THIS HANDBOOK PROVIDES CO.
TECHNICAL INFORMATION TO HEATING,
VENTILATING, AND AIR CONDITIONING
ENGINEERS, DESIGNERS AND PRACTITIONERS

MW00838044

HVAC:

Handbook of Heating, Ventilation and Air Conditioning for Design and Implementation

BY

ALI VEDAVARZ, PH.D., PE
Deputy Director of Engineering, New York City Capital Projects,
New York City Housing Authority and
Industry Professor, Polytechnic University, Brooklyn, NY

SUNIL KUMAR, PH.D.
Professor of Mechanical Engineering and Dean of Graduate School
Polytechnic University, Brooklyn, NY

MUHAMMED IQBAL HUSSAIN, PE
Mechanical Engineer, Department of Citywide Administrative Services
New York City, NY

2007

INDUSTRIAL PRESS INC.

NEW YORK

COPYRIGHT © 2007 by Industrial Press Inc., New York, NY.

Library of Congress Cataloging-in-Publication Data

Vedavarz, Ali.

HVAC: handbook of heating ventilation and air conditioning / Ali Vedavarz, Sunil Kumar, Muhammed Hussain.

p. cm.

ISBN 0-8311-3163-2

ISBN13 978-0-8311-3163-0

I. Heating--Handbooks, manuals, etc. 2. Ventilation--Handbooks, manuals, etc. 3. Air conditioning--Handbooks, manuals, etc. 4. Buildings--Environmental engineering--Handbooks, manuals, etc. I. Kumar, Sunil. II. Hussain, Muhammed Iqbal. III. Title.

TH7011.V46 2006
697--dc22

2006041837

Cover Photo: Image published with kind permission of CVRD and Bluhm Engineering.

INDUSTRIAL PRESS, INC.

989 Avenue of the Americas

New York, New York 10018 -5410

1st Edition

First Printing

10   9   8   7   6   5   4   3   2

Printed and bound in the United States of America

All rights reserved. This book or parts thereof may not be reproduced, stored in a retrieval system, or transmitted in any form without permission of the publishers.

TABLE OF CONTENTS

1. FUNDAMENTALS

1–1	Fundamentals of Thermodynamics
1–3	Conservation of Mass
1–3	First Law of Thermodynamics
1–4	Second Law, Reversibility, and Possible Processes
1–4	Thermodynamic Cycles
1–6	Fundamentals of Fluid Flow
1–6	Flow in Pipes and Ducts
1–11	Noise from Fluid Flow
1–11	Fundamentals of Heat Transfer
1–14	Overall Heat Transfer
1–15	Fins and Extended Surfaces
1–18	Some Details of Heat Exchange
1–19	Augmentation of Heat Transfer

2. PSYCHROMETRY

2–1	Psychrometrics
2–1	Ideal Gas Approximation
2–1	Equation of State
2–2	Humidity Ratio
2–2	Relative Humidity
2–2	Degree of Saturation
2–2	Wet Bulb Temperature
2–3	Partial Pressure of Water Vapor
2–4	Dew Point Temperature
2–4	Saturation
2–4	Enthalpy
2–5	Wet Bulb Temperature
2–6	Properties of Moist Air
2–7	Psychrometric Chart Presentation
2–12	Thermodynamic Properties of Water at Saturation
2–18	Thermodynamic Properties of Moist Air

3. AIR CONDITIONING PROCESSES

3–1	Introduction
3–1	Heating and Cooling Process
3–2	Cooling with Dehumidification
3–3	Heating with Humidification
3–3	Adiabatic Mixing of Two Air Streams
3–5	Evaporative Cooling
3–5	Heating and Air Conditioning System Cycles

4. INDOOR AIR QUALITY AND VENTILATION

4–1	Indoor Air Quality
4–1	Ventilation Procedure
4–5	Concentration of Air Pollutants
4–6	Indoor Air Quality Procedure
4–8	Filters
4–10	Hepa Filters
4–10	Carbon Media Filters
4–10	Fiber and Foam Filters
4–10	Ozone
4–10	Ultraviolet Light

5. LOAD ESTIMATING FUNDAMENTALS

5–1	Conduction
5–1	Thermal Conductivities of Materials
5–2	Convection
5–4	Thermal Radiation
5–4	Emissivities of Some Materials
5–6	Overall Heat Transfer Coefficient
5–8	Parallel Arrangement
5–11	Coefficient of Transmission

5. LOAD ESTIMATING FUNDAMENTALS
(Continued)

5–17	Relative Thermal Resistances of Building Materials
5–18	Surface Conductances and Resistances
5–18	Emittance Values of Various Surafces
5–19	Thermal Resistances of Plane Airspaces
5–21	Thermal Properties of Building and Insulating Materials
5–27	Coefficients of Heat Transmission of Various Fenestrations
5–28	Transmission Coefficients for Wood and Steel Doors
5–29	Outdoor Air Load Components

6. HEATING LOAD CALCULATIONS

6–1	Introduction
6–1	Calculating Design Heating Loads
6–2	Heat loss Through Walls, Roofs, and Glass Area
6–2	Heat Loss from Walls below Grade
6–3	Below-Grade Wall U-Factors
6–3	Heat Loss from Basement Floor Below Grade
6–4	Heat Loss Coefficients
6–4	Heat Loss from Floor Slab On Grade
6–6	Ventilation and Infiltration Heat Loss

7. COOLING LOAD CALCULATIONS

7–1	Transfer Function Method (TFM)
7–1	Heat Source in Conditioned Space
7–2	Heat Gain from Occupants
7–3	Heat Gain from Cooking Appliances
7–6	Heat Gain from Medical Equipments
7–6	Heat Gain from Computer
7–6	Heat Gain from Office Equipments
7–6	CLTD/SCL/CLF Calculation Procedure
7–7	Cooling Load by CLTD/SCL/CLF Method
7–8	Roof Numbers
7–9	CLTD for Roofs
7–11	CLTD for Walls
7–27	Code Number for Wall and Roof
7–28	Wall Types
7–31	CLTD for Glass
7–31	Zone Types for CLF Tables
7–31	Zone Types for SCL and CLF Tables
7–35	Residential Cooling Load Procedure
7–36	SCL for Glass
7–44	CLF for People and Unhooded Equipments
7–46	CLF for Hooded Equipments
7–47	Window GLF for Residences
7–49	CLTD for Residences
7–50	SC for Windows
7–50	SLF for Windows
7–50	Air Exchange Rates

8. DUCT DESIGN

8–1	Introduction
8–1	Pressure Head and Energy Equation
8–2	Friction Loss Analysis
8–7	Dynamic Losses
8–7	Ductwork Sectional Losses
8–8	Fan System Interface
8–8	Pressure Changes System
8–9	Duct System Design
8–9	Design Considerations
8–12	Duct Design Methods
8–13	Duct Design Procedures
8–13	Automated Duct Design
8–14	Duct Fitting Friction Loss Example
8–14	Equal Friction Method Example
8–15	Resistance in Low Pressure Duct System Example
8–15	Static Regain Method Example
8–17	Fitting Loss Coefficients

9.   PIPE SIZING

9–1   Pressure Drop Equations
9–1   Valve and Fitting Losses
9–3   Water Piping
9–3   Flow Rate Limitations
9–3   Noise Generation
9–3   Erosion
9–3   Allowances for Aging
9–4   Water Hammer
9–4   Hydronic System Piping
9–6   Valve and Fitting Pressure Drop
9–28   Service Water Piping
9–29   Plastic Pipe
9–29   Cold Water Pipe Sizing
9–31   Steam Flow in Pipes
9–31   Steam Flow Formulas
9–32   Vertical Pipes
9–32   Steam Piping
9–59   Gas Piping For Buildings
9–59   Residential Piping
9–61   Commercial-Industrial Piping
9–72   Compressed Air Systems
9–72   Compressed Air
9–78   Viscosity of Liquids
9–80   Piping
9–80   Types of Materials
9–91   Plastics Pipe
9–91   Joining Techniques
9–93   Standards for Specification and Identification
9–93   Design Parameters
9–96   Installation
9–97   Codes and Regulations
9–97   Pipe Fittings
9–97   Taper Pipe Thread
9–132   Laying Lengths of Pipe with Screwed Fittings
9–134   Allowable Spaces for Pipes
9–134   Expansion of Pipe
9–136   Corrosion Resistance
9–136   Pipe Support Spacing
9–139 Gate, Globe, and Check Valves
9–139   Operation
9–141   Maintenance Methods
9–142 Formulas for Sizing Control Valves
9–142   To Determine Valve Size
9–142   To Determine Valve Capacity
9–142   For Vapors Other Than Steam
9–143 Identification of Piping Systems
9–143   Dangerous Materials
9–143   Fire Protection Materials and Equipment
9–144   Safe Materials
9–144   Protective Materials
9–144   Method of Identification
9–144 Heat Losses in Piping
9–144   Heat Losses from Bare Pipe
9–145   Heat Losses from Steam Piping
9–157   Heat Loss from Insulated Pipe
9–158   Cold Surface Temperature

10.   HYDRONIC HEATING AND COOLING SYSTEM

10–1   Basic System
10–4   Temperature Classifications
10–4   Closed Hydronic System Components Design
10–4   Convectors or Terminal Units
10–4   Boiler
10–4   Air Eliminations Methods
10–6   Pressure Increase Due to Change in Temperature
10–6   Expansion Tank
10–7   Expansion Tank Sizing

10.   HYDRONIC HEATING AND COOLING SYSTEM
(Continued)

10–8   Characteristics of Centrifugal Pumps
10–8   Operating Characteristics
10–9   Pump Laws
10–9   Change of Performance
10–10   Centrifugal Pump Selection
10–10   Total Dynamic Head
10–11   Net Positive Suction Head (NPSH)
10–11 Pumping System
10–16   Parallel Pumping
10–17   Series Pumping
10–18 Design Procedures
10–18   Preliminary Equipment Layout
10–19   Final Pipe Sizing and Pressure Drop Determination
10–19   Final Pressure Drop
10–19   Final Pump Selection
10–19   Freeze Prevention

11.   ENERGY CALCULATION

11–1   Degree Day
11–1   65°F as the Base
11–2   Application of Degree Days
11–4   Predicting Fuel Consumption
11–5   Predicting Future Needs
11–7   Empirical Constants
11–7   Load Factor and Operating Hours
11–7   Limitations
11–8   Degree-Days Abroad
11–9   Degree Days for Various US Locations

12.   COMBUSTION

12–1   Combustion Basics
12–3   Efficiency Calculations
12–7   Saving Fuel with Combustion Controls
12–11   Combustion Considerations
12–11   Pressure and Flow Basic Principles
12–12   Atomizing Media Considerations
12–12   Combustion Air Considerations
12–13   Flue Gas Considerations
12–14   Gas Fuel Firing Considerations
12–14   Fuel Oil Firing Considerations
12–15   Operational Rules of Thumb
12–16   Common Application
12–20 Combustion Control Strategies
12–20   Control System Errors
12–20   Combustion Control Strategies
12–21   Parallel Positioning Systems
12–22   Fully Metered Control
12–23   Feedwater Control Systems
12–24   Draft Control
12–26   Oxygen Trim
12–27   Combustion Air Flow Control Techniques
12–28   Flue Gas Recirculation (FGR)
12–33 Fuel Oil Handling System Design
12–33   Determination of Required Flow Rate
12–34   Stand by Generator Loop Systems
12–34   Multiple Pumps
12–34   Burner Loop Systems
12–36   Maximum Inlet Suction
12–37   Pump Discharge Pressure
12–37   Piping System Design
12–37   Pump Set Control System Strategies

13. AIR CONDITIONING SYSTEMS

13–1   Air Conditioning Systems
13–1   Single Package Units
13–5   Single Package Installations
13–7   Installation of Split Systems
13–8   Zoning Unitary Installations
13–10   Selection Procedure
13–14   Evaporative Air Conditioning
13–14   Permissible Air Motion
13–17   Variable Volume AC System
13–18   Initial Costs
13–20   Cooling Considerations
13–21   Overlapping
13–22   Heat Recovery
13–22   Heating Cooling Systems
13–23   Air Systems
13–26   Controls
13–27   Air Water Systems
13–30   Sources of Internal Heat
13–31   Heat from Service Refrigeration
13–31   Exhaust Air Heat Recovery Systems
13–36   Heat Pumps
13–36   Reverse-Cycle Principle
13–36   Coefficient of Performance
13–37   Heating Season Performance Factor
13–37   Types of Heat Pumps
13–38   Air-to-Air Heat Pumps
13–39   Water-to-Water Heat Pumps
13–40   Water-to-Air Heat Pumps
13–40   Air-to-Water Heat Pumps
13–41   Ground Source Heat Pumps
13–41   Special Heat Sources
13–42   Operating and Installation Factors
13–42   Outdoor Temperature Effects
13–43   Thermostats
13–43   Heat Anticipators
13–44   Equipment Arrangement
13–44   Electrohydronic Heat Recovery
13–45   Cooling Cycle
13–47   System Design
13–47   Supplementary Heat
13–47   Optimized Data for Heat Pump
13–48   Development of Equations
13–48   Development of Tables
13–49   Selecting Air Handling Units
13–54   Well Water Air Conditioning
13–54   Heat Pump/Solar Energy Application
13–54   System Description and Operation
13–60   High Velocity Dual Duct Systems
13–60   Advantages and Disadvantages
13–60   Dual Duct Cycles
13–65   Duct Sizing Technique
13–65   Large vs. Small Ducts
13–66   Design Velocity
13–66   Maximum Velocity
13–67   Sizing High Pressure Ducts
13–68   Return Air Ducts
13–68   Low Pressure Ductwork
13–69   Basic Arrangement
13–69   Zoning
13–70   Ceiling Plenum
13–73   Modular Type Office Buildings
13–76   Constant Volume Mixing Units
13–77   Apparatus Floor Area
13–80   Construction Details
13–81   Automatic Control Applications
13–81   Rooftop Multizone Units
13–84   Multizone Unit Control
13–88   Damper Control
13–88   Economizer Control Cycle
13–88   Unit Ventilator Control

13. AIR CONDITIONING SYSTEMS
(Continued)

13–91   Hot Water System Control
13–94   Mixing Box Control
13–95   Rotary Air-to-Air Heat Exchanger Control
13–95   Automatic Control for Dual Duct System
13–97   Winterizing Chilled Water System
13–97   Water Circulation to Prevent Freeze-Up
13–99   Mechanical Draft Cooling Towers
13–102 Atmospheric Cooling Towers
13–104 Quantity of Cooling Water Required
13–105 Roof is a Location for AC Equipment
13–105 Advantages of Roof
13–106 Disadvantages of Roof
13–107 Servicing Cooling Plant
13–107 Servicing Cooling Plant for Summer Use
13–107 Water System
13–107 Air Handling System
13–107 Compressor Oil
13–107 Condenser
13–108 Refrigeration Unit
13–108 Check Oil
13–108 Compressor
13–108 Air Conditioning Equipment Maintenance
13–108 Air Handling Equipment
13–108 Air Distribution Equipment
13–108 Water-Using Equipment
13–108 Cooling Equipment
13–110 Air Conditioning Maintenance Schedule
13–111 Unit Air Conditioners
13–111 Central Systems
13–111 Condensing Water Circuit
13–112 Cooling Water System
13–112 Filters and Ducts
13–112 Air Conditioning Maintenance Procedure
13–112 Refrigerant Circuit and Controls
13–113 Condensing Water Circuit
13–113 Cooling Water System
13–113 Filters and Ducts
13–114 Rotating Apparatus
13–114 Unit Air Conditioners
13–114 Checklist for Air Conditioning Surveys

14. AIR HANDLING AND VENTILATION

14–1   Terminology, Abbreviations, and Definitions
14–3   Fan Laws
14–11   Fan Performance Curves
14–16   Class Limits for Fans
14–21   Fan Selection
14–26   Fan Inlet Connections
14–27   Fan Discharge Conditions
14–31   Useful Fan Formulas
14–32   Nomographs for Fan Horsepower
14–32   Monographs for Fan Horsepower and Actual Capacity
14–34   Fan Selection Questionnaire
14–37   Air Flow in Ducts
14–40   Pitot Traverse
14–40   Friction Losses
14–40   Correction for Roughness
14–40   Rectangular Duct
14–52   Air Balancing and Air Turning Hardware
14–56   Air Distribution
14–56   Fire Dampers and Fire Protection
14–56   Duct System Design
14–59   High Velocity System Design
14–68   Step by Step Design
14–68   Main Duct
14–70   Branch Trunk Ducts
14–71   Single Branch Lines
14–72   Duct Design by Computer
14–73   Fibrous Glass Duct Construction

14.   AIR HANDLING AND VENTILATION
(Continued)

14–75 Determining Required Air Volume
14–75 Estimating Weight of Metal
14–77 Apparatus Casing Construction
14–77 Condensate Drains for Air Conditioning Units
14–78 Air Filters and Dust Collectors
14–78 Air Filters
14–79 Dust Collectors
14–82 Dry Centrifugal Collectors
14–82 Wet Collectors
14–82 Fabric Collectors
14–83 Electrostatic Precipitators
14–83 Breeching Design and Construction
14–83 Expansion
14–84 Aerodynamics
14–85 Access
14–85 Round Breeching Construction
14–85 Rectangular Breeching Construction
14–90 Chimney Draft and Velocities
14–92 Forced Draft and Draft Control
14–94 Sizing of Large Chimneys
14–95 Chimney Design and Construction
14–96 Balancing Small Air Conditioning Systems
14–97 Balancing Medium and Large Systems
14–98 Balancing Duct Distribution
14–98 Balancing Systems Using Booster Fans
14–99 Air Balancing by Balancing and Testing Engineers

15.   STEAM HEATING SYSTEM DESIGN

15–1   Large Systems
15–1   Equivalent Direct Radiation
15–1   Piping Connections to Boilers
15–3   Direct Return Connection
15–3   Common Return Header
15–3   Two Boilers with Common Return Header and Hartford Connection
15–4   Two Boilers with Separate Direct Return Connections from Below
15–4   Separate Direct Return Connections
15–4   Connections to Steam Using Equipment
15–26 Piping Application
15–30 Industrial and Commercial Steam Requirements
15–39 Flash Steam Calculations
15–40 Sizing of Vertical Flash Tanks
15–40 To Size Flash Tank
15–41 To Size Float Trap
15–41 Airbinding
15–46 Estimating Friction in Hot Water Piping
15–49 Hot Water Heating Systems
15–49 Service Water Heating
15–49 Operating Water Temperature
15–49 Air Removal from System
15–49 Water Flow Velocity
15–49 Prevention of Freezing
15–49 Water Circulation below Mains
15–49 Limitation of Pressure
15–50 System Adaptability
15–50 Use of Waste Steam Heat
15–50 Heat from District Steam System
15–50 Summer Cooling
15–50 Types of Water Heating Systems
15–52 Design Recommendations for Hot Water Systems
15–52 Water Velocity
15–52 Pump Location
15–52 Air Venting
15–53 Balancing Circuits
15–53 Filling Pressure
15–53 Preventing Backflow
15–53 Connecting Returns to Boiler
15–53 Locating the Circulating Pump

15.   STEAM HEATING SYSTEM DESIGN
(Continued)

15–53 Sizing the Expansion Tank
15–54 Compressed Air to Reduce Tank Size
15–54 Piping Details
15–55 Design of Piping Systems
15–58 Design of Two Pipe Reversed Return System
15–58 Final Check of Pipe Sizes
15–58 Design of Two Pipe Direct Return System
15–59 Piping for One-Pipe Diversion System
15–59 Sizing Piping for Main
15–59 Sizing Piping for Branches
15–59 Pipe Size Check
15–60 Piping for One-pipe Series System
15–60 Combination of Piping Systems
15–60 Sizing Hot Water Expansion Tanks
15–60 Conditions Affecting Design
15–61 Sizing Hot Water Expansion Tanks
15–61 High Temperature Water Systems
15–63 High Temperature Drop
15–63 Heat Storage
15–63 Limitation of Corrosion
15–63 Pressurization of HTW System
15–63 Steam Pressurization
15–64 Gas Pressurization
15–64 Air Pressurization
15–64 Nitrogen Pressurization
15–65 Expansion Tanks
15–65 Expansion Conditions
15–65 Determining Expansion Tank Size
15–65 Location of Steam Pressurizing Tank
15–66 Nitrogen Pressurizing Tanks
15–66 Application of HTW for Process Steam
15–66 Circulating Pumps
15–67 Pumps for HTW Systems
15–67 Manufacturer's Information
15–67 Pump Specifications
15–68 Net Positive Suction Head
15–68 Effect of Cavitation Within Pump
15–68 Pump Construction for HTW Systems
15–68 Circulating Pump Seals
15–69 Boiler Recirculating Pump
15–69 Boilers for HTW Systems
15–69 Boiler Emergency Protection
15–69 Pipe, Valves, and Fittings for HTW Systems
15–69 Valve Installation
15–70 Welded Joints
15–70 Venting of Piping
15–70 Effect of Load Variation on Operation
15–71 Pipe Sizing for HTW Systems
15–73 Ratings of Steel Boilers
15–73 Ratings
15–74 Ratings for Steel Boilers
15–76 Stack Dimensions
15–81 Heating and Cooling Media
15–81 Brine
15–81 Glycerine
15–81 Glycol
15–81 Other Media
15–82 Warm Air Heating
15–82 Early Types
15–83 Current Types
15–85 Furnace Performance
15–85 Testing and Rating of Furnaces
15–86 Acceptable Limits
15–87 Selection of Furnace
15–87 Rule for Selection
15–87 Blower Characteristics
15–88 Blower Sizes
15–88 Duct System Characteristics
15–88 Trends
15–89 Warm Air Registers
15–90 Return Air Intakes

15.   STEAM HEATING SYSTEM DESIGN
(Continued)

15–91   Arrangement of Furnace and Ducts
15–94   Basic Thermostatic Controls
15–94   Continuous Air Circulation
15–95   Continuous Blower Operation
15–95   Intermittent Blower Operation
15–109   Steam Supplied Unit Heater
15–109   Gas Fired Radiant Heaters
15–112   Sizing of Steam Traps
15–117   Unit Heaters
15–124   Checklist for Heating System Servicing

16.   NOISE AND VIBRATION CONTROL

16–1   Noise and Vibration
16–1   Definitions and Terminology
16–2   Noise Criteria
16–2   Speech Interference Criteria
16–2   Sound Levels of Sources
16–7   Ratings and Standards
16–7   Airborne Sound Transmission
16–7   Vibration Isolation
16–9   Isolation Mount Selection
16–13   Airborne Noise Through Ducts
16–13   Regenerated Noise
16–13   Other Mechanical Noise Sources
16–14   Calculation of Sound Levels from HVAC Systems
16–14   Description of Decibels
16–14   Addition of Decibels
16–15   The Sabin
16–17   Determination of Sound Pressure Level
16–20   Noise in Ducted Systems
16–23   Fan Noise Generation
16–23   Estimating Fan Noise
16–24   Distribution of Sound Power at Branch Takeoffs
16–24   Attenuation of Untreated Duct
16–24   Duct Lining Attenuation
16–25   Sound Attenuation of Plenums
16–26   Duct Lining and Elbows
16–27   Open End Reflection Loss
16–27   Air Flow Noise
16–31   Flow Noise Generation of Silencers
16–31   Sound Transmission Through Duct Walls
16–32   Calculation of Sound Levels in Ducted Systems
16–36   Control of Cooling Tower Noise
16–36   Fan Noise
16–37   Water Noise
16–37   Drive Components
16–37   External Noise Sources
16–38   Configuration Factors
16–39   Location
16–39   Reducing Sound Generated
16–39   Half-Speed Operation
16–39   Oversizing of the Tower
16–39   Changing Leaving Conditions
16–40   Sound Absorbers
16–40   Obtaining Desired Sound Levels
16–40   Acoustical Problems in High Velocity Air Distribution
16–40   System Noise
16–42   Air Handling Apparatus Rooms
16–42   Selection of Fan Isolation Bases
16–42   Apparatus Casings
16–42   Dampers and Air Valves
16–43   Flexible Connectors
16–43   Air Distributing Systems
16–43   Duct Velocities
16–43   Choice of Duct Design Method
16–43   Ductwork Adjacent to Apparatus Room
16–44   Duct Connections to Apparatus Casings
16–44   Type Duct Construction
16–44   Fittings for High Velocity Ductwork

16.   NOISE AND VIBRATION CONTROL
(Continued)

16–45   Take-off Fittings
16–45   Dual Duct Area Ratio
16–46   Dampers as a Noise Generating Source
16–46   Sound Barrier for High Velocity Ductwork
16–46   Sound Traps
16–46   Cross Over of Horizontal Dual Duct Mains
16–47   Testing of High Pressure Ductwork
16–47   Terminal Devices
16–48   Radiation Protection at Wall Openings for Duct or Pipe
16–49   Medical Installations

17.   MOTORS AND STARTERS

17–1   NEMA Motor Classifications
17–1   Locked Rotor Torque
17–2   Classification of Single-Phase, Induction Motors by Design Letter
17–2   Torque, Speed, and Horsepower Ratings for Single-Phase Induction Motors
17–3   Classification by Environmental Protection and Method of Cooling
17–3   Standard Voltages and Frequencies for Motors
17–6   The National Electrical Code
17–6   Grounding
17–8   Motor and Load Dynamics, and Motor Heating
17–8   Torque Speed Relationships
17–9   Torque, Inertia, and Acceleration Time
17–10   Dynamics of the Motor and the Load
17–11   Motor Heating and Motor Life
17–12   Rotor Heating During Starting
17–12   Single Phase Motors
17–12   Types of Motors
17–15   Repulsion-Induction
17–15   Large Single-Phase Motors
17–16   Application
17–17   Loading
17–18   Motor Protection
17–18   Motor Selection
17–18   Analysis of Application
17–19   Polyphase Motors
17–19   Enclosure
17–20   Bearings
17–20   Quietness
17–20   Polyphase, Squirrel Cage Induction Motors
17–21   Speed Control
17–21   Two-Speed Polyphase, Squirrel Cage Induction Motors
17–21   Two Speed Motors Come in Two Types
17–23   Wound-Rotor Polyphase Induction Motors
17–24   Variable Speed
17–24   Synchronous Motors
17–25   Hermetic Type Motor Compressors
17–25   Hermetic Compressors to 5 hp
17–29   Starters
17–29   Motor Controllers
17–29   Overcurrent Protection
17–30   Overload Protection
17–31   Starters for Large AC Motors
17–33   Winding and Reduced-voltage Starting
17–33   Electric Utility Limitations
17–33   Minimizing Mechanical Shocks
17–33   Application
17–36   Types of Starters
17–36   Open Circuit Transition
17–37   Advantages and Disadvantages
17–39   Useful Formulas
17–39   Electric Motor Maintenance

18.   DESIGN PROCEDURE, ABBREVIATIONS, SYMBOLS

18–1   Design Procedure
18–1   Contract and Mechanical Drawings
18–1   HVAC Drawings
18–1   Floor Plans
18–5   Valve Symbols
18–6   Piping Symbols
18–7   Pipe Fittings Symbols
18–8   Abbreviations for Scientific and Engineering Terms
18–9   Lists of Abbreviations and Symbols

19.   CLIMATIC DESIGN INFORMATION

19–1   Climatic Design Conditions
19–1   Applicability and Characteristics of the Design Conditions
19–27 Dry Bulb and Wet Bulb Temperature for US Locations

20.   UNITS AND CONVERSIONS

20–1   U.S. Customary Unit System
20–1   Linear Measures
20–1   Surveyor's Measure
20–1   Nautical Measure
20–1   Square Measure
20–1   Cubic Measure
20–1   Shipping Measure
20–2   Dry Measure
20–2   Liquid Measure
20–2   Old Liquid Measure
20–2   Apothecaries' Fluid Measure
20–2   Avoirdupois or Commercial Weight
20–2   Troy Weight, Used for Weighing Gold and Silver
20–2   Apothecaries' Weight
20–2   Measures of Pressure
20–3   Miscellaneous

20.   UNITS AND CONVERSIONS
(Continued)

20–4   U.S. System And Metric System Conversion
20–4   Length and Area
20–4   Mass and Density
20–5   Volume and Flow
20–6   Force, Energy, Work, Torque and Power Conversion
20–7   Velocity and Acceleration
20–8   Metric Systems Of Measurement
20–8   Measures of Length
20–8   Square Measure
20–8   Surveyors Square Measure
20–8   Cubic Measure
20–8   Dry and Liquid Measure
20–8   Measures of Weight
20–10   Binary Multiples
20–10 Terminology of Sheet Metal

21.   INDEX

This Handbook provides comprehensive technical information in a modular form to heating, ventilating, and air conditioning (HVAC) designers and practitioners, namely engineers, architects, contractors, and plant engineers. It is also a handy reference for students mastering the intricacies of the
HVAC rudiments. Each chapter is self-contained to the extent possible and emphasis is placed on
graphical and tabular presentations of data that are useful for easy understanding of fundamentals
and solving problems of design, installation, and operation.

This Handbook draws upon the material presented in the *Handbook of Air Conditioning, Heating,
and Ventilating, Third Edition*, Industrial Press, which forms the basis of the presentation. New topics and chapters have been introduced and previous information updated or rewritten. Examples
using software solution tools have been added alongside traditional solutions using formulae from
the handbook. The organization, however, remains, in the literal sense, a handbook.

We gratefully acknowledge the contributors and editors of the aforementioned *Handbook of Air
Conditioning, Heating, and Ventilating*, whose knowledge is embedded throughout the present
book. We did not have the opportunity to meet any of them, but their written legacy has left an indel-
ible imprint on the present work.

An important source of information is the ASHRAE (American Society of Heating, Refrigerating,
and Air-Conditioning Engineers) repertoire of publications. ASHRAE serves as the authoritative,
and occasionally the sole, source of up-to-date HVAC related data and analysis. We acknowledge
their permission to use material from various publications, especially the latest ASHRAE Handbook
series.

ASHRAE Publications
1791 Tullie Circle, NE
Atlanta, GA 30329
Web Site: www.ashrae.org

We are also grateful to the Preferred Utilities corporation for making available their publication on the topic of combustion analysis, and consenting to let us base our combustion chapter on it.

Preferred Utilities Mfg. Corp
31-35 South Street
Danbury, CT 06810
Web Site: www.preferred-mfg.com

We acknowledge the input of our good friend, colleague, and HVAC critic, Mr. Naji Raad, whose experience in the profession provided a critical review of the manuscript. We thank our editors at Industrial Press, Mr. Christopher McCauley and Mr. Riccardo Heald, for their editorial input and suggestions, for reading the manuscript as it developed, and keeping the project on track; and Janet Romano for her cover design and production assistance. We acknowledge the effort of the many students at Polytechnic University who helped in researching for material, proofreading the manuscript, checking examples, and drawing figures. Those who deserve special recognition are Mr. Saurabh Shah and Mr. Christopher Bodenmiller for the graphics, Mr. Nayan Patel, Mr. Pranav Patel, and Mr. Prabodh Panindre for research, calculations, and proofing. Finally, we thank Kathleen McKenzie, freelance book editor, for her considerable contribution to this Handbook's style, format and readability.

Every effort has been made to prevent errors, but in a work of this scope it is inevitable that some may creep in. We request your forgiveness and will be grateful if you call any such errors to our attention by emailing them to info@industrialpress.com.

Ali Vedavarz, Sunil Kumar, Muhammed Iqbal Hussain

New York City
December 2006

Ali Vedavarz received his master of science degree in mechanical engineering from the University of Bridgeport in Connecticut and Ph.D. in mechanical engineering from Polytechnic University in Brooklyn, New York. Dr. Vedavarz is a member of ASME and ASHRAE and has published technical papers in ASME journals. Dr. Vedavarz is a licensed Professional Engineer in the State of New York and is currently the Deputy Director of Engineering (for Design) in the Office of Capital Projects at New York City Housing Authority. He is also an adjunct Industry Professor at Polytechnic University, Brooklyn, New York, where he teaches courses in HVAC design and energy systems.

Sunil Kumar received his bachelor's degree in mechanical engineering from the Indian Institute of Technology, Kharagpur, India, master's degrees in mechanical engineering and mathematics from the State University of New York at Buffalo, and a doctoral degree in mechanical engineering from the University of California at Berkeley. He is presently a Professor of Mechanical Engineering and the Dean of Graduate School and Associate Provost at Polytechnic University in Brooklyn, New York. Dr. Kumar has authored over 100 journal and conference papers in the area of thermal-fluid sciences and has extensive consulting and research experience in this subject area.

Muhammed Hussain received his bachelor's degree from Bangladesh University of Engineering and Technology, Dhaka, Bangladesh, and master's degree in mechanical engineering from Polytechnic University in Brooklyn, New York. He is a licensed Professional Engineer in the State of New York. Mr. Hussain is presently working as a mechanical design engineer in the Department of Citywide Administrative Services in New York City. Mr. Hussain is also a contributor to, and associate editor of, *Machinery's Handbook*.

FUNDAMENTALS OF THERMODYNAMICS

FUNDAMENTALS

This chapter covers the fundamentals of thermodynamics, fluid mechanics, and heat transfer as related to the theory and practice of air conditioning, heating and ventilation. Basic concepts needed for the HVAC professional are presented, while advanced topics are not considered. Excellent resources, such as the ASHRAE Handbook series and many great textbooks in the areas of thermal fluid sciences, treat the details and advanced topics that have been omitted from this focused chapter.

Fundamentals of Thermodynamics

Thermodynamics is the study of energy, its transformations, and its relation to states of matter or substance. Thermodynamics deals with equilibrium conditions that are typical of steady state, and any changes are considered to be quasi-equilibrium processes where change occurs slowly and incrementally so as to allow each incremental intermediate state to reach equilibrium before it advances further.

A pure substance has a homogeneous and invariable chemical composition. It can exist in more than one phase, but chemical composition is the same in all phases. If a substance exists as liquid at saturation temperature and pressure, it is called a saturated liquid. If the temperature of the liquid is lower than the saturation temperature for the existing pressure, it is called either a subcooled liquid (the temperature is lower than the saturation temperature for the given pressure) or a compressed liquid (the pressure is greater than the saturation pressure for the given temperature). When a substance exists as part liquid and part vapor at the saturation temperature, its quality is defined as the ratio of the mass of vapor to the total mass. Quality has meaning only when the substance is in a saturated state; i.e., at saturation pressure and temperature. If a substance exists as vapor at the saturation temperature, it is called saturated vapor. The term dry saturated vapor is used to emphasize that the quality of the substance is 100%. When the vapor is at a temperature greater than the saturation temperature, it is superheated vapor. The pressure and temperature of superheated vapor are independent properties, since the temperature can increase while the pressure remains constant. Gases are highly superheated vapors.

A property of a substance is any observable characteristic of the material. An intrinsic property of the material is one that does not depend on the shape or volume or mass of the material. Such properties are pressure and temperature, or properties that are usually expressed in the units of per unit mass, such as specific volume. This is in contrast with extrinsic properties which depend on the actual quantity of the material under consideration, such as volume. The thermodynamic state of a substance is defined by listing its intrinsic properties. The most common intrinsic thermodynamic properties are temperature T, pressure p, specific volume v (which is the inverse of density ρ), specific entropy s, specific enthalpy h, and specific internal energy u. It has been established that a thermodynamic state of a substance can be uniquely identified by two independent intrinsic properties. For example, temperature and pressure are such properties, except in the saturation region where the same temperature and pressure can have an infinite number of states corresponding to quality from 0 to 100%. Enthalpy (h) is defined by

$$h = u + pv \tag{1}$$

where u = internal energy per unit mass.

Each property in a given state has only one definite value, and any property always has the same value for a given state, regardless of how the substance arrived at that state. The thermodynamic property entropy s measures the molecular disorder of a system. The more mixed a system, the greater its entropy; conversely, an orderly or unmixed configuration is one of low entropy. Figs. 1-1a and 1-1b schematically show the liquid and vapor states of water using two properties to uniquely identify the states. Fig. 1-1a shows the states in (p, h) coordinates and a line showing the states along a constant temperature is also presented. Fig. 1-1b shows the same information in (T, s) coordinates and a constant pressure line is shown. Within the dome where the saturated states exist it is possible to increase the specific volume (and other intrinsic, per unit mass based properties) even when keeping the pressure and temperature constant (for example line B-A-C in Figs. 1-1a and 1-1b).

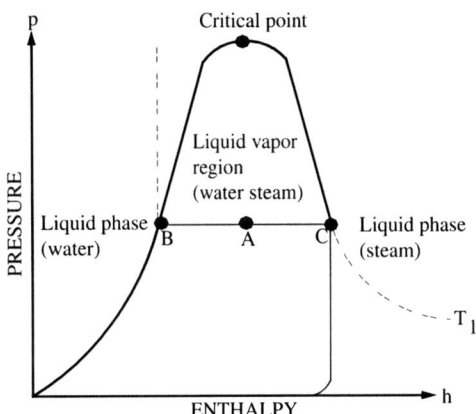

Fig 1-1a. Thermodynamic states of water in p-h coordinates

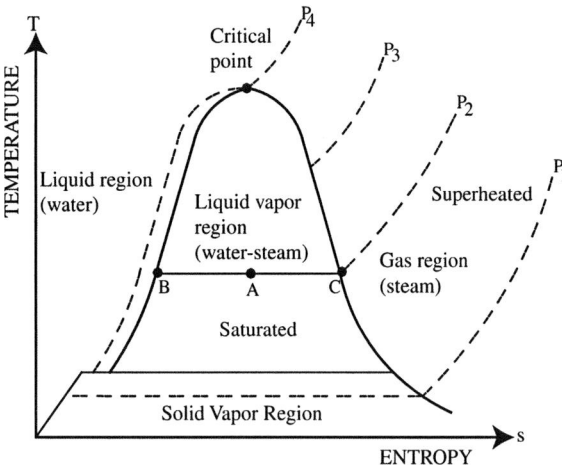

Fig 1-1b. Thermodynamic states of water in T-s coordinates

The specific heats at constant pressure C_p and volume C_v are defined as the heat added to a unit mass at constant pressure or volume, respectively, to cause temperature of the mass to increase by one unit. Mathematically, by using the first law for closed systems and the definition of work (described later in the chapter), these are defined as

$$C_v = \left(\frac{\partial u}{\partial T}\right)_v \qquad C_p = \left(\frac{\partial h}{\partial T}\right)_p \qquad (2)$$

For ideal gases the following holds true rigorously

$$du = C_v dT \qquad dh = C_p dT \qquad (3)$$

and for real gases this is a good engineering approximation. For incompressible substances the two specific heats are the same and the above expressions also holds. Thus, liquids and solids, which are treated as incompressible, are described by Equation (3).

The basic entity analyzed by thermodynamics is termed a thermodynamic system. A thermodynamic system is an identifiable or specific region in space or an identifiable or specific quantity of matter. It is bounded by the system surface or the system boundaries. The surroundings include everything external to the system, and the system is separated from the surroundings by the system boundaries. These boundaries can be movable or fixed, real or imaginary. There are two types of systems: closed and open. In a closed system, no mass enters or leaves the system. A closed system is thus a fixed mass system. In an open system, mass may enter or leave the system and therefore the boundaries of such a system are imaginary in some parts where the mass is exchanged with the surroundings. Energy can always cross the system boundaries, whether open or closed, except for an isolated closed system, which is one that does not allow energy to cross its boundaries. Almost all HVAC systems that will be studied here fall in the open system category.

Energy has the capacity for producing an effect on the system and is described differently depending on whether it is stored or is crossing the system boundary. Thermal (internal) energy is the energy possessed by the matter in a system caused by the internal motion of the molecules, the intermolecular forces, and other microscopic mechanisms of energy storage within the material. It is impossible to find the absolute (total) value of internal energy of a material, and it is therefore measured with reference to a standard state in which the value of the internal energy is arbitrarily set to zero. The internal energy is the sum of all these microscopic energies such that when the internal energy of an isolated closed system (fixed mass) changes, the result is a change in the temperature of the system. Internal energy is an intrinsic property of material and its value per unit mass can be used to uniquely define the state of the material. The specific internal energy u is the internal energy per unit mass. Potential energy is the energy possessed by a system due to the elevation of the system:

$$PE = mgz \qquad (4)$$

where m = mass;

g = local acceleration of gravity, and;

z = elevation above horizontal reference plane.

Potential energy is not an intrinsic property of material. Kinetic energy is the energy possessed due to the bulk velocity of the flowing material and is expressed as

$$KE = \frac{1}{2}mV^2 \qquad (5)$$

where V = velocity of a fluid stream.

Kinetic energy is not an intrinsic property of material.

The types of energy that are defined only when they cross the system boundaries are heat and work. Heat (Q) and work (W) cannot be stored and they only exist when energy is being transferred across a system boundary. Heat is the mechanism that transfers energy across the boundary of systems solely through temperature difference. Heat always flows from higher to lower temperatures. Heat is considered positive by convention when energy is added to a system (see Fig. 1-2). Work is the mechanism that transfers energy across the boundary of systems through forces and movement. (Here it has the traditional characterization: it is the product of force and distance.) If the total effect produced in the system can be reduced to the raising of a weight, then nothing but work has crossed the boundary. By convention work is considered positive when energy is removed from a system, i.e., the system does work on its surroundings (see Fig. 1-2). For example, when a system comprising a cylinder and movable piston expands so that the piston is moving outwards, work is done by the system on the surroundings and is therefore considered positive in any analysis of system. Mechanical or shaft work is the work associated with a rotating shaft such as a turbine, air compressor, or internal combustion engine. Flow work is energy associated with the movement of fluid in conjunction with forces of fluid pressure as it crosses the boundary of an open system. It can be more easily understood as the work done by the fluid to push itself against the other fluid particles as it forces itself to enter or exit the system. Work done by entering fluid streams is negative (pushing into the system), while work done by fluid streams exiting the system is positive (pushing the surroundings). The magnitude of flow work per unit mass is determined by the expression

$$\text{Flow work} = pv \qquad (6)$$

where p = pressure and;

  v = specific volume, or the inverse of density.

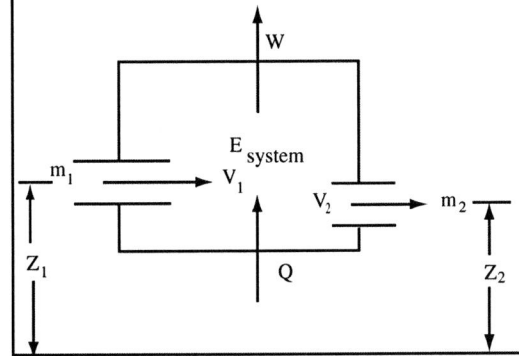

Fig 1-2. Energy flow in general thermodynamic system

A property of a system is any observable characteristic of the system. A process is a change in state that can be defined as any change in the properties of a system. A process is described by its initial and final equilibrium states, its path, and the interactions that take place across system boundaries as it goes forth. A cycle is a process or a series of processes wherein the initial and final states of the system are identical. Therefore, at the conclusion of a cycle, all properties have the same value they had at the beginning.

Conservation of Mass.—Conservation of mass in a closed system is the default since no mass leaves or enters the system. For an open system the conservation of mass indicates that the difference between the mass entering and leaving is equal to the increase of mass in the system. For the general case of multiple flow streams the conservation of mass is written as

$$\sum m_{\text{in}} - \sum m_{\text{out}} = [m_f - m_i]_{\text{system}} \qquad (7)$$

For steady flow processes the above can be modified as

$$\sum m_{\text{in}} = \sum m_{\text{out}} \qquad (8)$$

For flow through a pipe or duct the mass flow rate is related to the velocity by

$$\dot{m} = \rho VA = \frac{VA}{v} \qquad (9)$$

where ρ = density of the flowing fluid;

  A = cross-sectional area through which the fluid is flowing;

  V = velocity;

  v = specific volume, or the inverse of the density.

  i = indicate initial states; and

  f = indicate final states.

It is assumed that the velocity is uniform across the cross-section. If it is not, then V in the above mass flow rate definition is average velocity. A is normal to the direction of the fluid flow.

First Law of Thermodynamics.—The first law of thermodynamics is often called the law of the conservation of energy. After a system is defined, the conservation of energy states that

$$\text{energy in} - \text{energy out} = \text{increase in energy} \qquad (10)$$

Fig. 1-2 illustrates energy flows into and out of a thermodynamic system. For a closed system this is written as

$$Q - W = U_f - U_i = m(u_f - u_i) \qquad (11)$$

where m = mass of the system;

  U = internal energy of systems; and

  m = internal energy per unit mass;

For the general case of an open system with multiple mass flows in and out of the system, the energy balance can be written

$$\sum m_{\text{in}}\left(u + pv + \frac{V^2}{2} + gz\right)_{\text{in}} -$$

$$\sum m_{\text{out}}\left(u + pv + \frac{V^2}{2} + gz\right)_{\text{out}} + Q - W = \qquad (12)$$

$$\left[m_f\left(u + \frac{V^2}{2} + gz\right)_f - m_i\left(u + \frac{V^2}{2} + gz\right)_i\right]_{\text{system}}$$

The steady flow process is important in engineering applications. Steady flow signifies that no quantities associated with the system vary with time. Consequently,

$$\sum \dot{m}_{\text{in}}\left(u + pv + \frac{V^2}{2} + gz\right)_{\text{in}} -$$

$$\sum \dot{m}_{\text{out}}\left(u + pv + \frac{V^2}{2} + gz\right)_{\text{out}} + \dot{Q} - \dot{W} = 0 \qquad (13)$$

Here the addition of the dot on top of the variables m, Q, and W indicates the time derivative (d/dt) which yields the rate of mass flow, the rate of heat flow, and the rate of work done, respectively. In the above two equations the flow work of the entering and exiting streams is indicated by the pv terms, and, therefore, the W in the equations is the work done by moving system boundaries plus shaft work, and any other work not described by these categories. In the above energy conservation (Equations (12) and (13)) assume that velocity is uniform across the cross section. However, in real fluid systems it is not uniform due to viscosity of the fluid. The change to the kinetic energy term is discussed in the section Fundamentals of Fluid Flow.

Second Law, Reversibility, and Possible Processes.—The second law of thermodynamics can be expressed in many ways. Here it is being introduced to distinguish and quantify processes that can only proceed in one direction (irreversible) from those that are reversible. It also indicates which processes cannot exist.

The second law for a closed system is written as

$$dS \geq \frac{\delta Q}{T} \qquad S_f - S_i \geq \int_i^f \frac{\delta Q}{T} \qquad (14)$$

where the subscripts f and i indicate final and initial state, respectively, and the system entropy $S = ms$, where m is the mass of the system and s is specific entropy. The temperature T must be in absolute units (Kelvin or Rankine). The equality sign holds for reversible processes and the inequality for irreversible processes. The above form of the second law shows that the entropy of the system either increases or remains same, assuming the heat flow is positive. For adiabatic processes, that is where $Q = 0$, the right side of either Equation (14) vanishes, clearly indicating that entropy increases if the process is not reversible. For constant temperature processes

$$T(S_f - S_i) \geq Q \qquad (15)$$

where the equality holds for reversible processes. For an open system the above can be modified as

$$(S_f - S_i)_{\text{system}} + \sum (ms)_{\text{out}} - \sum (ms)_{\text{in}} \geq \int_i^f \frac{\delta Q}{T} \quad (16)$$

It is assumed in Equation (16) that the inlet and outlet properties remain invariant with time. For steady flow systems with invariant inlet and outlet properties the second law can be rewritten in the form

$$\sum (\dot{m}s)_{\text{out}} - \sum (\dot{m}s)_{\text{in}} \geq \int \frac{\dot{Q}}{T} \qquad (17)$$

The open system of Equation (17) can give insights about reversible and irreversible processes if we consider a single input, single output stream process. If the process is adiabatic, then the inlet and outlet entropies will be the same for reversible processes; otherwise the outlet entropy will be greater than the inlet. If the process is isothermal, then the difference between the rate of entropy flowing out and in will be equal to the heat addition rate divided by temperature only if the process is reversible. Adiabatic reversible processes are also termed isentropic because entropy remains same. On a thermodynamic chart where entropy is the horizontal axis, the adiabatic reversible processes will be vertical lines, but the irreversible processes will always veer right (towards increasing entropy) from their starting point. Thus, for any given

starting point, the only thermodynamically possible adiabatic processes are those that end in the half plane to the right of the vertical line drawn from the starting point in the thermodynamic chart where specific entropy is on the horizontal axis. Thus, the second law can show processes that are reversible, irreversible and possible, or impossible.

The second law for cycles is described next. It further refines the concept of possible and impossible series of processes occurring in a cycle.

Thermodynamic Cycles.—Thermodynamic cycles that make it possible to remove heat from cold spaces and dump the heat in hot ambient spaces are discussed here. These cycles make it possible for air conditioning and refrigeration systems to exist and they form the basis of HVAC engineering.

The performance of a refrigeration or air conditioning thermodynamic cycle is usually described by a coefficient of performance. COP is defined as the benefit of the cycle (amount of heat removed) divided by the required energy input to operate the cycle, or

$$COP = \frac{\text{useful refrigerating effect}}{\text{energy from external source}} \qquad (18)$$

The first law for cycles indicates that

$$\oint \delta Q = \oint \delta W$$
$$Q_{\text{net}} = W_{\text{net}} \qquad (19)$$
$$\dot{Q}_{\text{net}} = \dot{W}_{\text{net}}$$

where Q = heat added and;
           W = work done.

For the individual processes that make up the cycle, the first law for open systems is used. Since cyclic devices have only one working fluid and the mass flow rate of the fluid is the same through each process due to conservation of mass, the open system Equation (13) can be modified as below for each process in the cycle:

$$\dot{m}(h_{\text{out}} - h_{\text{in}}) + \dot{Q} - \dot{W} = 0 \qquad (20)$$

The kinetic and potential energy terms are usually neglected in comparison to enthalpy in refrigeration and air conditioning thermodynamic cycles because their magnitudes are usually several orders smaller than enthalpy.

The Carnot cycle is an ideal cycle that is made up of completely reversible processes and operates between two fixed temperatures. This cycle is useful since it is a thermodynamic ideal for refrigeration cycles that need to operate between two temperatures: the temperature of the conditioned space and the temperature of the external (hot) ambient. Also heat is transferred from the cold space to the ambient. The properties of the Carnot cycle are that it can be used as a refrigerator or a heat pump, as well as a work-producing device, depending on the input quantities. Fig. 1-3 shows the Carnot cycle on temperature entropy coordinates. Heat is withdrawn at the constant temperature T_R from the region to be refrigerated. Heat is rejected at the constant ambient temperature T_o. The cycle is completed by two isentropic processes that connect the high and low temperatures at the two extremes of entropy values. From Equation (17) the energy transfers are given by

$$Q_R = T_R(S_2 - S_1) \qquad \dot{Q}_R = \dot{m}T_R(s_2 - s_1) \quad (21)$$

$$Q_o = T_o(S_3 - S_4) \qquad \dot{Q}_R = \dot{m}T_o(s_2 - s_1) \quad (22)$$

Since the cycle is being run to remove the heat Q_R, the COP of the Carnot cycle will be

$$COP = \frac{Q_R}{W_R} = \frac{Q_R}{Q_o - Q_R} = \frac{T_R}{T_o - T_R} \quad (23)$$

where W_{net} work that would be supplied through isentropic processes of the cycle.

Equation (23) also shows that the COP of the ideal reversible Carnot cycle is a function only of the two absolute temperatures between which it operates.

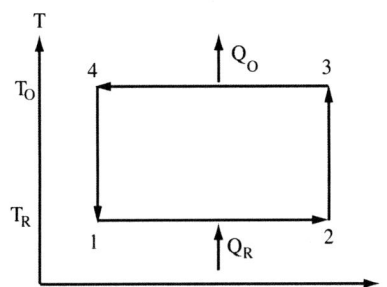

Fig 1-3. Carnot cycle

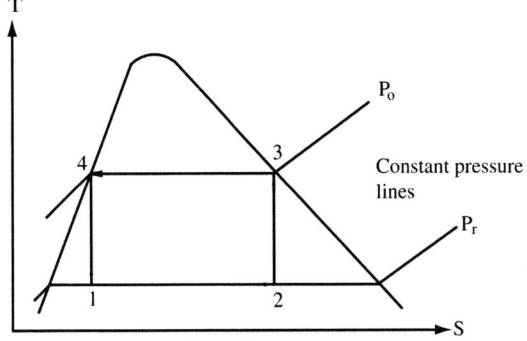

Fig 1-4. Possible thermodynamic realization of a Carnot cycle using a pure substance

The second law for cycles states that (1) no refrigerating cycle may have a COP higher than that for a reversible

cycle operated between the same temperature limits, and (2) all reversible cycles, when operated between the same temperature limits, have the same COP. Proofs of these statements are not presented here. They can be found in standard thermodynamics textbooks. Although the first law states that net heat flow into the cycle is equal to the net work done by the cycle (see Equation (19)), constraints are placed by the second law. For example, it is impossible to put heat into a system and convert it completely to work, a perfect conversion. The second law forces heat to be rejected (which is wasted), and the heat rejection should be to a different temperature reservoir than the temperature of the reservoir from which the heat is added for the cycle to exist. For refrigerating cycles it also establishes the only possible cycles are the ones in which the COP is less than the ideal COP, which is based only on the two extreme temperatures of the cycle.

The Carnot cycle can be created by exploiting the constant temperature and constant pressure characteristics of the phase change saturation region of pure substances for constant temperature heat addition and rejection processes. The isentropic processes that link the states between the high and low temperatures can now be processes between high and low pressures within the saturation dome. Movement from a low to high pressure is easy since pumps and compressors are available, and from high to low pressure can be achieved via turbines. This is shown in Fig. 1-4.

However, in a real device the Carnot cycle shown in Fig. 1-4 is difficult to obtain because of practical considerations. It is difficult to stop process heat addition/removal precisely at state 2. The compression from pressure of 2 to the higher pressure at 3 involves a substance that is mixed liquid and vapor at entry for which reliable compression devices are difficult to make (it is easy to either pump liquid alone or compress vapor). Similar problems occur at the expansion from 4 to 1, perhaps via a turbine, where the inlet is saturated liquid and the outlet is a wet saturated mixture of liquid and vapor. To overcome these problems the standard practical refrigeration cycle is shown in Figs. 1-5a and 1-5b. In this the constant temperature (and constant pressure) heat addition process ends when the entire saturated mixture has turned to saturated vapor at state 2 and a vapor compressor is used from pressure 2 to 3. From 3 to 4 the heat rejection is isobaric, and is only isothermal when in the saturation dome region. The isentropic expansion process from 4 to 1 of the Carnot cycle is replaced by a simple expansion valve that does not preserve entropy but preserves enthalpy. The advantage is that a moving device is avoided and a passive valve is replaced instead.

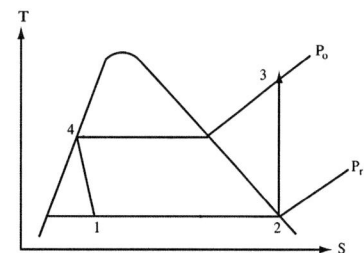

Fig 1-5a. Practical refrigeration cycle in (*T,s*) coordinates

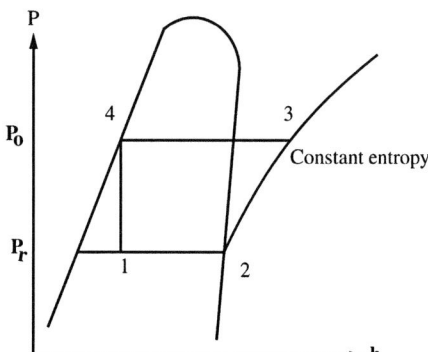

Fig 1-5b. Practical refrigeration cycle in *P-h* coordinates

A pure refrigerant or an azeotropic mixture can be used as the working fluid in the practical refrigerator to maintain constant temperature during phase changes through maintenance at constant pressure. Because of such concerns as high initial cost and increased maintenance requirements, the practical machine has one compressor, and the expander (engine or turbine) is replaced by a simple expansion valve. The valve throttles the refrigerant from high pressure to low pressure. The highest temperature in the cycle is at state 3. Thus, for ideal COP the temperature of 3 has to be used, and not that of state 4. The components of the refrigerator are sketched in Fig. 1-6. Because of the use of a compressor to go from the low temperature state 2 to high temperature state 3, the cycles are called vapor compression cycles.

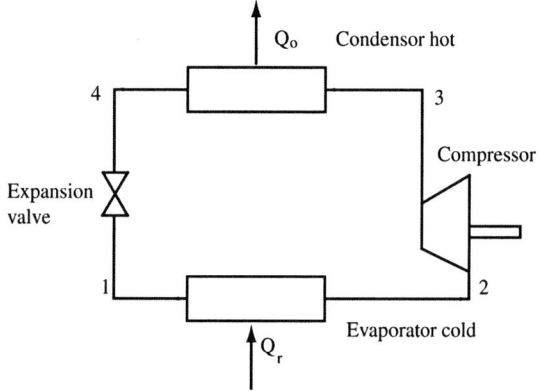

Fig. 1-6. Components of the refrigerator or air conditioner

Fundamentals of Fluid Flow

In addition to density discussed in the previous section, the other property that is of importance in fluid flow is viscosity. The viscosity of the fluid links the shear stress on a fluid layer to the local velocity gradient across the layer. In the terminology of Fig. 1-7, the following relation defines viscosity

$$\tau = \mu \frac{dV}{dy} \qquad (24)$$

where τ = shear stress (tangential force per unit area); and

μ = viscosity.

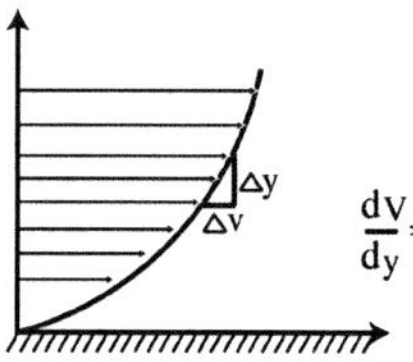

Fig 1-7. Velocity profiles and gradients in viscous flows

The density of air and water at standard conditions 68°F and 14.696 psi (sea level atmospheric pressure) are 0.075 lb_m/ft^3 and 62.3 lb_m/ft^3, respectively. All fluids are compressible to some degree; fluid density depends on pressure. Steady liquid flow may ordinarily be treated as incompressible, and incompressible flow analysis is satisfactory for gases and vapors at velocities below about 4000 to 8000 fpm, except in very long conduits. The units of viscosity are (force × time)/length^2. At standard conditions the viscosities of air and water are 1.2×10^{-5} lb_m/ft-s (= 3.7×10^{-7} lb_f-s/ft^2) and 6.7×10^{-4} lb_m/ft-s (= 2.1×10^{-5} lb_f-s/ft^2), respectively. Kinematic viscosity is viscosity divided by density. The values of kinematic viscosity at standard conditions for air and water are 1.7×10^{-4} ft^2/s and 1.08×10^{-5} ft^2/s, respectively. In general if the Mach number of the fluid is less than 0.30 the fluid can be considered incompressible.

In this chapter the fluid mechanics of pipe and duct flows are emphasized. This is because in HVAC systems flows in pipes and ducts are dominant methods of fluid transport, both airflow to the conditioned space and liquids that are the working fluids in the systems. External flows, such as flows of large fluid volumes over submerged objects, compressible flows such as in turbines and compressors, and the like are not discussed for the sake of brevity and relevance (or lack thereof).

Flow in Pipes and Ducts.—The conservation of mass (or continuity equation) follows the same formulation as described before in the thermodynamics section, Equations (8) and (9). For conservation of energy some simplifications and modifications can be made. For fluid mechanics analyses only conservation of mechanical energy is considered. If steady flow is considered along a single path system then the conservation of energy for open systems, Equation (13), can be rewritten as

$$\left(u + pv + \frac{V^2}{2} + gz\right)_{in} - \left(u + pv + \frac{V^2}{2} + gz\right)_{out} + \frac{\dot{Q}}{\dot{m}} = 0 \quad (25)$$

Here it is assumed that no work producing shafts or work producing moving boundaries are present and that the conservation of mass then permits the inlet and outlet mass flow rates to be the same. Pressure energy, kinetic energy, and potential energy are the mechanical energies of the flow. Since it was shown in the previous thermodynamics section that for most fluids, especially away from the saturation dome, the internal energy u is primarily a function of temperature, u is not considered a mechanical energy. The conservation of mechanical energy is then stated as

$$\left(pv + \frac{V^2}{2} + gz\right)_{in} - \left(pv + \frac{V^2}{2} + gz\right)_{out} = 0 \quad (26a)$$

$$\frac{p}{\rho} + \frac{V^2}{2} + gz = \text{constant} \quad (26b)$$

This is also the Bernoulli's equation, which is the conservation of mechanical energy in an ideal fluid with no losses, no heat additions/removal, and no work. Bernoulli's equation shows that the sum of pressure energy, kinetic energy, and potential energy is constant along a streamline of an ideal fluid. Even when temperature variations are present or the internal energies are not constant or heat transfer is present, the above mechanical energy conservation (and modifications presented below in case of losses) can be separately considered before the entire conservation of energy Equation (13) is eventually applied if needed.

In the case of real fluids, where viscosity introduces drag, loss in mechanical energy occurs. This loss of mechanical energy is usually converted to increase in internal energy or is dissipated as heat, as per general conservation of energy as described in the thermodynamics section. In such a case of losses Equation (26a) of conservation of mechanical energy (presented in the form of energy per unit mass) is rewritten as

$$\left(pv + \frac{V^2}{2} + gz\right)_{in} - \left(pv + \frac{V^2}{2} + gz\right)_{out} = E_{loss} \quad (27)$$

where E_{loss} = mechanical energy loss per unit mass, or rate of mechanical energy loss per unit mass flow rate.

If mechanical energy is added to the flow through appropriate forms of work such as shaft work, the above can be modified to include a source term for mechanical energy. This is shown in

$$\left(pv + \frac{V^2}{2} + gz\right)_{in} + -\left(pv + \frac{V^2}{2} + gz\right)_{out} \quad (28)$$
$$+ E_{mech} = E_{loss}$$

where E_{mech} = mechanical energy added into the pipe or duct flow via a device such as fan, blower, or pump.

Another consideration in the case of real fluids is the velocity V in Equation (28). The velocity V in the above is the average velocity through the pipe and is obtained from the mass flow rate. Because of the viscosity for real fluids, the velocity varies from zero at the duct or pipe walls to a maximum along the centerline. Since it is not mathematically true that the square of the average velocity is equal to the average of squared velocity unless the velocity profile is flat, this introduces an additional kinetic energy factor α in Equation (27) as follows:

$$\left(pv + \alpha\frac{V^2}{2} + gz\right)_{in} - \left(pv + \alpha\frac{V^2}{2} + gz\right)_{out} = E_{loss} \quad (29)$$

The kinetic energy factor is the ratio of the true kinetic energy of the flow to the kinetic energy represented by the mean or average velocity. It is shown that the value of this kinetic energy factor is 2.0 for laminar flow in circular pipes and 1.54 for laminar flow in wide rectangular channels. For turbulent flow the value is close to 1.0. Thus, for most HVAC applications, where the flow is turbulent, the original Bernoulli equation Equation (27), with losses is sufficient.

Reynolds number is an important unitless parameter in fluid mechanics. It is defined for flow in pipes or ducts as

$$Re = \frac{\rho VD}{\mu} \quad (30)$$

where D = diameter for circular pipes or a characteristic length for non-circular pipe.

For other cross-sections it can be the hydraulic diameter D_h which is defined as

$$D_h = \frac{4A}{P} \quad (31)$$

where A = cross-sectional area, and P = perimeter.

For external flows, characteristic length is usually the length of the object along the direction of the flow, or the value of the length's local coordinate depending on the application. For pipe and duct flows the flow is laminar if the Reynolds number is less than 2300 and turbulent for greater values. This value of the critical Reynolds number is observed via experiments. For external flows parallel to a surface the flow remains laminar until the local Reynolds number reaches 5×10^5. Thus, the critical Reynolds number for internal flow is 2300 and for the external flow is 5×10^5. If the Reynolds number exceeds the critical value, the flow transitions to turbulence; below the critical value, the flow is laminar.

Laminar flows are those where viscous effects dominate and the flow is orderly and layered. Fluid particles travel in smooth trajectories, without fluctuations. In steady internal flows, such as in pipes and ducts, the velocity profile is of a form that the forces due to pressure are balanced by viscous shear forces introduced by the presence of a wall (the velocity has to be zero at the wall). This gives rise to parabolic velocity profiles in the pipe or duct, where the velocity vanishes at the walls and is a maximum at the centerline.

Turbulent flows which typically have higher velocities than laminar flows, involve random perturbations or fluctuations of the velocity and pressure, characterized by an extensive hierarchy of scales or frequencies. Only flows involving random perturbations without order or periodicity are turbulent; the velocity in such a flow varies with time or locale of measurement (Fig. 1-8). Turbulence can be quantified by statistical factors. The velocity most often used in velocity profiles is the temporal average velocity, and the strength of the turbulence is characterized by the root mean square of the instantaneous variation in velocity about the temporal average velocity. The effects of turbulence cause fluid to diffuse momentum, heat, and mass very rapidly across the flow. Because of the rapid fluctuations, fluid particles do not travel in smooth trajectories. The fluctuation allows particles to cross layers and thus cause a greater uniformity of flow properties and characteristics than in the laminar case. Because of this the turbulent velocity profiles in pipes or ducts are flatter throughout the core of the flow around the centerline and only fall off to zero velocity at the walls in a small region near the walls. It is because of the flatter velocity profile that the kinetic energy factor in Equation (29) is near unity, usually ranging from 1.01 to 1.10.

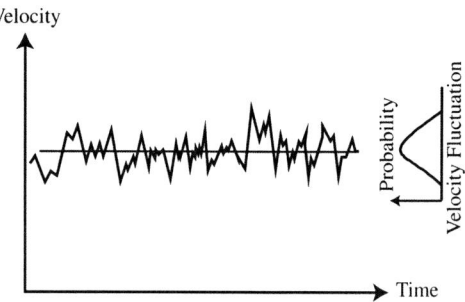

Fig 1-8. Velocity fluctuations with respect to time in turbulent flows

Time average velocity is defined by the Equation (32)

$$\bar{V} = \frac{1}{T}\int_0^T V dt \qquad (32)$$

The laminar and turbulent velocity profiles in a pipe flow are schematically compared in Fig. 1-9. Turbulent flow profiles are flat compared to the more pointed profiles of laminar flow. Near the wall, velocities of the tur-

bulent profile must drop to zero more rapidly than those of the laminar profile, so the shear stress and friction are much greater in the turbulent flow case.

The velocity profiles shown in Fig. 1-9 correspond to fully developed flows. Fully developed flow regions are far away from inlets, from sections of sudden changes in cross-section, and from sources of mechanical energy input. The entrance flow region is the region from an inlet to the location where the fully developed region starts. It corresponds to the length L_e of the pipe or duct needed for the flow to gradually change from its inlet profile to the new conditions.

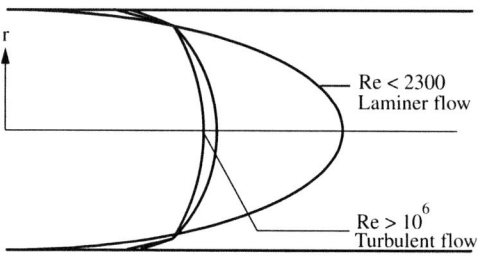

Fig 1-9. Laminar and turbulent velocity profiles in a circular duct

Note that if the cross-sectional area remains constant then by the conservation of mass the average velocity throughout the pipe, including the inlet and fully developed regions, remains the same although the shape of the profile changes.

With laminar flow following a rounded entrance, the entrance length L_e depends on the Reynolds number:

$$\frac{L_e}{D} \cong 0.06 Re \qquad (33)$$

At $Re = 2000$, a length of 120 diameters is needed to establish the fully developed parabolic velocity profile. However, the pressure gradient reaches the developed value of much sooner. With turbulent flow, a length of 80 to 100 diameters following the rounded entrance are needed for the velocity profile to become fully developed, but the friction loss per unit length reaches a value close to that of the fully developed flow value more quickly. After six diameters, the loss rate at a Reynolds number of 10^5 is only 14% above that of fully developed flow in the same length, while at 10^7 it is only 10% higher. For a sharp entrance, the flow separation causes a greater disturbance, but fully developed flow is achieved in about half the length required for a rounded entrance. With sudden expansion, the pressure change settles out in about eight times the diameter change (D_2-D_1), while the velocity profile takes at least a 50% greater distance to return to fully developed pipe flow.

The mechanical energy loss in a duct or pipe of constant cross-section due to friction is given by the following:

$$E_{\text{major-loss}} = E_{\text{loss-friction}} = f\frac{L}{D}\frac{V^2}{2} \qquad (34)$$

where f = friction factor.

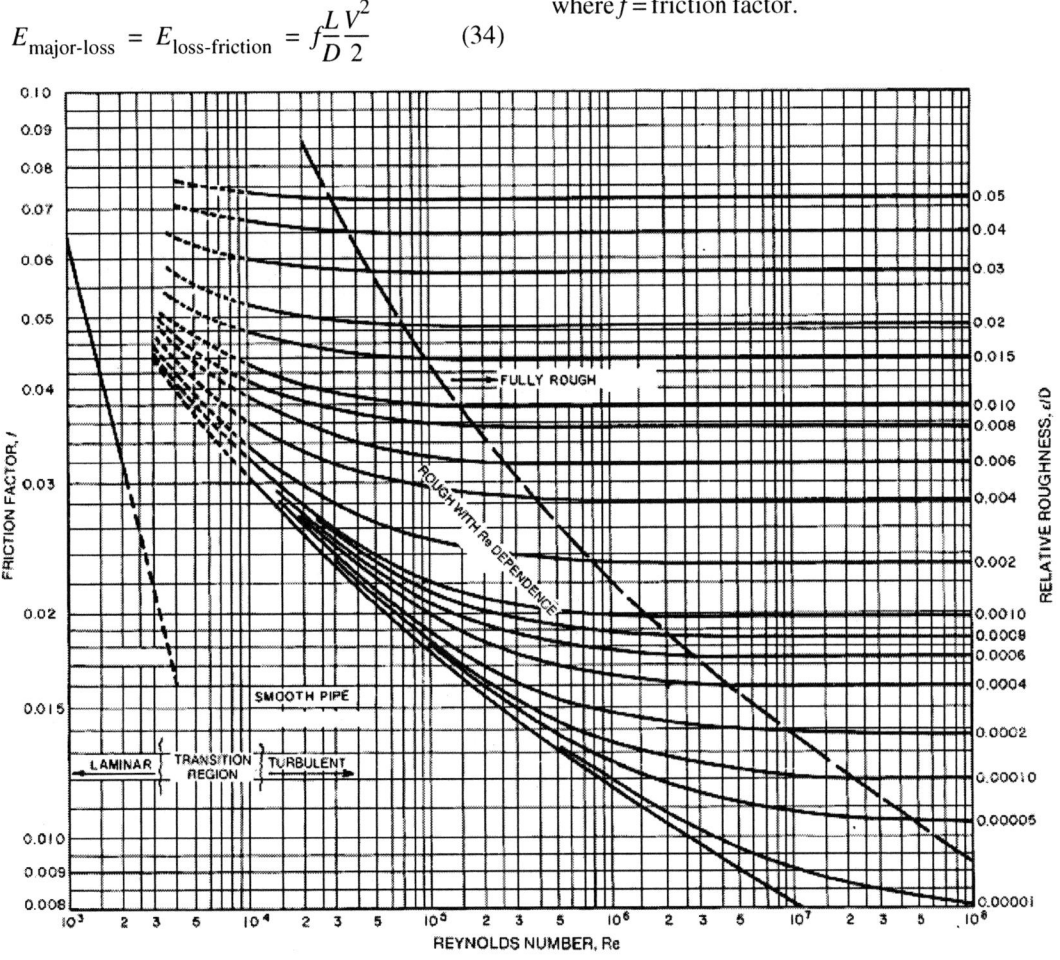

Fig 1-10. Friction factor (Moody's chart)

Losses due to friction are traditionally termed major losses in a pipe or duct system because for long pipes this loss dominates. However, for HVAC applications this may not be the case, and so the terminology of major losses may not be as appropriate as simple friction loss. Here L is the length of the pipe and D is the diameter. For noncircular ducts, the diameter may be replaced by the hydraulic diameter D_h. Friction factor is a function of the Reynolds number and the relative roughness of the pipe or duct walls. For large Reynolds numbers its value is fairly constant and is only a function of the roughness ε/D, where ε is the average height of roughness. This region is called the fully rough region. The value of friction factor is obtained via experiments and the values are given in Fig. 1-10 and in Equations (35) to (38).

In the laminar region, where the Reynolds number is less than 2300, the friction factor is independent of the roughness. This is because the dominant viscous effects suppress any fluctuations introduced by roughness. The value of f for this region is given as

$$f = \frac{64}{Re} \qquad (35)$$

for circular cross-section pipes. In non circular pipes exact values for f can be derived for laminar flow, and the use of hydraulic diameter in Equation (35) may lead to significant errors.

In turbulent flows for smooth pipes the friction factor is empirically correlated as

$$f = \frac{0.3164}{Re^{0.25}} \qquad \text{for} \quad Re < 10^5 \qquad (36)$$

$$f = 0.0032 + \frac{0.221}{Re^{0.237}} \quad \text{for} \quad 10^5 < Re < 3 \times 10^6 \qquad (37)$$

Another correlation for smooth pipes is

$$f = \frac{0.184}{Re^{0.20}} \qquad \text{for} \quad Re > 2 \times 10^4 \qquad (38)$$

For pipes and ducts that are not smooth, where a wall roughness ε is defined (in the units of length), the relative roughness ε/D plays an important role. In the fully rough region where the influence of Reynolds number is very small, the turbulent friction factor has been empirically correlated by

$$\frac{1}{\sqrt{f}} = 1.14 + 2\log\left(\frac{D}{\varepsilon}\right) \qquad (39)$$

In the other turbulent regime between the smooth walled pipes and the fully rough region several empirical correlations exist. A commonly used correlation is the Colebrook function given by

$$\frac{1}{\sqrt{f}} = 1.14 + 2\log\left(\frac{D}{\varepsilon}\right) - 2\log\left[1 + \frac{9.3D}{\varepsilon Re\sqrt{f}}\right] \qquad (40)$$

The use of hydraulic diameter D_h in the above correlations for turbulent flows is quite acceptable since errors up to 5% may be introduced as observed experimentally.

Mechanical energy losses other than friction loss described above in a pipe or duct are usually correlated by using a loss coefficient K:

$$E_{\text{loss-minor}} = E_{\text{loss-fixture}} = K\frac{V^2}{2} \qquad (41)$$

For inlets, the V in Equation (41) is velocity in the pipe after the entrance, and for outlets it is the velocity in the pipe before the exit. Thus, which velocity to use is a function of the geometry or of the type of the fitting or fixture. For a sudden expansion it is velocity before expansion and for a sudden contraction of cross sectional area it is velocity after contraction. The values of K are compiled via experiments and will be discussed in later chapters. It may be noted that although the true loss of mechanical energy occurs over a distance the formula lumps its effects at one location. For example, the inlet loss occurs over the entrance region but is lumped at the entrance by this formula. Note that these effects do not include the friction loss over the corresponding length, but only the additional losses associated with disturbances of flow and transitions. For systems with long pipe lengths these losses are a small portion of the total losses where the friction losses dominate and are traditionally called minor losses. However, for HVAC systems this is not the case and the multiple bends and junctions, size changes, and the presence of various fixtures and fittings ensure that these effects are a very significant part of the total loss.

Some Details of Relevant Flow Fields.—The presence of walls in fluid flows introduces velocity gradients in the flow field since the fluid necessarily has to be at zero velocity at the wall. This effect, termed friction, usually is present in the form of a boundary layer in fast moving flows. A boundary layer is the slender region near the wall where the velocity goes from the zero wall velocity to the free stream velocity. All the viscous effects are concentrated in the boundary layer. For flow around bodies, this layer (which is quite thin relative to distances in the flow direction) encompasses all viscous or turbulent actions, causing the velocity in it to vary rapidly from zero at the wall to that of the outer flow at its edge. Boundary layers are generally laminar near the start of their formation but may become turbulent downstream of the transition point.

For conduit or pipe flows, spacing between adjacent walls or within the pipe diameter is generally small compared with distances in the flow direction. As a result, layers from the walls meet at the centerline to fill the conduit. The region after the layers meet is the fully developed flow region that was discussed earlier. The length of the pipe or conduit where the boundary layers are still growing and have not yet met at the centerline is called the entrance region. Near the start of the straight conduit or pipe, the layer is very thin (and laminar in all probability), so the uniform velocity core outside has a velocity only slightly greater than the average velocity. As the layer grows in thickness, the slower velocity near the wall needs to increase in the uniform core to satisfy continuity. As the flow proceeds, the wall layers grow (and the centerline velocity increases) until they join, after an entrance length L_e. Application of the Bernoulli relation to the core flow indicates a decrease in pressure along the layer.

However, if the cross-sectional area is increasing along the flow so that average velocity decreases along the flow, the adverse pressure gradient can lead to flow separation. The development of the boundary layer in an adverse-pressure gradient situation (velocity at edge of layer decreasing in flow direction) causes the separation of the boundary layer where downstream from the separation point the fluid backflows near the wall. Separation is due to flow near the wall no longer having energy to move into the higher pressure imposed by the decrease in velocity at the edge of the layer. The locale of this separation is difficult to predict, especially for the turbulent boundary layer. Analyses verify the experimental observation that a turbulent boundary layer is less subject to separation than a laminar one because the flow in the turbulent layer has greater kinetic energy.

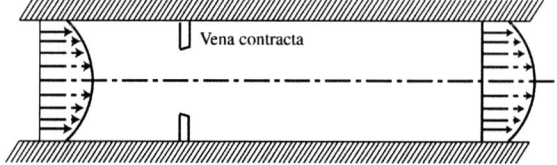

Fig 1-11a. Flow through orifice

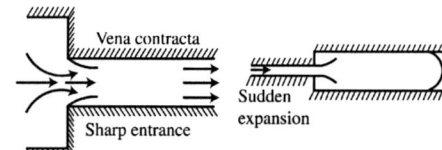

Fig 1-11b. Flow through sudden contraction or expansion

Flow separation is observed in several situations in HVAC equipment. Examples of flow through an orifice and through contractions and expansions are shown in Figs. 1-11a and 1-11b. The manifestation of separation is sudden pressure drop that is not recovered in the flow.

In liquid flow, gas- or vapor-filled pockets can occur if the absolute pressure is reduced to vapor pressure or less. In this case, a cavity or series of cavities form. This lowering of pressure may be due to flow separation or poor selection of operating parameters or equipment design. This is called cavitation and initial evidence of cavitation is the collapse noise of many small bubbles as they are carried by the flow into regions of higher pressure. The severity of cavitation increases as velocity increases or pressure decreases. Collapse of the cavities on or near solid boundaries becomes so frequent that the cumulative impact in time results in damage in the form of cavitations erosion of the surface or excessive vibration. As a result, pumps can lose efficiency or their parts may erode locally.

Noise from Fluid Flow.—Noise from fluid flow is especially important in HVAC systems where, for example, noisy ducts inside buildings can significantly cause complaints. Noise in flowing fluids results from unsteady flow fields and can be at discrete frequencies or broadly distributed over the audible range. With liquid flow, cavitation results in noise through the collapse of vapor bubbles. Noise in pumps or fittings (such as valves) can be easily eliminated by raising the system pressure. With severe cavitation, the resulting unsteady flow can produce by-product noise from induced vibration of adjacent parts.

Noise produced in pipes and ducts is especially associated with the loss through the valves and fittings. The sound pressure of noise in water pipe flow increases linearly with the head loss; the broadband noise increases, but only in the lower frequency range. Fitting-produced noise levels also increase with fitting loss (even without cavitation) and significantly exceed noise levels pipe flow. The relation between noise and loss associated with is because both involve excessive flow perturbations. A valve's pressure flow characteristics and structural elasticity may be such that for some operating point it oscillates, perhaps in resonance with part of the piping system, to produce excessive noise. A change in operating point conditions or details of valve geometry can result in significant noise reduction.

Pumps and blowers are strong potential noise sources. Turbo machinery noise is associated with blade-flow occurrences. Broadband noise results from vortex and turbulence interaction with walls and is primarily a function of the operating point of the machine. For blowers, noise is a minimum at the peak efficiency point. Narrow-band noise also occurs at the blade, crossing frequency and its harmonics. To reduce this noise, a designer

increases the clearances between impeller and housing, and spaces impeller blades unevenly around the circumference. However, this may be impractical because they lead to other problems.

Fundamentals of Heat Transfer

Heat is transfer of energy due to temperature difference. Solution of conservation of energy Equations (11) to (13) require the accurate assessment of heat transported into a closed or open system. Heat transfer theory is needed to quantify the rate at which heat will transfer for a given set of conditions. Although application of thermodynamic law requires the value of heat transfer be known, it does not provide any method to ascertain whether the required or prescribed heat transfer rate is feasible for the given system and available temperature differences. Thermal energy transfer always occurs in the direction of decreasing temperature.

Thermal conduction is the mechanism of heat transfer whereby energy is transported between parts of a continuum by the transfer of kinetic energy between particles or groups of particles at the atomic and subatomic levels. In liquids and gases, conduction is caused by elastic collision of molecules; in liquids and electrically nonconducting solids, it is caused by oscillations of the lattice structure (or phonons); in metals it occurs due to the motion of free electrons. In the study of engineering heat transfer, in contrast with physics, the underlying microscopic mechanism is not of interest and the entire conduction effect is lumped into understanding thermophysical properties.

Thermal conductivity k is defined as the ratio of heat flow rate per unit area to the local temperature gradient. This is given by Fourier's law,

$$\dot{Q} = -kA\frac{dT}{dx} \qquad (42)$$

where A = cross-sectional area (ft^2) normal to the heat flow; and

$\dot{Q}$ = rate of heat flow (Btu/hr).

In Equation (42) steady heat flow along the x direction is considered. The units for k are Btu-ft/hr-ft^2-°F and units of temperature T and distance x are °F and ft, respectively. The minus sign indicates that heat flow is positive in the direction of decreasing temperature (i.e., negative gradient). Thermal conductivity is an intrinsic property of a material and is tabulated in handbooks and property tables.

In solid opaque bodies, thermal conduction is the most significant heat transfer mechanism because there is no flow of material, and transport by other heat transfer mechanisms such as convection and radiation are not present. In fluids, thermal conduction dominates in the region very close to the flows solid boundary. However, in fluids the effects of conduction near the boundary are lumped into heat convection coefficients.

The distinction made between thermal convection and thermal conduction is this: Heat convection involves energy transfer or exchange at an interface, notably, the solid-fluid interface— the walls. Heat conduction occurs throughout the entire body of the transport mechanism. The heat transfer coefficient h is defined at the interface in the fluid region so that the rate of heat flow is related to the temperature difference by

$$\dot{Q} = hA(T_{surface} - T_{fluid}) \qquad (43)$$

where $T_{surface}$ = temperature of the solid surface; and

T_{fluid} = bulk or free stream temperature of the fluid (not the local temperature of the fluid near the surface)

Equation (43) relates the heat flow rate from the surface to the fluid. The units for h are Btu/hr-ft^2-°F. For pipe flows the fluid temperature in Equation (43) is the bulk mean temperature at the cross-section where the convective heat transport is being considered.

The heat transfer coefficient is an engineering concept that combines all microscopic energy transport processes near a solid-fluid interface into a single coefficient. The heat transfer coefficient is strongly a function of flow conditions and increases as flow velocities increase. It is not an intrinsic property of any material and it must computed or measured at the required flow configurations and geometries.

Thermal convection can be classified into two types: forced and natural. Forced convection occurs when fluid is flowing due to external mechanisms such as the case of it being driven by fans or pumps. Natural convection occurs in fluid that is normally quiescent, but is forced into motion by thermal buoyancy effects. For example, hot fluid near a hot wall rises because its density is lowered and colder fluid moves in to replace it, thereby setting up a loop that removes heat from the hot wall. In this case the value of h is strongly a function of temperature, the variations of the density with temperature, and the geometry of the system.

For internal flows through pipes and ducts the convective heat transfer coefficient stays constant along the direction of the flow in the fully developed region, i.e., after the entrance length region. For external flows the local convective heat transfer coefficient changes along the direction of the flow because the boundary layer keeps on growing, as opposed to internal flow where the boundary layers meet at the centerline at the end of the entrance region and no further changes in flow occur. The forced flow heat transfer correlations can be written generally as

$$Nu = CRe^n Pr^m \qquad (44)$$

where C, m, n = constants whose values are functions of the operating range and geometry, and

Nu = Nusselt number.

Nusselt number is given by

$$Nu = \frac{hL}{k} \qquad (45)$$

where L = characteristic length for the configuration; and

k = the thermal conductivity of the liquid.

The length in the Reynolds number is the same characteristic length as in the Nusselt number. For pipes the characteristic length is the diameter D or the hydraulic diameter D_h for non-circular pipes. For flat surfaces the length to be used is the entire length along the direction of flow for computing average heat transfer coefficient, or the local coordinate along the direction of the flow to compute the local heat transfer coefficient. The Prandtl number is a ratio of viscous and thermal diffusivities of the fluid and given by

$$Pr = \frac{\mu}{\rho\alpha} = \frac{\mu C_p}{k} \qquad (46)$$

where α = thermal diffusivity.

The thermal diffusivity is given by

$$\alpha = \frac{k}{\rho C_p} \qquad (47)$$

The general forced convection Equation (44) remains valid for flows inside pipe and ducts, as well as over flat surfaces and other objects. The constants C, n, and m for the above forced convection correlation are given in Table 1-1.

Table 1-1. Forced Convection Factors

Description of Flow	Characteristic Length	C	n	m
Laminar, fully developed flow in a circular pipe, constant surface temperature	Diameter D	3.66	0	0
Laminar, fully developed flow in a circular pipe, constant surface heat flux	Diameter D	4.36	0	0
Laminar, fully developed flow in a duct of square cross-section, constant surface temperature	Hydraulic diameter D_h	2.98	0	0
Laminar, fully developed flow in a duct of square cross-section, constant surface heat flux	Hydraulic diameter D_h	3.61	0	0
Laminar, fully developed flow in a duct of triangular cross-section, constant surface temperature	Hydraulic diameter D_h	2.47	0	0
Laminar, fully developed flow in a duct of triangular cross-section, constant surface heat flux	Hydraulic diameter D_h	3.11	0	0
Turbulent, fully developed flow in a pipe, heat added to fluid	Hydraulic diameter D_h	0.023	0.8	0.4
Turbulent, fully developed flow in a pipe, heat removed from fluid	Hydraulic diameter D_h	0.023	0.8	0.3

Table 1-1. *(Continued)* **Forced Convection Factors**

Description of Flow	Characteristic Length	C	n	m
Laminar flow parallel to flat surface, constant surface temperature, local heat transfer coefficient	Local coordinate in flow direction x	0.332	0.5	0.33
Laminar flow parallel to flat surface, constant surface temperature, average heat transfer coefficient	Length in flow direction L	0.664	0.5	0.33
Laminar flow parallel to flat surface, constant surface heat flux, local heat transfer coefficient	Local coordinate in flow direction x	0.453	0.5	0.33
Laminar flow parallel to flat surface, constant surface heat flux, average heat transfer coefficient	Length in flow direction L	0.68	0.5	0.33
Turbulent flow parallel to flat surface, constant surface temperature, local heat transfer coefficient	Local coordinate in flow direction x	0.0296	0.8	0.33
Turbulent flow parallel to flat surface, constant surface heat flux, local heat transfer coefficient	Local coordinate in flow direction x	0.0308	0.8	0.33
Cross-flow over a circular cylinder, average heat transfer coefficient, $0.4< Re <4$	Diameter D	0.989	0.33	0.33
Cross-flow over a circular cylinder, average heat transfer coefficient, $4< Re <40$	Diameter D	0.911	0.385	0.33
Cross-flow over a circular cylinder, average heat transfer coefficient, $40< Re <4000$	Diameter D	0.683	0.466	0.33
Cross-flow over a circular cylinder, average heat transfer coefficient, $4000< Re <40000$	Diameter D	0.193	0.618	0.33
Cross-flow over a circular cylinder, average heat transfer coefficient, $40000< Re <400000$	Diameter D	0.027	0.805	0.33
Cross-flow over tube bank rows, aligned inline square spacing, center to center distance on square $= 2D$	Diameter D^a	0.229	0.632	0.33
Flow over packed spheres	Diameter D	2.06	0.425	0.33

^{a} Note: Reynolds number in this case uses the maximum velocity in the space between tubes.

In the case of entry length flow in circular pipes the laminar correlation is modified as follows for the constant surface temperature case:

$$Nu = 3.66 + \frac{0.0668\left(\frac{D}{L}\right)RePr}{1 + 0.04\left[\left(\frac{D}{L}\right)RePr\right]^{\frac{2}{3}}} \tag{48}$$

where D = diameter and;

L = length of the pipe that includes the thermal entry length.

The Reynolds and Nusselt number are based on the diameter. The effects of thermal entry length on turbulent flows are not significant and the fully developed case can be used. Similarly, the effects of surface roughness are not noticeable in the heat transfer coefficient for turbulent flows (in contrast to the fluid mechanics friction factor), and thus need to be considered.

For flows parallel to flat surfaces the initial boundary layer is always laminar and makes the transition to the turbulent layer after the local Reynolds number becomes greater than critical. Thus, for flows that do become turbulent, the average heat transfer coefficient involves the initial laminar correlations, and then the turbulent. The average heat transfer coefficient for such cases is

$$Nu = (0.037Re^{0.80} - 871)Pr^{\frac{1}{3}} \tag{49}$$

Here the characteristic length is the length of the surface L in the direction of the flow, provided that Re based on this length is greater than the critical value 5×10^5.

A general formula for the average heat transfer coefficient for the external cross-flow over a cylinder, over the entire range of Reynolds numbers, is given by

$$Nu = 0.30 + \frac{0.62Re^{\frac{1}{2}}Pr^{\frac{1}{3}}}{\left[1 + (0.40Pr)^{\frac{2}{3}}\right]^{\frac{1}{4}}}\left[1 + \left(\frac{Re}{282000}\right)^{\frac{5}{8}}\right]^{\frac{4}{5}} \tag{50}$$

The general correlation for natural convection is given by

$$Nu = C(GrPr)^n = CRa^n \tag{51}$$

where C, n = are constants whose values depend on the operating range and geometry.

The Grashof number Gr is given by

$$Gr = \frac{L^3\rho^2\beta g\Delta T}{\mu^2} = \frac{L^3\rho^2\beta g|T_{surface} - T_{fluid}|}{\mu^2} \tag{52}$$

where ΔT = magnitude of the difference between the surface temperature and the free-stream or bulk fluid temperature.

The characteristic length L in the above natural convection correlations represents diameter for horizontal circular pipes, height for vertical plates or pipes, and radius for spheres. For vertical flat surfaces, the natural convection flows remain laminar until the value of $(GrPr)$ reaches 10^9. The Rayleigh number Ra is product of the Grashof and Prandtl numbers, and thus the critical Rayleigh number for natural convection over vertical flat plates is 10^9.

The values of the constants in Equation (51) the correlation for natural convection are given in the following table:

Table 1-2. Natural Convection Factors

Description of Flow	Characteristic length	C	n
Laminar, vertical surface, average heat transfer coefficient	Length L along flow	0.59	0.25
Turbulent, vertical surface, average heat transfer coefficient	Length L along flow	0.1	0.333
Horizontal surface, upper surface of heated plate or lower surface of cooled plate, average heat transfer coefficient, $10^4 < Ra < 10^7$	Plate surface area divided by perimeter	0.54	0.25
Horizontal surface, upper surface of heated plate or lower surface of cooled plate, average heat transfer coefficient, $10^7 < Ra < 10^{11}$	Plate surface area divided by perimeter	0.15	0.333
Horizontal surface, upper surface of cooled plate or lower surface of heated plate, average heat transfer coefficient, $10^5 < Ra < 10^{11}$	Plate surface area divided by perimeter	0.270	0.25
Horizontal cylinder, average heat transfer coefficient, $10^{-10} < Ra < 10^{-2}$	Diameter D	0.675	0.058
Horizontal cylinder, average heat transfer coefficient, $10^{-2} < Ra < 10^2$	Diameter D	1.02	0.148
Horizontal cylinder, average heat transfer coefficient, $10^2 < Ra < 10^4$	Diameter D	0.85	0.188
Horizontal cylinder, average heat transfer coefficient, $10^4 < Ra < 10^7$	Diameter D	0.48	0.25
Horizontal cylinder, average heat transfer coefficient, $10^7 < Ra < 10^{12}$	Diameter D	0.125	0.333

A correlation that covers the entire range of Ra for a vertical plate has been developed as

$$Nu = \left\{ 0.825 + \frac{0.387 Ra^{\frac{1}{6}}}{\left[1 + \left(\frac{0.492}{Pr} \right)^{\frac{9}{16}} \right]^{\frac{8}{27}}} \right\}^2 \quad (53)$$

Similarly a general correlation for a horizontal cylinder or pipe over the entire operating range for $Ra < 10^{12}$ has been formulated as

$$Nu = \left\{ 0.60 + \frac{0.387 Ra^{\frac{1}{6}}}{\left[1 + \left(\frac{0.559}{Pr} \right)^{\frac{9}{16}} \right]^{\frac{8}{27}}} \right\}^2 \quad (54)$$

Thermal radiation is the transport of heat via electromagnetic waves or photons. Whereas conduction and convection require a medium, radiation transport can occur in a vacuum. The rate of thermal radiant energy emitted by a surface depends on its absolute temperature. A surface is called black if it can absorb all incident radiation. The total energy W_b emitted per unit time per unit area of black surface to the hemispherical region above it is given by the Stefan-Boltzmann law:

$$\dot{Q} = A W_b = A \sigma T^4 \quad (55a)$$

where σ = Stefan-Boltzmann constant, and

   T = absolute temperature in absolute units (Rankine or Kelvin).

Substances and surfaces diverge in various ways from the Stefan-Boltzmann laws. W_b is the maximum emissive power at a surface temperature. Actual surfaces emit and absorb less than these maximums and are called non-black. The emissive power of a nonblack surface at temperature T radiating to the hemispherical region above it is written as

$$\dot{Q} = A W_b = A \varepsilon \sigma T^4 \quad (55b)$$

where ε = hemispherical emittance.

Emittance is a function of the material, the condition of its surface, and the temperature of the surface.

When radiation energy is incident on a surface, such as solar flux incident on a wall, the fraction of energy absorbed by the surface is the radiation absorptance. For engineering applications absorptance is taken to be equal to emittance. The rest of the incident radiation is reflected back and the reflectance is equal to 1– absorptance, which is equal to 1 – emittance.

If the surface is not completely opaque then some of energy is transmitted. An example is a pane of glass in a window. Incident radiation energy is either absorbed, reflected or transmitted. The relationship between these is

$$\text{Absorptance} + \text{Reflectance} + \text{Transmittance} = 1$$
$$\text{Absorptance} = \text{Emittance} \quad (56)$$

Overall Heat Transfer.—Many applications in HVAC involve different modes of heat transfer occurring in series or in parallel. For example, the loss of heat from a room to the cold outside ambient space through the walls involves three heat transfer steps: the transfer of heat from the indoor air to the inner surface of the wall via convection, the transfer of heat from the inner surface of the wall to the outer via conduction through the wall; and the transfer of heat from the outer surface to the cold ambient outdoors. If the temperatures of the indoor air and outdoor ambient spaces are T_1 and T_2 respectively, the rate of heat transport is given by

$$\dot{Q} = UA(T_1 - T_2) \quad (57)$$

where U = overall heat transfer coefficient.

If the wall temperatures are T_{w1} and T_{w2}, respectively at the inner and outer surfaces, and the corresponding heat transfer coefficients are h_1 and h_2, then the same heat transfer rate evaluated through the three individual steps is given by

$$\dot{Q} = h_1 A(T_1 - T_{w1}) = \frac{kA(T_{w1} - T_{w2})}{L}$$

$$= h_2 A(T_{w2} - T_2)$$

(58)

where k = thermal conductivity of the wall material; and

L = thickness of the wall in the direction of the flow of heat.

Combining Equation (57) and Equation (58) gives the expression for the overall heat transfer coefficient for this case as

$$\frac{1}{UA} = \frac{1}{h_1 A} + \frac{L}{kA} + \frac{1}{h_2 A}$$

(59)

The overall heat transfer coefficient can also be evaluated by considering thermal resistances. Through an analogy of flow of heat to flow of electricity through conductors where the driving potential is temperature difference, the thermal resistance can be defined as

$$R_{th} = \frac{\Delta T}{\dot{Q}}$$

(60)

where $\dot{Q}$ = heat flow rate analogous to electric current and;

R_{th} = is the thermal resistance.

Sometimes R_{th} is written without subscript as R. When many thermal steps are in series the thermal resistances add in series and the total resistance is related to the overall heat transfer coefficient. This is elaborated in Table 1-3.

Thus, the following can be used to compute the overall heat transfer coefficient when the resistances are in series:

$$\frac{1}{UA} = \sum R_{th}$$

(61)

If the resistances are not completely in series, then Equation (61) can be modified appropriately to account for the correct series/parallel addition of the thermal resistances.

Fins and Extended Surfaces.—Heat transfer from a surface, such as indoor radiator surfaces in heating and cooling systems, can be increased by attaching fins or extended surfaces that increase the area available for convective heat transfer. Fins provide a more compact heat transfer device with lower material costs for a given performance. Since heat flow rate is directly proportional to heat transfer coefficient, surface area, and temperature difference, increasing any of these three parameters will increase heat flow rate. However, increasing the convective heat transfer requires active processes such as introducing fans. Increasing surface area via extended

surfaces is a passive, inexpensive method of increasing heat flow.

Table 1-3. Solutions for Some Steady State Thermal Conduction Problems

System	Figure
Overall heat transfer coefficient U, where A is the reference surface chosen to define U $$R_{th} = \frac{1}{UA}$$	
Flat wall or curved wall if curvature is small (wall thickness less than 0.1 of inside diameter) $$R_{th} = \frac{L}{kA}$$	
Radial flow through a right circular cylinder $$R_{th} = \frac{\ln\left(\frac{r_0}{r_i}\right)}{2\pi k L}$$	
Buried cylinder $$R_{th} = \frac{\ln\left[\frac{(a + \sqrt{a^2 - r^2})}{r}\right]}{2\pi k L}$$ $$= \frac{\cosh^{-1}\left(\frac{a}{r}\right)}{2\pi k L}$$	
Radial flow in a hollow sphere $$R_{th} = \frac{\left(\frac{1}{r_i} - \frac{1}{r_0}\right)}{4\pi k}$$	
Convection at a surface of area A $$R_{th} = \frac{1}{hA}$$	
Improper contact between solids with contact conductance h_c $$R_{th} = \frac{1}{h_c A}$$	

Fin efficiency ϕ is defined as the ratio of the actual heat transferred from the fin to the heat that would be transferred if the entire fin were at its root or base temperature. This measure is needed because the temperature of the fin varies from its base to the tip as heat flows from the base to the tip and heat is lost from the lateral surfaces. Fin efficiency is low for long fins, thin fins, or fins made of low thermal conductivity material. For an infinitely long fin the fin efficiency asymptotically reaches zero. Fin efficiency decreases as the heat transfer coefficient increases because of increased heat flow. For natural convection in air cooled condensers and evaporators, where h for the air side is low, fins can be fairly large and fabricated from low conductivity materials such as steel, instead of copper or aluminum. For condensing and boiling, where large heat transfer coefficients are relevant, fins must be very short for optimal use of material. The value of fin efficiency is a function of fin geometry, and some shapes are shown in Fig. 1-12.

Fin effectiveness ε is a more important concept than ϕ, since it relates the heat flow from a surface A_b if it is covered by a fin to heat flow from a surface and not covered by a fin. It is defined in relation to fin efficiency as

$$\varepsilon = \frac{\dot{Q}_{\text{fin}}}{\dot{Q}_{\text{without fin}}} = \frac{\phi h A_s (T_b - T_a)}{h A_b (T_b - T_a)} = \frac{\phi A_s}{A_b} \quad (62)$$

where A_s = surface area of the fin; and

A_b = surface area covered by fin.

As the physical definition indicates effectiveness is greater than unity. It should be significantly greater than one to justify the additional expense and space needed for the fins. As fin length increases effectiveness will increase asymptotically to a maximum. Here T_b is the surface temperature of the unfinned surface, which is also equal to the temperature of the base of the fin. The maximum value of fin effectiveness for an infinitely long straight fin is given by

$$\varepsilon_{\max} = \sqrt{\frac{k}{h y_b}} \quad (63)$$

where y_b = half the thickness of the fin.

If a surface A is covered partially by a fin (or fins) so that the area covered by fin(s) is A_b and that not covered is $(A - A_b)$, then the heat flow from the entire area is given by

$$\dot{Q} = h(A - A_b)(T_b - T_a) + \varepsilon h A_b (T_b - T_a)$$
$$= h[A + (\varepsilon - 1)A_b](T_b - T_a) \quad (64)$$

The surface effectiveness ε_s of fins for the entire area A that is partially covered by the fins, as above, is given by

$$\varepsilon_s = \frac{\dot{Q}_{\text{with fins}}}{\dot{Q}_{\text{without fins}}} = 1 + (\varepsilon - 1)\frac{A_b}{A} \quad (65)$$

Thus, the surface effectiveness with fins is always greater than one.

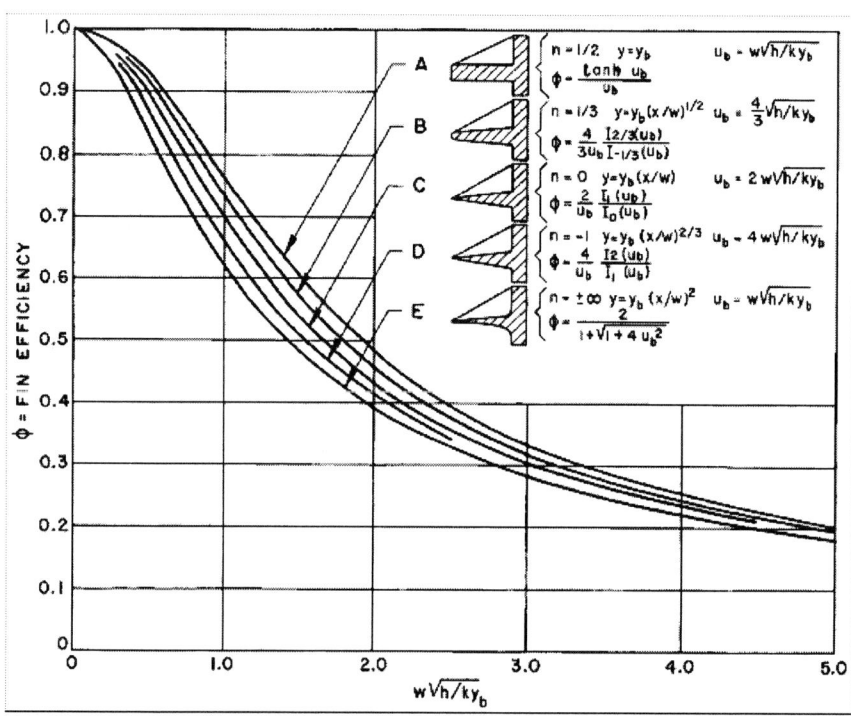

Fig 1-12. Efficiency of straight fins

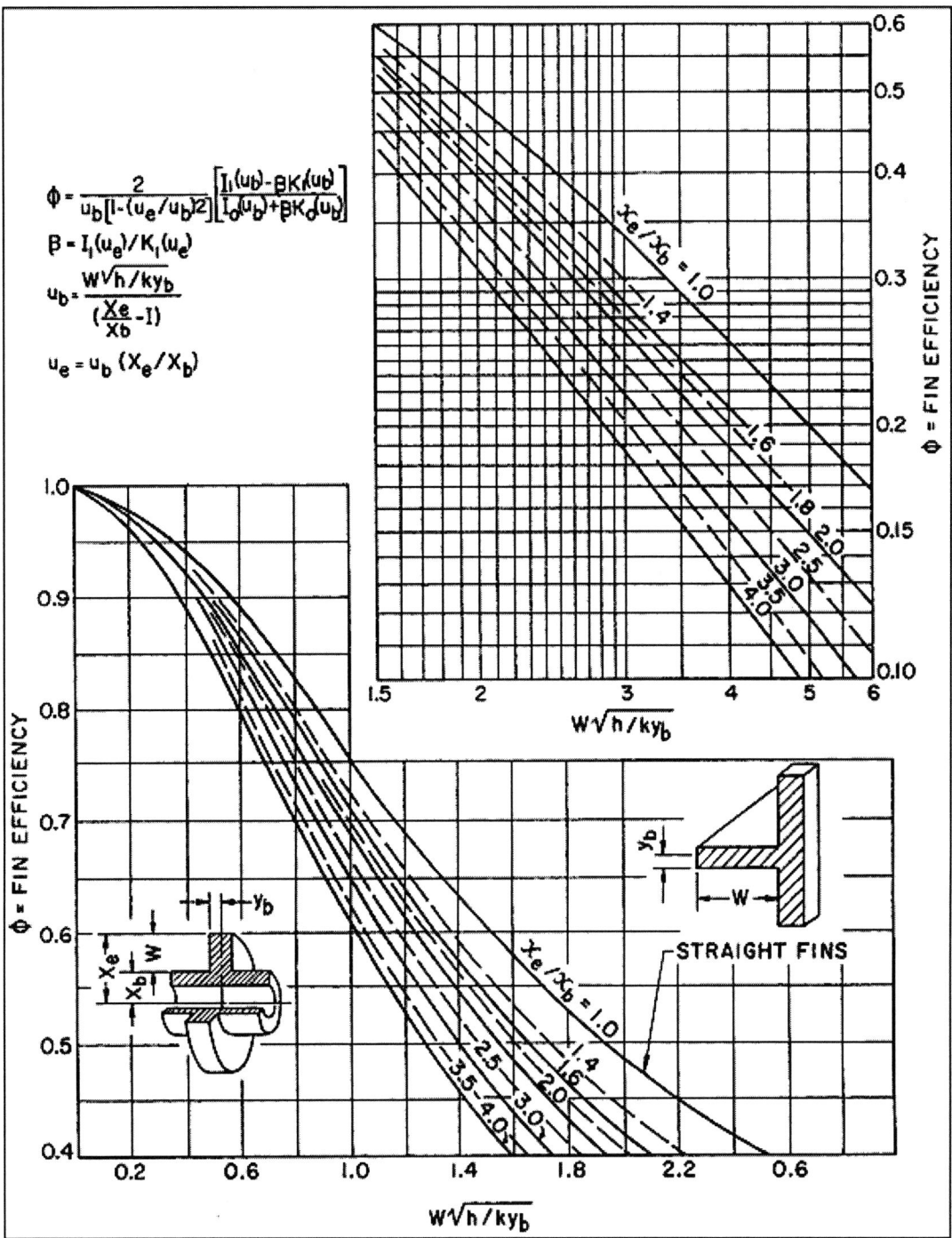

$$\phi = \frac{2}{u_b[1-(u_e/u_b)^2]}\left[\frac{I_1(u_b)-\beta K_1(u_b)}{I_0(u_b)+\beta K_0(u_b)}\right]$$

$$\beta = I_1(u_e)/K_1(u_e)$$

$$u_b = \frac{W\sqrt{h/ky_b}}{\left(\frac{X_e}{X_b}-1\right)}$$

$$u_e = u_b\,(X_e/X_b)$$

Fig 1-13. Fin efficiency for annular fins of constant thickness

Some Details of Heat Exchange.—In this section some mathematical developments of heat transfer in flowing streams are considered. Consider a flow in a pipe, tube, or duct. The energy equation under steady flow conditions Equation (13), neglecting variations in kinetic and potential energies and not considering any work done (other than flow work pv), for a differential distance along the flow direction is given as

$$\dot{m}\frac{dh}{dx}dx = \dot{q}_s dA_s = \dot{q}_s P dx \qquad (66)$$

where P = perimeter;

x = distance along the direction of the flow;

$h = u + pv$, enthalpy; and

$\dot{q}_s$ = heat flux (heat flow rate $\dot{Q}$ per unit area) entering the system from the boundary of the system, i.e., from the pipe surface.

Noting that the enthalpy for liquids and gases in the region way from the saturation region can be related to the temperature T by Equation (3) where C_p is the specific heat at constant pressure, the above energy balance equation is written as

$$\dot{m}C_p\frac{dT_m}{dx} = \dot{q}_s P \qquad (67)$$

In the above equation the temperature is the bulk mean temperature, averaged across the cross-section of the fluid, at distance x.

For the above configuration two cases can be considered: (1) the inner surface of the pipe is at a constant known temperature T_w or (2) there is a constant heat flux $\dot{q}_w$ of known magnitude at the pipe surface. The inlet bulk mean temperature (i.e., at x = 0) is assumed to be known and its value is taken to be T_{in}.

For the case of constant surface temperature, case (1), the energy balance is then rewritten by using the definition of the convective heat transfer coefficient defined at the interface of the fluid and the wall. This yields

$$\dot{m}C_p\frac{dT_m}{dx} = hP(T_w - T_m) \qquad (68)$$

which has an analytical solution if the heat transfer h is a constant (which is true for fully developed flows inside pipe, tubes, and ducts)

$$T_m = T_w - (T_w - T_{in})\exp\left(-\frac{hP}{\dot{m}C_p}x\right) \qquad (69)$$

For a pipe of length L and the corresponding surface area across which heat is added A_w (= PL), this leads expression for the exit temperature

$$T_{out} = T_w - (T_w - T_{in})\exp\left(-\frac{hP}{\dot{m}C_p}L\right)$$
$$= T_w - (T_w - T_{in})\exp\left(-\frac{hA_w}{\dot{m}C_p}\right) \qquad (70)$$

Note that the total heat added to the flow is

$$\dot{Q} = \dot{m}C_p(T_{out} - T_{in}) \qquad (71)$$

By combining Equations (70) and Equation (71) the following expression for the total heat added is formulated:

$$\dot{Q} = hA_w\left(\frac{(T_w - T_{out}) - (T_w - T_{in})}{\ln\left(\frac{(T_w - T_{out})}{(T_w - T_{in})}\right)}\right) \qquad (72)$$
$$= hA_w\Delta T_{lm}$$

where ΔT_{lm} = the log-mean temperature difference.

For the case of constant surface heat flux, case (2), the energy balance can be solved directly to yield

$$T_m = T_{in} + \frac{\dot{q}_w P}{\dot{m}C_p}x \qquad (73)$$

$$T_{out} = T_{in} + \frac{\dot{q}_w P}{\dot{m}C_p}L = T_{in} + \frac{\dot{q}_w A_w}{\dot{m}C_p} \qquad (74)$$

Thus, the temperature of the fluid increases linearly, for case (2) as opposed to the exponential temperature increase for the case of constant wall temperature, case (1). The wall temperature in this case also increases linearly if the heat transfer coefficient is a constant. This is due to the definition of the heat transfer coefficient which is rewritten as

$$T_w = T_m + \frac{\dot{q}_w}{h} \qquad (75)$$

The slopes of the wall temperature and fluid mean temperature are the same, and the offset is a constant value.

A more complicated case is that of two fluid streams exchanging heat through a common wall, such as in a heat exchanger. A hot stream flows on one side of the wall and a cold stream on the other side. In the process the hot stream cools down by losing some heat that is gained by the cold stream, which then warms up. With both the streams considered to be flowing in one direction, given by the coordinate x (such as in a parallel flow heat exchanger), and denoting T_h and T_c to be the local hot and cold stream bulk mean temperatures, respectively, the following set of equations is developed:

$$d\dot{Q} = \dot{m}_c C_c dT_c \qquad (76)$$

$$d\dot{Q} = -\dot{m}_h C_h dT_h \qquad (77)$$

$$dQ = U(T_h - T_c)dA \qquad (78)$$

where dA = incremental area measured along the direction; and

dT = changes of mean temperatures along the x direction.

The overall heat transfer coefficient is U, which includes the effects of convection at the wall surfaces on the hot and cold sides and the conduction through the wall. The above equations, after mathematical manipulations, yield the following solutions:

$$\dot{Q} = \dot{m}_c C_c (T_{c\,out} - T_{c\,in}) \qquad (79)$$

$$\dot{Q} = \dot{m}_h C_h (T_{h\,in} - T_{h\,out}) \qquad (80)$$

$$\dot{Q} = UA \left(\frac{(T_{h\,out} - T_{c\,out}) - (T_{h\,in} - T_{c\,in})}{\ln\left(\frac{T_{h\,out} - T_{c\,out}}{T_{h\,in} - T_{c\,in}}\right)} \right) \qquad (81)$$

The log-mean temperature difference is generally given as

$$\Delta T_{lm} = \frac{\Delta T_1 - \Delta T_2}{\ln\left(\frac{\Delta T_1}{\Delta T_2}\right)} \qquad (82)$$

where ΔT_1 = temperature differences at the first ends of the flow device, and

ΔT_2 = temperature differences at the second ends of the flow device.

In addition to the constant wall temperature case and the parallel flow case, the above equation also holds for a counterflow heat exchanger, where the hot and cold fluids enter at the opposite ends.

Augmentation of Heat Transfer.—Heat transfer augmentation techniques are desirable if the rate of heat flow is to be increased without substantial increase in equipment size and power requirement, and without a corresponding increase in undesirable side effects and losses. Techniques applied to augment (enhance) heat transfer can be classified as either passive methods, which require no direct application of external power, or active schemes, which require external power. Examples of passive techniques include incorporating rough surfaces, extended surfaces, displaced promoters, and vortex flow devices. Examples of active techniques include use of mechanical aids, surface vibration, fluid vibration, and electrostatic fields. The effectiveness of a given augmentation technique depends largely on the mode of heat transfer or the type of heat transfer device to which it is applied. Augmentation is typically used in components of a process or system where the thermal resistances are the highest resistance in the system. Augmentation is also used when it is to reduce the size of the heat transfer component.

Rough surfaces of the spiral repeated rib variety are widely used to improve in-tube heat transfer with water, as in flooded chillers. The roughness may be produced by spirally indenting the outer wall, forming the inner wall, or inserting coils. Longitudinal or spiral internal fins in tubes can be produced by extrusion or forming and give a substantial increase in the surface area. Twisted strips (vortex flow devices) can be inserted as original equipment or as retrofit devices. Microfin tubes (internally finned tubes with short fins around the circumference) are widely used in refrigerant evaporators and condensers. Since the gas entering the condenser in vapor compression refrigeration is superheated, a considerable portion of the condenser acts to de-superheat the flow (i.e., the gas is single phase).

The drawback to these passive techniques is that friction losses increase and the pressure drop may become very high. This requires additional pumping power. However, the increased friction factor may not require increased pumping power in certain cases if the flow rate can be adjusted or if the length of the heat exchanging surface can be reduced by a proper design. Another concern is increased fouling, which occurs when the corrugations or inserts trap impurities and particles that may be present in the flow. This would lead to degradation of flow characteristics and pressures. A related serious concern is the reduction of the heat transfer coefficients due to fouling. However, in general, fouled tubes with augmentation perform better than fouled plain tubes.

PSYCHROMETRY

PSYCHROMETRY

Psychrometrics.—Psychrometrics is the study of the measurement of the moisture content of atmospheric air (moist air). Atmospheric air, or moist air is a mixture of many gases and pollutants plus water vapor. The water vapor (moisture) in atmospheric air exists in a super-heated state at a very low pressure, usually less than 1 psia. One can also define atmospheric air as a mixture of dry air and water vapor (moisture). In 1949, a standard composition of dry air was defined by the International Joint Committee on Psychrometric Data as shown in Table 2-1.

Table 2-1. Composition of Dry Air

Constituent	Molecular Mass	Volume Fraction
Oxygen	32.000	0.2095
Nitrogen	28.016	0.7809
Argon	39.944	0.0093
Carbon dioxide	44.010	0.0003

In HVAC study, psychrometry is commonly taken to mean the study of atmospheric moisture and its effect on buildings and building systems.

Ideal Gas Approximation.—Atmospheric air pressure of 14.7 psi obeys the ideal gas law with sufficient accuracy for most engineering applications. Errors in calculating the fundamental psychrometric parameters, such as enthalpy, specific volume, and humidity ratio of saturated air at 14.7 psi are less than 0.7% for a temperature range of 60°F to 120°F when ideal gas relationships are used. Accordingly, we will assume that atmospheric air behaves as ideal gases with constant specific heat. Table 2-2 gives the properties of some ideal gases.

Table 2-2. Properties of Gases

Gas	Symbol	Relative Molecular Mass	R ft-lb$_f$/lb$_m$-R	C_p Btu/lb$_m$-R	C_p kJ/kg-°K	C_v Btu/lb$_m$-R	C_v kJ/kg-K	K
Air	...	28.97	53.34	0.240	1.00	0.171	0.716	1.400
Argon	Ar	39.94	38.66	0.125	0.523	0.075	0.316	1.667
Carbon dioxide	CO$_2$	44.01	35.10	0.203	0.85	0.158	0.661	1.285
Carbon monoxide	CO	28.01	55.16	0.249	1.04	0.178	0.715	1.399
Helium	He	4.003	386.0	1.250	5.23	0.753	3.153	1.667
Hydrogen	H$_2$	2.016	766.4	3.430	14.36	2.44	10.22	1.404
Methane	CH$_4$	16.04	96.35	0.532	2.23	0.403	1.690	1.320
Nitrogen	N$_2$	28.016	55.15	0.248	1.04	0.177	0.741	1.400
Oxygen	O$_2$	32.000	48.28	0.219	0.917	0.157	0.657	1.395
Steam	H$_2$O	18.016	85.76	0.445	1.863	0.335	1.402	1.329

Fundamental Parameters.—Atmospheric pressure or moist air pressure: Dalton's law for a mixture of ideal gases states that the mixture pressure is equal to the sum of the partial pressures of the constituents:

$$P = P_1 + P_2 + P_3 \qquad (1)$$

For atmospheric or moist air

$$P = P_{N_2} + P_{O_2} + P_{CO_2} + P_{Ar} + P_v \qquad (2)$$

Equation (2) can be written as

$$P = P_a + P_v \qquad (3)$$

where P_a = partial pressure of dry air (mixture of N$_2$, O$_2$, CO$_2$, Ar); and

P_v = partial pressure of water vapor

Equation of State.—The ideal gas for dry air and water vapor is as follows:

1. For dry air:

$$P_a V = n_a RT = m_a R_a T$$

$$\text{or} \qquad P_a = \rho_a R_a T \qquad (4)$$

$$\text{or} \qquad P_a v_a = R_a T$$

2. For water vapor:

$$P_v V = n_v RT = m_v R_v T$$

$$\text{or} \qquad P_v = \rho_v R_v T \qquad (5)$$

$$\text{or} \qquad P_v v_v = R_v T$$

where P_a = partial pressure of dry air;

P_v = partial pressure of water vapor;

V = total volume of mixture;

v = specific volume;

n_a = number of moles of dry air;

n_v = number of moles of water vapor;

R = universal gas constant; 1545.32 ft-lb$_f$/lb-mol-°R, or 8314.41 J/kg-mol-°K;

T = absolute temperature

The mixture also obeys the perfect gas equations:

$$PV = nRT \qquad \text{or}$$
$$(P_a + P_v)V = (n_a + n_v)RT \qquad (6)$$

where $P = P_a + P_v$ is the total pressure of mixture; and

$n = n_a + n_v$ is the total number of moles in the mixture.

To compare values for moist air assuming ideal gas behavior with actual table values, consider a saturated mixture of air and water vapor at 75°F. Table 2-3 gives the saturation pressure P_s of water as 0.43 lb$_f$/ft^2. For saturated air this is the partial pressure (P_v) of the vapor. The mass density is $1/v = 1/739.42$ or 0.001352 lb$_m$/ft^3. By Equation (5) we get

$$\frac{1}{v} = \rho = \frac{P_v}{R_v T} = \frac{0.43 \times 144}{85.78 \times (460 + 75)}$$

$$= 0.001349 \text{ lb}_m / \text{ft}^3$$

This result is accurate within about 0.2 percent. For non-saturated conditions water vapor is superheated and the agreement is generally better.

Humidity Ratio W.— The humidity ratio W is the ratio of the mass of the water vapor m_v to the mass of the dry air m_a in the mixture.

$$W = \frac{m_v}{m_a} \tag{7}$$

Relative Humidity ϕ.— The relative humidity is the ratio of the mole fraction of the water vapor x_v in a mixture to the mole fraction x_s of the water vapor in a saturated mixture at the same temperature and pressure:

$$\Phi = \left|\frac{x_v}{x_s}\right|_{T, P} \tag{8}$$

For a mixture of ideal gases, the mole fraction is equal to the partial pressure ratio of each constituent:

$$x_v = \frac{P_v}{P} \quad \text{and} \quad x_s = \frac{P_s}{P} \tag{9}$$

since the temperature of the dry air and the water vapor are assumed to be the same in the mixture. Substituting Equation (9) in Equation (8) we find

$$\Phi = \frac{P_v/P}{P_s/P} = \left|\frac{P_v}{P_s}\right|_{T, P} \tag{10}$$

where P_v = partial pressure of water vapor at temperature T; and

P_s = saturation pressure of water vapor at temperature T and pressure P (*Values of P_s may be obtained from Table 2-3*).

Using the ideal gas law we can derive a relation between the relative humidity ϕ and the humidity ratio W:

$$W = \frac{m_v}{m_a}$$

$$m_v = \frac{P_v V}{R_v T} \quad \text{and} \quad m_a = \frac{P_a V}{R_a T} \tag{11}$$

$$W = \frac{P_v R_a}{P_a R_v} \tag{12}$$

For the air-water vapor mixture, Equation (12) reduces to

$$W = \frac{18.015 P_v}{28.965 P_a} = 0.6219 \frac{P_v}{P_a}$$

$$= \frac{0.6219 P_v}{P - P_v} \tag{13}$$

Combining Equation (10) and Equation (13) gives

$$\Phi = \frac{W P_a}{0.6219 P_s} \tag{14}$$

Degree of Saturation.—The degree of saturation μ is the ratio of the humidity ratio W to the humidity ratio W_s of a saturated mixture at the same temperature and pressure:

$$\mu = \left|\frac{W}{W_s}\right|_{T, P} \tag{15}$$

Wet Bulb Temperature (T_w).—Fig. 2-1 is a schematic drawing of a device that measures wet and dry-bulb temperatures. The various instruments used to take these measurements are called psychrometers.

When unsaturated air is passed over a wetted thermometer bulb, water evaporates from the wetted surface and latent heat absorbed by the vaporizing water causes the temperature of the wetted surface and the enclosed thermometer bulb to fall. As soon as the wetted surface temperature drops below that of the surrounding atmosphere, heat begins to flow from the warmer air to the cooler surface, and the quantity of heat transferred in this manner increases with an increasing drop in temperature. On the other hand, as the surface temperature drops, the vapor pressure of the water becomes lower, and, hence, the rate of evaporation decreases. Eventually, a temperature is reached where the rate at which heat is transferred from the air to the wetted surface by convection and conduction is equal to the rate at which the wetted surface loses heat in the form of latent heat of vaporization. Thus, no further drop in temperature can occur. This temperature is known as the wet-bulb temperature (T_w).

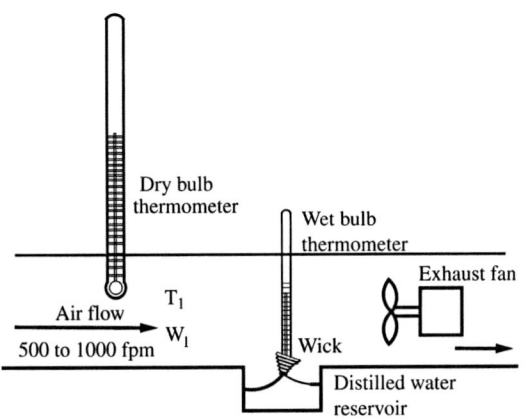

Fig 2-1. Psychrometry apparatus for measuring wet and dry- bulb temperatures

As moisture evaporates from the wetted bulb, the air surrounding the bulb becomes more humid. Therefore, in order to measure the wet-bulb temperature of the air in a given space, a continuous sample of the air must pass around the bulb. The purpose of the fan in Fig. 2-1 is to cause the air to be drawn across the wetted bulb. Conventional air velocities used are between 500 and 1000 fpm for normal size thermometer bulbs. Soft, fine-meshed cotton tubing is recommended for the wick; it should cover the bulb plus about an inch of the thermometer stem. The wick should be watched and replaced before it becomes dirty or crusty. Distilled water is recommended to give greater accuracy for a longer period of time.

Fig. 2-2 shows a device called a sling psychrometer. It is commonly used especially for checking conditions on a job. The instrument is rotated by hand to obtain the air movement across the bulbs. The instrument is rotated until no further change is indicated on the wet bulb. The reading taken at that time is the air wet-bulb temperature.

Thermodynamic wet-bulb temperature (T^*), sometimes called adiabatic saturation temperature, is discussed later.

Partial Pressure of Water Vapor (P_v).—Several equations for calculating this partial pressure have been proposed and used. Carrier's equation, first presented in 1911, has been frequently used with a high degree of accuracy. The equation makes use of the easily obtainable wet and dry-bulb temperatures, and its present form is

$$P_v = P_w - \frac{(P - P_w)(T - T_w)}{2831 - 1.43 T_w} \qquad (16)$$

where P_w = partial pressure of water vapor saturated at wet-bulb temperature T_w;

P = barometric pressure; and

T, T_w = dry and wet-bulb temperatures, respectively, in °F

P_v, P, and P_w must have consistent units, either in Hg or psia.

At temperatures below 32°F, Equation (16) applies only to temperatures of air and water vapor over supercooled water. For partial pressures of water vapor over ice, the denominator becomes $3160 - 0.09 T_w$, and P_w must be the partial pressure of water vapor over ice at T_w, the temperature of an iced wet bulb.

Example 1: A sample of moist air has a dry-bulb temperature of 80°F and a wet-bulb temperature of 70°F. The barometric pressure is 29.90 in. Hg. Determine the partial pressure of the water vapor and of the dry air in the sample of moist air.

Solution: From Table 2-3 at 70°F wet-bulb temperature, find $P_w = 0.3632$ psia. The barometric pressure of 29.90 in. Hg is converted by $(29.90)(0.491) = 14.681$ psia. By Equation (16)

$$P_v = P_w - \frac{(P - P_w)(T - T_w)}{2831 - 1.43 T_w}$$

$$= 0.3632 - \frac{(14.681 - 0.3632)(80 - 70)}{2831 - (1.43)(70)}$$

$$= 0.3107 \text{ psia}$$

Since $P = P_a + P_v$

$$P_a = P - P_v$$

$$= 14.681 - 0.3107$$

$$= 14.37 \text{ psia}$$

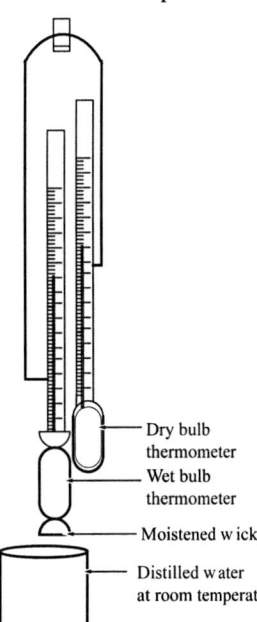

Fig 2-2. Sling psychrometer device for conveniently measuring wet and dry bulb temperatures

Dew Point Temperature (T_d).—During the various seasons of the year, especially during the summer months, in localities where the water supply is cool, it is common to see the outside surface of bare cold water pipes covered with moisture. Another common sight is that of a glass of ice water with its outside surface covered with a film of moisture. The term often used to describe the appearance of moisture on cold surfaces is sweating, as though the moisture came through the walls of the pipe or the glass.

What is actually happening is that the outside of the pipe or the glass is at or below the saturation temperature corresponding to the partial pressure of the water vapor in the surrounding air. This saturation temperature is known as the dew-point (T_d) temperature, the temperature at which condensation first starts to appear on the cold surface as the moist air is cooled at constant pressure.

Example 1, we calculated the partial pressure of the water vapor in the air to be 0.3107 psia. Referring to Table 2-3, we find that the saturation temperature corresponding to a pressure of 0.3107 psia is 65.5°F by interpolation. Therefore, 65.5°F is the dew-point temperature of the air sample. If any surface located in this air sample were at that temperature, moisture would start to condense on the surface.

Air itself does not condense nor does it have anything to do with the cooling and condensation of the water vapor. Actually, the same cooling and condensation of the water vapor would take place if no air were present and the entire process were carried out in a closed vessel under vacuum. Since this definition of the dew point temperature is in common use, however, we will use it in our discussion.

At the dew-point temperature and below, the air is said to be saturated because the air is mixed with the maximum possible weight of water vapor. If the mixture of air and water vapor is cooled at constant pressure, but remains above the dew-point temperature, there will be no condensation. However, as the mixture of air and water vapor is cooled, the volume of each component will contract in the same proportion because both are cooled through the same temperature range. In other words, if a mixture consisting of 1 pound of dry air and 0.15 pound of water vapor is cooled, the resulting smaller volume will still contain 1 pound of dry air and 0.15 pound of water vapor as both gases will contract in the same proportion. Changes in the temperature of an air-water vapor mixture do not affect the amount of water vapor mixed with each pound of air as long as the mixture is not cooled down to the dew-point temperature. Under these conditions, the mass of water vapor per pound of dry air will remain the same regardless of the temperature changes. An air-water vapor mixture at a dry-bulb temperature higher than its dew-point temperature is said to be unsaturated and the water vapor in the mixture is superheated.

At a given total pressure, the dew-point of a mixture is fixed by the humidity ratio W or by the partial pressure of the water vapor. Thus T_d, W, and P_v are not independent properties.

Saturation.—The term "saturation" denotes the maximum amount of water vapor that can exist in one cubic foot of space at a given temperature and is essentially independent of the mass and pressure of the air that may simultaneously exist in the same space. Frequently, we speak of "saturated air". However, it must be remembered that the air is not saturated; it is the contained water vapor that may be saturated at the air temperature.

Enthalpy.—The enthalpy of a mixture of ideal gases is equal to the sum of the enthalpies of each component:

$$h = h_a + W h_s \qquad (17)$$

Atmospheric air and water vapor mixture is usually referenced to the mass of dry air. This is because the amount of water vapor may vary during some processes but the amount of dry air typically remains constant. Each term in Equation (17) has units of energy per unit mass of dry air. With the assumption of ideal gas behavior, the enthalpy is a function of temperature only. If zero Fahrenheit or Celsius is selected as the reference state where the enthalpy of dry air is zero, and if the specific heats C_{pa} and C_{pv} are assumed to be constant, simple relations result:

$$\begin{aligned} h_a &= C_{pa} T \\ h_s &= h_g + C_{pv} T \end{aligned} \qquad (18)$$

where h_g = enthalpy of saturated vapor at that temperature, at 0°F is 1061.5 Btu/lb$_m$ and 2501.2 kJ/kg at 0°C

C_{pa}, C_{pv} = specific heat of air and vapor, respectively.

Using Equation (17) and (18) with C_{pa} and C_{pv} taken as 0.240 and 0.444 Btu/lb$_m$-°F, respectively, we have

$$h = (0.24T + W(1061.2 + 0.444T)) \text{ Btu/lb}_{ma} \qquad (19)$$

$$h = (1.0T + W(2501.3 + 1.86T)) \text{ kJ/kg} \qquad (20)$$

where C_{pa}, C_{pv} = 1.0 and 1.86 kJ/(kg°C), respectively.

Example 2: What is the enthalpy of saturated air at 70°F at standard atmospheric pressure?

Solution: As per Equation (13)

$$\begin{aligned} W &= 0.6219 \frac{P_s}{P_a} = 0.6219 \frac{P_s}{P - P_s} \\ &= 0.6219 \left(\frac{0.3633}{14.696 - 0.3633} \right) \\ &= 0.6219 \times \frac{0.3633}{14.3327} \\ &= 0.015764 \end{aligned}$$

As per Equation (19)

$$h = 0.24T + W(1061.2 + 0.444T)$$
$$= (0.24 \times 70 + 0.015764(1061.2 + 0.444 \times 70))$$
$$= 34.01 \text{ Btu/lb}_{ma}$$

Thermodynamic Wet-bulb Temperature (T^*).—

Fig. 2-3 represents an idealized, fully insulated flow device where unsaturated moist air enters at dry-bulb temperature T_1 enthalpy h_1, and humidity ratio W_1. When this air is brought into contact with the water at a lower temperature, the air is both cooled and humidified. If the system is fully insulated so that no heat is transferred into or out of the system, the process is adiabatic and if the water is at a constant temperature, the latent heat of evaporation can come only from the sensible heat given up by the air in cooling. The quantity of water present is assumed to be large (large surface area and quantity) compared to the amount evaporated into the air. We assume that there is no temperature gradient in the body of water.

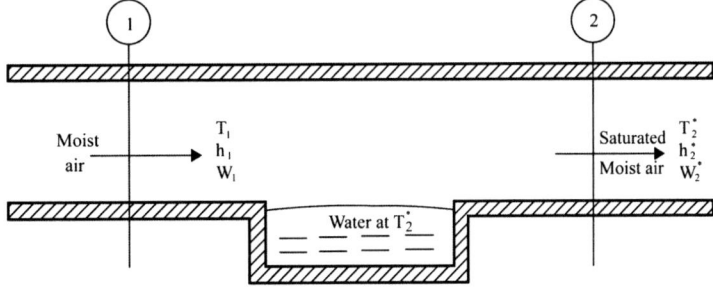

Fig 2-3. Adiabatic saturation of air

If the temperature reached by the air as it leaves the device where it is saturated is identical to the temperature of the water, this temperature is called the adiabatic saturation temperature or, more commonly, the thermodynamic wet-bulb temperature (T^*).

Thus, in Fig. 2-3, the saturated air leaving the device will have properties T_2^*, h_2^*, and W_2^*. Liquid water must be supplied to the device having an enthalpy h_{f2} at T_2^* for the process to be steady-flow. Assuming steady-flow conditions exist, the energy equation for the process is

$$h_1 + (W_2^* - W_1)h_{f2}^* = h_2^* \qquad (21)$$

The asterisk is used to denote properties at the thermodynamic wet-bulb temperature. The temperature corresponding to h_2 for the given values of h_1 and W_1 is the defined thermodynamic wet-bulb temperature.

Equation (21) is exact since it defines the thermodynamic wet-bulb temperature T^*. Substituting the approximate ideal gas relationship for h from Equation (19), the corresponding expression for h^* and the approximate relationship h_{f2} at T_2^* into Equation (21) and then solving for the humidity ratio W_1 gives

$$W_1 = \frac{(1093 - 0.556T^*)W_2^* - 0.240(T_1 - T^*)}{1093 + 0.444T_1 - T^*} \qquad (22)$$

where T_1 and T^* are in °F.

The corresponding equation in SI units is

$$W_1 = \frac{(2501 - 2.381T^*)W_2^* - (T_1 - T^*)}{2501 + 1.805T_1 - 4.186T^*} \qquad (23)$$

where T_1 and T^* are in °C.

Example 3: In an adiabatic saturator, the entering and leaving air pressure is 14.696 lb_f/in^2, the entering temperature is 70°F, and the leaving temperature is 60°F. Calculate the humidity ratio W and the relative humidity Φ?

Solution: After the adiabatic saturator, the relative humidity is 100% absorbing the water, so $P_{v2} = P_{s2}$. W_2 can be calculated by Equation (13)

$$W_2 = 0.6219\frac{P_v}{P_a} = 0.6219\frac{P_v}{P - P_v}$$
$$= 0.6219\left(\frac{0.2563}{14.696 - 0.2563}\right)$$
$$= 0.01104 \text{ lb}_v/\text{lb}_a$$

W_1 can be calculated by Equation (22)

$$W_1 = \frac{(1093 - 0.556T^*)W_2^* - 0.240(T_1 - T^*)}{1093 + 0.444T_1 - T^*}$$
$$= \frac{(1093 - 0.556 \times 60)0.01104 - 0.24(70 - 60)}{1093 + 0.444 \times 70 - 60}$$
$$= \frac{11.698 - 2.4}{1064.08}$$
$$= 0.008738$$

By applying Equation (13)

$$W_1 = 0.6219 \frac{P_v}{P_a}$$

$$0.008738 = 0.6219 \frac{P_v}{P - P_v}$$

$$0.008738 = \frac{0.6219 \times P_v}{14.696 - P_v}$$

$$P_v = 0.2036$$

By applying Equation (14)

$$\Phi = \frac{P_v}{P_s} \times 100$$

$$= \frac{0.2036}{0.36328} \times 100$$

$$= 56.04$$

The process discussed in this section is called the adiabatic saturation process. The usefulness of the foregoing discussion lies in the fact that the temperature of the saturated air-water-vapor mixture leaving the system is a function of the temperature, pressure, and relative humidity of the entering mixture and the exit pressure. Additionally, knowing the entering and exit pressures and temperatures, we may determine the relative humidity and humidity ratio of the entering mixture, as shown in Example 3.

In principle, there is a difference between the wet-bulb temperature T_w, and the temperature of adiabatic saturation T^*. The wet-bulb temperature is a function of both heat and mass transfer rates, while the adiabatic saturation temperature is a function of a thermodynamic equilibrium process. However, in practice, it has been found that for air-water-vapor mixtures at atmospheric pressures and temperatures, the wet-bulb and adiabatic saturation temperatures are essentially equal numerically.

Thermodynamic Properties of Moist Air.—Table 2-4 shows values of thermodynamic properties, for standard atmospheric pressure 14.696 psia or 29.92 in. Hg. The properties in this table are based on the thermodynamic temperature scale. This ideal scale differs only slightly from the practical temperature scales used for actual physical measurements.

Symbols used in Table 2-4 are:

T = Fahrenheit temperature;

W_s = humidity ratio at saturation, the condition at which the gaseous phase (moist air) exists in equilibrium with a condensed phase (liquid or solid) at the given temperature and pressure (standard atmospheric pressure). At given values of temperature and pressure, the humidity ratio W can have any value from zero and W_s.

$v_{as} = v_s - v_a$, the difference between the volume of moist air at saturation per lb of dry air, and the specific volume of the dry air itself, ft³/lb$_{da}$, at the same pressure and temperature.

v_s = volume of moist air at saturation per lb of dry air, ft³/lb$_{ma}$.

h_a = specific enthalpy of dry air, Btu/lb$_{da}$. The specific enthalpy of dry air has been assigned the value of zero at 0°F and standard atmospheric pressure.

$h_{as} = h_s - h_a$, the difference between the enthalpy of moist air at saturation, per lb of dry air, and the specific enthalpy of the dry air itself, Btu/lb$_{da}$, at the same pressure and temperature.

s_a = specific entropy of dry air, Btu/lb-°F (abs). The specific entropy of dry air has been assigned the value of zero at 0°F and standard atmospheric pressure.

s_s = specific entropy of moist air at saturation per lb of dry air, Btu/lb$_{da}$-°F (abs).

$h_w = h_s$ = specific enthalpy of condensed water (liquid or solid) in equilibrium with saturated air at a specified temperature and pressure, Btu/lb$_{water}$. Specific enthalpy of liquid water has been assigned the value of zero at its triple point (32.018°F) and saturation pressure.

Note: h_w is greater than the steam table enthalpy of saturated pure condensed phase by the amount of the enthalpy increase governed by the pressure increase from saturation pressure to one atmosphere, plus influence from the presence of air.

P_v = vapor pressure of water in saturated moist air, psia or in. Hg. P_v differs negligibly from the saturation vapor pressure of pure water P_s, at least for the conditions shown.

Example 4: What is the relative humidity of moist air that has a dry-bulb temperature of 70°F and a wet-bulb temperature of 60°F? The barometric pressure is 29.92 in. Hg.

Solution: Refer to Table 2-4, At 60°F wet-bulb, find h_s = 26.467 Btu/lb$_{da}$. At 70°F dry-bulb, find h_a =16.818 Btu/lb$_{da}$. Then,

$$h_{as} = 26.467 - 16.818 = 9.649 \quad Btu/lb_{da}$$

This is the heat of the vapor. Using Table 2-4, the value of h_{as} = 9.649 with corresponding value P_v of 0.4205 in. Hg. At 70°F dry-bulb, P_s= 0.73966 in. Hg. So, by Equation (10)

$$\Phi = \frac{P_v}{P_s} \times 100$$

$$= \frac{0.4205}{0.73966} \times 100$$

$$= 56.11$$

Example 5: Moist air exists at 70°F dry-bulb and 60°F dew-point when the barometric pressure is 29.92 in. Hg. What is the relative humidity of the moist air?

Solution: By definition, the 60°F dew-point temperature is the saturation temperature corresponding to the actual partial pressure of the water vapor in the air. From Table 2-4 at 60°F, find $P_v = P_s = 0.521930$ in. Hg. At 70°F, find $P_{vs} = P_s = 0.739660$ in. Hg. The relative humidity is

$$\Phi = \frac{P_v}{P_s} \times 100$$

$$= \frac{0.521930}{0.739660} \times 100$$

$$= 70.56 \%$$

Example 6: What is the enthalpy of moist air at 80°F dry-bulb temperature and 40% relative humidity? Barometric pressure is 29.92 in. Hg.

Solution: By Equation (19), $h = 0.240T + W(1061 + 0.444T)$. From Table 2-4 at 80°F, find $P_{vs} = P_s = 1.033020$ in. Hg. Relative humidity $\phi = P_v/P_s$; then, $P_v = \phi P_{vs} = 0.40(1.033020) = 0.413208$ in. Hg. By Equation (13)

$$W = 0.6219 \frac{P_v}{P - P_v}$$

$$= 0.6219 \left(\frac{0.413208}{29.92 - 0.413208} \right)$$

$$= 0.00871 \quad \text{lb}_v/\text{lb}_{da}$$

$$h = 0.24T + W(1061 + 0.444T)$$

$$= 0.24 \times 80 + 0.00871(1061 + 0.444 \times 80)$$

$$= 28.75 \quad \text{Btu/lb}_{da}$$

Example 7: Moist air exists at 70°F dry-bulb and 60°F dew-point when the barometric pressure is 29.92 in. Hg. Determine (1) humidity ratio, (2) saturation ratio, (3) relative humidity, (4) enthalpy, and (5) specific volume of dry air.

Solution: From Table 2-4 at dew-point temperature of 60°F, find $P_v = P_s = 0.52193$ in. Hg. By Equation (13),

$$W = 0.6219 \frac{P_v}{P - P_v}$$

$$= 0.6219 \left(\frac{0.52193}{29.92 - 0.52193} \right)$$

$$= 0.011 \text{ lb}_v/\text{lb}_{da}$$

From Table 2-4 at $T = 70°F$, find $W_s = 0.0158320$ lb$_v$/lb$_{da}$, find W_s. By Equation (15),

$$\mu = \frac{W}{W_s} = \frac{0.0110}{0.0158320} = 0.694795$$

From Table 2-4 at 70°F, find $P_v = P_s = 0.739660$ in. Hg. By Equation (21),

$$\Phi = \frac{P_v}{P_{vs}} \times 100 = \frac{0.52193}{0.739660} \times 100 = 70.56 \%$$

By Equation (21)

$$h = 0.240T + W(1061 + 0.444T)$$

$$= 0.240 \times 70 + 0.0110(1061 + 0.444(70))$$

$$= 28.8129 \quad \text{Btu/lb}_{da}$$

By Equation (5), $P_a V_a = R_a T$, where P_a is the partial pressure of the dry air in the moist air, may be used to find V_a. By Equation (3) $P_a = P - P_v = 29.92 - .52193 = 29.3981$ in. Hg. $= 14.434$ psia. By Equation (5)

$$P_a V_a = R_a T$$

$$V_a = \frac{R_a T}{P_a}$$

$$= \frac{53.352 \times (460 + 70)}{144 \times 14.434}$$

$$= 13.6043 \text{ ft}^3/\text{lb}$$

Graphical Representation of Psychrometric Chart.—To facilitate engineering computations, a graphical representation of the properties of moist air has been developed and is known as a psychrometric chart. Richard Mollier was the first to use such a chart with enthalpy as a coordinate. Modern day charts are somewhat different but still retain the enthalpy coordinate. ASHRAE has developed Mollier-type charts Figs. 2-5 and 2-6 the necessary range of variables. These charts contain all the necessary variables for carrying out HVAC computations. Because the chart is complex in design this section describes how each variable's curves appear so the user will see to which curves the examples refer.

Fig. 2-5 is the psychrometric chart for use at and above sea level. Fig. 2-6 is the psychrometric chart for use at and above 5000 ft. Dry bulb temperature is plotted along the horizontal axis. The dry bulb temperature lines are straight but not exactly parallel and incline slightly to the left. Humidity ratio is plotted along the vertical axis on the right hand side of the chart. The scale is uniform with horizontal lines parallel. The saturation curve slopes upward from left to right.

Dew point temperatures is also horizontal. Dry-bulb, wet-bulb, and dew point temperatures all coincide on the saturation curve.Relative humidity lines with shapes similar to the saturation curve appear at regular intervals.

The enthalpy scale is drawn obliquely on the left of the chart. Enthalpy lines inclined downward left to right. Although the wet bulb temperature lines appear to coincide with the enthalpy lines, they gradually diverge with respect to one another (i.e. they are not parallel). The spacing of the wet bulb lines is not uniform. Finally we note that specific volume lines also appear inclined from the upper left to the lower right, similar to enthalpy and wet bulb temperature lines they are not parallel.The enthalpy, specific volume, and humidity ratio scales are all based on unit mass of dry air, not unit mass of moist air.

A protractor with two scales appears at the upper left of Charts 1 and 2 of Figs. 2-5, and 2-6 respectively. One scale gives the sensible heat ratio and the other the ratio of enthalpy difference to humidity ratio difference.

Construction of the Psychrometric Chart: The charts of Figs. 2-5, and 2-6 are slightly different organizations. The ones here should be studied before any other psychrometric chart is used. To help the reader understand these charts, examples follow. But first, simplified versions of the chart is shown in Figs. 2-4a to 2-4g.

The location and positioning of the scales of the various properties as well as the constant value lines for these properties are shown in these simple charts which are not drawn to the actual scale. When you read the values or draw lines, always use a sharp drafting-type pencil and straight edge.

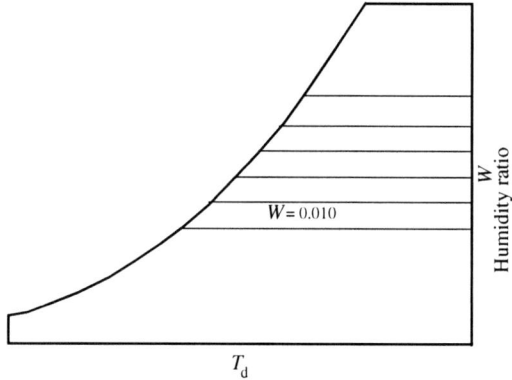

Fig 2-4b. Lines of constant humidity ratio (W)

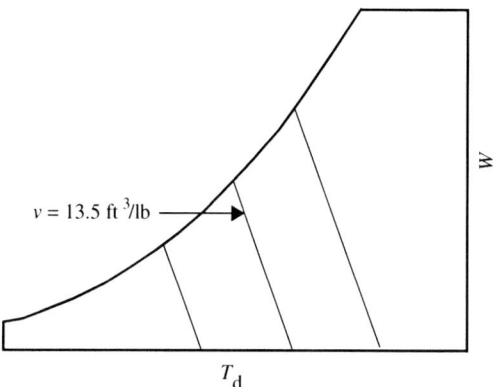

Fig 2-4c. Lines of constant specific volume v on the psychrometric chart

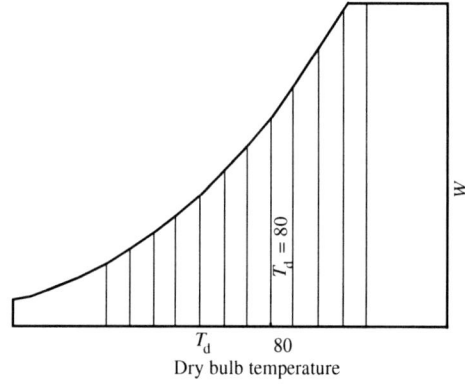

Fig 2-4a. Lines of constant dry bulb temperature t_d on the psychrometric chart

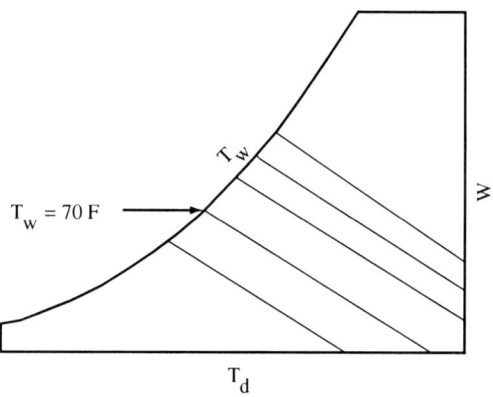

Fig 2-4d. Lines of constant wet bulb temperature T_w on the psychrometric chart

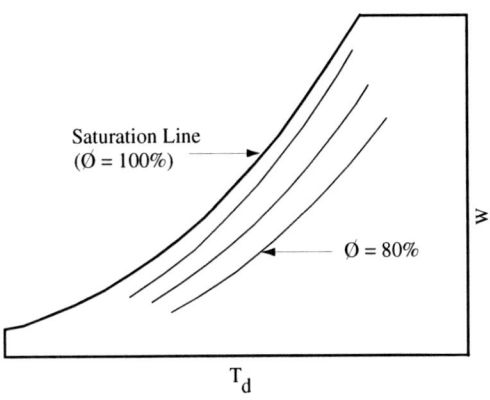

Fig 2-4e. Lines of constant relative humidity φ on the psychrometric chart

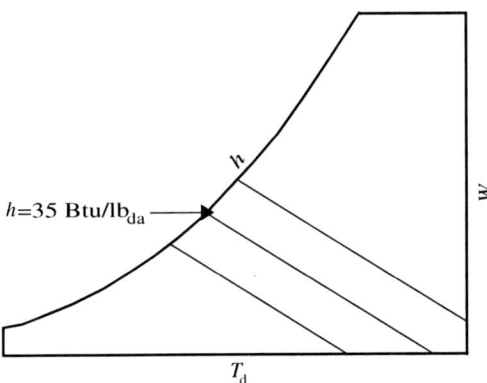

Fig 2-4f. Lines of constant enthalpy h on the psychrometric chart

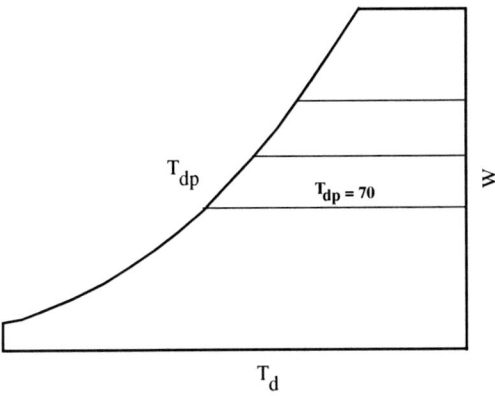

Fig 2-4g. Lines of constant dew point temperature T_{dp} on the psychrometric chart

Example 8: The air leaves a cooling coil is at 70°F T_d and 60°F T_w. What is its humidity ratio φ and specific enthalpy?

Solution: The intersection of the 70°F T_d and 60°F T_w lines defines the given state. This point on the chart is the reference from which all the other properties are determined.

Humidity Ratio W: Move horizontally to the right and read $W = 0.008778 \ lb_{mv}/ \ lb_{ma}$ on the vertical scale.

Relative Humidity φ: Interpolate between the 50 and 60% percent relative humidity lines and read 56.11%.

Enthalpy h: Follow a line of constant enthalpy upward to the left and read $h = 26.38$ Btu/lb_{ma} on the oblique scale.

Specific Volume v: Interpolate between the 13.5 and 14.0 specific volume lines and read $v = 13.65$ ft^3/lb_{ma}.

Dew Point T_{dp}: Move horizontally to the left from the reference point and read $T_{dp} = 53.7$ F on the saturation curve.

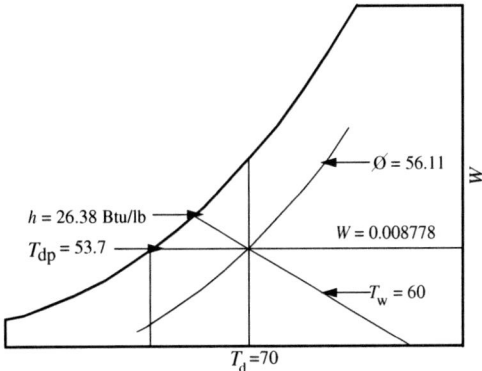

Solution of Example 8

Enthalpy h (alternate method): The nomograph in the upper left hand corner of Fig. 2-4g gives the difference D between the enthalpy of unsaturated moist air and the enthalpy of saturated air at the same wet-bulb temperature. Then $h = h_s + D$. For this example $h_s = 26.5$ Btu/lb_{ma}, $D = -0.1$ Btu/lb_{ma}, and $h = 26.5 - 0.1 = 26.4$ Btu/lb_{ma}.

Although psychrometric charts are useful in several aspects of HVAC design, the availability of computer programs to determine moist air properties has made some of these steps easier to carry out. These programs may be easily constructed from the basic equations of this chapter. Computer programs give the additional convenience of choice of units and arbitrary (atmospheric) pressures.

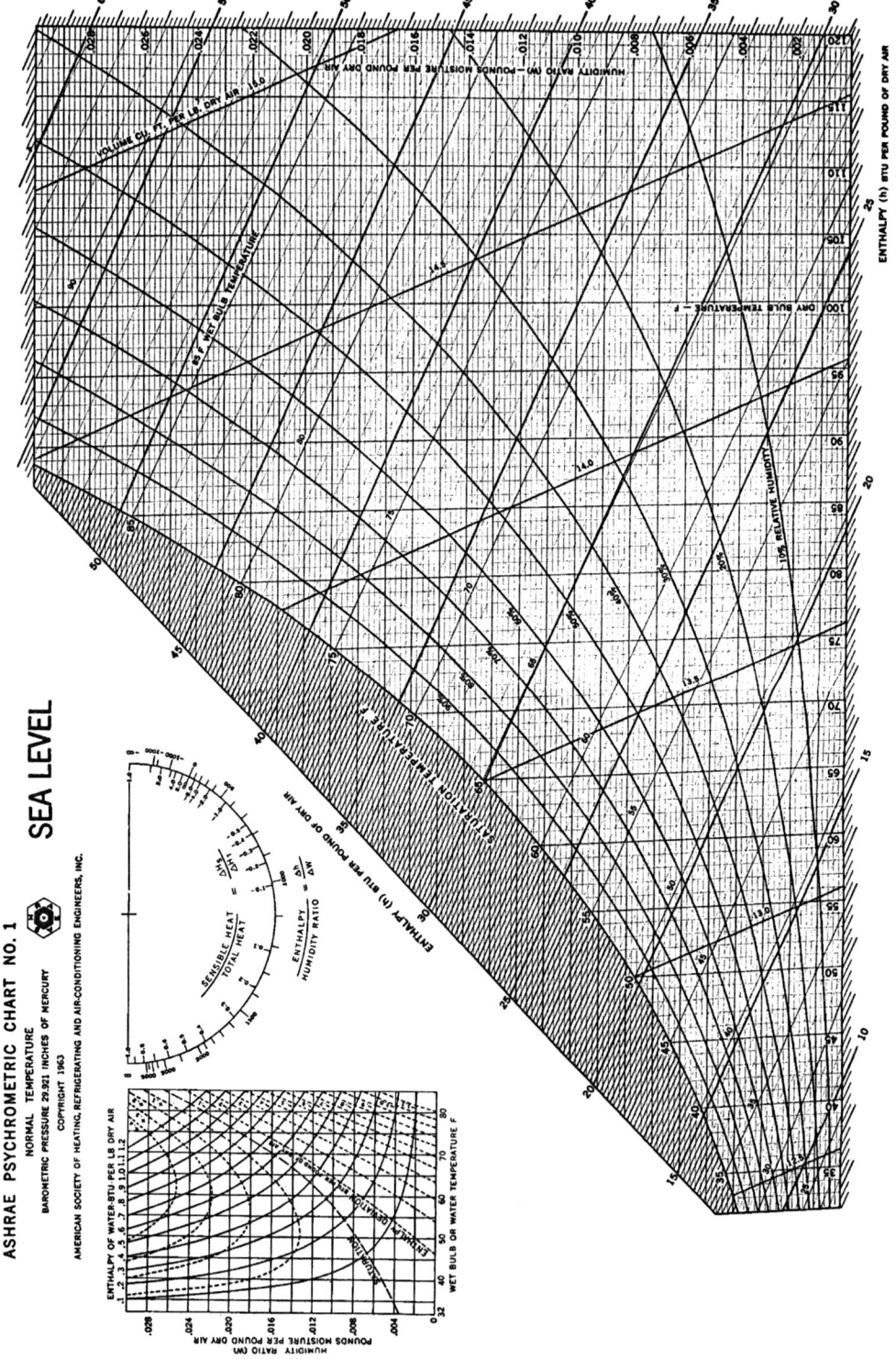

Fig 2-5. ASHRAE psychrometric chart

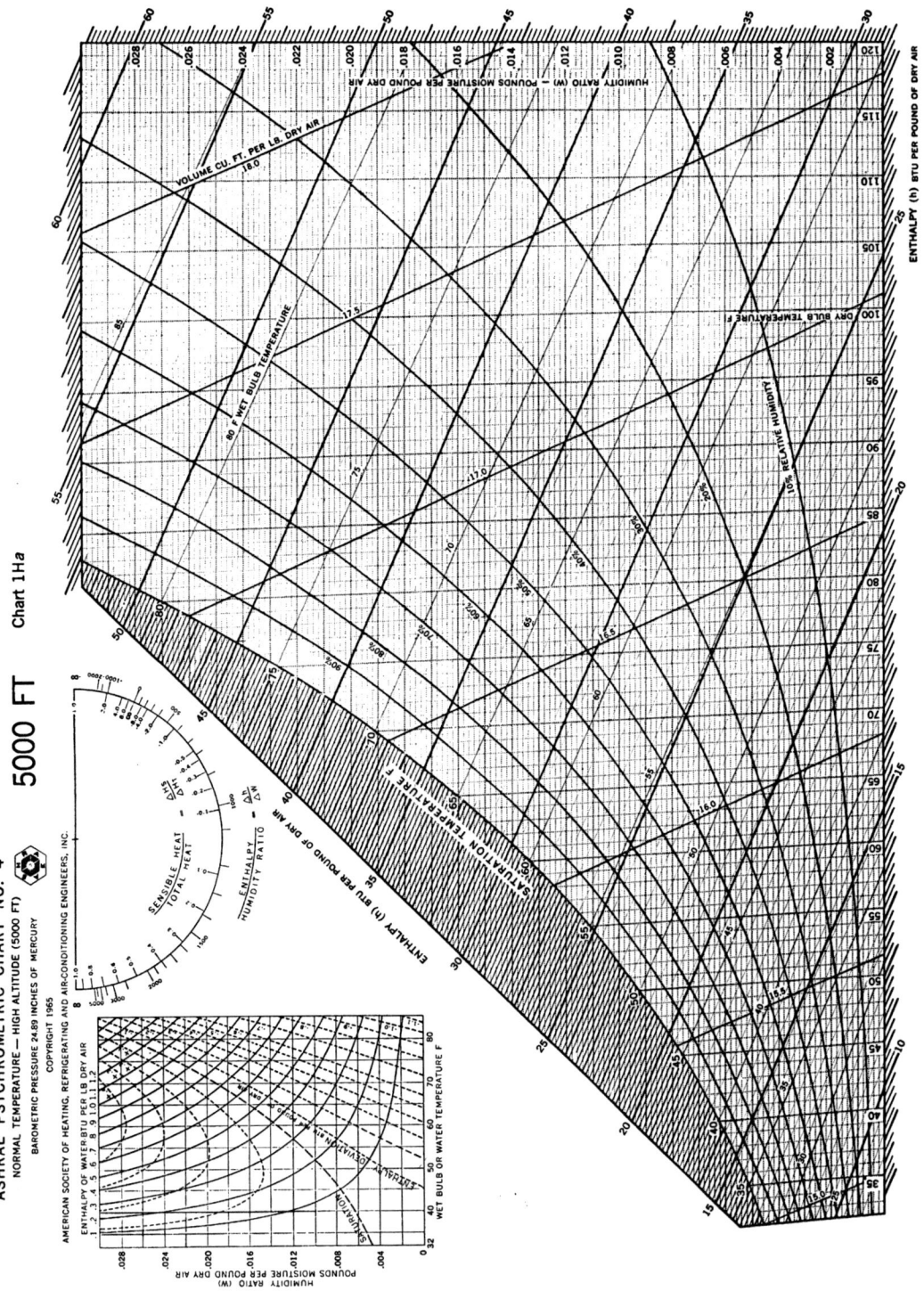

Fig 2-6. ASHRAE psychrometric chart (5000 ft)

Table 2-3. Thermodynamic Properties of Water at Saturation

Temp. °F	Absolute Pressure	Specific Volume ft³/lbₘ		Enthalpy Btu/lbₘ		Entropy Btu/ lbₘ-°F	
		Saturated Liquid	Saturated Vapor	Saturated Liquid	Saturated Vapor	Saturated Liquid	Saturated Vapor
T	P psi	v_f	v_g	h_f	h_g	s_f	s_g
−80	0.000116	0.01732	1953234	−193.50	1025.69	−0.4067	2.8045
−78	0.000135	0.01732	1685445	−192.71	1026.57	−0.4046	2.7900
−76	0.000157	0.01732	1456752	−191.92	1027.46	−0.4025	2.7757
−74	0.000182	0.01733	1260977	−191.12	1028.34	−0.4005	2.7615
−72	0.000211	0.01733	1093149	−190.32	1029.23	−0.3984	2.7475
−70	0.000245	0.01733	949067	−189.52	1030.11	−0.3963	2.7336
−68	0.000283	0.01733	825187	−188.71	1031.00	−0.3943	2.7199
−66	0.000326	0.01734	718508	−187.90	1031.88	−0.3922	2.7063
−64	0.000376	0.01734	626503	−187.08	1032.77	−0.3901	2.6929
−62	0.000433	0.01734	547041	−186.26	1033.65	−0.3881	2.6730
−60	0.000498	0.01734	478317	−185.44	1034.54	−0.3860	2.6665
−58	0.000571	0.01735	418803	−184.61	1035.42	−0.3839	2.6535
−56	0.000655	0.01735	367172	−183.78	1036.30	−0.3819	2.6406
−54	0.000750	0.01735	322336	−182.95	1037.19	−0.3798	2.6279
−52	0.000857	0.01735	283335	−182.11	1038.07	−0.3778	2.6153
−50	0.000979	0.01736	249381	−181.27	1038.96	−0.3757	2.6029
−48	0.001116	0.01736	219766	−180.42	1039.84	−0.3736	2.5906
−46	0.001271	0.01736	193909	−179.57	1040.73	−0.3716	2.5784
−44	0.001445	0.01736	171304	−178.72	1041.61	−0.3695	2.5663
−42	0.001642	0.01737	151518	−177.86	1042.50	−0.3675	2.5544
−40	0.001863	0.01737	134176	−177.00	1043.38	−0.3654	2.5426
−38	0.002111	0.01737	118959	−176.13	1044.27	−0.3633	2.5309
−36	0.002390	0.01738	105592	−175.26	1045.15	−0.3613	2.5193
−34	0.002702	0.01738	93828	−174.39	1046.03	−0.3592	2.5078
−32	0.003052	0.01738	83474	−173.51	1046.92	−0.3572	2.4965
−30	0.003443	0.01738	74341	−172.63	1047.80	−0.3551	2.4853
−28	0.003879	0.01739	66282	−171.74	1048.69	−0.3531	2.4742
−26	0.004366	0.01739	59161	−170.86	1049.57	−0.3510	2.4632
−24	0.004909	0.01739	52861	−169.96	1050.46	−0.3489	2.4523
−22	0.005514	0.01739	47281	−169.07	1051.34	−0.3469	2.4415
−20	0.006186	0.01740	42333	−168.16	1052.22	−0.3448	2.4309
−18	0.006933	0.01740	37943	−167.26	1053.11	−0.3428	2.4203
−16	0.007763	0.01740	34041	−166.35	1053.99	−0.3407	2.4098
−14	0.008683	0.01741	30572	−165.44	1054.87	−0.3387	2.3995
−12	0.009702	0.01741	27483	−164.52	1055.76	−0.3366	2.3892
−10	0.010830	0.01741	24730	−163.60	1056.64	−0.3346	2.3791
−8	0.012077	0.01741	22274	−162.68	1057.53	−0.3325	2.3690
−6	0.013456	0.01742	20081	−161.75	1058.41	−0.3305	2.3591
−4	0.014977	0.01742	18121	−160.82	1059.29	−0.3284	2.3492
−2	0.016654	0.01742	16367	−159.88	1060.17	−0.3264	2.3394
0	0.018502	0.01743	14797	−158.94	1061.06	−0.3243	2.3298
1	0.019495	0.01743	14073	−158.47	1061.50	−0.3233	2.3249
2	0.020537	0.01743	13388	−157.99	1061.94	−0.3223	2.3202
3	0.021629	0.01743	12740	−157.52	1062.38	−0.3212	2.3154
4	0.022774	0.01743	12125	−157.05	1062.82	−0.3202	2.3107
5	0.023975	0.01743	11543	−156.57	1063.26	−0.3192	2.3060
6	0.025233	0.01743	10991	−156.09	1063.70	−0.3182	2.3013
7	0.026552	0.01744	10468	−155.62	1064.14	−0.3171	2.2966
8	0.027933	0.01744	9971	−155.14	1064.58	−0.3161	2.2920
9	0.029379	0.01744	9500	−154.66	1065.03	−0.3151	2.2873
10	0.030894	0.01744	9054	−154.18	1065.47	−0.3141	2.2827
11	0.032480	0.01744	8630	−153.70	1065.91	−0.3130	2.2782
12	0.034140	0.01744	8228	−153.21	1066.35	−0.3120	2.2736
13	0.035878	0.01745	7846	−152.73	1066.79	−0.3110	2.2691
14	0.037696	0.01745	7483	−152.24	1067.23	−0.3100	2.2645
15	0.039597	0.01745	7139	−151.76	1067.67	−0.3089	2.2600

Table 2-3. *(Continued)* **Thermodynamic Properties of Water at Saturation**

Temp. °F	Absolute Pressure	Specific Volume ft³/lb$_m$		Enthalpy Btu/lb$_m$		Entropy Btu/ lb$_m$-°F	
		Saturated Liquid	Saturated Vapor	Saturated Liquid	Saturated Vapor	Saturated Liquid	Saturated Vapor
T	P psi	v_f	v_g	h_f	h_g	s_f	s_g
16	0.041586	0.01745	6811	−151.27	1068.11	−0.3079	2.2556
17	0.043666	0.01745	6501	−150.78	1068.55	−0.3069	2.2511
18	0.045841	0.01745	6205	−150.30	1068.99	−0.3059	2.2467
19	0.048113	0.01745	5924	−149.81	1069.43	−0.3049	2.2423
20	0.050489	0.01746	5657	−149.32	1069.87	−0.3038	2.2379
21	0.052970	0.01746	5404	−148.82	1070.31	−0.3028	2.2335
22	0.055563	0.01746	5162	−148.33	1070.75	−0.3018	2.2292
23	0.058271	0.01746	4932	−147.84	1071.19	−0.3008	2.2248
24	0.061099	0.01746	4714	−147.34	1071.63	−0.2997	2.2205
25	0.064051	0.01746	4506	−146.85	1072.07	−0.2987	2.2162
26	0.067133	0.01747	4308	−146.35	1072.50	−0.2977	2.2119
27	0.070349	0.01747	4119	−145.85	1072.94	−0.2967	2.2077
28	0.073706	0.01747	3940	−145.35	1073.38	−0.2956	2.2035
29	0.077207	0.01747	3769	−144.85	1073.82	−0.2946	2.1992
30	0.080860	0.01747	3606	−144.35	1074.26	−0.2936	2.1951
31	0.084669	0.01747	3450	−143.85	1074.70	−0.2926	2.1909
32	0.088640	0.01747	3302	−143.35	1075.14	−0.2915	2.1867
32*	0.088650	0.01602	3302.09	−0.02	1075.14	0.0000	2.1867
33	0.092290	0.01602	3178.16	0.99	1075.58	0.0020	2.1832
34	0.096070	0.01602	3059.49	2.00	1076.01	0.0041	2.1796
35	0.099980	0.01602	2945.68	3.00	1076.45	0.0061	2.1761
36	0.104030	0.01602	2836.61	4.01	1076.89	0.0081	2.1726
37	0.108220	0.01602	2732.15	5.02	1077.33	0.0102	2.1692
38	0.112570	0.01602	2631.89	6.02	1077.77	0.0122	2.1657
39	0.117070	0.01602	2535.88	7.03	1078.21	0.0142	2.1623
40	0.121720	0.01602	2443.69	8.03	1078.65	0.0162	2.1589
41	0.126540	0.01602	2355.24	9.04	1079.09	0.0182	2.1554
42	0.131530	0.01602	2270.43	10.04	1079.52	0.0202	2.1521
43	0.136690	0.01602	2189.04	11.04	1079.96	0.0222	2.1487
44	0.142030	0.01602	2110.94	12.05	1080.40	0.0242	2.1454
45	0.147550	0.01602	2035.92	13.05	1080.84	0.0262	2.1420
46	0.153260	0.01602	1963.87	14.05	1081.28	0.0282	2.1387
47	0.159170	0.01602	1894.73	15.06	1081.71	0.0302	2.1354
48	0.165270	0.01602	1828.3	16.06	1082.15	0.0321	2.1321
49	0.171580	0.01602	1764.46	17.06	1082.59	0.0341	2.1288
50	0.178110	0.01602	1703.20	18.06	1083.03	0.0361	2.1256
51	0.184840	0.01602	1644.26	19.06	1083.46	0.0381	2.1224
52	0.191810	0.01603	1587.65	20.07	1083.90	0.0400	2.1191
53	0.199000	0.01603	1533.24	21.07	1084.34	0.0420	2.1159
54	0.206430	0.01603	1480.91	22.07	1084.77	0.0439	2.1128
55	0.214100	0.01603	1430.62	23.07	1085.21	0.0459	2.1096
56	0.222020	0.01603	1382.21	24.07	1085.65	0.0478	2.1064
57	0.230200	0.01603	1335.67	25.07	1086.08	0.0497	2.1033
58	0.238640	0.01603	1290.87	26.07	1086.52	0.0517	2.1002
59	0.247350	0.01603	1247.78	27.07	1086.96	0.0536	2.0971
60	0.256350	0.01604	1206.32	28.07	1087.39	0.0555	2.0940
61	0.265620	0.01604	1166.4	29.07	1087.83	0.0575	2.0909
62	0.275190	0.01604	1127.95	30.07	1088.27	0.0594	2.0878
63	0.285060	0.01604	1090.96	31.07	1088.70	0.0613	2.0848
64	0.295240	0.01604	1055.33	32.07	1089.14	0.0632	2.0818
65	0.305740	0.01604	1021.00	33.07	1089.57	0.0651	2.0787
66	0.316560	0.01604	987.97	34.07	1090.01	0.0670	2.0758
67	0.327720	0.01605	956.12	35.07	1090.44	0.0689	2.0728
68	0.339210	0.01605	925.45	36.07	1090.88	0.0708	2.0698
69	0.351070	0.01605	895.87	37.07	1091.31	0.0727	2.0668
70	0.363280	0.01605	867.36	38.07	1091.75	0.0746	2.0639
71	0.375860	0.01605	839.88	39.07	1092.18	0.0765	2.0610

Table 2-3. *(Continued)* Thermodynamic Properties of Water at Saturation

Temp. °F	Absolute Pressure	Specific Volume ft³/lb_m		Enthalpy Btu/lb_m		Entropy Btu/ lb_m-°F	
		Saturated Liquid	Saturated Vapor	Saturated Liquid	Saturated Vapor	Saturated Liquid	Saturated Vapor
T	P psi	v_f	v_g	h_f	h_g	s_f	s_g
72	0.388820	0.01606	813.39	40.07	1092.61	0.0783	2.0580
73	0.402170	0.01606	787.87	41.07	1093.05	0.0802	2.0552
74	0.415920	0.01606	763.21	42.06	1093.48	0.0821	2.0523
75	0.430080	0.01606	739.44	43.06	1093.92	0.0840	2.0494
76	0.444650	0.01606	726.53	44.06	1094.35	0.0858	2.0465
77	0.459660	0.01607	699.8	45.06	1094.78	0.0877	2.0437
78	0.475100	0.01607	673.06	46.06	1095.22	0.0896	2.0409
79	0.491000	0.01607	652.46	47.06	1095.65	0.0914	2.0380
80	0.507360	0.01607	632.56	48.06	1096.08	0.0933	2.0352
81	0.524190	0.01608	613.37	49.06	1096.51	0.0951	2.0324
82	0.541500	0.01608	594.84	50.05	1096.95	0.0970	2.0297
83	0.559310	0.01608	576.92	51.05	1097.38	0.0988	2.0269
84	0.577630	0.01608	559.65	52.05	1097.81	0.1006	2.0242
85	0.596470	0.01609	542.94	53.05	1098.24	0.1025	2.0214
86	0.615840	0.01609	526.81	54.05	1098.67	0.1043	2.0187
87	0.635750	0.01609	511.22	55.05	1099.11	0.1061	2.0160
88	0.656220	0.01609	496.15	56.05	1099.54	0.1080	2.0133
89	0.677260	0.01610	481.61	57.04	1099.97	0.1098	2.0106
90	0.698890	0.01610	467.53	58.04	1100.40	0.1116	2.0079
91	0.721110	0.01610	453.93	59.04	1100.83	0.1134	2.0053
92	0.743940	0.01611	440.78	60.04	1101.26	0.1152	2.0026
93	0.767400	0.01611	428.06	61.04	1101.69	0.1170	2.0000
94	0.791500	0.01611	415.76	62.04	1102.12	0.1188	1.9973
95	0.816250	0.01612	403.86	63.03	1102.55	0.1206	1.9947
96	0.841660	0.01612	392.34	64.03	1102.98	0.1224	1.9921
97	0.867760	0.01612	381.21	65.03	1103.41	0.1242	1.9895
98	0.894560	0.01612	370.44	66.03	1103.84	0.1260	1.9870
99	0.922070	0.01613	360.01	67.03	1104.26	0.1278	1.9844
100	0.950310	0.01613	349.92	68.03	1104.69	0.1296	1.9819
101	0.979300	0.01613	340.15	69.03	1105.12	0.1314	1.9793
102	1.009040	0.01614	330.71	70.02	1105.55	0.1332	1.9768
103	1.039560	0.01614	321.55	71.02	1105.98	0.1349	1.9743
104	1.070880	0.01614	312.69	72.02	1106.40	0.1367	1.9718
105	1.103010	0.01615	304.10	73.02	1106.83	0.1385	1.9693
106	1.135970	0.01615	295.77	74.02	1107.26	0.1402	1.9668
107	1.169770	0.01616	287.73	75.01	1107.68	0.1420	1.9643
108	1.204440	0.01616	279.92	76.01	1108.11	0.1438	1.9619
109	1.239990	0.01616	272.36	77.01	1108.54	0.1455	1.9594
110	1.276440	0.01617	265.03	78.01	1108.96	0.1473	1.9570
111	1.313810	0.01617	257.93	79.01	1109.39	0.1490	1.9546
112	1.352120	0.01617	251.04	80.01	1109.81	0.1508	1.9521
113	1.391380	0.01618	244.38	81.01	1110.24	0.1525	1.9497
114	1.431620	0.01618	237.9	82.00	1110.66	0.1543	1.9474
115	1.472860	0.01619	231.63	83.00	1111.09	0.1560	1.9450
116	1.515120	0.01619	225.55	84.00	1111.51	0.1577	1.9426
117	1.558420	0.01619	219.65	85.00	1111.93	0.1595	1.9402
118	1.602770	0.01620	213.93	86.00	1112.36	0.1612	1.9379
119	1.648200	0.01620	208.37	87.00	1112.78	0.1629	1.9356
120	1.694740	0.01620	202.99	88.00	1113.20	0.1647	1.9332
121	1.742400	0.01621	197.76	89.00	1113.62	0.1664	1.9309
122	1.791170	0.01621	192.69	90.00	1114.05	0.1681	1.9286
123	1.841170	0.01622	187.78	90.99	1114.47	0.1698	1.9263
124	1.892330	0.01622	182.99	91.99	1114.89	0.1715	1.9240
125	1.944700	0.01623	178.36	92.99	1115.31	0.1732	1.9217
126	1.998310	0.01623	173.86	93.99	1115.73	0.1749	1.9195
127	2.053180	0.01623	169.49	94.99	1116.15	0.1766	1.9172
128	2.109340	0.01624	165.25	95.99	1116.57	0.1783	1.9150

Table 2-3. *(Continued)* **Thermodynamic Properties of Water at Saturation**

Temp. °F	Absolute Pressure	Specific Volume ft³/lb$_m$		Enthalpy Btu/lb$_m$		Entropy Btu/ lb$_m$-°F	
		Saturated Liquid	Saturated Vapor	Saturated Liquid	Saturated Vapor	Saturated Liquid	Saturated Vapor
T	P psi	v_f	v_g	h_f	h_g	s_f	s_g
129	2.166800	0.01624	161.12	96.99	1116.99	0.1800	1.9127
130	2.225600	0.01625	157.12	97.99	1117.41	0.1817	1.9105
131	2.285760	0.01625	153.23	98.99	1117.83	0.1834	1.9083
132	2.347300	0.01626	149.46	99.99	1118.25	0.1851	1.9061
133	2.410250	0.01626	145.78	100.99	1118.67	0.1868	1.9039
134	2.474630	0.01627	142.23	101.99	1119.08	0.1885	1.9017
135	2.540480	0.01627	138.76	102.99	1119.50	0.1902	1.8995
136	2.607820	0.01627	135.39	103.98	1119.92	0.1919	1.8974
137	2.676670	0.01628	132.12	104.98	1120.34	0.1935	1.8952
138	2.747070	0.01628	128.94	105.98	1120.75	0.1952	1.8930
139	2.819030	0.01629	125.85	106.98	1121.17	0.1969	1.8909
140	2.892600	0.01629	122.84	107.98	1121.58	0.1985	1.8888
141	2.967800	0.01630	119.92	108.98	1122.00	0.2002	1.8867
142	3.044650	0.01630	117.07	109.98	1122.41	0.2019	1.8845
143	3.123200	0.01631	114.31	110.98	1122.83	0.2035	1.8824
144	3.203450	0.01631	111.62	111.98	1123.24	0.2052	1.8803
145	3.285460	0.01632	109.00	112.98	1123.66	0.2068	1.8783
146	3.369240	0.01632	106.45	113.98	1124.07	0.2085	1.8762
147	3.454830	0.01633	103.98	114.98	1124.48	0.2101	1.8741
148	3.542260	0.01633	101.57	115.98	1124.89	0.2118	1.8721
149	3.631560	0.01634	99.22	116.98	1125.31	0.2134	1.8700
150	3.722770	0.01634	96.94	117.98	1125.72	0.2151	1.8680
151	3.815910	0.01635	94.72	118.99	1126.13	0.2167	1.8659
152	3.911010	0.01635	92.56	119.99	1126.54	0.2184	1.8639
153	4.008120	0.01636	90.46	120.99	1126.95	0.2200	1.8619
154	4.107270	0.01636	88.41	121.99	1127.36	0.2216	1.8599
155	4.208480	0.01637	86.41	122.99	1127.77	0.2233	1.8579
156	4.311800	0.01637	84.47	123.99	1128.18	0.2249	1.8559
157	4.417250	0.01638	82.58	124.99	1128.59	0.2265	1.8539
158	4.524880	0.01638	80.73	125.99	1128.99	0.2281	1.8519
159	4.634720	0.01639	78.94	126.99	1129.40	0.2297	1.8500
160	4.746800	0.01639	77.192	127.99	1129.81	0.2314	1.8480
161	4.861200	0.01640	75.488	128.99	1130.22	0.2330	1.8461
162	4.977800	0.01640	73.829	130.00	1130.62	0.2346	1.8441
163	5.096900	0.01641	72.213	131.00	1131.03	0.2362	1.8422
164	5.218300	0.01642	70.636	132.00	1131.43	0.2378	1.8403
165	5.342200	0.01642	69.101	133.00	1131.84	0.2394	1.8383
166	5.468500	0.01643	67.604	134.00	1132.24	0.2410	1.8364
167	5.597400	0.01643	66.146	135.00	1132.64	0.2426	1.8345
168	5.728700	0.01644	64.723	136.01	1133.05	0.2442	1.8326
169	5.862700	0.01644	63.336	137.01	1133.45	0.2458	1.8308
170	5.999300	0.01645	61.986	138.01	1133.85	0.2474	1.8289
171	6.138600	0.01646	60.666	139.01	1134.25	0.2490	1.8270
172	6.280600	0.01646	59.38	140.01	1134.66	0.2506	1.8251
173	6.425300	0.01647	58.128	141.02	1135.06	0.2521	1.8233
174	6.572900	0.01647	56.904	142.02	1135.46	0.2537	1.8214
175	6.723200	0.01648	55.711	143.02	1135.86	0.2553	1.8196
176	6.876500	0.01648	54.549	144.02	1136.26	0.2569	1.8178
177	7.032700	0.01649	53.414	145.03	1136.65	0.2585	1.8159
178	7.191800	0.01650	52.307	146.03	1137.05	0.2600	1.8141
179	7.353900	0.01650	51.226	147.03	1137.45	0.2616	1.8123
180	7.519100	0.01651	50.171	148.04	1137.85	0.2632	1.8105
181	7.687400	0.01651	49.143	149.04	1138.24	0.2647	1.8087
182	7.858900	0.01652	48.138	150.04	1138.64	0.2663	1.8069
183	8.033500	0.01653	47.158	151.05	1139.03	0.2679	1.8051
184	8.211400	0.01653	46.202	152.05	1139.43	0.2694	1.8034
185	8.392600	0.01654	45.267	153.05	1139.82	0.2710	1.8016

Table 2-3. *(Continued)* **Thermodynamic Properties of Water at Saturation**

Temp. °F	Absolute Pressure	Specific Volume ft³/lb_m		Enthalpy Btu/lb_m		Entropy Btu/ lb_m-°F	
		Saturated Liquid	Saturated Vapor	Saturated Liquid	Saturated Vapor	Saturated Liquid	Saturated Vapor
T	P psi	v_f	v_g	h_f	h_g	s_f	s_g
186	8.577000	0.01654	44.356	154.06	1140.22	0.2725	1.7998
187	8.764900	0.01655	43.465	155.06	1140.61	0.2741	1.7981
188	8.956200	0.01656	42.595	156.07	1141.00	0.2756	1.7963
189	9.151000	0.01656	41.746	157.07	1141.39	0.2772	1.7946
190	9.349300	0.01657	40.918	158.07	1141.78	0.2787	1.7929
191	9.551200	0.01658	40.108	159.08	1142.18	0.2803	1.7911
192	9.756700	0.01658	39.317	160.08	1142.57	0.2818	1.7894
193	9.965900	0.01659	38.544	161.09	1142.95	0.2834	1.7877
194	10.178800	0.01659	37.790	162.09	1143.34	0.2849	1.7860
195	10.395500	0.01660	37.052	163.10	1143.73	0.2864	1.7843
196	10.616000	0.01661	36.331	164.10	1144.12	0.2880	1.7826
197	10.840400	0.01661	35.628	165.11	1144.51	0.2895	1.7809
198	11.068700	0.01662	34.940	166.11	1144.89	0.2910	1.7792
199	11.301000	0.01663	34.268	167.12	1145.28	0.2926	1.7776
200	11.537400	0.01663	33.61	168.13	1145.66	0.2941	1.7759
201	11.777900	0.01664	32.968	169.13	1146.05	0.2956	1.7742
202	12.022500	0.01665	32.340	170.14	1146.43	0.2971	1.7726
203	12.271300	0.01665	31.726	171.14	1146.81	0.2986	1.7709
204	12.524400	0.01666	31.127	172.15	1147.20	0.3002	1.7693
205	12.781900	0.01667	30.540	173.16	1147.58	0.3017	1.7677
206	13.043600	0.01667	29.965	174.16	1147.96	0.3032	1.7660
207	13.309900	0.01668	29.404	175.17	1148.34	0.3047	1.7644
208	13.580600	0.01669	28.856	176.18	1148.72	0.3062	1.7628
209	13.855800	0.01669	28.319	177.18	1149.10	0.3077	1.7612
210	14.135700	0.01670	27.795	178.19	1149.48	0.3092	1.7596
212	14.709600	0.01671	26.780	180.20	1150.23	0.3122	1.7564
214	15.302500	0.01673	25.807	182.22	1150.98	0.3152	1.7532
216	15.915200	0.01674	24.878	184.24	1151.73	0.3182	1.7501
218	16.547900	0.01676	23.987	186.25	1152.48	0.3212	1.7469
220	17.201300	0.01677	23.134	188.27	1153.22	0.3241	1.7438
222	17.875900	0.01679	22.316	190.29	1153.96	0.3271	1.7407
224	18.572100	0.01680	21.533	192.31	1154.70	0.3301	1.7377
226	19.290500	0.01682	20.782	194.33	1155.43	0.3330	1.7347
228	20.031600	0.01683	20.062	196.35	1156.16	0.3359	1.7316
230	20.796100	0.01684	19.372	198.37	1156.89	0.3389	1.7287
232	21.584300	0.01686	18.709	200.39	1157.62	0.3418	1.7257
234	22.397000	0.01688	18.073	202.41	1158.34	0.3447	1.7227
236	23.234500	0.01689	17.463	204.44	1159.06	0.3476	1.7198
238	24.097700	0.01691	16.877	206.46	1159.77	0.3505	1.7169
240	24.986900	0.01692	16.314	208.49	1160.48	0.3534	1.7140
242	25.902800	0.01694	15.774	210.51	1161.19	0.3563	1.7111
244	26.846100	0.01695	15.255	212.54	1161.90	0.3592	1.7083
246	27.817200	0.01697	14.756	214.57	1162.60	0.3621	1.7055
248	28.816900	0.01698	14.276	216.60	1163.29	0.3649	1.7026
250	29.845700	0.01700	13.815	218.63	1163.99	0.3678	1.6998
252	30.904300	0.01702	13.372	220.66	1164.68	0.3706	1.6971
254	31.993400	0.01703	12.945	222.69	1165.37	0.3735	1.6943
256	33.113500	0.01705	12.147	226.73	1166.72	0.3764	1.6916
258	34.265300	0.01707	12.14	226.76	1166.73	0.3792	1.6889
260	35.449600	0.01708	11.759	228.79	1167.40	0.3820	1.6862
262	36.666900	0.01710	11.393	230.83	1168.08	0.3848	1.6835
264	37.918000	0.01712	11.041	232.87	1168.74	0.3876	1.6808
266	39.203500	0.01714	10.701	234.90	1169.41	0.3904	1.6781
268	40.524100	0.01715	10.374	236.94	1170.07	0.3932	1.6755
270	41.880600	0.01717	10.059	238.98	1170.72	0.3960	1.6729
272	43.273600	0.01719	9.755	241.03	1171.38	0.3988	1.6703
274	44.704000	0.01721	9.462	243.07	1172.02	0.4016	1.6677

Table 2-3. *(Continued)* **Thermodynamic Properties of Water at Saturation**

Temp. °F	Absolute Pressure	Specific Volume ft³/lb$_m$		Enthalpy Btu/lb$_m$		Entropy Btu/ lb$_m$-°F	
		Saturated Liquid	Saturated Vapor	Saturated Liquid	Saturated Vapor	Saturated Liquid	Saturated Vapor
T	P psi	v_f	v_g	h_f	h_g	s_f	s_g
276	46.172300	0.01722	9.179	245.11	1172.67	0.4044	1.6651
278	47.679400	0.01724	8.907	247.16	1173.31	0.4071	1.6626
280	49.226000	0.01726	8.644	249.20	1173.94	0.4099	1.6600
282	50.812800	0.01728	8.39	251.25	1174.57	0.4127	1.6575
284	52.440600	0.01730	8.146	253.30	1175.20	0.4154	1.6550
286	54.110300	0.01731	7.91	255.35	1175.82	0.4182	1.6525
288	55.822500	0.01733	7.681	257.40	1176.44	0.4209	1.6500
290	57.578000	0.01735	7.461	259.45	1177.05	0.4236	1.6476
292	59.377700	0.01737	7.248	261.51	1177.66	0.4264	1.6451
294	61.222400	0.01739	7.043	263.56	1178.26	0.4291	1.6427
296	63.112800	0.01741	6.844	265.62	1178.86	0.4318	1.6402
298	65.049800	0.01743	6.652	267.68	1179.45	0.4345	1.6378
300	67.034100	0.01745	6.467	269.74	1180.04	0.4372	1.6354

Table 2-4. Thermodynamic Properties of Moist Air at Standard Pressure

Temp	Humidity Ratio	Volume		Enthalpy		Entropy		Condensate Water		
								Enthalpy	Entropy	Vapor Press.
T	lb_w/lb_{da}	ft^3/lb_{da}		Btu/lb_{da}		Btu/lb_{da}-°F		Btu/lb	Btu/lb-°F	in. Hg
°F	W_s	v_a	v_s	h_a	h_s	s_a	s_s	h_w	s_w	p_s
−80	0.0000049	9.553	9.553	−19.221	−19.215	−0.04594	−0.04592	−193.45	−0.4067	0.000236
−78	0.0000057	9.604	9.604	−18.740	−18.734	−0.04468	−0.04466	−192.66	−0.4046	0.000275
−76	0.0000067	9.655	9.655	−18.259	−18.252	−0.04342	−0.04340	−191.87	−0.4025	0.000319
−74	0.0000078	9.705	9.705	−17.778	−17.770	−0.04217	−0.04215	−191.07	−0.4005	0.000371
−72	0.0000090	9.756	9.756	−17.298	−17.288	−0.04093	−0.04090	−190.27	−0.3984	0.000430
−70	0.0000104	9.807	9.807	−16.806	−16.817	−0.03969	−0.03966	−189.47	−0.3963	0.000498
−68	0.0000120	9.857	9.858	−16.336	−16.324	−0.03846	−0.03843	−188.66	−0.3943	0.000576
−66	0.0000139	9.908	9.908	−15.856	−15.841	−0.03724	−0.03720	−187.85	−0.3922	0.000665
−64	0.0000160	9.959	9.959	−15.375	−15.359	−0.03602	−0.03597	−187.04	−0.3901	0.000766
−62	0.0000184	10.009	10.010	−14.895	−14.876	−0.03481	−0.03476	−186.22	−0.3881	0.000882
−60	0.0000212	10.060	10.060	−14.414	−14.392	−0.03360	−0.03354	−185.39	−0.3860	0.001013
−58	0.0000243	10.111	10.111	−13.933	−13.908	−0.03240	−0.03233	−184.57	−0.3839	0.001163
−56	0.0000279	10.161	10.162	−13.453	−13.424	−0.03121	−0.03113	−183.74	−0.3819	0.001333
−54	0.0000319	10.212	10.213	−12.972	−12.939	−0.03002	−0.02993	−182.90	−0.3798	0.001526
−52	0.0000365	10.263	10.263	−12.492	−12.454	−0.02884	−0.02874	−182.06	−0.3778	0.001745
−50	0.0000416	10.313	10.314	−12.011	−11.968	−0.02766	−0.02755	−181.22	−0.3757	0.001992
−48	0.0000475	10.364	10.365	−11.531	−11.481	−0.02649	−0.02636	−180.37	−0.3736	0.002272
−46	0.0000541	10.415	10.416	−11.050	−10.994	−0.02533	−0.02518	−179.52	−0.3716	0.002587
−44	0.0000615	10.465	10.466	−10.570	−10.505	−0.02417	−0.02400	−178.67	−0.3695	0.002943
−42	0.0000699	10.516	10.517	−10.089	−10.016	−0.02302	−0.02283	−177.81	−0.3675	0.003343
−40	0.0000793	10.567	10.568	−9.609	−9.526	−0.02187	−0.02166	−176.95	−0.3654	0.003793
−38	0.0000898	10.617	10.619	−9.128	−9.034	−0.02073	−0.02049	−176.08	−0.3633	0.004299
−36	0.0001017	10.668	10.670	−8.648	−8.541	−0.01959	−0.01932	−175.21	−0.3613	0.004866
−34	0.0001150	10.719	10.721	−8.167	−8.047	−0.01846	−0.01816	−174.34	−0.3529	0.005502
−32	0.0001298	10.769	10.772	−7.687	−7.551	−0.01733	−0.01699	−173.46	−0.3572	0.006214
−30	0.0001465	10.820	10.822	−7.206	−7.053	−0.01621	−0.01583	−172.58	−0.3551	0.007009
−28	0.0001650	10.871	10.873	−6.726	−6.553	−0.01510	−0.01467	−171.70	−0.3531	0.007898
−26	0.0001858	10.921	10.924	−6.245	−6.051	−0.01399	−0.01351	−170.81	−0.3510	0.008890
−24	0.0002088	10.972	10.976	−5.765	−5.545	−0.01288	−0.01235	−169.92	−0.3489	0.009995
−22	0.0002346	11.022	11.027	−5.284	−5.038	−0.01178	−0.01118	−169.02	−0.3469	0.011226
−20	0.0002632	11.073	11.078	−4.804	−4.527	−0.01069	−0.01002	−168.12	−0.3448	0.012595
−18	0.0002950	11.124	11.129	−4.324	−4.013	−0.00960	−0.00885	−167.21	−0.3428	0.014117
−16	0.0003303	11.174	11.180	−3.843	−3.495	−0.00851	−0.00768	−166.30	−0.3407	0.015806
−14	0.0003694	11.225	11.232	−3.363	−2.973	−0.00743	−0.00650	−165.39	−0.3387	0.017679
−12	0.0004128	11.276	11.283	−2.882	−2.447	−0.00635	−0.00532	−164.47	−0.3366	0.019754
−10	0.0004608	11.326	11.335	−2.402	−1.915	−0.00528	−0.00414	−163.55	−0.3346	0.022050
−8	0.0005139	11.377	11.386	−1.922	−1.378	−0.00422	−0.00294	−162.63	−0.3325	0.024591
−6	0.0005726	11.427	11.438	−1.441	−0.835	−0.00316	−0.00174	−161.70	−0.3305	0.027397
−4	0.0006373	11.478	11.490	−0.961	−0.286	−0.00210	−0.00053	−160.77	−0.3284	0.030494
−2	0.0007088	11.529	11.542	−0.480	0.271	−0.00105	0.00069	−159.83	−0.3264	0.033909
0	0.0007875	11.579	11.594	0.000	0.835	0.00000	0.00192	−158.89	−0.3243	0.037671
1	0.0008298	11.604	11.620	0.240	1.121	0.00052	0.00254	−158.42	−0.3233	0.039694
2	0.0008742	11.630	11.646	0.480	1.408	0.00104	0.00317	−157.95	−0.3223	0.041814
3	0.0009207	11.655	11.672	0.721	1.699	0.00156	0.00380	−157.47	−0.3212	0.044037
4	0.0009695	11.680	11.699	0.961	1.991	0.00208	0.00443	−157.00	−0.3202	0.046370
5	0.0010207	11.706	11.725	1.201	2.286	0.00260	0.00506	−156.52	−0.3192	0.048814
6	0.0010743	11.731	11.751	1.441	2.584	0.00311	0.00570	−156.05	−0.3182	0.051375
7	0.0011306	11.756	11.778	1.681	2.884	0.00363	0.00272	−155.57	−0.3171	0.054060
8	0.0011895	11.782	11.804	1.922	3.188	0.00414	0.00700	−155.09	−0.3161	0.056872
9	0.0012512	11.807	11.831	2.162	3.494	0.00466	0.00766	−154.61	−0.3151	0.059819
10	0.0013158	11.832	11.857	2.402	3.804	0.00517	0.00832	−154.13	−0.3141	0.062901

Table 2-4. *(Continued)* **Thermodynamic Properties of Moist Air at Standard Pressure**

Temp	Humidity Ratio	Volume		Enthalpy		Entropy		Condensate Water		
								Enthalpy	Entropy	Vapor Press.
T	lb_w/lb_{da}	ft^3/lb_{da}		Btu/lb_{da}		Btu/lb_{da}-°F		Btu/lb	Btu/lb-°F	in. Hg
°F	W_s	v_a	v_s	h_a	h_s	s_a	s_s	h_w	s_w	p_s
11	0.0013835	11.857	11.884	2.642	4.117	0.00568	0.00898	−153.65	−0.3130	0.066131
12	0.0014544	11.883	11.910	2.882	4.433	0.00619	0.00966	−153.17	−0.3120	0.069511
13	0.0015286	11.908	11.937	3.123	4.753	0.00670	0.01033	−152.68	−0.3110	0.073049
14	0.0016062	11.933	11.964	3.363	5.077	0.00721	0.01102	−152.20	−0.3100	0.076751
15	0.0016874	11.959	11.991	3.603	5.404	0.00771	0.01171	−151.71	−0.3089	0.080623
16	0.0017724	11.984	12.018	3.843	5.736	0.00822	0.01241	−151.22	−0.3079	0.084673
17	0.0018613	12.009	12.045	4.084	6.072	0.00872	0.01312	−150.74	−0.3069	0.088907
18	0.0019543	12.035	12.072	4.324	6.412	0.00923	0.01383	−150.25	−0.3059	0.093334
19	0.0020515	12.060	12.099	4.564	6.757	0.00973	0.01455	−149.76	−0.3049	0.097962
20	0.0021531	12.085	12.127	4.804	7.107	0.01023	0.01528	−149.27	−0.3038	0.102798
21	0.0022592	12.110	12.154	5.044	7.462	0.01073	0.01602	−148.78	−0.3028	0.107849
22	0.0023703	12.136	12.182	5.285	7.822	0.01123	0.01677	−148.28	−0.3018	0.113130
23	0.0024863	12.161	12.209	5.525	8.187	0.01173	0.01753	−147.79	−0.3008	0.118645
24	0.0026073	12.186	12.237	5.765	8.558	0.01223	0.01830	−147.30	−0.2997	0.124396
25	0.0027339	12.212	12.265	6.005	8.935	0.01272	0.01908	−146.80	−0.2987	0.130413
26	0.0028660	12.237	12.293	6.246	9.318	0.01322	0.01987	−146.30	−0.2977	0.136684
27	0.0030039	12.262	12.321	6.486	9.708	0.01371	0.02067	−145.81	−0.2967	0.143233
28	0.0031480	12.287	12.349	6.726	10.104	0.01420	0.02148	−145.31	−0.2956	0.150066
29	0.0032984	12.313	12.378	6.966	10.507	0.01470	0.02231	−144.81	−0.2946	0.157198
30	0.0034552	12.338	12.406	7.206	10.917	0.01519	0.02315	−144.31	−0.2936	0.164631
31	0.0036190	12.363	12.435	7.447	11.335	0.01568	0.02400	−143.80	−0.2926	0.172390
32	0.0037895	12.389	12.464	7.687	11.760	0.01617	0.02487	−143.30	−0.2915	0.180479
32ª	0.0037900	12.389	12.464	7.687	11.760	0.01617	0.02487	0.02	0.0000	0.180500
33	0.0039470	12.414	12.492	7.927	12.170	0.01665	0.02570	1.03	0.0020	0.187910
34	0.0041090	12.439	12.521	8.167	12.587	0.01714	0.02655	2.04	0.0041	0.195590
35	0.0042770	12.464	12.550	8.408	13.010	0.01763	0.02740	3.05	0.0061	0.203560
36	0.0044520	12.490	12.579	8.648	13.441	0.01811	0.02827	4.05	0.0081	0.211810
37	0.0046330	12.515	12.608	8.888	13.878	0.01860	0.02915	5.06	0.0102	0.220350
38	0.0048200	12.540	12.637	9.128	14.322	0.01908	0.03004	6.06	0.0122	0.229200
39	0.0050140	12.566	12.667	9.369	14.773	0.01956	0.03095	7.07	0.0142	0.238350
40	0.0052160	12.591	12.696	9.609	15.233	0.02004	0.03187	8.07	0.0162	0.247840
41	0.0054240	12.616	12.726	9.849	15.700	0.02052	0.03281	9.08	0.0182	0.257650
42	0.0056400	12.641	12.756	10.089	16.175	0.02100	0.03375	10.08	0.0202	0.267810
43	0.0058630	12.667	12.786	10.330	16.660	0.02148	0.03472	11.09	0.0222	0.278310
44	0.0060940	12.692	12.816	10.570	17.152	0.02196	0.03570	12.09	0.0242	0.289180
45	0.0063340	12.717	12.846	10.810	17.653	0.02244	0.03669	13.09	0.0262	0.300420
46	0.0065810	12.743	12.877	11.050	18.164	0.02291	0.03770	14.10	0.0282	0.312060
47	0.0068380	12.768	12.908	11.291	18.685	0.02339	0.03873	15.10	0.0302	0.324080
48	0.0071030	12.793	12.939	11.531	19.215	0.02386	0.03978	16.10	0.0321	0.336510
49	0.0073780	12.818	12.970	11.771	19.756	0.02433	0.04084	17.10	0.0341	0.349370
50	0.0076610	12.844	13.001	12.012	20.306	0.02480	0.04192	18.11	0.0361	0.362640
51	0.0079550	12.869	13.033	12.252	20.868	0.02528	0.04302	19.11	0.0381	0.376360
52	0.0082590	12.894	13.065	12.492	21.441	0.02575	0.04415	20.11	0.0400	0.390540
53	0.0085730	12.920	13.097	12.732	22.025	0.02622	0.04529	21.11	0.0420	0.405180
54	0.0088970	12.945	13.129	12.973	22.621	0.02668	0.04645	22.11	0.0439	0.420300
55	0.0092330	12.970	13.162	13.213	23.229	0.02715	0.04763	23.11	0.0478	0.435920
56	0.0095800	12.995	13.195	13.453	23.850	0.02762	0.04884	24.11	0.0497	0.452050
57	0.0099380	13.021	13.228	13.694	24.484	0.02808	0.05006	25.11	0.0497	0.468700
58	0.0103090	13.046	13.262	13.934	25.131	0.02855	0.05132	26.11	0.0517	0.485890
59	0.0106920	13.071	13.295	14.174	25.792	0.02901	0.05259	27.11	0.0536	0.503630
60	0.0110870	13.096	13.329	14.415	26.467	0.02947	0.05389	28.11	0.0555	0.521930

Table 2-4. *(Continued)* Thermodynamic Properties of Moist Air at Standard Pressure

Temp	Humidity Ratio	Volume		Enthalpy		Entropy		Condensate Water		
								Enthalpy	Entropy	Vapor Press.
T	lb_w/lb_{da}	ft^3/lb_{da}		Btu/lb_{da}		Btu/lb_{da}-$°F$		Btu/lb	Btu/lb-°F	in. Hg
°F	W_s	v_a	v_s	h_a	h_s	s_a	s_s	h_w	s_w	p_s
61	0.0114960	13.122	13.364	14.655	27.157	0.02994	0.05522	29.12	0.0575	0.540820
62	0.0119190	13.147	13.398	14.895	27.862	0.03040	0.05657	30.11	0.0594	0.560320
63	0.0123550	13.172	13.433	15.135	28.582	0.03086	0.05795	31.11	0.0613	0.580410
64	0.0128050	13.198	13.468	15.376	29.318	0.03132	0.05936	32.11	0.0632	0.601130
65	0.0132700	13.223	13.504	15.616	30.071	0.03178	0.06080	33.11	0.0651	0.622520
66	0.0137500	13.248	13.540	15.856	30.840	0.03223	0.06226	34.11	0.0670	0.644540
67	0.0142460	13.273	13.577	16.097	31.626	0.03269	0.06376	35.11	0.0689	0.667250
68	0.0147580	13.299	13.613	16.337	32.431	0.03315	0.06529	36.11	0.0708	0.690650
69	0.0152860	13.324	13.650	16.577	33.254	0.03360	0.06685	37.11	0.0727	0.714790
70	0.0158320	13.349	13.688	16.818	34.097	0.03406	0.06844	38.11	0.0746	0.739660
71	0.0163950	13.375	13.726	17.058	34.959	0.03451	0.07007	39.11	0.0765	0.765670
72	0.0169760	13.400	13.764	17.299	35.841	0.03496	0.07173	40.11	0.0783	0.791670
73	0.0175750	13.425	13.803	17.539	36.743	0.03541	0.07343	41.11	0.0802	0.818820
74	0.0181940	13.450	13.843	17.779	37.668	0.03586	0.07516	42.11	0.0821	0.846840
75	0.0188330	13.476	13.882	18.020	38.615	0.03631	0.07694	43.11	0.0840	0.875670
76	0.0194910	13.501	13.923	18.260	39.583	0.03676	0.07875	44.10	0.0858	0.905330
77	0.0201700	13.526	13.963	18.500	40.576	0.03721	0.08060	45.10	0.0877	0.935890
78	0.0208710	13.551	14.005	18.741	41.592	0.03766	0.08250	46.10	0.0896	0.967330
79	0.0215940	13.577	14.046	18.981	42.633	0.03811	0.08444	47.10	0.0914	0.999700
80	0.0223400	13.602	14.089	19.222	43.701	0.03855	0.08642	48.10	0.0933	1.033020
81	0.0231090	13.627	14.132	19.462	44.794	0.03900	0.08844	49.10	0.0951	1.067280
82	0.0239020	13.653	14.175	19.702	45.913	0.03944	0.09052	50.10	0.0970	1.102520
83	0.0247200	13.678	14.220	19.943	47.062	0.03988	0.09264	51.09	0.0988	1.138820
84	0.0255630	13.703	14.264	20.183	48.238	0.04033	0.09481	52.09	0.1006	1.176080
85	0.0264330	13.728	14.310	20.424	49.445	0.04077	0.09703	53.09	0.1025	1.214450
86	0.0273290	13.754	14.356	20.664	50.681	0.04121	0.09930	54.09	0.1043	1.253880
87	0.0282540	13.779	14.403	20.905	51.949	0.04165	0.10163	55.09	0.1061	1.294430
88	0.0292080	13.804	14.450	21.145	53.250	0.04209	0.10401	56.09	0.1080	1.336130
89	0.0301890	13.829	14.498	21.385	54.582	0.04253	0.10645	57.09	0.1098	1.378930
90	0.0312030	13.855	14.547	21.626	55.951	0.04297	0.10895	58.08	0.1116	1.422980
91	0.0322470	13.880	14.597	21.866	57.355	0.06810	0.11150	59.08	0.1134	1.468240
92	0.0333230	13.905	14.647	22.107	58.794	0.04384	0.11412	60.08	0.1152	1.514710
93	0.0344330	13.930	14.699	22.347	60.271	0.04427	0.11680	61.08	0.1170	1.562480
94	0.0355770	13.956	14.751	22.588	61.787	0.04471	0.11955	62.08	0.1188	1.611540
95	0.0367570	13.981	14.804	22.828	63.343	0.04514	0.12237	63.08	0.1206	1.661960
96	0.0379720	14.006	14.858	23.069	64.940	0.04558	0.12525	64.07	0.1224	1.713720
97	0.0392250	14.032	14.913	23.309	66.578	0.04601	0.12821	65.07	0.1242	1.766850
98	0.0405160	14.057	14.969	23.550	68.260	0.04644	0.13124	66.07	0.1260	1.821410
99	0.0418480	14.082	15.026	23.790	69.988	0.04687	0.13434	67.07	0.1278	1.877450
100	0.0432190	14.107	15.084	24.031	71.761	0.04730	0.13752	68.07	0.1296	1.934920
101	0.0446340	14.133	15.143	24.271	73.583	0.04773	0.14079	69.07	0.1314	1.993960
102	0.0460900	14.158	15.203	24.512	75.452	0.04816	0.14413	70.06	0.1332	2.054470
103	0.0475920	14.183	15.264	24.752	77.373	0.04859	0.14756	71.06	0.1349	2.116610
104	0.0491400	14.208	15.326	24.993	79.346	0.04901	0.15108	72.06	0.1367	2.180370
105	0.0507370	14.234	15.390	25.233	81.375	0.04944	0.15469	73.06	0.1385	2.245810
106	0.0523830	14.259	15.455	25.474	83.460	0.04987	0.15839	74.06	0.1402	2.312970
107	0.0540770	14.284	15.521	25.714	85.599	0.05029	0.16218	75.06	0.1420	2.381730
108	0.0558260	14.309	15.588	25.955	87.799	0.05071	0.16608	76.05	0.1438	2.452320
109	0.0576280	14.335	15.657	26.195	90.061	0.05114	0.17008	77.05	0.1455	2.524730
110	0.0594860	14.360	15.727	26.436	92.386	0.05156	0.17418	78.05	0.1473	2.598910
111	0.0614010	14.385	15.799	26.677	94.776	0.05198	0.17839	79.05	0.1490	2.675000

Table 2-4. *(Continued)* **Thermodynamic Properties of Moist Air at Standard Pressure**

Temp	Humidity Ratio	Volume		Enthalpy		Entropy		Condensate Water		
								Enthalpy	Entropy	Vapor Press.
T	lb_w/lb_{da}	ft³/lb_{da}		Btu/lb_{da}		Btu/lb_{da}-°F		Btu/lb	Btu/lb-°F	in. Hg
°F	W_s	v_a	v_s	h_a	h_s	s_a	s_s	h_w	s_w	p_s
112	0.0633780	14.411	15.872	26.917	97.237	0.05240	0.18272	80.05	0.1508	2.753100
113	0.0654110	14.436	15.947	27.158	99.760	0.05282	0.18716	81.05	0.1525	2.832910
114	0.0675120	14.461	16.023	27.398	102.362	0.05324	0.19172	82.04	0.1543	2.914910
115	0.0696760	14.486	16.101	27.639	105.035	0.05366	0.19640	83.04	0.1560	2.998830
116	0.0719080	14.512	16.181	27.879	107.786	0.05408	0.20121	84.04	0.1577	3.084880
117	0.0742110	14.537	16.263	28.120	110.617	0.05450	0.20615	85.04	0.1595	3.173050
118	0.0765860	14.562	16.346	28.361	113.530	0.05492	0.21122	86.04	0.1612	3.263350
119	0.0790360	14.587	16.432	28.601	116.528	0.05533	0.21644	87.04	0.1629	3.355860
120	0.0815600	14.613	16.519	28.842	119.612	0.05575	0.22180	88.04	0.1647	3.450520
121	0.0841690	14.638	16.609	29.083	122.792	0.05616	0.22731	89.04	0.1664	3.547640
122	0.0868600	14.663	16.700	29.323	126.065	0.05658	0.23298	90.03	0.1681	3.647040
123	0.0896330	14.688	16.794	29.564	129.432	0.05699	0.23880	91.03	0.1698	3.748710
124	0.0925000	14.714	16.890	29.805	132.907	0.05740	0.24480	92.03	0.1715	3.852980
125	0.0954560	14.739	16.989	30.045	136.482	0.05781	0.25096	93.03	0.1732	3.959610
126	0.0985040	14.764	17.090	30.286	140.163	0.05823	0.25729	94.03	0.1749	4.068630
127	0.1016570	14.789	17.193	30.527	143.965	0.05864	0.26382	95.03	0.1766	4.180460
128	0.1049100	14.815	17.299	30.767	147.878	0.05905	0.27054	96.03	0.1783	4.294770
129	0.1082700	14.840	17.409	31.008	151.916	0.21800	0.27745	97.03	0.1800	4.411810
130	0.1117380	14.865	17.520	31.249	156.076	0.05986	0.28457	98.03	0.1817	4.531480
131	0.1153220	14.891	17.635	31.489	160.370	0.06027	0.29190	99.02	0.1834	4.653970
132	0.1190230	14.916	17.753	31.730	164.796	0.06068	0.29944	100.02	0.1851	4.779190
133	0.1228550	14.941	17.875	31.971	169.374	0.06109	0.30723	101.02	0.1868	4.907550
134	0.1268040	14.966	17.999	32.212	174.084	0.06149	0.31524	102.02	0.1885	5.038440
135	0.1308950	14.992	18.127	32.452	178.957	0.06190	0.32351	103.02	0.1902	5.172580
136	0.1351240	15.017	18.259	32.693	183.987	0.06230	0.33203	104.02	0.1919	5.309730
137	0.1394940	15.042	18.394	32.934	189.179	0.06271	0.34082	105.02	0.1935	5.449850
138	0.1440190	15.067	18.534	33.175	194.548	0.06311	0.35018	106.02	0.1952	5.593240
139	0.1486960	15.093	18.678	33.415	200.092	0.06351	0.35954	107.02	0.1969	5.739700
140	0.1535380	15.118	18.825	33.656	205.824	0.06391	0.36890	108.02	0.1985	5.889450
141	0.1586430	15.143	18.978	33.897	211.754	0.06431	0.37887	109.02	0.2002	6.042560
142	0.1637480	15.168	19.135	34.138	217.892	0.06471	0.38918	110.02	0.2019	6.199180
143	0.1691220	15.194	19.297	34.379	224.233	0.06511	0.39981	111.02	0.2035	6.358980
144	0.1746940	15.219	19.464	34.620	230.802	0.06551	0.41081	112.02	0.2052	6.522410
145	0.1804670	15.244	19.637	34.860	237.600	0.06591	0.42218	113.02	0.2068	6.689320
146	0.1864600	15.269	19.815	35.101	244.651	0.06631	0.43395	114.02	0.2085	6.860090
147	0.1926680	15.295	19.999	35.342	251.949	0.06671	0.44611	115.02	0.2101	7.034350
148	0.1991100	15.320	20.189	35.583	259.514	0.06710	0.45871	116.02	0.2118	7.212390
149	0.2057920	15.345	20.385	35.824	267.356	0.06750	0.47174	117.02	0.2134	7.394130
150	0.2127300	15.370	20.589	36.064	275.490	0.06790	0.48524	118.02	0.2151	7.579770
151	0.2199450	15.396	20.799	36.305	283.943	0.06829	0.49925	119.02	0.2167	7.769580
152	0.2274290	15.421	21.017	36.546	292.705	0.06868	0.51375	120.02	0.2184	7.963060
153	0.2352180	15.446	21.243	36.787	301.816	0.06908	0.52881	121.02	0.2200	8.160870
154	0.2433090	15.471	21.477	37.028	311.273	0.06947	0.54441	122.02	0.2216	8.362560
155	0.2517380	15.497	21.720	37.269	321.118	0.06986	0.56064	123.02	0.2233	8.568710
156	0.2605120	15.522	21.972	37.510	331.359	0.07025	0.57749	124.02	0.2249	8.779150
157	0.2696440	15.547	22.233	37.751	342.012	0.07065	0.59499	125.02	0.2265	8.993780
158	0.2791660	15.572	22.505	37.992	353.112	0.07104	0.61320	126.02	0.2281	9.212970
159	0.2891010	15.598	22.788	38.233	364.685	0.07143	0.63216	127.02	0.2297	9.436770
160	0.2994500	15.623	23.082	38.474	376.737	0.07181	0.65188	128.02	0.2314	9.664800
161	0.3102700	15.648	23.388	38.715	389.325	0.07220	0.67245	129.02	0.2330	9.897800
162	0.3215600	15.673	23.707	38.956	402.457	0.07259	0.69388	130.03	0.2346	10.135300

Table 2-4. *(Continued)* **Thermodynamic Properties of Moist Air at Standard Pressure**

Temp	Humidity Ratio	Volume		Enthalpy		Entropy		Condensate Water		
								Enthalpy	Entropy	Vapor Press.
T	lb_w/lb_{da}	ft^3/lb_{da}		Btu/lb_{da}		$Btu/lb_{da}\text{-}°F$		Btu/lb	Btu/lb-°F	in. Hg
°F	W_s	v_a	v_s	h_a	h_s	s_a	s_s	h_w	s_w	p_s
163	0.3333600	15.699	24.040	39.197	416.175	0.07298	0.71623	131.03	0.2362	10.377600
164	0.3457200	15.724	24.388	39.438	430.533	0.07337	0.73959	132.03	0.2378	10.625000
165	0.3586500	15.749	24.750	39.679	445.544	0.07375	0.76397	133.03	0.2394	10.877100
166	0.3722000	15.774	25.129	39.920	461.271	0.07414	0.78949	134.03	0.2410	11.134300
167	0.3863900	15.800	25.526	40.161	477.739	0.07452	0.81617	135.03	0.2426	11.396500
168	0.4013100	15.825	25.942	40.402	495.032	0.07491	0.84415	136.03	0.2442	11.664100
169	0.4169800	15.850	26.377	40.643	513.197	0.07529	0.87350	137.04	0.2458	11.937000
170	0.4334300	15.875	26.834	40.884	532.256	0.07567	0.90425	138.04	0.2474	12.214900
171	0.4507900	15.901	27.315	41.125	552.356	0.07606	0.93664	139.04	0.2490	12.498800
172	0.4690500	15.926	27.820	41.366	573.504	0.07644	0.97067	140.04	0.2506	12.788000
173	0.4882900	15.951	28.352	41.607	595.767	0.07682	1.00644	141.04	0.2521	13.082300
174	0.5086700	15.976	28.913	41.848	619.337	0.07720	1.04427	142.04	0.2537	13.383100
175	0.5301900	16.002	29.505	42.089	644.229	0.07758	1.08416	143.05	0.2553	13.689400
176	0.5529400	16.027	30.130	42.331	670.528	0.07796	1.12624	144.05	0.2569	14.001000
177	0.5771000	16.052	30.793	42.572	698.448	0.07834	1.17087	145.05	0.2585	14.319100
178	0.6027400	16.078	31.496	42.813	728.073	0.07872	1.21815	146.05	0.2600	14.643000
179	0.6300200	16.103	32.242	43.054	759.579	0.07910	1.26837	147.06	0.2616	14.973100
180	0.6591100	16.128	33.037	43.295	793.166	0.07947	1.32183	148.06	0.2632	15.309700
181	0.6901200	16.153	33.883	43.536	828.962	0.07985	1.37873	149.06	0.2647	15.652200
182	0.7233100	16.178	34.787	43.778	867.265	0.08023	1.43954	150.06	0.2663	16.001400
183	0.7588500	16.204	35.755	44.019	908.278	0.08060	1.50457	151.07	0.2679	16.356900
184	0.7970300	16.229	36.793	44.260	952.321	0.08098	1.57430	152.07	0.2694	16.719000
185	0.8381700	16.254	37.910	44.501	999.763	0.08135	1.64932	153.07	0.2710	17.088000
186	0.8825100	16.280	39.113	44.742	1050.892	0.08172	1.73006	154.08	0.2725	17.463400
187	0.9305700	16.305	40.416	44.984	1106.298	0.08210	1.81744	155.08	0.2741	17.846200
188	0.9827200	16.330	41.828	45.225	1166.399	0.08247	1.91210	156.08	0.2756	18.235700
189	1.0395100	16.355	43.365	45.466	1231.848	0.08284	2.01505	157.09	0.2772	18.632300
190	1.1015400	16.381	45.042	45.707	1303.321	0.08321	2.12733	158.09	0.2787	19.035800
191	1.1696500	16.406	46.882	45.949	1381.783	0.08359	2.25043	159.09	0.2803	19.446800
192	1.2447100	16.431	48.908	46.190	1468.237	0.08396	2.38589	160.10	0.2818	19.865200
193	1.3278800	16.456	51.151	46.431	1564.012	0.08433	2.53576	161.10	0.2834	20.291300
194	1.4202900	16.481	53.642	46.673	1670.431	0.08470	2.70208	162.11	0.2849	20.724400
195	1.5239600	16.507	56.435	46.914	1789.793	0.08506	2.88838	163.11	0.2864	21.166100
196	1.6407000	16.532	59.578	47.155	1924.187	0.08543	3.09787	164.12	0.2880	21.615200
197	1.7729900	16.557	63.137	47.397	2076.466	0.08580	3.33494	165.12	0.2895	22.071400
198	1.9247200	16.583	67.218	47.638	2251.102	0.08617	3.60647	166.13	0.2910	22.536700
199	2.0997500	16.608	71.923	47.879	2452.343	0.08653	3.91929	167.13	0.2926	23.009200
200	2.3045400	16.633	77.426	48.121	2688.205	0.08690	4.28477	168.13	0.2941	23.490600

[a] Extrapolated to represent metastable equilibrium with under cooled liquid.

AIR CONDITIONING PROCESSES

AIR CONDITIONING PROCESSES

Introduction.—The conservation of mass and energy is used in the study of air conditioning processes. Analysis of air conditioning processes is required for maintaining proper temperature and humidity in living space such as residential, commercial, and industrial facilities. The basic processes are as follows:

1) simple heating and cooling processes;

2) cooling with dehumidification;

3) heating with humidification;

4) adiabatic mixing of two air streams; and

5) evaporative cooling.

These air conditioning processes are represented in Fig. 3-1. Simple diagrams of the psychrometric chart are shown in Figs. 2-5 and 2-6.

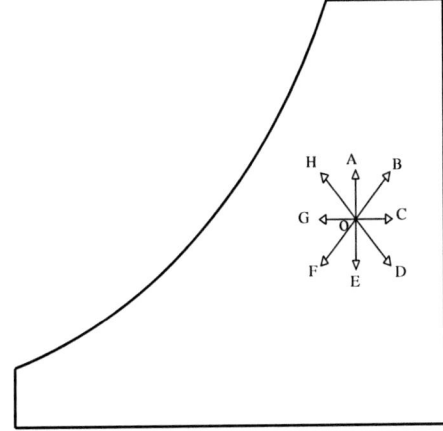

Fig 3-1. Fundamental air-conditioning processes

Process	Direction
Simple heating	O to C
Simple cooling	O to G
Humidification	O to A
Dehumidification	O to E
Evaporative cooling	O to H
Evaporative heating	O to D
Heating and humidification	O to B
Cooling and dehumidification	O to F

Simple Heating and Cooling (W = constant).—In some heating applications, air is heated without moisture being added. An example of this process is a heat pump with heating coil and no humidifier system. In the case of a simple cooling process, in some chilled water cooling applications air can be cooled without condensation. Figs. 3-2 and 3-4 shows schematics of simple heating process

and a simple cooling process, respectively. The simple psychrometric diagrams of these processes are shown Figs. 3-3 and 3-5 respectively.

Neglecting the fan work that may be present, the conservation of mass and energy equations are as follows.

Conservation of mass:

$$\dot{m}_{a1} = \dot{m}_{a2} = \dot{m}_a \tag{1}$$

$$\dot{m}_{v1} = \dot{m}_{v2} = \dot{m}_v \tag{2}$$

$$W_1 = W_2 = \text{constant} \tag{3}$$

Conservation of energy:

$$\dot{m}_a h_1 + \dot{q} = \dot{m}_a h_2 \tag{4}$$

$$\dot{q} = \dot{m}_a (h_2 - h_1) \tag{5}$$

$$h_1 = h_{a1} + W h_{v1} \tag{6}$$

$$h_2 = h_{a2} + W h_{v2} \tag{7}$$

By substituting Equations (6) and (7) in Equation (5) with assuming ideal gas law and approximating a proper acceptable value of W, for HVAC practice Equation (5) can be written in the following convenient form:

$$\dot{q}_h = 1.10 \times cfm \times (T_2 - T_1) \tag{8}$$

where $\dot{q}_h$ = heating load, Btu/hr

cfm = air flow rate of dry air, ft³/min

T_1 = entering temperature, °F

T_2 = leaving temperature, °F

Similarly, in the case of cooling the following convenient approximate form is used for HVAC practice:

$$\dot{q}_c = 1.10 \times cfm \times (T_1 - T_2) \tag{9}$$

where $\dot{q}_c$ = cooling load, Btu/hr

cfm = air flow rate of dry air, ft³/min

T_1 = entering temperature, °F

T_2 = leaving temperature, °F

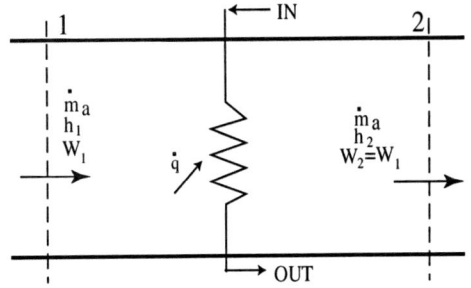

Fig 3-2. Schematic of simple cooling process (sensible cooling)

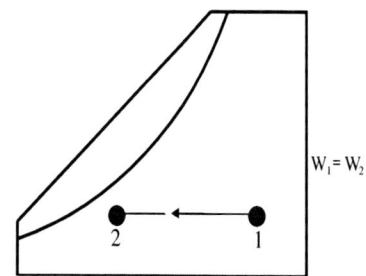

Fig 3-3. Psychrometric diagram of simple cooling process

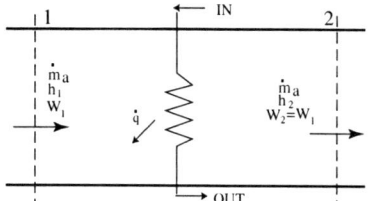

Fig 3-4. Schematic of simple heating process

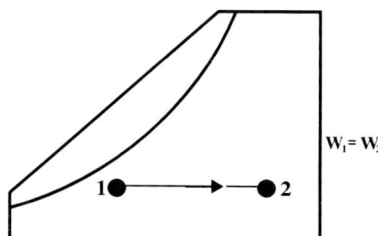

Fig 3-5. Psychrometric diagram of simple heating process

Example 1: Find the required heat to warm 2500 *cfm* of air at 60°F at 90% moisture humidity to 120°F without addition of moisture.

Solution: The mass flow rate of dry air is

$$\dot{m}_a = \frac{cfm}{v} = \frac{2500 \times 60}{13.2944} = 11283 \text{ lb}_m/\text{hr}$$

The specific volume of air at 60°F at 90% is 13.2944 from the psychrometric chart Fig. 2-5.

From the psychrometric chart Fig. 2-5 h_1 = 25.1 Btu/lb$_m$ and h_2 = 39.89 Btu/lb$_m$. By applying Equation (5)

$$\dot{q} = \dot{m}_a(h_2 - h_1)$$
$$= 11283(39.89 - 25.1)$$
$$= 166876 \text{ Btu/hr}$$

By applying the ASHRAE Equation (8)

$$\dot{q} = 1.10 \times cfm \times (T_2 - T_1)$$
$$= 1.10 \times 2500 \times (120 - 60)$$
$$= 165000 \text{ Btu/hr}$$

Cooling with Dehumidification.—In most of the cooling processes, the dew point temperature of the moist air entering the cooling coil is higher than the cooling coil surface temperature so that the water vapor in the entering air will be condensed on the cooling coil and then the condensate will be drained out. Because of this condition, the specific humidity of the leaving moist air will be lowered. The schematic cooling and dehumidification process is shown in Fig. 3-6. The air conditioning system on psychrometric chart representation of this process is shown in Fig. 3-7. The conservation of mass and energy equations for the cooling and dehumidification are as follows:

Conservation of mass:

$$\dot{m}_{a1} = \dot{m}_{a2} = \dot{m}_a \qquad (10)$$

$$\dot{m}_{v1} = \dot{m}_{v2} + \dot{m}_w \qquad (11)$$

$$\dot{m}_w = \dot{m}_a(W_1 - W_2) \qquad \text{where} \qquad W_1 > W_2 \quad (12)$$

Conservation of energy:

$$\dot{m}_a h_1 = \dot{m}_a h_2 + \dot{q} + \dot{m}_w h_w \qquad (13)$$

$$\dot{m}_a h_1 = \dot{m}_a h_2 + \dot{q} + \dot{m}_a(W_1 - W_2)h_w \qquad (14)$$

$$\dot{q} = \dot{m}_a(h_1 - h_2) - \dot{m}_a(W_1 - W_2)h_w \qquad (15)$$

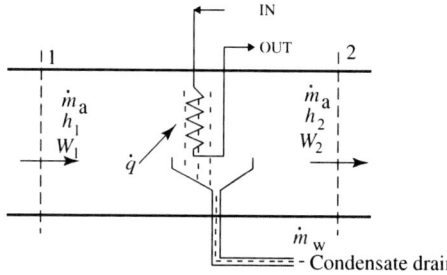

Fig 3-6. Schematic of cooling with dehumidifying process

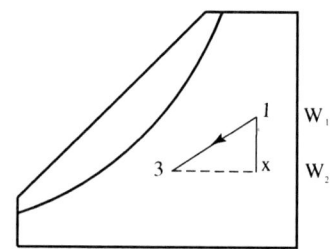

Fig 3-7. Psychrometric diagram of cooling with dehumidifying process

Example 2: What is the cooling capacity of a coil if 5000 *cfm* mixed air entering at 80°F and 67°F and leaving at 55°F at 90% relative humidity?

Solution: The mass flow rate of dry air is

$$\dot{m}_a = \frac{cfm}{v} = \frac{5000 \times 60}{13.833} = 21687 \text{ lb}_m/\text{hr}$$

The specific volume of air at 80°F and 67°F is 13.833 from the psychrometric chart (Fig. 2-5).

The enthalpy of air at entering $h_1 = 31.4$ Btu/lb$_m$, $W_1 = 0.0112$ lb$_v$/lb$_{da}$, $h_2 = 22.2$ Btu/lb$_m$, $W_2 = 0.0082$ lb$_v$/lb$_{da}$, and the enthalpy of condensation $h_w = 23.0$ Btu/lb$_v$. Applying the Equation (15)

$$\dot{q} = \dot{m}_a((h_1 - h_2) - (W_1 - W_2)h_w)$$
$$= 21687((31.4 - 22.2) - (0.0112 - 0.0082) \times 23)$$
$$= 198024 \text{ Btu}$$
$$= 16.5 \text{ ton}$$

Heating with Humidification.—In most commercial facilities such as large office spaces, hospitals, and modern schools where central heating and cooling HVAC systems are used, it is desirable to humidify the supplied heated air to various room and spaces in order to maintain comfortable relative humidity, especially in the locations where the outdoor relative humidity during winter season is very low. In the heating with humidification process, air first is heated by the heating coil or gas furnace and then is humidified by adding moisture before it is supplied to the space.

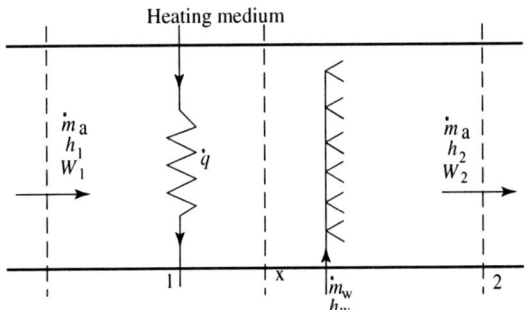

Fig 3-8. Schematic of heating with humidification process

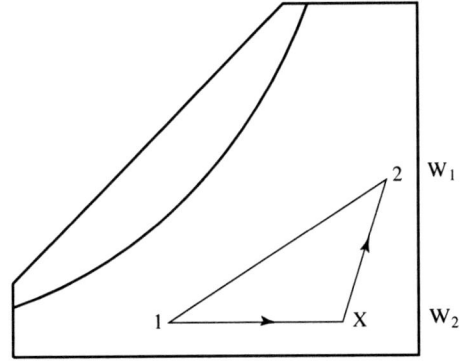

Fig 3-9. Psychrometric diagram of heating with humidification process

The schematic of this process is shown in Fig. 3-8. The air conditioning system on psychrometric chart representation of this process is shown in Fig. 3-9.

The conservation of the mass and energy equations are as follows:

Conservation of mass:

$$\dot{m}_{a1} = \dot{m}_{a2} = \dot{m}_a \tag{16}$$

$$\dot{m}_{v1} + \dot{m}_w = \dot{m}_{v2} \tag{17}$$

$$\dot{m}_w = \dot{m}_a(W_2 - W_1) \qquad \text{where } (W_2 < W_1) \tag{18}$$

Conservation of energy:

$$\dot{m}_a h_1 + \dot{q} + \dot{m}_w h_w = \dot{m}_a h_2 \tag{19}$$

$$\dot{m}_a h_1 + \dot{q} + \dot{m}_a(W_2 - W_1)h_w = \dot{m}_a h_2 \tag{20}$$

$$\dot{q} = \dot{m}_a(h_2 - h_1) + \dot{m}_a(W_1 - W_2)h_w \tag{21}$$

Equation (21) can be written in the following useful form:

$$\frac{h_2 - h_1}{W_2 - W_1} = \frac{\dot{q}}{\dot{m}_w} + h_w \tag{22}$$

Adiabatic Mixing of Two Air Streams.— Many air conditioning applications require the mixing of two air streams. This is particularly true for large buildings, and most process plants, office spaces, and hospitals, in which the space return air must be mixed with a certain required outdoor fresh air for proper ventilation before it enters the air conditioning unit. In this process, the heat transfer to the surrounding space is usually small and can be ignored. The schematic of this process is shown in Fig. 3-10. The psychrometric representation of this process is shown in Fig. 3-11. The mass and energy conservation equations for this process are as follows:

Conservation of mass:

$$\dot{m}_{a1} + \dot{m}_{a2} = \dot{m}_{a3} \tag{23}$$

$$\dot{m}_{v1} + \dot{m}_{v2} = \dot{m}_{v3} \tag{24}$$

$$\dot{m}_{a1}W_1 + \dot{m}_{a2}W_2 = \dot{m}_{a3}W_3 \tag{25}$$

Conservation of energy:

$$\dot{m}_{a1}h_1 + \dot{m}_{a2}h_2 = \dot{m}_{a3}h_3 \tag{26}$$

Combining Equations (23) to (26) gives:

$$\frac{h_2 - h_3}{h_3 - h_1} = \frac{W_2 - W_3}{W_3 - W_1} = \frac{\dot{m}_{a1}}{\dot{m}_{a2}} \tag{27}$$

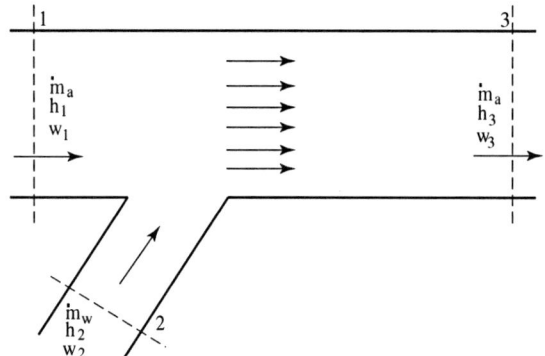

Fig 3-10. Adiabatic mixing of two streams process

Solving Equations (23) to (27) for h_3 and W_3 gives:

$$h_3 = \frac{\dfrac{\dot{m}_{a1}}{\dot{m}_{a2}} h_1 + h_2}{1 + \dfrac{\dot{m}_{a1}}{\dot{m}_{a2}}} \qquad (28)$$

and

$$W_3 = \frac{\dfrac{\dot{m}_{a1}}{\dot{m}_{a2}} W_1 + W_2}{1 + \dfrac{\dot{m}_{a1}}{\dot{m}_{a2}}} \qquad (29)$$

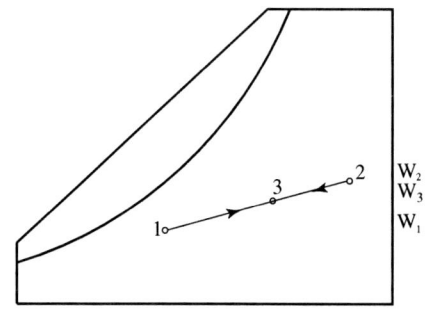

Fig 3-11. Psychrometric diagram of adiabatic mixing process

Example 3: Find the condition of mixed air in which 1500 cfm of outside air 90°F at 30% relative humidity is mixed with 4500 *cfm* return air of 75°F at 60% relative humidity.

Solution: First we will find out the outside air and return air properties. We are given these data:

$$cfm_{oa} = 1500 \qquad cfm_{ra} = 4500$$

$$T_{oa} = 90 \qquad T_{ra} = 75$$

$$\Phi_{oa} = 30 \qquad \Phi_{ra} = 60$$

By applying the psychrometry chart (Fig. 2-5)

$$\nu_{oa} = 14.04 \qquad \nu_{ra} = 13.70$$

$$W_{oa} = 0.009 \qquad W_{ra} = 0.0111$$

$$h_{oa} = 31.54 \qquad h_{ra} = 30.20$$

$$\dot{m}_{oa} = \frac{1500 \times 60}{14.04} \qquad \dot{m}_{ra} = \frac{4500 \times 60}{13.70}$$

$$= 6410 \qquad\qquad = 19708$$

The condition of the mixed air is

$$\dot{m}_m = \dot{m}_{oa} + \dot{m}_{ra} = 6410 + 19708 = 26118$$

$$h_m = \frac{h_{oa} \times \dot{m}_{oa} + h_{ra} \times \dot{m}_{ra}}{\dot{m}_m}$$

$$= \frac{31.54 \times 6410 + 30.20 \times 19708}{26118}$$

$$= 30.52 \ \text{Btu/lb}_m$$

$$W_m = \frac{W_{oa} \times \dot{m}_{oa} + W_{ra} \times \dot{m}_{ra}}{\dot{m}_m}$$

$$= \frac{0.009 \times 6410 + 0.0111 \times 19708}{26118}$$

$$= 0.0105 \ \ \text{lb}_v/\text{lb}_v$$

Example 4: Find the heat transfer rate and mass flow rate of a heating and adiabatic humidification process where 2000 *cfm* air enters at 40°F and 40% relative humidity and leaves at 110°F and a relative humidity of 30%.

Solution: First we will find out the outside air and return air properties. Given

$$cfm = 2000$$

$$T_1 = 40 \qquad T_2 = 110$$

$$\Phi_1 = 40\% \qquad \Phi_2 = 30\%$$

Mass flow rate of dry air

$$m_1 = \frac{cfm \times 60}{\nu} = \frac{2000 \times 60}{12.62} = 9508 \ \ \text{lb}_m/\text{hr}$$

The specific volume of air at 40°F and 40% is 12.62 from the psychrometry chart Fig. 2-5.

By applying the psychrometry chart (Fig. 2-5)

$$W_1 = 0.002 \qquad W_2 = 0.016$$

$$h_1 = 11.83 \qquad h_2 = 44.93$$

$$\dot{m}_2 = \dot{m}_a \qquad h_w = 1135$$

Steam flow rate,

$$\dot{m}_1 W_1 + \dot{m}_w = \dot{m}_2 W_2$$

$$\dot{m}_w = \dot{m}_1(W_2 - W_1)$$

$$= 9508(0.016 - 0.002)$$

$$= 133 \ \text{lb}_\text{m}/\text{hr}$$

Applying the energy balance equation for heating and humidifying equation

$$\dot{m}_1 h_1 + \dot{q} = \dot{m}_2 h_2 - \dot{m}_w h_w$$

$$\dot{q} = \dot{m}_2 h_2 - \dot{m}_1 h_1 - \dot{m}_w h_w$$

$$= \dot{m}_1(h_2 - h_1) - \dot{m}_w h_w$$

$$= 9508(44.93 - 11.83) - 133 \times 1135$$

$$= 163760 \ \text{Btu/hr}$$

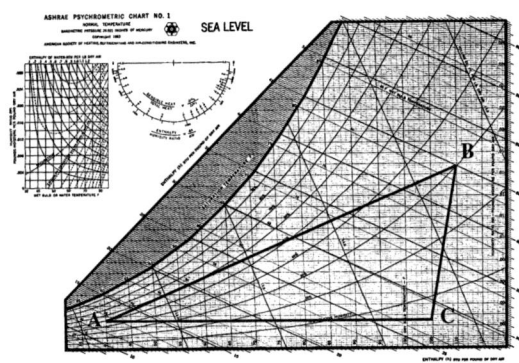

Psychrometric diagram of Example 4

Evaporative Cooling.—Conventional cooling systems such as rooftop and system air conditioning systems and heat pump systems operate on a refrigeration cycle that has high initial and operating and maintenance cost. The high operating cost is associated with the high electricity consumption of the compressor. The conventional refrigerant system can be used in any part of the world. However, in hot and dry climates, we can avoid the high cost of cooling by using the evaporative coolers. The evaporative cooler is based on a simple principle that as water evaporates, the latent heat of vaporization is absorbed from the water and the surrounding air. As a result, both water and the air are cooled during this process. The schematic process of evaporative cooling is shown in Fig. 3-12. The psychrometric representation of this process is shown in Fig. 3-13. During the humidification process the enthalpy of moist air and the wet-bulb temperature of the air remain approximately constant.

Conservation of mass:

$$\dot{m}_{a0} = \dot{m}_{a1} = \dot{m}_a \qquad (30)$$

$$\dot{m}_{v0} + \dot{m}_w = \dot{m}_{v1} \qquad (31)$$

$$\dot{m}_w = \dot{m}_a(W_1 - W_0) \qquad (32)$$

Conservation of energy:

$$\dot{m}_a h_0 = \dot{m}_a h_1$$

$$h_0 = h_1 \qquad (33)$$

or

$$T_{wb0} = T_{wb1}$$

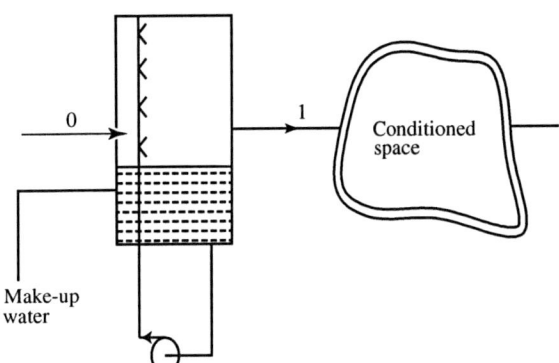

Fig 3-12. Evaporative cooling system

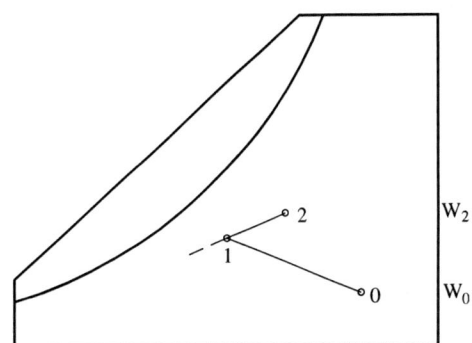

Fig 3-13. Psychrometric diagram for evaporative cooling system

Heating and Air Conditioning System Cycles.—Fig. 3-14 shows a schematic flow diagram of a simple air conditioning cycle. The psychrometric chart representation of a typical cooling and heating systems based on Fig. 3-14 are shown in Figs. 3-15 and 3-16.

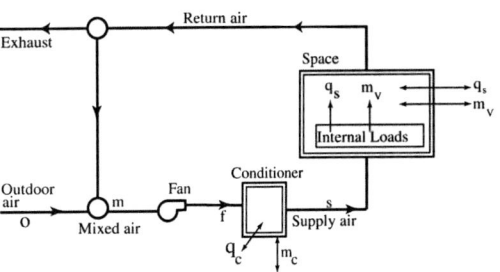

Fig 3-14. Air conditioning system

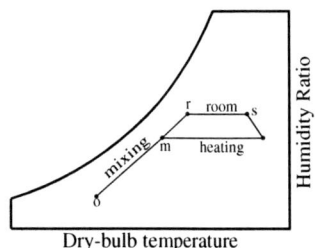

Fig 3-15. Psychrometric diagram of heating/humidifying process

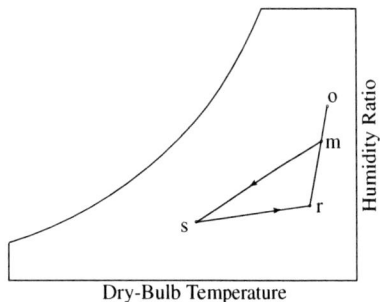

Fig 3-16. Air conditioning cooling system

The following examples will provide good practice and an approach to the analysis of HVAC cycles.

Example 5: Determine the sensible and latent heat load, if 5000 *cfm* conditioned air is supplied to a room at 55°F and 90% relative humidity. The space is to be maintained at 75°F at sensible heat factor (*SHF*) 0.80?

Solution: The total cooling load for the room is

$$\dot{q}_t = 1.10 \times cfm \times \Delta T$$
$$= 1.10 \times 5000 \times (75 - 55)$$
$$= 110000 \text{ Btu/hr}$$

Applying the sensible heat factor equation

$$SHF = \frac{\dot{q}_s}{\dot{q}_s + \dot{q}_l}$$

$$SHF = \frac{\dot{q}_s}{\dot{q}_t}$$

$$\dot{q}_s = \dot{q}_t \times SHF$$
$$= 110000 \times 0.80$$
$$= 88000 \text{ Btu/hr}$$

where $\dot{q}_t$ = total heat loss, Btu/hr

$\dot{q}_s$ = sensible heat loss, Btu/hr

$\dot{q}_l$ = latent heat loss, Btu/hr

Then latent heat is

$$\dot{q}_s + \dot{q}_l = \dot{q}_t$$
$$\dot{q}_l = \dot{q}_t - \dot{q}_s$$
$$= 110000 - 88000$$
$$= 22000 \text{ Btu/hr}$$

Example 6: A room is to be maintained at 75°F and 50% relative humidity. The outside air condition is 95°F and 60% relative humidity. The outdoor air requirements for the occupants is 500 *cfm*. The total heat gain to the space is 60,000 Btu/hr with a 0.80 *SHF*. Determine the quantity and the state of the air supplied to the space and the required capacity of cooling and dehumidifying equipment.

Solution: Assume that the conditions of air after the cooling coil is 55°F and 90% relative humidity. Now make a schematic diagram to locate the points on the psychrometric chart.

$$T_0 = 95 \qquad \Phi_0 = 60$$
$$T_2 = 55 \qquad \Phi_2 = 90$$
$$T_3 = 75 \qquad \Phi_3 = 50$$

$h_0 = 46.4 \qquad W_0 = 0.021 \qquad v_0 = 14.45$

$h_2 = 22.2 \qquad W_2 = 0.008 \qquad v_2 = 13.13$

$h_3 = 28.1 \qquad W_3 = 0.009 \qquad v_3 = 13.66$

Applying the energy balance equation around the room

$$\dot{m}_2 h_2 + \dot{q} = \dot{m}_2 h_3$$

$$\dot{m}_2 = \frac{\dot{q}}{(h_3 - h_2)}$$

$$= \frac{60000}{(28.1 - 22.2)}$$

$$= 10170 \text{ lb/hr}$$

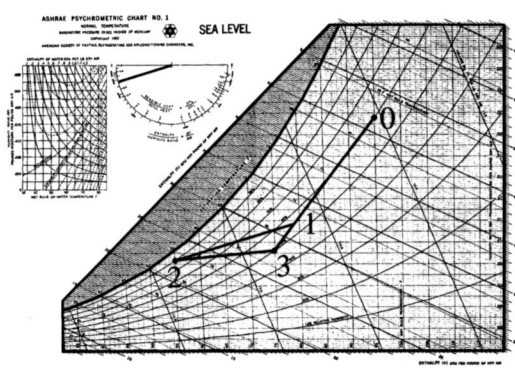

The flow rate of dry air is

$$cfm_{ra} = \dot{m}_2 v_3 = \frac{10170 \times 13.66}{60} = 2315 \text{ cfm}$$

The flow rate of outside air is

$$\dot{m}_4 = \frac{cfm_{oa}}{v} = \frac{500 \times 60}{14.45} = 2076 \text{ lb}_m/\text{hr}$$

The return air quantity will be (10170–2076) or 8094 lb_m/hr. Assume return air condition and room air condition are same.

Now we find the mixed air condition by the mixing of return air and outside air.

$$\dot{m}_1 = \dot{m}_0 + \dot{m}_4 = 8094 + 2076 = 10170 \text{ lb}$$

$$h_1 = \frac{h_0 \times \dot{m}_0 + h_4 \times \dot{m}_4}{\dot{m}_1}$$

$$= \frac{46.4 \times 2076 + 28.1 \times 8094}{10170}$$

$$= 31.84 \text{ Btu/lb}$$

$$W_1 = \frac{W_0 \times \dot{m}_0 + W_4 \times \dot{m}_4}{\dot{m}_1}$$

$$= \frac{0.021 \times 2076 + 0.009 \times 8094}{10170}$$

$$= 0.0115$$

Applying the energy balance equation around the cooling coil:

$$\dot{m}_1 h_1 = \dot{q}_c + \dot{m}_2 h_2$$

$$\dot{q}_c = \dot{m}_2(h_1 - h_2)$$

$$= 10170(31.84 - 22.2)$$

$$= 98038 \text{ Btu/hr}$$

$$= 8.17 \text{ ton}$$

Example 7: A room is to be maintained at 75°F and 50% relative humidity. The outside air is 30°F and 50% relative humidity. The outdoor air requirements for the occupants is 500 *cfm*. Sensible and latent heat losses from the spaces are 120,000 Btu/hr and 30,000 Btu/hr. Determine the quantity of air supplied at 120°F to the space and the required capacity of heating and humidifying equipment.

Solution: The figure below is the schematic for the problem.

$$SHF = \frac{\dot{q}_s}{\dot{q}_s + \dot{q}_l}$$

$$= \frac{120000}{120000 + 30000}$$

$$= 0.80$$

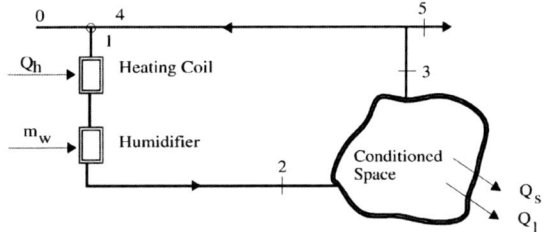

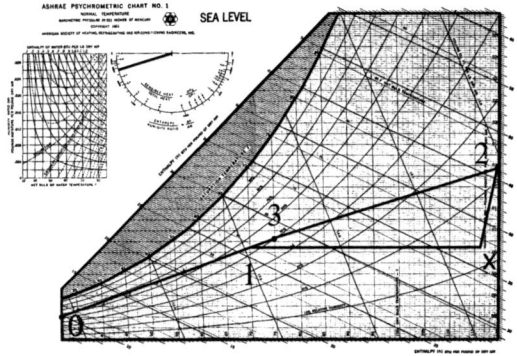

Draw a line at point 3 parallel to *SHF*= 0.80, which intersect 120°F at point 2.

Applying the energy balance equation around the room

$$\dot{m}_2 h_2 = \dot{m}_2 h_3 + \dot{q}_t$$

$$\dot{m}_2 = \frac{\dot{q}_t}{(h_3 - h_2)}$$

$$= \frac{150000}{(46.2 - 28.2)}$$

$$= 8333 \text{ lb/hr}$$

The flow rate of dry air is

$$cfm_{ra} = \dot{m}_2 v_3 = \frac{8333 \times 13.66}{60} = 1898 \text{ cfm}$$

The flow rate of outside air is

$$m_4 = \frac{cfm_{oa}}{v} = \frac{500 \times 60}{12.36} = 2427 \text{ lb/hr}$$

The return air quantity will be (8333–2427) or 5906 lb_m/hr. Assume return air condition and room air condition are the same. Neglecting the return fan effect.

Now we find the mixed air condition by the mixing of return air and outside air.

$$m_1 = m_0 + m_4 = 5906 + 2427 = 8333 \text{ lb}$$

$$h_1 = \frac{h_0 \times m_0 + h_4 \times m_4}{m_1}$$

$$= \frac{9.07 \times 2427 + 28.1 \times 5906}{8333}$$

$$= 22.55 \text{ Btu/lb}$$

$$W_1 = \frac{W_0 \times m_0 + W_4 \times m_4}{m_1}$$

$$= \frac{0.0017 \times 2427 + 0.009 \times 5906}{8333}$$

$$= 0.0068 \text{ lb/lb}$$

Applying the energy balance equation around the heating coil:

$$m_1 h_1 + \dot{q}_h = m_2 h_2$$

$$\dot{q}_h = m_2(h_2 - h_1)$$

$$= 8330(46.2 - 22.55)$$

$$= 197005 \text{ Btu/hr}$$

Applying the mass balance equation around the heating coil:

$$m_1 W_1 + m_w = m_2 W_2$$

$$m_w = m_1(W_2 - W_1)$$

$$= 8330(0.012 - 0.0068)$$

$$= 43.3 \text{ lb/hr}$$

Example 8: An existing building space will be an office space for 200 people. The space design loads are as follows:

Summer: 300,000 Btu/hr sensible (gain), 75,000 Btu/hr latent (gain)

Winter: 600,000 Btu/hr sensible (loss), negligible latent

Fan: 4 inch of water pressure drop with 80% efficiency

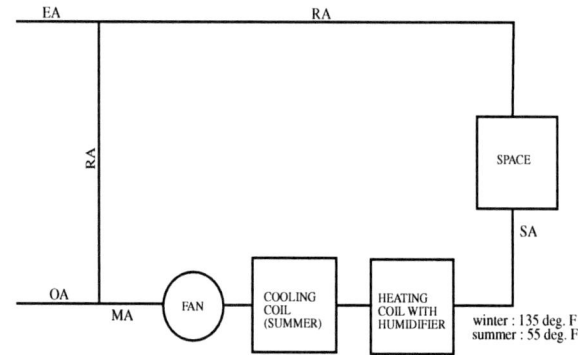

Find the

A) Summer air flow, *cfm*

B) Winter air flow, *cfm*

C) Cooling coil rating, tons

D) Sensible cooling coil rate, Btu/hr

E) Latent cooling coil rate, Btu/hr

F) Heating coil rating, MBH

G) Humidifier rating, gal/hr

Solution:

Location	Dry Bulb Temperature, T_{db}	Wet Bulb Temperature, T_{wb}	Relative Humidity	Enthalpy	Humidity Ratio
Summer					
OA	95	74	37.5	37.50	0.0133
RA	75		55.67	29.31	0.0103
SA	55		100	23.30	0.0092
MA					
Winter					
OA	7		100	2.883	0.0011
RA	72		50	26.42	0.0084
SA	135		7.65	41.77	0.0084
MA					

Summer cooling load:

$$\dot{q}_s = 1.10 \times cfm \times (T_{ra} - T_{sa})$$

$$cfm = \frac{\dot{q}_s}{1.10 \times (T_{ra} - T_{sa})}$$

$$= \frac{300000}{1.10 \times (75 - 55)}$$

$$= 13636$$

Mass of air:

$$\dot{m}_a = \frac{cfm \times 60}{v}$$

$$= \frac{13636 \times 60}{13.66}$$

$$= 59894 \text{ lb/h}$$

Mass of water:

$$\dot{m}_l = \frac{q_l}{1100}$$

$$= \frac{75000}{1100}$$

$$= 68.18 \quad \text{lb/h}$$

Humidity ratio of room air:

$$W_{ra} = W_{sa} + \frac{\dot{m}_l}{\dot{m}_a}$$

$$= 0.0092 + \frac{68.18}{59894}$$

$$= 0.010338$$

At humidity ratio 0.10338 and 75°F, $h_{ra} = 29.31$ Btu/hr.

Outside air requirement as per ASHRAE Code is 20 cfm/person. So the total outside air requirement = 200 × 20 = 4000 cfm.

Mass of air

$$\dot{m}_{oa} = \frac{4000 \times 60}{v}$$

$$= \frac{4000 \times 60}{14.26}$$

$$= 16830 \text{ lb/h}$$

The exhaust air will be 4000 cfm. So the return air will be 13636– 4000 = 9636 cfm and in mass 59894 –16830 = 43064 lb/h.

Mixed air condition:

$$h_m = \frac{\dot{m}_{oa} \times h_{oa} + \dot{m}_{ra} \times h_{ra}}{\dot{m}_{oa} + \dot{m}_{ra}}$$

$$= \frac{16830 \times 37.5 + 43064 \times 29.31}{59894}$$

$$= 31.61 \text{ Btu/lb}$$

$$W_m = \frac{\dot{m}_{oa} \times W_{oa} + \dot{m}_{ra} \times W_{ra}}{\dot{m}_{oa} + \dot{m}_{ra}}$$

$$= \frac{16830 \times 0.0133 + 43064 \times 0.0103}{59894}$$

$$= 0.0111$$

Fan power:

$$P = \frac{cfm \times \Delta p_t}{6350 \times \eta_f}$$

$$= \frac{13636 \times 4}{6350 \times 0.80}$$

$$= 10.737 \text{ hp}$$

$$= 8 \text{ kw}$$

Cooling coil capacity:

$$\dot{q}_{coil} = \dot{m}_a(h_m - h_s - (W_m - W_s)h_c)$$

$$= 59894(31.61 - 23.30 - (0.0111 - 0.0092)32.0)$$

$$= 494078 \text{ Btu/hr}$$

$$= 41.2 \text{Ton}$$

Winter load:

$$\dot{q}_s = 1.10 \times cfm \times (T_{ra} - T_{sa})$$

$$cfm = \frac{\dot{q}_s}{1.10 \times (T_{ra} - T_{sa})}$$

$$= \frac{600000}{1.10 \times (135 - 72)}$$

$$= 8568$$

Mass of air:

$$\dot{m}_a = \frac{cfm \times 60}{v}$$

$$= \frac{8568 \times 60}{13.56}$$

$$= 37911 \text{ lb/h}$$

Outside air requirement as per ASHRAE Code is 20 cfm/person. So the total outside air requirement = 200 × 20 = 4000 cfm.

Mass of air:

$$\dot{m}_{oa} = \frac{4000 \times 60}{v}$$

$$= \frac{4000 \times 60}{11.77}$$

$$= 20390 \text{ lb/h}$$

The exhaust air will be 4000 *cfm*. so the return air will be 8568– 4000 = 4568 *cfm* and in mass 37911 –20390 = 17521 lb/h.

Mixed air condition:

$$h_m = \frac{\dot{m}_{oa} \times h_{oa} + \dot{m}_{ra} \times h_{ra}}{\dot{m}_{oa} + \dot{m}_{ra}}$$

$$= \frac{20390 \times 2.88 + 17521 \times 26.42}{37911}$$

$$= 13.75 \text{ Btu/lb}$$

$$W_m = \frac{\dot{m}_{oa} \times W_{oa} + \dot{m}_{ra} \times W_{ra}}{\dot{m}_{oa} + \dot{m}_{ra}}$$

$$= \frac{20390 \times 0.0011 + 17521 \times 0.0084}{37911}$$

$$= 0.0044$$

Fan power:

$$P = \frac{cfm \times \Delta p_t}{6350 \times \eta_f}$$

$$= \frac{8568 \times 4}{6350 \times 0.80}$$

$$= 6.74 \text{ hp}$$

$$= 5.03 \text{ kw}$$

where Δp_t =total pressure loss, inches of water

η_f =efficiency of fan

Heating coil capacity:

$$\dot{q}_{coil} = \dot{m}_a(h_s - h_m + (W_s - W_m)h_c)$$

$$= 37911(41.77 - 13.75 + (0.0084 - 0.0044)32.0)$$

$$= 1067 \text{ MBH}$$

Humidifier rating:

$$\dot{m}_{humidifier} = \dot{m}_a(W_s - W_m)$$

$$= 37911(0.0084 - 0.0044)$$

$$= 152 \text{ lb/hr}$$

Example 9: A small space requires two zones. Maximum heat loss and heat gain for the zones are given below:

	Winter		Summer		Ventila-tion Require-ment
	Sensible	Latent	Sensible	Latent	
Room A	–48000	2000	60000	2000	600
Room B	–36000	2400	48000	2400	500

Space design condition:

Summer: 75°F

Winter: 75°F, 50% relative humidity

ROOM A	ROOM B

Winter Heat Gain
  Sensible Load: -48000 Btu/hr
  Latent Load: 2000 Btu/hr
 	
Summer Heat Loss
  Sensible Load: 60000 Btu/hr
  Latent Load: 2000 Btu/hr
	Winter Heat Gain
	  Sensible Load: -36000 Btu/hr
	  Latent Load: 2400 Btu/hr
	
	Summer Heat Loss
	  Sensible Load: 48000 Btu/hr
	  Latent Load: 2400 Btu/hr

Find:

A) The required fan capacity and cooling coil and heating coil capacity for double duct multi-zone system (duct loss = 2.0 inches of water).

B) The required fan capacity and cooling coil and heating coil capacity for variable volume with reheat (turn down 50% and cooling coil discharge 55°F (duct loss = 3.0 inches of water).

C) The required fan capacity and cooling coil and heating coil capacity for Four pipe induction (1:1 induction ratio) with primary air provided at 55°F and 130°F (duct loss = 3.0 inches of water).

D) Four pipe induction (1:1 induction ratio) with primary air provided at 55°F and 130°F.

Solution 4 (4-pipe fan coil units):

Location	Dry Bulb Temperature, T_{db}	Wet Bulb Temperature, T_{wb}	Relative Humidity	Enthalpy	Humidity Ratio
Summer					
OA	95	74	37.5	37.50	0.0133
RA	75	50			
SA	55		100	23.20	0.0m, m092
MA					
Winter					
OA	7		100	3.057	0.0013
RA	75		50	26.42	0.0093
SA	135				
MA					

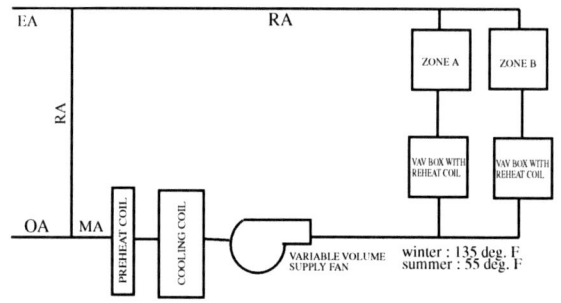

Room-A:

Summer cooling load:

$$\dot{q}_s = 1.10 \times cfm \times (T_{ra} - T_{sa})$$

$$cfm = \frac{\dot{q}_s}{1.10 \times (T_{ra} - T_{sa})}$$

$$= \frac{60000}{1.10 \times (75 - 55)}$$

$$= 2727$$

Mass of air:

$$\dot{m}_a = \frac{cfm \times 60}{v}$$

$$= \frac{2727 \times 60}{13.66}$$

$$= 11978 \text{ lb/h}$$

Mass of water:

$$\dot{m}_l = \frac{\dot{q}_l}{1100}$$

$$= \frac{2000}{1100}$$

$$= 1.82 \text{ lb/h}$$

Humidity ratio of room air:

$$W_{ra} = W_{sa} + \frac{\dot{m}_l}{\dot{m}_a}$$

$$= 0.0092 + \frac{1.82}{11978}$$

$$= 0.009352$$

Room temperature 75°F and humidity ratio 0.009352, relative humidity 50% and enthalpy h_{ra}= 28.15 Btu/h.

Outside air requirement = 600 cfm.

Mass of air:

$$\dot{m}_{oa} = \frac{cfm_{oa} \times 60}{v}$$

$$= \frac{600 \times 60}{14.26}$$

$$= 2524 \text{ lb/h}$$

The exhaust air will be 600 cfm. So the return air will be 2727− 600 = 2127 cfm and in mass 11978 −2524 = 9454 lb/hr.

Mixed air condition:

$$h_{ma} = \frac{\dot{m}_{oa} \times h_{oa} + \dot{m}_{ra} \times h_{ra}}{\dot{m}_{oa} + \dot{m}_{ra}}$$

$$= \frac{2524 \times 37.5 + 9454 \times 28.15}{11978}$$

$$= 30.12 \text{ Btu/lb}$$

$$W_{ma} = \frac{\dot{m}_{oa} \times W_{oa} + \dot{m}_{ra} \times W_{ra}}{\dot{m}_{oa} + \dot{m}_{ra}}$$

$$= \frac{2524 \times 0.0133 + 9454 \times 0.009352}{11978}$$

$$= 0.01018 \text{ lb of water/lb of air}$$

Fan power:

$$P = \frac{cfm \times \Delta p_t}{6350 \times \eta_f}$$

$$= \frac{2727 \times 2}{6350 \times 0.80}$$

$$= 1.07 \text{ hp}$$

$$= 0.80 \text{ kw}$$

Enthalpy after fan (due to fan power):

$$h_f = h_m + \frac{P \times 2545}{\dot{m}_a}$$

$$= 30.12 + \frac{0.80 \times 2545}{11978}$$

$$= 30.30 \text{ Btu/h}$$

$$W_f = W_m$$

$$= 0.01018$$

Cooling coil capacity (condensate water at 64°F h_c = 32.0 Btu/lb):

$$\dot{q}_{coil} = \dot{m}_a(h_f - h_s - (W_f - W_s)h_c)$$

$$= 11978(30.30 - 23.30 - (0.01018 - 0.0092)32.0)$$

$$= 83468 \text{ Btu/hr}$$

$$= 6.96 \text{ ton}$$

Winter supply temperature (same fan is applied, gives same cfm)

$$\dot{q}_s = 1.10 \times cfm \times (T_{sa} - T_{ra})$$

$$T_{sa} = T_{ra} + \frac{\dot{q}_s}{1.10 \times cfm}$$

$$= 75 + \frac{48000}{1.10 \times 2727}$$

$$= 91°F$$

Mass of water:

$$\dot{m}_l = \frac{\dot{q}_l}{1100}$$

$$= \frac{2000}{1100}$$

$$= 1.82$$

Supply air humidity ratio:

$$W_{sa} = W_{ra} - \frac{\dot{m}_l}{\dot{m}_a}$$

$$= 0.0093 - \frac{1.82}{11978}$$

$$= 0.009178$$

Corresponding temperature and humidity ratio of supply air the relative humidity & enthalpy of supply air 29.5% and 31.94 Btu/hr.

Mixed air condition:

$$h_{ma} = \frac{\dot{m}_{oa} \times h_{oa} + \dot{m}_{ra} \times h_{ra}}{\dot{m}_{oa} + \dot{m}_{ra}}$$

$$= \frac{2524 \times 3.057 + 9454 \times 26.42}{11978}$$

$$= 21.50 \text{ Btu/lb}$$

$$W_{ma} = \frac{\dot{m}_{oa} \times W_{oa} + \dot{m}_{ra} \times W_{ra}}{\dot{m}_{oa} + \dot{m}_{ra}}$$

$$= \frac{2524 \times 0.0013 + 9454 \times 0.009352}{11978}$$

$$= 0.0076$$

Fan power:

$$P = \frac{cfm \times \Delta p_t}{6350 \times \eta_f}$$

$$= \frac{2727 \times 2}{6350 \times 0.80}$$

$$= 1.07 \text{ hp}$$

$$= 0.80 \text{ kw}$$

Enthalpy after fan (due to fan power):

$$h_{fa} = h_{ma} + \frac{P \times 2545}{m_a}$$

$$= 21.50 + \frac{0.80 \times 2545}{11978}$$

$$= 21.66 \text{ Btu/h}$$

$$W_{fa} = W_{ma}$$

$$= 0.0076 \text{ lb of water/lb of air}$$

Heating coil capacity:

$$q_{coil} = \dot{m}_a(h_{sa} - h_{fa} + (W_{sa} - W_{fa})h_c)$$

$$= 11978(31.94 - 21.66 + (0.0092 - 0.0076)32.0)$$

$$= 124 \text{ MBH}$$

Humidifier rating

$$\dot{m}_{humidifier} = \dot{m}_a(W_{sa} - W_{fa})$$

$$= 11978(0.0092 - 0.0076)$$

$$= 19.17 \text{ lb/hr}$$

Room-B

Summer cooling load:

$$\dot{q}_s = 1.10 \times cfm \times (T_{ra} - T_{sa})$$

$$cfm = \frac{\dot{q}_s}{1.10 \times (T_{ra} - T_{sa})}$$

$$= \frac{48000}{1.10 \times (75 - 55)}$$

$$= 2182$$

Mass of air:

$$\dot{m}_a = \frac{cfm \times 60}{\nu}$$

$$= \frac{2182 \times 60}{13.66}$$

$$= 9584 \text{ lb/h}$$

Mass of water:

$$\dot{m}_l = \frac{q_l}{1100}$$

$$= \frac{2400}{1100}$$

$$= 2.18 \quad \text{lb/h}$$

Humidity ratio of room air:

$$W_{ra} = W_{sa} + \frac{\dot{m}_l}{\dot{m}_a}$$

$$= 0.0092 + \frac{2.18}{9584}$$

$$= 0.00943$$

Room temperature 75°F and humidity ratio 0.00943, relative humidity 50.85% and enthalpy $h_{ra}= 28.31$

Outside air requirement = 500 cfm.

Mass of air:

$$\dot{m}_{oa} = \frac{cfm_{oa} \times 60}{v}$$

$$= \frac{500 \times 60}{14.26}$$

$$= 2104 \text{ lb/h}$$

The exhaust air will be 500 cfm. So the return air will be 2182 – 500 = 1682 cfm and in mass 9584 – 2104 = 7480 lb/h.

Mixed air condition:

$$h_{ma} = \frac{\dot{m}_{oa} \times h_{oa} + \dot{m}_{ra} \times h_{ra}}{\dot{m}_{oa} + \dot{m}_{ra}}$$

$$= \frac{2104 \times 37.5 + 7480 \times 28.31}{9584}$$

$$= 30.32 \text{ Btu/lb}$$

$$W_{ma} = \frac{\dot{m}_{oa} \times W_{oa} + \dot{m}_{ra} \times W_{ra}}{\dot{m}_{oa} + \dot{m}_{ra}}$$

$$= \frac{2104 \times 0.0133 + 7480 \times 0.00943}{9584}$$

$$= 0.01027$$

Fan power:

$$P = \frac{cfm \times \Delta p_t}{6350 \times \eta_f}$$

$$= \frac{2182 \times 2}{6350 \times 0.80}$$

$$= 0.86 \text{ hp}$$

$$= 0.64 \text{ kw}$$

Enthalpy after fan (due to fan power):

$$h_{fa} = h_{ma} + \frac{P \times 2545}{\dot{m}_a}$$

$$= 30.32 + \frac{0.64 \times 2545}{9584}$$

$$= 30.49 \text{ Btu/h}$$

$$W_f = W_m$$

$$= 0.01027 \text{ lb of water/lb of air}$$

Cooling coil capacity (condensate water at 64°F $h_c = 32.0$ Btu/h):

$$\dot{q}_{coil} = \dot{m}_a(h_{fa} - h_{sa} - (W_{fa} - W_{sa})h_c)$$

$$= 9584(30.49 - 23.30 - (0.01027 - 0.0092)32.0)$$

$$= 68580 \text{ Btu/hr}$$

$$= 5.72 \text{ ton}$$

Winter supply temperature (same fan is applied, gives same cfm):

$$\dot{q}_s = 1.10 \times cfm \times (T_{sa} - T_{ra})$$

$$T_{sa} = T_{ra} + \frac{\dot{q}_s}{1.10 \times cfm}$$

$$= 75 + \frac{36000}{1.10 \times 2182}$$

$$= 90°F$$

Mass of water:

$$\dot{m}_l = \frac{\dot{q}_l}{1100}$$

$$= \frac{2400}{1100}$$

$$= 2.18 \text{ lb/h}$$

Supply air humidity ratio:

$$W_{sa} = W_{ra} - \frac{\dot{m}_l}{\dot{m}_a}$$

$$= 0.0093 - \frac{2.18}{9584}$$

$$= 0.009072$$

Corresponding temperature and humidity ratio of supply air the relative humidity & enthalpy of supply air 30.12% and 31.58 Btu/hr.

Mixed air condition:

$$h_{ma} = \frac{\dot{m}_{oa} \times h_{oa} + \dot{m}_{ra} \times h_{ra}}{\dot{m}_{oa} + \dot{m}_{ra}}$$

$$= \frac{2104 \times 3.057 + 7480 \times 26.42}{9584}$$

$$= 21.30 \text{ Btu/lb}$$

$$W_{ma} = \frac{\dot{m}_{oa} \times W_{oa} + \dot{m}_{ra} \times W_{ra}}{\dot{m}_{oa} + \dot{m}_{ra}}$$

$$= \frac{2104 \times 0.0013 + 7480 \times 0.009352}{9584}$$

$$= 0.0076 \text{ lb of water/lb of air}$$

Fan power:

$$P = \frac{cfm \times \Delta p_t}{6350 \times \eta_f}$$

$$= \frac{2182 \times 2}{6350 \times 0.80}$$

$$= 0.86 \text{ hp}$$

$$= 0.64 \text{ kw}$$

Enthalpy after fan (due to fan power):

$$h_{fa} = h_{ma} + \frac{P \times 2545}{\dot{m}_a}$$

$$= 21.30 + \frac{0.64 \times 2545}{9584}$$

$$= 21.47 \text{ Btu/h}$$

$$W_{fa} = W_{ma}$$

$$= 0.0076 \text{ lb of water/lb of air}$$

Heating coil capacity:

$$\dot{q}_{coil} = \dot{m}_a(h_{sa} - h_{fa} + (W_{sa} - W_{fa})h_c)$$

$$= 9584(31.58 - 21.47 + (0.0092 - 0.0076)32.0)$$

$$= 97 \text{ MBH}$$

Humidifier rating:

$$\dot{m}_{humidifier} = \dot{m}_a(W_{sa} - W_{fa})$$

$$= 9584(0.0092 - 0.0076)$$

$$= 15.33 \text{ lb/hr}$$

Solution 2 (VAV with Reheat):

Location	Dry-bulb Temperature, T_{db}	Wet-bulb Temperature, T_{wb}	Relative Humidity	Enthalpy	Humidity Ratio
Summer					
OA	95	74	37.5	37.50	0.0133
RA	75	50			
SA	55		100	23.20	0.0092

Location	Dry-bulb Temperature, T_{db}	Wet-bulb Temperature, T_{wb}	Relative Humidity	Enthalpy	Humidity Ratio
MA					
Winter					
OA	7		100	3.057	0.0013
RA	75		50	26.42	0.0093
SA	135				
MA					

Summer:
Maximum cooling load = 60000+48000= 108000 Btu/hr.

Summer cooling load:

$$\dot{q}_s = 1.10 \times cfm \times (T_{ra} - T_{sa})$$

$$cfm = \frac{\dot{q}_s}{1.10 \times (T_{ra} - T_{sa})}$$

$$= \frac{108000}{1.10 \times (75 - 55)}$$

$$= 4910$$

Mass of air:

$$\dot{m}_a = \frac{cfm \times 60}{v}$$

$$= \frac{4910 \times 60}{13.66}$$

$$= 21566 \text{ lb/h}$$

Now find out the maximum and minimum requirement of cfm VAV box for two zones. Minimum is the 50% of maximum capacities.

$$\dot{q}_s = 1.10 \times cfm_A \times (T_{ra} - T_{sa})$$

$$cfm_A = \frac{\dot{q}_s}{1.10 \times (T_{ra} - T_{sa})}$$

$$= \frac{60000}{1.10 \times (75 - 55)}$$

$$= 2728$$

$$\dot{q}_s = 1.10 \times cfm_B \times (T_{ra} - T_{sa})$$

$$cfm_B = \frac{\dot{q}_s}{1.10 \times (T_{ra} - T_{sa})}$$

$$= \frac{48000}{1.10 \times (75 - 55)}$$

$$= 2182$$

Room-A		Room-B	
Max. *cfm*	Min. *cfm*	Max. *cfm*	Min. *cfm*
2728	1364	2182	1091

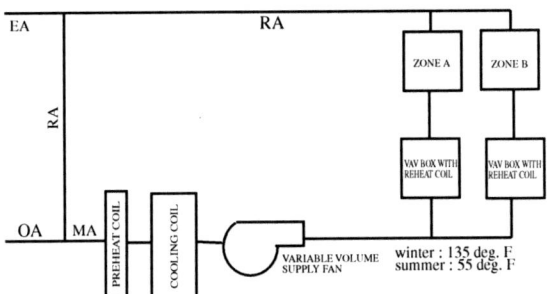

Mass of water:

$$\dot{m}_l = \frac{\dot{q}_{11} + \dot{q}_{12}}{1100}$$

$$= \frac{2000 + 2400}{1100}$$

$$= 4.0 \ \text{lb/h}$$

Humidity ratio of room air:

$$W_{ra} = W_{sa} + \frac{\dot{m}_l}{\dot{m}_a}$$

$$= 0.0092 + \frac{4.0}{21566}$$

$$= 0.00938$$

Room temperature 75°F and humidity ratio 0.00938, relative humidity 50.85% and enthalpy h_{ra} = 28.50 Btu/h.

Outside air requirement = 1100 cfm.

Mass of air:

$$\dot{m}_{oa} = \frac{cfm_{oa} \times 60}{v}$$

$$= \frac{1100 \times 60}{14.26}$$

$$= 4628 \ \text{lb/h}$$

The exhaust air will be 1100 cfm. So the return air will be 4910− 1100 = 3810 cfm and in mass 21566 −4628 = 16938 lb/h.

Mixed air condition

$$h_{ma} = \frac{\dot{m}_{oa} \times h_{oa} + \dot{m}_{ra} \times h_{ra}}{\dot{m}_{oa} + \dot{m}_{ra}}$$

$$= \frac{4628 \times 37.5 + 16938 \times 28.50}{21566}$$

$$= 30.43 \ \text{Btu/lb}$$

$$W_{ma} = \frac{\dot{m}_{oa} \times W_{oa} + \dot{m}_{ra} \times W_{ra}}{\dot{m}_{oa} + \dot{m}_{ra}}$$

$$= \frac{4628 \times 0.0133 + 16938 \times 0.00938}{21566}$$

$$= 0.01022$$

Fan power:

$$P = \frac{cfm \times \Delta p_t}{6350 \times \eta_f}$$

$$= \frac{4910 \times 3}{6350 \times 0.80}$$

$$= 2.9 \ \text{hp}$$

$$= 2.16 \ \text{kw}$$

Enthalpy after fan (due to fan power):

$$h_f = h_m + \frac{P \times 2545}{\dot{m}_a}$$

$$= 30.43 + \frac{2.16 \times 2545}{21566}$$

$$= 30.68 \ \text{Btu/h}$$

$$W_f = W_m$$

$$= 0.01098$$

Cooling coil capacity (condensate water at 64°F h_c = 32.0 Btu/h):

$$q_{coil} = \dot{m}_a(h_f - h_s - (W_f - W_s)h_c)$$

$$= 21566(30.68 - 23.20 - (0.01022 - 0.0092)32.0)$$

$$= 160610 \ \text{Btu/hr}$$

$$= 13.38 \text{Ton}$$

Winter:

During the winter period supplying 50% of maximum capacity.

For Room A, after the reheat coil supply air temperature:

$$\dot{q}_s = 1.10 \times cfm \times (T_{sa} - T_{ra})$$

$$T_{sa} = T_{ra} + \frac{\dot{q}_s}{1.10 \times cfm}$$

$$= 75 + \frac{48000}{1.10 \times 1364}$$

$$= 107°F$$

For Room B, after the reheat coil supply air temperature:

$$\dot{q}_s = 1.10 \times cfm \times (T_{sa} - T_{ra})$$

$$T_{sa} = T_{ra} + \frac{\dot{q}_s}{1.10 \times cfm}$$

$$= 75 + \frac{36000}{1.10 \times 1091}$$

$$= 105°F$$

Reheater capacity for Room A:

$$\dot{q}_{rh-1} = 1.10 \times cfm \times (T_{sa} - T_{ra})$$

$$= 1.10 \times 1364 \times (107 - 75)$$

$$= 48012 \text{ Btu/hr}$$

$$= 48MBH$$

Reheater capacity for Room B:

$$\dot{q}_{rh-2} = 1.10 \times cfm \times (T_{sa} - T_{ra})$$

$$= 1.10 \times 1091 \times (105 - 75)$$

$$= 36003 \text{ Btu/hr}$$

$$= 36MBH$$

Outside air requirement = 600+ 500 = 1100 *cfm*

Return air = 1364 +1091= 2455 *cfm*

Mixed air humidity ratio:

$$W_{ma} = \frac{\dot{m}_{oa} \times W_{oa} + \dot{m}_{ra} \times W_{ra}}{\dot{m}_{oa} + \dot{m}_{ra}}$$

$$= \frac{1100 \times 0.0013 + 1355 \times 0.0093}{2455}$$

$$= 0.0057$$

Supply air humidity ratio:

$$W_{sa} = W_{ra} - \frac{\dot{m}_l}{\dot{m}_a}$$

$$= 0.0093 - \frac{4}{\frac{21566}{2}}$$

$$= 0.00893$$

Humidifier rating:

$$\dot{m}_{humidifier} = \dot{m}_a(W_{sa} - W_{fa})$$

$$= \frac{21566}{2}(0.00893 - 0.0075)$$

$$= 15.4 \text{ lb/hr}$$

Solution 3 (Multizone):

Location	Dry Bulb Temperature, T_{db}	Wet Bulb Temperature, T_{wb}	Relative Humidity	Enthalpy	Humidity Ratio
Summer					
OA	95	74	37.5	37.50	0.0133
RA	75	50			
SA	55		100	23.20	0.0092
MA					
Winter					
OA	7		100	3.057	0.0013
RA	75		50	26.42	0.0093
SA	135				
MA					

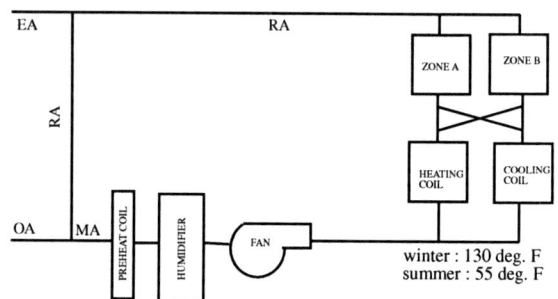

winter : 130 deg. F
summer : 55 deg. F

For Room A:

Maximum supply air in summer:

$$\dot{q}_s = 1.10 \times cfm \times (T_{ra} - T_{sa})$$

$$cfm = \frac{\dot{q}_s}{1.10 \times (T_{ra} - T_{sa})}$$

$$= \frac{60000}{1.10 \times (75 - 55)}$$

$$= 2728$$

Maximum supply air in winter:

$$\dot{q}_s = 1.10 \times cfm \times (T_{ra} - T_{sa})$$

$$cfm = \frac{\dot{q}_s}{1.10 \times (T_{ra} - T_{sa})}$$

$$= \frac{48000}{1.10 \times (130 - 75)}$$

$$= 794$$

Zone A capacity: 2728 *cfm* (maximum of summer and winter required *cfm*)

For room B:

Maximum Supply air in summer:

$$\dot{q}_s = 1.10 \times cfm \times (T_{ra} - T_{sa})$$

$$cfm = \frac{\dot{q}_s}{1.10 \times (T_{ra} - T_{sa})}$$

$$= \frac{48000}{1.10 \times (75 - 55)}$$

$$= 2182$$

Maximum supply air in winter:

$$\dot{q}_s = 1.10 \times cfm \times (T_{ra} - T_{sa})$$

$$cfm = \frac{\dot{q}_s}{1.10 \times (T_{ra} - T_{sa})}$$

$$= \frac{36000}{1.10 \times (130 - 75)}$$

$$= 595$$

Zone B capacity: 2182 *cfm* (maximum of summer and winter required *cfm*)

Total *cfm* = 2728+2182 = 4910 *cfm*

Mass of air:

$$\dot{m}_a = \frac{cfm \times 60}{v}$$

$$= \frac{4910 \times 60}{13.66}$$

$$= 21566 \text{ lb/h}$$

Mass of water:

$$m_l = \frac{\dot{q}_{l1} + \dot{q}_{l2}}{1100}$$

$$= \frac{2000 + 2400}{1100}$$

$$= 4.0$$

Humidity ratio of room air:

$$W_{ra} = W_{sa} + \frac{m_l}{m_a}$$

$$= 0.0092 + \frac{4.0}{21566}$$

$$= 0.00938$$

Room temperature 75°F and humidity ratio 0.00938, relative humidity 50.85% and enthalpy h_{ra}= 28.50 Btu/h.

Outside air requirement = 1100 *cfm*.

Mass of air:

$$m_{oa} = \frac{cfm_{oa} \times 60}{v}$$

$$= \frac{1100 \times 60}{14.26}$$

$$= 4628 \text{ lb/h}$$

The exhaust air will be 1100 *cfm*. So the return air will be 4910–1100 = 3810 *cfm* and in mass 21566 –4628 = 16938 lb/h.

Mixed air condition:

$$h_{ma} = \frac{m_{oa} \times h_{oa} + m_{ra} \times h_{ra}}{m_{oa} + m_{ra}}$$

$$= \frac{4628 \times 37.5 + 16938 \times 28.50}{21566}$$

$$= 30.43 \text{ Btu/lb}$$

$$W_{ma} = \frac{m_{oa} \times W_{oa} + m_{ra} \times W_{ra}}{m_{oa} + m_{ra}}$$

$$= \frac{4628 \times 0.0133 + 16938 \times 0.00938}{21566}$$

$$= 0.01022 \text{ lb of water/lb of air}$$

Fan power:

$$P = \frac{cfm \times \Delta p_t}{6350 \times \eta_f}$$

$$= \frac{4910 \times 3}{6350 \times 0.80}$$

$$= 2.9 \text{ hp}$$

$$= 2.16 \text{ kw}$$

Enthalpy after fan (due to fan power):

$$h_f = h_m + \frac{P \times 2545}{m_a}$$

$$= 30.43 + \frac{2.16 \times 2545}{21566}$$

$$= 30.68 \text{ Btu/h}$$

$$W_f = W_m$$

$$= 0.01098$$

Cooling coil capacity (condensate water at 64°F h_c = 32.0 Btu/h):

$$\dot{q}_{coil} = m_a(h_f - h_s - (W_f - W_s)h_c)$$
$$= 21566(30.68 - 23.30)$$
$$-(0.01022 - 0.0092)32.0$$
$$= 158453 \text{ Btu/hr}$$
$$= 13.20 \text{ ton}$$

Winter:

Applying the energy balance equation in Room A:

$$1.1 \times cfm_{h1} \times (130 - 75)$$
$$+ 1.1 \times (2728 - cfm_{h1}) \times (55 - 75) = 48000$$
$$60.5 \times cfm_{h1} - 60016 + 22 \times cfm_{h1} = 48000$$
$$82.5 cfm_{h1} = 108016$$
$$cfm_{h1} = 1310$$

Similarly for Room B:

$$1.1 \times cfm_{h2} \times (130 - 75)$$
$$+ 1.1 \times (2182 - cfm_{h2}) \times (55 - 75) = 36000$$
$$60.5 \times cfm_{h2} - 48004 + 22 \times cfm_{h2} = 36000$$
$$82.5 cfm_{h2} = 84004$$
$$cfm_{h2} = 1018$$

Air circulating through heating coil = 1310+1018 = 2328 *cfm*

Outside air requirement = 600 + 500 = 1100 *cfm*

Return air = 4910 *cfm*

Mixed air condition:

$$T_{ma} = \frac{cfm_{oa} \times T_{oa} + cfm_{ra} \times T_{ra}}{cfm_{oa} + cfm_{ra}}$$
$$= \frac{1100 \times 6 + 3810 \times 75}{4910}$$
$$= 59.54° \text{ F}$$
$$T_{fa} = T_{ma} + \frac{h_f}{c_p}$$
$$= 59.54 + \frac{0.25}{0.24}$$
$$= 60.58°\text{F}$$

Total heat load:

$$\dot{q}_h = 1.1 \times (cfm_{h1} + cfm_{h2}) \times (130 - 60.58)$$
$$= 1.10 \times (1310 + 1018) \times 69.42$$
$$= 154723 \text{ Btu/h}$$
$$= 155 \text{ Mbh}$$

Solution 4 (Four Pipe Induction):

Location	Dry Bulb Tempera-ture, T_{db}	Wet Bulb Tempera-ture, T_{wb}	Relative Humidity	Enthalpy	Humidity Ratio
		Summer			
OA	95	74	37.5	37.50	0.0133
RA	75	50			
SA	55		100	23.30	0.0092
MA					
		Winter			
OA	7		100	3.057	0.0013
RA	75		50	26.42	0.0093
SA	135				
MA					

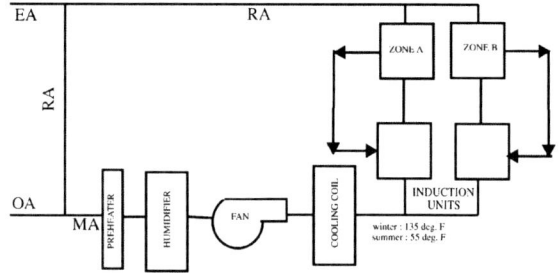

For Room A:

Maximum supply air in summer:

$$\dot{q}_s = 1.10 \times cfm \times (T_{ra} - T_{sa})$$
$$cfm = \frac{\dot{q}_s}{1.10 \times (T_{ra} - T_{sa})}$$
$$= \frac{60000}{1.10 \times (75 - 55)}$$
$$= 2728$$

Mass of air:

$$\dot{m}_{a1} = \frac{cfm \times 60}{v}$$
$$= \frac{2728 \times 60}{13.66}$$
$$= 11982 \text{ lb/h}$$

For room B:

Maximum supply air in summer:

$$\dot{q}_s = 1.10 \times cfm \times (T_{ra} - T_{sa})$$

$$cfm = \frac{\dot{q}_s}{1.10 \times (T_{ra} - T_{sa})}$$

$$= \frac{48000}{1.10 \times (75 - 55)}$$

$$= 2182$$

Mass of air:

$$\dot{m}_{a2} = \frac{cfm \times 60}{v}$$

$$= \frac{2182 \times 60}{13.66}$$

$$= 9584 \text{ lb/h}$$

Total cfm = 2728 + 2182 = 4910 cfm = 21566 lb/h

Fan capacity: 4910 cfm/2 = 2455 cfm

Mass of air:

$$\dot{m}_a = \frac{cfm \times 60}{v}$$

$$= \frac{4910 \times 60}{13.66}$$

$$= 21566 \text{ lb/h}$$

Mass of water:

$$\dot{m}_l = \frac{\dot{q}_{l1} + \dot{q}_{l2}}{1100}$$

$$= \frac{2000 + 2400}{1100}$$

$$= 4.0 \text{ lb/h}$$

Humidity ratio of room air:

$$W_{ra} = W_{sa} + \frac{\dot{m}_l}{\dot{m}_a}$$

$$= 0.0092 + \frac{4.0}{21566}$$

$$= 0.00938$$

Room temperature 75°F and humidity ratio 0.00938, relative humidity 50.85% and enthalpy h_{ra}= 28.50

Outside air requirement = 1100 cfm.

Mass of air:

$$\dot{m}_{oa} = \frac{cfm_{oa} \times 60}{v}$$

$$= \frac{1100 \times 60}{14.26}$$

$$= 4628 \text{ lb/h}$$

The exhaust air will be 1100 cfm. So the return air will be 2455 − 1100 = 1355 cfm and in mass 10783 − 4628 = 6155 lb/h.

Mixed air condition:

$$h_{ma} = \frac{cfm_{oa} \times h_{oa} + cfm_{ra} \times h_{ra}}{cfm_{oa} + cfm_{ra}}$$

$$= \frac{1100 \times 37.5 + 1355 \times 28.50}{2455}$$

$$= 32.53 \text{ Btu/lb}$$

$$W_{ma} = \frac{cfm_{oa} \times W_{oa} + cfm_{ra} \times W_{ra}}{cfm_{oa} + cfm_{ra}}$$

$$= \frac{1100 \times 0.0133 + 1355 \times 0.00938}{2455}$$

$$= 0.011081 \text{ lb of water/lb of air}$$

Fan power:

$$P = \frac{cfm \times \Delta p_t}{6350 \times \eta_f}$$

$$= \frac{2455 \times 3}{6350 \times 0.80}$$

$$= 1.45 \text{ hp}$$

$$= 1.08 \text{ kw}$$

Enthalpy after fan (due to fan power):

$$h_f = h_m + \frac{P \times 2545}{\dot{m}_a}$$

$$= 32.53 + \frac{1.08 \times 2545}{\dfrac{21566}{2}}$$

$$= 32.78 \text{ Btu/h}$$

$$W_f = W_m$$

$$= 0.01098 \text{ lb of water/lb of air}$$

Cooling coil capacity (condensate water at 64°F $h_c = 32.0$ Btu/h)

$$q_{coil} = \dot{m}_a(h_f - h_s - (W_f - W_s)h_c)$$

$$= \frac{21566}{2}(32.78 - 23.30 - (0.011 - 0.0092)32.0)$$

$$= 101602 \text{ Btu/hr}$$

$$= 8.46 \text{ ton}$$

Secondary cooling coil for room-A:

$$\dot{q}_{c1} = \frac{11982}{2}(26.42 - 23.30)$$

$$= 18692 \text{ Btu/hr}$$

Secondary heating coil for room-A:

$$\dot{q}_{h1} = 48000 + 1.10\left(\frac{2728}{2}\right)(75 - 55)$$

$$= 78008 \text{ Btu/hr}$$

Secondary cooling coil for room-B:

$$\dot{q}_{c2} = \frac{9584}{2}(26.42 - 23.30)$$

$$= 14952 \text{ Btu/hr}$$

Secondary heating coil for room-B:

$$\dot{q}_{h2} = 36000 + 1.10\left(\frac{2182}{2}\right)(75 - 55)$$

$$= 60002 \text{ Btu/hr}$$

INDOOR AIR QUALITY AND VENTILATION

INDOOR AIR QUALITY AND VENTILATION

Indoor Air Quality

Providing a comfortable and healthy indoor air quality for residential and commercial buildings (such as single family homes with central air conditioning systems, multiple dwelling buildings, commercial offices, and schools) is a major concern of HVAC engineers. Exposure to indoor pollutants can be more serious than exposure to outdoor pollutants since indoor concentrations of pollutants are generally higher than corresponding outdoor pollutants. ASHRAE Standards 62 provides many indoor air quality concerns. Table 4-1 provides concentrations of some pollutants found in indoor spaces.

Table 4-1. Sources, Possible Concentrations, and Indoor to Outdoor Concentration Ratios of Some Indoor Pollutants

Pollutant	Sources of Indoor Pollution	Possible Indoor Concentration	I/O Concentration Ratio	Location
Carbon monoxide	Combustion equipment, engines, faulty heating systems	100 ppm	>>1	Skating rinks, offices, homes, cars, shops
Respirable particles	Stoves, fireplaces, cigarettes, condensation of volatilize, aerosol sprays, responsions, cooking	100 to 500 $\mu g/m^3$	>>1	Homes, offices, cars, public facilities, bars, restaurants
Organic vapors	Combustion, solvents, resin products, pesticides, aerosol sprays	NA	>1	Homes, restaurants, public facilities, offices, hospitals
Nitrogen dioxide	Combustion, gas stoves, water heaters, dryers, cigarettes, engines	200 to 1000 $\mu g/m^3$	>>1	Homes, skating rinks
Sulfur dioxide	Heating system	20 $\mu g/m^3$	<1	
Total suspended particles without smoking	Combustion, responsions, heating system	100 $\mu g/m^3$	1	Homes, offices, transportation, restaurants
Sulfate	Matches, gas stoves	5 $\mu g/m^3$	<1	Homes, offices
Formaldehyde	Insulation, product binders, particle board	0.05 to 1.0 ppm	>1	Homes, offices
Radon and progeny	Building materials, groundwater, soil	0.1 to 200 nCi/m^3	>>1	Homes, buildings
Asbestos	Fireproofing insulation	$<10^6$ fiber/m^3	1	Homes, schools, offices
Mineral and synthetic fibers	Cloth, rugs, wallboard	NA	...	Homes, schools, offices
Carbon dioxide	Combustion, humans, pets	3000 ppm	>>1	Homes, schools, offices
Viable organisms	Humans, pets, rodents, insects, plants, fungi, humidifiers, air conditioners	NA	>1	Homes, hospitals, schools, offices, public facilities
Ozone	Electric arcing	20 ppb	<1	Airplanes
	Ultraviolet light sources	200 ppb	>1	Offices

ppb indicates parts per billion and ppm indicates parts per million.

Some symptoms of unacceptable indoor air quality are:
Headaches
Eye irritations
Fatigue
Breathing problems
Asthma attacks
Memory loss
Dizziness
Depression
Skin irritation
Sinus infections
Cold, flu, and viruses.

ASHRAE Standard 62-1989 provides two alternatives for maintaining acceptable air quality:
Ventilation procedure
Indoor air quality procedure.

Ventilation Procedure.—In ventilation procedure a minimum amount of acceptable outdoor air must be supplied to the conditioned space in order to maintain acceptable concentrations of indoor pollutants such as carbon dioxide (CO_2), odor, tobacco smoke generated by occupants, and other pollutant sources. Table 4-5 lists some indoor pollutants and their sources. Acceptable concentrations of the outdoor air pollutants are given in Table 4-1; and the required minimum amount of outdoor air is given in Table 4-2. Correct outdoor air requirements for ventilation of residential facilities are given in Table 4-3. Basically, a minimum of 15 cfm per person of the outdoor air is required to keep the indoor concentration of CO_2 below acceptable concentrations of 0.1% (1000 parts per million, ppm) assuming a typical generation of CO_2 per occupant. The minimum outdoor air requirement for ventilation given in Table 4-2 should be checked against local code requirements and use the local code requirements if it is more stringent.

Table 4-2. ASHRAE Standard 62-1989 Ventilation Rates

Application	Estimated Maximum[b] Occupancy/1000 ft² or 100 m²	Outdoor Air Requirements				Comments
		cfm/person	L/s person	cfm/ft²	L/s-m²	
Outdoor air requirements for ventilation commercial facilities[a] (offices, stores, shops, hotels, sports facilities)						
Dry Cleaners, Laundries						
Commercial laundry	10	25	13			Dry cleaning processes may require more air.
Commercial dry cleaner	30	30	15			
Storage, pick up	30	35	18			
Coin-operated laundries	20	15	8			
Coin-operated dry cleaner	20	15	8			
Food and Beverage Service						
Dining rooms	70	20	10			
Cafeteria, fast food	100	20	10			
Bars, cocktail lounges	100	30	15			Supplementary smoke-removal equipment may be required.
Kitchens (cooking)	20	15	8			Makeup air for hood exhaust may require more ventilating air. The sum of the outdoor air and transfer air of acceptable quality from adjacent spaces shall be sufficient to provide an exhaust rate of not less than 1.5 cfm/ft² (7.5 L/s-m²).
Garages, Repair, Service Stations						
Enclosed parking garage				1.50	7.50	Distribution among people must consider worker location and concentration of running engines; stands where engines are run must incorporate systems for positive engine exhaust withdrawal. Contaminant sensors may be used to control ventilation.
Auto repair rooms				1.50	7.50	
Hotels, Motels, Resorts, Dormitories				cfm/room[c]	L/s-room[c]	Independent of room size
Bedrooms				30	15	
Living rooms				30	15	
Baths				35	18	Installed capacity for intermittent use.
Lobbies	30	15	8			
Conference rooms	50	20	10			
Assembly rooms	120	15	8			
Dormitory sleeping areas	20	15	8			See also food and beverage services, merchandising, barber and beauty shops, garages.
Gambling casinos	120	30	15			Supplementary smoke-removal equipment may be required.
Offices						
Office space	7	20	10			Some office equipment may require local exhaust.
Reception areas	60	15	8			
Telecommunication centers and data entry areas	60	20	10			
Conference rooms	50	20	10			Supplementary smoke-removal equipment may be required.
Public Spaces				cfm/ft²[c]	L/s-m²[c]	
Corridors and utilities				0.05	0.25	
Public restrooms, cfm/water closet or urinal		50	25			Mechanical exhaust with no recirculation is recommended.
Locker and dressing rooms				0.5	2.5	
Smoking lounge	70	60	30			Normally supplied by transfer air, local mechanical exhaust with no recirculation recommended.
Elevators				1.0	5.0	Normally supplied by transfer air.
Retail Stores, Sales Floors, and Showroom Floors						
Basement and street	30			0.30	1.50	
Upper floors	20			0.20	1.00	
Storage rooms	15			0.15	0.75	
Dressing rooms				0.20	1.00	

Table 4-2. *(Continued)* **ASHRAE Standard 62-1989 Ventilation Rates**

Application	Estimated Maximum[b] Occupancy/1000 ft² or 100 m²	Outdoor Air Requirements				Comments
		cfm/person	L/s person	cfm/ft²	L/s-m²	
Outdoor air requirements for ventilation commercial facilities[a] (offices, stores, shops, hotels, sports facilities)						
Malls and arcades	20			0.20	1.00	
Shipping and receiving	10			0.20	1.00	
Warehouses	5			0.05	0.25	
Smoking lounge	70	60	30			Normally supplied by transfer air, local mechanical exhaust; exhaust with no recirculation recommended.
Specialty Shops						
Barbers	25	15	8			
Beauty shops	25	25	13			
Reducing salons	20	15	8			
Florists	8	15	8			Ventilation to optimize plant growth may dictate requirements.
Clothiers, furniture						
Hardware, drug stores, fabric stores	8	15	8			
Supermarkets	8	15	8			
Pet shops				1.00	5.00	
Sports and Amusement						
Spectator areas	150	15	8			When internal combustion engines are operated for maintenance of playing surfaces, increased ventilation rates may be required.
Game rooms	70	25	13			
Ice arenas (playing areas)				0.50	2.50	
Swimming pools (pool and deck area)				0.50	2.50	Higher values may be required for humidity control.
Playing floors (gymnasium)	30	20	10			
Ballrooms and discos	100	25	13			
Bowling alleys (seating areas)	70	25	13			
Theaters						
Ticket booths	60	20	10			Special ventilation will be needed to eliminate special stage effects (e.g., dry ice vapors, mists, etc.)
Lobbies	150	20	10			
Auditoriums	150	15	8			
Stages, studios	70	15	8			
Transportation						
Waiting rooms	100	15	8			
Platforms	100	15	8			Ventilation within vehicles may require special considerations.
Vehicles	150	15	8			
Workrooms						
Meat processing areas	10	15	8			Spaces maintained at low temperatures (−10°F to + 50°F, or −23°C to + 10°C) are not covered by these requirements unless the occupancy is continuous. Ventilation from adjoining spaces is permissible. When the occupancy is intermittent, infiltration will normally exceed the ventilation requirement.
Photo studios	10	15	8			
Darkrooms	10	15	8			
Pharmacies	10	15	8			
Bank vaults	10	15	8			
Duplicating, printing areas				0.50	2.50	Installed equipment must incorporate positive exhaust and control (as required) of undesirable contaminants (toxic or otherwise).

Table 4-2. *(Continued)* **ASHRAE Standard 62-1989 Ventilation Rates**

Application	Estimated Maximum[b] Occupancy/1000 ft² or 100 m²	Outdoor Air Requirements				Comments
		cfm/person	L/s person	cfm/ft²	L/s-m²	
Outdoor air requirements for ventilation commercial facilities[a] (offices, stores, shops, hotels, sports facilities)						
Institutional Facilities						
Education						
Classroom	50	15	8			Special contaminant control systems may be required for processes or functions including laboratory animal occupancy.
Laboratories	30	20	10			
Training shop	30	20	10			
Music rooms	50	15	8			
Libraries	20	15	8			
Locker rooms				0.50	2.50	
Corridors				0.10	0.50	
Auditoriums	150	15	8			
Smoking lounges	70	60	30			Normally supplied by transfer air. Local mechanical exhaust with no recirculation recommended.
Hospitals, Nursing and Convalescent Homes						
Patient rooms	10	25	13			Special requirements or codes and pressure relationships may determine minimum ventilation rates and filter efficiency. Procedures generating contaminants may require higher rates.
Medical procedure	20	15	8			
Operating rooms	20	30	15			
Recovery and ICU	20	15	8			
Autopsy rooms				0.50	2.50	Air shall not be recirculated into other spaces.
Physical Therapy	20	15	8			
Correctional Facilities						
Cells	20	20	10			
Dining halls	100	15	8			
Guard stations	40	15	8			

[a] Table prescribes supply rates of acceptable outdoor air required for acceptable indoor air quality. These values have been chosen to control CO_2 and other contaminants with an adequate margin of safety and to account for health variations among people, varied activity levels, and a moderate amount of smoking.

[b] Net occupiable space.

[c] Change of units

Table 4-3. Outdoor Air Requirements for Ventilation of Residential Facilities[a]
(Private Dwellings, Single, Multiple)

Applications	Outdoor Requirements	Comments
Living areas	0.35 air change per hour but not less than 15 cfm (7.5 L/s) per person	For calculating the air changes per hour, the volume of the living spaces shall include all areas within the conditioned space. The ventilation is normally satisfied by infiltration and natural ventilation. Dwellings with tight enclosures may require supplemental ventilation supply for fuel burning appliances, including fireplaces and mechanically exhausted appliances. Occupant loading shall be based on the number of bedrooms as follows: first bedroom, two persons; each additional bedroom, one person. Where higher occupant loadings are known, these shall be used.
Kitchens[b]	100 cfm (50 L/s) intermittent or 25 cfm (12 L/s) continuous or openable windows	Installed mechanical exhaust capacity[c]. Climatic conditions may affect choice of the ventilation system.
Baths, toilets	50 cfm (25 L/s) intermittent or 20 cfm (10 L/s) continuous or openable windows	Installed mechanical exhaust capacity
Garages		
Separate for each dwelling unit	100 cfm (50 L/s) per car	Normally satisfied by infiltration or natural ventilation.
Common for several units	1.5 cfm/ft² (7.5 L/s-in²)	

[a] In using this table, assume the outdoor air to be acceptable.

[b] Climatic conditions may affect choice of ventilation option chosen.

[c] The air exhausted from kitchens, bathrooms, and toilet rooms may utilize air supplied through adjacent living areas to compensate for the air exhausted. The air supplied shall meet the requirements of exhaust systems, and be of sufficient quantities to meet the requirements of this table.

Table 4-4. United States Ambient Air Quality Standards

Contaminant	Averaging Time	Primary Standard Levels	Secondary Standard Levels
Particulate matter	Annual (geometric mean)	75 µg/m³	60 µg/m³
	24h	260 µg/m³	150 µg/m³
Sulfur oxides	Annual (arithmetic mean)	80 µg/m³ (0.03 ppm)	
	24h	365 µg/m³ (0.14 ppm)	
	3h		130 µg/m³ (0.5 ppm)
Carbon monoxide	8h	10 mg/m³ (9 ppm)	10 mg/m³ (9 ppm)
	1h	40 mg/m³ (35 ppm)	40 mg/m³ (35 ppm)
Nitrogen dioxide	Annual (arithmetic mean)	100 µg/m³ (0.05 ppm)	100 µg/m³ (0.05 ppm)
Ozone	1h	240 µg/m³ (0.12 ppm)	240 µg/m³ (0.12 ppm)
Hydrocarbons (non-methane)	3h (6 am to 9 am)	160 µg/m³ (0.24 ppm)	160 µg/m³ (0.24 ppm)
Lead	3 months	1.5 µg/m³	1.5 µg/m³

Table 4-5. Indoor Air Pollutants and Sources

Sources	Contaminants
Outdoor	
Ambient air	SO₂, NO, NO₂, O₃, hydrocarbons, CO, particulates, bioaerosols
Motor vehicles	CO, Pb, hydrocarbons, particulates
Soil	Radon organics
Indoor	
Building construction materials	
Concrete, stone	Radon
Particle board, plywood	Formaldehyde
Insulation	Formaldehyde, fiberglass
Fire retardant	Asbestos
Adhesives	Organics
Paint	Mercury, organics
Building Contents	
Heating and cooking combustion appliances	CO, NO, NO₂, formaldehyde, particulates, organics
Furnishings	Organics
Water service, natural gas	Radon
Human occupants	CO, NO₂, organics, particulates, odors
Tobacco smoke	Fluorocarbons, vinyl chloride, organics
Aerosol sprays	Organics NH₂, odors
Cleaning and cooking products	Organics
Hobbies and crafts	

Sources	Contaminants
Damp organic materials, stagnant water Coil drain pans Humidifiers	Bioaerosols

Concentration of Air Pollutants.—The concentration of the indoor air pollutants depends on
1) strength of the outdoor and indoor pollutants; and
2) rate of pollutant removal.

The pollutant removal process can be achieved by dilution of the indoor air and use of local exhaust ventilation. Assuming the indoor air is thoroughly mixed and the concentrations are stable; the steady state indoor pollutant concentration can be given by Equation (1):

$$C_i = C_o + \frac{N}{Q_{oa}} \qquad (1)$$

where C_i = steady state indoor concentration, µg/ft³ or ppm (parts per million);
C_o = steady outdoor concentration, µg/ft³ or ppm (parts per million);
N = total indoor pollutant generated in the space, µg/min.; and
Q_{oa} = ventilation rate, cfm

Example 1: A 500 ft² school classroom is designed for 20 students.

What minimum rate of clean outdoor air requirement, is required for ventilation based on # of students.

What is the minimum amount of clean air is required based on 500 ft² classroom.

Solution: As per Table 4-2, for classroom the minimum outdoor air requirement is 15 cfm/person. So the total requirement for that classroom is (15 × 20) = 300 cfm.

As per Table 4-2, on the basis of area, the maximum occupancy will be 50 persons/1000 ft², so for 500 ft² the occupancy will be 25 people. As per Table 4-2, for classrooms the minimum outdoor air requirement is 15 cfm/person. So the total requirement for that classroom is 15 × 25 = 375 cfm.

Example 2: A person breathes carbon dioxide at a rate of 0.025 cfm. The CO_2 concentration in the supply ventilation air is 400 ppm. How much supply ventilation air is required to keep the room carbon dioxide concentration below 1000 ppm?

Solution: Given the rate pollutant generation is N = 0.025 cfm. The CO_2 concentration in the supply ventilation air is C_o = 400 ppm, and the indoor concentration C_s = 1000 ppm

$$C_i = C_o + \frac{N}{Q_{oa}}$$

$$Q_{oa} = \frac{N}{C_i - C_o}$$

$$= \frac{0.025 \times 10^6}{1000 - 400}$$

$$= 41.67 \text{ cfm}$$

Indoor Air Quality Procedure.—In this procedure, the minimum amount of outdoor air shown in Table 4-2 can be reduced by recirculating the room air and using air cleaning devices such as air filters. Using this procedure to minimize the amount of outdoor air for ventilation will considerably reduce energy consumption by HVAC systems during heating and cooling operations. The effectiveness of minimizing outdoor air is a function of type, efficiency, and location of the filter in the air distribution system however and of the rate of recirculated air. Excessive reduction of ventilation and infiltration to solve thermal comfort problems and to reduce energy consumption can affect indoor air quality and may be against code, so such procedures should be approached with care and be under the direction of an experienced registered professional engineer with expertise in HVAC analysis and design. HVAC design engineers and others concerned with building ventilation and indoor air quality should obtain a copy of ASHRAE Standard 62, Ventilation for Acceptable Indoor Air Quality. This standard, like all ASHRAE standards, is reviewed regularly and contains ventilation design and evaluation requirements for commercial and residential buildings. Before Engineers design a new building or analysis of an existing building, they must determine the version of Standard 62 that has been adopted by the local code authority. An existing building may be required to meet current code, or it may be grandfathered under an old code. If a project involves infiltration in residences, then ASHRAE Standards 119 and 136 should be consulted.

Fig. 4-1 represents an HVAC ventilation system that shows the installation of filters at two possible locations A and B. The filter at location A is at the recirculated air stream and filter at location B is at the mixed air stream. Variable air volume (VAV) systems can reduce the circulation air when thermal load is satisfied. This is accounted for by a flow reduction factor F_r. For any type of ventilation system, a mass balance equation for the contaminant can be written to determine the contamination concentration. The result of mass balance for the contaminant for different system arrangement based on Fig. 4-1 is given in Table 4-6. If the requirement for the space contamination is known, the equations in Table 4-6 can be used to determine the required outdoor flow rate. If the outdoor flow rate is specified, the equations in Table 4-6 can be used to

determine the concentration of the contaminant variables are:

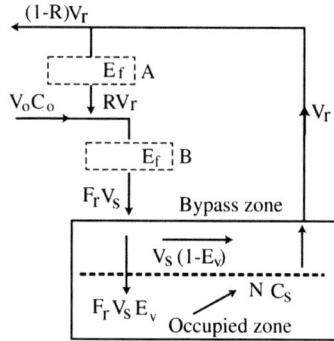

Fig 4-1. HVAC ventilation system schematic

A,B = filter location

V = volumetric flow

C = contaminant concentration

E = efficiency or effectiveness

F_r = flow reduction factor

N = contaminant generation rate

R = recirculation flow factor

Subscripts are:

f = filter
o = outdoor

r = return

s = supply

v = ventilation

Example 3: A smoking lounge is designed for 80 people. Table 4-2 lists a minimum outdoor air requirement of 60 cfm/person with 100% exhaust requirement (no recirculation) for smoking lounges. What should be the recirculation rate in order to reduce the outside air requirement by 15 cfm/person? The filter media must have a gravimetric efficiency of about 75%.

Solution:

$$Q_r \times E + Q_o = Q_s$$

$$Q_r = \frac{Q_s - Q_o}{E}$$

$$= \frac{(60 - 15)}{0.75}$$

$$= 60$$

$$Q_s = Q_r + Q_o$$

$$= 60 + 15$$

$$= 75 \text{ cfm/person}$$

Table 4-6. Required Outdoor Air or Space Contaminant Concentration with Recirculation and Filtration

Class	Filter Loca-tion	Flow	Temper-ature	Out-door air	Required Outdoor Air	Space Containment Concentration	Required Recirculation Rate
	Required Recirculation Rate						
I	None	VAV	Con-stant	100%	$V_o = \dfrac{N}{E_v F_r(C_s - C_o)}$	$C_s = C_o + \dfrac{N}{E_v F_r V_o}$	$RV_r = \dfrac{N + E_v V_o(C_o - C_s)}{E_v E_f C_s}$
II	A	Con-stant	Variable	Con-stant	$V_o = \dfrac{N - E_v RV_r E_f C_s}{E_v(C_s - C_o)}$	$C_s = \dfrac{N + E_v V_o C_o}{E_v(V_o + RV_r E_f)}$	$RV_r = \dfrac{N + E_v V_o(C_o - C_s)}{E_v F_r E_f C_s}$
III	A	VAV	Con-stant	Con-stant	$V_o = \dfrac{N - F_r E_v RV_r E_f C_s}{E_v(C_s - C_o)}$	$C_s = \dfrac{N + E_v V_o C_o}{E_v(V_o + F_r RV_r E_f)}$	$RV_r = \dfrac{N + E_f F_r V_o(C_o - C_s)}{E_v F_r E_f C_s}$
IV	A	VAV	Con-stant	Propor-tional	$V_o = \dfrac{N - F_r E_r RV_r E_f C_s}{E_v F_r(C_s - C_o)}$	$C_s = \dfrac{N + E_v V_o C_o}{E_v(V_o + RV_r E_f)}$	$RV_r = \dfrac{N + E_v V_o(C_o - C_s)}{E_v F_r E_f C_s}$
V	B	Con-stant	Variable	Con-stant	$V_o = \dfrac{N - E_v RV_r E_f C_s}{E_v(C_s - (1 - E_f)C_o)}$	$C_s = \dfrac{N + E_v V_o(1 - E_f)C_o}{E_v(V_o + RV_r E_f)}$	$RV_r = \dfrac{N + E_v V_o[(1 - E_f)C_o - C_s]}{E_v E_f C_s}$
VI	B	VAV	Con-stant	Con-stant	$V_o = \dfrac{N - F_r E_v RV_r E_f C_s}{E_v[C_s - (1 - E_f)C_o]}$	$C_s = \dfrac{N + E_v V_o(1 - E_f)C_o}{E_v(V_o + F_r RV_r E_f)}$	$RV_r = \dfrac{N + E_v V_o((1 - E_f)C_o - C_s)}{E_v F_r E_f C_s}$
VII	B	VAV	Con-stant	Propor-tional	$V_o = \dfrac{N - F_r E_v RV_r E_f C_s}{E_v F_r[(C_s - (1 - E_f)C_o)]}$	$C_s = \dfrac{N + E_v F_r V_o(1 - E_f)C_o}{E_v F_r(V_o + RV_r E_f)}$	$RV_r = \dfrac{N + E_v F_r V_o((1 - E_f)C_o - C_s)}{E_v F_r E_f C_s}$

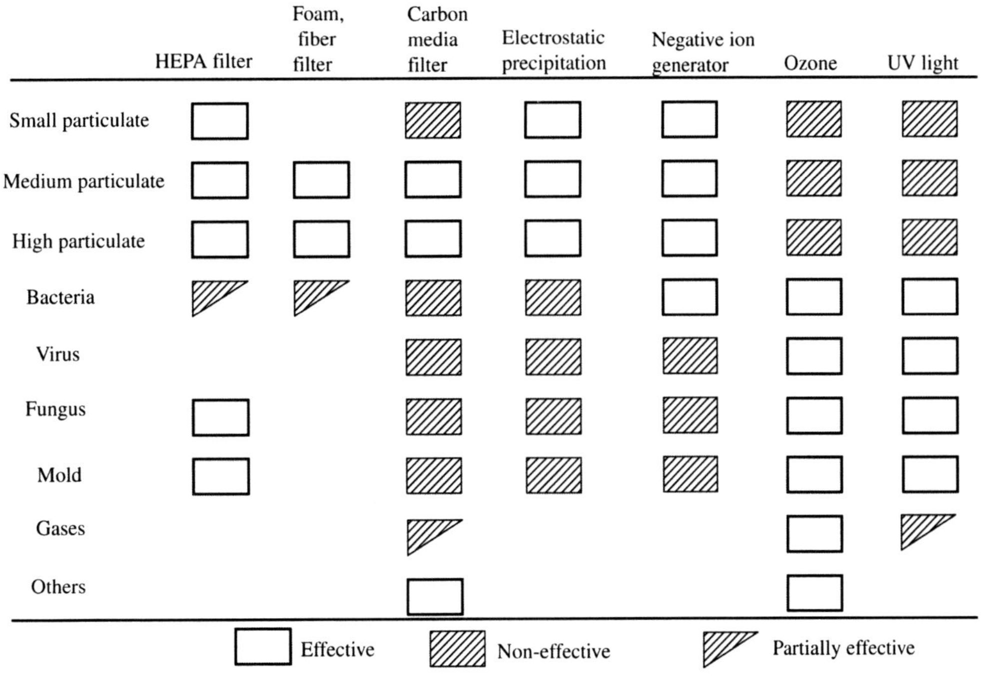

Fig 4-2. Filter selection

Example 4: A constant air volume system has a filter located at location A Fig. 4-1 and a filter efficiency of 80% for smoking; the particulate level in the occupied zone is 150 ppm. Assume average occupants produce 100 ppm, and 20 cfm of outdoor air/person is supplied. The ventilation effectiveness is 70% for the space. Find the rate of recirculation.

Solution: Applying filter efficiency 80%, ventilation effectiveness 70%, and flow reduction factor is equal to 1:

$$RV_r = \frac{N + E_v V_o (C_o - C_s)}{E_v F_r E_f C_s}$$

$$= \frac{100 + 0.70 \times 20 \times (0 - 150) \times 0.0283}{0.70 \times 1.00 \times 0.80 \times 150 \times 0.0283}$$

$$= 17.06 \text{ cfm/person}$$

The rate of supply air to the room = 20 + 17.06 = 37.06 *cfm*/person.

Filters.—Proper selection and use of air purification devices (filters) has a huge impact on maintaining acceptable indoor air quality. The purpose of filters is to remove contaminants from air we breathe. On average each human being breathes 23,000 times a day and moves around 435 ft^3 of the air, which is obviously a major concern. Indoor air pollution is considered the top environmental health problem and is regulated by EPA. With today's advancement in filter technology, a proper indoor air quality for tight buildings (energy saving buildings) can be maintained. In order to select an appropriate filter, we must first identify the problem and the indoor air pollution. Indoor air pollution consists of three major categories: particulates microbes, and gas/odors.

Particulates: Particulates consists of dust, dander (skin flakes), soot, pollen, and smoke particles that can flow in the air current sizes range from 0.001 to 1000 microns.

Microbes: Microbes are bacteria, germs, viruses, fungi, spores, and mold, size ranges from 0.001 to 10 microns.

Example 1: An united air cooled unit serves an office space having the following areas:

Description	Units	Room Size	Occu-pancy	Room Height
Private office	5	12'×15'		10'
Conference room	1	12'×25'		10'
Director's room	1	25'×25'	4 persons	10'
Smoking lounge	1	12'×12'		10'

What quantity of outside air must be brought into the air conditioning unit for ventilation? The supply fan capacity is 3600 cfm.

(b) How many air changes per hour (*ach*) are being used?

(c) What is the percent of outside air?

Solution:

Description	Units	Room Size	Area	Estimated Maximum Occupancy	Minimum Outside Air Requirements (cfm)	Volume
Private office	5	12'×15'	180	$= \frac{7}{1000} \times 180$ $= 1.26$ (1 person)	$5 \times 20 =$ 100 cfm	1800
Conference room	1	12'×25'	300	$= \frac{50}{1000} \times 300$ $= 15$ (15 people)	$15 \times 20 =$ 300 cfm	3000
Director's room	1	25'×25'	625	$= \frac{7}{1000} \times 625$ $= 4.375$ (4 people)	$4 \times 20 =$ 80 cfm	6250
Smoking lounge	1	12'×12'	144	$= \frac{70}{1000} \times 144$ $= 10.08$ (10 people)	$10 \times 60 =$ 600 cfm	1440
Minimum outside air					1080 cfm	12490

$$ach = \frac{cfm \times 60}{\text{volume}}$$

$$= \frac{1080 \times 60}{12490}$$

$$= 5.18$$

The percent of outside air:

$$= \frac{1080}{3600} \times 100$$

$$= 30\%$$

Gas and/or Odors: Example of indoor gases are benzene, formaldehyde, chloroform, hydrogen sulfide, and ammonia. These gases are released from furniture, cabinets, carpets, cleaning chemicals, copy machines, insulation, insect sprays, hair spray, etc. Size ranges from 0.0001 to 0.001 micron.

Fig. 4-3 shows the very wide range of particles and particle dispersoids along with the type of gas cleaning that could be appropriate for each case.

Air Filtration Technologies.—The main categories of air filtration technologies are:

    Filter (mechanical);

    Ionizers;

    Ozone generators; and

    UV light rays.

The capabilities of the different filter types are given in Fig. 4-3. It obvious from Fig. 4-3 that no single type filter can handle all types of pollutants. A combination of different filter types may be needed to improve removal of most air pollutants.

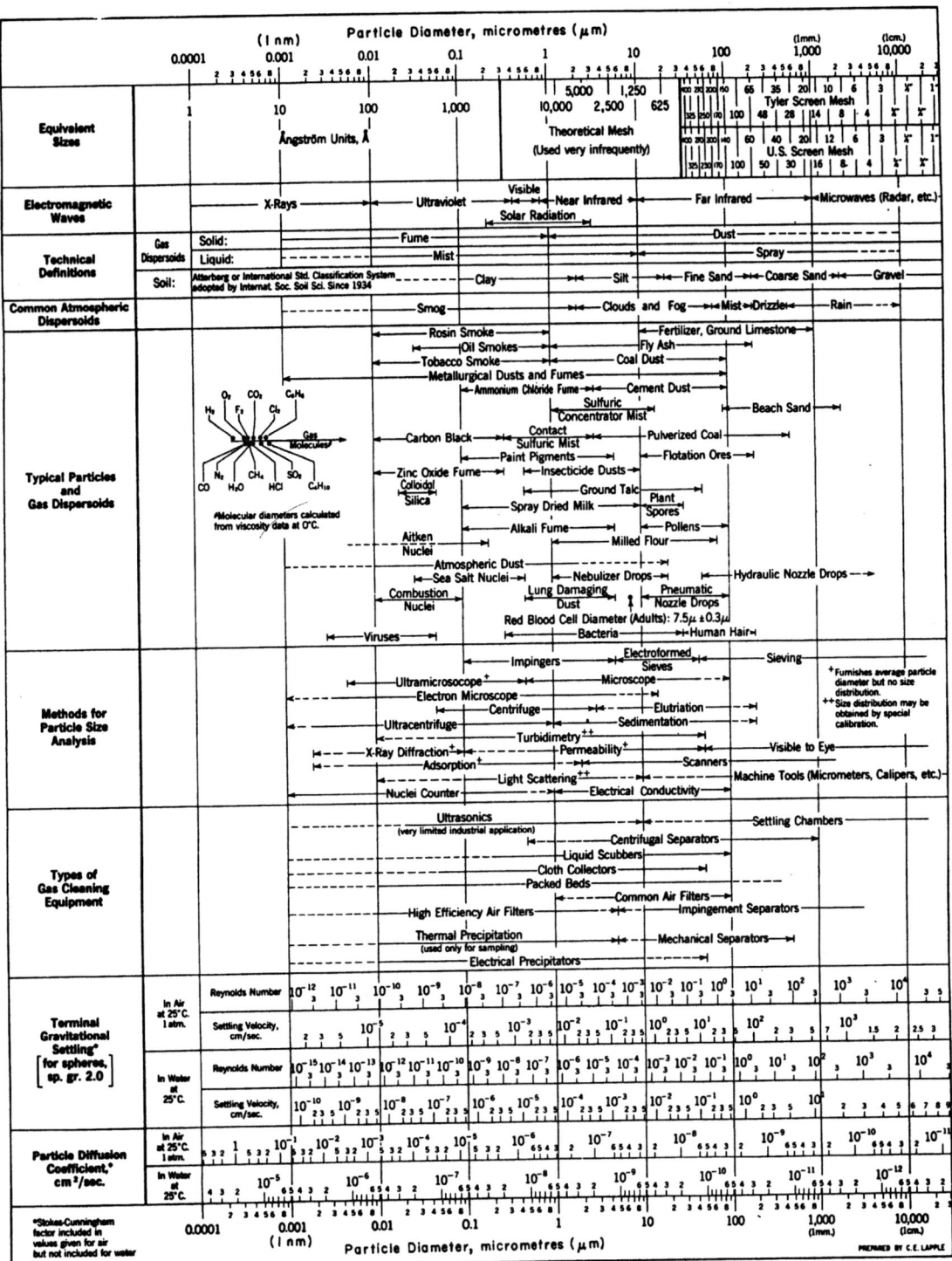

Fig 4-3. Characteristics of particles and particle dispersiods

Hepa Filters.—HEPA stands for high-efficiency particulate arrestance. HEPA filters use a powerful blower to force air through a very tight membrane to achieve high-efficiency particulate filtration.

Advantages: They are very efficient in the filtering of air that passes through filter. They filter to 0.03 micron.

Disadvantage: They require filter changes. The filter can act as a breeding ground for bacteria, mold, and fungus. They do not remove odors, gases, pesticides, viruses, and many bacteria. They reduce air flow due to the tight pores of the filter. They are generally not used in central systems and are sold as stand-alone units only.

Carbon Media Filters.—Carbon filters consist of carbon impregnated filter fabric or granulated carbon. These filters usually have a foam or fabric filter to hold the media Carbon has the unique capability to act as a physical filter by trapping particulates, and on a chemical basis by reacting with some odors and some of the heavy gases.

Advantages: They absorb odor, absorb some gases, filter particulate, installed in central or individual rooms.

Disadvantages: They require frequent changes, act as breeding ground for microorganisms, can easily become "blinded" and cease functioning. They reduce air flow.

Fiber and Foam Filters.—Fiber or open-cell foam filters rely on the air passing through a matrix of foam cells or fibers of fiberglass, wire, plastic, or cloth, Typically, these filters only stop medium to larger particulate.

Advantages: They are low cost, have low air resistance, and can be installed in central units.

Disadvantages: They only filter the air that passes through the filter. The particle build up can act as a breeding ground for bacteria. They only filter medium to large particulates.

Ozone.—Ozone is a gas of oxygen (an oxygen molecule containing three atoms instead of two, like hydrogen we breathe). The extra atom of ozone is known as a loose radical that looks for organics to attach to and thereby oxi-

dize. Ozone is known as a "friendly" oxidizer, due to the fact that it reverts back to oxygen after oxidation occurs.

Advantages: Ozone is an oxidizing gas that travels throughout the room and oxidizes all organics. Ozone can neutralize odors and gases. Ozone destroys microorganisms and does not reduce air flow. Ozone units can be installed in central units or in each rooms.

Disadvantages: Ozone has no effect on solid particles. Ozone exposure levels must be controlled.

Ultraviolet Light.—UV light rays have been used as a sanitizer by the medical profession for years. UV light can also sanitize air that is passed directly in its path.

Advantages: UV light can destroy bacteria, fungus, molds, and some gases. It does not reduce air flow. Can be installed in a central or individual room unit.

Disadvantages: UV light has no effect on particulates, needs direct close contact with a calculated exposure time. Humans must be shielded from exposure of UV light rays.

Filters vary in size, shape, initial cost and operating cost. Filters can be categorized by efficiency (ability to remove particulates), air flow resistance (pressure drop), and useful life (holding capacity). In general filters will permit pollutants to pass through with the air flow. Higher efficiency or density of a filter means more restriction on the airflow and more restriction to blower fan of an HVAC system. In general the filters with higher efficiency and lower air resistance should be considered for particulate application.

Example 2: Design a filter for a duct an HVAC system that requires 40,000 cfm of recirculated air with the pressure drop across the filter not to exceed 0.35 in.wc. Use the following filter media performance data.

Size	12"×24"×8"	24"×24"×8"	24"×24"×12"
cfm	850	1800	2100
Pressure drop	0.20 inch-wc	0.20 inch-wc	0.20 inch-wc

Solution

Size	12"×24"×8"	24"×24"×8"	24"×24"×12"
cfm	850	1800	2100
Pressure drop	0.20 inch -wc	0.20 inch -wc	0.20 inch -wc
As the pressure varies with filter rate, so the flow will be	$Q_n = Q_r\sqrt{\dfrac{P_n}{P_r}}$ $= 850 \times \sqrt{\dfrac{0.35}{0.20}}$ $= 1125$ cfm	$Q_n = Q_r\sqrt{\dfrac{P_n}{P_r}}$ $= 1800 \times \sqrt{\dfrac{0.35}{0.20}}$ $= 2381$ cfm	$Q_n = Q_r\sqrt{\dfrac{P_n}{P_r}}$ $= 2100 \times \sqrt{\dfrac{0.35}{0.20}}$ $= 2778$ cfm
The number of units	$n = \dfrac{40000}{1125} = 36$	$n = \dfrac{40000}{2381} = 17$	$n = \dfrac{40000}{2778} = 15$

LOAD ESTIMATING FUNDAMENTALS

LOAD ESTIMATING FUNDAMENTALS

Introduction

A basic understanding of all three modes of heat transfer, conduction, convection, and radiation, is important in heating, cooling, and ventilation calculations. At first we introduce the basic definitions of the modes of heat transfer, and then their applications will be discussed.

Conduction.—In gases and liquids, heat transfer by conduction can be defined as the net energy transfer due to random molecular motion (diffusion) in the absence of fluid bulk motion. In solids, heat conduction is due to vibrational motion of the molecules in the lattice and the flow of electrons. It should be noted that higher temperature of molecules is associated with higher molecular energy. The conduction heat transfer rate through any medium depends on the following:

1) geometry of the medium;

2) thickness of the medium;

3) type of the medium; and

4) temperature gradient across the medium.

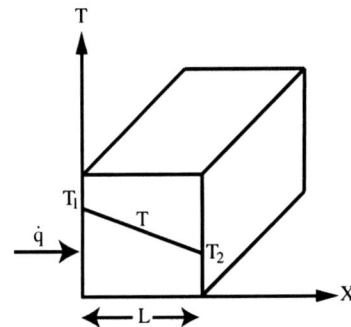

Fig 5-1. One- dimensional heat transfer by conduction

The conduction heat transfer rate can be quantified in the one-dimensional plane (Fig. 5-1) as

$$\dot{q} = -KA\frac{dT}{dX} \qquad (1)$$

where $\dot{q}$ is the rate of heat transfer, Btu/hr in the X direction, and K (Btu/ hr-ft-°R) is the thermal conductivity of the medium. Equation (1) is also called Fourier's law of heat conduction. The minus sign indicates heat transfer in the direction of decreasing temperature.

Thermal conductivity is a property of the substance and a function of temperature. The values of thermal conductivity of some materials at room temperature are given in Table 5-1, and the range of thermal conductivity of various materials at room temperature is given in Fig. 5-2. Thermal conductivity of substances is highest in solids,

then liquids, and it is lowest in gases. Thermal conductivity of gases increases with increase in temperature. However, with the exception of water, thermal conductivity of liquids increases with decrease of temperature.

Table 5-1. Thermal Conductivities (K) of Some Materials at Room Temperature

Material	Btu/hr-ft-°F	Material	Btu/hr-ft-°F
Diamond	1328.9400	Water (l)	0.3542
Silver	247.8762	Human skin	0.2138
Copper	231.6978	Wood (oak)	0.0982
Gold	183.1626	Helium (g)	0.0878
Aluminum	136.9386	Soft rubber	0.0751
Iron	46.3396	Refrigerant-12	0.0416
Mercury (l)	4.9344	Glass fiber	0.0248
Glass	0.4507	Air (g)	0.0150
Brick	0.4160	Urethane, rigid foam	0.0150

In most HVAC analysis, heat transfer can be assumed to be a one-dimensional steady state. Under steady state condition temperature distribution in the medium is linear, so Equation (1) can be written as

$$\dot{q} = -KA\frac{dT}{dX} \qquad (2)$$

Equation (2) can be rewritten as

$$\dot{q} = -\frac{\Delta T}{R} \qquad (3)$$

Where $R\left(\dfrac{\text{Btu}}{\text{hr-°F}}\right) = \dfrac{\Delta X}{KA}$ is called thermal resistance. On per unit area varies the corresponding R is called thermal resistance and it reciprocal is called thermal conductance as $C\left(\dfrac{\text{hr-°F}}{\text{Btu}}\right) = \dfrac{1}{R}$.

For insulating materials, unit thermal resistance R is called "R value" and represented as $R = \dfrac{L}{K}$ where L is the thickness of the insulating material. "R value" is the thermal resistance per unit area.

Equation (3) is similar to Ohm's law $I = \dfrac{\Delta V}{R}$ where I is analogous to $\dot{q}$, and ΔV is analogous to ΔT, if R is unit thermal resistance and $\dot{q}$ if it is the total resistance.

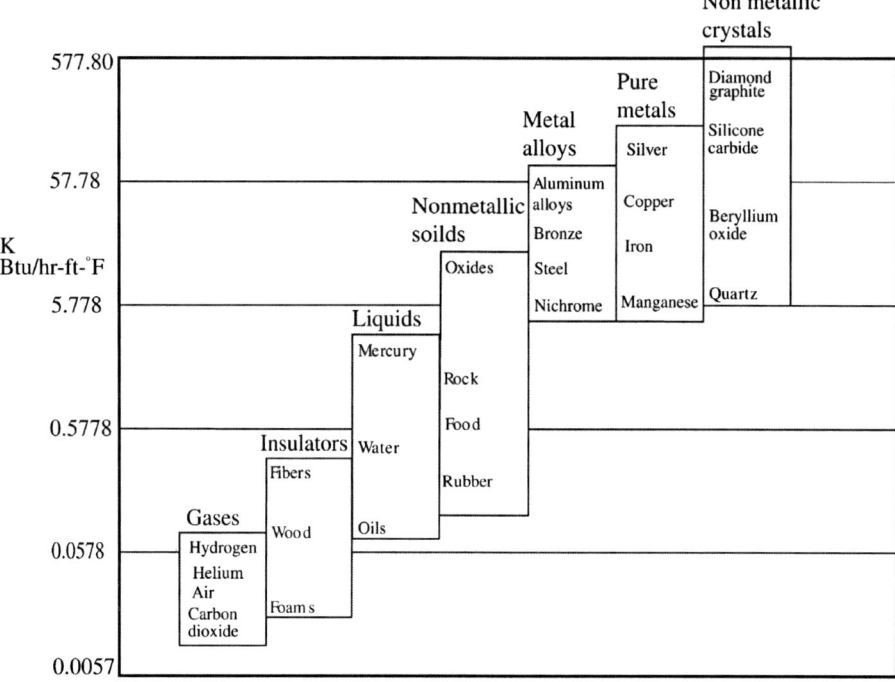

Fig 5-2. Range of thermal conductivity of various materials at different temperatures

Example 1: The wall of an industrial furnace is constructed from 2.0 ft thick fireclay brick having a thermal conductivity of 1.7 Btu/hr-ft-°F. Measurements made during steady state operation reveal temperatures of 800°F and 1150°F at the inner and outer surfaces, respectively. What is the rate of heat loss through a wall that is 2 ft by 6 ft?

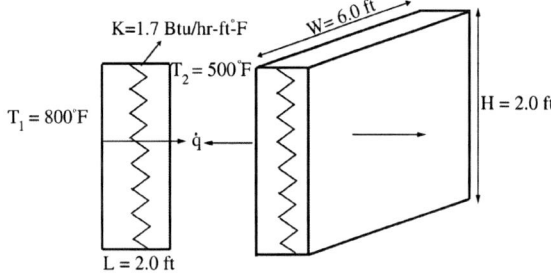

Solution: Known: Steady state conditions with prescribed wall thickness, area, thermal conductivity, and surface temperatures.

Find: Wall heat loss.

Schematic: shown.

Assumptions:

    1) steady state conditions

    2) one-dimensional conduction through the wall

    3) constant thermal conductivity

Analysis: Since heat transfer through the wall is by conduction, the heat flux may be determined from Furriers law. Using Equation (3), we have

$$\dot{q} = -KA\frac{\Delta T}{\Delta X}$$

$$\dot{q} = \frac{-KA(T_i - T_o)}{L}$$

$$\dot{q} = \frac{-K(T_i - T_o)}{L} \times A$$

$$= \frac{-1.7 \times (800 - 500) \times 2 \times 6}{2}$$

$$= -3060 \text{ Btu/hr}$$

Convection.— Convective heat transfer consists of the following two mechanisms, as shown in Fig. 5-3. Energy transfer by heat conduction, which is the energy transfer due to random molecular motion (diffusion); energy transfer by bulk fluid motion.

Convection heat transfer can be classified as one of either

    1) forced convection;

    2) natural convection;

    3) boiling; and

    4) condensation, as shown in Fig. 5-4.

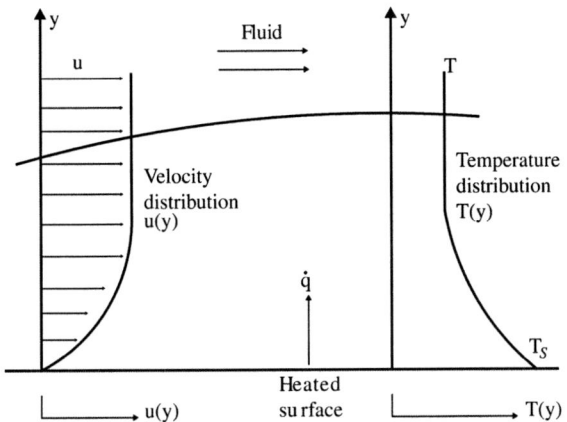

Fig 5-3. Boundary layer development in convection heat transfer

Despite the complexity of the convective heat transfer phenomenon, the rate of heat transfer can be written as

$$\dot{q} = h_c A(T_s - T_\infty) \qquad (4)$$

where $\dot{q}$ is the convection heat transfer rate per unit area, $h \left(\dfrac{\text{Btu}}{\text{hr ft}^{2\circ}F} \right)$ is the convection heat transfer coefficient (is also referred to as surface conductance), T_s is the surface temperature, and T_∞ is the fluid temperature far from the surface. The convection heat transfer coefficient is a property of the fluid and is a function of surface geometry, fluid motion, bulk fluid velocity and temperature. Typical values of convection heat transfer coefficient are given in Table 5-2.

The unit thermal resistance for convection can be written as $R = \dfrac{1}{h}$.

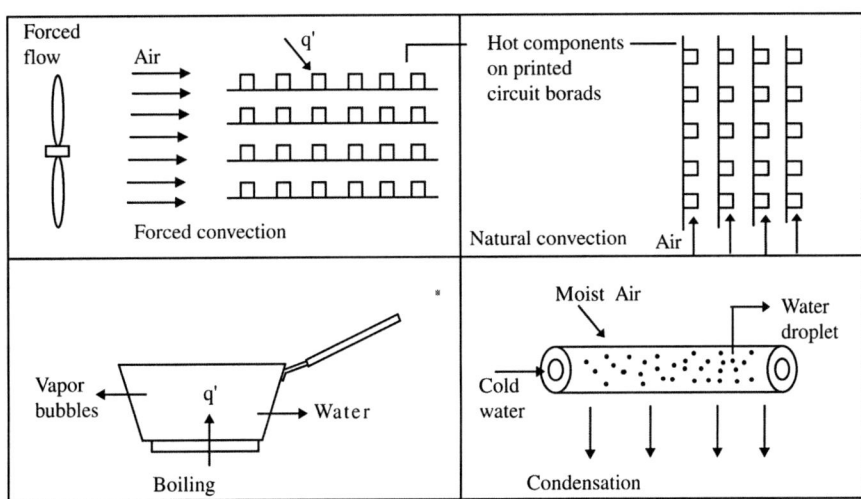

Fig 5-4. Convection heat transfer process

Table 5-2. Typical values of the Convection Heat Transfer coefficient

Process	h (Btu/(hr-ft^2-°F)
Free convection gases	0.25 – 5.0
Liquids	8 – 176
Forced convection gases	5 – 50
Liquids	15 – 3500
Convection with phase change boiling or condensation	440 – 17600

Example 2: Measuring Convection Heat Transfer Coefficient: A 6 ft long, 0.25 inch diameter electrical wire extends across a room with temperature 15°F, as shown in Fig. 5-5. Heat is generated in the wire as a result of resistance heating, and the surface temperature of the wire is measured to be 300°F in steady operation. Also, the voltage drop and electric current through the wire are measured to be 60 V and 1.50 A, respectively. Disregarding any heat transfer by radiation, determine the convection heat transfer coefficient for heat transfer between the outer surface of the wire and the air in the room.

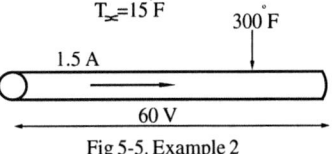

Fig 5-5. Example 2

Solution: The convection heat transfer coefficient for heat transferred from an electrically heated wire to air is to be determined by measuring temperatures when steady operating conditions are reached and electric power is consumed.

Assumptions:

1) Steady operating conditions exist since the temperature readings do not change with time.

2) Radiation heat transfer is negligible.

Analysis:

When steady operating conditions are reached, the rate of heat loss from the wire will equal the rate of heat generation in the wire as a result of resistance heating. That is,

$$\dot{q} = E_{generated}$$
$$= VI$$
$$= 60 \times 1.5$$
$$= 90 \text{ watts}$$
$$= 307 \text{ Btu/hr}$$

The surface area of the wire is

$$A = \pi \times D \times L$$
$$= \pi \times \frac{0.25}{12} \times 6$$
$$= 0.3929 \text{ ft}^2$$

Newton's law of cooling for convection heat transfer is expressed as

$$\dot{q} = hA(T_s - T_\infty)$$
$$h = \frac{\dot{q}}{A(T_s - T_\infty)}$$
$$= \frac{307}{0.3929(300 - 15)}$$
$$= 2.75 \text{ Btu/(hr-ft}^2\text{-}^\circ\text{F)}$$

Disregarding any heat transfer by radiation and thus assuming all the heat loss from the wire to occur by convection, the convection heat transfer coefficient determined by the above could be higher than actual.

Note that the simple setup described above can be used to determine average heat transfer coefficients from a variety of surfaces in air. Also, heat transfer by radiation can be eliminated by keeping the surrounding surfaces at the temperature of the wire.

Thermal Radiation.—Thermal radiation is energy emitted by matter that has a finite temperature. The matter could be in solid, liquid, or gas form. Unlike the transfer of energy in the case of conduction and convection, no material medium is required for the transfer of the radiation energy between two surfaces at a finite temperature. This is due to the fact that radiation energy is transferred by electromagnetic waves (or photons). It should be noted that regardless of the form of the matter (solid, liquid, or gas), the transfer of the emitted energy is as result of the changes in the electron configurations of the atoms or the molecules of the matter. The thermal radiation could be either emitted by the surface at a finite temperature Fig. 5-6 or incident on the surface Fig. 5-7. The incident thermal energy on the surface is called thermal irradiation.

There are four radiative properties: ε (emissivity), α (absorptivity), ρ (reflectivity), and τ (transmissibility). The radiative properties are functions of medium thickness, geometry, surface temperature, and radiation wavelength. The emissivities of some materials are given in Table 5-3.

For a semitransparent medium, three radiative properties obey the relationship:

$$\rho + \alpha + \tau = 1 \qquad (5)$$

For opaque (nontransparent) surfaces such as wood, metals, rocks there is transmission, and absorption and reflection are involved at the surface for which

$$\rho + \alpha = 1 \qquad (6)$$

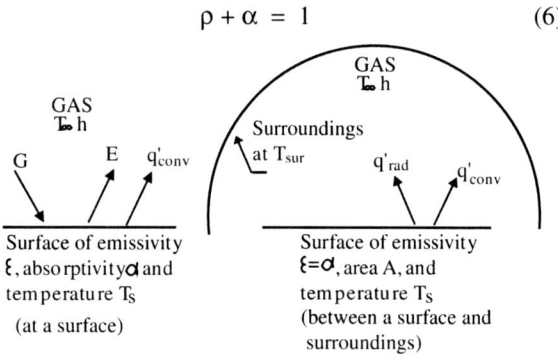

Fig 5-6. Radiation exchange

Table 5-3. Emissivities of Some Materials at 300°K

Material	Emissivity	Material	Emissivity
Aluminum foil	0.07	White paper	0.92 – 0.97
Anodized aluminum	0.82	Asphalt pavement	0.85 – 0.93
Polished copper	0.03	Red brick	0.93 – 0.96
Polished gold	0.03	Human skin	0.95
Polished silver	0.02	Wood	0.82 – 0.92
Polished stainless steel	0.17	Soil	0.93 – 0.96
Black paint	0.98	Water	0.96
White paint	0.90	Vegetation	0.92 – 0.96

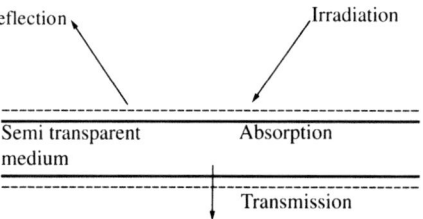

Fig 5-7. Absorption, Reflection, and Transmission processes associated with a semitransparent medium

An object or surface that can absorb all incident thermal energy ($\alpha = 1$) or can emit all the absorbed thermal energy ($\varepsilon = 1$) is called a black body (perfect absorber or radiator).

The emitted thermal energy of a black body is described by the Stefan Boltzmann law as

$$E_b = \sigma A T_s^4 \qquad (7)$$

or in terms of emissive energy per unit area as

$$\dot{q}_b = \sigma T_s^4 \qquad (8)$$

where $\dot{q} = \dfrac{E}{A}$.

In the above equation E (Btu/hr) is the emissive energy and $\sigma = 0.1714 \times 10^{-8}$ (Btu/hr-ft^2-R^4) is the Boltzman constant.

For real surfaces the emissive energy or absorptive energy can be written as

$$E = \varepsilon \sigma A T_s^4 \qquad \text{or in flux form}$$
$$\dot{q} = \varepsilon \sigma T_s^4 \qquad 0 < \varepsilon < 1 \qquad (9)$$

$$G = \alpha \sigma A T_{sur}^4 \qquad 0 < \alpha < 1 \qquad (10)$$

For a gray surface ($\alpha = \varepsilon$) the net radiation heat transfer can be expressed as

$$\dot{q} = \varepsilon \sigma (T_s^4 - T_{sur}^4) \qquad (11)$$

There are many situations in which the above equation can be expressed as

$$\dot{q} = h_r (T_s - T_{sur}) \qquad (12)$$

where the radiation heat transfer coefficient h_r is

$$h_r = \varepsilon \sigma (T_s + T_{sur})(T_s^2 + T_{sur}^2) \qquad (13)$$

Example 3: An uninsulated steam pipe passes through a room in which the air and walls are at 75°F. The outside diameter of the pipe is 3 inches, and its surface temperature and emissivity are 400°F and 0.8, respectively. What are the surface emissive power and irradiation?

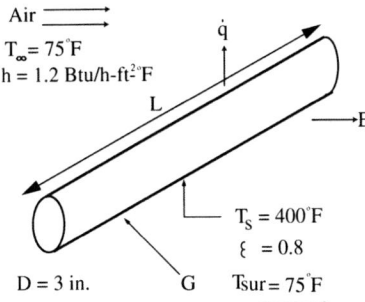

Air $\longrightarrow$
$T_\infty = 75°F$
$h = 1.2$ Btu/h-ft^{2}F
L
$\dot{q}$
E
$T_s = 400°F$
$\xi = 0.8$
$D = 3$ in.
G $T_{sur} = 75°F$

If the coefficient associated with free convection heat transfer from the surface to the air is 3 Btu/hr-ft^2-°F, what is the rate of heat loss from the surface per unit length of pipe?

Solution: Known: Uninsulated pipe of prescribed diameter, emissivity, and surface temperature in a room with fixed wall and air temperatures.

Find:
    1) surface emissive power and irradiation, and
    2) pipe heat loss per unit length.

Assumptions:
    1) steady state conditions,
    2) radiation exchange between the pipe and the room is between a small surface in a much larger enclosure,
    3) the surface emissivity and absorptivity are equal.

The surface emissive power may be evaluated from Equation (9):

$$\frac{E}{A} = \varepsilon \sigma T_s^4$$

$$= 0.80 \times 0.1714 \times 10^{-8} \times (460 + 400)^4$$

$$= 750 \text{ Btu/hr-ft}^2$$

$$\frac{G}{A} = \alpha \sigma T_{sur}^4$$

$$= 0.80 \times 0.1714 \times 10^{-8} \times (460 + 75)^4$$

$$= 19.25 \text{ Btu/hr-ft}^2$$

Heat loss from the pipe is due to convection to the room air and by radiation exchange with the walls. The heat loss per unit length of pipe is

$$q_t = q_{\text{convection}} + q_{\text{radiation}}$$

$$= h(\pi D L)(T_s - T_\infty) + \varepsilon(\pi D L)\sigma(T_s^4 - T_{sur}^4)$$

$$= (\pi D L)\left\{ h[T_s - T_\infty] + \varepsilon\sigma[T_s^4 - T_{sur}^4] \right\}$$

$$= \pi \frac{3}{12} 1 \{3(860 - 535)\}$$

$$+ 0.80 \times 0.1714 \times 10^{-8} \times [860^4 - 535^4]$$

$$= 0.7858 \times (975 + 637.72)$$

$$= 1268 \text{ Btu/hr per unit length of pipe}$$

Overall Heat Transfer Coefficient (*U* Factor) and Thermal Resistance Network.—Series wall composition: In many buildings walls are composed of multilayer as shown in Fig. 5-8. Using electrical resistance as an analogy, the overall thermal resistance *R* can be written as

$$R_{total} = R_{convection\ 1} + R_{conduction,\ wall\ 1} +$$

$$R_{conduction,\ wall\ 2} + R_{conduction,\ wall\ 3} + R_{convection\ 2} \quad (14)$$

$$R_{total} = \frac{1}{h_1 A} + \frac{L_1}{k_1 A} + \frac{L_2}{k_2 A} + \frac{L_3}{k_3 A} + \frac{1}{h_2 A}$$

Fig 5-8. Heat transfer resistance

It should be noted that in series arrangement, the heat transfer rate $\dot{q}$ and the cross sectional areas are assumed to be constant throughout. The overall heat transfer coefficient in this case is defined as

$$U_{overall} = \frac{1}{R_{total}} \quad (15)$$

Example 4: Determine the *U* value for a cavity wall consisting of face brick, 8 in. concrete block (138 lb/ft³), a ¾ in. air space as the cavity, another layer of the same type of concrete block, R-17 insulation, and ½ in. plasterboard.

Solution:

Component	Resistance
Outside air	0.17
Brick, 4-in. face	0.44
Concrete block, 8 in.	0.48
Air space, ¾ in.	1.00
Concrete block, 8 in.	0.48
Fiber insulation	17.00
Plasterboard, ½ in.	0.45
Inside air	0.68
Total *R* =	20.7

$U = 1/R_t = 1/20.7 = 0.048$ Btu/hr-ft²-°F

Example 5: Calculate the *U* factor of the 2 by 4 stud wall shown in Fig. 5-9. The studs are at 16 inch OC. There is 3.5 inches mineral fiber batt insulation (R-17) in the stud space. The inside finish is 0.5 inch gypsum wallboard; the outside is finished with rigid foam insulating sheathing (R-10) and 0.5 inch by 8 inch wood bevel lapped siding. The insulated cavity occupies approximately 70% of the transmission area; the studs, plates, and sills occupy 25%; and the headers occupy 5%.

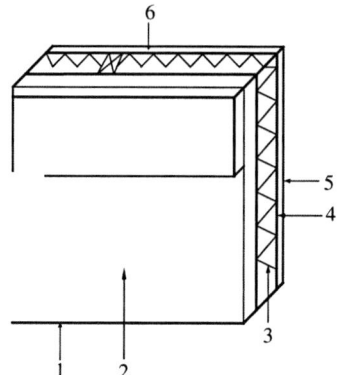

1. Outside surface
2. Wood bevelled lapped siding
3. Sheathing (rigid foam insulation)
4. Wood stud
5. Gypsum wallboard
6. Inside surface

Fig 5-9. Insulated wood frame wall Example 5

Solution: Assume *R* = 1.25 per inch for the wood framing. Also, assume the headers are solid wood in this case and group them with the studs, plates, and sills.

#	Element	*R* (Insulated Cavity)	*R* (Studs, Plates, Headers)
1	Outside surface, 15 mph wind	0.17	0.17
2	Wood bevel lapped siding	0.81	0.81
3	Rigid foam insulating sheathing	10.0	10.0
4	Mineral fiber batt insulation,	17.0	
5	Wood stud, nominal 2 × 4		4.38
6	Gypsum wallboard, 0.5 in	0.45	0.45
7	Inside surface, still air	0.68	0.68
	R	29.11	16.49
	U	0.0343	0.0643
	$U_{overall}$	$U = 0.0343 \times 0.70 + 0.0643 \times 0.30$ = 0.0433	

Example 6: Heat loss through an insulated hot water pipe. Hot water at 180°F flows in a steel pipe (K_{st} = 0.20 Btu-in./ft²-hr-°F) whose inner and outer diameters are D_i = 6.065 in. and D_o = 6.625 in., respectively. The pipe is covered with 2 in. thick glass wool insulation with K_{in} = 300 Btu-in./ft²-hr-°F. Heat is lost to surroundings at 40°F by natural convection and radiation, with a combined heat transfer coefficient outside h_o = 2 Btu/ft²-hr-°F and inside h_i =500 Btu/ft²-hr-°F. Determine the rate of heat loss from

the hot water per unit length of the pipe. Also determine the temperature drop across both pipe shell and insulation.

Solution: A steam pipe covered with glass wool insulation is subjected to convection on its surfaces. The rate of heat transfer per unit length and the temperature drop across the pipe and the insulation are to be determined.

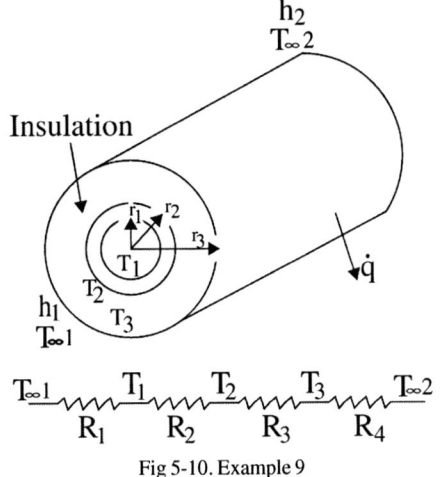

Fig 5-10. Example 9

Analysis: The thermal resistance network for this problem involves four resistances in series and is given in Fig. 5-10. Assume $L = 1$ ft.

$$R = \frac{1}{h_o A_o} + \frac{\ln\frac{r_3}{r_2}}{2\pi K_{in}L} + \frac{\ln\frac{r_2}{r_1}}{2\pi K_{st}L} + \frac{1}{h_i A_i}$$

$L = 1$ ft

$K_{in} = 0.20$ Btu-in./hr-ft^2-°F

$K_{st} = 300$ Btu-in./hr-ft^2-°F

$A_o = \pi D_o L = \pi \times \frac{6.625}{12} \times 1 = 1.73442$ ft^2

$A_i = \pi D_i L = \pi \times \frac{6.065}{12} \times 1 = 1.5878$ ft^2

$h_{in} = 500$ Btu/hr-ft^2-°F

$h_{out} = 2$ Btu/hr-ft^2-°F

$h_{in} = 500$ Btu/hr-ft^2-°F

$h_{out} = 2$ Btu/hr-ft^2-°F

$r_1 = \frac{6.065}{2} = 3.0325$

$r_2 = \frac{6.625}{2} = 3.3125$

$r_3 = 3.3125 + 2 = 5.3125$

$$R = \frac{1}{h_o A_o} + \frac{\ln\frac{r_3}{r_2}}{2\pi K_{in}L} + \frac{\ln\frac{r_2}{r_1}}{2\pi K_{st}L} + \frac{1}{h_i A_i}$$

$$= \frac{1}{2 \times 1.73} + \frac{\ln\frac{5.3125}{3.3125}}{2\pi \times \frac{0.20}{12} \times 1}$$

$$+ \frac{\ln\frac{3.3125}{3.0325}}{2\pi \times \frac{300}{12} \times 1} + \frac{1}{1.5878 \times 500}$$

$$= 0.289 + 4.5107 + 0.0005 + 0.00126$$

$$= 4.80146$$

$$U = \frac{1}{R} = \frac{1}{4.80146} = 0.20827$$

$\dot{q} = UA\Delta T$

$$= 0.20827 \times 2 \times \pi \times \frac{5.3125}{12} \times 1 \times (180 - 50)$$

$$= 75.31 \text{ Btu/hr per ft of pipe}$$

$$\dot{q} = \frac{T_i - T_o}{R} = \frac{T_i - T_{st}}{R_i + R_{st}} = \frac{T_i - T_{in}}{R_i + R_{st} + R_{in}}$$

$$\frac{T_i - T_{st}}{R_i + R_{st}} = \frac{T_i - T_o}{R}$$

$$\frac{180 - T_{st}}{0.00126 + 0.0005} = \frac{180 - 50}{4.80146}$$

$$\frac{180 - T_{st}}{0.00176} = 27.0751$$

$$T_{st} = 179.95°F$$

$$\frac{T_i - T_{st}}{R_i + R_{st} + R_{in}} = \frac{T_i - T_o}{R}$$

$$\frac{180 - T_{in}}{0.00126 + 0.0005 + 4.5107} = \frac{180 - 50}{4.80146}$$

$$\frac{180 - T_{in}}{4.51246} = 27.0751$$

$$T_{in} = 57.83°F$$

Parallel Arrangement: In many applications, the building wall has parallel arrangement as shown in Fig. 5-11. Using an electrical resistance analogy, the overall thermal resistance can be written as

$$\frac{1}{R_{total}} = \frac{1}{R_1} + \frac{1}{R_2} + \frac{1}{R_3}$$
$$= \frac{K_1 A_1}{L} + \frac{K_2 A_2}{L} + \frac{K_3 A_3}{L} \qquad (16)$$

For only two different materials Equation (16) can be written as

$$\frac{1}{R_{total}} = \frac{1}{R_1} + \frac{1}{R_2} = \frac{R_1 + R_2}{R_1 R_2}$$

or   (17)

$$R_{total} = \frac{R_1 R_2}{R_1 + R_2}$$

It should be noted that in parallel arrangement, the temperature difference across each material is assumed to be the same and all materials have the same thickness. The overall heat transfer coefficient in this case is defined as

$$U_{overall} = \frac{1}{R_{total}} \qquad (18)$$

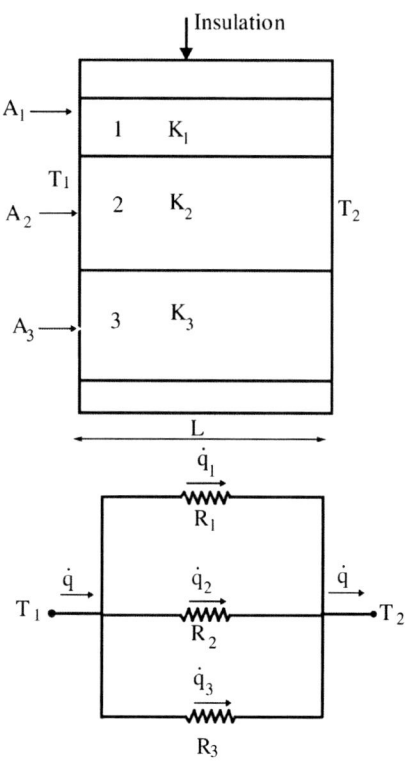

Fig 5-11. Thermal resistance network for three layers, parallel arrangements

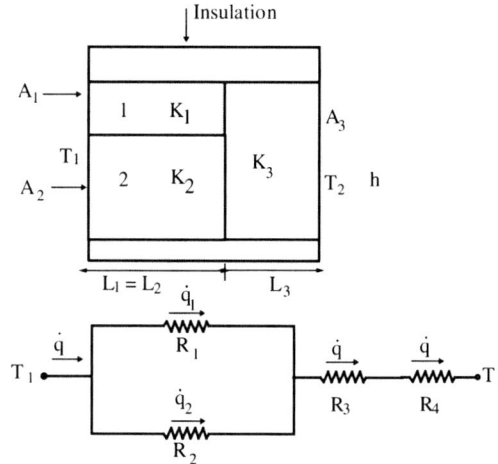

Fig 5-12. Thermal resistance network for combined arrangement

Example 7: Determine the U-value and the temperature at each point of change of material for the flat roof shown below. Roof has $\frac{3}{8}$-in. built-up roofing, $1\frac{1}{2}$-in. roof insulation, 2-in. thick, 80 lb/ft lightweight aggregate concrete on corrugated metal over steel joists with a metal lath and $\frac{3}{4}$ in. (sand) plaster ceiling. Disregard correction for framing.

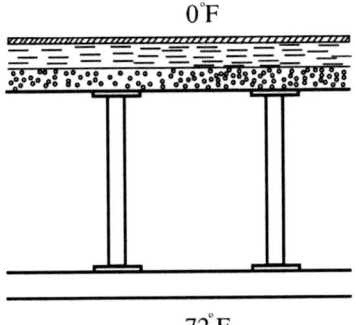

0°F

72°F

Solution:

Item	Element	R	$\sum R$	T_x °F
1	Outside surface	0.17	0.17	1.70
2	⅜" built up roofing	0.33	0.50	5.00
3	1½" roof insulation	4.50	5.00	50.06
4	2" 80 lb/ft concrete	0.80	5.80	58.08
5	Air space	0.61	6.41	64.19
6	Plaster	0.10	6.51	65.19
7	Inside surface, still air	0.68	7.19	72.00
	Total	7.19		

$$\frac{T_i - T_o}{R_t} = \frac{T_x - T_o}{R_x}$$

$$\frac{T_x - T_o}{\sum R_x} = \frac{T_i - T_o}{R_t}$$

$$\frac{T_x - 0}{\sum R_x} = \frac{72 - 0}{7.19}$$

$$\frac{T_x}{\sum R_x} = 10.013$$

Combined Series and Parallel Arrangement: Fig. 5-12 below is the example of the combined arrangement network. The total resistance in such an arrangement is

$$R_{total} = \frac{R_1 R_2}{R_1 + R_2} + R_3 + R_4 \tag{19}$$

Calculating Surface Temperature: For the series wall arrangement shown in Fig. 5-14, the surface temperature at point 3 can be can be calculated as follows.

$$T_3 = T_2 - \Delta T_{2-3}$$

$$\Delta T_{2-3} = T_2 - T_3 \tag{20}$$

$$= \frac{T_i - T_o}{R_3}$$

Example 8: Consider the wall section shown in Fig. 5-13. (a) Compute the temperatures of all surfaces. b)

Assuming that the moist air can diffuse through the gypsum and insulation from the inside, would you expect moisture to condense on surface 5? Explain. (c) Would moisture condense on surface 3? Explain. (d) Where should a vapor retardant be placed?

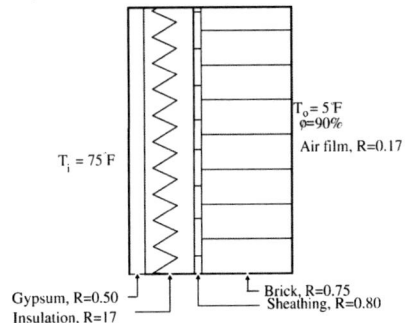

$T_i = 75$ F

$T_o = 5$ F
$\varphi = 90\%$
Air film, R=0.17

Gypsum, R=0.50
Insulation, R=17

Brick, R=0.75
Sheathing, R=0.80

Fig 5-13. Example 8

Solution:

Item	Element	R	$\sum R$	T_x °F
1	Outside surface	0.17	0.17	0.63
2	Brick	0.80	0.97	3.53
3	Sheathing	1.2	2.17	8.01
4	Insulation	17.0	19.17	70.82
5	Gypsum	0.45	19.62	72.48
6	Inside surface, still air	0.68	20.30	75.00
	Total	20.3		

$$\frac{T_i - T_o}{R_t} = \frac{T_x - T_o}{R_x}$$

$$\frac{T_x - T_o}{\sum R_x} = \frac{T_i - T_o}{R_t}$$

$$\frac{T_x - 0}{\sum R_x} = \frac{75 - 0}{20.3}$$

$$\frac{T_x}{\sum R_x} = 3.6946$$

(b) At 75°F and 30% φ, $T_{dp} = 41.53$°F, at surface 5, $T_5 = 72.48$°F, $T_5 > T_{dp}$ no condensation is expected.

(c) At surface 5, $T_3 = 8.01$°F, $T_5 < T_{dp}$. Condensation is expected.

(d) Place a vapor retarder at the location of 3 to avoid condensation.

Calculating Temperature of Unheated Space: Sometimes corridors, staircases, storage rooms, basement areas of a building are kept unheated for different reasons. Determining temperature of the unheated space is important for calculating heat loss from heated adjacent spaces. The temperature of the unheated space can be calculated from the following equation:

$$T_{unheated} = \frac{\sum_{in} UAT - \sum_{out} UAT}{\sum_{in} UA + \sum_{out} UA} \tag{21}$$

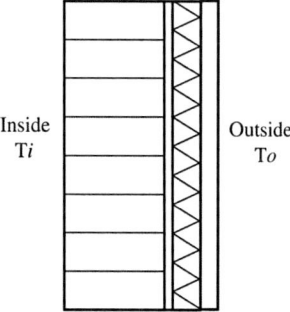

Fig 5-14. Thermal resistance network for three layers

Where subscript "in" is for the surfaces that transmit the heat into the unheated space and subscript "out" is for the surfaces that transmit the heat out of the unheated space.

Example 9: Consider the knee space shown in Fig. 5-15. The vertical dimension is 8 ft, the horizontal dimension is 6 ft, and the space is 25 ft long. The walls and roof surrounding the space have an overall heat transfer coefficient of about 0.40 Btu/hr-ft²-°F and 0.10 Btu/hr-ft²-°F respectively. Assuming an outdoor temperature of 0°F, an indoor temperature of 60°F, and room below the knee is 75°F, make a recommendation concerning the placement of water pipes in the knee space.

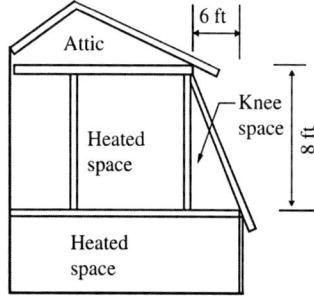

Fig 5-15. Example 9

Solution: The placement of water pipes depends on the temperature of the knee space in order to avoid freezing. Assume temperature in knee space is T_n. Now, by applying the energy balance equation,

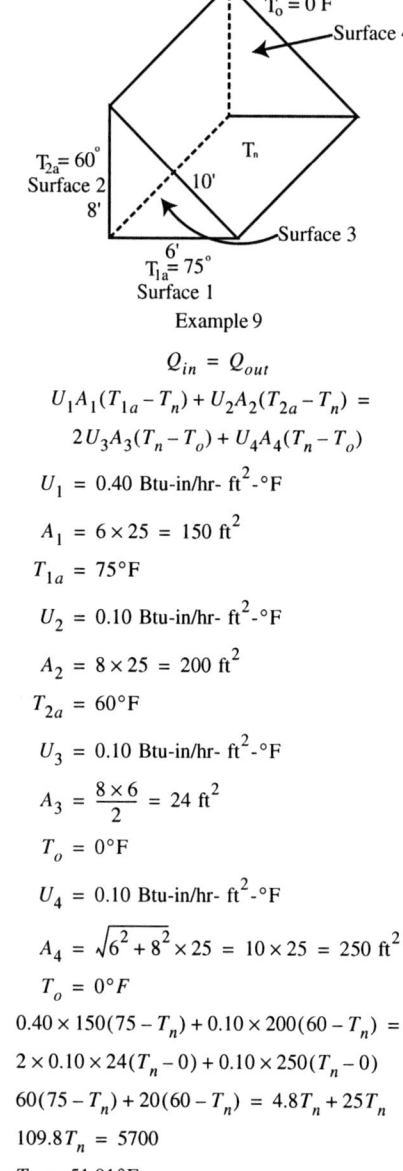

Example 9

$$Q_{in} = Q_{out}$$

$$U_1 A_1 (T_{1a} - T_n) + U_2 A_2 (T_{2a} - T_n) = 2U_3 A_3 (T_n - T_o) + U_4 A_4 (T_n - T_o)$$

$$U_1 = 0.40 \text{ Btu-in/hr- ft}^2\text{-°F}$$

$$A_1 = 6 \times 25 = 150 \text{ ft}^2$$

$$T_{1a} = 75\text{°F}$$

$$U_2 = 0.10 \text{ Btu-in/hr- ft}^2\text{-°F}$$

$$A_2 = 8 \times 25 = 200 \text{ ft}^2$$

$$T_{2a} = 60\text{°F}$$

$$U_3 = 0.10 \text{ Btu-in/hr- ft}^2\text{-°F}$$

$$A_3 = \frac{8 \times 6}{2} = 24 \text{ ft}^2$$

$$T_o = 0\text{°F}$$

$$U_4 = 0.10 \text{ Btu-in/hr- ft}^2\text{-°F}$$

$$A_4 = \sqrt{6^2 + 8^2} \times 25 = 10 \times 25 = 250 \text{ ft}^2$$

$$T_o = 0\text{°} F$$

$$0.40 \times 150(75 - T_n) + 0.10 \times 200(60 - T_n) = 2 \times 0.10 \times 24(T_n - 0) + 0.10 \times 250(T_n - 0)$$

$$60(75 - T_n) + 20(60 - T_n) = 4.8T_n + 25T_n$$

$$109.8T_n = 5700$$

$$T_n = 51.91\text{°F}$$

As temperature is above 40°F, we can place pipes in knee space.

Useful Tables.—The tables of varied wall and roof constructions (Table 5-4a to 5-4k) and tables for thermal resistances of various building materials (Table 5-5 to 5-11) are provided for user reference.

Table 5-4a. Coefficient of Transmission (U) of Frame Walls

		Construction 1		Construction 2	
Replace air space with 3.5 inch R-11 blanket insulation (new item 4)		Unit Resistance (R)			
	Construction	Between Framing	At Framing	Between Framing	At Framing
	1. Outside surface (15 mph wind)	0.17	0.17	0.17	0.17
	2. Siding, wood, 0.5 in.× 8 in. lapped (average)	0.81	0.81	0.81	0.81
	3. Sheathing, 0.5 in. asphalt impregnated	1.32	1.32	1.32	1.32
	4. Nonreflective air space, 3.5 in. (50° F mean; 10°F temperature difference)	1.01	…	11.00	…
	5. Nominal 2-in. × 4-in. wood stud	…	4.38	…	4.38
	6. Gypsum wallboard, 0.5 in.	0.45	0.45	0.45	0.45
	7. Inside surface (still air)	0.68	0.68	0.68	0.68
	Total thermal resistance (R)	$R_i = 4.44$	$R_s = 7.81$	$R_i = 14.43$	$R_s = 7.81$
$U = \dfrac{1}{R}$	*Coefficient of transmission (U)*	$U_i = 0.225$	$U_s = 0.128$	$U_i = 0.069$	$U_s = 0.128$
$U_{av} = U_i \times t_i + U_s \times t_s$	With 20% framing (typical of 2 in. × 4 in. studs @16 inch o.c.)	$U_{av} = 0.225 \times 0.80 + 0.128 \times 0.20$ $= 0.206$		$U_{av} = 0.069 \times 0.80 + 0.128 \times 0.20$ $= 0.081$	

These coefficients are expressed in Btu/hr-ft^2-°F difference in temperature between the air on the two sides, and are based on an outside wind velocity of 15 mph.

Table 5-4b. Coefficient of Transmission (U) of Solid Masonry Walls

		Construction 1		Construction 2
Replace furring strips and air space with 1 inch extruded polystyrene (new item 4)		Unit Resistance (R)		
	Construction	Between Framing	At Framing	Between Framing
	1. Outside surface (15 mph wind)	0.17	0.17	0.17
	2. Common brick, 8 in.	1.60	1.60	1.60
	3. Nominal 1-in. × 3-in. vertical furring	…	0.94	…
	4. Nonreflective air space, 0.75 in. (50°F mean; 10°F temperature difference)	1.01	…	5.00
	5. Gypsum wallboard, 0.5 in.	0.45	0.45	0.45
	6. Inside surface (still air)	0.68	0.68	0.68
	Total thermal resistance (R)	$R_i = 3.91$	$R_s = 3.84$	$R_i = 7.90$
$U = \dfrac{1}{R}$	*Coefficient of transmission (U)*	$U_i = 0.256$	$U_s = 0.260$	$U_i = 0.127$
$U_{av} = U_i \times t_i + U_s \times t_s$	With 20% framing (typical of 1 inch × 3 inch studs @16 inch o.c.)	$U_{av} = 0.225 \times 0.80 + 0.128 \times 0.20$ $= 0.206$		$U_{av} = 0.127$

Coefficients are expressed in Btu/hr- ft^2-°F difference in temperature between the air on the two sides, and are based on an outside wind velocity of 15 mph

Table 5-4c. Coefficient of Transmission (U) of Frame Partitions or Interior Walls

Replace air space with 3.5 inch R-11 blanket insulation (new item 3)		Construction 1		Construction 2	
		Unit Resistance (R)			
	Construction	Between Framing	At Framing	Between Framing	At Framing
	1. Inside surface (still air)	0.68	0.68	0.68	0.68
	2. Gypsum wallboard, 0.5 in.	0.45	0.45	0.45	0.45
	3. Nonreflective air space, 3.5 in. (50° F mean; 10°F temperature difference)	1.01	…	11.00	…
	4. Nominal 2-in. × 4-in. wood stud	…	4.38	…	4.38
	5. Gypsum wallboard 0.5 inch	0.45	0.45	0.45	0.45
	6. Inside surface (still air)	0.68	0.68	0.68	0.68
1 2 3 4 5 6	*Total thermal resistance (R)*	$R_i = 3.27$	$R_s = 6.64$	$R_i = 13.26$	$R_s = 6.64$
$U = \dfrac{1}{R}$	*Coefficient of transmission(U)*	$U_i = 0.306$	$U_s = 0.151$	$U_i = 0.075$	$U_s = 0.151$
$U_{av} = U_i \times t_i + U_s \times t_s$	With 10% framing (typical of 2 inch × 4 inch studs @24 inch o.c.)	$U_{av} = 0.306 \times 0.90 + 0.151 \times 0.10$ $= 0.290$		$U_{av} = 0.075 \times 0.90 + 0.151 \times 0.10$ $= 0.083$	

Coefficients are expressed in Btu/hr-ft²-°F difference in temperature between the air on the two sides, and are based on an still air (no wind) conditions on both sides.

Table 5-4d. Coefficient of Transmission (U) of Masonry Walls

Replace cinder aggregate block with 6 inch light weight aggregate block with cores filled (new item 4)		Construction 1		Construction 2	
		Unit Resistance (R)			
	Construction	Between Framing	At Framing	Between Framing	At Framing
	1. Outside surface (15 mph wind)	0.17	0.17	0.17	0.17
	2. Face brick, 4 in.	0.44	0.44	0.44	0.44
	3. Cement mortar, 0.50 inch	0.10	0.10	0.10	0.10
	4. Concrete block, cinder aggregate, 8 inch	1.72	1.72	2.99	2.99
	5. Reflective air space, 0.75 in (50° F mean; 30° F temperature difference)	2.77	…	2.77	…
	6. Nominal 1-in. × 3-in. vertical furring	…	0.94	…	0.94
	7. Gypsum wallboard, 0.5 in. foil backed	0.45	0.45	0.45	0.45
1 2 3 4 5 6 7 8	8. Inside surface (still air)	0.68	0.68	0.68	0.68
	Total thermal resistance (R)	$R_i = 6.33$	$R_s = 4.50$	$R_i = 7.60$	$R_s = 5.77$
$U = \dfrac{1}{R}$	*Coefficient of transmission (U)*	$U_i = 0.158$	$U_s = 0.222$	$U_i = 0.132$	$U_s = 0.173$
$U_{av} = U_i \times t_i + U_s \times t_s$	With 20% framing (typical of 1 inch × 3 inch vertical furring on masonry @16 inch o.c.)	$U_{av} = 0.158 \times 0.80 + 0.222 \times 0.20$ $= 0.171$		$U_{av} = 0.132 \times 0.80 + 0.173 \times 0.20$ $= 0.140$	

Coefficients are expressed in Btu/hr- ft²-°F difference in temperature between the air on the two sides, and are based on an still wind velocity of 15 mph.

Table 5-4e. Coefficient of Transmission (U) of Masonry Cavity Walls

Replace furring strips and gypsum wall board with 0.625 inch plaster (sand aggregate) applied directly to concrete fill 2.5 inch air space with vermiculite insulation (new items 3 and 7)		Construction 1		Construction 2
		Unit Resistance (R)		
	Construction	Between Framing	At Framing	Between Framing
	1. Outside surface (15 mph wind)	0.17	0.17	0.17
	2. Common brick, 8 in.	0.80	0.80	0.80
	3. Nonreflective air space, 2.5 in. (30°F mean; 10°F temperature difference)	1.10	1.10	5.32
	4. Concrete block, stone aggregate, 4 in.	0.71	0.71	0.71
	5. Nonreflective air space 0.75 in. (50° F mean; 10° F temperature difference)	1.01	…	…
	6. Nominal 1-in. × 3-in. vertical furring	…	0.94	…
	7. Gypsum wallboard, 0.5 in.	0.45	0.45	0.11
	8. Inside surface (still air)	0.68	0.68	0.68
	Total thermal resistance (R)	$R_i = 4.92$	$R_s = 4.85$	$R_i = 7.79$
$U = \dfrac{1}{R}$	*Coefficient of transmission (U)*	$U_i = 0.203$	$U_s = 0.206$	$U_i = 0.129$
$U_{av} = U_i \times t_i + U_s \times t_s$	With 20% framing (typical of 1 inch × 3 inch vertical furring on masonry @16 inch o.c.)	$U_{av} = 0.203 \times 0.80 + 0.206 \times 0.20$ $= 0.204$		$U_{av} = 0.129$

Coefficients are expressed in Btu/hr-ft^2-°F difference in temperature between the air on the two sides, and are based on an still wind velocity of 15 mph

Table 5-4f. Coefficient of Transmission (U) of Masonry Partitions

		Construction 1	Construction 2
Replace Concrete block with 4.0 inch gypsum tile (New Items 3)		Unit Resistance (R)	
	Construction		
	1. Inside surface (still air)	0.68	0.68
	2. Plaster, lightweight aggregate, 0.625 in.	0.39	0.39
	3. Concrete block, cinder aggregate, 4 in.	1.11	1.67
	4. Plaster, lightweight aggregate, 0.625 in.	0.39	0.39
	5. Inside surface (still air)	0.68	0.68
	Total thermal resistance (R)	$R_i = 3.25$	$R_i = 3.81$
$U = \dfrac{1}{R}$	*Coefficient of transmission (U)*	$U_i = 0.308$	$U_i = 0.262$

Coefficients are expressed in Btu/hr-ft^2-°F difference in temperature between the air on the two sides, and are based on an still wind velocity of 15 mph.

Table 5-4g. Coefficient of Transmission (U) of Frame Construction Ceiling and Floors

Assume unheated attic space above heated room with heat flow up- remove tile, felt, plywood, subfloor and air space -replace with r-19 blanket insulation (new item4)		Construction 1		Construction 2	
		Unit Resistance (R)			
Heated Room Below Unheated Space	Construction	Between Framing	At Framing	Between Framing	At Framing
	1. Bottom surface (still air)	0.61	0.61	0.61	0.61
	2. Metal lath and lightweight aggregate, plaster, 0.75 in.	0.47	0.47	0.47	0.47
	3. Nominal 2-in. × 8-in. floor joist	…	9.06	…	9.06
	4. Nonreflective airspace, 7.25-in.	0.93	…	19.00	…
	5. Wood subfloor, 0.75 in.	0.94	0.94	…	…
	6. Plywood, 0.625 in.	0.78	0.78	…	…
	7. Felt building membrane	0.06	0.06	…	…
	8. Resilient tile	0.05	0.05	…	…
	9. Top surface (still air)	0.61	0.61	0.61	0.61
	Total thermal resistance (R)	Ri = 4.45	Rs = 12.58	Ri = 20.69	Rs = 10.75
$U = \dfrac{1}{R}$	*Coefficient of transmission(U)*	Ui = 0.225	Us = 0.079	Ui = 0.048	Us = 0.093
$U_{av} = U_i \times t_i + U_s \times t_s$	With 10% framing (typical of 2 inch joists @ 16 inch o.c.)	$U_{av} = 0.225 \times 0.90 + 0.079 \times 0.10$ = 0.210		$U_{av} = 0.048 \times 0.90 + 0.093 \times 0.10$ = 0.053	

Coefficients are expressed in Btu/hr- ft2-°F difference in temperature between the air on the two sides, and are based on an still wind velocity of 15 mph

Table 5-4h. Coefficient of Transmission (U) of Flat Masonry Roofs with Built Up Roofing, with and without Suspended Ceilings (Winter conditions Upward flow)

Add rigid roof deck insulation, C = 0.24 (C= 1/R) (New item 7)		Construction 1	Construction 2
Heat Flow Up	Construction	Unit Resistance (R)	
	1. Inside surface (still air)	0.61	0.61
	1. Metal lath and lightweight aggregate plaster, 0.75 in.	0.47	0.47
	3. Nonreflective air space, greater than 3.5 in. (50°F mean;10°F temperature difference)	0.93	0.93
	4. Metal ceiling suspension system with metal hanger rods	0	0
	5. Corrugated metal deck	0	0
	6. Concrete slab, lightweight aggregate, 2 in.	2.22	2.22
	7. Rigid roof deck insulation (none)	…	4.17
	8. Built-up roofing, 0.375 in.	0.33	0.33
	9. Outside surface (15 mph wind)	0.17	0.17
	Total thermal resistance (R)	R_i = 4.73	R_i = 8.90
$U = \dfrac{1}{R}$	*Coefficient of transmission (U)*	U_i= 0.211	U_i= 0.112

Coefficients are expressed in Btu/hr- ft2-°F difference in temperature between the air on the two sides, and are based on an still wind velocity of 15 mph.

Table 5-4i. Coefficient of Transmission (U) of Wood Construction Flat Roofs and Ceilings (Winter conditions Upward flow)

Replace Roof deck insulation and 7.25 inches air space with 6 inch R-19 Blanket Insulation and 1.25 inches air space (New items 5 and 7)		Construction 1		Construction 2	
		Unit Resistance (R)			
Heat Flow Up	Construction (Heat Flow Up)	Between Framing	At Framing	Between Framing	At Framing
	1. Inside surface (still air)	0.61	0.61	0.61	0.61
	2. Acoustical tile, fiberboard, glued, 0.5 in.	1.25	1.25	1.25	1.25
	3. Gypsum wallboard, 0.5 in	0.45	0.45	0.45	0.45
	4. Nominal 2-in. × 8-in. ceiling joists	…	9.06	…	9.06
	5. Nonreflective air space, 7.25 in. (50°F mean; 10°F temperature difference)	0.93	…	1.05	…
	6. Plywood deck, 0.625 in.	0.78	0.78	0.78	0.78
	7. Rigid roof deck insulation, $C = 0.72$, $(R = 1/C)$	1.39	1.39	19.00	…
	8. Built-up roof	0.33	0.33	0.33	0.33
	9. Outside surface (15 mph wind)	0.17	0.17	0.17	0.17
	Total Thermal Resistance (R)	$R_i = 5.91$	$R_s = 14.04$	$R_i = 23.64$	$R_s = 12.65$
$U = \dfrac{1}{R}$	*Coefficient of Transmission (U)*	$U_i = 0.169$	$U_s = 0.071$	$U_i = 0.042$	$U_s = 0.079$
$U_{av} = U_i \times t_i + U_s \times t_s$	With 10% framing (typical of 2 in. joists @16 in. o.c.)	$U_{av} = 0.169 \times 0.90 + 0.071 \times 0.10$ $= 0.210$		$U_{av} = 0.042 \times 0.90 + 0.079 \times 0.10$ $= 0.053$	

Coefficients are expressed in Btu/hr- ft²-°F difference in temperature between the air on the two sides, and are based on an still wind velocity of 15 mph

Table 5-4j. Coefficient of Transmission (U) of Metal Construction Flat Roofs and Ceilings (Winter conditions Upward flow)

Replace rigid roof deck insulation (C= 0.24) and sand aggregate plaster with rigid roof deck insulation C=0.36 and lightweight aggregate plaster (new items 2 and 6)		Construction 1	Construction 2
	Construction (Heat Flow Up)	Unit Resistance (R)	
	1. Inside surface (still air)	0.61	0.61
	2. Metal lath and sand aggregate plaster, 0.75 in.	0.13	0.47
	3. Structural beam	0.00	0.00
	4. Nonreflective air space (50°F mean; 10°F temperature difference)	0.93	0.93
	5. Metal deck	0.00	0.00
	6. Rigid roof deck insulation, $C = 0.24$ $(R = 1/C)$	4.17	2.78
	7. Built-up roofing, 0.375 in.	0.33	0.33
	8. Outside surface (15 mph wind)	0.17	0.17
	Total thermal resistance (R)	$R_i = 6.34$	$R_i = 5.29$
$U = \dfrac{1}{R}$	*Coefficient of transmission (U)*	$U_i = 0.158$	$U_i = 0.189$

Coefficients are expressed in Btu/hr-ft²-°F difference in temperature between the air on the two sides, and are based on an still wind velocity of 15 mph

Table 5-4k. Coefficient of Transmission (U) of Pitched Roofs (Winter conditions Upward flow)

Find U_{av} heat flow down (summer conditions)	Construction (Heat Flow Up) (Reflective air space)	Construction 1		Construction 2	
		Unit Resistance (R)			
		Between Rafters	At Rafters	Between Rafters	At Rafters
	1. Inside surface (still air)	0.62	0.61	0.76	0.76
	2. Gypsum wallboard 0.5 in. foil backed	0.45	0.47	0.45	0.45
	3. Nominal 2-in. × 4-in. ceiling rafter	…	4.38	…	4.38
	4. 45° slope reflective air space, 3.5 in. (50°F mean, 30°F temperature difference)	2.17	…	4.33	…
	5. Plywood sheathing, 0.625 in.	0.78	0.78	0.78	0.78
	6. Felt building membrane	0.06	0.06	0.06	0.06
	7. Asphalt shingle roofing	0.44	0.44	0.44	0.44
	8. Outside surface (15 mph wind)	0.17	0.17	0.25	0.25
	Total thermal resistance (R)	$R_i = 4.69$	$R_s = 6.90$	$R_i = 7.07$	$R_s = 7.12$
$U = \dfrac{1}{R}$	*Coefficient of transmission (U)*	$U_i = 0.213$	$U_s = 0.145$	$U_i = 0.141$	$U_s = 0.140$
$U_{av} = U_i \times T_i + U_s \times T_s$	With 10% framing (typical of 2 inch joists @ 16 inch o.c.)	$U_{av} = 0.213 \times 0.90 + 0.145 \times 0.10$ $= 0.206$		$U_{av} = 0.141 \times 0.90 + 0.140 \times 0.10$ $= 0.141$	

Find U_{av} Heat flow down (Summer Conditions)	Construction (Heat Flow Up) (Non reflective air space)	Construction 3		Construction 4	
		Unit Resistance (R)			
		Between Rafters	At Rafters	Between Rafters	At Rafters
	1. Inside surface (still air)	0.62	0.61	0.76	0.76
	2. Gypsum wallboard 0.5 in. foil backed	0.45	0.47	0.45	0.45
	3. Nominal 2-in. × 4-in. ceiling rafter	…	4.38	…	4.38
	4. 45° slope reflective air space, 3.5 in. (50° F mean, 30°F temperature difference)	0.96	…	0.90	…
	5. Plywood sheathing, 0.625 in.	0.78	0.78	0.78	0.78
	6. Felt building membrane	0.06	0.06	0.06	0.06
	7. Asphalt shingle roofing	0.44	0.44	0.44	0.44
	8. Outside surface (15 mph wind)	0.17	0.17	0.25	0.25
	Total thermal resistance (R)	$R_i = 3.48$	$R_s = 6.90$	$R_i = 3.64$	$R_s = 7.12$
$U = \dfrac{1}{R}$	*Coefficient of transmission (U)*	$U_i = 0.287$	$U_s = 0.145$	$U_i = 0.275$	$U_s = 0.140$
$U_{av} = U_i \times t_i + U_s \times t_s$	With 10% framing (typical of 2 inch joists @ 16 inch o.c.)	$U_{av} = 0.287 \times 0.90 + 0.145 \times 0.10$ $= 0.273$		$U_{av} = 0.275 \times 0.90 + 0.140 \times 0.10$ $= 0.262$	

Coefficients are expressed in Btu/hr- ft²-°F difference in temperature between the air on the two sides, and are based on an still wind velocity of 15 mph.

Table 5-5. Relative Thermal Resistances of Building Materials

Material Description	Material Density lb/ft^3	Material Thickness in.	Resistance for Thickness Listed °F-ft^2-h/Btu	Material Description	Material Density lb/ft^3	Material Thickness in.	Resistance for Thickness Listed °F-ft^2-h/Btu
Building paper	...	...	0.06	Concrete block, 3 core, sand-gravel aggregate	...	8	1.11
Gypsum plaster, sand aggregate	105	½	0.09	Acoustical tile, wood or cane fiber	...	½	1.19
Structural glass	...	...	0.10	Fir, pine, and similar softwoods	32	1	1.25
Air surface, 15 mph wind, outside surface	...	...	0.17	Insulation board, impregnated	20	½	1.32
Gypsum or plaster board	50	⅜	0.32	Concrete, lightweight aggregate	80	4	1.50
Stone, lime, or sand		4	0.32	Air space, vertical, bounded by reflective material	...	¾ to 4	1.70
Concrete, sand-gravel aggregate	140	4	0.32	Concrete block, 3 core, cinder aggregate	...	8	1.72
Built-up roofing	70	⅜	0.33	Concrete block, 3 core, lightweight aggregate	...	8	2.00
Brick, face	130	4	0.44	Vermiculite, expanded	7	1	2.08
Still air surface, horiz., ordinary materials, heat flow up	...	...	0.61	Carpet and fibrous pad	...	...	2.08
Aluminum, steel, or vinyl over sheathing, hollow backed	...	...	0.61	Cellular glass insulation board	9	1	2.50
Plywood	34	½	0.63	Roof insulation, preformed for above deck	...	1	2.78
Still air surface, vertical, ordinary mtrls, horiz. heat flow	...	...	0.68	Mineral wool, loose fill, from slag glass or rock	2-5	1	3.33
Wood siding, bevel, ½ in 8 in lapped	...	...	0.81	Wood fiber, loose fill, hemlock, fir or redwood	2-3.5	1	3.33
Wood shingle siding, 16 in, 7 ½ in exposure	...	...	0.87	Plastic, foamed	1.62	1	3.45
Oak, maple, and similar hardwoods	45	1	0.91	Macerated paper or pulp	2-3.5	1	3.57
Air space, vertical, ordinary materials, horiz. heat flow	...	¾ to 4	0.97	Corkboard, without added binder	6.5-8	1	3.70
Clay tile, one cell deep	...	4	1.11	**Batt and Blankets Bounded by Nonreflective Materials**			
Wood fiber, multilayer, stitched expanded	1.5-2	1	3.70	Mineral wool, fibrous form, rock, slag, or glass	1.5-4	1	3.70
Cotton fiber	0.8-2	1	3.85	Wood fiber, multilayer, stitched expanded	1.5-2	1	3.70
Wood Fiber	3.2-3.6	1	4.00	Cotton fiber	0.8-2	1	3.85
				Wood fiber	3.2-3.6	1	4.00

Table 5-6. Surface Conductances and Resistances

Position of Surface	Direction of Heat Flow	Surface Emittance, ε						Position of Surface
		Non-reflective ε = 0.90		Reflective				
				ε = 0.20		ε = 0.05		
		h_i	R	h_i	R	h_i	R	
		Still Air						
Horizontal	Upward	1.63	0.61	0.91	1.10	0.76	1.32	Horizontal
Sloping-45°	Upward	1.60	0.62	0.88	1.14	0.73	1.37	Sloping-45°
Vertical	Horizontal	1.46	0.68	0.74	1.35	0.59	1.70	Vertical
Sloping-45°	Downward	1.32	0.76	0.60	1.67	0.45	2.22	Sloping-45°
Horizontal	Downward	1.08	0.92	0.37	2.70	0.22	4.55	Horizontal
Moving air	(Any position)	h_i	R					Moving air
15-mph wind (for winter)	Any	6.00	0.17	…	…	…	…	15-mph wind (for winter)
7.5-mph wind (for summer)	Any	4.00	0.25	…	…	…	…	7.5-mph wind (for summer)

Notes:
1) Surface conductance h_i and h_o measured in Btu/hr-ft^2-°F; resistance R in °F-ft^2-hr/Btu.
2) No surface has both an air space resistance value and a surface resistance value.
3) For ventilated attics or spaces above ceilings under summer conditions (heat flow down).
4) Conductances are for surfaces of the stated emittance facing virtual blackbody surroundings at the same temperature as the ambient air. Values are based on a surface air temperature difference of 10°F and for surface temperatures of 70°F.
5) Condensate can have a significant impact on surface emittance.

Table 5-7. Emittance Values of Various Surfaces and Effective Emittances of Air Spaces

Surface	Average Emittance ε	Effective Emittance ε_{eff} of Air Space	
		One Surface Emittance ε; Other, 0.9	Both Surface Emittance ε;
Aluminum foil, bright	0.05	0.05	0.03
Aluminum foil, with condensate just visible (> 0.7 gr/ft^2)	030	0.29	…
Aluminum foil, with condensate clearly visible (> 2.9 gr/ft^2)	0.70	0.65	…
Aluminum sheet	0.12	0.12	0.06
Aluminum coated paper, polished	0.20	0.20	0.11
Steel, galvanized, bright	0.25	0.24	0.15
Aluminum paint	0.50	0.47	0.35
Building materials: wood, paper, masonry, nonmetallic paints	0.90	0.82	0.82
Regular glass	0.84	0.77	0.72

Table 5-8. Thermal Resistances of Plain Air Spaces

Position of Air Space	Direction of Heat Flow	Mean Temp. °F	Temp Diff. °F	0.5 -in. Air Space					0.75 -in. Air Space				
		Air Space		Effective Emittance ε_{eff}					Effective Emittance ε_{eff}				
				0.03	0.05	0.2	0.5	0.82	0.03	0.05	0.2	0.5	0.82
Horiz.	Up	90	10	2.13	2.03	1.51	0.99	0.73	2.34	2.22	1.61	1.04	0.75
		50	30	1.62	1.57	1.29	0.96	0.75	1.71	1.66	1.35	0.99	0.77
		50	10	2.13	2.05	1.60	1.11	0.84	2.30	2.21	1.70	1.16	0.87
		0	20	1.73	1.70	1.45	1.12	0.91	1.83	1.79	1.52	1.16	0.93
		0	10	2.10	2.04	1.70	1.27	1.00	2.23	2.16	1.78	1.31	1.02
		−50	20	1.69	1.66	1.49	1.23	1.04	1.77	1.74	1.55	1.27	1.07
		−50	10	2.04	2.00	1.75	1.40	1.16	2.16	2.11	1.84	1.46	1.20
45° Slope	Up	90	10	2.44	2.31	1.65	1.06	0.76	2.96	2.78	1.88	1.15	0.81
		50	30	2.06	1.98	1.56	1.10	0.83	1.99	1.92	1.52	1.08	0.82
		50	10	2.55	2.44	1.83	1.22	0.90	2.90	2.75	2.00	1.29	0.92
		0	20	2.20	2.14	1.76	1.30	1.02	2.13	2.07	1.72	1.28	1.00
		0	10	2.63	2.54	2.03	1.44	1.10	2.72	2.62	2.08	1.47	1.12
		−50	20	2.08	2.04	1.78	1.42	1.17	2.05	2.01	1.76	1.41	1.16
		−50	10	2.62	2.56	2.17	1.66	1.33	2.53	2.47	2.10	1.62	1.30
Vertical	Horiz	90	10	2.47	2.34	1.67	1.06	0.77	3.50	3.24	2.08	1.22	0.84
		50	30	2.57	2.46	1.84	1.23	0.90	2.91	2.77	2.01	1.30	0.94
		50	10	2.66	2.54	1.88	1.24	0.91	3.70	3.46	2.35	1.43	1.01
		0	20	2.82	2.72	2.14	1.50	1.13	3.14	3.02	2.32	1.58	1.18
		0	10	2.93	2.82	2.20	1.53	1.15	3.77	3.59	2.64	1.73	1.26
		−50	20	2.90	2.82	2.35	1.76	1.39	2.90	2.83	2.36	1.77	1.39
		−50	10	3.20	3.10	2.54	1.87	1.46	3.72	3.60	2.87	2.04	1.56
45° Slope	Down	90	10	2.48	2.34	1.67	1.06	0.77	3.53	3.27	2.10	1.22	0.84
		50	30	2.64	2.52	1.87	1.24	0.91	3.43	3.23	2.24	1.39	0.99
		50	10	2.67	2.55	1.89	1.25	0.92	3.81	3.57	2.40	1.45	1.02
		0	20	2.91	2.80	2.19	1.52	1.15	3.75	3.57	2.63	1.72	1.26
		0	10	2.94	2.83	2.21	1.53	1.15	4.12	3.91	2.81	1.80	1.30
		−50	20	3.16	3.07	2.52	1.86	1.45	3.78	3.65	2.90	2.05	1.57
		−50	10	3.26	3.16	2.58	1.89	1.47	4.35	4.18	3.22	2.21	1.66
Horiz.	Down	90	10	2.48	2.34	1.67	1.06	0.77	3.55	3.29	2.10	1.22	0.85
		50	30	2.66	2.54	1.88	1.24	0.91	3.77	3.52	2.38	1.44	1.02
		50	10	2.67	2.55	1.89	1.25	0.92	3.84	3.59	2.41	1.45	1.02
		0	20	2.94	2.83	2.20	1.53	1.15	4.18	3.96	2.83	1.81	1.30
		0	10	2.96	2.85	2.22	1.53	1.16	4.25	4.02	2.87	1.82	1.31
		−50	20	3.25	3.15	2.58	1.89	1.47	4.60	4.41	3.36	2.28	1.69
		−50	10	3.28	3.18	2.60	1.90	1.47	4.71	4.51	3.42	2.30	1.71

Position of Air Space	Direction of Heat Flow	Mean Temp. °F	Temp Diff. °F	1.5-inch Air Space					3.5-inch Air Space				
		Air Space		0.03	0.05	0.2	0.5	0.82	0.03	0.05	0.2	0.5	0.82
Horiz.	Up	90	10	2.55	2.41	1.71	1.08	0.77	2.84	2.66	1.83	1.13	0.80
		50	30	1.87	1.81	1.45	1.04	0.80	2.09	2.01	1.58	1.10	0.80
		50	10	2.50	2.40	1.81	1.21	0.89	2.80	2.66	1.95	1.28	0.93
		0	20	2.01	1.95	1.63	1.23	0.97	2.25	2.18	1.79	1.32	1.03
		0	10	2.43	2.35	1.90	1.38	1.06	2.71	2.62	2.07	1.47	1.12
		−50	20	1.94	1.91	1.68	1.36	1.13	2.19	2.14	1.86	1.47	1.20
		−50	10	2.37	2.31	1.99	1.55	1.26	2.65	2.58	2.18	1.67	1.33
45° Slope	Up	90	10	2.92	2.73	1.86	1.14	0.80	3.18	2.96	1.97	1.18	0.82
		50	30	2.14	2.06	1.61	1.12	0.84	2.26	2.17	1.67	1.15	0.86
		50	10	2.88	2.74	1.99	1.29	0.94	3.12	2.95	2.10	1.34	0.96
		0	20	2.30	2.23	1.82	1.34	1.04	2.42	2.35	1.90	1.38	1.06
		0	10	2.79	2.69	2.12	1.49	1.13	2.98	2.87	2.23	1.54	1.16
		−50	20	2.22	2.17	1.88	1.49	1.21	2.34	2.29	1.97	1.54	1.25
		−50	10	2.71	2.64	2.23	1.69	1.35	2.87	2.79	2.33	1.75	1.39
Vertical	Horiz	90	10	3.99	3.66	2.25	1.27	0.87	3.69	3.40	2.15	1.24	0.85
		50	30	2.58	2.46	1.84	1.23	0.90	2.67	2.55	1.89	1.25	0.91
		50	10	3.79	3.55	2.39	1.45	1.02	3.63	3.40	2.32	1.42	1.01
		0	20	2.76	2.66	2.10	1.48	1.12	2.88	2.78	2.17	1.51	1.01
		0	10	3.51	3.35	2.51	1.67	1.23	3.49	3.33	2.50	1.67	1.23
		−50	20	2.64	2.58	2.18	1.66	1.33	2.82	2.75	2.30	1.73	1.37
		−50	10	3.31	3.21	2.62	1.91	1.48	3.40	3.30	2.67	1.94	1.50

Table 5-8. *(Continued)* **Thermal Resistances of Plain Air Spaces**

Position of Air Space	Direction of Heat Flow		Air Space		0.5 -in. Air Space					0.75 -in. Air Space				
			Mean Temp. °F	Temp Diff. °F	Effective Emittance ε_{eff}					Effective Emittance ε_{eff}				
					0.03	0.05	0.2	0.5	0.82	0.03	0.05	0.2	0.5	0.82
45° Slope	Down		90	10	5.07	4.55	2.56	1.36	0.91	4.81	4.33	2.49	1.34	0.90
			50	30	3.58	3.36	2.31	1.42	1.00	3.51	3.30	2.28	1.40	1.00
			50	10	5.10	4.66	2.85	1.60	1.09	4.74	4.36	2.73	1.57	1.08
			0	20	3.85	3.66	2.68	1.74	1.27	3.81	3.63	2.66	1.74	1.27
			0	10	4.92	4.62	3.16	1.94	1.37	4.59	4.32	3.02	1.88	1.34
			−50	20	3.62	3.50	2.80	2.01	1.54	3.77	3.64	2.90	2.05	1.57
			−50	10	4.67	4.47	3.40	2.29	1.70	4.50	4.32	3.31	2.25	1.68
Horiz.	Down		90	10	6.09	5.35	2.79	1.43	0.94	10.07	8.19	3.41	1.57	1.00
			50	30	6.27	5.63	3.18	1.70	1.14	9.60	8.17	3.86	1.88	1.22
			50	10	6.61	5.90	3.27	1.73	1.15	11.15	9.27	4.09	1.93	1.24
			0	20	7.03	6.43	3.91	2.19	1.49	10.90	9.52	4.87	2.47	1.62
			0	10	7.31	6.66	4.00	2.22	1.51	11.97	10.32	5.08	2.52	1.64
			−50	20	7.73	7.20	4.77	2.85	1.99	11.64	10.49	6.02	3.25	2.18
			−50	10	8.09	7.52	4.91	2.89	2.01	12.98	11.56	6.36	3.34	2.22

Thermal resistance values were determined from the relation, $R = 1/C$, where $C = h + \varepsilon_{eff} h_r$. h is conduction convection coefficient, $\varepsilon_{eff} h_r$ is radiation coefficient $= 0.0068\varepsilon_{eff}[(t_m + 460)/100]^3$, and t_m is the mean temperature of the air space. For extrapolation from this table to air spaces less than 0.5 in. (as in insulating window glass), assume $h = 0.159(1 + 0.0016 t_m)/l$, where l is the air space thickness in inches, and h is heat transfer through the air space only.

Values apply for ideal conditions, i.e., air spaces of uniform thickness bounded by plain, smooth, parallel surfaces with no air leakage to or from the space. Thermal resistance values for multiple air spaces must be based on careful estimates of mean temperature differences for each air space.

A single resistance value cannot account for multiple air spaces; each air space requires a separate resistance calculation that applies only for the established boundary conditions. Resistances of horizontal spaces with heat flow downward are substantially independent of temperature difference.

Interpolation is permissible for other values of mean temperature, temperature difference, and effective emittance ε_{eff}. Interpolation and moderate extrapolation for air spaces greater than 3.5 in. are also permissible.

Effective emittance ε_{eff} of the air space is given by $1/\varepsilon_{eff} = 1/\varepsilon_1 + 1/\varepsilon_2 - 1$, where ε_1 and ε_2 are the emittances of the surfaces of the air space.

Table 5-9. Typical Thermal Properties of Common Building and Insulating Materials[a]

		Density	Conductivity[c] (k)	Conductance (C)	Resistance[b] (R)		Specific Heat
					Per Inch Thickness (1/k)	For Thickness Listed (1/C)	
Description		lb/ft³	Btu-in./hr-ft²-°F	Btu/hr-ft²-°F	°F-ft²-hr/Btu-in.	°F-ft²-hr/Btu	Btu/lb-°F
Building Board							
Asbestos-cement board		120	4.0	...	0.25	...	0.24
Asbestos-cement board	0.125 in.	120	...	33.00	...	0.03	...
Asbestos-cement board	0.25 in.	120	...	16.50	...	0.06	...
Gypsum or plaster board	0.375 in.	50	...	3.10	...	0.32	0.26
Gypsum or plaster board	0.50 in.	50	...	2.22	...	0.45	...
Gypsum or plaster board	0.625 in.	50	...	1.78	...	0.56	...
Plywood (Douglas fir)		34	0.80		1.25		0.29
Plywood (Douglas fir)	0.25 in.	34	...	3.2	...	0.31	...
Plywood (Douglas fir)	0.375 in.	34	...	2.13	...	0.47	...
Plywood (Douglas fir)	0.5 in.	34	...	1.60	...	0.62	...
Plywood (Douglas fir)	0.625 in.	34	...	1.29	...	0.77	...
Plywood or wood panels	0.75 in.	34	...	1.07	...	0.93	0.29
Vegetable fiber board							
Sheathing, regular density	0.5 in.	18	...	0.76	...	1.32	0.31
	0.7812 in.	18	...	0.49	...	2.06	...
Sheathing intermediate density	0.5 in.	22	...	0.92	...	1.09	0.31
Nail-base sheathing	0.5 in.	25	...	0.94	...	1.06	0.31
Shingle backer	0.375 in.	18	...	1.06	...	0.94	0.31
Shingle backer	0.3125 in.	18	...	1.28	...	0.78	...
Sound deadening board	0.5 in.	15	...	0.74	...	1.35	0.30
Tile and lay-in panels, plain or acoustic		18	0.40		2.50		0.14
	0.5 in.	18	...	0.80	...	1.25	...
	0.75 in.	18	...	0.53	...	1.89	...
Laminated paperboard	...	30	0.50	...	2.00	...	0.33
Homogeneous board from repulped paper	...	30	0.50	...	2.00	...	0.28
Hardboard							...
Medium density	...	50	0.73	...	1.37	...	0.31
High density, service-tempered grade and service grade	...	55	0.82	...	1.22	...	0.32
High density, standard-tempered grade	...	63	1.00	...	1.00	...	0.32
Particle board							...
Low density	...	37	0.71	...	1.41	...	0.31
Medium density	...	50	0.94	...	1.06	...	0.31
High density	...	62	0.50	1.18	...	0.85	...
Underlayment	0.625 in.	40	...	1.22	...	0.82	0.29
Waferboard	...	37	0.63	...	1.59	...	...
Wood subfloor	0.75 in.	...	...	1.06	...	0.94	0.33
Building Membrane							
Vaporpermeable felt	...	...	16.7	...	0.06	...	...
Vaporseal, 2 layers of mopped 15 lb felt	...	...	8.35	...	0.12	...	...
Vaporseal, plastic film	...	...	...	...	Negl.	...	...
Finish Flooring Materials							
Carpet and fibrous pad		...	...	0.48	...	2.08	0.34
Carpet and rubber pad		...	...	0.81	...	1.23	0.33
Cork tile	0.125 in.	...	...	3.60	...	0.28	0.48
Terrazzo	1 in.	...	...	12.5	...	0.08	0.19
Tile asphalt, linoleum, vinyl, rubber		...	...	20.00	...	0.05	0.30
vinyl asbestos	0.2	...	...	...	...	...	0.24
ceramic	0.1	...	...	...	...	...	0.19
Wood, hardwood finish	0.75 in.	...	...	1.47	...	0.68	...

Table 5-9. *(Continued)* **Typical Thermal Properties of Common Building and Insulating Materials[a]**

Description	Density	Conductivity[c] (k)	Conductance (C)	Resistance[b] (R) Per Inch Thickness (1/k)	Resistance[b] (R) For Thickness Listed (1/C)	Specific Heat
	lb/ft³	Btu-in./hr-ft²-°F	Btu/hr-ft²-°F	°F-ft²-hr/Btu-in.	°F-ft²-hr/Btu	Btu/lb-°F
Insulating Materials						
Blanket and batt[d],[e]						
Mineral fiber, fibrous form processed from rock, slag, or glass						
approx. 3–4 in.	0.4-2.0	...	0.091	...	11	
approx. 3.5 in.	0.4-2.0	...	0.077	...	13	
approx. 3.5 in.	1.2-1.6	...	0.067	...	15	
approx. 5.5-6.5 in.	0.4-2.0	...	0.053	...	19	
approx. 5.5 in.	0.6-1.0	...	0.048	...	21	
approx. 6-7.5 in.	0.4-2.0	...	0.045	...	22	
approx. 8.25-10 in.	0.4-2.0	...	0.033	...	30	
approx. 10-13 in.	0.4-2.0	...	0.026	...	38	
Board and Slabs						
Cellular glass	8.0	0.33	...	3.03	...	0.18
Glass fiber, organic bonded	4.0-9.0	0.25	...	4.00	...	0.23
Expanded perlite, organic bonded	1.0	0.36	...	2.78	...	0.30
Expanded rubber (rigid)	4.5	0.22	...	4.55	...	0.40
Expanded polystyrene, extruded (smooth skin surface) (HCFC-12 exp.)	1.8-3.5	0.20	...	5.00	...	0.29
Expanded polystyrene, extruded (smooth skin surface) (HCFC-142b exp.),[f]	1.8-3.5	0.20	...	5.00	...	0.29
Expanded polystyrene, molded beads	1.00	0.26	...	3.85	...	...
	1.25	0.25	...	4	...	...
	1.50	0.24	...	4.17	...	...
	1.75	0.24	...	4.17	...	...
	2.0	0.23	...	4.35	...	...
Cellular polyurethane/polyisocyanurate) (CFC-11exp.) (unfaced)	1.5	0.16-0.18	...	6.25-5.56	...	0.38
Cellular polyisocyanurate (CFC-11 exp.) (gas-permeable facers)	1.5-2.5	0.16-0.18	...	6.25-5.56	...	0.22
Cellular polyisocyanurate[g] (CFC-11 exp.) (gas-impermeable facers)	2.0	0.14	...	7.04	...	0.27
Cellular phenolic (closed cell) (CFC-11, CFC-113 exp.)	3.0	0.12	...	8.20	...	...
Cellular phenolic (open cell)	1.8-2.2	0.23	...	4.40	...	...
Mineral fiber with resin binder	15.0	0.29	...	3.45	...	0.17
Mineral fiberboard, wet felted			...		...	...
Core or roof insulation	16-17	0.34	...	2.94	...	...
Acoustical tile	18	0.35	...	2.86	...	0.19
Acoustical tile	21	0.37	...	2.70	...	...
Mineral fiberboard, wet molded						
Acoustical tile	23	0.42	...	2.38	...	0.14
Wood or cane fiberboard					...	...
Acoustical tile 0.5 in.	...	...	0.80	...	1.25	0.31
Acoustical tile 0.75 in.	...	...	0.53	...	1.89	...
Interior finish (plank, tile)	15.0	0.35	...	2.86	...	0.32
Cement fiber slabs (shredded wood with Portland cement binder)	25-27.0	0.50-0.53	...	2.0-1.89	...	...
Cement fiber slabs (shredded wood with magnesia oxysulfide binder)	22	0.57	...	1.75	...	0.31
Loose Fill						
Cellulosic insulation (milled paper or wood pulp)	2.3-3.2	0.27-0.32	...	3.70-3.13	...	0.33
Perlite, expanded	2.0-4.1	0.27-0.31	...	3.7 - 3.3	...	0.26
	4.1 - 7.4	0.31 - 0.36	...	3.3 - 2.8	...	...
	7.4 - 11.0	0.36 - 0.42	...	2.8 - 2.4	...	...

Table 5-9. *(Continued)* **Typical Thermal Properties of Common Building and Insulating Materials[a]**

Description		Density	Conductivity[c] (k)	Conductance (C)	Resistance[b] (R) Per Inch Thickness (1/k)	Resistance[b] (R) For Thickness Listed (1/C)	Specific Heat
		lb/ft³	Btu-in./hr-ft²-°F	Btu/hr-ft²-°F	°F-ft²-hr/Btu-in.	°F-ft²-hr/Btu	Btu/lb-°F
Mineral fiber (rock, slag, or glass)[e]							
approx. 3.75 - 5 in.		0.6 - 2.0	…	…	…	11.0	0.17
approx. 6.5 - 8.75 in.		0.6 - 2.0	…	…	…	19.0	…
approx. 7.5 - 10 in.		0.6 - 2.0	…	…	…	22.0	…
approx. 10.25 - 13.75 in.		0.6 - 2.0	…	…	…	30.0	…
approx. 3.5 in (closed sidewall application)		2.0 - 3.5	…	…	…	12.0 - 14.0	…
Vermiculite, exfoliated		7.0 - 8.2	0.47	…	2.13	…	0.32
		4.0 - 6.0	0.44	…	2.27	…	…
Spray Applied							
Polyurethane foam		1.5 - 2.5	0.16 - 0.18	…	6.25 - 5.56	…	…
Ureaformaldehyde foam		0.7 - 1.6	0.22 - 0.28	…	4.55 - 3.57	…	…
Cellulosic fiber		3.5 - 6.0	0.29 - 0.34	…	3.45 - 2.94	…	…
Glass fiber		3.5 - 4.5	0.26 - 0.27	…	3.85 - 3.70	…	…
Reflective Insulation							
Reflective material (ε< 0.5) in center of ¾ in cavity forms two ⅜ in. vertical air spaces[h]		…	…	0.31	…	3.2	…
Roofing							
Asbestos - cement shingles		120	…	4.76	…	0.21	0.24
Asphalt roll roofing		70	…	6.50	…	0.15	0.36
Asphalt shingles		70	…	2.27	…	0.44	0.30
Built - up roofing	0.375 in.	70	…	3.00	…	0.33	0.35
Slate	0.5 in.	…	…	20.00	…	0.05	0.30
Wood shingles, plain and plastic film faced		…	…	1.06	…	0.94	0.31
Plastering Materials							
Cement plaster, sand aggregate		116	5.0	…	0.20	…	0.20
Sand aggregate	0.375 in.	…	…	13.3	…	0.08	0.20
Sand aggregate	0.75 in.	…	…	6.66	…	0.15	0.20
Gypsum plaster:							
Lightweight aggregate	0.5 in.	45	…	3.12	…	0.32	…
Lightweight aggregate	0.625 in.	45	…	2.67	…	0.39	…
Lightweight aggregate on metal lath	0.75 in.	…	…	2.13	…	0.47	…
Perlite aggregate		45	1.5	…	0.67	…	0.32
Sand aggregate		105	5.6	…	0.18	…	0.20
Sand aggregate	0.5 in.	105		11.1		0.09	
Sand aggregate	0.625 in.	105		9.1		0.11	
Sand aggregate on metal lath	0.75 in.			7.7		0.13	
Vermiculite aggregate		45	1.7		0.59		
Masonry Materials							
Masonry Units							
Brick, fired clay		150	8.4 - 10.2	…	0.12 - 0.10	…	…
		140	7.4 - 9.0	…	0.14 - 0.11	…	…
		130	6.4 - 7.8	…	0.16 - 0.12	…	…
		120	5.6 - 6.8	…	0.18 - 0.15	…	0.19
		110	4.9 - 5.9	…	0.20 - 0.17	…	…
		100	4.2 - 5.1	…	0.24 - 0.20	…	…
		90	3.6 - 4.3	…	0.28 - 0.24	…	…
		80	3.0 - 3.7	…	0.33 - 0.27	…	…
		70	2.5 - 3.1	…	0.40 - 0.33	…	…
Clay tile, hollow							…
1 cell deep	3 in.	…	…	1.25	…	0.80	0.21

Table 5-9. *(Continued)* **Typical Thermal Properties of Common Building and Insulating Materials**[a]

Description		Density	Conductivity[c] (k)	Conductance (C)	Resistance[b] (R)		Specific Heat
					Per Inch Thickness (1/k)	For Thickness Listed (1/C)	
		lb/ft³	Btu-in./hr-ft²-°F	Btu/hr-ft²-°F	°F-ft²-hr/Btu-in.	°F-ft²-hr/Btu	Btu/lb-°F
1 cell deep	4 in.	…	…	0.90	…	1.11	…
2 cells deep	6 in.	…	…	0.66	…	1.52	…
2 cells deep	8 in.	…	…	0.54	…	1.85	…
2 cells deep	10 in.	…	…	0.45	…	2.22	…
3 cells deep	12 in.	…	…	0.40	…	2.50	…
Concrete blocks [i, j]							
Limestone aggregate							
8 in., 36 lb, 138 lb/ft³ concrete, 2 cores		…	…	…	…	…	…
Same with perlite filled cores		…	0.48	…	2.1	…	…
12 in., 55 lb, 138 lb/ft³ concrete, 2 cores		…	…	…	…	…	…
Same with perlite filled cores		…	0.27	…	3.7	…	…
Normal weight aggregate (sand and gravel)							
8 in, 33 - 36 lb, 126 - 136 lb/ft³ concrete, 2 or 3 cores		…	…	0.90 - 1.03	…	1.11 - 0.97	0.22
Same with perlite filled cores		…	…	0.50	…	2.0	…
Same with vermiculite filled cores		…	…	0.52 - 0.73	…	1.92 - 1.37	…
12 in., 50 lb, 125 lb/ft³ concrete, 2 cores		…	…	0.81	…	1.23	0.22
Medium weight aggregate (combinations of normal weight and lightweight aggregate)							
8 in., 26 - 29 lb, 97 - 112 l lb/ft³ concrete, 2 or 3 cores.		…	…	0.58 - 0.78	…	1.71 - 1.28	…
Same with perlite filled cores		…	…	0.27 - 0.44	…	3.7 - 2.3	…
Same with vermiculite filled cores		…	…	0.30	…	3.3	…
Same with molded EPS (beads) filled cores		…	…	0.32	…	3.2	…
Same with molded EPS inserts in cores		…	…	0.37	…	2.7	…
Lightweight aggregate (expanded shale, clay, slate or slag, pumice)							
6 in., 16 - 17 lb 85 - 87 lb/ft³ concrete, 2 or 3 cores		…	…	0.52 - 0.61	…	1.93 - 1.65	…
Same with perlite filled cores		…	…	0.24	…	4.2	…
Same with vermiculite filled cores		…	…	0.33	…	3	…
8 in., 19 - 22 lb, 72 - 86 lb/ft³ concrete		…	…	0.32 - 0.54	…	3.2 - 1.90	…
Same with perlite filled cores		…	…	0.15 - 0.23	…	6.8 - 4.4	…
Same with vermiculite filled cores		…	…	0.19 - 0.26	…	5.3 - 3.9	…
Same with molded EPS (beads) filled cores		…	…	0.21	…	4.8	…
Same with UF foam filled cores		…	…	0.22	…	4.5	…
Same with molded EPS inserts in cores		…	…	0.29	…	3.5	…
12 in., 32 - 36 lb, 80 - 90 lb/ft³ concrete, 2 or 3 cores.		…	…	0.38 - 0.44	…	2.6 - 2.3	…
Same with perlite filled cores		…	…	0.11 - 0.16	…	9.2 - 6.3	…
Same with vermiculite filled cores		…	…	0.17	…	5.8	…
Stone, lime, or sand		180	72	…	0.01	…	…
Quartzitic and sandstone		160	43	…	0.02	…	…
		140	24	…	0.04	…	…
		120	13	…	0.08	…	0.19
Calcitic, dolomitic, limestone, marble, and granite		180	30	…	0.03	…	…
		160	22	…	0.05	…	…
		140	16	…	0.06	…	…
		120	11	…	0.09	…	0.19
		100	8	…	0.13	…	…
Gypsum partition tile							
3 by 12 by 30 in., solid		…	…	0.79	…	1.26	0.19

Table 5-9. *(Continued)* **Typical Thermal Properties of Common Building and Insulating Materials[a]**

Description	Density	Conductivity[c] (k)	Conductance (C)	Resistance[b] (R) Per Inch Thickness (1/k)	Resistance[b] (R) For Thickness Listed (1/C)	Specific Heat
	lb/ft³	Btu-in./hr-ft²-°F	Btu/hr-ft²-°F	°F-ft²-hr/Btu-in.	°F-ft²-hr/Btu	Btu/lb-°F
3 by 12 by 30 in., 4 cells	...	...	0.74	...	1.35	...
4 by 12 by 30 in., 3 cells	...	...	0.60	...	1.67	...
Concretes[j]						
Sand and gravel or stone aggregate concretes (concretes with more than 50% quartz or quartzite sand have conductivities in the higher end of the range)	150	10.0 - 20.0	...	0.10 - 0.05	...	
	140	9.0 - 18.0	...	0.11 - 0.06	...	0.19 - 0.20
	130	7.0 - 13.0	...	0.14 - 0.08	...	...
Limestone concretes	140	11.1	...	0.09	...	...
	120	7.9	...	0.13	...	...
	100	5.5	...	0.18	...	...
Gypsum - fiber concrete (87.5% gypsum, 12.5% wood chips)	51	1.66	...	0.60	...	0.21
Cement/lime, mortar, and stucco	120	9.7	...	0.10	...	...
	80	4.5	...	0.22	...	...
Lightweight aggregate concretes			...		...	...
	120	6.4 - 9.1	...	0.16 - 0.11	...	...
Expanded shale, clay, or slate; expanded slags; cinders; pumice (with density up to 100 lb/ft³); and scoria (sanded concretes have conductivities in the higher end of the range)	100	4.7 - 6.2	...	0.21 - 0.16	...	0.20
	80	3.3 - 4.1	...	0.30 - 0.24	...	0.20
	60	2.1 - 2.5	...	0.48 - 0.40	...	...
	40	1.3	...	0.78	...	...
Perlite, vermiculite, and polystyrene beads	50	1.8 - 1.9	...	0.55 - 0.53	...	...
	40	1.4 - 1.5	...	0.71 - 0.67	...	0.15 - 0.23
	30	1.1	...	0.91	...	...
	20	0.8	...	1.25	...	...
Foam concretes	120	5.4	...	0.19	...	...
	100	4.1	...	0.24	...	...
	80	3.0	...	0.33	...	...
	70	2.5	...	0.40	...	...
Foam concretes and cellular concretes	60	2.1	...	0.48	...	...
	40	1.4	...	0.71	...	...
	20	0.8	...	1.25	...	...
Siding Materials (on Flat Surface)						
Shingles						
Asbestos - cement	120	...	4.75	...	0.21	...
Wood, 16 in. 7.5 in. exposure	...	...	1.15	...	0.87	0.31
Wood, double, 16 in. 12 in. exposure	...	...	0.84	...	1.19	0.28
Wood, plus ins. backer board, 0.312 in	...	...	0.71	...	1.40	0.31
Siding						
Asbestos - cement, 0.25 in. lapped	...	...	4.76	...	0.21	0.24
Asphalt roll siding	...	...	6.50	...	0.15	0.35
Asphalt insulating siding (0.5 in bed.)	...	...	0.69	...	1.46	0.35
Hardboard siding, 0.4375 in.	...	...	1.49	...	0.67	0.28
Wood, drop, 1in. by 8 in.	...	...	1.27	...	0.79	0.28
Wood, bevel, 0.5 in. by 8 in., lapped	...	...	1.23	...	0.81	0.28
Wood, bevel, 0.75in. by 10 in., lapped	...	...	0.95	...	1.05	0.28
Wood, plywood, 0.375 in., lapped	...	...	1.69	...	0.59	0.29
Aluminum, steel, or vinyl[k,l] over sheathing	...	...		...		...
Hollow - backed	...	...	1.64	...	0.61	0.29
Insulating - board backed nominal 0.375 in.	...	...	0.55	...	1.82	0.32
Insulating - board backed nominal 0.375 in., foil backed	...	...	0.34	...	2.96	...
Architectural (soda - lime float) glass	158	6.9		...		...

Table 5-9. *(Continued)* **Typical Thermal Properties of Common Building and Insulating Materials[a]**

Description	Density	Conductivity[c] (k)	Conductance (C)	Resistance[b] (R) Per Inch Thickness (1/k)	Resistance[b] (R) For Thickness Listed (1/C)	Specific Heat
	lb/ft^3	Btu-in./hr-ft^2-°F	Btu/hr-ft^2-°F	°F-ft^2-hr/Btu-in.	°F-ft^2-hr/Btu	Btu/lb-°F
Woods (12% Moisture Content)[m]						
Hard woods						0.39
Oak	41.2 - 46.8	1.12 - 1.25		0.89 - 0.80		...
Birch	42.6 - 45.4	1.16 - 1.22		0.87 - 0.82		...
Maple	39.8 - 44.0	1.09 - 1.19		0.92 - 0.84		...
Ash	38.4 - 41.9	1.06 - 1.14		0.94 - 0.88		...
Softwoods						0.39[n]
Southern pine	35.6 - 41.2	1.00 - 1.12		1.00 - 0.89		...
Douglas fir - larch	33.5 - 36.3	0.95 - 1.01		1.06 - 0.99		...
Southern cypress	31.4 - 32.1	0.90 - 1.01		1.11 - 1.09		...
Hem - fir, spruce - pine - fir	24.5 - 31.4	0.74 - 0.90		1.35 - 1.11		...
West coast woods, cedars	21.7 - 31.4	0.68 - 0.90		1.48 - 1.11		...
California redwood	24.5 - 28.0	0.74 - 0.82		1.35 - 1.22		...

[a] Values are for a mean temperature of 75°F. Representative values for dry materials are intended as design (not specification) values for materials in normal use. Thermal values of insulating materials may differ from design values depending on their in-situ properties (e.g., density and moisture content, orientation, etc.) and variability experienced during manufacture. For properties of a particular product, use the value supplied by the manufacturer or by unbiased tests.

[b] Resistance values are the reciprocals of C before rounding off C to two decimal places.

[c] To obtain thermal conductivities in Btu/hr-ft-°F, divide the K-factor by 12 in./ft.

[d] Does not include paper backing and facing, it any. Where insulation forms a boundary (reflective or otherwise) of an airspace, see Tables 5-7 and 5-8 for the insulating value of an air space with the appropriate effective emittance and temperature conditions of the space.

[e] Conductivity varies with fiber diameter. Batt, blanket, and loose-fill mineral fiber insulations are manufactured to achieve specified R-values, the most common of which are listed in the table. Due to differences in manufacturing processes and materials, the product thicknesses, densities, and thermal conductivities vary over considerable ranges for a specified R-value.

[f] Insulating values of acoustical tile vary, depending on density of the board and on type, size, and depth of perforations.

[g] Values are for aged products with gas-impermeable facers on the two major surfaces. An aluminum foil facer of 0.001 inch thickness or greater is generally considered impermeable to gases.

[h] Cavity is framed with 0.75 inch wood furring strips. Caution should be used in applying this value for other framing materials. The reported value was derived from tests and applies to the reflective path only. The effect of studs or furring strips must be included in determining the overall performance of the wall.

[i] Values for fully grouted block may be approximated using values for concrete with a similar unit weight.

[j] Values for concrete block and concrete are at moisture contents representative of normal use.

[k] Values for metal or vinyl siding applied over flat surfaces vary widely, depending on amount of ventilation of airspace beneath the siding; whether airspace is reflective or nonreflective; and on thickness, type, and application of insulating backing used. Values are averages for use as design guides.

[l] Vinyl specific heat = 0.25 Btu/lb °F

[m] The conductivity values listed are for heat transfer across the grain. The thermal conductivity of wood varies linearly with the density, and the density ranges listed are those normally found for the wood species given. If the density of the wood species is not known, use the mean conductivity value. For extrapolation to other moisture contents, the following empirical equation may be used:

$$k = 0.1791 + \frac{(1.874 \times 10^{-2} + 5.753 \times 10^{-4}M)\rho}{1 + 0.01M}$$

where ρ is density of the moist wood in lb/ft^3. and M is the moisture content in percent.

[n] From Wilkes (1979), an empirical equation for the specific heat of moist wood at 75°F is as follows:

$$c_p = \frac{(0.299 + 0.01M)}{(1 + 0.01M)} + \Delta c_p \quad \text{where } \Delta c_p \text{ accounts for the heat of absorption and is denoted by}$$

$$\Delta c_p = M(1.921 \times 10^{-3} - 3.168 \times 10^{-5}M) \quad \text{where } M \text{ is the moisture content in percent by mass.}$$

Table 5-10. Overall Coefficients of Heat Transmission of Various Fenestrations

Product Type		Glass Only		Vertical Installations									
Frame Type				Operable (including Sliding and Swinging Glass Doors)					Fixed				
Glazing	Glazing Type	Center of Glass	Edge of Glass	Aluminum without Thermal Break	Aluminum with Thermal Break	Reinforced Vinyl/Aluminum Clad Wood	Wood/Vinyl	Insulated Fiberglass/Vinyl	Aluminum without Thermal Break	Aluminum with Thermal Break	Reinforced Vinyl/Aluminum Clad Wood	Wood/Vinyl	Insulated Fiberglass/Vinyl
	Single Glazing												
Single Glazing	⅛ in. glass	1.04	1.04	1.27	1.08	0.90	0.89	0.81	1.13	1.07	0.98	0.98	0.94
	¼ in. acrylic/polycarbonate	0.88	0.88	1.14	0.96	0.79	0.78	0.71	0.99	0.92	0.84	0.84	0.81
	⅛ in. acrylic/polycarbonate	0.96	0.96	1.21	1.02	0.85	0.83	0.76	1.06	1.00	0.91	0.91	0.87
	Double Glazing												
Double Glazing	¼ in. air space	0.55	0.64	0.87	0.65	0.57	0.55	0.49	0.69	0.63	0.56	0.56	0.53
	½ in. air space	0.48	0.59	0.81	0.60	0.53	0.51	0.44	0.64	0.57	0.50	0.50	0.48
	¼ in. argon space	0.51	0.61	0.84	0.62	0.55	0.53	0.46	0.66	0.59	0.53	0.52	0.50
	½ in. argon space	0.45	0.57	0.79	0.58	0.51	0.49	0.43	0.61	0.54	0.48	0.48	0.45
	Double Glazing, $e = 0.60$ on surface 2 or 3												
	¼ in. air space	0.52	0.62	0.84	0.63	0.55	0.53	0.47	0.67	0.60	0.54	0.53	0.51
	½ in. air space	0.44	0.56	0.78	0.57	0.50	0.48	0.42	0.60	0.53	0.47	0.47	0.45
	¼ in. argon space	0.47	0.58	0.81	0.59	0.52	0.50	0.44	0.63	0.56	0.50	0.49	0.47
	½ in. argon space	0.41	0.54	0.76	0.55	0.48	0.46	0.40	0.58	0.51	0.45	0.44	0.42
	Double Glazing, $e = 0.40$ on surface 2 or 3												
	¼ in. air space	0.49	0.60	0.82	0.61	0.53	0.51	0.45	0.64	0.58	0.51	0.51	0.49
	½ in. air space	0.40	0.54	0.75	0.54	0.48	0.45	0.40	0.57	0.50	0.44	0.44	0.41
	¼ in. argon space	0.43	0.56	0.78	0.57	0.50	0.47	0.41	0.59	0.53	0.46	0.46	0.44
	½ in. argon space	0.36	0.51	0.72	0.52	0.45	0.43	0.37	0.53	0.47	0.41	0.40	0.38
	Double Glazing, $e = 0.20$ on surface 2 or 3												
	¼ in. air space	0.45	0.57	0.79	0.58	0.51	0.49	0.43	0.61	0.54	0.48	0.48	0.45
	½ in. air space	0.35	0.50	0.71	0.51	0.44	0.42	0.36	0.53	0.46	0.40	0.39	0.37
	¼ in. argon space	0.38	0.52	0.74	0.53	0.46	0.44	0.38	0.55	0.48	0.42	0.42	0.40
	½ in. argon space	0.30	0.46	0.67	0.47	0.41	0.39	0.33	0.48	0.41	0.36	0.35	0.33
	Double Glazing, $e = 0.10$ on surface 2 or 3												
	¼ in. air space	0.42	0.55	0.77	0.56	0.49	0.47	0.41	0.59	0.52	0.46	0.45	0.43
	½ in. air space	0.32	0.48	0.69	0.49	0.42	0.40	0.35	0.50	0.43	0.37	0.37	0.35
	¼ in. argon space	0.35	0.50	0.71	0.51	0.44	0.42	0.36	0.53	0.46	0.40	0.39	0.37
	½ in. argon space	0.27	0.44	0.65	0.45	0.39	0.37	0.31	0.46	0.39	0.33	0.33	0.31
	Double Glazing, $e = 0.05$ on surface 2 or 3												
	¼ in. air space	0.41	0.54	0.76	0.55	0.48	0.46	0.40	0.58	0.51	0.45	0.44	0.42
	½ in. air space	0.30	0.46	0.67	0.47	0.41	0.39	0.33	0.48	0.41	0.36	0.35	0.33
	¼ in. argon space	0.33	0.48	0.70	0.49	0.43	0.41	0.35	0.51	0.44	0.38	0.38	0.36
	½ in. argon space	0.25	0.42	0.63	0.44	0.38	0.36	0.30	0.44	0.37	0.32	0.31	0.29
	Triple Glazing												
Triple Glazing	¼ in. air spaces	0.38	0.52	0.72	0.51	0.44	0.43	0.38	0.55	0.48	0.42	0.41	0.40
	½ in. air spaces	0.31	0.47	0.67	0.46	0.40	0.39	0.34	0.49	0.42	0.36	0.35	0.34
	¼ in. argon spaces	0.34	0.49	0.69	0.48	0.42	0.41	0.35	0.51	0.45	0.39	0.38	0.36
	½ in. argon spaces	0.29	0.45	0.65	0.44	0.38	0.37	0.32	0.47	0.40	0.34	0.34	0.32
	Triple Glazing, $e = 0.20$ on surface 2, 3, 4 or 5												
	¼ in. air spaces	0.33	0.48	0.69	0.47	0.41	0.40	0.35	0.50	0.44	0.38	0.37	0.36
	½ in. air spaces	0.25	0.42	0.62	0.41	0.36	0.35	0.30	0.43	0.37	0.31	0.30	0.29
	¼ in. argon spaces	0.28	0.45	0.65	0.44	0.38	0.37	0.32	0.46	0.40	0.34	0.33	0.32
	½ in. argon spaces	0.22	0.40	0.60	0.39	0.34	0.33	0.28	0.41	0.34	0.29	0.28	0.27
	Triple Glazing, $e = 0.20$ on surfaces 2 or 3 and 4 or 5												
	¼ in. air spaces	0.29	0.45	0.65	0.44	0.38	0.37	0.32	0.47	0.40	0.34	0.34	0.32
	½ in. air spaces	0.20	0.39	0.58	0.38	0.32	0.31	0.27	0.39	0.33	0.27	0.26	0.25
	¼ in. argon spaces	0.23	0.41	0.61	0.40	0.34	0.33	0.29	0.42	0.35	0.30	0.29	0.28
	½ in. argon spaces	0.17	0.36	0.56	0.36	0.30	0.29	0.25	0.37	0.30	0.25	0.24	0.23

Table 5-10. *(Continued)* **Overall Coefficients of Heat Transmission of Various Fenestrations**

Product Type		Glass Only		Vertical Installations									
Frame Type				Operable (including Sliding and Swinging Glass Doors)					Fixed				
Glazing	Glazing Type	Center of Glass	Edge of Glass	Aluminum without Thermal Break	Aluminum with Thermal Break	Reinforced Vinyl/Aluminum Clad Wood	Wood/Vinyl	Insulated Fiberglass/Vinyl	Aluminum without Thermal Break	Aluminum with Thermal Break	Reinforced Vinyl/Aluminum Clad Wood	Wood/Vinyl	Insulated Fiberglass/Vinyl
Triple Glazing	**Triple Glazing, e = 0.10 on surfaces 2 or 3 and 4 or 5**												
	¼ in. air spaces	0.27	0.44	0.64	0.43	0.37	0.36	0.31	0.45	0.39	0.33	0.32	0.31
	½ in. air spaces	0.18	0.37	0.57	0.36	0.31	0.30	0.25	0.37	0.31	0.25	0.25	0.23
	¼ in. argon spaces	0.21	0.39	0.59	0.39	0.33	0.32	0.27	0.40	0.34	0.28	0.27	0.26
	½ in. argon spaces	0.14	0.34	0.54	0.33	0.28	0.27	0.23	0.34	0.28	0.22	0.21	0.20
Quadruple Glazing	**Quadruple Glazing, e = 0.10 on surfaces 2 or 3 and 4 or 5**												
	¼ in. air spaces	0.22	0.40	0.60	0.39	0.34	0.33	0.28	0.41	0.34	0.29	0.28	0.27
	½ in. air spaces	0.15	0.35	0.54	0.34	0.29	0.28	0.24	0.35	0.28	0.23	0.22	0.21
	¼ in. argon spaces	0.17	0.36	0.56	0.36	0.30	0.29	0.25	0.37	0.30	0.25	0.24	0.23
	½ in. argon spaces	0.12	0.32	0.52	0.32	0.27	0.26	0.22	0.32	0.26	0.20	0.20	0.19
	¼ in. krypton spaces	0.12	0.32	0.52	0.32	0.27	0.26	0.22	0.32	0.26	0.20	0.20	0.19

1. All heat transmission coefficients in this table include film resistances and are based on winter conditions of 0°F outdoor air temperature and 70°F indoor air temperature, with 15 mph outdoor air velocity and zero solar flux. With the exception of single glazing, small changes in the indoor and outdoor temperatures will not significantly affect overall U - factors. The coefficients are for vertical positions except skylight and sloped glazing values, which are for 20° from horizontal with heat flow up.

2. Glazing layer surfaces are numbered from outdoor to the indoor. Double, triple and quadruple refer to the number of glazing panels. All data are based on ⅛ inch glass, unless otherwise noted. Thermal conductivities are: 0.53 Btu/hr-ft^2-°F for glass. and 0.11 Btu/hr-ft^2-°F for acrylic and polycarbonate.

3. Standard spacers are metal. Edge-of-glass effects assumed to extend over the 2 ½ in. band around perimeter of each glazing unit.

Table 5-11. Transmission Coefficients for Wood and Steel Doors

Nominal Door Thickness, in.	Description	No Storm Door	Wood Storm Door[a]	Metal Storm Door[b]
	Wood Doors[c],[d]			
1⅜	Panel door with ⁷⁄₁₆ in. panels[e]	0.57	0.33	0.37
1⅜	Hollow core flush door	0.47	0.30	0.32
1⅜	Solid core flush door	0.39	0.26	0.28
1¾	Panel door with ⁷⁄₁₆ in. panels	0.54	0.32	0.36
1¾	Hollow core flush door	0.46	0.29	0.32
1¾	Panel door with 1⅛ in. panels	0.39	0.26	0.28
1¾	Solid core flush door	0.40		0.26
2¼	Solid core flush door	0.27	0.20	0.21
	Steel Doors[d]			
1¾	Fiberglass or mineral wool core with steel stiffeners, no thermal break[f]	0.60		
1¾	Paper honeycomb core without thermal break	0.56		
1¾	Solid urethane foam core without thermal break	0.40		
1¾	Solid fire rated mineral fiberboard core without thermal break	0.38		
1¾	Polystyrene core without thermal break (18 gage commercial steel)	0.35		
1¾	Polyurethane core without thermal break (18 gage commercial steel)	0.29		
1¾	Polyurethane core without thermal break (24 gage residential steel)	0.29		
1¾	Polyurethane core with thermal break and wood perimeter (24 gage residential steel)	0.20		
1¾	Solid urethane foam core with thermal break[a]	0.20		

[a] Values for wood storm door are for approximately 50% area.
[b] Values for metal storm door are for any percent glass.
[c] Values are based on a nominal 32 in. by 80 in. door size with no glazing.
[d] Outside air conditions: 15 mph wind speed, 0°F air temperature; inside air conditions: natural convection, 70°F air temperature.
[e] 55% panel area.
[f] Hotbox data on a nominal 3 ft by 7 ft door size with no glazing.

Note: All U-factors for exterior doors in this table are for doors with no glazing, except for storm doors, which are in addition to the main exterior door. Any glazing area in exterior doors should be included with the appropriate glass type and analyzed as a window. Interpolation and moderate extrapolation are permitted for door thicknesses other than those specified.

Outdoor Air Load Components.—Outdoor air can be introduced to the conditioned spaces through windows, doors, HVAC equipment and other openings. Outdoor air load is a large portion of the total heating or cooling loads. The amount of outdoor air load is required for the proper sizing of HVAC equipment.

Basic Concepts and Terminologies.—*Ventilation:* Ventilation is the intentional introduction of outside air into a space. Ventilation can be forced ventilation or it can be in which the outside air is forced into a space by mechanical means such as a fan; window or natural ventilation, in which the outside air enters the space through window openings. In order to achieve natural ventilation, the space pressure must be less than the outside air pressure to allow the flow of air into the space. In natural ventilation, it is difficult to measure and control the air flow rate. In the case of the forced ventilation, the air flow can be controlled and measured.

Infiltration: Ventilation should not be confused with infiltration; infiltration is uncontrolled flow of outdoor air into a space through wall and window cracks, and other unintentional openings such as doors and entrances to the building.

Ex-filtration: Ex-filtration is the uncontrolled flow of indoor air to outside through wall and window cracks, and other unintentional openings such as doors and entrances to the building.

Air Handling Unit: Fig. 5-16 shows a schematic of a simple air handling unit. The air is returned from the conditioned space is called return air (RA), the part of the return air that is exhausted is called exhaust air (EA), the amount of outdoor air is added to the unexhausted return air is called outside air (OA). The outside air flow being introduced by an air handler to the conditioned space is also called outside air fraction (X_{oa}), which is the ratio of the outside air flow to the total supply air flow rate; it is also called percent of outside air when expressed as a percent. If the amount EA is larger than OA, the space should be kept below atmospheric pressure. If the amount of EA is less than the OA, the space should be pressurized. If the amount of EA is equal to OA the space should be kept at atmospheric pressure. Conventional air handlers usually provide 10-40% outside air. 100% outside air means no recirculation of the return air through the air handling unit and all return air is exhausted separately to outside by means of ceiling or wall mounted exhaust fans. An air handler that provides 100% outdoor air is called a make-up air unit.

Infiltration Air Flow Analysis: The infiltration airflow rate *cfm* can be calculated by two methods: air change method or crack method. The crack method is used to estimate the air leakage through windows, doors, and certain

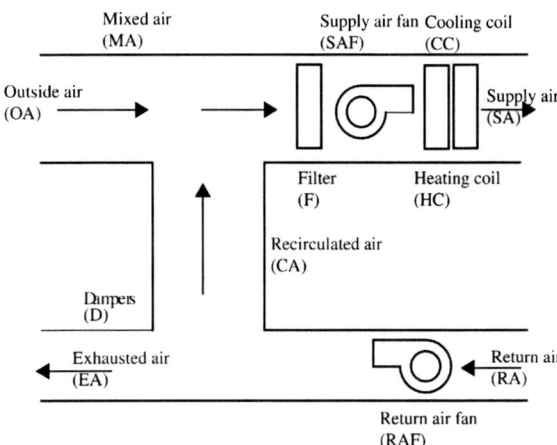

Fig 5-16. Simple all-air-handling unit with associated airflows

walls. The crack method is based on scientific principles and is more accurate if the leakage characteristics and the pressure differences can be accurately calculated. Otherwise, the air change method may be used. In this book the air change method and the crack method for the simple, single zone spaces will be discussed. For detailed discussion and analysis of the crack method, readers should refer to ASHRAE Standards.

Air Change Method: The infiltration rate can be calculated as

$$cfm = \frac{ACH \times V}{60} \qquad (22)$$

where *cfm* = infiltration rate in ft³/min;

V = gross space volume in ft³, and

ACH = air change per hour.

Air change per hour means the number times the volume of the space can be displaced by infiltration air flow in one hour. Table 5-12 provides values of ACH.

Table 5-12. Change Rates as a Function of Airtightness

Class	Outdoor Design Temperature, °F									
	50	40	30	20	10	0	−10	−20	−30	−40
Tight	0.41	0.43	0.45	0.47	0.49	0.51	0.53	0.55	0.57	0.59
Medium	0.69	0.73	0.77	0.81	0.85	0.89	0.93	0.97	1.00	1.05
Loose	1.11	1.15	1.20	1.23	1.27	1.30	1.35	1.40	1.43	1.47

Note: Values are for 15 mph wind and indoor temperature of 68°F.

Crack Method for Single Zone Space: A simple single zone approach for calculating air infiltration rates in residential houses requires an effective leakage area of 0.016. The data in Table 5-13 can be used to estimate the leakage area of a building. The total leakage area for a building is the sum of all individual components listed in Table 5-14.

Table 5-13. Local Shielding Class

Class	Description
1	No obstructions or local shielding
2	Light local shielding; few obstructions, few trees, or small shed
3	Moderate local shielding; some obstructions within two house heights, thick hedge, solid fence, or one neighboring house
4	Heavy shielding; obstructions around most of perimeter, buildings or trees within 30 ft in most directions; typical suburban shielding
5	Very heavy shielding; large obstructions surrounding perimeter within two house heights; typical downtown shielding

Table 5-14. Stack Coefficient C_s

	House Height (Stories)		
	One	Two	Three
Stack coefficient	0.0150	0.0299	0.0449

Table 5-15. Wind Coefficient C_w

	House Height (Stories)		
Shielding Class	One	Two	Three
1	0.0119	0.0157	0.0184
2	0.0092	0.0121	0.0143
3	0.0065	0.0086	0.0101
4	0.0039	0.0051	0.0060
5	0.0012	0.0016	0.0018

Using the effective leakage area, the infiltration air flow rate can be calculated as

$$cfm = A_l\sqrt{C_s\Delta T + C_w V^2} \qquad (23)$$

where *cfm* = air flow rate
A_l = effective leakage area, in.^{2}
C_S = stack coefficient, cfm^2/in$^{.4}$-°F
ΔT = average indoor-outdoor temp. difference, °F
V = average wind speed, mph

C_w = wind coefficient, cfm^2/in^4- mph^2.

The value of C_w depends on the local shielding class of the building. The different shielding classes are listed in Table 5-13. The values of C_s for one, two, and three story houses are given in Table 5-14. The values of C_w for one, two, and three story houses are given in Table 5-15. The Heights of the one, two, and three story buildings are 8, 16, and 24 feet, respectively.

Example 10: A double-sider, weather-stripped window is mounted in a masonry wall and is caulked. The window is 6 ft by 8 ft and is on the second story of an unshielded building. The design wind velocity is 15 mph; the inside temperature is 70°F while the outside temperature is 0°F. Estimate the cfm of infiltration air.

Solution: The leakage area method is used.

From Table 5-16 for a double-sider, weather-stripped window, the best estimate for infiltration area is 0.037 in^2/ft of crack length.

From Table 5-16, for the window frame leakage in the wall, the best estimate is 0.0 19 in^2/ft^2.

Infiltration
area = 0.031(6 + 6 + 6 + 8 + 8) + (0.019)(6 × 8) = 1.968 in^2

From Table 5-14, this window is classed as class 1 shielding. From Table 5-14, C_s = 0.0299 for a two-story window. For a two-story window with class 1 shielding, C_w = 0.0157, from Table 5-15. Substitution yields:

$$cfm = A_l\sqrt{C_s\Delta T + C_w V^2}$$
$$= 1.968\sqrt{(0.0299 \times 70) + (0.0157 \times 15^2)}$$
$$= 4.667 \ cfm$$

Table 5-16. Effective Leakage Area of Building Components (0.016 in. of Water Pressure Difference)

Components	Units (see note)	Best	Mini- mum	Maxi- mum	Components	Units (see note)	Best	Mini- mum	Maxi- mum
Ceiling					Piping/ plumbing/ wiring penetrations				
General	in^2/ ft^2	0.026	0.011	0.04	Uncaulked	in^2 ea	0.90	0.31	3.7
Drop	in^2/ ft^2	0.0027	0.00066	0.003	Caulked	in^2 ea	0.30	0.16	0.30
Ceiling penetrations					Vents				
Whole-house fans	in^2 ea	3.1	0.25	3.3	Bathroom with damper closed	in^2 ea	1.60	0.39	3.1
Recessed lights	in^2 ea	1.6	0.23	3.3	Bathroom with damper open	in^2 ea	3.1	0.95	3.4
Ceiling/Flue vent	in^2 ea	4.8	4.3	4.8	Dryer with damper	in^2 ea	0.46	0.45	1.1
Surface-mounted lights	in^2 ea	0.13			Dryer without damper	in^2 ea	2.3	1.9	5.3
Chimney	in^2 ea	4.5	3.3	5.6	Kitchen with damper open	in^2 ea	6.2	2.2	11
Crawl space					Kitchen with damper closed	in^2 ea	0.80	0.16	1.1
General (area for exposed wall)	in^2/ ft^2	0.144	0.1	0.24	Kitchen with tight gasket	in^2 ea	0.16		
8 in by 16 in vents	in^2 ea	20			Walls (exterior)				
Door frame					Cast-in-place concrete	in^2/ ft^2	0.007	0.0007	0.026
General	in^2 ea	1.9	0.37	3.9	Clay brick cavity wall, finished	in^2/ ft^2	0.0098	0.0007	0.033
Masonry, not caulked	in^2/ ft^2	0.07	0.024	0.07	Precast concrete panel	in^2/ ft^2	0.017	0.0004	0.024
Masonry, caulked	in^2/ ft^2	0.014	0.004	0.014	Lightweight concrete block, unfinished	in^2/ ft^2	0.05	0.019	0.058

Table 5-16. *(Continued)* **Effective Leakage Area of Building Components (0.016 in. of Water Pressure Difference)**

Components	Units (see note)	Best	Mini-mum	Maxi-mum	Components	Units (see note)	Best	Mini-mum	Maxi-mum
Wood, not caulked	in^2 / ft^2	0.024	0.009	0.024	Lightweight concrete block, painted or stucco	in^2 / ft^2	0.016	0.0075	0.016
Wood, caulked	in^2 / ft^2	0.004	0.001	0.004	Heavyweight concrete block, unfinished	in^2 / ft^2	0.0036		
Trim	in^2 / lftc	0.05			Continuous air infiltration barrier	in^2 / ft^2	0.0022	0.0008	0.003
Jamb	in^2 / lftc	0.4	0.3	0.5	Rigid sheathing	in^2 / ft^2	0.005	0.0042	0.006
Threshold	in^2 / lftc	0.1	0.06	1.1					
Doors					**Window framing**				
Attic/crawl space, not weatherstripped	in^2 ea	4.6	1.6	5.7	Masonry, uncaulked	in^2 / ft^2	0.094	0.082	0.148
Attic/crawl space, weatherstripped	in^2 ea	2.8	1.2	2.9	Masonry, caulked	in^2 / ft^2	0.019	0.016	0.03
Attic fold down, not weatherstripped	in^2 ea	6.8	3.6	13	Wood, uncaulked	in^2 / ft^2	0.025	0.022	0.039
Attic fold down, weatherstripped	in^2 ea	3.4	2.2	6.7	Wood, caulked	in^2 / ft^2	0.004	0.004	0.007
Attic fold down, with insulated box	in^2 ea	0.6			**Windows**				
Attic from unconditioned garage	in^2 ea	0	0	0	Awning, not weatherstripped	in^2 / ft^2	0.023	0.011	0.035
Double, not weatherstripped	in^2 / ft^2	0.16	0.10	0.32	Awning, weatherstripped	in^2 / ft^2	0.012	0.006	0.017
Double, weatherstripped	in^2 / ft^2	0.12	0.04	0.33	Casement, weatherstripped	in^2 / lftc	0.011	0.005	0.14
Elevator (passenger)	in^2 ea	0.04	0.022	0.054	Casement, not weatherstripped	in^2 / lftc	0.013		
General, average	in^2 / lftc	0.015	0.011	0.021	Double horizontal slider, not weatherstripped	in^2 / lftc	0.052	0.0009	0.16
Interior (pocket, on top floor)	in^2 ea	2.2			Double horizontal slider, wood, weatherstripped	in^2 / lftc	0.026	0.0070	0.081
Interior (stairs)	in^2 / lftc	0.04	0.012	0.070	Double horizontal slider, aluminum, weatherstripped	in^2 / lftc	0.034	0.027	0.038
Mail slot	in^2 / lftc	0.20			Double-hung, not weatherstripped	in^2 / lftc	0.12	0.040	0.29
Sliding exterior glass patio	in^2 ea	3.4	0.46	9.3	Double-hung, weatherstripped	in^2 / lftc	0.031	0.009	0.089
Sliding exterior glass patio	in^2 / ft^2	0.079	0.009	0.22	Double-hung with storm, not-weatherstripped	in^2 / lftc	0.046	0.040	0.080
Storm (difference between with and without)	in^2 ea	0.90	0.46	0.96	Double-hung with storm, weatherstripped	in^2 / lftc	0.037	0.021	0.050
Single, not weatherstripped	in^2 ea	3.3	1.9	8.2	Double-hung with pressurized track, weatherstripped	in^2 / lftc	0.023	0.018	0.026
Single, weatherstripped	in^2 ea	1.9	0.60	4.2	Jalousie	in^2 / louver	0.524		
Vestibule (subtract per each location)	in^2 ea	1.6			Lumped	in^2 / lfts	0.022	0.00042	0.097
Electrical outlets / Switches					Single horizontal slider, weatherstripped	in^2 / lfts	0.031	0.009	0.097
No gaskets	in^2 ea	0.38	0.08	0.96	Single horizontal slider, aluminum	in^2 / lfts	0.04	0.013	0.097
With gaskets	in^2 ea	0.023	0.012	0.54	Single horizontal slider, wood	in^2 / lfts	0.021	0.013	0.047
Furnace					Single horizontal slider, wood clad	in^2 / lfts	0.030	0.025	0.038
Sealed (or no) combustion	in^2 ea	0	0	0	Sill	in^2 / lftc	0.0099	0.0065	0.010
Retention head or stack damper	in^2 ea	4.6	3.1	4.6	Storm inside, heat shrink	in^2 / lfts	0.00085	0.00042	0.00085
Retention head and stack damper	in^2 ea	3.7	2.8	4.6	Storm inside, rigid sheet with magnetic seal	in^2 / lfts	0.0056	0.00085	0.011
Floors over crawl spaces					Storm inside, flexible sheet with mechanical seal	in^2 / lfts	0.0072	0.00085	0.039
General	in^2 / ft^2	0.032	0.006	0.071					
Without ductwork in crawl space	in^2 / ft^2	0.0285							
With ductwork in crawl space	in^2 / ft^2	0.0324							
Fireplace									
With damper closed	in^2 / ft^2	0.62	0.14	1.3					
With damper open	in^2 / ft^2	5.04	2.09	5.47					
With glass doors	in^2 / ft^2	0.58	0.06	0.58					
With insert and damper closed	in^2 / ft^2	0.52	0.37	0.66					
With insert and damper open	in^2 / ft^2	0.94	0.58	1.3					
Gas water heater	in^2 ea	3.1	2.3	3.9					

Table 5-16. *(Continued)* **Effective Leakage Area of Building Components (0.016 in. of Water Pressure Difference)**

Components	Units (see note)	Best	Mini-mum	Maxi-mum	Components	Units (see note)	Best	Mini-mum	Maxi-mum
Joints					Storm inside, rigid sheet with mechanical seal	in^2 / lfts	0.019	0.0021	0.039
Ceiling-wall	in^2 / lftc	0.070	0.0075	0.12					
Sole plate, floor/wall, uncaulked	in^2 / lftc	0.20	0.018	0.26	Storm outside, pressurized track	in^2 / lfts	0.025		
Sole plate, floor/wall, caulked	in^2 / lftc	0.04	0.0035	0.056	Storm outside, 2-track	in^2 / lfts	0.058		
Top plate, band joist	in^2 / lftc	0.005	0.0035	0.018	Storm outside, 3-track	in^2 / lfts	0.116		

Note: Air leakage areas are based on values found in the literature. The effective air leakage area (in square inches) is based on a pressure difference of 0.016 inch of water and $C_D = 1$.

Abbreviations: ft^2 = gross area in square feet area, lftc = linear foot of crack, lfts = linear foot of sash, ea = each

Outdoor Air Load Calculations: The outdoor air load is a large portion of the total conditioned space load. The total condition space load could be heating, cooling, humidification, and dehumidification loads. The rate of sensible energy consumption for heating and cooling is given by

$$\dot{q}_s = cfm\rho c_p \Delta T \qquad (24)$$

where $\dot{q}_s$ = sensible heat load

   cfm = air flow rate

   c_p = specific heat of air

   ρ = air density

   ΔT = indoor-outdoor temperature difference

The above equation can be simplified to a more convenient form as

$$\dot{q}_s = 1.10 cfm \Delta T \qquad (25)$$

where $\dot{q}_s$ = sensible heat load

   cfm = air flow rate in cfm

   ΔT = indoor-outdoor temperature difference °F

The rate of latent energy consumption for humidification and dehumidification load is given by

$$\dot{q}_l = cfm\rho h_{fg} \Delta W \qquad (26)$$

where $\dot{q}_l$ = latent heat load

   h_{fg} = latent heat of water

   ΔW = indoor-outdoor humidity ratio difference of air

The above equation can be simplified in more convenient form as

$$\dot{q}_l = 4840 cfm \Delta W \qquad (27)$$

where $\dot{q}_l$ = latent heat load

   cfm = airflow rate in cfm

ΔW = Indoor-outdoor humidity ratio difference of air

Example 11: A building is 18 ft wide by 40 ft long and 20 ft high. The indoor conditions are 75°F and 50% ϕ, and outside conditions are 0°F and saturated. The infiltration rate is estimated to be 0.75 *ach*. Calculate the sensible and latent heat loss.

Solution: The volume of the room

$$\text{Volume} = 18 \times 40 \times 20$$
$$= 14400 \text{ ft}^3$$

The cfm

$$cfm = \frac{\text{Volume} \times n}{60}$$
$$= \frac{14400 \times 0.75}{60}$$
$$= 180$$

From the psychrometric chart (See Fig 2-5.)

$$W_i = 0.00926$$
$$W_o = 0.0009$$

The sensible heat is:

$$\dot{q}_s = 1.10 \times cfm \times \Delta T$$
$$= 1.10 \times 180 \times (75 - 0)$$
$$= 14850 \text{ Btu/hr}$$

The latent heat is:

$$\dot{q}_l = 4840 \times cfm \times \Delta W$$
$$= 4840 \times 180 \times (0.00926 - 0.0009)$$
$$= 7283 \text{ Btu/hr}$$

Example 12: A 4 ft by 4 ft ventilation opening is in a wall facing in the prevalent wind direction. There are adequate openings in the roof for the passage of exhaust air. Estimate the ventilation rate for a 25-mph wind.

Solution: The ventilation rate

$$cfm = 88 \times 0.55 \times A \times V$$
$$= 88 \times 0.55 \times 16 \times 25$$
$$= 19360$$

Basic Components of Heating and Cooling Loads: The basic components of the heating and cooling loads are shown in Fig. 5-17. The procedure for the heating and cooling load calculations will be discussed in Chapters 6 and 7.

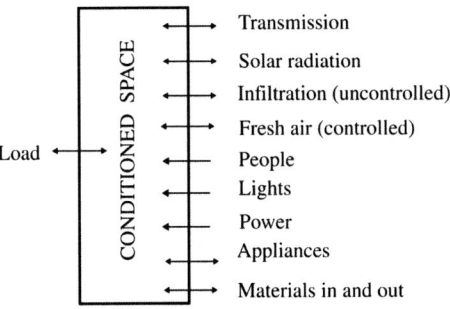

Fig 5-17. Components of heating and cooling loads

Example 13: A small factory with a 12 ft high ceiling is shown in the following sketch. There are 15 employees normally in the shop area, 10 customers, and 2 employees in the office area. On a winter day when the outside temperature is 0°F, the office is maintained at 75°F, 25% φ, and the shop is kept at 70°F with no humidity control. Determine for each area: (a) the infiltration, cfm

(b) minimum required outside air, cfm

(c) sensible heat loss due to infiltration, Btu/h

(d) latent heat loss due to infiltration, Btu/h

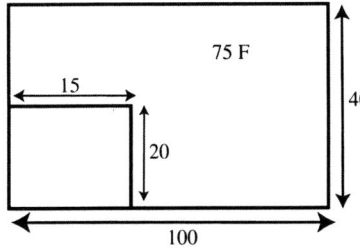

Solution: (a) Office area:

$$volume = 20 \times 15 \times 12$$
$$= 3600 \text{ ft}^3$$

Assume 2 *ach* due to heavy traffic.

$$cfm = \frac{volume \times ach}{60}$$
$$= \frac{3600 \times 2}{60}$$
$$= 120$$

Auto repairs area

$$volume = 40 \times 100 \times 12 - 3600$$
$$= 44400 \text{ ft}^3$$

Assume 3 *ach* due to heavy traffic.

$$cfm = \frac{volume \times ach}{60}$$
$$= \frac{44400 \times 3}{60}$$
$$= 2220$$

(b) Minimum outside air for office = $20 \times 2 = 40$ *cfm*. Minimum outside air for auto repair shop = $1.5 \times (4000-300) = 5550$ *cfm*.

(c) The sensible heat loss for office:

$$\dot{q}_s = 1.10 \times cfm \times \Delta T$$
$$= 1.10 \times 40 \times (75 - 15)$$
$$= 2640 \text{ Btu/hr}$$

The sensible heat loss for the shop

$$\dot{q}_s = 1.10 \times cfm \times \Delta T$$
$$= 1.10 \times 5550 \times (75 - 15)$$
$$= 335775 \text{ Btu/hr}$$

(d) The latent heat loss in the office

$$\dot{q}_l = 4840 \times cfm \times \Delta W$$
$$= 4840 \times 40 \times (0.0046 - 0.0008)$$
$$= 735 \text{ Btu/hr}$$

The latent heat for the shop is zero, because no humidity control is required.

HEATING LOAD CALCULATION

HEATING LOAD CALCULATIONS

Introduction

Heating load must be calculated for peak building heating demand. For example, let's assume that the coldest days (peak heating demand) and hours during the heating season are five consecutive days in the month of January from 5:00 AM to 9:00 AM. In this case, the heating boiler or the HVAC unit must be sized to handle the heating load on these coldest days even though during the other months and days the heating load is much lower. It should be noted also during the coldest days and hours the following assumptions are very accurate:

1) The variation in outdoor temperature is very minimal and is nearly constant.
2) Solar heat gain is not a big factor, so it can be ignored.
3) Heat gain from internal sources can reasonably be ignored.
4) Heat storage of the building structure can be ignored.

With the above reasonable assumptions we can conclude that the heat transfer process for the heating load calculations is steady state. Of course it should be noted that for the annual energy consumption analysis of the building, the variation in outdoor temperature, solar heat gain, heat storage of the structure, and heat gain from internal sources such as lights, people, and appliances cannot be ignored and must be included in the analysis. In this case, the heat transfer process is instantaneous and the transfer function method described in the 2001 ASHRAE Fundamental Handbook should be used for the analysis.

In this book we present the procedure for carrying out residential heating load calculations; for commercial and other institutional facilities, the 2001 ASHRAE Fundamentals Handbook should be consulted. The summary of the Residential heating load calculations is given in Table 6-1.

Table 6-1. Summary of Loads, Equations and References for Calculating Design Heating Loads in Residential and Light Commercial Buildings

Heating Load	Equation	Reference, Table, Description
Roofs, ceilings, walls, glass	$\dot{q} = UA\Delta T$	U: Chapter 5, Tables 5-4a to 5-4k, and 5-9 (Btu/hr-ft²-°F) ΔT: Temperature difference between inside and outside design dry bulbs. For temperatures in unheated spaces, see Equation (2); for attic temperatures, see Equation (3), Chapter 5 Equation (21) (°F) A: Area calculated from plans (ft²) $\dot{q}$: Heat loss (Btu/hr)
Walls below grade	$\dot{q} = UA\Delta T$	U: See Table 6-2 (Btu/hr-ft²-°F) ΔT: $T_i - T_f$ $\dot{q}$: Heat loss (Btu/hr) T_f: $T_{ave} - A$, Use Fig. 6-3 for A and Fig. 6-4 for T_{ave}
Floors:		
Above grade	$\dot{q} = UA\Delta T$	U: Chapter 5, Tables 5-4a to 5-4k, and 5-9 (Btu/hr-ft²-°F) ΔT: $T_i - T_f$ (°F) A: Area calculated from plans (ft²) $\dot{q}$: Heat loss (Btu/hr)
On grade	$\dot{q} = F_2 P\Delta T$	ΔT: Indoor outdoor temperature differences (°F) F_2: See Table 6-5 (Btu/hr-ft-°F) P: Floor slab perimeter
Below grade	$\dot{q} = UA\Delta T$	P: Perimeter of slab ΔT: $T_i - T_f$ (°F) $T_f = T_{ave} - A$ U: See Table 6-3
Infiltration and ventilation air:		
Sensible	$\dot{q}_s = 0.018 Q\Delta T$	Q: Volume rate of outdoor air entering building (ft³/hr) ΔT: Indoor outdoor temperature differences (°F)
Latent	$\dot{q}_l = 80.7 Q\Delta W$	ΔW: Indoor outdoor humidity ratio difference (lb$_v$/lb$_a$) ΔT: Indoor outdoor temperature differences (°F)

Note: SI equations for infiltration and ventilation air are $q_s = 1.20 Q\Delta T$ and $q_l = 3.0 Q\Delta W$ where q is in watts, Q is in (l/s) and W is in (g/kg).

Heat loss Through Walls, Roofs, Glass Area of the windows, and Ceilings.—In this case Equation (1) below can be used as stated in Table 6-1 to calculate the heat loss from walls, roofs, glass area of windows, and the ceilings.

$$\dot{q} = UA\Delta T = UA(T_i - T_o) \qquad (1)$$

where $\dot{q}$ = heat transfer, Btu/hr

U = overall heat transfer coefficient or the U factor, Btu/hr- ft²-°F

A = area, ft²

ΔT = indoor-outdoor temperature difference °F

The design indoor-outdoor temperature for different locations is given in tables in Chapter 19. The U values or surface conductance of different materials are given in Table 5-9. In the case of heat loss through unheated spaces such as attics, Equation (1) can be written as

$$\dot{q} = UA(T_i - T_a) \qquad (2)$$

where T_a = temperature °F of the unheated space and can be calculated from Equation (21) in Chapter 5, assuming no ventilation heat loss. If ventilation heat loss is included, T_a can be calculated by using ASHRAE Fundamental Handbook.

Example 1: A house has a pitched roof shown in figure below.

$U_{roof} = 0.60$

$U_{ceiling} = 0.169$

The attic is unvented during the winter if the outside temperature is 0°F and inside temperature is 75°F. Determine the heat loss through the ceiling.

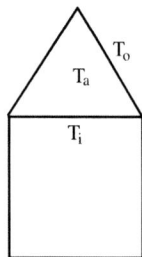

Solution: Given

$$A_{ceiling} = 800 \text{ ft}^2$$

$$A_{roof} = 932 \text{ ft}^2$$

$$U_{ceiling} = 0.169$$

$$U_{roof} = 0.60$$

To find T_a:

$$U_{roof} \times A_{roof} \times (T_a - T_o) = U_{clg} \times A_{clg} \times (T_i - T_o)$$

$$0.60 \times 932 \times (T_a - 0) = 0.169 \times 800 \times (75 - T_a)$$

$$T_a = \frac{0.169 \times 800 \times 75}{0.60 \times 932 + 0.169 \times 800}$$

$$= 14.00°F$$

The heat loss through the ceiling is:

$$\dot{q} = UA\Delta T$$

$$= 0.169 \times 800 \times (75 - 14)$$

$$= 8247 \text{ Btu/hr}$$

Heat Loss from Walls below Grade.—The heat flow (heat loss) from the portion of the walls below grade is two-dimensional and cannot be estimated with one dimensional heat conduction analysis. It can be categorized in parts as follows:

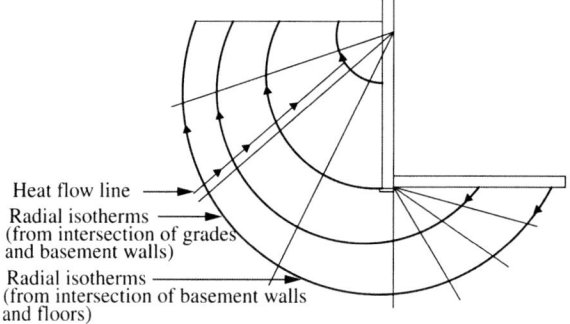

Heat flow line
Radial isotherms (from intersection of grades and basement walls)
Radial isotherms (from intersection of basement walls and floors)

Fig 6-1. Heat flow from basement

1) Below grade walls with no insulation and with un-insulated floor such as the basement wall and the floor as shown in Fig. 6-1. From Fig. 6-1 is obvious that the isotherm lines are radial, and also the heat flow at the basement floor is concentrated at the perimeter of the basement floor.

2) Completely insulated wall and floor. In this case the isotherm lines will be horizontal parallel to the grade line; and the heat flow line will be vertical.

3) Partially insulated below grade walls are as shown in Fig. 6-2. The isotherm lines is between radial and horizontal; heat flow lines in this case are diagonal, and are almost evenly spread over the wall below the insulation portion.

For any of the above cases, the heat loss from walls below grade can be calculated from the following equation

$$\dot{q} = UA(T_i - T_f) \qquad (3)$$

where T_i = temperature in °F of the unheated space and can be calculated from Equation (21) in Chapter 5 assuming no ventilation heat loss. If ventilation heat loss is included, T_i can be calculated from the ASHRAE Fundamental Handbook.

$T_f = T_{ave} - A$ °F, T_{ave} is the mean winter air temperature shown in Table 6-4 for various United States cities; and A°F is the ground temperature which can be found from Fig. 6-3.

U = heat loss coefficient from basement walls and floor that can be obtained from Tables 6-2 and 6-3.

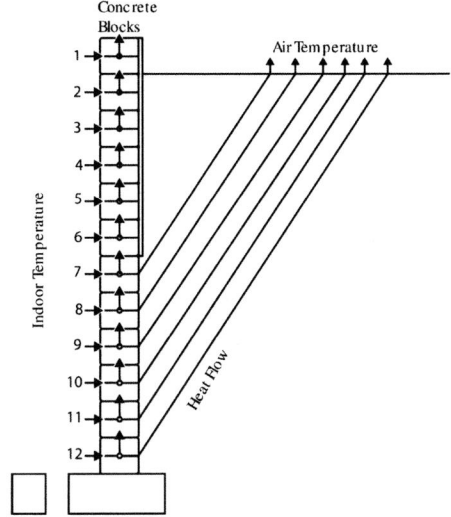

Fig 6-2. Heat flow path for partially insulated basement wall

Table 6-2. Below Grade Wall U-Factors, Btu/h-ft²-°F

Depth ft	Path Length Through Soil, ft	Heat Loss Coefficient, Btu/hr-ft²-°F[a]							
		Uninsulated	Σ[b]	R-4.17	Σ[b]	R-8.34	Σ[b]	R-12.5	Σ[b]
0 to 1	0.68	0.410	Σ[b]	0.152	Σ[b]	0.093	Σ[b]	0.067	Σ[b]
1 to 2	2.27	0.222	0.632	0.116	0.268	0.079	0.172	0.059	0.126
2 to 3	3.88	0.155	0.787	0.094	0.362	0.068	0.240	0.053	0.179
3 to 4	5.52	0.119	0.906	0.079	0.441	0.060	0.300	0.048	0.227
4 to 5	7.05	0.096	1.002	0.069	0.510	0.053	0.353	0.044	0.271
5 to 6	8.65	0.079	1.081	0.060	0.570	0.048	0.401	0.040	0.311
6 to 7	10.28	0.069	1.150	0.054	0.624	0.044	0.445	0.037	0.348

[a] Soil conductivity was assumed to be 9.6 Btu/hr-ft²-°F
[b] Σ = heat loss to current depth.

Note: The second column under each level of insulation is a summation of the first column and second column figures above it.

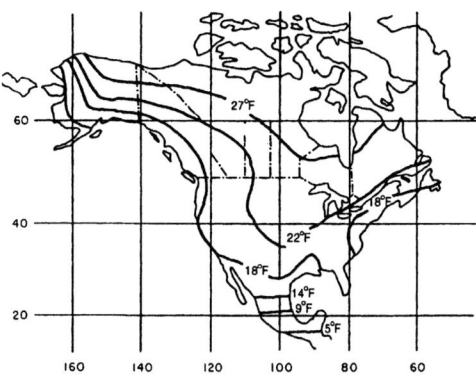

Fig 6-3. Lines of constant amplitude of ground temperature

Heat Loss from Basement Floor Below Grade.—
Heatloss from basement floor below grade can be calculated by the following equation:

$$\dot{q} = UA\Delta T = UA(T_i - T_f)$$

where $\Delta T = T_i - T_f$ same as for the case for wall below grade described above.

U = overall heat loss coefficient shown on Table 6-3.

Table 6-3. Below-Grade Through Basement Floor, U Factors Btu/hr-ft²-°F

Depth of foundation wall below grade, ft	Heat loss coefficient, Btu/hr-ft²-°F			
	Shortest width of house, ft			
	20	24	28	32
5	0.032	0.029	0.026	0.023
6	0.030	0.027	0.025	0.022
7	0.029	0.026	0.023	0.021

Table 6-4. Average Winter Air Temperatures for Selected Cities in the United States

State and City	Average Winter Temperature	
	°F	°C
Arkansas, Little Rock	50.5	10.6
Colorado, Denver	37.6	3.44
District of Columbia, Washington	45.7	7.94
Illinois, Chicago	35.8	2.44
Kentucky, Louisville	44.0	6.70
Maine, Portland	33.0	0.60
Michigan, Alpena	29.7	−1.3
Minnesota, Duluth	23.4	−4.8
Montana, Glasgow	26.4	−3.1
New York, Syracuse	35.2	1.8
North Dakota, Monot	22.4	−5.3
Oklahoma, Oklahoma City	48.3	9.39

Table 6-5. Heat Loss Coefficients F_2 for Slab Floors (Btu/hr-ft-°F)

Construction	Insulation	Degree-Days (65°F)		
		2950	5350	7433
8 in. block wall, brick facing	Uninsulated	0.62	0.68	0.72
	R-5.4 from edge to footer	0.48	0.50	0.56
4 in. block wall, brick facing	Uninsulated	0.80	0.84	0.93
	R-5.4 from edge to footer	0.47	0.49	0.54
Metal stud wall, stucco	Uninsulated	1.15	1.20	1.34
	R-5.4 from edge to footer	0.51	0.53	0.58
Poured concrete wall with duct near perimeter	Uninsulated	1.84	2.12	2.73
	R-5.4 from edge to footer 3 ft under floor	0.64	0.72	0.90

Heat Loss from Floor Slab On Grade.—The heat loss from floor slab on grade can be calculated from the following equation:

$$\dot{q} = F_2 \times P \times \Delta T$$

where F_2 = heat loss coefficient, shown in Table 6-5 Btu/h-°F;

P = perimeter of exposed edge of floor ft;

ΔT = temperature difference in outside and inside in °F.

The concrete slabs are categorized in two parts as follows:

1) Heated floor slab by heating pipes or warm air ducts, see Fig. 6-4.

2) Unheated floor slab, see Figs. 6-5, 6-6, and 6-7.

Example 2: Determine the heat loss for a semi attached basement in New York City which is 40 feet in length, 16 feet width, and 8 feet height of standard concrete construction of which 4 feet is below the grade. Calculate the heat loss.

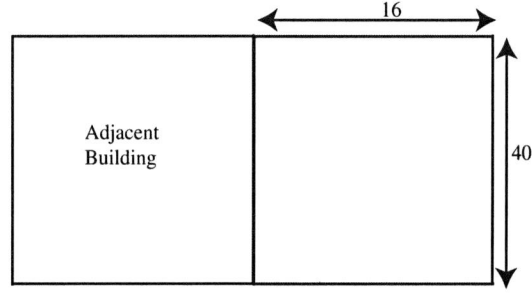

Solution: Given

$$U_{\text{wall}} = 0.171$$

The wall below grade:

$$\Delta T = T_i - T_f$$
$$= 70 - (35.5 - 18)$$
$$= 52.5°F$$

The unheated perimeter P is

$$P = 16 + 40 + 16$$
$$= 72 \text{ ft}$$

	U Table 6-2	A	$\dot{q} = UA\Delta T$
1st floor	0.41	72	1549.8
2nd floor	0.222	72	839.16
3rd floor	0.155	72	585.90
4th floor	0.119	72	449.82
Total heat loss below grade			3424.68

The heat loss through the wall above grade

$$P = 72 \text{ ft}$$
$$A = 72 \times 4 = 288 \text{ ft}^2$$
$$\Delta T = 70 - 0 = 70$$
$$\dot{q} = UA\Delta T$$
$$= 0.171 \times 288 \times (70 - 0)$$
$$= 3447.26 \text{ Btu/hr}$$

Basement floor below grade:

$$\Delta T = T_i - T_f$$
$$= 70 - (35.5 - 18)$$
$$= 52.5°F$$
$$U = 0.032$$
$$A = 40 \times 16 = 640 \text{ ft}^2$$
$$\dot{q} = UA\Delta T$$
$$= 0.032 \times 640 \times 52.5$$
$$= 1075.2 \text{ Btu/hr}$$

Total heat loss below grade	3424.68
Total heat loss above grade	3447.36
Total heat loss on floor	1075.2
Total heat loss	7947.24

Example 3: Determine the heat loss from the floor slab on grade with the 30' by 20' dimensions. Assuming 8' block wall brick facing, uninsulated.

Solution:
$$\dot{q} = F_2 P(T_i - T_o)$$

$$T_i - T_o = 70 - 0 = 70° \text{ F}$$

$$P = 2(30 + 20) = 100 \text{ ft}$$

$$F_2 = 0.62 \text{ Btu/hr-ft-F from Table 5}$$

$$\dot{q} = F_2 P (T_i - T_o)$$

$$= 0.62 \times 100 \times 70$$

$$= 4340 \text{ Btu/hr}$$

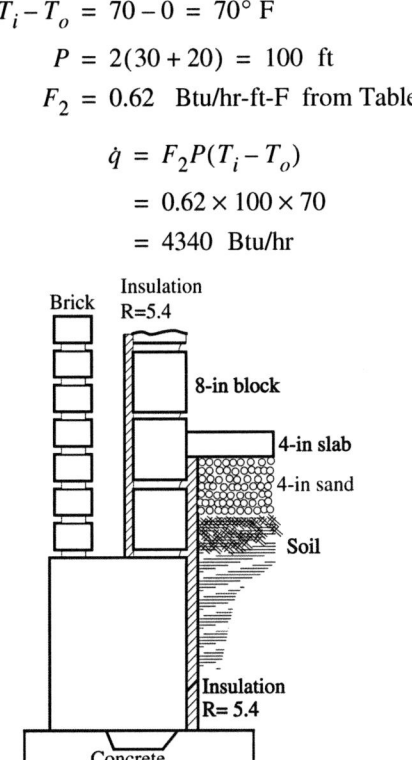

Fig 6-4. Concrete wall slab on grade foundation insulation

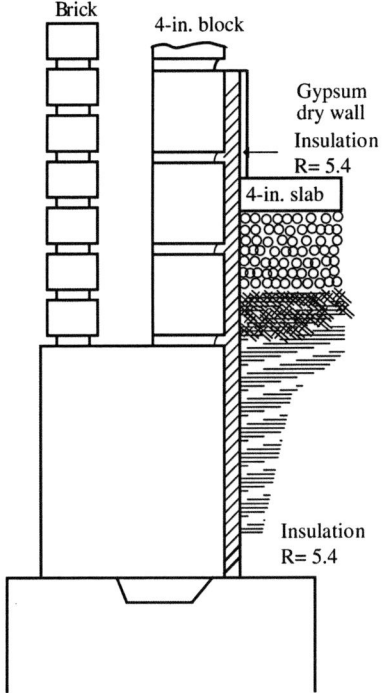

Fig 6-5. 8-inch block wall slab on grade foundation insulation

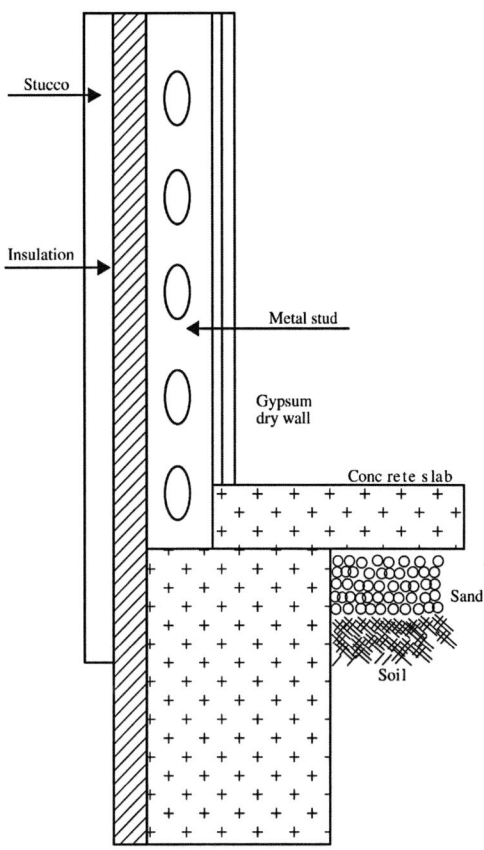

Fig 6-6. 4-inch block wall slab on grade foundation insulation

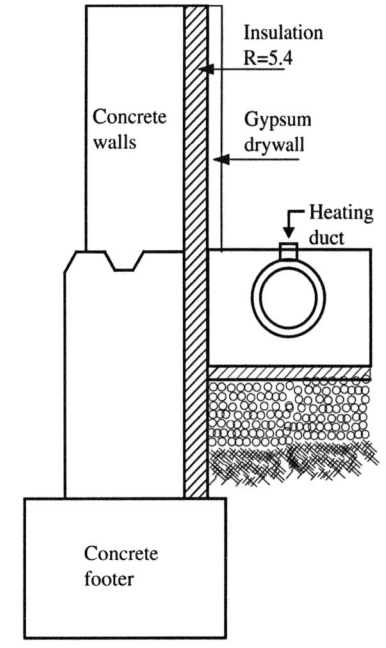

Fig 6-7. Metal stud wall slab on grade foundation insulation

In both heated and unheated floor slabs, the majority of the heat loss is from the perimeter of the floor slab. It is recommended that the perimeter of the floor slab be insulated for energy conservation.

Ventilation and Infiltration Heat Loss.—Once the air flow rate in cfm is computed by the air change method discussed in Chapter 5. The sensible and latent ventilation heat loss can be calculated by the following equations.

$$\dot{q}_s = 1.10 cfm\Delta T \tag{4}$$

where $\dot{q}_s$ = sensible heat load (Btu/hr);
  cfm = air flow rate cfm; and
  ΔT = indoor outdoor temperature difference (°F)

$$\dot{q}_l = 4840 cfm\Delta W \tag{5}$$

where $\dot{q}_l$ = latent load (Btu/hr);
  cfm = air flow rate cfm; and
  ΔW = Indoor outdoor humidity ratio difference of air (lb_v/lb_a)

Example 4: Calculate the heat loss of a room that is 17 ft in length, 13 ft width, and 8 ft height as shown in figure below.

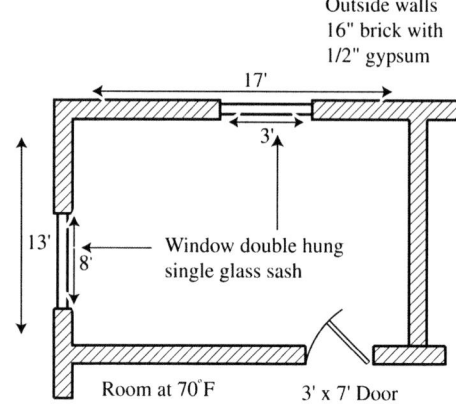

Outside walls
16" brick with
1/2" gypsum

17'

3'

13'

8'

Window double hung
single glass sash

Room at 70°F

3' x 7' Door

Solution: Given

$$U_{wall} = 0.25$$

$$U_{glass} = 0.89$$

$$U_{ceiling} = 0.15$$

Item	Dimension	U	ΔT	Heat Loss (Btu/hr)
Wall	17×10+13×10−(8×6)−(3×6) =234 ft²	0.25	70	4095
Glass	(8×6)+(3×6)=66 ft²	0.89	70	4112
Ceiling	17×13=221 ft²	0.15	70	2320
Infiltration	Volume=17×13×10=2210 ft³ Assume *ach* =1, *cfm*=2210×1/60=36.83		70	2836
Total heat loss				13,363

COOLING LOAD CALCULATIONS

COOLING LOAD CALCULATIONS

Because of numerous factors and conditions, the heat transfer process for space heat gains, unlike space heat losses, is not steady state and must be analyzed carefully and accurately in order to calculate the cooling load. For example, the heat storage of the materials of a building structure and interior furniture is an important factor. These surfaces and objects will store the thermal energy, and then they will transfer the heat to the room air when they become warmer than room air. This means the instantaneous heat gain for a given space does not convert immediately to the cooling load. Fig. 7-1 shows the difference between the instantaneous heat gain and instantaneous cooling load due to thermal storage.

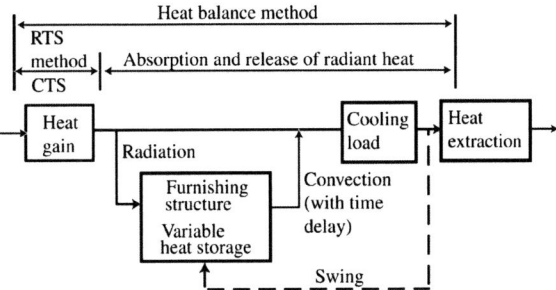

Fig 7-1. The difference between the instantaneous heat gain and instantaneous cooling load due to thermal storage

Cooling load calculations are based on the fundamental concept of heat balance the calculation of which is difficult and time consuming. There are different methods for calculating cooling load.

Transfer Function Method (TFM).—Total Equivalent Temperature Differential and system of Time Averaging (TETD/TA).

In this book we will discuss only the Cooling Load Temperature Differences, Solar Cooling Load, and Cooling Load Factors (CLTD/SCL/CLF) procedure. For details of the other procedures, the reader can refer to the ASHRAE Fundamentals Handbook. The Transfer Function Method (TFM) is an approximation of the heat balance method. The CLTD/SCL/CLF method is a simplified version of the TFM which applies to the certain types of buildings for which data are available. The application data are presented in the ASHRAE Handbooks.

Manual calculation that rely on this method become tedious for peak cooling load since a lot of data analysis is required. In this book a detailed example of this procedure along with the reference data are given. Computer programs and software are available for computing cooling load calculations that are less time consuming and are very efficient. They provide accurate results to experienced users. This book includes the demo of the Trace

Load 700 program by Trane Company. This software is among the most commonly used software in the United States. An example of heating and cooling load calculations by Trace Load 700 is also presented in this chapter.

Basic Definitions.—*Heat Flow Rate:* Heat flow rate is divided into four parts which must be carefully differentiated from one another 1) space heat gain; 2) space cooling load; 3) space heat extraction rate; and 4) cooling coil load.

Space Heat Gain: This is instantaneous rate of energy transfer in the form of heat that enters into and/or is generated within the space at a given time. Heat gain can be sensible or latent heat gain. The modes of space heat gain are:

1) solar radiation through transparent building surfaces;

2) heat conduction through exterior walls, roof, windows and interior partitions, ceilings and floors;

3) heat generation within the space by occupants, appliances, and lights; and

4) energy transfer to the space as a result of ventilation and infiltration of the outdoor air.

Sensible or Latent Heat Gain: Sensible heat gain is the energy added by conduction, convection and/or radiation. Latent heat gain occurs when moisture is added to the conditioned space by occupants and moisture generating equipment such as humidifiers.

Space Cooling Load: This is amount of heat that must be removed to maintain constant space temperature. The sum of all instantaneous space heat gain at a given time is not equal to cooling and must be differentiated.

Radiant Heat Gain: This is space heat gain by radiation, which is not immediately converted to cooling load due to thermal storage in building construction materials and interior objects.

Space Heat Extraction Rate: This is the rate of actual heat removal from the space when the space temperature swings above and below its preset value. Swings of room temperature may occur during the intermediate operation of the cooling system. Space extraction rate is equal to the cooling load if the space temperature remains constant.

Cooling Coil Load: The rate at which heat is removed from the space by the cooling coil is equal to the space peak cooling load plus other external loads such as addition of outside air for ventilation and heat loss from distribution air duct or piping systems passing through the conditioned space.

Heat Source in Conditioned Space.—People and lighting are the major source of the heat gain in a conditioned space. Minor sources such as a ceiling return plenum are shown in Fig. 7-2.

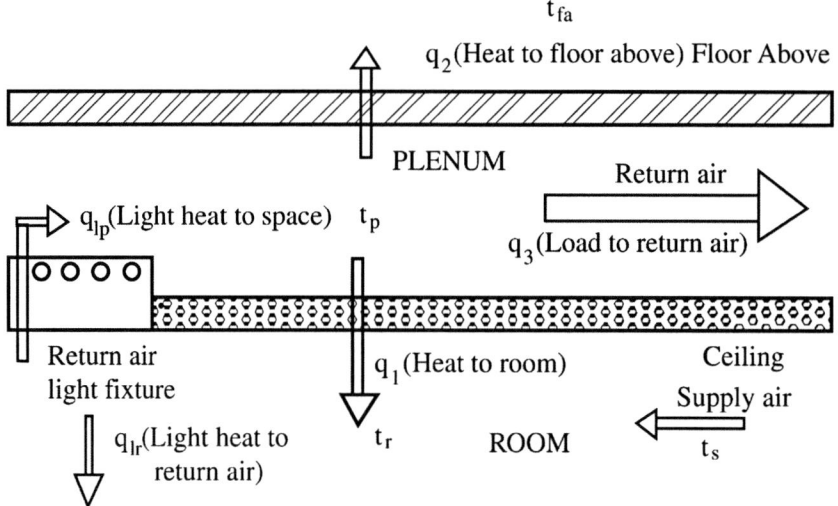

Fig 7-2. Heat balance of typical ceiling return plenum

Table 7-1. Rates of Heat Gain From Occupants

Degree of Activity	Location	Total Heat Btu/hr		Sensible Heat, Btu/hr	Latent Heat, Btu/hr	% Sensible Heat that is Radiant	
		Adult Male	Adjusted, M/F[a]			Low V	High V
Seated at theater	Theater, matinee	390	330	225	105		
Seated at theater, night	Theater, night	390	350	245	105	60	27
Seated, very light work	Offices, hotels, apartments	450	400	245	155		
Moderately active office work	Offices, hotels, apartments	475	450	250	200		
Standing, light work; walking	Department store; retail store	550	450	250	200	58	38
Walking, standing	Drug store, bank	550	500	250	250		
Sedentary work	Restaurant[b]	490	550	275	275		
Light bench work	Factory	800	750	275	475		
Moderate dancing	Dance hall	900	850	305	545	49	35
Walking 3 mph; light machine work	Factory	1000	1000	375	625		
Bowling[c]	Bowling alley	1500	1450	580	870		
Heavy work	Factory	1500	1450	580	870	54	19
Heavy machine work; lifting	Factory	1600	1600	635	965		
Athletics	Gymnasium	2000	1800	710	1090		

[a] Adjusted heat gain is based on 85% of that for an adult male. A child is 75% of that for an adult male.
[b] Adjusted heat gain includes 60 Btu/hr for food per individual (30 Btu/hr sensible and 30 Btu/hr latent)
[c] Figure one person per alley actually bowling, and all others as sitting (400 Btu/hr) or standing or walking slowly (550 Btu/hr).

Tabulated values are based on 75°F room dry bulb temperature. For 80°F room dry bulb, the total heat remains the same, but the sensible heat values should be decreased by approximately 20%, and the latent heat values increased accordingly.

All values are rounded to nearest 5 Btu/hr.

The rate of sensible heat and latent heat (moisture) gain given up by people in the occupied space is given in Table 7-1. It should be noted that the conversion of the sensible heat gain from people to the occupied space is a function of the thermal storage characteristic of the interior space. However, the latent heat from people is instantaneous.

In the case of lighting, only a portion of heat is transferred instantaneously by convection into the conditioned space. The remaining portion is in the form of radiation that affects the conditioned space once it is absorbed and then released by the interior objects in the space. The absorbed radiation energy contributes to the space cooling load only after a time lag, so part of this energy is rera-

diating after lights have been turned off, as shown in Fig. 7-3.

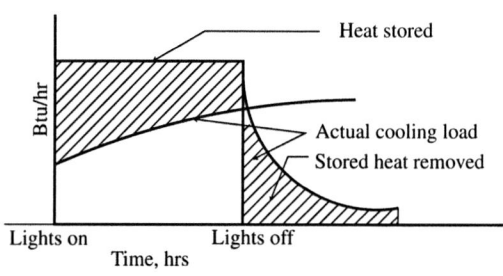

Fig 7-3. Thermal storage effect in cooling load from lights

Table 7-2. Recommended Rates of Heat Gain From Typical Commercial Cooking Appliances[a]

Appliance	Size	Energy Rate, Btu/hr		Recommended Rate of Heat Gain, [a]Btu/hr			
				Without hood			With hood
		Rated	Standby	Sensible	Latent	Total	Sensible
Electrical appliances (without hood)							
Barbeque (pit), per pound of food capacity	80 to 300 lb	136	...	86	50	136	42
Barbeque (pressurized), per pound of food capacity	44 lb	327	...	109	54	163	50
Blender, per quart of capacity	1 to 4 qt	1,550	...	1,000	520	1,520	480
Braising pan, per quart of capacity	108 to 140 qt	360	...	180	95	275	132
Cabinet (large hot holding)	16.2 to 17.3 ft^3	7,100	...	610	340	960	290
Cabinet (large hot serving)	37.4 to 406 ft^3	6,820	...	610	310	920	280
Cabinet (large proofing)	16 to 17 ft^3	693	...	610	310	920	280
Cabinet (small hot holding)	3.2 to 6.4 ft^3	3,070	...	270	140	410	130
Cabinet (very hot holding)	17.3 ft^3	21,000	...	1,880	960	2,830	850
Can opener		580	...	580	...	580	0
Coffee brewer	12 cup/2 burners	5,660	...	3,750	1,910	5,660	1,810
Coffee heater, per boiling burner	1 to 2 burners	2,290	...	1,500	790	2,290	720
Coffee heater, per warming burner	1 to 2 burners	340	...	230	110	340	110
Coffee/hot water boiling urn, per quart of capacity	11.6 qt	390	...	256	132	388	123
Coffee brewing urn (large), per quart of capacity	23 to 40 qt	2,130	...	1,420	710	2,130	680
Coffee brewing urn (small), per quart of capacity	10.6 qt	1,350	...	908	445	1,353	416
Cutter (large)	18 in. bowl	2,560	...	2,560	...	2,560	0
Cutter (small)	14 in. bowl	1,260	...	1,260	...	1,260	0
Cutter and mixer (large)	30 to 48 qt	12,730	...	12,730	...	12730	0
Dishwasher (hood type, chemical sanitizing), per 100 dishes/hr	950 to 2000 dishes/hr	1,300	...	170	370	540	170
Dishwasher (hood type, water sanitizing), per 100 dishes/hr	950 to 2000 dishes/hr	1,300	...	190	420	610	190
Dishwasher (conveyor type, chemical sanitizing), per 100 dishes/hr	5000 to 9000 dishes/hr	1,160	...	140	330	470	150
Dishwasher (conveyor type, water sanitizing), per 100 dishes/hr	5000 to 9000 dishes/hr	1,160	...	150	370	520	170
Display case (refrigerated), per 10 ft^3 of interior	6 to 67 ft^3	1,540	...	617	0	617	0
Dough roller (large)	2 rollers	5,490	...	5,490	...	5,490	0
Dough roller (small)	1 roller	1,570	...	140	...	140	0
Egg cooker	12 eggs	6,140	...	2,900	1,940	4,850	1,570
Food processor	2.4 qt	1,770	...	1,770	...	1,770	0
Food warmer (infrared bulb), per lamp	1 to 6 bulbs	850	...	850	...	850	850
Food warmer (shelf type), per ft^2 of surface	3 to 9 ft^2	930	...	740	190	930	260
Food warmer (infrared tube), per ft of length	39 to 53 in.	990	...	990	...	990	990
Food warmer (well type), per ft^3 of well	0.7 to 2.5 ft^3	3,620	...	1,200	610	1,810	580
Freezer (large)	73	4,570	...	1,840	...	1,840	0
Freezer (small)	18	2,760	...	1,090	...	1,090	0
Griddle/grill (large), per ft^2 of cooking surface	4.6 to 11.8 ft^2	9,200	...	615	343	958	343
Griddle/grill (small), per ft^2 of cooking surface	2.2 to 4.5 ft^2	8,300	...	545	308	853	298
Hot dog broiler	48 to 56 hot dogs	3,960	...	340	170	510	160
Hot plate (double burner, high speed)		16,720	...	7,810	5,430	13,240	6,240
Hot plate (double burner, stockpot)		13,650	...	6,380	4,440	10,820	5,080
Hot plate (single burner, high speed)		9,550	...	4,470	3,110	7,580	3,550
Hot water urn (large), per quart of capacity	56 qt	416	...	161	52	213	68
Hot water urn (small), per quart of capacity	8 qt	738	...	285	95	380	123
Ice maker (large)	220 lb/day	3,720	...	9,320	...	9,320	0

Table 7-2. *(Continued)* **Recommended Rates of Heat Gain From Typical Commercial Cooking Appliances**[a]

Appliance	Size	Energy Rate, Btu/hr		Recommended Rate of Heat Gain, [a]Btu/hr			
				Without hood			With hood
		Rated	Standby	Sensible	Latent	Total	Sensible
Ice maker (small)	110 lb/day	2,560	...	6,410	...	6,410	0
Microwave oven (heavy duty, commercial)	0.7 ft^3	8,970	...	8,970	...	8,970	0
Microwave oven (residential type)	1 ft^3	2,050 to 4,780	...	2,050 to 4,780	...	2,050 to 4780	0
Mixer (large), per quart of capacity	81 qt	94	...	94	...	94	0
Mixer (small), per quart of capacity	12 to 76 qt	48	...	48	...	48	0
Press cooker (hamburger)	300 patties/hr	7,510	...	4,950	2,560	7510	2,390
Refrigerator (large), per 10 ft^3 of interior space	25 to 74 ft^3	753	...	300	...	300	0
Refrigerator (small), per 10 ft^3 of interior space	6 to 25 ft^3	1,670	...	665	...	665	0
Rotisserie	300 hamburgers/hr	10,920	...	7,200	3,720	10,920	3,480
Serving cart (hot), per cubic foot of well	1.8 to 3.2 ft^3	2,050	...	680	340	1,020	328
Serving drawer (large)	252 to 336 dinner rolls	3,750	...	480	34	510	150
Serving drawer (small)	84 to 168 dinner rolls	2,730	...	340	34	380	110
Skillet (tilting), per quart of capacity	48 to 132 qt	580	...	293	161	454	218
Slicer, per square foot of slicing carriage	0.65 to 0.97 ft^2	680	...	682	...	682	216
Soup cooker, per quart of well	7.4 to 11.6 qt	416	...	142	78	220	68
Steam cooker, per cubic foot of compartment	32 to 64 qt	20,700	...	1,640	1,050	2,690	784
Steam kettle (large), per quart of capacity	80 to 320 qt	300	...	23	16	39	13
Steam kettle (small), per quart of capacity	24 to 48 qt	840	...	68	45	113	32
Syrup warmer, per quart of capacity	11.6 qt	284	...	94	52	146	45
Toaster (bun toasts on one side only)	1400 buns/hr	5,120	...	2,730	2,420	5,150	1,640
Toaster (large conveyor)	720 slices/hr	10,920	...	2,900	2,560	5,460	1,740
Toaster (small conveyor)	360 slices/hr	7,170	...	1,910	1,670	3,580	1,160
Toaster (large pop up)	10 slice	18,080	...	9,590	8,500	18,080	5,800
Toaster (small pop up)	4 slice	8,430	...	4,470	3,960	8,430	2,700
Waffle iron	75 in^2	5,600	...	2,390	3,210	5,600	1,770
Electric, Exhaust Hood Required							
Broiler (conveyor infrared), per ft^2 of cooking area	2 to 102 ft^2	19,230	...	...	...	...	3,840
Broiler (single deck infrared), per ft^2 of broiling area	2.6 to 9.8 ft^2	10,870	...	...	...	...	2,150
Charbroiler, per linear foot of cooking surface	2 to 8 linear ft	11,000	9,300	...	...	...	2,800
Fryer (deep fat)	35 to 50 lb oil	48,000	2,900	...	...	...	1,200
Fryer (pressurized), per pound of fat capacity	13 to 33 lb	1565	...	...	...	...	59
Oven (full size convection)		41,000	4,600	...	...	...	2,900
Oven (large deck baking with 537 ft^3 decks), per cubic foot of oven space	15 to 46 ft^3	1,670	...	...	...	...	69
Oven (roasting), per cubic foot of oven space	7.8 to 23 ft^3	27,350	...	...	...	...	113
Oven (small convection), per cubic foot of oven space	1.4 to 5.3 ft^3	10,340	...	...	...	...	147
Oven (small deck baking with 272 ft^3 decks), per cubic foot of oven space	7.8 to 23 ft^3	2,760	...	...	...	...	113
Open range top, per 2 element section	2 to 6 elements	14,000	4,600	...	...	...	2,100
Range (hot top/fry top), per ft^2 of cooking surface	4 to 8 ft^2	7,260	...	...	...	...	2,690
Range (oven section), per ft^3 of oven space	4.2 to 11.3 ft^3	3,940	...	...	...	...	160
Griddle, per linear ft of cooking surface	2 to 8 linear ft	19,500	3,100	...	...	...	1,400
Gas, no hood required							
Broiler, per ft^2 of broiling area	2.7 ft^2	14,800	660[b]	5,310	2,860	8,170	1,220
Cheese melter, per ft^2 of cooking surface	2.5 to 5.1 ft^2	10,300	660[b]	3,690	1,980	5,670	850

Table 7-2. *(Continued)* **Recommended Rates of Heat Gain From Typical Commercial Cooking Appliances[a]**

Appliance	Size	Energy Rate, Btu/hr		Recommended Rate of Heat Gain, [a]Btu/hr			
				Without hood			With hood
		Rated	Standby	Sensible	Latent	Total	Sensible
Dishwasher (hood type, chemical sanitizing), per 100 dishes/hr	950 to 2,000 dishes/hr	1,740	660[b]	510	200	710	230
Dishwasher (hood type, water sanitizing), per 100 dishes/hr	950 to 2,000 dishes/hr	1,740	660[b]	570	220	790	250
Dishwasher (conveyor type, chemical sanitizing), per 100 dishes/hr	5,000 to 9,000 dishes/hr	1,370	660[b]	330	70	400	130
Dishwasher (conveyor type, water sanitizing), per 100 dishes/hr	5,000 to 9,000 dishes/hr	1,370	660[b]	370	80	450	140
Griddle/grill (large), per ft² of cooking surface	4.6 to 11.8 ft²	17,000	330	1,140	610	1,750	460
Griddle/grill (small), per ft² of cooking surface	2.5 to 4.5 ft²	14,400	330	970	510	1,480	400
Hot plate	2 burners	19,200	1,325[b]	11,700	3,470	15,200	3,410
Oven (pizza), per ft² of hearth	6.4 to 12.9 ft²	4,740	660[b]	623	220	843	85
Gas, Exhaust Hood Required							
Braising pan, per quart of capacity	105 to 140 qt	9,840	660[b]	...	...	...	2,430
Broiler, per ft² of broiling area	3.7 to 3.9 ft²	21,800	530	...	...	...	1,800
Broiler (large conveyor, infrared), per ft² of cooking area/minute	2 to 102 ft²	51,300	1,990	...	...	...	5,340
Broiler (standard infrared), per ft² of broiling area	2.4 to 9.4 ft²	1,940	530	...	...	...	1,600
Charbroiler (large), per linear ft of cooking area	2 to 8 linear ft	36,000	22,000	...	...	...	3,800
Fryer (deep fat)	35 to 50 oil capacity	80,000	5,600	...	...	...	1,900
Oven (bake deck), per ft³ of oven space	5.3 to 16.2 ft³	7,670	660b	...	...	...	140
Oven (convection), full size		70,000	29,400	...	...	...	5,700
Oven (pizza), per ft² of oven hearth	9.3 to 25.8 ft²	7,240	660[b]	...	...	...	130
Oven (roasting), per ft³ of oven space	9 to 28 ft³	4,300	660[b]	...	...	...	77
Oven (twin bake deck), per ft³ of oven space	11 to 22 ft³	4,390	660[b]	...	...	...	78
Range (burners), per 2 burner section	2 to 10 burners	33,600	1,325	...	...	...	6,590
Range (hot top or fry top),/ft² of cooking surface	3 to 8 ft²	11,800	330	...	...	...	3,390
Range (large stock pot)	3 burners	100,000	1,990	...	...	...	19,600
Range (small stock pot)	2 burners	40,000	1,330	...	...	...	7,830
Griddle, per linear foot of cooking surface	2 to 8 linear ft	25,000	6,300				1,600
Range top, open burner (per 2 burner section)	2 to 6 elements	40,000	13,600	...	...	...	2,200
Steam							
Compartment steamer, per pound of food capacity/hr	46 to 450 lb	280	...	22	14	36	11
Dishwasher (hood type, chemical sanitizing), per 100 dishes/hr	950 to 2,000 dishes/hr	3,150	...	880	380	1,260	410
Dishwasher (hood type, water sanitizing), per 100 dishes/hr	950 to 2,000 dishes/hr	3,150	...	980	420	1,400	450
Dishwasher (conveyor, chemical sanitizing), per 100 dishes/hr	5,000 to 9,000 dishes/hr	1,180	...	140	330	470	150
Dishwasher (conveyor, water sanitizing), per 100 dishes/hr	5,000 to 9,000 dishes/hr	1,180	...	150	370	520	170
Steam kettle, per quart of capacity	13 to 32 qt	500	...	39	25	64	19

[a] In some cases, heat gain data are given per unit of capacity.
[b] Standby input rating is given for entire appliance regardless of size.

Table 7-3. Typical Heat Gain from Medical Equipment

Typical Equipment	Medical Nameplate, W	Equipment Peak, W	Average, W
Anesthesia system	250	177	166
Blanket warmer	500	504	221
Blood pressure meter	180	33	29
Blood warmer	360	204	114
ECG/RESP	1440	54	50
Electro surgery	1000	147	109
Endoscope	1688	605	596
Harmonical scalpel	230	60	59
Hysteroscopic pump	180	35	34
Laser sonics	1200	256	229
Optical microscope	330	65	63
Pulse oximeter	72	21	20
Stress treadmill	N/A	198	173
Ultrasound system	1800	1063	1050
Vacuum suction	621	337	302
X-ray system	968	…	82
X-ray system	1725	534	480
X-ray system	2070	…	18

Table 7-4. Recommended Heat Gain from Typical Laboratory Equipment

Typical Equipment	Nameplate, W	Peak, W	Average, W
Analytical balance	7	7	7
Centrifuge	138	89	87
Centrifuge	288	136	132
Centrifuge	5500	1176	730
Electrochemical analyzer	50	45	44
Electrochemical analyzer	100	85	84
Flame photometer	180	107	105
Fluorescent microscope	150	144	143
Fluorescent microscope	200	205	178
Function generator	58	29	29
Incubator	515	461	451
Incubator	600	479	264
Incubator	3125	1335	1222
Orbital shaker	100	16	16
Oscilloscope	72	38	38
Oscilloscope	345	99	97
Rotary evaporator	75	74	73
Rotary evaporator	94	29	28
Spectronics	36	31	31
Spectrophotometer	575	106	104
Spectrophotometer	200	122	121
Spectrophotometer	N/A	127	125
Spectro fluorometer	340	405	395
Thermocycler	1840	965	641
Thermocycler	N/A	233	198
Tissue culture	475	132	46
Tissue culture	2346	1178	1146

Table 7-5. Recommended Heat Gain from Typical Computer Equipment

Computer Equipment	Continuous, W	Energy Saver Mode, W
Computers		
Average value	55	20
Conservative value	65	25

Computer Equipment	Continuous, W	Energy Saver Mode, W
Highly conservative value	75	30
Monitors Displaying Windows		
Small monitor (13 to 15 in.)	55	0
Medium monitor (16 to 18 in.)	70	0
Large monitor (19 to 20 in.)	80	0

Table 7-6. Recommended Heat Gain from Typical Laser Printers and Copiers

	Continuous, W	1 page/min, W	Idle, W
Laser Printers			
Small desktop	130	75	10
Desktop	215	100	35
Small office	320	160	70
Large office	550	275	125
Copiers			
Desktop copier	400	85	20
Office copier	1,100	400	300

Table 7-7. Recommended Heat Gain from Miscellaneous Office Equipment

Appliances	Maximum Input Rating, W	Recommended Rate of Heat Gain, W
Mail-processing equipment		
Folding machine	125	80
Inserting machine, 3,600 to 6,800 pieces/hr	600 to 3,300	390 to 2,150
Labeling machine, 1,500 to 30,000 pieces/hr	600 to 6,600	390 to 4,300
Postage meter	230	150
Vending machines		
Cigarette	72	72
Cold food/beverage	1,150 to 1,920	575 to 960
Hot beverage	1,725	862
Snack	240 to 275	240 to 275
Other		
Bar code printer	440	370
Cash registers	60	48
Check processing workstation, 12 pockets	4,800	2,470
Coffee maker, 10 cups	1,500	1050 W sensible, 1540 Btu/hr latent
Microfiche reader	85	85
Microfilm reader	520	520
Microfilm reader/printer	1,150	1150
Microwave oven, 1 ft^3	600	400
Paper shredder	250 to 3,000	200 to 2420
Water cooler, 32 qt/hr	700	350

CLTD/SCL/CLF Calculation Procedure.—The CLTD/SCL/CLF method is a simplified version of the TFM. In order to use simple direct one-step hand calculations, CLTDs, SCLs, and CLFs are developed to include the effect of

1) time lag in conductive heat gain through opaque exterior surfaces, and

2) time delay by thermal storage in converting radiant heat gain to cooling load.

When data are available, this simplification allows us to calculate cooling load manually. For more details of this procedure and the assumptions for obtaining the data, refer to 2001 ASHRAE Fundamental Handbook. The summary of this procedure is given in the Table 7-8.

Table 7-8. Procedure for Calculating Space Design Cooling Load by CLTD/SCL/CLF Method

External Cooling Load	
Roofs, walls, and conduction through glass	$\dot{q} = UA(CLTD)$ U = design heat transfer coefficient for roof or wall from Chapter 5 A = area of roof, wall, or glass, calculated from building plans $CLTD$ = cooling load temperature difference, roof, wall, or glass, Tables 7-11 to 7-22
Solar load through glass	$\dot{q} = A(SC)(SCL)$ SC = design heat transfer coefficient for roof or wall from Chapter 5 SCL = solar cooling load factor with no interior shade or with shade, Tables 7-25 to 7-32
Cooling load from partitions, ceilings, floors	$\dot{q} = UA(T_o - T_{rc})$ U = design heat transfer coefficient for partition, ceiling, or floor, from Chapter 5 A = area of partition, ceiling, or floor, calculated from building plans T_o = temperature in adjacent space T_{rc} = inside design temperature (constant) in conditioned space
Internal Cooling Load	
People	$\dot{q}_{\text{sensible}} = N(\text{Sensible heat gain})CLF$ $\dot{q}_{\text{latent}} = N(\text{Latent heat gain})$ N = number of people in space, from best available source. Sensible and latent heat gain from occupancy, Table 7-1. CLF = cooling load factor, by hour of occupancy, Table 7-34 *Note:* CLF 1.0 with high density or 24-hr occupancy and/or if cooling off at night or during weekends.
Lights	$\dot{q}_{el} = 3.41WF_{ul}F_{sa}(CLF)$ W = watts input from electrical plans or lighting fixture data F_{ul} = lighting use factor, as appropriate F_{sa} = special allowance factor, as appropriate CLF = cooling load factor, by hour of occupancy, Table 7-34 *Note:* CLF = 1.0 with 24-hr light usage and/or if cooling off at night or during weekends.
Power	$\dot{q}_p = 2545PE_FCLF$ P = horsepower rating from electrical plans or manufacturer's data E_F = efficiency factors and arrangements to suit circumstances CLF = cooling load factor, by hour of occupancy, Table 7-34 *Note:* CLF = 1.0 with 24-hr light usage and/or if cooling off at night or during weekends.
Appliances	$\dot{q}_{\text{sensible}} = q_{\text{input}}F_UF_{R(CLF)} = q_{\text{input}}F_{L(CLF)}$ q_{input} = rated energy input from appliances—Tables 7-2 and 7-7 F_U = usage factors from the general principles section F_R = radiation factors from the general principles section F_L = load factors from the general principles section CLF = cooling load factor, by scheduled hours and hooded or not, Tables 7-34 and 7-35 *Note 1:* CLF = 1.0 with 24-hr light usage and/or if cooling off at night or during weekends. *Note 2:* Set latent load = 0 if appliance under exhaust hood.
Ventilation and infiltration air	$\dot{q}_{\text{sensible}} = 1.10cfm(T_o - T_i)$ $\dot{q}_{\text{latent}} = 4840cfm(W_o - W_i)$ $\dot{q}_{\text{total}} = 4.5cfm(h_o - h_i)$ cfm = ventilation cfm from ASHRAE Standard 62; infiltration from Chapter 5 T_o = outside air temperature, °F T_i = inside air temperature, °F W_o = outside air humidity ratio, lb (water)/lb (dry air) W_i = inside air humidity ratio, lb (water)/lb (dry air) h_o = outside air enthalpy, Btu/lb (dry air) h_i = inside air enthalpy, Btu/lb (dry air)

Table 7-9. Roof Numbers Used in Tables 7-10 -7-19

Mass Location[a]	Suspended Ceiling	R Value, hr-ft²-°F/Btu	B7 Wood 1 in.	C12 HW Concrete 2 in.	A3, Steel Deck	Attic-Ceiling Combination
Mass inside the insulation	Without	0 to 5	b	2	b	b
		5 to 10	b	2	b	b
		10 to 15	b	4	b	b
		15 to 20	b	4	b	b
		20 to 25	b	5	b	b
		25 to 30	b	b	b	b
	With	0 to 5	b	5	b	b
		5 to 10	b	8	b	b
		10 to 15	b	13	b	b
		15 to 20	b	13	b	b
		20 to 25	b	14	b	b
		25 to 30	b	b	b	b
Mass evenly placed	Without	0 to 5	1	2	1	1
		5 to 10	2	b	1	2
		10 to 15	2	b	1	2
		15 to 20	4	b	2	2
		20 to 25	4	b	2	4
		25 to 30	b	b	b	b
	With	0 to 5	b	3	1	b
		5 to 10	4	b	1	b
		10 to 15	5	b	2	b
		15 to 20	9	b	2	b
		20 to 25	10	b	4	b
		25 to 30	10	b	b	b
Mass outside the insulation	Without	0 to 5	b	2	b	b
		5 to 10	b	3	b	b
		10 to 15	b	4	b	b
		15 to 20	b	5	b	b
		20 to 25	b	5	b	b
		25 to 30	b	b	b	b
	With	0 to 5	b	3	b	b
		5 to 10	b	3	b	b
		10 to 15	b	4	b	b
		15 to 20	b	5	b	b
		20 to 25	b	b	b	b
		25 to 30	b	b	b	b

[a] The 2 in. concrete is considered massive and the others non massive.
[b] Denotes a roof that is not possible with the chosen parameters.

Table 7-10. July Cooling Load Temperature Differences (CLTDs) for Calculating Cooling Load

Roof No.	1	2	3	4	5	6	7	8	9	10	11	12	13	14	15	16	17	18	19	20	21	22	23	24	Roof No.
													Solar Time, hr												
Flat Roofs 24° North Latitude																									
1	0	−2	−4	−5	−6	−6	−3	9	26	44	62	76	87	92	92	86	74	58	39	23	14	8	4	2	1
2	2	0	−2	−4	−5	−6	−5	1	14	30	48	64	77	86	90	89	82	70	53	36	23	14	8	5	2
3	12	8	5	2	0	−2	−2	3	11	22	35	47	59	68	74	77	74	68	58	47	37	29	22	16	3
4	16	11	6	3	0	−2	−3	−4	−1	5	15	27	41	55	67	75	80	80	76	67	55	43	32	23	4
5	21	16	12	8	5	3	1	1	4	10	19	30	42	52	61	68	71	70	66	59	50	41	33	27	5
8	28	24	20	17	14	11	9	9	10	14	20	27	35	43	49	54	58	58	56	52	47	42	37	32	8
9	31	25	20	16	12	9	6	4	3	5	10	17	26	36	46	54	61	65	66	63	58	51	44	37	9
10	36	31	27	22	19	15	12	9	8	8	11	16	22	30	37	45	52	56	59	59	56	52	47	41	10
14	34	32	30	27	25	23	21	19	19	19	21	24	27	32	36	40	43	45	46	45	44	42	39	37	14
Flat Roofs 32° North Latitude																									
1	0	−2	−4	−5	−6	−6	−1	11	27	45	62	76	86	91	91	85	75	59	41	25	15	9	5	2	1
2	2	0	−2	−4	−5	−6	−4	3	16	32	48	64	76	85	89	88	82	70	55	38	24	15	9	5	2
3	12	8	5	2	0	−2	−1	4	12	23	35	48	59	68	74	76	74	68	59	48	38	29	22	17	3
4	17	11	7	3	1	−1	−3	−3	0	6	16	28	42	55	66	75	79	80	76	67	56	44	33	24	4
5	21	16	12	8	5	3	1	1	5	12	21	31	42	52	61	67	71	70	66	59	51	42	34	27	5
8	29	25	21	17	14	12	10	9	11	15	21	28	35	43	49	54	57	58	57	53	48	43	38	33	8
9	32	26	21	16	12	9	6	4	4	6	11	18	27	37	46	54	61	65	66	64	59	52	45	38	9
10	37	32	27	23	19	15	12	10	9	9	12	16	23	30	38	45	52	56	59	59	56	52	47	42	10
14	35	32	30	28	25	23	21	20	19	20	22	24	28	32	36	40	43	45	46	46	44	42	40	37	14
Flat Roofs 40° North Latitude																									
1	0	−2	−4	−5	−6	−6	0	13	29	45	60	73	83	88	88	83	73	60	43	26	15	9	5	2	1
2	2	0	−2	−4	−5	−6	−4	4	17	32	48	62	74	82	86	85	80	70	56	39	25	15	9	5	2
3	12	8	5	2	0	−2	0	5	13	24	35	47	57	66	72	74	73	67	59	48	38	30	23	17	3
4	17	11	7	3	1	−1	−3	−3	0	7	17	29	42	54	65	73	77	78	74	67	56	45	34	24	4
5	21	16	12	8	5	3	1	2	6	12	21	31	41	51	60	66	69	69	65	59	51	42	34	27	5
8	28	24	21	17	14	12	10	10	12	16	21	28	35	42	48	53	56	57	56	52	48	43	38	33	8
9	32	26	21	16	13	9	6	4	4	7	12	19	27	36	45	53	59	63	64	63	58	52	45	38	9
10	37	32	27	23	19	15	12	10	9	10	12	17	23	30	37	44	50	55	57	58	56	52	47	42	10
14	35	32	30	27	25	23	21	20	19	20	22	24	28	32	36	39	42	44	45	45	44	42	40	37	14
Flat Roofs 48° North Latitude																									
1	0	−2	−4	−5	−6	−5	3	15	29	44	58	69	78	83	83	79	71	59	44	29	17	9	5	2	1
2	2	0	−2	−4	−5	−5	−2	6	19	32	47	60	70	78	82	81	76	68	55	41	27	16	10	5	2
3	12	8	5	2	0	−1	1	6	14	24	35	45	55	63	68	71	70	65	58	48	38	30	23	17	3
4	17	12	7	3	1	−1	−3	−2	2	8	18	29	40	52	62	69	73	74	71	65	55	45	34	25	4
5	21	16	12	8	5	3	2	3	7	13	21	31	40	49	57	63	66	66	63	58	50	42	34	27	5
8	28	24	20	17	14	11	10	10	12	16	21	27	34	40	46	51	54	55	54	51	47	42	37	32	8
9	31	26	21	16	12	9	6	5	5	8	12	19	27	35	43	51	57	60	62	61	57	51	44	38	9
10	36	31	27	22	19	15	12	10	9	10	13	17	23	29	36	43	48	53	55	56	54	51	46	41	10
14	34	32	29	27	25	23	21	20	19	20	22	24	27	31	35	38	41	43	44	44	43	41	39	36	14

1. Direct application of data: Dark surface; Indoor temperature of 78°F; Outdoor maximum temperature of 95°F with mean temperature of 85°F and daily range of 21°F; Solar radiation typical of clear day on 21st day of month; Outside surface resistance of 0.333 hr-ft^2-°F/Btu; Inside surface film resistance of 0.685 hr-ft^2-°F/Btu.

2. Adjustment to table data: Design temperatures: Corrected $CLTD = CLTD + (78 - T_r) + (T_m - 85)$ where T_r = inside room temperature; T_m = mean outdoor temperature; T_m = maximum outdoor temperature − daily range/2; No adjustment recommended for color; No adjustment recommended for ventilation of air space above a ceiling.

Table 7-11. August Cooling Load Temperature Differences (CLTDs) for Calculating Cooling Load

Roof No.	Solar Time, hr																								Roof No.
	1	2	3	4	5	6	7	8	9	10	11	12	13	14	15	16	17	18	19	20	21	22	23	24	
Flat Roofs 24° North Latitude																									
1	−1	−2	−4	−5	−6	−7	−5	5	22	41	59	75	86	91	91	84	72	55	35	21	13	8	4	1	1
2	1	−1	−2	−4	−5	−6	−6	−1	11	27	45	62	76	85	89	88	80	67	50	33	21	13	8	4	2
3	11	7	4	2	−1	−2	−3	1	9	20	33	46	57	67	73	75	73	66	55	44	35	27	21	15	3
4	15	10	6	3	0	−2	−3	−4	−3	3	13	25	39	53	65	74	79	79	74	64	53	41	30	22	4
5	20	15	11	7	5	2	0	0	2	8	17	28	40	51	60	66	69	69	64	56	47	39	32	25	5
8	27	23	19	16	13	11	8	7	9	13	18	25	33	41	48	53	56	56	54	50	45	40	35	31	8
9	29	24	19	15	11	8	6	3	2	4	8	16	24	34	48	53	60	63	64	61	56	49	42	35	9
10	34	30	25	21	18	14	11	9	7	7	9	14	20	28	36	43	50	55	57	57	54	50	45	39	10
14	33	31	28	26	24	22	20	18	17	18	19	22	26	30	34	38	41	43	44	43	42	40	38	35	14
Flat Roofs 32° North Latitude																									
1	−1	−2	−4	−5	−6	−7	−4	6	23	41	58	72	82	88	88	82	70	54	36	21	13	8	4	1	1
2	1	−1	−2	−4	−5	−6	−6	−1	11	27	44	60	73	82	86	85	78	66	50	33	21	13	8	4	2
3	11	7	4	1	−1	−2	−2	1	9	20	32	44	56	65	71	73	70	64	54	44	35	27	20	15	3
4	15	10	6	3	0	−2	−3	−4	−2	3	13	25	38	51	63	71	76	76	72	63	52	40	30	22	4
5	19	15	11	7	4	2	0	0	3	9	17	28	39	49	58	64	67	67	62	55	47	39	31	25	5
8	26	23	19	16	13	10	8	8	9	13	18	25	32	40	46	51	54	55	53	49	44	39	35	30	8
9	29	24	19	15	11	8	5	3	3	4	9	15	24	33	43	51	58	61	62	60	55	48	41	35	9
10	34	29	25	21	17	14	11	9	7	7	10	14	20	27	35	42	48	53	55	55	53	49	44	39	10
14	32	30	28	25	23	21	19	18	17	17	19	22	25	29	33	37	40	42	43	42	41	39	37	35	14
Flat Roofs 40° North Latitude																									
1	−1	−2	−4	−5	−6	−7	−3	7	22	39	55	68	78	83	83	77	67	53	36	22	13	7	4	1	1
2	1	−1	−3	−4	−5	−6	−5	0	11	26	42	57	69	77	81	80	74	63	48	33	21	13	8	4	2
3	10	7	4	1	−1	−2	−2	2	9	19	30	42	53	61	67	69	67	61	52	43	34	26	20	15	3
4	15	10	6	2	0	−2	−4	−4	−2	4	13	24	36	49	59	67	72	72	68	61	50	39	29	21	4
5	19	14	10	7	4	2	0	0	3	9	17	26	37	46	55	61	64	63	60	53	45	37	30	24	5
8	25	22	18	15	12	10	8	7	9	12	17	24	31	38	44	49	51	52	51	47	43	38	34	29	8
9	28	23	18	14	11	8	5	3	3	4	8	15	23	32	41	48	55	58	59	57	52	46	40	34	9
10	33	28	24	20	17	13	10	8	7	7	9	13	19	26	33	40	46	50	53	53	50	47	42	37	10
14	31	29	26	24	22	20	18	17	16	17	18	21	24	28	32	35	38	40	41	41	39	37	35	33	14
Flat Roofs 48° North Latitude																									
1	−1	−3	−4	−5	−6	−7	−3	7	21	36	50	62	71	76	76	72	63	50	35	21	13	7	4	1	1
2	1	−1	−3	−4	−5	−6	−5	1	11	25	39	52	63	71	75	74	69	59	46	32	21	13	7	4	2
3	10	6	3	1	−1	−3	−2	2	9	18	28	39	48	56	61	64	62	57	50	40	32	25	19	14	3
4	14	9	5	2	0	−2	−4	−4	−2	4	12	22	34	45	55	62	66	67	64	57	48	37	28	20	4
5	18	13	10	6	4	1	0	0	3	8	16	25	34	43	50	56	59	59	56	50	43	35	29	23	5
8	24	20	17	14	11	9	7	7	8	12	16	22	28	35	40	45	48	48	47	44	40	36	32	28	8
9	26	22	17	13	10	7	4	3	2	4	8	14	21	29	37	45	50	54	55	53	49	44	38	32	9
10	31	26	22	19	15	12	10	7	6	7	9	13	18	24	31	37	42	46	49	49	47	44	40	35	10
14	29	27	25	23	21	19	17	16	15	16	17	20	23	26	29	33	35	37	38	38	37	35	33	31	14

1. Direct application of data: Dark surface; Indoor temperature of 78°F; Outdoor maximum temperature of 95°F with mean temperature of 85°F and daily range of 21°F; Solar radiation typical of clear day on 21st day of month; Outside surface resistance of 0.333 hr-ft^2-°F/Btu; Inside surface film resistance of 0.685 hr-ft^2-°F/Btu.

2. Adjustment to table data: Design temperatures: Corrected $CLTD = CLTD + (78 - T_r) + (T_m - 85)$ where T_r = inside room temperature; T_m = mean outdoor temperature; T_m = maximum outdoor temperature − daily range/2; No adjustment recommended for color; No adjustment recommended for ventilation of air space above a ceiling.

Table 7-12. July Cooling Load Temperature Differences (CLTDs) for Calculating Cooling Load from Sunlit Walls 24° North Latitude

Wall Facing	1	2	3	4	5	6	7	8	9	10	11	12	13	14	15	16	17	18	19	20	21	22	23	24	Wall Facing
WALL NO 1																									
N	1	0	-1	-2	-3	-2	5	13	17	18	19	22	26	28	30	32	34	34	27	17	11	7	5	3	N
NE	1	0	-1	-2	-3	0	17	39	51	53	48	39	32	30	30	30	28	24	18	13	10	7	5	3	NE
E	1	0	-1	-2	-3	0	18	44	59	63	59	48	36	32	31	30	28	24	19	13	10	7	5	3	E
SE	1	0	-1	-2	-3	-2	8	25	38	44	45	42	35	32	31	30	27	24	18	13	10	7	5	3	SE
S	1	0	-1	-2	-3	-3	-1	3	8	12	18	24	29	31	31	30	27	23	18	13	9	7	4	3	S
SW	1	0	-1	-2	-3	-3	-1	3	8	13	17	22	29	40	51	58	59	52	36	20	12	8	5	3	SW
W	2	0	-1	-2	-2	-3	-1	3	8	13	17	22	27	42	59	73	80	75	52	27	14	9	5	3	W
NW	2	0	-1	-2	-2	-3	-1	3	8	13	17	22	27	37	50	62	69	67	48	25	13	8	5	3	NW
WALL NO 2																									
N	5	3	2	0	-1	-2	-1	2	7	12	15	18	20	23	25	28	30	32	32	29	23	17	12	8	N
NE	5	3	2	0	-1	-2	0	9	23	36	44	46	43	38	34	32	31	29	26	22	18	14	10	7	NE
E	5	3	2	0	-1	-2	0	10	26	42	52	55	52	44	38	35	32	30	27	23	18	14	10	8	E
SE	5	3	2	0	-1	-2	-1	4	14	26	35	40	41	38	35	33	31	29	26	22	18	14	10	7	SE
S	5	3	1	0	-1	-2	-2	-1	1	4	8	13	19	24	27	29	29	28	26	22	17	13	10	7	S
SW	6	4	2	1	-1	-2	-2	-1	1	5	9	13	18	24	32	42	50	54	52	44	33	22	15	10	SW
W	8	5	2	1	0	-1	-2	-1	1	5	9	13	17	23	33	46	59	69	71	61	45	30	19	12	W
NW	7	4	2	1	-1	-1	-2	-1	1	5	9	13	17	22	30	40	51	60	62	55	41	28	18	12	NW
WALL NO 3																									
N	8	5	4	2	1	0	1	5	8	11	14	16	19	21	24	26	29	30	30	26	21	17	13	10	N
NE	7	5	3	2	1	0	4	14	25	34	38	38	36	35	33	32	31	29	26	22	19	15	12	9	NE
E	7	5	3	2	1	0	5	16	29	39	45	46	43	40	37	35	33	30	27	23	19	16	12	10	E
SE	7	5	3	2	0	0	2	8	17	25	31	34	35	34	33	32	31	29	26	22	18	15	12	9	SE
S	7	5	3	1	0	-1	-1	0	2	5	9	13	18	22	25	26	26	26	23	20	17	14	11	9	S
SW	10	7	5	3	1	0	0	1	3	6	9	13	17	24	32	40	46	48	45	37	30	23	18	14	SW
W	13	9	6	4	2	1	0	1	3	6	9	13	17	24	34	46	56	62	59	50	39	30	23	17	W
NW	12	8	6	4	2	1	0	1	3	6	9	13	17	22	30	39	48	54	53	45	35	27	21	16	NW
WALL NO 4																									
N	12	8	6	4	2	1	0	0	3	6	10	13	15	18	21	23	26	28	30	30	28	24	20	15	N
NE	10	7	5	3	2	0	0	3	10	20	29	36	39	39	37	35	34	32	30	27	24	20	16	13	NE
E	10	8	5	3	2	1	0	3	11	22	34	43	47	46	43	40	37	34	32	28	25	21	17	13	E
SE	10	7	5	3	2	0	0	1	5	13	21	28	33	35	35	35	33	32	30	27	24	20	16	13	SE
S	10	7	5	3	2	0	-1	-1	-1	1	4	7	11	16	20	24	26	27	27	25	22	19	16	12	S
SW	15	11	7	5	3	1	0	-1	0	1	4	7	11	15	21	29	37	43	47	47	42	35	27	21	SW
W	20	14	9	6	4	2	0	0	0	2	4	7	11	15	21	30	41	52	60	61	56	46	36	27	W
NW	18	13	9	6	3	1	0	0	0	2	4	7	11	15	20	27	36	45	52	54	50	42	33	25	NW
WALL NO 5																									
N	13	11	9	7	5	3	2	3	5	7	10	12	14	16	19	21	23	25	27	27	25	22	19	16	N
NE	13	11	8	7	5	3	3	6	12	20	26	31	33	33	32	32	31	31	29	27	24	21	18	16	NE
E	14	11	9	7	5	4	3	6	13	22	31	36	39	39	37	36	35	33	31	29	26	22	19	16	E
SE	13	10	8	6	5	3	2	4	8	14	20	25	28	30	30	30	30	28	26	24	21	18	15	13	SE
S	11	9	7	6	4	3	2	1	1	3	5	7	11	14	18	20	22	23	23	22	20	18	16	14	S
SW	18	15	12	9	7	5	3	3	3	4	5	8	11	14	20	26	32	38	41	40	36	31	27	22	SW
W	23	19	15	12	9	7	5	4	4	4	6	8	11	15	20	28	37	45	51	51	47	41	34	28	W
NW	21	17	14	11	8	6	4	3	3	4	6	8	11	14	19	25	32	40	45	46	42	37	31	26	NW
WALL NO 6																									
N	14	12	10	8	7	5	4	5	6	8	10	11	13	15	17	20	22	24	25	25	23	21	19	16	N
NE	14	12	10	8	7	5	5	8	14	20	25	28	29	30	30	30	30	29	28	26	24	22	19	17	NE
E	15	13	11	9	7	6	6	9	15	22	29	33	35	35	34	34	33	32	30	28	26	23	20	18	E
SE	14	12	10	8	7	5	4	6	10	14	19	23	26	27	28	28	28	27	25	23	21	19	16	14	SE
S	12	10	8	7	5	4	3	3	4	5	8	11	14	16	18	19	20	21	21	19	17	16	14	12	S
SW	19	16	14	11	9	7	6	5	5	6	7	9	11	15	19	25	30	34	36	36	33	29	26	22	SW
W	24	21	17	14	12	9	8	7	6	7	8	10	12	15	20	27	35	42	46	46	42	37	33	28	W
NW	22	19	16	13	11	8	7	6	6	6	7	9	11	14	18	24	31	37	41	41	38	34	29	25	NW
WALL NO 7																									
N	14	12	11	9	8	7	7	7	9	10	11	12	14	15	17	19	20	22	23	22	21	19	17	16	N
NE	16	14	12	11	9	8	9	12	17	21	24	26	26	27	27	28	28	27	26	25	23	21	19	17	NE
E	17	15	13	11	10	9	9	13	19	24	28	30	31	31	31	30	30	28	27	25	23	21	19	18	E
SE	15	13	12	10	9	7	7	9	13	16	20	22	24	25	25	26	26	25	23	22	20	18	17	15	SE
S	12	10	9	8	7	6	5	5	5	6	7	9	11	14	16	17	18	19	19	18	17	16	15	13	S
SW	19	17	15	13	11	10	8	8	8	8	9	11	13	16	20	24	28	31	32	30	28	26	23	21	SW
W	24	21	19	16	14	12	11	10	10	10	11	12	14	17	22	28	34	39	40	39	36	32	29	26	W
NW	21	19	17	15	13	11	10	9	9	9	10	11	13	16	20	24	30	34	36	35	32	29	26	24	NW
WALL NO 9																									
N	19	16	14	11	9	7	5	4	4	5	6	8	10	12	14	16	18	21	23	25	26	25	23	21	N
NE	18	16	13	11	9	7	5	4	6	9	15	20	25	29	30	31	31	31	31	30	28	26	24	21	NE
E	19	17	14	12	9	7	6	5	5	10	17	24	30	34	36	36	36	35	34	32	30	28	25	22	E
SE	18	15	13	11	9	7	5	4	4	6	10	15	20	24	27	28	29	29	29	29	27	25	23	21	SE
S	15	13	11	9	8	6	4	3	2	2	3	4	6	8	11	14	17	20	21	22	22	21	19	18	S
SW	26	22	18	15	12	10	8	6	4	4	4	5	7	9	12	16	21	27	32	36	37	36	33	30	SW
W	33	28	23	19	16	13	10	8	6	5	5	6	7	9	12	16	22	30	37	44	47	46	43	38	W
NW	30	25	21	18	14	11	9	7	5	5	5	6	7	9	12	15	20	26	33	38	41	41	38	34	NW

Table 7-12. July Cooling Load Temperature Differences (CLTDs) for Calculating Cooling Load from Sunlit Walls 24° North Latitude *(Continued)*

Wall Facing	1	2	3	4	5	6	7	8	9	10	11	12	13	14	15	16	17	18	19	20	21	22	23	24	Wall Facing
WALL NO 10																									
N	18	16	14	12	10	8	6	5	5	6	7	8	10	12	14	16	18	20	22	24	24	24	22	21	N
NE	19	16	14	12	9	8	6	6	7	11	16	20	24	27	29	30	30	30	30	29	28	26	24	21	NE
E	20	17	15	12	10	8	6	6	8	12	18	24	29	32	34	34	35	34	33	32	30	28	25	23	E
SE	18	16	13	11	9	7	6	5	6	8	11	16	20	23	25	27	28	29	29	28	27	25	23	21	SE
S	15	14	12	10	8	6	5	4	3	3	3	4	6	9	11	14	17	19	20	21	21	20	19	17	S
SW	26	22	19	16	13	11	8	7	5	5	5	6	7	9	12	16	21	26	31	34	35	34	32	29	SW
W	32	28	24	20	17	14	11	9	7	6	6	7	8	10	13	17	23	30	37	42	44	43	40	37	W
NW	29	25	22	18	15	12	10	8	6	6	6	6	8	10	12	16	21	27	32	37	39	38	36	33	NW
WALL NO 11																									
N	17	16	14	13	11	10	8	8	8	8	9	10	11	12	14	15	17	18	20	21	22	21	20	19	N
NE	19	17	16	14	12	11	10	9	11	14	17	21	23	25	26	26	27	27	27	26	26	24	23	21	NE
E	21	19	17	15	13	12	10	10	12	15	19	24	27	29	30	30	30	30	29	28	26	25	23	21	E
SE	18	17	15	13	12	10	9	8	9	11	14	17	19	21	23	24	25	25	25	24	23	22	21	20	SE
S	14	13	12	11	9	8	7	6	5	5	5	6	6	8	10	12	14	15	17	18	18	18	17	16	S
SW	23	21	19	17	15	13	12	10	9	9	9	9	10	11	14	17	20	24	28	30	30	29	27	25	SW
W	29	26	24	21	19	17	15	13	12	11	11	11	12	13	15	18	23	28	33	36	37	36	34	32	W
NW	26	24	21	19	17	15	13	12	10	10	10	10	11	12	14	17	20	25	29	32	33	33	31	29	NW
WALL NO 12																									
N	17	16	14	13	12	10	9	8	8	9	9	10	11	12	14	15	16	18	19	20	21	20	19	18	N
NE	20	18	16	15	13	12	11	10	12	14	17	20	22	24	25	25	26	26	26	25	24	23	22	21	NE
E	21	19	18	16	14	13	12	11	13	16	19	23	26	28	29	29	29	29	28	27	26	25	23	21	E
SE	19	17	16	14	13	11	10	9	10	11	14	16	19	21	22	23	24	24	25	24	24	23	21	20	SE
S	14	13	12	11	10	9	8	7	6	6	6	7	8	10	11	13	15	16	17	17	17	17	16	15	S
SW	23	21	19	17	16	14	12	11	10	10	9	10	11	12	14	17	20	23	26	28	28	28	26	25	SW
W	29	26	24	22	20	18	16	14	13	12	12	12	12	13	15	18	22	27	31	35	35	35	33	31	W
NW	26	24	22	20	18	16	14	13	11	11	11	11	12	13	14	17	20	24	28	31	32	31	30	28	NW
WALL NO 14																									
N	17	16	15	14	13	12	11	11	10	10	11	11	12	12	13	14	15	16	17	18	18	18	18	17	N
NE	20	19	18	17	16	15	14	13	14	15	17	19	21	22	22	23	24	24	24	24	24	23	22	21	NE
E	22	21	20	19	17	16	15	15	15	17	19	21	23	25	26	26	27	27	27	27	26	25	24	23	E
SE	19	18	17	16	15	14	13	12	13	14	16	18	19	20	21	21	22	22	22	22	22	21	21	20	SE
S	14	13	12	12	11	10	9	9	8	8	8	8	9	10	11	12	13	14	15	15	15	15	15	15	S
SW	22	21	20	18	17	16	15	14	13	12	12	12	13	13	14	16	18	20	22	24	25	24	24	23	SW
W	27	26	24	23	21	20	19	17	16	16	15	15	15	15	16	18	21	24	27	29	30	30	30	29	W
NW	24	23	22	21	19	18	17	16	15	14	14	14	14	14	15	17	19	21	24	26	27	27	27	26	NW
WALL NO 15																									
N	21	19	17	15	13	11	9	8	7	6	6	7	8	9	11	13	15	17	19	21	22	23	23	22	N
NE	22	20	18	16	14	11	10	8	7	8	11	14	18	22	24	26	28	29	29	29	29	28	26	24	NE
E	24	22	19	17	14	12	10	9	8	9	12	16	21	25	29	31	32	33	33	33	32	30	29	26	E
SE	22	20	17	15	13	11	9	8	7	7	8	11	14	17	20	23	25	26	27	27	27	26	25	24	SE
S	17	16	14	13	11	9	8	6	5	4	4	4	5	6	8	10	13	15	17	19	19	20	20	19	S
SW	29	26	24	21	18	15	13	11	9	7	6	6	6	7	9	11	15	19	23	27	31	32	32	31	SW
W	37	33	30	26	23	20	16	14	11	9	8	8	8	9	10	12	16	21	26	32	37	40	40	39	W
NW	33	30	27	24	21	18	15	12	10	8	7	7	7	8	9	12	15	19	23	28	33	35	36	35	NW
WALL NO 16																									
N	20	18	17	15	14	12	11	9	8	8	8	8	9	10	11	13	14	16	17	19	20	21	21	21	N
NE	22	21	19	17	15	13	12	10	10	10	12	15	18	21	23	24	26	27	27	27	27	26	25	24	NE
E	24	22	20	18	16	14	12	11	10	11	13	17	20	24	26	28	30	30	31	31	30	29	28	26	E
SE	21	20	18	16	14	13	11	10	9	9	10	12	14	17	19	21	23	24	25	25	25	24	24	23	SE
S	17	16	14	13	12	10	9	8	6	6	5	5	6	7	8	10	12	14	16	17	18	18	18	17	S
SW	27	25	23	21	19	17	15	13	11	10	9	8	8	9	10	12	15	18	22	25	28	29	29	28	SW
W	34	32	29	26	24	21	18	16	14	12	11	10	10	11	11	13	16	20	25	30	33	36	36	35	W
NW	30	28	26	24	21	19	17	14	12	11	10	9	9	10	11	12	15	18	22	26	30	32	32	32	NW

1. Direct application of data: Dark surface; Indoor temperature of 78°F; Outdoor maximum temperature of 95°F with mean temperature of 85°F and daily range of 21°F; Solar radiation typical of clear day on 21st day of month; Outside surface resistance of 0.333 hr-ft²-°F/Btu; Inside surface film resistance of 0.685 hr-ft²-°F/Btu.

2. Adjustment to table data: Design temperatures: Corrected $CLTD = CLTD + (78 - T_r) + (T_m - 85)$ where T_r = inside room temperature; T_m = mean outdoor temperature; T_m = maximum outdoor temperature − daily range/2; No adjustment recommended for color; No adjustment recommended for ventilation of air space above a ceiling.

Table 7-13. July Cooling Load Temperature Differences (CLTDs) for Calculating Cooling Load from Sunlit Walls 32° North Latitude

Wall Facing	\multicolumn{24}{Solar Time, hr}																								Wall Facing
	1	2	3	4	5	6	7	8	9	10	11	12	13	14	15	16	17	18	19	20	21	22	23	24	
WALL NO 1																									
N	1	0	-1	-2	-3	-2	6	12	14	15	18	22	25	28	29	29	30	31	27	17	11	7	5	3	N
NE	1	0	-1	-2	-3	1	21	41	49	48	41	33	29	29	30	29	28	24	19	14	10	7	5	3	NE
E	1	0	-1	-2	-3	1	23	48	61	64	59	48	36	32	31	30	28	24	19	14	10	7	5	3	E
SE	1	0	-1	-2	-3	-1	12	29	42	50	52	49	42	35	32	30	28	24	19	14	10	7	5	3	SE
S	1	0	-1	-2	-3	-3	0	4	8	16	25	34	40	42	41	36	30	25	19	13	10	7	5	3	S
SW	2	0	-1	-2	-2	-2	0	4	8	13	17	23	34	47	58	65	64	57	41	22	13	8	5	3	SW
W	2	1	-1	-2	-2	-2	0	4	8	13	17	22	27	42	59	73	80	77	58	30	15	9	6	3	W
NW	2	0	-1	-2	-2	-2	0	4	8	13	17	21	26	32	43	56	65	66	52	27	14	8	5	3	NW
WALL NO 2																									
N	5	3	2	0	-1	-2	-1	3	7	10	13	15	18	22	25	27	28	29	30	28	23	17	12	8	N
NE	5	3	2	0	-1	-2	1	11	25	37	42	42	38	34	32	31	30	29	26	23	18	14	10	7	NE
E	5	3	2	0	-1	-2	1	13	30	45	54	56	52	45	38	35	32	30	27	23	18	14	11	8	E
SE	5	3	2	0	-1	-2	0	6	17	29	39	45	47	44	40	36	33	30	27	23	18	14	10	8	SE
S	5	3	2	0	-1	-2	-2	-1	1	5	11	18	26	33	37	39	37	34	29	24	19	14	10	7	S
SW	7	4	2	1	-1	-2	-2	-1	2	5	9	13	18	26	37	47	56	60	58	49	36	25	16	11	SW
W	8	5	3	1	0	-1	-2	-1	2	5	9	13	17	23	33	46	59	69	72	64	48	32	20	13	W
NW	7	4	2	1	-1	-2	-2	-1	2	5	9	13	17	22	27	36	46	55	60	55	42	29	19	12	NW
WALL NO 3																									
N	8	5	3	2	1	0	2	5	7	9	12	15	18	21	23	25	26	28	28	25	21	17	13	10	N
NE	7	5	3	2	1	0	6	16	26	33	35	35	33	32	31	31	30	28	26	22	18	15	12	9	NE
E	7	5	4	2	1	0	7	19	31	41	46	47	44	40	37	35	33	31	27	23	19	16	13	10	E
SE	7	5	3	2	1	0	3	10	20	29	35	39	40	39	36	35	33	30	27	23	19	16	13	10	SE
S	7	5	3	2	0	0	-1	1	3	6	12	18	25	30	33	34	33	30	27	23	19	16	12	10	S
SW	11	8	5	3	2	0	0	1	3	6	9	13	19	27	36	44	50	53	49	41	33	25	20	15	SW
W	13	10	7	4	2	1	1	2	4	6	9	13	17	24	34	45	56	62	62	52	41	32	24	18	W
NW	12	9	6	4	2	1	0	1	3	6	9	13	16	21	27	35	44	51	52	45	35	28	21	16	NW
WALL NO 4																									
N	11	8	6	4	2	0	0	0	3	6	8	11	14	17	20	22	25	26	28	28	27	23	19	15	N
NE	10	7	5	3	2	0	0	3	11	21	29	34	36	35	34	33	32	31	29	27	24	20	16	13	NE
E	10	8	5	4	2	1	0	4	13	25	36	44	48	47	44	40	37	34	32	29	25	21	17	13	E
SE	10	8	5	3	2	0	0	2	7	15	24	32	38	41	41	39	37	34	32	29	25	21	17	13	SE
S	10	8	5	3	2	0	-1	-1	0	2	5	9	15	22	28	32	34	34	33	30	26	21	17	14	S
SW	17	12	8	5	3	1	0	0	0	2	4	7	11	17	24	32	41	48	53	52	47	38	30	23	SW
W	21	15	10	6	4	2	0	0	0	2	4	8	11	15	21	30	41	52	60	63	58	49	38	28	W
NW	18	13	9	6	3	1	0	0	0	2	4	7	11	15	19	25	32	41	48	52	49	42	33	25	NW
WALL NO 5																									
N	13	11	8	6	5	3	2	3	5	7	8	10	12	15	18	20	22	24	25	25	24	21	18	16	N
NE	13	10	8	6	5	3	3	7	13	20	26	29	30	30	30	30	30	29	28	26	24	21	18	15	NE
E	14	11	9	7	5	4	3	7	15	24	32	38	40	39	38	37	35	34	32	29	26	23	20	17	E
SE	13	11	9	7	5	3	3	5	9	16	23	28	33	35	35	34	33	32	31	28	25	22	19	16	SE
S	13	10	8	6	5	3	2	2	2	3	6	10	14	20	24	27	29	29	28	27	24	21	18	15	S
SW	20	16	13	10	8	6	4	3	3	4	6	9	11	16	22	29	36	42	45	44	40	35	29	24	SW
W	24	20	16	12	9	7	5	4	4	5	6	9	11	15	20	28	37	46	52	53	49	42	36	29	W
NW	21	17	14	11	8	6	4	3	3	4	6	8	11	14	18	23	29	37	42	44	41	36	31	25	NW
WALL NO 6																									
N	14	12	10	8	6	5	4	5	6	7	9	10	12	14	17	19	20	22	23	23	22	20	18	16	N
NE	14	12	10	8	7	5	6	9	15	20	24	26	27	28	28	28	28	27	26	24	21	19	16	14	NE
E	16	13	11	9	7	6	6	10	17	24	30	34	36	36	35	34	34	32	31	29	26	23	21	18	E
SE	15	13	11	9	7	6	5	7	11	16	22	26	30	31	32	32	31	31	29	27	25	22	20	17	SE
S	14	12	10	8	6	5	4	3	4	5	7	10	14	18	22	25	26	27	26	25	23	20	18	16	S
SW	21	18	15	12	10	8	7	6	6	6	7	9	12	16	22	28	34	38	40	39	36	32	28	25	SW
W	25	21	18	15	12	10	8	7	7	7	8	10	12	15	20	27	35	42	47	47	44	39	34	29	W
NW	22	18	15	13	10	8	7	6	6	8	9	11	14	17	22	28	34	39	39	37	33	29	25	22	NW
WALL NO 7																									
N	13	12	10	9	8	7	7	7	8	9	10	11	13	14	16	18	19	20	21	21	20	18	17	15	N
NE	15	13	12	10	9	8	9	13	17	21	23	24	25	25	26	26	26	26	25	24	22	21	19	17	NE
E	17	15	13	12	10	9	10	15	20	25	29	31	32	32	32	31	31	30	29	27	25	23	21	19	E
SE	16	14	12	11	9	8	8	11	14	19	22	25	27	28	28	28	28	27	25	24	22	20	18	16	SE
S	14	12	11	9	8	7	6	6	6	7	9	12	15	18	21	23	23	23	23	22	20	19	17	16	S
SW	21	18	16	14	12	11	9	9	9	9	10	11	14	18	22	27	32	35	35	34	31	28	26	23	SW
W	24	22	19	17	15	13	11	10	10	10	11	12	14	17	22	28	34	39	41	40	37	34	30	27	W
NW	21	19	16	14	12	11	9	9	9	9	10	11	13	15	18	23	28	32	35	34	31	29	26	23	NW
WALL NO 9																									
N	18	15	13	11	9	7	5	4	4	4	6	7	9	11	13	15	17	20	21	23	24	24	22	20	N
NE	18	16	13	11	9	7	5	5	6	10	15	21	25	27	28	29	29	29	29	27	25	23	21	19	NE
E	20	17	14	12	10	8	6	5	7	11	18	25	31	35	37	37	36	36	34	33	31	28	26	23	E
SE	19	16	14	11	9	7	6	5	5	8	12	17	23	27	31	32	33	33	32	31	30	27	25	22	SE
S	18	15	13	11	9	7	5	4	3	3	5	7	11	15	20	23	26	27	28	27	25	23	20	18	S
SW	28	24	20	17	14	11	9	7	5	5	5	6	7	9	13	18	23	30	35	40	41	40	37	33	SW
W	34	29	24	20	16	13	10	8	6	6	6	6	8	10	12	17	22	30	37	44	48	48	44	39	W
NW	29	25	21	17	14	11	9	7	5	5	5	6	7	9	12	15	19	24	30	36	39	40	37	34	NW

Table 7-13. July Cooling Load Temperature Differences (CLTDs) for Calculating Cooling Load from Sunlit Walls 32° North Latitude *(Continued)*

Wall Facing	Solar Time, hr																								Wall Facing
	1	2	3	4	5	6	7	8	9	10	11	12	13	14	15	16	17	18	19	20	21	22	23	24	
WALL NO 10																									
N	18	15	13	11	9	7	6	5	5	5	6	7	9	11	13	15	17	19	21	22	23	23	21	20	N
NE	18	16	14	11	9	7	6	6	8	12	16	20	23	26	27	28	28	29	29	28	27	25	23	21	NE
E	20	17	15	12	10	8	7	6	9	13	19	25	30	33	35	35	35	35	34	32	31	28	26	23	E
SE	19	17	14	12	10	8	6	6	6	9	13	18	22	26	29	31	32	32	31	31	29	27	25	22	SE
S	18	16	13	11	9	7	6	4	4	3	4	6	8	12	15	19	22	25	26	26	26	24	22	20	S
SW	28	24	21	18	15	12	9	7	6	5	6	6	8	10	14	18	24	29	34	38	39	38	35	32	SW
W	34	29	25	21	18	14	11	9	7	7	6	7	8	10	13	17	23	30	37	42	45	44	42	38	W
NW	29	25	21	18	15	12	10	8	6	6	6	6	8	10	12	15	19	25	30	35	37	37	35	32	NW
WALL NO 11																									
N	16	15	13	12	11	9	8	7	7	8	8	9	10	11	13	14	16	17	19	20	20	20	19	18	N
NE	19	17	15	14	12	11	9	9	11	14	17	20	22	23	24	25	25	26	26	25	25	23	22	20	NE
E	21	19	17	15	14	12	11	11	13	16	21	25	28	30	31	31	31	31	30	28	27	25	23	23	E
SE	20	18	16	14	13	11	10	9	10	12	15	19	22	25	26	27	28	28	28	27	26	25	23	22	SE
S	17	16	14	13	11	10	8	7	7	6	7	8	10	12	15	18	20	22	22	23	22	21	20	19	S
SW	25	23	21	19	17	15	13	11	11	10	10	10	11	12	15	19	23	27	30	33	33	32	30	28	SW
W	30	27	24	22	19	17	15	13	12	11	11	11	11	13	15	18	23	28	33	37	38	38	35	33	W
NW	26	23	21	19	17	15	13	11	10	10	10	10	10	11	12	14	16	19	23	27	31	32	32	30	NW
WALL NO 12																									
N	16	15	14	12	11	10	9	8	8	8	9	9	10	11	13	14	15	17	18	19	20	19	18	17	N
NE	19	17	16	14	13	12	10	10	12	14	17	20	22	23	23	24	25	25	25	25	24	23	22	21	NE
E	22	20	18	16	15	13	12	12	14	17	21	24	27	29	29	30	30	30	30	29	28	27	25	23	E
SE	20	18	17	15	14	12	11	10	11	13	16	19	21	24	25	26	27	27	27	27	26	25	23	22	SE
S	17	16	14	13	12	10	9	8	7	7	8	9	10	12	15	17	19	21	21	22	21	21	20	18	S
SW	25	23	21	19	17	15	14	12	11	11	11	11	12	13	15	18	22	26	29	31	31	31	29	27	SW
W	29	27	25	22	20	18	16	15	13	13	12	12	13	14	16	19	23	27	32	35	36	36	34	32	W
NW	25	23	21	19	17	15	14	12	11	11	11	11	11	12	14	16	19	22	26	29	30	30	29	27	NW
WALL NO 14																									
N	16	15	14	13	12	12	11	10	10	10	10	10	11	12	12	13	14	15	16	17	17	17	17	16	N
NE	20	19	18	17	15	14	13	13	14	15	17	19	20	21	21	22	22	23	23	23	23	21	21	21	NE
E	23	22	20	19	18	17	16	15	16	18	20	22	24	26	26	27	27	27	27	27	26	25	25	24	E
SE	21	20	19	17	16	15	14	13	14	14	16	18	20	21	23	23	24	24	25	25	24	24	23	22	SE
S	17	16	15	14	13	12	11	11	10	10	10	10	11	12	14	15	17	18	19	19	19	19	18	18	S
SW	24	23	22	20	19	18	17	15	15	14	14	13	14	14	16	18	20	23	25	27	27	27	26	25	SW
W	28	27	25	24	22	21	19	18	17	16	16	15	16	16	17	19	21	24	27	30	31	31	31	29	W
NW	24	23	21	20	19	17	16	15	14	14	13	13	14	14	15	16	18	20	23	25	26	26	26	25	NW
WALL NO 15																									
N	20	18	16	14	13	11	9	7	6	6	6	6	7	9	10	12	14	16	17	19	21	22	22	21	N
NE	22	20	17	15	13	11	9	8	7	9	11	14	18	21	23	25	26	27	28	28	27	27	25	24	NE
E	24	22	19	17	15	12	10	9	8	10	13	17	22	26	30	32	33	34	34	33	32	31	29	27	E
SE	23	21	19	16	14	12	10	8	7	8	9	12	16	20	23	26	28	30	30	30	30	29	27	25	SE
S	21	19	17	15	13	11	9	7	6	5	5	6	8	10	14	17	20	22	24	25	25	24	22	22	S
SW	32	29	26	23	20	17	14	12	10	8	7	7	7	8	10	13	16	21	26	30	34	36	36	34	SW
W	38	35	31	27	24	20	17	14	12	10	9	8	8	9	10	12	16	21	26	32	37	40	41	40	W
NW	32	29	26	23	20	17	15	12	10	8	7	7	7	8	9	11	14	17	22	27	31	34	34	34	NW
WALL NO 16																									
N	19	18	16	15	13	12	10	9	8	7	7	8	8	9	10	12	13	15	16	18	19	20	20	20	N
NE	22	20	18	17	15	13	11	10	10	10	12	15	18	20	22	23	24	25	26	26	26	25	25	23	NE
E	25	23	21	19	16	15	13	11	11	12	14	18	22	25	27	29	30	31	31	31	31	30	28	27	E
SE	23	21	19	18	16	14	12	10	10	10	11	13	16	19	22	24	26	27	28	28	28	27	26	25	SE
S	20	19	17	15	14	12	11	9	8	7	6	6	7	9	11	13	16	18	20	22	22	22	22	21	S
SW	30	28	26	23	21	18	16	14	12	11	10	9	9	10	11	13	16	20	24	28	31	32	32	31	SW
W	35	33	30	27	24	22	19	17	14	13	12	11	11	12	14	16	20	25	30	34	36	37	36	36	W
NW	29	28	26	23	21	19	16	14	12	11	10	9	9	10	11	12	14	17	21	25	28	30	31	31	NW

1. Direct application of data: Dark surface; Indoor temperature of 78°F; Outdoor maximum temperature of 95°F with mean temperature of 85°F and daily range of 21°F; Solar radiation typical of clear day on 21st day of month; Outside surface resistance of 0.333 hr-ft^2-°F/Btu; Inside surface film resistance of 0.685 hr-ft^2-°F/Btu.

2. Adjustment to table data: Design temperatures: Corrected $CLTD = CLTD + (78 - T_r) + (T_m - 85)$ where T_r = inside room temperature; T_m = mean outdoor temperature; T_m = maximum outdoor temperature − daily range/2; No adjustment recommended for color; No adjustment recommended for ventilation of air space above a ceiling.

Table 7-14. July Cooling Load Temperature Differences (CLTDs) for Calculating Cooling Load from Sunlit Walls 40° North Latitude

Wall Facing	1	2	3	4	5	6	7	8	9	10	11	12	13	14	15	16	17	18	19	20	21	22	23	24	Wall Facing
WALL NO 1																									
N	1	0	−1	−2	−3	−1	7	11	11	13	17	21	25	27	29	29	28	29	27	17	11	7	5	3	N
NE	1	0	−1	−2	−3	2	24	42	47	43	35	28	27	28	29	29	27	24	20	14	10	7	5	3	NE
E	1	0	−1	−2	−2	2	28	51	62	64	59	48	36	31	30	30	28	25	20	14	10	7	5	3	E
SE	1	0	−1	−2	−3	0	15	32	46	55	58	56	49	39	33	31	28	25	20	14	10	7	5	3	SE
S	1	0	−1	−2	−3	−2	0	4	11	21	33	43	50	52	50	44	34	27	20	14	10	7	5	3	S
SW	2	0	−1	−2	−2	−2	0	4	8	13	17	25	39	53	64	70	69	61	45	24	13	8	5	3	SW
W	2	1	−1	−2	−2	−2	1	4	8	13	17	21	27	42	59	73	80	79	62	32	16	9	6	3	W
NW	2	0	−1	−2	−2	−2	0	4	8	13	17	21	25	29	38	50	61	64	55	29	15	9	5	3	NW
WALL NO 2																									
N	5	3	2	0	−1	−2	−1	3	7	9	11	14	18	21	24	26	27	28	28	27	22	17	12	8	N
NE	5	3	2	0	−1	−2	2	13	26	36	39	37	33	31	29	29	29	28	26	23	18	14	10	7	NE
E	5	3	2	0	−1	−1	2	15	32	47	55	57	52	44	38	34	32	30	27	23	19	14	11	8	E
SE	5	3	2	0	−1	−2	0	8	20	33	43	50	53	51	45	39	35	31	28	24	19	14	11	8	SE
S	5	3	2	0	−1	−2	−2	−1	2	7	14	24	33	42	47	48	46	40	33	27	21	15	11	8	S
SW	7	4	2	1	0	−1	−2	0	2	5	9	13	20	30	41	53	61	65	62	53	39	27	17	11	SW
W	8	5	3	1	0	−1	−2	0	2	5	9	13	17	23	33	46	59	69	73	66	50	34	22	14	W
NW	8	4	2	1	−1	−2	−2	−1	2	5	9	13	17	21	25	32	41	51	57	54	42	29	19	12	NW
WALL NO 3																									
N	7	5	3	2	1	0	2	5	7	8	11	14	17	20	23	24	25	26	27	24	20	16	13	10	N
NE	7	5	3	2	0	0	7	17	26	31	33	31	30	29	29	29	29	28	25	22	18	15	12	9	NE
E	7	5	4	2	1	1	8	21	33	42	47	47	44	40	37	35	33	31	28	24	20	16	13	10	E
SE	8	5	4	2	1	0	4	12	22	32	39	44	46	44	41	38	35	32	29	24	20	16	13	10	SE
S	8	6	4	2	1	0	0	1	4	9	16	24	31	38	41	42	40	36	31	26	22	17	14	11	S
SW	12	9	6	4	2	1	1	2	4	6	9	14	21	30	40	49	55	57	54	45	36	28	21	16	SW
W	14	10	7	5	3	1	1	2	4	6	9	13	17	24	34	45	56	63	63	54	43	33	25	19	W
NW	12	8	6	4	2	1	0	2	3	6	9	13	16	20	25	32	40	48	50	44	35	27	21	16	NW
WALL NO 4																									
N	11	8	6	4	2	0	0	1	3	5	7	10	13	16	19	22	24	26	27	27	26	22	19	15	N
NE	10	7	5	3	2	0	0	4	12	21	29	32	33	32	31	30	30	29	28	26	23	20	16	13	NE
E	10	8	5	4	2	1	1	5	15	27	38	45	49	47	44	40	37	34	32	29	25	21	17	14	E
SE	11	8	6	4	2	1	0	2	8	17	27	36	43	46	46	44	41	37	34	30	26	22	18	14	SE
S	11	8	6	4	2	1	0	−1	0	2	6	13	20	28	35	41	43	42	39	35	30	24	19	15	S
SW	18	13	9	6	3	2	0	0	0	2	5	8	12	18	27	36	46	53	57	57	51	42	33	25	SW
W	21	15	10	7	4	2	1	0	1	2	5	8	11	15	21	30	40	51	60	64	60	50	40	30	W
NW	18	13	9	6	3	1	0	0	0	2	4	8	11	15	19	23	30	37	45	49	48	41	33	25	NW
WALL NO 5																									
N	13	10	8	6	5	3	2	3	5	6	8	9	12	14	17	19	21	23	24	24	23	21	18	15	N
NE	13	10	8	6	5	3	3	7	14	20	25	27	28	28	28	28	28	28	27	26	23	21	18	15	NE
E	14	11	9	7	5	4	4	8	17	26	33	39	40	40	38	37	35	34	32	29	26	23	20	17	E
SE	14	12	9	7	5	4	3	6	11	18	25	32	37	39	39	38	37	35	33	30	27	24	20	17	SE
S	15	12	9	7	5	4	3	2	3	4	8	13	19	25	31	35	36	36	34	32	28	24	21	18	S
SW	22	18	14	11	8	6	5	4	4	5	6	9	12	17	25	33	40	46	49	48	44	38	32	26	SW
W	25	20	16	13	10	7	5	4	4	5	7	9	11	15	20	28	37	45	52	54	50	44	37	30	W
NW	21	17	13	10	8	6	4	3	4	4	6	8	11	14	17	21	27	34	40	42	40	35	30	25	NW
WALL NO 6																									
N	13	11	9	8	6	5	4	5	6	7	8	10	12	14	16	18	20	21	22	23	21	20	17	15	N
NE	14	12	10	8	6	5	6	10	15	20	23	25	25	26	26	27	27	27	26	25	23	21	18	16	NE
E	16	13	11	9	7	6	7	11	18	25	31	35	36	36	35	35	34	33	31	29	26	24	21	18	E
SE	16	14	11	9	8	6	6	8	13	18	24	29	33	35	36	35	34	33	32	29	27	24	21	18	SE
S	16	13	11	9	7	6	5	4	4	6	9	13	18	24	28	31	33	33	31	29	27	24	21	18	S
SW	23	19	16	14	11	9	7	6	6	7	8	10	13	18	24	31	37	42	44	43	40	35	31	27	SW
W	26	22	18	15	13	10	8	7	7	7	8	10	12	15	20	27	35	42	47	48	45	40	35	30	W
NW	21	18	15	12	10	8	7	6	6	6	8	9	11	14	16	21	26	32	36	38	36	32	28	25	NW
WALL NO 7																									
N	13	12	10	9	7	6	6	7	8	8	9	11	12	14	16	17	18	19	20	20	19	18	16	15	N
NE	15	13	11	10	9	8	9	13	17	20	22	23	23	24	24	25	25	25	24	23	22	20	18	16	NE
E	17	15	13	12	10	9	11	16	21	26	30	32	32	32	32	32	31	30	29	27	25	23	21	19	E
SE	17	15	13	12	10	9	9	12	16	21	25	28	31	32	32	32	31	30	29	27	25	23	21	19	SE
S	16	14	13	11	10	8	7	7	7	9	12	15	19	23	26	28	29	29	28	26	24	22	20	18	S
SW	23	20	18	16	13	12	10	10	10	10	11	12	15	20	25	30	35	38	39	37	34	31	28	15	SW
W	25	22	20	17	15	13	12	11	11	11	11	12	13	14	17	22	28	34	39	42	41	38	34	28	W
NW	20	18	16	14	12	10	9	9	9	9	9	10	11	13	15	17	21	26	30	33	33	30	28	23	NW
WALL NO 9																									
N	17	15	13	11	9	7	5	4	4	4	5	7	8	10	12	15	17	19	21	22	23	23	22	20	N
NE	18	15	13	11	9	7	5	5	5	6	10	16	20	23	25	26	27	27	28	28	27	26	25	23	NE
E	20	17	14	12	10	8	6	5	7	12	19	26	32	36	37	37	37	36	34	33	31	29	26	23	E
SE	20	17	15	12	10	8	6	5	6	9	13	19	25	31	34	36	37	36	35	34	32	29	26	23	SE
S	21	18	15	12	10	8	6	5	4	3	4	6	10	14	20	25	29	33	34	34	32	30	27	24	S
SW	31	26	22	18	15	12	9	7	6	5	5	6	8	10	14	19	26	33	39	43	45	44	40	36	SW
W	35	30	25	21	17	14	11	8	7	6	6	7	8	10	12	16	22	30	37	44	48	48	45	41	W
NW	29	25	21	17	14	11	9	7	5	5	5	6	7	9	11	14	18	22	28	34	37	38	36	33	NW

Table 7-14. July Cooling Load Temperature Differences (CLTDs) for Calculating Cooling Load from Sunlit Walls 40° North Latitude *(Continued)*

Wall Facing	Solar Time, hr																								Wall Facing
	1	2	3	4	5	6	7	8	9	10	11	12	13	14	15	16	17	18	19	20	21	22	23	24	
WALL NO 10																									
N	17	15	13	11	9	7	6	5	5	5	6	7	8	10	12	14	17	18	20	22	22	22	21	19	N
NE	18	16	13	11	9	7	6	6	8	12	16	20	22	24	25	26	27	27	27	27	26	24	22	20	NE
E	20	17	15	12	10	8	7	7	10	14	20	26	31	34	35	36	36	35	34	33	31	28	26	23	E
SE	21	18	15	13	10	8	7	6	7	10	15	20	25	30	33	34	35	35	34	33	31	29	26	23	SE
S	21	18	15	13	11	9	7	5	4	4	5	7	11	15	20	24	28	31	32	32	31	29	26	24	S
SW	31	27	23	19	16	13	10	8	7	6	6	7	8	11	15	20	26	32	38	41	42	41	38	35	SW
W	34	30	26	22	18	15	12	9	8	7	7	7	8	10	13	17	23	30	37	42	45	45	42	39	W
NW	28	24	21	18	15	12	10	8	6	6	6	6	8	10	12	14	18	23	28	33	35	36	34	31	NW
WALL NO 11																									
N	16	14	13	12	10	9	8	7	7	7	8	9	10	11	12	14	15	17	18	19	20	19	18	17	N
NE	18	17	15	13	12	10	9	9	11	14	17	20	21	22	23	23	24	24	25	25	24	23	21	20	NE
E	21	19	17	16	14	12	11	11	13	17	22	26	29	30	31	31	31	31	30	29	27	25	24	23	E
SE	21	19	17	16	14	12	11	10	11	14	17	21	24	27	29	30	31	31	30	30	29	27	25	23	SE
S	20	18	16	15	13	11	10	9	8	8	8	10	13	16	19	23	25	27	28	28	27	25	24	22	S
SW	28	25	23	20	18	16	14	12	11	11	10	11	12	14	17	21	25	30	33	36	36	35	33	30	SW
W	31	28	25	22	20	18	16	14	12	12	11	12	12	13	15	19	23	28	33	37	39	38	36	33	W
NW	25	23	20	18	16	14	12	11	10	9	9	10	11	12	13	15	18	22	26	29	31	31	29	27	NW
WALL NO 12																									
N	16	14	13	12	11	10	8	8	8	8	9	10	11	12	14	15	16	17	18	19	19	18	17	16	N
NE	18	17	15	14	13	11	10	10	12	14	17	19	21	21	22	23	23	24	24	24	23	22	21	20	NE
E	22	20	18	17	15	13	12	12	14	17	21	25	28	29	30	30	30	30	30	29	28	27	25	24	E
SE	22	20	18	16	15	13	12	11	12	14	17	21	24	26	28	29	30	30	30	29	28	27	25	23	SE
S	20	19	17	15	14	12	11	10	9	9	9	11	13	16	19	22	24	26	26	26	25	23	22	21	S
SW	27	25	23	21	19	17	15	14	12	12	12	12	12	14	17	20	24	28	32	34	34	34	32	30	SW
W	30	28	25	23	21	19	17	15	14	13	13	13	13	14	16	19	23	27	32	35	37	36	35	33	W
NW	24	22	20	19	17	15	13	12	11	10	10	11	11	12	13	15	18	21	25	28	29	29	28	26	NW
WALL NO 14																									
N	15	15	14	13	12	11	10	10	10	10	10	10	10	11	12	13	14	15	15	16	17	17	16	16	N
NE	19	18	17	16	15	14	13	13	14	15	17	18	19	20	20	21	21	22	22	22	22	22	21	20	NE
E	23	22	21	19	18	17	16	15	16	18	21	23	25	26	27	27	28	28	28	27	26	25	24	23	E
SE	23	21	20	19	18	16	15	15	15	16	18	20	22	24	25	26	27	27	27	27	26	26	25	24	SE
S	20	19	18	17	16	15	14	13	12	12	12	12	14	15	17	19	21	22	23	23	23	23	22	21	S
SW	26	25	24	22	21	19	18	17	16	15	15	15	15	16	17	19	22	25	27	29	30	30	29	28	SW
W	29	27	26	24	23	21	20	18	17	16	16	16	16	16	17	19	21	24	27	30	32	32	31	30	W
NW	23	22	21	19	18	17	16	15	14	13	13	13	13	14	14	15	17	19	21	24	25	25	25	24	NW
WALL NO 15																									
N	19	18	16	14	12	10	9	7	6	6	6	6	7	8	9	11	13	15	17	19	20	21	21	20	N
NE	21	19	17	15	13	11	9	8	7	9	11	14	18	20	22	23	25	25	26	26	26	26	25	23	NE
E	25	22	20	17	15	12	10	9	9	10	14	18	23	27	30	32	34	34	34	33	32	31	29	27	E
SE	25	22	20	17	15	13	11	9	8	8	10	14	18	22	26	30	32	33	34	33	33	31	30	27	SE
S	25	22	20	17	15	13	11	9	7	6	6	6	7	10	13	17	21	25	28	30	30	29	27	25	S
SW	35	32	28	25	22	18	16	13	11	9	8	8	8	9	11	14	18	23	28	33	37	39	39	37	SW
W	39	35	32	28	24	21	18	15	12	10	9	8	8	9	10	13	16	21	26	32	38	41	42	41	W
NW	31	28	26	23	20	17	14	12	10	8	7	7	7	8	9	11	13	16	20	25	29	32	33	33	NW
WALL NO 16																									
N	18	17	16	14	13	11	10	9	8	7	7	7	8	9	10	11	13	14	16	17	18	19	20	20	N
NE	21	20	18	16	14	13	11	10	10	11	13	15	17	19	21	22	23	24	24	25	25	24	24	23	NE
E	25	23	21	19	17	15	13	11	11	12	15	19	22	26	28	30	31	31	32	32	31	30	29	27	E
SE	25	23	21	19	17	15	13	11	10	11	12	15	18	21	25	27	29	30	31	31	31	30	29	27	SE
S	24	22	20	18	16	14	12	11	9	8	8	8	9	11	14	17	20	23	25	27	27	27	27	25	S
SW	33	30	28	25	23	20	18	15	13	12	11	10	10	11	12	15	18	22	27	30	33	35	35	34	SW
W	36	33	31	28	25	22	20	17	15	13	12	11	11	11	12	14	17	20	25	30	34	37	38	37	W
NW	29	27	25	23	20	18	16	14	12	11	10	9	9	10	11	12	14	16	19	23	27	29	30	30	NW

1. Direct application of data: Dark surface; Indoor temperature of 78°F; Outdoor maximum temperature of 95°F with mean temperature of 85°F and daily range of 21°F; Solar radiation typical of clear day on 21st day of month; Outside surface resistance of 0.333 hr-ft²-°F/Btu; Inside surface film resistance of 0.685 hr-ft²-°F/Btu.

2. Adjustment to table data: Design temperatures: Corrected $CLTD = CLTD + (78 - T_r) + (T_m - 85)$ where T_r = inside room temperature; T_m = mean outdoor temperature; T_m = maximum outdoor temperature − daily range/2; No adjustment recommended for color; No adjustment recommended for ventilation of air space above a ceiling.

Table 7-15. July Cooling Load Temperature Differences (Clads) for Calculating Cooling Load from Sunlit Walls 48° North Latitude

Wall Facing	1	2	3	4	5	6	7	8	9	10	11	12	13	14	15	16	17	18	19	20	21	22	23	24	Wall Facing
																									Solar Time, hr
										WALL NO 1														
N	1	0	−1	−2	−2	3	9	10	10	13	17	21	24	27	28	28	27	27	27	21	13	8	5	3	N
NE	1	0	−1	−2	−1	10	30	42	44	38	30	26	26	28	29	29	27	24	20	15	10	7	5	3	NE
E	1	0	−1	−2	−1	10	34	54	63	64	58	47	35	31	30	29	28	25	20	15	10	7	5	3	E
SE	2	0	−1	−2	−2	4	19	36	50	59	63	61	55	45	36	31	28	25	20	15	10	7	5	3	SE
S	2	0	−1	−2	−2	−2	1	5	15	28	41	52	59	62	59	51	40	29	22	15	11	7	5	3	S
SW	2	1	−1	−2	−2	−1	1	5	8	12	18	29	45	59	70	75	74	65	49	29	16	9	6	3	SW
W	2	1	−1	−2	−2	−1	1	5	9	13	17	21	26	41	58	72	80	80	67	41	20	11	6	4	W
NW	2	0	−1	−2	−2	−2	1	5	8	12	17	21	24	27	33	45	56	62	57	37	19	10	6	3	NW
										WALL NO 2														
N	6	3	2	0	−1	−1	1	5	7	9	11	14	17	21	24	26	27	27	27	27	24	18	13	9	N
NE	5	3	2	0	−1	0	6	18	29	36	37	34	30	28	28	28	28	26	23	19	14	11	8	NE
E	5	3	2	0	−1	0	6	20	36	49	56	57	52	44	38	34	31	29	27	23	19	15	11	8	E
SE	5	3	2	0	−1	−1	2	11	23	36	48	55	58	56	51	43	37	33	29	24	20	15	11	8	SE
S	6	4	2	0	−1	−1	−1	0	3	9	19	30	41	50	55	57	54	47	38	30	23	17	12	8	S
SW	8	5	3	1	0	−1	−1	0	2	6	9	14	22	33	46	58	66	69	67	57	44	30	20	13	SW
W	9	6	3	1	0	−1	−1	0	3	6	9	13	17	22	32	45	58	69	73	69	55	38	25	15	W
NW	8	5	3	1	0	−1	−1	0	2	5	9	13	17	20	24	29	37	46	54	54	46	33	22	14	NW
										WALL NO 3														
N	8	6	4	2	1	1	3	5	7	8	11	14	17	20	22	24	25	25	26	25	21	17	14	10	N
NE	7	5	3	2	1	3	11	20	27	31	30	29	28	28	28	28	28	27	25	22	19	15	12	9	NE
E	8	5	4	2	1	3	12	24	36	44	48	48	44	40	37	35	33	31	28	24	20	16	13	10	E
SE	8	6	4	2	1	1	6	15	25	35	43	49	51	49	45	41	37	34	30	26	21	17	14	11	SE
S	9	6	4	3	1	0	0	2	5	12	20	29	38	45	49	50	47	42	36	30	24	19	15	12	S
SW	13	9	7	4	2	1	1	2	4	6	10	15	24	34	45	54	60	61	58	50	39	31	23	18	SW
W	15	11	8	5	3	2	2	2	4	7	9	13	16	23	33	45	55	62	64	58	46	36	27	20	W
NW	12	9	6	4	2	1	1	2	4	6	9	13	16	19	23	29	37	44	49	46	38	29	22	17	NW
										WALL NO 4														
N	12	9	6	4	2	1	1	2	4	6	8	10	13	16	19	21	24	25	26	26	23	19	16	N
NE	10	8	5	3	2	1	2	7	15	23	29	31	31	30	29	29	29	28	28	26	23	20	17	13	NE
E	11	8	6	4	2	1	2	8	18	30	40	47	49	48	44	40	37	34	31	29	25	21	18	14	E
SE	11	8	6	4	2	1	1	4	11	20	30	40	47	51	51	49	45	40	36	32	27	23	18	14	SE
S	12	9	6	4	2	1	0	0	1	3	9	16	25	34	43	48	51	50	46	40	34	27	22	17	S
SW	20	14	10	6	4	2	1	0	1	3	5	8	13	20	30	40	50	58	62	61	55	46	36	27	SW
W	24	17	11	7	5	2	1	0	1	3	5	8	11	15	21	29	40	51	60	64	62	54	43	32	W
NW	20	14	10	6	4	2	0	0	1	2	5	8	11	14	18	22	27	34	42	47	47	43	35	27	NW
										WALL NO 5														
N	13	11	9	7	5	3	3	4	5	6	8	10	12	14	17	19	21	22	23	24	23	21	19	16	N
NE	13	10	8	6	5	4	5	10	16	22	25	26	26	26	27	27	27	27	27	25	23	21	18	15	NE
E	14	12	9	7	5	4	6	11	20	28	35	40	41	40	39	37	35	34	32	29	27	23	20	17	E
SE	15	12	10	8	6	4	4	7	13	20	28	35	40	43	44	42	40	38	35	32	29	25	21	18	SE
S	16	13	11	8	6	5	3	3	3	6	10	16	23	31	37	41	43	43	40	37	32	28	24	20	S
SW	24	19	15	12	9	7	5	4	4	5	7	9	13	19	27	36	44	50	53	52	48	41	35	29	SW
W	27	21	17	14	10	8	6	5	5	6	7	9	11	15	20	27	36	45	52	55	52	46	39	32	W
NW	21	17	14	11	8	6	5	4	4	5	6	8	11	14	16	20	25	31	37	41	40	36	31	26	NW
										WALL NO 6														
N	14	12	10	8	6	5	5	6	6	7	8	10	12	14	16	18	19	21	22	22	22	20	18	16	N
NE	14	12	10	8	6	6	7	12	17	21	23	24	24	25	25	26	26	26	26	25	23	21	18	16	NE
E	16	14	11	9	8	7	9	14	20	27	33	36	37	37	36	35	34	33	31	29	27	24	21	19	E
SE	17	14	12	10	8	7	7	10	15	21	27	33	37	39	40	39	38	36	34	32	29	26	23	20	SE
S	18	15	13	11	9	7	6	5	6	8	12	17	23	29	34	37	39	39	37	34	31	28	24	21	S
SW	25	21	18	15	12	10	8	7	7	7	9	11	14	20	27	34	40	45	48	47	43	39	34	29	SW
W	27	23	19	16	13	11	9	8	8	8	9	10	12	15	20	27	34	42	47	49	47	42	37	32	W
NW	22	18	15	13	10	8	7	6	7	8	9	11	14	16	19	24	29	34	37	36	33	29	25	NW
										WALL NO 7														
N	13	12	10	9	8	7	7	8	8	8	9	11	12	14	16	17	18	19	20	20	19	18	16	15	N
NE	15	13	11	10	9	9	11	15	18	21	22	22	22	23	24	24	25	25	24	23	21	20	18	16	NE
E	17	16	14	12	10	10	13	18	23	28	31	33	33	33	32	32	32	31	30	28	26	24	22	20	E
SE	18	16	14	13	11	10	11	14	18	23	27	31	34	35	35	35	34	33	32	30	27	25	23	21	SE
S	19	17	15	13	11	10	9	8	9	11	15	19	23	28	31	34	34	34	32	30	28	26	23	21	S
SW	25	22	19	17	15	13	12	11	11	11	12	14	17	22	28	33	38	41	42	40	37	34	31	28	SW
W	26	23	21	18	16	14	12	12	11	11	12	13	14	17	22	28	34	39	42	42	40	36	33	29	W
NW	21	18	16	14	12	11	10	9	9	9	10	11	13	14	17	20	24	28	32	33	31	28	26	23	NW
										WALL NO 9														
N	18	15	13	11	9	7	5	5	5	5	6	7	8	10	12	14	17	19	20	22	23	23	22	20	N
NE	18	15	13	11	9	7	6	6	8	12	17	21	23	25	25	26	26	27	27	27	26	24	22	20	NE
E	20	17	15	12	10	8	6	6	9	15	22	28	34	37	38	38	37	36	35	33	31	29	26	23	E
SE	21	18	15	13	10	8	7	6	7	10	16	22	28	34	38	41	41	40	39	37	34	31	28	25	SE
S	24	20	17	14	11	9	7	5	4	4	5	8	12	18	24	30	35	39	40	40	38	35	31	27	S
SW	34	29	24	20	16	13	10	8	7	6	6	7	8	11	15	22	29	36	43	47	49	48	44	39	SW
W	37	32	27	22	18	15	12	9	7	7	7	6	7	8	10	12	16	22	29	37	44	49	50	47	43	W
NW	29	25	21	18	14	17	9	7	6	5	5	6	7	9	11	14	17	21	26	31	36	38	36	33	NW

Table 7-15. July Cooling Load Temperature Differences (Clads) for Calculating Cooling Load from Sunlit Walls 48° North Latitude *(Continued)*

Wall Facing	Solar Time, hr																								Wall Facing
	1	2	3	4	5	6	7	8	9	10	11	12	13	14	15	16	17	18	19	20	21	22	23	24	
WALL NO 10																									
N	17	15	13	11	9	7	6	5	5	6	6	7	9	10	12	14	16	18	20	21	22	22	21	19	N
NE	18	15	13	11	9	7	6	7	10	13	17	20	22	23	24	25	26	26	26	26	25	24	22	20	NE
E	20	18	15	13	10	8	7	8	11	16	22	28	32	35	36	36	36	35	34	33	31	29	26	23	E
SE	22	19	16	14	11	9	7	7	9	12	17	22	28	33	36	38	39	39	38	36	34	31	28	25	SE
S	24	21	18	15	12	10	8	6	6	5	5	7	9	14	19	24	30	34	37	38	38	36	34	31	S
SW	34	29	25	21	17	14	11	9	8	7	7	7	9	12	17	22	29	36	41	45	46	45	42	38	SW
W	36	32	27	23	19	16	13	10	9	8	7	8	9	10	13	17	23	30	37	42	46	46	44	41	W
NW	29	25	22	18	15	12	10	8	7	6	6	7	8	10	12	14	17	21	26	31	34	35	34	32	NW
WALL NO 11																									
N	16	15	13	12	10	9	8	8	8	8	8	9	10	11	12	14	15	17	18	19	19	19	19	18	N
NE	18	16	15	13	12	10	10	10	12	15	18	20	21	22	22	23	23	24	24	24	23	22	21	20	NE
E	22	20	18	16	14	12	12	12	15	19	23	27	30	32	32	32	32	32	31	30	29	28	26	24	E
SE	23	21	19	17	15	13	12	12	13	15	19	23	27	30	33	34	34	34	33	32	31	29	27	25	SE
S	23	21	19	17	15	13	12	10	10	9	10	12	16	19	23	27	30	32	33	33	31	30	28	26	S
SW	30	28	25	22	20	18	15	14	13	12	12	12	13	15	18	23	28	32	36	39	39	38	36	33	SW
W	32	29	26	23	21	19	16	15	13	12	12	12	13	14	16	19	23	28	33	38	40	40	38	35	W
NW	25	23	21	18	16	14	13	11	10	10	10	10	11	12	13	15	17	20	24	28	30	30	29	27	NW
WALL NO 12																									
N	16	15	13	12	11	10	9	8	8	8	8	9	10	11	12	14	15	16	17	18	19	19	18	17	N
NE	18	17	15	14	12	11	11	11	13	15	18	19	20	21	22	22	23	23	24	23	23	22	21	20	NE
E	22	20	19	17	15	14	13	13	16	19	23	26	29	30	31	31	31	31	30	30	29	27	26	24	E
SE	23	21	20	18	16	14	13	13	14	16	19	23	26	29	31	33	33	33	32	32	30	29	27	25	SE
S	23	22	20	18	16	14	13	12	11	11	11	13	16	19	23	26	29	31	31	31	30	29	27	25	S
SW	30	28	25	23	21	19	17	15	14	13	13	13	14	16	19	22	27	31	35	37	38	37	35	33	SW
W	32	29	26	24	22	19	17	16	15	14	13	13	14	14	16	19	23	27	32	36	38	38	36	34	W
NW	25	23	21	19	17	15	14	12	11	11	11	11	11	12	13	15	17	20	23	26	29	29	28	27	NW
WALL NO 14																									
N	16	15	14	13	12	11	11	10	10	10	10	10	11	11	12	13	14	15	15	16	17	17	17	16	N
NE	19	18	17	16	15	14	13	13	14	16	17	18	19	20	20	21	21	21	22	22	22	21	21	20	NE
E	24	22	21	20	18	17	16	16	18	20	22	24	26	27	28	28	28	28	28	28	28	27	26	25	E
SE	24	23	22	20	19	18	17	16	17	18	20	22	24	26	28	29	29	30	30	29	29	28	27	26	SE
S	24	22	21	20	18	17	16	15	14	14	14	15	16	18	21	23	25	27	27	28	27	27	26	25	S
SW	29	27	26	24	23	21	20	19	18	17	16	16	16	17	19	21	24	27	30	32	33	32	32	30	SW
W	30	28	27	25	23	22	20	19	18	17	16	16	16	17	18	19	22	24	28	30	32	33	32	31	W
NW	23	22	21	20	18	17	16	15	14	13	13	13	13	14	14	15	17	18	21	23	24	25	25	24	NW
WALL NO 15																									
N	19	18	16	14	13	11	9	8	7	6	6	7	7	8	10	11	13	15	17	18	20	21	21	20	N
NE	21	19	17	15	13	11	9	8	8	10	13	16	18	20	22	23	24	25	25	26	26	25	24	23	NE
E	25	22	20	17	15	13	11	9	10	12	15	20	25	29	32	34	34	35	34	34	33	31	30	27	E
SE	27	24	21	18	16	14	11	10	9	10	12	16	20	25	29	33	35	37	37	37	36	34	32	29	SE
S	29	26	23	20	17	15	12	10	8	7	7	7	9	12	17	21	26	30	33	35	36	35	33	31	S
SW	38	35	31	27	24	20	17	14	12	10	9	8	9	10	12	15	20	25	31	36	40	42	42	41	SW
W	40	37	33	29	26	22	19	16	13	11	10	9	9	10	11	13	16	21	26	32	38	41	43	42	W
NW	31	29	26	23	20	17	15	12	10	9	8	7	7	8	8	9	11	13	16	19	23	28	31	32	NW
WALL NO 16																									
N	18	17	16	15	13	12	10	9	8	8	8	8	8	9	10	11	13	14	16	17	18	19	19	19	N
NE	21	19	18	16	14	13	11	10	10	12	14	16	18	19	20	22	22	23	24	24	24	24	23	22	NE
E	25	23	21	19	17	15	13	12	12	14	17	20	24	27	29	31	32	32	32	32	31	30	29	27	E
SE	27	25	22	20	18	16	14	12	12	12	14	17	20	24	27	30	32	34	34	34	33	32	31	29	SE
S	28	26	23	21	19	16	14	12	11	10	9	10	11	14	17	21	24	28	30	32	33	32	31	30	S
SW	36	33	31	28	25	22	19	17	15	13	12	11	11	12	13	16	20	24	29	33	36	38	38	38	SW
W	37	35	32	29	26	23	21	18	16	14	13	12	12	12	14	17	20	25	30	34	37	39	38	38	W
NW	29	27	25	23	21	18	16	14	12	11	10	9	9	10	11	12	13	16	19	22	25	28	29	29	NW

1. Direct application of data: Dark surface; Indoor temperature of 78°F; Outdoor maximum temperature of 95°F with mean temperature of 85°F and daily range of 21°F; Solar radiation typical of clear day on 21st day of month; Outside surface resistance of 0.333 hr-ft²-°F/Btu; Inside surface film resistance of 0.685 hr-ft²-°F/Btu.

2. Adjustment to table data: Design temperatures: Corrected $CLTD = CLTD + (78 - T_r) + (T_m - 85)$ where T_r = inside room temperature; T_m = mean outdoor temperature; T_m = maximum outdoor temperature − daily range/2; No adjustment recommended for color; No adjustment recommended for ventilation of air space above a ceiling.

Table 7-16. August Cooling Load Temperature Differences (CLTDs) for Calculating Cooling Load from Sunlit Walls 24° North Latitude

Wall Facing	1	2	3	4	5	6	7	8	9	10	11	12	13	14	15	16	17	18	19	20	21	22	23	24	Wall Facing
WALL NO 1																									
N	1	0	-1	-2	-3	-3	0	6	9	12	17	21	25	28	29	29	27	26	20	13	9	7	4	3	N
NE	1	0	-1	-2	-3	-2	8	31	44	46	41	33	29	29	30	29	27	23	17	13	9	7	5	3	NE
E	1	0	-1	-2	-3	-2	10	39	59	65	60	49	36	32	31	30	27	23	18	13	10	7	5	3	E
SE	1	0	-1	-2	-3	-2	5	26	43	52	54	51	43	35	32	30	27	23	17	13	9	7	5	3	SE
S	1	0	-1	-2	-3	-3	-2	2	8	17	26	35	41	43	42	37	30	24	18	13	9	7	4	3	S
SW	2	0	-1	-2	-2	-3	-2	2	7	12	17	23	34	48	60	67	68	57	35	19	12	8	5	3	SW
W	2	0	-1	-2	-2	-3	-1	3	7	12	17	21	27	43	61	75	82	73	45	23	13	8	5	3	W
NW	1	0	-1	-2	-3	-3	-2	2	7	12	17	21	25	32	44	56	63	60	38	20	12	8	5	3	NW
WALL NO 2																									
N	5	3	1	0	-1	-2	-2	-1	2	5	9	13	17	21	24	27	27	27	26	23	18	14	10	7	N
NE	5	3	2	0	-1	-2	-1	5	17	30	38	39	36	33	31	30	30	28	25	21	17	13	10	7	NE
E	5	3	2	0	-1	-2	-1	6	22	40	52	56	52	45	39	35	32	29	26	22	17	13	10	7	E
SE	5	3	2	0	-1	-2	-2	3	15	29	40	47	49	46	41	36	33	30	26	22	17	13	10	7	SE
S	5	3	1	0	-1	-2	-2	-2	0	4	11	19	27	34	38	40	38	34	29	23	18	14	10	7	S
SW	6	4	2	1	-1	-2	-2	-2	1	4	8	13	18	26	37	49	58	62	59	47	34	23	15	10	SW
W	7	4	2	1	0	-1	-2	-2	1	4	8	13	17	23	33	47	61	70	70	58	41	27	18	11	W
NW	6	4	2	1	-1	-2	-2	-2	0	4	8	12	17	21	27	36	45	54	55	47	34	23	15	10	NW
WALL NO 3																									
N	7	5	3	2	0	-1	-1	1	3	6	9	13	16	20	22	24	25	25	24	21	17	14	11	9	N
NE	7	5	3	2	0	0	2	10	20	28	32	32	31	30	30	30	29	27	25	21	18	14	12	9	NE
E	7	5	3	2	1	0	2	13	27	38	45	46	43	40	37	35	33	30	26	23	19	15	12	10	E
SE	7	5	3	2	1	0	1	8	18	29	36	41	41	39	37	35	33	30	26	22	19	15	12	9	SE
S	7	5	3	2	0	-1	-1	0	2	6	12	19	25	30	34	35	34	31	27	23	19	15	12	9	S
SW	11	8	5	3	2	0	0	0	2	5	9	13	19	27	37	46	52	54	49	40	31	25	19	14	SW
W	12	9	6	4	2	1	0	1	3	5	9	12	16	24	34	46	57	62	57	47	37	28	22	16	W
NW	10	7	5	3	1	0	0	0	2	5	9	12	16	20	27	35	44	49	46	38	30	24	18	14	NW
WALL NO 4																									
N	10	7	5	3	2	0	-1	-1	0	2	4	8	11	15	18	21	24	25	26	25	23	19	16	13	N
NE	10	7	5	3	2	0	0	1	6	15	24	30	33	33	32	32	31	30	28	26	23	19	16	13	NE
E	10	7	5	3	2	0	0	1	8	20	32	42	46	46	44	40	37	34	31	28	24	20	16	13	E
SE	10	7	5	3	2	0	0	0	5	13	23	32	39	42	42	40	37	35	32	28	24	20	16	13	SE
S	10	7	5	3	2	0	-1	-1	-1	1	4	9	16	22	28	33	35	35	33	30	25	21	17	13	S
SW	16	11	8	5	3	1	0	-1	-1	1	3	7	11	16	24	33	42	50	54	52	46	37	29	22	SW
W	18	13	9	6	3	2	0	-1	0	1	4	7	11	15	21	30	42	53	60	61	54	44	34	25	W
NW	16	11	8	5	3	1	0	-1	-1	1	3	7	10	14	19	25	32	40	47	48	43	36	28	21	NW
WALL NO 5																									
N	11	9	7	6	4	3	2	1	2	3	5	8	10	13	16	19	21	22	23	22	20	18	16	14	N
NE	12	10	8	6	4	3	2	4	9	16	22	26	27	28	28	28	29	28	27	25	23	20	17	15	NE
E	13	11	9	7	5	3	3	4	11	20	29	36	39	38	37	36	35	33	31	28	25	22	19	16	E
SE	13	11	9	7	5	3	2	3	8	15	22	29	33	35	35	34	32	30	28	25	22	19	16	16	SE
S	13	10	8	6	5	3	2	1	1	3	6	10	15	20	25	28	30	30	29	27	24	21	18	15	S
SW	19	16	13	10	7	5	4	3	3	4	5	8	11	15	22	30	37	43	46	44	39	34	28	24	SW
W	22	18	14	11	9	6	5	3	3	4	6	8	11	14	20	28	37	46	51	50	45	39	33	27	W
NW	18	15	12	9	7	5	3	2	2	3	5	7	10	13	17	23	29	36	40	40	37	32	27	22	NW
WALL NO 6																									
N	12	10	8	7	5	4	3	3	3	4	6	8	10	13	15	17	19	20	21	20	19	17	16	14	N
NE	14	11	10	8	6	5	4	6	11	16	21	23	25	25	26	27	27	27	26	24	22	20	18	16	NE
E	15	13	11	9	7	6	5	7	13	21	28	32	34	35	34	34	33	32	30	28	25	23	20	18	E
SE	15	13	11	9	7	5	4	6	10	16	22	27	30	32	32	32	32	31	29	27	25	22	20	17	SE
S	14	12	10	8	6	5	4	3	2	4	7	10	15	19	23	26	27	27	26	25	23	20	18	16	S
SW	21	18	15	12	10	8	6	5	5	6	7	9	11	16	22	28	34	39	41	39	36	32	28	24	SW
W	23	20	17	14	11	9	7	6	6	6	7	9	11	15	20	27	35	42	46	44	41	36	31	27	W
NW	19	16	14	11	9	7	6	5	5	5	7	8	11	13	17	22	28	33	36	36	33	29	26	22	NW
WALL NO 7																									
N	12	10	9	8	7	5	5	5	5	6	7	9	11	13	15	16	17	18	19	18	17	16	14	13	N
NE	14	13	11	10	8	7	7	10	14	18	20	22	22	23	24	25	25	25	24	22	21	19	18	16	NE
E	16	15	13	11	10	8	8	12	17	23	27	30	31	31	30	30	30	29	28	26	24	22	20	18	E
SE	16	14	12	11	9	8	7	10	14	18	22	26	28	28	29	29	29	28	27	25	23	21	20	18	SE
S	14	12	11	9	8	7	6	5	6	7	9	12	15	19	21	23	24	24	23	22	20	19	17	16	S
SW	20	18	16	14	12	10	9	8	8	9	10	11	14	18	22	28	32	35	35	33	31	28	25	23	SW
W	23	20	18	16	14	12	10	9	9	10	10	12	13	17	22	28	34	39	39	37	34	31	28	26	W
NW	19	17	15	13	11	9	8	8	7	7	8	10	12	14	18	22	27	31	32	30	28	26	23	21	NW
WALL NO 9																									
N	15	13	11	9	8	6	4	3	2	2	3	4	6	8	11	13	16	18	20	21	21	21	19	17	N
NE	17	15	13	10	8	7	5	4	4	7	11	17	21	24	26	27	27	28	28	27	26	24	22	20	NE
E	19	16	14	11	9	7	6	4	4	5	9	15	22	29	33	35	36	36	35	34	32	30	28	25	E
SE	19	16	14	11	9	7	5	4	4	6	11	17	23	28	31	33	33	33	33	31	29	27	24	22	SE
S	18	15	13	11	9	7	5	4	3	2	3	4	7	11	16	20	24	27	28	28	27	25	23	20	S
SW	28	24	20	16	13	11	8	6	5	4	4	5	6	9	12	17	24	30	36	41	42	40	36	32	SW
W	32	27	23	19	15	12	10	7	6	5	5	5	7	9	12	16	22	30	38	44	46	45	41	37	W
NW	26	22	19	15	13	10	8	6	4	4	4	5	6	8	11	14	18	24	30	35	37	36	33	30	NW

Table 7-16. August Cooling Load Temperature Differences (CLTDs) for Calculating Cooling Load from Sunlit Walls 24° North Latitude *(Continued)*

Wall Facing	Solar Time, hr																								Wall Facing
	1	2	3	4	5	6	7	8	9	10	11	12	13	14	15	16	17	18	19	20	21	22	23	24	
WALL NO 10																									
N	15	13	12	10	8	6	5	4	3	3	4	5	6	9	11	13	16	18	19	20	20	20	19	17	N
NE	17	15	13	11	9	7	6	5	6	9	13	17	20	23	24	26	27	27	27	27	25	24	22	20	NE
E	19	17	14	12	10	8	6	5	7	11	16	22	28	31	33	34	34	34	33	32	30	27	25	22	E
SE	19	17	14	12	10	8	6	5	6	8	12	17	22	26	29	31	32	32	32	31	29	27	24	22	SE
S	18	16	13	11	9	7	6	4	3	3	4	5	8	12	16	20	23	25	27	27	26	24	23	20	S
SW	28	24	21	17	14	12	9	7	6	5	5	6	7	10	13	18	24	30	35	38	39	37	35	31	SW
W	31	27	23	20	16	13	10	8	7	6	6	6	8	9	12	17	23	30	37	42	43	42	39	35	W
NW	26	22	19	16	13	11	8	7	5	5	5	5	7	9	11	15	19	24	29	33	34	34	32	29	NW
WALL NO 11																									
N	14	13	12	10	9	8	7	6	6	6	6	7	8	9	11	13	14	16	17	18	18	17	16	15	N
NE	18	16	14	13	11	10	9	8	9	11	14	17	20	21	22	23	24	24	24	24	23	22	21	19	NE
E	20	18	17	15	13	12	10	9	11	14	18	23	26	28	29	30	30	30	29	29	27	26	24	22	E
SE	20	18	16	14	13	11	10	9	9	11	15	18	22	25	26	27	28	28	28	27	26	25	23	21	SE
S	17	16	14	13	11	10	8	7	6	6	7	8	10	13	16	18	21	22	23	23	22	21	20	19	S
SW	25	23	21	18	16	14	13	11	10	9	9	9	10	12	15	18	23	27	31	33	33	32	30	27	SW
W	28	25	23	20	18	16	14	12	11	10	10	10	11	12	14	18	23	28	33	36	37	35	33	31	W
NW	23	21	19	17	15	13	11	10	9	8	8	9	9	10	11	13	15	18	22	26	29	29	27	25	NW
WALL NO 12																									
N	14	13	12	11	10	8	7	7	6	6	6	7	8	9	11	12	14	15	16	17	17	17	16	15	N
NE	18	16	15	14	12	11	10	9	10	12	14	17	19	20	21	22	23	23	24	23	23	22	21	19	NE
E	21	19	17	16	14	13	11	11	12	14	18	22	25	27	28	29	29	29	29	28	27	26	24	22	E
SE	20	18	17	15	14	12	11	10	10	12	15	18	21	24	25	26	27	27	27	27	26	24	23	21	SE
S	17	16	14	13	12	10	9	8	7	7	7	8	10	13	15	18	20	21	22	22	22	21	20	18	S
SW	25	23	21	19	17	15	14	12	11	10	10	10	11	13	15	18	22	26	30	31	31	30	29	27	SW
W	28	25	23	21	19	17	15	14	12	11	11	11	12	13	15	18	22	27	31	34	35	34	32	30	W
NW	23	21	19	17	15	14	12	11	10	9	9	10	10	11	13	15	18	22	25	27	28	27	26	24	NW
WALL NO 14																									
N	14	13	12	12	11	10	9	9	8	8	8	8	9	9	10	11	12	13	14	15	15	15	15	14	N
NE	18	17	16	15	14	13	12	12	12	13	15	16	18	19	19	20	21	21	21	21	21	21	20	19	NE
E	22	21	19	18	17	16	15	14	14	16	18	21	23	24	25	26	26	26	26	26	26	25	24	23	E
SE	21	19	18	17	16	15	14	13	13	14	16	18	20	21	23	23	24	24	25	24	24	23	23	22	SE
S	17	16	15	14	13	12	11	11	10	9	9	10	11	12	14	16	17	18	19	19	19	19	18	18	S
SW	24	23	21	20	19	18	16	15	14	14	13	13	13	14	15	17	20	23	25	27	27	27	26	25	SW
W	26	25	24	22	21	19	18	17	16	15	15	14	15	15	16	18	20	24	27	29	30	30	29	28	W
NW	22	20	19	18	17	16	15	14	13	12	12	12	12	12	13	14	15	17	19	21	23	24	24	23	NW
WALL NO 15																									
N	17	16	14	13	11	9	8	6	5	4	4	4	5	6	8	10	12	14	16	18	19	19	19	18	N
NE	21	19	17	15	13	11	9	7	6	7	9	12	15	18	20	22	24	25	26	26	26	25	24	22	NE
E	24	21	19	16	14	12	10	8	7	8	11	15	20	24	28	30	32	32	33	32	31	30	28	26	E
SE	23	21	18	16	14	12	10	8	7	7	8	11	15	20	23	26	28	30	30	31	30	29	27	25	SE
S	21	19	17	15	13	11	9	7	6	5	4	4	6	8	10	14	17	20	23	24	25	25	24	23	S
SW	32	29	26	23	20	17	14	12	9	8	7	6	7	8	9	12	16	21	26	31	34	36	36	34	SW
W	35	32	29	25	22	19	16	13	11	9	8	7	7	8	9	12	15	20	26	32	37	39	39	38	W
NW	29	26	24	21	18	15	13	11	9	1	6	6	6	7	9	11	13	17	21	26	29	31	32	31	NW
WALL NO 16																									
N	16	15	14	13	12	10	9	8	6	6	5	6	6	7	8	10	11	13	15	16	17	18	18	17	N
NE	21	19	17	16	14	12	11	9	8	9	10	12	15	17	19	21	22	23	24	24	24	24	23	22	NE
E	24	22	20	18	16	14	12	11	10	10	12	16	19	23	26	28	29	30	30	30	30	29	27	26	E
SE	23	21	19	17	15	14	12	10	9	9	10	13	16	19	22	24	26	27	28	28	27	26	25	25	SE
S	20	19	17	15	14	12	11	9	8	7	6	6	7	9	11	13	16	19	21	22	23	23	22	21	S
SW	30	28	25	23	20	18	16	14	12	10	9	9	9	9	11	13	16	20	24	28	31	32	32	31	SW
W	33	31	28	26	23	20	18	15	13	12	10	10	10	10	11	13	16	20	25	30	33	35	35	35	W
NW	27	25	23	21	19	17	15	13	11	9	8	8	8	9	10	11	13	16	20	24	26	28	28	28	NW

1. Direct application of data: Dark surface; Indoor temperature of 78°F; Outdoor maximum temperature of 95°F with mean temperature of 85°F and daily range of 21°F; Solar radiation typical of clear day on 21st day of month; Outside surface resistance of 0.333 hr-ft^2-°F/Btu; Inside surface film resistance of 0.685 hr-ft^2-°F/Btu.

2. Adjustment to table data: Design temperatures: Corrected $CLTD = CLTD + (78 - T_r) + (T_m - 85)$ where T_r = inside room temperature; T_m = mean outdoor temperature; T_m = maximum outdoor temperature − daily range/2; No adjustment recommended for color; No adjustment recommended for ventilation of air space above a ceiling.

Table 7-17. August Cooling Load Temperature Differences (CLTDs) for Calculating Cooling Load from Sunlit Walls 32° North Latitude

Wall Facing	Solar Time, hr																								Wall Facing
	1	2	3	4	5	6	7	8	9	10	11	12	13	14	15	16	17	18	19	20	21	22	23	24	
WALL NO 1																									
N	1	0	-1	-2	-3	-3	1	5	8	12	17	21	25	27	29	28	27	24	20	14	9	7	4	3	N
NE	1	0	-1	-2	-3	-1	11	32	42	42	35	28	27	28	29	29	27	23	15	13	9	7	5	3	NE
E	1	0	-1	-2	-3	-1	15	42	60	65	60	49	36	31	30	29	27	23	18	13	10	7	5	3	E
SE	1	0	-1	-2	-3	-2	8	29	47	57	60	57	50	39	33	30	27	23	18	13	10	7	5	3	SE
S	1	0	-1	-2	-3	-3	-1	3	12	23	35	44	51	54	52	45	36	27	19	13	10	7	5	3	S
SW	2	0	-1	-2	-2	-3	-1	3	7	12	17	25	39	55	67	73	72	61	39	21	12	8	5	3	SW
W	2	0	-1	-2	-2	-3	-1	3	7	12	17	21	27	42	60	75	81	75	49	25	14	8	5	3	W
NW	1	0	-1	-2	-3	-3	-1	3	7	12	17	21	25	29	38	50	59	58	41	22	12	8	5	3	NW
WALL NO 2																									
N	5	3	1	0	-1	-2	-2	-1	2	5	9	13	17	21	24	26	27	27	25	23	18	14	10	7	N
NE	5	3	1	0	-1	-2	-1	6	18	29	35	35	32	30	29	29	29	28	25	21	17	13	10	7	NE
E	5	3	2	0	-1	-2	0	8	25	41	52	56	52	45	38	34	32	29	26	22	18	14	10	7	E
SE	5	3	2	0	-1	-2	-1	5	17	31	44	52	54	52	46	40	35	31	27	22	18	14	10	7	SE
S	5	3	2	0	-1	-2	-2	-2	1	7	15	25	35	43	48	49	47	42	34	27	20	15	11	8	S
SW	7	4	2	1	0	-1	-2	-1	1	4	8	13	20	30	42	54	63	67	63	51	37	25	16	11	SW
W	7	5	2	1	0	-1	-2	-1	1	4	8	12	17	23	33	46	60	70	71	60	43	29	19	12	W
NW	7	4	2	1	-1	-2	-2	-1	1	4	8	12	17	21	25	32	41	49	52	46	35	24	16	10	NW
WALL NO 3																									
N	7	5	3	1	0	-1	0	1	3	6	9	12	16	19	22	24	25	25	23	21	17	14	11	9	N
NE	7	5	3	2	0	0	3	11	20	27	29	29	28	28	28	29	28	27	24	21	17	14	12	9	NE
E	7	5	3	2	1	0	4	15	28	39	45	47	43	40	37	35	33	30	27	23	19	15	12	10	E
SE	7	5	4	2	1	0	2	10	21	31	40	45	47	44	41	38	35	32	28	23	19	16	13	10	SE
S	8	6	4	2	1	0	-1	0	3	9	16	25	32	39	42	43	41	37	32	26	22	17	14	11	S
SW	11	8	6	4	2	1	0	1	3	5	9	13	21	30	41	50	57	58	53	43	34	26	20	15	SW
W	13	9	6	4	2	1	0	1	3	5	9	12	16	24	34	46	56	62	59	49	38	29	22	17	W
NW	10	7	5	3	1	0	0	1	2	5	8	12	16	19	25	32	40	46	45	38	30	24	18	14	NW
WALL NO 4																									
N	10	7	5	3	2	0	-1	-1	0	2	4	7	11	14	18	21	24	25	25	24	22	19	16	13	N
NE	10	7	5	3	2	0	0	1	7	15	23	28	30	30	29	29	29	27	25	22	19	16	14	12	NE
E	10	7	5	3	2	0	0	2	10	21	33	42	47	47	44	40	37	34	31	28	24	20	16	13	E
SE	10	8	5	3	2	1	0	1	6	15	26	36	43	47	47	45	41	37	34	30	25	21	17	13	SE
S	11	8	6	4	2	1	-1	-1	0	2	6	13	21	29	36	42	44	44	41	35	30	24	19	15	S
SW	17	12	8	5	3	1	0	-1	0	1	4	7	11	18	26	37	47	55	59	57	50	40	31	23	SW
W	19	14	9	6	4	2	0	0	0	1	4	7	10	15	21	30	41	52	60	61	55	46	35	26	W
NW	16	11	8	5	3	1	0	-1	0	1	4	7	10	14	18	23	29	37	43	45	42	35	28	21	NW
WALL NO 5																									
N	11	9	7	6	4	3	2	1	2	3	5	7	10	13	16	18	20	22	22	22	20	18	16	13	N
NE	12	10	8	6	4	3	2	4	9	16	21	24	25	25	26	27	27	27	26	24	22	20	17	14	NE
E	13	11	9	7	5	3	3	5	13	22	30	36	39	39	37	36	35	33	31	28	25	22	19	16	E
SE	14	11	9	7	5	4	3	4	9	16	24	32	37	40	40	39	37	35	33	30	26	23	20	17	SE
S	15	12	9	7	5	4	2	2	2	4	8	13	19	26	31	35	38	37	35	32	28	25	21	18	S
SW	21	17	14	11	8	6	4	3	3	4	6	8	11	17	25	33	41	47	50	48	43	37	31	26	SW
W	23	18	15	12	9	7	5	4	3	4	6	8	11	14	20	28	37	46	51	51	46	40	34	28	W
NW	18	15	12	9	7	5	3	2	2	3	5	7	10	13	16	21	27	33	38	38	35	31	26	22	NW
WALL NO 6																									
N	12	10	8	7	5	4	3	3	3	4	6	8	10	12	15	17	19	20	20	20	19	17	15	14	N
NE	13	11	9	8	6	5	4	7	11	16	20	22	23	24	24	25	26	26	25	24	22	20	17	15	NE
E	15	13	11	9	7	6	5	8	15	22	29	33	35	35	34	34	33	32	30	28	25	23	20	18	E
SE	16	13	11	9	7	6	5	7	11	17	24	29	33	36	36	35	34	33	31	29	26	23	21	18	SE
S	16	14	11	9	8	6	5	4	4	6	9	14	19	24	28	32	34	34	32	30	27	24	21	19	S
SW	22	19	16	13	11	9	7	6	6	6	7	9	12	17	24	31	38	43	44	43	39	34	30	26	SW
W	24	20	17	14	12	9	7	6	6	6	8	9	11	15	20	27	35	42	46	45	41	37	32	28	W
NW	19	16	13	11	9	7	6	5	5	5	7	8	11	13	16	20	25	31	34	34	32	29	25	22	NW
WALL NO 7																									
N	12	10	9	8	7	5	5	5	5	6	7	9	11	13	14	16	17	18	18	18	17	16	14	13	N
NE	14	12	11	9	8	7	7	10	14	17	19	20	21	22	23	23	24	24	23	22	20	19	17	15	NE
E	17	15	13	11	10	8	9	13	18	24	28	30	31	31	31	31	30	29	28	26	24	22	20	18	E
SE	17	15	13	11	10	9	8	11	15	20	25	28	31	32	32	31	30	29	27	25	23	21	19	17	SE
S	17	15	13	11	10	8	7	7	7	9	12	16	20	24	27	29	30	29	28	26	24	22	20	18	S
SW	22	20	17	15	13	11	10	9	9	9	10	12	15	20	25	30	35	38	38	36	33	30	28	25	SW
W	23	21	18	16	14	12	11	10	9	10	11	12	13	17	22	28	34	39	40	38	35	32	29	26	W
NW	18	16	14	12	11	9	8	7	7	8	9	10	12	14	16	20	25	29	30	29	27	25	23	20	NW
WALL NO 9																									
N	15	13	11	9	8	6	4	3	2	2	3	4	6	8	11	13	16	18	20	21	21	20	19	17	N
NE	17	14	12	10	8	6	5	4	4	7	12	16	20	22	24	25	25	26	26	25	23	21	19	17	NE
E	19	16	14	11	9	7	6	5	6	9	16	23	29	34	36	36	35	34	32	30	28	25	22	20	E
SE	20	17	14	12	10	8	6	5	5	7	12	18	25	31	35	37	37	37	36	34	32	29	26	23	SE
S	21	18	15	12	10	8	6	4	3	3	4	6	10	15	20	26	30	33	35	35	33	30	27	24	S
SW	30	26	21	18	14	12	9	7	5	5	5	7	9	14	19	26	33	40	44	45	43	40	35	30	SW
W	32	28	23	19	16	12	10	8	6	5	5	6	7	9	12	16	22	30	37	44	47	46	42	38	W
NW	25	22	18	15	12	10	8	6	4	4	4	5	6	8	11	14	17	22	27	32	35	35	32	29	NW

Table 7-17. August Cooling Load Temperature Differences (CLTDs) for Calculating Cooling Load from Sunlit Walls 32° North Latitude (Continued)

Wall Facing										Solar Time, hr															Wall Facing
	1	2	3	4	5	6	7	8	9	10	11	12	13	14	15	16	17	18	19	20	21	22	23	24	
WALL NO 10																									
N	15	13	11	10	8	6	5	4	3	3	4	5	6	8	11	13	15	17	19	20	20	20	18	17	N
NE	17	15	13	11	9	7	5	5	6	9	13	16	19	21	23	24	25	26	26	25	25	23	21	19	NE
E	20	17	14	12	10	8	6	6	7	12	17	23	28	32	34	34	34	34	33	32	30	28	25	22	E
SE	20	17	15	12	10	8	6	5	6	9	14	19	25	29	33	35	35	35	35	33	31	29	26	23	SE
S	21	18	16	13	11	9	7	5	4	4	5	7	11	15	20	25	29	32	33	33	32	29	27	24	S
SW	30	26	22	19	15	13	10	8	6	5	5	6	8	10	15	20	26	33	38	42	42	41	38	34	SW
W	32	28	24	20	17	14	11	9	7	6	6	6	8	10	12	17	23	30	37	42	43	43	40	36	W
NW	25	22	19	16	13	10	8	6	5	5	5	5	7	9	11	14	18	22	27	31	33	32	30	28	NW
WALL NO 11																									
N	14	13	12	10	9	8	7	6	5	5	6	7	8	9	11	12	14	16	17	17	17	17	16	15	N
NE	17	16	14	13	11	10	8	8	9	11	14	17	18	20	21	21	22	23	23	23	22	21	20	19	NE
E	21	19	17	15	13	12	10	10	11	15	19	23	27	29	30	30	30	30	30	29	28	26	24	22	E
SE	21	19	17	15	14	12	10	10	10	13	16	20	24	27	29	30	31	31	30	30	28	27	25	23	SE
S	20	18	17	15	13	12	10	9	8	8	8	10	13	16	20	23	26	28	28	28	27	26	24	22	S
SW	27	25	22	20	18	16	14	12	11	10	10	10	11	13	16	20	25	30	34	36	36	35	32	30	SW
W	29	26	23	21	19	16	14	13	11	11	10	11	11	12	15	18	23	28	33	36	37	36	34	31	W
NW	22	20	18	16	14	13	11	10	9	8	8	9	9	11	12	14	17	21	24	27	28	28	26	24	NW
WALL NO 12																									
N	14	13	12	11	9	8	7	7	6	6	6	7	8	9	11	12	14	15	16	17	17	16	16	15	N
NE	17	16	14	13	12	10	9	9	10	12	14	16	18	19	20	21	22	22	22	22	21	20	19	19	NE
E	21	19	18	16	14	13	11	11	12	15	19	23	26	28	29	29	29	29	29	28	27	26	24	23	E
SE	21	20	18	16	15	13	12	11	11	13	16	20	23	26	28	29	30	30	29	29	28	26	25	23	SE
S	20	19	17	15	14	12	11	10	9	9	9	11	13	16	19	22	25	26	27	27	26	25	24	22	S
SW	27	25	23	20	18	17	15	13	12	11	11	11	12	14	16	20	24	29	32	34	34	33	31	29	SW
W	28	26	24	21	19	17	15	14	13	12	11	12	12	13	15	18	22	27	31	34	35	34	33	31	W
NW	22	20	18	17	15	13	12	11	10	9	9	9	10	11	12	14	17	20	23	26	27	26	25	24	NW
WALL NO 14																									
N	14	13	12	11	11	10	9	8	8	8	8	8	9	9	10	11	12	13	14	15	15	15	15	14	N
NE	18	17	16	15	14	13	12	11	12	13	14	16	17	18	18	19	20	20	20	21	20	20	19	19	NE
E	22	21	20	18	17	16	15	14	15	16	19	21	23	25	26	26	26	27	27	26	26	25	24	23	E
SE	22	21	20	19	17	16	15	14	14	15	17	19	22	24	25	26	27	27	27	27	26	25	24	23	SE
S	20	19	18	17	16	15	14	13	12	12	12	12	14	16	18	20	22	23	24	24	24	23	22	21	S
SW	26	25	23	22	20	19	18	17	16	IS	14	14	14	15	17	19	22	25	27	29	30	29	28	27	SW
W	27	26	24	23	21	20	18	17	16	15	15	15	15	15	16	18	20	24	27	29	30	30	29	28	W
NW	21	20	19	18	16	15	14	13	12	12	12	12	12	13	14	16	18	20	22	23	23	23	23	22	NW
WALL NO 15																									
N	17	16	14	13	11	9	8	6	5	4	4	4	5	6	8	10	12	14	16	17	18	19	19	18	N
NE	20	18	16	14	12	10	9	7	6	7	9	12	14	17	19	21	22	23	24	25	25	24	23	22	NE
E	24	21	19	16	14	12	10	8	8	8	11	16	20	25	28	31	32	33	33	32	31	30	28	26	E
SE	25	22	19	17	15	12	10	9	7	8	9	13	17	22	26	29	32	33	34	33	33	31	29	27	SE
S	25	22	20	17	15	13	11	9	7	6	5	6	7	10	14	18	22	26	29	30	31	30	29	27	S
SW	34	31	28	24	21	18	15	13	10	9	7	7	7	8	10	13	18	23	29	34	37	39	39	37	SW
W	36	33	30	26	23	19	16	14	11	9	8	7	7	8	10	12	15	20	26	32	37	39	40	39	W
NW	28	25	23	20	18	15	13	10	9	7	6	6	6	7	8	10	13	16	20	24	27	30	30	29	NW
WALL NO 16																									
N	16	15	14	13	11	10	9	7	6	6	5	5	6	7	8	10	11	13	14	16	17	17	17	17	N
NE	20	18	17	15	13	12	10	9	8	9	10	12	14	16	18	19	21	22	23	23	23	23	22	21	NE
E	24	22	20	18	16	14	12	11	10	11	13	16	20	24	26	28	29	30	30	30	30	29	28	26	E
SE	25	23	21	18	16	14	13	11	10	10	11	14	17	21	24	27	29	30	31	31	30	28	27	27	SE
S	24	22	20	18	16	14	13	11	9	8	8	8	9	11	14	17	21	24	26	27	28	28	27	26	S
SW	32	30	27	25	22	20	17	15	13	11	10	10	9	10	12	14	18	22	27	31	34	35	35	34	SW
W	33	31	29	26	23	21	18	16	14	12	11	10	10	10	11	13	16	20	25	29	33	35	36	35	W
NW	26	24	22	20	18	16	14	12	11	9	8	8	8	9	9	11	13	15	19	22	25	27	27	27	NW

1. Direct application of data: Dark surface; Indoor temperature of 78°F; Outdoor maximum temperature of 95°F with mean temperature of 85°F and daily range of 21°F; Solar radiation typical of clear day on 21st day of month; Outside surface resistance of 0.333 hr-ft^2-°F/Btu; Inside surface film resistance of 0.685 hr-ft^2-°F/Btu.

2. Adjustment to table data: Design temperatures: Corrected $CLTD = CLTD + (78 - T_r) + (T_m - 85)$ where T_r = inside room temperature; T_m = mean outdoor temperature; T_m = maximum outdoor temperature – daily range/2; No adjustment recommended for color; No adjustment recommended for ventilation of air space above a ceiling.

Table 7-18. August Cooling Load Temperature Differences (CLTDs) for Calculating Cooling Load from Sunlit Walls 40° North Latitude

Wall Facing	1	2	3	4	5	6	7	8	9	10	11	12	13	14	15	16	17	18	19	20	21	22	23	24	Wall Facing
												WALL NO 1													
N	1	0	−1	−2	−3	−2	1	4	7	12	16	20	24	27	28	28	26	23	20	14	10	7	4	3	N
NE	1	0	−1	−2	−3	−1	14	32	39	37	29	25	26	27	28	28	26	23	18	13	9	7	4	3	NE
E	1	0	−1	−2	−3	0	18	44	60	64	59	48	35	31	30	29	27	23	18	13	10	7	5	3	E
SE	1	0	−1	−2	−3	−1	11	32	50	61	65	63	56	45	35	31	28	24	18	13	10	7	5	3	SE
S	1	0	−1	−2	−3	−3	−1	4	15	29	42	53	60	63	60	53	42	29	20	14	10	7	5	3	S
SW	2	0	−1	−2	−2	−3	−1	3	7	12	17	29	45	61	72	77	75	64	42	23	13	8	5	3	SW
W	2	0	−1	−2	−2	−3	−1	3	7	12	16	20	26	41	59	73	80	75	53	27	14	9	5	3	W
NW	1	0	−1	−2	−3	−3	−1	3	7	12	16	20	24	27	34	45	54	56	43	23	13	8	5	3	NW
												WALL NO 2													
N	5	3	1	0	−1	−2	−2	0	2	5	8	12	16	20	23	26	27	26	25	22	18	14	10	7	N
NE	5	3	1	0	−1	−2	0	7	19	28	32	31	29	27	27	28	28	27	25	21	17	13	10	7	NE
E	5	3	2	0	−1	−2	0	10	27	43	53	56	52	44	38	34	31	29	26	22	18	14	10	7	E
SE	5	3	2	0	−1	−2	−1	6	19	34	47	56	59	57	51	44	37	32	28	23	18	14	10	8	SE
S	5	3	2	0	−1	−2	−2	−1	2	9	19	30	42	51	57	58	55	48	39	30	22	16	11	8	S
SW	7	4	2	1	0	−1	−2	−1	1	4	8	13	22	34	47	59	68	71	67	54	39	26	17	11	SW
W	8	5	2	1	0	−1	−2	−1	1	4	8	12	16	22	32	46	59	69	71	61	45	30	19	12	W
NW	7	4	2	0	−1	−2	−2	−1	1	4	8	12	16	20	24	29	37	45	50	45	35	24	16	10	NW
												WALL NO 3													
N	6	5	3	1	0	−1	0	1	3	5	8	12	15	19	21	23	24	24	23	20	17	14	11	9	N
NE	7	5	3	2	0	0	4	12	20	25	26	26	26	26	27	27	27	26	24	21	17	14	11	9	NE
E	7	5	3	2	1	0	5	16	29	40	46	46	43	39	36	34	32	30	26	23	19	15	12	10	E
SE	8	6	4	2	1	0	3	11	23	34	43	49	51	49	45	41	37	33	29	24	20	16	13	10	SE
S	9	6	4	2	1	0	0	1	5	12	20	30	39	46	50	51	48	43	36	30	24	19	15	12	S
SW	12	9	6	4	2	1	0	1	3	5	9	14	23	34	45	55	61	62	57	46	36	28	22	16	SW
W	13	9	6	4	2	1	0	1	3	5	9	12	16	23	33	45	56	62	60	50	39	30	23	17	W
NW	10	7	5	3	1	0	0	1	3	5	8	12	15	19	23	29	36	43	43	37	30	23	18	14	NW
												WALL NO 4													
N	10	7	5	3	2	0	−1	−1	0	2	4	7	10	14	17	21	23	24	25	24	22	19	16	13	N
NE	10	7	5	3	2	0	0	2	8	16	22	26	27	27	27	28	27	27	25	22	19	16	12	NE
E	10	7	5	3	2	0	0	3	11	23	34	43	47	46	43	40	36	34	31	28	24	20	16	13	E
SE	11	8	5	4	2	1	0	2	7	17	28	39	47	51	52	49	45	40	36	31	26	22	17	14	SE
S	12	9	6	4	2	1	0	−1	0	3	8	16	26	35	43	49	52	51	47	41	34	27	21	16	S
SW	18	13	9	6	3	2	0	0	0	1	4	7	12	20	29	41	51	59	63	61	53	43	33	25	SW
W	20	14	9	6	4	2	0	0	0	1	4	7	10	14	21	29	40	51	60	61	56	47	36	27	W
NW	16	11	8	5	3	1	0	−1	0	1	4	7	10	14	18	22	27	34	40	43	41	35	28	21	NW
												WALL NO 5													
N	11	9	7	5	4	3	2	1	2	3	5	7	10	13	15	18	20	21	22	21	20	18	16	13	N
NE	12	10	8	6	4	3	2	5	10	16	20	22	23	23	24	25	26	26	25	24	22	19	17	14	NE
E	13	11	9	7	5	3	3	6	14	23	31	37	39	39	37	36	34	33	31	28	25	22	19	16	E
SE	14	12	9	7	5	4	3	5	10	18	26	34	40	43	44	42	40	38	35	31	28	24	21	17	SE
S	16	13	11	8	6	4	3	2	3	5	10	16	24	31	37	42	44	44	41	37	32	28	24	20	S
SW	22	18	15	11	9	6	5	4	3	4	6	8	12	19	27	36	45	51	53	51	46	39	33	27	SW
W	23	19	15	12	9	7	5	4	4	4	6	8	10	14	19	27	37	45	51	52	47	41	34	28	W
NW	18	14	11	9	7	5	3	2	2	3	5	7	10	13	16	19	25	30	35	37	34	30	26	21	NW
												WALL NO 6													
N	12	10	8	7	5	4	3	3	3	4	5	7	10	12	14	17	18	19	20	20	18	17	15	13	N
NE	13	11	9	7	6	5	4	7	11	16	19	20	21	22	23	24	24	24	23	21	19	17	15	NE
E	15	13	11	9	7	6	6	9	15	23	29	33	35	35	34	33	33	32	30	28	25	23	20	18	E
SE	16	14	12	10	8	6	6	8	12	19	26	32	36	39	40	39	37	36	33	31	28	25	22	19	SE
S	18	15	13	11	9	7	5	5	5	7	11	17	23	29	34	38	40	40	37	34	31	27	24	21	S
SW	24	20	17	14	12	9	8	6	6	6	8	10	14	19	26	34	41	46	48	46	42	37	32	28	SW
W	24	21	17	14	12	9	8	6	6	7	8	9	11	14	20	27	34	42	46	46	42	37	33	28	W
NW	18	15	13	11	9	7	5	5	5	5	6	8	10	13	15	19	23	28	32	33	31	28	24	21	NW
												WALL NO 7													
N	11	10	9	8	6	5	5	5	5	6	7	8	10	12	14	16	17	17	18	17	16	15	14	13	N
NE	13	12	10	9	8	7	7	10	14	16	18	19	19	20	21	22	23	23	22	21	20	18	17	15	NE
E	16	15	13	11	10	8	9	13	19	24	28	31	31	31	31	30	30	29	28	26	24	22	20	18	E
SE	18	16	14	12	11	9	9	12	16	21	26	31	34	35	35	34	34	32	31	29	27	24	22	20	SE
S	19	17	15	13	11	10	8	8	9	11	14	19	24	28	32	34	35	34	33	30	28	26	23	21	S
SW	24	21	19	16	14	12	11	10	10	10	11	13	16	22	27	33	38	41	41	39	36	33	30	27	SW
W	24	21	18	16	14	12	11	10	10	10	11	12	13	16	21	27	34	38	40	38	35	32	29	26	W
NW	18	16	14	12	10	9	8	7	7	7	8	9	10	12	13	16	19	23	27	29	28	26	24	20	NW
												WALL NO 9													
N	15	13	11	9	7	6	4	3	2	2	3	4	6	8	10	13	15	17	19	20	20	20	19	17	N
NE	16	14	12	10	8	6	5	4	5	8	12	16	19	21	22	23	24	25	25	24	23	21	19	NE
E	19	16	14	11	9	7	6	5	6	10	17	24	30	34	36	36	36	35	33	32	30	28	25	22	E
SE	21	18	15	12	10	8	6	5	5	8	13	20	27	33	38	40	41	40	38	36	34	31	27	24	SE
S	24	20	17	14	11	9	7	5	4	4	5	8	12	18	25	31	36	40	41	41	38	35	31	27	S
SW	32	27	23	19	15	12	10	8	6	5	5	6	7	10	15	21	29	36	43	48	49	47	42	37	SW
W	33	28	23	19	16	13	10	8	6	5	5	6	7	9	12	16	22	29	37	43	47	46	43	38	W
NW	25	21	18	15	12	10	7	6	4	4	4	5	6	8	11	13	16	20	25	30	33	33	31	28	NW

Table 7-18. August Cooling Load Temperature Differences (CLTDs) for Calculating Cooling Load from Sunlit Walls 40° North Latitude *(Continued)*

Wall Facing	Solar Time, hr																								Wall Facing
	1	2	3	4	5	6	7	8	9	10	11	12	13	14	15	16	17	18	19	20	21	22	23	24	
WALL NO 10																									
N	15	13	11	9	8	6	5	4	3	3	3	4	6	8	10	13	15	17	18	19	20	19	18	17	N
NE	17	14	12	10	9	7	5	5	6	9	12	15	18	20	21	22	23	24	25	24	24	22	21	19	NE
E	19	17	14	12	10	8	6	6	8	12	18	24	29	32	34	34	34	34	33	32	30	27	25	22	E
SE	21	18	16	13	11	9	7	6	7	10	15	21	27	32	36	38	39	38	37	36	33	30	27	24	SE
S	24	21	18	15	12	10	8	6	5	5	6	9	13	19	25	30	35	38	39	38	37	34	31	27	S
SW	32	28	24	20	16	13	11	8	7	6	6	6	8	11	16	22	29	36	41	45	45	44	40	36	SW
W	32	28	24	20	17	14	11	9	7	6	6	6	8	9	12	17	23	30	36	41	44	43	40	37	W
NW	24	21	18	15	13	10	8	6	5	4	5	5	7	9	11	13	17	21	25	29	31	31	29	27	NW
WALL NO 11																									
N	14	13	11	10	9	8	7	6	5	5	6	6	7	9	10	12	14	15	16	17	17	17	16	15	N
NE	17	15	14	12	11	9	8	8	9	11	14	16	17	18	19	20	21	22	22	22	21	21	19	18	NE
E	20	19	17	15	13	12	10	10	12	15	20	24	27	29	30	30	30	30	29	29	27	26	24	22	E
SE	22	20	18	16	14	13	11	10	11	14	17	22	26	30	32	33	34	33	33	32	30	28	26	24	SE
S	23	21	19	17	15	13	12	10	9	9	10	12	16	19	24	28	31	33	33	33	32	30	28	26	S
SW	29	26	24	21	19	17	15	13	12	11	11	11	12	14	18	22	27	32	36	39	39	37	35	32	SW
W	29	26	24	21	19	17	15	13	12	11	10	11	11	12	14	18	22	28	33	36	37	36	34	32	W
NW	21	20	18	16	14	12	11	9	8	8	8	8	9	10	12	14	16	19	23	26	27	26	25	23	NW
WALL NO 12																									
N	14	13	12	10	9	8	7	6	6	6	6	7	8	9	10	12	13	15	16	16	16	16	15	15	N
NE	17	15	14	13	11	10	9	9	10	12	14	16	17	18	19	20	20	21	21	21	21	20	19	18	NE
E	21	19	17	16	14	13	11	11	13	16	19	23	26	28	29	29	29	29	28	27	26	24	23	22	E
SE	23	21	19	17	15	14	12	12	12	14	18	22	25	29	31	32	32	32	32	31	30	28	26	25	SE
S	23	21	20	18	16	14	13	11	10	10	11	13	16	19	23	27	29	31	32	32	31	29	27	25	S
SW	29	27	24	22	20	18	16	14	13	12	12	12	13	15	18	22	27	31	35	37	37	36	34	31	SW
W	28	26	24	22	19	17	16	14	13	12	12	12	12	13	15	18	22	27	31	34	35	35	33	31	W
NW	21	19	18	16	14	13	11	10	9	9	9	9	10	11	12	14	16	19	22	24	25	25	24	23	NW
WALL NO 14																									
N	13	13	12	11	10	10	9	8	8	8	8	8	9	10	11	12	13	14	14	14	14	14	14	14	N
NE	17	16	15	14	13	12	12	11	12	13	14	15	16	17	17	18	19	19	20	20	20	19	19	18	NE
E	22	21	20	18	17	16	15	14	15	17	19	21	23	25	26	26	26	27	27	26	26	25	24	23	E
SE	24	22	21	20	19	17	16	15	15	16	18	21	23	25	27	28	29	29	29	29	28	27	26	25	SE
S	24	22	21	20	18	17	16	15	14	14	14	15	16	19	21	23	25	27	28	28	28	27	26	25	S
SW	28	27	25	24	22	21	19	18	17	16	15	15	15	16	18	21	24	27	30	31	32	32	31	29	SW
W	27	26	24	23	21	20	19	17	16	15	15	15	15	16	18	20	23	27	29	30	30	30	30	28	W
NW	20	19	18	17	16	15	14	13	12	11	11	11	11	12	13	14	15	17	19	21	22	22	22	21	NW
WALL NO 15																									
N	17	15	14	12	11	9	8	6	5	4	4	4	5	6	7	9	11	13	15	17	18	18	18	18	N
NE	19	18	16	14	12	10	8	7	6	7	9	11	14	16	18	19	21	22	23	23	24	23	22	21	NE
E	24	21	19	16	14	12	10	8	8	9	12	16	21	25	29	31	32	33	33	32	31	30	28	26	E
SE	26	23	21	18	15	13	11	9	8	8	10	14	19	24	28	32	35	36	37	36	35	33	31	29	SE
S	29	26	23	20	17	15	12	10	8	7	6	7	9	12	17	21	26	31	34	36	36	35	34	31	S
SW	37	33	30	26	23	19	16	14	11	9	8	7	8	9	11	15	19	25	31	37	40	42	42	40	SW
W	36	33	30	26	23	20	16	14	11	9	8	8	8	10	12	15	20	26	32	37	39	40	39	37	W
NW	27	25	22	20	17	15	12	10	8	7	6	6	7	8	10	12	15	18	22	26	28	29	28	27	NW
WALL NO 16																									
N	16	15	14	12	11	10	9	7	6	6	5	5	6	7	8	9	11	12	14	15	16	17	17	17	N
NE	19	18	16	15	13	12	10	9	8	9	10	12	14	16	17	18	19	21	21	22	22	22	21	20	NE
E	24	22	20	18	16	14	12	11	10	11	13	17	21	24	26	28	29	30	30	30	30	29	27	26	E
SE	26	24	22	20	17	15	13	12	11	11	12	15	19	23	27	30	32	33	34	34	33	32	30	28	SE
S	28	26	23	21	19	16	14	12	11	9	9	9	11	13	17	21	25	28	31	32	33	33	31	30	S
SW	35	32	29	27	24	21	18	16	14	12	11	10	10	11	13	15	19	24	29	33	36	38	38	36	SW
W	34	32	29	26	24	21	18	16	14	12	11	10	10	10	11	13	16	20	24	29	33	35	36	35	W
NW	25	23	22	20	18	16	14	12	10	9	8	8	8	9	11	12	15	18	21	24	25	26	26	26	NW

1. Direct application of data: Dark surface; Indoor temperature of 78°F; Outdoor maximum temperature of 95°F with mean temperature of 85°F and daily range of 21°F; Solar radiation typical of clear day on 21st day of month; Outside surface resistance of 0.333 hr-ft^2-°F/Btu; Inside surface film resistance of 0.685 hr-ft^2-°F/Btu.

2. Adjustment to table data: Design temperatures: Corrected $CLTD = CLTD + (78 - T_r) + (T_m - 85)$ where T_r = inside room temperature; T_m = mean outdoor temperature; T_m = maximum outdoor temperature − daily range/2; No adjustment recommended for color; No adjustment recommended for ventilation of air space above a ceiling.

Table 7-19. August Cooling Load Temperature Differences (CLTDs) for Calculating Cooling Load from Sunlit Walls 48° North Latitude

WALL NO 1

Wall Facing	1	2	3	4	5	6	7	8	9	10	11	12	13	14	15	16	17	18	19	20	21	22	23	24	Wall Facing
N	1	0	-1	-2	-3	-2	2	4	7	11	15	20	23	26	27	27	26	23	20	14	10	7	4	2	N
NE	1	0	-1	-2	-3	0	16	32	36	32	24	22	24	26	28	28	26	23	18	13	9	7	4	3	NE
E	1	0	-1	-2	-3	1	21	45	60	63	58	47	34	30	29	28	26	23	18	13	10	7	5	3	E
SE	2	0	-1	-2	-3	-1	13	34	52	64	69	68	61	50	37	31	27	24	19	14	10	7	5	3	SE
S	2	0	-1	-2	-2	-3	0	6	19	34	49	60	68	71	67	59	47	33	22	15	10	7	5	3	S
SW	2	1	-1	-2	-2	-2	0	3	7	11	17	32	50	65	76	81	78	66	45	24	13	8	5	3	SW
W	2	0	-1	-2	-2	-2	0	3	7	11	16	20	25	40	58	72	79	75	55	28	15	9	5	3	W
NW	1	0	-1	-2	-3	-3	-1	3	7	11	15	20	23	26	29	39	50	54	44	24	13	8	5	3	NW

WALL NO 2

Wall Facing	1	2	3	4	5	6	7	8	9	10	11	12	13	14	15	16	17	18	19	20	21	22	23	24	Wall Facing
N	5	3	1	0	0	-2	-2	0	2	5	8	12	16	19	23	25	26	26	24	22	18	14	10	7	N
NE	5	3	1	0	-1	-2	0	8	19	27	29	27	25	25	26	27	26	24	21	17	13	10	7	5	NE
E	5	3	2	0	-1	-2	1	12	28	43	52	55	51	43	37	33	30	28	26	22	18	14	10	7	E
SE	5	3	2	0	-1	-2	0	7	21	36	50	59	63	62	56	47	39	33	28	23	18	14	11	8	SE
S	6	4	2	1	-1	-1	-2	-1	3	11	23	36	48	58	64	65	62	54	43	33	24	17	12	8	S
SW	7	5	2	1	0	-1	-2	-1	1	4	8	13	23	37	51	63	72	74	70	57	41	28	18	12	SW
W	8	5	3	1	0	-1	-2	-1	1	4	8	12	16	21	31	45	58	68	70	62	46	31	20	13	W
NW	7	4	2	0	-1	-2	-2	-1	1	4	8	12	16	19	23	27	33	41	46	44	34	24	16	10	NW

WALL NO 3

Wall Facing	1	2	3	4	5	6	7	8	9	10	11	12	13	14	15	16	17	18	19	20	21	22	23	24	Wall Facing
N	6	5	3	1	0	-1	0	1	3	5	8	11	15	18	21	23	24	23	23	20	17	14	11	9	N
NE	7	5	3	2	0	0	4	12	20	23	23	23	23	24	25	26	26	25	23	20	17	14	11	9	NE
E	7	5	3	2	1	0	6	17	30	40	45	46	42	38	36	34	32	29	26	22	19	15	12	10	E
SE	8	6	4	2	1	0	4	12	24	36	45	52	55	54	49	43	39	34	30	25	21	17	13	10	SE
S	9	7	5	3	1	0	0	2	6	14	24	35	45	52	57	58	55	48	40	33	26	21	16	12	S
SW	13	9	6	4	2	1	0	1	3	5	9	15	25	37	49	58	64	65	59	49	38	30	23	17	SW
W	13	9	7	4	2	1	0	1	3	5	8	12	15	22	33	44	54	61	60	50	40	31	23	18	W
NW	10	7	5	3	1	0	0	1	2	5	8	11	15	18	21	26	33	39	41	36	29	23	18	13	NW

WALL NO 4

Wall Facing	1	2	3	4	5	6	7	8	9	10	11	12	13	14	15	16	17	18	19	20	21	22	23	24	Wall Facing
N	10	7	5	3	2	0	-1	-1	0	2	4	7	10	13	17	20	22	24	24	24	22	19	16	13	N
NE	9	7	5	3	2	0	0	2	8	15	21	24	24	25	25	26	26	26	24	22	19	15	12	10	NE
E	10	7	5	3	2	0	0	3	12	23	35	43	46	46	42	39	36	33	30	27	24	20	16	13	E
SE	11	8	6	4	2	1	0	2	8	18	30	41	50	55	56	53	48	42	37	32	27	22	18	14	SE
S	13	9	7	4	2	1	0	-1	0	4	10	19	30	40	50	56	59	58	53	46	37	30	23	17	S
SW	19	13	9	6	4	2	0	0	0	1	4	7	12	21	32	44	54	63	66	64	56	45	35	26	SW
W	20	14	10	6	4	2	0	0	0	1	4	7	10	14	20	29	39	50	59	61	56	47	37	28	W
NW	15	11	8	5	3	1	0	-1	0	1	3	6	10	13	17	20	25	31	37	40	39	34	27	21	NW

WALL NO 5

Wall Facing	1	2	3	4	5	6	7	8	9	10	11	12	13	14	15	16	17	18	19	20	21	22	23	24	Wall Facing
N	11	9	7	6	4	3	2	1	2	3	5	7	10	13	16	18	20	22	22	22	20	18	16	13	N
NE	12	9	8	6	4	3	2	4	9	16	21	24	25	25	26	27	27	27	26	24	22	20	17	14	NE
E	13	11	9	7	5	3	3	5	13	22	30	36	39	39	37	36	35	33	31	28	25	22	19	16	E
SE	15	12	9	7	5	4	3	4	9	16	24	32	37	40	40	39	37	35	33	30	26	23	21	18	SE
S	18	15	9	7	5	4	2	2	2	4	8	13	19	26	31	35	38	37	35	32	28	25	26	22	S
SW	24	19	14	11	8	6	4	3	3	4	6	8	11	17	25	33	41	47	50	48	43	37	35	29	SW
W	23	19	15	12	9	7	5	4	3	4	6	8	11	14	20	28	37	46	51	51	46	40	34	28	W
NW	17	14	12	9	7	5	3	2	2	3	5	7	10	13	16	21	27	33	38	38	35	31	25	21	NW

WALL NO 6

Wall Facing	1	2	3	4	5	6	7	8	9	10	11	12	13	14	15	16	17	18	19	20	21	22	23	24	Wall Facing
N	11	10	8	7	5	0	3	3	3	4	5	7	9	12	14	16	18	19	19	19	18	17	15	13	N
NE	12	11	9	7	6	4	5	7	11	15	17	18	19	20	21	22	23	23	23	22	20	18	16	14	NE
E	15	13	11	9	7	6	6	10	16	23	29	33	35	34	34	33	32	31	30	28	25	23	20	17	E
SE	17	15	12	10	8	6	6	8	13	20	27	34	39	42	43	41	40	38	35	32	29	26	23	20	SE
S	20	17	14	12	10	8	6	5	5	9	14	20	27	33	39	43	45	45	42	39	35	31	27	23	S
SW	25	21	18	15	12	10	8	7	6	7	8	10	14	21	28	36	43	48	50	48	44	39	34	29	SW
W	24	21	17	14	12	10	8	7	6	7	8	9	11	14	19	26	34	41	45	45	42	37	33	28	W
NW	18	15	12	10	8	7	5	4	4	5	6	8	10	12	14	17	21	26	30	31	29	27	23	20	NW

WALL NO 7

Wall Facing	1	2	3	4	5	6	7	8	9	10	11	12	13	14	15	16	17	18	19	20	21	22	23	24	Wall Facing
N	11	10	9	7	6	5	5	5	5	6	7	8	10	12	14	15	16	17	17	17	16	15	14	13	N
NE	13	11	10	9	7	6	7	10	13	16	16	17	18	19	20	21	21	21	21	20	19	18	16	14	NE
E	16	15	13	11	10	8	10	14	19	24	28	30	31	30	30	30	30	29	28	26	24	22	20	18	E
SE	19	17	15	13	11	10	10	13	17	23	28	33	36	37	37	37	35	34	32	30	28	26	23	21	SE
S	21	19	16	14	12	11	9	9	10	13	17	22	27	32	36	39	40	39	37	34	32	29	26	23	S
SW	25	22	20	17	15	13	11	11	10	10	11	13	18	23	29	35	40	43	43	41	38	34	31	28	SW
W	24	21	18	16	14	12	11	10	10	10	10	12	13	16	21	27	33	38	40	38	35	32	29	26	W
NW	17	15	13	11	10	8	7	7	7	7	8	10	11	13	15	17	21	25	27	27	25	23	21	19	NW

WALL NO 9

Wall Facing	1	2	3	4	5	6	7	8	9	10	11	12	13	14	15	16	17	18	19	20	21	22	23	24	Wall Facing
N	15	13	11	9	7	6	4	3	2	2	3	4	5	8	10	12	15	17	19	20	20	20	18	17	N
NE	16	14	12	10	8	6	5	4	5	8	12	15	17	19	20	21	22	23	24	24	23	22	20	18	NE
E	19	16	14	11	9	7	6	5	6	11	17	24	30	34	36	36	35	34	33	31	30	27	25	22	E
SE	22	18	16	13	10	8	6	5	6	9	14	21	29	35	40	43	44	43	41	38	35	32	28	25	SE
S	26	22	19	15	13	10	8	6	5	4	6	9	15	21	28	35	41	45	47	46	43	39	35	30	S
SW	34	29	24	20	16	13	10	8	6	5	5	6	7	11	16	23	31	39	46	50	51	49	45	39	SW
W	33	28	24	20	16	13	10	8	6	5	5	6	7	9	11	15	21	28	36	43	46	46	43	38	W
NW	24	20	17	14	12	9	7	5	4	4	4	4	6	8	10	13	15	19	23	28	31	31	30	27	NW

Table 7-19. August Cooling Load Temperature Differences (CLTDs) for Calculating Cooling Load from Sunlit Walls 48° North Latitude (Continued)

Wall Facing											Solar Time, hr													Wall Facing
	1	2	3	4	5	6	7	8	9	10	11	12	13	14	15	16	17	18	19	20	21	22	23	24	
WALL NO 10																									
N	15	13	11	9	8	6	5	4	3	3	3	4	6	8	10	12	14	16	18	19	19	19	18	16	N
NE	16	14	12	10	8	7	5	5	6	9	12	15	16	18	19	20	22	23	23	23	23	21	20	18	NE
E	19	17	14	12	10	8	6	6	8	13	18	24	29	32	33	34	34	33	32	31	29	27	25	22	E
SE	22	19	16	14	11	9	7	6	8	11	16	22	29	34	38	41	41	41	40	37	35	32	29	25	SE
S	27	23	19	16	13	11	9	7	6	6	7	11	16	22	28	34	39	43	44	43	41	38	34	31	S
SW	34	29	25	21	17	14	11	9	7	6	6	7	8	12	17	24	31	38	44	47	48	46	43	38	SW
W	33	28	24	20	17	14	11	9	7	6	6	6	8	9	12	16	22	29	36	41	43	43	40	37	W
NW	23	20	17	15	12	10	8	6	5	4	4	5	6	8	10	13	15	19	23	27	29	29	28	26	NW
WALL NO 11																									
N	14	12	11	10	9	8	7	6	5	5	6	6	7	9	10	12	13	15	16	17	17	16	16	15	N
NE	16	15	13	12	10	9	8	8	9	11	13	15	16	17	18	19	20	20	21	21	20	20	19	17	NE
E	20	18	17	15	13	12	10	10	12	15	20	24	27	29	30	30	30	30	29	28	27	26	24	22	E
SE	23	21	19	17	15	13	12	11	12	15	19	23	28	32	34	36	36	36	35	33	32	30	28	25	SE
S	26	24	21	19	17	15	13	12	11	10	12	14	18	23	27	32	35	37	38	37	36	33	31	29	S
SW	31	28	25	22	20	18	16	14	12	11	11	11	12	15	19	24	29	34	39	41	41	39	37	34	SW
W	29	26	24	21	19	17	15	13	12	11	10	11	11	12	14	17	22	27	32	36	37	36	34	32	W
NW	21	19	17	15	13	12	10	9	8	8	8	8	9	10	11	13	15	18	21	24	25	25	24	22	NW
WALL NO 12																									
N	13	12	11	10	9	8	7	6	6	6	6	7	8	9	10	12	13	14	15	16	16	16	15	14	N
NE	16	15	13	12	11	10	9	9	10	11	13	15	16	16	17	18	19	20	20	20	20	19	18	17	NE
E	21	19	17	16	14	13	11	11	13	16	20	23	26	28	28	29	29	29	28	28	27	26	24	22	E
SE	24	22	20	18	16	14	13	12	13	15	19	23	27	30	33	34	35	34	34	33	31	30	28	26	SE
S	26	24	22	20	18	16	14	13	12	12	13	15	18	22	26	30	33	35	36	36	34	33	31	28	S
SW	31	28	26	23	21	19	17	15	14	13	12	12	13	16	19	24	28	33	37	39	39	38	36	33	SW
W	28	26	24	22	19	17	16	14	13	12	12	12	12	13	15	18	21	26	31	34	35	35	33	31	W
NW	20	19	17	15	14	12	11	10	9	8	8	9	9	10	12	13	15	17	20	23	24	24	23	22	NW
WALL NO 14																									
N	13	12	12	11	10	9	9	8	8	8	8	8	8	9	10	11	12	13	13	14	14	14	14	14	N
NE	16	16	15	14	13	12	11	11	11	12	13	14	15	16	16	17	17	18	18	19	19	18	18	17	NE
E	22	21	19	18	17	16	15	14	15	17	19	21	23	25	25	26	26	26	26	26	26	25	24	23	E
SE	25	24	22	21	20	18	17	16	16	17	19	22	25	27	29	30	31	31	31	31	30	29	28	26	SE
S	26	25	24	22	21	19	18	17	16	15	16	17	19	21	24	27	29	31	32	32	31	30	29	28	S
SW	30	28	26	25	23	22	20	19	18	17	16	16	16	17	19	22	25	28	31	33	34	33	32	31	SW
W	27	26	24	23	21	20	18	17	16	15	15	15	15	15	16	18	20	23	26	29	30	30	29	28	W
NW	19	18	17	16	15	14	13	12	11	11	11	11	11	11	12	13	14	16	18	20	21	21	21	20	NW
WALL NO 15																									
N	16	15	14	12	11	9	7	6	5	4	4	4	5	6	7	9	11	13	15	16	17	18	18	17	N
NE	19	17	15	13	12	10	8	7	6	7	9	11	13	15	17	18	19	20	21	22	22	22	21	20	NE
E	23	21	19	16	14	12	10	8	8	9	12	16	21	25	29	31	32	32	32	32	31	30	28	26	E
SE	27	24	21	19	16	14	11	9	8	9	11	15	20	25	30	34	37	39	39	38	37	35	33	30	SE
S	32	29	25	22	19	16	14	11	9	8	7	8	11	14	19	25	30	35	39	41	41	40	38	35	S
SW	39	35	31	28	24	20	17	14	12	10	9	8	8	9	12	16	21	27	33	39	43	44	44	42	SW
W	36	33	30	26	23	20	17	14	11	10	8	8	8	9	11	15	20	25	31	36	39	40	39	39	W
NW	26	24	21	19	16	14	12	10	8	7	6	6	6	7	8	10	12	14	17	21	24	26	27	27	NW
WALL NO 16																									
N	16	15	14	12	11	10	8	7	6	6	5	5	6	6	8	9	11	12	14	15	16	17	17	16	N
NE	18	17	16	14	13	11	10	8	8	9	10	12	13	15	16	17	18	19	20	21	21	21	20	19	NE
E	24	22	20	18	16	14	12	11	10	11	14	17	21	24	26	28	29	30	30	30	29	28	27	26	E
SE	28	25	23	20	18	16	14	12	11	12	13	16	20	24	28	32	34	35	36	36	35	34	32	30	SE
S	31	29	26	23	21	18	16	14	12	11	10	11	13	16	19	24	28	32	35	37	37	37	35	33	S
SW	36	34	31	28	25	22	19	17	15	13	12	11	11	11	13	16	21	26	31	35	38	40	40	39	SW
W	34	32	29	26	24	21	18	16	14	12	11	10	10	10	11	13	15	19	24	29	33	35	36	35	W
NW	24	22	21	19	17	15	13	11	10	9	8	7	7	8	9	10	12	14	16	19	22	24	25	24	NW

1. Direct application of data: Dark surface; Indoor temperature of 78°F; Outdoor maximum temperature of 95°F with mean temperature of 85°F and daily range of 21°F; Solar radiation typical of clear day on 21st day of month; Outside surface resistance of 0.333 hr-ft²-°F/Btu; Inside surface film resistance of 0.685 hr-ft²-°F/Btu.

2. Adjustment to table data: Design temperatures: Corrected $CLTD = CLTD + (78 - T_r) + (T_m - 85)$ where T_r = inside room temperature; T_m = mean outdoor temperature; T_m = maximum outdoor temperature − daily range/2; No adjustment recommended for color; No adjustment recommended for ventilation of air space above a ceiling.

Table 7-20. Thermal Properties and Code Numbers Used in Wall and Roof Descriptions

Code Number	Description	Thickness and Thermal Properties						Code Number
		L	k	ρ	c_p	R	Mass	
A0	Outside surface resistance	0.0	0.0	0.0	0.0	0.33	0.0	A0
A1	1 in. stucco	0.0833	0.4	116.0	0.20	0.21	9.7	A1
A2	4 in. face brick	0.333	0.77	125.0	0.22	0.43	41.7	A2
A3	Steel siding	0.005	26.0	480.0	0.10	0.00	2.4	A3
A4	½ in. slag	0.0417	0.11	70.0	0.40	0.38	2.2	A4
A5	Outside surface resistance	0.00	0.00	0.0	0.0	0.33	0.0	A5
A6	Finish	0.0417	0.24	78.0	0.26	0.17	3.3	A6
A7	4 in. face brick	0.333	0.77	125.0	0.22	0.43	41.7	A7
B1	Air space resistance	0.00	0.00	0.0	0.0	0.91	0.0	B1
B2	1 in. insulation	0.083	0.025	2.0	0.2	3.33	0.2	B2
B3	2 in. insulation	0.167	0.025	2.0	0.2	6.67	0.3	B3
B4	3 in. insulation	0.25	0.025	2.0	0.2	1.19	0.5	B4
B5	1 in. insulation	0.0833	0.025	5.7	0.2	3.33	0.5	B5
B6	2 in. insulation	0.167	0.025	5.7	0.2	6.67	1.0	B6
B7	1 in. wood	0.0833	0.07	37.0	0.6	1.19	3.1	B7
B8	2.5 in. wood	0.2083	0.07	37.0	0.6	2.98	7.7	B8
B9	4 in. wood	0.333	0.07	37.0	0.6	4.76	12.3	B9
B10	2 in. wood	0.167	0.07	37.0	0.6	2.39	6.2	B10
B11	3 in. wood	0.25	0.07	37.0	0.6	3.57	9.3	B11
B12	3 in. insulation	0.25	0.025	5.7	0.2	10.00	1.4	B12
B13	4 in. insulation	0.333	0.025	5.7	0.2	13.33	1.9	B13
B14	5 in. insulation	0.417	0.025	5.7	0.2	16.67	2.4	B14
B15	6 in. insulation	0.500	0.025	5.7	0.2	20.00	2.9	B15
B16	0.15 in. insulation	0.0126	0.025	5.7	0.2	0.50	0.1	B16
B17	0.3 in. insulation	0.0252	0.025	5.7	0.2	1.00	0.1	B17
B18	0.45 in. insulation	0.0379	0.025	5.7	0.2	1.50	0.2	B18
B19	0.61 in. insulation	0.0505	0.025	5.7	0.2	2.00	0.3	B19
B20	0.76 in. insulation	0.0631	0.025	5.7	0.2	2.50	0.4	B20
B21	1.36 in. insulation	0.1136	0.025	5.7	0.2	4.50	0.6	B21
B22	1.67 in. insulation	0.1388	0.025	5.7	0.2	5.50	0.8	B22
B23	2.42 in. insulation	0.2019	0.025	5.7	0.2	8.00	1.2	B23
B24	2.73 in. insulation	0.2272	0.025	5.7	0.2	9.00	1.3	B24
B25	3.33 in. insulation	0.2777	0.025	5.7	0.2	11.00	1.6	B25
B26	3.64 in. insulation	0.3029	0.025	5.7	0.2	12.00	1.7	B26
B27	4.54 in. insulation	0.3786	0.025	5.7	0.2	15.00	2.2	B27
C1	4 in. clay file	0.333	0.33	70.0	0.2	1.01	23.3	C1
C2	4 in. lightweight concrete block	0.333	0.22	38.0	0.2	1.51	12.7	C2
C3	4 in. heavyweight concrete block	0.333	0.47	61.0	0.2	0.71	20.3	C3
C4	4 in. common brick	0.333	0.42	120.0	0.2	0.79	40.0	C4
C5	4 in. heavyweight concrete	0.333	1.00	140.0	0.2	0.33	46.7	C5
C6	8 in. clay tile	0.667	0.33	70.0	0.2	2.00	46.7	C6
C7	8 in. lightweight concrete block	0.667	0.33	38.0	0.2	2.00	25.3	C7
C8	8 in. heavyweight concrete block	0.667	0.6	61.0	0.2	1.11	40.7	C8
C9	8 in. common brick	0.667	0.42	120.0	0.2	1.59	80.0	C9
C10	8 in. heavyweight concrete	0.667	1.0	140.0	0.2	0.67	93.4	C10
C11	12 in. heavyweight concrete	1.0	1.0	140.0	0.2	1.00	140.0	C11
C12	2 in. heavyweight concrete	0.167	1.0	140.0	0.2	0.17	23.3	C12
C13	6 in. heavyweight concrete	0.5	1.0	140.0	0.2	0.50	70.0	C13
C14	4 in. lightweight concrete	0.333	0.1	40.0	0.2	3.33	13.3	C14
C15	6 in. lightweight concrete	0.5	0.1	40.0	0.2	5.00	20.0	C15
C16	8 in. lightweight concrete	0.667	0.1	40.0	0.2	6.67	26.7	C16
C17	8 in. lightweight concrete block (filled)	0.667	0.08	18.0	0.2	8.34	12.0	C17
C18	8 in. heavyweight concrete block (filled)	0.667	0.34	53.0	0.2	1.96	35.4	C18
C19	12 in. lightweight concrete block (filled)	1.000	0.08	19.0	0.2	12.50	19.0	C19
C20	12 in. heavyweight concrete block (filled)	1.000	0.39	56.0	0.2	2.56	56.0	C20
E0	Inside surface resistance	0.0	0.00	0.0	0.0	0.69	0.0	E0
E1	¾ in. plaster or gypsum	0.0625	0.42	100.0	0.2	0.15	6.3	E1
E2	½ in. slag or stone	0.0417	0.83	55.0	0.40	0.05	2.3	E2
E3	⅜ in. felt and membrane	0.0313	0.11	70.0	0.40	0.29	2.2	E3
E4	Ceiling air space	0.0	0.00	0.0	0.0	1.00	0.0	E4
E5	Acoustic tile	0.0625	0.035	30.0	0.2	1.79	1.9	E5

L = thickness, ft ρ = density, lb/ft^3 R = thermal resistance, °F-ft^2-hr/Btu k = thermal conductivity, Btu/hr-ft-°F C_p = specific heat, Btu/lb-°F Mass= unit mass, lb/ft^2.

Table 7-21a. Wall Types, Mass Located Inside Insulation, for Use with Tables 7-10 to 7-19

Secondary Material	R value, ft²-°F-hr/Btu	Principal Wall Material[a]													
		A1	A2	B7	B10	C1	C2	C3	C4	C5	C6	C7	C8	C17	C18
Stucco and/or plaster	0.0 to 2.0	...	...	...	...	...	...	...	...	...	...	...	...	...	...
	2.0 to 2.5	...	5	...	...	...	...	...	...	5	...	...	...	...	...
	2.5 to 3.0	...	5	...	...	3	...	2	5	6	...	...	5	...	...
	3.0 to 3.5	...	5	...	...	4	2	2	5	6	...	...	6	...	...
	3.5 to 4.0	...	5	...	...	4	2	3	6	6	10	4	6	...	5
	4.0 to 4.75	...	6	...	...	5	2	4	6	6	11	5	10	...	10
	4.75 to 5.5	...	6	...	...	5	2	4	6	6	11	5	10	...	10
	5.5 to 6.5	...	6	...	...	5	2	5	10	7	12	5	11	...	10
	6.5 to 7.75	...	6	...	...	5	4	5	11	7	16	10	11	...	11
	7.75 to 9.0	...	6	...	...	5	4	5	11	7	...	10	11	...	11
	9.0 to 10.75	...	6	...	...	5	4	5	11	7	...	10	11	4	11
	10.75 to 12.75	...	6	...	...	5	4	5	11	11	...	10	11	4	11
	12.75 to 15.0	...	10	...	...	10	4	5	11	11	...	10	11	9	12
	15.0 to 17.5	...	10	...	...	10	5	5	11	11	...	11	12	10	16
	17.5 to 20.0	...	11	...	...	10	5	9	11	11	...	15	16	10	16
	20.0 to 23.0	...	11	...	...	10	9	9	16	11	...	15	16	10	16
	23.0 to 27.0	...	...	...	...	...	...	...	...	...	...	16		15	
Steel or other light weight siding	0.0 to 2.0	...	...	...	...	...	...	...	...	...	...	...	...	...	...
	2.0 to 2.5	...	3	...	...	...	...	2	3	5	...	...	...	...	...
	2.5 to 3.0	...	5	...	...	2	...	2	5	3	...	...	5	...	...
	3.0 to 3.5	...	5	...	...	3	1	2	5	5	...	...	5	...	...
	3.5 to 4.0	...	5	...	...	3	2	2	5	5	6	3	5	...	5
	4.0 to 4.75	...	6	...	...	4	2	2	5	5	10	4	6	...	5
	4.75 to 5.5	...	6	...	...	5	2	2	6	6	11	5	6	...	6
	5.5 to 6.5	...	6	...	...	5	2	3	6	6	11	5	6	...	6
	6.5 to 7.75	...	6	...	...	5	2	3	6	6	11	5	6	...	10
	7.75 to 9.0	...	6	...	...	5	2	3	6	6	12	5	6	...	11
	9.0 to 10.75	...	6	...	...	5	2	3	6	6	12	5	6	4	11
	10.75 to 12.75	...	6	...	...	5	2	3	6	7	12	6	11	4	11
	12.75 to 15.0	...	6	...	...	5	2	4	6	7	12	10	11	5	11
	15.0 to 17.5	...	10	...	...	6	4	4	10	7	...	10	11	9	11
	17.5 to 20.0	...	10	...	...	10	4	4	10	11	...	10	11	10	11
	20.0 to 23.0	...	11	...	...	10	4	5	11	11	...	10	11	10	16
	23.0 to 27.0	...	...	...	...	...	...	...	...	...	...	10	...	11	16
Face brick	0.0 to 2.0	...	...	...	...	...	...	...	...	...	...	...	...	...	...
	2.0 to 2.5	3	...	...	...	...	...	...	...	11	...	...	...	...	...
	2.5 to 3.0	5	11	...	...	...	...	6	11	12	...	...	...	...	...
	3.0 to 3.5	5	12	5	...	11	...	11	12	12	...	...	12	...	...
	3.5 to 4.0	5	12	6	...	12	6	12	12	13	...	...	12	...	...
	4.0 to 4.75	6	13	6	10	13	10	12	12	13	...	11	...	...	16
	4.75 to 5.5	6	13	6	11	...	11	12	13	13	...	16	...	...	...
	5.5 to 6.5	6	13	6	11	...	11	12	13	13	...	...	...	...	...
	6.5 to 7.75	6	13	6	11	...	11	13	...	13	...	...	...	...	...
	7.75 to 9.0	6	13	10	16	...	11	13	...	13	...	...	...	...	...
	9.0 to 10.75	6	14	10	16	...	11	13	...	14	...	...	...	16	...
	10.75 to 12.75	6	14	10	16	...	11	13	...	14	...	...	...	16	...
	12.75 to 15.0	6	...	11	16	...	12	13	...	...	...	...	...	...	...
	15.0 to 17.5	10	...	11	...	...	12	13	...	...	...	...	...	...	...
	17.5 to 20.0	10	...	11	...	...	16	...	...	...	...	...	...	...	...
	20.0 to 23.0	11	...	15	...	...	16	...	...	...	...	...	...	...	...
	23.0 to 27.0	...	...	...	...	...	16	...	...	...	...	...	...	...	...

[a] See Table 7-20 for definition of code letters

... Denotes a wall that is not possible with the chosen set of parameters.

Table 7-21b. Wall Types, Mass Located Inside Insulation, for Use with Tables 7-10 to 7-19

Secondary Material	R value, ft^2-°F-hr/Btu	Principal Wall Material[a]														
		A1	A2	B7	B9	B10	C1	C2	C3	C4	C5	C6	C7	C8	C17	C18
Stucco and/or plaster	0.0 to 2.0	1	3	...	...	...	...	...	1	3	1	...	...	...	...	...
	2.0 to 2.5	1	3	1	...	...	2	...	2	4	4	...	...	5	...	...
	2.5 to 3.0	1	4	1	...	...	2	2	2	4	4	...	...	5	...	...
	3.0 to 3.5	1	...	1	...	...	2	2	...	...	...	10	4	5	...	4
	3.5 to 4.0	1	...	1	...	2	...	4	...	...	...	10	4	...	...	4
	4.0 to 4.75	1	...	1	...	2	...	...	...	...	...	10	4	...	...	4
	4.75 to 5.5	1	...	1	...	2	...	...	...	...	...	...	...	...	...	...
	5.5 to 6.5	1	...	2	10	4	...	...	...	...	...	...	...	...	...	...
	6.5 to 7.75	1	...	2	11	4	...	...	...	...	...	...	...	...	...	...
	7.75 to 9.0	1	...	2	16	4	...	...	...	...	...	...	...	...	...	...
	9.0 to 10.75	1	...	2	16	4	...	...	...	...	...	...	...	...	4	...
	10.75 to 12.75	1	...	2	...	5	...	...	...	...	...	...	...	...	4	...
	12.75 to 15.0	2	...	2	...	5	...	...	...	...	...	...	...	...	...	...
	15.0 to 17.5	2	...	2	...	5	...	...	...	...	...	...	...	...	...	...
	17.5 to 20.0	2	...	2	...	9	...	...	...	...	...	...	...	...	...	...
	20.0 to 23.0	2	...	4	...	9	...	...	...	...	...	...	...	...	...	...
	23.0 to 27.0	...	...	...	...	9	...	...	...	...	...	...	...	...	...	...
Steel or other light weight siding	0.0 to 2.0	1	3	...	...	...	...	...	1	3	2	...	...	...	...	...
	2.0 to 2.5	1	3	1	...	...	2	...	1	3	2	...	...	3	...	...
	2.5 to 3.0	1	4	1	...	...	2	1	2	4	4	...	...	3	...	...
	3.0 to 3.5	1	...	1	...	...	4	1	...	...	...	5	2	4	...	4
	3.5 to 4.0	1	...	1	...	2	...	2	...	...	...	5	2	...	...	4
	4.0 to 4.75	1	...	1	...	2	...	...	...	...	...	10	4	...	...	4
	4.75 to 5.5	1	...	1	...	2	...	...	...	...	...	...	...	...	...	...
	5.5 to 6.5	1	...	1	10	2	...	...	...	...	...	...	...	...	...	...
	6.5 to 7.75	1	...	1	11	4	...	...	...	...	...	...	...	...	...	...
	7.75 to 9.0	1	...	2	16	4	...	...	...	...	...	...	...	...	...	...
	9.0 to 10.75	1	...	2	16	4	...	...	...	...	...	...	...	...	2	...
	10.75 to 12.75	1	...	2	...	4	...	...	...	...	...	...	...	...	4	...
	12.75 to 15.0	1	...	2	...	5	...	...	...	...	...	...	...	...	...	...
	15.0 to 17.5	1	...	2	...	5	...	...	...	...	...	...	...	...	...	...
	17.5 to 20.0	1	...	2	...	5	...	...	...	...	...	...	...	...	...	...
	20.0 to 23.0	2	...	4	...	9	...	...	...	...	...	...	...	...	...	...
	23.0 to 27.0	...	...	...	...	9	...	...	...	...	...	...	...	...	...	...
Face brick	0.0 to 2.0	3	6	...	...	...	...	...	...	...	6	...	...	...	...	...
	2.0 to 2.5	3	10	...	...	...	...	...	5	10	10	...	...	...	...	...
	2.5 to 3.0	4	10	5	...	...	5	...	5	10	11	...	...	10	...	...
	3.0 to 3.5	...	11	5	...	...	10	5	5	11	11	15	10	10	...	10
	3.5 to 4.0	...	11	5	...	10	10	5	5	11	11	16	10	16	...	10
	4.0 to 4.75	...	11	...	...	11	10	5	5	16	11	...	10	16	...	16
	4.75 to 5.5	...	11	...	...	11	10	5	10	16	16	...	10	16	...	16
	5.5 to 6.5	...	16	...	...	...	10	9	10	16	11	...	11	16	...	16
	6.5 to 7.75	...	16	...	...	...	11	9	10	16	16	...	16	16	...	...
	7.75 to 9.0	...	16	...	...	...	15	9	10	16	...	...	15	16	...	...
	9.0 to 10.75	...	16	...	...	...	15	10	10	...	16	...	16	...	10	...
	10.75 to 12.75	...	16	...	...	...	16	10	10	...	...	...	16	...	15	...
	12.75 to 15.0	...	16	...	...	...	16	10	10	...	16	...	...	...	15	...
	15.0 to 17.5	...	...	...	...	...	16	10	15	...	...	...	...	...	16	...
	17.5 to 20.0	...	...	...	...	...	16	15	15	...	...	...	...	...	16	...
	20.0 to 23.0	...	...	...	...	...	...	15	16	...	...	...	...	...	...	...
	23.0 to 27.0	...	...	...	...	...	...	15	...	...	...	...	...	...	...	...

[a] See Table 7-20 for definition of code letters

... Denotes a wall that is not possible with the chosen set of parameters.

Table 7-21c. Wall Types, Mass Located Inside Insulation, for Use with Tables 7-10 to 7-19

Secondary Material	R value, ft²-°F-hr/Btu	A1	A2	B7	B9	B10	C1	C2	C3	C4	C5	C6	C7	C8	C17	C18
Stucco and/or plaster	0.0 to 2.0	1	3	…	…	…	…	…	1	3	3	…	…	…	…	…
	2.0 to 2.5	1	3	1	…	…	2	…	2	4	4	…	…	5	…	…
	2.5 to 3.0	1	4	1	…	…	2	2	2	4	4	…	…	5	…	…
	3.0 to 3.5	1	…	1	…	…	2	2	…	…	…	10	4	5	…	4
	3.5 to 4.0	1	…	1	…	2		4	…	…	…	10	4	…	…	4
	4.0 to 4.75	1	…	1	…	2			…	…	…	10	4	…	…	4
	4.75 to 5.5	1	…	1	…	2	…	…	…	…	…	…	…	…	…	…
	5.5 to 6.5	1	…	2	10	4	…	…	…	…	…	…	…	…	…	…
	6.5 to 7.75	1	…	2	11	4	…	…	…	…	…	…	…	…	…	…
	7.75 to 9.0	1	…	2	16	4	…	…	…	…	…	…	…	…	…	…
	9.0 to 10.75	1	…	2	16	4	…	…	…	…	…	…	…	…	4	…
	10.75 to 12.75	1	…	2	…	5	…	…	…	…	…	…	…	…	4	…
	12.75 to 15.0	2	…	2	…	5	…	…	…	…	…	…	…	…	…	…
	15.0 to 17.5	2	…	2	…	5	…	…	…	…	…	…	…	…	…	…
	17.5 to 20.0	2	…	2	…	9	…	…	…	…	…	…	…	…	…	…
	20.0 to 23.0	2	…	4	…	9	…	…	…	…	…	…	…	…	…	…
	23.0 to 27.0	…	…	…	…	9	…	…	…	…	…	…	…	…	…	…
Steel or other light weight siding	0.0 to 2.0	1	3	…	…	…	…	…	1	3	2	…	…	…	…	…
	2.0 to 2.5	1	3	1	…	…	2		1	3	2	…	…	3	…	…
	2.5 to 3.0	1	4	1	…	…	2	1	2	4	4	…	…	3	…	…
	3.0 to 3.5	1	…	1	…	…	4	1	…	…	…	5	2	4	…	4
	3.5 to 4.0	1	…	1	…	2	…	2	…	…	…	5	2	…	…	4
	4.0 to 4.75	1	…	1	…	2	…	…	…	…	…	10	4	…	…	4
	4.75 to 5.5	1	…	1	…	2	…	…	…	…	…	…	…	…	…	…
	5.5 to 6.5	1	…	1	10	2	…	…	…	…	…	…	…	…	…	…
	6.5 to 7.75	1	…	1	11	4	…	…	…	…	…	…	…	…	…	…
	7.75 to 9.0	1	…	2	16	4	…	…	…	…	…	…	…	…	…	…
	9.0 to 10.75	1	…	2	16	4	…	…	…	…	…	…	…	…	2	…
	10.75 to 12.75	1	…	2	…	4	…	…	…	…	…	…	…	…	4	…
	12.75 to 15.0	1	…	2	…	5	…	…	…	…	…	…	…	…	…	…
	15.0 to 17.5	1	…	2	…	5	…	…	…	…	…	…	…	…	…	…
	17.5 to 20.0	1	…	2	…	5	…	…	…	…	…	…	…	…	…	…
	20.0 to 23.0	2	…	4	…	9	…	…	…	…	…	…	…	…	…	…
	23.0 to 27.0	…	…	…	…	9	…	…	…	…	…	…	…	…	…	…
Face brick	0.0 to 2.0	3	6	…	…	…	…	…	…	…	6	…	…	…	…	…
	2.0 to 2.5	3	10	…	…	…	…	…	5	10	10	…	…	…	…	…
	2.5 to 3.0	4	10	5	…	…	5		5	10	11	…	…	10	…	…
	3.0 to 3.5	…	11	5	…	…	10	5	5	11	11	15	10	10	…	10
	3.5 to 4.0	…	11	5	…	10	10	5	5	11	11	16	10	16	…	10
	4.0 to 4.75	…	11	…	…	11	10	5	5	16	11	…	10	16	…	16
	4.75 to 5.5	…	11	…	…	11	10	5	10	16	16	…	10	16	…	16
	5.5 to 6.5	…	16	…	…	…	10	9	10	16	11	…	11	16	…	16
	6.5 to 7.75	…	16	…	…	…	11	9	10	16	16	…	16	16	…	…
	7.75 to 9.0	…	16	…	…	…	15	9	10	16	…	…	15	16	…	…
	9.0 to 10.75	…	16	…	…	…	15	10	10	…	16	…	16	…	10	…
	10.75 to 12.75	…	16	…	…	…	16	10	10	…	…	…	16	…	15	…
	12.75 to 15.0	…	16	…	…	…	16	10	10	…	16	…	…	…	15	…
	15.0 to 17.5	…	…	…	…	…	16	10	15	…	…	…	…	…	16	…
	17.5 to 20.0	…	…	…	…	…	16	15	15	…	…	…	…	…	16	…
	20.0 to 23.0	…	…	…	…	…	…	15	16	…	…	…	…	…	16	…
	23.0 to 27.0	…	…	…	…	…	…	15	…	…	…	…	…	…	…	…

[a] See Table 7-20 for definition of code letters

… Denotes a wall that is not possible with the chosen set of parameters.

Table 7-22. Cooling Load Temperature Differences (CLTD) for Conduction Through Glass

Solar Time, hr	CLTD, °F	Solar Time, hr	CLTD, °F	Solar Time, hr	CLTD, °F
0100	1	0900	2	1700	13
0200	0	1000	4	1800	12
0300	−1	1100	7	1900	10
0400	−2	1200	9	2000	8
0500	−2	1300	12	2100	6
0600	−2	1400	13	2200	4
0700	−2	1500	14	2300	3
0800	0	1600	14	2400	2

Table 7-23a. Zone Types for Use With CLF Tables, Interior Rooms

	Zone Parameter[a]			Zone Type	
Room Location	Middle Floor	Ceiling Type	Floor Covering	People and Equipment	Lights
Single story	N/A	N/A	Carpet	C	B
	N/A	N/A	Vinyl	D	C
Top floor	2.5 in. concrete	with	Carpet	D	C
	2.5 in. concrete	with	Vinyl	D	D
	2.5 in. concrete	without	[b]	D	B
	1 in. wood	[b]	[b]	D	B
Bottom floor	2.5 in. concrete	with	Carpet	D	C
	2.5 in. concrete	[b]	Vinyl	D	D
	2.5 in. concrete	without	Carpet	D	D
	1 in. wood	[b]	Carpet	D	C
	1 in. wood	[b]	Vinyl	D	D
Mid floor	2.5 in. concrete	N/A	Carpet	D	C
	2.5 in. concrete	N/A	Vinyl	D	D
	1 in. wood	N/A	[b]	C	B

[a] Fourteen zone parameters are defined in Chapter 26, *1997 ASHRAE Fundamentals Handbook*
[b] The effect of inside shade is negligible in this case.

Table 7-23b. Zone Types for Use with SCL and CLF Tables, Single-Story Building

	Zone Parameters[a]			Zone Type			Error Bands	
No. walls	Floor Covering	Partition Type	Inside Shade	Glass Solar	People and Equipment	Lights	Plus	Minus
1 or 2	Carpet	Gypsum	[b]	A	B	B	9	2
1 or 2	Carpet	Concrete block	[b]	B	C	C	9	0
1 or 2	Vinyl	Gypsum	Full	B	C	C	9	0
1 or 2	Vinyl	Gypsum	Half to None	C	C	C	16	0
1 or 2	Vinyl	Concrete block	Full	C	D	D	8	0
1 or 2	Vinyl	Concrete block	Half to None	D	D	D	10	6
3	Carpet	Gypsum	[b]	A	B	B	9	2
3	Carpet	Concrete block	Full	A	B	B	9	2
3	Carpet	Concrete block	Half to None	B	B	B	9	0
3	Vinyl	Gypsum	full	B	C	C	9	0
3	Vinyl	Gypsum	Half to None	C	C	C	16	0
3	Vinyl	Concrete block	Full	B	C	C	9	0
3	Vinyl	Concrete block	Half to None	C	C	C	16	0
4	Carpet	Gypsum	[b]	A	B	B	6	3
4	Vinyl	Gypsum	Full	B	C	C	11	6
4	Vinyl	Gypsum	Half to None	C	C	C	19	−1

[a] Fourteen zone parameters are defined in Chapter 26, *1997 ASHRAE HandbookFundamentals*
[b] The effect of inside shade is negligible in this case

Table 7-23c. Zone Types for Use with SCL and CLF Tables, Middle Floor of Multi-Story Building

No. of Walls	Mid-Floor	Ceiling Type	Floor Covering	Partition Type	Inside Shade	Glass Solar	People and Equipment	Lights	Plus	Minus
				Zone Parameters[a]			Zone Type		Error Band	
1 or 2	2.5 in. Concrete	With	Carpet	Gypsum		B	B	C	6	6
	2.5 in. Concrete	With	Carpet	Concrete block	Full	C	C	C	1	4
	2.5 in. Concrete	With	Carpet	Concrete block	Half to None	C	C	C	10	4
	2.5 in. Concrete	With	Vinyl	Gypsum	Full	C	D	D	10	4
	2.5 in. Concrete	With	Vinyl	Gypsum	Half to None	D	D	D	6	12
	2.5 in. Concrete	With	Vinyl	Concrete block	…	D	D	D	3	7
	2.5 in. Concrete	Without	Carpet	Gypsum	…	B	B	D	6	6
	2.5 in. Concrete	Without	Carpet	Concrete block	…	C	C	D	10	4
	2.5 in. Concrete	Without	Vinyl	Gypsum	Full	B	C	C	11	6
	2.5 in. Concrete	Without	Vinyl	Gypsum	Half to None	C	C	C	9	7
	2.5 in. Concrete	Without	Vinyl	Concrete block	…	C	C	D	9	−1
	1 in. Wood	…	…	Gypsum	…	A	A	A	0	0
	1 in. Wood	…	…	Concrete block	…	B	A	B	6	8
3	2.5 in. Concrete	With	Carpet	Gypsum	…	B	B	C	6	6
	2.5 in. Concrete	With	Carpet	Concrete block	Full	B	C	C	6	6
	2.5 in. Concrete	With	Carpet	Concrete block	Half to None	C	C	C	1	4
	2.5 in. Concrete	With	Vinyl	Gypsum	Full	C	D	D	10	4
	2.5 in. Concrete	With	Vinyl	Gypsum	Half to None	D	D	D	7	12
	2.5 in. Concrete	With	Vinyl	Concrete block	Full	C	D	D	10	−1
	2.5 in. Concrete	With	Vinyl	Concrete block	Half to None	D	D	D	7	12
	2.5 in. Concrete	Without	Carpet	Gypsum	…	B	B	C	6	6
	2.5 in. Concrete	Without	Carpet	Concrete block	Full	C	C	C	1	4
	2.5 in. Concrete	Without	Carpet	Concrete block	Half to None	B	C	C	6	6
	2.5 in. Concrete	Without	Vinyl	Gypsum	Full	B	C	C	11	6
	2.5 in. Concrete	Without	Vinyl	Gypsum	Half to None	C	C	C	9	7
	2.5 in. Concrete	Without	Vinyl	Concrete block	Full	B	C	C	11	−2
	2.5 in. Concrete	Without	Vinyl	Concrete block	Half to None	C	C	C	9	−1
	1 in. Wood	…	…	Gypsum	…	A	A	A	0	0
	1 in. Wood	…	…	Concrete block	…	A	A	B	10	0
4	2.5 in. Concrete	With	Carpet	Gypsum	…	B	C	C	6	6
	2.5 in. Concrete	With	Vinyl	Gypsum	Full	C	C	C	14	6
	2.5 in. Concrete	With	Vinyl	Gypsum	Half to None	C	C	C	26	6
	2.5 in. Concrete	Without	Carpet	Gypsum	…	B	A	C	6	6
	2.5 in. Concrete	Without	Vinyl	Gypsum	Full	B	A	C	7	6
	2.5 in. Concrete	Without	Vinyl	Gypsum	Half to None	B	A	C	20	6
	1 in. Wood	…	…	…	…	A	A	B	−2	2

[a] Fourteen zone parameters are defined in Chapter 26, *1997 ASHRAE Handbook Fundamentals*.

Table 7-23d. Zone Types for Use with SCL and CLF Tables, First Floor of Multi-story Building

		Zone Parameters[a]				Zone Type			Error	Band
No. of Walls	Mid-Floor	Ceiling Type	Floor Covering	Partition Type	Inside Shade	Glass Solar	People and Equipment	Lights	Plus	Minus
	2.5 in. Concrete	With	Carpet	Gypsum	Full	A	C	B	7	1
	2.5 in. Concrete	With	Carpet	Gypsum	Half to None	B	C	B	9	2
	2.5 in. Concrete	With	Carpet	Concrete block	Full	B	D	C	9	2
	2.5 in. Concrete	With	Carpet	Concrete block	Half to None	C	D	C	0	0
	2.5 in. Concrete	With	Vinyl	Gypsum	Full	C	D	D	19	0
	2.5 in. Concrete	With	Vinyl	Gypsum	Half to None	C	D	D	26	0
	2.5 in. Concrete	With	Vinyl	Concrete block	Full	D	D	D	6	3
	2.5 in. Concrete	With	Vinyl	Concrete block	Half to None	D	D	D	16	3
	2.5 in. Concrete	Without	Carpet	Gypsum		B	C	B	9	2
	2.5 in. Concrete	Without	Carpet	Concrete block	Full	C	D	C	19	0
	2.5 in. Concrete	Without	Carpet	Concrete block	Half to None	C	D	C	16	0
1 or 2	2.5 in. Concrete	Without	Vinyl	Gypsum	Full	C	D	D	19	6
	2.5 in. Concrete	Without	Vinyl	Gypsum	Half to None	D	D	D	6	6
	2.5 in. Concrete	Without	Vinyl	Concrete block	Full	C	D	D	16	0
	2.5 in. Concrete	Without	Vinyl	Concrete block	Half to None	D	D	D	6	3
	1 in. Wood	...	Carpet	Gypsum	Full	A	A	B	2	-2
	1 in. Wood	...	Carpet	Gypsum	Half to None	B	A	B	6	6
	1 in. Wood	...	Carpet	Concrete block	Full	B	B	C	6	6
	I in. Wood	...	Carpet	Concrete block	Half to None	C	B	C	7	3
	I in. Wood	...	Vinyl	Gypsum	Full	B	B	B	18	6
	1 in. Wood	...	Vinyl	Gypsum	Half to None	C	B	B	14	3
	1 in. Wood	...	Vinyl	Concrete block	Full	C	C	D	14	3
	1 in. Wood	...	Vinyl	Concrete block	Half to None	D	C	D	2	4
	2.5 in. Concrete	With	Carpet	Gypsum	Full	A	C	B	7	1
	2.5 in. Concrete	With	Carpet	Gypsum	Half to None	B	C	B	9	2
	2.5 in. Concrete	With	Carpet	Concrete block		B	C	B	9	2
	2.5 in. Concrete	With	Vinyl	Gypsum	Full	C	D	C	19	0
	2.5 in. Concrete	With	Vinyl		Half to None	C	D	C	26	0
	2.5 in. Concrete	With	Vinyl	Concrete block	Full	C	D	C	19	0
	2.5 in. Concrete	Without	Carpet	Gypsum		B	C	B	9	2
	2.5 in. Concrete	Without	Carpet	Concrete block	Full	B	C	B	9	2
	2.5 in. Concrete	Without	Carpet	Concrete block	Half to None	C	C	B	0	0
3	2.5 in., Concrete	Without	Vinyl	Gypsum	Full	C	D	C	19	6
	2.5 in. Concrete	Without	Vinyl		Half to None	C	D	C	26	0
	2.5 in. Concrete	Without	Vinyl	Concrete block	Full	C	D	C	19	0
	1 in. Wood	...	Carpet	Gypsum	Full	A	A	B	2	-2
	1 in. Wood	...	Carpet	Gypsum	Half to None	B	A	B	6	6
	1 in. Wood	...	Carpet	Concrete block		B	B	B	6	6
	1 in. Wood	...	Vinyl	Gypsum	Full	B	B	C	18	6
	1 in. Wood	...	Vinyl	Gypsum	Half to None	C	B	C	14	3
	1 in. Wood	...	Vinyl	Concrete block	Full	C	B	C	7	3
	1 in. Wood	...	Vinyl	Concrete block	Half to None	C	B	C	14	3
	2.5 in. Concrete	With	Carpet	Gypsum	Full	A	B	B	4	-4
	2.5 in. Concrete	With	Carpet	Gypsum	Half to None	B	B	B	18	6
	2.5 in. Concrete	With	Vinyl	Gypsum	...	C	C	C	19	3
	2.5 in. Concrete	Without	Carpet	Gypsum	...	B	C	C	7	6
4	2.5 in. Concrete	Without	Vinyl	Gypsum	...	B	C	C	31	6
	1 in. Wood	...	Carpet	Gypsum	Full	A	B	A	0	0
	I in. Wood	...	Carpet	Gypsum	Half to None	A	B	A	12	0
	1 in. Wood	...	Vinyl	Gypsum	Full	B	B	B	16	8
	1 in. Wood	...	Vinyl	Gypsum	Half to None	C	8	B	20	6

[a] Fourteen zone parameters are defined in Chapter 26, *1997 ASHRAE Handbook Fundamentals*.

Table 7-23e. Zone Types for Use with SCL and CLF Tables, Top Floor of Multi-story Building

No. of Walls	Mid-Floor	Ceiling Type	Floor Covering	Partition Type	Inside Shade	Glass Solar	People and Equipment	Lights	Plus	Minus
1 or 2	2.5 in. Concrete	With	Carpet	Gypsum	Full	A	A	B	2	4
	2.5 in. Concrete	With	Carpet	Gypsum	Half to None	A	A	B	7	−2
	2.5 in. Concrete	With	Carpet	Concrete block	Full	B	A	C	9	6
	2.5 in. Concrete	With	Carpet	Concrete block	Half to None	B	A	C	14	2
	2.5 in. Concrete	With	Vinyl	Gypsum	Full	B	A	C	8	6
	2.5 in. Concrete	With	Vinyl	Gypsum	Half to None	C	A	C	12	10
	2.5 in. Concrete	With	Vinyl	Concrete block	Full	C	B	D	7	7
	2.5 in. Concrete	With	Vinyl	Concrete block	Half to None	C	B	D	19	0
	2.5 in. Concrete	Without	Carpet	Gypsum	…	A	A	B	−4	4
	2.5 in. Concrete	Without	Carpet	Concrete block	…	A	A	C	7	4
	2.5 in. Concrete	Without	Vinyl	Gypsum	…	A	A	B	7	4
	2.5 in. Concrete	Without	Vinyl	Concrete block	Full	B	A	C	8	6
	2.5 in. Concrete	Without	Vinyl	Concrete block	Half to None	B	A	C.	10	6
	1 in. Wood	…	…	Gypsum	…	A	A	B	−3	3
	1 in. Wood	…	…	Concrete block	…	A	B	C	13	3
3	2.5 in. Concrete	With	Carpet	Gypsum	Full	A	B	B	2	4
	2.5 in. Concrete	With	Carpet	Gypsum	Half to None	A	A	B	7	−2
	2.5 in. Concrete	With	Carpet	Concrete block	Full	A	A	C	7	−2
	2.5 in. Concrete	With	Carpet	Concrete block	Half to None	B	A	C	9	6
	2.5 in. Concrete	With	Vinyl	Gypsum	Full	B	A	C	8	6
	2.5 in. Concrete	With	Vinyl	Gypsum	Half to None	C	A	C	12	10
	2.5 in. Concrete	With	Vinyl	Concrete block	Full	B	A	C	9	2
	2.5 in. Concrete	With	Vinyl	Concrete block	Half to None	C	A	C	12	7
	2.5 in. Concrete	Without	Carpet	…	…	A	A	B	2	4
	2.5 in. Concrete	Without	Vinyl	Gypsum	Full	A	A	B	7	4
	2.5 in. Concrete	Without	Vinyl	Gypsum	Half to None	A	A	B	4	4
	2.5 in. Concrete	Without	Vinyl	Concrete block	Full	A	A	B	7	4
	2.5 in. Concrete	Without	Vinyl	Concrete block	Half to None	B	A	B	2	6
	1 in. Wood	…	…	Gypsum	…	A	A	B	−3	3
	1 in. Wood	…	…	Concrete block	…	A	A	B	6	3
4	2.5 in. Concrete	With	Carpet	Gypsum	Full	A	A	B	9	6
	2.5 in. Concrete	With	Carpet	Gypsum	Half to None	B	A	B	6	4
	2.5 in. Concrete	With	Vinyl	Gypsum	Full	B	C	C	7	14
	2.5 in. Concrete	With	Vinyl	Gypsum	Half to None	B	B	C	24	4
	2.5 in. Concrete	Without	Carpet	Gypsum	Full	A	A	B	4	6
	2.5 in. Concrete	Without	Carpet	Gypsum	Half to None	A	A	B	−6	6
	2.5 in. Concrete	Without	Vinyl	Gypsum	Full	A	A	B	4	6
	2.5 in. Concrete	Without	Vinyl	Gypsum	Half to None	A	A	B	7	0
	1 in. Wood	…	…	…	…	A		B	0	8

[a] Fourteen zone parameters are defined in Chapter 26, *1997 ASHRAE Handbook Fundamentals*.

Residential Cooling Load Procedure.—The CLTD/SCL/CLF procedure described above applies to commercial and institutional buildings. In case of residential structures, the cooling load calculation can by simplified based on the following factors.

Cooling Load Determinations: The cooling load calculation is divided among sensible and latent cooling loads. The sensible cooling loads are due to:

heat gains through walls, floor, and ceilings;

heat gain through windows;

heat gain from infiltration and ventilation; and

occupancy.

In this procedure many rooms may be considered one zone. To properly calculate cooling load for a whole building, cooling load and the amount of required conditioned air for each room must be calculated separately, then added to find the total cooling load.

Residential buildings can be categorized as 1) detached single family, 2) multi-family, and 3) light commercial buildings. Generally, in a design of one story single family buildings, a single zone, single thermostat is recommended. For two story single family buildings, two zones with separate thermostats is recommended for energy saving.

Latent cooling loads are due to:

outdoor air;

occupants; and

miscellaneous sources such as cooking, laundry, and bathing.

The summary of residential cooling load calculation procedure is given in the Table 7-24.

Table 7-24. Summary of Procedures for Residential Cooling Load Calculations

Load Source	Equations
Glass and window areas	$\dot{q} = (GLF)\,A$ GLF = glass load factors may be found in Tables 7-36 and 7-37 according to window orientation, type of glass, type of interior shading, and outdoor design temperature; and A = glass area.
Doors	$\dot{q} = U_d A (CLTD)$ U_d = design heat transfer coefficient for door from Chapter 5; A = area of door, calculated from building plans; and $CLTD$ = cooling load temperature difference, Tables 7-38 to 7-39.
Above-grade exterior walls	$\dot{q} = U_w A (CLTD)$ U_W = design heat transfer coefficient for exterior wall from Chapter 5; A = area of exterior wall, calculated from building plans; and $CLTD$ = cooling load temperature difference, Tables 7-38 to 7-39.
Partitions to unconditioned space	$\dot{q} = U_p A (T_o - T_i)$ U_p = design heat transfer coefficient for partitions to unconditioned space from Chapter 5; A = area of unconditioned space or partitions, calculated from building plans; T_o = outside air temperature, °F; and T_i = inside air temperature, °F
Ceilings and roofs	$\dot{q} = U_r A (CLTD)$ U_r = design heat transfer coefficient for ceilings or roof from Chapter 5; A = area of ceilings or roof, calculated from building plans; and $CLTD$ = cooling load temperature difference, Tables 7-38 to 7-39.
Exposed floors	$\dot{q} = U_f A (CLTD)$ U_f = design heat transfer coefficient for exposed floor from Chapter 5; A = area of ceilings or roof, calculated from building plans; and $CLTD$ = cooling load temperature difference, Tables 7-38 to 7-39.
Infiltration	$\dot{q} = 1.1\, cfm \Delta T \qquad cfm = ach \times \dfrac{\text{room volume}}{60}$ cfm = ventilation cfm T_o = outside air temperature, °F T_i = inside air temperature, °F ACH = Air exchange rates given in Tables 7-43 and 7-44
Internal loads: People, appliances, lights	$\dot{q} = N \times 230 \;\; \text{Btu/person}$ N = number of people in space Divide occupants evenly among rooms not used as bedrooms. If number of occupants is not known, assume two people for first bedroom and one person for each additional bedroom. $\dot{q} = 1600 \;\; \text{Btu/hr}$
Total loads	Total cooling load = $LF \times$ Sum of individual sensible cooling load componenets LF = Load factors are from Fig. 7-4, according to outdoor design humidity ratio and airtightness classification.

Table 7-25. July Solar Cooling Load (SCL) for Sunlit Glass 24° North Latitude

Wall Facing	Solar Time, hr																								Wall Facing
	1	2	3	4	5	6	7	8	9	10	11	12	13	14	15	16	17	18	19	20	21	22	23	24	
ZONE TYPE A																									
N	0	0	0	0	0	19	35	36	36	38	40	42	42	40	38	39	43	32	11	6	3	1	1	0	N
NE	0	0	0	0	0	54	124	150	144	115	78	58	49	44	38	32	25	14	6	3	1	1	0	0	NE
E	0	0	0	0	0	57	139	177	180	154	107	68	54	46	40	33	25	14	6	3	1	1	0	0	E
SE	0	0	0	0	0	26	74	104	114	106	83	59	50	44	38	32	25	14	6	3	1	1	0	0	SE
S	0	0	0	0	0	5	15	23	30	35	40	43	43	40	37	32	24	14	6	3	1	1	0	0	S
SW	0	0	0	0	0	5	15	23	30	35	39	42	61	88	110	118	105	62	24	12	6	3	1	1	SW
W	1	0	0	0	0	5	15	23	30	35	39	41	67	116	160	186	184	118	44	21	11	5	3	1	W
NW	1	0	0	0	0	5	15	23	30	35	39	41	51	83	122	151	158	106	39	19	9	5	2	1	NW
ZONE TYPE B																									
N	2	2	1	1	1	16	30	32	32	35	37	39	40	39	37	39	42	33	16	10	7	5	4	3	N
NE	2	1	1	1	1	47	105	128	126	106	78	62	55	50	44	38	31	20	12	9	6	5	3	3	NE
E	2	2	1	1	1	49	118	151	158	141	105	74	63	55	48	41	33	22	13	10	7	5	4	3	E
SE	2	1	1	1	1	23	63	89	100	95	78	60	53	48	43	37	30	20	12	8	6	4	3	2	SE
S	1	1	1	1	0	5	13	20	26	31	36	39	40	38	36	32	26	17	10	7	5	4	3	2	S
SW	5	3	3	2	1	5	13	20	26	31	35	38	55	79	98	106	98	63	33	22	15	11	8	6	SW
W	7	6	4	3	2	6	14	21	27	32	35	38	61	102	141	165	167	115	56	37	26	18	13	10	W
NW	6	5	4	3	2	6	14	21	27	32	35	38	47	75	108	134	142	102	48	32	22	16	11	8	NW
ZONE TYPE C																									
N	5	5	4	4	4	19	31	31	30	32	35	36	36	35	34	36	39	31	14	11	9	8	7	6	N
NE	8	7	6	6	5	50	104	120	114	92	65	53	50	47	43	38	32	23	16	14	12	11	10	9	NE
E	9	8	6	7	6	53	117	143	143	123	88	62	56	51	47	42	35	26	19	16	14	13	11	10	E
SE	7	6	6	5	4	26	64	85	92	85	68	51	47	44	40	36	30	21	15	12	11	10	9	8	SE
S	4	4	3	3	3	7	14	20	25	29	33	36	36	34	32	29	24	15	10	8	7	6	5	5	S
SW	10	9	8	7	7	10	17	23	28	32	34	37	53	75	92	97	87	53	26	20	17	14	13	11	SW
W	15	14	12	11	10	13	20	25	30	34	36	38	60	99	132	152	150	97	43	31	26	22	19	17	W
NW	13	12	10	9	8	12	19	24	29	33	35	37	45	72	103	125	129	87	36	27	22	19	16	14	NW
ZONE TYPE D																									
N	8	8	7	6	6	17	27	27	27	29	31	33	33	33	33	34	37	30	17	15	13	12	10	9	N
NE	12	11	10	9	8	43	86	100	97	82	63	54	52	49	46	42	37	29	23	21	18	16	15	13	NE
E	14	13	11	10	9	46	97	118	121	108	83	64	59	56	52	47	41	33	27	24	21	19	17	16	E
SE	11	10	9	8	7	24	53	71	77	74	62	50	47	45	42	38	33	26	21	18	16	15	13	12	SE
S	6	6	5	5	4	7	13	18	22	25	29	32	32	31	30	28	24	18	13	11	10	9	8	7	S
SW	15	14	12	11	10	12	18	22	26	29	31	34	47	64	79	84	78	53	32	27	24	21	19	17	SW
W	23	21	19	17	15	17	22	26	29	32	34	36	53	84	112	130	130	91	50	42	36	32	29	26	W
NW	20	18	16	14	13	15	20	24	28	31	33	34	41	63	88	106	111	80	43	35	30	27	24	22	NW

Table 7-26. July Solar Cooling Load (SCL) for Sunlit Glass 32° North Latitude

Wall Facing	Solar Time, hr																								Wall Facing
	1	2	3	4	5	6	7	8	9	10	11	12	13	14	15	16	17	18	19	20	21	22	23	24	
ZONE TYPE A																									
N	0	0	0	0	0	23	31	30	33	36	39	41	41	39	36	33	36	35	12	6	3	1	1	0	N
NE	0	0	0	0	0	73	128	143	128	94	62	52	46	42	38	32	26	16	6	3	1	1	0	0	NE
E	0	0	0	0	0	78	149	182	152	155	107	68	54	46	40	33	26	16	6	3	2	1	0	0	E
SE	0	0	0	0	0	37	85	118	133	129	107	75	55	46	40	33	26	16	6	3	2	1	0	0	SE
S	0	0	0	0	0	7	16	24	32	44	56	64	63	55	43	35	27	17	7	3	2	1	0	0	S
SW	0	0	0	0	0	7	16	24	30	35	39	50	80	111	131	135	120	78	29	14	7	3	2	1	SW
W	1	0	0	0	0	7	16	24	30	35	39	41	67	115	160	188	189	140	50	24	12	6	3	1	W
NW	1	0	0	0	0	7	16	24	30	35	39	41	42	64	103	137	152	121	42	20	10	5	2	1	NW
ZONE TYPE B																									
N	2	2	1	1	1	20	26	26	29	33	36	38	39	38	36	33	36	35	15	10	7	5	4	3	N
NE	2	1	1	1	1	62	109	123	114	89	65	57	52	47	42	37	30	22	12	9	6	5	3	3	NE
E	2	2	1	1	1	66	127	156	160	142	106	75	63	55	48	41	34	24	14	10	7	5	4	3	E
SE	2	2	1	1	1	32	72	101	116	116	100	76	60	53	46	40	32	23	13	9	7	5	4	3	SE
S	2	1	1	1	1	6	14	21	28	39	50	57	58	52	43	36	30	21	12	8	6	4	3	2	S
SW	5	4	3	2	2	7	15	21	27	32	35	46	71	98	117	123	112	79	39	27	19	13	10	7	SW
W	8	6	5	3	3	8	15	21	27	32	35	37	60	102	140	166	171	133	61	40	28	20	14	11	W
NW	6	5	4	3	2	7	15	21	27	32	35	37	39	59	92	121	136	113	49	32	22	16	11	8	NW
ZONE TYPE C																									
N	5	5	4	4	3	23	27	25	28	31	34	35	36	35	33	30	34	33	14	10	9	7	7	6	N
NE	7	7	6	5	5	65	106	115	102	76	54	50	47	45	42	37	32	24	16	13	12	10	9	8	NE
E	9	8	7	7	6	70	125	135	145	124	89	62	56	52	47	42	36	28	20	17	15	13	12	10	E
SE	8	7	6	6	5	36	73	97	107	104	87	64	52	47	43	39	33	25	17	14	13	11	10	9	SE
S	5	5	4	4	3	9	16	21	27	37	47	53	52	46	38	32	27	20	12	10	8	7	7	6	S
SW	12	11	10	9	8	13	19	24	29	32	35	44	69	93	108	111	99	67	31	24	20	17	15	13	SW
W	16	14	13	12	10	15	21	26	31	34	36	38	59	99	133	153	154	115	46	33	27	23	20	18	W
NW	13	11	10	9	8	13	19	25	29	32	35	36	38	57	88	114	124	99	37	26	21	18	16	14	NW
ZONE TYPE D																									
N	8	7	6	6	5	20	24	22	25	28	30	32	33	32	31	30	32	32	17	14	12	11	10	9	N
NE	11	10	9	8	8	55	87	95	88	69	54	51	49	47	44	40	36	29	22	20	18	16	14	13	NE
E	14	13	12	11	10	60	103	121	123	110	84	65	60	56	53	48	43	35	28	25	22	20	18	16	E
SE	12	11	10	9	8	32	61	81	90	90	79	62	53	50	46	42	38	31	24	21	19	17	15	14	SE
S	8	7	7	6	5	9	15	19	24	32	40	45	46	42	36	32	28	22	16	14	12	11	10	9	S
SW	18	16	15	13	12	15	20	24	27	30	32	40	60	79	93	97	89	66	38	32	28	25	22	20	SW
W	24	22	20	18	16	19	23	27	30	33	35	36	53	85	112	131	133	106	53	44	38	34	30	27	W
NW	19	17	15	14	12	16	20	24	28	30	33	34	35	51	75	97	107	89	42	34	30	26	23	21	NW

Table 7-27. July Solar Cooling Load (SCL) for Sunlit Glass 40° North Latitude

Wall Facing	1	2	3	4	5	6	7	8	9	10	11	12	13	14	15	16	17	18	19	20	21	22	23	24	Wall Facing
												ZONE TYPE A													
N	0	0	0	0	1	25	27	28	32	35	38	40	40	39	36	31	31	36	12	6	3	1	1	0	N
NE	0	0	0	0	2	85	129	134	112	75	55	48	44	40	37	32	26	18	7	3	2	1	0	0	NE
E	0	0	0	0	2	93	157	185	183	154	106	67	53	45	39	33	26	18	7	3	2	1	0	0	E
SE	0	0	0	0	1	47	95	131	150	150	131	97	63	49	41	34	27	18	7	3	2	1	0	0	SE
S	0	0	0	0	0	9	17	25	41	64	85	97	96	84	63	42	31	20	8	4	2	1	0	0	S
SW	0	0	0	0	0	9	17	24	30	35	39	64	101	133	151	152	133	93	35	17	8	4	2	1	SW
W	1	0	0	0	0	9	17	24	30	35	38	40	65	114	158	187	192	156	57	27	13	6	3	2	W
NW	1	0	0	0	0	9	17	24	30	35	38	40	40	50	84	121	143	130	46	22	11	5	3	1	NW
												ZONE TYPE B													
N	2	2	1	1	1	22	23	24	28	32	35	37	38	37	35	32	31	35	16	10	7	5	4	3	N
NE	2	1	1	1	2	73	109	116	101	73	58	52	48	45	41	36	30	23	13	9	6	5	3	3	NE
E	2	2	1	1	2	80	133	159	162	143	105	74	63	55	48	41	34	25	15	10	7	5	4	3	E
SE	2	2	1	1	1	40	81	112	131	134	122	96	69	58	49	42	35	26	15	10	8	6	4	3	SE
S	2	2	1	1	1	8	15	21	36	56	74	86	87	79	63	46	37	27	16	11	8	6	4	3	S
SW	6	5	4	3	2	9	16	22	27	31	36	58	89	117	135	138	126	94	46	31	21	15	11	8	SW
W	8	6	5	4	3	9	16	22	27	31	35	37	59	101	139	166	173	147	66	43	30	21	15	11	W
NW	6	5	4	3	2	9	16	22	27	31	34	37	37	46	76	108	128	119	51	33	22	16	11	8	NW
												ZONE TYPE C													
N	5	5	4	4	4	24	23	24	27	30	33	34	35	34	32	29	29	34	14	10	8	7	6	6	N
NE	7	6	6	5	6	75	106	107	88	61	49	47	45	43	40	36	31	25	16	13	11	10	9	8	NE
E	9	8	8	7	8	83	130	148	145	124	89	62	56	52	47	43	37	30	20	17	15	13	12	11	E
SE	9	8	7	6	6	45	82	107	121	121	107	82	59	51	47	42	36	29	19	16	14	13	11	10	SE
S	7	7	6	5	5	12	18	23	36	54	70	79	79	70	54	40	33	26	16	13	12	10	9	8	S
SW	14	12	11	10	9	15	21	26	29	33	36	57	86	110	124	125	111	80	37	28	23	20	17	15	SW
W	17	15	13	12	11	17	22	27	31	34	36	37	59	98	132	153	156	128	50	35	28	24	21	19	W
NW	12	11	10	9	8	14	20	25	29	32	34	36	36	44	73	102	118	107	39	26	21	17	15	13	NW
												ZONE TYPE D													
N	8	7	6	6	6	21	21	21	24	27	29	31	32	31	30	28	29	32	17	14	12	11	10	9	N
NE	11	10	9	8	9	63	87	90	77	58	49	48	46	44	42	39	35	29	22	19	17	15	14	12	NE
E	15	13	12	11	11	70	107	123	124	110	85	65	60	57	53	48	43	37	29	25	22	20	18	16	E
SE	14	13	11	10	10	39	68	90	102	104	95	78	60	55	51	47	42	35	27	24	21	19	17	16	SE
S	11	10	9	8	7	12	17	21	32	46	59	67	69	63	52	41	36	30	22	19	17	15	14	12	S
SW	21	19	17	15	14	18	22	25	28	31	34	51	74	94	106	109	100	78	45	37	33	29	26	23	SW
W	25	23	20	18	17	21	24	28	30	33	34	35	53	84	112	130	135	116	57	46	39	35	31	28	W
NW	18	16	15	13	12	17	21	24	27	30	32	33	34	41	64	87	101	94	42	33	29	25	22	20	NW

Table 7-28. July Solar Cooling Load (SCL) for Sunlit Glass 48° North Latitude

Wall Facing	Solar Time, hr																								Wall Facing
	1	2	3	4	5	6	7	8	9	10	11	12	13	14	15	16	17	18	19	20	21	22	23	24	
ZONE TYPE A																									
N	0	0	0	0	14	28	24	27	31	34	37	38	38	37	35	31	27	34	25	9	4	2	1	1	N
NE	0	0	0	0	32	101	130	126	95	61	49	44	41	38	35	31	26	19	10	4	2	1	0	0	NE
E	0	0	0	0	31	112	165	188	182	153	104	65	51	43	38	32	27	19	10	4	2	1	0	0	E
SE	0	0	0	0	11	58	106	143	164	168	152	119	77	54	43	35	28	20	10	4	2	1	1	0	SE
S	0	0	0	0	3	11	18	30	58	90	116	130	130	116	88	56	37	24	12	5	3	1	1	0	S
SW	1	0	0	0	3	11	18	24	30	34	46	82	122	152	168	166	146	106	50	22	11	5	3	1	SW
W	1	1	0	0	3	11	18	24	30	34	36	38	64	112	156	186	193	167	89	36	17	9	4	2	W
NW	1	0	0	0	3	11	18	24	30	34	36	38	38	40	67	106	134	134	76	30	14	7	3	2	NW
ZONE TYPE B																									
N	2	2	1	1	13	25	21	24	28	32	34	36	36	36	34	31	28	34	26	12	8	6	4	3	N
NE	2	1	1	1	28	86	111	110	88	62	53	49	45	42	39	35	30	23	15	9	6	5	3	3	NE
E	2	2	1	1	27	95	141	163	163	143	105	74	62	54	47	41	34	27	17	11	8	6	4	3	E
SE	3	2	2	1	10	50	91	123	1	151	141	116	83	64	53	45	37	29	19	12	9	6	5	4	SE
S	3	2	2	1	3	10	16	26	50	78	101	115	118	109	88	62	45	34	22	15	11	8	6	4	S
SW	7	6	4	3	5	11	17	22	27	31	41	72	107	134	150	152	138	107	61	37	26	18	13	10	SW
W	10	7	5	4	5	11	17	22	27	31	34	35	58	99	137	164	174	156	93	51	34	24	17	13	W
NW	7	5	4	3	4	11	17	22	27	30	33	35	36	38	61	95	119	121	75	38	25	18	13	9	NW
ZONE TYPE C																									
N	5	5	4	4	15	26	21	24	27	30	32	33	34	33	31	29	26	33	25	12	9	8	7	6	N
NE	7	6	6	5	31	86	106	100	76	51	46	44	43	41	39	35	31	25	18	13	11	10	9	8	NE
E	10	9	8	7	32	97	136	151	146	124	89	62	56	51	47	43	38	31	23	18	16	14	12	11	E
SE	10	9	8	7	16	54	90	118	133	136	125	101	71	56	50	45	39	33	24	19	16	14	13	11	SE
S	10	9	8	7	9	14	20	29	51	75	95	106	106	96	76	53	40	32	23	18	16	14	12	11	S
SW	16	14	13	11	13	18	23	27	30	33	42	71	103	126	138	137	122	92	51	33	27	23	20	18	SW
W	18	16	14	13	14	19	24	28	31	33	35	36	58	96	130	152	158	138	77	41	31	26	23	20	W
NW	12	11	10	9	10	16	21	25	28	31	33	34	35	36	59	90	111	110	63	30	22	18	16	14	NW
ZONE TYPE D																									
N	8	7	7	6	15	23	20	22	24	27	29	30	31	31	30	28	26	31	25	15	13	11	10	9	N
NE	11	10	9	8	28	71	88	85	68	50	47	45	44	43	41	38	34	29	23	19	17	15	13	12	NE
E	15	14	12	11	30	81	112	126	126	111	85	66	61	57	53	49	44	38	31	26	23	21	19	17	E
SE	16	14	13	12	18	47	76	99	113	117	111	94	72	61	56	51	46	40	32	27	24	22	20	18	SE
S	15	14	12	11	12	16	20	27	44	64	80	90	93	86	72	55	45	39	31	26	23	21	19	17	S
SW	24	22	20	18	18	21	24	27	30	32	39	63	88	107	119	120	111	89	57	43	38	33	30	27	SW
W	27	24	22	20	20	23	26	29	31	33	34	35	52	83	110	130	136	123	78	50	43	38	33	30	W
NW	19	17	15	14	14	18	21	24	27	29	31	32	33	34	53	78	95	96	60	36	30	26	23	21	NW

Table 7-29. August Solar Cooling Load (SCL) for Sunlit Glass 24° North Latitude

Wall Facing	1	2	3	4	5	6	7	8	9	10	11	12	13	14	15	16	17	18	19	20	21	22	23	24	Wall Facing
ZONE TYPE A																									
N	0	0	0	0	0	5	16	23	29	35	39	41	41	39	36	30	26	14	6	3	1	1	0	0	N
NE	0	0	0	0	0	23	102	129	122	91	61	51	46	42	37	31	23	10	5	2	1	1	0	0	NE
E	0	0	0	0	0	27	129	177	184	160	110	69	55	46	39	32	23	11	5	2	1	1	0	0	E
SE	0	0	0	0	0	15	83	125	143	138	113	78	56	47	39	32	24	11	5	2	1	1	0	0	SE
S	0	0	0	0	0	2	13	21	32	46	59	66	66	58	46	34	25	11	5	2	1	1	0	0	S
SW	0	0	0	0	0	2	13	21	29	34	38	51	83	118	141	147	127	59	25	12	6	3	1	1	SW
W	1	0	0	0	0	2	13	21	29	34	38	41	69	121	166	193	184	88	37	18	9	4	2	1	W
NW	0	0	0	0	0	2	13	21	29	34	38	41	42	65	102	132	137	68	27	13	7	3	2	1	NW
ZONE TYPE B																									
N	1	1	1	1	0	4	14	19	25	31	35	37	38	37	35	31	27	17	10	7	5	3	3	2	N
NE	2	1	1	1	1	20	86	110	107	84	62	55	50	46	41	35	28	16	11	8	5	4	3	2	NE
E	2	2	1	1	1	23	110	151	160	144	107	75	63	55	47	40	31	19	13	9	7	5	4	3	E
SE	2	1	1	1	1	13	71	106	123	123	105	78	62	53	46	39	30	18	12	9	6	5	3	3	SE
S	2	1	1	1	1	2	11	18	28	40	52	59	60	55	45	36	28	17	11	7	5	4	3	2	S
SW	5	4	3	2	2	3	12	19	25	31	35	46	74	104	125	133	119	64	37	25	18	13	9	7	SW
W	7	5	4	3	2	3	12	19	25	31	35	37	62	106	146	171	167	90	50	34	23	17	12	9	W
NW	5	4	3	2	2	3	12	19	25	31	34	37	39	59	91	118	123	67	36	24	17	12	9	7	NW
ZONE TYPE C																									
N	4	4	3	3	3	6	15	20	25	29	32	34	34	33	31	27	24	15	9	8	7	6	5	5	N
NE	7	6	5	5	4	23	87	104	96	72	51	47	45	43	39	35	28	18	14	12	10	9	8	7	NE
E	9	8	7	6	6	28	111	144	146	127	90	62	55	51	46	41	34	23	18	16	14	12	11	10	E
SE	8	7	6	6	5	17	73	103	114	110	92	66	53	48	43	38	31	21	16	14	12	11	10	9	SE
S	5	5	4	4	3	5	13	20	28	39	48	54	54	48	40	32	25	15	11	9	8	7	6	6	S
SW	12	11	10	9	8	9	17	23	28	32	34	45	71	98	116	120	105	51	29	23	19	17	15	13	SW
W	15	13	12	11	9	10	18	24	29	33	35	37	61	102	137	157	149	72	38	29	24	21	18	16	W
NW	10	9	8	8	7	8	16	22	27	31	34	36	37	56	86	110	112	55	28	21	17	15	13	12	NW
ZONE TYPE D																									
N	6	6	5	5	4	7	14	17	21	25	28	30	31	30	29	27	24	17	12	11	10	9	8	7	N
NE	10	9	8	7	7	21	72	86	81	65	50	47	46	44	41	37	32	24	20	17	16	14	13	11	NE
E	14	12	11	10	9	26	91	118	122	110	84	63	59	55	51	46	40	31	26	23	21	19	17	15	E
SE	12	11	10	9	8	17	61	85	96	94	82	64	54	50	47	42	36	28	23	21	19	17	15	14	SE
S	8	7	6	6	5	6	12	17	24	33	41	46	47	44	38	32	27	19	15	13	12	11	10	9	S
SW	18	16	15	13	12	12	18	22	26	29	32	40	62	83	99	104	94	53	37	32	28	25	22	20	SW
W	22	20	18	16	15	15	20	24	28	31	33	35	54	87	116	133	129	72	47	39	34	31	27	25	W
NW	16	14	13	12	10	11	17	21	25	28	31	33	34	50	74	93	97	54	34	28	25	22	20	18	NW

Solar Time, hr

Table 7-30. August Solar Cooling Load (SCL) for Sunlit Glass 32° North Latitude

Wall Facing	Solar Time, hr																								Wall Facing
	1	2	3	4	5	6	7	8	9	10	11	12	13	14	15	16	17	18	19	20	21	22	23	24	
ZONE TYPE A																									
N	0	0	0	0	0	7	15	22	29	34	38	39	40	38	35	30	24	16	6	3	1	1	0	0	N
NE	0	0	0	0	0	37	103	121	106	72	53	47	43	40	36	30	23	12	5	2	1	1	0	0	NE
E	0	0	0	0	0	44	136	179	184	159	109	68	53	45	38	31	24	12	5	2	1	1	0	0	E
SE	0	0	0	0	0	25	91	136	157	158	137	100	64	50	41	33	24	12	5	3	1	1	0	0	SE
S	0	0	0	0	0	3	13	24	44	68	88	99	100	88	67	45	29	15	6	3	2	1	0	0	S
SW	0	0	0	0	0	3	13	22	28	34	39	65	105	139	160	161	138	73	30	14	7	3	2	1	SW
W	1	0	0	0	0	3	13	22	28	34	37	39	68	119	165	192	186	106	41	20	10	5	2	1	W
NW	0	0	0	0	0	3	13	22	28	34	37	39	40	50	84	117	129	79	30	14	7	3	2	1	NW
ZONE TYPE B																									
N	1	1	1	1	0	7	13	19	25	30	34	36	37	36	34	30	25	18	10	7	5	3	3	2	N
NE	2	1	1	1	1	32	87	104	93	68	55	50	47	43	39	34	27	17	10	7	5	4	3	2	NE
E	2	2	1	1	1	38	115	153	161	144	107	74	63	54	47	40	31	20	13	9	7	5	4	3	E
SE	2	2	1	1	1	22	78	116	137	140	127	99	70	58	49	41	32	21	13	10	7	5	4	3	SE
S	2	2	1	1	1	4	12	21	38	59	77	88	90	83	67	49	36	23	15	10	7	6	4	3	S
SW	6	5	3	3	2	4	12	19	25	30	35	58	92	123	142	147	130	78	43	29	20	15	11	8	SW
W	7	5	4	3	2	5	13	19	25	30	34	36	61	105	145	170	168	105	54	36	25	18	13	10	W
NW	5	4	3	2	2	4	12	19	25	30	34	36	37	46	75	104	116	75	36	24	17	12	9	6	NW
ZONE TYPE C																									
N	4	4	3	3	3	8	14	19	24	28	31	33	33	33	31	27	23	17	9	8	7	6	5	5	N
NE	6	6	5	4	4	35	87	97	83	58	46	44	43	41	38	33	28	19	13	11	10	9	8	7	NE
E	9	8	7	6	6	42	115	145	146	126	90	61	55	50	46	41	34	24	18	16	14	12	11	10	E
SE	9	8	7	6	6	26	79	112	127	126	111	84	59	52	46	41	34	24	18	16	14	12	11	10	SE
S	7	7	6	5	5	7	15	23	39	57	72	81	81	73	58	42	32	21	16	13	12	10	9	8	S
SW	14	12	11	10	9	11	18	23	28	32	35	57	89	115	131	132	114	64	34	26	22	19	17	15	SW
W	15	14	12	11	10	12	19	24	29	32	35	36	60	101	136	156	151	86	41	31	25	22	19	17	W
NW	10	9	8	7	6	9	16	22	27	30	33	35	35	44	72	98	106	64	28	20	17	14	13	11	NW
ZONE TYPE D																									
N	6	6	5	5	4	9	13	17	21	25	27	29	30	30	29	26	23	18	12	11	10	9	8	7	N
NE	10	9	8	7	6	30	71	81	71	53	45	44	43	41	39	35	31	23	19	17	15	13	12	11	NE
E	14	12	11	10	9	37	95	119	123	110	84	63	59	55	51	46	40	32	26	23	21	19	17	15	E
SE	14	12	11	10	9	25	67	92	106	108	99	79	61	55	51	46	40	32	26	23	21	19	17	15	SE
S	11	10	9	8	7	9	15	21	34	48	61	69	71	65	55	43	35	27	22	19	17	15	14	12	S
SW	21	19	17	15	14	15	20	24	27	30	33	51	76	98	112	115	103	65	43	36	32	28	26	23	SW
W	23	21	19	17	15	16	21	25	28	31	33	34	53	86	115	133	131	83	49	41	36	32	28	25	W
NW	15	14	12	11	10	11	17	21	25	28	30	32	32	40	62	84	91	60	33	27	24	21	19	17	NW

Table 7-31. August Solar Cooling Load (SCL) for Sunlit Glass 40° North Latitude

Wall Facing	Solar Time, hr																								Wall Facing
	1	2	3	4	5	6	7	8	9	10	11	12	13	14	15	16	17	18	19	20	21	22	23	24	
ZONE TYPE A																									
N	0	0	0	0	0	9	15	22	28	33	36	38	38	37	34	29	23	17	6	3	1	1	0	0	N
NE	0	0	0	0	0	48	102	112	89	58	47	43	41	38	34	29	23	13	5	3	1	1	0	0	NE
E	0	0	0	0	0	58	140	179	183	157	107	66	52	43	37	31	23	13	5	3	1	1	0	0	E
SE	0	0	0	0	0	35	99	145	170	174	158	122	78	54	42	33	25	14	6	3	1	1	0	0	SE
S	0	0	0	0	0	5	14	31	61	93	119	133	134	120	93	60	35	19	8	4	2	1	0	0	S
SW	0	0	0	0	0	5	14	21	28	33	45	83	125	158	176	174	147	86	34	16	8	4	2	1	SW
W	1	0	0	0	0	5	14	21	28	33	36	38	66	117	162	189	185	120	45	22	11	5	3	1	W
NW	0	0	0	0	0	5	14	21	28	33	36	38	38	40	67	103	121	87	31	15	7	4	2	1	NW
ZONE TYPE B																									
N	1	1	1	1	0	8	13	19	24	29	32	35	35	35	33	29	24	19	10	7	5	3	3	2	N
NE	2	1	1	1	1	41	87	96	80	56	49	46	43	41	37	32	26	17	10	7	5	4	3	2	NE
E	2	2	1	1	1	50	119	153	160	143	105	73	61	53	46	39	31	21	13	9	7	5	4	3	E
SE	2	2	1	1	1	30	84	124	148	155	145	119	84	64	53	44	34	23	15	11	8	6	4	3	SE
S	3	2	2	1	1	5	12	27	53	81	104	118	121	112	92	66	45	30	19	14	10	7	5	4	S
SW	7	5	4	3	2	6	13	19	25	29	40	73	110	139	157	159	140	90	48	32	23	16	12	9	SW
W	8	6	4	3	2	6	13	19	25	29	33	35	59	103	142	167	168	116	56	38	26	19	14	10	W
NW	5	4	3	2	2	5	12	19	24	29	32	35	35	37	61	92	108	81	36	24	16	12	8	6	NW
ZONE TYPE C																									
N	4	4	3	3	3	10	14	19	24	27	30	32	32	31	29	26	22	18	9	8	6	6	5	4	N
NE	6	5	5	4	4	44	85	89	70	47	42	41	40	38	36	32	27	19	13	11	9	8	7	7	NE
E	9	8	7	6	6	54	118	145	145	125	88	60	54	49	45	40	34	25	18	16	14	12	11	10	E
SE	10	9	8	7	6	35	85	119	137	140	128	102	71	56	49	43	36	27	20	18	16	14	12	11	SE
S	10	9	8	7	6	10	16	30	53	78	98	108	109	99	80	56	39	28	21	18	15	14	12	11	S
SW	15	14	12	11	10	13	19	24	28	31	41	72	105	130	144	142	122	75	39	30	25	22	19	17	SW
W	15	14	12	11	10	13	19	24	28	31	34	35	58	99	134	154	151	98	43	31	26	22	19	17	W
NW	9	8	8	7	6	9	16	21	26	29	32	33	33	35	58	87	100	71	28	20	16	14	12	11	NW
ZONE TYPE D																									
N	6	5	5	4	4	10	13	17	21	24	26	28	29	29	28	25	22	19	12	11	9	8	8	7	N
NE	9	8	7	7	6	37	70	74	61	44	41	41	40	39	37	34	29	23	18	16	14	12	11	10	NE
E	14	12	11	10	9	47	97	119	122	110	83	62	58	54	50	46	40	33	26	23	21	19	17	15	E
SE	15	14	12	11	10	32	72	99	115	120	113	95	72	60	55	50	44	36	29	26	23	21	19	17	SE
S	15	14	12	11	10	12	17	27	46	66	82	92	95	89	75	58	45	36	29	26	23	21	19	17	S
SW	23	21	19	17	15	17	21	25	28	30	38	63	89	110	123	124	111	76	48	41	36	32	29	26	SW
W	23	21	19	17	15	17	21	25	28	30	32	33	52	85	113	131	130	92	50	42	36	32	29	26	W
NW	14	13	12	10	9	12	16	20	24	27	29	30	31	33	51	74	85	64	32	26	22	20	18	16	NW

Table 7-32. August Solar Cooling Load (SCL) for Sunlit Glass 48° North Latitude

Wall Facing	Solar Time, hr																								Wall Facing
	1	2	3	4	5	6	7	8	9	10	11	12	13	14	15	16	17	18	19	20	21	22	23	24	
ZONE TYPE A																									
N	0	0	0	0	0	10	15	21	27	31	34	36	36	34	32	28	22	18	6	3	1	1	0	0	N
NE	0	0	0	0	0	57	100	101	74	49	43	40	38	36	32	28	22	14	5	3	1	1	0	0	NE
E	0	0	0	0	0	70	143	178	179	153	104	63	49	41	35	29	23	14	6	3	1	1	0	0	E
SE	0	0	0	0	0	43	104	152	180	187	175	142	95	58	43	33	25	15	6	3	1	1	0	0	SE
S	0	0	0	0	0	6	15	40	78	116	146	162	163	147	117	77	42	23	10	5	2	1	1	0	S
SW	1	0	0	0	0	6	14	21	26	31	55	99	143	174	189	183	154	96	37	18	9	4	2	1	SW
W	1	0	0	0	0	6	14	21	26	31	34	36	63	113	157	185	183	131	47	23	11	6	3	1	W
NW	0	0	0	0	0	6	14	21	26	31	34	36	36	34	53	89	111	92	32	15	7	4	2	1	NW
ZONE TYPE B																									
N	1	1	1	1	0	9	13	118	23	28	31	33	33	33	31	28	23	19	10	7	5	3	2	2	N
NE	2	1	1	1	0	49	85	87	67	48	44	42	40	38	35	31	25	18	10	7	5	4	3	2	NE
E	2	2	1	1	1	60	121	152	158	140	103	70	59	51	44	37	30	21	13	9	7	5	4	3	E
SE	3	2	1	1	1	37	89	130	156	167	160	136	99	69	56	45	36	26	16	11	8	6	5	3	SE
S	4	3	2	2	1	6	13	34	67	100	127	144	148	138	115	83	54	37	24	17	12	9	7	5	S
SW	7	5	4	3	2	7	13	19	24	25	49	87	124	153	169	168	147	101	52	35	25	18	13	10	SW
W	8	6	4	3	2	7	13	19	24	28	31	33	57	99	138	166	166	125	58	39	27	19	14	10	W
NW	4	3	3	2	1	6	13	18	23	28	31	33	33	33	49	79	99	84	36	23	16	11	5	6	NW
ZONE TYPE C																									
N	4	3	3	3	2	10	14	19	23	26	28	30	30	30	28	25	21	18	9	7	6	5	5	4	N
NE	6	5	4	4	4	51	83	81	58	40	39	38	37	36	33	30	25	19	12	10	9	8	7	6	NE
E	9	8	7	6	6	64	119	143	143	122	86	58	52	48	43	39	33	26	18	16	14	12	11	10	E
SE	11	10	9	8	7	42	90	125	145	151	142	118	84	59	51	45	38	30	22	19	17	15	13	12	SE
S	12	11	10	9	8	12	18	38	68	97	119	131	133	122	100	71	47	35	25	22	19	17	15	14	S
SW	17	15	13	12	11	14	20	24	28	31	50	86	119	143	154	150	129	85	42	32	27	24	21	19	SW
W	15	14	12	11	10	14	19	24	27	30	32	33	56	96	130	151	149	107	44	32	26	22	19	17	W
NW	9	8	7	6	6	10	16	21	25	28	30	31	32	31	47	76	93	75	27	19	15	13	11	10	NW
ZONE TYPE D																									
N	6	5	5	4	4	10	12	16	20	23	25	26	27	27	26	24	21	19	12	10	9	8	7	7	N
NE	9	8	7	6	6	43	68	67	51	39	38	38	37	36	34	31	28	22	17	15	13	12	11	9	NE
E	14	12	11	10	9	54	98	118	121	108	82	61	56	53	49	45	39	33	26	23	21	19	17	15	E
SE	17	15	14	12	11	38	76	104	122	129	125	109	84	65	59	53	47	39	32	28	25	23	21	19	SE
S	19	17	15	14	12	15	19	35	58	82	101	112	115	109	94	73	54	44	36	32	28	25	23	21	S
SW	25	23	20	18	17	19	22	25	28	30	45	74	101	121	132	132	118	85	52	44	39	35	31	28	SW
W	23	21	19	17	15	18	21	24	27	29	31	32	50	82	110	128	129	99	51	42	36	32	29	26	W
NW	13	12	11	10	9	12	16	20	23	25	27	29	29	29	42	65	79	67	30	25	21	19	17	15	NW

Table 7-33. Cooling Load Factors (CLF) For People and Unhooded Equipment

Hours in Space	Number of Hours After Entry into Space or Equipment Turned On																								Hours in Space
	1	2	3	4	5	6	7	8	9	10	11	12	13	14	15	16	17	18	19	20	21	22	23	24	
ZONE TYPE A																									
2	0.75	0.88	0.18	0.08	0.04	0.02	0.01	0.01	0.01	0.01	0.00	0.00	0.00	0.00	0.00	0.00	0.00	0.00	0.00	0.00	0.00	0.00	0.00	0.00	2
4	0.75	0.88	0.93	0.95	0.22	0.10	0.05	0.03	0.02	0.02	0.01	0.01	0.01	0.01	0.00	0.00	0.00	0.00	0.00	0.00	0.00	0.00	0.00	0.00	4
6	0.75	0.88	0.93	0.95	0.97	0.97	0.23	0.11	0.06	0.04	0.03	0.02	0.02	0.01	0.01	0.01	0.01	0.00	0.00	0.00	0.00	0.00	0.00	0.00	6
8	0.75	0.88	0.93	0.95	0.97	0.97	0.98	0.98	0.24	0.11	0.06	0.04	0.03	0.02	0.02	0.01	0.01	0.01	0.01	0.01	0.00	0.00	0.00	0.00	8
10	0.75	0.88	0.93	0.95	0.97	0.97	0.98	0.98	0.99	0.99	0.24	0.12	0.07	0.04	0.03	0.02	0.02	0.01	0.01	0.01	0.01	0.01	0.00	0.00	10
12	0.75	0.88	0.93	0.96	0.97	0.98	0.98	0.98	0.99	0.99	0.99	0.99	0.25	0.12	0.07	0.04	0.03	0.02	0.02	0.02	0.01	0.01	0.01	0.01	12
16	0.76	0.89	0.94	0.96	0.97	0.98	0.98	0.99	0.99	0.99	0.99	0.99	1.00	1.00	1.00	1.00	0.25	0.12	0.07	0.05	0.03	0.03	0.02	0.02	16
18	0.77	0.89	0.94	0.96	0.97	0.98	0.98	0.99	0.99	0.99	0.99	1.00	1.00	1.00	1.00	1.00	1.00	1.00	0.25	0.12	0.07	0.05	0.03	0.03	18
ZONE TYPE B																									
2	0.65	0.74	0.16	0.11	0.08	0.06	0.05	0.04	0.03	0.02	0.02	0.01	0.01	0.01	0.01	0.00	0.00	0.00	0.00	0.00	0.00	0.00	0.00	0.00	2
4	0.65	0.75	0.81	0.85	0.24	0.17	0.13	0.10	0.07	0.06	0.04	0.03	0.03	0.02	0.02	0.01	0.01	0.01	0.01	0.00	0.00	0.00	0.00	0.00	4
6	0.65	0.75	0.81	0.85	0.89	0.91	0.29	0.20	0.15	0.12	0.09	0.07	0.05	0.04	0.03	0.02	0.02	0.01	0.01	0.01	0.01	0.01	0.00	0.00	6
8	0.65	0.75	0.81	0.85	0.89	0.91	0.93	0.95	0.31	0.22	0.17	0.13	0.10	0.08	0.06	0.05	0.04	0.03	0.02	0.02	0.01	0.01	0.01	0.01	8
10	0.65	0.75	0.81	0.85	0.89	0.91	0.93	0.95	0.96	0.97	0.33	0.24	0.18	0.14	0.11	0.08	0.06	0.05	0.04	0.03	0.02	0.02	0.01	0.01	10
12	0.66	0.76	0.81	0.86	0.89	0.92	0.94	0.95	0.96	0.97	0.98	0.98	0.34	0.24	0.19	0.14	0.11	0.08	0.06	0.05	0.04	0.03	0.02	0.02	12
16	0.69	0.78	0.83	0.87	0.90	0.92	0.94	0.95	0.96	0.97	0.98	0.98	0.99	0.99	0.99	0.99	0.35	0.25	0.19	0.15	0.11	0.09	0.07	0.05	16
18	0.71	0.80	0.85	0.88	0.91	0.93	0.95	0.96	0.97	0.98	0.98	0.99	0.99	0.99	0.99	0.99	1.00	1.00	0.35	0.25	0.19	0.15	0.11	0.09	18
ZONE TYPE C																									
2	0.60	0.68	0.14	0.11	0.09	0.07	0.06	0.05	0.04	0.03	0.03	0.02	0.02	0.01	0.01	0.01	0.01	0.01	0.01	0.00	0.00	0.00	0.00	0.00	2
4	0.60	0.68	0.74	0.79	0.23	0.18	0.14	0.12	0.10	0.08	0.06	0.05	0.04	0.04	0.03	0.02	0.02	0.02	0.01	0.01	0.01	0.01	0.01	0.01	4
6	0.61	0.69	0.74	0.79	0.83	0.86	0.28	0.22	0.18	0.15	0.12	0.10	0.08	0.07	0.06	0.05	0.04	0.03	0.03	0.02	0.02	0.01	0.01	0.01	6
8	0.61	0.69	0.75	0.79	0.83	0.86	0.89	0.91	0.32	0.26	0.21	0.17	0.14	0.11	0.09	0.08	0.06	0.05	0.04	0.04	0.03	0.02	0.02	0.02	8
10	0.62	0.70	0.75	0.80	0.83	0.86	0.89	0.91	0.92	0.94	0.35	0.28	0.23	0.18	0.15	0.12	0.10	0.08	0.07	0.06	0.05	0.04	0.03	0.03	10
12	0.63	0.71	0.76	0.81	0.84	0.87	0.89	0.91	0.93	0.94	0.95	0.96	0.37	0.29	0.24	0.19	0.16	0.13	0.11	0.09	0.07	0.06	0.05	0.04	12
16	0.68	0.74	0.79	0.83	0.86	0.89	0.91	0.92	0.94	0.95	0.96	0.96	0.97	0.98	0.98	0.98	0.39	0.31	0.25	0.21	0.17	0.14	0.11	0.09	16
18	0.72	0.78	0.82	0.85	0.88	0.90	0.92	0.93	0.94	0.95	0.96	0.97	0.97	0.98	0.98	0.99	0.99	0.99	0.39	0.31	0.26	0.21	0.17	0.14	18
ZONE TYPE D																									
2	0.59	0.67	0.13	0.09	0.08	0.06	0.05	0.05	0.04	0.04	0.03	0.03	0.02	0.02	0.02	0.01	0.01	0.01	0.01	0.01	0.01	0.01	0.01	0.01	2
4	0.60	0.67	0.72	0.76	0.20	0.16	0.13	0.11	0.10	0.08	0.07	0.06	0.05	0.05	0.04	0.03	0.03	0.03	0.02	0.02	0.02	0.01	0.01	0.01	4
6	0.61	0.68	0.73	0.77	0.80	0.83	0.26	0.20	0.17	0.15	0.13	0.11	0.09	0.08	0.07	0.06	0.05	0.05	0.04	0.03	0.03	0.03	0.02	0.02	6
8	0.62	0.69	0.74	0.77	0.80	0.83	0.85	0.87	0.30	0.24	0.20	0.17	0.15	0.13	0.11	0.10	0.08	0.07	0.06	0.05	0.05	0.04	0.04	0.03	8
10	0.63	0.70	0.75	0.78	0.81	0.84	0.86	0.88	0.89	0.91	0.33	0.27	0.22	0.19	0.17	0.14	0.12	0.11	0.09	0.08	0.07	0.06	0.05	0.05	10
12	0.65	0.71	0.76	0.79	0.82	0.84	0.87	0.88	0.90	0.91	0.92	0.93	0.35	0.29	0.24	0.21	0.18	0.16	0.13	0.12	0.10	0.09	0.08	0.07	12
16	0.70	0.76	0.80	0.83	0.85	0.87	0.89	0.90	0.92	0.93	0.94	0.95	0.95	0.96	0.96	0.97	0.38	0.31	0.26	0.23	0.20	0.17	0.15	0.13	16
18	0.74	0.80	0.83	0.85	0.87	0.89	0.91	0.92	0.93	0.94	0.95	0.95	0.96	0.97	0.97	0.97	0.98	0.98	0.39	0.32	0.27	0.23	0.20	0.17	18

Table 7-34. Cooling Load Factors (CLF) For Lights

Lights On	Number of Hours after Lights Turned On																								Lights On
	1	2	3	4	5	6	7	8	9	10	11	12	13	14	15	16	17	18	19	20	21	22	23	24	
ZONE TYPE A																									
8	0.85	0.92	0.95	0.96	0.97	0.97	0.97	0.98	0.13	0.06	0.04	0.03	0.02	0.02	0.02	0.01	0.01	0.01	0.01	0.01	0.01	0.01	0.01	0.01	8
10	0.85	0.93	0.95	0.97	0.97	0.97	0.98	0.98	0.98	0.98	0.14	0.07	0.04	0.03	0.02	0.02	0.02	0.02	0.02	0.02	0.01	0.01	0.01	0.01	10
12	0.86	0.93	0.96	0.97	0.97	0.98	0.98	0.98	0.98	0.98	0.98	0.98	0.14	0.07	0.04	0.03	0.03	0.02	0.02	0.02	0.02	0.02	0.02	0.02	12
16	0.87	0.94	0.96	0.97	0.98	0.98	0.98	0.99	0.99	0.99	0.99	0.99	0.99	0.99	0.99	0.99	0.15	0.08	0.05	0.04	0.03	0.03	0.03	0.02	16
ZONE TYPE B																									
8	0.75	0.85	0.90	0.93	0.94	0.95	0.95	0.96	0.23	0.12	0.08	0.05	0.04	0.04	0.03	0.03	0.03	0.02	0.02	0.02	0.02	0.02	0.02	0.01	8
10	0.75	0.86	0.91	0.93	0.94	0.95	0.95	0.96	0.96	0.97	0.24	0.13	0.08	0.06	0.05	0.04	0.04	0.03	0.03	0.03	0.03	0.02	0.02	0.02	10
12	0.76	0.86	0.91	0.93	0.95	0.95	0.96	0.96	0.97	0.97	0.97	0.97	0.24	0.14	0.09	0.07	0.05	0.05	0.04	0.04	0.03	0.03	0.03	0.03	12
16	0.77	0.88	0.92	0.95	0.96	0.96	0.97	0.97	0.97	0.98	0.98	0.98	0.98	0.98	0.98	0.99	0.25	0.15	0.10	0.07	0.06	0.05	0.05	0.04	16
ZONE TYPE C																									
8	0.72	0.80	0.84	0.87	0.88	0.89	0.90	0.91	0.23	0.15	0.11	0.09	0.08	0.07	0.07	0.06	0.05	0.05	0.05	0.04	0.04	0.03	0.03	0.03	8
10	0.73	0.81	0.85	0.87	0.89	0.90	0.91	0.92	0.92	0.93	0.25	0.16	0.13	0.11	0.09	0.08	0.08	0.07	0.06	0.06	0.05	0.05	0.04	0.04	10
12	0.74	0.82	0.86	0.88	0.90	0.91	0.92	0.92	0.93	0.94	0.94	0.95	0.26	0.18	0.14	0.12	0.10	0.09	0.08	0.08	0.07	0.06	0.06	0.05	12
16	0.77	0.85	0.89	0.91	0.92	0.93	0.93	0.94	0.95	0.95	0.95	0.96	0.96	0.97	0.97	0.97	0.28	0.20	0.16	0.13	0.12	0.11	0.10	0.09	16
ZONE TYPE D																									
8	0.66	0.72	0.76	0.79	0.81	0.83	0.85	0.86	0.25	0.20	0.17	0.15	0.13	0.12	0.11	0.10	0.09	0.08	0.07	0.06	0.06	0.05	0.04	0.04	8
10	0.68	0.74	0.77	0.80	0.82	0.84	0.86	0.87	0.88	0.90	0.28	0.23	0.19	0.17	0.15	0.14	0.12	0.11	0.10	0.09	0.08	0.07	0.06	0.06	10
12	0.70	0.75	0.79	0.81	0.83	0.85	0.87	0.88	0.89	0.90	0.91	0.92	0.30	0.25	0.21	0.19	0.17	0.15	0.13	0.12	0.11	0.10	0.09	0.08	12
16	0.75	0.80	0.83	0.85	0.87	0.88	0.89	0.90	0.91	0.92	0.93	0.94	0.94	0.95	0.96	0.96	0.34	0.28	0.24	0.21	0.19	0.17	0.15	0.14	16

Table 7-35. Cooling Load Factors For Hooded Equipment

Hours in Operation	Number of Hours After Equipment Turned on																								Hours in Operation
	1	2	3	4	5	6	7	8	9	10	11	12	13	14	15	16	17	18	19	20	21	22	23	24	
ZONE TYPE A																									
2	0.64	0.83	0.26	0.11	0.06	0.03	0.01	0.01	0.01	0.01	0.00	0.00	0.00	0.00	0.00	0.00	0.00	0.00	0.00	0.00	0.00	0.00	0.00	0.00	2
4	0.64	0.83	0.90	0.93	0.31	0.14	0.07	0.04	0.03	0.03	0.01	0.01	0.01	0.01	0.00	0.00	0.00	0.00	0.00	0.00	0.00	0.00	0.00	0.00	4
6	0.64	0.83	0.90	0.93	0.96	0.96	0.33	0.16	0.09	0.06	0.04	0.03	0.03	0.01	0.01	0.01	0.01	0.00	0.00	0.00	0.00	0.00	0.00	0.00	6
8	0.64	0.83	0.90	0.93	0.96	0.96	0.97	0.97	0.34	0.16	0.09	0.06	0.04	0.03	0.03	0.01	0.01	0.01	0.01	0.01	0.00	0.00	0.00	0.00	8
10	0.64	0.83	0.90	0.93	0.96	0.96	0.97	0.97	0.99	0.99	0.34	0.17	0.10	0.06	0.04	0.03	0.03	0.01	0.01	0.01	0.01	0.01	0.01	0.00	10
12	0.64	0.83	0.90	0.94	0.96	0.97	0.97	0.97	0.99	0.99	0.99	0.99	0.36	0.17	0.10	0.06	0.04	0.03	0.03	0.03	0.01	0.01	0.01	0.01	12
16	0.66	0.84	0.91	0.94	0.96	0.97	0.97	0.99	0.99	0.99	0.99	0.99	1.00	1.00	1.00	1.00	0.36	0.17	0.10	0.07	0.04	0.04	0.04	0.03	16
18	0.67	0.84	0.91	0.94	0.96	0.97	0.97	0.99	0.99	0.99	0.99	1.00	1.00	1.00	1.00	1.00	1.00	1.00	0.36	0.17	0.10	0.08	0.07	0.04	18
ZONE TYPE B																									
2	0.50	0.63	0.23	0.16	0.11	0.09	0.07	0.06	0.04	0.03	0.03	0.01	0.01	0.01	0.01	0.00	0.00	0.00	0.00	0.00	0.00	0.00	0.00	0.00	2
4	0.50	0.64	0.73	0.79	0.34	0.24	0.19	0.14	0.10	0.09	0.06	0.04	0.04	0.03	0.03	0.01	0.01	0.01	0.01	0.00	0.00	0.00	0.00	0.00	4
6	0.50	0.64	0.73	0.79	0.84	0.87	0.41	0.29	0.21	0.17	0.13	0.10	0.07	0.06	0.04	0.03	0.03	0.01	0.01	0.01	0.01	0.01	0.01	0.00	6
8	0.50	0.64	0.73	0.79	0.84	0.87	0.90	0.93	0.44	0.31	0.24	0.19	0.14	0.11	0.09	0.07	0.06	0.04	0.03	0.03	0.01	0.01	0.01	0.01	8
10	0.50	0.64	0.73	0.79	0.84	0.87	0.90	0.93	0.94	0.96	0.47	0.34	0.26	0.20	0.16	0.11	0.09	0.07	0.06	0.04	0.03	0.03	0.03	0.01	10
12	0.51	0.66	0.73	0.80	0.84	0.89	0.91	0.93	0.94	0.96	0.97	0.97	0.49	0.34	0.27	0.20	0.16	0.11	0.09	0.07	0.06	0.05	0.04	0.03	12
16	0.56	0.69	0.76	0.81	0.86	0.89	0.91	0.93	0.94	0.96	0.97	0.97	0.99	0.99	0.99	0.99	0.50	0.36	0.27	0.21	0.16	0.14	0.13	0.10	16
18	0.59	0.71	0.79	0.83	0.87	0.90	0.93	0.94	0.96	0.97	0.97	0.99	0.99	0.99	0.99	0.99	1.00	1.00	0.50	0.36	0.27	0.23	0.21	0.16	18
ZONE TYPE C																									
2	0.43	0.54	0.20	0.16	0.13	0.10	0.09	0.07	0.06	0.04	0.04	0.03	0.03	0.01	0.01	0.01	0.01	0.01	0.01	0.00	0.00	0.00	0.00	0.00	2
4	0.43	0.54	0.63	0.70	0.33	0.26	0.20	0.17	0.14	0.11	0.09	0.07	0.06	0.06	0.04	0.03	0.03	0.03	0.01	0.01	0.01	0.01	0.01	0.01	4
6	0.44	0.56	0.63	0.70	0.76	0.80	0.40	0.31	0.26	0.21	0.17	0.14	0.11	0.10	0.09	0.07	0.06	0.04	0.04	0.03	0.03	0.02	0.01	0.01	6
8	0.44	0.56	0.64	0.70	0.76	0.80	0.84	0.87	0.46	0.37	0.30	0.24	0.20	0.16	0.13	0.11	0.09	0.07	0.06	0.06	0.04	0.03	0.03	0.03	8
10	0.46	0.57	0.64	0.71	0.76	0.80	0.84	0.87	0.89	0.91	0.50	0.40	0.33	0.26	0.21	0.17	0.14	0.11	0.10	0.09	0.07	0.06	0.06	0.04	10
12	0.47	0.59	0.66	0.73	0.77	0.81	0.84	0.87	0.90	0.91	0.93	0.94	0.53	0.41	0.34	0.27	0.23	0.19	0.16	0.13	0.10	0.09	0.09	0.07	12
16	0.54	0.63	0.70	0.76	0.80	0.84	0.87	0.89	0.91	0.93	0.94	0.94	0.96	0.97	0.97	0.97	0.56	0.44	0.36	0.30	0.24	0.22	0.20	0.16	16
18	0.60	0.69	0.74	0.79	0.83	0.86	0.89	0.90	0.91	0.93	0.94	0.96	0.96	0.97	0.97	0.99	0.99	0.99	0.56	0.44	0.37	0.33	0.30	0.24	18
ZONE TYPE D																									
2	0.41	0.53	0.19	0.13	0.11	0.09	0.07	0.07	0.06	0.06	0.04	0.04	0.03	0.03	0.03	0.01	0.01	0.01	0.01	0.01	0.01	0.01	0.01	0.01	2
4	0.43	0.53	0.60	0.66	0.29	0.23	0.19	0.16	0.14	0.11	0.10	0.09	0.07	0.07	0.06	0.04	0.04	0.04	0.03	0.03	0.03	0.02	0.01	0.01	4
6	0.44	0.54	0.61	0.67	0.71	0.76	0.37	0.29	0.24	0.21	0.19	0.16	0.13	0.11	0.10	0.09	0.07	0.07	0.06	0.04	0.04	0.04	0.04	0.03	6
8	0.46	0.56	0.63	0.67	0.71	0.76	0.79	0.81	0.43	0.34	0.29	0.24	0.21	0.19	0.16	0.14	0.11	0.10	0.09	0.07	0.07	0.06	0.06	0.06	8
10	0.47	0.57	0.64	0.69	0.73	0.77	0.80	0.83	0.84	0.87	0.47	0.39	0.31	0.27	0.24	0.20	0.17	0.16	0.13	0.11	0.10	0.09	0.09	0.07	10
12	0.50	0.59	0.66	0.70	0.74	0.77	0.81	0.83	0.86	0.87	0.89	0.90	0.50	0.41	0.34	0.30	0.26	0.23	0.19	0.17	0.14	0.13	0.13	0.11	12
16	0.57	0.66	0.71	0.76	0.79	0.81	0.84	0.86	0.89	0.90	0.91	0.93	0.93	0.94	0.94	0.96	0.54	0.44	0.37	0.33	0.29	0.26	0.24	0.21	16
18	0.63	0.71	0.76	0.79	0.81	0.84	0.87	0.89	0.90	0.91	0.93	0.93	0.94	0.96	0.96	0.96	0.97	0.97	0.56	0.46	0.39	0.35	0.33	0.29	18

Table 7-36. Window Glass Load Factors (GLFs) for Single Family Detached Residences[*]

Design	Regular Single Glass						Regular Double Glass						Heat Absorbing Double Glass						Clear Triple Glass			Design
Temp., °F	85	90	95	100	105	110	85	90	95	100	105	110	85	90	95	100	105	110	85	90	95	Temp., °F
No Inside Shading																						
North	34	36	41	47	48	50	30	30	34	37	38	41	20	20	23	25	26	28	27	27	30	**North**
NE and NW	63	65	70	75	77	83	55	56	59	62	63	66	36	37	39	42	44	44	50	50	53	**NE and NW**
East and West	88	90	95	100	102	107	77	78	81	84	85	88	51	51	54	56	59	59	70	70	73	**East and West**
SE and SW[a]	79	81	86	91	92	98	69	70	73	76	77	80	45	46	49	51	54	54	62	63	65	**SE and SW**[a]
South	53	55	60	65	67	72	46	47	50	53	54	57	31	31	34	36	39	39	42	42	45	**South**
Draperies, Venetian Blinds, Translucent Roller Shades, Fully Drawn																						
North	18	19	23	27	29	33	16	16	19	22	23	26	13	14	16	18	19	21	15	16	18	**North**
NE and NW	32	33	38	42	43	47	29	30	32	35	36	39	24	24	27	29	29	32	28	28	30	**NE and NW**
East and West	45	46	50	54	55	59	40	41	44	46	47	50	33	33	36	38	38	41	39	39	41	**East and West**
SE and SW	40	41	46	49	51	55	36	37	39	42	43	46	29	30	32	34	35	37	35	36	38	**SE and SW**
South[a]	27	28	33	37	38	42	24	25	28	31	31	34	20	21	23	25	26	28	23	24	26	**South**[a]
Opaque Roller Shades, Fully Drawn																						
North	14	15	20	23	25	29	13	14	17	19	20	23	12	12	15	17	17	20	13	13	15	**North**
NE and NW	25	26	31	34	36	40	23	24	27	30	30	33	21	22	24	26	27	29	23	23	26	**NE and NW**
East and West	34	36	40	44	45	49	32	33	36	38	39	42	29	30	32	34	35	37	32	32	35	**East and West**
SE and SW	31	32	36	40	42	46	29	30	33	35	36	39	26	27	29	31	32	34	29	29	31	**SE and SW**
South[a]	21	22	27	30	32	36	20	20	23	26	27	30	18	19	21	23	24	26	19	20	22	**South**[a]

[a] Correct by +30% for latitude of 48° and by −30% for latitude of 32°. Use linear interpolation for latitude from 40° to 48° and from 40° to 32°.

To obtain *GLF* for other combinations of glass and/or inside shading:

$$GLF_a = \left(\frac{SC_a}{SC_t}\right)(GLF_t - U_t D_t) + U_a D_t$$

where DR = daily range;

T_o = outdoor design temperature;

SC_a = shading coefficient given in Table 7-41;

U_a = factors given in Table 5-6;

$D_t = T_a - 75$

$T_a = T_o - DR/2$

a = alternate values; and

t = alternate and table values.

[*] Glass load factors (*GLFs*) for single-family detached houses, duplexes, or multi-family residences, with both east and west exposed walls or only north and south exposed walls, Btu/hr-ft^2.

Table 7-37. Window Glass Load Factors (GLFs) for Multi-Family Detached Residences[*]

Design	Regular Single Glass						Regular Double Glass						Heat-Absorbing Double Glass						Clear Triple Glass			Design
Temp., °F	85	90	95	100	105	110	85	90	95	100	105	110	85	90	95	100	105	110	85	90	95	Temp., °F
No Inside Shading																						
North	40	44	49	54	58	64	34	36	39	42	44	47	23	24	26	29	30	33	30	32	34	**North**
NE	88	89	91	95	97	100	78	79	80	83	84	85	52	52	53	55	55	57	71	71	73	**NE**
East	136	137	139	142	144	147	120	121	122	125	126	127	79	79	81	83	83	84	109	109	111	**East**
SE	129	130	134	139	141	144	109	113	116	119	120	122	72	75	77	79	79	81	99	103	105	**SE**
South	88	91	96	101	105	110	76	78	81	84	86	89	50	52	54	56	58	60	68	70	72	**South**
SW	154	159	164	169	174	179	134	137	140	143	145	148	89	91	93	95	97	99	121	123	125	**SW**
West	174	178	183	188	192	197	151	154	157	160	162	165	100	102	104	106	108	110	137	139	141	**West**
NW	123	127	132	137	141	147	107	109	112	115	117	121	71	72	75	77	79	81	96	98	100	**NW**
Draperies, Venetian Blinds, Translucent Roller Shades, Fully Drawn																						
North	21	25	29	33	36	40	18	21	23	26	28	31	15	17	19	21	23	25	17	19	21	**North**
NE	43	44	46	50	51	52	39	40	41	44	45	46	33	33	34	36	36	37	39	39	40	**NE**
East	67	68	70	74	75	76	61	62	63	65	66	67	50	50	51	54	54	55	60	60	61	**East**
SE	64	65	69	73	74	77	58	59	61	63	64	66	48	48	50	52	52	54	57	57	59	**SE**
South	45	48	52	56	59	63	40	42	44	47	49	52	33	34	36	39	40	42	38	40	42	**South**
SW	79	83	87	91	94	98	70	72	75	78	80	83	57	59	62	64	66	68	68	69	71	**SW**
West	89	92	96	100	103	107	79	81	84	86	88	91	65	66	69	71	72	75	76	78	80	**West**
NW	63	66	70	74	77	81	56	58	61	63	66	68	46	48	50	52	54	56	54	55	57	**NW**
Opaque Roller Shades, Fully Drawn																						
North	17	21	25	29	32	36	15	17	20	23	25	28	14	15	18	20	22	24	15	16	18	**North**
NE	33	34	35	39	40	42	31	32	33	36	35	37	29	28	30	32	32	34	32	31	33	**NE**
East	51	52	53	57	61	65	48	49	50	53	52	55	45	45	46	48	48	49	49	49	50	**East**
SE	49	50	53	57	58	61	46	47	49	52	52	55	42	43	45	47	47	49	46	46	48	**SE**
South	35	38	42	46	49	53	32	34	37	40	42	42	29	31	33	35	37	39	32	33	35	**South**
SW	61	65	69	73	77	81	57	59	62	65	67	70	52	54	56	58	60	62	56	58	60	**SW**
West	68	71	75	80	83	87	64	66	68	71	73	76	58	60	62	64	66	68	63	64	66	**West**
NW	49	52	56	60	63	67	45	47	50	53	55	58	41	43	45	47	49	51	45	46	48	**NW**

To obtain GLF for other combinations of glass and/or inside shading:

$$GLF_a = \left(\frac{SC_a}{SC_t}\right)(GLF_t - U_t D_t) + U_a D_t$$

where DR = daily range;

T_o = outdoor design temperature;

SC_a = shading coefficient given in Table 7-41;

U_a = factors given in Table 5-6;

$D_t = T_a - 75$

$T_a = T_o - DR/2$

a = alternate values; and

t = alternate and table values.

[*] Glass load factors (GLFs) for single-family detached houses, duplexes, or multifamily residences, with both east and west exposed walls or only north and south exposed walls, Btu/hr-ft^2.

Table 7-38. CLTD Values for Single Family Residences*

Daily Temperature Range[a]	85°F L	85°F M	90°F L	90°F M	90°F H	95°F L	95°F M	95°F H	100°F M	100°F H	105°F M	110°F H
All Walls and Doors												
North	8	3	13	8	3	18	13	8	18	13	18	23
NE and NW	14	9	19	14	9	24	19	14	24	19	24	29
East and West	18	13	23	18	13	28	23	18	28	23	28	33
SE and SW	16	11	21	16	11	26	21	16	26	21	26	31
South	11	6	16	11	6	21	16	11	21	16	21	26
Roofs and Ceilings												
Attic or flat built-up	42	37	47	42	37	51	47	42	51	47	51	56
Floors and Ceilings												
Under conditioned space, over unconditioned room, or over crawl space	9	4	12	9	4	14	12	9	14	12	14	19
Partitions												
Inside or shaded	9	4	12	9	4	14	12	9	12	12	14	19

[a] L denotes low daily range, less than 16°F; M denotes medium daily range, 16 to 25°F; and H denotes high daily range, greater than 25°F.

Table 7-39. CLTD Values for Multi-Family Residences*

Daily Temperature Range[a]		85 L	85 M	90 L	90 M	90 H	95 L	95 M	95 H	100 M	100 H	105 M	110 H	Daily Temperature Range[b]	
Walls and doors[c]															
N	Light	14	11	19	16	12	24	21	17	26	22	27	32	Light	N
	Medium	13	10	18	15	11	23	20	16	25	21	26	31	Medium	
	Heavy	9	6	15	11	7	20	16	12	21	17	22	27	Heavy	
NE	Light	23	17	28	22	17	33	27	22	32	26	31	36	Light	NE
	Medium	20	15	25	20	16	30	25	21	29	25	29	34	Medium	
	Heavy	16	12	21	17	13	26	22	18	26	22	26	31	Heavy	
E	Light	32	27	37	32	27	43	38	32	42	37	42	47	Light	E
	Medium	30	24	34	29	24	40	34	29	39	33	39	44	Medium	
	Heavy	23	18	28	23	18	34	29	23	33	28	33	38	Heavy	
SE	Light	31	27	35	31	26	41	37	31	42	37	42	47	Light	SE
	Medium	28	22	32	27	22	37	32	27	37	33	38	43	Medium	
	Heavy	21	16	26	22	17	32	27	22	31	27	32	37	Heavy	
S	Light	25	22	29	26	22	35	31	26	36	32	37	43	Light	S
	Medium	22	18	26	22	18	31	26	22	31	27	32	38	Medium	
	Heavy	16	11	20	16	12	26	21	17	26	21	27	33	Heavy	
SW	Light	39	36	44	40	35	50	46	40	51	47	52	58	Light	SW
	Medium	33	29	37	34	29	44	40	35	45	40	46	52	Medium	
	Heavy	23	18	28	24	19	36	31	25	35	30	36	42	Heavy	
W	Light	44	41	48	45	40	54	51	46	56	52	57	63	Light	W
	Medium	37	33	41	38	33	46	42	38	48	43	49	55	Medium	
	Heavy	26	22	31	27	23	37	32	27	37	32	38	44	Heavy	
NW	Light	33	30	37	34	30	43	39	34	44	40	45	50	Light	NW
	Medium	28	25	32	29	24	37	33	29	39	35	40	45	Medium	
	Heavy	20	16	25	20	16	31	29	21	31	26	32	37	Heavy	
Roof and Ceiling															
Attic or Flat built-up	Light	58	53	65	60	55	70	65	60	70	65	72	77	Light	Attic or Flat built-up
	Medium or heavy	21	18	23	21	18	25	23	21	25	23	25	28	Medium or heavy	
Floors and Ceiling															
Under or over unconditioned space, crawl space		9	4	12	9	4	14	12	9	14	12	14	19		Under or over unconditioned space, crawl space
Partitions															
Inside or shaded		9	4	12	9	4	14	12	9	14	12	14	19		Inside or shaded

[a] L denotes low daily range, less than 16°F; M denotes medium daily range, 16 to 25°F; and H denotes high daily range, greater than 25°F.
[b] L denotes low daily range, less than 16°F; M denotes medium daily range, 16 to 25°F; and H denotes high daily range, greater than 25°F.
[c] Light denotes lightweight; medium denotes medium-weight; and heavy denotes heavyweight construction.

* Cooling load temperature differences (CLTDs) for multi-family, low-rise or single-family detached if zoned with separate temperature control for each zone, °F.

Table 7-40. Potential Errors for Roof and Wall CLTDs in Tables 7-10 to 7-19

Roof Number	Error %		Wall Number	Error%	
	Plus	Minus		Plus	Minus
1	13	5	1	18	7
2	13	5	2	17	8
3	12	5	3	17	7
4	13	5	4	16	7
5	11	4	5	13	8
6	...	...	6	14	6
7	...	...	7	12	6
8	10	4	...	...	...
9	10	4	9	13	6
10	9	3	10	10	6
11	...	...	11	8	3
12	...	...	12	4	7
13	7	4	13	4	4
14	5	4	14	5	8
15	...	...	15	11	6
16	...	...	16	8	7

Table 7-41. Shading Coefficients (SCs) and U-Factors (Btu/hr-ft^2-°F) for Residential Windows

	Inside Shade					
	None		Drapery, Venetian Blind, or Translucent Roller Shade		Opaque Roller Shade	
Glass Type	SC	U	SC	U	SC	U
Single	1.00	1.04	0.50	0.81	0.38	0.81
Double	0.88	0.61	0.45	0.55	0.36	0.55
Heat-absorbing	0.58	0.45	0.37	0.44	0.33	0.44
Triple	0.80	0.44	0.44	0.40	0.36	0.40

Table 7-42. Shade Line Factors (SLFs)

Direction Window Faces	Latitude, Degrees N						
	24	32	36	40	44	48	52
East	0.8	0.8	0.8	0.8	0.8	0.8	0.8
SE	1.8	1.6	1.4	1.3	1.1	1.0	0.9
South	9.2	5.0	3.4	2.6	2.1	1.8	1.5
SW	1.8	1.6	1.4	1.3	1.1	1.0	0.9
West	0.8	0.8	0.8	0.8	0.8	0.8	0.8

Shadow length below the overhang equals the shade line factor times the overhang width. Values are averages for the 5 hours of greatest solar intensity on August 1.

Table 7-43. Winter Air Exchange Rates (*ach*) as Function of Airtightness

Class	Outdoor Design Temperature, °F									
	50	40	30	20	10	0	−10	−20	−30	−40
Tight	0.41	0.43	0.45	0.47	0.49	0.51	0.53	0.55	0.57	0.59
Medium	0.69	0.73	0.77	0.81	0.85	0.89	0.93	0.97	1.00	1.05
Loose	1.11	1.15	1.20	1.23	1.27	1.30	1.35	1.40	1.43	1.47

Values are for 15 mph wind and indoor temperature of 68° F.

Table 7-44. Summer Air Exchange Rates (*ach*) as Function of Airtightness

Class	Outdoor Design Temperature °F					
	85	90	95	100	105	110
Tight	0.33	0.34	0.35	0.36	0.37	0.38
Medium	0.46	0.48	0.50	0.52	0.54	0.56
Loose	0.68	0.70	0.72	0.74	0.76	0.78

Values are for 7.5 mph wind and indoor temperature of 75° F.

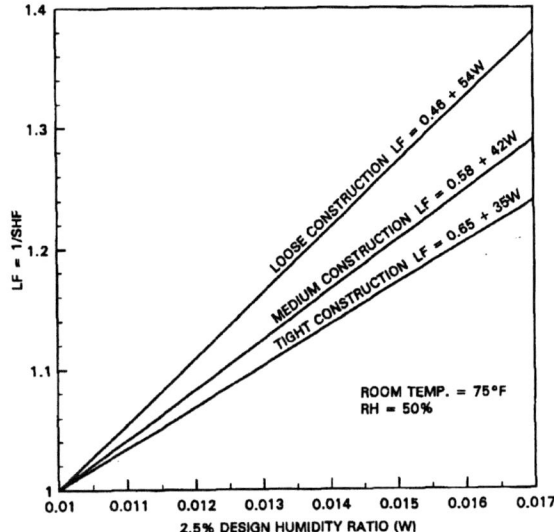

Fig 7-4. Effect of infiltration on latent load factor

Example 1: A typical single-family house is shown in the following figure. Calculate the heating and cooling load by hand calculations using CLTD method, as well as by Trace Load 700 software.

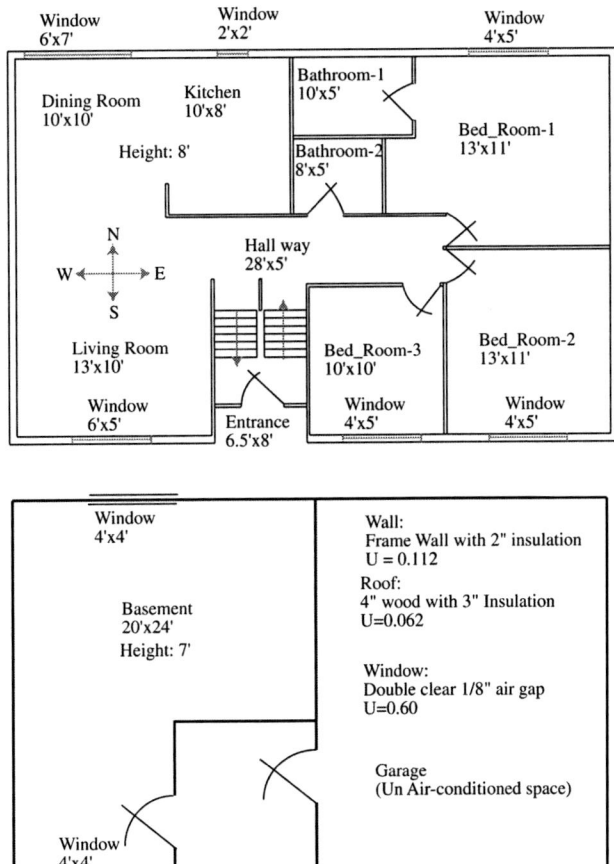

Find out the cooling load and heating load?

Solution: The following tables contain the calculations for each room of the example. The first ten tables represent CLTD calculations as done without computer software, the remainder were produced by the Trace Load software.

Table 7-45a. Dining Room Heat Loss/Gain by CLTD Method

Floor area 100 ft²									Ceiling height 8 ft			
Source		Unit		Unit					Sensible Btu/hr	Latent Btu/hr	Temp. Diff.	Heat Loss
Wall W	80	ft²	55.6	CLTD			0.112	U	498.18	…	57	510.72
Wall N	38	ft²	55.6	CLTD			0.112	U	236.64	…	57	242.60
Glass N	42	ft²	42.77	SCL	0.88	SC			1580.77	…	…	…
Glass N	42	ft²	8.0	CLTD			0.60	U	201.6		57	1513.00
Floor area	100	ft²	0	TD	…	…	0.594	U	0	…	0	0
Roof	100	ft²	30.3	CLTD	…	…	0.062	U	187.86	…	57	354.00
Infiltration	13.33	cfm	8.11	TD (S)	…	…	0	Td (W)	118.92	165	57	835.80
Occupants	0	persons	450	Btu-hr/person	…	…	…	…	0	0	…	…
Lighting	100	W	3.414	Btu-hr/watt	…	…	…	…	341	…	…	…
Computer	0	W	3.414	Btu-hr/watt	…	…	…	…	0	…	…	…
Equipment	0	W	3.414	Btu-hr/watt	…	…	…	…	0	…	…	0
Sum									3165	165		3456.12
Total cooling load									3330	Total heating load		3456

Table 7-46a. Kitchen Heat Loss/Gain by CLTD Method

Floor Area	80	ft²							Ceiling Height		8	ft
Source		Unit		Unit		Unit			Sensible Btu/hr	Latent Btu/hr	Temp. Diff.	Heat Loss
Wall N	76	ft²	23.6	CLTD				0.112	U	200.88	…	57	485.19
Glass N	4	ft²	30.4	SCL	0.88	SC				107.00	…		
Glass N	4	ft²	13.2	CLTD				0.60	U	31.68		57	136.80
Roof	80	ft²	18.9	CLTD				0.062	U	93.75	…	57	282.72
Infiltration	11	cfm	13.0	TD(S)						157.3	373	57	689.7
Occupants	0	persons	450	Btu-hr/person						0.00	…	…	…
Lighting	80	W	3.414	Btu-hr/watt						272.8	…	…	…
Computer	0	W	3.414	Btu-hr/watt						0	…	…	0
Equipment		W	3.414	Btu-hr/watt						…	…	…	…
Sum										863.41	373		1594.41
Total cooling load										1236	Total heating load		1595

Table 7-47a. Bathroom-1 Heat Loss/Gain by CLTD Method

Floor area = 50 ft²										Ceiling height 8 ft			
Source		Unit		Unit		Unit				Sensible Btu/hr	Latent Btu/hr	Temp. Diff.	Heat Loss
Wall N	80	ft²	24.1	CLTD				0.112	U	216.00	…	57	510.72
Roof	50	ft²	21.8	CLTD				0.062	U	67.58	…	57	176.7
Infiltration	7	cfm	12.33	TD(S)				0		95.0	226.0	67	491
Occupants	0	person	450	Btu-hr/person				=		0	0	…	…
Lighting	50	W	3.414	Btu-hr/watt				=		170.5	…	…	…
Computer	0	W	3.414	Btu-hr/watt				=		0	…	…	…
Equipment		W	3.414	Btu-hr/watt				=		0	…	…	0
Sum										549.08	226.0		1178.42
Total cooling load										775	Total heating load		1178

Table 7-48a. Bathroom-2 Heat Loss/Gain by CLTD Method

Floor area 40 ft²										Ceiling height 8ft			
Source		Unit		Unit						Sensible Btu/hr	Latent Btu/hr	Temp. Diff.	Heat Loss
Roof	40	ft²	18.9	CLTD				0.062	U	46.87	…	57	141.36
Infiltration	4	cfm	16	TD(S)				0		78.00	186.00	57	250.80
Occupants	0	person	450	Btu-hr/person				=		0	0	…	…
Lighting	40	W	3.414	Btu-hr/watt				=		136.56	…	…	…
Computer	0	W	3.414	Btu-hr/watt				=		0	…	…	…
Equipment		W	3.414	Btu-hr/watt				=		0	…	…	0
Sum										261.43	186.00		615
Total cooling load										447	Total heating load		615

Table 7-49a. Bedroom-1 Heat Loss/Gain by CLTD Method

Floor area 143 ft²										Ceiling height 8 ft			
Source										Sen. Btuh	Lat. Btuh	Temp. Diff.	Heat Loss
Wall	N	84	ft²	30.5	CLTD			0.112	U	286.95	...	57	536.26
Glass	N	20	ft²	30.50	SCL	0.96	SC			585.60	...	...	...
Glass	N	20	ft²	12.8	CLTD			0.60	U	152.16		57	684.00
Wall	E	88	ft²	30.5	CLTD			0.112	U	300.61	...	57	561.80
Roof		143	ft²	16.4	CLTD			0.062	U	145.40	...	57	505.36
Infiltration		19	cfm	11	TD(S)			0		272.00	657	57	1191.3
Occupants		2	persons	450	Btu-hr/person			=		500	450	...	...
Lighting		143	W	3.414	Btu-hr/watt			=		487.63	...	...	...
Computer		0	W	3.414	Btu-hr/watt			=		0	...	...	...
Equipment			W	3.414	Btu-hr/watt			=		0	...	...	0
Ventilation		40	cfm	16	TD(S)			0		571	1378	57	2508.00
Sum										3301.15	2485.00		5986.72
Total cooling load										5786	Total heating load		5987

Table 7-50a. Bedroom-2 Heat Loss/Gain by CLTD Method

Floor area 143 ft²										Ceiling height 8 ft			
Source										Sen. Btuh	Lat. Btuh	Temp. Diff.	Heat Loss
Wall	S	84	ft²	50.7	CLTD			0.112	U	476.98	...	57	536.26
Glass	S	20	ft²	118.0	SCL	1.00	SC			2360.00	...		
Glass	S	20	ft²	10.0	CLTD			0.60	U	120.00		57	684.00
Wall	E	88	ft²	50.7	CLTD			0.112	U	499.70	...	57	561.79
Roof		143	ft²	13.5	CLTD			0.062	U	119.69	...	57	505.36
Infiltration		19	cfm	11.85	TD(S)			0		248.0	619	57	1191.3
Occupants		1	person	450	Btu-hr/person			=		250	200	...	...
Lighting		143	W	3.414	Btu-hr/watt			=		487.63	...	...	...
Equipment			W	3.414	Btu-hr/watt			=		0	...	...	0
Ventilation		20	cfm	11.85	TD(S)			0		261.00	650	57	1254.0
Sum										4823.00	1469		4732.72
Total cooling load										6292	Total heating load		4732

Table 7-51a. Bedroom-3 Heat Loss/Gain by CLTD Method

Floor area = 100 ft²										Ceiling height 8ft			
Source										Sen. Btuh	Lat. Btuh	Temp. Diff.	Heat Loss
Wall	S	64	ft²	51.7	CLTD			0.112	U	370.58	...	57	408.58
Glass	S	16	ft²	120	SCL	1.00	SC			1920.00	...	...	...
Glass	S	16	ft²	11.7	CLTD			0.60	U	112.32		57	547.2
Roof		100	ft²	14.5	CLTD			0.062	U	89.90	...	57	374
Infiltration		13.33	cfm	12	TD(S)			0		175.96	529.0	57	353.4
Occupants		1	person	450	Btu-hr/person			=		250	200.0	...	...
Lighting		100	W	3.414	Btu-hr/watt			=		341.41	...	...	...
Computer		0	W	3.414	Btu-hr/watt			=		0	...	...	...
Equipment											...	...	0
Ventilation		20	cfm	12.0	TD(S)			0		264.00	650.0	57	1254.0
Sum										3524.17	1379.0		2937.18
Total cooling load										4903	Total heating load		2937

Table 7-52a. Entrance Heat Loss/Gain by CLTD Method

Floor area = 52 ft²										Ceiling height 8 ft			
Source										Sen. Btuh	Lat. Btuh	Temp. Diff.	Heat Loss
Wall	S	31	ft²	44.7	CLTD			0.112	U	155.20	…	57	197.90
Glass	S	21	ft²	206	SCL	0.88	SC			3806.88	…		
Glass	S	21	ft²	−6.3	CLTD			0.60	U	−71.38		57	718.20
Roof		52	ft²	−10.5	CLTD			0.062	U	−33.85	…	57	183.77
Infiltration		9	cfm	12	TD(S)					118.8	357.0	57	564.30
Occupants		0	person	450	Btu-hr/person			=		0	…	…	…
Lighting		52	W	3.414	Btu-hr/watt			=		177.31	…	…	…
Computer		0	W	3.414	Btu-hr/watt			=		0	…	…	…
Equipment			W	3.414	Btu-hr/watt			=		0	…	…	…
Sum										4220.66	357.0		1664.17
Total cooling load										4577	Total heating load		1664

Table 7-53a. Living Room Heat Loss/Gain by CLTD Method

Floor area 130 ft²										Ceiling height 8 ft			
Source										Sen. Btuh	Lat. Btuh	Temp. Diff.	Heat Loss
Wall	W	80	ft²	37.3	CLTD			0.112	U	334.20	…	57	510.72
Wall	S	74	ft²	37.3	CLTD			0.112	U	309.14	…	57	472.42
Glass	S	30	ft²	177	SCL	0.88	SC			4672.80	…		
Glass	S	30	ft²	4.2	CLTD			0.60	U	75.60		57	1026.00
Roof		130	ft²	3.80	CLTD			0.062	U	30.63	…	57	459.42
Infiltration		17	cfm	5	TD(S)			0		81.00	395.00	57	1065.90
Occupants		0	P	450	Btu-hr/person			=		…	…	…	…
Lighting		130	W	3.414	Btu-hr/watt			=		443.82	…	…	…
Computer		0	W	3.414	Btu-hr/watt			=		…	…	…	…
Equipment			W	3.414	Btu-hr/watt			=		…	…	…	…
Sum										5947.19	395 .00		3534.46
Total cooling load										6342	Total heating load		3534

Table 7-54a. Basement Heat Loss/Gain by CLTD Method

Floor area 480 ft²										Ceiling height 7 ft			
Source										Sen. Btuh	Lat. Btuh	Temp. Diff.	Heat Loss
Wall	W	168	ft²	35.2	CLTD			0.112	U	662.0	…	57	1072.51
Wall	N	140	ft²	24.1	CLTD			0.112	U	377.88	…	57	893.76
Glass	N	16	ft²	30.5	SCL	0.88	SC			429.44	…		
Glass	N	16	ft²	12.8	CLTD			0.60	U	122.88		57	547.20
Wall	S	140	ft²	51.7	CLTD			0.112	U	810.66	…	57	893.76
Glass	S	16	ft²	120	SCL	0.88	SC	0.60	U	1689.60	…		
Glass	S	16	ft²	11.7	CLTD			0.60	U	112.32		57	547.2
Roof		0	ft²	0	CLTD			0.062	U	0	…	57	0
Infiltration		52	cfm	16	TD(S)			0		915.20	2205	57	3260.4
Occupants		0	person	450	Btu-hr/person			=		…	…	…	…
Lighting		480	W	3.414	Btu-hr/watt			=		1638.72	…	…	…
Sum										6758.7	2205		7214.83
Total cooling load										8963	Total heating load		7214

Room Checksums

Bedroom-1

COOLING COIL PEAK / CLG SPACE PEAK / HEATING COIL PEAK

COOLING COIL PEAK — Peaked at Time: Mo/Hr: 8/14, Outside Air: OADB/WB/HR: 88/76/114
CLG SPACE PEAK — Mo/Hr: 7/13, OADB: 87
HEATING COIL PEAK — Mo/Hr: 13/1, OADB: 15

	COOLING COIL PEAK Space Sens.+Lat. Btu/h	Plenum Sens.+Lat Btu/h	Net Total Btu/h	Percent Of Total (%)	CLG SPACE PEAK Space Sensible Btu/h	Percent Of Total (%)	HEATING COIL PEAK Space Peak Space Sens Btu/h	Coil Peak Tot Sens Btu/h	Percent Of Total (%)
Envelope Loads									
Skylite Solar	0	0	0	0.00	0	0.00	0	0	0.00
Skylite Cond	0	0	0	0.00	0	0.00	0	0	0.00
Roof Cond	145	0	145	2.55	157	5.45	-506	-506	9.08
Glass Solar	584	0	584	10.23	658	22.81	0	0	0.00
Glass Cond	154	0	154	2.69	149	5.16	-720	-720	12.92
Wall Cond	561	0	561	9.83	670	23.21	-1,095	-1,095	19.65
Partition	0	0	0	0.00	0	0.00	0	0	0.00
Exposed Floor	0	0	0	0.00	0	0.00	0	0	0.00
Infiltration	929		929	16.27	264	9.13	-1,211	-1,211	21.73
Sub Total ==>	2,373	0	2,373	41.56	1,898	65.76	-3,533	-3,533	63.37
Internal Loads									
Lights	488	0	488	8.55	488	16.91	0	0	0.00
People	900	0	900	15.76	500	17.33	500	500	-8.97
Misc	0	0	0	0.00	0	0.00	0	0	0.00
Sub Total ==>	1,388	0	1,388	24.31	988	34.24	500	500	-8.97
Ceiling Load	0	0	0	0.00	0	0.00	0	0	0.00
Ventilation Load	0		1,949	34.13	0	0.00	0	-2,542	45.60
Ov/Undr Sizing	0	0		0.00	0	0.00	0	0	0.00
Exhaust Heat		0						0	0.00
Sup. Fan Heat								0	0.00
Ret. Fan Heat	0	0		0.00				0	0.00
Duct Heat Pkup	0	0		0.00				0	0.00
Reheat at Design				0.00				0	0.00
Grand Total ==>	3,761	0	5,710	100.00	2,886	100.00	-3,033	-5,574	100.00

COOLING COIL SELECTION

	Total Capacity ton	MBh	Sens Cap. MBh	Coil Airflow cfm	Enter DB °F	WB °F	HR gr/lb	Leave DB °F	WB °F	HR gr/lb
Main Clg	0.5	5.7	3.3	119	79.3	67.3	81.4	53.3	51.7	54.8
Aux Clg	0.0	0.0	0.0	0	0.0	0.0	0.0	0.0	0.0	0.0
Opt Vent	0.0	0.0	0.0	0	0.0	0.0	0.0	0.0	0.0	0.0
Total	0.5	5.7								

HEATING COIL SELECTION

	Capacity MBh	Coil Airflow cfm	Ent °F	Lvg °F
Main Htg	-5.6	119	52.9	94.8
Aux Htg	0.0	0	0.0	0.0
Preheat	-0.1	119	52.9	53.3
Humidif	0.0	0	0.0	0.0
Opt Vent	0.0	0	0.0	0.0
Total	-5.6			

AREAS

	Gross Total	Glass ft²	Glass (%)
Floor	143		
Part	0		
ExFlr	0		
Roof	143	0	0
Wall	192	20	10

ENGINEERING CKS

	Cooling	Heating
% OA	33.5	33.5
cfm/ft²	0.83	0.83
cfm/ton	250.60	
ft²/ton	300.51	
Btu/hr-ft²	39.93	
No. People	2	

TEMPERATURES

	Cooling	Heating
SADB	53.3	94.8
Plenum	75.0	72.0
Return	75.0	72.0
Ret/OA	79.3	52.9
Fn MtrTD	0.0	0.0
Fn BldTD	0.0	0.0
Fn Frict	0.0	0.0

AIRFLOWS

	Cooling	Heating
Vent	40	40
Infil	19	19
Supply	119	119
MinStop/Rh	0	0
Return	138	138
Exhaust	59	59
Rm Exh	0	0
Auxil	0	0

Room Checksums

Bedroom-2

COOLING COIL PEAK

Peaked at Time: Mo/Hr: 8/13
Outside Air: OADB/WB/HR: 87/75/111

	Space Sens. + Lat. Btu/h	Plenum Sens. + Lat. Btu/h	Net Total Btu/h	Percent Of Total (%)
Envelope Loads				
Skylite Solar	0	0	0	0.00
Skylite Cond	0	0	0	0.00
Roof Cond	129	0	129	2.04
Glass Solar	2,394	0	2,394	37.88
Glass Cond	140	0	140	2.22
Wall Cond	939	0	939	14.86
Partition	0	0	0	0.00
Exposed Floor	0	0	0	0.00
Infiltration	868		868	13.74
Sub Total ==>	4,471	0	4,471	70.75
Internal Loads				
Lights	488	0	488	7.72
People	450		450	7.12
Misc	0	0	0	0.00
Sub Total ==>	938	0	938	14.84
Ceiling Load	0	0	0	0.00
Ventilation Load	0	0	910	14.41
Ov/Undr Sizing	0	0	0	0.00
Exhaust Heat		0	0	0.00
Sup. Fan Heat		0	0	0.00
Ret. Fan Heat		0	0	0.00
Duct Heat Pkup		0	0	0.00
Reheat at Design		0	0	0.00
Grand Total ==>	5,409	0	6,319	100.00

CLG SPACE PEAK

Mo/Hr: 9/12
OADB: 78

	Space Sensible Btu/h	Percent Of Total (%)
Envelope Loads		
Skylite Solar	0	0.00
Skylite Cond	0	0.00
Roof Cond	26	0.53
Glass Solar	3,150	64.41
Glass Cond	34	0.69
Wall Cond	884	18.07
Partition	0	0.00
Exposed Floor	0	0.00
Infiltration	60	1.22
Sub Total ==>	4,153	84.91
Internal Loads		
Lights	488	9.98
People	250	5.11
Misc	0	0.00
Sub Total ==>	738	15.09
Ceiling Load	0	0.00
Ventilation Load	0	0.00
Ov/Undr Sizing	0	0.00
Grand Total ==>	4,891	100.00

HEATING COIL PEAK

Mo/Hr: 13/1
OADB: 15

	Space Peak Space Sens Btu/h	Coil Peak Tot Sens Btu/h	Percent Of Total (%)
Envelope Loads			
Skylite Solar	0	0	0.00
Skylite Cond	0	0	0.00
Roof Cond	-506	-506	11.11
Glass Solar	0	0	0.00
Glass Cond	-720	-720	15.81
Wall Cond	-1,095	-1,095	24.05
Partition	0	0	0.00
Exposed Floor	0	0	0.00
Infiltration	-1,211	-1,211	26.61
Sub Total ==>	-3,533	-3,533	77.58
Internal Loads			
Lights	0	0	0.00
People	250	250	-5.49
Misc	0	0	0.00
Sub Total ==>	250	250	-5.49
Ceiling Load	0	0	0.00
Ventilation Load		-1,271	27.91
Ov/Undr Sizing	0	0	0.00
Exhaust Heat		0	0.00
OA Preheat Diff.		0	0.00
RA Preheat Diff.		0	0.00
Additional Reheat		0	0.00
System Plenum Heat		0	0.00
Grand Total ==>	-3,283	-4,553	100.00

TEMPERATURES

	Cooling	Heating
SADB	58.8	82.9
Plenum	75.0	72.0
Return	75.0	72.0
Ret/OA	75.9	67.8
Fn MtrTD	0.0	0.0
Fn BldTD	0.0	0.0
Fn Frict	0.0	0.0

AIRFLOWS

	Cooling	Heating
Vent	20	20
Infil	19	19
Supply	270	270
MinStop/Rh	0	0
Return	289	289
Exhaust	39	39
Rm Exh	0	0
Auxil	0	0

ENGINEERING CKS

	Cooling	Heating
% OA	7.4	7.4
cfm/ft²	1.89	1.89
cfm/ton	512.66	
ft²/ton	271.56	
Btu/hr·ft²	44.19	-31.84
No. People	1	

AREAS

	Gross Total	Glass ft²	(%)
Floor	143		
Part	0		
ExFlr	0		
Roof	143	0	0
Wall	192	20	10

COOLING COIL SELECTION

	Total Capacity ton	Total Capacity MBh	Sens Cap. MBh	Coil Airflow cfm	Enter DB °F	WB °F	HR gr/lb	Leave DB °F	WB °F	HR gr/lb
Main Clg	0.5	6.3	4.9	270	75.9	63.6	68.4	58.8	55.9	62.3
Aux Clg	0.0	0.0	0.0	0	0.0	0.0	0.0	0.0	0.0	0.0
Opt Vent	0.0	0.0	0.0	0	0.0	0.0	0.0	0.0	0.0	0.0
Total	0.5	6.3								

HEATING COIL SELECTION

	Capacity MBh	Coil Airflow cfm	Ent °F	Lvg °F
Main Htg	-4.6	270	67.8	82.9
Aux Htg	0.0	0	0.0	0.0
Preheat	0.0	0	0.0	0.0
Humidif	0.0	0	0.0	0.0
Opt Vent	0.0	0	0.0	0.0
Total	-4.6			

Room Checksums

Bedroom-3

COOLING COIL PEAK

Peaked at Time: Mo/Hr: 8/13
Outside Air: OADB/WB/HR: 87/75/111

	Space Sens. + Lat. Btu/h	Plenum Sens. + Lat Btu/h	Net Total Btu/h	Percent Of Total (%)
Envelope Loads				
Skylite Solar	0	0	0	0.00
Skylite Cond	0	0	0	0.00
Roof Cond	90	0	90	1.79
Glass Solar	1,915	0	1,915	38.04
Glass Cond	112	0	112	2.23
Wall Cond	369	0	369	7.34
Partition	0		0	0.00
Exposed Floor	0		0	0.00
Infiltration	703		703	13.96
Sub Total ==>	3,190	0	3,190	63.35
Internal Loads				
Lights	341	0	341	6.78
People	450		450	8.94
Misc	0	0	0	0.00
Sub Total ==>	791	0	791	15.72
Ceiling Load	0	0	0	0.00
Ventilation Load		1,054	1,054	20.93
Ov/Undr Sizing	0	0	0	0.00
Exhaust Heat		0	0	0.00
Sup. Fan Heat			0	0.00
Ret. Fan Heat		0	0	0.00
Duct Heat Pkup		0	0	0.00
Reheat at Design			0	0.00
Grand Total ==>	3,981	0	5,035	100.00

CLG SPACE PEAK

Mo/Hr: 10/13
OADB: 70

	Space Sensible Btu/h	Percent Of Total (%)
Envelope Loads		
Skylite Solar	0	0.00
Skylite Cond	0	0.00
Roof Cond	-61	-1.69
Glass Solar	2,826	77.66
Glass Cond	-44	-1.21
Wall Cond	396	10.87
Partition	0	0.00
Exposed Floor	0	0.00
Infiltration	-68	-1.88
Sub Total ==>	3,047	83.75
Internal Loads		
Lights	341	9.38
People	250	6.87
Misc	0	0.00
Sub Total ==>	591	16.25
Ceiling Load	0	0.00
Ventilation Load	0	0.00
Exhaust Heat	0	0.00
OA Preheat Diff.		
RA Preheat Diff.		
Additional Reheat		
System Plenum Heat		
Grand Total ==>	3,639	100.00

HEATING COIL PEAK

Mo/Hr: 13/1
OADB: 15

	Space Peak Space Sens Btu/h	Coil Peak Tot Sens Btu/h	Percent Of Total (%)
Envelope Loads			
Skylite Solar	0	0	0.00
Skylite Cond	0	0	0.00
Roof Cond	-354	-354	11.04
Glass Solar	0	0	0.00
Glass Cond	-576	-576	17.97
Wall Cond	-408	-408	12.71
Partition	0	0	0.00
Exposed Floor	0	0	0.00
Infiltration	-847	-847	26.43
Sub Total ==>	-2,184	-2,184	68.15
Internal Loads			
Lights	0	0	0.00
People	250	250	-7.80
Misc	0	0	0.00
Sub Total ==>	250	250	-7.80
Ceiling Load	0	0	0.00
Ventilation Load		-1,271	39.65
Ov/Undr Sizing	0	0	0.00
Exhaust Heat	0	0	0.00
OA Preheat Diff.	0	0	0.00
RA Preheat Diff.	0	0	0.00
Additional Reheat	0	0	0.00
System Plenum Heat	0	0	0.00
Grand Total ==>	-1,934	-3,205	100.00

TEMPERATURES

	Cooling	Heating
SADB	55.0	82.6
Plenum	75.0	72.0
Return	75.0	72.0
Ret/OA	76.4	65.0
Fn MtrTD	0.0	0.0
Fn BldTD	0.0	0.0
Fn Frict	0.0	0.0

AIRFLOWS

	Cooling	Heating
Vent	20	20
Infil	13	13
Supply	163	163
MinStop/Rh		
Return	177	177
Exhaust	33	33
Rm Exh	0	0
Auxil	0	0

ENGINEERING CKS

	Cooling	Heating
% OA	12.3	12.3
cfm/ft²	1.63	1.63
cfm/ton	389.00	
ft²/ton	238.33	
Btu/hr·ft²	50.35	
No. People	1	

AREAS

	Gross Total	Glass ft²	(%)
Floor	100		
Part	0		
ExFlr	0		
Roof	100	0	0
Wall	80	16	20

COOLING COIL SELECTION

	Total Capacity ton	MBh	Sens Cap. MBh	Coil Airflow cfm	Enter DB/WB/HR °F °F gr/lb	Leave DB/WB/HR °F °F gr/lb
Main Clg	0.4	5.0	3.5	163	76.4 62.3 61.7	55.0 51.7 51.7
Aux Clg	0.0	0.0	0.0	0	0.0 0.0 0.0	0.0 0.0 0.0
Opt Vent	0.0	0.0	0.0	0	0.0 0.0 0.0	0.0 0.0 0.0
Total	0.4	5.0	5.0			

HEATING COIL SELECTION

	Capacity MBh	Coil Airflow cfm	Ent °F	Lvg °F
Main Htg	-3.2	163	65.0	82.6
Aux Htg	0.0	0	0.0	0.0
Preheat	0.0	0	0.0	0.0
Humidif	0.0	0	0.0	0.0
Opt Vent	0.0	0	0.0	0.0
Total	-3.2			

Room Checksums

Basement

COOLING COIL PEAK

Peaked at Time: Mo/Hr: 8 / 14
Outside Air: OADB/WB/HR: 88 / 76 / 114

	Space Sens. + Lat. Btu/h	Plenum Sens. + Lat Btu/h	Net Total Btu/h	Percent Of Total (%)
Envelope Loads				
Skylite Solar	0	0	0	0.00
Skylite Cond	0	0	0	0.00
Roof Cond	0	0	0	0.00
Glass Solar	2,172	0	2,172	27.73
Glass Cond	246	0	246	3.14
Wall Cond	2,298	0	2,298	29.33
Partition	0		0	0.00
Exposed Floor	0		0	0.00
Infiltration	3,118		3,118	39.80
Sub Total ==>	7,834	0	7,834	100.00
Internal Loads				
Lights	0	0	0	0.00
People	0		0	0.00
Misc	0		0	0.00
Sub Total ==>	0		0	0.00
Ceiling Load	0	0	0	0.00
Ventilation Load	0	0	0	0.00
Ov/Undr Sizing	0		0	0.00
Exhaust Heat		0	0	0.00
Sup. Fan Heat		0	0	0.00
Ret. Fan Heat		0	0	0.00
Duct Heat Pkup		0	0	0.00
Reheat at Design		0	0	0.00
Grand Total ==>	7,834	0	7,834	100.00

CLG SPACE PEAK

Mo/Hr: 8 / 13
OADB: 87

	Space Sensible Btu/h	Percent Of Total (%)
Envelope Loads		
Skylite Solar	0	0.00
Skylite Cond	0	0.00
Roof Cond	0	0.00
Glass Solar	2,402	42.15
Glass Cond	224	3.94
Wall Cond	2,239	39.28
Partition	0	0.00
Exposed Floor	0	0.00
Infiltration	834	14.63
Sub Total ==>	5,699	100.00
Internal Loads		
Lights	0	0.00
People	0	0.00
Misc	0	0.00
Sub Total ==>	0	0.00
Ceiling Load	0	0.00
Ventilation Load	0	0.00
Ov/Undr Sizing	0	0.00
Grand Total ==>	5,699	100.00

HEATING COIL PEAK

Mo/Hr: 13 / 1
OADB: 15

	Space Peak Space Sens Btu/h	Coil Peak Tot Sens Btu/h	Percent Of Total (%)
Envelope Loads			
Skylite Solar	0	0	0.00
Skylite Cond	0	0	0.00
Roof Cond	0	0	0.00
Glass Solar	0	0	0.00
Glass Cond	-1,152	-1,152	15.78
Wall Cond	-3,719	-3,719	50.95
Partition	0	0	0.00
Exposed Floor	0	0	0.00
Infiltration	-4,067	-4,067	55.72
Sub Total ==>	-8,937	-8,937	122.45
Internal Loads			
Lights	1,638	1,638	-22.45
People	0	0	0.00
Misc	0	0	0.00
Sub Total ==>	1,638	1,638	-22.45
Ceiling Load	0	0	0.00
Ventilation Load	0	0	0.00
Ov/Undr Sizing	0	0	0.00
Exhaust Heat		0	0.00
OA Preheat Diff.		0	0.00
RA Preheat Diff.		0	0.00
Additional Reheat		0	0.00
System Plenum Heat		0	0.00
Grand Total ==>	-7,299	-7,299	100.00

TEMPERATURES

	Cooling	Heating
SADB	51.4	102.2
Plenum	75.0	72.0
Return	75.0	72.0
Ret/OA	0.0	0.0
Fn MtrTD	0.0	0.0
Fn BldTD	0.0	0.0
Fn Frict		

AIRFLOWS

	Cooling	Heating
Vent	0	0
Infil	64	64
Supply	217	217
MinStop/Rh	0	0
Return	281	281
Exhaust	64	64
Rm Exh	0	0
Auxil	0	0

ENGINEERING CKS

	Cooling	Heating
% OA	0.0	0.0
cfm/ft²	0.45	0.45
cfm/ton	332.40	
ft²/ton	735.24	
Btu/hr-ft²	16.32	-15.21
No. People	0	

HEATING COIL SELECTION

	Capacity MBh	Coil Airflow cfm	Ent °F	Lvg °F
Main Htg	-7.3	217	72.0	102.2
Aux Htg	0.0	0	0.0	0.0
Preheat	0.0	0	0.0	0.0
Humidif	0.0	0	0.0	0.0
Opt Vent	0.0	0	0.0	0.0
Total	-7.3			

COOLING COIL SELECTION

	Total Capacity ton	Sens Cap. MBh	Coil Airflow cfm	Enter DB/WB/HR °F / °F / gr/lb	Leave DB/WB/HR °F / °F / gr/lb
Main Clg	0.7	7.8	5.6	217	75.0 / 62.6 / 65.0	51.4 / 49.9 / 51.0
Aux Clg	0.0	0.0	0.0	0	0.0 / 0.0 / 0.0	0.0 / 0.0 / 0.0
Opt Vent	0.0	0.0	0.0	0	0.0 / 0.0 / 0.0	0.0 / 0.0 / 0.0
Total	0.7	7.8				

AREAS

	Gross Total	Glass ft²	Glass (%)
Floor	480		
Part	0		
ExFlr	0		
Roof	0	0	0
Wall	616	32	5

Room Checksums

Dining Room

COOLING COIL PEAK

Peaked at Time: Mo/Hr: 6 / 18
Outside Air: OADB/WB/HR: 83 / 69 / 83

	Space Sens. + Lat. Btu/h	Plenum Sens. + Lat. Btu/h	Net Total Btu/h	Percent Of Total (%)
Envelope Loads				
Skylite Solar	0	0	0	0.00
Skylite Cond	0	0	0	0.00
Roof Cond	188	0	188	5.64
Glass Solar	1,581	0	1,581	47.49
Glass Cond	202	0	202	6.06
Wall Cond	734	0	734	22.04
Partition	0	0	0	0.00
Exposed Floor	0	0	0	0.00
Infiltration	284	0	284	8.53
Sub Total ==>	2,988	0	2,988	89.75
Internal Loads				
Lights	341	0	341	10.25
People	0	0	0	0.00
Misc	0	0	0	0.00
Sub Total ==>	341	0	341	10.25
Ceiling Load	0	0	0	0.00
Ventilation Load	0	0	0	0.00
Ov/Undr Sizing	0	0	0	0.00
Exhaust Heat	0	0	0	0.00
Sup. Fan Heat	0	0	0	0.00
Ret. Fan Heat	0	0	0	0.00
Duct Heat Pkup	0	0	0	0.00
Reheat at Design	0	0	0	0.00
Grand Total ==>	3,329	0	3,329	100.00

CLG SPACE PEAK

Mo/Hr: 6 / 18
OADB: 83

	Space Sensible Btu/h	Percent Of Total (%)
Envelope Loads		
Skylite Solar	0	0.00
Skylite Cond	0	0.00
Roof Cond	188	5.94
Glass Solar	1,581	49.96
Glass Cond	202	6.37
Wall Cond	734	23.19
Partition	0	0.00
Exposed Floor	0	0.00
Infiltration	119	3.76
Sub Total ==>	2,823	89.21
Internal Loads		
Lights	341	10.79
People	0	0.00
Misc	0	0.00
Sub Total ==>	341	10.79
Ceiling Load	0	0.00
Ventilation Load	0	0.00
Ov/Undr Sizing	0	0.00
Grand Total ==>	3,164	100.00

HEATING COIL PEAK

Mo/Hr: 13 / 1
OADB: 15

	Space Peak Space Sens Btu/h	Coil Peak Tot Sens Btu/h	Percent Of Total (%)
Envelope Loads			
Skylite Solar	0	0	0.00
Skylite Cond	0	0	0.00
Roof Cond	-354	-354	10.21
Glass Solar	0	0	0.00
Glass Cond	-1,512	-1,512	43.64
Wall Cond	-751	-751	21.69
Partition	0	0	0.00
Exposed Floor	0	0	0.00
Infiltration	-847	-847	24.46
Sub Total ==>	-3,464	-3,464	100.00
Internal Loads			
Lights	0	0	0.00
People	0	0	0.00
Misc	0	0	0.00
Sub Total ==>	0	0	0.00
Ceiling Load	0	0	0.00
Ventilation Load	0	0	0.00
Ov/Undr Sizing	0	0	0.00
Exhaust Heat	0	0	0.00
OA Preheat Diff.	0	0	0.00
RA Preheat Diff.	0	0	0.00
Additional Reheat	0	0	0.00
System Plenum Heat	0	0	0.00
Grand Total ==>	-3,464	-3,464	100.00

TEMPERATURES

	Cooling	Heating
SADB	61.3	87.0
Plenum	75.0	72.0
Return	75.0	72.0
Ret/OA	75.0	72.0
Fn MtrTD	0.0	0.0
Fn BldTD	0.0	0.0
Fn Frict	0.0	0.0

AIRFLOWS

	Cooling	Heating
Vent	0	0
Infil	13	13
Supply	207	207
MinStop/Rh	0	0
Return	221	221
Exhaust	13	13
Rm Exh	0	0
Auxil	0	0

ENGINEERING CKS

	Cooling	Heating
% OA	0.0	0.0
cfm/ft²	2.07	2.07
cfm/ton	747.33	
ft²/ton	360.48	
Btu/hr·ft²	33.29	-34.64
No. People	0	

AREAS

	Gross Total	Glass ft²	Glass (%)
Floor	100		
Part	0		
ExFlr	0		
Roof	100	0	0
Wall	160	42	26

COOLING COIL SELECTION

	Total Capacity ton	MBh	Sens Cap. MBh	Coil Airflow cfm	Enter DB/WB/HR °F	°F	gr/lb	Leave DB/WB/HR °F	°F	gr/lb
Main Clg	0.3	3.3	3.2	207	75.0	62.6	65.0	61.3	57.3	63.8
Aux Clg	0.0	0.0	0.0	0	0.0	0.0	0.0	0.0	0.0	0.0
Opt Vent	0.0	0.0	0.0	0	0.0	0.0	0.0	0.0	0.0	0.0
Total	0.3	3.3								

HEATING COIL SELECTION

	Capacity MBh	Coil Airflow cfm	Ent °F	Lvg °F
Main Htg	-3.5	207	72.0	87.0
Aux Htg	0.0	0	0.0	0.0
Preheat	0.0	0	0.0	0.0
Humidif	0.0	0	0.0	0.0
Opt Vent	0.0	0	0.0	0.0
Total	-3.5			

Room Checksums

Entrance

COOLING COIL PEAK
Peaked at Time: Mo/Hr: 10 / 12
Outside Air: OADB/WB/HR: 69 / 58 / 56

	Space Sens. + Lat Btu/h	Plenum Sens. + Lat Btu/h	Net Total Btu/h	Percent Of Total (%)
Envelope Loads				
Skylite Solar	0	0	0	0.00
Skylite Cond	0	0	0	0.00
Roof Cond	-42	0	-42	-1.06
Glass Solar	3,807	0	3,807	95.10
Glass Cond	-80	0	-80	-1.99
Wall Cond	155	0	155	3.87
Partition	0		0	0.00
Exposed Floor	0		0	0.00
Infiltration	-59		-59	-1.46
Sub Total ==>	3,781	0	3,781	94.46
Internal Loads				
Lights	222	0	222	5.54
People	0		0	0.00
Misc	0	0	0	0.00
Sub Total ==>	222	0	222	5.54
Ceiling Load	0	0	0	0.00
Ventilation Load	0	0	0	0.00
Ov/Undr Sizing	0		0	0.00
Exhaust Heat	0			0.00
Sup. Fan Heat	0			0.00
Ret. Fan Heat	0			0.00
Duct Heat Pkup	0			0.00
Reheat at Design	0	0		0.00
Grand Total ==>	4,003	0	4,003	100.00

CLG SPACE PEAK
Mo/Hr: 10 / 12
OADB: 69

	Space Sensible Btu/h	Percent Of Total (%)
Envelope Loads		
Skylite Solar	0	0.00
Skylite Cond	0	0.00
Roof Cond	-42	-1.06
Glass Solar	3,807	95.16
Glass Cond	-80	-1.99
Wall Cond	155	3.87
Partition	0	0.00
Exposed Floor	0	0.00
Infiltration	-61	-1.52
Sub Total ==>	3,779	94.45
Internal Loads		
Lights	222	5.55
People	0	0.00
Misc	0	0.00
Sub Total ==>	222	5.55
Ceiling Load	0	0.00
Ventilation Load	0	0.00
Ov/Undr Sizing	0	0.00
Grand Total ==>	4,001	100.00

HEATING COIL PEAK
Mo/Hr: 13 / 1
OADB: 15

	Space Peak Space Sens Btu/h	Coil Peak Tot Sens Btu/h	Percent Of Total (%)
Envelope Loads			
Skylite Solar	0	0	0.00
Skylite Cond	0	0	0.00
Roof Cond	-230	-230	13.26
Glass Solar	0	0	0.00
Glass Cond	-756	-756	43.60
Wall Cond	-197	-197	11.38
Partition	0	0	0.00
Exposed Floor	0	0	0.00
Infiltration	-551	-551	31.76
Sub Total ==>	-1,734	-1,734	100.00
Internal Loads			
Lights	0	0	0.00
People	0	0	0.00
Misc	0	0	0.00
Sub Total ==>	0	0	0.00
Ceiling Load	0	0	0.00
Ventilation Load	0	0	0.00
Ov/Undr Sizing	0	0	0.00
OA Preheat Diff.			0.00
RA Preheat Diff.			0.00
Additional Reheat			0.00
System Plenum Heat			0.00
Grand Total ==>	-1,734	-1,734	100.00

TEMPERATURES

	Cooling	Heating
SADB	65.0	76.3
Plenum	75.0	72.0
Return	75.0	72.0
Ret/OA	75.0	72.0
Fn MtrTD	0.0	0.0
Fn BldTD	0.0	0.0
Fn Frict	0.0	0.0

AIRFLOWS

	Cooling	Heating
Vent	0	0
Infil	9	9
Supply	359	359
MinStop/Rh	0	0
Return	368	368
Exhaust	9	9
Rm Exh	0	0
Auxil	0	0

ENGINEERING CKS

	Cooling	Heating
% OA	0.0	0.0
cfm/ft²	5.52	5.52
cfm/ton	1,075.86	
ft²/ton	194.85	
Btu/hr·ft²	61.59	-26.68
No. People	0	

COOLING COIL SELECTION

	Total Capacity ton	MBh	Sens Cap. MBh	Coil Airflow cfm	Enter DB/WB/HR °F °F gr/lb	Leave DB/WB/HR °F °F gr/lb
Main Clg	0.3	4.0	4.0	359	75.0 60.5 55.6	65.0 56.7 55.6
Aux Clg	0.0	0.0	0.0	0	0.0 0.0 0.0	0.0 0.0 0.0
Opt Vent	0.0	0.0	0.0	0	0.0 0.0 0.0	0.0 0.0 0.0
Total	0.3	4.0				

HEATING COIL SELECTION

	Capacity MBh	Coil Airflow cfm	Ent °F	Lvg °F
Main Htg	-1.7	359	72.0	76.3
Aux Htg	0.0	0	0.0	0.0
Preheat	0.0	0	0.0	0.0
Humidif	0.0	0	0.0	0.0
Opt Vent	0.0	0	0.0	0.0
Total	-1.7			-1.7

AREAS

	Gross Total ft²	Glass ft²	(%)
Floor	65		
Part	0		
ExFlr	0		
Roof	65	0	0
Wall	52	21	40

Room Checksums

Kitchen

COOLING COIL PEAK

Peaked at Time: Mo/Hr: 8/15
Outside Air: OADB/WB/HR: 88/76/115

	Space Sens. + Lat. Btu/h	Plenum Sens. + Lat Btu/h	Net Total Btu/h	Percent Of Total (%)
Envelope Loads				
Skylite Solar	0	0	0	0.00
Skylite Cond	0	0	0	0.00
Roof Cond	94	0	94	7.58
Glass Solar	107	0	107	8.64
Glass Cond	32	0	32	2.56
Wall Cond	201	0	201	16.24
Partition	0		0	0.00
Exposed Floor	0		0	0.00
Infiltration	530		530	42.87
Sub Total ==>	962	0	962	77.90
Internal Loads				
Lights	273	0	273	22.10
People	0		0	0.00
Misc	0	0	0	0.00
Sub Total ==>	273	0	273	22.10
Ceiling Load	0	0	0	0.00
Ventilation Load	0	0	0	0.00
Ov/Undr Sizing	0		0	0.00
Exhaust Heat		0	0	0.00
Sup. Fan Heat			0	0.00
Ret. Fan Heat		0	0	0.00
Duct Heat Pkup		0	0	0.00
Reheat at Design			0	0.00
Grand Total ==>	1,235	0	1,235	100.00

CLG SPACE PEAK

Mo/Hr: 7/16
OADB: 89

	Space Sensible Btu/h	Percent Of Total (%)
Envelope Loads		
Skylite Solar	0	0.00
Skylite Cond	0	0.00
Roof Cond	126	13.61
Glass Solar	111	11.96
Glass Cond	33	3.53
Wall Cond	221	23.89
Partition	0	0.00
Exposed Floor	0	0.00
Infiltration	162	17.48
Sub Total ==>	651	70.47
Internal Loads		
Lights	273	29.53
People	0	0.00
Misc	0	0.00
Sub Total ==>	273	29.53
Ceiling Load	0	0.00
Ventilation Load	0	0.00
Ov/Undr Sizing	0	0.00
Grand Total ==>	925	100.00

HEATING COIL PEAK

Mo/Hr: 13/1
OADB: 15

	Space Peak Space Sens Btu/h	Coil Peak Tot Sens Btu/h	Percent Of Total (%)
Envelope Loads			
Skylite Solar	0	0	0.00
Skylite Cond	0	0	0.00
Roof Cond	-283	-283	17.82
Glass Solar	0	0	0.00
Glass Cond	-144	-144	9.06
Wall Cond	-484	-484	30.46
Partition	0	0	0.00
Exposed Floor	0	0	0.00
Infiltration	-678	-678	42.66
Sub Total ==>	-1,589	-1,589	100.00
Internal Loads			
Lights	0	0	0.00
People	0	0	0.00
Misc	0	0	0.00
Sub Total ==>	0	0	0.00
Ceiling Load	0	0	0.00
Ventilation Load	0	0	0.00
Ov/Undr Sizing	0	0	0.00
OA Preheat Diff.	0	0	0.00
RA Preheat Diff.	0	0	0.00
Additional Reheat	0	0	0.00
System Plenum Heat	0	0	0.00
Grand Total ==>	-1,589	-1,589	100.00

TEMPERATURES

	Cooling	Heating
SADB	55.1	106.2
Plenum	75.0	72.0
Return	75.0	72.0
Ret/OA	75.0	72.0
Fn MtrTD	0.0	0.0
Fn BldTD	0.0	0.0
Fn Frict	0.0	0.0

AIRFLOWS

	Cooling	Heating
Vent	0	0
Infil	11	11
Supply	42	42
MinStop/Rh	0	0
Return	52	52
Exhaust	11	11
Rm Exh	0	0
Auxil	0	0

ENGINEERING CKS

	Cooling	Heating
% OA	0.0	0.0
cfm/ft²	0.52	0.52
cfm/ton	404.74	
ft²/ton	777.11	
Btu/hr-ft²	15.44	-19.86
No. People	0	

AREAS

	Gross Total	Glass ft²	Glass (%)
Floor	80		
Part	0		
ExFlr	0		
Roof	80,	0	
Wall	80	4	5

COOLING COIL SELECTION

	Total Capacity ton	Total Capacity MBh	Sens Cap. MBh	Coil Airflow cfm	Enter DB/WB/HR °F	Enter DB/WB/HR °F	Enter DB/WB/HR gr/lb	Leave DB/WB/HR °F	Leave DB/WB/HR °F	Leave DB/WB/HR gr/lb
Main Clg	0.1	1.2	0.9	42	75.0	62.6	65.0	55.1	52.4	54.4
Aux Clg	0.0	0.0	0.0	0	0.0	0.0	0.0	0.0	0.0	0.0
Opt Vent	0.0	0.0	0.0	0	0.0	0.0	0.0	0.0	0.0	0.0
Total	0.1	1.2								

HEATING COIL SELECTION

	Capacity MBh	Coil Airflow cfm	Ent °F	Lvg °F
Main Htg	-1.6	42	72.0	106.2
Aux Htg	0.0	0	0.0	0.0
Preheat	0.0	0	0.0	0.0
Humidif	0.0	0	0.0	0.0
Opt Vent	0.0	0	0.0	0.0
Total	-1.6			

Room Checksums

Living_room

COOLING COIL PEAK
Peaked at Time: Mo/Hr: 9/13
Outside Air: OADB/WB/HR: 79/68/88

	Space Sens.+Lat Btu/h	Plenum Sens.+Lat Btu/h	Net Total Btu/h	Percent Of Total (%)
Envelope Loads				
Skylite Solar	0	0	0	0.00
Skylite Cond	0	0	0	0.00
Roof Cond	30	0	30	0.49
Glass Solar	4,649	0	4,649	74.41
Glass Cond	75	0	75	1.21
Wall Cond	573	0	573	9.18
Partition	0		0	0.00
Exposed Floor	0		0	0.00
Infiltration	476		476	7.62
Sub Total ==>	5,805	0	5,805	92.90
Internal Loads				
Lights	444	0	444	7.10
People	0		0	0.00
Misc	0	0	0	0.00
Sub Total ==>	444		444	7.10
Ceiling Load	0	0	0	0.00
Ventilation Load	0	0	0	0.00
Ov/Undr Sizing	0	0	0	0.00
Exhaust Heat	0	0	0	0.00
Sup. Fan Heat		0	0	0.00
Ret. Fan Heat		0	0	0.00
Duct Heat Pkup		0	0	0.00
Reheat at Design		0	0	0.00
Grand Total ==>	6,248	0	6,248	100.00

CLG SPACE PEAK
Mo/Hr: 10/13
OADB: 70

	Space Peak Space Sensible Btu/h	Percent Of Total (%)
Envelope Loads		
Skylite Solar	0	0.00
Skylite Cond	0	0.00
Roof Cond	-80	-1.34
Glass Solar	5,298	89.03
Glass Cond	-83	-1.39
Wall Cond	461	7.75
Partition	0	0.00
Exposed Floor	0	0.00
Infiltration	-89	-1.49
Sub Total ==>	5,508	92.54
Internal Loads		
Lights	444	7.46
People	0	0.00
Misc	0	0.00
Sub Total ==>	444	7.46
Ceiling Load	0	0.00
Ventilation Load	0	0.00
Ov/Undr Sizing		
Exhaust Heat		
OA Preheat Diff.		
RA Preheat Diff.		
Additional Reheat		
System Plenum Heat		
Grand Total ==>	5,951	100.00

HEATING COIL PEAK
Mo/Hr: 13/1
OADB: 15

	Space Peak Space Sens Btu/h	Coil Peak Tot Sens Of Total Btu/h	Percent (%)
Envelope Loads			
Skylite Solar	0	0	0.00
Skylite Cond	0	0	0.00
Roof Cond	-460	-460	12.70
Glass Solar	0	0	0.00
Glass Cond	-1,080	-1,080	29.82
Wall Cond	-981	-981	27.07
Partition	0	0	0.00
Exposed Floor	0		0.00
Infiltration	-1,101	-1,101	30.41
Sub Total ==>	-3,622	-3,622	100.00
Internal Loads			
Lights	0	0	0.00
People	0	0	0.00
Misc	0	0	0.00
Sub Total ==>	0	0	0.00
Ceiling Load	0	0	0.00
Ventilation Load	0	0	0.00
Exhaust Heat	0	0	0.00
OA Preheat Diff.	0	0	0.00
RA Preheat Diff.	0	0	0.00
Additional Reheat	0	0	0.00
System Plenum Heat	0	0	0.00
Grand Total ==>		-3,622	100.00

TEMPERATURES

	Cooling	Heating
SADB	65.0	78.1
Plenum	75.0	72.0
Return	75.0	72.0
Ret/OA	75.0	72.0
Fn MtrTD	0.0	0.0
Fn BldTD	0.0	0.0
Fn Frict	0.0	0.0

AIRFLOWS

	Cooling	Heating
Vent	0	0
Infil	17	17
Supply	534	534
MinStop/Rh	0	0
Return	551	551
Exhaust	17	17
Rm Exh	0	0
Auxil	0	0

ENGINEERING CKS

	Cooling	Heating
% OA	0.0	0.0
cfm/ft²	4.11	4.11
cfm/ton	1,025.33	
ft²/ton	249.67	
Btu/hr·ft²	48.06	-27.86
No. People	0	

AREAS

	Gross Total	Glass ft²	Glass (%)
Floor	130		
Part	0		
ExFlr	0		
Roof	130	0	0
Wall	184	30	16

COOLING COIL SELECTION

	Total Capacity ton	MBh	Sens Cap. MBh	Coil Airflow cfm	Enter DB/WB/HR °F/°F/gr/lb	Leave DB/WB/HR °F/°F/gr/lb
Main Clg	0.5	6.3	5.9	534	75.0/60.4/55.0	65.0/56.4/54.1
Aux Clg	0.0	0.0	0.0	0	0.0/0.0/0.0	0.0/0.0/0.0
Opt Vent	0.0	0.0	0.0	0	0.0/0.0/0.0	0.0/0.0/0.0
Total	0.5	6.3				

HEATING COIL SELECTION

	Capacity MBh	Coil Airflow cfm	Ent °F	Lvg °F
Main Htg	-3.6	534	72.0	78.1
Aux Htg	0.0	0	0.0	0.0
Preheat	0.0	0	0.0	0.0
Humidif	0.0	0	0.0	0.0
Opt Vent	0.0	0	0.0	0.0
Total	-3.6			

Room Checksums

Bath_1

COOLING COIL PEAK

Peaked at Time: Mo/Hr: 8 / 16
Outside Air: OADB/WB/HR: 88 / 75 / 113

	Space Sens. + Lat. Btu/h	Plenum Sens. + Lat Btu/h	Net Total Btu/h	Percent Of Total (%)
Envelope Loads				
Skylite Solar	0	0	0	0.00
Skylite Cond	0	0	0	0.00
Roof Cond	68	0	68	8.72
Glass Solar	0	0	0	0.00
Glass Cond	0	0	0	0.00
Wall Cond	215	0	215	27.79
Partition	0		0	0.00
Exposed Floor	0		0	0.00
Infiltration	322		322	41.47
Sub Total ==>	605	0	605	77.99
Internal Loads				
Lights	171	0	171	22.01
People	0	0	0	0.00
Misc	0	0	0	0.00
Sub Total ==>	171	0	171	22.01
Ceiling Load	0	0	0	0.00
Ventilation Load	0	0	0	0.00
Ov/Undr Sizing	0		0	0.00
Exhaust Heat	0	0	0	0.00
Sup. Fan Heat			0	0.00
Ret. Fan Heat	0	0	0	0.00
Duct Heat Pkup	0		0	0.00
Reheat at Design			0	0.00
Grand Total ==>	775	0	775	100.00

CLG SPACE PEAK

Mo/Hr: 7 / 16
OADB: 89

	Space Sensible Btu/h	Percent Of Total (%)
Envelope Loads		
Skylite Solar	0	0.00
Skylite Cond	0	0.00
Roof Cond	79	13.50
Glass Solar	0	0.00
Glass Cond	0	0.00
Wall Cond	232	39.89
Partition	0	0.00
Exposed Floor	0	0.00
Infiltration	101	17.33
Sub Total ==>	412	70.72
Internal Loads		
Lights	171	29.28
People	0	0.00
Misc	0	0.00
Sub Total ==>	171	29.28
Ceiling Load	0	0.00
Ventilation Load	0	0.00
Exhaust Heat	0	0.00
OA Preheat Diff.		
RA Preheat Diff.		
Additional Reheat		
System Plenum Heat		
Grand Total ==>	583	100.00

HEATING COIL PEAK

Mo/Hr: 13 / 1
OADB: 15

	Space Peak Space Sens Btu/h	Coil Peak Tot Sens Btu/h	Percent Of Total (%)
Envelope Loads			
Skylite Solar	0	0	0.00
Skylite Cond	0	0	0.00
Roof Cond	-177	-177	15.94
Glass Solar	0	0	0.00
Glass Cond	0	0	0.00
Wall Cond	-509	-509	45.90
Partition	0	0	0.00
Exposed Floor	0	0	0.00
Infiltration	-424	-424	38.17
Sub Total ==>	-1,110	-1,110	100.00
Internal Loads			
Lights	0	0	0.00
People	0	0	0.00
Misc	0	0	0.00
Sub Total ==>	0	0	0.00
Ceiling Load	0	0	0.00
Ventilation Load	0	0	0.00
Ov/Undr Sizing	0	0	0.00
Exhaust Heat	0	0	0.00
OA Preheat Diff.	0	0	0.00
RA Preheat Diff.	0	0	0.00
Additional Reheat	0	0	0.00
System Plenum Heat	0	0	0.00
Grand Total ==>	-1,110	-1,110	100.00

TEMPERATURES

	Cooling	Heating
SADB	55.2	109.8
Plenum	75.0	72.0
Return	75.0	72.0
Ret/OA	75.0	72.0
Fn MtrTD	0.0	0.0
Fn BldTD	0.0	0.0
Fn Frict	0.0	0.0

AIRFLOWS

	Cooling	Heating
Vent	0	0
Infil	7	7
Supply	26	26
MinStop/Rh	0	0
Return	33	33
Exhaust	7	7
Rm Exh	0	0
Auxil	0	0

ENGINEERING CKS

	Cooling	Heating
% OA	0.0	0.0
cfm/ft²	0.53	0.53
cfm/ton	407.78	
ft²/ton	773.91	
Btu/hr·ft²	15.51	
No. People	0	

HEATING COIL SELECTION

	Capacity MBh	Coil Airflow cfm	Ent °F	Lvg °F
Main Htg	-1.1	26	72.0	109.8
Aux Htg	0.0	0	0.0	0.0
Preheat	0.0	0	0.0	0.0
Humidif	0.0	0	0.0	0.0
Opt Vent	0.0	0	0.0	0.0
Total	-1.1			

COOLING COIL SELECTION

	Total Capacity ton	MBh	Sens Cap. MBh	Coil Airflow cfm	Enter DB/WB/HR °F	°F	gr/lb	Leave DB/WB/HR °F	°F	gr/lb
Main Clg	0.1	0.8	0.6	26	75.0	62.6	65.0	55.2	52.5	54.6
Aux Clg	0.0	0.0	0.0	0	0.0	0.0	0.0	0.0	0.0	0.0
Opt Vent	0.0	0.0	0.0	0	0.0	0.0	0.0	0.0	0.0	0.0
Total	0.1	0.8	0.8							

AREAS

	Gross Total	Glass ft²	(%)
Floor	50	0	0
Part	0		
ExFlr	0		
Roof	50		
Wall	80	0	0

Room Checksums

Bath_2

COOLING COIL PEAK

Peaked at Time: Mo/Hr: 8 / 15
Outside Air: OADB/WB/HR: 88 / 76 / 115

	Space Sens. + Lat. Btu/h	Plenum Sens. + Lat Btu/h	Net Total Btu/h	Percent Of Total (%)
Envelope Loads				
Skylite Solar	0	0	0	0.00
Skylite Cond	0	0	0	0.00
Roof Cond	47	0	47	10.45
Glass Solar	0	0	0	0.00
Glass Cond	0	0	0	0.00
Wall Cond	0	0	0	0.00
Partition	0		0	0.00
Exposed Floor	0		0	0.00
Infiltration	265		265	59.09
Sub Total ==>	312	0	312	69.54
Internal Loads				
Lights	137		137	30.46
People	0	0	0	0.00
Misc	0		0	0.00
Sub Total ==>	137		137	30.46
Ceiling Load	0	0	0	0.00
Ventilation Load	0	0	0	0.00
Ov/Undr Sizing		0	0	0.00
Exhaust Heat		0	0	0.00
Sup. Fan Heat			0	0.00
Ret. Fan Heat		0	0	0.00
Duct Heat Pkup		0	0	0.00
Reheat at Design		0	0	0.00
Grand Total ==>	448	0	448	100.00

CLG SPACE PEAK

Mo/Hr: 7 / 17
OADB: 88

	Space Sensible Btu/h	Percent Of Total (%)
Envelope Loads		
Skylite Solar	0	0.00
Skylite Cond	0	0.00
Roof Cond	71	25.18
Glass Solar	0	0.00
Glass Cond	0	0.00
Wall Cond	0	0.00
Partition	0	0.00
Exposed Floor	0	0.00
Infiltration	74	26.37
Sub Total ==>	145	51.55
Internal Loads		
Lights	137	48.45
People	0	0.00
Misc	0	0.00
Sub Total ==>	137	48.45
Ceiling Load	0	0.00
Ventilation Load	0	0.00
Ov/Undr Sizing	0	0.00
Grand Total ==>	282	100.00

HEATING COIL PEAK

Mo/Hr: 13 / 1
OADB: 15

	Space Peak Space Sens Btu/h	Coil Peak Tot Sens Btu/h	Percent Of Total (%)
Envelope Loads			
Skylite Solar	0	0	0.00
Skylite Cond	0	0	0.00
Roof Cond	-142	-142	29.46
Glass Solar	0	0	0.00
Glass Cond	0	0	0.00
Wall Cond	0	0	0.00
Partition	0	0	0.00
Exposed Floor	0	0	0.00
Infiltration	-339	-339	70.54
Sub Total ==>	-480	-480	100.00
Internal Loads			
Lights	0	0	0.00
People	0	0	0.00
Misc	0	0	0.00
Sub Total ==>	0	0	0.00
Ceiling Load	0	0	0.00
Ventilation Load	0	0	0.00
Ov/Undr Sizing		0	0.00
Exhaust Heat		0	0.00
OA Preheat Diff.		0	0.00
RA Preheat Diff.		0	0.00
Additional Reheat		0	0.00
System Plenum Heat		0	0.00
Grand Total ==>		-480	100.00

TEMPERATURES

	Cooling	Heating
SADB	50.7	113.4
Plenum	75.0	72.0
Return	75.0	72.0
Ret/OA	0.0	0.0
Fn MtrTD	0.0	0.0
Fn BldTD	0.0	0.0
Fn Frict	0.0	

AIRFLOWS

	Cooling	Heating
Vent	0	0
Infil	5	5
Supply	10	10
MinStop/Rh	0	0
Return	16	16
Exhaust	5	5
Rm Exh	0	0
Auxil	0	0

ENGINEERING CKS

	Cooling	Heating
% OA	0.0	0.0
cfm/ft²	0.26	0.26
cfm/ton	278.82	
ft²/ton	1,071.07	
Btu/hr-ft²	11.20	-12.01
No. People	0	

AREAS

	Gross Total	Glass ft²	(%)
Floor	40		
Part	0		
ExFlr	0		
Roof	40	0	0
Wall	0	0	0

COOLING COIL SELECTION

	Total Capacity ton	MBh	Sens Cap. MBh	Coil Airflow cfm	Enter DB °F	WB °F	HR gr/lb	Leave DB °F	WB °F	HR gr/lb
Main Clg	0.0	0.5	0.3	10	75.0	62.6	65.0	50.7	47.1	42.3
Aux Clg	0.0	0.0	0.0	0	0.0	0.0	0.0	0.0	0.0	0.0
Opt Vent	0.0	0.0	0.0	0	0.0	0.0	0.0	0.0	0.0	0.0
Total	0.0	0.5								

HEATING COIL SELECTION

	Capacity MBh	Coil Airflow cfm	Ent °F	Lvg °F
Main Htg	-0.5	10	72.0	113.4
Aux Htg	0.0	0	0.0	0.0
Preheat	0.0	0	0.0	0.0
Humidif	0.0		0.0	0.0
Opt Vent	0.0		0.0	0.0
Total	-0.5			

System Checksums

System - 1   **Fan Coil**

COOLING COIL PEAK

Peaked at Time: Mo/Hr: 8 / 13
Outside Air: OADB/WB/HR: 87 / 75 / 111

	Space Sens. + Lat. Btu/h	Plenum Sens. + Lat Btu/h	Net Total Btu/h	Percent Of Total (%)
Envelope Loads				
Skylite Solar	0	0	0	0.00
Skylite Cond	0	0	0	0.00
Roof Cond	769	0	769	1.95
Glass Solar	14,825	0	14,825	37.71
Glass Cond	1,298	0	1,298	3.30
Wall Cond	5,583	0	5,583	14.20
Partition	0		0	0.00
Exposed Floor	0		0	0.00
Infiltration	8,353		8,353	21.24
Sub Total ==>	30,827	0	30,827	78.41
Internal Loads				
Lights	2,904	0	2,904	7.39
People	1,800	0	1,800	4.58
Misc	0	0	0	0.00
Sub Total ==>	4,704	0	4,704	11.97
Ceiling Load	0	0	0	0.00
Ventilation Load	0	0	3,785	9.63
Ov/Undr Sizing	0		0	0.00
Exhaust Heat		0	0	0.00
Sup. Fan Heat			0	0.00
Ret. Fan Heat	0	0	0	0.00
Duct Heat Pkup		0	0	0.00
Reheat at Design			0	0.00
Grand Total ==>	35,531	0	39,317	100.00

CLG SPACE PEAK

Mo/Hr: 8 / 13
OADB: 87

	Space Sensible Btu/h	Percent Of Total (%)
Envelope Loads		
Skylite Solar	0	0.00
Skylite Cond	0	0.00
Roof Cond	463	1.44
Glass Solar	19,833	61.94
Glass Cond	435	1.36
Wall Cond	5,990	18.71
Partition	0	0.00
Exposed Floor	0	0.00
Infiltration	1,395	4.36
Sub Total ==>	28,115	87.81
Internal Loads		
Lights	2,904	9.07
People	1,000	3.12
Misc	0	0.00
Sub Total ==>	3,904	12.19
Ceiling Load	0	0.00
Ventilation Load	0	0.00
Ov/Undr Sizing	0	0.00
Grand Total ==>	32,020	100.00

HEATING COIL PEAK

Mo/Hr: 13 / 1
OADB: 15

	Space Peak Space Sens Btu/h	Coil Peak Tot Sens Btu/h	Percent Of Total (%)
Envelope Loads			
Skylite Solar	0	0	0.00
Skylite Cond	0	0	0.00
Roof Cond	-3,011	-3,011	9.23
Glass Solar	0	0	0.00
Glass Cond	-6,659	-6,659	20.41
Wall Cond	-9,239	-9,239	28.31
Partition	0	0	0.00
Exposed Floor	0	0	0.00
Infiltration	-11,276	-11,276	34.56
Sub Total ==>	-30,185	-30,185	92.51
Internal Loads			
Lights	1,638	1,638	-5.02
People	1,000	1,000	-3.06
Misc	0	0	0.00
Sub Total ==>	2,638	2,638	-8.09
Ceiling Load	0	0	0.00
Ventilation Load	0	-5,083	15.58
Ov/Undr Sizing	0	0	0.00
Exhaust Heat		0	0.00
OA Preheat Diff.		0	0.00
RA Preheat Diff.		0	0.00
Additional Reheat		0	0.00
Grand Total ==>	-27,547	-32,630	100.00

TEMPERATURES

	Cooling	Heating
SADB	60.3	84.7
Plenum	75.0	72.0
Return	75.0	72.0
Ret/OA	75.5	69.7
Fn MtrTD	0.0	0.0
Fn BldTD	0.0	0.0
Fn Frict	0.0	0.0

AIRFLOWS

	Cooling	Heating
Vent	80	80
Infil	177	177
Supply	1,948	1,948
MinStop/Rh	0	0
Return	2,125	2,125
Exhaust	257	257
Rm Exh	0	0
Auxiliary	0	0

ENGINEERING CKS

	Cooling	Heating
% OA	4.1	4.1
cfm/ft²	1.46	1.46
cfm/ton	594.54	
ft²/ton	406.24	
Btu/hr-ft²	29.54	
No. People	4	

COOLING COIL SELECTION

	Total Capacity ton	MBh	Sens Cap. MBh	Coil Airflow cfm	Enter DB/WB/HR °F °F gr/lb			Leave DB/WB/HR °F °F gr/lb		
Main Clg	3.3	39.3	29.7	1,948	75.5	62.7	64.7	60.3	56.0	60.2
Aux Clg	0.0	0.0	0.0	0	0.0	0.0	0.0	0.0	0.0	0.0
Opt Vent	0.0	0.0	0.0	0	0.0	0.0	0.0	0.0	0.0	0.0
Total	**3.3**	**39.3**								

HEATING COIL SELECTION

	Capacity MBh	Coil Airflow cfm	Ent °F	Lvg °F
Main Htg	-32.6	1,948	69.7	84.7
Aux Htg	0.0	0	0.0	0.0
Preheat	0.0	0	0.0	0.0
Humidif	0.0	0	0.0	0.0
Opt Vent	0.0	0	0.0	0.0
Total	**-32.6**			

AREAS

	Gross Total	Glass ft²	(%)
Floor	1,331		
Part	0		
ExFlr			
Roof	851	0	0
Wall	1,636	185	11

System Component Selection Summary

System Description: System - 1
System Type: Fan Coil
Number of Zones: 10
Number of Rooms: 10

Component	Sizing Method	Location	Quantity
Cooling			
Main Clg Coil	Block	Room	10
Primary Clg Fan	Peak	Room	10
Heating			
Main Htg Coil	Peak	Room	10
Miscellaneous			
System Exhaust Fan	Vent+Inf-RmExh	System	1
Return Fan	Return Airflow	System	1

Coil Location — Cooling Coil Selection

System	Zone	Room	Component	Time Of Peak Mo/Hr	Total Capacity ton	MBh	Sensible Capacity MBh	Airflow At Coil Peak cfm	Enter DB °F	WB °F	HR gr/lb	Leave DB °F	WB °F	HR gr/lb
		Basement	Main Clg Coil	8/14	0.7	7.8	5.6	217	75.0	62.6	65.0	51.4	49.9	51.0
		Bath_1	Main Clg Coil	8/16	0.1	0.8	0.6	26	75.0	62.6	65.0	55.2	52.5	54.6
		Bath_2	Main Clg Coil	8/15	0.0	0.5	0.3	10	75.0	62.6	65.0	50.7	47.1	42.3
		Bedroom-1	Main Clg Coil	8/14	0.5	5.7	3.3	119	79.3	67.3	81.4	53.3	51.7	54.8
		Bedroom-2	Main Clg Coil	8/13	0.5	6.3	4.9	270	75.9	63.6	68.4	58.8	55.9	62.3
		Bedroom-3	Main Clg Coil	8/13	0.4	5.0	3.5	163	76.4	62.3	61.7	55.0	51.7	51.7
		Dining Room	Main Clg Coil	6/18	0.3	3.3	3.2	207	75.0	62.6	65.0	61.3	57.3	63.8
		Entrance	Main Clg Coil	10/12	0.3	4.0	4.0	359	75.0	60.5	55.6	65.0	56.7	55.6
		Kitchen	Main Clg Coil	8/15	0.1	1.2	0.9	42	75.0	62.6	65.0	55.1	52.4	54.4
		Living_room	Main Clg Coil	9/13	0.5	6.3	5.9	534	75.0	60.4	55.0	65.0	56.4	54.1

Coil Location — Heating Coil Selection

System	Zone	Room	Component	Total Capacity MBh	Airflow cfm	Entering DB °F	Entering HR gr/lb	Leaving DB °F	Leaving HR gr/lb
		Basement	Main Htg Coil	-7.3	217	72.0		102.2	
		Bath_1	Main Htg Coil	-1.1	26	72.0		109.8	
		Bath_2	Main Htg Coil	-0.5	10	72.0		113.4	
		Bedroom-1	Main Htg Coil	-5.6	119	52.9		94.8	
		Bedroom-2	Main Htg Coil	-4.6	270	67.8		82.9	
		Bedroom-3	Main Htg Coil	-3.2	163	65.0		82.6	
		Dining Room	Main Htg Coil	-3.5	207	72.0		87.0	
		Entrance	Main Htg Coil	-1.7	359	72.0		76.3	
		Kitchen	Main Htg Coil	-1.6	42	72.0		106.2	
		Living_room	Main Htg Coil	-3.6	534	72.0		78.1	

Component Location — Miscellaneous Component Selection

System	Zone	Room	Component	Design Airflow cfm	Ach/hr	Outside Air %	SADB Clg °F	SADB Htg °F	Minimum Airflow cfm

System Component Selection Summary

Component Location			Miscellaneous Component Selection					
System	Zone	Room	Component	Design Airflow cfm	Design Airflow Ach/hr	Outside Air %	SADB Clg °F	SADB Htg °F	Minimum Airflow cfm
System - 1									
System - 1									
			System Exhaust Fan	257					
			Return Fan	2,125					
		Basement	Diffuser	217	3.4	0.0	51.4	102.2	
		Basement	Primary Fan	217	3.4	0.0	51.4		
		Bath_1	Primary Fan	26	4.0	0.0	55.2		
		Bath_1	Diffuser	26	4.0	0.0	55.2	109.8	
		Bath_2	Primary Fan	10	2.0	0.0	50.7		
		Bath_2	Diffuser	10	2.0	0.0	50.7	113.4	
		Bedroom-1	Diffuser	119	6.3	33.5	53.3	94.8	
		Bedroom-1	Primary Fan	119	6.3	33.5	53.3		
		Bedroom-2	Diffuser	270	14.2	7.4	58.8	82.9	
		Bedroom-2	Primary Fan	270	14.2	7.4	58.8		
		Bedroom-3	Primary Fan	163	12.2	12.3	55.0		
		Bedroom-3	Diffuser	163	12.2	12.3	55.0	82.6	
		Dining Room	Diffuser	207	15.6	0.0	61.3	87.0	
		Dining Room	Primary Fan	207	15.6	0.0	61.3		
		Entrance	Primary Fan	359	41.4	0.0	65.0		
		Entrance	Diffuser	359	41.4	0.0	65.0	76.3	
		Kitchen	Diffuser	42	3.9	0.0	55.1	106.2	
		Kitchen	Primary Fan	42	3.9	0.0	55.1		
		Living_room	Primary Fan	534	30.8	0.0	65.0		
		Living_room	Diffuser	534	30.8	0.0	65.0	78.1	

Load / Airflow Summary

Description **		Floor Area ft²	People #	Coil Cooling Sensible Btu/h	Coil Cooling Total Btu/h	Space Design Max SA cfm	Air Changes ach/hr	VAV Minimum SA cfm	Main Coil Heating Sensible Btu/h	Heating Fan Max SA cfm	Percent OA Clg	Percent OA Htg	ASHRAE 62-89 OA fraction
Dining Room	Rm/Zn Tot	100	0.0	3,164	3,329	207	15.55	0	-3,464	207	0.0	0.0	
Kitchen	Rm/Zn Tot	80	0.0	863	1,235	42	3.91	0	-1,589	42	0.0	0.0	
Bath_1	Rm/Zn Tot	50	0.0	549	775	26	3.95	0	-1,110	26	0.0	0.0	
Bedroom-1	Rm/Zn Tot	143	2.0	3,275	5,710	119	6.25	0	-5,574	119	33.5	33.5	
Bedroom-2	Rm/Zn Tot	143	1.0	4,850	6,319	270	14.16	0	-4,553	270	7.4	7.4	
Bedroom-3	Rm/Zn Tot	100	1.0	3,513	5,035	163	12.24	0	-3,205	163	12.3	12.3	
Entrance	Rm/Zn Tot	65	0.0	4,001	4,003	359	41.41	0	-1,734	359	0.0	0.0	
Living_room	Rm/Zn Tot	130	0.0	5,853	6,248	534	30.80	0	-3,622	534	0.0	0.0	
Basement	Rm/Zn Tot	480	0.0	5,629	7,834	217	3.39	0	-7,299	217	0.0	0.0	
Bath_2	Rm/Zn Tot	40	0.0	262	448	10	1.95	0	-480	10	0.0	0.0	
System - 1	Sys Tot/Ave	1,331	4.0	31,958	40,938	1,948			-32,630	1,948	4.1	4.1	
System - 1	Sys Block	1,331	4.0	29,734	39,317	1,948			-32,630	1,948	4.1	4.1	

ENGINEERING CHECKS

Description	Type	COOLING					HEATING			Floor Area ft²
		% OA	cfm/ft²	cfm/ton	ft/ton	Btu/hr-ft²	% OA	cfm/ft²	Btu/hr-ft²	
Dining Room	Zone	0.00	2.07	747.3	360.5	33.29	0.00	2.07	-34.64	100
Kitchen	Zone	0.00	0.52	404.7	777.1	15.44	0.00	0.52	-19.86	80
Bath_1	Zone	0.00	0.53	407.8	773.9	15.51	0.00	0.53	-22.20	50
Bedroom-1	Zone	33.54	0.83	250.6	300.5	39.93	33.54	0.83	-38.98	143
Bedroom-2	Zone	7.41	1.89	512.7	271.6	44.19	7.41	1.89	-31.84	143
Bedroom-3	Zone	12.25	1.63	389.0	238.3	50.35	12.25	1.63	-32.05	100
Entrance	Zone	0.00	5.52	1,075.9	194.9	61.59	0.00	5.52	-26.68	65
Living_room	Zone	0.00	4.11	1,025.3	249.7	48.06	0.00	4.11	-27.86	130
Basement	Zone	0.00	0.45	332.4	735.2	16.32	0.00	0.45	-15.21	480
Bath_2	Zone	0.00	0.26	278.8	1,071.1	11.20	0.00	0.26	-12.01	40
System - 1	System - Fan Coil	4.11	1.46	594.5	406.2	29.54	4.11	1.46	-24.52	1,331

PEAK COOLING LOADS
MAIN SYSTEM

Description		Floor Area ft²	Peak Time Mo/Hr	OA Cond. DB/WB °F		Room Dry Bulb °F	SPACE Supply Dry Bulb °F	Space Air Flow cfm	Space Sensible Load Btu/h	Space Latent Load Btu/h	Peak Time Mo/Hr	OA Cond. DB/WB °F		Supply Dry Bulb °F	COIL Coil Air Flow cfm	Coil Sensible Load Btu/h	Coil Latent Load Btu/h
Dining Room	Rm/Zn Tot	100	6/18	83	69	75	61.3	207	3,164	165	6/18	83	69	61.3	207	3,164	165
Kitchen	Rm/Zn Tot	80	7/16	89	73	75	55.1	42	925	237	8/15	88	76	56.4	42	863	373
Bath_1	Rm/Zn Tot	50	7/16	89	73	75	55.2	26	583	148	8/16	88	75	56.3	26	549	226
Bedroom-1	Rm/Zn Tot	143	7/13	87	72	75	53.3	119	2,886	767	8/14	88	76	54.7	119	3,275	2,435
Bedroom-2	Rm/Zn Tot	143	9/12	78	68	75	58.7	270	4,891	492	8/13	87	75	59.8	270	4,850	1,469
Bedroom-3	Rm/Zn Tot	100	10/13	70	59	75	55.0	163	3,639	205	8/13	87	75	57.1	163	3,513	1,522
Entrance	Rm/Zn Tot	65	10/12	69	58	75	65.0	359	4,001	2	10/12	69	58	65.0	359	4,001	2
Living_room	Rm/Zn Tot	130	10/13	70	59	75	65.0	534	5,951	4	9/13	79	68	65.2	534	5,853	395
Basement	Rm/Zn Tot	480	8/13	87	75	75	51.4	217	5,699	2,079	8/14	88	76	51.7	217	5,629	2,205
Bath_2	Rm/Zn Tot	40	7/17	88	72	75	50.7	10	282	108	8/15	88	76	52.4	10	262	186
System - 1	Sys Tot/Ave	1,331		87	75	75	60.3	1,948	32,020	4,207		87	75	60.8	1,948	31,958	8,980
System - 1	Sys Block	1,331	8/13	87	75	75	60.3	1,948	28,691	6,840	8/13	87	75	61.8	1,948	29,734	9,583

PEAK HEATING LOADS
MAIN SYSTEM

Description		Floor Area ft²	Peak Time Mo/Hr	OA Cond. DB/WB °F		Room Dry Bulb °F	SPACE Supply Dry Bulb °F	Space Air Flow cfm	Space Sensible Load Btu/h	Peak Time Mo/Hr	OA Cond. DB/WB °F		Supply Dry Bulb °F	COIL Coil Air Flow cfm	Coil Sensible Load Btu/h
Dining Room	Rm/Zn Tot	100	13/1	15	10	72	87.0	207	-3,464	13/1	15	10	87.0	207	-3,464
Kitchen	Rm/Zn Tot	80	13/1	15	10	72	106.2	42	-1,589	13/1	15	10	106.2	42	-1,589
Bath_1	Rm/Zn Tot	50	13/1	15	10	72	109.8	26	-1,110	13/1	15	10	109.8	26	-1,110
Bedroom-1	Rm/Zn Tot	143	13/1	15	10	72	94.8	119	-3,033	13/1	15	10	94.8	119	-5,574
Bedroom-2	Rm/Zn Tot	143	13/1	15	10	72	82.9	270	-3,283	13/1	15	10	82.9	270	-4,553
Bedroom-3	Rm/Zn Tot	100	13/1	15	10	72	82.6	163	-1,934	13/1	15	10	82.6	163	-3,205
Entrance	Rm/Zn Tot	65	13/1	15	10	72	76.3	359	-1,734	13/1	15	10	76.3	359	-1,734
Living_room	Rm/Zn Tot	130	13/1	15	10	72	78.1	534	-3,622	13/1	15	10	78.1	534	-3,622
Basement	Rm/Zn Tot	480	13/1	15	10	72	102.2	217	-7,299	13/1	15	10	102.2	217	-7,299
Bath_2	Rm/Zn Tot	40	13/1	15	10	72	113.4	10	-480	13/1	15	10	113.4	10	-480
System - 1	Sys Tot/Ave	1,331		15	10	72	84.7	1,948	-27,547		15	10	84.7	1,948	-32,630
System - 1	Sys Block	1,331	13/1	15	10	72	84.7	1,948	-27,547	13/1	15	10	84.7	1,948	-32,630

DUCT DESIGN

DUCT DESIGN

Introduction

This chapter is adapted mainly from ASHRAE Fundamentals Handbook (2001). Air ducts deliver conditioned air from HVAC units to the space to be conditioned, and, depending on the design, may also bring fresh and recirculated air to the units. Proper design of ducts facilitates distribution of air that is balanced throughout the conditioned space, thereby avoiding areas of under supply as well as over supply. Improper design can additionally lead to excessive noise, discomfort, and adverse health effects. The ducts should be designed so that a proper balance between high flow rates, which cause noise and vibration, and low flow rates, which cause buildup of contaminants in the ducts and pose health risks, is achieved. Interior duct lining and outside insulation can also be used to reduce noise transmitted to the interior space.

Pressure Head and Energy Equation.—A given fluid mass has three components of mechanical energy: kinetic energy (due to motion), potential energy (due to gravity and height), and pressure energy (due to fluid pressure). As this fluid mass travels, the total mechanical energy does not stay conserved along the path of flow and is dissipated due to energy losses. These losses are categorized as two different types: major losses due to presence of friction introduced by duct walls, and the so-called minor losses due to sudden expansions/contractions and fluid mixing in joints, junctions, fittings, equipment, inlets/outlets, and the like. The major friction losses are due to the momentum exchange between molecules and between volumes of adjacent layers moving at different velocities. The layers move at different velocities because of fluid viscosity: the layer next to the duct wall has to be at zero local velocity (no-slip boundary condition) and the successive layers toward the centerline have increasingly higher velocities. In HVAC practice the minor losses are termed dynamic losses.

Considering the average values of the fluid (air in the case of ducts considered in this chapter) velocity, pressure, and height, where the average is taken across the cross-section at a given location along the duct, we can write the energy equation for conservation of mechanical energy in a steady flow:

$$\frac{\rho v_1^2}{2g_c} + p_{s1} + \frac{g}{g_c}\rho z_1 = \qquad (1)$$
$$\frac{\rho v_2^2}{2g_c} + p_{s2} + \frac{g}{g_c}\rho z_2 + \Delta p_{t,1\text{-}2}$$

where v = average duct velocity, fps;

g_c = gravitational constant, 32.2 lb_m-ft/lb_f-sec^2;

p_s = static pressure, lb_f/ft^2;

ρ = density, lb_m/ft^3;

g = acceleration due to gravity, ft/sec^2;

z = elevation, ft; and

$\Delta p_{t\,1\text{-}2}$ = total pressure loss due to friction and dynamic losses between sections 1 and 2, lb_f/ft^2.

The above equation is the conservation of mechanical energy per unit volume, and is so presented to keep the terms in the units of pressure. Sections 1 and 2 are two sections along a single duct system (i.e., no branches and multiple parallel paths for fluid flow). For HVAC ducts through which air flows, the potential energy terms in the energy equation do not play a significant role because of the low density of air.

The kinetic energy term $\dfrac{\rho v^2}{2g_c}$ is the velocity pressure:

$$P_v = \frac{\rho v^2}{2g_c} \qquad (2)$$

The total pressure is given as:

$$P_t = P_v + P_s \qquad (3)$$

The velocity pressure for air can be written as

$$P_v = \rho\left(\frac{v}{4005}\right)^2 \qquad (4)$$

where ρ = density, lb_f/ft^3;

P_v = velocity pressure, in. of water;

P_s = static pressure, in. of water; and

v = average velocity, fpm

Air velocity is calculated by

$$v = \frac{144Q}{A} \qquad (5)$$

where Q = air flow rate, *cfm*;

A = cross-sectional area of duct, in^2; and

v = fluid mean velocity, fpm

In HVAC practice it common to refer to pressure as head, and often head and pressure are used interchangeably. Head is the height of fluid in a column that would give the same pressure at the base of the column as the static pressure. For liquids such as water the head is usually specified in terms of the height of water or other liquid in the column. However, for gases such as air, the height specified is customarily in terms of the equivalent height of water. When such a value is presented, it is usually written as "in. of water" to indicate that the head is not in terms of the height of the flowing fluid, but is in terms of a height of water that would give the same pressure.

To derive the equation in terms of head of the flowing fluid, Equation (1) is divided by $\rho g/g_c$, which will result in:

$$\frac{v_1^2}{2g} + \frac{p_{s1}g_c}{\rho\,g} + z_1 = \frac{v_2^2}{2g} + \frac{p_{s2}g_c}{\rho\,g} + z_2 + h_{t,\,1\text{-}2} \quad (6)$$

where $h_{t,1\text{-}2} = \dfrac{g_c \Delta p_{t,\,1-2}}{\rho g}$ = lost head, ft;

z = static head, ft;

$\dfrac{p_s g_c}{\rho\,g}$ = static pressure head, ft; and

$\dfrac{v^2}{2g}$ = velocity head, ft.

In HVAC systems all gases and liquids are assumed incompressible. The above equations are valid for incompressible fluids. The energy equation has to be complemented by the conservation of mass, which indicates that the mass flow rate at sections 1 and 2 are the same in a continuous single branch duct system. Since the fluid is incompressible, this also indicates that the volume flow rates (equal to the product of velocity and cross-sectional area) are the same at the two sections. If the duct cross-sectional area is constant then the velocities at the two sections are equal.

Friction Loss Analysis.—Friction losses occur along the entire duct length.

For fluid flow in conduits, friction loss can be calculated by the Darcy equation:

$$\Delta p_f = \frac{12fL}{D_h}\rho\left(\frac{V}{1097}\right)^2 \quad (7)$$

where Δp_f = friction losses in terms of total pressure, in. of water;

f = friction factor, dimensionless;

D_h = hydraulic diameter, in.;

V = velocity of air, fpm; and

ρ = density of air, lb_m/ft^3

Within the region of laminar flow (Reynolds numbers less than 2000), friction factor is a function of Reynolds number only $f = 64/Re$. For completely turbulent flow, the friction factor depends on Reynolds number, duct surface roughness, and internal protuberances such as joints. Between the bounding limits of hydraulically smooth behavior and fully rough behavior is a transitional roughness zone where the friction factor depends on both roughness and Reynolds number. In this transitionally rough, turbulent zone the friction factor f is calculated by Colebrook's equation. Colebrook's transition curve

merges asymptotically into the curves representing laminar and completely turbulent flow. Because Colebrook's equation cannot be solved explicitly for f, we use iterative techniques (same as Equation (40) in Chapter 1 and Equation (4) in Chapter 9).

$$\frac{1}{\sqrt{f}} = -2\log\left(\frac{12\varepsilon}{3.7D_h} + \frac{2.51}{R_e\sqrt{f}}\right) \quad (8)$$

where ε = material absolute roughness factor, ft; and

Re = Reynolds number

A simplified formula for calculating friction factor, developed by Altshul (Altshul et al. 1975) and modified by Tsal, is

$$f' = 0.11\left(\frac{12\varepsilon}{D_h} + \frac{68}{R_e}\right)^{0.25}$$

$$f = \begin{cases} f' & \text{for } f' \geq 0.018 \\ 0.85f' + 0.0028 & \text{for } f' < 0.018 \end{cases} \quad (9)$$

Friction factors obtained from the Altshul-Tsal equation are within 1.6% of those obtained by Colebrook's equation. The friction factor is also presented on a Moody Chart (see Fig. 1-10 in Chapter 1.)

Reynolds number (Re) can be calculated by the equation:

$$Re = \frac{D_h V}{7200\nu} \quad (10)$$

where $\nu = (\mu/\rho)$ kinematic viscosity, ft^2/sec.

For standard air, Re can be calculated by

$$Re = 8.56 D_h V \quad (11)$$

Roughness Factors: The roughness factors ε listed in Table 8-2 are recommended for use with the Colebrook or Altshul-Tsal equation. These values include not only material, but also duct construction, joint type, and joint spacing.

Manufacturers' data indicate that absolute roughness for fully extended nonmetallic flexible ducts ranges from 0.0035 to 0.015 ft. For fully extended flexible metallic ducts, absolute roughness ranges from 0.0004 to 0.007 ft. This range covers flexible duct with supporting wire exposed to flow or duct with wire covered by the material.

Table 8-1. Velocity Equivalents of Velocity Pressures

Pressure P_v in. of Water	Velocity V ft/min	Pressure P_v in. of Water	Velocity V ft/min	Pressure P_v in. of Water	Velocity V ft/min	Pressure P_v in. of Water	Velocity V ft/min	Pressure P_v in. of Water	Velocity V ft/min	Pressure P_v in. of Water	Velocity V ft/min	Pressure P_v in. of Water	Velocity V ft/min	Pressure P_v in. of Water	Velocity V ft/min
0.01	400.5	0.43	2626.3	0.85	3692.4	1.27	4513.4	1.69	5206.5	2.11	5817.6	2.53	6370.3	2.95	6878.8
0.02	566.4	0.44	2656.6	0.86	3714.1	1.28	4531.1	1.7	5221.9	2.12	5831.4	2.54	6382.9	2.96	6890.5
0.03	693.7	0.45	2686.6	0.87	3735.6	1.29	4548.8	1.71	5237.2	2.13	5845.1	2.55	6395.5	2.97	6902.1
0.04	801.0	0.46	2716.3	0.88	3757.0	1.30	4566.4	1.72	5252.5	2.14	5858.8	2.56	6408.0	2.98	6913.7
0.05	895.5	0.47	2745.7	0.89	3778.3	1.31	4583.9	1.73	5267.8	2.15	5872.5	2.57	6420.5	2.99	6925.3
0.06	981.0	0.48	2774.7	0.90	3799.5	1.32	4601.4	1.74	5283.0	2.16	5886.1	2.58	6433.0	3.00	6936.9
0.07	1059.6	0.49	2803.5	0.91	3820.5	1.33	4618.8	1.75	5298.1	2.17	5899.7	2.59	6445.4	3.01	6948.4
0.08	1132.8	0.50	2832.0	0.92	3841.5	1.34	4636.1	1.76	5313.2	2.18	5913.3	2.60	6457.9	3.02	6959.9
0.09	1201.5	0.51	2860.1	0.93	3862.4	1.35	4653.4	1.77	5328.3	2.19	5926.9	2.61	6470.3	3.03	6971.5
0.10	1266.5	0.52	2888.0	0.94	3883.0	1.36	4670.6	1.78	5343.3	2.20	5940.4	2.62	6482.7	3.04	6983.0
0.11	1328.3	0.53	2915.7	0.95	3903.6	1.37	4687.7	1.79	5358.3	2.21	5953.9	2.63	6495.0	3.05	6994.4
0.12	1387.4	0.54	2943.1	0.96	3924.1	1.38	4704.8	1.80	5373.3	2.22	5967.3	2.64	6507.4	3.06	7005.9
0.13	1444.0	0.55	2970.2	0.97	3944.5	1.39	4721.8	1.81	5388.2	2.23	5980.7	2.65	6519.7	3.07	7017.3
0.14	1498.5	0.56	2997.1	0.98	3964.7	1.40	4738.8	1.82	5403.0	2.24	5994.1	2.66	6532.0	3.08	7028.7
0.15	1551.1	0.57	3023.7	0.99	3984.9	1.41	4755.7	1.83	5417.9	2.25	6007.5	2.67	6544.2	3.09	7040.1
0.16	1602.0	0.58	3050.1	1.00	4005.0	1.42	4772.5	1.84	5432.6	2.26	6020.8	2.68	6556.5	3.10	7051.5
0.17	1651.3	0.59	3076.3	1.01	4025.0	1.43	4789.3	1.85	5447.4	2.27	6034.1	2.69	6568.7	3.11	7062.9
0.18	1699.2	0.60	3102.3	1.02	4044.9	1.44	4806.0	1.86	5462.1	2.28	6047.4	2.70	6580.9	3.12	7074.2
0.19	1745.7	0.61	3128.0	1.03	4064.6	1.45	4822.7	1.87	5476.8	2.29	6060.7	2.71	6593.1	3.13	7085.6
0.20	1791.1	0.62	3153.5	1.04	4084.3	1.46	4839.3	1.88	5491.4	2.30	6073.9	2.72	6605.2	3.14	7096.9
0.21	1835.3	0.63	3178.9	1.05	4103.9	1.47	4855.8	1.89	5506.0	2.31	6087.1	2.73	6617.3	3.15	7108.2
0.22	1878.5	0.64	3204.0	1.06	4123.4	1.48	4872.3	1.90	5520.5	2.32	6100.2	2.74	6629.5	3.16	7119.4
0.23	1920.7	0.65	3228.9	1.07	4142.8	1.49	4888.7	1.91	5535.0	2.33	6113.4	2.75	6641.5	3.17	7130.7
0.24	1962.0	0.66	3253.7	1.08	4162.1	1.50	4905.1	1.92	5549.5	2.34	6126.5	2.76	6653.6	3.18	7141.9
0.25	2002.5	0.67	3278.2	1.09	4181.3	1.51	4921.4	1.93	5563.9	2.35	6139.5	2.77	6665.6	3.19	7153.2
0.26	2042.2	0.68	3302.6	1.10	4200.5	1.52	4937.7	1.94	5578.3	2.36	6152.6	2.78	6677.7	3.20	7164.4
0.27	2081.1	0.69	3326.8	1.11	4219.5	1.53	4953.9	1.95	5592.7	2.37	6165.6	2.79	6689.7	3.21	7175.5
0.28	2119.2	0.70	3350.8	1.12	4238.5	1.54	4970.1	1.96	5607.0	2.38	6178.6	2.80	6701.6	3.22	7186.7
0.29	2156.8	0.71	3374.7	1.13	4257.4	1.55	4986.2	1.97	5621.3	2.39	6191.6	2.81	6713.6	3.23	7197.9
0.30	2193.6	0.72	3398.4	1.14	4276.2	1.56	5002.2	1.98	5635.5	2.40	6204.5	2.82	6725.5	3.24	7209.0
0.31	2229.9	0.73	3421.9	1.15	4294.9	1.57	5018.3	1.99	5649.7	2.41	6217.4	2.83	6737.5	3.25	7220.1
0.32	2265.6	0.74	3445.2	1.16	4313.5	1.58	5034.2	2.00	5663.9	2.42	6230.3	2.84	6749.3	3.26	7231.2
0.33	2300.7	0.75	3468.4	1.17	4332.1	1.59	5050.1	2.01	5678.1	2.43	6243.2	2.85	6761.2	3.27	7242.3
0.34	2335.3	0.76	3491.5	1.18	4350.5	1.60	5066.0	2.02	5692.2	2.44	6256.0	2.86	6773.1	3.28	7253.4
0.35	2369.4	0.77	3514.4	1.19	4368.9	1.61	5081.8	2.03	5706.2	2.45	6268.8	2.87	6784.9	3.29	7264.4
0.36	2403.0	0.78	3537.1	1.20	4387.3	1.62	5097.5	2.04	5720.3	2.46	6281.6	2.88	6796.7	3.30	7275.4
0.37	2436.1	0.79	3559.7	1.21	4405.5	1.63	5113.2	2.05	5734.3	2.47	6294.4	2.89	6808.5	3.31	7286.5
0.38	2468.8	0.80	3582.2	1.22	4423.7	1.64	5128.9	2.06	5748.3	2.48	6307.1	2.90	6820.3	3.32	7297.5
0.39	2501.1	0.81	3604.5	1.23	4441.8	1.65	5144.5	2.07	5762.2	2.49	6319.8	2.91	6832.0	3.33	7308.4
0.40	2533.0	0.82	3626.7	1.24	4459.8	1.66	5160.1	2.08	5776.1	2.50	6332.5	2.92	6843.7	3.34	7319.4
0.41	2564.5	0.83	3648.7	1.25	4477.7	1.67	5175.6	2.09	5790.0	2.51	6345.1	2.93	6855.5	3.35	7330.4
0.42	2595.5	0.84	3670.6	1.26	4495.6	1.68	5191.1	2.10	5803.8	2.52	6357.7	2.94	6867.1	3.36	7341.3

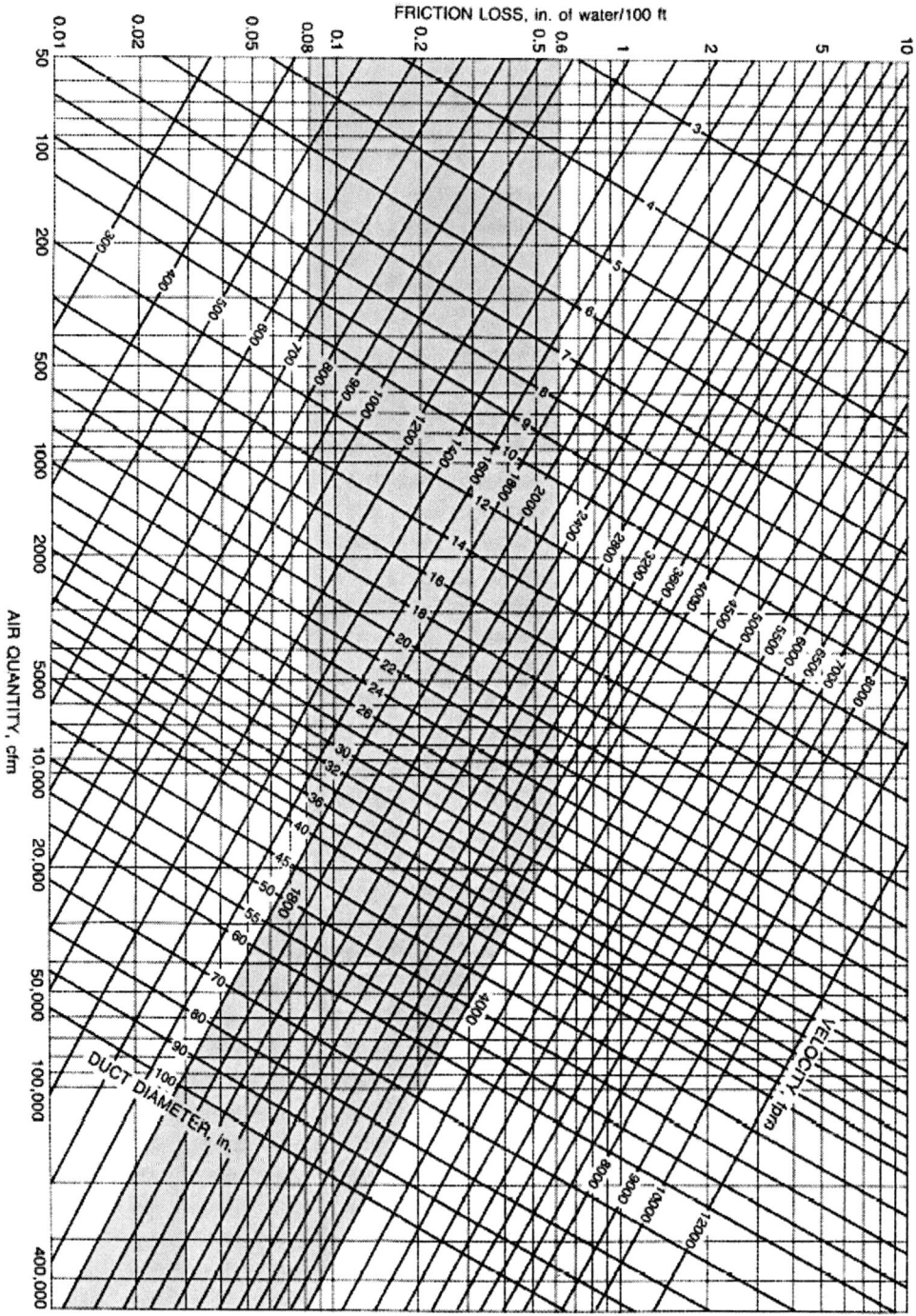

Fig 8-1. Friction chart for round duct ($\rho = 0.075$ lb_m/ft^3 and $\varepsilon = 0.0003$ ft)

Table 8-2. Duct Roughness

Duct Material	Factors Roughness Category	Absolute Roughness ε, ft
Uncoated carbon steel, clean (0.00015 ft)	smooth	0.0001
PVC plastic pipe (0.00003 to 0.00015 ft)		
Aluminum (0.000015 to 0.0002 ft)		
Galvanized steel, longitudinal seams, 4 ft joints (0.00016 to 0.00032 ft)	medium smooth	0.0003
Galvanized steel, continuously rolled, spiral seams, 10 ft joints (0.0002 to 0.0004 ft)		
Galvanized steel, spiral seam with 1, 2, and 3 ribs, 12 ft joints (0.00029 to 0.00038 ft)		
Galvanized steel, longitudinal seams, 2.5 ft joints (0.0005 ft)	average	0.0005
Fibrous glass duct, rigid	medium rough	0.003
Fibrous glass duct liner, air side with facing material (0.005 ft)	rough	0.01
Fibrous glass duct liner, air side spray coated (0.015 ft)		
Flexible duct, metallic (0.004 to 0.007 ft when fully extended)		
Flexible duct, all types of fabric and wire (0.0035 to 0.015 ft when fully extended)		
Concrete (0.001 to 0.01 ft)		

Friction Chart: Fluid resistance caused by friction in round ducts can be determined by the friction chart (Fig. 8-1). This chart is based on standard air flowing through round galvanized ducts with beaded slip couplings on 48 in. centers, equivalent to an absolute roughness of 0.0003 ft.

Changes in barometric pressure, temperature, and humidity affect air density, air viscosity, and Reynolds number. No corrections to Fig. 8-1 are needed for (1) duct materials with a medium smooth roughness factor; (2) temperature variations in the order of ±30°F from 70°F; (3) elevations to 1500 ft, and (4) duct pressures from −20 in. of water to +20 in. of water relative to the ambient pressure. These individual variations in temperature, elevation, and duct pressure result in duct losses within ±5% of the standard air friction chart.

For duct materials other than those categorized as medium smooth in Table 8-2 and for variations in temperature, barometric pressure (elevation), and duct pressures (outside the range listed), calculate the friction loss in a duct by the Altshul-Tsal and Darcy equations.

Noncircular Ducts: A momentum analysis can relate average wall shear stress to pressure drop per unit length for fully developed turbulent flow in a passage of arbitrary shape but uniform longitudinal cross-sectional area. This analysis leads to the definition of hydraulic diameter:

$$D_h = \frac{4A}{P} \qquad (12)$$

where D_h = hydraulic diameter, in.

A = duct area, in^2

P = perimeter of cross section, in.

While hydraulic diameter is often used to correlate noncircular data, exact solutions for laminar flow in non-circular passages show that such practice causes some inconsistencies. No exact solutions exist for turbulent flow. Tests over a limited range of turbulent flow indicate that fluid resistance is the same for equal lengths of duct for equal mean velocities of flow as long as the ducts have the same ratio of cross-sectional area to perimeter. From a series of experiments using round, square, and rectangular ducts having essentially have the same hydraulic diameter, it is found that each duct, for most purposes, the same flow resistance at equal mean velocities. Tests also indicate that experimental rectangular duct data for airflow over the range typical of HVAC systems can be correlated satisfactorily using Equation (8) together with hydraulic diameter, particularly when a realistic experimental uncertainty is accepted. These tests support using hydraulic diameter to correlate noncircular duct data.

Rectangular Ducts: The relationship between rectangular and round ducts that is used to determine size equivalency based on equal flow, resistance, and length. This relationship, Equation (13), is the basis for Table 8-3:

$$D_e = \frac{1.30(ab)^{0.625}}{(a+b)^{0.250}} \qquad (13)$$

where D_e = circular equivalent of rectangular duct for equal length, fluid resistance, and air flow, in.;

a = length one side of duct in.; and

b = length adjacent side of duct in.

To determine equivalent round duct diameter, use Table 8-3. Equations (8) or (9) and (10) must be used to determine pressure loss.

Flat Oval Ducts: Equation (14) will be applied to convert circular equivalent of a flat oval duct for equal airflow, resistance, and length. Equations (8) or (9) and (10) shall be used to determine friction loss.

$$D_e = \frac{1.55 AR^{0.625}}{P^{0.250}}$$

$$AR = \frac{\pi a^2}{4} + a(A - a) \qquad (14)$$

$$P = \pi a + 2(A - a)$$

where AR = cross-sectional area of flat oval duct

P = perimeter of flat oval duct, in.;

A = major axis of flat oval duct, in.;

a = minor axis of flat oval duct, in.

Table 8-3. Equivalent Rectangular Duct Dimensions

Circular Duct Dia, in.	Length One Side of Rectangular Duct (a) in.																			
	4	5	6	7	8	9	10	12	14	16	18	20	22	24	26	28	30	32	34	36
	Length Adjacent Side of Rectangular Duct (b) in.																			
5	5	...	...	...	...	...	...	...	...	...	...	...	...	...	...	...	...	...	...	...
5.5	6	5	...	...	...	...	...	...	...	...	...	...	...	...	...	...	...	...	...	...
6	8	6	...	...	...	...	...	...	...	...	...	...	...	...	...	...	...	...	...	...
6.5	9	7	6	...	...	...	...	...	...	...	...	...	...	...	...	...	...	...	...	...
7	11	8	7	...	...	...	...	...	...	...	...	...	...	...	...	...	...	...	...	...
7.5	13	10	8	...	...	...	...	...	...	...	...	...	...	...	...	...	...	...	...	...
8	15	11	9	8	...	...	...	...	...	...	...	...	...	...	...	...	...	...	...	...
8.5	17	13	10	9	...	...	...	...	...	...	...	...	...	...	...	...	...	...	...	...
9	20	15	12	10	8	...	...	...	...	...	...	...	...	...	...	...	...	...	...	...
9.5	22	17	13	11	9	...	...	...	...	...	...	...	...	...	...	...	...	...	...	...
10	25	19	15	12	10	9	...	...	...	...	...	...	...	...	...	...	...	...	...	...
10.5	29	21	16	14	12	10	...	...	...	...	...	...	...	...	...	...	...	...	...	...
11	32	23	18	15	13	11	10	...	...	...	...	...	...	...	...	...	...	...	...	...
11.5	...	26	20	17	14	12	11	...	...	...	...	...	...	...	...	...	...	...	...	...
12	...	29	22	18	15	13	12	...	...	...	...	...	...	...	...	...	...	...	...	...
12.5	...	32	24	20	17	15	13	...	...	...	...	...	...	...	...	...	...	...	...	...
13	...	35	27	22	18	16	14	12	...	...	...	...	...	...	...	...	...	...	...	...
13.5	...	38	29	24	20	17	15	13	...	...	...	...	...	...	...	...	...	...	...	...
14	...	...	32	26	22	19	17	14	...	...	...	...	...	...	...	...	...	...	...	...
14.5	...	...	35	28	24	20	18	15	...	...	...	...	...	...	...	...	...	...	...	...
15	...	...	38	30	25	22	19	16	14	...	...	...	...	...	...	...	...	...	...	...
16	...	...	45	36	30	25	22	18	15	...	...	...	...	...	...	...	...	...	...	...
17	...	...	...	41	34	29	25	20	17	16	...	...	...	...	...	...	...	...	...	...
18	...	...	...	47	39	33	29	23	19	17	...	...	...	...	...	...	...	...	...	...
19	...	...	...	54	44	38	33	26	22	19	18	...	...	...	...	...	...	...	...	...
20	...	...	...		50	43	37	29	24	21	19	...	...	...	...	...	...	...	...	...
21	...	...	...	...	57	48	41	33	27	23	20	...	...	...	...	...	...	...	...	...
22	...	...	...	...	64	54	46	36	30	26	23	20	...	...	...	...	...	...	...	...
23	...	...	...	...	...	60	51	40	33	28	25	22	...	...	...	...	...	...	...	...
24	...	...	...	...	...	66	57	44	36	31	27	24	22	...	...	...	...	...	...	...
25	...	...	...	...	...	...	63	49	40	34	29	26	24	...	...	...	...	...	...	...
26	...	...	...	...	...	...	69	54	44	37	32	28	26	24	...	...	...	...	...	...
27	...	...	...	...	...	...	76	59	48	40	35	31	28	25	...	...	...	...	...	...
28	...	...	...	...	...	...	...	64	52	43	38	33	30	27	26	...	...	...	...	...
29	...	...	...	...	...	...	...	70	56	47	41	36	32	29	27	...	...	...	...	...
30	...	...	...	...	...	...	...	76	61	51	44	39	35	31	29	28	...	...	...	...
31	...	...	...	...	...	...	...	82	66	55	47	41	37	34	31	29	...	...	...	...
32	...	...	...	...	...	...	...	89	71	59	51	44	40	36	33	31	...	...	...	...
33	...	...	...	...	...	...	...	96	76	64	54	48	42	38	35	33	30	...	...	...
34	...	...	...	...	...	...	...	...	82	68	58	51	45	41	37	35	32	...	...	...
35	...	...	...	...	...	...	...	...	88	73	62	54	48	44	40	37	34	32	...	...
36	...	...	...	...	...	...	...	...	95	78	67	58	51	46	42	39	36	34	...	...
37	...	...	...	...	...	...	...	...	101	83	71	62	55	49	45	41	38	36	34	...
38	...	...	...	...	...	...	...	...	108	89	76	66	58	52	47	44	40	38	36	...
39	...	...	...	...	...	...	...	...	...	95	80	70	62	55	50	46	43	40	37	36
40	...	...	...	...	...	...	...	...	...	101	85	74	65	58	53	49	45	42	39	37
41	...	...	...	...	...	...	...	...	...	107	91	78	69	62	56	51	47	44	41	39
42	...	...	...	...	...	...	...	...	...	114	96	83	73	65	59	54	50	46	44	41
43	...	...	...	...	...	...	...	...	...	120	102	88	77	69	62	57	53	49	46	43
44	...	...	...	...	...	...	...	...	...	...	107	93	81	73	66	60	55	51	48	45
45	...	...	...	...	...	...	...	...	...	...	113	98	86	76	69	63	58	54	50	47
46	...	...	...	...	...	...	...	...	...	...	120	103	90	80	72	66	61	56	53	49
47	...	...	...	...	...	...	...	...	...	...	126	108	95	84	76	69	64	59	55	52
48	...	...	...	...	...	...	...	...	...	...	133	114	100	89	80	73	67	62	58	54
49	...	...	...	...	...	...	...	...	...	...	140	120	105	93	84	76	70	65	60	56
50	...	...	...	...	...	...	...	...	...	...	147	126	110	98	88	80	73	68	63	59
51	...	...	...	...	...	...	...	...	...	...	...	132	115	102	92	83	76	71	66	61
52	...	...	...	...	...	...	...	...	...	...	...	139	121	107	96	87	80	74	69	64
53	...	...	...	...	...	...	...	...	...	...	...	145	127	112	100	91	83	77	71	67
54	...	...	...	...	...	...	...	...	...	...	...	152	133	117	105	95	87	80	74	70
55	...	...	...	...	...	...	...	...	...	...	...	...	139	123	110	99	91	84	78	72
56	...	...	...	...	...	...	...	...	...	...	...	...	145	128	114	104	95	87	81	75
57	...	...	...	...	...	...	...	...	...	...	...	...	151	134	119	108	98	91	84	78
58	...	...	...	...	...	...	...	...	...	...	...	...	158	139	124	112	102	94	87	81
59	...	...	...	...	...	...	...	...	...	...	...	...	165	145	130	117	107	98	91	85
60	...	...	...	...	...	...	...	...	...	...	...	...	172	151	135	122	111	102	94	88

Dynamic Losses.—Dynamic losses result from flow disturbances caused by duct-mounted equipment and fittings that change the air flow path's direction and/or area. These fittings include entries, exits, elbows, transitions, and junctions. Fluid resistance of fittings and local loss coefficients are presented in three forms: tables, curves, and equations.

Local Loss Coefficients: The dimensionless coefficient C is used for fluid resistance because this coefficient has the same value in dynamically similar streams (i.e., streams with geometrically similar stretches, equal Reynolds numbers, and equal values of other criteria necessary for dynamic similarity). The fluid resistance coefficient represents the ratio of total pressure loss to velocity pressure at the referenced cross section:

$$C = \frac{\Delta P_j}{\rho\left(\dfrac{V}{1097}\right)^2} = \frac{\Delta P_j}{P_v} \tag{15}$$

where C = local loss coefficient, dimensionless

ΔP_j = total pressure loss, in. of water

P_v = velocity pressure loss, in. of water

Dynamic losses occur along a duct length and cannot be separated from friction losses. For ease of calculation, dynamic losses are assumed to be concentrated at a section (local) and to exclude friction. Frictional losses must be considered only for relatively long fittings. Generally, fitting friction losses are accounted for by measuring duct lengths from the centerline of one fitting to that of the next fitting. For fittings closely coupled (less than six hydraulic diameters apart), the flow pattern entering subsequent fittings differs from the flow pattern used to determine loss coefficients. Adequate data for these situations are unavailable.

For all fittings, except junctions, calculate the total pressure loss at a section is calculated by

$$\Delta P_j = C_o P_{v,o} \tag{16}$$

where the subscript o is the cross section at which the velocity pressure is referenced. The dynamic loss is based on the actual velocity in the duct, not the velocity in an equivalent noncircular duct.

For the cross section to reference a fitting loss coefficient, refer to Step 4 in this chapter entitled section on HVAC *Duct Design Procedures.* Where necessary (unequal area fittings), convert a loss coefficient from section o to section i using Equation (17), where V is the velocity at the respective sections:

$$C_i = \frac{C_o}{\left(\dfrac{V_i}{V_o}\right)^2} \tag{17}$$

For converging and diverging flow junctions total pressure losses through the straight (main) section are calculated as

$$\Delta P_j = C_{c,s} P_{v,c} \tag{18}$$

For total pressure losses through the branch section,

$$\Delta P_j = C_{c,b} P_{v,c} \tag{19}$$

where $P_{v,c}$ is the velocity pressure at the common section c, and $C_{c,s}$ and $C_{c,b}$ are losses for the straight (main) and branch flow paths, respectively, each referenced to the velocity pressure at section c. To convert junction local loss coefficients referenced to straight and branch velocity pressures, use the equation:

$$C_i = \frac{C_{c,i}}{\left(\dfrac{V_i}{V_c}\right)^2} \tag{20}$$

where C_i = local loss coefficient referenced to calculated section (see subscripts), dimensionless;

$C_{c,i}$ = straight ($C_{c,s}$) or branch local loss, coefficient referenced to dynamic pressure at common section, dimensionless;

V_i = velocity at section to which C_i is being referenced, fpm;

V_c = velocity at common section, fpm;

b = branch;

s = straight (main) section; and

c = common section.

The junction of two parallel streams moving at different velocities is characterized by turbulent mixing of the streams, accompanied by pressure losses. In the course of this mixing, an exchange of momentum takes place between the particles moving at different velocities, finally resulting in the equalization of the velocity distributions in the common stream. The jet with higher velocity loses a part of its kinetic energy by transmitting it to the slower moving jet. The loss in total pressure before and after mixing is always large and positive for the higher velocity jet and increases with an increase in the amount of energy transmitted to the lower velocity jet. Consequently, the local loss coefficient defined by Equation (20) will always be positive. The energy stored in the lower velocity jet increases as a result of mixing. The loss in total pressure and the local loss coefficient can, therefore, also have negative values for the lower velocity jet.

Ductwork Sectional Losses.—*Darcy-Weisbach Equation:* Total pressure loss in a duct section is calculated by combining Equations (7) and (15) in terms of Δp, where ΣC is the summation of local loss coefficients within the duct section. Each fitting loss coefficient must be referenced to that section's velocity pressure.

$$\Delta P = \left(\frac{12fL}{D_h} + \Sigma C\right)\rho\left(\frac{V}{1097}\right)^2 \qquad (21)$$

Fan System Interface.—*Fan Inlet and Outlet Conditions:* Fan performance data measured in the field may show lower performance capacity than manufacturers' ratings. The most common causes of deficient performance of the fan/system combination are improper outlet connections, nonuniform inlet flow, and swirl at the fan inlet. These conditions alter the aerodynamic characteristics of the fan so that its full flow potential is not realized. One bad connection can reduce fan performance far below its rating. No data have been published that account for the effects of fan inlet and outlet flexible vibration connectors.

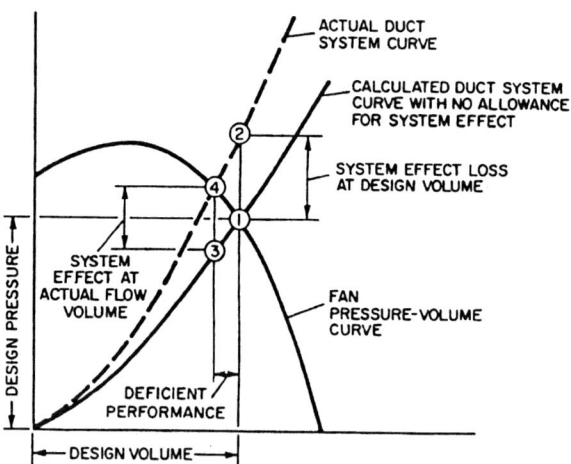

Fig 8-2. Deficient system performance with system effect ignored

Normally, a fan is tested with open inlets and a section of straight duct attached to the outlet (ASHRAE Standard 51). This set up results in uniform flow into the fan and efficient static pressure recovery on the fan outlet. If good inlet and outlet conditions are not provided in the actual installation, the performance of the fan suffers. The designer must consider the effects of poor inlet outlet conditions, and the pressure requirements of the fan, as calculated by standard duct design procedures, must increase.

Fig. 8-2 illustrates deficient fan/system performance. The system pressure losses have been determined accurately, and a fan has been selected for operation at point 1. However, no allowance has been made for the effect of system connections to the fan on fan performance. To compensate, a fan system effect must be added to the calculated system pressure losses to determine the actual system curve. The point of intersection between the fan performance curve and the actual system curve is point 4. The actual flow volume is, therefore, deficient by the difference from 1 to 4. To achieve design flow volume, a fan system effective pressure loss equal to the pressure difference between points 1 and 2 should be added to the calcu-

lated system pressure losses, and the fan should be selected to operate at point 2.

Pressure Changes System.—In a duct of constant diameter or constant cross-sectional area, the velocity or dynamic pressure does not change between the inlet and the outlet. This is because velocity pressure is a function of velocity and the velocity remains constant in a duct of uniform cross-section. The static pressure drops along the direction of flow in the duct as given by the equation for friction losses, Equation (6). The total pressure, which is the sum of the static and velocity pressures, therefore decreases at the same rate as the static pressure along the length of the constant area duct.

The pressure losses at entrances, exits, fittings and junctions are related to the local velocity pressure as described in the previous sections. To graphically demonstrate the pressure losses, a simple duct system is considered in Fig. 8-3a. Two different diameter ducts are attached in this simple example, and entrance and exit are connected to the atmosphere. The flow rate of air through the system is Q. Location 1 is at atmospheric pressure and is sufficiently far away from the inlet so that the velocity is zero. Location 9 is sufficiently far away from the exit and the velocity there is assumed zero. The pressure deficit at the location 9, relative to the inlet static pressure at location 1, is the duct system pressure loss for the given flow rate. As the flow rate increases this pressure loss will increase, and conversely, the pressure loss will decrease as the flow rate decreases, reaching zero pressure drop for zero flow. The relationship between the system pressure drop and the flow rate gives rise to the system pressure loss curve, as the one shown in Fig. 8-2 in the previous section. The pressure deficit has to be made up by introducing a fan in the system, as shown in Fig. 8-3b.

The pressure changes in Fig. 8-3a are described as follows. At location 1 the velocity of the air is zero and therefore the velocity pressure is zero. The static pressure and the total pressure are therefore equal to the local atmospheric pressure. As the entrance of the system is approached, the velocity starts to increase. This results in an increase of velocity pressure. Since the total energy is conserved, the total pressure remains constant and the static pressure decreases. At the entrance, location 2, the velocity reaches the value needed to maintain the air flow rate of Q and remains constant thereafter until the duct cross-section changes at location 5. Thus the velocity pressure remains constant between location 2 and location 5. The dynamic losses at the inlet cause a further drop in the static pressure between locations 2 and 3. Location 3 is very close to 2, although the separation distance has been exaggerated in the figure for clarity. Near the end of the first section of the duct system, location 4, and near the beginning of the second duct, location 6, the dynamic losses due to expansion affect the total and static pressures.

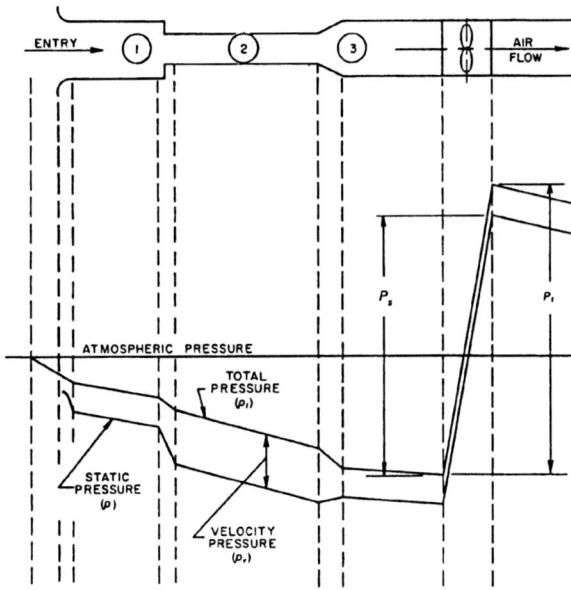

Fig 8-3a. Pressure changes in system

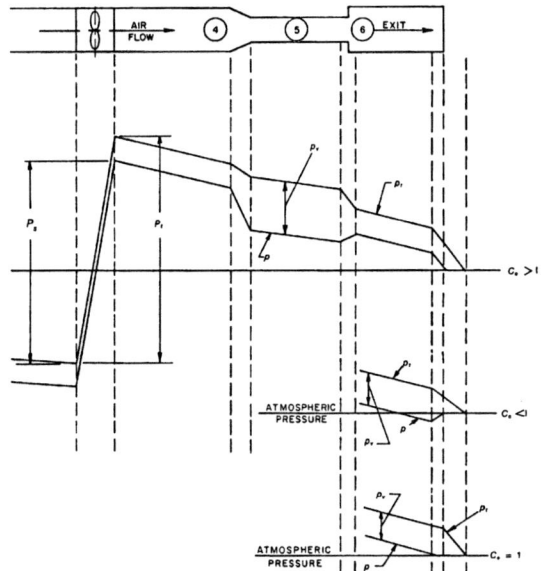

Fig 8-3b. Pressure changes in system

Location 4 is very near location 5 and location 6 is very close to 5, but the respective separations in the figure are also exaggerated for clarity, as before. The velocity pressure reduces at location 5, where the increase of diameter results in a drop in velocity and the associated velocity pressure. This reduced velocity pressure remains constant between location 5 and the exit, location 8. At the exit the exit pressure loss affects the total and static pressures, between a location 7 very close to the exit and the exit, location 8. After the exit the total pressure remains con-

stant and the gradual slowing of the air results in the decrease of the velocity pressure and the corresponding recovery (gain) of the static pressure. At location 9, which is at a distance far enough from the outlet that the velocity is zero, the velocity pressure is zero and the static and total pressures are the same. The difference between this pressure at 9 and the pressure upstream of the inlet at 9 is the system pressure drop and needs to be compensated for the flow to actually occur. The common way of compensating this pressure drop is to introduce a fan in the system that has the same pressure rise for the given flow rate Q. This is demonstrated in Fig. 8-3b and the fan selection was shown if Fig. 8-2.

Duct System Design

Design Considerations.—*Space Pressure Relationships:* Space pressure is determined by fan location and duct system arrangement. For example, a supply fan that pumps air into a space increases space pressure; an exhaust fan reduces space pressure. If both supply and exhaust fans are used, space pressure depends on the relative capacity of the fans. Space pressure is positive if supply exceeds exhaust and negative if exhaust exceeds supply.

Fire and Smoke Management: Because duct systems can convey smoke, hot gases, and fire from one area to another and can accelerate a fire within the system, fire protection is an essential part of air conditioning and ventilation system design. Generally, fire safety codes require compliance with the standards of national organizations. NFPA Standard 90A examines fire safety requirements for (1) ducts, connectors, and appurtenances; (2) plenums and corridors; (3) air outlets, air inlets, and fresh air intakes; (4) air filters; (5) fans; (6) electric wiring and equipment; (7) air-cooling and -heating equipment; (8) building construction, including protection of penetrations; and (9) controls, including smoke control.

Fire safety codes often refer to the testing and labeling practices of nationally recognized laboratories, such as Factory Mutual and Underwriters Laboratories (UL). The Building Materials Directory compiled by UL lists fire and smoke dampers that have been tested and meet the requirements of UL Standards 555 and 555S. This directory also summarizes maximum allowable sizes for individual dampers and assemblies of these dampers. Fire dampers are 1.5 hr or 3 hr fire-rated. Smoke dampers are classified by (1) temperature degradation ambient air or high temperature (250°F minimum), and (2) leakage at 1 and 4 in. of water pressure difference (8 and 12 in. of water classification optional). Smoke dampers are tested under conditions of maximum airflow. UL's Fire Resistance Directory lists the fire resistance of floor/roof and ceiling assemblies with and without ceiling fire dampers.

Duct Insulation: In all new construction (except low-rise residential buildings), air-handling ducts and plenums installed as part of an HVAC air distribution system should be thermally insulated. Duct insulation for new low-rise residential buildings should be in compliance with ASHRAE Standard 90.2. Existing buildings should meet the requirements of ASHRAE Standard 100. The insulation thicknesses in these standards are minimum values. Economic and thermal considerations may justify higher insulation levels. Additional insulation, vapor retarders, or both may be required to limit vapor transmission and condensation. Duct heat gains or losses must be known for the calculation of supply air quantities, supply air temperatures, and coil loads. To estimate duct heat transfer and entering or leaving air temperatures, the following equations are used:

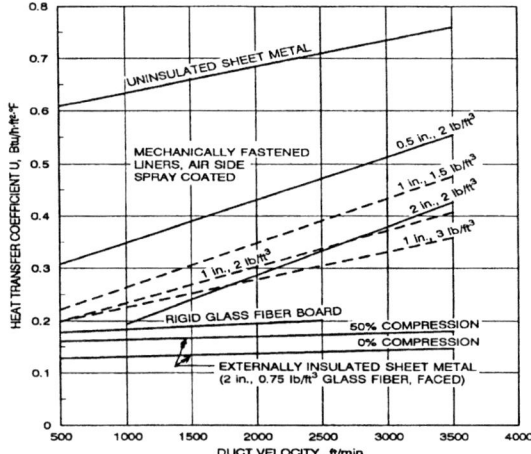

Fig 8-4a. Rigid ducts

$$q_l = \frac{UPL}{12}\left[\frac{(T_e + T_l)}{2} - T_a\right]$$

$$T_e = \frac{T_l(y+1) - 2T_a}{(y-1)} \qquad (22)$$

$$T_l = \frac{T_e(y-1) + 2T_a}{(y+1)}$$

$$y = \frac{10 A V \rho C_p}{UPL} \qquad \text{for rectangular ducts}$$

$$y = \frac{2.5 D V \rho C_p}{UL} \qquad \text{for round ducts} \qquad (23)$$

where q_l = heat loss/gain through duct walls, Btu/hr (negative for heat gain);

$\quad U$ = overall heat transfer coefficient of duct wall, Btu/hr-ft²-°F;

$\quad P$ = perimeter of bare or insulated duct, in.;

$\quad L$ = duct length, ft;

$\quad T_e$ = temperature of air entering duct, °F;

$\quad T_l$ = temperature of air leaving duct, °F;

$\quad T_a$ = temperature of air surrounding duct, °F;

$\quad y$ = constants, based on above formula; and

$\quad V$ = average velocity, fpm

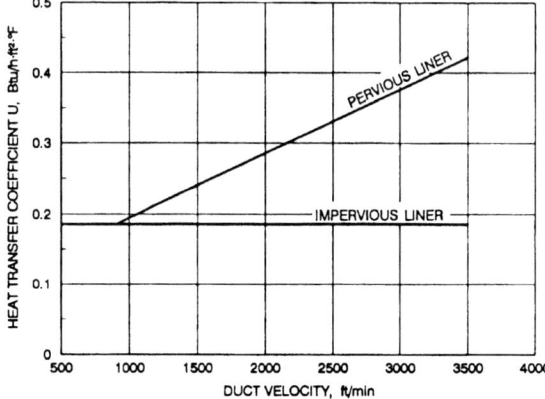

Fig 8-4b. Insulated flexible ducts

Use Fig. 8-4a to determine U-factors for insulated and uninsulated ducts. Lauvray (1978) has shown the effects of (1) compressing insulation wrapped externally on sheet metal ducts and (2) insulated flexible ducts with air-porous liners. For a 2 in. thick, 0.75 lb$_m$/ft³ fibrous glass blanket compressed 50% during installation, the heat transfer rate increases approximately 20% (see Fig. 8-4a). Pervious flexible duct liners also influence heat transfer significantly (see Fig. 8-4b). At 2500 fpm, the pervious liner U-factor is 0.33 Btu/hr-ft²-°F; for an impervious liner, $U = 0.19$ Btu/hr-ft²-°F.

Example 1: A 40 ft length of 18 in. by 24 in. uninsulated sheet metal duct, freely suspended, conveys heated air through a space maintained above freezing at 40°F. Based on heat loss calculations for the heated zone, 1800 *cfm* of standard air ($C_p = 0.24$ Btu/lb$_m$-°F) at a supply air temperature of 122°F is required. The duct is connected directly to the heated zone. Determine the temperature of the air entering the duct and the duct heat loss.

Solution: Calculate duct velocity:

$$V = \frac{144 \times 1800 \text{ cfm}}{(24 \text{ in.})(36 \text{ in.})} = 600 \text{ fpm}$$

Calculating entering air temperature:

$$U = 0.73$$

$$P = 2(18 + 24) = 84 \text{ in.}$$

$$y = \frac{10 \times 18 \times 24 \times 600 \times 0.075 \times 0.24}{0.73 \times 84 \times 40} = 19.02$$

$$T_e = \frac{122 \times (19.02 + 1) - (2 \times 40)}{(19.02 - 1)} = 131.10°F$$

Calculate duct heat loss:

$$q_l = \frac{0.73 \times 84 \times 40}{12}\left(\frac{131.10 + 122}{2} - 40\right)$$

$$= 17690 \text{ Btu/hr.}$$

Example 2: Same as Example 1, except the duct is insulated externally with 2 in. thick fibrous glass with a density of 0.75 lb_m/ft^3. The insulation is wrapped with 0% compression.

Solution: All values except U remain the same as in Example 1. From Fig. 8-4a, $U = 0.15$ Btu/hr-ft^2-°F at 2900 fpm.

Calculate duct velocity:

$$V = \frac{144 \times 1800 \text{ cfm}}{(24 \text{ in.})(36 \text{ in.})} = 600 \text{ fpm}$$

Calculate entering air temperature:

$$U = 0.15$$
$$P = 2(18 + 24) = 84 \text{ in.}$$
$$y = \frac{10 \times 18 \times 24 \times 600 \times 0.075 \times 0.24}{0.15 \times 84 \times 40} = 92.57$$
$$T_e = \frac{122 \times (92.57 + 1) - (2 \times 40)}{(92.57 - 1)} = 123.79°F$$

Calculate duct heat loss

$$q_l = \frac{0.15 \times 84 \times 40}{12}\left(\frac{123.79 + 122}{2} - 40\right)$$

$$= 3482 \text{ Btu/hr}$$

Insulating this duct reduces heat loss to 80% of the uninsulated value.

Duct System Leakage: Leakage in all unsealed ducts varies considerably with the fabricating machinery used, the methods for assembly, and installation workmanship.

System Component Design Velocities: Table 8-4 summarizes face velocities for HVAC components in built-up systems. In most cases the values are abstracted from pertinent chapters in the ASHRAE Handbook—Systems and Equipment; final selection of the components should be based on data in these chapters or from manufacturers.

Louvers require special treatment since the blade shapes, angles, and spacing cause significant variations in louver-free area and performance (pressure drop and water penetration). Selection and analysis should be based on test data obtained in accordance with AMCA Standard 500-L (1999). This standard presents both pressure drop and water penetration test procedures and a uniform method for calculating the free area of a louver. Tests are conducted on a 48 in^2 louver with the frame mounted flush in the wall. For the water penetration tests, the rainfall is 4 in./hr, no wind, and the water flow down the wall is 0.25 gpm per linear foot of louver width.

Table 8-4. Recommended Duct Velocities and Typical Velocities and Pressure Losses of Various HVAC Components

Designation	Residences	Schools, Theaters, Public Buildings	Industrial Buildings
Recommended Velocities, fpm			
Main ducts	700–900	1000–1300	1200–1800
Branch ducts	600	600–900	800–1000
Branch risers	500	600–700	800
Components			
Outdoor air intakes[a]	500	500	500
Filters[a]	250	300	350
Heating coils[a]	450	500	600
Cooling coils[a]	450	500	600
Air washers[a]	500	500	500
Fan outlets	1000–1600	1300–2000	1600–2400
Maximum Velocities, fpm			
Main ducts	800–1200	1100–1600	1300–2200
Branch ducts	700–1000	800–1300	1000–1800
Branch risers	650–800	800–1200	1000–1600
Components			
Outdoor air intakes[a]	800	900	1200
Filters[a]	300	350	350
Heating coils[a]	500	600	700
Cooling coils[a]	450	500	600
Air washers	500	500	500
Fan outlets	1700	1500–2200	1700–2800

[a] These velocities are for total face area, not net free area; other velocities in table are for net free area.

Component	Static Pressure Loss, in. w.g.
Supply plenum	0.50
Static regain supply duct	0.30
Supply grille	0.05
HEPA	0.70
Raised floor perforations	0.05
Ducted return	0.40
Return plenum	0.05
Cooling coil	0.35
Bag filters	0.80
30/30 prefilters	0.30

Air flow carried by duct, cfm	Maximum velocity, fpm
1000–3000	2500
3000–6000	3000
6000–10000	3500
10000–15000	4000
15000–25000	4500
25000–40000	5000
40000–60000	6000

Use Fig. 8-5 for preliminary sizing of air intake and exhaust louvers. For air quantities greater than 7000 *cfm* per louver, the air intake gross louver openings are based on 400 fpm; for exhaust louvers, 500 fpm is used for air quantities of 5000 *cfm* per louver and greater. For air quantities less than these, refer to Fig. 8-5. These criteria are presented on a per louver basis (i.e., each louver in a bank of louvers) to include each louver frame. Representative production-run louvers were used in establishing Fig. 8-5, and all data used in that analysis are based on AMCA standard tests. For louvers larger than 16 ft^2, the free areas are greater than 45%, while for louvers less than 16 ft^2, the free areas are less than 45%. Unless specific louver data are analyzed, no louver should have a face area less than 4 ft^2. If debris collection on the screen of an intake louver is possible, or if louvers are located at grade with adjacent pedestrian traffic, louver face velocity should not exceed 100 fpm.

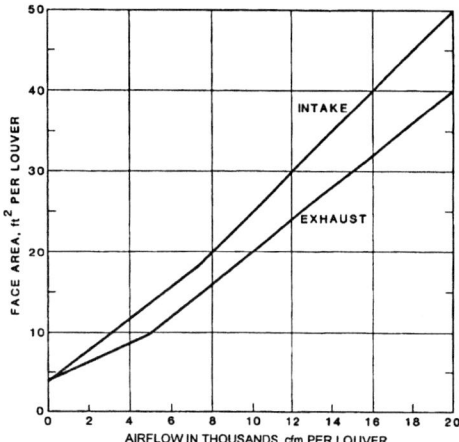

Fig 8-5. Criteria for louver sizing

Parameters Used to Establish Fig. 8-5	Intake Louver	Exhaust Louver
Minimum free area (48 in^2 test section),%	45	45
Water penetration, oz/ft^2, 0.25hr	negligible (less than 0.2)	n/a
Maximum static pressure drop, in. of water	0.15	0.25

Table 8-5. Typical Duct Design Velocities

Duct Element	Face Velocity, fpm
Louvers	
Intake	
7000 *cfm* and greater	400
Less than 7000 *cfm*	
Exhaust	
5000 *cfm* and greater	500
Less than 5000 *cfm*	
Filters	
Panel filters	
Viscous impingement	200 to 800
Dry-type, extended-surface	

Duct Element	Face Velocity, fpm
Flat (low efficiency)	Duct velocity up to 750
Pleated media (intermediate efficiency)	
HEPA	250
Renewable media filters	
Moving-curtain viscous impingement	500
Moving-curtain dry media electronic air cleaners	200
Ionizing type	150 to 350
Heating coils	
Steam and hot water	500 to 1000 200 min., 1500 max.
Electric	
Open wire	Refer to mfg. data
Finned tubular	Refer to mfg. data
Dehumidifying coils	400 to 500
Air washers	
Spray type	300 to 600
Cell type	Refer to mfg. data
High-velocity spray type	1200 to 1800

System and Duct Noise: The major sources of noise from air conditioning systems are diffusers, grilles, fans, ducts, fittings, and vibrations. Sound control for terminal devices consists of selecting devices that meet the design goal under all operating conditions and installing them properly so that no additional sound is generated. The sound power output of a fan is determined by the type of fan, air flow, and pressure. Sound control in the duct system requires proper duct layout, sizing, and provision for installing duct attenuators, if required. The noise generated by a system increases with both duct velocity and system pressure.

Testing and Balancing: Each air duct system should be tested, adjusted, and balanced. To properly determine fan total (or static) pressure from field measurements taking into account fan system effect, refer to the section *Fan System Interface.*

Duct Design Methods.—Duct design methods for HVAC systems and for exhaust systems conveying vapors, gases, and smoke are the equal friction method, the static regain method, and the T-method. Equal friction and static regain are non optimizing methods, while the T-method is a practical optimization method.

To ensure that system designs are acoustically acceptable, noise generation should be analyzed and sound attenuators and/or acoustically lined duct provided where necessary. Dampers must be installed throughout systems designed with equal friction, static regain, and the T-method because inaccuracies are introduced into these design methods by duct size round-off and the effect of close coupled fittings on total pressure loss calculations.

Equal Friction Method: In the equal friction method, ducts are sized for a constant pressure loss per unit length. The shaded area of the friction chart (Fig. 8-1) is the suggested range of friction rate and air velocity. When energy cost is high and installed ductwork cost is low, a low friction rate design is more economical. For low energy cost and high duct cost, a higher friction rate is more economical. After initial sizing, calculate the total pressure loss for all duct sections, and then resize sections to balance pressure losses at each junction.

Static Regain Method: The objective of the static regain method is to obtain the same static pressure at diverging flow junctions by changing downstream duct sizes. This design objective can be developed by rearranging Equation (6) and setting $P_{s,2}$ equal to $P_{s,1}$ (neglecting thermal gravity effect term). Thus,

$$P_{s,1} - P_{s,2} = \Delta P_{t,1-2} - \left(\frac{\rho V_1^2}{2g_c} - \frac{\rho V_2^2}{2g_c} \right)$$

and   (24)

$$\Delta P_{t,1-2} = \left(\frac{\rho V_1^2}{2g_c} - \frac{\rho V_2^2}{2g_c} \right)$$

where $\Delta P_{t,1-2}$ is the total pressure loss from upstream of junction 1 to upstream of junction 2, or the terminal of section 2.

The classical static regain method is based on Equation (25), where R is the static pressure regain factor, and ΔP_r is the static pressure regain between junctions

$$\Delta P_r = R \left(\frac{\rho V_1^2}{2g_c} - \frac{\rho V_2^2}{2g_c} \right)$$ (25)

Typically R values ranging from 0.5 to 0.95 have been used. This uncertainty exists because the splitting of mass at junctions and dynamic (fitting) losses between junctions are ignored. The classical static regain method using an R-value should not be used because R is not predictable.

Duct Design Procedures.—The general procedure for HVAC system duct design is as follows:

1) Study the building plans and arrange the supply and return outlets to provide proper distribution of air within each space. Adjust calculated air quantities for duct heat gains or losses and duct leakage. Also, adjust the supply, return, and/or exhaust air quantities to meet space pressurization requirements.

2) Select outlet sizes from manufacturers' data.

3) Sketch the duct system, connecting supply outlets and return intakes with the air handling units/air conditioners. Space allocated for supply and return ducts often dictates system layout and ductwork shape. Use round ducts whenever feasible and avoid close-coupled fittings.

4) Divide the system into sections and number each section. A duct system should be divided at all points where flow, size, or shape changes. Assign fittings to the section toward the supply and return (or exhaust) terminals.

5) Size ducts by the selected design method. Calculate system total pressure loss; then select the fan.

6) Lay out the system in detail. If duct routing and fittings vary significantly from the original design, recalculate the pressure losses. Reselect the fan if necessary.

7) Resize duct sections to approximately balance pressures at each junction.

8) Analyze the design for objectionable noise levels, and specify sound attenuators as necessary. Refer to *Noise in Ducted Systems.*

Automated Duct Design.— Now a days duct design calculations have been automated by computers. From drawing sheets, computer calculate and it places the exact size of duct and even it notify if there is any conflicts with the installation of other ducts or pipes. Automated duct design offers following features such as:

1) optimization of duct design
2) provide pressure loss in fittings
3) provide pressure loss in ducts
4) required static pressure of fan
5) duct construction and thermal analysis
6) balancing analysis
7) system noise analysis
8) interference with other ducts or pipes
9) material takeoffs; and
10) documentation.

Example 3: Select the return duct sizes and the approximate frictional losses.

Duct	cfm	Length
A	4000	10
B	2000	40
C	2000	50

Solution: Select the duct sizes based on friction loss of 0.05 in. of water/100 ft length.

Duct	cfm	Duct Sizes	Equiv. Dia	Velocity	Velocity Pressure in. of water/feet	C_o	Loss	Losses	at end
A	4000	30×20	26.64	1033	0.0665	0	0.05/100×10	0.05	0.05
B	2000	20×18	20.73	853	0.0453	0.11 + 0.08 + 0.23 = 0.42	0.05 / 100 × 40 +.450 ×.42	0.309	0.359
C	2000	20×18	20.73	853	0.0453	0.11 + 0.08 + 0.23 = 0.42	0.05 / 100 × 40 +.450 ×.42	0.439	0.489

In branch B, elbow, mitered 90°, single thickness vanes $C_o = 0.11$

For butterfly damper $\theta = 0$ and $H/W = 0.90$, $C_o = 0.08$

Wye, symmetrical dovetail, $Q_b/Q_c = 0.50$ $C_b = 0.23$ as $A_b/A_c = 0.50$.

As points B and C have different pressures, to balance the system, now we can choose different duct size for branch B to have the same pressure as C. The pressure on duct B will be 0.05×50/40 = 0.0625, then the duct size will be 19.80 in. In this case, the volume damper will be applied in branch C to balance the system. We can apply 27 in. diameter branch A and 20 in. in branch B and C.

Duct Fitting Friction Loss Example.—The sheet metal draftsman, during preparation of shop drawings, should analyze duct locations that are schematically indicated on the mechanical drawings. He must prevent these ducts from conflicting with other building components because certain conditions may require duct fittings with high resistance to air flow. When space permits, fittings should be selected with low friction-loss factors and economical fabrication and erection characteristics.

Example 4: Calculate the friction loss of a 24 × 12 straight clinch tap to handle 4000 *cfm* which connects to a supply plenum with an air velocity of 1000 fpm. where:

$$\text{Area of branch} = \frac{24 \times 12}{12 \times 12} = 2 \text{ ft}^2.$$

Let V_1 = branch-duct velocity; V_2 = plenum velocity = 1000 fpm. Then

$$V_1 = \frac{cfm}{A} = \frac{4000}{2}$$

$$V_1 = 2000 \text{ fpm}$$

$$\frac{V_1}{V_2} = \frac{2000}{1000} = 2$$

A sharp contraction that doubles air velocity has a fraction of velocity pressure loss of 0.32. Table 8-1, velocity pressure for 2,000 fpm = 0.25 in. of water.

$$\text{Fitting loss} = 0.32 \times 0.25$$
$$= 0.08 \text{ in. of water}$$

Example 5: What is the friction loss of a 18 in. diameter, 5-piece 90° elbow with a 27 in. throat radius and an air velocity of 3100 fpm?

From Table 8-1, velocity pressure for 3100 fpm = 0.60 in. water. From Table 8-15, C_o =0.15.

$$\text{Fitting loss} = 0.15 \times 0.60$$
$$= 0.09 \text{ in. of water}$$

Elbows Example.—Job specifications generally require rectangular elbows to have a throat radius equal to the cheek width. Where space conditions prevent installation of full-radius elbows, square throat, square-heel elbow with double-thickness turning vane are usually used. The draftsman should draw radius elbows whenever possible as they are fabricated more economically than the vaned type. However, handling and field-erection conditions of large elbows should be studied to determine the most economical installation: one-piece radius

elbows, multiple-section radius elbows, or square throat vaned elbows.

Air flow resistance in elbows is influenced by the ratio of the throat radius to the cheek width and by aspect ratio, which is the relationship of the elbow height to the cheek width. The draftsman must also be aware that offsets are combinations of beveled elbows and similarly affect air-flow resistance.

Using type 1 elbow as a comparative standard, if throat radius is reduced to one-half its cheek width, the elbow resistance would be increased approximately 1.63 times, as in type 2. If throat radius is reduced to one-quarter the cheek width, the resistance would be 2.0 to 2.75 times greater, as in type 3.

The elbow is type 1 and has a fraction of velocity pressure loss of 0.13. From Table 8-1; an air velocity of 2002 fpm = 0.25 in. of water, elbow loss = 0.13 × 0.25 = 0.0325 in. of water.

Example 6: Find the resistance of a 90° elbow, 48 in. wide by 12 in. high, with a 12 in. throat radius, and carrying 2400 *cfm* of air.

$$V = \frac{cfm}{A} = \frac{2400 \times 144}{48 \times 12} = 600 \text{ fpm}$$

From Table 8-1: 600 fpm = 0.01683 in. of water

From Table 8-28: H/W_0= 12/48=0.25, W_1/W_0=1, C_o=1.14

Elbow loss = 1.14 × 0.01683 = 0.019 in. water.

Equal Friction Method Example.—To design a duct system by the equal friction method, a friction factor per 100 ft of equivalent length is determined by selecting the maximum duct velocity that would satisfy sound criteria for the space.

Example 7: An air velocity of 1440 fpm was selected for a public school ventilation system of 12000 *cfm*. Find the duct width for a 20 in. high main, and also the friction loss per 100 ft of equivalent length.

Solution: Let W = required duct width. To find the ft^2 area of a duct with a capacity of 12,000 *cfm* at 1,440 fpm:

$$A = \frac{cfm}{V} = \frac{12000}{1440}$$

$$A = \frac{W \times 20}{144}$$

Substituting:

$$\frac{W \times 20}{144} = \frac{12000}{1440}$$

$$W = 60$$

$$\text{Duct size} = 60 \times 20$$

Therefore, a 60 × 20 duct is equivalent to one of 37 in. diameter.

A 37 in. diameter duct at 12000 *cfm* has a friction loss per 100 ft of 0.09 in. water.

The friction factor of 0.09 in. would be used for all duct sizes in an equal friction design.

Example 8: Using a friction loss per 100 ft of 0.09 in. water, calculate the velocity and size of a branch duct that is 14 in. high and has a capacity of 1,800 *cfm*.

A duct of 1,800 *cfm* at 0.09 in. water = 18 in. diameter

A 18 in. diameter is 19×14, where

$$A = \frac{19 \times 14}{144} = 1.85 \ ft^2$$

$$V = \frac{Q}{A} = \frac{1800}{1.85}$$

$$V = 974 \ fpm$$

For low pressure systems of equal to friction design, the friction loss per 100 ft of equivalent length of 0.07–0.15 in. water. Total duct resistance is then determined by multiplying the equivalent length of the longest run by the factor selected and dividing by 100.

Example 9: Find the friction loss of a duct run with an equivalent length of 350 ft and a friction loss of 0.09 in. per 100 ft.

Solution:
$$FL = \frac{EQL \times EF}{100}$$

where FL = friction loss;
   EQL = equivalent length, ft; and
   FF = friction factor, loss per 100 ft.

$$FL = \frac{EQL \times FF}{100} = \frac{350 \times 0.09}{100} = 0.315 \ in \ water$$

When a decrease in velocity occurs in the duct at the fan discharge, a static pressure regain equal to 0.75 of the velocity pressure difference of the fan discharge and duct should be allowed:

$$Regain = 0.75(P_v \ fan - P_v \ duct)$$

Example 10: Find the static pressure regain when a fan outlet velocity of 2400 fpm discharges into a duct increaser where the velocity decreases to 1600 fpm.

Regain = $0.75(P_v \ fan - P_v \ duct)$

From Table 8-1: 2400 fpm = 0.36 in. of water; 1600 fpm = 0.16 in. of water

Regain = 0.75(0.36 − 0.16) = 0.75(0.20)

Regain = 0.15 in. wg

Resistance in Low Pressure Duct System Example.—Total resistance in low pressure duct systems is the sum of duct, equipment, entrance, and discharge, less the pressure gain at fan discharge.

Although the equal friction method of finding resistance is convenient because calculations are held to a minimum, branch ducts present difficulties using equal friction because at close proximity to the fan have the greatest amount of pressure, require maximum damping, and are not easily balanced for design air quantities. A

refinement is to size these branch ducts at a greater friction loss factor so the pressure available may be partially or fully utilized. However, velocities must neither be excessive nor generate objectionable noise in the space.

Example 11: Calculate the size of a branch duct that will use pressure available at the take-off of a main in an air-conditioning system for a printing plant. where:

Branch duct volume = 1400 *cfm*

Branch duct depth = 10 in.

Equivalent length = 125 ft.

Pressure loss at take-off = 0.035 in. water

Pressure required at supply diffuser = 0.20 in. water

Main duct pressure at take-off = 0.885 in. water

Solution: From previous example:

$$FL = \frac{EQL \times FF}{100}$$

Converting

$$FF = \frac{100 \times FL}{EQL}$$

Loss at take off	0.035 in.
Pressure required at outlet	0.200 in.
Total	0.235 in.

Friction loss of branch = 0.885 − 0.235 = 0.65 in.

$$FF = \frac{100 \times 0.65 \, in.}{125} = 0.52 \ in./100 \ ft$$

1400 ft at 0.52 in./100 ft = 12 in. diameter

12 in. diameter in rectangular duct = 12 in. × 10 in.

Static Regain Method Example.—The following is a comparative analysis of two ducts for an air conditioning supply system of 16,000 *cfm*:

Duct Size	Area, ft²	Velocity, fpm	Velocity Pressure	Friction/100 ft
48″ ×24″	8	2000	0.25 in.	0.15 in.
24″ × 24″	4	4000	1.00 in.	0.84 in.

In the 24" × 24" duct, velocity pressure is 4 times greater and the friction factor is 5.6 times greater than 48" × 24". To hold high velocity duct losses at a minimum and to maintain a constant static pressure throughout the system, the *Static Regain Method Example* is used, where the velocity pressure of each section in a duct run is reduced an amount equivalent to the friction loss of the previous section. The following formula is convenient to calculate duct sizes for a static regain which is assumed to have a 50 percent efficiency.

$$P_{vd} = P_{vu} - 2FL$$

where FL = friction loss in preceding duct section;
   P_{vd} = velocity pressure in downstream duct; and
   P_{vu} = velocity pressure in upstream duct.

Example 12: A 22-in.-diameter cold duct has a volume of 12500 *cfm*, a velocity of 5000 fpm, and a 3500 *cfm* branch take-off at a location 26 feet from a sound trap. The friction loss in this portion is 0.35 in. wg.

Solution: Find the required duct size after the branch tap. where:

From Table 8-1: 5000 fpm = 1.56 in. of water.

$FL = 0.35$ in.

cfm in downstream duct = $12500 - 3500 = 9000$.

$$P_{vd} = P_{vu} - 2FL$$
$$= 1.56 - 2 \times 0.35$$
$$= 0.86 \text{ in. of water}$$

From Table 8-1: 0.86 in. of water = 3714 fpm.

A duct for 9000 *cfm* at 3700 fpm is 22 in. diameter.

The above example explains the plenum duct principle to achieve static regain. As each duct segment has a different friction loss, a separate tabulation should be used to summarize total system resistance and the most critical duct run (that having the most resistance), not necessarily the longest, is used for the total.

A branch duct to a terminal unit is generally made the size of the unit inlet. However, when a branch feeds more than one unit, the duct may be sized to use a portion of excessive pressure, such as a take-off at close proximity to the fan. Generally, a high-loss take-off fitting, such as a tee, is used to absorb some excess of pressure available for the total resistance requirement of the branch duct, fittings, terminal unit, and outlets.

Design range for high-velocity systems is 4000 to 6000 fpm for the initial main duct, at a friction loss of about 1.0 in. to 1.5 in. per 100 ft.

Fitting Loss Coefficients

Table 8-6. Supply or Return Rectangular Elbow without Vane

C_p Values								
	Height to Width Ratio H/W							
r/W	0.25	0.5	1.00	2.00	3.00	4.00	6.00	8.00
0.5	1.53	1.38	1.18	1.00	1.00	1.06	1.16	1.18
0.75	0.57	0.52	0.44	0.39	0.39	0.4	0.43	0.44
1	0.27	0.25	0.21	0.18	0.18	0.19	0.21	0.21
1.5	0.22	0.2	0.17	0.14	0.14	0.15	0.17	0.17
2	0.2	0.18	0.15	0.13	0.13	0.14	0.15	0.15
Angle Factor K								
θ	20	30	45	60	75	90	150	180
K	0.31	0.45	0.6	0.78	0.9	1	1.28	1.4

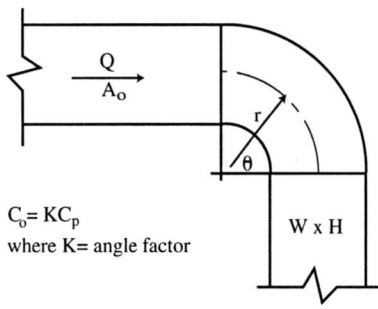

$C_o = KC_p$
where K = angle factor

Table 8-7. Supply or Return Rectangular Elbow with One Splitter Vane

C_p Values								
	Height to Width Ratio H/W							
r/W	0.25	0.5	1	2	3	4	6	8
0.6	0.36	0.27	0.25	0.3	0.35	0.39	0.46	0.52
0.7	0.22	0.16	0.14	0.15	0.16	0.17	0.19	0.21
0.8	0.15	0.11	0.09	0.09	0.09	0.1	0.11	0.12
0.9	0.11	0.08	0.07	0.06	0.06	0.06	0.07	0.07
1	0.09	0.06	0.05	0.04	0.04	0.04	0.05	0.05
Angle Factor K								
θ	0	30	45	60	90			
K	0	0.45	0.6	0.78	1			
Curve Ratio CR								
r/W	0.6	0.7	0.8	0.90	1			
CR	0.302	0.408	0.48	0.535	0.577			
Throat Radius/Width Ratio R/W								
r/W	0.6	0.7	0.8	0.9	1			
R/W	0.1	0.2	0.3	0.4	0.5			

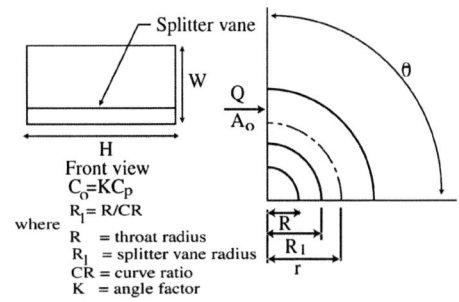

Front view
$C_o = KC_p$
$R_1 = R/CR$
where R = throat radius
R_1 = splitter vane radius
CR = curve ratio
K = angle factor

Table 8-8. Supply or Return Rectangular Elbow Mitered

C_o Values						
	Height to Width Ratio H/W					
θ	0.25	0.5	1	2	4	6
30	0.18	0.17	0.16	0.15	0.13	0.12
45	0.38	0.37	0.34	0.31	0.27	0.25
60	0.6	0.59	0.55	0.49	0.43	0.39
90	1.3	1.27	1.18	1.07	0.92	0.85

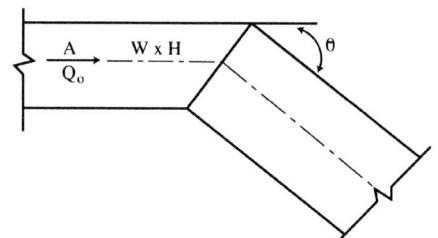

Table 8-9. Supply or Return Rectangular Elbow Mitered 90° Single Thickness Vanes

r in.	s in.	L in.	C_o Values
2.0	1.5	0	0.11
2.0	1.5	0.75	0.12
4.5	3.25	0	0.33

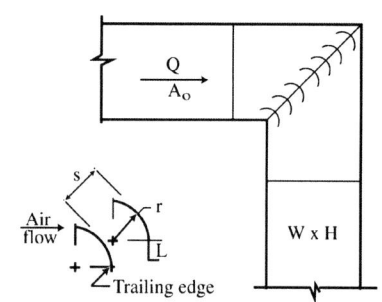

Table 8-10. Supply or Return Rectangular Elbow Mitered 90° Double Thickness Vanes

r in.	s in.	C_o Values
2.0	1.5	0.38
2.0	2.125	0.25
4.5	3.25	0.41

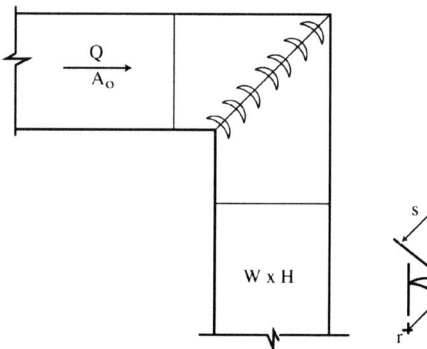

Table 8-11. Supply or Return Rectangular Elbow Z Shaped

H/W	C_p Values L/W								
	0.4	0.6	0.8	1	1.2	1.6	2	4	8.0
0.25	0.68	0.99	1.77	2.89	3.97	4.6	4.6	3.39	3.03
0.5	0.66	0.96	1.72	2.81	3.86	4.47	4.47	3.3	2.94
1	0.62	0.9	1.61	2.63	3.61	4.18	4.18	3.08	2.75
2	0.56	0.81	1.45	2.37	3.25	3.76	3.76	2.77	2.48
3	0.51	0.75	1.34	2.18	3.00	3.47	3.47	2.56	2.28
4	0.48	0.70	1.26	2.05	2.82	3.26	3.26	2.4	2.15
6	0.45	0.65	1.16	1.89	2.6	3.01	3.01	2.22	1.98
$R_e/1000$	10	30	40	60	100	140	500		
K_r	1.4	1.19	1.14	1.09	1.04	1	1		

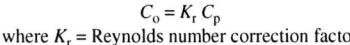

$$C_o = K_r\, C_p$$

where K_r = Reynolds number correction factor

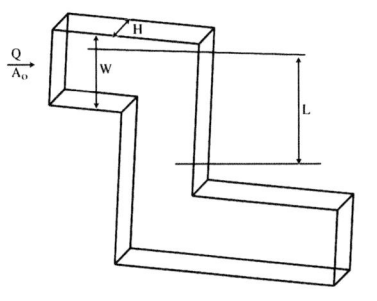

Table 8-12. Supply or Return Rectangular Damper

	H/W	C_o Values θ						
		0	10	20	30	50	60	70
Butterfly Damper	0.12	0.04	0.3	1.1	3	23	60	190
	0.25	0.08	0.33	1.18	3.3	26	70	210
	1	0.08	0.33	1.18	3.3	26	70	210
	L/R							
Parallel Blades Damper	0.3	0.52	0.79	1.49	2.20	8.73	14.15	32.11
	0.4	0.52	0.84	1.56	2.25	9.00	16.00	37.73
	0.6	0.52	0.92	1.66	2.45	9.77	21.75	53.78
	0.8	0.52	0.96	1.69	2.55	10.03	22.8	65.46
	1.0	0.52	1.00	1.76	2.66	10.53	23.84	73.23
	1.5	0.52	1.08	1.83	2.78	11.21	27.56	97.41
Opposed Blades Damper	0.3	0.52	0.79	1.91	3.77	19.46	70.12	295.21
	0.4	0.52	0.85	2.07	4.61	26.73	92.9	346.25
	0.6	0.52	1.00	2.46	5.99	41.26	143.69	440.25
	0.8	0.52	1.08	2.66	6.96	56.47	193.92	520.27
	1.0	0.52	1.17	2.91	7.31	71.68	245.45	576
	1.5	0.52	1.38	3.16	9.51	107.41	361	717.05

$$\frac{L}{R} = \frac{NW}{2(H+W)}$$

where
N = number of damper blades
W = duct dimension parallel to blade axis, in
H = duct height, in
L = sum of damper blade lengths, in
R = perimeter of duct, in

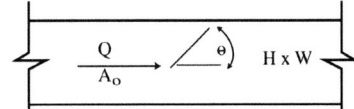

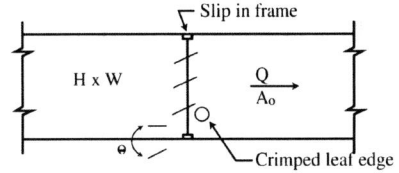

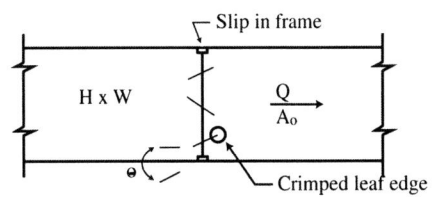

Table 8-13. Supply and Return Circular Elbow of r/D = 1.5

D in.	C_o 90°	45°
3	0.30	0.18
4	0.21	0.13
5	0.16	0.10
6	0.14	0.08
7	0.12	0.07
8	0.11	0.07
9	0.11	0.07
10	0.11	0.07

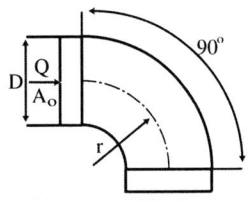

Die stamped 90° elbows

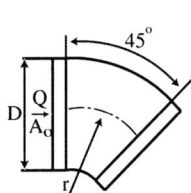

Die stamped 45° elbows

Table 8-14. Supply and Return Circular Elbow of r/D = 1.5

D in.	C_o 90°	C_o 60°	C_o 45°	Figure
4	0.57	0.45	0.34	
6	0.43	0.34	0.26	
8	0.34	0.27	0.21	
10	0.28	0.23	0.17	
12	0.26	0.20	0.16	
14	0.25	0.19	0.15	
16	0.25	0.19	0.15	

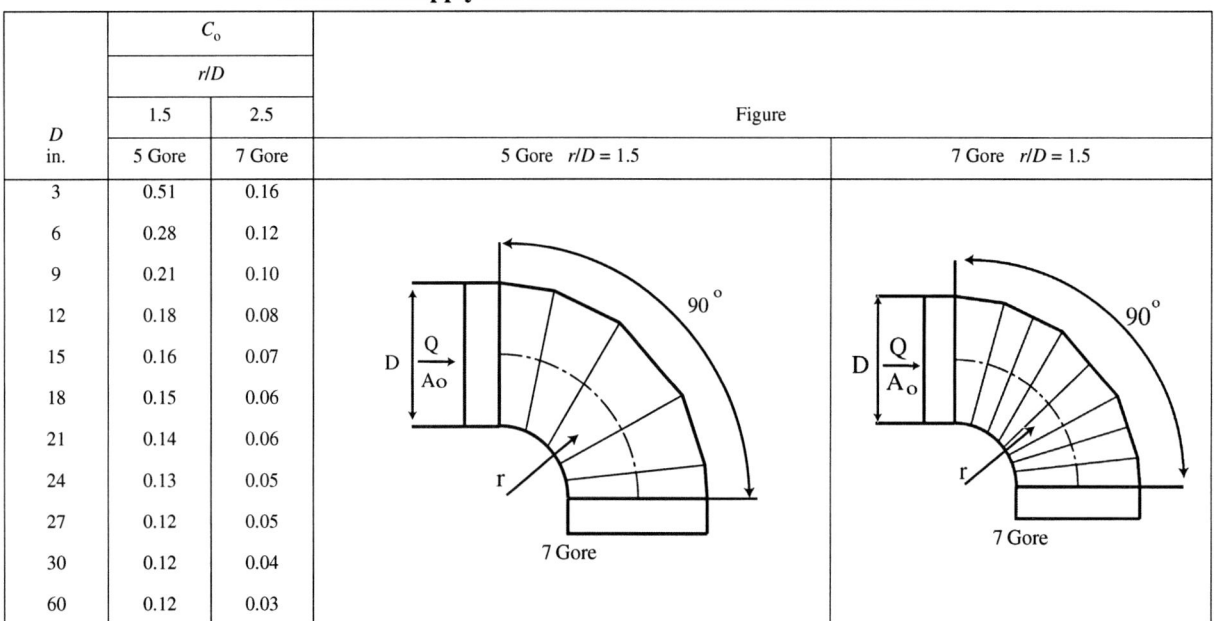

Table 8-15. Supply and Return Circular Elbow Made of Gore

D in.	C_o r/D 1.5 — 5 Gore	C_o r/D 2.5 — 7 Gore	Figure
3	0.51	0.16	
6	0.28	0.12	
9	0.21	0.10	
12	0.18	0.08	
15	0.16	0.07	
18	0.15	0.06	
21	0.14	0.06	
24	0.13	0.05	
27	0.12	0.05	
30	0.12	0.04	
60	0.12	0.03	

Table 8-16. Supply and Return Elbow, r/D =1.5

D in	C_o 3 Gore 60°	C_o 3 Gore 45°	C_o Mitered 45°	Figures
3	0.40	0.31	0.34	
6	0.21	0.17	0.34	
9	0.16	0.13	0.34	
12	0.14	0.11	0.34	
15	0.12	0.11	0.34	
18	0.11	0.09	0.34	
21	0.10	0.08	0.34	
24	0.09	0.08	0.34	
27	0.09	0.07	0.34	
30	0.09	0.07	0.34	
60	0.09	0.07	0.34	

Table 8-17. Supply Air System from Plenum to Rectangular Duct

$$D_h = \frac{2H_0 W_0}{H_0 + W_0}$$

θ is larger of θ_1 and θ_2

A_o/A_1	L/D_h	\multicolumn{9}{c}{C_o Values — θ}								
		0	20	30	45	60	90	120	150	180
0.10	0.05	0.46	0.38	0.33	0.30	0.28	0.31	0.36	0.41	0.46
	0.10	0.46	0.30	0.23	0.19	0.17	0.23	0.30	0.38	0.46
	0.15	0.46	0.25	0.18	0.15	0.14	0.21	0.29	0.37	0.46
	0.30	0.46	0.22	0.16	0.13	0.13	0.20	0.28	0.37	0.46
0.20	0.05	0.42	0.35	0.30	0.27	0.25	0.29	0.33	0.37	0.42
	0.10	0.42	0.27	0.21	0.18	0.15	0.21	0.27	0.35	0.42
	0.15	0.42	0.23	0.17	0.13	0.13	0.19	0.26	0.34	0.42
	0.30	0.42	0.20	0.15	0.12	0.12	0.18	0.26	0.34	0.42
0.40	0.05	0.34	0.28	0.25	0.22	0.20	0.23	0.26	0.30	0.34
	0.10	0.34	0.22	0.17	0.14	0.12	0.17	0.22	0.28	0.34
	0.15	0.34	0.18	0.14	0.11	0.10	0.15	0.21	0.27	0.34
	0.30	0.34	0.16	0.12	0.10	0.10	0.15	0.21	0.27	0.34
0.60	0.05	0.25	0.21	0.18	0.16	0.15	0.17	0.19	0.22	0.25
	0.10	0.25	0.16	0.13	0.11	0.09	0.12	0.16	0.21	0.25
	0.15	0.25	0.14	0.10	0.08	0.08	0.11	0.16	0.20	0.25
	0.30	0.25	0.12	0.09	0.07	0.07	0.11	0.15	0.20	0.25
0.80	0.05	0.15	0.12	0.11	0.10	0.09	0.10	0.12	0.13	0.15
	0.10	0.15	0.10	0.07	0.06	0.05	0.07	0.10	0.12	0.15
	0.15	0.15	0.08	0.06	0.05	0.04	0.07	0.09	0.12	0.15
	0.30	0.15	0.07	0.05	0.04	0.04	0.07	0.09	0.12	0.15

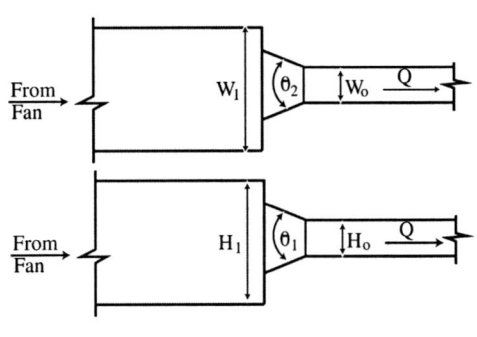

Table 8-18. Supply Rectangular Diffuser

A_1/A_0	$R_e/1000$	\multicolumn{7}{c}{C_o Values — θ}						
		10	20	30	45	60	90	120
2	50	0.51	0.63	0.80	0.96	1.04	1.09	1.09
	100	0.50	0.63	0.80	0.96	1.04	1.09	1.09
	200	0.47	0.63	0.74	0.93	1.02	1.08	1.08
	400	0.42	0.62	0.74	0.93	1.02	1.08	1.08
4	50	0.38	0.63	0.76	0.91	1.03	1.07	1.07
	100	0.36	0.59	0.72	0.88	1.02	1.07	1.07
	200	0.31	0.53	0.67	0.83	0.96	1.06	1.06
	400	0.27	0.53	0.67	0.83	0.96	1.06	1.06

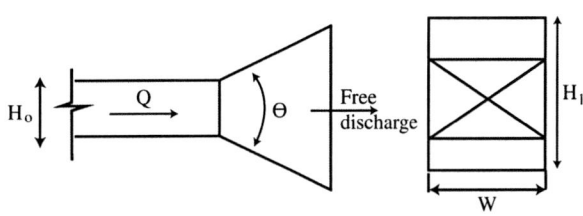

Table 8-19. Supply Air Systems Variable Inlet/Outlet Areas with 90° Elbow

H/W_1	\multicolumn{7}{c}{C_o Values — W_o/W_1}						
	0.6	0.8	1	1.2	1.4	1.6	2
0.25	0.63	0.92	1.24	1.64	2.14	2.71	4.24
1	0.61	0.87	1.15	1.47	1.86	2.3	3.36
4	0.53	0.7	0.9	1.17	1.49	1.84	2.64

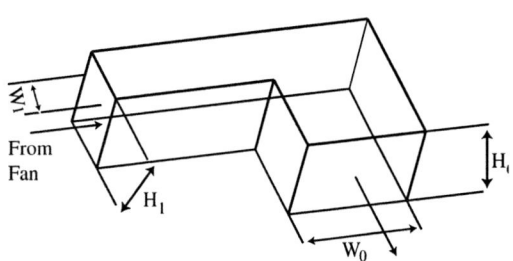

Table 8-20. Supply Air Systems Transition from Rectangular to Rectangular

A_o/A_1	C_o Values								
	θ								
	10	15	30	45	60	90	120	150	180
0.10	0.05	0.05	0.05	0.07	0.08	0.19	0.29	0.37	0.43
0.25	0.05	0.04	0.04	0.06	0.07	0.17	0.27	0.35	0.41
0.50	0.06	0.05	0.05	0.06	0.07	0.14	0.20	0.26	0.27
1.00	0.00	0.00	0.00	0.00	0.00	0.00	0.00	0.00	1.00
2.00	0.56	0.52	0.96	1.40	1.48	1.52	1.48	1.44	1.40
4.00	2.72	3.04	6.72	9.60	10.88	11.20	11.04	10.72	10.56

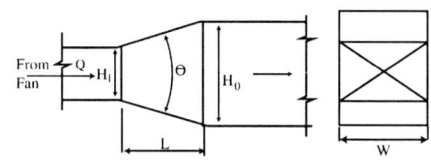

Table 8-21. Supply Air Systems Transition from Round to Rectangular

A_o/A_1	C_o Values								
	θ								
	10	15	30	45	60	90	120	150	180
0.10	0.05	0.05	0.05	0.07	0.08	0.19	0.29	0.37	0.43
0.25	0.06	0.05	0.04	0.06	0.07	0.17	0.27	0.35	0.41
0.50	0.06	0.07	0.05	0.06	0.06	0.12	0.18	0.24	0.26
1.00	0.00	0.00	0.00	0.00	0.00	0.00	0.00	0.00	0.00
2.00	0.60	0.84	1.20	1.32	1.32	1.32	1.28	1.24	1.20
4.00	4.00	5.76	8.32	9.28	9.92	10.24	10.24	10.24	10.24

θ is greater of θ_1 or θ_2

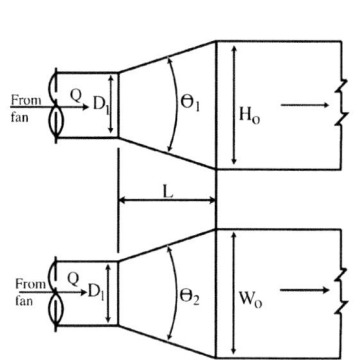

Table 8-22. Supply Air System Diverging Wye of Type $A_s + A_b \geq A_c$

A_s/A_c	A_b/A_c	C_b Values						
		Q_b/Q_c						
		0.1	0.2	0.4	0.5	0.6	0.8	0.9
0.50	0.25	3.44	0.70	0.20	0.17	0.16	0.17	0.18
	0.50	11.00	2.37	0.64	0.52	0.47	0.47	0.48
0.75	0.25	2.19	0.55	0.31	0.33	0.35	0.37	0.39
	0.50	13.00	2.50	0.47	0.34	0.31	0.36	0.43
1.00	0.25	3.44	0.78	0.33	0.30	0.31	0.42	0.46
	0.50	15.50	3.00	0.62	0.48	0.42	0.42	0.46

A_s/A_c	A_b/A_c	C_s Values						
		Q_s/Q_c						
		0.1	0.2	0.4	0.5	0.6	0.8	0.9
0.50	0.25	8.75	1.62	0.17	0.05	0.00	−0.02	0.00
	0.50	7.50	1.12	0.06	0.05	0.09	0.19	0.22
0.75	0.25	19.13	3.38	0.28	0.05	−0.02	0.00	0.06
	0.50	20.81	3.23	0.14	−0.02	−0.05	−0.02	0.03
1.00	0.25	46.00	9.50	1.31	0.52	0.14	−0.05	−0.01
	0.50	35.00	6.75	0.75	0.24	0.00	−0.09	−0.04

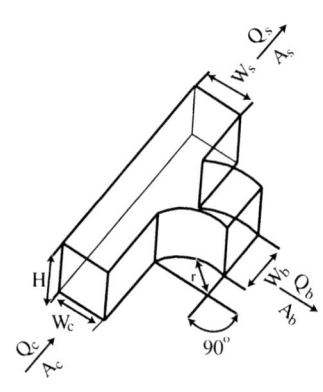

Table 8-23. Supply Air System Diverging 45° Wye of Type $A_s + A_b > A_c$, $A_s = A_c$

A_s/A_c	A_b/A_c	C_b Values					
		Q_b/Q_c					
		0.1	0.2	0.4	0.5	0.6	0.8
0.10	0.60	0.52	0.57	0.64	0.67	0.70	0.73
0.20	2.24	0.56	0.44	0.51	0.54	0.58	0.62
0.30	5.94	1.08	0.52	0.44	0.46	0.49	0.54
0.40	10.56	1.88	0.71	0.35	0.31	0.31	0.34
0.50	17.75	3.25	1.14	0.40	0.31	0.30	0.31
0.60	26.64	5.04	1.76	0.50	0.36	0.32	0.30
0.70	37.73	7.23	2.56	0.67	0.44	0.35	0.30
0.80	49.92	9.92	3.48	0.87	0.55	0.42	0.32
Q_s/Q_c	0.10	0.20	0.50	0.60	0.80		
C_s	32.00	6.50	0.40	0.17	0.03		

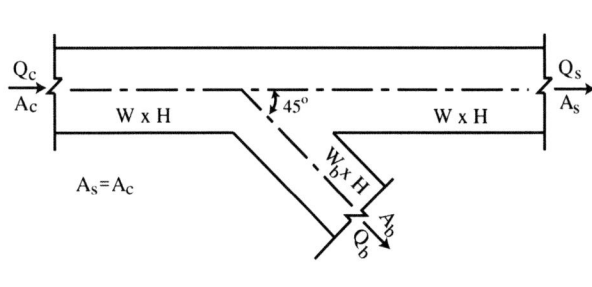

Table 8-24. Supply Air System Diverging Tee of the Type $A_s + A_b > A_c$, $A_s = A_c$

A_s/A_c	A_b/A_c	C_b Values					
		Q_b/Q_c					
		0.2	0.3	0.4	0.5	0.6	0.7
0.20	5.16	1.28	1.03	0.99	0.94	0.92	0.90
0.30	10.26	1.78	1.28	1.16	1.06	1.01	0.97
0.40	15.84	2.24	1.48	1.11	0.88	0.80	0.75
0.50	24.25	3.03	1.89	1.35	1.03	0.91	0.84
0.60	34.56	4.04	2.41	1.64	1.22	1.04	0.94
0.70	46.55	5.17	3.00	2.00	1.44	1.20	1.06
Q_s/Q_c	0.20	0.30	0.40	0.50	0.60		
C_s	6.50	2.22	0.87	0.40	0.17		

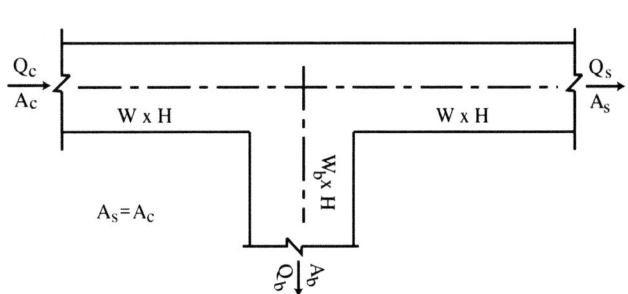

Table 8-25. Supply Air System Diverging Tee Rectangular Main to Round Tap

A_s/A_c	C_b Values						
	Q_b/Q_c						
	0.2	0.3	0.4	0.5	0.6	0.7	0.8
0.30	2.67	1.58	1.20	1.03	0.94	0.88	0.85
0.40	4.20	2.25	1.58	1.27	1.10	1.00	0.94
0.50	6.19	3.13	2.07	1.58	1.32	1.16	1.06
0.60	8.63	4.20	2.67	1.96	1.58	1.35	1.20
0.70	11.51	5.48	3.38	2.41	1.89	1.58	1.38

A_s/A_c	C_b Values						
	Q_s/Q_c						
	0.1	0.2	0.3	0.4	0.5	0.6	0.7
0.30	3.48	0.31	0.04				
0.40	7.55	0.98	0.18	0.04			
0.50	13.18	2.03	0.49	0.13	0.04		
0.60	20.38	3.48	0.98	0.31	0.10	0.04	
0.70	29.15	5.32	1.64	0.60	0.23	0.09	0.04

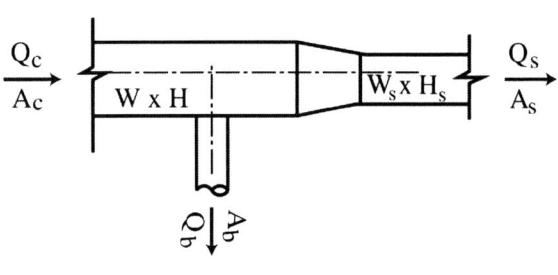

Table 8-26. Supply Air System Diverging Tee

	C_b Values				
	Q_b/Q_c				
A_s/A_c	0.2	0.4	0.5	0.6	0.8
0.20	0.73	0.34	0.32	0.32	0.34
0.30	1.65	0.47	0.37	0.34	0.32
0.40	3.10	0.73	0.51	0.41	0.34
0.50	5.08	1.12	0.73	0.54	0.38
0.60	7.59	1.65	1.03	0.73	0.47
0.70	10.63	2.31	1.42	0.98	0.58
0.80	14.20	3.10	1.90	1.28	0.73
	C_b Values				
	Q_s/Q_c				
A_s/A_c	0.2	0.4	0.5	0.6	0.8
0.40	0.98	0.04			
0.50	2.03	0.13	0.04		
0.60	3.48	0.31	0.10	0.04	
0.70	5.32	0.60	0.23	0.09	
0.80	7.55	0.98	0.42	0.18	0.04

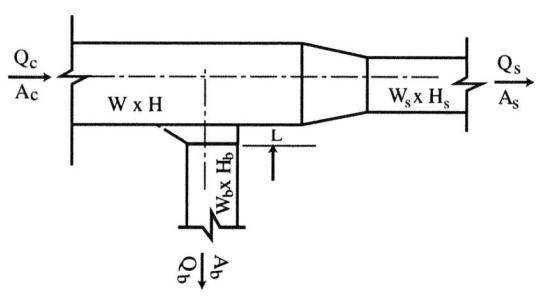

Table 8-27. Return or Exhaust from Plenum to Circular Ducts

	C_o Values									
	r/D_1									
A_o/A_1	0.00	0.02	0.04	0.05	0.06	0.08	0.1	0.12	0.16	0.2
1.5	0.22	0.15	0.12	0.1	0.09	0.07	0.05	0.04	0.03	0.01
2	0.13	0.08	0.07	0.06	0.05	0.04	0.03	0.02	0.02	0.01
2.5	0.08	0.05	0.04	0.04	0.03	0.02	0.02	0.01	0.01	0.00
3	0.06	0.04	0.03	0.02	0.02	0.02	0.01	0.01	0.01	0.00
4	0.03	0.02	0.02	0.01	0.01	0.01	0.01	0.01	0.00	0.00

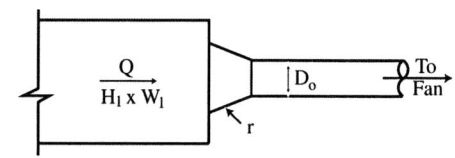

Table 8-28. Return or Exhaust Variable Inlet/Outlet Areas Elbow, 90 Degree

	C_o Values						
	W_1/W_o						
H/W_o	0.6	0.8	1	1.2	1.4	1.6	2.00
0.25	1.76	1.43	1.24	1.14	1.09	1.06	1.06
1	1.7	1.36	1.15	1.02	0.95	0.9	0.84
4	1.46	1.1	0.9	0.81	0.76	0.72	0.66

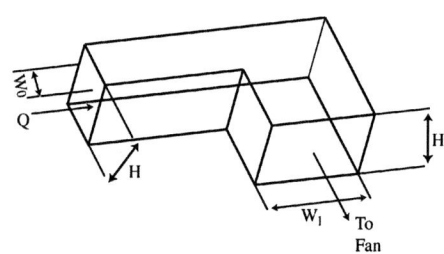

Table 8-29. Return or Exhaust Transition from Rectangular to Rectangular

A_o/A_1	C_o Values							
	θ							
	10	15	30	45	60	90	120	180
0.10	0.24	0.26	0.53	0.69	0.82	0.93	0.93	0.91
0.25	0.17	0.19	0.42	0.60	0.68	0.70	0.69	0.66
0.50	0.14	0.13	0.24	0.35	0.37	0.38	0.37	0.35
1.00	0.00	0.00	0.00	0.00	0.00	0.00	0.00	0.00
2.00	0.23	0.20	0.20	0.24	0.28	0.54	0.78	1.09
4.00	0.81	0.64	0.64	0.88	1.12	2.78	4.38	6.60

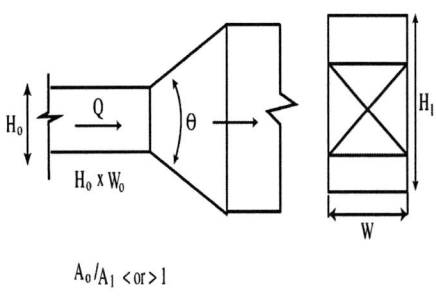

$A_o/A_1 <$ or > 1

Table 8-30. Return or Exhaust Transition from Rectangular to Round

A_o/A_1	C_o Values							
	θ							
	10	15	30	45	60	90	120	180
0.06	0.3	0.54	0.65	0.77	0.88	0.95	0.98	0.93
0.1	0.3	0.5	0.64	0.75	0.84	0.89	0.91	0.88
0.25	0.25	0.36	0.52	0.58	0.62	0.64	0.64	0.64
0.5	0.15	0.21	0.3	0.33	0.33	0.33	0.32	0.3
1	0	0	0	0	0	0	0	0
2	0.24	0.28	0.2	0.22	0.24	0.49	0.73	1.04
4	0.89	0.78	0.7	0.88	1.12	2.72	4.33	6.58
6	1.89	1.67	1.49	1.98	2.52	6.51	10.14	15.14
10	5.09	5.32	5.05	6.5	8.05	19.06	29.07	43.05

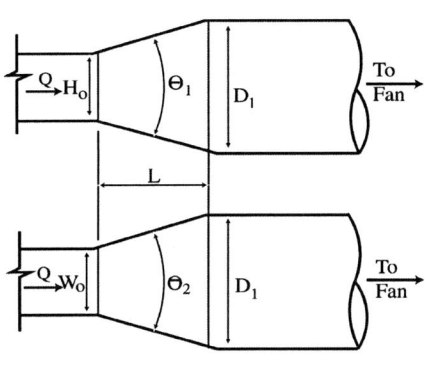

Table 8-31. Return or Exhaust Converging Tee Round Tap to Rectangular Main

Q_b/Q_c	0.30	0.40	0.50	0.60	0.70	0.80
C_b	0.64	0.94	1.27	1.43	1.40	1.45

Q_s/Q_c	0.30	0.40	0.50	0.60	0.70	0.80
C_s	6.54	3.74	2.23	1.33	0.76	0.38

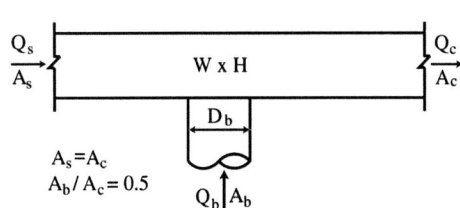

$A_s = A_c$
$A_b / A_c = 0.5$

Table 8-32. Return or Exhaust Converging Tee 45 Degree Entry Branch

Q_b/Q_c	0.30	0.40	0.50	0.60	0.70	0.80
C_b	−0.64	0.53	0.76	0.79	0.93	0.79

Q_s/Q_c	0.30	0.40	0.50	0.60	0.70	0.80
C_b	6.54	3.74	2.23	1.33	0.76	0.38

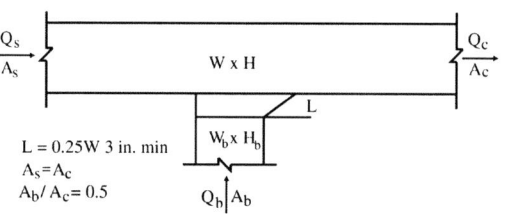

L = 0.25W 3 in. min
$A_s = A_c$
$A_b/A_c = 0.5$

Table 8-33. Return or Exhaust Transition from Round to Plenum

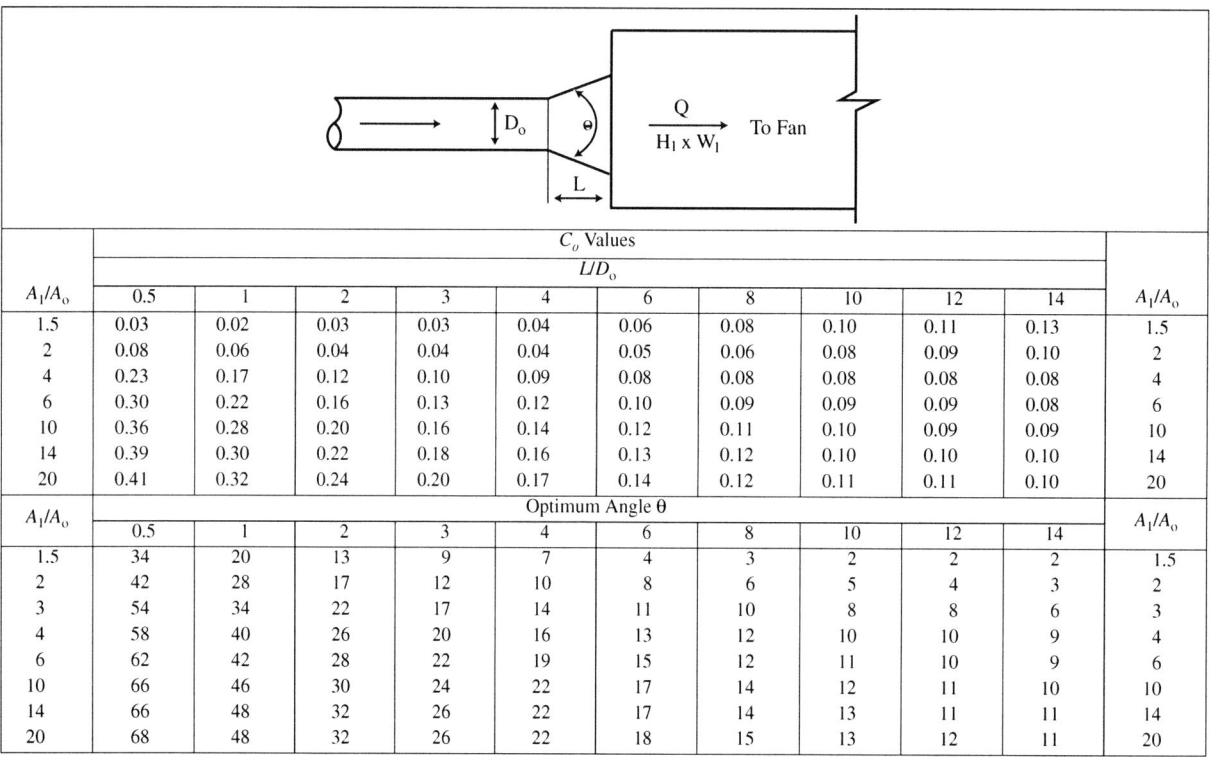

A_1/A_o	C_o Values										A_1/A_o
	L/D_o										
	0.5	1	2	3	4	6	8	10	12	14	
1.5	0.03	0.02	0.03	0.03	0.04	0.06	0.08	0.10	0.11	0.13	1.5
2	0.08	0.06	0.04	0.04	0.04	0.05	0.06	0.08	0.09	0.10	2
4	0.23	0.17	0.12	0.10	0.09	0.08	0.08	0.08	0.08	0.08	4
6	0.30	0.22	0.16	0.13	0.12	0.10	0.09	0.09	0.09	0.08	6
10	0.36	0.28	0.20	0.16	0.14	0.12	0.11	0.10	0.09	0.09	10
14	0.39	0.30	0.22	0.18	0.16	0.13	0.12	0.10	0.10	0.10	14
20	0.41	0.32	0.24	0.20	0.17	0.14	0.12	0.11	0.11	0.10	20
A_1/A_o	Optimum Angle θ										A_1/A_o
	0.5	1	2	3	4	6	8	10	12	14	
1.5	34	20	13	9	7	4	3	2	2	2	1.5
2	42	28	17	12	10	8	6	5	4	3	2
3	54	34	22	17	14	11	10	8	8	6	3
4	58	40	26	20	16	13	12	10	10	9	4
6	62	42	28	22	19	15	12	11	10	9	6
10	66	46	30	24	22	17	14	12	11	10	10
14	66	48	32	26	22	17	14	13	11	11	14
20	68	48	32	26	22	18	15	13	12	11	20

Table 8-34. Return or Exhaust Transition from Round to Round

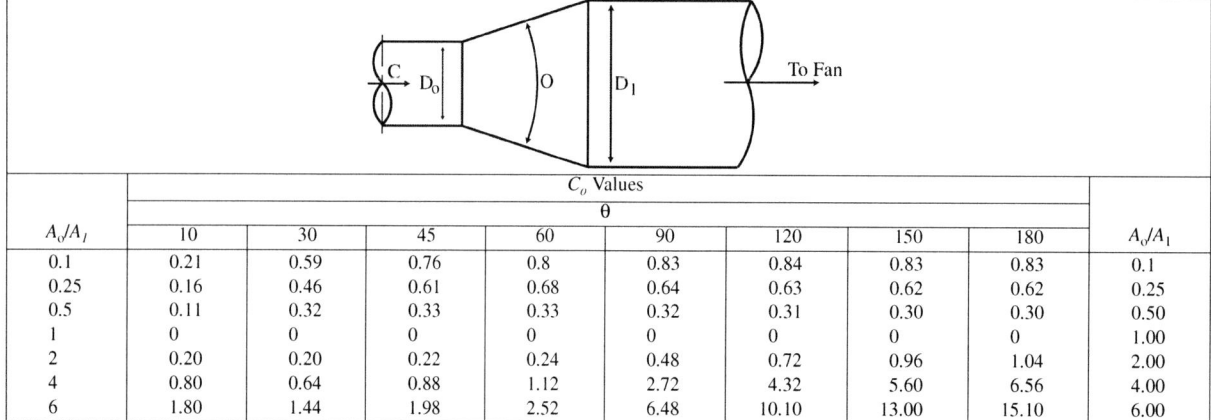

A_o/A_1	C_o Values								A_o/A_1
	θ								
	10	30	45	60	90	120	150	180	
0.1	0.21	0.59	0.76	0.8	0.83	0.84	0.83	0.83	0.1
0.25	0.16	0.46	0.61	0.68	0.64	0.63	0.62	0.62	0.25
0.5	0.11	0.32	0.33	0.33	0.32	0.31	0.30	0.30	0.50
1	0	0	0	0	0	0	0	0	1.00
2	0.20	0.20	0.22	0.24	0.48	0.72	0.96	1.04	2.00
4	0.80	0.64	0.88	1.12	2.72	4.32	5.60	6.56	4.00
6	1.80	1.44	1.98	2.52	6.48	10.10	13.00	15.10	6.00

Table 8-35. Return or Exhaust Transition from Round to Rectangular

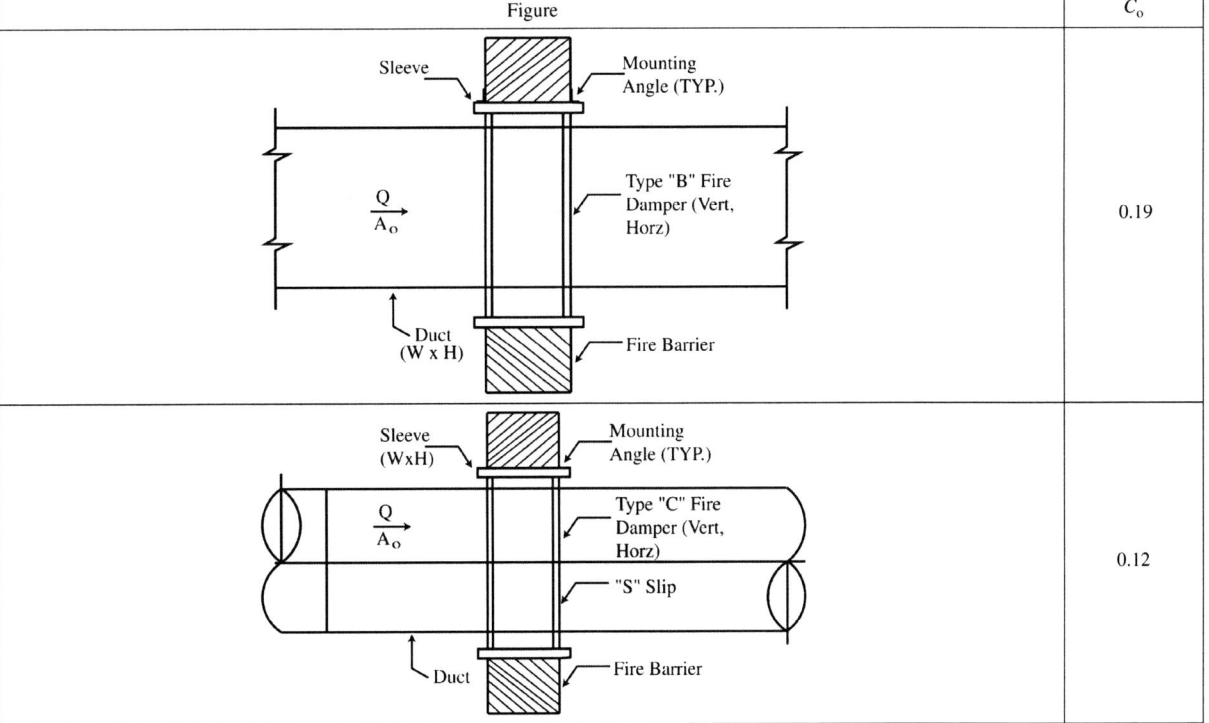

A_o/A_1	C_o Values								A_o/A_1
	θ								
	10	15	30	45	60	90	120	180	
0.1	0.3	0.5	0.64	0.75	0.84	0.89	0.91	0.88	0.1
0.25	0.25	0.36	0.52	0.58	0.62	0.64	0.64	0.64	0.25
0.5	0.15	0.21	0.30	0.33	0.33	0.33	0.32	0.3	0.5
1	0.00	0.00	0.00	0.00	0.00	0.00	0.00	0.00	1
2	0.24	0.28	0.2	0.22	0.24	0.49	0.73	1.04	2
4	0.89	0.78	0.7	0.88	1.12	2.72	4.33	6.58	4
6	1.89	1.67	1.49	1.98	2.52	6.51	10.14	15.14	6

Table 8-36. Fire Damper

Figure	C_o
Sleeve — Mounting Angle (TYP.) — $\frac{Q}{A_o}$ — Type "B" Fire Damper (Vert, Horz) — Duct (W x H) — Fire Barrier	0.19
Sleeve (WxH) — Mounting Angle (TYP.) — $\frac{Q}{A_o}$ — Type "C" Fire Damper (Vert, Horz) — "S" Slip — Duct — Fire Barrier	0.12

Table 8-37. Return or Exhaust Wye Merging at 30° Converging

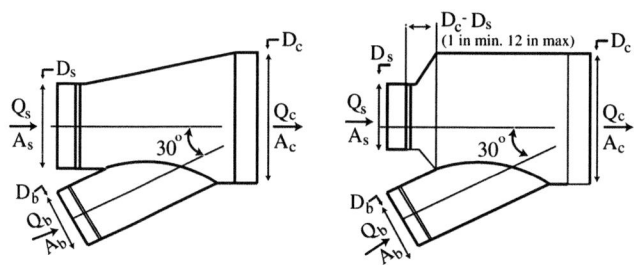

A_s/A_c	A_b/A_c	C_b Values							A_b/A_c	A_s/A_c
		Q_b/Q_c								
		0.2	0.3	0.4	0.5	0.6	0.7	0.8		
0.3	0.2	−1.77	0.08	0.59	0.77	0.84	0.88	0.92	0.2	0.3
	0.4	−10.08	−2.52	−0.41	0.32	0.59	0.67	0.68	0.4	
	0.6	−23.45	−6.44	−1.68	−0.03	0.57	0.76	0.77	0.6	
	0.8	−42.01	−11.77	−3.32	−0.38	0.69	1.02	1.03	0.8	
	1	−65.79	−18.53	−5.32	−0.73	0.94	1.45	1.47	1	
0.4	0.2	−0.85	0.39	0.71	0.82	0.87	0.9	0.94	0.2	0.4
	0.4	−6.48	−1.37	0.02	0.48	0.64	0.67	0.66	0.4	
	0.6	−15.37	−3.84	−0.71	0.33	0.67	0.75	0.71	0.6	
	0.8	−27.65	−7.16	−1.59	0.25	0.86	1.00	0.93	0.8	
	1	−43.35	−11.33	−2.63	0.26	1.21	1.42	1.31	1	
0.5	0.2	−0.36	0.54	0.77	0.85	0.88	0.9	0.95	0.2	0.5
	0.4	−4.59	−0.79	0.22	0.54	0.64	0.66	0.64	0.4	
	0.6	−11.13	−2.56	−0.28	0.45	0.67	0.69	0.65	0.6	
	0.8	−20.12	−4.88	−0.83	0.46	0.85	0.9	0.81	0.8	
	1	−31.58	−7.77	−1.43	0.59	1.19	1.26	1.12	1	
0.6	0.2	−0.1	0.62	0.79	0.85	0.87	0.9	0.95	0.2	0.6
	0.4	−3.55	−0.5	0.3	0.55	0.62	0.63	0.62	0.4	
	0.6	−8.8	−1.92	−0.12	0.45	0.61	0.62	0.57	0.6	
	0.8	−16	−3.76	−0.54	0.46	0.74	0.76	0.67	0.8	
	1	−25.14	−6.02	−0.99	0.58	1.02	1.04	0.9	1	
0.7	0.2	0.05	0.65	0.80	0.85	0.87	0.89	0.94	0.2	0.7
	0.4	−3	−0.38	0.31	0.52	0.59	0.6	0.59	0.4	
	0.6	−7.58	−1.67	−0.11	0.38	0.52	0.53	0.49	0.6	
	0.8	−13.83	−3.3	−0.53	0.33	0.58	0.59	0.52	0.8	
	1	−21.76	−5.3	−0.97	0.38	0.76	0.78	0.67	1	
0.8	0.2	0.11	0.65	0.79	0.84	0.86	0.88	0.94	0.2	0.8
	0.4	−2.75	−0.36	0.28	0.48	0.55	0.56	0.57	0.4	
	0.6	−7.05	−1.64	−0.2	0.26	0.41	0.43	0.41	0.6	
	0.8	−12.88	−3.26	−0.69	0.13	0.38	0.42	0.37	0.8	
	1	−20.27	−5.24	−1.23	0.06	0.45	0.51	0.43	1	
0.9	0.2	0.12	0.64	0.78	0.82	0.85	0.88	0.93	0.2	0.9
	0.4	−2.7	−0.4	0.22	0.43	0.5	0.53	0.54	0.4	
	0.6	−6.97	−1.77	−0.35	0.12	0.28	0.32	0.32	0.6	
	0.8	−12.74	−3.49	−0.97	−0.12	0.16	0.23	0.22	0.8	
	1	−20.06	−5.61	−1.66	−0.34	0.11	0.21	0.18	1	

Table 8-38. Return or Exhaust Wye Merging at 30° Converging

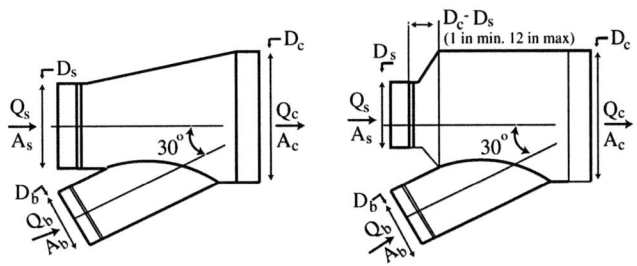

A_s/A_c	A_b/A_c	\multicolumn{7}{c}{C_s Values Q_s/Q_c}	A_b/A_c	A_s/A_c
		0.2	0.3	0.4	0.5	0.6	0.7	0.8		
0.3	0.2	−7.59	−2.48	−0.79	−0.06	0.29	0.47	0.57	0.2	0.3
	0.4	−3.49	−0.8	0.02	0.35	0.49	0.56	0.6	0.4	
	0.6	−1.7	−0.13	0.32	0.49	0.56	0.6	0.61	0.6	
	0.8	−0.72	0.23	0.48	0.57	0.6	0.61	0.62	0.8	
	1	−0.11	0.45	0.58	0.61	0.62	0.62	0.62	1	
0.4	0.2	−13.76	−4.74	−1.81	−0.59	−0.02	0.24	0.36	0.2	0.4
	0.4	−6.62	−1.88	−0.46	0.07	0.3	0.38	0.41	0.4	
	0.6	−3.48	−0.73	0.04	0.31	0.41	0.43	0.43	0.6	
	0.8	−1.77	−0.12	0.31	0.44	0.46	0.46	0.44	0.8	
	1	−0.69	0.26	0.47	0.51	0.5	0.47	0.44	1	
0.5	0.2	−21.64	−7.61	−3.07	−1.19	−0.34	0.05	0.22	0.2	0.5
	0.4	−10.59	−3.21	−1.02	−0.2	0.13	0.26	0.29	0.4	
	0.6	−5.72	−1.43	−0.24	0.16	0.3	0.33	0.31	0.6	
	0.8	−3.06	−0.49	0.16	0.35	0.39	0.37	0.33	0.8	
	1	−1.39	0.1	0.41	0.46	0.44	0.39	0.33	1	
0.6	0.2	−31.26	−11.09	−4.56	−1.89	−0.68	−0.12	0.1	0.2	0.6
	0.4	−15.4	−4.8	−1.65	−0.48	−0.01	0.17	0.2	0.4	
	0.6	−8.41	−2.25	−0.54	0.03	0.22	0.26	0.24	0.6	
	0.8	−4.59	−0.9	0.03	0.3	0.34	0.31	0.25	0.8	
	1	−2.2	−0.06	0.39	0.46	0.42	0.34	0.27	1	
0.7	0.2	−42.62	−15.17	−6.31	−2.68	−1.04	−0.29	0.01	0.2	0.7
	0.4	−21.07	−6.64	−2.36	−0.77	−0.14	0.09	0.15	0.4	
	0.6	−11.56	−3.19	−0.86	−0.08	0.18	0.23	0.19	0.6	
	0.8	−6.37	−1.35	−0.08	0.27	0.34	0.29	0.21	0.8	
	1	−3.12	−0.21	0.4	0.49	0.43	0.33	0.23	1	
0.8	0.2	−55.7	−19.86	−8.29	−3.56	−1.43	−0.46	−0.06	0.2	0.8
	0.4	−27.58	−8.74	−3.16	−1.09	−0.26	0.05	0.11	0.4	
	0.6	−15.17	−4.24	−1.20	−0.19	0.15	0.22	0.17	0.6	
	0.8	−8.4	−1.84	−0.18	0.28	0.36	0.3	0.2	0.8	
	1	−4.15	−0.35	0.44	0.56	0.49	0.36	0.22	1	
0.9	0.2	−70.51	−25.16	−10.53	−4.54	−1.84	−0.62	−0.12	0.2	0.9
	0.4	−34.94	−11.09	−4.03	−1.41	−0.37	0.02	0.1	0.4	
	0.6	−19.24	−5.40	−1.56	−0.28	0.15	0.23	0.17	0.6	
	0.8	−10.66	−2.37	−0.27	0.31	0.41	0.34	0.21	0.8	
	1	−5.29	−0.49	0.52	0.67	0.57	0.41	0.23	1	

Table 8-39. Return or Exhaust Wye Merging at 45° Converging

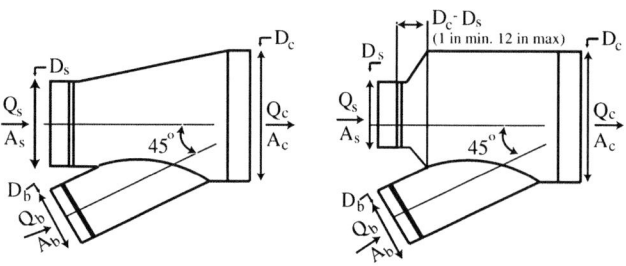

A_s/A_c	A_b/A_c	C_b Values							A_b/A_c	A_s/A_c
		Q_b/Q_c								
		0.2	0.3	0.4	0.5	0.6	0.7	0.8		
0.3	0.2	−1.77	0.13	0.66	0.85	0.93	0.97	1.03	0.2	0.3
	0.4	−10.26	−2.48	−0.3	0.47	0.77	0.88	0.93	0.4	
	0.6	−24.26	−6.68	−1.73	0.01	0.66	0.88	0.91	0.6	
	0.8	−43.6	−12.34	−3.54	−0.43	0.72	1.11	1.15	0.8	
	1	−68.43	−19.56	−5.79	−0.94	0.86	1.45	1.49	1	
0.4	0.2	−0.64	0.54	0.85	0.95	0.99	1.03	1.09	0.2	0.4
	0.4	−6.02	−1.05	0.28	0.72	0.87	0.91	0.92	0.4	
	0.6	−14.65	−3.42	−0.38	0.61	0.93	0.99	0.95	0.6	
	0.8	−26.56	−6.55	−1.15	0.62	1.18	1.29	1.19	0.8	
	1	−41.83	−10.54	−2.09	0.68	1.56	1.71	1.53	1	
0.5	0.2	0.04	0.79	0.97	1.02	1.04	1.07	1.14	0.2	0.5
	0.4	−3.53	−0.24	0.59	0.83	0.89	0.88	0.85	0.4	
	0.6	−8.9	−1.46	0.43	0.97	1.09	1.06	0.97	0.6	
	0.8	−16.35	−3.09	0.27	1.24	1.45	1.38	1.2	0.8	
	1	−25.9	−5.15	0.11	1.63	1.95	1.83	1.52	1	
0.6	0.2	−0.08	0.7	0.91	0.98	1.01	1.05	1.14	0.2	0.6
	0.4	−4.14	−0.68	0.26	0.57	0.68	0.71	0.72	0.4	
	0.6	−10.28	−2.48	−0.34	0.37	0.61	0.67	0.66	0.6	
	0.8	−18.84	−4.92	−1.12	0.16	0.58	0.67	0.61	0.8	
	1	−29.83	−8.04	−2.07	−0.08	0.58	0.7	0.56	1	
0.7	0.2	0.25	0.83	0.97	1.01	1.04	1.08	1.17	0.2	0.7
	0.4	−2.92	−0.27	0.43	0.65	0.72	0.73	0.73	0.4	
	0.6	−7.55	−1.55	0.03	0.53	0.68	0.69	0.65	0.6	
	0.8	−14.01	−3.3	−0.46	0.43	0.68	0.69	0.58	0.8	
	1	−22.32	−5.53	−1.07	0.33	0.72	0.71	0.48	1	
0.8	0.2	0.5	0.91	1.01	1.03	1.05	1.09	1.18	0.2	0.8
	0.4	−2	0.05	0.56	0.71	0.75	0.74	0.74	0.4	
	0.6	−5.52	−0.87	0.31	0.65	0.72	0.7	0.64	0.6	
	0.8	−10.42	−2.1	0.01	0.62	0.75	0.69	0.53	0.8	
	1	−16.73	−3.68	−0.35	0.61	0.79	0.68	0.38	1	
0.9	0.2	0.68	0.98	1.03	1.05	1.06	1.09	1.18	0.2	0.9
	0.4	−1.29	0.29	0.66	0.76	0.77	0.75	0.74	0.4	
	0.6	−3.94	−0.34	0.52	0.73	0.75	0.7	0.63	0.6	
	0.8	−7.64	−1.18	0.37	0.76	0.78	0.67	0.48	0.8	
	1	−12.42	−2.27	0.18	0.8	0.83	0.62	0.26	1	

Table 8-40. Return or Exhaust Wye Merging at 45° Converging

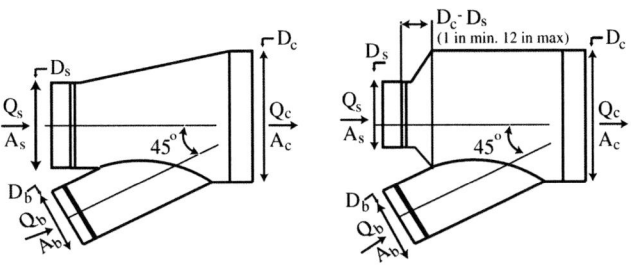

A_s/A_c	A_b/A_c	C_s Values							A_b/A_c	A_s/A_c
		Q_s/Q_c								
		0.2	0.3	0.4	0.5	0.6	0.7	0.8		
0.30	0.20	−5.14	−1.67	−0.44	0.12	0.42	0.58	0.67	0.20	0.30
	0.40	−2.22	−0.34	0.25	0.49	0.60	0.67	0.70	0.40	
	0.60	−0.75	0.24	0.52	0.62	0.67	0.70	0.72	0.60	
	0.80	0.07	0.55	0.66	0.69	0.70	0.71	0.72	0.80	
	1.00	0.60	0.74	0.75	0.73	0.73	0.72	0.72	1.00	
0.40	0.20	−9.48	−3.34	−1.23	−0.31	0.12	0.33	0.42	0.20	0.40
	0.40	−4.51	−1.13	−0.13	0.25	0.40	0.46	0.47	0.40	
	0.60	−1.97	−0.17	0.31	0.46	0.50	0.50	0.48	0.60	
	0.80	−0.54	0.35	0.54	0.57	0.55	0.52	0.49	0.80	
	1.00	0.37	0.68	0.68	0.64	0.58	0.54	0.50	1.00	
0.50	0.20	−15.18	−5.49	−2.21	−0.81	−0.16	0.14	0.26	0.20	0.50
	0.40	−7.54	−2.16	−0.57	0.02	0.25	0.32	0.33	0.40	
	0.60	−3.62	−0.69	0.09	0.33	0.39	0.38	0.35	0.60	
	0.80	−1.41	0.11	0.44	0.49	0.47	0.41	0.36	0.80	
	1.00	0.00	0.61	0.65	0.59	0.51	0.43	0.36	1.00	
0.60	0.20	−22.29	−8.18	−3.41	−1.39	−0.46	−0.03	0.13	0.20	0.60
	0.40	−11.37	−3.44	−1.09	−0.23	0.10	0.21	0.22	0.40	
	0.60	−5.77	−1.35	−0.17	0.20	0.30	0.30	0.25	0.60	
	0.80	−2.59	−0.21	0.33	0.43	0.41	0.34	0.26	0.80	
	1.00	−0.57	0.51	0.63	0.57	0.47	0.37	0.27	1.00	
0.70	0.20	−30.88	−11.42	−4.85	−2.08	−0.80	−0.21	0.02	0.20	0.70
	0.40	−16.08	−5.02	−1.73	−0.52	−0.05	0.11	0.13	0.40	
	0.60	−8.47	−2.19	−0.48	0.06	0.22	0.22	0.17	0.60	
	0.80	−4.16	−0.64	0.18	0.37	0.36	0.28	0.19	0.80	
	1.00	−1.41	0.33	0.60	0.55	0.44	0.32	0.20	1.00	
0.80	0.20	−41.01	−15.25	−6.55	−2.88	−1.19	−0.41	−0.10	0.20	0.80
	0.40	−21.71	−6.91	−2.50	−0.86	−0.22	0.01	0.05	0.40	
	0.60	−11.78	−3.22	−0.87	−0.10	0.13	0.16	0.10	0.60	
	0.80	−6.16	−1.20	0.00	0.29	0.31	0.23	0.12	0.80	
	1.00	−2.58	0.06	0.53	0.54	0.42	0.28	0.14	1.00	
0.90	0.20	−52.75	−19.69	−8.53	−3.81	−1.63	−0.63	−0.22	0.20	0.90
	0.40	−28.34	−9.15	−3.41	−1.26	−0.41	−0.10	−0.04	0.40	
	0.60	−15.78	−4.48	−1.35	−0.30	0.03	0.09	0.03	0.60	
	0.80	−8.67	−1.93	−0.25	0.20	0.26	0.18	0.06	0.80	
	1.00	−4.14	−0.34	0.42	0.50	0.39	0.24	0.08	1.00	

Table 8-40a. Return or Exhaust Converging Tee $D_c \leq 10$ in.

Dc-Ds　1" min. 12" max

$\frac{Q_s}{A_s}$ Ds　90°　Dc $\frac{Q_c}{A_c}$

1"　Db　1" 1"

$Q_b \uparrow A_b$

A_s/A_c	A_b/A_c	C_b Values Q_b/Q_c							A_b/A_c	A_s/A_c
		0.2	0.3	0.4	0.5	0.6	0.7	0.8		
0.3	0.2	−1.55	0.36	0.89	1.08	1.16	1.19	1.23	0.2	0.3
	0.4	−9.68	−1.94	0.24	1.00	1.29	1.39	1.42	0.4	
	0.6	−23.33	−5.84	−0.92	0.81	1.45	1.65	1.66	0.6	
	0.8	−42.30	−11.19	−2.43	0.65	1.78	2.14	2.13	0.8	
	1	−66.70	−18.08	−4.39	0.42	2.19	2.74	2.72	1	
0.4	0.2	−0.54	0.71	1.04	1.15	1.2	1.22	1.26	0.2	0.4
	0.4	−5.81	−0.67	0.73	1.19	1.35	1.39	1.39	0.4	
	0.6	−14.59	−2.97	0.2	1.26	1.6	1.67	1.6	0.6	
	0.8	−26.77	−6.09	−0.45	1.43	2.04	2.16	2.03	0.8	
	1	−42.45	−10.12	−1.30	1.63	2.58	2.75	2.54	1	
0.5	0.2	0.04	0.91	1.13	1.2	1.22	1.24	1.29	0.2	0.5
	0.4	−3.67	−0.01	0.96	1.26	1.34	1.35	1.32	0.4	
	0.6	−9.70	−1.41	0.78	1.46	1.64	1.63	1.53	0.6	
	0.8	−18.07	−3.32	0.57	1.78	2.11	2.09	1.89	0.8	
	1	−28.89	−5.81	0.27	2.16	2.67	2.63	2.31	1	
0.6	0.2	0.39	1.03	1.18	1.22	1.24	1.26	1.3	0.2	0.6
	0.4	−2.42	0.35	1.05	1.25	1.29	1.27	1.22	0.4	
	0.6	−6.73	−0.50	1.08	1.54	1.63	1.57	1.45	0.6	
	0.8	−12.81	−1.72	1.1	1.91	2.07	1.97	1.73	0.8	
	1	−20.68	−3.33	1.09	2.35	2.6	2.44	2.03	1	
0.7	0.2	0.62	1.1	1.21	1.23	1.24	1.26	1.31	0.2	0.7
	0.4	−1.59	0.58	1.11	1.25	1.27	1.24	1.18	0.4	
	0.6	−4.86	0.02	1.22	1.54	1.57	1.5	1.35	0.6	
	0.8	−9.50	−0.79	1.35	1.91	1.97	1.82	1.54	0.8	
	1	−15.53	−1.89	1.46	2.34	2.43	2.19	1.73	1	
0.8	0.2	0.76	1.14	1.22	1.24	1.24	1.26	1.31	0.2	0.8
	0.4	−1.06	0.71	1.13	1.24	1.24	1.2	1.13	0.4	
	0.6	−3.69	0.31	1.27	1.5	1.5	1.41	1.25	0.6	
	0.8	−7.42	−0.29	1.42	1.83	1.83	1.65	1.35	0.8	
	1	−12.30	−1.12	1.56	2.21	2.2	1.92	1.4	1	
0.9	0.2	0.85	1.16	1.22	1.23	1.24	1.25	1.3	0.2	0.9
	0.4	−0.74	0.77	1.12	1.2	1.2	1.16	1.08	0.4	
	0.6	−2.98	0.44	1.24	1.42	1.41	1.31	1.13	0.6	
	0.8	−6.17	−0.07	1.36	1.69	1.66	1.47	1.13	0.8	
	1	−10.36	−0.79	1.46	1.98	1.92	1.61	1.06	1	

Table 8-40b. Return or Exhaust Converging Tee $D_c \leq 10$ in.

A_s/A_c	A_b/A_c	C_s Values							A_b/A_c	A_s/A_c
		Q_s/Q_c								
		0.2	0.3	0.4	0.5	0.6	0.7	0.8		
0.3	0.2	7.19	2.8	1.57	1.08	0.84	0.71	0.63	0.2	0.3
	0.4	4.59	2.09	1.3	0.96	0.78	0.67	0.61	0.4	
	0.6	3.71	1.82	1.19	0.9	0.74	0.65	0.59	0.6	
	0.8	3.26	1.67	1.12	0.86	0.72	0.63	0.58	0.8	
	1	2.52	1.36	0.95	0.75	0.65	0.58	0.54	1	
0.4	0.2	12.25	4.42	2.26	1.39	0.97	0.74	0.6	0.2	0.4
	0.4	7.32	3.08	1.74	1.16	0.85	0.67	0.56	0.4	
	0.6	5.72	2.61	1.54	1.05	0.79	0.63	0.53	0.6	
	0.8	4.13	1.98	1.21	0.85	0.65	0.53	0.46	0.8	
	1	3.69	1.80	1.12	0.79	0.62	0.51	0.44	1	
0.5	0.2	17.76	6.27	3.07	1.79	1.16	0.81	0.6	0.2	0.5
	0.4	10.24	4.23	2.29	1.43	0.98	0.71	0.54	0.4	
	0.6	7.9	3.53	1.99	1.27	0.88	0.65	0.5	0.6	
	0.8	5.57	2.59	1.49	0.96	0.67	0.5	0.38	0.8	
	1	5.05	2.36	1.36	0.88	0.62	0.46	0.35	1	
0.6	0.2	22.64	8.06	3.91	2.23	1.39	0.92	0.63	0.2	0.6
	0.4	12.9	5.39	2.88	1.75	1.14	0.78	0.55	0.4	
	0.6	8.2	3.69	2.04	1.25	0.81	0.55	0.38	0.6	
	0.8	7.06	3.26	1.81	1.11	0.72	0.48	0.33	0.8	
	1	6.61	3	1.65	1	0.65	0.43	0.28	1	
0.7	0.2	25.82	9.48	4.66	2.65	1.63	1.04	0.68	0.2	0.7
	0.4	14.92	6.47	3.48	2.09	1.33	0.87	0.58	0.4	
	0.6	9.51	4.41	2.42	1.45	0.9	0.57	0.35	0.6	
	0.8	8.6	3.99	2.18	1.29	0.79	0.49	0.28	0.8	
	1	8.49	3.77	2.01	1.16	0.7	0.41	0.22	1	
0.8	0.2	26.38	10.3	5.22	3.01	1.85	1.17	0.74	0.2	0.8
	0.4	12.79	5.92	3.23	1.91	1.17	0.72	0.42	0.4	
	0.6	10.57	5.1	2.81	1.66	1.01	0.6	0.33	0.6	
	0.8	10.37	4.8	2.59	1.5	0.88	0.5	0.25	0.8	
	1	10.98	4.71	2.43	1.36	0.77	0.41	0.18	1	
0.9	0.2	23.73	10.34	5.54	3.28	2.05	1.3	0.81	0.2	0.9
	0.4	12.21	6.28	3.55	2.12	1.29	0.77	0.42	0.4	
	0.6	11.62	5.81	3.23	1.89	1.13	0.64	0.32	0.6	
	0.8	12.73	5.79	3.07	1.74	0.99	0.53	0.23	0.8	
	1	14.52	5.94	2.97	1.61	0.87	0.42	0.14	1	

Table 8-40c. Return or Exhaust Converging Tee $D_c > 10$ in.

| A_s/A_c | A_b/A_c | C_b Values | | | | | | | A_b/A_c | A_s/A_c |
| | | Q_b/Q_c | | | | | | | | |
		0.2	0.3	0.4	0.5	0.6	0.7	0.8		
0.3	0.2	−2.16	−0.04	0.58	0.81	0.9	0.93	0.94	0.2	0.3
	0.4	−11.09	−2.78	−0.38	0.48	0.82	0.93	0.94	0.4	
	0.6	−25.85	−7.21	−1.86	0.06	0.8	1.05	1.05	0.6	
	0.8	−46.56	−13.39	−3.89	−0.47	0.85	1.28	1.3	0.8	
	1	−73.33	−21.37	−6.48	−1.12	0.94	1.63	1.68	1	
0.4	0.2	−1.18	0.26	0.69	0.84	0.91	0.93	0.93	0.2	0.4
	0.4	−7.03	−1.46	0.11	0.67	0.87	0.93	0.91	0.4	
	0.6	−16.60	−4.17	−0.69	0.52	0.95	1.06	1.01	0.6	
	0.8	−29.99	−7.90	−1.73	0.4	1.15	1.33	1.24	0.8	
	1	−47.31	−12.70	−3.04	0.29	1.45	1.74	1.61	1	
0.5	0.2	−0.62	0.43	0.75	0.86	0.91	0.93	0.93	0.2	0.5
	0.4	−4.67	−0.72	0.38	0.76	0.89	0.92	0.9	0.4	
	0.6	−11.17	−2.42	−0.03	0.76	1.01	1.05	0.98	0.6	
	0.8	−20.22	−4.71	−0.50	0.87	1.29	1.33	1.2	0.8	
	1	−31.92	−7.63	−1.07	1.06	1.71	1.77	1.56	1	
0.6	0.2	−0.27	0.54	0.78	0.88	0.91	0.93	0.93	0.2	0.6
	0.4	−3.15	−0.25	0.55	0.82	0.9	0.92	0.91	0.4	
	0.6	−7.64	−1.30	0.38	0.91	1.05	1.04	0.98	0.6	
	0.8	−13.83	−2.65	0.26	1.15	1.36	1.33	1.19	0.8	
	1	−21.84	−4.35	0.18	1.54	1.85	1.77	1.54	1	
0.7	0.2	−0.03	0.61	0.81	0.89	0.92	0.94	0.94	0.2	0.7
	0.4	−2.10	0.07	0.66	0.85	0.91	0.93	0.92	0.4	
	0.6	−5.18	−0.54	0.65	1	1.07	1.05	1	0.6	
	0.8	−9.37	−1.24	0.78	1.33	1.41	1.33	1.21	0.8	
	1	−14.78	−2.09	1.03	1.84	1.94	1.78	1.56	1	
0.8	0.2	0.15	0.67	0.83	0.9	0.93	0.94	0.95	0.2	0.8
	0.4	−1.34	0.3	0.74	0.88	0.93	0.94	0.95	0.4	
	0.6	−3.39	0.01	0.84	1.06	1.09	1.06	1.03	0.6	
	0.8	−6.11	−0.22	1.15	1.46	1.45	1.35	1.25	0.8	
	1	-9.59	-0.44	1.63	2.06	2.00	1.80	1.61	1	
0.9	0.2	0.28	0.71	0.85	0.91	0.94	0.96	0.97	0.2	0.9
	0.4	−0.76	0.47	0.8	0.91	0.94	0.96	0.98	0.4	
	0.6	−2.04	0.42	0.99	1.11	1.12	1.09	1.09	0.6	
	0.8	−3.63	0.55	1.42	1.55	1.49	1.38	1.32	0.8	
	1	−5.64	0.8	2.08	2.22	2.06	1.84	1.69	1	

Table 8-40d. Return or Exhaust Converging Tee D_c > 10 in.

A_s/A_c	A_b/A_c	C_s Values							A_b/A_c	A_s/A_c
		Q_s/Q_c								
		0.2	0.3	0.4	0.5	0.6	0.7	0.8		
0.30	0.20	7.11	2.49	1.33	0.90	0.70	0.60	0.54	0.20	0.30
	0.40	3.57	1.58	1.00	0.76	0.64	0.57	0.52	0.40	
	0.60	2.59	1.32	0.90	0.72	0.62	0.56	0.52	0.60	
	0.80	2.25	1.23	0.87	0.70	0.61	0.56	0.52	0.80	
	1.00	2.17	1.21	0.86	0.70	0.61	0.55	0.52	1.00	
0.40	0.20	12.10	3.91	1.85	1.08	0.74	0.55	0.45	0.20	0.40
	0.40	5.51	2.21	1.23	0.82	0.61	0.49	0.42	0.40	
	0.60	3.78	1.76	1.07	0.75	0.58	0.48	0.41	0.60	
	0.80	3.27	1.63	1.02	0.73	0.57	0.47	0.41	0.80	
	1.00	3.25	1.62	1.02	0.73	0.57	0.47	0.41	1.00	
0.50	0.20	16.99	5.39	2.42	1.32	0.81	0.54	0.38	0.20	0.50
	0.40	7.27	2.87	1.51	0.93	0.63	0.45	0.34	0.40	
	0.60	4.95	2.27	1.29	0.84	0.58	0.43	0.33	0.60	
	0.80	4.48	2.15	1.25	0.82	0.57	0.43	0.33	0.80	
	1.00	4.76	2.22	1.28	0.83	0.58	0.43	0.33	1.00	
0.60	0.20	20.32	6.54	2.92	1.54	0.89	0.54	0.33	0.20	0.60
	0.40	8.37	3.44	1.80	1.06	0.67	0.43	0.28	0.40	
	0.60	5.98	2.82	1.57	0.97	0.62	0.41	0.27	0.60	
	0.80	5.98	2.82	1.57	0.97	0.62	0.41	0.27	0.80	
	0.90	6.38	2.92	1.61	0.98	0.63	0.42	0.27	0.90	
	1.00	6.94	3.07	1.66	1.00	0.64	0.42	0.28	1.00	
0.70	0.20	20.74	7.01	3.21	1.70	0.96	0.54	0.29	0.20	0.70
	0.40	8.52	3.84	2.06	1.21	0.73	0.44	0.24	0.40	
	0.60	6.97	3.44	1.92	1.14	0.70	0.42	0.24	0.60	
	0.80	8.10	3.73	2.02	1.19	0.72	0.43	0.24	0.80	
	1.00	10.30	4.30	2.23	1.28	0.76	0.45	0.25	1.00	
0.80	0.20	17.35	6.57	3.21	1.75	0.99	0.55	0.27	0.20	0.80
	0.40	7.77	4.09	2.31	1.37	0.81	0.46	0.23	0.40	
	0.60	8.36	4.24	2.37	1.39	0.83	0.47	0.23	0.60	
	0.80	11.49	5.05	2.66	1.52	0.88	0.50	0.24	0.80	
	1.00	15.64	6.13	3.05	1.68	0.96	0.53	0.26	1.00	
0.90	0.20	10.05	5.20	2.91	1.70	0.99	0.55	0.25	0.20	0.90
	0.40	6.73	4.34	2.60	1.57	0.93	0.52	0.24	0.40	
	0.60	11.01	5.45	3.00	1.74	1.01	0.56	0.25	0.60	
	0.80	17.18	7.05	3.58	1.98	1.13	0.61	0.28	0.80	
	1.00	24.12	8.85	4.23	2.26	1.26	0.67	0.31	1.00	

Table 8-41. Return or Exhaust Converging Symmetrical 60° Wye, $D_{b1} \geq D_{b2}$

NOTE: $D_{b1} \leq D_{b2}$　　(1 in. min. or 12 in. max.)

| A_{b1}/A_c | A_{b2}/A_c | C_{b1} Values | | | | | | | A_{b2}/A_c | A_{b1}/A_c |
| | | Q_{b1}/Q_c | | | | | | | | |
		0.2	0.3	0.4	0.5	0.6	0.7	0.8		
0.2	0.2	−1.89	−0.09	0.41	0.62	0.74	0.8	0.8	0.2	0.2
	0.3	−1.89	−0.09	0.41	0.62	0.74	0.8	0.8	0.3	
0.4	0.2	−14	−4.26	−1.24	−0.1	0.33	0.5	0.57	0.2	0.4
	0.3	−9.91	−2.86	−0.69	0.07	0.3	0.4	0.49	0.3	
	0.4	−6.22	−2.15	−0.57	0.19	0.55	0.72	0.79	0.4	
0.5	0.2	−23.8	−7.44	−2.64	−0.85	−0.13	0.16	0.26	0.2	0.5
	0.3	−16.91	−5.16	−1.73	−0.46	0.04	0.23	0.29	0.3	
	0.4	−10.07	−2.9	−0.82	−0.07	0.21	0.3	0.31	0.4	
0.6	0.2	−39.31	−12.13	−4.35	−1.54	−0.4	0.06	0.22	0.2	0.6
	0.3	−27.69	−8.75	−3.2	−1.13	−0.29	0.05	0.17	0.3	
	0.4	−16.07	−5.38	−2.04	−0.71	−0.17	0.04	0.12	0.4	
	0.6	−7.86	−2.6	−0.99	−0.26	0	0.14	0.21	0.6	
0.7	0.2	−54.52	−17.03	−6.21	−2.27	−0.68	−0.04	0.19	0.2	0.7
	0.3	−38.02	−12.54	−4.92	−2.01	−0.76	−0.22	0.01	0.3	
	0.4	−21.41	−8.05	−3.64	−1.75	−0.84	−0.4	−0.17	0.4	
	0.6	−11.7	−4.97	−2.59	−1.4	−0.76	−0.37	−0.15	0.6	
	0.7	−16.68	−6.9	−3.29	−1.61	−0.8	−0.29	0.02	0.7	
0.8	0.2	−69.73	−21.93	−8.08	−3.0	−0.95	−0.13	0.15	0.2	0.8
	0.4	−26.76	−10.71	−5.24	−2.78	−1.52	−0.84	−0.45	0.4	
	0.6	−15.54	−7.35	−4.2	−2.54	−1.53	−0.89	−0.51	0.6	
	0.8	−25.49	11.19	−5.59	−2.96	−1.6	−0.72	−0.18	0.8	
0.9	0.2	−89.56	−28.39	−10.59	−4.04	−1.41	−0.36	0.01	0.2	0.9
	0.4	−32.88	−14.6	−7.98	−4.74	−2.91	−1.79	−1.1	0.4	
	0.6	−23.08	−12.11	−7.45	−4.84	−3.15	−2.01	−1.26	0.6	
	0.8	−31.63	−15.05	−8.44	−5.11	−3.18	−1.9	−1.07	0.8	
	0.9	−35.19	−16.07	−8.7	−5.18	−3.19	−1.88	−1.08	0.9	
1	0.2	−109.39	−34.85	−13.11	−5.09	−1.86	−0.59	−0.13	0.2	1
	0.4	−39	−18.5	−10.71	−6.71	−4.29	−2.74	−1.74	0.4	
	0.6	−30.62	−16.87	−10.7	−7.13	−4.77	−3.13	−2.02	0.6	
	0.8	−37.76	−18.91	−11.29	−7.26	−4.76	−3.09	−1.96	0.8	
	0.9	−41.32	−19.93	−11.55	−7.32	−4.77	−3.07	−1.98	0.9	

Table 8-42. Return or Exhaust Converging Symmetrical 60° Wye, $D_{b1} \geq D_{b2}$

NOTE: $D_{b1} \leq D_{b2}$ (1 in. min. or 12 in. max.)

A_{b1}/A_c	A_{b2}/A_c	0.2	0.3	0.4	0.5	0.6	0.7	0.8	0.9	A_{b2}/A_c	A_{b1}/A_c
0.2	0.2	−1.89	−0.09	0.41	0.62	0.74	0.8	0.8	0.79	0.2	0.2
	0.3	−1.89	−0.09	0.41	0.62	0.74	0.8	0.8	0.79	0.3	
0.4	0.2	−1	0.16	0.53	0.67	0.71	0.72	0.72	0.71	0.2	0.4
	0.3	−2.9	−0.44	0.4	0.79	0.98	1.05	1.06	1.05	0.3	
	0.4	−6.22	−2.15	−0.57	0.19	0.55	0.72	0.79	0.85	0.4	
0.5	0.2	−0.01	0.56	0.71	0.82	0.89	0.92	0.9	0.89	0.2	0.5
	0.3	−1.17	0.44	0.88	1.11	1.25	1.29	1.25	1.23	0.3	
	0.4	−2.93	−0.21	0.48	0.73	0.84	0.88	0.87	0.82	0.4	
0.6	0.2	0.07	0.77	0.98	1.06	1.08	1.08	1.06	1.04	0.2	0.6
	0.4	−2.12	0.06	0.6	0.83	0.95	0.98	0.95	0.91	0.4	
	0.6	−7.86	−2.6	−0.99	−0.26	0	0.14	0.21	0.25	0.6	
0.7	0.2	−0.4	0.55	0.86	0.98	1.02	1.04	1.03	1.02	0.2	0.7
	0.4	−3.09	−0.44	0.36	0.71	0.89	0.97	0.98	0.97	0.4	
	0.6	−9.82	−3.47	−1.41	−0.48	−0.04	0.21	0.36	0.45	0.6	
	0.7	−16.68	−6.9	−3.29	−1.61	−0.8	−0.29	0.02	0.22	0.7	
0.8	0.2	−0.87	0.33	0.73	0.9	0.97	1	1	0.99	0.2	0.8
	0.4	−4.06	−0.93	0.11	0.59	0.83	0.96	1.01	1.03	0.4	
	0.6	−11.78	−4.34	−1.83	−0.7	−0.09	0.28	0.51	0.65	0.6	
	0.8	−25.49	−11.19	−5.59	−2.96	−1.6	−0.72	−0.18	0.19	0.8	
0.9	0.2	−0.34	0.54	0.85	0.97	1.03	1.04	1.03	1.01	0.2	0.9
	0.4	−4.98	−1.39	−0.12	0.47	0.78	0.95	1.04	1.09	0.4	
	0.6	−14.28	−5.64	−2.53	−1.08	−0.3	0.18	0.49	0.7	0.6	
	0.8	−27.77	−12.18	−6.22	−3.35	−1.79	−0.81	−0.19	0.23	0.8	

Column header structure: C_{b2} Values, Q_{b2}/Q_c

PIPE SIZING

PIPE SIZING

The working fluids in HVAC systems are mainly water, steam, refrigerants, natural gas and oil. Pipes and pipe networks are used to appropriately distribute the working fluids throughout the system. Pipes must be correctly sized to ensure that pressures and flow rates are balanced and that the flow rates are maintained at design values. In this chapter the principles and methods of pipe sizing are discussed.

HVAC piping systems are characterized by relatively short pipe lengths and by the presence of many valves and fixtures. As a result the cumulative pressure loss due to valves and fixtures is at least as important as the pressure drop due to friction in the pipes. The pressure drop, the pipe length and diameter, the pipe roughness, the fluid density, the flow rate and the Reynolds number, and the loss characteristics of the individual fixtures used are all interrelated. The easiest computation is calculating the pressure loss for a system for a given flow rate when the fluid and its properties are known, the pipe material roughness, diameter and length are given, fixture types and their respective positions are known. For most other computations an iterative scheme may be needed.

Additional details can be found in the reference material published by ASHRAE, notably the ASHRAE Handbook series.

Pressure Drop Equations

The pressure drop due to friction in a fully developed fluid flow inside a pipe is described by the Darcy-Weisbach equation:

$$\Delta P = f\left(\frac{L}{D}\right)\left(\frac{\rho}{g_c}\right)\left(\frac{V^2}{2}\right) \tag{1}$$

where ΔP = pressure drop in lb_f/ft^2;

f = friction factor, dimensionless ;

L = length of pipe, ft;

D = internal diameter of pipe, ft;

ρ = fluid density at mean temperature, lb_m/ft^3;

V = average velocity, fps; and

g_c = units conversion factor, 32.2 ft-lb_m/lb_f-sec^2

This equation is often presented in head or specific energy form as

$$h_f = \left(\frac{\Delta P}{\rho}\right)\left(\frac{g_c}{g}\right) = (f)\left(\frac{L}{D}\right)\left(\frac{V^2}{2g}\right) \tag{2}$$

where h_f = head loss, ft

g = acceleration of gravity, ft/sec^2

The friction factor f is a function of pipe roughness ε, inside diameter D, and parameter Re, the Reynolds number:

$$Re = \frac{\rho VD}{\mu} \tag{3}$$

where Re = Reynolds number, dimensionless;

ε = absolute roughness of pipe wall, ft; and

μ = dynamic viscosity of fluid, lb_m/ft-sec.

The friction factor is presented on a Moody chart (See Fig 1-10. on page 9) giving f as a function of Re with ε/D as a parameter:

$$\frac{1}{\sqrt{f}} = 1.74 - 2\log\left(\frac{2\varepsilon}{D} + \frac{18.7}{Re\sqrt{f}}\right) \tag{4}$$

Another formulation for calculating pressure drop is the Hazen-Williams equation, which is expressed as

$$\Delta P = 3.022L\left(\frac{V}{C}\right)^{1.852}\left(\frac{1}{D}\right)^{1.167}\left(\frac{\rho g}{g_c}\right) \tag{5}$$

$$h_f = 3.022L\left(\frac{V}{C}\right)^{1.852}\left(\frac{1}{D}\right)^{1.167} \tag{6}$$

where C = roughness factor.

This method is less widely used. However it is popular for hydraulic calculations for sprinkler systems. Typical values of C are 150 for plastic pipe and copper tubing, 140 for new steel pipe, down to 100 and below for badly corroded or very rough pipe.

Valve and Fitting Losses.—The pressure loss in piping system due to valves and fittings is usually much greater than that of a straight pipe run. One formulation expresses losses as

$$\Delta P = K\left(\frac{\rho}{g_c}\right)\left(\frac{V^2}{2}\right) \qquad (lb_f/ft^2) \tag{7}$$

$$h_f = K\left(\frac{V^2}{2g}\right) \qquad ft \tag{8}$$

where K = geometry and size dependent loss coefficient.

The pressure loss for valves can also be formulated as

$$Q = C_v\sqrt{\Delta P} \tag{9}$$

where Q = volumetric flow, gpm;

C_v = valve coefficient, and

ΔP = pressure drop, psi.

Table 9-1. K Factors– Screwed Pipe Fittings

Nominal Pipe Dia., in.	90° Standard Elbow	90° Long-Radius Elbow	45° Elbow	Return Bend	Tee-Line	Tee-Branch	Globe Valve	Gate Valve	Angle Valve	Swing Check Valve	Bell-Mouth Inlet	Square Inlet	Projected Inlet
⅜	2.5	…	0.38	2.5	0.9	2.7	20	0.4	…	8	0.05	0.5	1
½	2.1	…	0.37	2.1	0.9	2.4	14	0.33	…	5.5	0.05	0.5	1
¾	1.7	0.92	0.35	1.7	0.9	2.1	10	0.28	6.1	3.7	0.05	0.5	1
1	1.5	0.78	0.34	1.5	0.9	1.8	9	0.24	4.6	3	0.05	0.5	1
1¼	1.3	0.65	0.33	1.3	0.9	1.7	8.5	0.22	3.6	2.7	0.05	0.5	1
1½	1.2	0.54	0.32	1.2	0.9	1.6	8	0.19	2.9	2.5	0.05	0.5	1
2	1.0	0.42	0.31	1.0	0.9	1.4	7	0.17	2.1	2.3	0.05	0.5	1
2½	0.85	0.35	0.3	0.85	0.9	1.3	6.5	0.16	1.6	2.2	0.05	0.5	1
3	0.8	0.31	0.29	0.8	0.9	1.2	6	0.14	1.3	2.1	0.05	0.5	1
4	0.7	0.24	0.28	0.7	0.9	1.1	5.7	0.12	1.0	2	0.05	0.5	1

Table 9-2. *K* Factors–Flanged Welded Pipe Fittings

Nominal Pipe Dia., in.	90° Standard Elbow	90° Long-Radius Elbow	45° Long-Radius Elbow	Return Bend Standard	Return Bend Long Radius	Tee Line	Tee Branch	Globe Valve	Gate Valve	Angle Valve	Swing Check Valve
1	0.43	0.41	0.22	0.43	0.43	0.26	1.00	13.00	…	4.80	2.00
1¼	0.41	0.37	0.22	0.41	0.38	0.25	0.95	12.00	…	3.70	2.00
1½	0.40	0.35	0.21	0.40	0.35	0.23	0.90	10.00	…	3.00	2.00
2	0.38	0.30	0.20	0.38	0.30	0.20	0.84	9.00	0.34	2.50	2.00
2½	0.35	0.28	0.19	0.35	0.27	0.18	0.79	8.00	0.27	2.30	2.00
3	0.34	0.25	0.18	0.34	0.25	0.17	0.76	7.00	0.22	2.20	2.00
4	0.31	0.22	0.18	0.31	0.22	0.15	0.70	6.50	0.16	2.10	2.00
6	0.29	0.18	0.17	0.29	0.18	0.12	0.62	6.00	0.10	2.10	2.00
8	0.27	0.16	0.17	0.27	0.15	0.10	0.58	5.70	0.08	2.10	2.00
10	0.25	0.14	0.16	0.25	0.14	0.09	0.53	5.70	0.06	2.10	2.00
12	0.24	0.13	0.16	0.24	0.13	0.08	0.50	5.70	0.05	2.10	2.00

Table 9-3. Approximate Range of Variation for *K* Factors

90° Elbow	Regular threaded	±20% above 2 in.	Tee	Threaded, line or branch	±25%
		±40% below 2 in.		Flanged, line or branch	±35%
	Long-radius threaded	±25%	Globe Valve	Threaded	±25%
	Regular flanged	±35%		Flanged	±25%
	Long-radius flanged	±30%	Gate Valve	Threaded	±25%
45° Elbow	Regular threaded	±10%		Flanged	±50%
	Long-radius flanged	±10%	Angle Valve	Threaded	±20%
Return Bend (180°)	Regular threaded	±25%		Flanged	±50%
	Regular flanged	±35%	Check Valve	Threaded	±50%
	Long-radius flanged	±30%		Flanged	200%

Table 9-4. Equivalent Length Feet of Pipe for 90° Elbows

| Velocity, fps | Pipe Size | | | | | | | | | | | | | Velocity, fps |
	½	1	1¼	1½	2	2½	3	4	5	6	8	10	12	
1	1.20	2.20	3.00	3.50	4.50	5.40	6.70	8.60	10.50	12.20	15.40	18.70	22.20	1
2	1.40	2.50	3.30	3.90	5.10	6.00	7.50	9.50	11.70	13.70	17.30	20.80	24.80	2
3	1.50	2.70	3.60	4.20	5.40	6.40	8.00	10.20	12.50	14.60	18.40	22.30	26.50	3
4	1.50	2.80	3.70	4.40	5.60	6.70	8.30	10.60	13.10	15.20	19.20	23.20	27.60	4
5	1.60	2.90	3.90	4.50	5.90	7.00	8.70	11.10	13.60	15.80	19.80	24.20	28.80	5
6	1.70	3.00	4.00	4.70	6.00	7.20	8.90	11.40	14.00	16.30	20.50	24.90	29.60	6
7	1.70	3.00	4.10	4.80	6.20	7.40	9.10	11.70	14.30	16.70	21.00	25.50	30.30	7
8	1.70	3.10	4.20	4.90	6.30	7.50	9.30	11.90	14.60	17.10	21.50	26.10	31.00	8
9	1.80	3.20	4.30	5.00	6.40	7.70	9.50	12.20	14.90	17.40	21.90	26.60	31.60	9
10	1.80	3.20	4.30	5.10	6.50	7.80	9.70	12.40	15.20	17.70	22.20	27.00	32.00	10

Water Piping

Flow Rate Limitations.—Noise, erosion, and installation and operating costs all limit the maximum and minimum velocities in piping systems.

For a given volume or mass flow rate of water, if the pipe diameter is too small (leading to higher velocities and pressure drops) the noise levels, pipe erosion, and pumping costs can be unfavorable. On the other hand, if the pipe diameters are too large, the installation costs may be excessive. Therefore, in addition to the equations presented so far, sizes must be chosen that take into account these considerations.

Guidelines based on the annual operating hours (Table 9-5) and based on the type of service (Table 9-6) have been developed. There are many other upper limits available from various sources. One recommendation places a velocity limit of 4 fps for 2 in. and smaller pipes, and a pressure drop of 4 ft of water per 100 ft of piping for pipes of diameter larger than 2 in. Another recommendation limits the maximum velocity to be 15 fps in any case.

Table 9-5. Maximum Water Velocities to Minimize Erosion

Normal Operation, hr/yr	Velocity, fps
1500	15
2000	14
3000	13
4000	12
6000	10

Table 9-6. Velocity Design Criteria

Fluid	Condition	Service	Velocity, fps
Water	Cold	Pump discharge	6 to 9
Water	Cold	Supply headers	3 to 8
Water	Hot	Boiler feed mains	8 to 12
Water	Hot or cold	Pump suction and drains	4 to 7
Boiler feed	Hot or cold		6 to 15
Pump suction and drain lines	Hot or cold		4 to 7
Acids and chemicals	All	General	5 to 9
Slurry mixtures	All	General	3 to 5
Air, gases, and steam	Wet (0 to 49 psig)	General	65 to 100
Air, gases, and steam	Wet (50 psig and up)	General	100 to 180
Air, gases, and steam	Dry (200 psig and up)	General	120 to 350

Noise Generation.—Velocity dependent noise in pipes and piping systems results from any or all of four sources: turbulence, cavitation, release of entrained air, and water hammer. Velocities on the order of 10 to 17 fps lie within the range of allowable noise levels for residential and commercial buildings. Generally, systems with longer pipe and with more numerous fittings and valves are noisier. Due to the fact that systematic experiments have not been conducted, no detailed correlations relating sound level to flow velocity in generalized systems are available.

The noise generated by fluid flow in a pipe increases sharply if cavitation or the release of entrained air occurs. Usually the combination of a high water velocity with a change in flow direction or a decrease in the cross section of a pipe causing a sudden pressure drop is necessary to cause cavitation.

Some data are available for predicting hydrodynamic (liquid) noise generated by control valves. A correlation to predict hydrodynamic noise from control valves is

$$SL = 10\log C_v + 20\log \Delta P - 30\log t + 5 \qquad (10)$$

where SL = sound level, dB;

$\quad C_v$ = valve coefficient, gpm/(psi)$^{0.5}$;

$\quad Q$ = flow rate, gpm;

$\quad p$ = pressure drop across valve, psi; and

$\quad t$ = downstream pipe wall thickness, in.

Air entrained in water usually has a higher partial pressure than the water. Even when flow rates are small enough to avoid cavitation, the release of entrained air may create noise. Every effort should be made to vent the piping system or otherwise remove entrained air.

Erosion.—Erosion in piping systems is caused by water bubbles, particulates and/or other solid matter impinging on the inner surface of the pipe. Generally, at velocities lower than 100 fps erosion is not significant as long as there is no cavitation. When solid matter is entrained in fluid at high velocities, erosion occurs rapidly, especially in bends. Thus, high velocities should not be used in systems where sand or other solids are present or where slurries are transported.

Allowances for Aging.—With age the internal surfaces of pipes become increasingly rough, which reduces available flow with fixed pressure supply. However, designing with excessive age allowances may result in oversized piping. Age related decreases in capacity depend on type of water, type of pipe material, temperature of water, type of system (open or closed) causes include:

1) Sliming (biological growth or deposited soil on the pipe walls), which occurs mainly in unchlorinated, raw water systems.

2) Caking of calcareous salts, which occurs in hard water (i.e., water bearing calcium salts) and increases with water temperature.

3) Corrosion (incrustations of ferrous and ferric hydroxide on the pipe walls), which occurs in metal pipe in soft water. Because oxygen is necessary for corrosion to take place, significantly more corrosion takes place in open systems.

Allowances for expected decreases in capacity are sometimes treated as a specific amount (percentage).

It is recommended that 15% to 20% allowance be added to the friction drop in new pipes for closed systems (equivalent to 8% to 12% decrease in capacity). For open systems the added allowance in the friction drop should be increased by 75% to 90%. Differentiation based on the corrosive potential of different metals could be considered by noting the iron has the highest corrosion, followed by galvanized steel, lead, copper and copper alloys (brass). For example in an experiment reported in literature, copper pipes had a capacity loss of 25% to 65% after 4 years of cold and hot water use, while aged ferrous pipes had capacity loss of 40 to 80%. Plastic pipes are generally found to be unaffected by corrosion, even after 30 years of use.

Age related flow data are available for use in the Hazen-Williams equation. These are not presented in this handbook.

Water Hammer.—Water hammer occurs when any moving fluid (not just water) is abruptly stopped, as when a valve closes suddenly a large pressure can develop. While detailed analysis requires knowledge of the elastic properties of the pipe and the flow-time history, the limiting case of rigid pipe and instantaneous closure is simple to calculate. Under these conditions, reduces the effective value.

$$\Delta P_h = \frac{\rho c_s V}{g_c} \qquad (11)$$

where ΔP_h = pressure rise caused by water hammer, lb_f/ft^2;

ρ = fluid density, lb_m/ft^3;

c_s = velocity of sound in fluid, fps;

g_c = units conversion factor, 32.2 ft-lb_m/lb_f-sec^2; and

V = fluid flow velocity, fps.

The c_s for water is 4720 fps.

Other Considerations.—Not discussed in detail in this chapter, but of potentially great importance, are a number of physical and chemical considerations: pipe and fitting design, materials, and joining methods must be appropriate for working pressures and temperatures encountered, as well as suitably resistant to chemical attack by the fluid.

For fluids not included in this chapter or for piping materials of different dimensions, manufacturers' literature frequently supplies pressure drop charts. In any event, if the manufacturer supplied the relevant pressure drop charts or correlations, that information should be used.

Hydronic System Piping

The Darcy-Weisbach equation with friction factors from the Moody chart or Colebrook equation (or, alternatively, the Hazen-Williams equation) is fundamental to calculating pressure drop in hot and chilled water piping; however, charts obtained from these equations (such as Figs. 9-1, 9-2, and 9-3) provide easy determination of pressure drops for specific fluids and pipe standards.

The Reynolds numbers represented on the charts in Figs. 9-1, 9-2, and 9-3 are all in the turbulent flow regime. For smaller pipes and/or lower velocities, the Reynolds number may fall into the laminar regime for which expressions from Chapter 1 can be used.

Most tables and charts for water are calculated for properties at 60°F. Using these for hot water introduces some error, although the answers are conservative (i.e., cold water calculations overstate the pressure drop for hot water). However, if the use of 60°F water charts for 200°F water produces errors in excess of 20% then this charts should not be used.

For designing the piping system most common approach is to determine the pipe size for desired flow rate and allowable pressure drop. Usually a pipe diameter is first selected using no fittings in the computation and then modifying the calculations to include the influence of all the fittings. A rule of thumb for the initial computations without including fittings is to increase the design length of the pipe by a factor of 1.5 to 2.0 of the actual to approximately account for the pressure drop in the fittings.

The general range of pipe friction loss used for design of hydronic systems is between 1 and 4 ft of water per 100 ft of pipe. A value of 2.5 ft/100 ft represents the mean to which most systems are designed.

Closed-loop hydronic system piping is generally sized below certain upper limits, such as a velocity limit of 4 fps for 2 in. pipe and under, and a pressure drop limit of 4 ft per 100 ft for piping over 2 in. in diameter described earlier. This is to keep piping noise at a low level.

Water velocity noise is caused by free air, sharp pressure drops, turbulence, or a combination of these, which in turn cause cavitation or flashing of water into vapor. Therefore, higher velocities may be used if proper precautions are taken to eliminate air and turbulence.

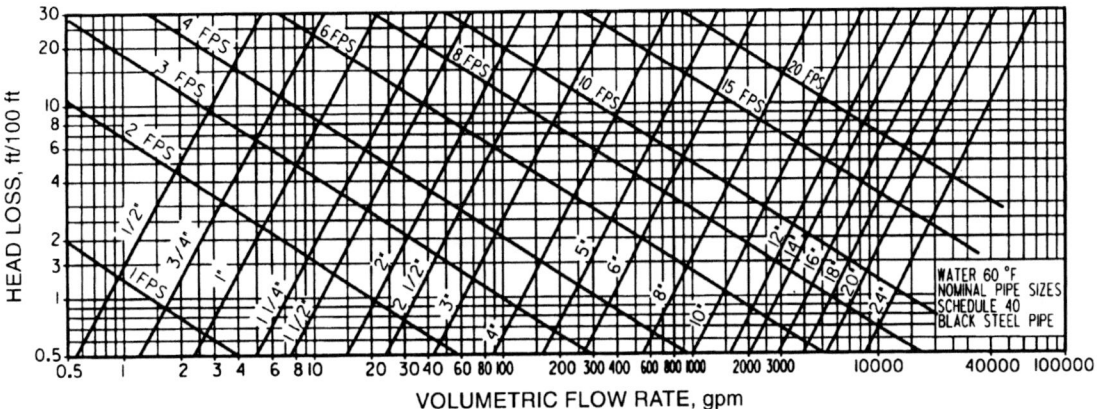

Fig 9-1. Friction loss for water in commercial steel pipe

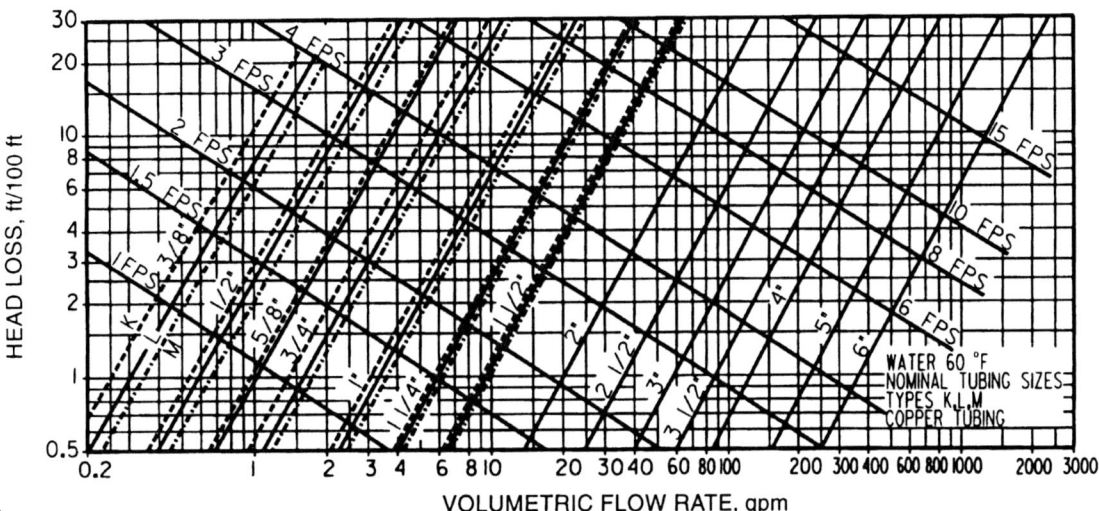

Fig 9-2. Friction loss for water in copper tubing (Types K, L, M)

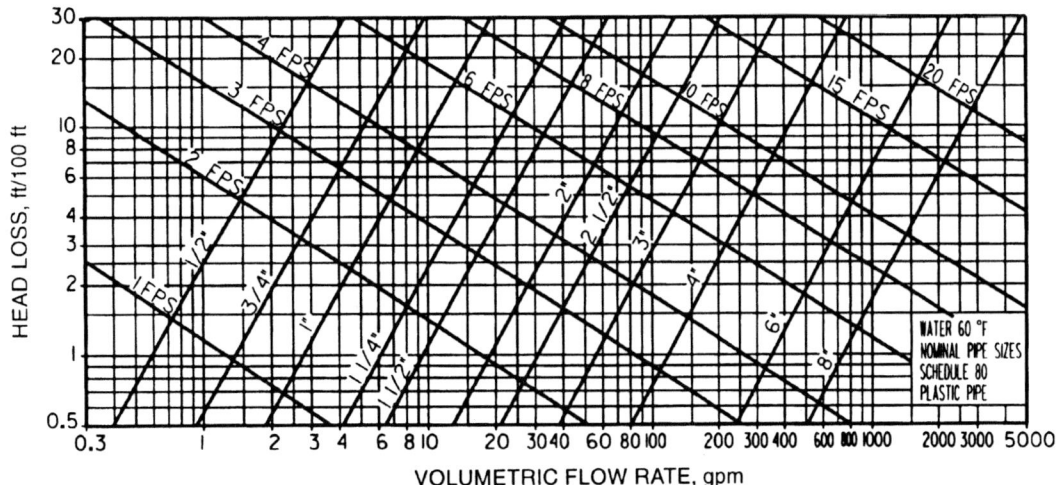

Fig 9-3. Friction loss for water in plastic pipe (Schedule 80)

Table 9-7. Iron and Copper Elbow Equivalents

Fitting	Iron Pipe	Copper Tubing
Elbow, 90°	1.00	1.00
Elbow, 45°	0.70	0.70
Elbow, 90° long-radius	0.50	0.50
Elbow, welded, 90°	0.50	0.50
Reduced coupling	0.40	0.40
Open return bend	1.00	1.00
Angle radiator valve	2.00	3.00
Radiator or convector	3.00	4.00
Boiler or heater	3.00	4.00
Open gate valve	0.50	0.70
Open globe valve	12.00	17.00

Table 9-8. Proper Flow and Pressure Required During Flow for Different Fixtures

Fixture	Flow Pressure, psig[a]	Flow, gpm
Ordinary basin faucet	8	3.0
Self closing basin faucet	12	2.5
Sink faucet ⅜ inch	10	4.5
Sink faucet ½ inch	5	4.5
Dish washer	15–25	[b]
Bathtub faucet	5	6.0
Laundry tube cock ¼ inch	5	5.0
Shower	12	3–10
Ball valve for closet	15	3.0
Flush valve for closet	10–20	15–40[c]
Flush valve for urinal	15	15.0
Garden hose, 50 ft, and sill cock	30	5

[a] Flow pressure is the pressure in the pipe at the entrance to the particular fixture considered.
[b] Varies; see manufacturers, data.
[c] Wide range due to variation in design and type of flush valve closets.

In addition to causing flow noise in piping systems, air allows oxygen to react with piping materials and sometimes even prevents flow in parts of a system. Air enters the system through open interfaces such as in holding or expansion tanks, or in the form of dissolved air already present in makeup water. Most well designed hydronic systems therefore use air separation devices. The solubility of air increases with increasing pressure and/or decreasing temperature. Air separation devices should therefore ideally be located at lowest pressure and/or highest temperature points. However, due to practical constraints, the devices may usually be located elsewhere; for example, in the basement where the pressure is not necessarily the lowest. An example, in apartment buildings where the pressure is lower at the higher floors, higher velocities should be used in the returns that bring the water to separation units may be located in the basement.

Maximum velocities to minimize erosion are established Table 9-5 using noise as the criteria. Minimum velocities are recommended to address air solubility considerations. Velocities must be high enough to ensure that parasitic air in the system is dissolved and carried by the water to the separation units. Velocities greater than 2 fps are recommended for pipes less than or equal 2 in. diameter. For larger diameter pipes the velocities should be greater than that corresponding to a head loss of 0.75 ft/100 ft. The velocity criteion for different flow types is given in Table 9-6.

Valve and Fitting Pressure Drop.—Valves and fittings can be listed in elbow equivalents, with an elbow being equivalent to a length of straight pipe. Table 9-4 lists equivalent lengths of 90° elbows; Table 9-7 lists elbow equivalents for valves and fittings for iron and copper.

Pressure drop through pipe tees varies with flow through the branch. Fig. 9-4 illustrates pressure drops for tees of equal inlet and outlet sizes and for the flow patterns illustrated. As an estimate of the upper limit to tee losses, a pressure or head loss coefficient of 1.0 may be assumed for entering and leaving flows.

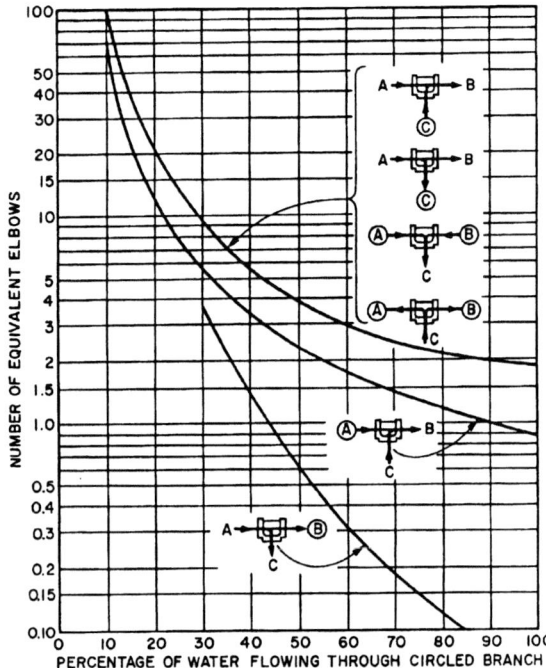

Fig 9-4. Elbow equivalents of tees at various flow conditions

1. Chart is based on straight tees (i.e., branches A, B, and C are the same size).

2. Pressure loss in desired circuit is obtained by selecting the proper curve according to illustrations, determining the flow at the circled branch, and multiplying the pressure loss for the same size elbow at the flow rate in the circled branch by the equivalent elbows indicated.

3. When the size of an outlet is reduced, the equivalent elbows shown on the chart do not apply. Therefore, the maximum loss for any circuit for any flow will not exceed 2 elbow equivalents at the maximum flow occurring in any branch of the tee.

4. Top curve is average of 4 curves, one for each circuit shown.

Table 9-9. Equivalent Resistance of Valves and Fittings

Nominal Pipe Diameter, in.	Valve or Fitting									
	Globe Valve Open	Gate Valve				Angle Valve Open	Close Return Bend	Tee		Ordinary Entrances[a]
		¾ Closed	½ Closed	¼ Closed	Open			Through Run	Through Side[b]	
	Equivalent Resistance, Feet of Pipe									
½	16	40	10	2	0.3	9.0	4.0	1.0	4.0	0.9
¾	22	55	14	3	0.5	12.0	5.0	1.4	5.0	1.2
1	27	70	17	4	0.6	15.0	6.0	1.7	6.0	1.5
1¼	37	90	22	4	0.8	18.0	8.0	2.3	8.0	2.0
1½	44	110	28	6	0.9	21.0	10.0	2.7	9.0	2.4
2	55	140	35	7	1.2	28.0	13.0	3.5	12.0	3.0
2½	65	160	40	8	1.4	32.0	15.0	4.2	14.0	3.3
3	80	200	50	10	1.6	41.0	18.0	5.0	17.0	4.5
3½	100	240	60	12	2.0	50.0	21.0	6.0	19.0	5.0
4	120	275	69	14	2.2	55.0	25.0	7.0	21.0	6.0
5	140	325	81	16	2.9	70.0	30.0	8.5	27.0	7.5
6	160	400	100	20	3.5	80.0	36.0	10.1	34.0	9.0
8	220	525	131	26	4.5	110.0	50.0	14.0	44.0	12.0
10	...	700	175	35	5.5	140.0	60.0	17.0	55.0	15.0
12	...	800	200	40	6.5	160.0	72.0	19.0	65.0	16.5
14	...	950	238	48	8.0	190.0	85.0	23.0	75.0	20.0
16	...	1100	272	52	9 0	220.0	100.0	26.0	88.0	22.0
18	...	1300	325	65	10.0	250.0	115.0	30.0	110.0	25.0

Nominal Pipe Diameter, Inches	Valve or Fitting									
	Sudden Contraction[c]			Borda Entrance	Reducing Tee[d]		90° Elbow			45° Elbow
	D/d=4	D/d=2	D/d=4/3		D/d=2	D/d=4/3	Standard	Medium Sweep	Long Sweep	
	Equivalent Resistance, Feet of Pipe									
½	0.8	0.6	0.3	1.4	1.5	1.3	1.5	1.3	1.0	0.8
¾	1.0	0.8	0.5	1.9	2.0	1.8	2.0	1.8	1.4	1.0
1	1.3	1.0	0.6	2.5	2.6	2.4	2.6	2.4	1.7	1.3
1¼	0.6	1.3	0.8	3.5	3.5	3.1	3.5	3.1	2.3	1.6
1½	2.0	1.5	0.9	4.0	4.5	3.7	4.5	3.7	2.7	2.0
2	2.5	1.9	1.2	5.0	5.3	4.5	5.3	4.5	3.5	2.5
2½	3.0	2.2	1.4	6.0	6.3	5.5	6.3	5.5	4.2	3.0
3	3.7	2.8	1.6	7.5	8.0	6.9	8.0	6.9	5.0	3.7
3½	4.4	3.3	2.0	9.0	9.5	8.0	9.5	8.0	6.0	4.4
4	5.0	3.7	2.2	11.0	11.5	9.5	11.0	9.5	7.0	5.0
5	6.0	4.7	2.9	12.0	12.5	12.0	13.0	12.0	8.5	6.0
6	7.5	5.6	3.5	15.0	16.0	14.0	16.0	14.0	10.1	7.5
8	11.0	7.2	4.5	19.0	20.0	18.0	20.0	18.0	14.0	10.0
10	13.0	9.5	5.5	24.0	25.0	22.0	25.0	22.0	17.0	13.0
12	15.0	11.0	6.5	29.0	31.0	26.0	31.0	26.0	19.0	...
14	17.0	12.5	8.0	34.0	36.0	30.0	36.0	30.0	23.0	...
16	9.0	15.0	9.0	38.0	40.0	35.0	40.0	35.0	26.0	...
18	21.0	16.5	10.0	43.0	45.0	40.0	45.0	40.0	30.0	...

[a] Into pipe of given diameter from tank, etc.
[b] For flow making 90° turn.
[c] Use pipe size of small diameter. For sudden enlargements, $d/D = \frac{1}{4}$, values are same as for reducing tee, $D/d = 2$; $d/D = \frac{1}{2}$, values are same as for Tee, Through run; $d/D = 4/3$ values are same as for sudden contraction, $D/d = 4/3$.
[d] For run of tee. Use pipe size of small diameter.

Table 9-10. Volume Flow at 1 Fpm in Pipe and Tube

Nominal Diameter in.	Schedule 40 Pipe			Schedule 80 Pipe			Type K Copper Tube		
	ft³/min	gpm	lbs/min (60°F Water)	ft³/min	gpm	lbs/min (60°F Water)	ft³/min	gpm	lbs/min (60°F Water)
⅛	0.0004	0.003	0.025	0.0003	0.002	0.016	0.0002	0.0014	0.012
¼	0.0007	0.005	0.044	0.0005	0.004	0.031	0.0005	0.0039	0.033
⅜	0.0013	0.010	0.081	0.0010	0.007	0.061	0.0009	0.0066	0.055
½	0.0021	0.016	0.132	0.0016	0.012	0.102	0.0018	0.0113	0.094
¾	0.0027	0.028	0.232	0.0030	0.025	0.213	0.0030	0.0267	0.189
1	0.0062	0.046	0.387	0.0050	0.037	0.312	0.0054	0.0404	0.338
1¼	0.0104	0.078	0.649	0.0880	0.067	0.555	0.0085	0.0632	0.53
1½	0.0141	0.106	0.882	0.0123	0.092	0.765	0.0196	0.1465	1.22
2	0.0233	0.174	1.454	0.0206	0.154	1.28	0.0209	0.1565	1.31
2½	0.0332	0.248	2.073	0.0294	0.220	1.830	0.0323	0.2418	2.02
3	0.0514	0.383	3.201	0.0460	0.344	2.870	0.0461	0.3446	2.88
3½	0.0682	0.513	4.287	0.0617	0.458	3.720	0.0625	0.4675	3.91
4	0.0884	0.660	5.516	0.0800	0.597	4.970	0.0811	0.6068	5.07
5	0.1390	1.040	8.674	0.126	0.947	7.940	0.1259	0.9415	7.87
6	0.2010	1.500	12.52	0.182	1.355	11.300	0.1797	1.3440	11.2
8	0.348	2.600	21.68	0.3180	2.380	19.800	0.3135	2.3446	19.6
10	0.5470	4.100	34.16	0.5560	4.165	31.130	0.4867	3.4405	30.4
12	0.7850	5.870	48.5	0.7060	5.280	44.040	0.6978	5.2194	43.6
14	1.0690	7.030	58.64	0.852	6.380	53.180	…	…	…
16	1.3920	9.180	76.58	1.117	8.360	69.730	…	…	…
18	1.5530	11.120	96.93	1.418	10.61	88.500	…	…	…
20	1.9250	14.400	120.56	1.755	13.13	109.51	…	…	…

Nominal Diameter in.	Type L Copper Tube			Type M Copper Tube			Type DWV Copper Drain Tube		
	ft³/min	gpm	lbs/min (60°F Water)	ft³/min	gpm	lbs/min (60°F Water)	ft³/min	gpm	lbs/min (60°F Water)
⅛	0.0002	0.002	0.014	0.0002	0.002	0.014	…	…	…
¼	0.0005	0.004	0.034	0.0006	0.004	0.036	…	…	…
⅜	0.0010	0.008	0.063	0.0011	0.008	0.069	…	…	…
½	0.0016	0.012	0.101	0.0018	0.013	0.110	…	…	…
¾	0.0034	0.025	0.210	0.0036	0.027	0.224	…	…	…
1	0.0057	0.043	0.358	0.0061	0.045	0.379	…	…	…
1¼	0.0087	0.065	0.545	0.0091	0.068	0.569	0.0091	0.068	0.569
1½	0.0124	0.093	0.770	0.0133	0.100	0.83	0.0129	0.097	0.850
2	0.0215	0.161	1.34	0.0220	0.165	1.35	0.0227	0.170	1.417
2½	0.0331	0.248	2.07	0.0340	0.254	2.12	…	…	…
3	0.0473	0.354	2.96	0.0485	0.363	3.03	0.0502	0.376	3.13
3½	0.064	0.479	4.00	0.0653	0.488	4.08	…	…	…
4	0.0841	0.622	5.20	0.0834	0.626	5.23	0.0876	0.655	5.47
5	0.1296	0.969	8.10	0.1313	0.982	8.20	0.1352	1.152	8.33
6	0.1862	1.393	11.6	0.1885	1.00	11.78	0.1936	1.448	12.08
8	0.3253	2.434	20.3	0.3304	2.472	20.70	…	…	…
10	0.5050	3.777	21.6	0.5131	3.838	32.10	…	…	…
12	0.7291	5.454	45.6	0.7357	5.503	46.00	…	…	…

Table 9-11. Friction Loss in ⅛-Inch Schedule 40 Steel Pipe[a]

Flow Rate			60° Water		180° Water		300° Water	
gpm	ft³/sec	Velocity, ft/sec	Flow, lb/hr	Pressure Loss, ft/100 ft	Flow, lb/hr	Pressure Loss, ft/100 ft	Flow, lb/hr	Pressure Loss, ft/100 ft
0.2	0.000446	1.13	100	4.62	97	3.58	92	3.14
0.3	0.000668	1.69	150	9.52	146	7.63	138	6.81
0.4	0.000891	2.26	200	1 6.0	194	13.1	184	11.8
0.5	0.00111	2.82	250	24.0	243	20.1	230	18.2
0.6	0.00134	3.39	300	33.4	291	28.4	276	26.0
0.7	0.00156	3.95	350	44.6	340	38.3	322	35.2
0.8	0.00178	4.52	400	57.1	389	49.6	368	45.7
0.9	0.00201	5.08	450	71.1	439	62.5	414	57.4
1.0	0.00223	5.65	500	86.6	486	76.4	460	70.7
1.2	0.00267	6.77	600	122	583	109	552	101
1.4	0.00312	7.90	700	164	680	148	644	137
1.6	0.00356	9.03	800	213	777	194	735	181
1.8	0.00401	10.2	900	264	874	241	827	225
2.0	0.00446	11.3	1000	324	972	298	919	278

[a] To calculate the velocity (V_x) or the pressure drop (H_x) through pipe other than schedule 40, use the following relationships:

$$V_x = V_{40}\left(\frac{D_{40}}{D_x}\right)^2 \qquad H_x = H_{40}\left(\frac{D_{40}}{D_x}\right)^5$$

Table 9-12. Friction Loss in ¼-Inch Schedule 40 Steel Pipe[a]

Flow Rate			60° Water		180° Water		300° Water	
gpm	ft³/sec	Velocity, ft/sec	Flow, lb/hr	Pressure Loss, ft/100 ft	Flow, lb/hr	Pressure Loss, ft/100 ft	Flow, lb/hr	Pressure Loss, ft/100 ft
0.4	0.000891	1.23	200	3.65	194	2.86	184	2.52
0.6	0.00134	1.85	300	7.54	291	6.11	276	5.47
0.8	0.00178	2.47	400	12.7	389	5.92	368	9.53
1.0	0.00223	3.08	500	19.1	486	16.2	460	14.7
1.2	0.00267	3.70	600	26.8	583	22.9	552	21.10
1.4	0.00312	4.32	700	35.6	680	30.9	644	28.4
1.6	0.00356	4.93	800	45.6	777	39.9	735	36.9
1.8	0.00401	5.55	900	56.9	874	50.2	827	46.5
2.0	0.00446	6.17	1000	69.4	972	61.8	919	57.2
2.5	0.00557	7.71	1250	106	1215	95.4	1149	89.0
3.0	0.00668	9.25	1500	150	1457	137	1379	128
3.5	0.0078	10.8	1950	202	1700	185	1609	173
4.0	0.00891	12.3	2000	261	1943	240	1839	225
4.5	0.01000	13.9	2250	328	2186	304	2069	285
5.0	0.0111	15.4	2500	402	2429	374	2298	351

Table 9-13. Friction Loss in ⅜-Inch Schedule 40 Steel Pipe[a]

Flow Rate			60°F Water		180°F Water		300°F Water	
gpm	ft³/sec	Velocity, ft/sec	Flow, lb/hr	Pressure Loss, ft/100 ft	Flow, lb/hr	Pressure Loss, ft/100 ft	Flow, lb/hr	Pressure Loss, ft/100 ft
0.6	0.00134	1.01	300	1.72	291	1.33	276	1.17
0.8	0.00178	1.34	400	2.88	389	2.28	368	2.02
1.0	0.00223	1.68	500	4.29	486	3.46	460	3.09
1.5	0.00334	2.52	750	8.92	729	7.44	690	6.74
2.0	0.00446	3.36	1000	15.2	972	12.9	912	11.8
2.5	0.00557	4.20	1250	22.9	1215	19.8	1149	18.2
3.0	0.00668	5.04	1500	32.2	1457	28.3	1379	26.1
3.5	0.00780	5.88	1750	43.0	1700	38.2	1609	35.4
4.0	0.00891	6.72	2000	55.3	1943	49.5	1839	46.0
4.5	0.0100	7.56	2250	69.2	2186	62.5	2069	58.1
5.0	0.0111	8.40	2500	84.8	2429	76.9	2298	71.7
6.0	0.0134	10.1	3000	120	2915	110	2758	102
7.0	0.0156	11.8	3500	162	3401	149	3218	139
8.0	0.0178	13.4	4000	209	3887	194	3677	182
9.0	0.0201	15.1	4500	263	4372	245	4137	230
10.0	0.0223	16.8	5000	323	4858	302	4597	283

Table 9-14. Friction Loss in ½-Inch Schedule 40 Steel Pipe[a]

Flow Rate			60°F Water		180°F Water		300°F Water	
gpm	ft³/sec	Velocity, ft/sec	Flow, lb/hr	Pressure Loss, ft/100 ft	Flow, lb/hr	Pressure Loss, ft/100 ft	Flow, lb/hr	Pressure Loss, ft/100 ft
1.0	0.00223	1.06	500	1.38	486	1.08	460	0.946
1.5	0.00334	1.58	750	2.86	729	2.30	690	2.05
2.0	0.00446	2.11	1000	4.81	972	3.95	919	3.56
2.5	0.00557	2.64	1250	7.22	1215	6.05	1149	5.49
3.0	0.00668	3.17	1500	10.1	1457	8.58	1379	7.83
3.5	0.00780	3.70	1750	13.4	1700	11.5	1609	10.6
4.0	0.00891	4.22	2000	17.2	1943	14.9	1839	13.7
4.5	0.0100	4.75	2250	21.4	2186	18.8	2069	17.3
5.0	0.0111	5.28	2500	26.1	2429	23.0	2298	21.3
6.0	0.0134	6.34	3000	36.8	2915	32.9	2758	30.5
7.0	0.0156	7.39	3500	49.4	3401	44.5	3218	41.4
8.0	0.0178	8.45	4000	63.2	3887	57.4	3677	53.4
9.0	0.0201	9.5	4500	79.6	4372	72.7	4137	67.8
10.0	0.0223	10.6	5000	97.5	4858	89.6	4597	83.7
11.0	0.0245	11.6	5500	118	5344	108	5056	101
12.0	0.0267	12.7	6000	139	5830	128	5516	120
13.0	0.0290	13.7	6500	162	6316	151	5976	141
14.0	0.0312	14.8	7000	188	6801	175	6435	164
15.0	0.0334	15.8	7500	214	7287	200	6895	188

Table 9-15. Friction Loss in ¾-Inch Schedule 40 Steel Pipe[a]

Flow Rate		Velocity, ft/sec	60°F Water		180°F Water		300°F Water	
gpm	ft³/sec		Flow, lb/hr	Pressure Loss, ft/100 ft	Flow, lb/hr	Pressure Loss, ft/100 ft	Flow, lb/hr	Pressure Loss, ft/100 ft
1	0.00223	0.602	500	0.358	486	0.269	460	0.231
1.5	0.00334	0.903	750	0.734	729	0.566	690	0.494
2	0.00446	1.20	1000	1.22	972	0.96	919	0.848
2.5	0.00557	1.50	1250	1.82	1215	1.46	1149	1.130
3.0	0.00668	1.8 1	1500	2.51	1457	2.05	1379	1.184
3.5	0.0078	2.11	1750	3.32	1700	2.75	1609	2.48
4.0	0.00891	2.41	2000	4.25	1943	3.54	1839	3.21
4.5	0.0100	2.71	2250	5.27	2186	4.44	2069	4.04
5	0.0111	3.01	2500	6.4	2429	5.44	2298	4.96
6	0.0134	3.61	3000	8.98	2915	7.73	2758	7.09
7.0	0.0156	4.21	3500	12	3401	10.4	3218	9.57
8.0	0.0178	4.81	4000	15.3	3587	13.5	3677	12.4
9	0.0201	5.42	4500	19.1	4372	16.9	4137	15.7
10	0.0223	6.02	5000	23.3	4858	20.8	4597	19.3
11	0.0245	6.62	5500	28	5344	25.1	5056	23.3
12	0.0267	7.22	6000	32.5	5830	29.7	55 16	27.6
13	0.0290	7.82	6500	38.4	6316	34.8	5976	32.4
14	0.0312	8.42	7000	44.3	6801	40.1	6435	37.4
15	0.0334	9.03	7500	50.7	7287	46.2	6895	43.1
16	0.0356	9.63	8000	57.2	7773	52.3	7355	48.8
17	0.0379	10.2	8500	64.4	8259	59.1	7814	55.2
18	0.0401	10.8	9000	71.6	8745	65.9	8274	61.6
19	0.0423	11.4	9500	79.6	9231	73.4	8734	68.6
20	0.0446	12.0	10000	87.9	9716	81.2	9193	76.0
22.0	0.049	13.2	11000	106	10688	97.9	10113	91.8
24.0	0.0535	14.4	12000	125	11660	117	11032	109
26.0	0.0579	15.6	13000	146	12631	139	11951	128
28.0	0.0624	16.8	14000	169	13602	158	12871	148
30.0	0.0668	18.1	15000	193	14575	181	13790	170

Table 9-16. Friction Loss in 1-Inch Schedule 40 Steel Pipe[a]

Flow Rate			60°F Water		180°F Water		300°F Water	
gpm	ft³/sec	Velocity, ft/sec	Flow, lb/hr	Pressure Loss, ft/100 ft	Flow, lb/hr	Pressure Loss, ft/100 ft	Flow, lb/hr	Pressure Loss, ft/100 ft
1	0.00267	0.371	500	0.113	486	0.0830	460	0.0700
2	0.00446	0.742	1000	0.381	972	0.290	919	0.252
3	0.00668	1.11	1500	0.778	1457	0.0612	1379	0.540
4	0.00891	1.48	2000	1.30	1943	1.05	1839	0.936
5	0.0111	1.86	2500	1.94	2429	1.59	2298	1.43
6	0.0134	2.23	3000	2.71	2915	2.25	2758	2.04
7	0.0156	2.60	3500	3.59	3401	3.03	3218	2.75
8	0.0178	2.97	4000	4.59	3887	4.08	3677	3.56
9	0.0201	3.34	4500	5.70	4372	4.89	4137	4.48
10	0.0223	3.71	5000	6.94	4858	6.00	4597	5.51
12	0.0267	4.45	6000	9.76	5830	8.54	5516	7.87
14	0.0312	5.20	7000	13.0	6801	11.6	6435	10.7
16	0.0356	5.94	8000	16.8	7773	15	7355	13.9
18	0.0401	6.68	9000	21.0	8745	18.9	8274	17.5
20	0.0446	7.42	10000	25.7	9716	23.2	9193	21.6
22	0.0490	8.17	11000	30.8	10688	28.1	10113	26.1
24	0.0535	8.91	12000	36.2	11660	33.1	11032	30.9
26	0.0579	9.65	13000	42.5	12631	38.9	11951	36.3
28	0.0624	10.4	14000	48.9	13603	45	12871	42.0
30	0.0668	11.1	15000	55.9	14575	51.6	13790	48.2
32	0.0713	11.9	1 6000	63.2	15546	58.4	14709	54.7
34	0.0758	12.6	17000	71.3	16518	66.1	15629	61.9
36	0.0802	13.4	18000	79.6	17490	74	16548	69.3
38	0.0847	14.1	19000	88.2	18461	82.1	17467	77.0
40	0.0891	14.8	20000	97.7	19433	91.1	18387	85.4
42	0.0936	15.6	21000	107	20404	100	19306	94.1
44	0.0980	16.3	22000	118	21376	110	20225	103
46	0.102	17.1	23000	128	22348	120	21145	113
48	0.107	17.8	24000	139	23319	130	22064	122
50	0.111	18.6	25000	151	24291	141	22984	133
55	0.123	20.4	27500	182	26720	171	25282	161
60	0.134	22.3	30000	215	29149	203	27580	191
65	0.145	24.1	32500	252	31578	241	29879	224
70	0.156	26.0	35000	279	34007	276	32177	260
75	0.167	27.8	37500	332	36437	316	34475	297
80	0.178	29.7	40000	379	38866	360	36774	339
85	0.189	31.6	42500	428	41295	407	39072	384
90	0.201	33.4	45000	477	43724	454	41370	428
95	0.212	35.3	47500	531	46153	506	43669	477
100	0.223	37.1	50000	588	48582	561	45967	529

Table 9-17. Friction Loss in 1½-Inch Schedule 40 Steel Pipe[a]

Flow Rate		Velocity, ft/sec	60°F Water		180°F Water		300°F Water	
gpm	ft³/sec		Flow, lb/hr	Pressure Loss, ft/100 ft	Flow, lb/hr	Pressure Loss, ft/100 ft	Flow, lb/hr	Pressure Loss, ft/100 ft
2	0.00446	0.315	1	0.0490	0.972	0.0358	0.919	0.0302
3	0.00668	0.473	1.5	0.0993	1.457	0.0741	1.379	0.0632
4	0.00891	0.630	2	0.165	1.943	0.125	1.838	0.108
5	0.0111	0.788	2.5	0.243	2.429	0.188	2.298	0.164
6	0.0134	0.946	3	0.336	2.915	0.263	2.758	0.231
7	0.0156	1.10	3.5	0.443	3.401	0.350	3.218	0.308
8	0.0178	1.26	4	0.562	3.887	0.449	3.677	0.398
9	0.0201	1.42	4.5	0.695	4.372	0.560	4.137	0.498
10	0.0223	1.58	5	0.839	4.858	0.682	4.597	0.610
12	0.0267	1.89	6	1.17	5.830	0.962	5.516	0.867
14	0.0312	2.21	7	1.54	6.801	1.29	6.435	1.16
16	0.0356	2.52	8	1.98	7.773	1.66	7.355	1.51
18	0.0401	2.84	9	2.45	8.745	2.09	8.274	1.90
20	0.0446	3.15	10	2.98	9.716	2.55	9.193	2.34
22	0.0490	3.47	11	3.56	10.69	3.08	10.11	2.82
24	0.0535	3.78	12	4.18	11.66	3.63	11.03	3.33
26	0.0579	4.1	13	4.85	12.63	4.25	11.95	3.92
28	0.0624	4.41	14	5.59	13.6	4.91	12.87	4.51
30	0.0668	4.73	15	6.35	14.57	5.6	13.79	5.17
32	0.0713	5.04	16	7.17	15.55	6.35	14.71	5.89
34	0.0758	5.36	17	8.04	16.52	7.15	15.63	6.6
36	0.0802	5.67	18	8.97	17.49	8.00	16.55	7.40
38	0.0847	5.99	19	10.3	18.46	9.21	17.47	8.69
40	0.0891	6.30	20	11.0	19.43	9.84	18.39	9.15
42	0.0936	6.62	21	12.0	20.40	10.8	19.31	10.1
44	0.0980	6.93	22	13.1	21.38	11.9	20.27	11.0
46	0.102	7.25	23	14.3	22.35	12.9	21.14	12.0
48	0.107	7.56	24	15.5	23.32	14.1	22.06	13.1
50	0.111	7.88	25	16.8	24.29	15.3	22.98	14.2
55	0.123	8.67	27.5	20.2	26.72	18.5	25.28	17.2
60	0.134	9.46	30	23.8	29.15	21.8	27.58	20.4
65	0.145	10.2	32.5	27.7	31.58	25.5	29.88	23.8
70	0.156	11.0	35	32.0	34.01	29.5	32.18	27.6
75	0.167	11.8	37.5	36.6	36.44	33.8	34.48	31.7
80	0.178	12.6	40	41.4	38.87	38.5	36.77	36.1
85	0.189	13.4	42.5	46.6	41.29	43.4	39.07	40.7
90	0.201	14.2	45	52.1	43.72	45.6	41.37	45.7
95	0.212	15.0	47.5	57.8	46.15	54.0	43.67	50.8
100	0.223	15.8	50	63.9	48.58	59.8	45.97	56.0
110	0.245	17.3	55	77.0	53.44	72.2	50.56	67.7
120	0.267	18.9	60	91.3	58.3	85.9	55.16	80.6
130	0.290	20.5	65	107	63.16	101	59.76	94.5
140	0.312	22.1	70	123	68.01	117	64.35	110
150	0.334	23.6	75	141	72.87	134	68.95	126
160	0.356	25.2	80	161	77.73	152	73.55	143
170	0.379	26.8	85	181	82.59	172	78.14	162
180	0.401	28.4	90	202	87.45	192	82.74	181
190	0.423	29.9	95	225	92.31	214	87.34	202
200	0.446	31.5	100	248	97.16	236	91.93	223

Table 9-18. Friction Loss in 2-Inch Schedule 40 Steel Pipe[a]

Flow Rate			60°F Water		180°F Water		300°F Water	
gpm	ft³/sec	Velocity, ft/sec	Flow, lb/hr	Pressure Loss, ft/100 ft	Flow, lb/hr	Pressure Loss, ft/100 ft	Flow, lb/hr	Pressure Loss, ft/100 ft
2	0.00446	0.191	1	0.0150	0.972	0.0108	0.919	0.00897
4	0.00891	0.382	2	0.0498	1.943	0.0368	1.838	0.0313
6	0.0134	0.574	3	0.101	2.915	0.0766	2.758	0.0659
8	0.0178	0.765	4	0.168	3.887	0.130	3.677	0.113
10	0.0223	0.956	5	0.249	4.858	0.196	4.597	0.172
12	0.0267	1.15	6	0.346	5.830	0.275	5.516	0.244
14	0.0312	1.34	7	0.455	6.801	0.366	6.435	0.325
16	0.0356	1.53	8	0.580	7.773	0.471	7.355	0.422
18	0.0401	1.72	9	0.717	8.745	0.588	8.274	0.529
20	0.0446	1.91	10	0.868	9.716	0.718	9.193	0.648
22	0.0490	2.10	11	1.03	10.69	0.861	10.11	0.777
24	0.0535	2.29	12	1.21	11.66	1.02	11.03	0.924
26	0.0579	2.49	13	1.40	12.63	1.18	11.95	1.08
28	0.0624	2.68	14	1.6	13.6	1.36	12.87	1.24
30	0.0668	2.87	15	1.83	14.57	1.56	13.79	1.42
35	0.0780	3.35	17.5	2.43	17.00	2.10	1 6.09	1.93
40	0.0891	3.82	20	3.11	19.43	2.71	18.39	2.50
45	0.1000	4.30	22.5	3.89	21.86	3.42	20.69	3.14
50	0.111	4.78	25	4.74	24.29	4.19	22.98	3.87
55	0.123	5.26	27.5	5.67	26.72	5.05	25.28	4.69
60	0.134	5.74	30	6.68	29.15	5.98	27.58	5.52
65	0.145	6.21	32.5	7.79	31.58	7.00	29.88	6.48
70	0.156	6.69	35	8.96	34.01	8.09	32.18	7.52
75	0. 167	7.17	37.5	10.2	36.44	9.26	34.48	8.63
80	0.178	7.65	40	11.6	38.87	10.5	36.77	9.82
85	0. 189	8.13	42.5	13.0	41.29	11.9	39.07	11.1
90	0.201	8.6	45	14.5	43.72	13.2	41.37	12.4
95	0.212	9.08	47.5	16.1	46.15	14.7	43.67	13.7
100	0.223	9.56	50	17.8	48.58	16.3	45.97	15.2
110	0.245	10.5	55	21.3	53.44	19.7	50.56	18.4
120	0.267	11.5	60	25.3	58.3	23.4	55.16	21.9
130	0.290	12.4	65	29.5	63.0	27.4	59.76	25.7
140	0.312	13.4	70	34.0	68.01	31.7	64.35	29.7
150	0.334	14.3	75	39.0	72.87	36.4	68.95	34.2
160	0.356	15.3	80	44.2	77.73	41.4	73.55	38.9
170	0.379	16.3	85	49.7	82.59	46.6	78.14	44.0
180	0.401	17.2	90	55.5	87.45	52.1	82.74	48.8
190	0.423	18.2	95	61.7	92.31	58.1	87.34	54.4
200	0.446	19.1	100	68.2	97.16	64.2	91.93	60.2
220	0.490	21.0	110	82.4	106.9	77.7	101.1	72.9
240	0.535	22.9	120	97.6	116.6	92.4	110.3	86.7
260	0.579	24.9	130	114	126.3	108	119.5	102
280	0.624	26.8	140	132	136	125	128.7	118
300	0.668	28.7	150	152	145.7	144	137.9	136
320	0.713	30.6	160	171	155.5	163	147.1	154
340	0.758	32.5	170	194	165.2	184	156.3	174
360	0.802	34.4	180	217	174.9	207	165.5	195
380	0.847	36.3	190	242	184.6	230	174.7	217
400	0.891	38.2	200	267	194.3	255	183.9	241

Table 9-19. Friction Loss in 2½-Inch Schedule 40 Steel Pipe[a]

Flow Rate		Velocity, ft/sec	60°F Water		180°F Water		300°F Water	
gpm	ft³/sec		Flow, lb/hr	Pressure Loss, ft/100 ft	Flow, lb/hr	Pressure Loss, ft/100 ft	Flow, lb/hr	Pressure Loss, ft/100 ft
4	0.00891	0.268	2	0.0215	1.943	0.0157	1.838	0.0131
6	0.0134	0.402	3	0.0432	2.915	0.0322	2.758	0.0274
8	0.0178	0.536	4	0.0715	3.887	0.0542	3.677	0.0465
10	0.0223	0.670	5	0.106	4.858	0.0814	4.597	0.0705
12	0.0267	0.804	6	0.146	5.830	0.113	5.516	0.0990
14	0.0312	0.938	7	0.193	6.801	0.151	6.435	0.133
16	0.0356	1.07	8	0.245	7.773	0.194	7.355	0.172
18	0.0401	1.21	9	0.301	8.745	0.241	8.274	0.214
20	0.0446	1.34	10	0.365	9.716	0.294	9.193	0.262
22	0.0490	1.47	11	0.433	10.69	0.352	10.11	0.315
24	0.0535	1.61	12	0.507	11.66	0.414	11.03	0.372
26	0.0579	1.74	13	0.585	12.63	0.482	11.95	0.434
28	0.0624	1.88	14	0.667	13.6	0.555	12.87	0.501
30	0.0668	2.01	15	0.76	14.57	0.632	13.79	0.572
35	0.078	2.35	19.5	1.01	17.00	0.849	16.09	0.771
40	0.0891	2.68	20	1.29	19.43	1.100	18.39	1.02
45	0.100	3.02	22.5	1.6	21.86	1.37	20.69	1.26
50	0.111	3.35	25	1.94	24.29	1.68	22.98	1.54
55	0.123	3.69	29.5	2.33	26.72	2.03	25.28	1.86
60	0.134	4.02	30	2.94	29.15	2.40	27.58	2.21
65	0.145	4.36	32.5	3.19	31.58	2.81	29.88	2.59
70	0.156	4.69	35	3.66	34.01	3.24	32.18	3.00
75	0.167	5.03	37.5	4.17	36.44	3.71	34.48	3.43
80	0.178	5.36	40	4.72	38.87	4.21	36.72	3.90
85	0.189	5.70	42.5	5.28	41.29	4.73	39.07	4.38
90	0.201	6.03	45	5.89	43.72	5.29	41.37	4.90
95	0.212	6.37	47.5	6.53	46.15	5.88	43.67	5.46
100	0.223	6.70	50	7.09	48.58	6.51	45.97	6.04
110	0.245	7.37	55	8.63	53.44	7.83	50.56	7.30
120	0.267	8.04	60	10.2	58.30	9.26	55.16	8.63
130	0.290	8.71	65	11.9	63.0	10.9	59.76	10.2
140	0.312	9.38	70	14.3	68.01	12.6	64.36	11.8
150	0.334	10.1	75	15.7	72.87	14.4	68.96	13.5
160	0.356	10.7	80	17.8	77.73	16.4	73.55	15.4
170	0.379	11.4	85	20.1	82.59	18.5	78.14	17.3
180	0.401	12.1	90	22.3	87.45	20.7	82.74	19.4
190	0.423	12.7	95	24.8	92.31	23.1	87.34	21.6
200	0.446	13.4	100	27.3	97.16	25.5	91.93	23.9
220	0.490	14.7	110	33.0	106.9	30.8	101.1	28.9
240	0.535	16.1	120	39.0	116.6	36.6	110.3	34.3
260	0.579	17.4	130	45.7	126.3	43.0	119.5	40.3
280	0.624	18.8	140	52.7	136.0	49.7	128.7	46.7
300	0.668	20.1	150	60.4	145.7	57	137.9	53.6
350	0.780	23.5	175	81.7	170.0	77.5	160.9	72.8
400	0.891	26.8	200	107	194.3	101	183.9	95.3
450	1.003	30.2	225	134	218.6	127	206.9	120
500	1.114	33.5	250	164	242.9	157	229.8	148
550	1.225	36.9	275	199	267.2	190	252.8	179
600	1.337	40.2	300	236	291.5	226	275.8	213

Table 9-20. Friction Loss in 3-Inch Schedule 40 Steel Pipe[a]

Flow Rate		Velocity, ft/sec	60°F Water		180°F Water		300°F Water	
gpm	ft³/sec		Flow, lb/hr	Pressure Loss, ft/100 ft	Flow, lb/hr	Pressure Loss, ft/100 ft	Flow, lb/hr	Pressure Loss, ft/100 ft
5	0.0111	0.217	2.5	0.0113	2.429	0.00732	2.298	0.00681
10	0.0223	0.434	5	0.0375	4.858	0.0281	4.596	0.0241
15	0.0334	0.651	7.5	0.0764	7.287	0.0587	6.895	0.0510
20	0.0446	0.868	10	0.128	9.716	0.0997	9.193	0.0876
25	0.0557	1.09	12.5	0.19	12.15	0.151	11.49	0.134
30	0.0668	1.30	15	0.262	14.57	0.212	13.79	0.189
35	0.0780	1.52	17.5	0.348	17.00	0.284	1 6.09	0.255
40	0.0891	1.74	20	0.442	19.43	0.365	18.39	0.329
45	0.100	1.95	22.5	0.549	21.86	0.458	20.69	0.413
50	0.111	2.17	25	0.666	24.29	0.559	22.98	0.507
55	0.123	2.39	27.5	0.792	26.72	0.67	25.28	0.609
60	0.134	2.6	30	0.927	29.15	0.789	27.58	0.720
65	0.145	2.82	32.5	1.08	31.58	0.926	29.88	0.847
70	0.156	3.04	35	1.24	34.01	1.06	32.18	0.974
75	0. 167	3.25	37.5	1.41	36.44	1.22	34.48	1.12
50	0.178	3.47	40	1.59	38.87	1.38	36.77	1.27
85	0.189	3.69	42.5	1.77	41.29	1.55	39.07	1.42
90	0.201	3.91	45	1.97	43.72	1.73	41.37	1.6
95	0.212	4.12	47.5	2.19	46.15	1.92	43.67	1.77
100	0.223	4.34	50	2.46	48.58	2.16	45.97	1.97
110	0.245	4.77	55	2.89	53.44	2.56	50.56	2.37
120	0.267	5.21	60	3.40	58.3	3.03	55.16	2.81
130	0.290	5.64	65	3.99	63.16	3.55	59.76	3.30
140	0.312	6.08	70	4.56	68.01	4.10	64.35	3.82
150	0.334	6.51	75	5.2 1	72.87	4.71	68.95	4.38
160	0.356	6.94	80	5.88	77.73	5.33	73.55	4.97
170	0.379	7.38	85	6.61	82.59	6.01	78.14	5.59
150	0.401	7.81	90	7.37	87.45	6.72	82.74	6.27
190	0.423	8.25	95	8.20	92.31	7.50	87.34	7.00
200	0.446	8.68	100	9.01	97.16	8.27	91.93	7.71
220	0.490	9.55	110	10.9	106.9	10.0	101.1	9.34
240	0.535	10.4	120	12.8	116.6	11.9	110.3	11.1
260	0.579	11.3	130	15.0	126.3	13.9	119.5	13.0
280	0.624	12.2	140	17.2	136	16	128.7	15.0
300	0.668	13.0	150	19.7	145.7	18.4	137.9	17.2
320	0.713	13.9	160	22.4	155.5	20.9	147.1	19.7
340	0.758	14.8	170	25.2	165.2	23.6	156.3	22.1
360	0.802	15.6	180	28.2	174.9	26.4	165.5	24.8
380	0.847	16.5	190	31.3	184.6	29.4	174.7	27.7
400	0.891	17.4	200	34.6	194.3	32.5	183.9	30.6
420	0.936	18.2	210	38.1	204.0	35.9	193.1	33.7
440	0.980	19.1	220	41.7	213.8	39.3	202.2	37.0
460	1.025	20.0	230	45.5	223.5	43	211.4	40.4
480	1.069	20.8	240	49.5	233.2	46.8	220.6	43.9
500	1.114	21.7	250	53.6	242.9	50.7	229.8	47.7
600	1.337	26	300	76.5	291.5	72.7	275.8	68.4
700	1.56	30.4	350	104	340.1	98.8	321.8	93.1
800	1.782	34.7	400	135	388.7	129	367.7	122
1,000	2.228	43.4	500	210	485.8	202	459.7	190

Table 9-21. Friction Loss in 3½-Inch Schedule 40 Steel Pipe[a]

Flow Rate		Velocity, ft/sec	60°F Water		180°F Water		300°F Water	
gpm	ft³/sec		Flow, lb/hr	Pressure Loss, ft/100 ft	Flow, lb/hr	Pressure Loss, ft/100 ft	Flow, lb/hr	Pressure Loss, ft/100 ft
5	0.0111	0.162	2.5	0.00564	2.429	0.00406	2.298	0.00337
10	0.0223	0.323	5	0.0188	4.858	0.0139	4.597	0.0118
15	0.0334	0.487	7.5	0.0380	7.287	0.0288	6.895	0.0248
20	0.0446	0.649	10	0.0632	9.716	0.0487	9.193	0.0423
25	0.0557	0.811	12.5	0.0936	12.15	0.117	11.49	0.0642
30	0.0668	0.974	15	0.130	14.57	0.103	13.79	0.0907
35	0.0780	1.14	17.5	0.171	17.00	0.137	16.09	0.121
40	0.0891	1.30	20	0.218	19.43	0.176	18.39	0.157
45	0.1000	1.46	22.5	0.269	21.86	0.219	20.69	0.197
50	0.111	1.62	25	0.326	24.29	0.268	22.98	0.241
60	0.134	1.95	30	0.455	29.15	0.379	27.58	0.343
70	0.156	2.27	35	0.604	34.01	0.509	32.18	0.463
80	0.178	2.6	40	0.774	38.87	0.658	36.77	0.602
90	0.201	2.92	45	0.963	43.72	0.827	41.37	0.758
100	0.223	3.25	50	1.17	48.58	1.01	45.97	0.930
110	0.245	3.57	55	1.4	53.44	1.22	50.56	1.12
120	0.267	3.89	60	1.64	58.3	1.44	55.16	1.33
130	0.290	4.22	65	1.91	63.0	1.68	59.76	1.55
140	0.312	4.54	70	2.2	68.01	1.95	64.35	1.8
150	0.334	4.87	75	2.50	72.87	2.22	68.95	2.06
160	0.356	5.19	80	2.82	77.73	2.52	73.55	2.34
170	0.379	5.52	85	3.17	82.59	2.96	78.14	2.63
180	0.401	5.84	90	3.53	87.45	3.17	82.74	2.95
190	0.423	6.17	95	3.91	92.31	3.53	87.34	3.28
200	0.446	6.49	100	4.32	97.16	3.90	91.93	3.63
220	0.490	7.14	110	5.18	106.9	4.70	101.3	4.38
240	0.535	7.79	120	6.12	116.6	5.58	110.3	5.21
260	0.579	8.44	130	7.16	126.3	6.56	119.5	6.13
280	0.624	9.09	140	8.22	136	7.55	128.7	7.05
300	0.668	9.74	150	9.39	145.7	8.66	137.9	8.09
320	0.713	10.4	160	10.6	155.5	9.86	147.1	9.22
340	0.758	11.0	170	12.0	165.2	11.1	156.3	10.4
360	0.802	11.7	180	13.4	174.9	12.4	165.5	11.6
380	0.847	12.3	190	14.8	184.6	13.8	174.7	12.9
400	0.891	13.0	200	16.4	194.3	15.3	183.9	14.4
420	0.936	13.6	210	18.1	204.0	16.9	193.1	15.8
440	0.98	14.3	220	21.6	213.8	18.5	202.2	17.3
460	1.025	14.9	230	21.5	223.5	20.2	211.4	18.9
480	1.069	15.6	240	23.4	233.2	21.9	220.6	20.6
500	1.114	16.2	250	30.7	242.9	23.8	229.8	22.4
600	1.337	19.5	300	36.2	291.5	34.2	275.8	32.2
700	1.56	22.7	350	49.1	340.0	46.4	321.8	43.7
800	1.782	26.0	400	63.8	388.7	60.7	367.7	57.1
1000	2.228	32.5	500	99.2	485.8	94.6	459.7	89.1
1100	2.451	35.7	550	119	534.4	114	505.6	108
1200	2.674	38.9	600	142	583.0	136	551.6	128
1300	2.896	42.2	650	166	631.6	160	597.6	150
1400	3.119	45.4	700	193	680.1	185	643.5	174
1500	3.342	48.7	750	221	728.7	212	689.5	200

Table 9-22. Friction Loss in 4-Inch Schedule 40 Steel Pipe[a]

Flow Rate		Velocity, ft/sec	60°F Water		180°F Water		300°F Water	
gpm	ft³/sec		Flow, lb/hr	Pressure Loss, ft/100 ft	Flow, lb/hr	Pressure Loss, ft/100 ft	Flow, lb/hr	Pressure Loss, ft/100 ft
20	0.0446	0.504	10	0.0345	9.716	0.0262	9.193	0.0226
30	0.0668	0.756	15	0.0706	14.457	0.055	13.79	0.0481
40	0.0981	1.01	20	0.118	19.43	0.0939	18.39	0.0831
50	0.111	1.26	25	0.176	24.29	0.143	22.98	0.127
60	0.134	1.51	30	0.245	29.15	0.201	27.58	0.180
70	0.156	1.76	35	0.325	34.01	0.269	32.18	0.242
80	0.178	2.02	40	0.414	38.87	0.347	36.77	0.315
90	0.201	2.27	45	0.514	43.72	0.434	41.37	0.395
100	0.223	2.52	50	0.624	48.58	0.532	45.97	0.485
110	0.245	2.77	55	0.741	53.44	0.637	50.56	0.582
120	0.267	3.02	60	0.875	58.3	0.754	55.16	0.692
130	0.290	3.28	65	1.02	63.16	0.882	59.76	0.81
140	0.312	3.53	70	1.16	68.01	1.02	64.35	0.934
150	0.334	3.78	75	1.33	72.87	1.16	68.95	1.07
160	0.356	4.03	80	1.50	77.73	1.32	73.55	1.22
170	0.379	4.28	85	1.68	82.59	1.48	78.14	1.37
180	0.401	4.54	90	1.87	87.45	1.66	82.74	1.54
190	0.423	4.78	95	2.07	92.31	1.84	87.34	1.71
200	0.446	5.04	100	2.28	97.16	2.04	91.93	1.89
220	0.490	5.54	110	2.74	106.9	2.46	101.1	2.28
240	0.535	6.05	120	3.23	116.6	2.91	110.3	2.70
260	0.579	6.55	130	3.76	126.3	3.40	119.5	3.17
280	0.624	7.06	140	4.33	136	3.94	128.7	3.67
300	0.668	7.56	150	4.94	145.7	4.51	137.9	4.2
320	0.713	8.06	160	5.59	155.5	5.12	147.1	4.78
340	0.758	8.57	170	6.28	165.2	5.77	156.3	5.38
360	0.802	9.07	180	7.01	174.9	6.46	165.5	6.04
380	0.847	9.58	190	7.81	184.6	7.21	174.7	6.74
400	0.891	10.1	200	8.59	194.3	7.95	183.9	7.44
420	0.936	10.6	210	9.47	204.0	8.75	193.1	8.20
440	0.980	11.1	220	10.3	213.8	9.59	202.2	8.98
460	1.025	11.6	230	11.3	223.5	10.5	211.4	9.82
480	1.069	12.1	240	12.2	233.2	11.4	220.6	10.7
500	1.114	12.6	250	13.3	242.9	12.4	229.8	11.6
600	1.337	15.1	300	18.9	291.5	17.7	275.8	16.6
700	1.56	17.6	350	25.6	340.1	24.1	321.8	22.7
800	1.782	20.2	400	33.2	388.7	31.4	367.7	29.5
900	2.005	22.7	450	41.8	437.2	39.7	413.7	37.4
1000	2.228	25.2	500	51.5	485.8	48.9	459.7	46.0
1100	2.451	27.7	550	62.0	534.4	58.9	505.6	55.5
1200	2.674	30.2	600	73.6	583.0	70.1	551.6	66.2
1300	2.896	32.8	650	86.5	631.6	82.5	597.6	77.8
1400	3.119	35.3	700	99.8	680.1	95.3	643.5	89.9
1500	3.342	37.8	750	115	728.7	109	689.5	103
1600	3.565	40.3	800	130	777.3	125	735.5	118
1700	3.788	42.8	850	147	825.9	141	781.4	133
1800	4.010	45.0	900	165	874.5	158	827.4	149
1900	4.233	47.9	950	183	923.1	176	873.4	166
2000	4.456	50.4	1000	203	971.6	195	919.3	184

Table 9-23. Friction Loss in 6-Inch Schedule 40 Steel Pipe[a]

Flow Rate		Velocity, ft/sec	60°F Water		180°F Water		300°F Water	
gpm	ft³/sec		Flow, lb/hr	Pressure Loss, ft/100 ft	Flow, lb/hr	Pressure Loss, ft/100 ft	Flow, lb/hr	Pressure Loss, ft/100 ft
20	0.0446	0.222	10	0.00489	9.716	0.00359	9.193	0.00302
40	0.0891	0.444	20	0.0164	19.43	0.0125	18.39	0.0107
60	0.134	0.666	30	0.0336	29.15	0.0262	27.58	0.0228
80	0.178	0.888	40	0.0562	38.87	0.0446	36.77	0.0394
100	0.223	1.11	50	0.0841	48.58	0.0676	45.97	0.0602
120	0.267	1.33	60	0.117	58.30	0.0952	55.16	0.0852
140	0.312	1.55	70	0.155	68.01	0.127	64.35	0.115
160	0.356	1.78	80	0.197	97.73	0.164	73.55	0.148
180	0.401	2.00	90	0.245	87.45	0.206	82.74	0. 186
200	0.446	2.22	100	0.297	97.16	0.252	91.93	0.229
220	0.490	2.44	110	0.353	106.9	0.302	101.2	0.275
240	0.535	2.66	120	0.415	116.6	0.355	110.3	0.325
260	0.579	2.89	130	0.484	126.3	0.417	119.5	0.383
280	0.624	3.11	140	0.554	136	0.48	128.7	0.440
300	0.668	3.33	150	0.628	145.7	0.547	137.9	0.503
320	0.713	3.55	160	0.710	155.4	0.621	147.1	0.572
340	0.758	3.78	170	0.797	165.2	0.702	156.3	0.647
360	0.802	4.00	180	0.857	194.9	0.756	165.5	0.698
380	0.847	4.22	190	0.983	184.6	0.870	174.7	0.804
400	0.891	4.44	200	1.08	194.3	0.961	183.9	0.889
420	0.936	4.66	210	1.19	204.0	1.06	193.1	0.978
440	0.980	4.89	220	1.29	213.8	1.16	202.2	1.07
460	1.025	5.11	230	1.40	223.5	1.26	211.4	1.17
480	1.07	5.33	240	1.53	233.2	1.37	220.6	1.27
500	1.11	5.55	250	1.64	242.9	1.48	229.8	1.38
600	1.34	6.66	300	2.33	291.5	2.13	275.8	1.98
700	1.56	7.77	350	3.13	340.1	2.87	321.8	2.68
800	1.78	8.88	400	4.06	388.7	3.75	367.7	3.51
900	2.01	9.99	450	5.08	437.2	4.71	413.7	4.41
1000	2.23	11.1	500	6.24	485.8	5.84	459.7	5.46
1100	2.45	12.2	550	7.49	534.4	7.03	505.6	6.58
1200	2.67	13.3	600	8.89	583.0	8.34	551.6	7.82
1300	2.90	14.4	650	10.4	631.6	9.78	597.6	9.18
1400	3.12	15.5	700	12.0	680.1	11.4	643.5	10.6
1500	3.34	16.7	750	13.7	728.7	13.0	689.5	12.2
1600	3.56	17.8	800	15.6	777.3	14.8	735.5	13.9
1700	3.79	18.9	850	17.6	825.9	16.7	781.4	15.7
1800	4.01	20.0	900	19.7	874.5	18.6	827.4	17.5
1900	4.23	21.1	950	21.9	923.1	20.8	873.4	19.5
2000	4.46	22.2	1000	24.2	971.6	23.0	919.3	21.6
2100	4.68	23.3	1050	26.7	1020	25.4	965.3	23.8
2200	4.90	24.4	1100	29.3	1069	27.8	1011	26.2
2300	5.12	25.5	1150	31.8	1117	30.3	1057	28.5
2400	5.35	26.6	1200	34.7	1166	33.0	1103	31.0
2500	5.57	27.8	1250	37.8	1215	35.9	1149	33.8
2600	5.79	28.9	1300	40.8	1263	38.9	1195	36.6
2700	6.02	30.0	1350	44	1312	41.9	1241	39.4
2800	6.24	31.1	1400	47.0	1360	44.9	1287	42.3
3000	6.68	33.3	1500	53.7	1457	51.4	1379	48.4

Table 9-24. Friction Loss in 8-Inch Schedule 40 Steel Pipe[a]

Flow Rate			60°F Water		180°F Water		300°F Water	
gpm	ft³/sec	Velocity, ft/sec	Flow, lb/hr	Pressure Loss, ft/100 ft	Flow, lb/hr	Pressure Loss, ft/100 ft	Flow, lb/hr	Pressure Loss, ft/100 ft
20	0.0446	0.128	10	0.0013	9.716	0.000940	9.193	0.000783
40	0.0891	0.257	20	0.00431	19.43	0.00320	18.39	0.00272
60	0.134	0.385	30	0.00881	29.49	0.00667	27.58	0.00573
80	0.178	0.513	40	0.0146	38.87	0.0113	36.77	0.00978
100	0.223	0.641	50	0.0217	48.58	0.0170	45.97	0.0149
120	0.267	0.770	60	0.0301	58.3	0.0238	55.16	0.0210
140	0.312	0.898	70	0.0398	68.01	0.0316	64.35	0.028
160	0.356	1.03	80	0.0507	77.73	0.0408	73.55	0.0362
180	0.401	1.15	90	0.0625	87.45	0.0507	82.74	0.0453
200	0.446	1.28	100	0.0758	97.16	0.062	91.93	0.0556
220	0.490	1.41	110	0.0899	106.9	0.0742	101.1	0.0667
240	0.535	1.54	120	0.105	116.6	0.0876	110.3	0.0788
260	0.579	1.67	130	0.122	126.3	0.102	119.5	0.0920
280	0.624	1.8	140	0.140	136.0	0.117	128.7	0.106
300	0.668	1.92	150	0.159	145.7	0.134	137.9	0.121
320	0.713	2.05	160	0.179	155.5	0.151	147.1	0.138
340	0.758	2.18	170	0.200	165.2	0.170	156.2	0.155
360	0.802	2.31	180	0.222	174.9	0.19	165.5	0.173
380	0.847	2.44	190	0.246	184.6	0.210	174.7	0.193
400	0.891	2.57	200	0.269	194.3	0.232	183.9	0.212
450	1.003	2.89	225	0.335	218.6	0.290	206.9	0.267
500	1.11	3.21	250	0.410	242.9	0.358	229.8	0.330
550	1.23	3.53	275	0.488	267.2	0.430	252.8	0.396
600	1.34	3.85	300	0.577	291.5	0.511	275.8	0.472
650	1.45	4.17	325	0.675	315.8	0.599	298.8	0.553
700	1.56	4.49	350	0.773	340.1	0.689	321.8	0.639
750	1.67	4.81	375	0.882	364.4	0.788	344.8	0.731
800	1.78	5.13	400	0.994	388.7	0.896	367.7	0.830
850	1.89	5.45	425	1.12	412.9	1.01	390.7	0.938
900	2.01	5.77	450	1.25	437.2	1.13	413.7	1.05
950	2.12	6.09	475	1.38	461.5	1.25	436.7	1.17
1000	2.23	6.41	500	1.52	485.8	1.39	459.7	1.29
1200	2.67	7.70	600	2.16	583	1.98	551.6	1.85
1400	3.12	8.98	700	2.90	680.1	2.69	643.5	2.51
1600	3.56	10.3	800	3.77	777.3	3.51	735.5	3.28
1800	4.01	11.5	900	4.64	874.5	4.41	827.4	4.14
2000	4.46	12.8	1000	5.84	971.6	5.45	919.3	5.12
2200	4.90	14.1	1100	6.98	1069	6.55	1011	6.18
2400	5.35	15.4	1200	8.32	1166	7.8	1103	7.36
2600	5.79	16.7	1300	9.72	1263	9.0	1195	8.6
2800	6.24	18.0	1400	11.2	1360	10.6	1287	9.97
3000	6.68	19.2	1500	12.9	1457	12.2	1379	11.4
3200	7.13	20.5	1600	14.6	1555	13.8	1471	13.0
3400	7.58	21.8	1700	17.4	1652	15.6	1563	14.7
3600	8.02	23.1	1800	18.4	1749	17.5	1655	16.5
3800	8.47	24.4	1900	20.5	1846	19.5	1747	18.4
4000	8.91	25.7	2000	22.6	1943	21.5	1839	20.2
4500	10.03	28.9	2250	28.5	2186	27.2	2069	25.5
5000	11.1	32.1	2500	35.2	2429	33.6	2298	31.7

Table 9-25. Friction Loss in 10-Inch Schedule 40 Steel Pipe[a]

Flow Rate			60°F Water		150°F Water		300°F Water	
gpm	ft³/sec	Velocity, ft/sec	Flow, lb/hr	Pressure Loss, ft/100 ft	Flow, lb/hr	Pressure Loss, ft/100 ft	Flow, lb/hr	Pressure Loss, ft/100 ft
100	0.223	0.407	50	0.00725	48.58	0.00555	45.96	0.00478
120	0.267	0.488	60	0.00999	58.3	0.00773	55.16	0.00670
140	0.312	0.570	70	0.0132	68.01	0.0103	64.35	0.00895
160	0.356	0.651	80	0.0167	77.73	0.0131	73.55	0.0115
180	0.401	0.732	90	0.0207	87.45	0.0163	82.74	0.0144
200	0.446	0.814	100	0.0249	97.0	0.0199	91.93	0.0176
220	0.490	0.895	110	0.0296	106.9	0.0239	101.1	0.0211
240	0.535	0.976	120	0.0346	116.6	0.028	110.3	0.0249
260	0.579	1.06	130	0.0402	126.3	0.0325	119.5	0.0289
280	0.624	1.14	140	0.0459	136	0.0374	128.7	0.0333
300	0.668	1.22	150	0.0520	145.7	0.0427	137.9	0.0380
350	0.780	1.42	175	0.0687	170.0	0.0570	1 60.9	0.0513
400	0.891	1.63	200	0.0878	194.3	0.0733	183.9	0.0663
450	1.003	1.83	225	0.109	218.6	0.0917	206.9	0.0834
500	1.11	2.03	250	0.132	242.9	0.113	229.8	0.102
550	1.23	2.24	275	0.157	267.2	0.135	252.8	0.123
600	1.34	2.44	300	0.185	291.5	0.159	275.8	0.145
650	1.45	2.64	325	0.215	315.8	0.186	298.8	0.171
700	1.56	2.85	350	0.247	340.1	0.214	321.8	0.197
750	1.67	3.05	375	0.281	364.4	0.247	344.8	0.226
800	1.78	3.25	400	0.318	388.7	0.279	367.7	0.257
850	1.89	3.46	425	0.355	412.9	0.312	390.7	0.288
900	2.01	3.66	450	0.395	437.2	0.349	413.7	0.322
950	2.12	3.87	475	0.438	461.5	0.387	436.7	0.360
1000	2.23	4.07	500	0.483	485.8	0.429	459.7	0.396
1200	2.67	4.88	600	0.681	583.0	0.614	551.6	0.570
1400	3.12	5.70	700	0.917	680.1	0.832	643.5	0.771
1600	3.56	6.51	800	1.18	777.3	1.08	735.5	1.00
1800	4.01	7.32	900	1.48	874.5	1.36	827.4	1.27
2000	4.46	8.14	1000	1.81	971.6	1.68	919.3	1.57
2200	4.90	8.95	1100	2.19	1069	2.03	1011	1.90
2400	5.35	9.76	1200	2.58	1166	2.40	1103	2.23
2600	5.79	10.6	1300	3.03	1263	2.82	1195	2.63
2800	6.24	11.4	1400	3.49	1360	3.25	1287	3.05
3000	6.68	12.2	1500	3.99	1457	3.74	1379	3.50
3200	7.13	13.0	1600	4.52	1555	4.23	1471	3.97
3400	7.58	13.8	1700	5.07	1652	4.78	1563	4.48
3600	8.02	14.6	1800	5.69	1749	5.36	1655	5.03
3800	8.47	15.5	1900	6.31	1846	5.97	1747	5.6
4000	8.91	16.3	2000	7.00	1943	6.63	1839	6.22
4500	10.03	18.3	2250	8.8	2186	8.34	2069	7.82
5000	11.1	20.3	2500	10.8	2429	10.3	2298	9.65
6000	13.4	24.4	3000	15.6	2915	14.8	2758	13.9
7000	15.6	28.5	3500	21.0	3401	20.0	3218	18.9
8000	17.8	32.5	4000	27.6	3887	26.2	3677	24.8
9000	20.1	36.6	4500	34.5	4372	33.1	4137	31.2
10000	22.3	40.7	5000	42.7	4858	40.9	4597	38.6

Table 9-26. Friction Loss in 12-Inch Schedule 40 Steel Pipe[a]

Flow Rate		Velocity, ft/sec	60°F Water		180°F Water		300°F Water	
gpm	ft³/sec		Flow, lb/hr	Pressure Loss, ft/100 ft	Flow, lb/hr	Pressure Loss, ft/100 ft	Flow, lb/hr	Pressure Loss, ft/100 ft
120	0.267	0.344	60	0.00445	58.3	0.00338	55.16	0.00291
140	0.312	0.401	70	0.00583	68.01	0.00448	64.35	0.00385
160	0.356	0.459	80	0.00739	77.73	0.00572	73.55	0.00497
180	0.401	0.5 16	90	0.00911	87.45	0.00708	82.74	0.00617
200	0.446	0.573	100	0.011	97.0	0.00864	91.93	0.00751
220	0.490	0.631	110	0.0130	106.9	0.0103	101.1	0.00902
240	0.535	0.688	120	0.0152	116.6	0.0121	110.3	0.0106
260	0.579	0.745	130	0.0176	126.3	0.0140	119.5	0.0123
280	0.624	0.802	140	0.0201	136	0.016	128.7	0.0142
300	0.668	0.86	150	0.0228	145.7	0.0183	137.9	0.0162
400	0.891	1.15	200	0.0384	194.3	0.0312	183.9	0.0279
500	1.11	1.43	250	0.0574	242.9	0.0479	229.8	0.0431
600	1.34	1.72	300	0.0805	291.5	0.0676	275.8	0.0612
700	1.56	2.01	350	0.107	340.1	0.0908	321.8	0.0826
800	1.78	2.29	400	0.136	388.7	0.118	367.7	0.107
900	2.01	2.58	450	0.170	437.2	0.146	413.7	0.135
1000	2.23	2.87	500	0.207	485.8	0.18	459.7	0. 166
1200	2.67	3.44	600	0.293	583.0	0.258	551.6	0.237
1400	3.12	4.01	700	0.312	680.1	0.348	643.5	0.320
1600	3.56	4.59	800	0.504	777.3	0.451	735.5	0.419
1800	4.01	5.0	900	0.629	874.5	0.567	827.4	0.530
2000	4.46	5.73	1000	0.772	971.6	0.700	919.3	0.649
2200	4.90	6.31	1100	0.927	1069	0.84	1011	0.785
2400	5.35	6.88	1200	1.1	1166	1.00	1103	0.933
2600	5.79	7.45	1300	1.28	1263	1.17	1195	1.10
2800	6.24	8.03	1400	1.47	1361	1.35	1287	1.26
3000	6.68	8.6	1500	1.68	1457	1.55	1379	1.45
3200	7.13	9.17	1600	1.90	1555	1.77	1471	1.65
3400	7.58	9.75	1700	2.15	1652	2.00	1563	1.86
3600	8.02	10.3	1800	2.39	1749	2.21	1655	2.08
3800	8.47	10.9	1900	2.65	1846	2.47	1747	2.2
4000	8.91	11.5	2000	3.04	1943	2.73	1839	2.57
4500	10.03	12.9	2250	3.70	2186	3.47	2069	3.26
5000	11.1	14.3	2500	4.53	2429	4.27	2298	3.99
5500	12.3	15.8	2750	5.44	2672	5.13	2528	4.83
6000	13.4	17.2	3000	6.49	2915	6.12	2758	5.75
6500	14.5	18.6	3250	7.60	3158	7.17	2988	6.74
7000	15.6	20.1	3500	8.76	3401	8.33	3218	7.83
7500	16.7	21.5	3750	10.1	3644	9.55	3448	8.98
8000	17.8	22.9	4000	11.4	3887	10.9	3677	10.2
8500	18.9	24.4	4250	12.8	4129	12.3	3907	10.5
9000	20.1	25.8	4500	14.3	4372	13.7	4137	12.9
9500	21.2	27.2	4750	1 6.0	4615	15.2	4367	14.4
10000	22.3	28.7	5000	17.7	4858	16.9	4597	1 6.0
12000	26.7	34.4	6000	25.3	5830	24.2	5516	22.9
14000	31.2	40.1	7000	34.5	6801	33.0	6435	31.3
16000	35.6	45.9	8000	44.8	7773	43.2	7355	40.9
18000	40.1	51.6	9000	56.7	8745	54.6	8274	51.8
20000	44.6	57.3	10000	70.0	9716	67.5	9193	63.9

Table 9-27. Friction Loss in 14-Inch Schedule 40 Steel Pipe[a]

Flow Rate		Velocity, ft/sec	60°F Water		180°F Water		300°F Water	
gpm	ft³/sec		Flow, lb/hr	Pressure Loss, ft/100 ft	Flow, lb/hr	Pressure Loss, ft/100 ft	Flow, lb/hr	Pressure Loss, ft/100 ft
200	0.446	0.474	100	0.00698	97.16	0.00541	91.93	0.00468
250	0.557	0.593	125	0.0104	121.5	0.00814	114.9	0.00751
300	0.668	0.711	150	0.0144	145.7	0.0114	137.9	0.0101
350	0.78	0.830	195	0.0189	170.0	0.0152	160.9	0.0135
400	0.891	0.948	200	0.0242	194.3	0.0196	183.9	0.0174
500	1.114	1.19	250	0.0362	242.9	0.0296	229.8	0.0266
600	1.34	1.42	300	0.0506	291.5	0.0421	275.8	0.0377
700	1.56	1.66	350	0.0672	340.1	0.0565	321.8	0.0509
800	1.78	1.90	400	0.0855	388.7	0.0727	367.7	0.066
900	2.01	2.13	450	0.107	437.2	0.0913	413.7	0.0835
1000	2.23	2.37	500	0.129	485.8	0.112	459.7	0.102
1100	2.45	2.61	550	0.155	534.4	0.135	505.6	0.123
1200	2.67	2.85	600	0.183	583	0.159	551.6	0.146
1300	2.90	3.08	650	0.212	631.6	0.186	597.6	0.172
1400	3.12	3.32	700	0.243	680.1	0.214	643.5	0.197
1500	3.34	3.56	750	0.278	728.7	0.246	689.5	0.227
1600	3.56	3.79	800	0.314	777.3	0.278	735.5	0.258
1700	3.79	4.03	850	0.350	825.9	0.312	781.4	0.290
1800	4.01	4.27	900	0.391	874.5	0.348	827.4	0.323
1900	4.43	4.50	950	0.432	923.1	0.387	873.4	0.359
2000	4.46	4.74	1000	0.478	971.6	0.429	919.3	0.398
2500	5.57	5.93	1250	0.932	1215	0.666	1149	0.617
3000	6.68	7.11	1500	1.04	1457	0.951	1379	0.888
3500	7.80	8.30	1750	1.40	1700	1.29	1609	1.21
4000	8.91	9.48	2000	1.81	1943	1.68	1839	1.57
4500	10.02	10.7	2250	2.28	2186	2.12	2069	1.98
5000	11.1	11.9	2500	2.79	2429	2.62	2298	2.44
6000	13.4	14.2	3000	3.96	2915	3.74	2758	3.52
7000	15.6	16.6	3500	5.35	3401	5.09	3218	4.79
8000	17.8	19.0	4000	6.99	3887	6.65	3697	6.26
9000	20.1	21.3	4500	8.78	4372	8.43	4137	7.93
10000	22.3	23.7	5000	10.8	4858	10.3	4597	9.79
11000	24.5	26.1	5500	13.1	5344	12.5	5056	11.8
12000	26.7	28.5	6000	15.6	5830	14.9	5516	14.0
13000	29.0	30.8	6500	18.2	6316	17.5	5976	16.4
14000	31.2	33.2	7000	21.0	6801	20.2	6435	19
15000	33.4	35.6	7500	24.2	7287	23.2	6895	21.9
16000	35.6	37.9	8000	27.6	7773	26.4	7355	24.9
17000	37.9	40.3	8500	31	8259	29.7	7814	28.0
18000	40.1	42.7	9000	34.8	8745	33.4	8274	31.4
19000	42.3	45.0	9500	38.7	9230	37.2	8734	35.0
20000	44.6	47.4	10000	42.5	9716	41.2	9193	38.7
22000	49.0	52.2	11000	51.6	10690	49.9	10110	47.0
24000	53.5	56.9	12000	61.4	11660	59.4	11030	55.8
26000	57.9	61.6	13000	72.1	12630	69.7	11950	65.6
28000	62.4	66.4	14000	83.6	13600	80.8	12870	76.0
30000	66.8	71.1	15000	95.9	14570	92.7	13790	87.2

Table 9-28. Friction Loss in 16-Inch Schedule 40 Steel Pipe[a]

Flow Rate			60°F Water		180°F Water		300°F Water	
gpm	ft³/sec	Velocity, ft/sec	Flow, lb/hr	Pressure Loss, ft/100 ft	Flow, lb/hr	Pressure Loss, ft/100 ft	Flow, lb/hr	Pressure Loss, ft/100 ft
300	0.668	0.545	150	0.00757	145.7	0.00590	139.9	0.00516
400	0.891	0.726	200	0.0126	194.3	0.0101	183.9	0.00894
500	1.114	0.908	250	0.0189	242.9	0.0154	229.8	0.0136
600	1.34	1.09	300	0.0263	291.5	0.0215	275.8	0.0193
700	1.56	1.27	350	0.0349	340.1	0.0289	231.8	0.0259
800	1.78	1.45	400	0.0446	388.7	0.0371	367.7	0.0335
900	2.01	1.63	450	0.0552	437.2	0.0465	413.7	0.0423
1000	2.23	1.82	500	0.0671	485.8	0.0568	459.7	0.0517
1200	2.67	2.18	600	0.0945	583	0.0812	551.6	0.0738
1400	3.12	2.54	700	0.126	680.1	0.108	643.5	0.0998
1600	3.56	2.90	800	0.159	777.3	0.14	735.5	0.129
1800	4.01	3.27	900	0.199	874.5	0.178	827.4	0.03
2000	4.46	3.63	1000	0.246	971.6	0.217	919.3	0.201
2500	5.57	4.54	1250	0.374	1215	0.336	1149	0.311
3000	6.68	5.45	1500	0.530	1457	0.479	1379	0.447
3500	7.8	6.35	1750	0.709	1700	0.652	1609	0.605
4000	8.91	7.26	2000	0.918	1943	0.853	1839	0.790
4500	10.02	8.17	2250	1.16	2186	1.07	2069	0.999
5000	11.1	9.08	2500	1.42	2429	1.32	2298	1.23
6000	13.4	10.9	3000	2.01	2915	1.88	2758	1.76
7000	15.6	12.7	3500	2.74	3401	2.56	3218	2.40
8000	17.8	14.5	4000	3.54	3887	3.35	3677	3.13
9000	20.1	16.3	4500	4.44	4372	4.19	4137	3.96
10000	22.3	18.2	5000	5.48	4858	5.17	4597	4.88
11000	24.5	20.0	5500	6.63	5344	6.26	5056	5.90
12000	26.7	21.8	6000	7.82	5830	7.45	5516	7.03
13000	29.0	23.6	6500	9.18	6300	8.75	5976	8.24
14000	31.2	25.4	7000	10.6	6801	10.1	6435	9.55
15000	33.4	27.2	7500	12.2	7287	11.6	6895	10.9
16000	35.6	29.0	8000	13.9	7773	13.2	7355	12.4
17000	37.9	30.9	8500	15.5	8259	14.9	7814	14.1
18000	40.1	32.7	9000	17.4	8745	16.8	8294	15.8
19000	42.3	34.5	9500	19.4	9231	18.7	8734	17.6
20000	44.6	36.3	10000	21.5	9716	20.7	9193	19.5
22000	49.0	39.9	11000	26	10690	25.0	10110	23.5
24000	53.5	43.6	12000	31.0	11660	29.8	11030	28
26000	57.9	47.2	13000	36.3	12630	34.6	11950	32.8
28000	62.4	50.8	14000	41.8	13600	40.2	12870	38.1
30000	66.8	54.5	15000	47.9	14570	46.1	13790	43.7
32000	71.3	58.1	16000	54.5	15550	52.4	14710	49.7
34000	75.8	61.7	17000	61.6	16520	59.2	15630	56.1
36000	80.2	65.4	18000	69.1	17490	66.4	16550	62.9
38000	84.7	69	19000	77.0	18460	94.0	17470	70.2
40000	89.1	72.6	20000	85.3	19430	82.0	18390	77.7
42000	93.6	76.2	21000	94.0	20400	90.4	19310	85.7
44000	98	79.9	22000	103	21380	99.2	20230	94.0
46000	102.5	83.5	23000	113	22350	108	21140	103
48000	107	87.1	24000	123	23320	118	22060	112
50000	111	90.8	25000	133	24290	128	22980	121

Table 9-29. Friction Loss in 18-Inch Schedule 40 Steel Pipe[a]

Flow Rate		Velocity, ft/sec	60°F Water		180°F Water		300°F Water	
gpm	ft³/sec		Flow, lb/hr	Pressure Loss, ft/100 ft	Flow, lb/hr	Pressure Loss, ft/100 ft	Flow, lb/hr	Pressure Loss, ft/100 ft
300	0.668	0.430	150	0.00429	145.7	0.00333	137.9	0.00288
400	0.891	0.574	200	0.00717	194.3	0.00565	183.9	0.00496
500	1.114	0.717	250	0.0106	242.9	0.00854	229.8	0.00754
600	1.34	0.861	300	0.0148	291.5	0.0120	275.8	0.0111
700	1.56	1.00	350	0.0198	340.1	0.0161	321.8	0.0149
800	1.78	1.15	400	0.0250	388.7	0.0207	367.7	0.0186
900	2.01	1.29	450	0.0311	437.2	0.0258	413.7	0.0232
1000	2.23	1.43	500	0.0378	485.8	0.0315	459.7	0.0285
1200	2.67	1.72	600	0.0529	583.0	0.0446	551.6	0.0405
1400	3.12	2.01	700	0.0702	680.1	0.06	643.5	0.0547
1600	3.56	2.30	800	0.0901	777.3	0.0776	735.5	0.0710
1800	4.01	2.58	900	0.112	874.5	0.0972	827.4	0.0893
2000	4.46	2.87	1000	0.137	971.6	0.119	919.3	0.110
2500	5.57	3.59	1250	0.208	1215	0.184	1149	0.170
3000	6.68	4.30	1500	0.294	1457	0.263	1379	0.244
3500	7.80	5.02	1750	0.392	1700	0.356	1608	0.331
4000	8.91	5.74	2000	0.508	1943	0.463	1839	0.431
4500	10.02	6.45	2250	0.636	2186	0.577	2069	0.538
5000	11.1	7.17	2500	0.980	2429	0.717	2298	0.670
6000	13.4	8.61	3000	1.08	2915	1.03	2758	0.961
7000	15.6	10.0	3500	1.50	3401	1.40	3218	1.31
8000	17.8	11.5	4000	1.94	3887	1.82	3677	1.71
9000	20.1	12.9	4500	2.44	4372	2.29	4137	2.15
10000	22.3	14.3	5000	3.00	4858	2.82	4597	2.66
12000	26.7	17.2	6000	4.29	5830	4.06	5516	3.81
14000	31.2	20.1	7000	5.81	6801	5.52	6435	5.2
16000	35.6	22.9	8000	7.56	7773	7.19	7355	6.78
18000	40.1	25.8	9000	9.54	8745	9.1	8274	8.6
20000	44.6	28.7	10000	11.8	9716	11.2	9193	10.6
22000	49.0	31.6	11000	14.2	10680	13.6	10113	12.8
24000	53.5	34.4	12000	16.8	11660	16.1	11030	15.2
26000	57.9	37.3	13000	19.7	12630	18.9	11950	17.8
28000	62.4	40.2	14000	22.9	13600	22.0	12870	20.7
30000	66.8	43.0	15000	26.2	14570	25.2	13790	23.8
32000	71.3	45.9	16000	29.8	15550	28.6	14710	27.0
34000	95.8	48.8	17000	33.6	16520	32.3	15630	30.5
36000	80.2	51.6	18000	37.6	17490	36.2	16550	34.2
38000	84.7	54.5	19000	41.9	18460	40.3	17470	38.1
40000	89.1	57.4	20000	46.4	19430	44.7	18390	42.2
42000	93.6	60.2	21000	51.1	20410	49.2	19310	46.5
44000	98	63.1	22000	56.1	21380	54.0	20230	51.1
46000	102	66	23000	61.3	22350	59.0	21150	55.9
48000	107	68.9	24000	66.7	23320	64.3	22060	60.7
50000	111	71.7	25000	72.2	24290	69.7	22980	65.8
55000	123	78.9	27500	87.3	26720	84.3	25280	79.7
60000	134	86.1	30000	104	29150	100	27580	94.8
65000	145	93.2	32500	122	31580	118	29880	111
70000	156	100.4	35000	142	34010	139	32180	129

Table 9-30. Friction Loss in 20-Inch Schedule 40 Steel Pipe[a]

Flow Rate			60°F Water		180°F Water		300°F Water	
gpm	ft³/sec	Velocity, ft/sec	Flow, lb/hr	Pressure Loss, ft/100 ft	Flow, lb/hr	Pressure Loss, ft/100 ft	Flow, lb/hr	Pressure Loss, ft/100 ft
300	0.668	0.346	150	0.00255	145.7	0.00195	137.9	0.00169
400	0.891	0.462	200	0.00424	194.3	0.00331	183.9	0.00288
500	1.114	0.577	250	0.00631	242.9	0.00499	229.8	0.00438
600	1.34	0.692	300	0.00879	291.5	0.00701	275.8	0.00619
700	1.56	0.808	350	0.0116	340.1	0.00934	321.8	0.00829
800	1.78	0.923	400	0.0147	388.7	0.0120	367.7	0.0107
900	2.01	1.039	450	0.0183	437.2	0.0150	413.7	0.0134
1000	2.23	1.15	500	0.0221	485.8	0.0183	459.7	0.0164
1200	2.67	1.38	600	0.0310	583.0	0.0258	551.6	0.0233
1400	3.12	1.62	700	0.0410	680.1	0.0347	643.5	0.0315
1600	3.56	1.85	800	0.0526	777.3	0.0448	735.5	0.0408
1800	4.01	2.08	900	0.0654	874.5	0.0562	827.4	0.0513
2000	4.46	2.31	1000	0.0796	971.6	0.0688	919.3	0.0630
2500	5.57	2.89	1250	0.1210	1215	0.106	1149	0.0973
3000	6.68	3.46	1500	0.170	1457	0.151	1379	0.139
3500	7.8	4.04	1750	0.229	1700	0.204	1609	0.189
4000	8.91	4.62	2000	0.294	1943	0.264	1839	0.246
4500	10.02	5.19	2250	0.368	2186	0.326	2069	0.324
5000	11.1	5.77	2500	0.450	2429	0.410	2298	0.381
6000	13.4	6.92	3000	0.639	2915	0.587	2758	0.548
7000	15.6	8.08	3500	0.860	3401	0.796	3218	0.744
8000	17.8	9.23	4000	1.11	3887	1.03	3677	0.968
9000	20.1	10.39	4500	1.41	4372	1.31	4137	1.23
10000	22.3	11.5	5000	1.72	4858	1.61	4596	1.51
12000	26.7	13.8	6000	2.46	5830	2.32	5516	2.17
14000	31.2	16.2	7000	4.03	6801	3.72	6435	3.51
16000	35.6	18.5	8000	4.32	7773	4.1	7355	3.86
18000	40.1	20.8	9000	5.45	8745	5.18	8274	4.88
20000	44.6	23.1	10000	6.71	9716	6.39	9193	6.02
22000	49.0	25.4	11000	8.11	10690	7.73	10110	7.27
24000	53.5	27.7	12000	9.59	11660	9.16	11030	8.64
26000	59.9	30.0	13000	11.3	12630	10.8	11950	10.2
28000	62.4	32.3	14000	13.0	13600	12.5	12870	11.8
30000	66.8	34.6	15000	14.9	14570	14.3	13790	13.5
32000	71.3	36.9	16000	17.0	15550	16.3	14790	15.4
34000	75.8	39.2	17000	19.1	16520	18.4	15630	17.3
36000	80.2	41.5	1 8000	21.4	17490	20.6	16550	19.4
38000	84.7	43.9	19000	23.9	18460	23.0	17470	21.7
40000	89.1	46.2	20000	26.4	19430	25.4	18390	24.0
42000	93.6	48.5	21000	29.1	20400	28	19310	26.5
44000	98	50.8	22000	32.0	21380	30.8	20230	29.1
46000	102	53.1	23000	34.9	22350	33.6	21140	31.7
48000	107	55.4	24000	38	23320	36.6	22060	34.5
50000	111	59.7	25000	41.2	24290	39.6	22980	37.4
60000	134	69.2	30000	59.2	29150	57.1	27580	53.9
70000	156	80.8	35000	80.1	34010	77.7	32180	73.4
80000	178	92.3	40000	105	38870	101	36770	95.4
90000	201	103.9	45000	133	43720	129	41370	121
100000	223	115.4	50000	164	48580	158	45970	150

Table 9-31. Friction Loss in 24-Inch Schedule 40 Steel Pipe[a]

Flow Rate		Velocity, ft/sec	60°F Water		180°F Water		300°F Water	
gpm	ft³/sec		Flow, lb/hr	Pressure Loss, ft/100 ft	Flow, lb/hr	Pressure Loss, ft/100 ft	Flow, lb/hr	Pressure Loss, ft/100 ft
300	0.668	0.239	150	0.00105	145.7	0.000879	137.9	0.000683
400	0.891	0.319	200	0.00195	194.3	0.00134	183.9	0.00116
500	1.114	0.399	250	0.00259	242.9	0.00202	229.8	0.00176
600	1.34	0.479	300	0.0036	291.5	0.00283	275.8	0.00247
700	1.56	0.559	350	0.00474	340.1	0.00376	321.8	0.00330
800	1.78	0.638	400	0.00604	388.7	0.00482	367.7	0.00425
900	2.01	0.718	450	0.00747	437.2	0.006	413.7	0.00531
1000	2.23	0.798	500	0.00903	485.8	0.00731	459.7	0.00650
1200	2.67	0.958	600	0.0125	583.0	0.0103	551.6	0.00917
1400	3.12	1.12	700	0.0167	680.1	0.0138	643.5	0.0124
1600	3.56	1.28	800	0.0213	977.3	0.0177	735.5	0.0160
1800	4.01	1.44	900	0.0265	874.5	0.0222	827.4	0.0201
2000	4.46	1.6	1000	0.0321	971.6	0.0272	919.3	0.0247
2500	5.59	1.99	1250	0.0485	1215	0.0417	1149	0.0380
3000	6.68	2.39	1500	0.0683	1457	0.0593	1379	0.0544
3500	7.8	2.79	1950	0.0909	1700	0.0797	1609	0.0733
4000	8.91	3.19	2000	0.117	1943	0.103	1839	0.0953
4500	10.02	3.59	2250	0.146	2186	0.130	2069	0.120
5000	11.1	3.99	2500	0.178	2429	0.16	2298	0.148
6000	13.4	4.79	3000	0.253	2915	0.229	2758	0.212
7000	15.6	5.59	3500	0.340	3401	0.309	3218	0.288
8000	17.8	6.38	4000	0.439	3887	0.402	3677	0.375
9000	20.1	7.18	4500	0.550	4372	0.507	4137	0.473
10000	22.3	7.98	5000	0.674	4858	0.624	4597	0.0584
12000	26.7	9.58	6000	0.957	5830	0.892	5516	0.777
14000	31.2	11.2	7000	1.30	6801	1.25	6435	0.114
16000	35.6	12.8	8000	1.68	7773	1.58	7355	0.149
18000	40.1	14.4	9000	2.13	8745	2.00	8274	1.88
20000	44.6	16.0	10000	2.61	9716	2.47	9193	2.32
22000	49.0	17.6	11000	3.15	10690	2.98	10110	2.81
24000	53.5	19.2	12000	3.73	11660	3.55	11030	3.33
26000	57.9	20.7	13000	4.38	12630	4.15	11950	3.91
28000	62.4	22.3	14000	5.06	13600	4.82	12870	4.54
30000	66.8	23.9	15000	5.80	14570	5.52	13790	5.20
34000	75.8	27.1	17000	7.39	16520	7.07	15630	6.66
38000	84.7	30.3	19000	9.24	18460	8.85	17470	8.35
42000	93.6	33.5	21000	11.3	20400	10.8	19310	10.2
46000	102	36.7	23000	13.5	22350	12.9	21140	12.2
50000	111	39.9	25000	15.9	24290	15.3	22980	14.4
60000	134	47.9	30000	22.8	29150	22.0	27580	20.8
70000	156	55.9	35000	31.1	34000	29.9	32180	28.2
80000	178	63.8	40000	40.4	38870	39.0	36770	36.8
90000	201	71.8	45000	51.2	43720	49.3	41370	46.6
100000	223	79.8	50000	63.1	48580	60.9	45970	57.6
110000	245	87.8	55000	76.4	53440	73.9	50560	69.8
120000	267	95.8	60000	90.5	58300	87.5	55160	82.6
130000	290	103.7	65000	106	63160	103	59760	97.2
140000	312	112	70000	123	68010	120	64350	113
150000	334	120	75000	142	72870	137	68950	130

Service Water Piping.—Sizing of service water pipe systems differs from sizing of process lines in that design flows in service water piping are determined by the probability of simultaneous operation of a multiplicity of individual loads such as water closets, urinals, lavatories, sinks, and showers. The full flow characteristics of each load device are readily obtained from manufacturers; however, service water piping sized to handle all load devices simultaneously would be seriously oversized. Thus, a major issue in sizing service water pipe system is to determining the diversity of the loads. Plumbing design is usually constrained by building or plumbing codes, which specify the individual and collective loads to be used for pipe sizing. Frequently used codes contain procedures quite similar to those shown here. The designer must be aware of the applicable code for the location being considered.

ture supplied through that pipe by its weight from Table 9-32, adding the products, and then referring to the appropriate curve of Figs. 9-5, 9-6, or 9-7 to find the demand corresponding to the total fixture units. The demands for outlets and listed in Table 9-32 (e.g., hose connections and airconditioning apparatus) that are likely to impose continuous demand during heavy use of the weighted fixtures should be estimated separately and added to calculated demand for fixtures that are used intermittently to estimate total demand.

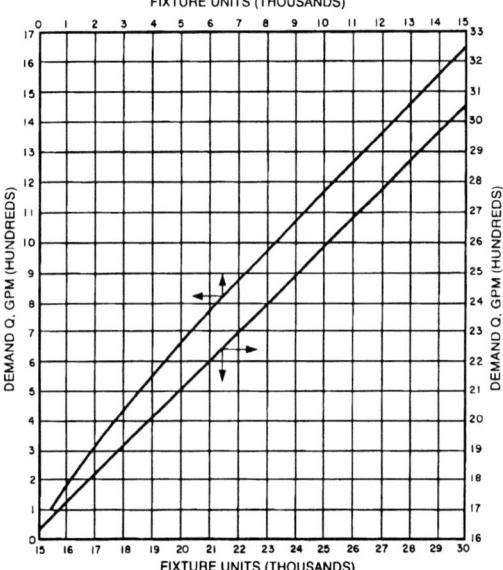

Fig 9-5. Demand versus fixture units

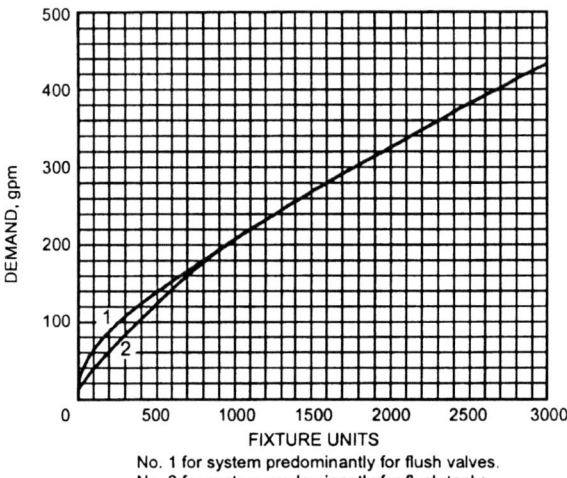

No. 1 for system predominantly for flush valves.
No. 2 for system predominantly for flush tanks.

Fig 9-6. Estimate curves for demand load

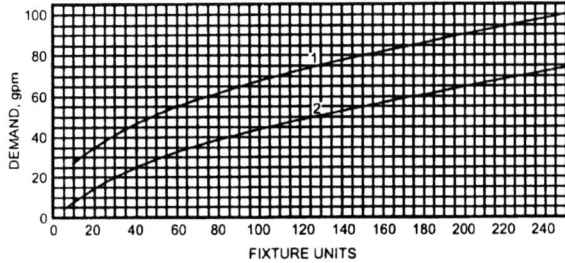

No. 1 for system predominantly for flush valves.
No. 2 for system predominately for flush tanks.

Fig 9-7. Estimate curves for demand load on enlarged scale

The designer must be aware of special considerations; for example, toilet usage at sports arenas will probably have much less diversity than the codes allow and thus may require larger supply piping than the minimum specified by the codes. Table 9-8 gives the rate of flow desirable for many common fixtures and the average pressure necessary to give said rate of flow.

In estimating the load, the rate of flow is frequently computed in fixture units, which are relative indicators of flow. Table 9-32 gives the demand weights in terms of fixture units for different plumbing fixtures under several conditions of service, and Fig. 9-5 gives the estimated demand in gallons per minute corresponding to any total number of fixture units. The estimated demand load for fixtures used intermittently on any supply pipe can be obtained by multiplying the number of each kind of fix-

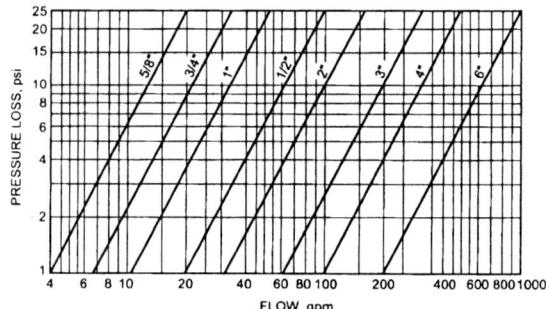

Fig 9-8. Pressure loss in disk type water meters

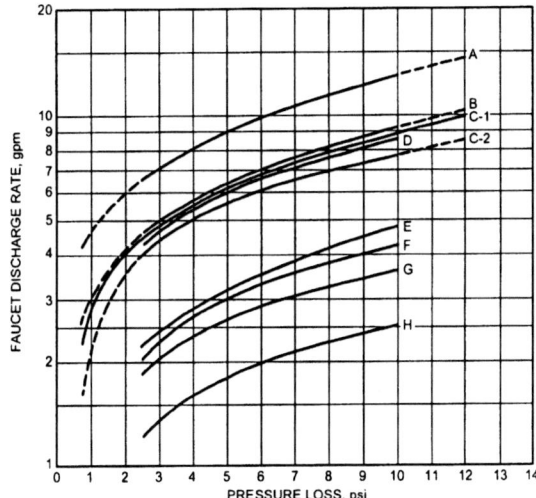

A. 1/2 in. laundry bibb (old style)
B. Laundry compression faucet
C-1. 1/2 in. compression sink faucet (mfr. 1)
C-2. 1/2 in. compression sink faucet (mfr. 2)
D. Combination compression bathtub faucets (both open)
E. Combination compression sink faucet
F. Basin faucet
G. Spring self-closing faucet
H. Slow self-closing faucet
(Dashed lines indicate recommended extrapolation)

Fig 9-9. Variation of pressure loss with flow rate
for various faucets and cocks

The curves in Figs. 9-5, 9-6, or 9-7 are based on use patterns in residential buildings and can be erroneous for other usages.

As water flows through a pipe, the pressure continually decreases along the pipe due to loss of energy from friction. The problem is then to first ascertain the minimum pressure in the street main and then the minimum pressure required to operate the fixture that is farthest from the mains in terms of pressure drop encountered by the flow as water travels from the mains to the fixture. The pressure differential overcomes both the friction pressure drop in the piping distributing system (pipes plus fittings, valves, etc.) and the difference in elevation between the water main and the highest fixture. The pressure loss component (in psi) resulting from the difference in elevation between the street main and the highest fixture can be obtained by multiplying the difference in elevation in feet by the conversion factor 0.434. Approximate design pressure losses and flow limits for disk-type meters for various rates of flow are given in Fig. 9-8. Manufacturers give data on exact pressure losses and capacities.

Fig. 9-9 shows the variation of pressure loss with rate of flow for various faucets and cocks. The water demand for hose bibbs or other large-demand fixtures taken off the building main frequently results in inadequate water supply to the upper floor of a building. This condition can be

prevented by sizing the distribution system so that the pressure drops from the street main to all fixtures are the same. An ample building main (not less than 1 in. where possible) should be maintained until all branches to hose bibbs have been connected. Where the street main pressure is excessive, a pressure reducing valve is used to prevent water hammer or excessive pressure at the fixtures, the hose bibbs should be connected ahead of the reducing valve.

The principles involved in sizing upfeed and downfeed systems are the same. In the downfeed system, however, the difference in elevation between the overhead supply mains and the fixtures provides the pressure required to overcome pipe friction. Because friction pressure loss and height pressure loss are not additive, as in an upfeed system, smaller pipes may be used with a downfeed system.

Plastic Pipe.—The maximum safe water velocity in a thermoplastic piping system under most operating conditions is typically 5 fps; however, higher velocities can be used in cases where the operating characteristics of valves and pumps are known so that sudden changes in flow velocity can be controlled. The total pressure in the system at any time (operating pressure plus surge of water hammer) should not exceed 150% of the pressure rating of the system.

Procedure for Sizing Cold Water Systems.—The recommended procedure for sizing piping systems is outlined below.

1) Sketch the main lines, risers, and branches, and indicate the fixtures to be served. Indicate the rate of flow of each fixture.

2) Using Table 9-32, compute the demand weights of the fixtures in fixture units.

3) Determine the total demand in fixture units and, using Figs. 9-5, 9-6, or 9-7, find the expected demand.

4) Determine the equivalent length of pipe in the main lines, risers, and branches. Because the sizes of the pipes are not known, the exact equivalent length of various fittings cannot be determined. Add the equivalent lengths, starting at the street main and proceed along the service line, the main line of the building, and up the riser to the top fixture of the group served.

5) Determine the average minimum pressure in the street main and the minimum pressure required for the operation of the topmost fixture, which should be 8 to 25 psi.

6) Calculate the approximate design value of the average pressure drop per 100 ft of equivalent length of pipe determined in step 4.

$$\Delta P = \frac{(P_s - 0.434H - P_f - P_m) \times 100}{L} \qquad (12)$$

where ΔP = average pressure loss per 100 ft of equivalent
length of pipe, psi;
P_s = pressure in street main, psig;

P_f = minimum pressure required to operate topmost fixture, psig;

P_m = pressure drop through water meter, psi;

H = height of highest fixture above street main, ft; and

L = equivalent length determined in step 4, ft

If the system is downfeed supply from a gravity tank, height of water in the tank, converted to psi by multiplying by 0.434, replaces the street main pressure, and the term 0.434H is added instead of subtracted in calculating ΔP. In this case, H is the vertical distance of the fixture below the bottom of the tank. From the expected rate of flow determined in step 3 and the value of ΔP calculated in step 6, choose the sizes of pipe from Figs. 9-1, 9-2, or 9-3.

Table 9-32. Demand Weights of Fixtures in Fixture Units[*]

Fixture or Group[a]	Occupancy	Type of Supply Control	Weight in Fixture Units[b]
Water closet	Public	Flush valve	10
Water closet	Public	Flush tank	5
Pedestal urinal	Public	Flush valve	10
Stall or wall urinal	Public	Flush valve	5
Stall or wall urinal	Public	Flush tank	3
Lavatory	Public	Faucet	2
Bathtub	Public	Faucet	4
Shower head	Public	Mixing valve	4
Service sink	Office, etc.	Faucet	3
Kitchen sink	Hotel or restaurant	Faucet	4
Water closet	Private	Flush valve	6
Water closet	Private	Flush tank	3
Lavatory	Private	Faucet	1
Bathtub	Private	Faucet	2
Shower head	Private	Mixing valve	2
Bathroom group	Private	Flush valve for closet	8
Bathroom group	Private	Flush tank for closet	6
Separate shower	Private	Mixing valve	2
Kitchen sink	Private	Faucet	2
Laundry trays (1 to 3)	Private	Faucet	3
Combination fixture	Private	Faucet	3

[a] For fixtures not listed, weights may be assumed by comparing the fixture to a listed one using water in similar quantities and at similar rates.

[b] The given weights are for total demand. For fixtures with both hot and cold water supplies, the weights for maximum separate demands can be assumed to be 75% of the listed demand for the supply.

Source: Hunter (1941).

At this point, estimate the equivalent pipe length of the fittings on the direct line from the street main to the highest fixture. The exact equivalent length of the various fittings cannot be determined since the pipe sizes of the building main, riser, and branch leading to the highest fixture are not yet known, but a first approximation is necessary for a tentative selection of pipe sizes. If the computed pipe sizes differ from those used in determining the equivalent length of pipe fittings, a recalculation using the computed pipe sizes for the fittings will be necessary.

Table 9-33. Allowable Number of 1-Inch Flush Valves Served by Various Sizes of Water Pipes

Pipe Size, in.	No. of 1 in. Flush Valves
1¼	1
1½	2–4
2	5–12
2½	13–25
3	26–40
4	41–100

Table 9-33 is a guide to minimum pipe sizing where flush valves are used. Velocities exceeding 10 fps cause undesirable noise in the piping system. This usually governs the size of larger pipes in the system, while in small pipe sizes, the friction loss usually governs the selection because the velocity is low compared to friction loss. Velocity is the governing factor in downfeed systems, where friction loss is usually neglected. Velocity in branches leading to pump suctions should not exceed 5 fps.

If the street pressure is too low to adequately supply upper-floor fixtures, the pressure must be increased. Constant or variable speed booster pumps, alone or in conjunction with gravity supply tanks, or hydro pneumatic systems may be used.

Flow control valves for individual fixtures under varying pressure conditions automatically adjust the flow at the fixture to a predetermined quantity. These valves allow the designer to (1) limit the flow at the individual outlet to the minimum suitable for the purpose, (2) hold the total demand for the system more closely to the required minimum, and (3) design the piping system as accurately as is practicable for the requirements.

[*] For supply outlets likely to impose continuous demands, estimate continuous supply separately, and add to total demand for fixtures.

Steam Flow in Pipes

Background of Steam Flow Formulas.—The flow relationships equations in common use originated with Darcy and Weisbach, both of whom worked with flow of water. The Darcy-Weisbach equation for drop in pressure head for water flow has been carried forward to this time in its original form, which included a friction factor f as follows:

$$h_f = \frac{fLV^2}{2gD} \tag{13}$$

where h_f = head loss in feet of fluid flowing;

 f = friction factor;

 L = length of pipe in feet; and

 D = internal diameter of pipe in feet.

 V = average velocity, fps; and

 g_c = units conversion factor, 32.2 ft-lb$_m$/lb$_f$-sec^2

The best approach to the study of steam flow in pipes consists in utilizing concepts of fluid flow, and in particular the chart prepared by Moody. This chart gives the relation between friction factor and Reynolds number for various degrees of roughness of the surface of the pipe is shown in Fig. 1-10.

Table 9-34. Pressure Drops Used for Sizing Steam Pipe[a]

Initial Steam Pressure, psig	Pressure Drop per 100 ft	Total Pressure Drop in Steam Supply Piping
Vacuum return	2 to 4 oz/in²	1 to 2 psi
0	0.5 oz/in²	1 oz/in²
1	2 oz/in²	1 to 4 oz/in²
2	2 oz/in²	8 oz/in²
5	4 oz/in²	1.5 psi
10	8 oz/in²	3 psi
15	1 psi	4 psi
30	2 psi	5 to 10 psi
50	2 to 5 psi	10 to 15 psi
100	2 to 5 psi	15 to 25 psi
150	2 to 10 psi	25 to 30 psi

[a] Equipment, control valves, and so forth must be selected based on delivered pressures.

Computation Based on Data.—Using similar concepts incorporated in the Moody chart for fluid flow, a method can be derived for the sizing of steam pipes. Twenty six working charts (from Figs. 9-10 to 9-35) that summarize the method in graphical form are presented on subsequent pages. A detailed example of the necessary

calculations that were made to establish a single point on the charts follows:

If the following variables are known:
1) absolute viscosity, μ
2) density, ρ
3) velocity of steam, V
4) inside diameter of pipe, D
5) absolute roughness of pipe surface, e

The pressure drop per 100-ft length of pipe may be calculated by the Moody chart and Equation (13).

The variables listed are functions of other parameters. For example, the first two variables of absolute viscosity and density depend upon the steam pressure and the steam condition (i.e., wet, dry, or superheated). The fourth variable of inside diameter depends upon the nominal pipe size and the schedule number of the pipe. For example, a 2-inch Schedule 40 commercial steel pipe has an inside diameter of 2.067 inches, while a 2-inch Schedule 80 commercial steel pipe has an inside diameter of 1.939 inches. The fifth variable of absolute surface roughness depends on the material used in the pipe.

Assume that the pressure drop is sought for 39 ft of 3-inch Schedule 40 commercial-steel pipe when 12 lb/min of saturated steam is flowing at an initial pressure of 15.7 psia. The first step of the solution is to determine steam properties. This can be done in the 10 steps that follow:

1) Density = 1/25.17 = 0.03973 lb/ft³ (from steam tables by interpolation).
2) Absolute viscosity $\mu = 9.0 \times 10^{-6}$ lb/ft-sec.
3) Inside diameter $D = 0.2557$ ft (from piping tables).
4) Velocity

$$V = \frac{\dot{m}}{\rho A} = \frac{12}{0.03973 \times \left[\frac{\pi}{4} \times 0.2557^2\right]}$$

$$= 5882 \text{ fpm}$$

where $\dot{m}$ = steam flowing lbs/min;

 A = cross-sectional area of inside of pipe.

5) For the next step involving the Moody chart, the Reynolds number and relative roughness must be computed:

$$Re = \frac{\rho VD}{\mu} = \frac{0.03973 \times 5882 \times 0.2557}{9.0 \times 10^{-6} \times 60}$$

$$= 1.107 \times 10^5$$

6) Absolute surface roughness $e = 0.00015$ ft.

7) Relative roughness $\frac{e}{D} = \frac{0.00015}{0.2557} = 0.0005867$.

8) On the Moody chart, the intersection of the e/D line of 0.0005867 and the Re line of 1.107×10^5 is located.
9) Friction factor $f = 0.00206$ (from Moody chart). Appropriate values are substituted in Equation (13) to obtain.
10) Head loss

$$h_f = \frac{fLv^2}{D2g} = \frac{0.0206 \times 37 \times (5882)^2}{0.2557 \times 2 \times 32.2 \times 3600}$$

$$= 446 \ \text{ft}$$

11) Pressure drop

$$\Delta P = \frac{\rho h_f}{144} = \frac{0.03973 \times 446}{144} = 0.123 \ \text{psi}$$

The Page-Konzo Working Charts.—Tedious calculations of the preceding type can be practically eliminated by the use of 20 working charts as shown on subsequent Figs. 9-15 to 9-35, which were designed by Page and Konzo. The computations were made for Schedule 40 and 80 commercial steel pipe. Chart scales show the following variables:

1) Weight rate of flow in pounds per minute (abscissa).
2) Pressure drop in psi per 100 ft length of pipe (left ordinate).
3) Pressure drop in ounces per square inch per 100 ft length of pipe (right ordinate) for the convenience of those who utilize this unit of pressure drop.
4) Constant velocity lines (sloping downward to the right).
5) Constant diameter lines (sloping upward to the right).

Examples of Use of Charts: Case 1. *When pressure drop is the dependent variable.* The sample problem already described can be readily solved by means of the working charts. It was required to determine the pressure drop in 37 ft of 3 inch Schedule 40 commercial steel pipe when 12 lb/min of saturated steam was flowing at an initial pressure of 15.7 psia. The first chart Figs. 9-15 to 9-35 will be used since it applies to Schedule 40 pipe and to a pressure range of 14.7 to 16.6 psia.

Locate the flow rate of 12 lb/min on the right ordinate. Proceed to the left on the chart until the 3-inch diameter line is intersected. Then proceed down to obtain a pressure drop of 0.333 psi per 100 ft of length. The pressure drop for 37 ft of pipe is 0.37 × 0.333, or 0.123 psi. This result is the same as that of the detailed method previously given.

Case 2. *When weight flow rate is the dependent variable.* What is the flow rate in lb/min of saturated steam at 15.0 psia through a Schedule 40 commercial steel pipe of 1-inch diameter, 190 ft long, for a pressure drop of 1.1 psi?

The pressure drop per 100 ft length is 1.1 × 100/190, or 0.579 psi. Since the initial pressure is 3.3 psig, utilize the second chart. Locate the value of 0.579 psi at the bottom, and proceed vertically until the intersection with the 1-inch diameter line is reached. Then proceed horizontally to the right to obtain a weight flow rate of 0.98 lb/min.

Case 3. *When pipe diameter is the dependent variable.* When given an initial pressure of 19 psia, a pressure drop of 0.5 psi per 100-ft length, and saturated steam to be transported at a rate of 25 lbs/min, what are pipe size and steam velocity?

Select the second chart Fig. 9-20 for pressures between 16.7 to 19.7 psia. Locate 0.5 psi on the bottom and proceed vertically. Next locate 25 lb/min on the ordinate and proceed horizontally. The intersection of these two lines lies between two commercial pipe sizes. A 4-inch pipe could be used, but the weight flow is 32.9 lb/min, which is considerably larger than necessary. On the other hand, a 3½ inch pipe gives a weight flow of 23.1 lb/min. The 3½ inch pipe will be preferred, since a flow rate of 25 lb/min would result in a pressure drop of 0.575 psi, which is only slightly larger than the given value of 0.5 psi. The steam velocity is 8000 fps.

Vertical Pipes.—If the pipe in a given piping system rises to a higher level in the direction of flow, an additional pressure drop is involved equal in magnitude to the product of the density and the change in elevation. Similarly, if the pipe drops to a lower level in the direction of flow, a pressure increase is involved equal to the density times the change in elevation. In Table 9-35 is shown the relationship between the pressure drop (per 10-ft length) and the absolute pressure of saturated steam. For low pressures or small changes in elevation the correction is negligible, but for high pressures and large changes in elevation the corrections may be significantly large.

Any correction for changes in elevation should be algebraically added to the pressure drop determined for frictional effects alone.

Table 9-35. Pressure Drop in Saturated Steam for 10 ft Change in Pipe Elevation

Steam Pressure, psia	Pressure Drop, psi per 10 ft Change	Steam Pressure, psia	Pressure Drop, psi per 10 ft Change
10	0.0018	80	0.0130
15	0.0027	100	0.0151
20	0.0035	150	0.0230
25	0.0045	200	0.0300
30	0.0050	300	0.0450
40	0.0065	400	0.0600
60	0.0097	500	0.0750

Steam Piping.—Pressure losses in steam piping for flows of dry or nearly dry steam are governed by Equations (1) through (7). This section incorporates these principles with other information specific to steam systems.

Pipe Sizes: Required pipe sizes for a given load in steam heating depend on the following factors:

- The initial pressure and the total pressure drop that can be allowed between the source of supply and the end of the return system.
- The maximum velocity of steam allowable for quiet and dependable operation of the system, taking into consideration the direction of condensate flow.
- The equivalent length of the run from the boiler or source of steam supply to the farthest heating unit.

Initial Pressure and Pressure Drop: Table 9-35 lists pressure drops commonly used with corresponding initial steam pressures for sizing steam piping. Several factors, such as initial pressure and pressure required at the end of the line, should be considered, but it is most important that (1) the total pressure drop does not exceed the initial gage pressure of the system (and in practice it should never exceed one-half the initial gage pressure); (2) the pressure drop is not great enough to cause excessive velocities; (3) a constant initial pressure be maintained, except on systems specially designed for varying initial pressures (e.g., subatmospheric pressure), which normally operate under controlled partial vacuums; and (4) for gravity return systems, the pressure drop to the heating units does not exceed the water column available for removing condensate (i.e., the height above the boiler water line of the lowest point on the steam main, on the heating units, or on the dry return).

Maximum Velocity: For quiet operation, steam velocity should be 8000 to 12000 fpm, with a maximum of 15000 fpm. The lower the velocity, the quieter the system. When the condensate must flow against the steam, even in limited quantity, the velocity of the steam must not exceed limits above which the disturbance between the steam and the counter flowing water may (1) produce objectionable sound, such as water hammer, or (2) result in the retention of water in certain parts of the system until the steam flow is reduced sufficiently to permit the water to pass. The velocity at which these disturbances take place is a function of (1) pipe size; (2) pitch of the pipe if it runs horizontally; (3) the quantity of condensate flowing against the steam; and (4) the freedom of the piping from water pockets that, under certain conditions, act as a restriction in pipe size. Table 9-36 lists maximum capacities for various size steam lines.

Table 9-36. Comparative Capacity of Steam Lines at Various Pitches for Steam and Condensate Flowing in Opposite Directions

Pitch of Pipe, in./10 ft	Nominal Pipe Diameter, in.									
	¾		1		1¼		1½		2	
	Capacity	Maximum Velocity	Capacity	Maximum Velocity	Capacity	Maximum Velocity	Capacity	Maximum Velocity	Capacity	Maximum Velocity
¼	3.2	8	6.8	9	11.8	11	19.8	12	42.9	15
½	4.1	11	9	12	15.9	14	25.9	16	54	18
1	5.7	13	11.7	15	19.9	17	33	19	68.8	24
1½	6.4	14	12.8	17	24.6	20	37.4	22	83.3	27
2	7.1	16	14.8	19	27	22	42	24	92.9	30
3	8.3	17	17.3	22	31.3	25	46.8	26	99.6	32
4	9.9	22	19.2	24	33.4	26	50.8	28	102.4	32
5	10.5	22	20.5	25	38.5	31	59.2	33	115	33

Equivalent Length of Run: All tables for the flow of steam in pipes based on pressure drop must allow for pipe friction, as well as for the resistance of fittings and valves. These resistances are generally stated in terms of straight pipe; that is, a certain fitting produces a drop in pressure equivalent to the stated number of feet of straight run of the same size of pipe.

Table 9-37 gives the number of feet of straight pipe usually allowed for the more common types of fittings and valves. In all pipe sizing tables in this chapter, the length of run refers to the equivalent length of run as distinguished from the actual length of pipe. A common sizing method is to assume the length of run and to check this assumption after pipes are sized. For this purpose, the length of run is usually assumed to be double the actual length of pipe.

Table 9-37. Equivalent Length of Fittings to be Added to Pipe Run

Nominal Pipe Diameter, in.	Length to be Added to Run, ft				
	Standard Elbow	Side Outlet Tee[a]	Gate Valve[b]	Globe Valve[b]	Angle Valve[b]
½	1.3	3	0.3	14	7
¾	1.8	4	0.4	18	10
1	2.2	5	0.5	23	12
1¼	3	6	0.6	29	15
1½	3.5	7	0.8	34	18
2	4.3	8	1.0	46	22
2½	5	11	1.1	54	27
3	6.5	13	1.4	66	34
3½	8	15	1.6	80	40
4	9	18	1.9	92	45
5	11	22	2.2	112	56
6	13	27	2.8	136	67
8	17	35	3.7	180	92
10	21	45	4.6	230	112
12	27	53	5.5	270	132
14	30	63	6.4	310	152

[a] Values apply only to a tee used to divert the flow in the main to the last riser.
[b] Valve in full-open position.

Advantages of Form of Working Charts.—Any given form of working charts for steam flow will have inherent advantages as well as limitations. The forms shown in the working charts were ultimately chosen after a study of the limitations and advantages of these as well as other forms.

The charts as given have two limitations, which were not been considered as unsurmountable.

1) For complete coverage over a wide range of steam pressures, a large number of charts are required. The first chart for a range of pressures from 14.7 psia to 16.6 psia was actually based on values for 15.7 psia. Similarly, the second chart for a range of pressures from 16.7 psia to 19.7 psia was based on values for 18.0 psia. For higher steam pressures, successively larger ranges of steam pressures were used to give the same order of accuracy as those embodied in the first two. In this connection, the maximum deviation in all the values shown was limited to 7%, which was regarded as reasonable considering the accuracy of the original data involved.

2) In order to cover the cases of pipes other than Schedule 40 (or, in the case of the last four charts on Schedule 80 pipe) commercial steel or wrought iron, either separate charts or conversion factors would be necessary.

In spite of the obvious limitations of the form used, the advantages were considered to outweigh the disadvantages:

1) All the data for a particular steam condition are presented on one chart. For most practical applications, the engineer is able to solve a problem without reference to other charts.

2) The solution to any problem can be started at any place on the chart, provided any two of the four variables are known. As shown by the three sample problems, any variable on the chart can be the dependent variable.

3) The complete determination of the problem is made. Information is obtained not only about pressure drop, but also weight flow, diameter, and velocity. It is possible to observe how a change in any one of the four variables will affect the other three.

4) The flow charts are similar in form to those in common use for water and air flow so that familiarity with such existing charts can be extended to these new charts for steam flow.

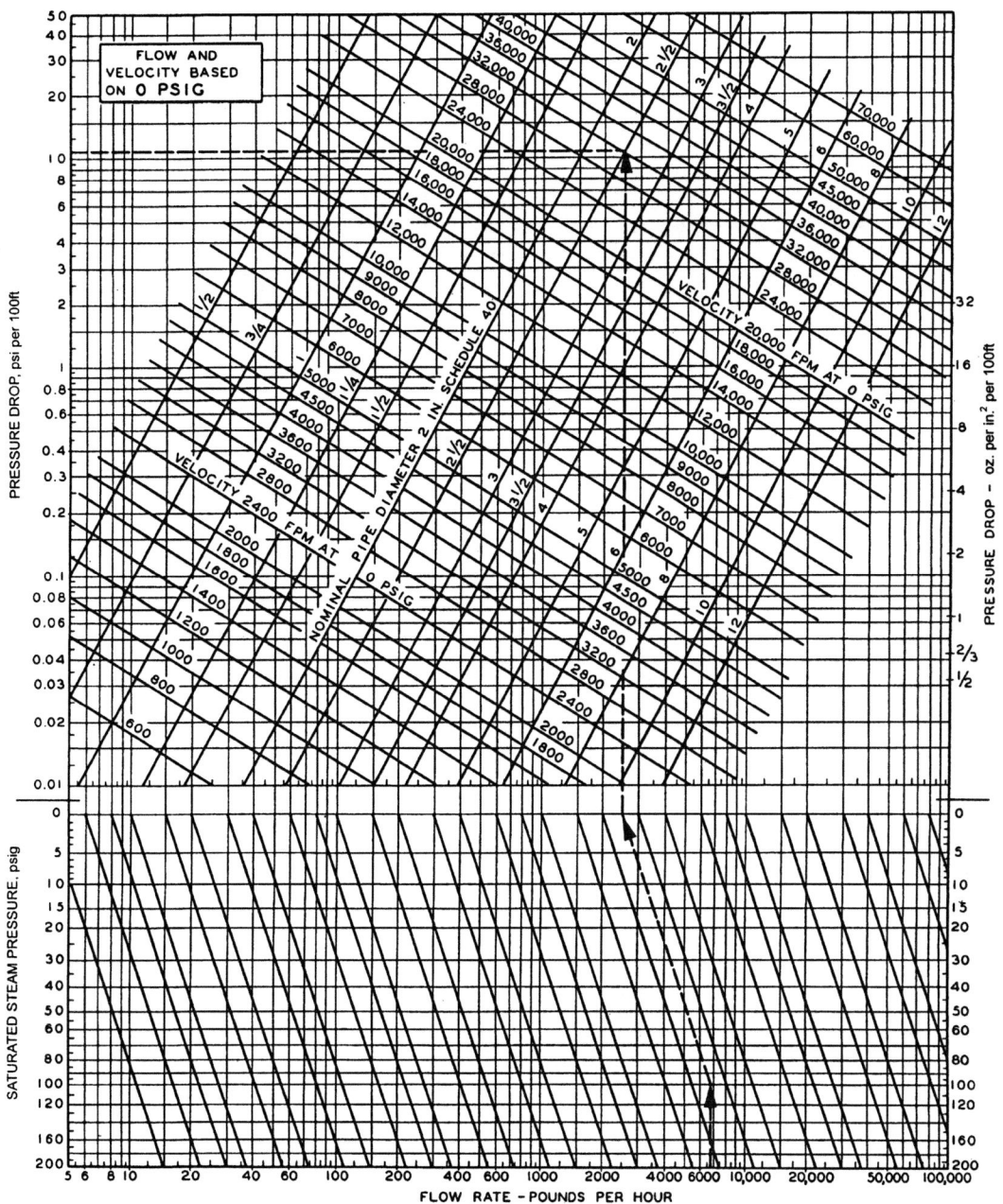

Fig 9-10. Flow rate and velocity of steam in Schedule 40 pipe at saturation pressure of 0 psig

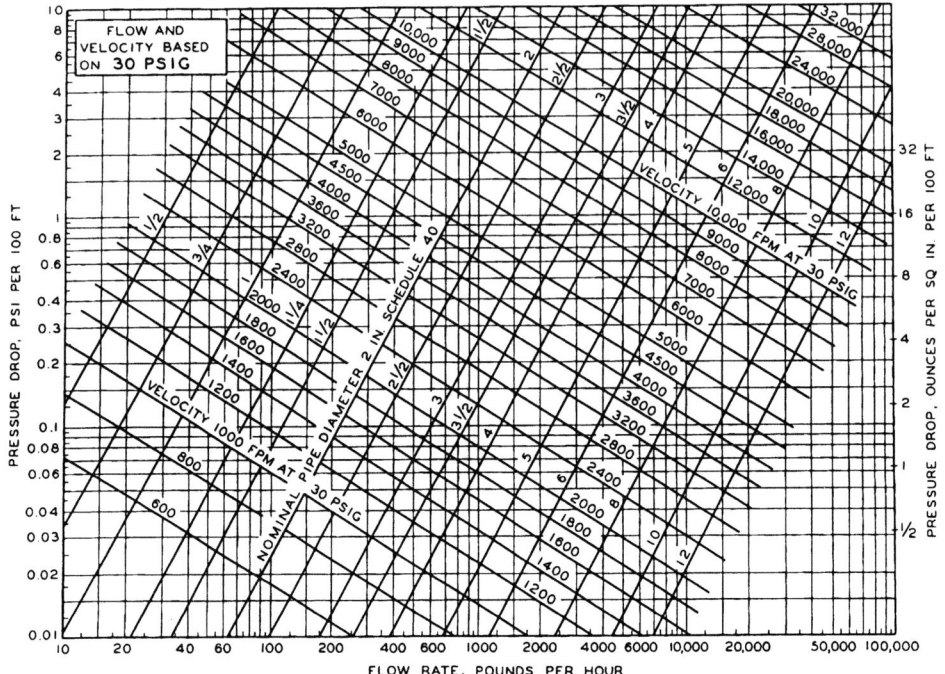

Notes: Based on Moody Friction Factor where flow of condensate does not inhibit the flow of steam.
May be used for steam pressures from 23 to 37 psig with an error not exceeding 9%.

Fig 9-11. Flow rate and velocity of steam in Schedule 40 pipe at saturation pressure of 30 psig

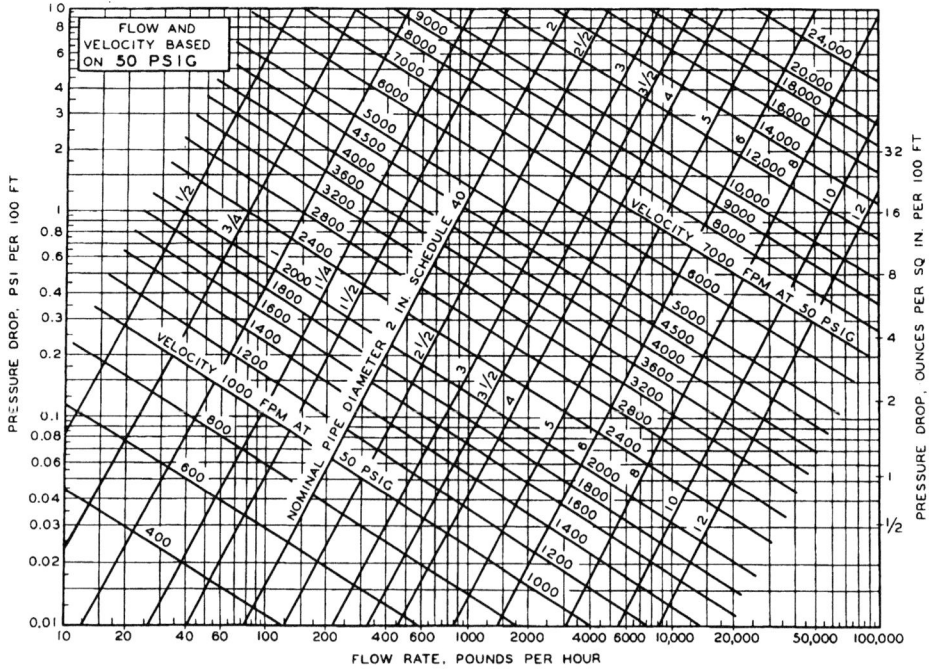

Notes: Based on Moody Friction Factor where flow of condensate does not inhibit the flow of steam.
May be used for steam pressures from 40 to 60 psig with an error not exceeding 8%.

Fig 9-12. Flow rate and velocity of steam in Schedule 40 pipe at saturation pressure of 50 psig

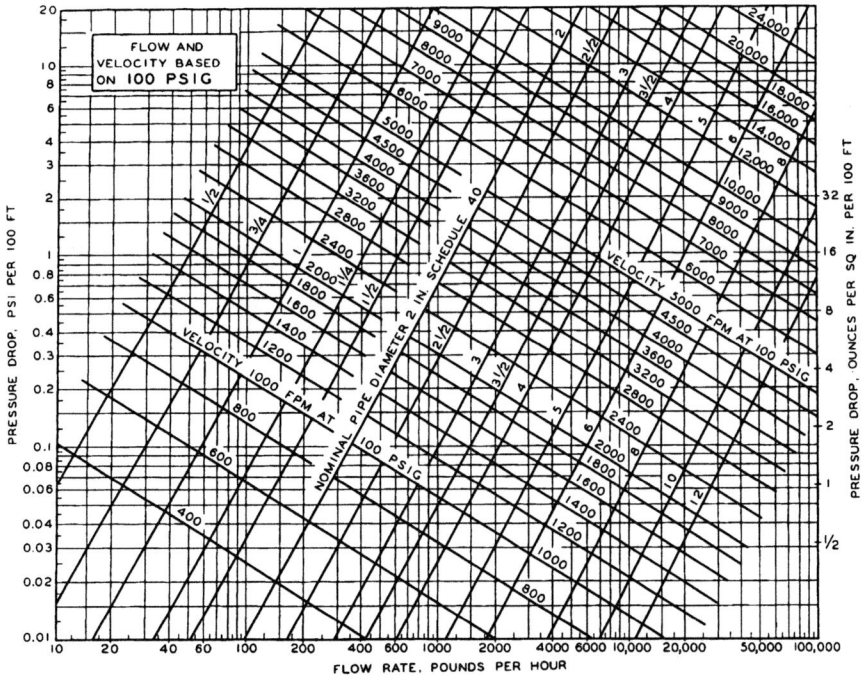

Notes: Based on Moody Friction Factor where flow of condensate does not inhibit the flow of steam.
May be used for steam pressures from 85 to 120 psig with an error not exceeding 8%.

Fig 9-13. Flow rate and velocity of steam in Schedule 40 pipe at saturation pressure of 100 psig

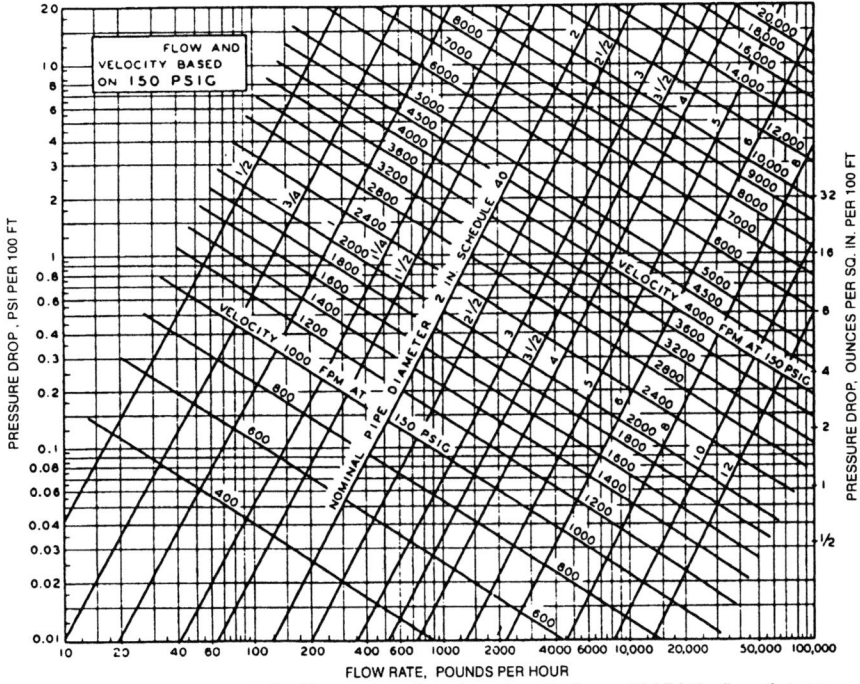

Notes: Based on Moody Friction Factor where flow of condensate does not inhibit the flow of steam.
May be used for steam pressures from 127 to 180 psig with an error not exceeding 8%.

Fig 9-14. Flow rate and velocity of steam in Schedule 40 pipe at saturation pressure of 150 psig

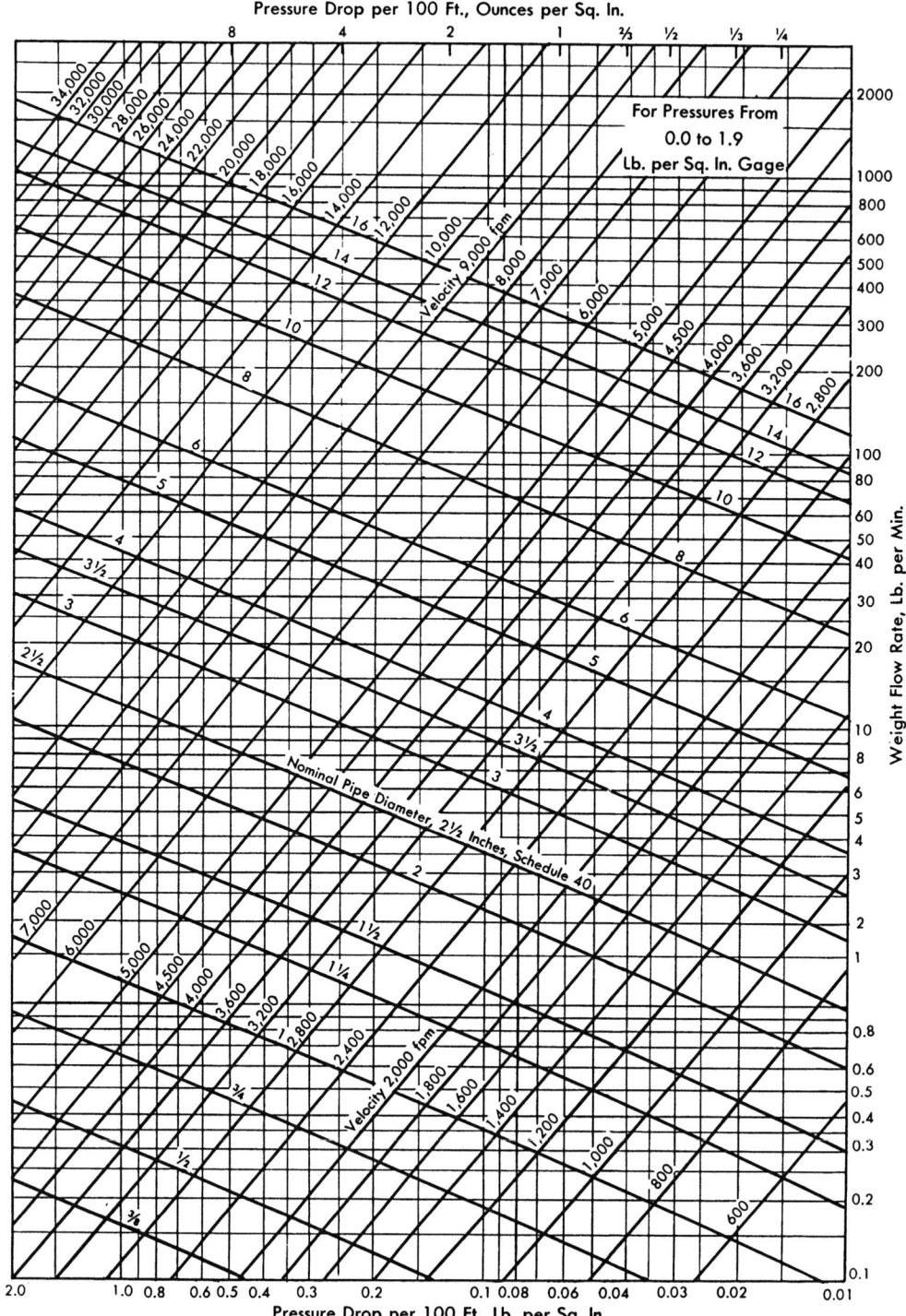

Fig 9-15. For pressure from 0.0 to 1.99 lb/inch^2 gage

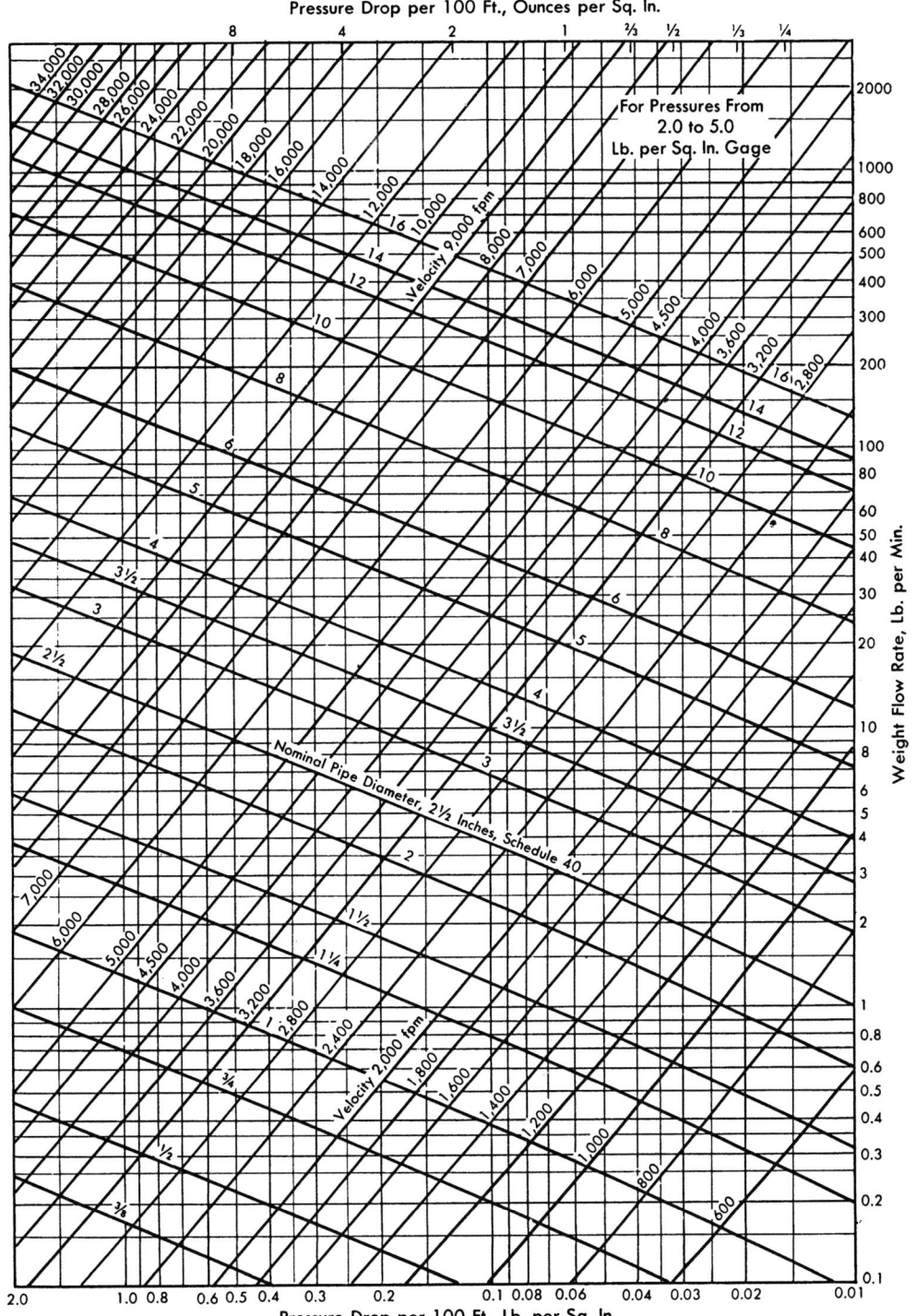

Fig 9-16. For pressure from 2.0 to 5.0 psig

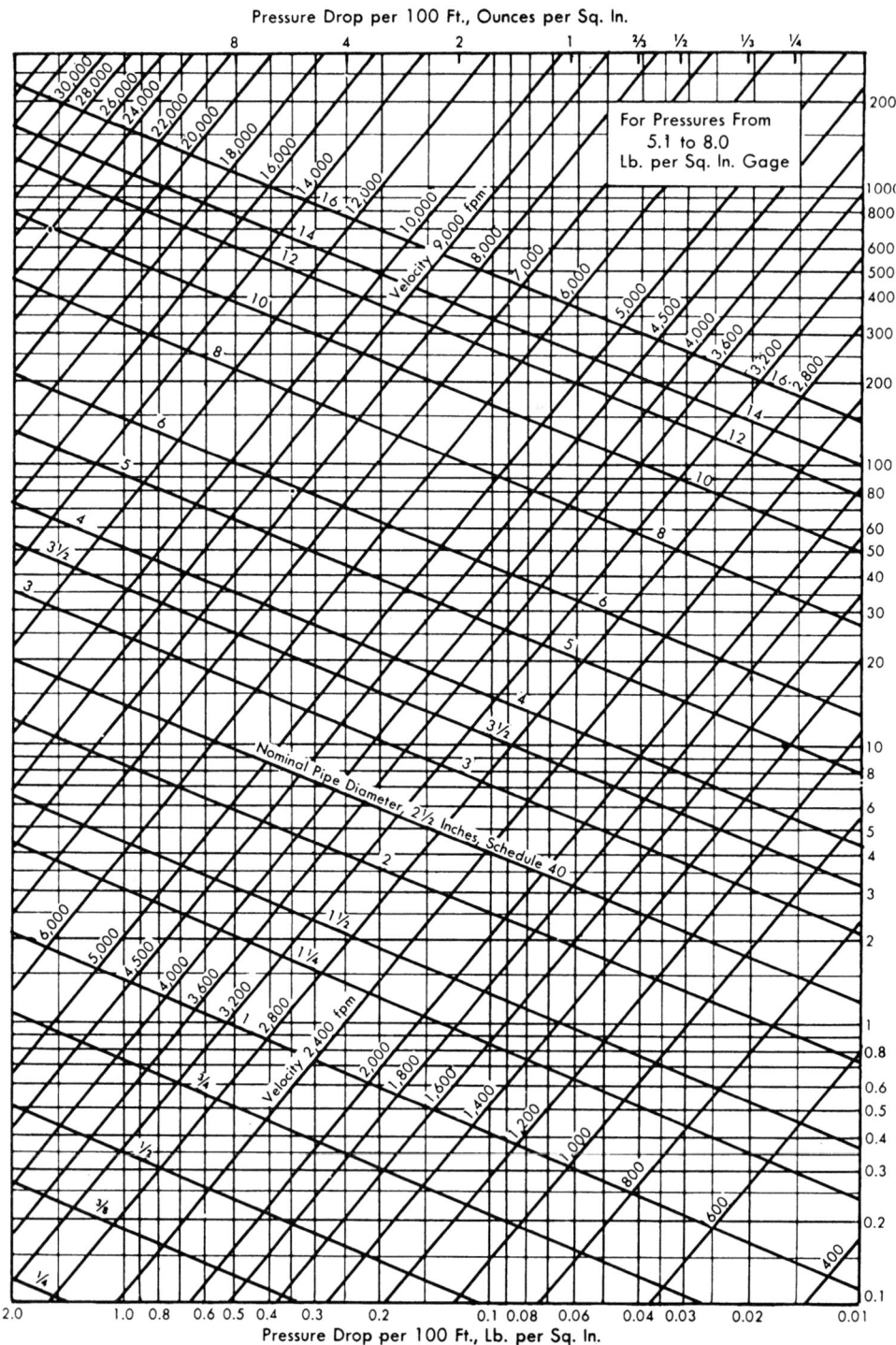

Fig 9-17. For pressure from 5.1 to 8.0 psig

Pressure Drop per 100 Ft., Ounces per Sq. In.

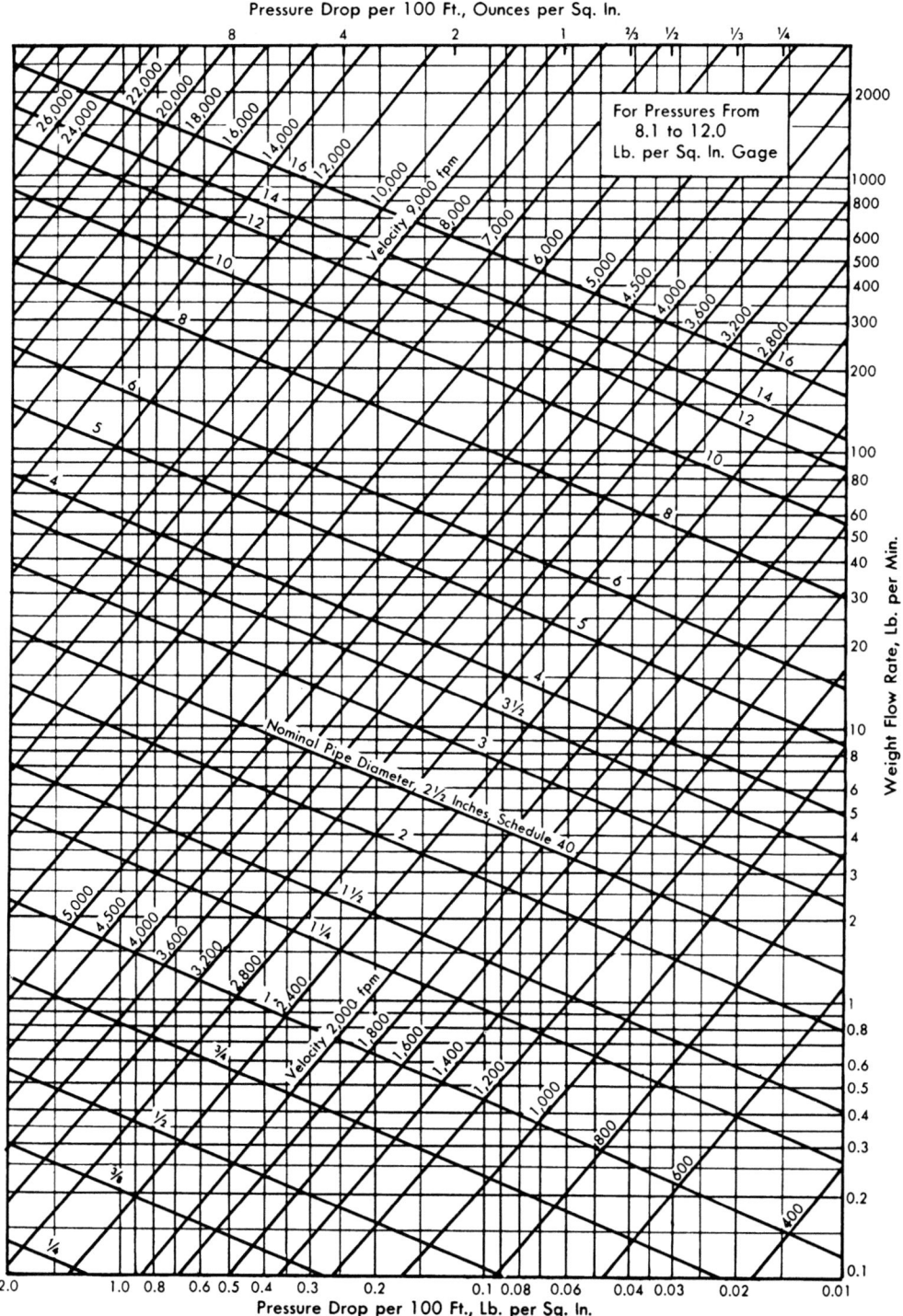

Fig 9-18. For pressure from 8.1 to 12.0 psig

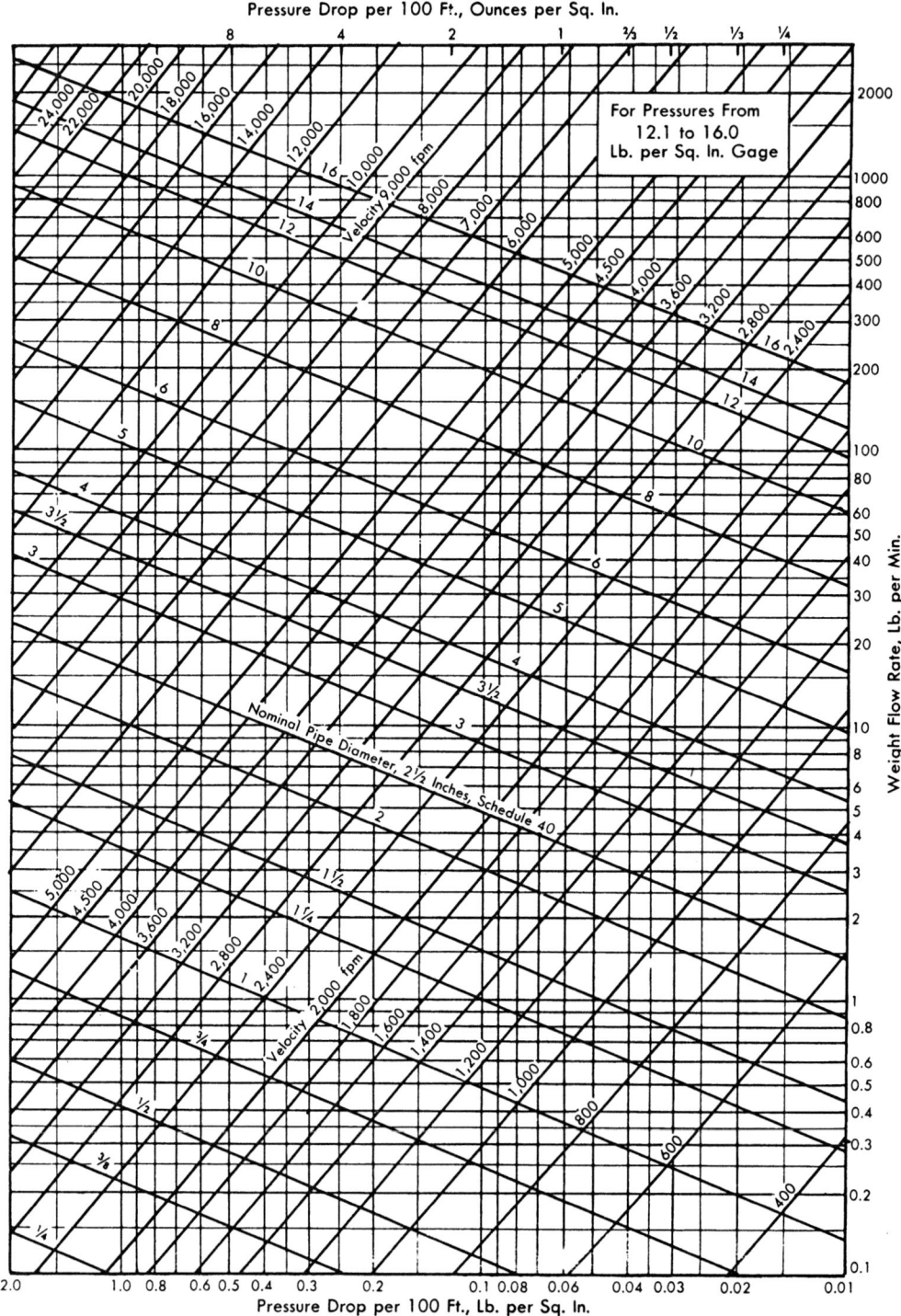

Fig 9-19. For pressure from 12.1 to 16.0 psig

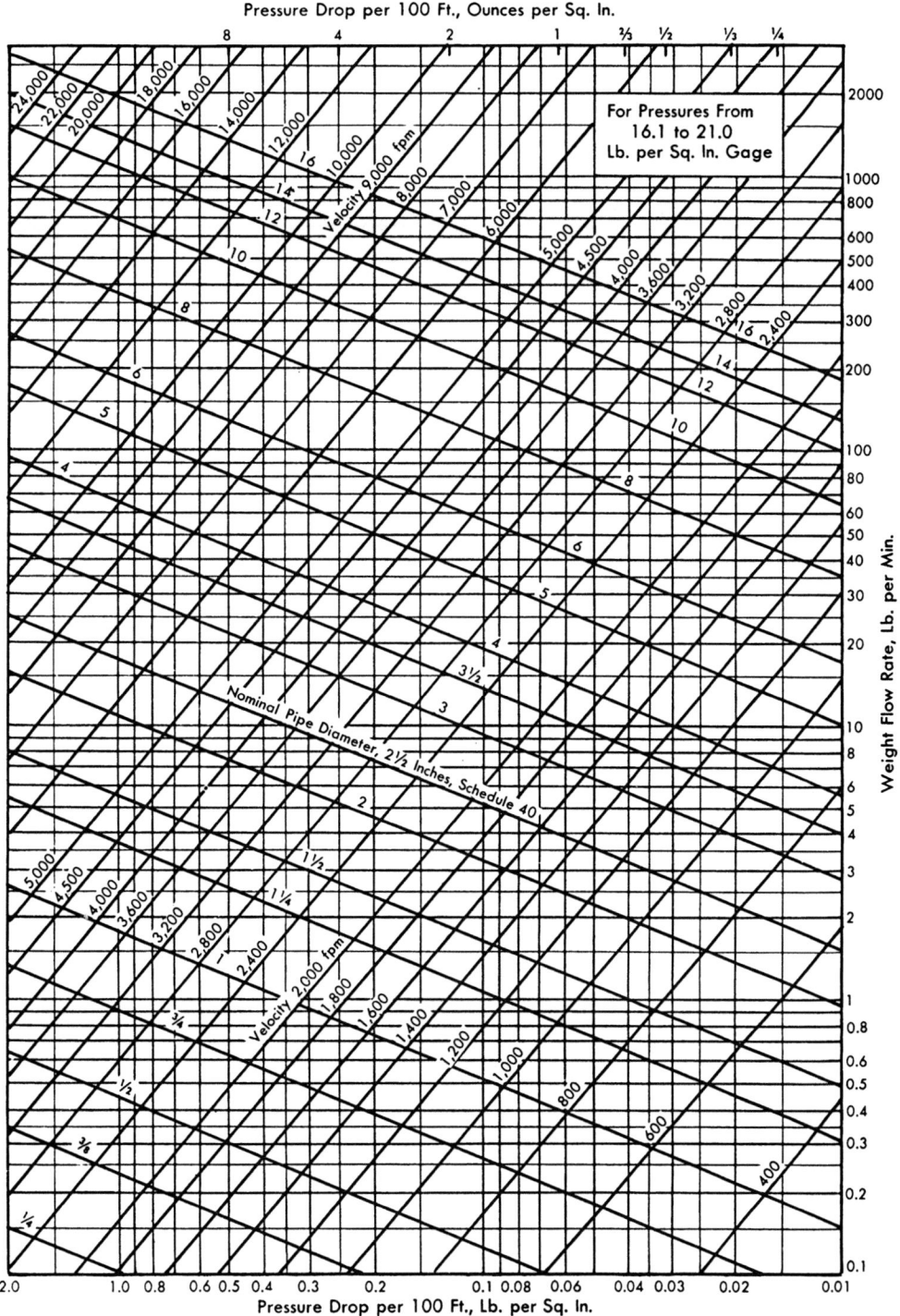

Fig 9-20. For pressure from 16.1 to 21.0 psig

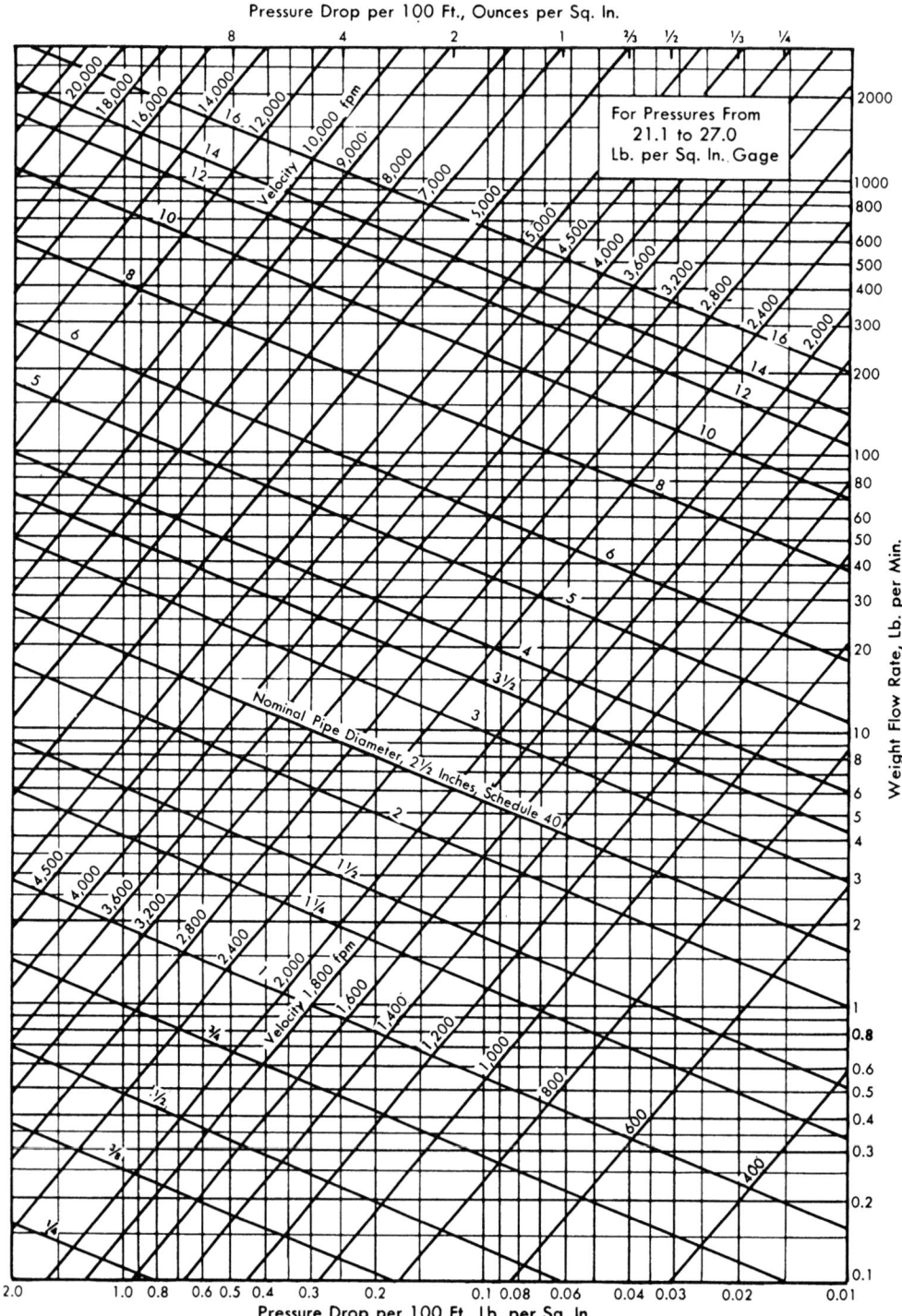

Fig 9-21. For pressure from 21.1 to 27.0 psig

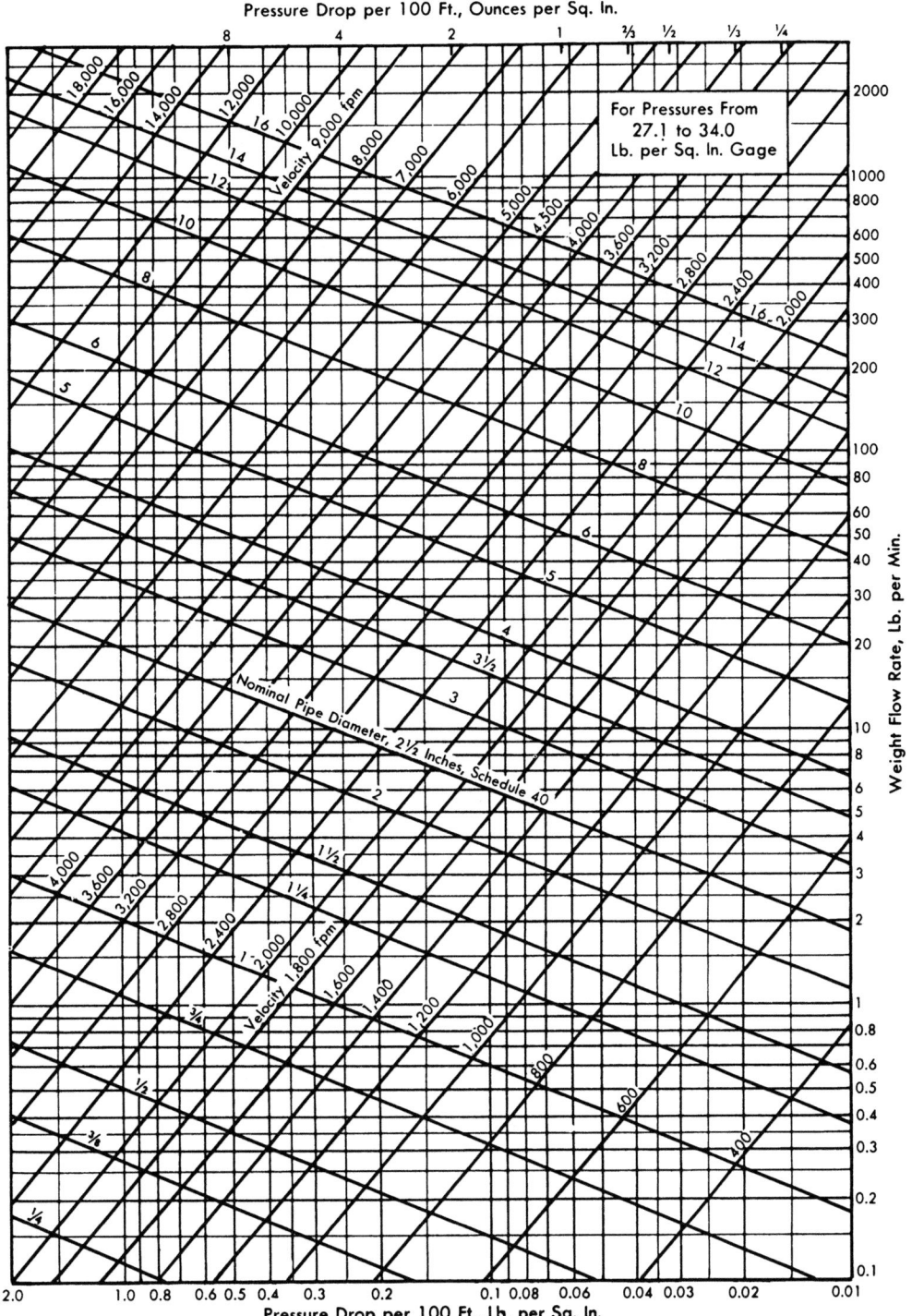

Fig 9-22. For pressure from 27.1 to 34.0 psig

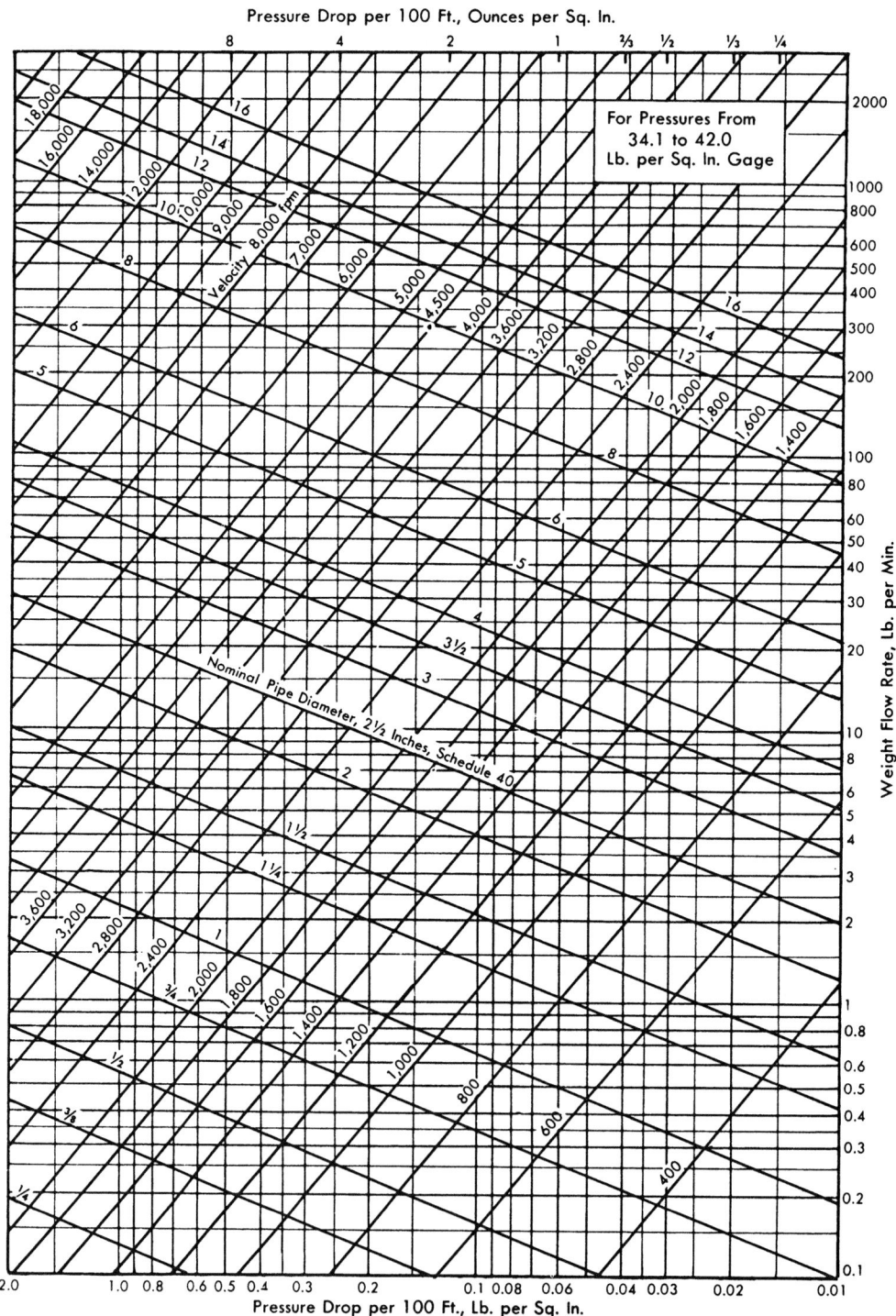

Fig 9-23. For pressure from 34.1 to 42.0 psig

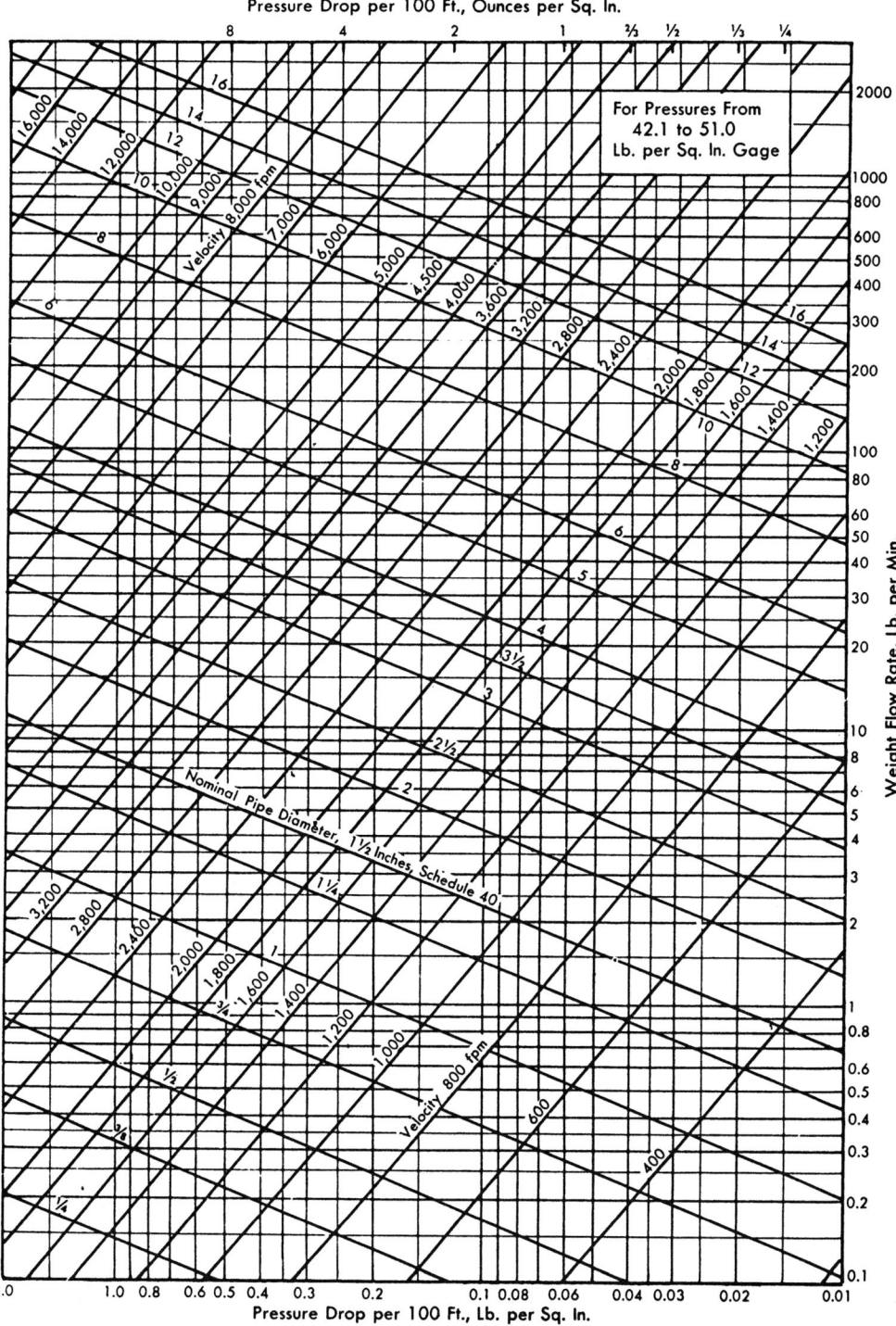

Fig 9-24. For pressure from 42.1 to 51.0 psig

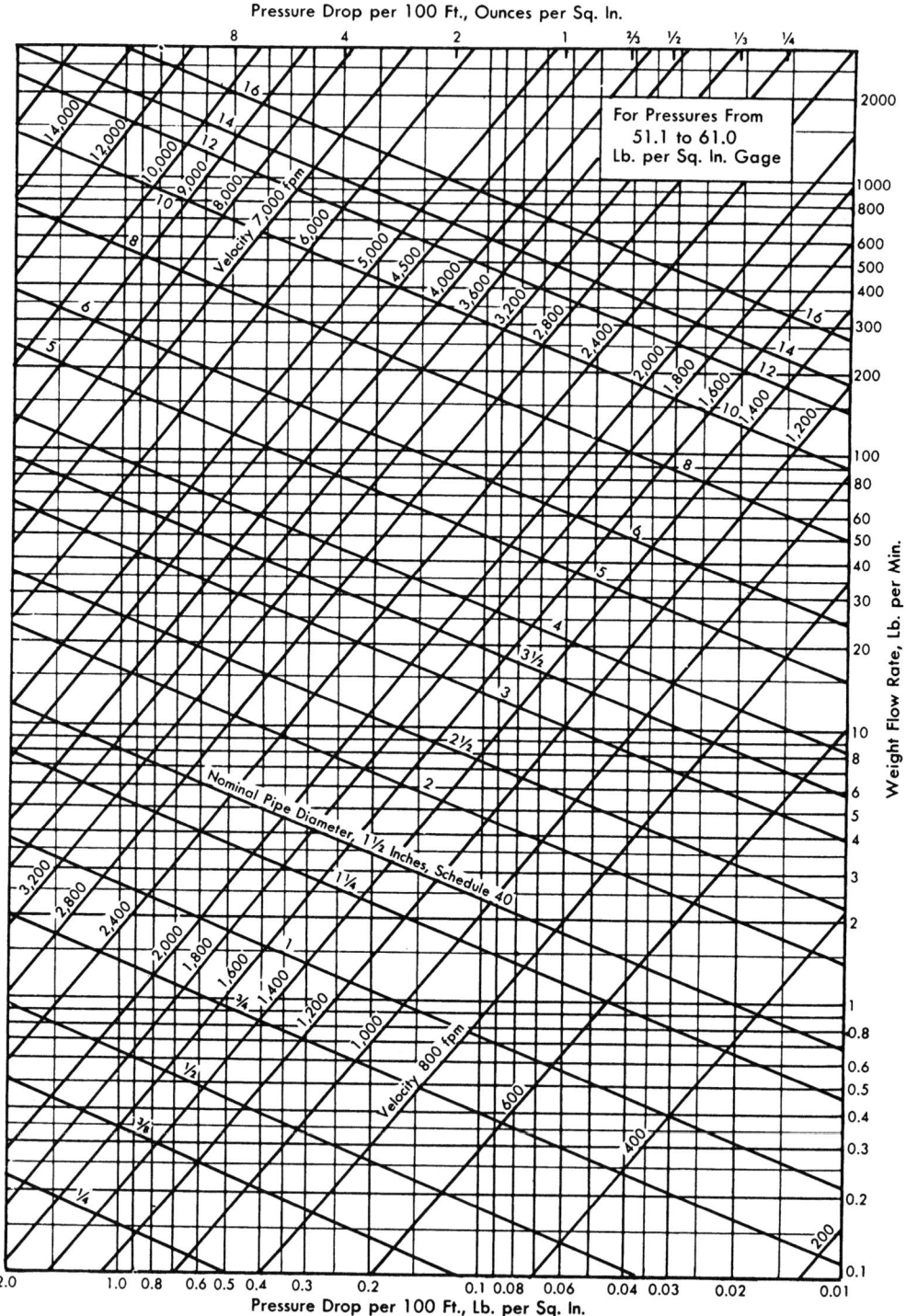

Fig 9-25. For pressure from 51.1 to 61.0 psig

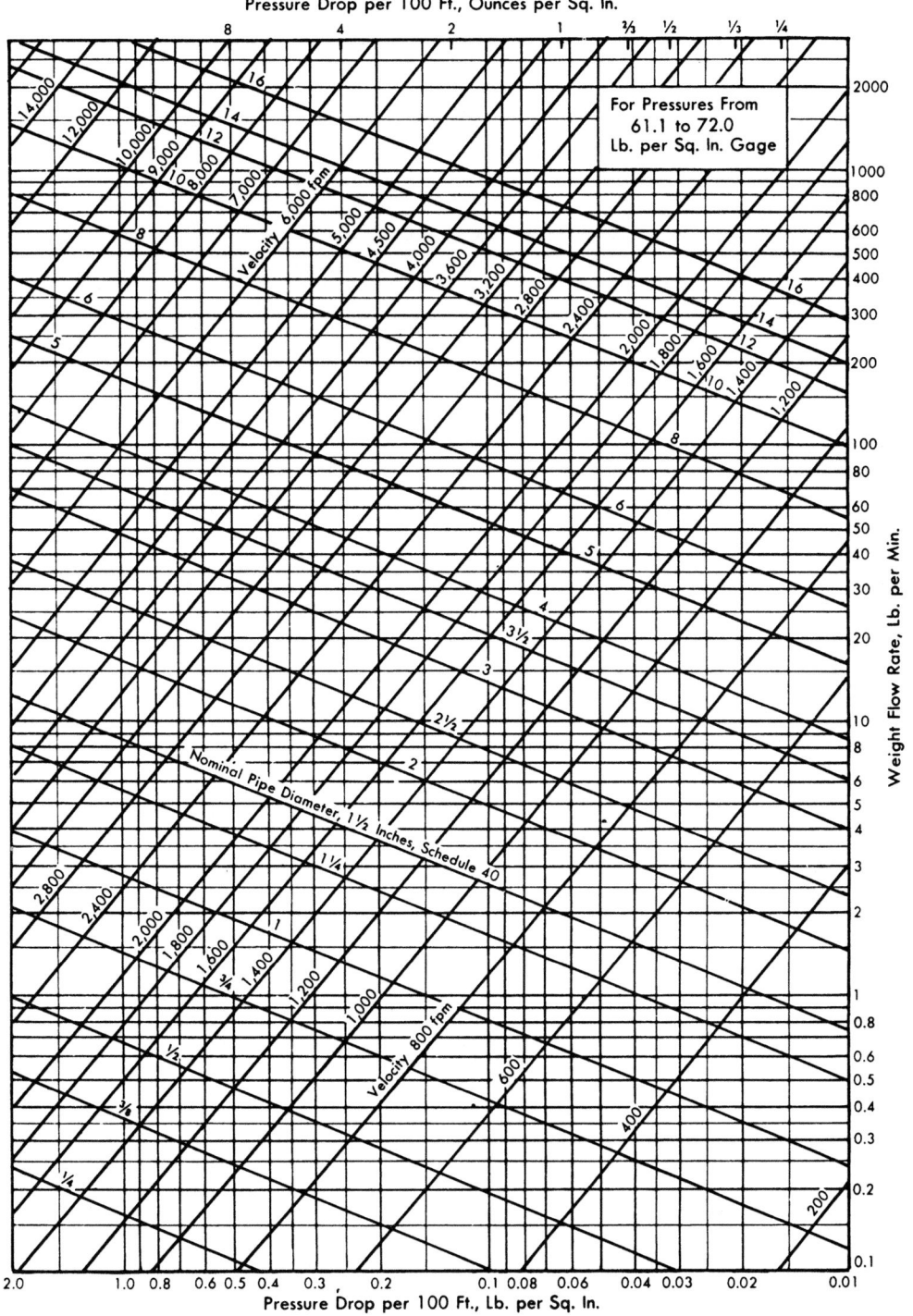

Fig 9-26. For pressure from 61.1 to 72.0 psig

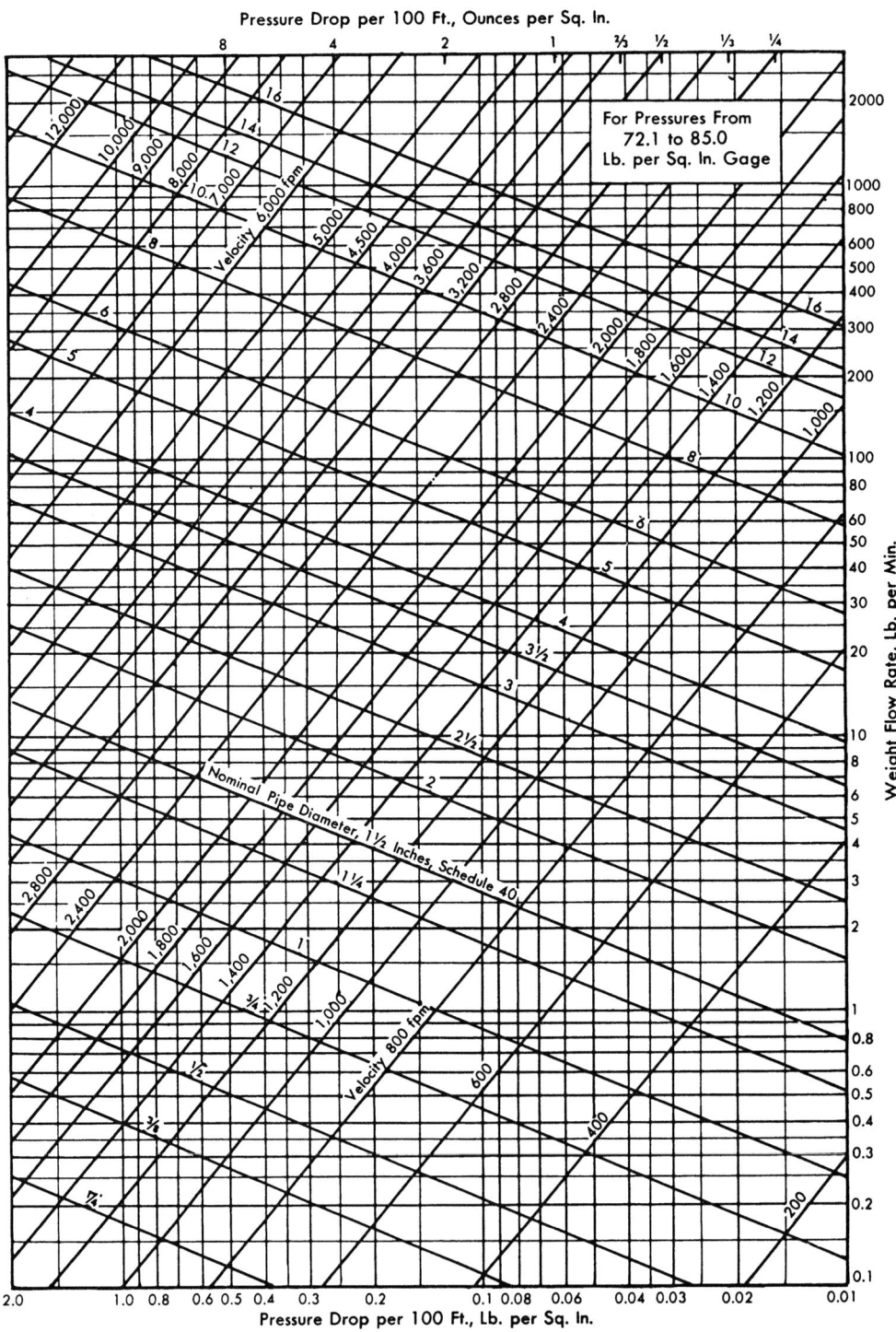

Pressure Drop per 100 Ft., Ounces per Sq. In.

For Pressures From
72.1 to 85.0
Lb. per Sq. In. Gage

Pressure Drop per 100 Ft., Lb. per Sq. In.

Fig 9-27. For pressure from 72.1 to 85.0 psig

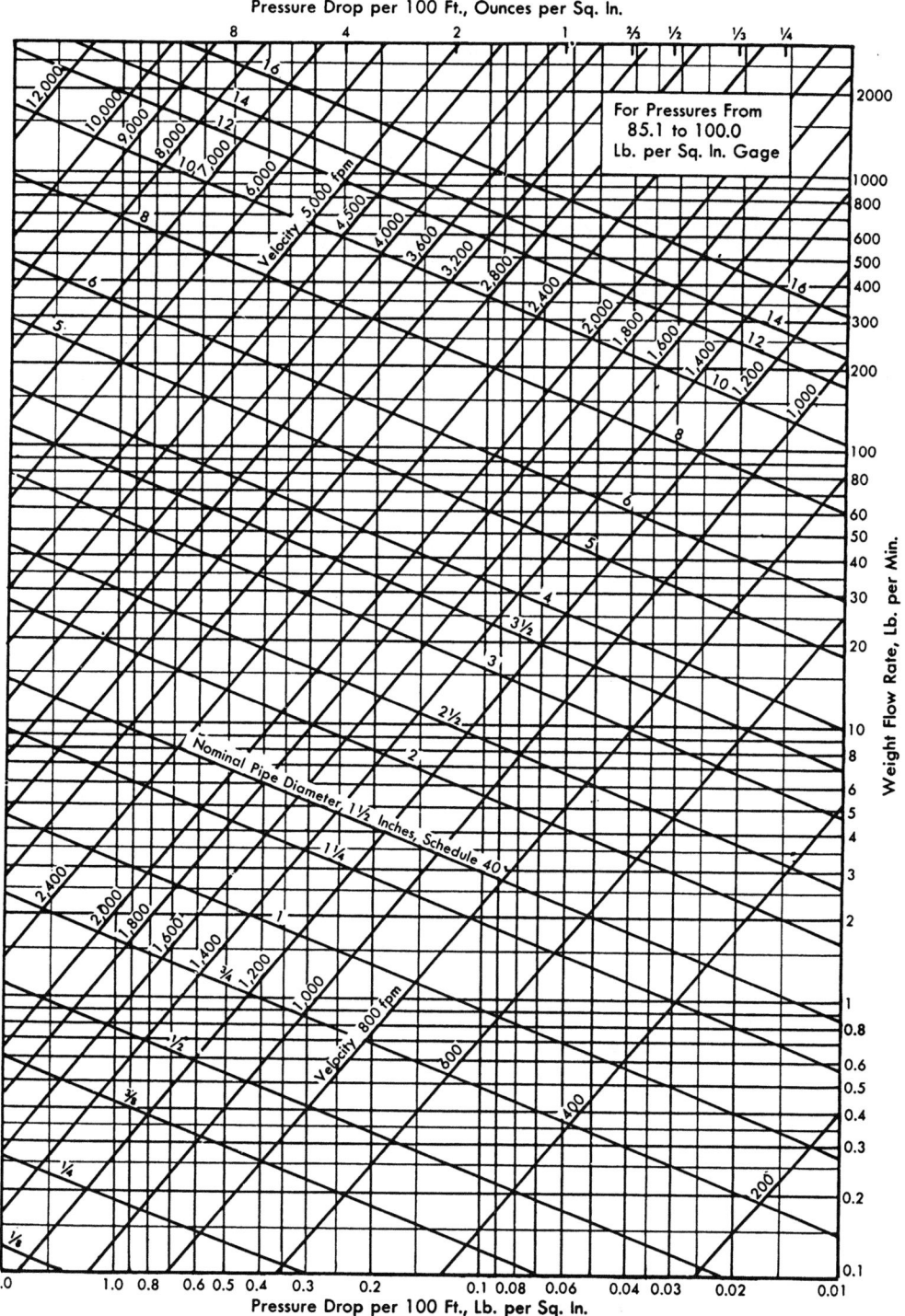

Pressure Drop per 100 Ft., Ounces per Sq. In.

For Pressures From
85.1 to 100.0
Lb. per Sq. In. Gage

Weight Flow Rate, Lb. per Min.

Pressure Drop per 100 Ft., Lb. per Sq. In.

Fig 9-28. For pressure from 85.1 to 100.0 psig

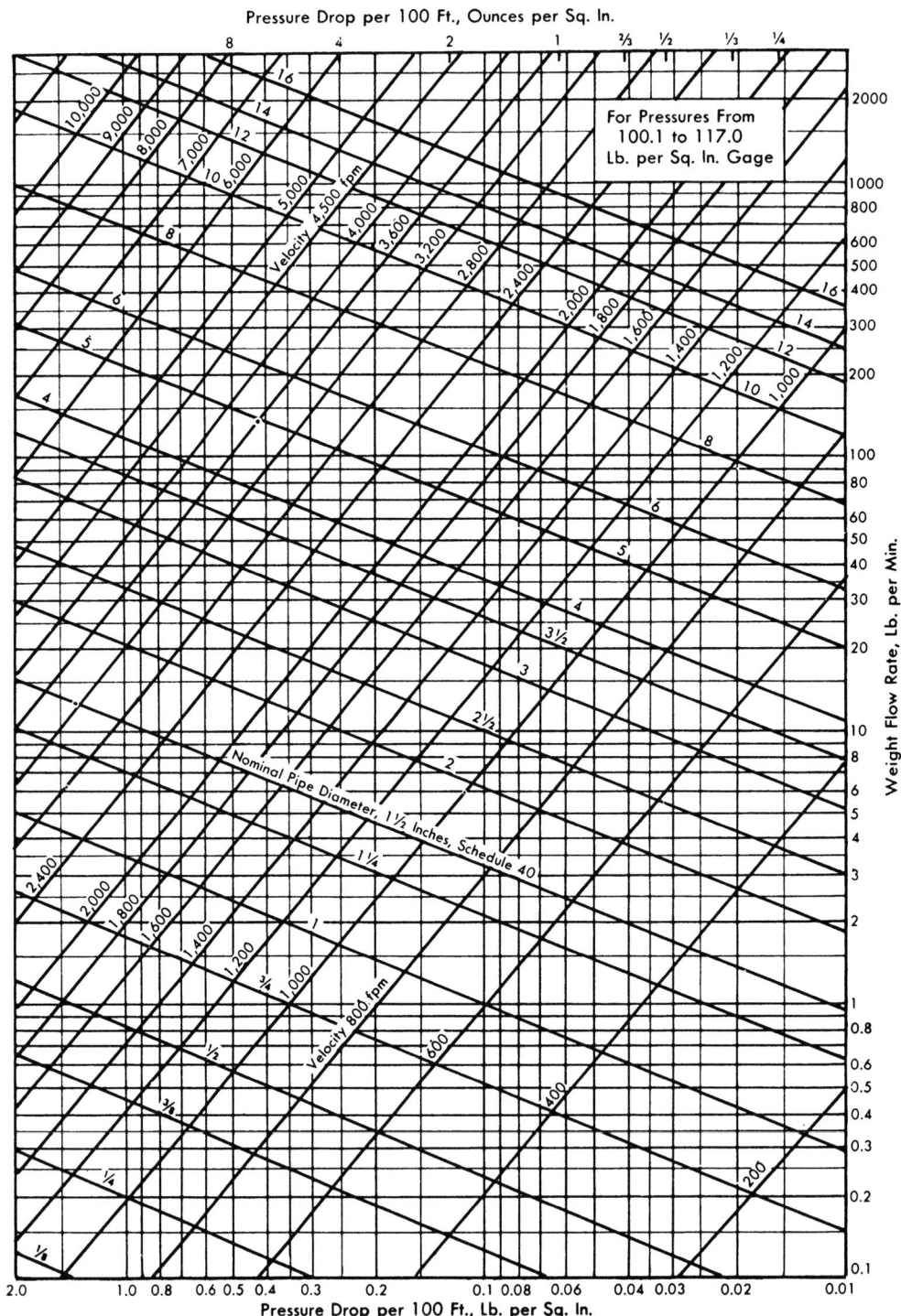

Fig 9-29. For pressure from 101.1 to 117.0 psig

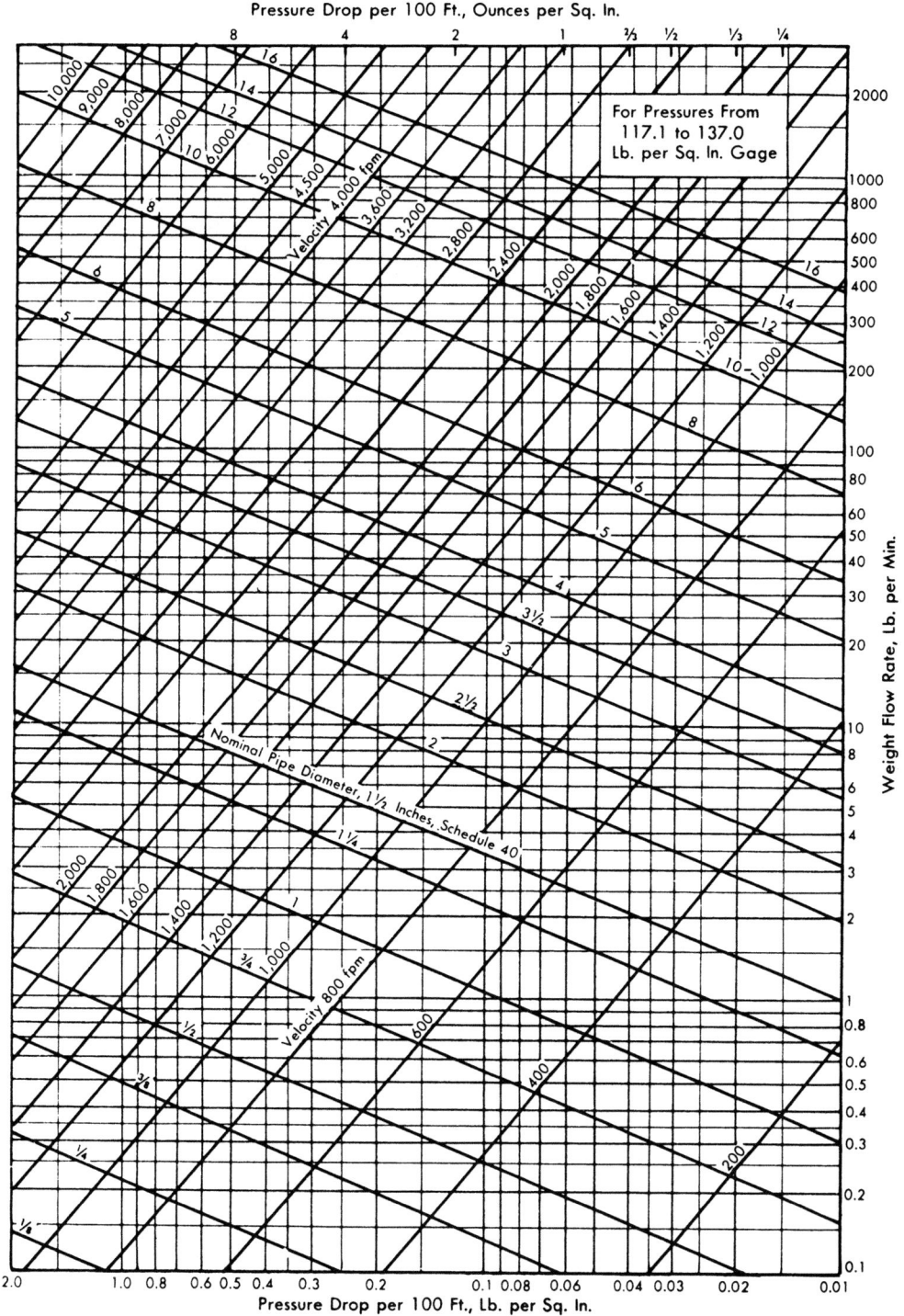

Fig 9-30. For pressure from 117.1 to 137.0 psig

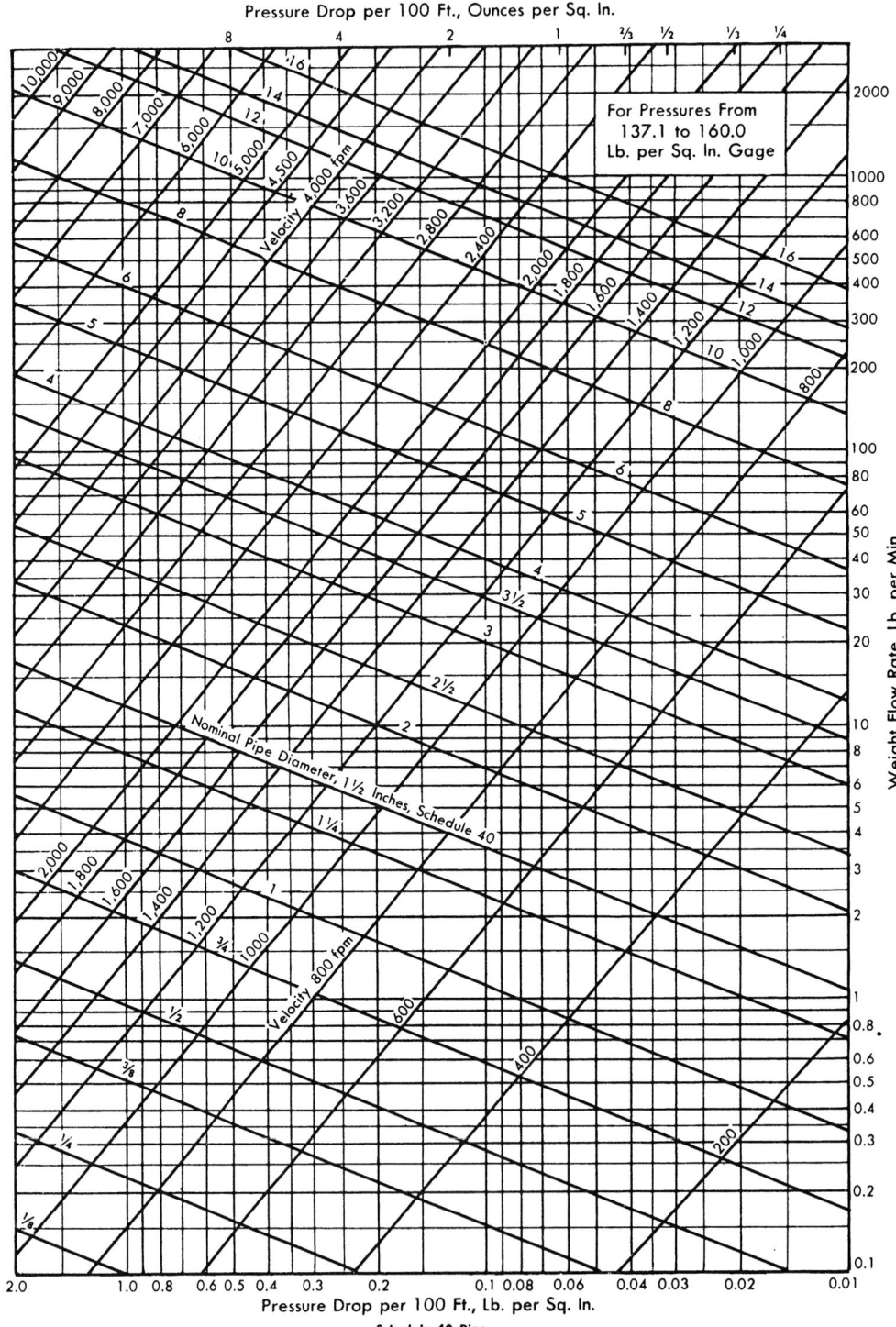

Fig 9-31. For pressure from 137.1 to 160.0 psig

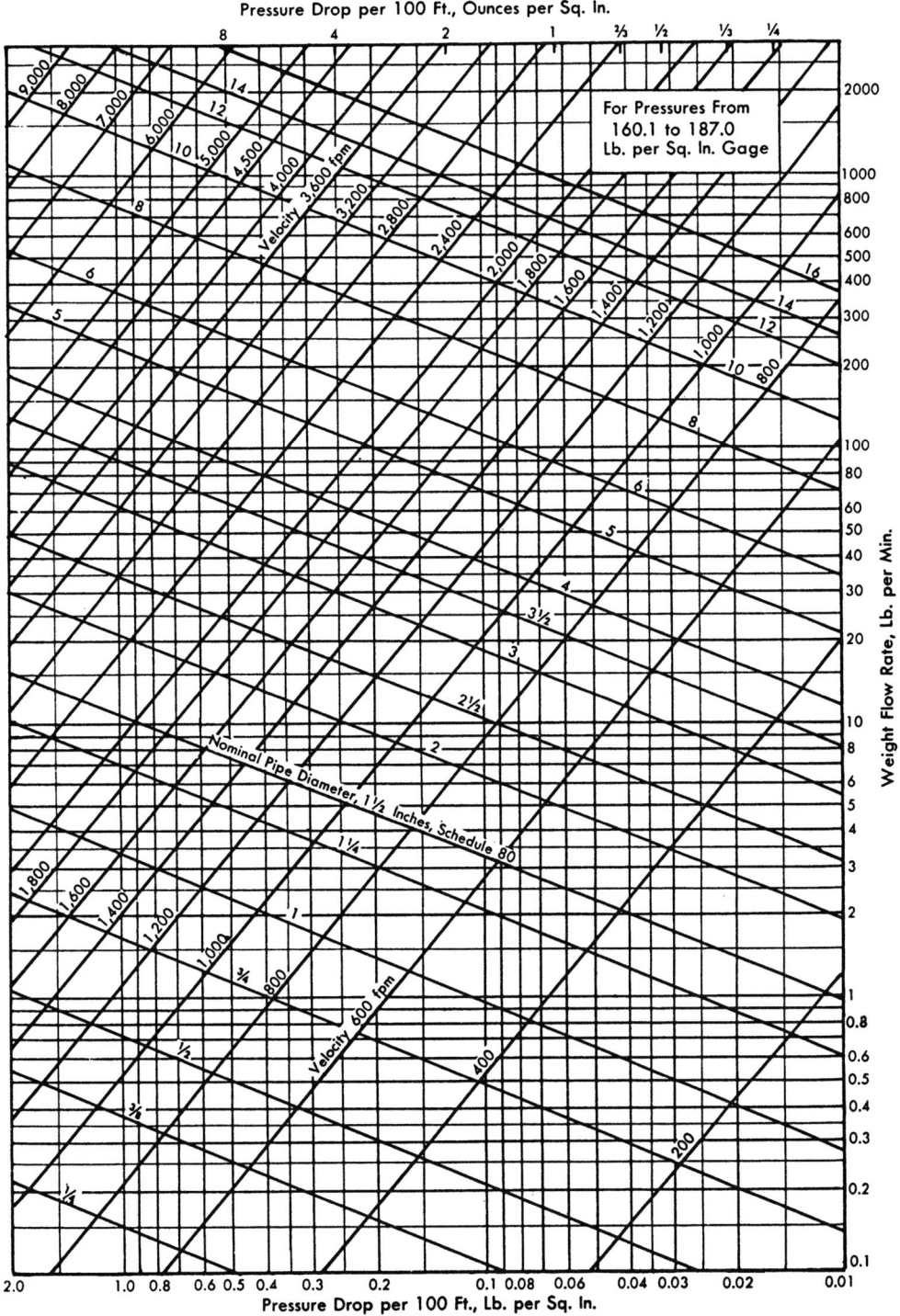

Fig 9-32. For pressure from 160.1 to 187.0 psig

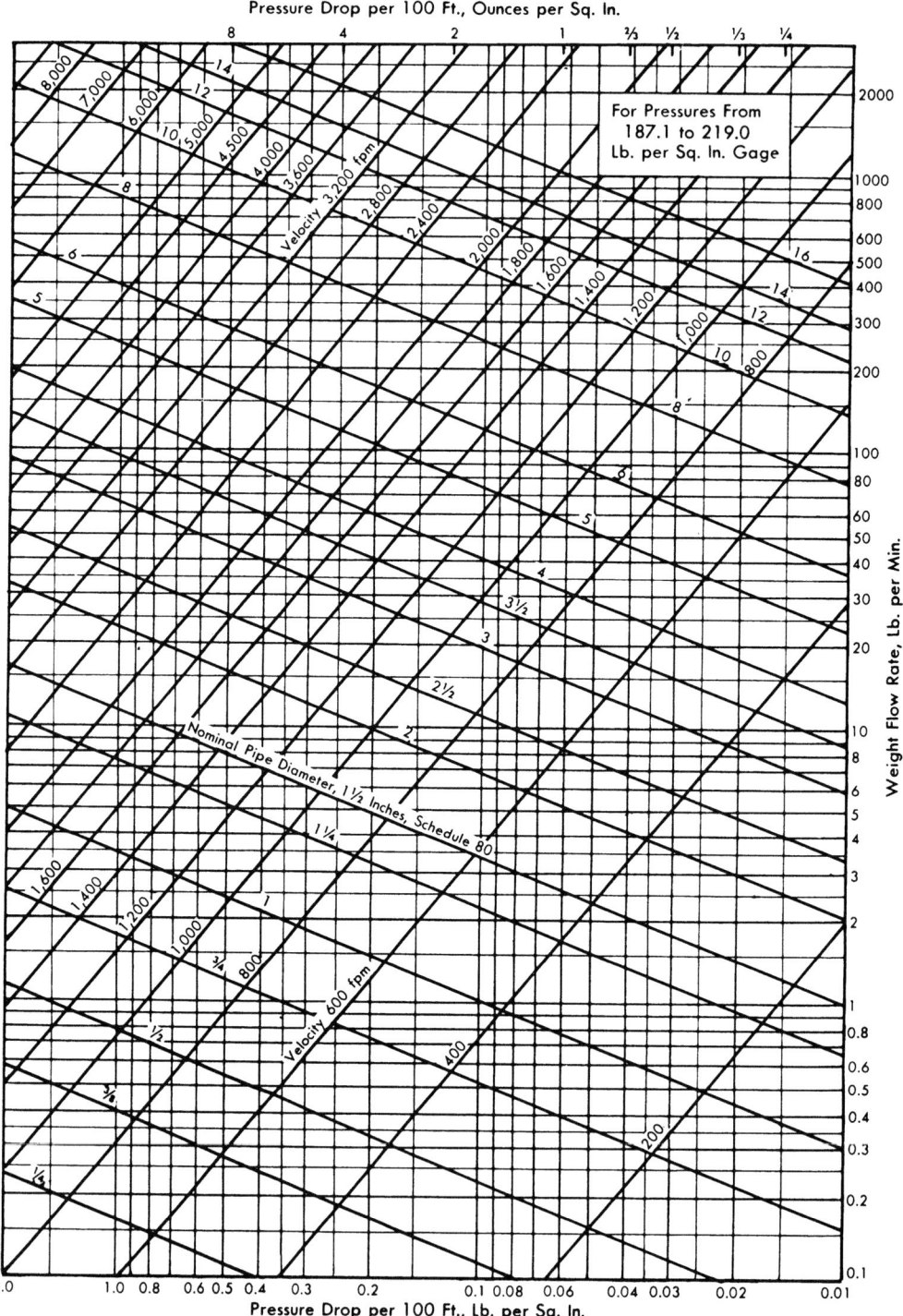

Fig 9-33. For pressure from 187.1 to 219.0 psig

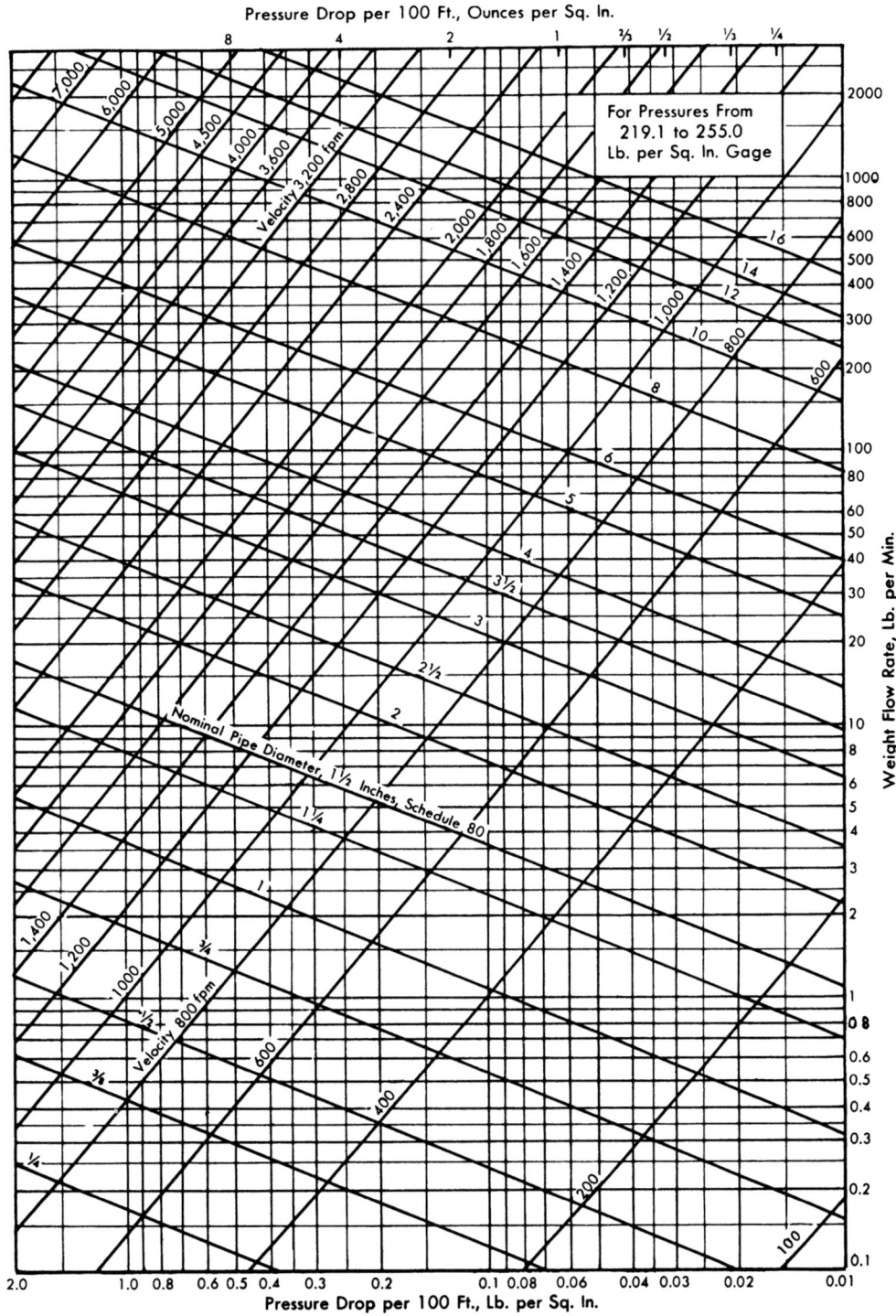

Fig 9-34. For pressure from 219.1 to 255.0 psig

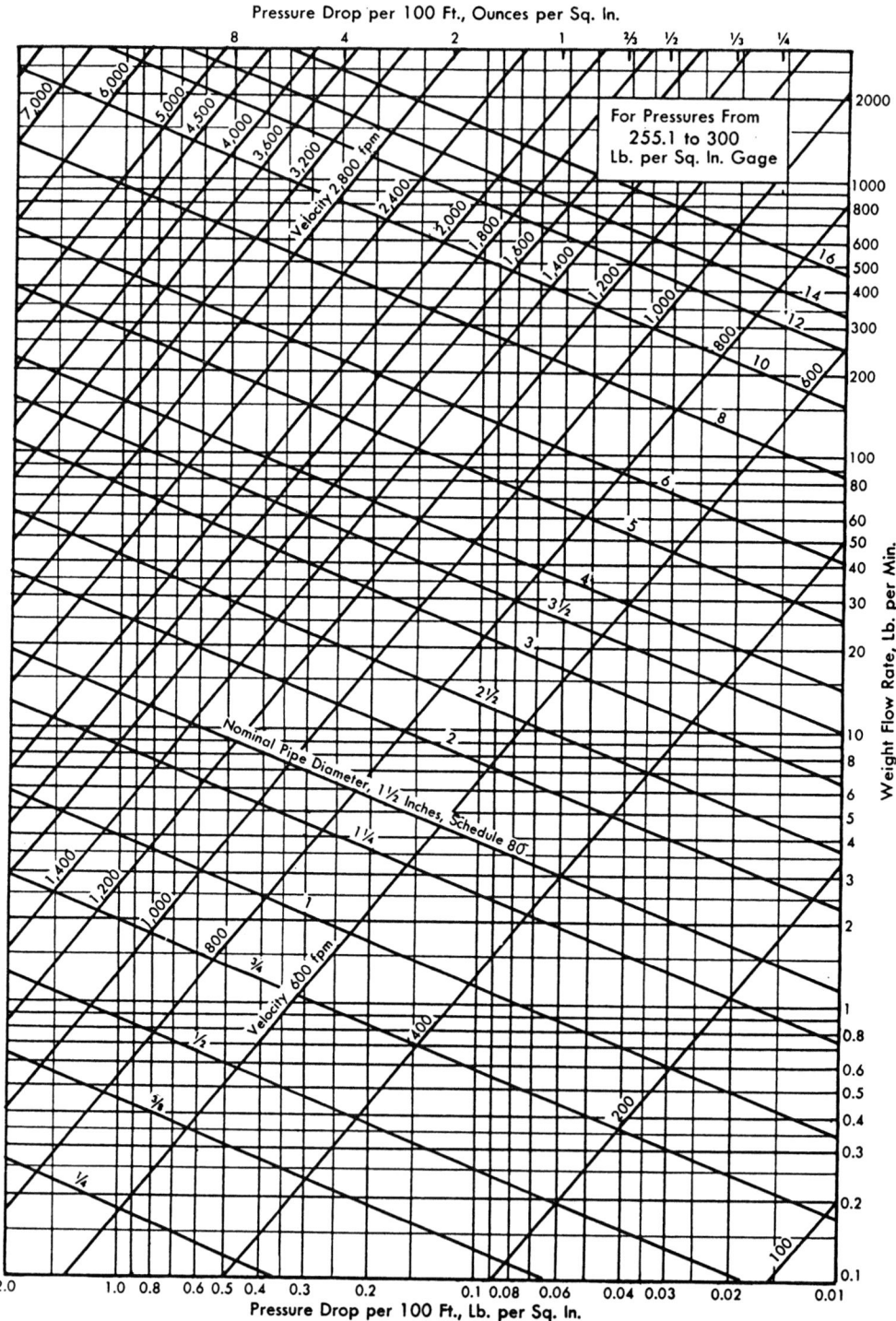

Fig 9-35. For pressure from 255.1 to 300.0 psig

Gas Piping For Buildings

Residential Piping.—Recommendations for the installation of gas piping in buildings other than industrial and commercial are given in ANSI-Z21.30 of the American National Standards Institute, sponsored by the American Gas Association. Among the provisions of this standard are the following:

These standards apply only to low pressure (not in excess of ½ psi) gas piping systems in buildings, extending from the gas meter outlet to the inlet connections of appliances, and the installation and operation of residential and commercial gas appliances supplied through such systems by public utilities. They are intended to cover the design, fabrication, installation, tests, and operation of such systems for fuel gases such as natural gas, manufactured gas, liquefied petroleum gas-air, or mixtures thereof. They are not intended to cover systems distributing undiluted liquefied petroleum gas. They are also not intended to cover systems or portions of systems supplying equipment engineered, designed, and installed for specific manufacturing, production processing and power generating applications, such as large and high pressure boilers, melting and treating furnaces, and production ovens. For piping in gas distribution systems, in gas manufacturing plants, in gas compressing stations, and in gas processing plants, refer to the latest edition of Code for Fuel Gas Piping, ANSI B31.2.

It is recommended that before installation of a gas piping system, a piping sketch or plan be prepared showing the proposed location of the piping as well as the size of different branches. Adequate consideration should be given to future demands and provisions made for added gas service.

Piping shall be of such size and so installed as to provide a supply of gas sufficient to meet the maximum demand without undue loss of pressure between the meter and the appliance or appliances. The size of gas pipe depends upon the following factors:

1) allowable loss in pressure from meter to appliance;
2) maximum gas consumption to be provided for;
3) length of pipe and number of fittings;
4) specific gravity of the gas; and
5) diversity factor.

It is recommended that the pressure loss in any piping system from the gas meter to any appliance at the maximum probable gas demand not exceed 0.3 inch water column.

The volume of gas to be provided for (in ft³/hr) shall be determined, whenever possible, directly from manufacturer Btu ratings, the appliances to be installed, and the heating value of the gas to be used.

Table 9-38. Gas Pipe Sizes, Low Pressures, Residential Piping (for Pressure Not Over ½ psig, Pressure Drop of 0.30 in. Water, and Gas of 0.60 Specific Gravity)

Total Length of Pipe, ft	Diameter of Pipe in. (IPS)									
	½	¾	1	1¼	1½	2	3	4	6	8
	Capacity in ft³/hr									
15	76	172	345	750	1220	2480	6500	13880	38700	99000
30	52	120	241	535	850	1780	4700	9700	27370	55850
45	43	99	199	435	700	475	3900	9900	23350	45600
60	38	86	173	380	610	1290	3450	6800	19330	39500
75	...	77	55	345	545	1120	3000	6000	17310	35300
90	...	70	14	310	490	1000	2700	5500	15800	32250
105	...	65	131	285	450	920	2450	5100	14620	29850
120	...	...	120	270	420	860	2300	4800	13680	29920
150	...	...	109	242	380	780	2090	4350	12240	25000
180	...	...	100	225	350	720	1950	4000	11160	22800
210	...	...	92	205	320	660	1780	3700	10330	21100
240	...	...	...	190	300	620	1680	3490	9600	19740
270	...	...	...	178	285	580	1580	3250	9000	186,0
300	...	...	...	70	270	545	1490	3000	8500	17660
450	...	...	...	140	226	450	1230	2500	7000	14420
600	...	...	...	119	192	390	1030	2130	6000	12480

Table 9-39. Multipliers to Be Used with Gas Pipe Sizing Tables for Various Specific Gravities

Specific Gravity	Multiplier	Specific Gravity	Multiplier
0.35	1.31	1.00	0.775
0.40	1.23	1.10	0.740
0.45	1.16	1.20	0.707
0.50	1.10	1.30	0.680
0.55	1.04	1.40	0.655
0.60	1.00	1.50	0.633
0.65	0.962	1.60	0.612
0.70	0.926	1.70	0.594
0.75	0.895	1.80	0.577
0.80	0.867	1.90	0.565
0.85	0.841	2.00	0.547
0.90	0.817	2.10	0.535

To obtain the ft³/hr of gas required divide the total Btu input of all appliances by the average Btu heating value per ft³ of the gas. The value of average Btu per ft³ of the gas in the area of installation may be obtained from the local gas company.

Capacities of different sizes and lengths of pipe in ft³/hr with a pressure drop of 0.3 inch of water column for gas of 0.60 specific gravity are shown in Table 9-38. In using this table, no allowance for an ordinary number of fittings is necessary.

Table 9-38 on residential gas pipeline capacities is based on the Pole formula:

$$Q = 1350\left(\frac{d^5 p}{0.33 Ls}\right)^{\frac{1}{2}}$$

where Q = flow in ft³/hr;
 d = nominal pipe diameter, in.;
 p = pressure drop, inches of water, over length L;
 L = length of pipe in ft; and
 s = specific gravity of gas.

Table 9-38 is a solution of this formula for various lengths L and pipe sizes when p is ½ inch, and s is 0.60. For other values of s, multiply the values of gas flow in the table by the multipliers given in Table 9-39.

The diversity factor is the percentage of the total connected load in use at any one time and is an important factor in determining the correct pipe size to be used in multifamily dwellings. It is dependent upon the number and kinds of gas appliances being installed. Consult the local gas company or the authority having jurisdiction for the diversity factor that should be used in sizing pipe.

Extensions to existing piping shall conform to the pipe capacity table. Existing piping shall be converted to the proper size of pipe where necessary. In no case shall extensions be made to existing pipe that is smaller than permitted by the pipe capacity table.

Gas piping in buildings shall be wrought iron or steel pipe complying with the American National Standard for Wrought Steel and Wrought Iron Pipe, ANSI-B36.10. The connecting of pipe by welding is permissible. Threaded pipe fittings (except stop cocks or valves) shall be malleable iron or steel when used with wrought iron or steel pipe. Where approved by the authority having jurisdiction, cast iron fittings in sizes 4 inches and larger may be used with wrought iron and steel pipe, and copper or brass pipe in iron pipe sizes assembled with threaded fittings of the same materials may be used with gases not corrosive to such materials.

Gas piping and fittings shall be clear and free from cutting burrs and defects in structure or threading and shall be thoroughly brushed and scale blown.

Pipe, fittings, valves, etc., removed from any existing installation shall not be reused until they have been thoroughly cleaned, inspected, and ascertained to be equivalent to new material.

No pipe smaller than standard ½ inch iron pipe size shall be used in any concealed location.

Concealed piping should be located in hollow rather than in solid partitions.

Piping in solid floors such as concrete shall be laid in channels in the floor suitably covered to permit access to the piping with a minimum of damage to the building. Piping in contact with earth or other material that may corrode the piping shall be protected against corrosion in an approved manner. Piping shall not be laid in cinders.

When piping that shall be concealed is installed, unions, running threads, right and left couplings, bushings, and swing joints made by combinations of fittings shall not be used.

When it is necessary to insert fittings in piping that has been installed in a concealed location, the piping may be reconnected by the use of a ground joint union with the nut center punched to prevent loosening by vibration.

The building structure shall not be weakened by the installation of any gas piping. Before any beams or joists are cut or notched, special permission should be obtained from the authority having jurisdiction.

All piping shall be graded not less than ¼ in. in 15 feet to prevent traps. All horizontal lines shall grade to risers and from the risers to the meter or to the appliance.

Gas piping shall not be supported by other piping but shall be supported to maintain proper grade with pipe hooks, metal pipe straps, bands, or hangers suitable for the size of pipe, and of proper strength and quality at proper intervals so that the piping cannot be moved accidentally from the installed position.

Spacing of supports in piping installations shall not be greater than the following:

½ inch pipe	6 feet
¾ inch or 1 inch pipe	8 feet
1¼ inch or longer (horizontal) pipe	10 feet
1¼ inch or longer (vertical) pipe	every floor level

Gas piping shall be protected against freezing temperatures. When piping must be exposed to wide ranges or sudden changes in temperatures, special care shall be taken to prevent stoppages.

Where there are overhanging kitchens or other rooms built beyond foundation walls in which gas appliances are installed, care shall be taken to avoid placing the piping where it will be exposed to low temperatures (40°F or below for manufactured gas) or to extreme changes of temperatures. In such cases the piping shall be brought up inside the building proper and run around the sides of the room in the most practical manner.

Pipe shall not be bent. Fittings shall be used when making turns in the gas piping.

A drip shall be provided at any point in the line of pipe where condensate may collect. Where condensation is excessive, a drip should be provided at the outlet of the meter. This drip should be so installed as to constitute a trap, where in an accumulation of condensate will shut off the flow of gas before it will run back into the meter.

All drips shall be installed only in such locations that they will be readily accessible to permit cleaning or emptying. A drip shall not be located where the condensate is likely to freeze. The size of any drip used shall be determined by the capacity and the exposure of the piping that drains to it and in accordance with recommendations of the local gas company.

A tee fitting with the bottom outlet plugged or capped instead of an elbow fitting shall be used at the bottom of any riser to catch any dirt or other foreign materials.

Gas pipe inside any building shall not be run in or through an air duct, clothes chute, chimney or flue, ventilating duct, dumb waiter or elevator shaft.

No device shall be placed inside the gas pipe or fittings that will reduce the cross-sectional area or otherwise obstruct the free flow of gas through the pipe and fittings.

All branch outlet pipes shall be taken from the top or sides of horizontal lines and not from the bottom. Where a branch outlet is placed on a main supply line before it is known what size of pipe will be connected to it, the outlet shall be of the same size as the line that supplies it.

Where piping is run from one building to another, it shall be adequately protected against freezing temperatures and shall be graded toward a suitable drip.

Where manufactured gas is distributed, underground piping shall be one size larger than that specified by the accompanying table, but in no case less than $1\frac{1}{4}$ inch.

Where local conditions require it, underground piping shall be protected against corrosion by coating or by other suitable means.

Lines supplying gas pilots for oil burning appliances shall be accessible, not less than $\frac{1}{2}$ inch standard pipe size and shall not be exposed to extreme temperatures.

In multiple tenant buildings supplied through a master meter, or where meters are not readily accessible from the appliance location, an individual shut-off valve for each apartment or for each separate house line shall be provided at a convenient point of general accessibility.

Before any system of gas piping is finally put in service, it shall be carefully tested to assure that it is gas tight. Where any part of the system is to be enclosed or concealed, this test should precede the work of closing in. To be tested for tightness the piping may be filled with city gas, air or inert gas but not with any other gas or liquid. In no case shall oxygen ever be used. The piping shall stand a pressure of at least 6 inches of mercury measured with a manometer or slope gage for a period of not less than 10 minutes without showing any drop in pressure.

Commercial-Industrial Piping.—The following are among the recommendations of American Gas Association for consumer-owned gas piping not covered by American National Standard Requirements for Gas Appliances and Gas Piping Installations, ANSI-Z21.30. They do not cover undiluted liquefied petroleum gas, but do cover natural gas, manufactured gas, liquefied petroleum gas-air or mixtures of these gases for industrial installations at any pressure, and all other nonresidential installations at operating pressures in excess of $\frac{1}{2}$ psig.

It is recommended that before designers proceed with the installation of a gas piping system, a piping sketch or plan be prepared showing the proposed location and size of the piping and the various loads. Adequate consideration should be given to future loads and provisions made for added gas service.

Piping other than entry shall not be buried underground inside of buildings. Avoid running piping through crawl spaces. Where gas piping must be run in crawl spaces, tunnels or unfrequented basements, continuous ventilation should be provided.

Piping in crawl spaces should be treated in the same manner as other above ground piping with respect to painting and insulation if necessary. Entering piping buried inside the building beyond the wall must be encased in a protective pipe of larger diameter. It is recommended that such casing extend at least 4 inches outside of the building wall, being left open at that point, and sealed at the inside end of the casing, and a removable threaded inspection plug be provided in the casing.

When it is practical to do so, outdoor gas piping in industrial plant yards should be installed above ground. Such piping must be securely supported and located where it will be protected from physical damage. Where soil conditions are unstable and settling of piping or foundation walls might occur, adequate measures shall be provided to prevent excessive stressing of the piping. Avoid locating piping in cinder fill.

Where the gas supply pressure is higher than that at which the gas utilization equipment is designed to operate, a gas pressure regulator shall be installed. Where used, gas pressure regulators should maintain the gas pressure to the burner supply line within plus or minus 10% of the operating gage pressure between maximum and minimum firing rates. These limitations do not apply to regulators known as "zero governors" used in connection with gas-air proportioning and mixing systems.

Regulators of the spring loaded, dead weight or pressure balanced type are preferred. Spring, weight loaded, or exposed lever type regulators must have springs, levers, and weights covered by a suitable housing.

Pressure regulators of the diaphragm type, except zero governors, generally require venting. An adequately sized independent vent to a safe point outside the building should be provided when the regulator is such that a ruptured diaphragm would cause a hazard. Means should likewise be provided to prevent water, insects or foreign materials from entering the vent pipe.

Standard weight or Schedule 40 steel pipe is acceptable and generally used for gas pressures up to 125 psig.

Welded joints should be used wherever practical. Compression or gland type fittings may be used if adequately braced so that neither the gas pressure nor external physical damage will force the joint apart. Pipe shall be fully inserted in gland or compression type of joints before assembly is completed. Screw fittings should be malleable cast iron, steel castings, or forgings. In sizes 4 inches and larger, cast iron fittings may be used.

Cast iron pipe of 4 inch size and larger equipped with standardized mechanical joints may be used for underground service for pressures up to 50 psig.

For gases containing sulphur compounds, copper and its alloys may prove unsuitable for gas piping. Consult the gas company before using these materials. For copper tubing, brazed (melting point over 1000°F) or flared joints should be used.

For copper and brass pipe, threaded or brazed joints (melting point over 1000°F) should be used. Compression or gland type couplings shall not be used in above ground installations.

Piping shall be of such a size and so installed as to provide a supply of gas sufficient to meet the requirements of demand and pressure at the point of use. The proper size depends upon the following factors:
  1) maximum gas consumption to be accommodated;
  2) diversity of load;
  3) allowable loss in pressure from the start of the pipe to the end;
  4) length of pipe and number and size of fittings, valves, and control devices;
  5) specific gravity of the gas; and
  6) allowance for any probable future change in consumption, specific gravity, or heating value of gas.

The volume of gas to be provided for (in ft³/hr) shall be determined directly from the manufacturer's input ratings of the equipment served. When input rating is not indicated, the gas company should be contacted for estimated volume of gas to be supplied.

Natural Gas Flow Tables: The following tables are designed primarily for use in sizing natural gas systems in industrial plants where, for safety reasons, gas pressures rarely exceed 20 psig. The accuracy of pipe sizing for natural gas in the pressure range 1–20 psig is satisfactory for use in architectural engineering and plant engineering offices.

The Weymouth formula, used for pipes 3 inches and larger in diameter, is

$$Q = 28d^{2.667}\sqrt{\left(\frac{(P_1^2 - P_2^2)}{GL}\right)\frac{520}{T}}$$

The Cox formula, used for pipes under 3 inches diameter, is

$$Q = 33.3\sqrt{\frac{(P_1^2 - P_2^2)d^5}{GL}}$$

where Q = rate of flow in ft³/hr;
  d = internal diameter of pipe in inch;
  L = length of pipe in miles;
  G = specific gravity of gas, here taken as 0.60 (air = 1.0);
  T = absolute temperature in °F of the flowing gas;
  P_1 = initial absolute pressure in psi; and
  P_2 = terminal absolute pressure in psi

Capacities of pipes to carry gas depend, among other things, on the altitude above sea level of the considered installation. Table 9-41a are computed for three specific altitudes, 500, 2500 and 4500 ft above sea level, and are sufficiently accurate within the three selected ranges 0 – 1500, 1500 –3500 and 3500 – 5500 ft above sea level.

Specific gravity of the gas is selected as 0.60 (air = 1.0). For gases having specific gravity other than 0.60, multiply pipe length by correction factor F appearing in Table 9-43.

To coincide with table parameters, express flow rate in ft³/hr (*cfh*), pressure in lbs/in² gage (psig), pipe diameter in inches, and length in feet. Equivalent resistance in fittings and valves, expressed in feet of straight pipe, should be added to the actual length of pipe.

Key to Solve Examples 1 to 7

	Follow Examples 1 to 7						
	1	2	3	4	5	6	7
Flow, ft³/hr	known	known	known	known	?	known	known
Pipe Length, ft	known	known	known	?	known	known	known
Initial pressure Psig	known	known	?	known	known	?	?
Pressure drop, psi	known	?	known	known	known	?	known
Pipe size, in.	?	known	known	known	known	known	?
Terminal pressure, psig	?	?	?	?	?	known	known
Specific gravity	0.60	0.60	0.60	0.60	0.60	other 0.60	0.60

Example 1: Given: flow 50000 ft³/hr of gas
  Pipe length 1000 ft
  Initial pressure 10 psig
  Pressure drop 1 psi
  Altitude of installation 500 ft above sea level
  Find: Pipe size

Solution: 1) From Table 9-41a the pressure drop factor corresponding to initial pressure of 10 psig and pressure drop of 1 psi is found to be 48.

2) Pressure drop factor for 100 ft is (48×100)/1000 = 4.8

3) Locate next smallest pressure drop factor per 100 ft to 4.8 from Tables 9-40c in the 50,000 ft³/hr row is 6" in.

Table 9-40a. Pressure Drop Factors for Use in Tables 9-41a to 9-42b

Flow ft³/hr	Nominal Pipe Diameter in.								
	½	¾	1	1¼	1½	2	2½	3	4
	(0.622)	(0.824)	(1.049)	(1.610)	(1.610)	(2.067)	(2.469)	(3.068)	(4.026)
	Pressure Drop Factor per 100 Feet of Pipe								
100	1.10	0.27	0.08	…	…	…	…	…	…
200	4.40	1.08	0.32	0.08	…	…	…	…	…
300	9.90	2.43	0.73	0.18	0.09	…	…	…	…
400	17.60	4.32	1.29	0.33	0.15	…	…	…	…
500	27.50	6.7	2.02	0.51	0.24	0.07	…	…	…
600	39.6	9.7	2.90	0.74	0.34	0.10	…	…	…
700	54.0	13.2	3.95	1.00	0.46	0.13	…	…	…
800	70.4	17.3	5.2	1.31	0.6 2	0.17	0.07	…	…
900	89.2	21.9	6.5	1.66	0.77	0.22	0.09	…	…
1000	100	27.0	8.1	2.05	0.95	0.27	0.11	…	…
1100	133	32.6	9.8	2.48	1.15	0.33	0.13	…	…
1200	159	38.9	11.6	2.95	1.36	0.39	0.16	…	…
1300	…	45.6	13.6	3.46	1.6	0.46	0.19	0.06	…
1400	…	52.9	15.8	4.01	1.86	0.53	0.22	0.07	…
1500	…	60.7	18.2	4.61	2.13	0.61	0.25	0.08	…
1600	…	69.1	20.7	5.2	2.43	0.70	0.29	0.09	…
1700	…	78.8	23.3	5.9	2.74	0.79	0.32	0.11	…
1800	…	87.4	26.1	6.6	3.07	0.88	0.36	0.12	…
1900	…	97.4	29.1	7.4	3.42	0.98	0.40	0.13	…
2000	…	108	32.3	8.2	3.79	1.09	0.45	0.15	…
2100	…	119	35.6	9.0	4.18	1.20	0.49	0.16	…
2200	…	132	39.1	9.9	4.58	1.32	0.54	0.18	…
2300	…	143	42.7	10.8	5.0	1.44	0.59	0.20	…
2400	…	…	46.5	11.8	5.5	1.57	0.64	0.21	…
2500	…	…	50.4	12.8	5.9	1.70	0.70	0.23	…
2600	…	…	54.5	13.8	6.4	1.84	0.76	0.25	…
2700	…	…	58.8	14.9	6.9	1.98	0.80	0.27	0.06
2800	…	…	63.2	16.1	7.4	2.13	0.88	0.29	0.07
2900	…	…	67.8	17.2	8.0	2.28	0.94	0.31	0.07
3000	…	…	72.6	18.4	8.5	2.44	1.01	0.33	0.08
3100	…	…	77.5	19.7	9.1	2.61	1.07	0.36	0.08
3200	…	…	82.6	21.0	9.7	2.78	1.14	0.38	0.09
3300	…	…	87.8	22.3	10.3	2.96	1.22	0.40	0.09
3400	…	…	93.3	23.7	11.0	3.14	1.29	0.43	0.10
3500	…	…	98.8	25.1	11.6	3.33	1.37	0.45	0.11
3600	…	…	105	26.5	12.3	3.52	1.45	0.48	0.11
3700	…	…	110	28.0	13.0	3.72	1.53	0.51	0.12
3800	…	…	116	29.6	13.7	3.92	1.61	0.53	0.13
3900	…	…	123	31.2	14.4	4.13	1.70	0.56	0.13
4000	…	…	129	32.8	15.2	4.35	1.79	0.59	0.14
4100	…	…	136	34.4	15.9	4.57	1.88	0.62	0.15
4200	…	…	…	36.1	16.7	4.79	1.97	0.65	0.15
4300	…	…	…	37.9	17.5	5.5	2.07	0.68	0.16
4400	…	…	…	39.6	18.3	5.3	2.16	0.72	0.17
4500	…	…	…	41.5	19.2	5.5	2.26	0.75	0.18
4600	…	…	…	43.3	20.0	5.8	2.36	0.78	0.18
4700	…	…	…	45.2	20.9	6.0	2.47	0.82	0.19

Table 9-40b. (continued) Pressure Drop Factors for Use in Tables 9-41a to 9-42b

Flow ft³/hr	Nominal Pipe Diameter, in.							
	1¼	1½	2	2½	3	4	6	8
	(1.260)	(1.610)	(2.067)	(2.469)	(3.068)	(4.026)	(6.065)	(7.981)
	Pressure Drop Factor per 100 ft of Pipe							
5200	55.4	25.6	7.3	3.02	1.0	0.24	...	...
5400	59.7	27.6	7.9	3.26	1.08	0.25	...	...
5600	64.2	29.7	8.5	3.50	1.16	0.27	...	...
5800	69.0	31.9	9.1	3.76	1.25	0.29	...	...
6000	73.8	41.3	9.8	4.02	1.33	0.31	...	...
6200	78.8	36.4	10.4	4.29	1.42	0.34	...	...
6400	84.0	38.8	11.1	4.57	1.51	0.36	...	...
6600	89.3	41.3	11.8	4.87	1.61	0.38	...	...
6800	94.8	43.8	12.6	5.2	1.71	0.40	...	...
7000	100	46.4	13.3	5.5	1.81	0.43	...	...
7200	106	49.1	14.1	5.8	1.92	0.45	...	...
7400	112	51.9	14.9	6.1	2.02	0.48	...	...
7600	118	54.7	15.7	6.5	2.13	0.50	...	...
7800	125	57.6	16.5	6.8	2.24	0.53	...	...
8000	131	60.6	17.4	7.2	2.37	0.56	...	...
8200	138	63.7	18.3	7.5	2.49	0.58	...	...
8400	...	66.8	19.2	7.9	2.61	0.61	...	...
8600	...	70.0	20.1	8.3	2.73	0.64	0.07	...
8800	...	73.3	21.0	8.7	2.86	0.67	0.08	...
9000	...	76.7	22.0	9.1	3.0	0.70	0.08	...
9200	...	80.2	23.0	9.5	3.13	0.74	0.08	...
9400	...	83.7	24.0	9.9	3.27	0.77	0.09	...
9600	...	87.3	25.0	10.3	3.41	0.8	0.09	...
9800	...	90.9	26.1	10.8	3.55	0.83	0.09	...
10000	...	94.7	27.2	11.2	3.70	0.87	0.10	...
11000	...	115	32.9	13.5	4.47	1.05	0.12	...
12000	...	136	39.1	16.1	5.3	1.25	0.14	...
13000	...	...	45.9	18.9	6.3	1.47	0.17	...
14000	...	...	53.2	21.9	7.2	1.70	0.18	...
15000	...	...	61.1	25.1	8.3	1.95	0.22	...
16000	...	...	69.6	28.6	9.5	2.22	0.25	...
17000	...	...	78.5	32.3	10.7	2.51	0.28	...
18000	...	...	88	36.2	12.0	2.81	0.32	0.07
19000	...	...	98	40.3	13.3	3.14	0.35	0.08
20000	...	...	109	44.7	14.8	3.47	0.39	0.09
21000	...	...	120	49.3	16.3	3.83	0.43	0.1
22000	...	...	131	54.1	17.9	4.20	0.47	0.11
23000	...	...	144	59.1	19.6	4.59	0.52	0.12
24000	...	...	...	64.3	21.3	5.00	0.56	0.13
25000	...	...	...	69.8	23.1	5.4	0.61	0.14
26000	...	...	...	75.5	25.0	5.9	0.66	0.15
27000	...	...	...	81.4	27.0	6.3	0.71	0.17
28000	...	...	...	87.6	29.0	6.8	0.77	0.18
29000	...	...	...	93.9	31.1	7.3	0.82	0.19
30000	...	...	...	101	33.3	7.8	0.88	0.20
31000	...	...	...	107	35.5	8.4	0.94	0.22
32000	...	...	...	114	37.9	8.9	1.0	0.23
33000	...	...	...	122	40.3	9.5	1.07	0.25
34000	...	...	...	129	42.7	10.0	1.13	0.26
35000	...	...	...	137	45.3	10.6	1.20	0.28

Table 9-40c. (continued) Pressure Drop Factors for Use in Tables 9-41a to 9-42b

Flow ft³/hr	Nominal Pipe Diameter, in.							
	3	4	6	8	10	12	14	16
	3.068	4.026	(6.065)	7.981	(10.02)	(12.00)	(13.25)	(15.25)
	Pressure Drop Factor per 100 ft of Pipe							
36000	47.9	11.3	1.27	0.29	...	...	...	...
37000	50.6	11.9	1.34	0.31	0.09	...	...	...
38000	53.4	12.5	1.41	0.33	0.10	...	...	...
39000	56.2	13.2	1.49	0.35	0.10	...	...	...
40000	59.1	13.9	1.57	0.36	0.11	...	...	...
41000	62.1	14.6	1.65	0.38	0.11	...	...	...
42000	65.2	15.3	1.73	0.40	0.12	...	...	...
43000	68.3	16.1	1.81	0.42	0.13	...	...	...
44000	71.6	16.8	1.89	0.44	0.13	...	...	...
45000	74.8	17.6	1.98	0.46	0.14	...	...	...
46000	78.2	18.4	2.07	0.48	0.14	...	...	...
47000	81.6	19.2	2.16	0.50	0.15	...	...	...
48000	85.2	20.0	2.25	0.52	0.16	...	...	...
49000	88.7	20.9	2.35	0.55	0.16	...	...	...
50000	92.4	21.7	2.44	0.57	0.17	...	...	...
52000	99.9	23.5	2.64	0.61	0.18	...	...	...
54000	108	25.3	2.85	0.66	0.20	...	...	...
56000	116	27.2	3.07	0.71	0.21	...	...	...
58000	124	29.2	3.29	0.76	0.23	...	...	...
60000	133	31.3	3.32	0.82	0.24	...	...	...
62000	142	33.9	3.76	0.87	0.26	...	...	...
64000	...	35.6	4.00	0.93	0.28	...	...	...
66000	...	37.8	4.26	0.99	0.29	...	...	...
68000	...	40.2	4.52	1.05	0.31	...	...	...
70000	...	42.6	4.79	1.11	0.33	...	...	...
72000	...	45.0	5.1	1.18	0.35	0.13	...	...
74000	...	47.6	5.4	1.24	0.37	0.14	...	...
76000	...	50.2	5.7	1.31	0.39	0.15	...	...
78000	...	52.8	6.0	1.38	0.41	0.16	...	...
80000	...	55.6	6.3	1.45	0.43	0.17	...	...
82000	...	58.4	6.6	1.52	0.45	0.17	...	...
84000	...	61.3	6.9	1.6	0.47	0.18	...	...
86000	...	64.2	7.2	1.68	0.50	0.19	...	...
88000	...	67.3	7.6	1.76	0.52	0.20	...	...
90000	...	70.3	7.9	1.84	0.55	0.21	...	...
92000	...	73.5	8.3	1.92	0.57	0.22	...	...
94000	...	76.7	8.6	2.00	0.59	0.23	...	...
96000	...	80.0	9.0	2.00	0.62	0.24	...	...
98000	...	83.4	9.4	2.18	0.65	0.25	...	...
100000	...	86.9	9.8	2.27	0.67	0.26	0.15	...
110000	...	105	11.8	2.74	0.81	0.31	0.18	...
120000	...	125	14.1	3.27	0.97	0.37	0.22	...
130000	...	147	16.5	3.83	1.14	0.44	0.26	...
140000	...	...	19.2	4.45	1.32	0.50	0.30	0.14
150000	...	...	22.0	5.1	1.51	0.58	0.34	0.16
160000	...	...	25.0	5.8	1.72	0.66	0.39	0.18
170000	...	...	28.3	6.6	1.95	0.74	0.44	0.21
180000	...	...	31.7	7.4	2.18	0.83	0.49	0.23
190000	...	...	35.3	8.2	2.43	0.93	0.55	0.26
200000	...	...	39.1	9.1	2.69	1.03	0.61	0.29

Table 9-40d. (continued) Pressure Drop Factors for Use in Tables 9-41a to 9-42b

Flow ft³/hr	Nominal Pipe Diameter, in.							
	6	8	10	12	14	16	18	20
	(6.065)	(7.981)	(10.02)	(12)	(13.25)	(15.25)	17.25	(19.25)
	Pressure Drop Factor per 100 ft of Pipe							
210000	43.1	10.0	2.97	1.14	0.67	0.32	…	…
220000	47.3	11.0	3.26	1.25	0.73	0.35	0.18	0.1
230000	51.7	12.0	3.56	1.36	0.80	0.38	0.20	0.11
240000	56.3	13.1	3.88	1.48	0.87	0.41	0.21	0.12
250000	61.1	14.2	4.20	1.61	0.95	0.45	0.23	0.13.
260000	66.1	15.3	4.55	1.74	1.03	0.49	0.25	0.14
270000	71.3	16.5	4.91	1.88	1.11	0.52	0.27	0.15
280000	76.7	17.8	5.53	2.02	1.19	0.56	0.20	0.16
290000	82.2	19.1	5.7	2.17	1.28	0.6	0.31	0.17
300000	88.0	20.4	6.1	2.32	1.37	0.65	0.33	0.19
310000	94.0	21.8	6.5	2.47	1.46	0.69	0.36	0.20
320000	100	23.2	6.9	2.64	1.55	0.73	0.38	0.21
330000	106	24.7	7.3	2.8	1.65	0.78	0.41	0.23
340000	113	26.2	7.8	2.98	1.75	0.83	0.43	0.24
350000	120	27.8	8.2	3.15	1.86	0.88	0.46	0.25
360000	127	29.4	8.7	3.34	1.97	0.93	0.48	0.27
370000	134	31.1	9.2	3.52	2.08	0.98	0.51	0.28
380000	141	32.8	9.7	3.72	2.19	1.04	0.54	0.30
390000	…	34.5	10.2	3.92	2.31	1.09	0.57	0.32
400000	…	36.3	10.8	4.12	2.43	1.15	0.6	0.33
420000	…	40.0	11.9	4.54	2.68	1.27	0.66	0.37
440000	…	43.9	13.0	4.98	2.94	1.39	0.72	0.4
460000	…	48	14.2	5.5	3.21	1.52	0.79	0.44
480000	…	52.3	15.5	5.9	3.5	1.65	0.86	0.48
500000	…	56.7	16.8	6.4	3.79	1.79	0.93	0.52
520000	…	61.3	18.2	7.0	4.10	1.94	1.00	0.56
540000	…	66.1	19.7	7.5	4.43	2.1	1.08	0.60
560000	…	71.1	21.1	8.1	4.76	2.25	1.17	0.65
580000	…	76.3	22.6	8.7	5.1	2.41	1.25	0.70
600000	…	81.6	24.2	9.3	5.5	2.58	1.34	0.75
620000	…	87.2	25.9	9.9	5.8	2.76	1.43	0.80
640000	…	92.9	27.6	10.5	6.2	2.94	1.52	0.85
660000	…	98.8	29.3	11.2	6.6	3.13	1.62	0.90
680000	…	105	31.1	11.9	7.0	3.32	1.72	0.96
700000	…	111	33.0	12.6	7.4	3.52	1.82	1.02
720000	…	118	34.9	13.3	7.9	3.72	1.93	1.08
740000	…	124	36.9	14.1	8.3	3.93	2.04	1.14
760000	…	131	38.9	14.9	8.8	4.14	2.15	1.20
780000	…	138	41.0	15.7	9.2	4.37	2.26	1.26
800000	…	…	43.1	16.5	9.7	4.59	2.38	1.33
820000	…	…	45.3	17.3	10.2	4.83	2.5	1.39
840000	…	…	47.5	18.2	10.7	5.1	2.63	1.46
860000	…	…	49.8	19.0	11.2	5.3	2.75	1.53
580000	…	…	52.1	20.0	11.8	5.6	2.88	1.61
900000	…	…	54.5	20.9	12.3	5.8	3.02	1.68
920000	…	…	57.0	21.8	12.8	6.1	3.15	1.76
940000	…	…	59.5	22.8	13.4	6.3	3.29	1.83
960000	…	…	62.0	23.37	14.0	6.6	3.43	1.91
980000	…	…	64.6	24.7	14.6	6.9	3.57	1.99
1000000	…	…	67.3	25.58	15.2	7.2	3.72	2.07

Table 9-41a. Pressure Drop of Gas in Pipe, Initial Pressure Known

Altitude, ft	Initial Pressure, psig																					
3500-5500	1	2	3	4	5	6	7	8	9	10	11	12	13	14	15	16	17	18	19	20	21	22
1500-3500		1	2	3	4	5	6	7	8	9	10	11	12	13	14	15	16	17	18	19	20	21
0-1500			1	2	3	4	5	6	7	8	9	10	11	12	13	14	15	16	17	18	19	20
Pressure Drop, psi	Pressure Drop Factor (From Tables 9-40a to 9-40d)																					
0.1	3	3	3	3	3	4	4	4	4	4	5	5	5	5	5	6	6	6	6	6	7	7
0.2	5	6	6	7	7	7	8	8	9	9	9	10	10	11	11	11	12	12	13	13	13	13
0.3	8	9	9	10	10	11	12	12	13	13	14	15	15	16	16	17	18	18	19	19	20	20
0.4	11	11	12	13	14	15	15	16	17	18	19	19	20	21	22	23	23	24	25	26	27	27
0.5	13	14	15	16	17	18	19	20	21	22	23	24	25	26	27	28	29	30	31	32	33	34
0.6	...	17[a]	18[b]	19	21	22	23	24	25	27	28	29	30	31	33	34	35	36	37	39	40	41
0.7	...	20[a]	21[b]	22	24	25	27	28	29	31	32	34	35	36	38	39	41	42	43	45	46	48
0.8	...	22[a]	24[b]	26	27	29	30	32	34	35	37	38	40	42	43	45	46	48	50	51	53	54
0.9	...	25[a]	27[b]	29	31	32	34	36	38	40	41	43	45	47	49	50	52	54	56	58	59	61
1.0	...	28[a]	30[b]	32	34	36	38	40	42	44	46	48	50	52	54	56	58	60	62	64	66	68
1.1	...	30[a]	33[b]	35	37	39	41	44	46	48	50	52	55	57	59	61	63	66	68	70	72	75
1.2	...	33[a]	36[b]	38	40	43	45	48	50	52	55	57	60	62	64	67	69	72	74	76	79	81
1.3	...	36[a]	38[b]	41	44	46	49	51	54	57	59	62	65	67	70	72	75	77	80	83	85	88
1.4	...	38[a]	41[b]	44	47	50	52	55	58	61	64	66	69	72	75	78	80	83	86	89	92	94
1.5	...	41[a]	44[b]	47	50	53	56	59	62	65	68	71	74	77	80	83	86	89	92	98	98	101
1.6	...	...	47[a]	50[b]	53	36	60	63	66	69	72	76	79	82	85	88	92	95	98	101	104	108
1.7	...	...	49[a]	53[b]	56	60	63	66	70	73	77	80	83	87	90	94	97	100	104	107	111	114
1.8	...	...	52[a]	56[b]	59	63	67	70	74	77	81	85	88	92	95	99	103	106	110	113	117	120
1.9	...	...	55[a]	59[b]	63	66	70	74	78	82	85	89	93	97	101	104	108	112	116	120	123	127
2.0	...	...	58[a]	62[b]	66	70	74	78	82	86	90	94	98	102	106	110	113	118	122	126	130	134
2.1	...	...	60[a]	64[b]	69	73	77	81	85	90	94	98	102	106	111	115	119	123	127	132	136	140
2.2	...	...	63[a]	67[b]	72	76	81	85	89	94	98	103	107	111	116	120	125	129	133	138	142	147
2.3	...	...	66[a]	70[b]	75	79	84	89	93	98	102	107	112	116	121	125	130	135	139	144	148	153
2.4	...	...	68[a]	73[b]	78	83	87	92	87	102	107	111	116	121	126	131	135	140	145	150	155	159
2.5	...	...	71[a]	76[b]	81	86	91	96	101	106	111	116	121	126	131	136	141	146	151	156	161	166
2.6	...	...	...	79[a]	84[b]	89	94	99	105	110	115	120	125	131	136	141	146	151	157	162	167	172
2.7	...	...	...	81[a]	87[b]	92	97	103	108	114	119	124	130	135	141	146	151	157	162	168	173	178
2.8	...	...	...	84[a]	90[b]	95	101	106	112	118	123	129	134	140	146	151	157	162	168	174	179	185
2.9	...	...	...	87[a]	93[b]	98	104	110	116	122	127	133	139	145	151	155	162	168	174	180	185	191
3.0	...	...	...	89[a]	95[b]	101	107	113	119	125	131	137	143	149	155	161	167	173	179	185	191	197
3.1	...	...	...	92[a]	98[b]	104	111	117	123	129	135	142	148	154	160	166	173	179	185	191	197	204
3.2	...	...	...	95[a]	101[b]	108	114	120	127	133	139	146	152	159	165	171	178	184	191	197	203	210
3.3	...	...	...	97[a]	104[b]	111	117	124	130	137	143	150	157	163	170	176	183	190	196	203	209	216
3.4	...	...	...	100[a]	107[b]	114	120	127	134	141	147	154	161	168	175	181	188	195	202	209	215	222
3.5	...	...	...	103[a]	110[b]	117	124	131	138	145	151	159	166	173	180	186	194	201	208	215	221	228
3.6	...	...	...	...	112[a]	120[b]	127	134	141	148	155	163	170	177	184	191	199	206	213	220	227	234
3.7	...	...	...	...	115[a]	122[b]	130	137	145	152	159	167	174	182	189	196	204	211	219	226	233	241
3.8	...	...	...	...	118[a]	125[b]	133	141	148	156	163	171	179	186	194	201	209	217	224	232	239	247
3.9	...	...	...	...	121[a]	128[b]	136	144	152	160	167	175	183	191	199	206	214	222	230	238	245	253
4.0	...	...	...	...	123[a]	131[b]	139	147	155	163	171	179	187	195	203	211	219	227	235	243	251	259
4.1	...	...	...	...	126[a]	134[b]	142	150	159	167	175	183	191	200	208	216	224	232	241	249	257	265
4.2	...	...	...	...	129[a]	137[b]	145	154	162	171	179	187	196	204	213	221	229	238	246	255	263	271
4.3	...	...	...	...	131[a]	140[b]	148	157	166	174	183	191	200	209	217	226	234	243	252	260	269	277
4.4	...	...	...	...	134[a]	143[b]	151	160	169	178	187	195	204	213	222	231	239	248	257	266	275	283
4.5	...	...	...	...	136[a]	145[b]	154	163	172	181	190	199	208	217	226	235	244	253	262	271	280	289
4.6	...	...	...	...	...	148[a]	157[b]	167	176	185	194	203	213	222	231	240	249	259	268	277	286	295
4.7	...	...	...	...	...	151[a]	160[b]	170	179	188	198	207	217	226	235	245	254	264	273	282	292	301
4.8	...	...	...	...	...	153[a]	163[b]	173	182	192	202	211	221	230	240	250	259	260	278	288	298	307
4.9	...	...	...	...	...	156[a]	166[b]	176	186	196	205	215	225	235	245	254	264	274	284	294	303	313
5.0	...	...	...	...	...	159[a]	169[b]	179	189	199	209	219	229	239	249	259	269	279	289	299	309	319

[a] This figure valid for altitudes of 1500–3500 and 3500–5500 feet above sea level only.
[b] This figure valid for altitudes of 3500–5500 feet above sea level only.

Table 9-41b. Pressure Drop of Gas in Pipe, Initial Pressure Known

Altitude, ft	Initial Pressure, psig															
3500–5500	7	8	9	10	11	12	13	14	15	16	17	18	19	20	21	22
1500–3500	6	7	8	9	10	11	12	13	14	15	16	17	18	19	20	21
0–1500	5	6	7	8	9	10	11	12	13	14	15	16	17	18	19	20
Pressure Drop, psi	Pressure Drop Factor (From Tables 9-40a to 9-40d)															
5.1	172[a]	182[b]	192	202	213	223	233	243	253	264	274	284	294	304	315	325
5.2	175[a]	185[b]	196	206	216	227	237	248	258	268	299	289	300	310	320	331
5.3	178[a]	188[b]	199	209	220	231	241	252	262	273	284	294	305	315	326	337
5.4	180[a]	191[b]	202	213	224	234	245	256	267	278	288	299	310	321	332	343
5.5	183[a]	194[b]	205	216	227	238	249	260	271	282	292	304	315	326	337	348
5.6	186[a]	197[b]	208	220	231	242	253	264	276	287	297	309	320	332	343	354
5.7	189[a]	200[b]	211	223	234	246	257	268	280	291	302	314	325	337	348	360
5.8	191[a]	203[b]	215	226	238	249	261	273	284	296	307	319	331	342	354	365
5.9	194[a]	206[b]	218	230	241	253	265	277	289	300	312	324	336	348	359	371
6.0	197[a]	209[b]	221	233	245	257	269	281	293	305	317	329	341	353	365	377
6.1	...	212[a]	224[b]	236	248	260	273	285	297	309	321	334	346	358	370	383
6.2	...	215[a]	227[b]	239	252	264	277	289	301	314	326	339	351	363	376	388
6.3	...	217[a]	230[b]	243	255	268	280	293	306	318	331	343	356	369	381	394
6.4	...	220[a]	233[b]	246	259	271	284	297	310	323	335	348	361	374	387	399
6.5	...	223[a]	236[b]	249	262	275	288	301	314	327	340	353	366	379	392	405
6.6	...	225[a]	239[b]	252	265	279	292	305	318	331	345	358	371	384	397	411
6.7	...	228[a]	242[b]	255	269	282	295	309	322	336	349	362	376	389	403	416
6.8	...	231[a]	245[b]	258	272	286	299	313	326	340	354	367	381	394	408	422
6.9	...	234[a]	248[b]	262	275	289	303	317	330	344	358	372	386	400	413	428
7.0	...	237[a]	251[b]	265	279	293	307	321	335	349	363	377	391	405	419	433
7.1	...	...	253[a]	268[b]	282	296	310	324	339	353	367	381	395	410	424	438
7.2	...	...	256[a]	271[b]	285	300	314	328	343	357	372	386	400	415	429	443
73	...	...	259[a]	274[b]	288	303	318	332	347	361	376	391	404	420	434	449
7.4	...	...	262[a]	277[b]	292	306	321	336	351	366	380	395	409	425	440	454
7.5	...	...	265[a]	280[b]	295	310	325	340	355	370	385	400	414	430	445	460
7.6	...	...	268[a]	283[b]	298	313	328	344	359	374	389	404	419	435	450	465
7.7	...	...	270[a]	286[b]	301	316	332	347	363	378	393	409	424	440	455	470
7.8	...	...	273[a]	289[b]	304	320	335	351	367	382	398	413	429	445	460	476
7.9	...	...	276[a]	292[b]	307	323	339	355	371	386	402	418	434	449	465	481
8	...	...	278[a]	294[b]	310	326	342	358	374	390	406	422	438	454	470	486
8.1	...	...	...	297[a]	313[b]	330	346	362	378	394	411	427	443	459	475	492
8.2	...	...	...	300[a]	316[b]	333	349	366	382	398	415	431	448	464	480	497
8.3	...	...	...	303[a]	319[b]	336	353	369	386	402	419	436	452	469	485	502
8.4	...	...	...	306[a]	322[b]	339	356	373	390	406	423	440	457	474	490	507
8.5	...	...	...	309[a]	325[b]	343	360	377	394	410	428	445	462	479	495	512
8.6	...	...	...	311[a]	328[b]	346	363	380	397	414	432	449	466	483	500	518
8.7	...	...	...	314[a]	331[b]	349	366	384	401	418	436	453	471	488	505	523
8.8	...	...	...	317[a]	334[b]	352	370	387	405	422	440	458	475	493	510	528
8.9	...	...	...	320[a]	337[b]	355	373	391	409	426	444	462	480	498	515	533
9.0	...	...	...	322[a]	340[b]	358	376	394	412	430	448	466	484	502	520	538
9.1	...	...	...	...	343[a]	361[b]	379	398	416	434	452	470	489	507	525	543
9.2	...	...	...	...	346[a]	364[b]	383	401	420	438	456	475	493	512	530	548
9.3	...	...	...	...	349[a]	367[b]	386	405	423	442	460	479	498	516	535	553
9.4	...	...	...	...	352[a]	370[b]	389	408	427	446	464	483	502	521	540	558
9.5	...	...	...	...	354[a]	373[b]	392	411	430	449	468	487	506	525	544	563
9.6	...	...	...	...	357[a]	376[b]	396	415	434	453	472	492	511	530	549	567
9.7	...	...	...	...	360[a]	379[b]	399	418	437	457	476	496	515	534	554	573
9.8	...	...	...	...	363[a]	382[b]	402	421	441	461	480	500	519	539	559	578
9.9	...	...	...	...	365[a]	385[b]	405	425	445	464	484	504	524	544	563	583
10.0	...	...	...	...	368[a]	388[b]	408	428	448	468	488	508	528	548	568	588

[a] This figure valid for altitudes of 3500-5500 feet above sea level only.
[b] This figure valid for altitudes of 1500-3500 and 3500-5500 feet above sea level only.

Table 9-42a. Pressure Drop of Gas in Pipe, Terminal Pressure Known

Altitude, ft	Initial Pressure, psig																					
3500-5500	1	2	3	4	5	6	7	8	9	10	11	12	13	14	15	16	17	18	19	20	21	22
1500-3500		1	2	3	4	5	6	7	8	9	10	1 1	12	13	14	15	16	17	18	19	20	21
0-1500			1	2	3	4	5	6	7	8	9	10	11	12	13	14	15	16	17	18	19	20
Pressure Drop, psi	Pressure Drop Factor (From Tables 9-40a to 9-40d)																					
0.1	3	3	3	3	3	4	4	4	4	4	5	5	5	5	5	6	6	6	6	6	7	7
0.2	5	6	6	7	7	7	8	8	9	9	9	10	10	11	11	11	12	12	13	13	13	14
0.3	8	9	9	10	11	11	12	12	13	14	14	15	15	16	17	17	28	18	19	20	20	21
0.4	11	12	12	13	14	15	16	16	17	18	19	20	20	21	22	23	24	24	25	26	27	28
0.5	14	15	16	17	18	19	20	21	22	23	24	25	26	27	28	29	30	31	32	33	34	35
0.6	16	18	19	20	21	22	24	25	26	27	28	30	31	32	33	34	36	37	38	39	40	42
0.7	19	21	22	23	25	26	28	29	30	32	33	35	36	37	39	40	42	43	44	46	47	49
0.8	22	24	25	27	28	30	32	33	35	36	38	40	41	43	44	46	48	49	51	52	54	56
0.9	25	27	29	30	32	34	36	38	39	41	43	45	47	48	50	52	54	56	57	59	61	63
1.0	28	30	32	34	36	38	40	42	44	46	48	50	52	54	56	58	60	62	64	66	68	70
1.1	31	33	35	37	39	42	44	46	48	50	53	55	57	59	61	64	66	68	70	72	75	77
1.2	34	36	38	41	43	46	48	50	53	55	58	60	62	65	67	70	72	74	77	79	82	84
1.3	37	39	42	44	47	50	52	55	57	60	63	65	68	70	73	76	78	81	83	86	89	91
1.4	39	42	45	48	51	53	56	59	62	65	67	70	73	76	79	81	84	87	90	93	95	98
1.5	42	45	48	51	54	57	60	63	66	69	72	75	78	81	84	87	90	93	96	99	102	105
1.6	45	49	52	55	58	61	65	68	71	74	77	81	84	87	90	93	97	100	103	106	109	113
1.7	48	52	55	59	62	65	69	72	76	99	82	86	89	93	96	99	103	106	110	113	116	120
1.8	51	55	59	62	66	69	73	77	80	84	87	91	95	98	102	105	109	113	116	120	123	127
1.9	55	58	62	66	70	74	77	81	85	89	93	96	100	104	108	112	115	119	123	127	131	134
2.0	58	62	66	70	74	78	82	86	90	94	98	102	106	110	114	118	122	126	130	134	138	142
2.1	61	65	69	73	77	82	86	90	94	98	103	107	111	115	119	124	128	132	136	140	145	149
2.2	64	68	73	77	81	86	90	95	99	103	108	112	117	121	125	130	134	139	143	147	152	156
2.3	67	72	76	81	85	90	95	99	104	108	113	118	122	127	131	136	141	145	150	154	159	164
2.4	70	75	80	84	89	94	99	104	108	113	118	123	128	132	137	142	147	152	156	161	166	171
2.5	73	78	83	88	93	98	103	108	113	118	123	128	133	138	143	148	153	158	163	168	173	178
2.6	76	82	87	92	97	102	108	113	118	123	128	134	139	144	149	154	160	165	170	175	180	186
2.7	80	85	90	96	101	107	112	117	123	128	134	139	144	150	155	161	166	171	197	182	188	193
2.8	83	88	94	100	105	111	116	122	128	133	139	144	150	156	161	167	172	178	184	189	195	200
2.9	86	92	98	104	109	115	121	127	133	138	144	150	156	162	167	173	179	185	191	196	202	208
3.0	89	95	101	107	113	119	125	131	137	143	149	155	161	167	173	179	185	191	197	203	209	215
3.1	93	99	105	111	117	124	130	136	42	148	155	161	167	173	179	186	192	198	204	210	217	223
3.2	96	102	109	115	122	128	134	141	147	154	160	166	173	179	186	192	198	205	211	218	224	230
3.3	99	106	113	119	126	132	139	146	152	159	165	172	179	185	192	198	205	212	218	225	231	238
3.4	103	109	116	123	130	137	143	150	57	165	171	177	184	191	198	205	211	218	225	232	239	245
3.5	106	113	120	127	134	141	148	155	162	169	176	183	190	197	204	211	218	225	232	239	246	253
3.6	109	117	124	131	138	145	153	160	167	174	181	189	196	203	210	217	225	231	239	246	253	261
3.7	113	120	128	135	142	150	157	165	172	179	187	194	202	209	216	224	231	239	246	253	261	268
3.8	116	124	131	139	147	154	162	169	177	185	192	200	207	215	223	230	238	245	253	261	268	276
3.9	120	128	135	143	151	199	167	194	182	190	198	206	213	221	229	237	245	252	260	268	276	284
4.0	123	131	139	147	155	163	171	199	187	195	203	211	219	227	235	243	251	259	267	295	283	291
4.2	130	139	147	155	164	172	181	189	199	206	214	223	231	239	248	256	265	273	281	290	298	307
4.4	137	146	155	164	172	181	190	199	208	216	225	234	243	252	260	269	278	287	296	304	313	322
4.6	144	154	163	172	180	190	200	209	218	227	236	246	256	264	273	282	292	301	310	319	328	338
4.8	152	161	171	180	190	200	209	219	228	238	248	257	267	276	286	296	305	315	324	334	344	353
5.0	159	169	199	189	199	209	219	229	239	249	259	269	279	289	299	309	319	329	339	349	359	369

Table 9-42b. Pressure Drop of Gas in Pipe, Terminal Pressure Known

Altitude, ft	Initial Pressure, psig																					
3500-5500	1	2	3	4	5	6	7	8	9	10	11	12	13	14	15	16	17	18	19	20	21	22
1500-3500		1	2	3	4	5	6	7	8	9	10	1 1	12	13	14	15	16	17	18	19	20	21
0-1500			1	2	3	4	5	6	7	8	9	10	11	12	13	14	15	16	17	18	19	20
Pressure Drop, psi	Pressure Drop Factor (From Tables 9-40a to 9-40d)																					
5.1	163	173	183	193	203	214	224	234	244	254	265	275	285	295	305	316	326	336	346	356	367	377
5.2	166	197	187	198	208	218	229	239	250	260	270	281	291	302	312	322	333	343	354	364	374	385
5.3	170	181	191	202	213	223	234	244	255	266	276	287	297	308	319	329	340	350	361	372	382	393
5.4	174	185	195	206	217	228	239	249	260	271	282	293	303	314	325	336	347	357	368	379	390	401
5.5	178	189	200	211	222	233	244	255	266	277	288	299	310	321	332	343	354	365	376	387	398	409
5.6	181	193	204	215	226	237	249	260	271	282	293	305	316	327	338	349	361	372	383	394	405	417
5.7	185	197	208	219	231	242	254	265	276	288	299	311	322	333	345	356	368	379	390	402	413	425
5.8	189	201	212	224	235	247	259	270	282	293	305	317	328	340	351	363	375	386	398	409	411	433
5.9	193	205	217	228	240	252	264	276	287	299	311	323	335	346	358	370	382	394	405	417	429	441
6.0	197	209	221	233	245	257	269	281	293	305	317	329	341	353	365	377	389	401	413	425	437	449
6.1	201	213	225	237	249	262	294	286	298	310	323	335	347	359	371	384	396	408	420	432	445	457
6.2	205	217	229	242	254	267	279	291	304	316	329	341	353	366	378	391	403	415	428	440	453	465
6.3	209	221	234	246	259	272	284	297	309	321	335	347	360	372	385	398	410	423	435	448	461	473
6.4	212	225	238	251	264	276	289	302	315	327	340	353	366	379	392	404	417	430	443	456	468	481
6.5	216	229	242	255	268	281	294	307	320	333	346	359	372	385	398	411	424	437	450	463	476	489
6.6	220	234	247	260	273	286	300	313	326	339	352	366	379	392	405	418	432	445	458	471	484	498
6.7	224	238	250	265	278	291	305	318	332	345	358	372	385	399	412	425	439	452	466	479	492	506
6.8	228	242	256	269	283	296	310	324	337	351	364	378	392	405	419	432	446	460	473	487	500	514
6.9	233	246	260	274	288	302	315	329	343	357	370	384	398	412	426	440	453	467	481	495	509	522
7.0	237	251	265	279	293	307	320	335	349	363	377	391	405	49	433	447	461	475	489	503	517	531
7.1	241	255	269	283	297	312	326	340	354	368	382	397	411	425	439	454	468	482	496	510	525	539
7.2	245	259	274	288	302	317	331	346	360	374	389	403	418	432	446	461	475	490	504	518	533	547
7.3	249	264	278	293	307	322	337	351	366	380	395	410	424	439	453	468	483	497	512	526	541	556
7.4	253	268	283	297	312	327	342	357	371	386	401	416	430	445	460	475	490	505	519	534	549	564
7.5	257	272	287	302	317	332	347	362	377	392	407	422	437	452	467	482	497	512	527	542	557	572
7.6	261	277	292	307	322	337	353	368	383	398	413	429	444	459	474	489	505	520	535	550	565	581
7.7	266	281	296	312	327	343	358	373	389	404	420	435	450	466	481	497	512	527	543	558	574	589
7.8	270	285	301	317	332	348	363	379	395	410	426	441	457	473	488	504	59	535	551	566	582	597
7.9	274	290	306	322	337	353	369	385	401	416	432	488	464	480	495	511	527	543	559	574	590	606
8.0	278	294	310	326	342	358	374	390	406	422	438	454	470	486	502	518	534	550	566	582	598	614
8.1	283	299	315	331	347	364	380	396	412	428	445	461	477	493	509	526	542	558	574	590	607	623
8.2	287	303	320	336	353	369	385	402	418	435	451	467	484	500	517	533	549	566	582	599	615	631
8.3	291	308	325	341	358	374	390	408	424	441	457	474	491	507	524	540	557	574	590	607	623	639
8.4	296	312	329	346	363	380	396	413	430	447	464	480	497	514	531	548	564	581	598	615	632	648
8.5	300	317	334	351	368	385	402	419	436	453	470	487	504	521	538	555	572	589	606	623	640	657
8.6	304	322	339	356	373	390	408	425	442	459	476	494	511	528	545	562	580	597	614	631	648	666
8.7	309	326	344	361	378	396	413	431	448	465	483	500	518	535	552	570	587	605	622	639	657	674
8.8	313	331	348	366	384	401	419	436	454	472	489	507	524	542	560	577	595	612	630	648	665	683
8.9	318	336	353	371	389	407	425	442	460	478	495	514	531	549	567	585	603	620	638	656	693	692
9.0	322	340	358	376	394	412	430	448	466	484	502	520	538	556	574	592	610	628	646	664	682	700
9.2	331	350	368	386	405	423	442	460	478	497	515	534	552	570	589	607	626	644	662	681	699	718
9.4	340	359	378	397	415	434	453	472	491	509	528	547	566	585	603	622	641	660	679	697	716	735
9.6	349	369	388	407	426	445	465	484	503	522	541	561	580	599	618	637	657	676	695	714	733	753
9.8	359	378	398	417	437	457	476	496	515	535	555	574	594	613	633	653	672	692	711	731	751	770
10.0	368	388	408	428	448	468	488	508	528	548	568	588	608	628	648	668	688	708	728	748	768	788

Example 2: Given:

flow 300000 ft^3/hr;

pipe length 2000 ft;

initial pressure 15 psig;

pipe size 10 in.

Altitude of installation 1000 ft above sea level.

Find: Pressure drop

Solution: (a) From Table 9-40d, 6.1 is the pressure drop factor per 100 ft corresponding to 300,000 ft^3/hr flow and 10 inch pipe size.

(b) For 2000 ft length the pressure drop factor is $(6.1 \times 2000) \div 100 = 122$.

(c) From Table 9-41a under initial pressure of 15 psig, pressure drop factor of 122 corresponds to a pressure drop of 2.15 psi.

Example 3: Given:

flow 6800 ft^3/hr;

pipe length 500 ft;

pressure drop 0.5 psi;

pipe size 2½ inches;

altitude of installation 2500 ft above sea level.

Find: Required initial pressure

Solution: (a) From Table 9-40b; 5.2 is the pressure drop factor per 100 ft corresponding to 6800 ft^3/hr flow and 2½ in. pipe size.

(b) For 500 ft, pressure drop factor is $(5.2 \times 500) \div 100 = 26$.

(c) From Tables 9-41a &9-41b, initial pressure of 13 psig corresponds to pressure drop of 0.5 psi and pressure drop factor of 26.

Example 4: Given:

flow 400000 ft^3/hr;

pipe diameter 12 in.;

initial pressure 20 psig;

pressure drop 2 psi;

altitude of installation 500 ft above sea level.

Find: Pipe length causing 2 psi pressure drop.

Solution: (a) From Table 9-41a,134 is the pressure drop factor corresponding to initial pressure of 20 psig and 2 psi pressure drop.

(b) From Table 9-40d, 4.12 is the pressure drop factor per 100 ft corresponding to a flow of 400000 ft^3/hr through a 12 inch pipe.

(c) The pipe length is L = 134 ×100÷4.12=3250 ft.

Example 5: Given:

Pipe length, 1500 ft

Initial pressure, 14 psig

pressure drop, 3 psi

inside pipe diameter, 12 in.

altitude of installation, 4000 ft above sea level

Find: Flow capacity of pipe?

Solution: (a) From Tables 9-41a, 149 is the pressure drop factor corresponding to 14 psig initial pressure, and 3 psi pressure drop.

(b) The pressure drop factor per 100 ft is $(149 \times 100) \div 1500 = 9.9$.

(c) From Table 9-40d, 620,000 ft^3/hr corresponds to pressure drop factor per 100 ft equal to 9.9 under the 12 inch diameter column.

Example 6: Given:

specific gravity, 0.65;

flow, 7400 ft^3/hr;

pipe length, 1850 ft;

terminal pressure, 16 psig;

pipe size, 2½ in.;

altitude of installation, 2500 ft above sea level.

Find: Necessary initial pressure.

Solution: (a) From Table 9-40b; 6.1 is the pressure drop factor per 100 ft corresponding to 7400 ft^3/hr flow and 2½ inch pipe size.

(b) For a specific gravity of 0.65, find correction factor $F = 1.08$ from Table 9-43. Multiply length of 1850×1.08, obtaining an equivalent length of 2000 ft.

(c) For 2000 ft equivalent length the pressure drop factor is $(6.1 \times 2000) \div 100 = 122$.

(d) From Table 9-42a, under terminal pressure of 16 psig, the pressure drop factor of 122 corresponds to a pressure drop of 2.0 psi. Therefore, initial pressure is 16 + 2 = 18 psig.

Example 7: Given:

flow 25000 ft^3/hr;

pipe length 1200 ft;

pressure drop 3 psig;

terminal pressure 7 psig;

Altitude of installation 4500 ft above sea level.

Find: Pipe size.

Solution: (a) From Tables 9-42a, the pressure drop factor corresponding to terminal pressure of 7 psig and pressure drop of 3 psi is found to be 125.

(b) The pressure drop factor per 100 ft is $(125 \times 100) \div 1200 = 10.4$.

(c) Locate the next smallest pressure drop factor per 100 ft from Table 9-40b in the 25,000 ft^3/hr row, here 5.4. The corresponding required pipe size is 4 inches.

Table 9-43. Correction Factors for Specific Gravity

Specific Gravity	Correction Factor F	Specific Gravity	Correction Factor F
0.35	0.58	0.85	1.42
0.40	0.67	0.90	1.50
0.45	0.75	0.95	1.58
0.50	0.83	1.00	1.67
0.55	0.92	1.10	1.83
0.60	1.00	1.20	2.00
0.65	1.08	1.30	2.17
0.70	1.17	1.40	2.33
0.75	1.25	1.50	2.50
0.80	1.33		

Pressure Drop of Air Pipes: The nomograph permits the rapid calculation of pressure drops in steel pipe and the sizing of air lines.

The Formulas: The Darcy formula for pressure drop of any gas can be written*

$$\frac{\Delta P}{100} = \frac{0.00705 f (scfm)^2 S_g^2}{\rho d^5} \tag{14}$$

where $\Delta P/100$ = pressure drop per 100 ft of pipe, psi;

f = friction factor;

$scfm$ = cubic feet per minute at standard conditions, (14.9 psia and 60 °F);

S_g = specific gravity of gas (air = 1);

d = inside diameter of pipe, in.;

ρ = gas density, lb/ft³.

From the perfect gas law, air density can be written

$$\rho = \frac{2.70 P}{t + 460} \tag{15}$$

where P = absolute pressure, psia; and

t = temperature, °F.

For fully turbulent flow in steel pipes

$$f = 0.189 N_R^{-0.189} \tag{16}$$

where

$$N_R = \frac{28.92 \times scfm \times S_g}{d\mu} \tag{17}$$

μ = gas viscosity, centipoises

Substituting (17) into (16),

$$f = \frac{0.1008 d^{0.187} \mu^{0.187}}{scfm^{0.187}} \tag{18}$$

*See Crane Company's Flow of Fluids.

In the temperature range 60 to 150°F, $\mu^{0.187}$ for air varies only from 0.472 to 0.482, so that 0.477 can be taken as an average value and Equation (18) becomes

$$f = \frac{0.0481 d^{0.187}}{scfm^{0.187}} \tag{19}$$

Substituting (19) and (15) into (14),

$$\Delta P/100 = \frac{1.25 \times 10^{-4}(t+460) scfm^{1.813}}{(p+14.7) d^{4.813}} \tag{20}$$

where P = gage pressure, psig.

The nomograph of Fig. 9-38 is a graphical solution of Equation (20).

Example 8: What is the pressure drop of 200 *scfm* of air at 60°F and 100 psig average pressure flowing through a standard 3 in. steel pipe?

Solution: Substituting in Equation (20),

$$\frac{\Delta P}{100} = \frac{1.25 \times 10^{-4}(60+460)(200)^{1.813}}{(100+14.7)(3.068)^{4.813}}$$

$$= \frac{1.25 \times 10^{-4} \times 520 \times 150000}{114.7 \times 220}$$

$$= 0.038 \text{ psi}$$

Solution by Nomograph: Align $t = 60$°F with $P = 100$ psig and read air density $\rho = 0.60$ lb/ft³. Align this latter value with *scfm* = 200 and mark intersection on pivot line. Align this intersection with $d = 3$-in. nominal diameter and $P = 0.038$ psi per 100 feet of pipe.

Compressed Air Systems

Compressed Air.—Pressure and quality of compressed air must be determined before design of a system begins.

Instrument air is supplied at pressures of 60–100 psig and generally reduced to 25 psig for most instruments. This air must be filtered and dried.

Cleaning and testing operations utilize full pressure air up to 100 psig and need not be filtered.

Compressed air quantities for sewage lift are determined by the height of the lift and sewage flow in gallons per minute. Compressor capacity may be determined from Equation (21):

$$A = \frac{S(34+h)}{255} \tag{21}$$

where A = compressor capacity, ft³/min of free air;

h = lift against which sewage is to be discharged, ft; and

S = flow of sewage during discharge, gpm.

Systems with storage tanks are better than tankless compressed air systems for use with pneumatic ejectors. The effect of the tank is to impart 50% more lift, resulting in a more efficient ejector.

Laboratory air requirements are variable. Lab tables should be supplied with 20-psig air, but only 5-10 psig in cases where there is extensive use made of air operated mixers or agitators. Secondary filtering may be advisable. Occasionally, 1000-psig air may be required.

Pipe Sizing: Sizes and capacities of compressed air pipe may be computed from Equation (22) or (23) or Table 9-45

$$d = 13.5\sqrt{(cfm)/V} \qquad (22)$$

$$cfm = 58\sqrt{\frac{Pd^5}{WL}} \qquad (23)$$

where d = pipe inner diameter, in.;

cfm = flow, ft^3/min;

V = velocity, fpm;

P = pressure difference, psi;

W = entering air density, lb/ft^3;

L = length of pipe, ft.

Ascertainment of peak capacities for compressed air systems is largely a matter of judgement. It is necessary to consider the probable use factors, determined by the devices requiring compressed air, the estimated number of people who will be drawing air from the system, and the pattern of air use, with special attention paid to periods of high load.

For example, compressed air demand in a two person laboratory may reach 20 *cfm* of free air per laboratory, depending on the number of air outlets ($\frac{1}{8}$-in. orifices) in use.

Table 9-47 gives free air discharge through orifices at various pressures.

Where a number of small pipe branches are involved, application of Table 9-48 is helpful in arriving at relative capacities of pipe headers.

Fig. 9-36, a chart of air quantities vs. number of laboratories, was drawn in connection with the design of a specific installation. Similar charts can be easily drawn for any installation as an aid to pipe sizing. The chart reflects specific conditions and the designers judgment in each case. In Fig. 9-36, two person laboratories were required with 20-psig supply. A 150% contingency factor is used to cover any peak load.

Air Compressors: Compressors may be single- or two-stage, water or air cooled. The single-stage pump is used for general plumbing work with pressures up to 125 psig; the two-stage pump is used for higher pressures. An air-cooled compressor may be considered for outdoor installation; a water-cooled unit for indoor installation, or where high pressures are required, or where water supply and drainage are conveniently available. Reciprocating or rotary type compressors may be used where oil-free air is required. A compressor oversized 50% of design load is not objectionable.

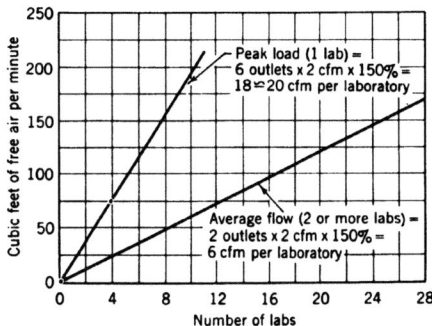

Fig 9-36. Compressed air charts

Receiver tanks are recommended where peak loads are sudden; they also tend to dampen pulsations, maintaining a more uniform pressure. Receivers may be purchased with the compressor as part of a package unit: however, this is recommended only for installations under 75 *cfm* demand. Capacities of ASME approved receivers are suggested in Table 9-44.

Relief valves and gages, along with drains and support features, are generally an integral part of the compressor unit.

Filters and Regulators: Filters for the removal by oils, dust, water, and other impurities should be given very careful consideration and selected on the basis of manufacturer's ratings. Regulators are available for reduction of compressor output to any desired pressure. Combination filter regulators are used close to the outlets or the air-using equipment being served. Very little maintenance is required where proper filters are chosen.

Table 9-44. Receiver for Compressed Air System

Compressor Capacity, *cfm*	ASME Receiver Dimensions		
	Diameter, in.	Length, ft	Volume, ft³
45	14	4	4½
110	13	6	11
190	24	6	19
340	30	7	34
570	36	8	57
960	42	10	96
2115	48	12	151
3120	54	14	223
4400	60	16	314
6000	66	18	428

Pipe, Valves, Fittings: Materials for compressed air piping up to 150 psig working pressure and not over 6 in. diameter, should be Schedule 40 galvanized steel. Type L copper tube and Delrin (DuPont) plastic pipe with heat fusion joints are suitable for working pressures to 100 psig. At higher pressures and in the larger pipe sizes, Schedule 40 black steel pipe with welded joints may be considered for an economical installation.

Fittings for steel pipe may be screwed galvanized malleable iron (ANSI-B16.3); or, socket-welding or threaded forged steel (ANS1-B16.11). Valves and checks, ⅜-2 in., should be brass, 150 lb, with screwed ends (ASTM B62); larger valves (above 2 in.) should be welded or flanged forged steel, 150 lb.

Testing: Piping should be tested hydrostatically at 1½ times the maximum operating pressure, or 50 psig, whichever is greater, then purged dry before the system is placed in service. Testing with air or inert gases may be desirable in some instances, allowing for detection with soap bubbles.

The piping system should be kept dirt-free with filters; however, addition of dirt pickets or blowout valves at the base of piping drops is frequently advisable.

Example 9: Given: 14 two person laboratories, 3 air service stations, and 6 air operated ventilation damper controls.

Solution: A: Minimum size pipe ⅜ inch per outlets. B: Peak load demand for one laboratory from Fig. 9-37. Table 9-47, discharges through orifices, also Fig. 9-36 for use factors. D, E, F, H, J. Accumulation of air quantities. Header sizes from Table 9-48. Size J from Table 9-45. G, I. Hose outlets sized. K. Negligible demand.

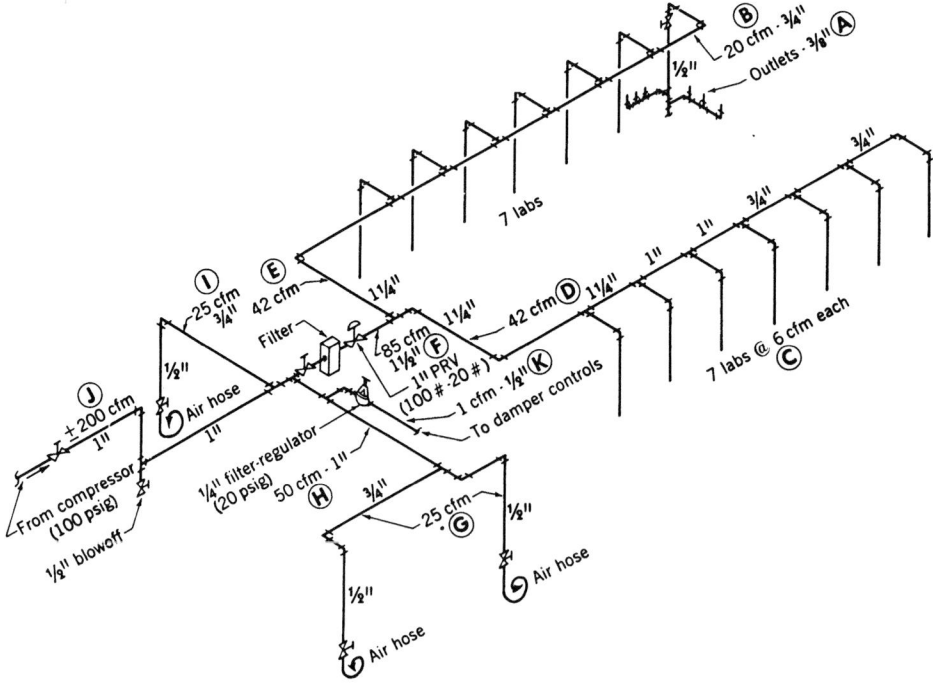

Fig 9-37. Pipe sizing Example 9

NOMOGRAPH FOR PRESSURE DROP OF AIR IN PIPES

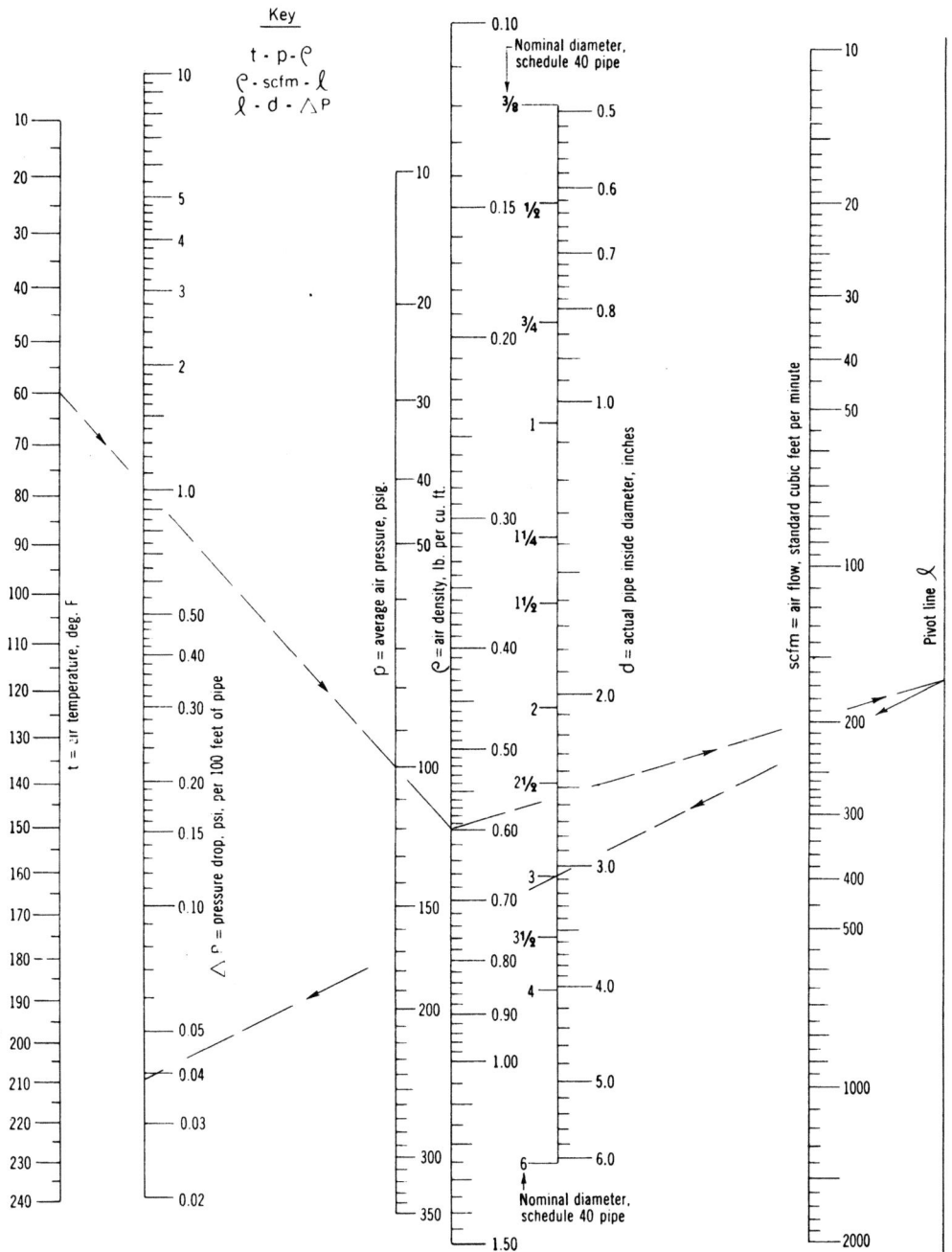

Fig 9-38. Nomograph for calculating pressure drops in steel pipe and sizing of air in pipes

Table 9-45. Loss of Air Pressure in psi per 1000 ft of Pipe due to Friction

ft³/min Free Air	Equivalent Compressed Air ft³/min	60-Psig Initial Pressure — Nominal Pipe Diameter in.								Equivalent Compressed Air ft³/min	80-Psig Initial Pressure — Nominal Pipe Diameter in.							
		½	¾	1	1¼	1½	2	2½	3		½	¾	1	1¼	1½	2	2½	3
10	1.96	10.0	1.53	0.43	0.10	...	...	...	...	1.55	7.90	1.21	0.34	...	...	...	...	...
20	3.94	39.7	5.99	1.71	0.39	0.18	...	...	...	3.10	31.4	4.72	1.35	0.31	...	...	...	...
30	5.89	...	13.85	3.86	0.88	0.40	...	...	...	4.65	70.8	10.9	3.04	0.69	0.31	...	...	...
40	7.86	...	24.7	6.85	1.59	0.71	0.19	...	...	6.20	...	19.5	5.40	1.25	0.56	...	...	...
50	9.84	...	38.6	10.7	2.48	1.10	0.30	...	...	7.74	...	30.5	8.45	1.96	0.87	...	...	...
60	11.81	...	55.57	15.4	3.58	1.57	0.43	...	...	9.29	...	43.8	12.16	2.82	1.24	0.34	...	...
70	13.75	...	...	21.0	4.87	2.15	0.57	0.22	...	10.82	...	59.8	16.6	3.84	1.70	0.45	...	...
80	15.72	...	...	27.4	6.37	2.82	0.75	0.29	...	12.40	...	78.2	21.6	5.03	2.22	0.59	...	...
90	17.65	...	...	34.7	8.05	3.57	0.57	0.95	0.37	13.95	...	...	27.4	6.35	2.82	0.75	...	...
100	19.60	...	...	42.8	9.95	4.40	1.18	0.46	...	15.5	...	...	33.8	7.85	3.47	0.93	0.36	...
125	19.4	[3½]	...	46.2	12.4	6.90	1.83	0.71	0.14	19.4	...	...	46.2	12.4	5.45	1.44	0.56	...
150	29.45	0.15	...	...	22.4	9.90	2.64	1.02	0.32	23.2	...	...	76.2	17.7	7.82	2.08	0.81	...
175	34.44	0.20	...	...	30.8	13.40	3.64	1.40	0.43	27.2	...	...	...	24.8	10.6	2.87	1.10	...
200	39.40	0.27	[4]	...	39.7	17.60	4.71	1.83	0.57	31.0	[3½]	...	...	31.4	13.9	3.72	1.44	0.45
250	49.20	0.42	0.21	...	...	27.5	7.37	2.85	0.89	38.7	0.33	...	...	49.0	21.7	5.82	2.25	0.70
300	58.90	0.60	0.31	[4½]	...	39.6	10.55	4.11	1.30	46.5	0.47	[4]	...	70.6	31.2	8.35	3.24	1.03
350	68.8	0.82	0.42	0.23	...	54.0	14.4	5.60	1.76	54.2	0.65	0.33	...	...	42.5	11.4	4.42	1.39
400	78.8	1.06	0.53	0.30	...	...	18.6	7.30	2.30	62.0	0.84	42	...	...	55.5	14.7	5.76	1.82
450	88.4	1.35	0.70	0.38	...	...	23.7	9.20	2.90	69.7	1.06	0.55	[4½]	...	...	18.7	7.25	2.29
500	98.4	1.67	0.85	0.46	...	...	29.7	11.4	3.60	77.4	1.32	0.67	0.30	...	...	23.3	9.0	2.84
600	118.1	2.40	1.22	0.67	...	...	42.3	16.4	5.17	92.9	1.89	0.96	0.53	...	...	33.4	12.9	4.08
700	137.5	3.27	1.67	0.91	...	...	57.8	22.3	7.00	108.2	2.58	1.32	0.72	...	...	45.7	17.6	5.52
800	157.2	4.26	2.18	1.20	...	...	...	29.2	9.16	124.0	3.36	1.72	0.95	...	...	59.3	23.1	7.15
900	176.5	5.40	2.76	1.51	...	...	...	39.0	11.6	139.5	4.26	2.18	1.19	...	...	...	29.2	9.17
1000	196.0	6.65	3.40	1.87	[5]	[6]	[8]	45.7	14.3	155	5.27	2.68	1.48	[5]	[6]	...	36.1	11.3
1500	294.5	15.0	7.6	4.2	2.32	0.87	0.29	...	32.3	232	11.8	6.0	3.32	1.83	0.69	[8]	81.7	25.5
2000	394.0	26.6	13.6	7.5	4.18	1.53	0.36	[10]	57.5	310	21.0	10.7	5.9	3.30	1.21	0.29	...	45.3
2500	492	41.7	21.3	11.6	6.4	2.42	0.57	0.17	...	387	32.9	16.8	9.2	5.1	1.91	0.45	[10]	70.9
3000	589	60.0	30.1	16.7	9.2	3.48	0.81	0.24	...	465	47.4	24.2	13.2	7.3	2.74	0.64	0.19	...
3500	688	...	41.7	22.6	12.8	4.68	1.07	0.33	...	542	64.5	32.8	17.8	10.1	3.70	0.85	0.26	...
4000	788	...	54.5	29.7	16.5	6.17	1.44	0.44	[12]	620	...	43.0	23.4	13.0	4.87	1.14	0.34	...
4500	884	...	...	37.9	20.8	7.8	1.83	0.55	0.21	697	...	54.8	29.8	16.4	6.15	1.44	0.43	[12]
5000	984	...	...	46.4	25.7	9.7	2.26	0.67	0.27	774	...	67.4	36.7	20.3	7.65	1.78	0.53	0.21
6000	1181	...	...	...	37.0	13.9	3.25	0.98	0.38	929	...	...	53.0	29.2	11.0	2.57	0.77	0.29
7000	1375	...	...	...	50.3	18.7	4.43	1.34	0.51	1082	...	...	72.1	39.8	14.8	3.40	1.06	0.40
8000	1572	...	...	...	...	24.7	5.80	1.73	0.71	1240	...	...	...	52.1	19.5	4.57	1.36	0.56
9000	1765	...	...	...	...	31.3	7.33	2.20	0.87	1395	...	...	...	65.8	24.7	5.78	1.74	0.69
10000	1960	...	...	...	...	38.6	9.05	2.72	1.06	1550	...	...	...	...	30.5	7.15	2.14	0.84
11000	2165	...	...	...	...	46.7	10.9	3.29	1.28	1710	...	...	...	...	36.8	8.61	2.60	1.01
12000	2362	...	...	...	...	55.5	13.0	3.90	1.51	1860	...	...	...	...	43.8	10.3	3.08	1.19
13000	2560	...	...	...	...	...	15.2	4.58	1.77	2020	...	...	...	...	51.7	12.0	3.62	1.40
14000	2750	...	...	...	...	...	17.7	5.32	2.07	2170	...	...	...	...	60.2	14.0	4.20	1.63
15000	2945	...	...	...	...	...	20.3	6.10	2.36	2320	...	...	...	...	68.5	16.0	4.82	1.86
16000	3144	...	...	...	...	...	23.1	6.95	2.70	2480	...	...	...	...	78.2	18.2	5.48	2.13
18000	3530	...	...	...	...	...	29.2	8.80	3.42	2790	...	...	...	...	...	23.0	6.95	2.70
20000	3940	...	...	...	...	...	36.2	10.8	4.22	3100	...	...	...	...	...	28.6	8.55	3.33
22000	4330	...	...	...	...	...	43.7	13.2	5.12	3410	...	...	...	...	...	34.5	10.4	4.04
24000	4724	...	...	...	...	...	51.9	15.6	5.92	3720	...	...	...	...	...	41.0	12.3	4.69
26000	5120	...	...	...	...	...	...	18.3	7.15	4030	...	...	...	...	...	48.2	14.4	5.60
28000	5500	...	...	...	...	...	...	21.3	8.30	4350	...	...	...	...	...	55.9	16.8	6.50
30000	5890	...	...	...	...	...	...	24.4	9.40	4650	...	...	...	...	...	64.2	19.3	7.5

Reprinted, by permission, from compressed Air and Gas Handbook, published by Compressed Air and Gas Institute, New York, N.Y.

Table 9-46. Loss of Air Pressure in psi per 1000 ft of pipe due to friction

ft³/min Free Air	Equivalent ft³/min Compressed Air	60-Psig Initial Pressure — Nominal Pipe Dia., Inches								Equivalent ft³/min Compressed Air	80-Psig Initial Pressure — Nominal Pipe Dia., Inches							
		½	¾	1	1¼	1½	2	2½	3		½	¾	1	1¼	1½	2	2½	3
10	1.28	6.5	0.99	0.28	...	...	...	...	...	1.05	5.35	0.82	0.23	...	...	...	...	...
20	2.56	25.9	3.90	1.11	0.25	0.11	...	...	...	2.11	21.3	3.21	0.92	0.21	...	...	...	...
30	3.84	58.5	9.01	2.51	0.57	0.26	...	...	...	3.16	48.0	7.42	2.07	0.47	0.21	...	...	...
40	5.12	...	16.0	4.45	1.03	0.46	...	...	...	4.21	...	13.2	3.67	0.85	0.38	...	...	...
50	6.41	...	25.1	6.96	1.61	0.11	0.19	...	...	5.26	...	20.6	5.72	1.33	0.59	...	...	...
60	7.68	...	36.2	10.0	2.32	1.02	0.28	...	...	6.32	...	29.7	8.25	1.86	0.84	0.23	...	...
70	8.96	...	49.3	13.7	3.16	1.40	0.37	...	...	7.38	...	40.5	11.2	2.61	1.15	0.31	...	...
80	10.24	...	64.5	17.8	4.14	1.83	0.49	0.19	...	8.42	...	53.0	14.7	3.41	1.51	0.40	...	...
90	11.52	...	82.8	22.6	5.23	2.32	0.62	0.24	...	9,47	...	68.0	18.6	4.30	1.91	0.51	0.20	...
100	12.81	...	...	27.9	6.47	2.86	0.77	0.30	...	10.50	...	...	22.9	5.32	2.36	0.63	0.25	...
125	15.82	...	...	48.6	10.2	4.49	1.19	0.46	...	13.15	...	...	39.9	8.4	3.70	0.98	0.38	...
150	19.23	...	...	62.8	14.6	6.43	1.72	0.66	0.21	15.79	...	...	51.6	12.0	5.30	1.41	0.55	0.17
175	22.40	[3½]	...	...	19.8	8.72	2.36	0.91	0.28	18.41	[3½]	...	...	16.3	7.2	1.95	0.75	0.24
200	25.62	0.17	...	...	25.9	11.4	3.06	1.19	0.37	21.05	...	...	...	21.3	9.4	2.52	0.98	0.31
250	31.64	0.27	[4]	...	40.4	17.9	4.78	1.85	0.58	26.30	0.22	...	...	33.2	14.7	3.94	1.53	0.48
300	38.44	0.39	0.2	...	58.2	25.8	6.85	2.67	0.84	31.60	0.32	[4]	...	47.3	21.2	5.62	2.20	0.70
350	44.80	0.53	0.27	[4½]	...	35.1	9.36	3.64	1.14	36.80	0.44	0.22	...	...	28.8	7.7	3.00	0.94
400	51.24	0.69	0.35	0.19	...	45.8	12.1	4.75	1.50	42.10	0.57	0.28	[4½]	...	37.6	10.0	3.91	1.23
450	57.65	0.88	0.46	0.25	...	58.0	15.4	5.98	1.89	47.30	0.72	0.37	[20]	...	47.7	12.7	4.92	1.55
500	63.28	1.09	0.55	0.30	...	71.6	19.2	7.42	2.34	52.60	0.89	0.46	0.25	...	58.8	15.7	6.1	1.93
600	76.88	1.56	0.79	0.44	...	...	27.6	10.7	3.36	63.20	1.28	0.65	0.36	...	...	22.6	8.8	2.76
700	89.60	2.13	1.09	0.59	...	...	37.7	14.5	4.55	73.80	1.75	0.89	0.49	...	...	30.0	11.9	3.74
800	102.5	2.77	1.42	0.78	...	...	49.0	19.0	5.89	84.20	2.28	1.17	0.64	...	...	40.2	15.6	4.85
900	115.3	3.51	1.80	0.99	...	...	62.3	24.1	7.6	94.70	2.89	1.48	0.81	...	...	51.2	19.8	6.2
1000	128.1	4.35	2.21	1.22	[5]	[6]	76.9	29.8	9.3	105.1	3.57	1.82	1.00	[5]	[6]	63.2	24.5	7.7
1500	192.3	9.8	4.9	2.73	1.51	0.57	[8]	67.0	21.0	157.9	8.0	4.10	2.25	1.24	0.47	[8]	55.0	17.2
2000	256.2	17.3	8.8	4.9	2.72	0.99	0.24	...	37.4	210.5	14.2	7.30	4.0	2.24	0.82	0.19	...	30.7
2500	316.4	27.2	13.8	8.3	4.2	1.57	0.37	[10]	58.4	263.0	22.3	11.4	6.2	3.4	1.30	0.31	[10]	48.0
3000	384.6	39.1	20.0	10.9	6.0	2.26	0.53	...	84.1	316	32.1	16.4	9.0	4.9	1.86	0.43	...	69.2
3500	447.8	58.2	27.2	14.7	8.2	3.04	0.70	0.22	...	368	47.7	22.3	121	6.9	2.51	0.57	0.18	...
4000	512.4	69.4	35.5	19.4	10.7	4.01	0.94	0.28	...	421	57.0	29.2	15.9	8.9	3.30	0.77	0.23	...
4500	576.5	...	45.0	24.5	13.5	5.10	1.19	0.36	[12]	473	...	37.0	20.1	11.1	4.2	0.98	0.29	[12]
5000	632.8	...	55.6	30.2	16.8	6.30	1.47	0.44	0.17	526	...	45.7	24.8	13.9	5.2	1.21	0.36	...
6000	768.8	...	80.0	43.7	24.1	9.10	2.11	0.64	0.24	632	...	65.7	35.8	19.8	7.5	1.74	0.52	0.20
7000	896.0	...	...	59.5	32.8	12.2	2.88	0.87	0.33	738	...	...	48.8	26.9	10.0	2.37	0.72	0.27
8000	1025	...	...	77.5	42.9	16.1	3.77	1.12	0.46	842	...	...	63.1	35.2	13.2	3.10	0.93	0.38
9000	1153	...	...	...	54.3	20.4	4.77	1.43	0.57	947	...	...	...	44.7	16.7	3.93	1.18	0.47
10000	1280	...	...	...	67.1	25.1	5.88	1.77	0.69	1051	...	...	...	55.2	20.6	4.85	1.46	0.57
11000	1410	...	...	...	...	30.4	7.10	2.14	0.83	1156	...	...	...	...	25.0	5.8	1.76	0.68
12000	1540	...	...	...	...	36.2	8.5	2.54	0.98	1262	...	...	...	...	29.7	7.0	2.09	0.81
13000	1668	...	...	...	...	42.6	9.8	2.98	1.15	1368	...	...	...	...	35.0	8.1	2.44	0.95
14000	1795	...	...	...	...	49.2	11.5	3.46	1.35	1473	...	...	...	...	40.3	9.7	2.85	1.11
15000	1923	...	...	...	...	56.6	13.2	3.97	1.53	1579	...	...	...	...	46.5	10.9	3.26	1.26
16000	2050	...	...	...	...	64.5	15.0	4.52	1.75	1683	...	...	...	...	53.0	12.4	3.72	1.45
18000	2310	...	...	...	...	81.5	19.0	5.72	2.22	1893	...	...	...	...	66.9	15.6	4.71	1.83
20000	2560	...	...	...	...	...	23.6	7.0	2.74	2150	...	...	...	...	...	19.4	5.8	2.20
22000	2820	...	...	...	...	...	28.5	8.5	3.33	2315	...	...	...	...	...	23.4	7.1	2.74
24000	3080	...	...	...	...	...	33.8	10.0	3.85	2525	...	...	...	...	...	27.8	8.4	3.17
26000	3338	...	...	...	...	...	39.7	11.9	4.65	2735	...	...	...	...	...	32.6	9.8	3.83
28000	3590	...	...	...	...	...	46.2	13.8	5.40	2946	...	...	...	...	...	37.9	11.4	4.4
30000	3850	...	...	...	...	...	53.0	15.9	6.17	3158	...	...	...	...	...	43.5	13.1	5.1

Reprinted, by permission, from compressed Air and Gas Handbook, published by Compressed Air and Gas Institute, New York, N.Y.

Table 9-47. Discharge of Air Through Orifices

Pressure Before Orifice, Psig	Diameter of Orifice, in.										
	1/64	1/32	1/16	1/8	1/4	3/8	1/2	5/8	3/4	7/8	1
	Discharge, ft³ of Free Air per min										
1	0.028	0.112	0.450	1.80	7.18	16.2	28.7	45.0	64.7	88.1	115
2	0.04	0.158	0.633	2.53	10.1	22.8	40.5	63.3	91.2	124	162
3	0.048	0.194	0.775	3.10	12.4	27.8	49.5	77.5	111	152	198
4	0.056	0.223	0.892	3.56	14.3	32.1	57.0	89.2	128	175	228
5	0.062	0.248	0.993	3.97	15.9	35.7	63.5	99.3	143	195	254
6	0.068	0.272	1.09	4.34	17.4	39.1	69.5	109	156	213	278
7	0.073	0.293	1.17	4.68	18.7	42.2	75.0	117	168	230	300
9	0.083	0.331	1.32	5.30	21.1	47.7	84.7	132	191	260	339
12	0.095	0.379	1.52	6.07	24.3	54.6	97.0	152	218	297	388
15	0.105	0.420	1.68	6.72	26.9	60.5	108	168	242	329	430
20	0.123	0.491	1.96	7.86	31.4	70.7	126	196	283	385	503
25	0.140	0.562	2.25	8.98	35.9	80.9	144	225	323	440	575
30	0.158	0.633	2.53	10.1	40.5	91.1	162	253	365	496	648
35	0.176	0.703	2.81	11.3	45.0	101	180	281	405	551	720
40	0.194	0.774	3.10	12.4	49.6	112	198	310	446	607	793
45	0.211	0.845	3.38	13.5	54.1	122	216	338	487	662	865
50	0.229	0.916	3.66	14.7	58.6	132	235	366	528	718	938
60	0.264	1.060	4.23	16.9	61.6	152	271	423	609	823	1082
70	0.300	1.200	4.39	19.2	76.7	173	307	479	690	939	1227
80	0.335	1.340	5.36	21.4	85.7	193	343	536	771	1050	1371
90	0.370	1.480	5.92	23.1	94.8	213	379	592	853	1161	1516
100	0.406	1.620	6.49	26.0	104	234	415	649	934	1272	1661
110	0.441	1.760	7.05	28.2	113	254	452	705	1016	1383	1806
120	0.476	1.910	7.62	30.5	122	274	488	762	1097	1494	1951
125	0.494	1.980	7.90	31.6	126	284	506	790	1138	1549	2023

Table 9-48. Relative Discharge Capacities of Pipe

Nominal Dia. of Larger Pipe, in.	Nominal Diameter of Smaller Pipe, in.															
	1/8	1/4	3/8	1/2	3/4	1	1¼	1½	2	2½	3	3½	4	4½	5	6
	Approximate Number of Small Pipe Flows Handled by Larger Pipe															
1/8	1	...	...	...	...	...	...	...	...	...	...	...	...	...	...	...
1/4	2.1	1	...	...	...	...	...	...	...	...	...	...	...	...	...	...
3/8	4.5	2.1	1	...	...	...	...	...	...	...	...	...	...	...	...	...
1/2	8	3.8	1.8	1	...	...	...	...	...	...	...	...	...	...	...	...
3/4	15	8	3.6	2	1	...	...	...	...	...	...	...	...	...	...	...
1	30	15	6.6	3.7	1.8	1	...	...	...	...	...	...	...	...	...	...
1¼	60	25	13	7	3.6	2	1	...	...	...	...	...	...	...	...	...
1½	90	40	20	10	5.5	2.9	1.5	1	...	...	...	...	...	...	...	...
2	165	75	35	20	10	5.5	2.7	1.9	1	...	...	...	...	...	...	...
2½	255	120	55	30	16	8	4.3	2.9	1.6	1	...	...	...	...	...	...
3	440	210	100	55	27	15	7.0	5	2.7	1.7	1	...	...	...	...	...
3½	630	300	140	80	40	21	11	7	3.9	2.5	1.4	1	...	...	...	...
4	870	400	190	100	55	30	15	10	5.3	3.4	2	1.4	1	...	...	...
4½	1150	540	250	140	70	40	20	13	7.0	4.5	2.6	1.8	1.3	1	...	...
5	1500	720	330	180	90	50	25	17	9.0	6.0	3.5	2.4	1.8	1.3	1	...
6	2400	1130	530	300	150	80	40	28	15	9.0	5.5	3.8	2.8	2.1	1.6	1

Viscosity of Liquids.—Viscosity is the property of a fluid by which it resists any force tending to produce flow or, in other terms, it is the fluids ability to resist shear; it is independent of specific gravity. The chart below gives the absolute and kinematic viscosity of liquids.

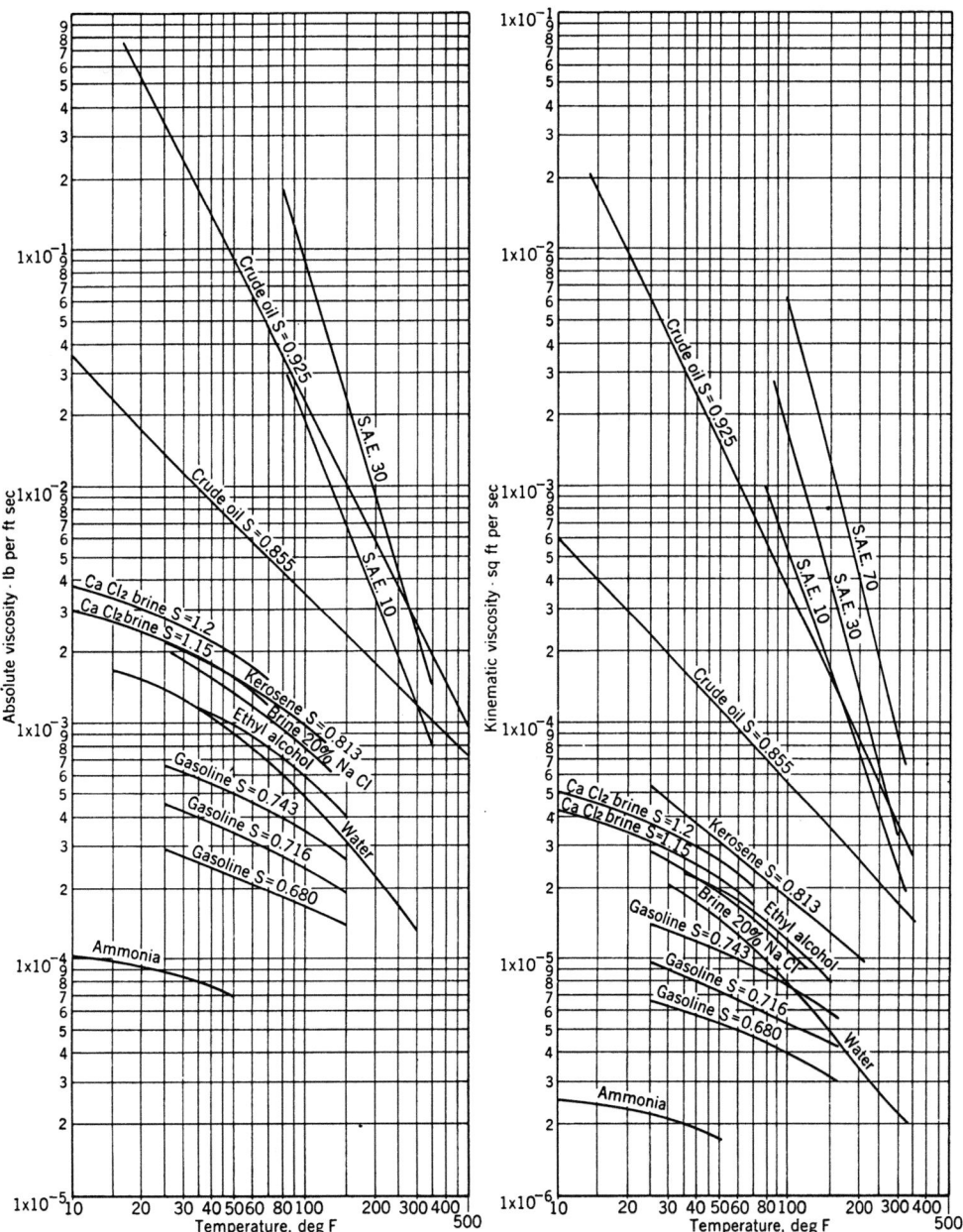

Fig 9-39. Viscosity of liquids with temperature

Piping

Copper drainage tube has been developed specifically for sanitary drainage service. It can be installed by a simple soldering operation in which the solder is drawn into the joint by capillary action. A complete selection of drainage fittings, featuring long radius elbows, are available for soldered connection to copper tube. These fittings also include fittings worth one or more outlets threaded for use with brass or copper pipe or with slip joints. Bends, both adjustable and fixed, with suitable flanges for closet connections, are also available.

Soldered drainage fittings are installed by the same technique that most plumbers developed with respect to water lines.

With respect to residences, the actual selection of sizes in most instances is controlled by code requirements, but 3-inch copper tube stack with not more than three branch intervals will accommodate 30 fixture units (for no more than two water closets). Where size is not fixed by code, a sanitary engineer or other qualified designer would prob-ably specify a 3-inch stack, which will easily fit between 2 × 4 studs. Copper drainage tube may be used equally well in multi-story buildings. Vent headers and waste lines should be long enough to take up expansion in the stacks.

Types of Materials.—Type *K* copper water tube is recommended for use with soldered or compression fittings, for general plumbing involving relatively severe service conditions, and for heating, gas, steam, oil lines and underground service.

Type *L* copper water tube can also be used with soldered or compression fittings, and is intended for general plumbing work involving relatively less severe conditions than with Type *K*, the wall thickness being thinner than Type *K*.

Type *M*, with thinner walls than either Type *K* or Type *L*, is recommended for use with soldered fittings only, for interior application, for heating and for waste, vent, soil, and other nonpressure applications.

Table 9-49. Dimensional and Capacity Data – Schedule 40 Steel Pipe

Diameter, in.			Wall Thickness, in.	Cross-Sectional Area, in^2			Weight, lb/ft		
Nominal	Actual Inside	Actual Outside		Outside	Inside	Metal	Pipe Alone	Water in Pipe	Pipe with Water
⅛	0.269	0.405	0.068	0.129	0.057	0.072	0.25	0.028	0.278
¼	0.364	0.540	0.088	0.229	0.104	0.125	0.43	0.045	0.475
⅜	0.493	0.675	0.091	0.358	0.191	0.167	0.57	0.083	0.653
½	0.622	0.840	0.109	0.554	0.304	0.250	0.86	0.132	0.992
¾	0.824	1.050	0.113	0.866	0.533	0.333	1.14	0.232	1.372
1	1.049	1.315	0.133	1.358	0.864	0.494	1.68	0.375	2.055
1¼	1.380	1.660	0.140	2.164	1.495	0.669	2.28	0.649	2.929
1½	1.600	1.900	0.145	2.835	2.036	0.799	2.72	0.882	3.602
2	2.067	2.375	0.154	4.431	3.356	1.075	3.66	1.454	5.114
2½	2.469	2.875	0.203	6.492	4.788	1.704	5.80	2.073	7.873
3	3.068	3.500	0.216	9.621	7.393	2.228	7.58	3.201	10.781
3½	3.548	4.000	0.226	12.568	9.888	2.680	9.11	4.287	13.397
4	4.026	4.500	0.237	15.903	12.730	3.173	10.80	5.516	16.316
5	5.047	5.563	0.258	24.308	20.004	4.304	14.70	8.674	23.52
6	6.065	6.625	0.280	34.474	28.89	5.584	19.00	12.52	31.52
8	7.981	8.625	0.322	58.426	50.030	8.396	28.60	21.68	50.28
10	10.020	10.950	0.365	90.790	78.85	11.90	40.50	34.16	74.66
12	11.938	12.750	0.406	127.67	113.09	15.77	53.60	48.50	102.10
14	13.126	14.000	0.437	153.94	135.33	18.6	63.30	58.64	121.94
16	15.000	16.000	0.500	201.06	176.71	24.35	82.80	76.58	159.38
18	16.876	18.000	0.562	254.47	223.68	30.79	105.00	96.93	201.93
20	18.814	20.000	0.593	314.16	278.01	36.15	123.00	120.46	243.46

Nominal Dia., in.	Circumference in.		Surface Area ft^2/ Lineal ft		Contents of Pipe per Lineal ft		Lineal ft to Contain		
	Outside	Inside	Outside	Inside	ft^3	Gal	ft^3	1 gal	1 lb of Water
⅛	1.27	0.84	0.106	0.070	0.0004	0.003	2533.775	338.740	35.714
¼	1.69	1.14	0.141	0.095	0.0007	0.005	1383.789	185.000	22.222
⅜	2.12	1.55	0.177	0.129	0.0013	0.010	754.360	100.850	12.048
½	2.65	1.95	0.221	0.167	0.0021	0.016	473.906	63.360	7.576
¾	3.29	2.58	0.275	0.215	0.0037	0.028	270.034	36.100	4.310
1	4.13	3.29	0.344	0.274	0.0062	0.045	166.618	22.280	2.667
1¼	5.21	4.33	0.435	0.361	0.0104	0.077	96.275	12.870	1.541
1½	5.96	5.06	0.497	0.422	0.0141	0.106	70.733	9.460	1.134
2	7.46	6.49	0.622	0.540	0.0233	0.174	42.913	5.740	0.688
2½	9.02	7.75	0.753	0.654	0.0332	0.248	30.077	4.020	0.482
3	10.96	9.63	0.916	0.803	0.0514	0.383	19.479	2.600	0.312
3½	12.56	11.14	1.047	0.928	0.0682	0.513	14.565	1.950	0.233
4	14.13	12.64	1.178	1.052	0.0884	0.660	11.312	1.510	0.181
5	17.47	15.84	1.456	1.319	0.1390	1.040	7.198	0.960	0.115
6	20.81	19.05	1.734	1.585	0.2010	1.500	4.984	0.670	0.080
8	27.09	25.07	2.258	2.090	0.3480	2.600	2.878	0.380	0.046
10	33.77	31.47	2.814	2.622	0.5470	4.100	1.826	0.240	0.029
12	40.05	37.70	3.370	3.140	0.7850	5.870	1.273	0.170	0.021
14	47.12	44.76	3.930	3.722	1.0690	7.030	1.067	0.140	0.017
16	53.41	51.52	4.440	4.310	1.3920	9.180	0.814	0.110	0.013
18	56.55	53.00	4.712	4.420	1.5530	11.120	0.644	0.090	0.010
20	62.83	59.09	5.236	4.920	1.9250	14.400	0.519	0.070	0.008

Table 9-50. Dimensional and Capacity Data – Schedule 80 Steel Pipe

Diameter, in.			Wall Thickness, in.	Cross-Sectional Area, in²			Weight, lb/ft		
Nominal	Actual Inside	Actual Outside		Outside	Inside	Metal	Pipe Alone	Water in Pipe	Pipe with Water
⅛	0.215	0.405	0.095	0.129	0.036	0.093	0.314	0.016	0.330
¼	0.302	0.540	0.119	0.229	0.072	0.157	0.535	0.031	0.566
⅜	0.423	0.675	0.126	0.358	0.141	0.217	0.738	0.061	0.799
½	0.546	0.840	0.147	0.554	0.234	0.320	1.087	0.102	1.189
¾	0.742	1.050	0.154	0.866	0.433	0.433	1.730	0.213	1.686
1	0.957	1.315	0.179	1.358	0.719	0.639	2.171	0.312	2.483
1¼	1.278	1.660	0.191	2.164	1.283	0.881	2.960	0.555	3.551
1½	1.500	1.900	0.200	2.835	1.767	1.068	3.631	0.765	4.396
2	1.939	2.375	0.218	4.431	2.540	1.770	5.022	1.280	6.302
2½	2.323	2.875	0.276	6.492	4.238	2.254	7.661	1.830	9.491
3	2.900	3.500	0.300	9.621	6.605	3.016	10.252	2.870	13.122
3½	3.364	4.000	0.318	12.568	8.890	3.678	12.505	3.720	16.225
4	3.826	4.500	0.337	15.903	11.496	4.407	14.983	4.970	19.953
5	4.813	5.563	0.375	24.308	18.196	6.112	20.778	7.940	28.718
6	5.761	6.625	0.432	34.740	26.069	8.405	28.573	11.300	39.873
8	7.625	8.625	0.500	58.426	45.666	12.760	43.388	19.800	63.188
10	9.564	10.750	0.593	90.790	71.870	18.920	64.400	31.300	95.530
12	11.376	12.750	0.687	127.670	101.640	26.030	88.600	44.040	132.640
14	12.500	14.000	0.750	153.940	122.720	31.220	107.000	53.180	160.150
16	14.314	16.000	0.843	201.060	160.920	40.140	137.000	69.730	206.730
18	16.126	18.000	0.937	254.470	204.240	50.230	171.000	88.500	259.500
20	17.938	20.000	1.031	314.160	252.720	61.440	209.000	109.100	318.510

Nominal Dia., in.	Circumference in.		Surface Area ft²/ Lineal ft		Contents of Pipe per Lineal ft		Lineal ft to Contain		
	Outside	Inside	Outside	Inside	ft³	Gal	ft³	1 gal	1 lb of Water
⅛	1.270	0.675	0.106	0.056	0.00033	0.0019	3070	527	101.010
¼	1.690	0.943	0.141	0.079	0.00052	0.0037	1920	271	32.260
⅜	2.120	1.328	0.177	0.111	0.00098	0.0073	1370	137	16.390
½	2.650	1.715	0.221	0.143	0.00162	0.0122	616	82	9.800
¾	3.290	2.330	0.275	0.194	0.003	0.0255	334	39.200	4.690
1	4.130	3.010	0.344	0.251	0.005	0.0374	200	26.800	3.210
1¼	5.210	4.010	0.435	0.334	0.00880	0.0666	114	15.000	1.800
1½	5.960	4.720	0.497	0.393	0.01230	0.0918	81.50	10.900	1.310
2	7.460	6.090	0.622	0.507	0.02060	0.1535	49.80	6.520	0.780
2½	9.030	7.320	0.753	0.610	0.02940	0.220	34.000	4.550	0.550
3	10.960	9.120	0.916	0.760	0.0460	0.344	21.700	2.910	0.350
3½	12.560	10.580	1.047	0.882	0.0617	0.458	16.250	2.180	0.270
4	14.130	12.020	1.178	1.002	0.0800	0.597	12.500	1.675	0.200
5	17.470	15.150	1.456	1.262	0.1260	0.947	7.950	1.055	0.130
6	20.810	18.100	1.734	1.510	0.1820	1.355	5.500	0.738	0.090
8	27.090	24.000	2.258	2.000	0.3180	2.380	3.140	0.420	0.050
10	33.770	30.050	2.814	2.503	0.5560	4.165	1.800	0.241	0.030
12	40.050	35.720	3.370	2.975	0.7060	5.280	1.420	0.189	0.020
14	47.120	39.270	3.930	3.271	0.8520	6.380	1.180	0.157	0.019
16	53.410	44.700	4.440	3.746	1.1170	8.360	0.895	0.119	0.014
18	56.550	50.660	4.712	4.220	1.4180	10.610	0.705	0.094	0.011
20	62.830	56.350	5.236	4.694	1.7550	13.300	0.570	0.076	0.009

Table 9-51. Dimensional and Capacity Data – Type K Copper Tube

Nominal	Diameter, in. Actual Inside	Diameter, in. Actual Outside	Wall Thickness, in.	Cross-Sectional Area, in^2 Outside	Cross-Sectional Area, in^2 Inside	Cross-Sectional Area, in^2 Metal	Weight lb/ft Pipe Alone	Weight lb/ft Water in Pipe	Weight lb/ft Pipe with Water
¼	0.311	0.375	0.035	0.110	0.076	0.034	0.145	0.033	0.167
⅜	0.402	0.500	0.049	0.196	0.127	0.069	0.269	0.055	0.324
½	0.527	0.625	0.049	0.307	0.218	0.089	0.344	0.094	0.438
⅝	0.652	0.750	0.049	0.442	0.334	0.08	0.418	0.145	0.563
¾	0.745	0.875	0.065	0.601	0.436	0.165	0.641	0.189	0.830
1	0.995	1.125	0.065	0.993	0.777	0.216	0.839	0.338	1.177
1¼	1.245	1.375	0.065	1.484	1.217	0.267	1.04	0.53	1.57
1½	1.481	1.625	0.072	2.072	1.722	0.350	1.36	1.22	2.58
2	1.959	2.125	0.083	3.546	3.013	0.533	2.06	1.31	3.37
2½	2.435	2.625	0.095	5.409	4.654	0.755	2.93	2.02	4.95
3	2.907	3.125	0.109	7.669	6.634	1.035	4.00	2.88	6.88
3½	3.385	3.625	0.120	10.321	8.999	1.322	5.12	3.91	9.03
4	3.857	4.125	0.134	13.361	11.682	1.679	6.51	5.07	11.58
5	4.805	5.125	0.16	20.626	18.126	2.500	9.67	7.87	17.54
6	5.741	6.125	0.192	29.453	25.874	3.579	13.9	11.2	25.1
8	7.583	8.125	0.271	51.826	45.138	6.888	25.9	19.6	45.5
10	9.449	10.125	0.338	80.463	70.085	10.378	40.3	30.4	70.7
12	11.315	12.125	0.405	115.395	100.480	14.915	57.8	43.6	101.4

Nominal Dia., in.	Circumference, in. Outside	Circumference, in. Inside	Surface Area ft^2/ Lineal ft Outside	Surface Area ft^2/ Lineal ft Inside	Contents of Pipe per Lineal ft ft^3	Contents of Pipe per Lineal ft Gal	Lineal ft to Contain ft^3	Lineal ft to Contain 1 gal	Lineal ft to Contain 1 lb of Water
¼	1.178	0.977	0.098	0.081	0.00052	0.00389	1923	257	30.8
⅜	1.570	1.262	0.131	0.105	0.00088	0.00658	1136	152	18.2
½	1.963	1.655	0.164	0.138	0.00151	0.1129	662	88.6	10.6
⅝	2.355	2.047	0.196	0.171	0.00232	0.1735	431	57.6	6.9
¾	2.748	2.339	0.229	0.195	0.00303	0.02664	330	37.5	5.28
1	3.533	3.124	0.294	0.260	0.00540	0.04039	185	24.8	2.96
1¼	4.318	3.909	0.360	0.326	0.00845	0.06321	118	15.8	1.89
1½	5.103	4.650	0.425	0.388	0.01958	0.14646	51.1	6.83	0.817
2	6.673	6.151	0.556	0.513	0.02092	0.15648	47.8	6.39	0.765
2½	8.243	7.646	0.688	0.637	0.03232	0.2418	30.9	4.14	0.495
3	9.813	9.128	0.818	0.761	0.04607	0.3446	21.7	2.90	0.347
3½	11.388	10.634	0.949	0.886	0.06249	0.46745	15.8	2.14	0.257
4	12.953	12.111	1.080	1.009	0.08113	0.60682	12.3	1.65	0.197
5	16.093	15.088	1.341	1.257	0.12587	0.9415	7.94	1.06	0.127
6	19.233	18.027	1.603	1.502	0.17968	1.3440	5.56	0.744	0.089
8	25.513	23.811	2.126	1.984	0.3135	2.3446	3.19	0.426	0.051
10	31.793	29.67	2.649	2.473	0.48670	3.4405	2.05	0.291	0.033
12	38.073	35.529	3.173	2.961	0.69778	5.2194	1.43	0.192	0.023

PIPING

Table 9-52. Dimensional and Capacity Data – Type L Copper Tube

Nominal	Diameter, in.		Wall Thickness, in.	Cross-Sectional Area, in²			Weight lb/ft		
	Actual Inside	Actual Outside		Outside	Inside	Metal	Pipe Alone	Water in Pipe	Pipe with Water
¼	0.315	0.375	0.030	0.110	0.078	0.032	0.126	0.034	0.160
⅜	0.430	0.500	0.035	0.196	0.145	0.051	0.198	0.063	0.261
½	0.545	0.625	0.040	0.307	0.233	0.074	0.285	0.101	0.386
⅝	0.666	0.750	0.042	0.442	0.348	0.094	0.362	0.151	0.513
¾	0.785	0.875	0.045	0.601	0.484	0.117	0.455	0.210	0.665
1	1.025	1.125	0.050	0.993	0.825	0.168	0.655	0.358	1.013
1¼	1.127	1.375	0.055	1.484	1.256	0.228	0.884	0.545	1.429
1½	1.505	1.625	0.06	2.072	1.778	0.294	1.14	0.77	1.91
2	1.985	2.125	0.070	3.546	3.093	0.453	1.75	1.34	3.09
2½	2.465	2.625	0.08	5.409	4.770	0.639	2.48	2.07	4.55
3	2.945	3.125	0.090	7.669	6.808	0.861	3.33	2.96	6.29
3½	3.425	3.625	0.100	10.321	9.214	1.107	4.29	4.00	8.29
4	3.905	4.125	0.110	13.361	11.971	1.390	5.38	5.20	10.58
5	4.875	5.125	0.125	20.626	18.659	1.967	7.61	8.10	15.71
6	5.845	6.125	0.140	29.453	26.817	2.636	10.2	11.6	21.8
8	7.725	8.125	0.200	51.826	46.849	4.977	19.3	20.3	39.6
10	9.625	10.125	0.250	80.463	72.722	7.741	30.1	31.6	61.7
12	11.565	12.125	0.280	115.395	104.994	10.401	40.4	45.6	86.0

Nominal Dia., in.	Circumference in.		Surface Area ft²/ Lineal ft		Contents of Pipe per Lineal ft		Lineal ft to Contain		
	Outside	Inside	Outside	Inside	ft³	Gal	ft³	1 gal	1 lb of Water
¼	1.178	0.989	0.098	0.082	0.00054	0.0040	1852	250	29.6
⅜	1.570	1.350	0.131	0.113	0.00100	0.0075	1000	133	16.00
½	1.963	1.711	0.164	0.143	0.00162	0.0121	617.3	82.6	9.87
⅝	2.355	2.091	0.196	0.174	0.00242	0.0181	413.2	55.2	6.61
¾	2.748	2.465	0.229	0.205	0.00336	0.2510	297.6	40.5	4.76
1	3.533	3.219	0.294	0.268	0.00573	0.0429	174.5	23.3	2.79
1¼	4.318	3.972	0.360	0.331	0.00872	0.0652	114.7	15.3	1.83
1½	5.103	4.726	0.425	0.394	0.01237	0.0925	80.84	10.8	1.29
2	6.673	6.233	0.556	0.519	0.02147	0.1606	46.58	6.23	0.745
2½	8.243	7.740	0.688	0.645	0.03312	0.2478	30.19	4.04	0.483
3	9.813	9.247	0.818	0.771	0.04728	0.3537	21.15	2.83	0.338
3½	11.388	10.760	0.949	0.897	0.06398	0.4786	15.63	2.09	0.251
4	12.953	12.262	1.08	1.022	0.08313	0.6218	12.03	1.61	0.192
5	16.093	15.308	1.341	1.276	0.12958	0.9693	7.220	1.03	0.123
6	19.233	18.353	1.603	1.529	0.18622	1.393	5.371	0.718	0.0592
8	25.513	24.465	2.126	2.039	0.3253	2.434	3.074	0.411	0.0492
10	31.793	30.223	2.649	2.519	0.50501	3.777	1.98	0.265	0.0317
12	38.073	36.314	3.173	3.026	0.72912	5.454	1.372	0.183	0.0219

Table 9-53. Dimensional and Capacity Data – Type M Copper Tube

Diameter, in.			Wall Thickness, in.	Cross-Sectional Area, in^2			Weight lb/ft		
Nominal	Actual Inside	Actual Outside		Outside	Inside	Metal	Pipe Alone	Water in Pipe	Pipe with Water
⅜	0.4500	0.5000	0.0250	0.1960	0.1590	0.0370	0.1450	0.0690	0.2140
½	0.5690	0.6250	0.0280	0.3070	0.2540	0.0530	0.2040	0.1100	0.3140
¾	0.8110	0.8750	0.0320	0.6010	0.5160	0.0850	0.3280	0.2240	0.5520
1	1.0550	1.1250	0.0350	0.9930	0.8740	0.1190	0.4650	0.379	0.8440
1¼	1.2910	1.3750	0.0420	1.4800	1.3100	0.1700	0.6820	0.569	1.251
1½	1.5270	1.6250	0.0490	2.0700	1.8300	0.2400	0.9400	0.830	1.770
2	2.0090	2.1250	0.0580	3.5500	3.1700	0.3800	1.4600	1.350	2.810
2½	2.4950	2.6250	0.0650	5.4100	4.8900	0.5200	2.0300	2.120	4.150
3	2.9810	3.1250	0.0720	7.6700	6.9800	0.6900	2.6800	3.030	5.710
3½	3.4590	3.6250	0.0830	10.3200	9.4000	0.9240	3.5800	4.080	7.660
4	3.9350	4.1250	0.0950	13.3600	12.1500	1.2100	4.6600	5.230	9.890
5	4.9070	5.1250	0.1090	20.6300	18.9000	1.7300	6.6600	8.200	14.860
6	5.8810	6.1250	0.1220	29.4500	25.1500	2.3000	8.9200	11.780	20.700
8	7.7850	8.1250	0.1700	51.8300	47.5800	4.2500	16.5000	20.700	37.200
10	9.7010	10.1250	0.2120	80.4600	73.8800	6.5800	25.6000	32.100	57.700
12	11.617	12.1250	0.2540	115.4700	105.9900	9.4800	36.7000	46.000	82.700

Nominal Dia., in.	Circumference in.		Surface Area ft^2/ Lineal ft		Contents of Pipe per Lineal Ft		Lineal Ft to Contain		
	Outside	Inside	Outside	Inside	ft^3	Gal	ft^3	1 gal	1 lb of Water
⅜	1.57	1.413	0.131	0.118	0.0011	0.00823	909	122	14.5
½	1.963	1.787	0.164	0.149	0.00176	0.01316	568	76.0	9.09
¾	2.748	2.547	0.229	0.212	0.00358	0.02678	379	37.3	4.47
1	3.533	3.313	0.294	0.276	0.00607	0.0454	164.7	22.0	2.64
1¼	4.318	4.054	0.36	0.338	0.0091	0.06807	109.9	14.7	1.76
1½	5.103	4.795	0.425	0.4	0.01333	0.09971	75.02	10.0	1.20
2	6.673	6.308	0.556	0.526	0.02201	0.16463	45.43	6.08	0.727
2½	8.243	7.834	0.688	0.653	0.03396	0.25402	29.45	3.94	0.471
3	9.813	9.36	0.818	0.78	0.04847	0.36256	20.63	2.76	0.33
3½	11.388	10.867	0.949	0.906	0.06525	0.48813	15.33	2.05	0.246
4	12.953	12.356	1.08	1.03	0.08368	0.62593	11.95	1.60	0.191
5	16.093	15.408	1.341	1.284	0.13125	0.98175	7.62	1.02	0.122
6	19.233	18.466	1.603	1.539	0.18854	1.410	5.30	0.709	0.849
8	25.513	24.445	2.126	2.037	0.33044	2.2472	3.03	0.405	0.484
10	31.793	30.461	2.649	2.538	0.51306	3.838	1.91	0.261	0.312
12	38.073	36.477	3.173	3.039	0.73569	5.503	1.36	0.182	0.217

Table 9-54. Dimensional and Capacity Data – Copper Drainage Tube

Nominal	Diameter, in. Actual Inside	Diameter, in. Actual Outside	Wall Thickness, in.	Cross-Sectional Area, in^2 Outside	Cross-Sectional Area, in^2 Inside	Cross-Sectional Area, in^2 Metal	Weight lb/ft Pipe Alone	Weight lb/ft Water in Pipe	Weight lb/ft Pipe with Water
1¼	1.295	1.375	0.040	1.484	1.317	0.167	0.650	0.572	1.222
1½	1.541	1.625	0.042	2.072	1.865	0.207	0.809	0.809	1.618
2	2.041	2.125	0.042	3.546	3.272	0.274	1.070	1.420	2.490
3	3.035	3.125	0.045	7.669	7.234	0.435	1.690	3.140	4.830
4	4.009	4.125	0.058	13.361	12.623	0.738	2.870	5.480	8.350
5	4.981	5.125	0.072	20.626	19.486	1.140	4.430	8.460	12.890
6	5.590	6.125	0.083	29.453	27.890	1.563	6.10	12.100	15.200

Nominal Diameter in.	Circumference in. Outside	Circumference in. Inside	Surface Area ft^2/ Lineal ft Outside	Surface Area ft^2/ Lineal ft Inside	Contents of Pipe per Lineal ft ft^3	Contents of Pipe per Lineal ft Gal	Lineal ft to Contain ft^3	Lineal ft to Contain 1 gal	Lineal ft to Contain 1 lb of Water
1¼	4.318	4.068	0.360	0.339	0.00914	0.0684	109.400	14.600	1.750
1½	5.103	4.841	0.425	0.403	0.01294	0.09680	97.300	10.300	1.240
2	6.673	6.412	0.556	0.534	0.02271	0.16990	44.000	5.890	0.707
3	9.813	9.535	0.818	0.795	0.05020	0.37550	19.920	2.660	0.319
4	12.953	12.595	1.080	1.050	0.08760	0.65520	11.420	1.530	0.184
5	16.093	15.648	1.341	1.304	0.13523	1.15200	7.390	0.868	0.104
6	19.233	18.721	1.603	1.560	0.19356	1.44780	5.170	0.690	0.083

Table 9-55. Dimensions of Stainless Steel Pipe

Nominal	Outside Diameter	Nominal Wall Thickness in. Schedule 5S	Nominal Wall Thickness in. Schedule 10S	Nominal Wall Thickness in. Schedule 40S	Nominal Wall Thickness in. Schedule 80S	Weight Plain Ends, lb/ft Schedule 5S	Weight Plain Ends, lb/ft Schedule 10S	Weight Plain Ends, lb/ft Schedule 40S	Weight Plain Ends, lb/ft Schedule 80S
⅛	0.405	…	0.049	0.068	0.095	…	0.19	0.24	0.31
¼	0.540	…	0.065	0.088	0.119	…	0.33	0.42	0.54
⅜	0.675	…	0.065	0.091	0.126	…	0.42	0.57	0.74
½	0.840	0.065	0.083	0.109	0.147	0.54	0.67	0.85	1.09
¾	1.050	0.065	0.083	0.113	0.154	0.69	0.86	1.13	1.47
1	1.315	0.065	0.109	0.133	0.179	0.87	1.40	1.68	2.17
1¼	1.660	0.065	0.109	0.140	0.191	1.11	1.81	2.27	3.00
1½	1.900	0.065	0.109	0.145	0.200	1.28	2.09	2.72	3.63
2	2.375	0.065	0.109	0.154	0.218	1.61	2.64	3.65	5.02
2½	2.875	0.083	0.120	0.203	0.276	2.48	3.53	5.79	7.66
3	3.500	0.083	0.120	0.216	0.300	3.03	4.33	7.58	10.25
3½	4.000	0.083	0.120	0.226	0.318	3.48	4.97	9.11	12.51
4	4.500	0.083	0.120	0.237	0.337	3.92	5.61	10.79	14.98
5	5.563	0.109	0.134	0.258	0.375	6.36	7.77	14.62	20.78
6	6.625	0.109	0.134	0.280	0.432	7.60	9.29	18.97	28.57
8	8.625	0.109	0.148	0.322	0.500	9.93	13.40	28.55	43.39
10	10.750	0.134	0.165	0.365	0.500	15.23	18.70	40.48	54.74
12	12.750	0.156	0.180	0.375	0.500	22.22	24.20	49.56	65.42

Table 9-56. Dimensional and Capacity Data – Threadless Copper Pipe

Diameter, in.			Wall Thickness, in.	Area of Bore, in^2	ft^2 of Surface/Lineal ft		Weight, lb/ft	Allowable Internal Pressure, psi		
Nominal	Actual Outside	Actual Inside			Outside	Inside		At 100°	At 200°	At 300°
¼	0.540	0.410	0.065	0.132	0.141	0.107	0.376	1500	1380	1190
⅜	0.675	0.545	0.065	0.233	0.179	0.143	0.483	1170	1070	930
½	0.840	0.710	0.065	0.396	0.220	0.186	0.613	920	850	730
¾	1.050	0.920	0.065	0.665	0.275	0.241	0.780	730	670	580
1	1.315	1.185	0.065	1.100	0.344	0.310	0.989	580	530	460
1¼	1.66	1.530	0.065	1.84	0.435	0.401	1.26	450	420	360
1½	1.900	1.970	0.065	2.46	0.497	0.464	1.45	400	360	310
2	2.375	2.245	0.065	3.96	0.622	0.588	1.83	300	280	240
2½	2.875	2.745	0.065	5.92	0.753	0.719	2.22	250	230	200
3	3.500	3.334	0.083	8.73	0.9	0.874	3.45	260	240	210
3½	4.000	3.810	0.095	11.4	1.05	0.998	4.52	270	250	210
4	4.500	4.286	0.107	14.4	1.18	1.12	5.72	270	240	210
5	5.562	5.298	0.132	22.0	1.46	1.39	8.73	270	250	210
6	6.625	6.309	0.158	31.3	1.73	1.65	12.4	270	250	220
8	8.625	8.215	0.205	53.3	2.26	2.15	21.0	270	250	220
10	10.750	10.238	0.256	82.3	2.81	2.68	32.7	270	250	220
12	12.750	12.124	0.313	115.4	3.34	3.18	47.4	280	260	220

All weights in these tables are calculated values. Values in these tables for allowable internal pressure are based on the formula:

$$P = \frac{2St_m}{D - 0.80t_m}$$

where

P = maximum rated internal working pressure, psi;

t_m = pipe wall thickness, in.;

D = outside diameter of pipe, in.; and

S = allowable stress in material due to internal pressure, psi
6000 at 100°; 5500 at 200°; 4750 at 300°; and 3000 at 400°.

Table 9-57. Dimensional and Capacity Data – Refrigeration Field Service Copper Tube

Diameter, in.			Wall Thickness, in.	Area of Bore, in^2	ft^2 of Surface/Lineal ft		Weight, lb/ft	Allowable Internal Pressure, psi		
Nominal	Actual Outside	Actual Inside			Outside	Inside		At 100°	At 200°	At 300°
⅛	0.125	0.065	0.030	0.0033	0.0327	0.0170	0.0347	3130	2870	2480
3/16	0.188	0.128	0.030	0.013	0.0492	0.0335	0.0577	1990	1820	1570
¼	0.250	0.190	0.030	0.0284	0.0655	0.0497	0.0804	1450	1330	1150
5/16	0.312	0.248	0.032	0.0483	0.0817	0.0649	0.109	1230	1120	970
⅜	0.375	0.311	0.032	0.076	0.0982	0.0814	0.134	1010	920	800
½	0.500	0.436	0.032	0.149	0.131	0.114	0.182	740	680	590
⅝	0.625	0.555	0.035	0.242	0.164	0.145	0.251	640	590	510
¾	0.750	0.680	0.035	0.363	0.196	0.178	0.305	520	480	410

Table 9-58. Dimensional and Capacity Data – Standard Copper Pipe

	Diameter, in.		Wall Thickness, in.	Cross-Sectional Area, in²			Weight lb/ft		
Nominal	Actual Inside	Actual Outside		Outside	Inside	Metal	Pipe Alone	Water in Pipe	Pipe with Water
⅛	0.281	0.405	0.062	0.129	0.062	0.067	0.259	0.0269	0.286
¼	0.376	0.540	0.082	0.229	0.111	0.118	0.457	0.0481	0.505
⅜	0.495	0.675	0.090	0.358	0.192	0.166	0.641	0.0831	0.724
½	0.626	0.840	0.107	0.554	0.308	0.246	0.955	0.1338	1.09
¾	0.822	1.050	0.114	0.866	0.531	0.335	1.30	0.2306	1.53
1	1.063	1.315	0.126	1.358	0.888	0.470	1.82	0.3856	2.21
1¼	1.368	1.66	0.146	2.165	1.469	0.696	2.69	0.6375	3.33
1½	1.600	1.900	0.150	2.835	2.011	0.824	3.20	0.8731	4.07
2	2.063	2.375	0.156	4.430	3.343	1.087	4.22	1.451	5.67
2½	2.501	2.875	0.187	6.492	4.913	1.579	6.12	2.133	8.25
3	3.062	3.500	0.219	9.621	7.364	2.945	8.75	3.196	11.95
3½	3.500	4.000	0.250	12.566	9.621	2.945	11.4	4.176	15.6
4	4.000	4.500	0.250	15.904	12.566	3.338	12.9	5.454	18.4
5	5.062	5.562	0.250	24.300	20.122	4.178	16.2	8.734	24.9
6	6.125	6.625	0.250	34.471	29.468	5.003	19.4	12.79	32.2
8	8.001	8.625	0.312	58.426	50.281	8.145	31.6	21.82	53.4
10	10.020	10.750	0.365	90.761	78.854	11.907	46.2	34.23	80.4
12	12.000	12.750	0.375	127.675	113.098	14.577	56.5	49.09	105.6

Nominal Dia., in.	Circumference in.		Surface Area ft²/ Lineal ft		Contents of Pipe per Lineal ft		Lineal ft to Contain		
	Outside	Inside	Outside	Inside	ft³	gal	1 ft³	1 gal	1 lb of Water
⅛	1.272	0.883	0.106	0.074	0.00043	0.00322	2325.6	310.6	37.17
¼	1.696	1.181	0.141	0.098	0.00077	0.00576	1298.7	173.6	20.79
⅜	2.121	1.555	0.177	0.130	0.00133	0.00995	751.9	100.5	12.03
½	2.639	1.967	0.220	0.164	0.00214	0.01601	467.3	62.5	7.47
¾	3.299	2.582	0.275	0.215	0.00369	0.0276	271.0	36.2	4.34
1	4.131	3.340	0.344	0.278	0.00617	0.04615	162.1	21.7	2.59
1¼	5.215	4.298	0.435	0.358	0.01020	0.07630	98.0	13.1	1.57
1½	5.969	5.027	0.497	0.419	0.01397	0.10450	71.6	9.57	1.15
2	7.461	6.481	0.622	0.540	0.02322	0.17369	43.1	5.76	0.689
2½	9.032	7.857	0.753	0.655	0.03412	0.25522	29.3	3.92	0.469
3	10.996	9.620	0.916	0.802	0.05114	0.38253	19.6	2.61	0.313
3½	12.566	10.966	1.047	0.916	0.06681	0.49974	15.0	2.00	0.239
4	14.137	12.566	1.178	1.047	0.08726	0.65270	11.5	1.53	0.183
5	17.474	15.903	1.456	1.325	0.13974	1.0453	7.2	0.96	0.114
6	20.813	19.242	1.734	1.603	0.20464	1.5307	4.9	0.65	0.078
8	27.096	25.136	2.258	2.095	0.34917	2.6118	2.9	0.38	0.046
10	33.772	31.479	2.814	2.623	0.54760	4.096	1.8	0.24	0.029
12	40.055	37.699	3.338	3.142	0.78540	5.8748	1.3	0.17	0.020

Table 9-59. Dimensional and Capacity Data – Extra Strong Copper Pipe

Nominal	Actual Inside	Actual Outside	Wall Thickness, in.	Outside	Inside	Metal	Pipe Alone	Water in Pipe	Pipe with Water
⅛	0.205	0.405	0.100	0.129	0.033	0.096	0.391	0.0144	0.385
¼	0.294	0.540	0.123	0.229	0.067	0.162	0.625	0.0294	0.654
⅜	0.421	0.675	0.127	0.358	0.139	0.219	0.847	0.0606	0.908
½	0.542	0.84	0.149	0.554	0.231	0.323	1.25	0.100	1.35
¾	0.736	1.050	0.157	0.866	0.425	0.441	1.71	0.1844	1.89
1	0.951	1.315	0.182	1.358	0.710	0.648	2.51	0.3081	2.82
1¼	1.272	1.66	0.194	2.165	1.271	0.894	3.46	0.5519	4.01
1½	1.494	1.900	0.203	2.835	1.753	1.082	4.19	0.7606	4.95
2	1.933	2.375	0.221	4.430	2.934	1.496	5.8	1.273	7.07
2½	2.315	2.875	0.280	6.492	4.209	2.283	8.5	1.827	10.7
3	2.892	3.500	0.304	9.621	6.569	3.052	11.8	2.851	14.7
3½	3.358	4.000	0.321	12.566	8.859	3.707	14.4	3.845	18.2
4	3.818	4.500	0.341	15.904	11.451	4.453	17.3	4.970	22.3
5	4.792	5.562	0.375	24.300	18.033	6.267	23.7	7.827	31.5
6	5.751	6.625	0.437	34.471	25.973	8.498	32.9	11.27	44.2
8	7.625	8.625	0.500	58.426	45.663	12.763	49.5	19.82	69.3
10	9.750	10.750	0.500	90.761	74.660	16.101	62.4	32.40	94.8

Nominal Dia., in.	Outside	Inside	Outside	Inside	ft³	gal	ft³	1 gal	1 lb of Water
⅛	1.272	0.644	0.106	0.054	0.00097	0.00726	1030.9	137.7	16.50
¼	1.696	0.924	0.141	0.077	0.00047	0.00172	2127.7	581.4	69.44
⅜	2.121	1.323	0.177	0.110	0.00023	0.00352	4347.8	284.1	34.01
½	2.639	1.703	0.220	0.142	0.0016	0.01197	625.0	83.5	10.00
¾	3.299	2.312	0.275	0.193	0.00295	0.02207	393.0	45.3	5.42
1	4.131	2.988	0.344	0.249	0.00493	0.03688	202.8	27.1	3.25
1¼	5.215	3.996	0.435	0.333	0.00883	0.06605	113.3	15.1	1.81
1½	5.969	4.694	0.497	0.391	0.01217	0.09103	82.2	11.0	1.31
2	7.461	6.073	0.622	0.506	0.02037	0.15237	49.1	6.56	0.785
2½	9.032	7.273	0.753	0.606	0.02923	0.21864	34.2	4.57	0.547
3	10.996	9.086	0.916	0.757	0.04562	0.34124	21.9	2.93	0.351
3½	12.566	10.549	1.047	0.879	0.06152	0.46017	16.3	2.17	0.260
4	14.137	11.995	1.178	1.000	0.07952	0.59481	12.6	1.68	0.201
5	17.474	15.055	1.456	1.255	0.12523	0.93672	8.0	1.07	0.128
6	20.813	18.067	1.734	1.506	0.18037	1.3492	5.5	0.74	0.089
8	27.096	23.955	2.258	1.996	0.31710	2.3719	3.2	0.42	0.050
10	33.772	30.631	2.814	2.553	0.51847	3.8782	1.9	0.26	0.031

Table 9-60. Lead Pipe

Inside Diameter, in.	Class of Pipe[a]	Commercial Designations[b]		Wall Thickness, in.	Minimum Outside Circumference, in.	Weight per ft	
		East	West			lbs	oz
Water Service Pipe							
$\frac{3}{8}$	50	A	S	0.143	$2\frac{1}{16}$	1	4
	75	AA	XS	0.175	$2\frac{1}{8}$	1	8
	100	AAA	XXS	0.256	$2\frac{5}{8}$	2	8
$\frac{1}{2}$	50	A	S	0.149	$2\frac{3}{8}$	1	8
	75	AA	XS	0.188	$2\frac{5}{8}$	2	0
	100	AAA	XXS	0.256	$3\frac{1}{16}$	3	0
$\frac{5}{8}$	50	A	S	0.197	$3\frac{1}{16}$	2	8
	75	AA	XS	0.228	$3\frac{1}{4}$	3	0
	100	AAA	XXS	0.256	$3\frac{7}{16}$	3	8
$\frac{3}{4}$	50	A	S	0.203	$3\frac{1}{2}$	3	0
	75	AA	XS	0.231	$3\frac{11}{16}$	3	8
	100	AAA	XXS	0.293	$4\frac{1}{16}$	4	12
	50	A	S	0.214	$4\frac{5}{16}$	4	0
	75	AA	XS	0.246	$4\frac{9}{16}$	4	12
	100	AAA	XXS	0.298	$4\frac{7}{8}$	6	0
$1\frac{1}{4}$	50	A	S	0.210	$5\frac{1}{8}$	4	12
	75	AA	XS	0.258	$5\frac{3}{8}$	6	0
	100	AAA	XXS	0.320	$5\frac{3}{16}$	7	12
$1\frac{1}{2}$	50	A	S	0.242	$6\frac{1}{16}$	6	8
	75	AA	XS	0.288	$6\frac{3}{8}$	8	0
	100	AAA	XXS	0.386	7	11	4
2	50	A	S	0.252	$7\frac{3}{4}$	8	12
	75	AA	XS	0.376	$8\frac{1}{2}$	13	12
	100	AAA	XXS	0.504	$9\frac{5}{16}$	19	8
Soil and Waste Pipe							
$1\frac{1}{4}$		D	XL	0.118	$4\frac{1}{2}$	2	8
		C	L	0.139	$4\frac{11}{16}$	3	0
		B	M	0.171	$4\frac{7}{8}$	3	12
$1\frac{1}{2}$		D	XL	0.138	$5\frac{7}{16}$	3	8
		C	L	0.165	$5\frac{5}{8}$	4	4
		B	M	0.191	$5\frac{3}{4}$	5	0
2		D	XL	0.142	$7\frac{1}{16}$	4	12
		C	L	0.177	$7\frac{1}{4}$	6	0
		B	M	0.205	$7\frac{7}{16}$	7	0
$2\frac{1}{2}$		D	XL	0.125	$8\frac{1}{2}$	5	0
		B	M	0.250	$9\frac{5}{16}$	10	10
3		D	XL	0.125	$10\frac{1}{16}$	6	0
		B	M	0.250	$10\frac{7}{8}$	12	8
4		D	XL	0.125	$13\frac{3}{16}$	8	0
		B	M	0.250	14	16	6
5		D	XL	0.125	$16\frac{3}{8}$	10	0
		B	M	0.250	$17\frac{1}{8}$	20	4
6		D	XL	0.125	$19\frac{1}{2}$	11	12
		B	M	0.250	$20\frac{1}{4}$	24	2

[a] Class of pipe also indicates maximum working pressure in psi.
[b] Designations ordinarily used east and west, respectively, of the Illinois–Indiana State line.

Plastics Pipe.—The following information covers the characteristics and applications of thermoplastics piping. The word thermoplastics differentiates this group of plastic piping from one composed of different plastics materials which are called thermosets. While thermoplastic materials can be softened and hardened repeatedly by heating and cooling, thermosets cannot. Thermoset piping materials are not discussed below since they are normally restricted to specialized industrial applications.

Plastics piping technology is still relatively new, hence its technical data tend to become obsolete within a few years. Continued awareness of the latest product information is, therefore, a must for the serious practitioner.

The principal advantages of plastics piping are its light weight, its quick-joining techniques, its high resistance to corrosion, its chemical inertness, and generally lower friction losses.

The following are the major, or most common, thermoplastics piping materials: acrylonitrile butadiene styrene (ABS); polyethylene (PE); polybutylene (PB); polypropylene (PP); polyvinyl chloride (PVC); and chlorinated polyvinyl chloride (CPVC). Although these plastics piping materials have overlapping characteristics, each does have certain properties and capabilities that are highly suitable for specific applications. Each is also readily available commercially.

Thermoplastic piping can be divided into two categories, *rigid* and *flexible*. A brief description of the more common applications of the major thermoplastics piping materials is as follows:

Acrylonitrile Butadiene Styrene (ABS): This pipe is a rigid type and is found most commonly in drain, waste, and vent (DWV) systems, building drains, building sewers, well casings, electrical and communications conduits and rainwater conductors. Although ABS can be used as pressure piping, it is generally used in non-pressure systems because of its lower hydrostatic design stress rating.

Polyethylene (PE): This is a member of the polyolefin family of plastics. *PE* is flexible and is usually found underground in such applications as natural gas distribution lines, gas service, water service, and turf and agricultural irrigation systems. It also serves as a reliner for deteriorated gas or sewer mains.

Polybutylene (PB): This is a flexible material resembling a high density polyethylene but has advantages in pressure and heat resistance performance. In addition to those applications common to PE, PB piping can be used for hot and cold water distribution.

Polypropylene (PP): This pipe is another member of the polyolefin family, but it differs from polyethylene and Polybutylene in that it is more rigid and may be used at slightly higher temperatures than *PE* Also, it is common to chemical waste systems because of its high degree of chemical resistance.

Polyvinyl Chloride (PVC): PVC is the most widely used thermoplastic pipe. It is a rigid type that is used for *DWV* systems, water service and water mains, electrical and communications conduits, turf and agricultural irrigation, well casings, building sewers and sewer mains, and chemical process piping.

Chlorinated Polyvinyl Chloride (CPVC): This pipe is a variation of PVC sometimes known as Type IV PVC. It is designed to withstand higher temperatures and therefore has application in both hot and cold water distribution, as well as in hot chemical systems.

Joining Techniques.—Common joining techniques for thermoplastics piping include solvent cementing, elastomeric sealing, mechanical coupling, heat fusion, flaring, insert fitting, flanging, and threading.

Solvent Cementing: A technique used on ABS, PVC, and CPVC pipe, where it requires socket-type fittings or bell ends. However, PE, PB, and PP pipe, because of their high resistance to chemicals, cannot be joined by this method. The solvent cement is applied to both pipe and fitting, momentarily dissolving the surfaces of each. The pipe and fitting are then joined while the cement is still wet. Once the solvent evaporates (usually in only 2 to 3 minutes), the bond sets permanently. However, it must be remembered that specific cements are designed for use only with designated plastics materials.

Elastomeric Sealing: This has applications in joining PVC piping with diameter 6 inches and above. In these larger pipe sizes solvent cementing becomes difficult. Such piping is manufactured with integral grooved bells on the end of each length of pipe. A specially designed rubber ring is placed into the groove. The straight end of the next pipe is then pushed into the bell, and the elastomeric seal forms a pressure-tight fitting. These types of joints are commonly used in underground applications, such as water, sewer, and irrigation piping.

Mechanical Couplings: This technique is available in a number of proprietary designs, and can join plastic piping to itself or to other materials. In some cases, stiffeners are inserted into the pipe with a metal clamp or collar which is placed over the pipe and then tightened, Some mechanical couplings afford pull-out resistance while others are designed only to maintain operating pressure.

Heat Fusion: This method is used to join PE, PB, or PP piping. Heat fusion with a hot-air torch was a common practice at one time. However, since fittings of nearly every configuration are now easily obtained, it is a technique that is rarely applied today. Various heating tools still are available for fusing pipe ends together with socket fittings or for plain butt fusion. In butt fusion the plain ends of pipe are heated, and are pressed or *butted* together while still hot. Cooling brings about a permanently fused joint.

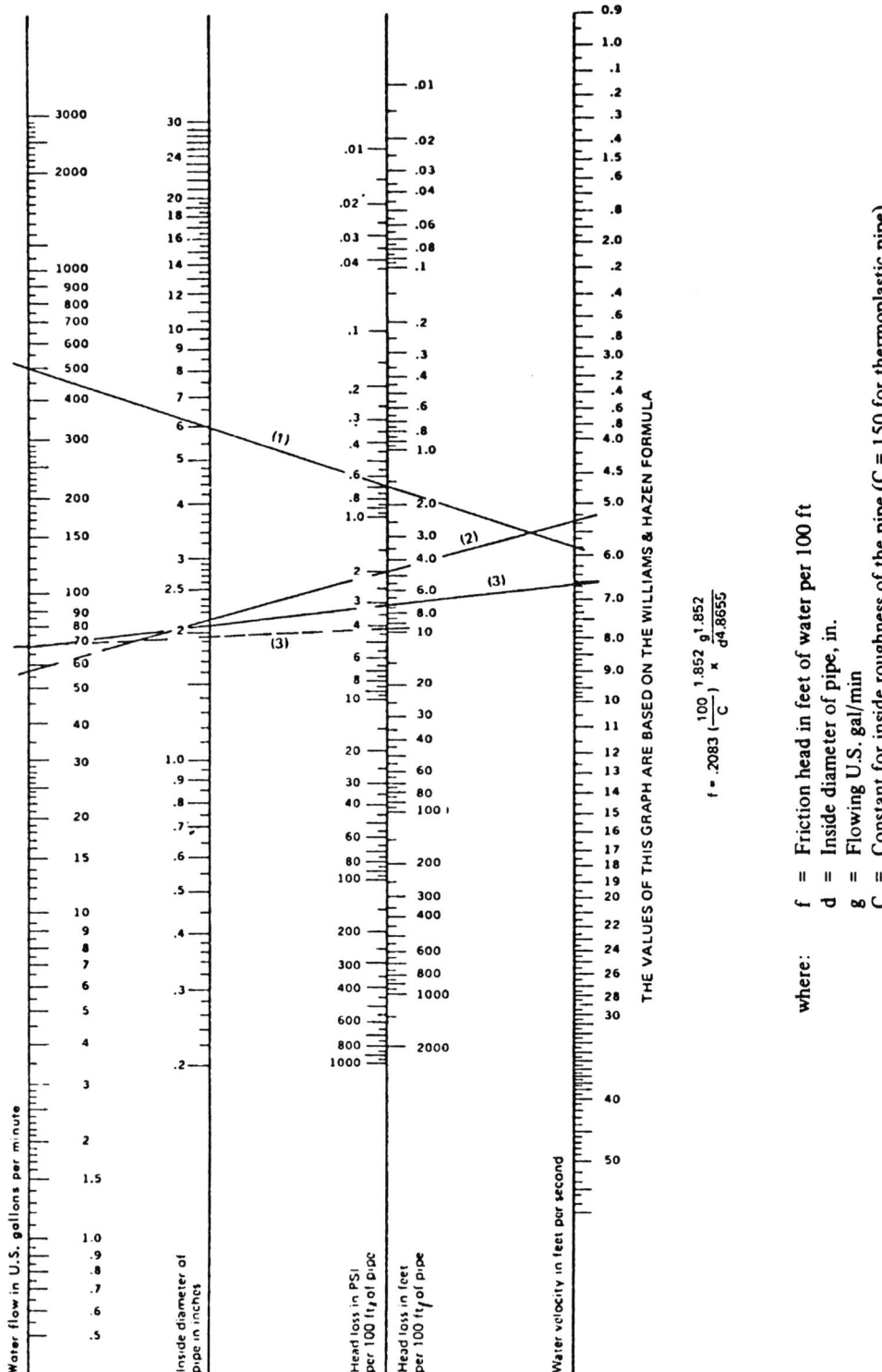

Fig 9-40. Flow loss characteristics of water flow through rigid plastic pipe

Flaring: Flaring involves the use of tools designed specifically for the purpose. Flexible plastics such as PE and PB can be cold-flared for joining with flare nuts. This technique is commonly used for fitting transitions.

Insert Fittings: This consists of metallic or plastic inserts that are forced into the ends of the pipe. A stainless steel hose clamp is then placed on the outside of the pipe and tightened. This type of joint may also be used as a transition fitting for joining plastic pipe to pipe of some other material.

Flanging: This is often required in industrial process piping systems at various points where frequent assembly and disassembly is necessary. Flanges with bolt-holes can be solvent-cemented to the plain ends of PVC pipe in the make-up of such joints.

Threading: This can be accomplished on rigid plastic pipe by using special thread cutters. Such pipe must have wall thicknesses conforming to Schedule 80 or 120, since Schedule 40 plastic pipe lacks sufficient wall thickness to support threads. Also, for plastic pipe a Teflon tape or an emulsion is used, rather than standard pipe dope. A strap wrench is used to tighten the fitting, with care taken not to overseas the connection.

Standards for Specification and Identification.—

Although there are standards for plastics piping published by several agencies, the industry has concentrated most of its standards-writing activities with the American Society for Testing and Materials (ASTM).

Volume 34 of the ASTM standards is a complete collection dealing with thermoplastics piping. These standards specify dimensional data and tolerances, pressure and temperature capabilities, as well as other physical characteristics such as impact resistance, crush resistance, and tensile strength. Familiarity with these standards is of great importance when designing and installing plastic piping systems.

Most ASTM standards require that the pipe be clearly marked with the name of the manufacturer, the plastic material from which the pipe was extruded, the nominal diameter of the pipe, the ASTM standard to which it was manufactured, and with whatever certifying agencies that are required. Pipe markings must be clearly visible throughout the length of the pipe and should be of sufficient permanence that they will not rub off during normal handling. Pipe or fittings which are not identified in the manner specified should never be accepted.

Design Parameters.—The basic design parameters for plastics piping, such as thermal expansion, chemical resistance, flow characteristics, and pressure ratings are essentially the same as for any other piping material. The only difference lies in the numerical values of these parameters.

Coefficients of thermal expansion for a number of piping materials are given in Table 9-61. The data show that plastic pipe undergoes far greater dimensional change than metal pipe for a given temperature differential. However, the force of expansion generated in plastics is so much less than in metal that potentially destructive stresses are also substantially smaller in magnitude. Nevertheless, where temperature differentials of more than 30°F are anticipated, provision for the control of thermal movement must be made. Some recommendations follow:

Table 9-61. Coefficients of Thermal Expansion[a]

Material	Nominal Coefficients $\times 10^{-5}$ in./in.°F
ABS- Acrylonitrile butadiene styrene	4.0–6.0
PE (Polyethylene) – Type-1	10.0
PE (Polyethylene) – Type-II	8.0–9.0
PE (Polyethylene) – Type-III	7.0
PE (Polyethylene) – Type-IV high molecular weight	6.0
PVC Type -I – Rigid and unplasticized poly vinyl chloride; PVC 1120 and PVC 1220	3.0–3.5
PVC Type -II– Rubber modified poly vinyl chloride; PVC 2110, 2112, 2116, and 2120	3.0–5.0
CPVC Chlorinated poly vinyl chloride. Formerly designated as PVC 4120.	3.5
SR - Styrene rubber	3.3–5.0
PB -Polybutylene	7.2
PP - Polypropylene	4.0–4.8
CAB- Cellubose acetate butynate	8.0–9.5
Acetyl	4.5–5.0
Steel	0.65
Cast iron	0.56
Copper	0.98

[a] These values are independent of pipe diameter.

Below Ground: Small-diameter piping can be *snaked* in the trench; that is, laid in the trench in a sinuous configuration rather than in a straight line. Large-diameter piping must be provided with expansion loops. Prolonged exposure of plastic pipe to sunlight while it awaits burial in the trench will cause heating and therefore expansion. Thus, before the final connection is made, piping should be allowed to cool to operating temperature. Otherwise, after connection the potential of failure from joint pull-out will exist.

Above Ground: Piping systems with many changes of direction and relatively short runs usually do not require expansion control. The DWV system in a single-family dwelling would be one such system. The DWV system in a multistory building, however, would require some attention to thermal expansion, specifically in vertical stacks, which run in a straight line through the entire height of the building. In such non-pressure applications, it is recommended that restraint fittings or O-ring expansion joints be installed at all points of potential strain.

Chemical Resistance: Generally plastics are impervious to a wider range of chemicals than are metals. However, they are not resistant to all chemicals. Factors that determine the suitability of each particular plastic material when exposed to a certain chemical include:

1) the specific chemical and its concentration;

2) the specific plastic compound within the pipe or fitting;

3) the joining method;

4) the dimensions of the pipe and fittings;

5) the pressure;

6) the temperature;

7) the period of contact with the chemical;

8) other service conditions that may introduce stress concentrations in pipe or fittings.

Water solutions of neutral inorganic salts such as sodium chloride, aluminum potassium sulfate, calcium chloride, copper sulfate, potassium sulfate, and zinc chloride generally have the same effect on thermoplastics piping materials as does water alone. With organic chemicals in a specific series, such as alcohols, ketones, or organic acids, the resistance of a particular plastic increases as the molecular weight of the chemical increases. Thus, one type of PVC is not suitable for transporting ethyl acetate at 73°F, but it may be used with butyl acetate at that temperature. Complete technical data on chemical resistance can be obtained from the Society of the Plastics Industry. It is strongly recommended, however, that each user satisfy himself by means of tests approximating actual conditions, or from previous experience, before a particular plastic piping system is chosen to transport a specific chemical.

Flow Characteristics: The head losses that occur because of liquid flowing in plastic piping systems are calculated using the William and Hazen formula, in a similar manner as those for other piping materials. In this formula, the constant for inside roughness (C) of plastic is 150. Because the surface of plastic pipe is smooth and slippery, its frictional resistance is considerably less than that of other piping materials. Further, the C value remains fairly constant over extended periods of use due to the material's inherent resistance to corrosion and to the build-up of scale.

Fig. 9-40 provides a nomograph giving the flow capacity for water in different standard commercial sizes of thermoplastic pipe.

Pressure Ratings: The recommended pressure ratings for plastics pipes that meet current ASTM standards are given in Tables 9-62 through 9-72. Threaded *PVC* and *ABS* pipe should be pressure rated at 50 percent of the non-threaded rating. The pressure ratings shown make some allowance for surge and water hammer. However, when excessive surges and water hammer are likely to be

encountered, extra allowance should be made, or protective devices installed.

The plastics piping industry uses two-dimensional systems for pressure pipe. One is the Schedule system (Schedule 40, 80, and 120) which emulates the Iron Pipe Sizes (IPS) used in metal piping. The other, referred to as the standard dimension ratio (SDR) system, is unique to plastics pipe. This latter system results in uniform pressure ratings regardless of pipe diameter, while in the Schedule system pressure ratings vary according to diameter. Pressure ratings are temperature dependent. Ratings shown in the Tables are at 73°F, and a derating factor must be employed when a designer or engineer considers use at elevated temperatures.

Table 9-62. Standard Thermoplastic Dimension Ratios (SDR) and Water Pressure Rating (PR) at 23 °C (73° F) for SDR-PR ABS Plastic Pipe

Standard Dimension Ratio	ABS Pipe Material			
	ABS 1316	ABS 2112	ABS 1210	ABS 1208
	Pressure Rating, psia			
13.5	250	200	160	125
17	200	160	125	100
21	160	125	100	…
26	125	100	…	…
Pressure Rating, psi	Standard Dimension Ratio			
250	13.5	…	…	…
200	17	13.5	…	…
160	21	17	13.5	…
125	26	21	17	13.5
100	…	26	21	17

Table 9-63. Water Pressure Ratings at 23°C (73°F) for Schedule 40 ABS Plastic Pipe

Nominal Pipe Size in.	Pressure Ratings, psia			
	ABS 1208	ABS 1210	ABS 1316	ABS 2112
½	240	300	480	370
¾	190	240	390	300
1	180	220	360	280
1¼	150	180	290	230
1½	130	170	260	210
2	110	140	220	170
2½	120	150	240	190
3	100	130	210	160
3½	90	120	190	150
4	90	110	180	140
5	80	110	160	120
6	…	90	140	110
8	…	80	120	100
10	…	…	110	90
12	…	…	110	80

Table 9-64. Water Pressure Ratings at 23°C (73°F) for Schedule 80 ABS Plastic Pipe

Nominal Pipe Size in.	ABS 1208		ABS 1210		ABS 1318		ABS 2112	
	Unthreaded	Threaded	Unthreaded	Threaded	Unthreaded	Threaded	Unthreaded	Threaded
½	340	170	420	210	680	340	530	260
¾	280	140	340	170	550	280	430	210
1	250	130	320	160	500	250	390	200
1¼	210	100	260	130	420	210	330	160
1½	190	90	240	120	380	190	290	150
2	160	80	200	100	320	160	250	130
2½	170	80	210	110	340	170	270	130
3	150	…	190	90	300	150	230	120
3½	140	…	170	90	280	140	220	110
4	130	…	160	…	260	130	200	100
5	120	…	140	…	230	120	180	90
6	110	…	140	…	220	110	170	90
8	100	…	120	…	200	100	150	80
10	90	…	120	…	190	90	150	…
12	90	…	110	…	180	90	140	…

Table 9-65. Standard Thermoplastic Pipe Dimension Ratios (SDR) and Water Pressure Ratings (PR) at 23 °C (73° F) for SDR-PR PE Plastic Pipe Outside Diameter Control

Standard Dimension Ratio	Pressure Rating, psia		
	PE 3406, PE 3306, PE 2306	PE 2305	PE 1404
11	125	100	80
13.5	100	80	…
17	80	…	…
Pressure Rating psi	Standard Dimension Ratio		
125	11	…	…
100	13.5	11	…
80	17	13.5	11
80	15	11.5	9

Standard Dimension Ratio	PE 3406, PE 3306, PE 2306	PE 2305	PE 1404
	Pressure Rating, psi		
5.3	200	160	125
7	160	125	100
9	125	100	80
11.5	100	80	…
15	80	…	…
Pressure Rating, psi	Standard Dimension Ratio		
200	5.3	…	…
160	7	5.3	…
125	9	7	5.3
100	11.5	9	7
80	15	11.5	9

Table 9-66. Water Pressure Ratings at 23 °C (73°F) for Schedule 40 PE Plastic Pipe, Inside Diameter Control

Nominal Pipe Size in.	Pressure Ratings, psi		
	PE 2306, PE 3306, PE 3406	PE 2305	PE 1404
½	190	150	120
¾	150	120	100
1	140	110	90
1¼	120	90	70
1½	100	80	70
2	90	70	60
2½	100	80	60
3	80	70	50
4	70	60	NPR
6	60	NPR	NPR

Table 9-67. Water Pressure Ratings at 23 °C (73°F) for Schedule 40 PE Plastic Pipe, Outside Diameter Control

Nominal Pipe Size in.	Pressure Rating, psia					
	PE 2306, PE 3306, PE 3406		PE 2305		PE 1404	
	SCH 40	SCH 80	SCH 40	SCH 80	SCH 40	SCH 80
½	188	267	149	212	119	170
¾	152	217	120	172	96	137
1	142	199	113	158	90	126
1¼	116	164	92	130	74	104
1½	104	148	83	118	66	94
2	87	127	69	101	55	81
2½	96	134	76	106	61	85
3	83	118	66	94	53	75
3½	75	109	60	86	50	69
4	70	102	55	81	NPR	65
5	61	91	50	72	NPR	58
6	55	88	NPR	70	NPR	56
8	50	…	NPR	…	NPR	…

Table 9-68. Standard Thermoplastic Pipe Dimension Ratios (SDR) and Water Pressure Ratings (PR) at 23 °C (73° F) for PVC Plastic Pipe

Standard Dimension Ratio	CPVC 4120 PVC 1120 and PVC 1220	PVC 2116	PVC 2112	PVC 2110
	Pressure Rating, psi			
13.5	315	250	200	160
17	250	200	160	125
21	200	160	125	100
26	160	125	100	…
32.5	125	100	…	…
Pressure Rating, psi	Standard Dimension Ratio			
315	13.5	…	…	…
250	17	13.5	…	…
200	21	17	13.5	…
160	26	21	17	13.5
125	32.5	26	21	17
100	41	32.5	26	21

Table 9-69. Water Pressure Ratings at 23 °C (73° F) for Schedule 80 PVC Plastic Pipe

Nominal Pipe Size in.	Pressure Ratings, psi							
	CPVC 4120 PVC 1120 PVC 1120		PVC 2216		PVC 2112		PVC 2110	
	Unthreaded	Threaded	Unthreaded	Threaded	Unthreaded	Threaded	Unthreaded	Threaded
½	850	420	680	340	530	260	420	210
¾	690	340	550	280	430	210	340	170
1	630	320	500	250	390	200	320	160
1¼	520	260	420	210	320	160	260	130
1½	470	240	380	190	290	150	240	120
2	400	200	320	160	250	130	200	100
2½	420	340	340	170	260	130	210	110
3	370	190	300	150	230	120	190	90
3½	350	170	280	140	220	110	170	90
4	320	160	260	130	200	100	160	80
5	290	140	230	120	180	90	140	…
6	280	140	220	110	170	90	140	…
8	250	120	200	100	150	80	120	…
10	230	120	190	90	150	…	120	…
12	230	110	180	90	140	…	110	…

Table 9-70. Water Pressure Ratings at 23 °C (73° F) for Schedule 120 PVC Plastic Pipe

Nominal Pipe Size in.	Pressure Ratings, psi							
	CPVC 4120 PVC 1120 PVC 1220		PVC 2116		PVC 2112		PVC 2110	
	Unthreaded	Threaded	Unthreaded	Threaded	Unthreaded	Threaded	Unthreaded	Threaded
½	1010	510	810	410	630	320	510	250
¾	770	390	620	310	480	240	390	190
1	720	360	570	290	450	220	360	180
1¼	600	300	480	240	370	190	300	150
1½	540	270	430	210	340	170	270	130
2	470	240	380	190	290	150	240	120
2½	470	230	370	190	290	150	230	120
3	440	220	360	180	280	140	220	110
3½	380	190	310	150	240	120	190	100
4	430	220	340	170	270	130	220	110
5	400	200	320	160	250	120	200	100
6	370	190	300	150	230	120	190	90
8	380	180	290	140	230	110	180	90
10	370	180	290	140	230	110	180	90
12	340	170	270	140	210	110	170	80

Table 9-71. Standard Thermoplastic Pipe Dimension Ratios (SDR) and Water Pressure Rating (PR) at 23 for SDR-PR PB Plastic Pipe

Standard Dimension Ratio	PB 2110
	Pressure Rating, psi
9	200
11.5	160
15	125

Table 9-72. Water Pressure Ratings at 23 °C (73°F) for Schedule 40 PVC Plastic Pipe

Nominal Pipe Size in.	Pressure Rating, psi			
	PVC1120 PVC1120 CPVC 4120	PVC 2116	PVC 2110	PVC 2112
½	600	450	300	370
¾	480	390	240	300
1	450	360	220	280
1¼	370	290	180	230
1½	330	260	170	210
2	280	220	140	170
2½	300	240	150	190
3	260	210	130	160
3½	240	190	120	150
4	220	180	110	140
5	190	160	100	120
6	180	140	90	110
8	160	120	80	100
10	140	110	…	90
12	130	110	…	80

Installation.—*Storage Handling:* Exposure to direct sunlight for extended periods of time (longer than one year) can have detrimental effects on plastics pipe. Piping that must be stored outdoors should be covered and placed in racks that give continuous support to prevent sagging or draping. Because plastic pipe is softer than metal, it is more susceptible to damage by abrasion or gouging. Therefore, such practices as dragging the pipe over rough ground or over sharp projections, or throwing it from trucks when unloading it, should be avoided. Dropping plastic piping from great heights, particularly in cold weather, should also be avoided since at lower temperatures plastics tend to lose some of their impact resistance.

Above Ground: Rigid plastics piping must be supported above ground at intervals that will prevent sagging. Ordinary pipe hangers and brackets may be used, as long as overtightening is avoided and they do not cut, abrade, or distort the pipe. Valves should be properly anchored so that their use will not apply a torque to the piping. Since the strength of plastics piping is dependent on temperature, such piping should not be installed near hot objects or in areas of high ambient temperature.

Below Ground: The most critical aspects of below-ground installation are the preparation of the trench and the backfilling after installation. The trench bottom must support the pipe evenly throughout its entire length, hence, the use of blocks to attain desired grade is to be avoided. Where a smooth trench bottom cannot be attained in the initial excavation, a bed of sand or fine granular soil should be placed on the bottom of the trench. Care must be exercised to keep rocks and boulders from coming into direct contact with the piping.

Selected backfill materials should be used to surround the pipe. It should be placed in layers; each soil layer should be sufficiently compacted to uniformly develop lateral passive soil forces during the backfill operation. As an added protective measure during installation, it may often be advisable to have the pipe under pressure during backfilling procedures.

Codes and Regulations.—The degree to which plastics piping is allowed in mechanical and plumbing systems varies widely from one jurisdiction to another. Therefore, before plastics piping is specified or installed, it is advisable to consult the regulatory agency having jurisdiction. One municipality, for example, may allow the use of plastic DWV piping in any type of building, while another may restrict its use according to building height or occupancy. It is, therefore essential that an engineer or designer have a clear understanding of any such restrictions well in advance of installation.

Because plastic are combustible materials, penetrations of fire-resistive walls and floors by plastics piping or conduit must be considered to preserve the endurance ratings of rated walls and floors. Industry-sponsored research indicates that after installation such penetrations must be carefully sealed with a non-combustible material. However, a preliminary check should be made to assure that the jurisdictional authority does not prohibit the installation of plastics piping in fire resistive construc-

tion. And if use is permitted, requirements for proper closure should be followed.

Pipe Fittings

Taper Pipe Thread.—The American Standard for Pipe Threads, originally known as the Briggs Standard was formulated by Robert Briggs about 1862. By 1886, most American manufacturers had adopted this standard, the adoption being formalized by its adoption by the ASME.

The accompanying data are from the ANSI B2.1 standards adopted by ANSI with ASME and AGA as the sponsor organizations.

For all dimensions see corresponding reference letters in Table 9-73. Angle between sides of thread is 60°. Taper of thread on diameter is $\frac{3}{4}$ inch per foot.

The basic maximum thread depth K of the truncated thread is $0.8 \times$ pitch of thread. The crest and root are truncated a minimum of $0.033 \times$ pitch for all pitches. Maximum truncation for crest and root are: $0.096 \times$ pitch for 27 threads per inch; $0.088 \times$ pitch for 18 threads per inch, $0.098 \times$ pitch for 14 threads per inch; $0.073 \times$ pitch for 11 $\frac{1}{2}$ threads per inch; $0.062 \times$ pitch for 8 threads per inch.

These fittings are rated for maximum saturated steam pressures of 150 psig and for maximum liquid and gas service pressures at 150°F of 300 psig.

All fittings are threaded with American Standard Pipe Threads and have taper threads, except $\frac{1}{8}$, $\frac{1}{4}$ and $\frac{3}{8}$ in. wrought couplings and caps that may have straight threads.

Size of all fittings listed indicates nominal inside diameter of port.

Table 9-73. American National Standard Taper Pipe Threads

| Nominal Pipe Diameter in. | Outside Diameter, in. B | Number of Threads per in. | Pitch Diameter, in. | | Length of Effective Thread, in. C | Length of Hand Tight Engagement, in. D | Length of Imperfect Threads, in. | Max. Depth of Thread, in. K | Root Diameter at Small End, in. G |
			End of External Thread F	End of Internal Thread E					
1/16	0.3125	27	0.27118	0.28118	0.2611	0.16	0.1285	0.02963	0.2416
1/8	0.405	27	0.36351	0.37476	0.2639	0.180	0.1285	0.02963	0.3339
1/4	0.540	18	0.47739	0.48989	0.4018	0.200	0.1928	0.04444	0.4329
3/8	0.675	18	0.61201	0.62701	0.0478	0.240	0.1928	0.04444	0.5676
1/2	0.840	14	0.75843	0.77843	0.5337	0.320	0.2478	0.05714	0.7013
3/4	1.050	14	0.96768	0.98887	0.5457	0.339	0.2478	0.05714	0.9105
1	1.315	11½	1.21363	1.23863	0.6828	0.400	0.3017	0.06957	1.1441
1¼	1.660	11½	1.55713	1.58338	0.7068	0.420	0.3017	0.06957	1.4876
1½	1.900	11½	1.79609	1.82234	0.7235	0.420	0.3017	0.06957	1.7265
2	2.375	11½	2.26902	2.29627	0.7565	0.436	0.3017	0.06957	2.1995
2½	2.875	8	2.71953	2.76216	1.1375	0.682	0.4337	0.10000	2.6195
3	3.500	8	3.34062	3.38850	1.2000	0.766	0.4337	0.10000	3.2406
3½	4.000	8	3.83750	3.88881	1.2500	0.821	0.4337	0.10000	3.7375
4	4.500	8	4.33438	4.38712	1.3000	0.844	0.4337	0.10000	4.2344
5	5.563	8	5.39073	5.44929	1.4063	0.937	0.4337	0.10000	5.2907
6	6.625	8	6.44609	6.50597	1.5125	0.958	0.4337	0.10000	6.3461
8	8.625	8	8.43359	8.50003	1.7125	1.063	0.4337	0.10000	8.3336
10	10.750	8	10.54531	10.62094	1.9250	1.210	0.4337	0.10000	10.4453
12	12.750	8	12.53281	12.61781	2.1250	1.360	0.4337	0.10000	12.4328
14 OD[a]	14.000	8	13.77500	13.87262	2.2500	1.562	0.4337	0.10000	13.6750
16 OD[a]	16.000	8	15.76250	15.87575	2.4500	1.812	0.4337	0.10000	15.6625
18 OD[a]	18.000	8	17.75000	17.87500	2.6500	2.000	0.4337	0.10000	17.6500
20 OD[a]	20.000	8	19.73750	19.87031	2.8500	2.125	0.4337	0.10000	19.6375
24 OD[a]	24.000	8	23.71250	23.86094	3.2500	2.375	0.4337	0.10000	23.6125

[a] OD indicates outer diameter.

Maximum Pressures (Gage): Fittings of all sizes, 25 psi for saturated steam; sizes 36 inches and smaller, 43 psi maximum nonshock working hydraulic pressure, or 25 psi maximum gas pressure at or near the ordinary range of air temperatures.

The flange diameters, bolt circles, and number of bolts are the same as the 125 lb American Standard with a reduction in the thickness of flanges and the bolt diameters, thereby maintaining interchangeability with the 125 lb American Standard flanges. The face-to-face and center to face dimensions of fittings are the same as the 125 Ib. American Standard (Class 125) cast iron flanged fittings.

Special degree elbows, ranging from 1 to 45° inclusive shall have the same center to face dimensions given for 45° elbows and those over 45° and up to 90° inclusive shall have the same center-to-face dimensions as given for 90° elbows. The angle designation of an elbow is its deflection from straight line flow and is the angle between the flange faces.

Side outlet elbows and side outlet tees shall have all openings on intersecting center lines.

Tees, side outlet tees, and crosses 16 inches and smaller, reducing on the outlet or branch, have the same dimensions center-to-face and face-to-face as straight size fittings, corresponding to the size of the larger opening. Sizes 18 inches and larger, reducing on the outlet, are made in two lengths, depending on the size of the outlet.

Class 125 cast iron pipe flanges and fittings are rated as follows for maximum saturated steam service pressures (gage): 125 psi for sizes 1 to 12 inches, inclusive; 100 psi for sizes 14 to 24 inches, inclusive; and 50 psi for sizes 30 to 48 inches, inclusive. For maximum water service pressures (gage) at or near the ordinary range of air temperature: 175 psi for sizes 1 to 12 inches, inclusive, and 150 psi for sizes 14 to 48 inches, inclusive, for flanges only.

The sizes from 54 to 96 inches are included for convenience where special fittings with larger flanges are required and do not necessarily carry a definite rating.

Bolt holes straddle the center lines and are in multiples of four, so that fittings may be made to face in any quarter. For bolts smaller than $1\frac{3}{4}$ inches the bolt holes shall be drilled $\frac{1}{8}$ inch larger in diameter than the nominal diameter of the bolt. Holes for bolts $1\frac{3}{4}$ inches and larger shall be drilled $\frac{1}{4}$ inch larger than nominal diameter of bolts.

The bolt holes of these cast-iron flanges and flanged fittings need not be spot faced for ordinary service except as follows: In sizes 12 inches and smaller when rough flanges, after facing, are oversized more than $\frac{1}{8}$ inch in thickness, they shall be spot faced to the specified thickness of flange (minimum) with a plus tolerance of $\frac{1}{16}$ inch. In sizes 14 inches to 24 inches, inclusive, when rough flanges, after facing, are oversized more than $\frac{3}{16}$ inch in thickness they shall be spot faced to the specified thickness of flange (minimum) with a plus tolerance of $\frac{1}{16}$ inch.

These fittings are for maximum saturated steam service of 125 psig in sizes 1 to 12 inches included, 100 psig for 14 to 24 inches included and 50 psig for sizes 30 to 48 inches included. The fittings are to be designed to withstand twice these pressures in hydrostatic tests.

These data apply to reducing tees; crosses and laterals. In the drawing, the tee, extreme left, top row, is reducing on outlet. Top row, next to left, tee is reducing on one run and outlet. Top row, next to right, side outlet tee or cross is reducing on both outlets. Top row, extreme right, side outlet tee or cross is reducing on one run and outlets. Cross, bottom row, extreme left, reducing on both outlets. Next to left, bottom row, cross is reducing on one run and both outlets. Bottom row, next to right, 45° lateral is reducing on branch. Bottom row, extreme right, 45° lateral is reducing on one run and branch.

Side outlet tees, with outlet at 90° or any other angle, straight or reducing, have the same dimensions center-to-face as regular tees having the same reductions. In a side outlet tee the larger of the two side outlets governs the center-to-face dimension "J".

Table 9-74. 125 and 250 LB Cast Iron Screwed Fittings

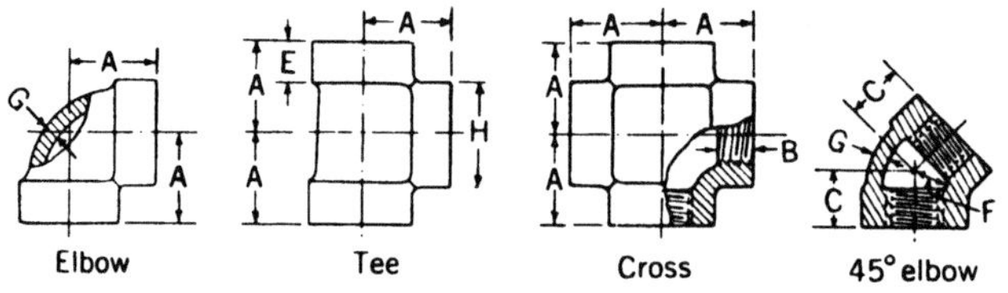

Elbow   Tee   Cross   45° elbow

Nominal Pipe Diameter, in.	A	C	B Min	E Min	F Min	F Max	G	A Min
				Fittings for 125 psi				
¼	0.81	0.73	0.32	0.38	0.540	0.584	0.110	0.93
⅜	0.95	0.80	0.36	0.44	0.695	0.919	0.120	1.12
½	1.12	0.88	0.43	0.50	0.840	0.897	0.130	1.34
¾	1.31	0.98	0.50	0.56	1.050	1.109	0.155	1.63
1	1.50	1.12	0.58	0.62	1.315	1.385	0.190	1.95
1¼	1.95	1.29	0.69	0.69	1.66	1.730	0.185	2.39
1½	1,94	1.43	0.70	0.75	1.900	1.970	0.200	2.68
2	2.25	1.68	0.75	0.84	2.375	2.445	0.220	3.28
2½	2.90	1.95	0.92	0.94	2.895	2.975	0.240	3.86
3	3.08	2.19	0.98	1.00	3.500	3.600	0.260	4.62
3½	3.42	2.39	1.03	1.06	4.000	4.100	0.280	5.20
4	3.79	2.61	1.08	1.12	4.500	4.600	0.310	5.79
5	4.50	3.05	1:18	1.18	5.563	5.663	0.380	7.05
6	5.13	3.46	1.28	1.28	6.625	6.925	0.430	8.28
8	6.56	4.28	1.49	1.47	8.625	8.925	0.550	10.63
10	[a]8.08	5.0	1.68	1.68	1.75	10.85	0.69	13.12
12	[a]9.50	5.97	1.88	1.88	12.750	12.850	0.800	15.47
				Fittings for 250 psi				
¼	0.94	0.81	0.43	0.49	0.540	0.584	0.18	1.17
⅜	1.06	0.88	0.47	0.55	0.675	0.919	0.18	1.36
½	1.25	1.00	0.57	0.60	0.840	0.899	0.20	1.59
¾	1.44	1.13	0.64	0.68	1.050	1.109	0.23	1.88
1	1.63	1.31	0.95	0.76	1.315	1.385	0.28	2.24
1¼	1.94	1.50	0.84	0.88	1.660	1.730	0.33	2.73
1½	2.13	1.69	0.89	0.97	1.900	1.990	0.35	3.07
2	2.50	2.00	1.00	1.12	2.375	2.445	0.39	3.74
2½	2.94	2.25	1.19	1.3	2.875	2.975	0.43	4.60
3	3.38	2.50	1.23	1.40	3.500	3.600	0.48	5.36
3½	3.75	2.63	1.28	1149	4.000	4.100	0.52	5.98
4	4.13	2.81	1.33	1.57	4.500	4.600	0.56	6.61
5	4.88	3.19	1.43	1.94	5.563	5.663	0.66	9.92
6	5.63	3.50	1.53	1.91	6.625	6.725	0.74	9.24
8	7.00	4.31	1.92	2.24	8.625	8.925	0.90	11.73
10	8.63	5.19	1.93	2.58	10.750	10.85	1.08	14.37
12	10.00	6.00	2.13	2.91	12.750	12.850	1.24	16.84

[a] This applies to elbows and tees only.

All dimensions given are in inches.

Table 9-75. 150 LB Malleable Iron Screwed Fittings

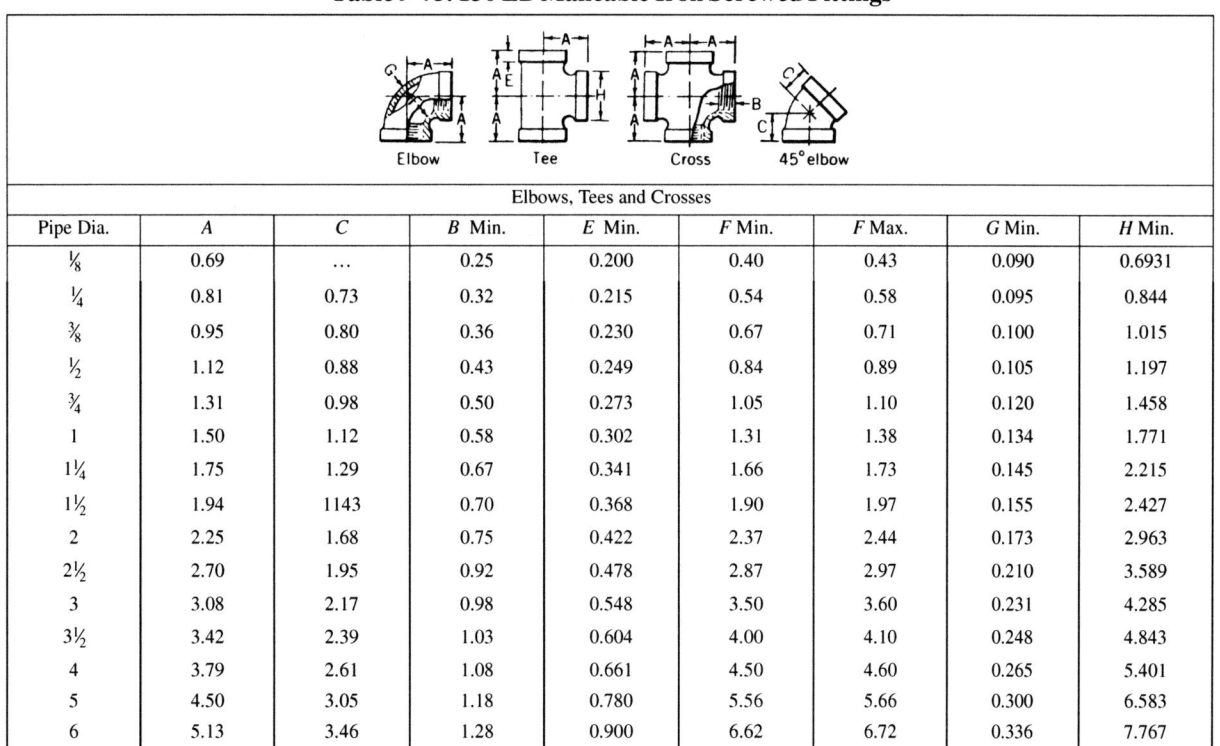

Elbow   Tee   Cross   45° elbow

				Elbows, Tees and Crosses				
Pipe Dia.	A	C	B Min.	E Min.	F Min.	F Max.	G Min.	H Min.
⅛	0.69	…	0.25	0.200	0.40	0.43	0.090	0.6931
¼	0.81	0.73	0.32	0.215	0.54	0.58	0.095	0.844
⅜	0.95	0.80	0.36	0.230	0.67	0.71	0.100	1.015
½	1.12	0.88	0.43	0.249	0.84	0.89	0.105	1.197
¾	1.31	0.98	0.50	0.273	1.05	1.10	0.120	1.458
1	1.50	1.12	0.58	0.302	1.31	1.38	0.134	1.771
1¼	1.75	1.29	0.67	0.341	1.66	1.73	0.145	2.215
1½	1.94	1143	0.70	0.368	1.90	1.97	0.155	2.427
2	2.25	1.68	0.75	0.422	2.37	2.44	0.173	2.963
2½	2.70	1.95	0.92	0.478	2.87	2.97	0.210	3.589
3	3.08	2.17	0.98	0.548	3.50	3.60	0.231	4.285
3½	3.42	2.39	1.03	0.604	4.00	4.10	0.248	4.843
4	3.79	2.61	1.08	0.661	4.50	4.60	0.265	5.401
5	4.50	3.05	1.18	0.780	5.56	5.66	0.300	6.583
6	5.13	3.46	1.28	0.900	6.62	6.72	0.336	7.767

All dimensions given are in inches.

Table 9-76. Straight and Reducing Couplings (Cast)

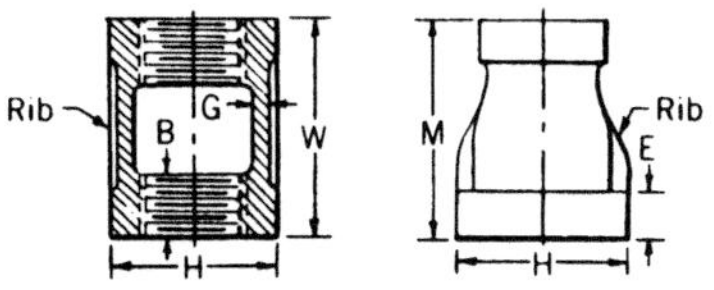

Pipe Dia.	B Min.	E Min.	G Min.	H Min.	Rib Thickness	W	M
⅛	0.25	0.20	0.09	0.693	0.09	0.96	…
¼	0.32	0.215	0.095	0.844	0.095	1.06	1.00
⅜	0.36	0.23	0.100	1.015	0.100	1.16	1.13
½	0.43	0.249	0.105	1.197	0.105	1.34	1.25
¾	0.50	0.273	0.12	1.458	0.120	1.52	1.44
1	0.58	0.302	0.134	1.771	0.134	1.67	1.69
1¼	0.67	0.341	0.145	2.153	0.145	1.93	2.06
1½	0.70	0.368	0.155	2.427	0.155	2.15	2.31
2	0.75	0.422	0.173	2.963	0.173	2.53	2.81
2½	0.92	0.478	0.210	3.589	0.210	2.88	3.25
3	0.98	0.548	0.231	4.285	0.231	3.18	3-69
3½	1.03	0.604	0.248	4.843	0.248	3.43	4.00
4	1.08	0.661	0.265	5.401	0.265	3.69	4.38

All dimensions given in inches.

Table 9-77. 150 LB Malleable Iron Screwed Fittings (2)

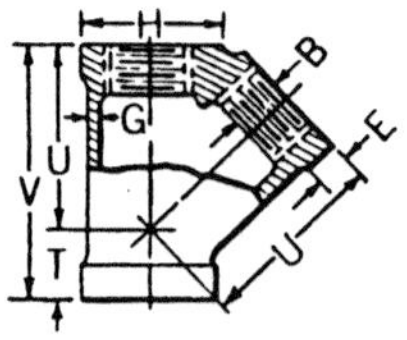

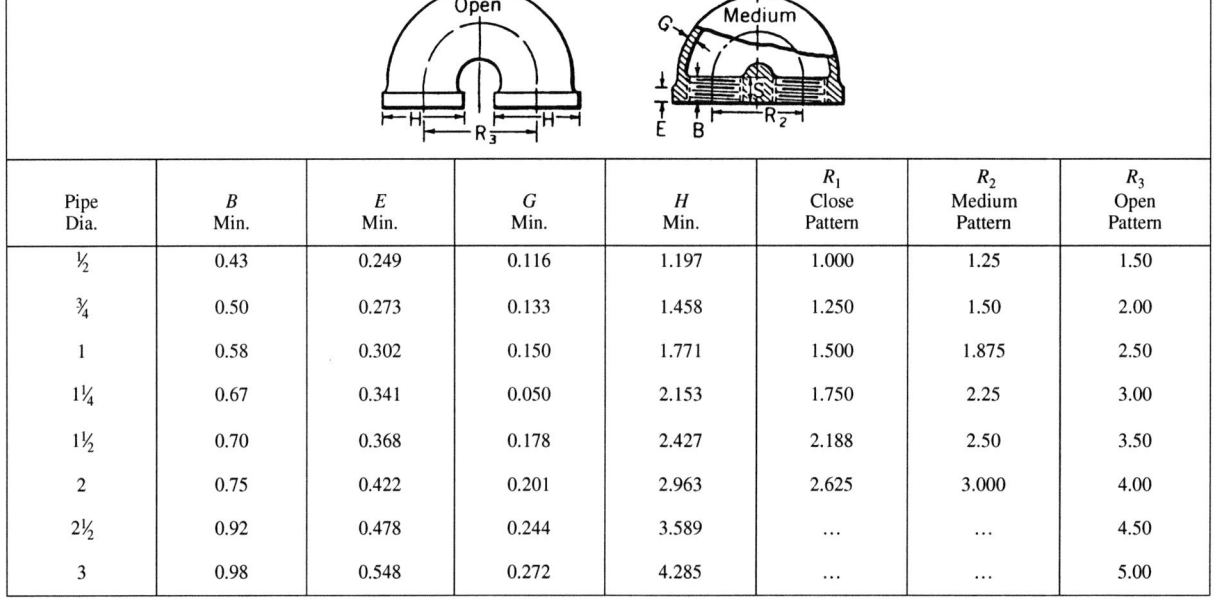

45° Y-Branches (Straight Sizes)

Pipe Dia.	B Min.	E Min.	G Min.	H Min.	T	U	V
⅜	0.36	0.23	0.100	1.015	0.50	1.43	1.93
½	0.43	0.249	0.105	1.197	0.61	1.91	2.32
¾	0.50	0.273	0.120	1.458	0.92	2.05	2.77
1	0.58	0.302	0.134	1.971	0.85	2.43	3.28
1¼	0.67	0.341	0.145	2.153	1.02	2.92	3.94
1½	0.70	0.368	0.155	2.429	1.10	3.28	4.38
2	0.95	0.422	0.193	2.963	1.24	3.93	5.17
2½	0.92	0.478	0.210	3.589	1.52	4.73	6.25
3	0.98	0.548	0.231	4.285	1.71	5.55	7.26
3½	1.03	0.604	0.248	4.843	1.85	6.25	8.10
4	1.08	0.661	0.265	5.401	2.01	6.97	8.98

Table 9-78. Close, Medium and Open Pattern Return Bends

Pipe Dia.	B Min.	E Min.	G Min.	H Min.	R_1 Close Pattern	R_2 Medium Pattern	R_3 Open Pattern
½	0.43	0.249	0.116	1.197	1.000	1.25	1.50
¾	0.50	0.273	0.133	1.458	1.250	1.50	2.00
1	0.58	0.302	0.150	1.771	1.500	1.875	2.50
1¼	0.67	0.341	0.050	2.153	1.750	2.25	3.00
1½	0.70	0.368	0.178	2.427	2.188	2.50	3.50
2	0.75	0.422	0.201	2.963	2.625	3.000	4.00
2½	0.92	0.478	0.244	3.589	…	…	4.50
3	0.98	0.548	0.272	4.285	…	…	5.00

All dimensions given in inches.

Table 9-79. 300 LB Malleable Iron Screwed Fittings

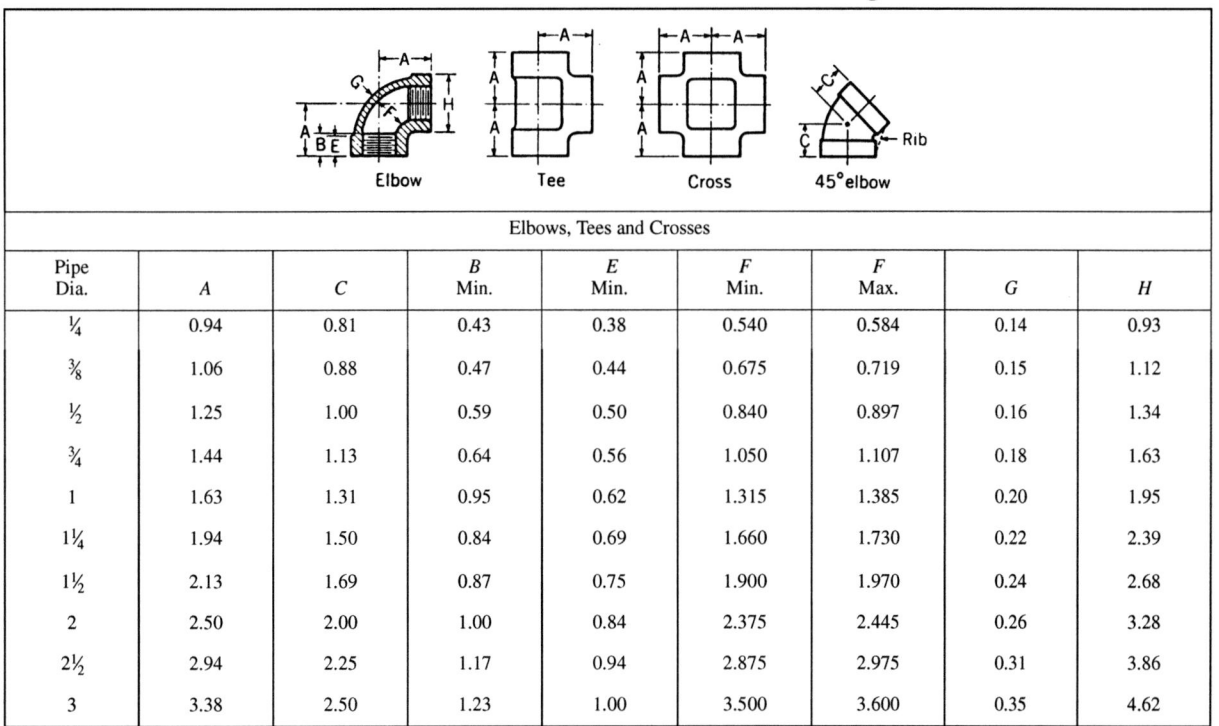

Pipe Dia.	A	C	B Min.	E Min.	F Min.	F Max.	G	H
¼	0.94	0.81	0.43	0.38	0.540	0.584	0.14	0.93
⅜	1.06	0.88	0.47	0.44	0.675	0.719	0.15	1.12
½	1.25	1.00	0.59	0.50	0.840	0.897	0.16	1.34
¾	1.44	1.13	0.64	0.56	1.050	1.107	0.18	1.63
1	1.63	1.31	0.95	0.62	1.315	1.385	0.20	1.95
1¼	1.94	1.50	0.84	0.69	1.660	1.730	0.22	2.39
1½	2.13	1.69	0.87	0.75	1.900	1.970	0.24	2.68
2	2.50	2.00	1.00	0.84	2.375	2.445	0.26	3.28
2½	2.94	2.25	1.17	0.94	2.875	2.975	0.31	3.86
3	3.38	2.50	1.23	1.00	3.500	3.600	0.35	4.62

(Elbows, Tees and Crosses)

Table 9-80. Coupling

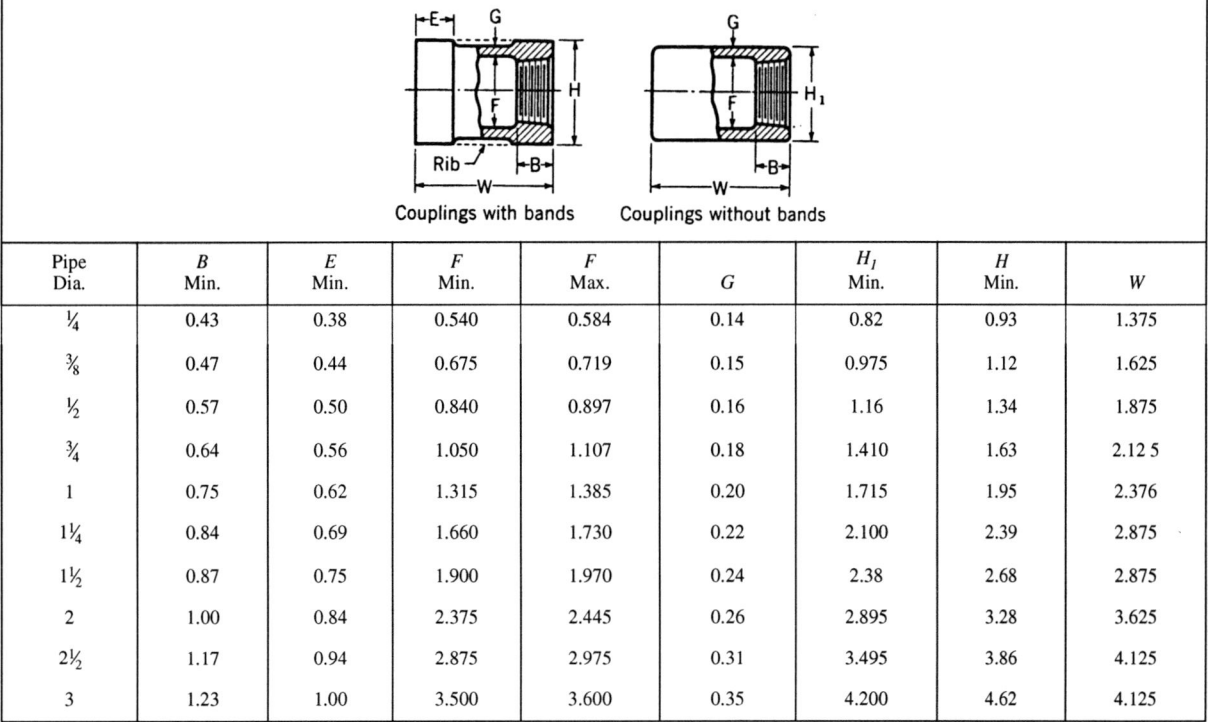

Pipe Dia.	B Min.	E Min.	F Min.	F Max.	G	H₁ Min.	H Min.	W
¼	0.43	0.38	0.540	0.584	0.14	0.82	0.93	1.375
⅜	0.47	0.44	0.675	0.719	0.15	0.975	1.12	1.625
½	0.57	0.50	0.840	0.897	0.16	1.16	1.34	1.875
¾	0.64	0.56	1.050	1.107	0.18	1.410	1.63	2.12 5
1	0.75	0.62	1.315	1.385	0.20	1.715	1.95	2.376
1¼	0.84	0.69	1.660	1.730	0.22	2.100	2.39	2.875
1½	0.87	0.75	1.900	1.970	0.24	2.38	2.68	2.875
2	1.00	0.84	2.375	2.445	0.26	2.895	3.28	3.625
2½	1.17	0.94	2.875	2.975	0.31	3.495	3.86	4.125
3	1.23	1.00	3.500	3.600	0.35	4.200	4.62	4.125

All dimensions given in inches.

Table 9-81. Class 25 Cast Iron Flanged Fittings

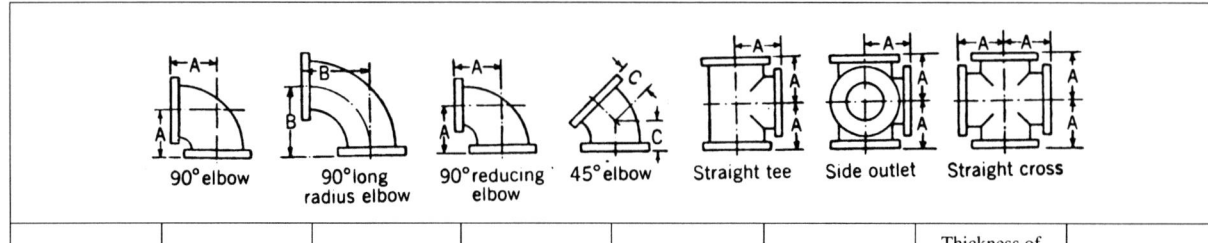

90° elbow   90° long radius elbow   90° reducing elbow   45° elbow   Straight tee   Side outlet   Straight cross

Nominal Pipe Diameter	Center-to-Face A	Center-to-Face B	Center-to-Face C	Face-to-Face A + A	Diameter of Flange	Thickness of Flange (Min)	Body Wall Thickness (Min)
4	6½	9	4	13	9	¾	0.42
5	7½	10¼	4½	15	10	¾	0.44
6	8	11½	5	16	11	¾	0.44
8	9	14	5½	18	13½	¾	0.46
10	11	16½	6½	22	16	⅞	0.50
12	12	19	7½	24	19	1	0.54
14	14	21½	7½	28	21	1⅛	0.57
16	15	24	8	30	23½	1⅛	0.60
18	16½	26½	8½	33	25	1¼	0.64
20	18	29	9½	36	27 ½	1¼	0.67
24	22	34	11	44	32	1⅜	0.76
30	25	41½	15	50	38¾	1½	0.88
36	28	49	18	56	46	1⅝	0.99
42	31	56½	21	62	53	1¾	1.1
48	34	64	24	68	59½	2	1.26
54	39	71½	27	78	66¼	2¼	1.35
60	44	79	30	88	73	2¼	1.39
72	53	94	36	106	86½	2½	1.62

All dimensions given are in inches.

Crosses and laterals, both straight and reducing, shall be reinforced where necessary to compensate for the inherent weakness in the casting design.

Class 250 pipe flanges and fittings are rated as follows for maximum saturated steam service pressures (gage): 250 psia for sizes 1 to 12 inches, inclusive; 200 psia for sizes 14 to 24 inches, inclusive; 100 psia for sizes 30 to 48 inches, inclusive. For maximum water service pressures (gage) at or near the ordinary range of air temperature: 400 psia for sizes 1 to 12 inches, inclusive; 300 psia for sizes 14 to 48 inches, inclusive, for flanges only.

Bolts shall be of carbon steel with American National Standard regular unfinished square heads or American National Standard heavy unfinished hexagonal heads and the nuts shall be of carbon steel with American National Standard heavy hexagonal dimensions, all as specified in American National Standard for Wrench Head Bolts and Nuts and Wrench Openings. For bolts $1\frac{3}{4}$ in. diameter and larger, bolt-studs with a nut on each end are recommended.

Hexagonal nuts for pipe sizes 1 inch to 16 inches can be conveniently pulled up with open wrenches of minimum design of heads. Hexagonal nuts for pipe sizes 18 inches to 48 inches can be conveniently pulled up with box wrenches. All bolts, or bolt-studs if used, and all nuts shall be threaded in accordance with American National Standard for Screw Threads Coarse Thread Series, Class 2 Fit.

Bolt holes of these flanges and fittings need not be spotfaced except when the rough flanges, after facing, are oversized by certain amounts specified in the standard and depending on the nominal size.

Reducing elbows carry same dimensions, center-to-face, as straight size elbows corresponding to the size of the larger opening.

All Class 250 cast iron flanges have a $\frac{1}{16}$ inch raised face. This raised face is included in the face-to-face, center-to-face, and minimum thickness of flange dimensions.

Reducing elbows carry the same dimensions center-to-face as regular straight size elbows corresponding to the size of the larger opening. Tees 16 inches and smaller reducing on the outlet have the same dimensions center to face and face-to-face as straight size fittings corresponding to the size of the larger opening. Sizes 18 inches and larger reducing on the outlet are made in two lengths, depending on the size of the outlet.

Special degree elbows ranging from 1 to 45°, inclusive, have the same center-to-face dimensions given for 45° elbows, and those over 45° and up to 90°, inclusive, shall have the same center-to-face dimensions given for 90° elbows. The angle designation of an elbow is its deflection from straight line flow and is the angle between the flange faces.

Reducers, for all reductions, use the same face-to-face dimensions given in the above table of dimensions for the larger opening.

For drilling templates, pressure ratings, and bolt holes, see Table 9-84. Class 250 Cast Iron Flanges . ANSI-B31.5 Refrigeration Piping Code and ANSI-B9.1 Safety Code for Mechanical Refrigeration require that:

Refrigerant working pressure not exceed 250 psi in Schedule 40 ferrous pipe, and butt-welded pipe shall not exceed 2 inches in size. Refrigerant liquid ferrous pipe, $1\frac{1}{2}$-inch and smaller, shall be of Schedule 80. Refrigerant tubing shall not be lighter than Type L for field assembly or Type M for shop assembly.

Soft annealed copper tubing erected on the premises shall not be used in sizes exceeding $\frac{3}{4}$ inch.

Pipe thinner than Schedule 40 ferrous, or regular brass, shall not be threaded. For refrigerants, cast iron shall conform to ASTM A126, Class B higher strength gray iron with not less than 31000 psi tensile strength.

Screwed joints are limited by the Piping Code not to be over 3 inches nominal size for refrigerant pressures 250 psi or less, $1\frac{1}{4}$ inches for refrigerant pressures above 250 psi and not over 4 inches for brine. Screwed on flanges are not permitted in sizes larger than the above. Bushings are not permitted for reductions of a single pipe size. For screwed brass or copper refrigerant pipe extra heavy fittings are required.

Flanged joints are used for sizes greater than the above, and in many cases for smaller sizes.

Welding is almost universally accepted as the standard method of assembly of ferrous piping systems today, except that valves are flanged and flanged unions are used where disassembly is frequent.

In soldering for nonferrous materials the clearance between the two surfaces is maintained within narrow limits. The solder, with suitable flux, is run into this narrow annulus in a molten condition. The joint depends on the large area of contact and of shear. Hard solder is ordinarily a silver base alloy, melting above 1000°F, whereas soft solder is ordinarily a tin base alloy, melting below 500°F.

Flared compression fittings are permitted by the Piping Code for refrigerant lines not over $\frac{3}{4}$ inch outside diameter of annealed copper tubing, provided joints are exposed for visual inspection.

A principle of design in this standard is to maintain a fixed position for the flanged edge with reference to the body of the fitting. The addition of any facing is beyond the outside edge of the flange except for the $\frac{1}{16}$ inch raised face in the 150 lb and 300 lb standards.

Center-to-contact surface or center-to-flanged edge dimensions for all openings shall be the same as those of straight size fittings of the largest opening. The contact surface-to-contact surface or flanged edge-to-flanged edge dimension for all reductions of reducers and eccentric reducers shall be as listed for the larger opening.

Side outlet elbows, side outlet tees, and side outlet crosses, shall have all openings on intersecting center-lines and the center-to-contact surface dimensions of the side outlet shall be the same as for the largest opening. Long radius elbows with side outlet shall have the side outlet on the radial center-line of the elbow and the center to contact surface dimension of the side outlet shall be the same as for the regular 90° elbow of the largest opening. The accompanying data on steel butt-welding fittings is from an American National Standards Institute standard sponsored by the Mechanical Contractors Association of America, Manufacturers Standardization Society of the Valve and Fittings Industry, and American Society of Mechanical Engineers.

The standard covers overall dimensions, tolerances, and marking for wrought and cast carbon steel and alloy-steel welding fittings. Welding ends are to be in accordance with ANSI-B16.25.

In this standard *wrought* is used to denote fittings made of pipe, tubing, plate, or forgings. Fittings shall be designed so that the pressure rating may be calculated as for straight seamless pipe of the same or equivalent material in accordance with the rules established in the various sections of the Code for Pressure Piping (ANSI-B31).

The *size* of the fittings in the accompanying tables is identified by the corresponding *nominal pipe size*. For fittings 14 inches and larger the outer diameter of the pipe corresponds with the nominal size.

One of the principles of this standard is the maintenance of a fixed position for the welding ends with reference to the centerline of the fittings or the overall dimensions, as the case may be.

The actual bursting pressure of the fittings covered by this standard shall at least equal the computed bursting pressure of seamless pipe of the schedule number (or nominal wall thickness) and material designated by the marking on the fitting. To determine the bursting pressure of the fittings, straight seamless pipe of the designated schedule (or nominal wall thickness) and material shall be welded to each end, each pipe being at least equal in length to twice the outside diameter of the pipe and having proper end closures, applied beyond the minimum length of straight pipe; hydrostatic pressure shall be applied until either the fitting or one of the pipes welded there to bursts.

Hydrostatic testing of wrought fittings is not required in this standard. Cast welding fittings shall be hydrostatically tested. All fittings shall be capable of withstanding without leakage a test pressure equal to that prescribed in the specification for the pipe with which the fitting is recommended.

Traps in cast iron soil pipe lines shall provide minimum water seal as follows: 2-inch pipe, 2-inch seal; 3 to 6 inch,

$2\frac{1}{2}$-inch seal, 8 to 12 inches, 3-inches seal. In the case of 15-inch pipe a $3\frac{1}{2}$ inch seal is required.

Screw plugs and tapped openings in fittings shall have American National Standard taper pipe threads. The threads shall be in accordance with the American National Standard for Pipe Threads, B2.1, or with the National Bureau of Standards Handbook, Screw Thread Standards for Federal Services, of the current issue.

Screw joint drainage fittings were developed around 1880 by the Durham House Drainage Company of New York and are often referred to as Durham fittings. At that time soil pipes and drains had been required by the then recent legislation to be of plumbers cast iron soil pipe. This ruling was made in the City of New York, while in Chicago soil pipes were required to be of lead or plumbers cast iron pipe.

In order to form a continuous passageway with no pockets or obstructions where foreign matter could collect and gradually accumulate, it was necessary to design a special type of screw fitting. These fittings are made with the inside diameter approximately equal to the nominal size of standard weight (Schedule 40, ANSI B36.10) wrought pipe. The thread chamber is designed so that the end of the pipe, when screwed into the fitting to make a tight joint, will come close to the shoulder in the fitting, thereby making a practically continuous passage. The threading of these fittings required special care and the threads on the pipe were cut to suit the threads in the fitting.

These screwed drainage fittings follow the general proportions of other castiron screwed fittings, except that the shapes and center-to-end dimensions are designed to suit the particular service for which they are intended. Manufacturing practice in the case of the drainage fittings, however, as they developed, differed to a considerable extent in center-to-end dimensions as well as in some other respects, which finally led to an extensive study of the situation by the Manufacturer's Standardization Society of the Valve and Fittings Industry. This study resulted in the development of a standard practice of the industry for these fittings as indicated by this present standard.

All fittings shall be threaded with American National Standard Taper Pipe Threads, and the variations in threading shall be limited to one turn small and no turn large, except for screwed openings without shoulder, which shall be limited to one turn large and one turn small, from the gaging notch on the plug when working gages are used.

When gaging internal threads the notch shall be flush with the bottom of the chamfer, which shall be considered the intersection of the chamfer cone and the pitch cone of the thread. This depth is approximately equal to one-half thread from the face of the fitting.

Table 9-82. Class 125 Cast Iron Flanged Fittings (1)

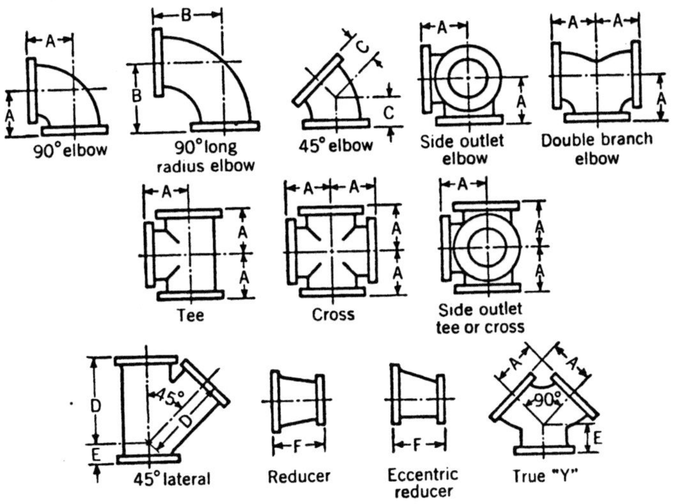

Nominal Pipe Diameter	Center to face						Body Wall Thickness	Dia. of Flange	Thickness of Flange
	A	*B*	*C*	*D*	*E*	*F*			
1	3½	5	1¾	5¾	1¾	...	5/16	4¼	7/16
1¼	3¾	5½	2	6¼	1¾	...	5/16	4⅝	½
1½	4	6	2¼	7	2	...	5/16	5	9/16
2	4½	6½	2½	8	2½	5	5/16	6	⅝
2½	5	7	3	9½	2½	5½	5/16	7	11/16
3	5½	7¾	3	10	3	6	⅜	7½	¾
3½	6	8½	3½	11½	3	6½	7/16	8½	13/16
4	6½	9	4	12	3	7	½	9	15/16
5	7½	10¼	4½	13½	3½	8	½	10	15/16
6	8	11½	5	14½	3½	9	9/16	11	1
8	9	14	5½	17½	4½	11	⅝	13½	1⅛
10	11	16½	6½	20½	5	12	¾	16	1 3/16
12	12	19	7½	24½	5½	14	13/16	19	1¼
14 OD	14	21½	7½	27	6	16	⅞	21	1⅜
16 OD	15	24	8	30	6½	18	1	23½	1 7/16
18 OD	16½	26½	8½	32	7	19	1 1/16	25	1 9/16
20 OD	18	29	9½	35	8	20	1⅛	27½	1 11/16
24 OD	22	34	11	40½	9	24	1¼	32	1⅞
30 OD	25	41½	15	49	10	30	1 7/16	38¾	2⅛
36 OD	28	49	18	...	...	36	1⅝	46	2⅜
42 OD	31	56½	21	...	...	42	1 1/16	53	2⅝
48 OD	34	64	24	...	...	48	2	59½	2¾

All dimensions given in inches. OD indicates outer diameter.

PIPE FITTING

Table 9-83. Class 125 Cast Iron Flanged Fittings (2)

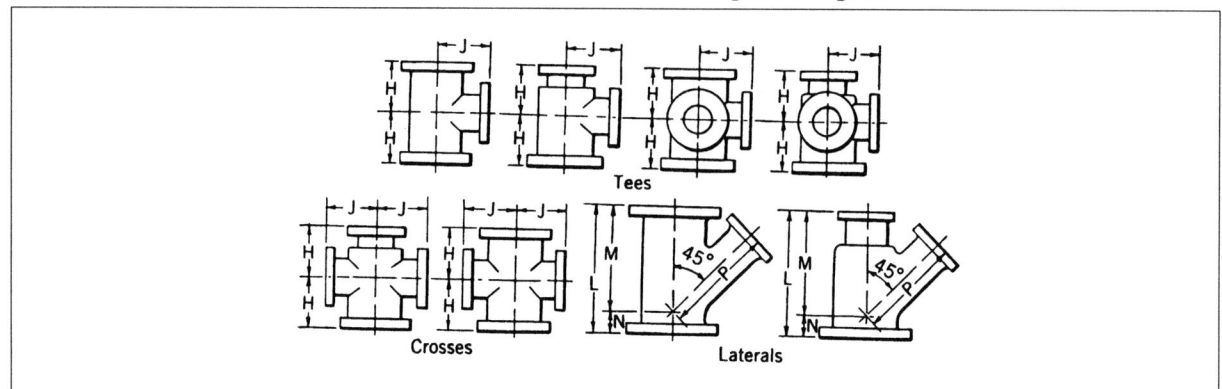

Nominal Pipe Diameter	Size of Outlet and Smaller	Center-to-Face Run H	Center-to-Face Outlet J	Size of Branch and Smaller	Face-to-Face Run L	Center-to-Face Run M	Center-to-Face Run N	Center-to-Face Branch P
1	1	3½	3½	1	7½	5¾	1¾	5¾
1¼	1¼	3¼	3¼	1¼	8	6¼	1¾	6¼
1½	1½	4	4	1½	9	7	2½	7
2	2	4½	4½	2	10½	8	2½	8
2½	2½	5	5	2½	12	9½	2½	9½
3	3	5½	5½	3	13	10	3	10
3½	3½	6	6	3½	14½	11½	3	11½
4	4	6½	6½	4	15	12	3	12
5	5	7½	7½	5	17	13½	3½	13½
6	6	8	8	6	18	14½	3½	14½
8	8	9	9	8	22	17½	4½	17½
10	10	11	11	10	25½	20½	5	20½
12	12	12	12	12	30	24½	5½	24½
14 OD	14	14	14	14	33	27	6	27
16 OD	16	15	15	16	36½	30	6½	30
18 OD	12	13	15½	8	26	25	1	57½
20 OD	14	14	17	10	28	27	1	29½
24 OD	16	15	19	12	32	31½	½	34½
30 OD	20	18	23	14	39	39	0	42
36 OD	24	20	26	…	…	…	…	…

All dimensions given in inches.

Table 9-84. Class 250 Cast Iron Flanges

Nominal Pipe Diameter	Diameter of Flange	Thickness of Flange[a] (Min.)	Diameter of Bolt Circle[b]	Diameter of Bolt Holes[b]	Number of Bolts	Size of Bolts	Length of Bolts[c]	Size Ring of Gasket
1	$4\frac{7}{8}$	$\frac{11}{16}$	$3\frac{1}{2}$	$\frac{3}{4}$	4	$\frac{5}{8}$	$2\frac{1}{2}$	$1 \times 2\frac{7}{8}$
$1\frac{1}{4}$	$5\frac{1}{4}$	$\frac{3}{4}$	$3\frac{7}{8}$	$\frac{3}{4}$	4	$\frac{5}{8}$	$2\frac{1}{2}$	$1\frac{1}{4} \times 3\frac{1}{4}$
$1\frac{1}{2}$	$6\frac{1}{8}$	$\frac{13}{16}$	$4\frac{1}{2}$	$\frac{7}{8}$	4	$\frac{3}{4}$	$2\frac{3}{4}$	$1\frac{1}{2} \times 3\frac{3}{4}$
2	$6\frac{1}{2}$	$\frac{7}{8}$	5	$\frac{3}{4}$	8	$\frac{5}{8}$	$2\frac{3}{4}$	$2 \times 4\frac{3}{8}$
$2\frac{1}{2}$	$7\frac{1}{2}$	1	$5\frac{7}{8}$	$\frac{7}{8}$	8	$\frac{3}{4}$	$3\frac{1}{4}$	$2\frac{1}{2} \times 5\frac{1}{8}$
3	$8\frac{1}{4}$	$1\frac{1}{8}$	$6\frac{5}{8}$	$\frac{7}{8}$	8	$\frac{3}{4}$	$3\frac{1}{2}$	$3 \times 5\frac{7}{8}$
$3\frac{1}{2}$	9	$1\frac{3}{16}$	$7\frac{1}{4}$	$\frac{7}{8}$	8	$\frac{3}{4}$	$3\frac{1}{2}$	$3\frac{1}{2} \times 6\frac{1}{2}$
4	10	$1\frac{1}{4}$	$7\frac{7}{8}$	$\frac{7}{8}$	8	$\frac{3}{4}$	$3\frac{3}{4}$	$4 \times 7\frac{1}{8}$
5	11	$1\frac{3}{8}$	$9\frac{1}{4}$	$\frac{7}{8}$	8	$\frac{3}{4}$	4	$5 \times 8\frac{1}{2}$
6	$12\frac{1}{2}$	$1\frac{7}{16}$	$10\frac{5}{8}$	$\frac{7}{8}$	12	$\frac{3}{4}$	4	$6 \times 9\frac{7}{8}$
8	15	$1\frac{5}{8}$	13	1	12	$\frac{7}{8}$	$4\frac{1}{2}$	$8 \times 12\frac{1}{8}$
10	$17\frac{1}{2}$	$1\frac{7}{8}$	$15\frac{1}{4}$	$1\frac{1}{8}$	16	1	$5\frac{1}{4}$	$10 \times 14\frac{1}{4}$
12	$20\frac{1}{2}$	2	$17\frac{3}{4}$	$1\frac{1}{4}$	16	$1\frac{1}{8}$	$5\frac{1}{2}$	$12 \times 16\frac{5}{8}$
14 OD	23	$2\frac{1}{8}$	$20\frac{1}{4}$	$1\frac{1}{4}$	20	$1\frac{1}{8}$	6	$13\frac{1}{4} \times 19\frac{1}{8}$
16 OD	$25\frac{1}{2}$	$2\frac{1}{4}$	$22\frac{1}{2}$	$1\frac{3}{8}$	20	$1\frac{1}{4}$	$6\frac{1}{4}$	$15\frac{1}{4} \times 21\frac{1}{4}$
18 OD	28	$2\frac{3}{8}$	$24\frac{3}{4}$	$1\frac{3}{8}$	24	$1\frac{1}{4}$	$6\frac{1}{2}$	$17 \times 23\frac{1}{2}$
20 OD	$30\frac{1}{2}$	$2\frac{1}{2}$	27	$1\frac{3}{8}$	24	$1\frac{1}{4}$	$6\frac{3}{4}$	$19 \times 25\frac{3}{4}$
24 OD	36	$2\frac{3}{4}$	32	$1\frac{11}{16}$	24	$1\frac{1}{2}$	$7\frac{3}{4}$	$23 \times 30\frac{1}{2}$
30 OD	43	3	$39\frac{1}{4}$	2	28	$1\frac{3}{4}$	$8\frac{1}{2}$	$20 \times 37\frac{1}{2}$
36 OD	50	$3\frac{3}{8}$	46	$2\frac{1}{4}$	32	2	$9\frac{1}{2}$	$34\frac{1}{2} \times 44$
42 OD	57	$3\frac{11}{16}$	$52\frac{3}{4}$	$2\frac{1}{4}$	36	2	$10\frac{1}{4}$	$40\frac{1}{4} \times 50\frac{3}{4}$
49 OD	65	4	$60\frac{3}{4}$	$2\frac{1}{4}$	40	2	$10\frac{3}{4}$	$46 \times 58\frac{3}{4}$

[a] All Class 250 cast iron flanges have a $\frac{1}{16}$ raised face. This raised face is included in the face-to-face, center-to-face, and the minimum thickness of flange dimensions.

[b] Drilling templates are in multiples of four, so that fittings may be made to face in any quarter, and bolt holes straddle the center line. For bolts smaller than $1\frac{1}{2}$ inch the bolt holes shall be drilled $\frac{1}{8}$ inch larger in diameter than the nominal diameter of the bolt. Holes for bolts $1\frac{3}{4}$ inch shall be drilled $\frac{1}{4}$ inch larger in diameter than the nominal diameter of the bolt. Holes for bolts $1\frac{3}{4}$ inch and larger shall be drilled $\frac{1}{4}$ inch larger than nominal diameter of bolts.

[c] The bolt holes of these cast iron flanges and flanged fittings need not be spot faced for ordinary service except as follows: In sizes 12 inches and smaller, when rough flanges, after facing, are oversized more than $\frac{1}{8}$ inch in thickness, they shall be spot-faced to the specified thickness of flange (minimum) with a plus tolerance of $\frac{1}{16}$ inch. In sizes 14 to 24 inches, inclusive, when rough flanges, after facing, are oversized more than $\frac{3}{16}$ inch in thickness they shall be spot-faced to the specified thickness of flange (minimum) with a plus tolerance of $\frac{1}{16}$ inch. In sizes 30 inches and larger, when rough flanges, after facing, are oversized more than $\frac{1}{4}$ inch in thickness, they shall be spot-faced to the specified thickness of flange (minimum) with a plus tolerance of $\frac{1}{8}$ inch.

All dimensions given in inches.

Table 9-85. Cast Iron Flanged Fittings For Refrigerant Piping

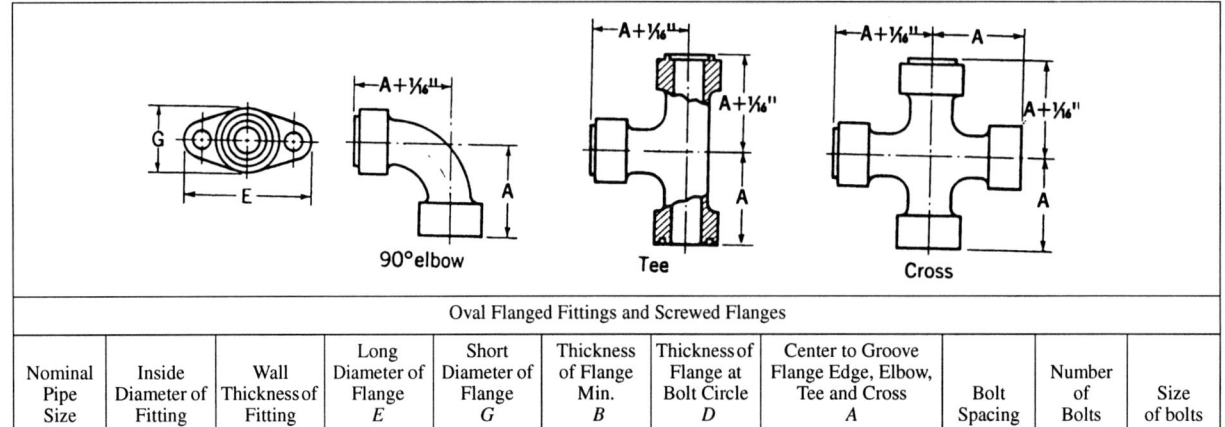

Nominal Pipe Size	Inside Diameter of Fitting	Wall Thickness of Fitting	Long Diameter of Flange E	Short Diameter of Flange G	Thickness of Flange Min. B	Thickness of Flange at Bolt Circle D	Center to Groove Flange Edge, Elbow, Tee and Cross A	Bolt Spacing	Number of Bolts	Size of bolts
$\frac{1}{4}$	$\frac{3}{8}$	$\frac{1}{4}$	$3\frac{7}{16}$	$1\frac{3}{16}$	$\frac{13}{16}$	$\frac{1}{2}$	$2\frac{3}{8}$	$2\frac{1}{4}$	2	$\frac{1}{2}$
$\frac{3}{8}$	$\frac{1}{2}$	$\frac{1}{4}$	$3\frac{11}{16}$	$1\frac{3}{16}$	$\frac{15}{16}$	$\frac{9}{16}$	$2\frac{1}{2}$	$2\frac{1}{2}$	2	$\frac{1}{2}$
$\frac{1}{2}$	$\frac{5}{8}$	$\frac{1}{4}$	$3\frac{7}{8}$	$1\frac{3}{16}$	1	$\frac{5}{8}$	$2\frac{3}{4}$	$2\frac{3}{4}$	2	$\frac{1}{2}$
$\frac{3}{4}$	$\frac{3}{16}$	$\frac{1}{4}$	$4\frac{1}{8}$	$2\frac{1}{8}$	$1\frac{1}{8}$	$\frac{11}{16}$	$3\frac{1}{4}$	3	2	$\frac{1}{2}$

Oval Flanged Fittings and Screwed Flanges

Table 9-86. Square Flanged Fittings and Screwed Flanges

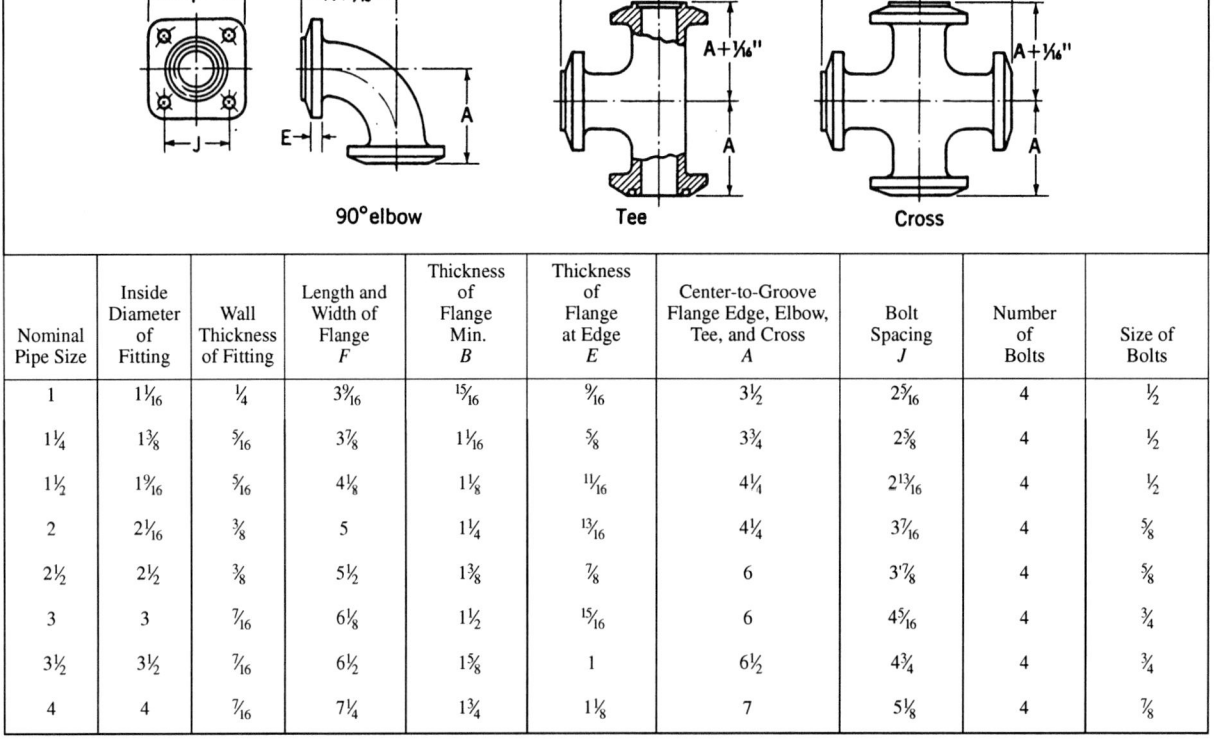

Nominal Pipe Size	Inside Diameter of Fitting	Wall Thickness of Fitting	Length and Width of Flange F	Thickness of Flange Min. B	Thickness of Flange at Edge E	Center-to-Groove Flange Edge, Elbow, Tee, and Cross A	Bolt Spacing J	Number of Bolts	Size of Bolts
1	$1\frac{1}{16}$	$\frac{1}{4}$	$3\frac{9}{16}$	$\frac{15}{16}$	$\frac{9}{16}$	$3\frac{1}{2}$	$2\frac{5}{16}$	4	$\frac{1}{2}$
$1\frac{1}{4}$	$1\frac{3}{8}$	$\frac{5}{16}$	$3\frac{7}{8}$	$1\frac{1}{16}$	$\frac{5}{8}$	$3\frac{3}{4}$	$2\frac{5}{8}$	4	$\frac{1}{2}$
$1\frac{1}{2}$	$1\frac{9}{16}$	$\frac{5}{16}$	$4\frac{1}{8}$	$1\frac{1}{8}$	$\frac{11}{16}$	$4\frac{1}{4}$	$2\frac{13}{16}$	4	$\frac{1}{2}$
2	$2\frac{1}{16}$	$\frac{3}{8}$	5	$1\frac{1}{4}$	$\frac{13}{16}$	$4\frac{1}{4}$	$3\frac{7}{16}$	4	$\frac{5}{8}$
$2\frac{1}{2}$	$2\frac{1}{2}$	$\frac{3}{8}$	$5\frac{1}{2}$	$1\frac{3}{8}$	$\frac{7}{8}$	6	$3\frac{7}{8}$	4	$\frac{5}{8}$
3	3	$\frac{7}{16}$	$6\frac{1}{8}$	$1\frac{1}{2}$	$\frac{15}{16}$	6	$4\frac{5}{16}$	4	$\frac{3}{4}$
$3\frac{1}{2}$	$3\frac{1}{2}$	$\frac{7}{16}$	$6\frac{1}{2}$	$1\frac{5}{8}$	1	$6\frac{1}{2}$	$4\frac{3}{4}$	4	$\frac{3}{4}$
4	4	$\frac{7}{16}$	$7\frac{1}{4}$	$1\frac{3}{4}$	$1\frac{1}{8}$	7	$5\frac{1}{8}$	4	$\frac{7}{8}$

All dimensions given in inches.

Table 9-87. Round Flanged Fittings and Screwed Flanges

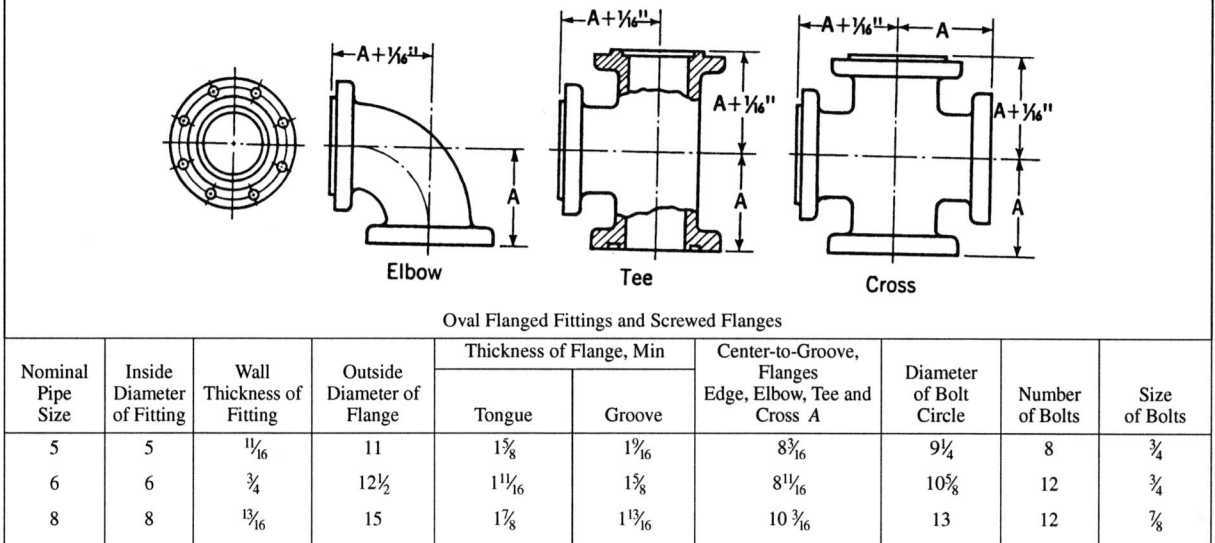

Elbow   Tee   Cross

Oval Flanged Fittings and Screwed Flanges

Nominal Pipe Size	Inside Diameter of Fitting	Wall Thickness of Fitting	Outside Diameter of Flange	Thickness of Flange, Min		Center-to-Groove, Flanges Edge, Elbow, Tee and Cross *A*	Diameter of Bolt Circle	Number of Bolts	Size of Bolts
				Tongue	Groove				
5	5	$\frac{11}{16}$	11	$1\frac{5}{8}$	$1\frac{9}{16}$	$8\frac{3}{16}$	$9\frac{1}{4}$	8	$\frac{3}{4}$
6	6	$\frac{3}{4}$	$12\frac{1}{2}$	$1\frac{11}{16}$	$1\frac{5}{8}$	$8\frac{11}{16}$	$10\frac{5}{8}$	12	$\frac{3}{4}$
8	8	$\frac{13}{16}$	15	$1\frac{7}{8}$	$1\frac{13}{16}$	$10\frac{3}{16}$	13	12	$\frac{7}{8}$
10	10	$\frac{15}{16}$	$17\frac{1}{2}$	$2\frac{1}{8}$	$2\frac{1}{16}$	$11\frac{11}{16}$	$15\frac{1}{4}$	16	1
12	12	1	$20\frac{1}{2}$	$2\frac{1}{4}$	$2\frac{3}{16}$	$13\frac{3}{16}$	$17\frac{3}{4}$	16	$1\frac{1}{8}$

All dimensions given in inches.

Table 9-88. Steel Pipe Flange Facing, All Pressures

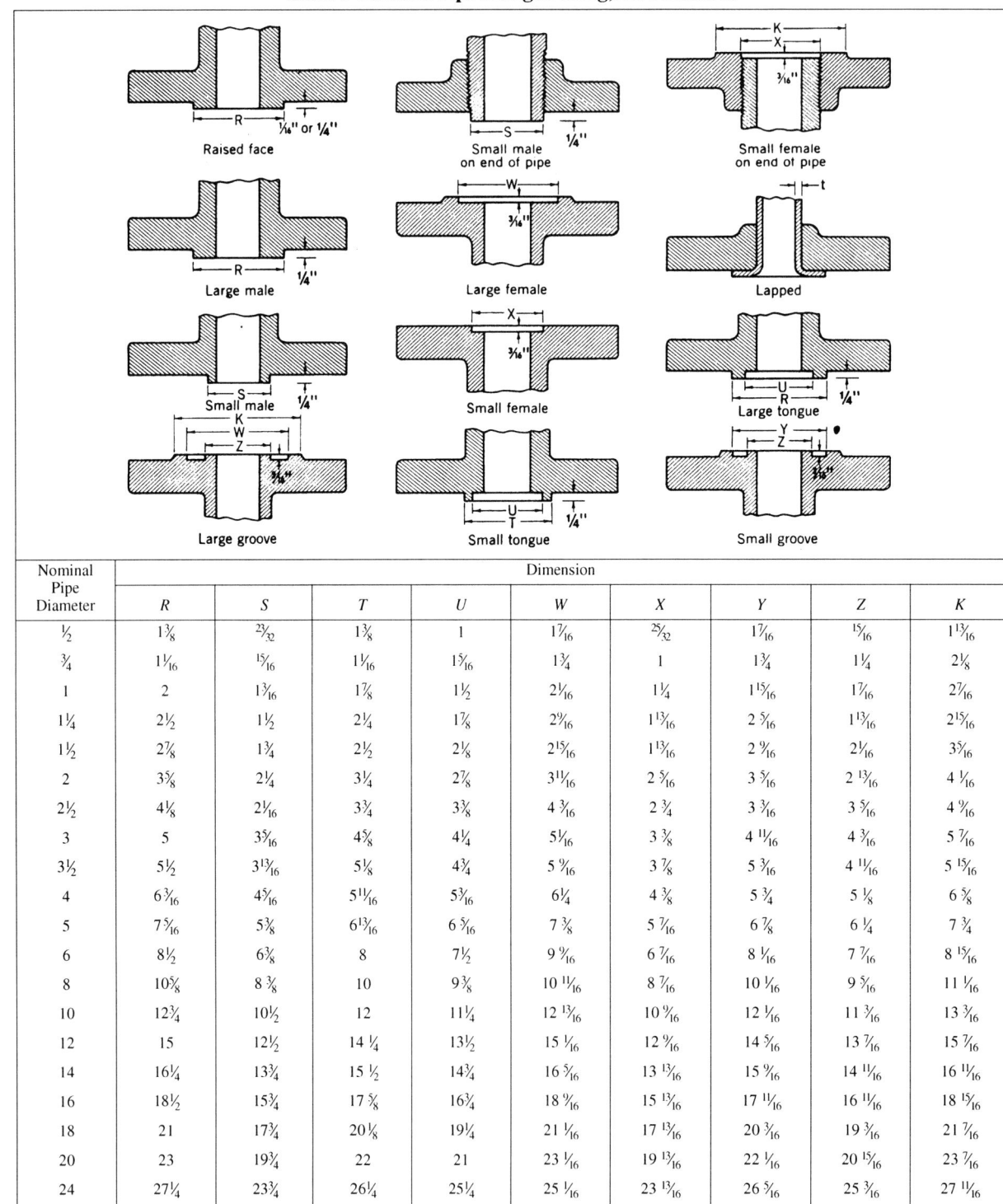

Nominal Pipe Diameter	Dimension								
	R	S	T	U	W	X	Y	Z	K
$\frac{1}{2}$	$1\frac{3}{8}$	$\frac{23}{32}$	$1\frac{3}{8}$	1	$1\frac{7}{16}$	$\frac{25}{32}$	$1\frac{7}{16}$	$\frac{15}{16}$	$1\frac{13}{16}$
$\frac{3}{4}$	$1\frac{1}{16}$	$\frac{15}{16}$	$1\frac{1}{16}$	$1\frac{5}{16}$	$1\frac{3}{4}$	1	$1\frac{3}{4}$	$1\frac{1}{4}$	$2\frac{1}{8}$
1	2	$1\frac{3}{16}$	$1\frac{7}{8}$	$1\frac{1}{2}$	$2\frac{1}{16}$	$1\frac{1}{4}$	$1\frac{15}{16}$	$1\frac{7}{16}$	$2\frac{7}{16}$
$1\frac{1}{4}$	$2\frac{1}{2}$	$1\frac{1}{2}$	$2\frac{1}{4}$	$1\frac{7}{8}$	$2\frac{9}{16}$	$1\frac{13}{16}$	$2\frac{5}{16}$	$1\frac{13}{16}$	$2\frac{15}{16}$
$1\frac{1}{2}$	$2\frac{7}{8}$	$1\frac{3}{4}$	$2\frac{1}{2}$	$2\frac{1}{8}$	$2\frac{15}{16}$	$1\frac{13}{16}$	$2\frac{9}{16}$	$2\frac{1}{16}$	$3\frac{5}{16}$
2	$3\frac{5}{8}$	$2\frac{1}{4}$	$3\frac{1}{4}$	$2\frac{7}{8}$	$3\frac{11}{16}$	$2\frac{5}{16}$	$3\frac{5}{16}$	$2\frac{13}{16}$	$4\frac{1}{16}$
$2\frac{1}{2}$	$4\frac{1}{8}$	$2\frac{1}{16}$	$3\frac{3}{4}$	$3\frac{3}{8}$	$4\frac{3}{16}$	$2\frac{3}{4}$	$3\frac{3}{16}$	$3\frac{5}{16}$	$4\frac{9}{16}$
3	5	$3\frac{5}{16}$	$4\frac{5}{8}$	$4\frac{1}{4}$	$5\frac{1}{16}$	$3\frac{3}{8}$	$4\frac{11}{16}$	$4\frac{3}{16}$	$5\frac{7}{16}$
$3\frac{1}{2}$	$5\frac{1}{2}$	$3\frac{13}{16}$	$5\frac{1}{8}$	$4\frac{3}{4}$	$5\frac{9}{16}$	$3\frac{7}{8}$	$5\frac{3}{16}$	$4\frac{11}{16}$	$5\frac{15}{16}$
4	$6\frac{3}{16}$	$4\frac{5}{16}$	$5\frac{11}{16}$	$5\frac{3}{16}$	$6\frac{1}{4}$	$4\frac{3}{8}$	$5\frac{3}{4}$	$5\frac{1}{8}$	$6\frac{5}{8}$
5	$7\frac{5}{16}$	$5\frac{3}{8}$	$6\frac{13}{16}$	$6\frac{5}{16}$	$7\frac{3}{8}$	$5\frac{7}{16}$	$6\frac{7}{8}$	$6\frac{1}{4}$	$7\frac{3}{4}$
6	$8\frac{1}{2}$	$6\frac{3}{8}$	8	$7\frac{1}{2}$	$9\frac{9}{16}$	$6\frac{7}{16}$	$8\frac{1}{16}$	$7\frac{7}{16}$	$8\frac{15}{16}$
8	$10\frac{5}{8}$	$8\frac{3}{8}$	10	$9\frac{3}{8}$	$10\frac{11}{16}$	$8\frac{7}{16}$	$10\frac{1}{16}$	$9\frac{5}{16}$	$11\frac{1}{16}$
10	$12\frac{3}{4}$	$10\frac{1}{2}$	12	$11\frac{1}{4}$	$12\frac{13}{16}$	$10\frac{9}{16}$	$12\frac{1}{16}$	$11\frac{3}{16}$	$13\frac{3}{16}$
12	15	$12\frac{1}{2}$	$14\frac{1}{4}$	$13\frac{1}{2}$	$15\frac{1}{16}$	$12\frac{9}{16}$	$14\frac{5}{16}$	$13\frac{7}{16}$	$15\frac{7}{16}$
14	$16\frac{1}{4}$	$13\frac{3}{4}$	$15\frac{1}{2}$	$14\frac{3}{4}$	$16\frac{5}{16}$	$13\frac{13}{16}$	$15\frac{9}{16}$	$14\frac{11}{16}$	$16\frac{11}{16}$
16	$18\frac{1}{2}$	$15\frac{3}{4}$	$17\frac{5}{8}$	$16\frac{3}{4}$	$18\frac{9}{16}$	$15\frac{13}{16}$	$17\frac{11}{16}$	$16\frac{11}{16}$	$18\frac{15}{16}$
18	21	$17\frac{3}{4}$	$20\frac{1}{8}$	$19\frac{1}{4}$	$21\frac{1}{16}$	$17\frac{13}{16}$	$20\frac{3}{16}$	$19\frac{3}{16}$	$21\frac{7}{16}$
20	23	$19\frac{3}{4}$	22	21	$23\frac{1}{16}$	$19\frac{13}{16}$	$22\frac{1}{16}$	$20\frac{15}{16}$	$23\frac{7}{16}$
24	$27\frac{1}{4}$	$23\frac{3}{4}$	$26\frac{1}{4}$	$25\frac{1}{4}$	$25\frac{1}{16}$	$23\frac{13}{16}$	$26\frac{5}{16}$	$25\frac{3}{16}$	$27\frac{11}{16}$

All dimensions given in inches.

Table 9-89. 150 and 300 lb Steel Flanged Fittings

Elbow 45° elbow Tee Cross

45° lateral Reducer Eccentric reducer True "Y"

Nominal Pipe Diameter	Inside Diameter of Fitting	Minimum Wall Thickness	Flange Diameter	Flange Thickness	Dimensions to Contact Surface of Raised Face				
					AA	BB	CC	EE	FF
150 Pound Fittings									
1	1	1/4	4 1/4	7/16	3 1/2	5	1 3/4	5 3/4	1 3/4
1 1/4	1 1/4	1/4	4 5/8	1/2	3 3/4	5 1/2	2	6 1/4	1 3/4
1 1/2	1 1/2	1/4	5	9/16	4	6	2 1/4	7	2
2	2	1/4	6	5/8	4 1/2	6 1/2	2 1/2	8	2 1/2
2 1/2	2 1/2	1/4	7	11/16	5	7	3	9 1/2	2 1/2
3	3	1/4	7 1/2	3/4	5 1/2	7 3/4	3	10	3
3 1/2	3 1/2	1/4	8 1/2	13/16	6	8 1/2	3 1/2	11 1/2	3
4	4	1/4	9	15/16	6 1/2	9	4	12	3
5	5	9/32	10	15/16	7 1/2	10 1/4	4 1/2	13 1/2	3 1/2
6	6	9/32	11	1	8	11 1/2	5	14 1/2	3 1/2
8	8	5/16	13 1/2	1 1/8	9	14	5 1/2	17 1/2	4 1/2
10	10	11/32	16	1 3/16	11	16 1/2	6 1/2	20 1/2	5
12	12	3/8	10	1 1/4	12	19	7 1/2	24 1/2	5 1/2
14	13 1/4	13/32	21	1 3/8	14	21 1/2	7 1/2	27	6
16	15 1/4	7/16	23 1/2	1 7/16	15	24	8	30	6 1/2
18	17 1/4	15/32	25	1 7/16	16 1/2	26 1/2	8 1/2	32	7
20	19 1/4	1/2	27 1/2	1 11/16	18	29	9 1/2	35	8
24	23 1/4	9/16	32	1 7/8	22	34	11	40 1/2	9
300 Pound Fittings									
1	1	1/4	4 7/8	11/16	4	5	2 1/4	6 1/2	2
1 1/4	1 1/4	1/4	5 1/4	3/4	4 1/4	5 1/2	2 1/2	7 1/4	2 1/4
1 1/2	1 1/2	1/4	6 1/8	13/16	4 1/2	6	2 3/4	8 1/2	2 1/2
2	2	1/4	6 1/2	7/8	5	6 1/2	3	9	2 1/2
2 1/2	2 1/2	1/4	7 1/2	1	5 1/2	7	3 1/2	10 1/2	2 1/2
3	3	9/32	8 1/4	1 1/8	6	7 3/4	3 1/2	11	3
3 1/2	3 1/2	9/32	9	1 3/16	6 1/2	8 1/2	4	12 1/2	3
4	4	5/16	10	1 1/4	7	9	4 1/2	13 1/2	3
5	5	3/8	11	1 3/8	8	10 1/4	5	15	3 1/2
6	6	3/8	12 1/2	1 7/16	8 1/2	11 1/2	5 1/2	17 1/2	4
8	8	7/16	15	1 5/8	10	14	6	20 1/2	5
10	10	1/2	17 1/2	1 7/8	11 1/2	16 1/2	7	24	5 1/2
12	12	9/16	20 1/2	2	13	19	8	27 1/2	6
14	13 1/4	5/8	23	2 1/8	15	21 1/2	8 1/2	31	6 1/2
16	15 1/4	11/16	25 1/2	2 1/4	16 1/2	24	9 1/2	34 1/2	7 1/2
18	17	3/4	28	2 3/8	18	26 1/2	10	37 1/2	8
20	19	13/16	30 1/2	2 1/2	19 1/2	29	10 1/2	40 1/2	8 1/2
24	23	15/16	36	2 3/4	22 1/2	34	12	47 1/2	10

All dimensions given in inches.

Table 9-90. 400, 900 lbs Steel Flanged Fittings

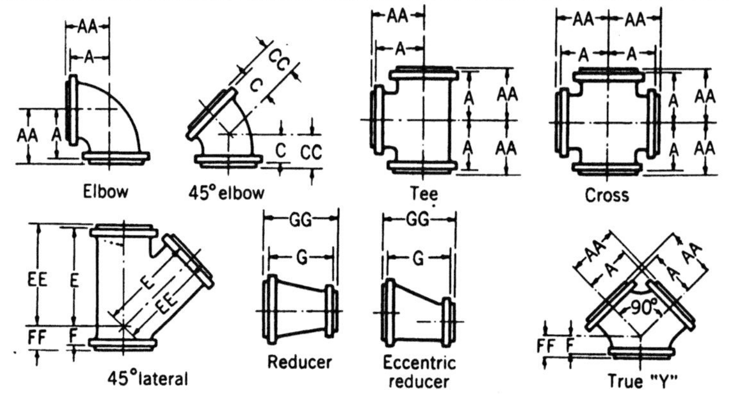

Elbow 45° elbow Tee Cross

45° lateral Reducer Eccentric reducer True "Y"

Nominal Pipe Diameter	Flange Diameter	Flange Thickness	Wall Thickness	Inside Diameter of Fitting	Dimensions to Contact Surface of Raised Face				
					AA	CC	EE	FF	GG
400 lb Fittings									
½ to 3½	Use 600 lb dimensions in these sizes								
4	10	1⅜	⅜	4	8	5½	16	4½	8¼
5	11	1½	⁷⁄₁₆	5	9	6	16¾	5	9¼
6	12½	1⅝	⁷⁄₁₆	6	9¾	6¼	18¾	5¼	10
8	15	1⅞	⁹⁄₁₆	8	11¾	6¾	22¼	5¾	12
10	17½	2⅛	1¹⁄₁₆	10	13¼	7¾	25¾	6¼	13½
12	20½	2¼	¾	12	18	8¾	29¾	6½	15¼
14	23	2⅜	¹³⁄₁₆	13⅛	16¼	9¼	32¾	7	16½
16	25½	2½	⅛	15	17¾	10¼	36¼	8	18½
18	28	2⅝	¹⁵⁄₁₆	17	19¼	10¾	39¼	8½	19½
20	30½	2¾	1 ¹⁄₁₆	18⅞	20¾	11¼	42¾	9	21
24	36	3	1³⁄₁₆	22⅝	24¼	12¾	50¼	10½	24½
900 lb Fittings									
½ to 2½	Use 1500 lb dimensions in these sizes								
3	9½	1½	¹³⁄₃₂	2⅞	7½	5½	14½	4½	7¾
4	11½	1¾	½	3⅞	9	6½	17½	5½	9¼
5	13¾	2	¹⁹⁄₃₂	4¾	11	7½	21	6½	11¼
6	15	2³⁄₁₆	²³⁄₃₂	5¾	12	8	22½	6½	12¼
8	18½	2½	⅞	7½	14½	9	27½	7½	14¾
10	21½	2¾	1¹⁄₁₆	9⅜	16½	10	31½	8½	16¾
12	24	3⅛	1¼	11⅛	19	11	34½	9	17¾
14	25¼	3⅜	1⅜	12¼	20¼	11½	36½	9½	19
16	27¾	3½	1⁹⁄₁₆	14	22¼	12½	40¾	10½	21
18	31	4	1¾	15¾	24	13¼	45½	12	24½
20	33¾	4¼	1²⁹⁄₃₂	17½	26	14½	50¼	13	26½
24	41	5½	2⁹⁄₃₂	21	30½	18	60	15½	30½

All dimensions given in inches.

Table 9-91. 600 and 1500 lb Steel Flanged Fittings

Nominal Pipe Diameter	Flange Diameter	Flange Thickness	Wall Thickness	Inside Diameter of Fitting	Dimensions to Contact Surface of Raised Face				
					AA	CC	EE	FF	GG
600 lb Fittings									
1/2	3 3/4	9/16	1/4	1/2	3 1/4	2	5 3/4	1 3/4	5
3/4	4 5/8	5/8	1/4	3/4	3 3/4	2 1/2	6 3/4	2	5
1	4 7/8	11/16	1/4	1	4 1/4	2 1/2	7 1/4	2 1/4	5
1 1/4	5 1/4	13/16	1/4	1 1/4	4 1/2	2 3/4	8	2 1/2	5
1 1/2	6 1/8	7/8	1/4	1 1/2	4 3/4	3	9	2 3/4	5
2	6 1/2	1	1/4	2	5 3/4	4 1/4	10 1/4	3 1/2	6
2 1/2	7 1/2	1 1/8	9/32	2 1/2	6 1/2	4 1/2	11 1/2	3 1/2	6 3/4
3	8 1/4	1 1/4	5/16	3	7	5	12 3/4	4	7 1/4
3 1/2	9	1 3/8	11/32	3 1/2	7 1/2	5 1/2	14	4 1/2	7 3/4
4	10 3/4	1 1/2	3/8	4	8 1/2	6	16 1/2	4 1/2	8 3/4
5	13	1 3/4	7/16	5	10	7	19 1/2	6	10 1/4
6	14	1 7/8	1/2	6	11	7 1/2	21	6 1/2	11 1/4
8	16 1/2	2 3/16	5/8	7 7/8	13	8 1/2	24 1/2	7	13 1/4
10	20	2 1/2	3/4	9 3/4	15 1/2	9 1/2	29 1/2	8	15 3/4
12	22	2 5/8	29/32	11 3/4	16 1/2	10	31 1/2	8 1/2	16 3/4
14	23 3/4	2 3/4	31/32	12 7/8	17 1/2	10 3/4	34 1/4	9	17 3/4
16	27	3	1 3/32	14 3/4	19 1/2	11 3/4	38 1/2	10	19 3/4
18	29 1/4	3 1/4	1 7/32	16 1/2	21 1/2	12 1/4	42	10 1/2	21 3/4
20	32	3 1/2	1 11/32	18 1/4	23 1/2	13	45 1/2	11	23 3/4
24	37	4	1 19/32	22	27 1/2	14 3/4	53	13	27 3/4
1500 lb Fittings									
1/2	4 3/4	7/8	1/4	1/2	4 1/4	3	…	…	…
3/4	5 1/8	1	1/4	11/16	4 1/2	3 1/4	…	…	…
1	5 7/8	1 1/8	1/4	7/8	5	3 1/2	9	2 1/2	5
1 1/4	6 1/4	1 1/8	5/16	1 1/8	5 1/2	4	10	3	5 3/4
1 1/2	7	1 1/4	3/8	1 3/8	6	4 1/4	11	3 1/2	6 1/4
2	8 1/2	1 1/2	7/16	1 7/8	7 1/4	4 3/4	13 1/4	4	7 1/4
2 1/2	9 5/8	1 5/8	1/2	2 1/4	8 1/4	5 1/4	15 1/4	4 1/2	8 1/4
3	10 1/2	1 7/8	5/8	2 3/4	9 1/4	5 3/4	17 1/4	5	9 1/4
4	12 1/4	2 1/8	3/4	3 5/8	10 3/4	7 1/4	19 1/4	6	10 3/4
5	14 3/4	2 7/8	29/32	4 3/8	13 1/4	8 3/4	23 1/4	7 1/2	13 3/4
6	15 1/2	3 1/4	1 3/32	5 3/8	13 7/8	9 3/8	24 7/8	8 1/8	14 1/2
8	19	3 5/8	1 13/32	7	16 3/8	10 7/8	29 7/8	9 1/8	17
10	23	4 1/4	1 23/32	8 3/4	19 1/2	12	36	10 1/4	20 1/4
12	26 1/2	4 7/8	2	10 3/8	22 1/4	13 1/4	40 3/4	12	23
14	29 1/2	5 1/4	2 3/16	11 3/8	24 3/4	14 1/4	44	12 1/2	25 3/4
16	32 1/2	5 3/4	2 1/2	13	27 1/4	16 1/4	48 1/4	14 3/4	28 1/4
18	36	6 3/8	2 13/16	14 5/8	30 1/4	17 3/4	53 1/4	16 1/2	31 1/2
20	38 3/4	7	3 1/8	16 3/8	32 3/4	18 3/4	57 3/4	17 3/4	34
24	46	8	3 23/32	19 5/8	38 1/4	20 3/4	67 1/4	20 1/2	39 3/4

All dimensions given in inches.

Table 9-92. Steel Butt-Welded Fittings

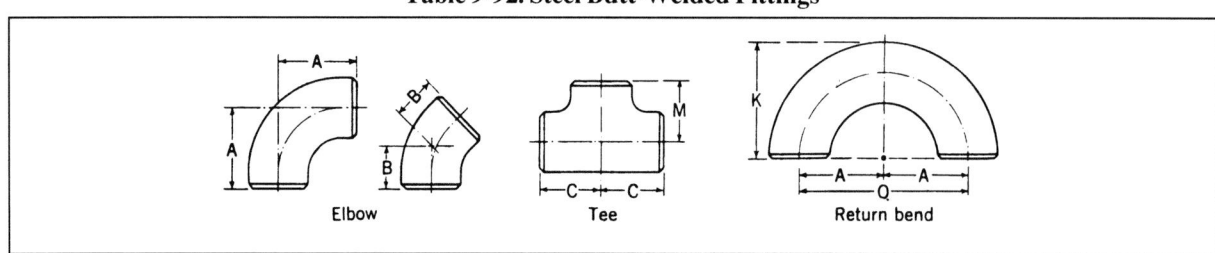

Elbow   Tee   Return bend

Nominal Pipe Size	Outside Diameter at Bevel	Center-to-End				180° Returns[a]	
		90° Elbows	45° Elbows	Tees, Run	Tees, Outlet		
		A	B	C	M	O	K
1	1.315	1½	⅞	1½	1½	3	2³⁄₁₆
1¼	1.66	1⅞	1	1⅞	1⅞	3¾	2¾
1½	1.9	2¼	1⅛	2¼	2¼	4½	3¼
2	2.375	3	1⅜	2½	2½	6	4³⁄₁₆
2½	2.875	3¾	1¾	3	3	7½	5³⁄₁₆
3	3.500	4½	2	3⅜	3⅜	9	6¼
3½	4.000	5½	2¼	3¾	3¾	10½	7¼
4	4.500	6	2½	4⅛	4⅛	12	8¼
5	5.563	7½	3⅛	4⅞	4⅞	15	10⁵⁄₁₆
6	6.625	9	3¾	5⅝	5⅝	18	12⁵⁄₁₆
8	8.625	12	5	7	7	24	16
10	10.75	15	6¼	8½	8½	30	20⅜
12	12.75	18	7½	10	10	36	24⅜
14	14.00	21	8¾	11	…	42	28
16	16.00	24	10	12	…	48	32
18	18.00	27	11¼	13 ½	…	54	36
20	20.00	30	12½	15	…	60	40
24	24.00	36	15	17	…	72	48

[a] Dimension A=½ dimension O.

All dimensions given in inches.

Table 9-93. Reducers

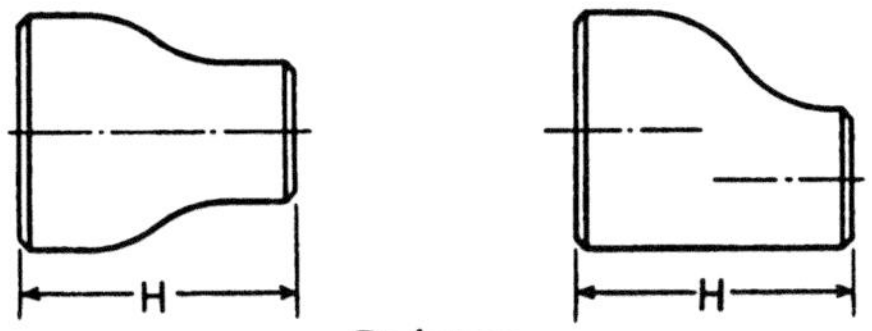

Reducers

Nominal Pipe Size	End-to-End H	Nominal Pipe Size	End-to-End H	Nominal Pipe Size	End-to-End H	Nominal Pipe Size	End-to-End H
1 × ¾	2	3 × 2½	3½	6 × 5	5½	14 × 12	13
1 × ½	2	3 × 2	3½	6 × 4	5½	14 × 10	13
		3 × ½	3½	6 × 3½	5½	14 × 8	13
1¼ × 1	2	3 × 1¼	3½	6 × 3	5½	14 × 6	13
1¼ × ¾	2			6 × 2½	5½		
1¼ × ½	2	3½ × 3	4			16 × 14	14
		3½ × 2½	4	8 × 6	6	16 × 12	14
1½ × 1¼	2 ½	3 ½ × 2	4	8 × 5	6	16 × 10	14
1½ × 1	2 ½	3 ½ × 2½	4	8 × 4	6	16 × 8	14
1½ × ¾	2 ½	3 ½ × 1 ¼	4	8 × 3 ½	6		
1½ × ½	2 ½					18 × 16	15
		4 × 3½	4	10 × 8	7	18 × 14	15
2 × 1½	3	4 × 3		10 × 6	7	18 × 12	15
2 × 1½	3	4 × 2½	4	10 × 5	7	18 × 10	15
2 × 1	3	4 × 2	4	10 × 4	7		
2 × ¾	3	4 × 1½	4			20 × 18	20
				12 × 10	8	20 × 16	20
2 ½ × 2	3 ½	5 × 4	5	12 × 8	8	20 × 14	20
2½ ×1½	3 ½	5 × 3½	5	12 × 6	8	20 × 12	20
2½ × 1¼	3 ½	5 × 3	5	12 × 5	8		
2 ½ × 1	3 ½	5 × 2½	5			24 × 20	20
		5 × 2	5			24 × 18	20
						24 × 16	20

All dimensions given in inches.

Table 9-94. Steel Socket Welded Fittings

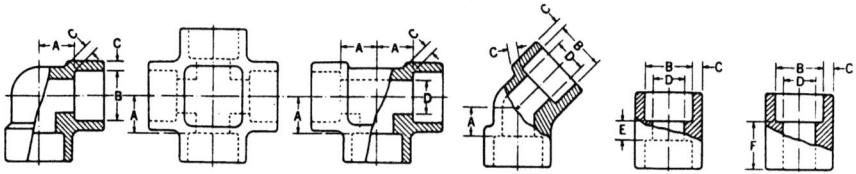

Table 9-95. Elbows, Tees and Crosses

Nominal Pipe Size	Center to Bottom of Socket		Bore Diameter of Socket	Minimum Socket Wall Thickness			Bore Diameter of Fitting		
	Schedule 40 and 160	Schedule 160		Schedule 40	Schedule 80	Schedule 160	Schedule 40	Schedule 80	Schedule 160
	A		Minimum B	C			D		
⅛	⁷⁄₁₆	…	0.420	0.125	0.125	…	0.269	0.215	…
¼	⁷⁄₁₆	…	0.555	0.125	0.149	…	0.364	0.302	…
⅜	¹⁷⁄₃₂	…	0.69	0.125	0.158	…	0.493	0.423	…
½	⅝	¾	0.855	0.136	0.184	0.234	0.622	0.546	0.466
¾	¾	⅞	1.065	0.141	0.193	0.273	0.824	0.742	0.614
1	⅞	1¹⁄₁₆	1.330	0.166	0.224	0.313	1.049	0.957	0.815
1¼	1¹⁄₁₆	1¼	1.675	0.175	0.239	0.313	1.38	1.278	1.160
1½	1¼	1½	1.915	0.181	0.250	0.351	1.61	1.500	1.338
2	1½	1⅝	2.406	0.193	0.293	0.429	2.067	1.939	1.689
2½	1⅝	2¼	2.906	0.254	0.345	0.469	2.469	2.323	2.125
3	2¼	2½	3.535	0.270	0.375	0.546	3.068	2.900	2.626

Table 9-96. Steel Socket Welded Fittings 45° Elbows, Couplings, and Half Couplings

Nominal Pipe Size	Center to Bottom of Socket		Bore Diameter of Socket Minimum	Socket Wall Thickness Minimum			Bore Diameter of Fitting		
	Schedule 40 and 160	Schedule160		Schedule 40	Schedule 80	Schedule 160	Schedule40	Schedule 80	Schedule 160
	A		B	C			D		
⅛	⁵⁄₁₆	…	⅝	0.420	0.125	0.125	…	0.269	0.215
¼	⁵⁄₁₆	…	⅝	0.555	0.125	0.149	…	0.364	0.302
⅜	⁵⁄₁₆	…	¹¹⁄₁₆	0.69	0.125	0.158	…	0.493	0.423
½	⁷⁄₁₆	½	⅞	0.855	0.136	0.184	0.234	0.622	0.546
¾	½	⁹⁄₁₆	¹⁵⁄₁₆	1.065	0.141	0.193	0.273	0.824	0.742
1	⁹⁄₁₆	¹¹⁄₁₆	1⅛	1.330	0.166	0.224	0.313	1.049	0.957
1¼	¹¹⁄₁₆	¹³⁄₁₆	1³⁄₁₆	1.675	0.175	0.239	0.313	1.38	1.278
1½	¹³⁄₁₆	1	1¼	1.915	0.181	0.250	0.351	1.61	1.500
2	1	1⅛	1⅝	2.406	0.193	0.273	0.429	2.067	1.939
2½	1⅛	1¼	1¹¹⁄₁₆	2.906	0.254	0.345	0.469	2.469	2.323
3	1¼	1⅜	1¾	3.535	0.270	0.375	0.546	3.068	2.900

All dimensions given in inches.

Table 9-97. Cast Brass Solder Joint Fittings

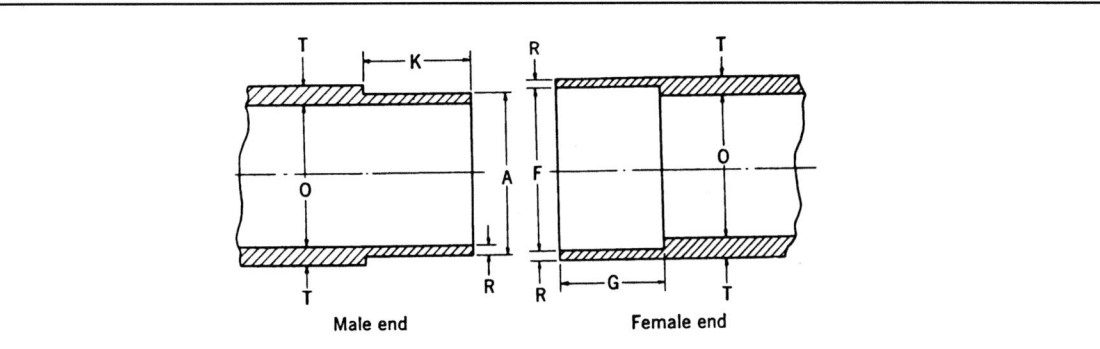

Male end   Female end

Dimensions of Solder-Joint Ends

Standard Water Tube Size	Male End			Female End			Metal Thickness, Minimum		Inside Diameter of Fitting O
	Outside Diameter A		Length K	Inside Diameter F		Depth G			
	Minimum	Maximum	Minimum	Minimum	Maximum	Minimum	Body T	Joint R	Minimum
¼	0.374	0.376	⅜	0.378	0.380	⁵⁄₁₆	0.08	0.048	0.31
⅜	0.499	0.501	⁷⁄₁₆	0.503	0.505	⅜	0.09	0.048	0.43
½	0.624	0.626	⁹⁄₁₆	0.628	0.630	½	0.09	0.054	0.54
¾	0.874	0.876	¹³⁄₁₆	0.878	0.880	¾	0.10	0.06	0.78
1	1.1235	1.1265	³¹⁄₃₂	1.1285	1.1305	²⁹⁄₃₂	0.11	0.066	1.02
1¼	1.3735	1.3765	1¹⁄₃₂	1.3785	1.3805	³¹⁄₃₂	0.12	0.072	1.26
1½	1.623	1.627	1⁵⁄₃₂	1.629	1.6315	1³⁄₃₂	0.13	0.078	1.50
2	2.123	2.127	1¹³⁄₃₂	2.129	2.1315	1¹¹⁄₃₂	0.15	0.090	1.98
2½	2.623	2.627	1¹⁷⁄₃₂	2.629	2.6315	1¹⁵⁄₃₂	0.17	0.102	2.46
3	3.123	3.127	1²³⁄₃₂	3.129	3.1315	1²¹⁄₃₂	0.19	0.114	2.94
3½	3.623	3.627	1³¹⁄₃₂	3.629	3.632	1²⁹⁄₃₂	0.20	0.12	3.42
4	4.123	4.127	2 ⁷⁄₃₂	4.129	4.132	2⁵⁄₃₂	0.22	0.132	3.90
5	5.123	5.127	2²³⁄₃₂	5.129	5.132	2²¹⁄₃₂	0.28	0.168	4.87
6	6.123	6.127	3⁵⁄₃₂	6.129	6.132	3³⁄₃₂	0.34	0.204	5.84
8	8.123	8.127	4¹⁄₃₂	8.129	8.132	3³¹⁄₃₂	0.375	0.310	7.72

All dimensions given in inches.

Table 9-98. Dimensions of Elbows and Tees

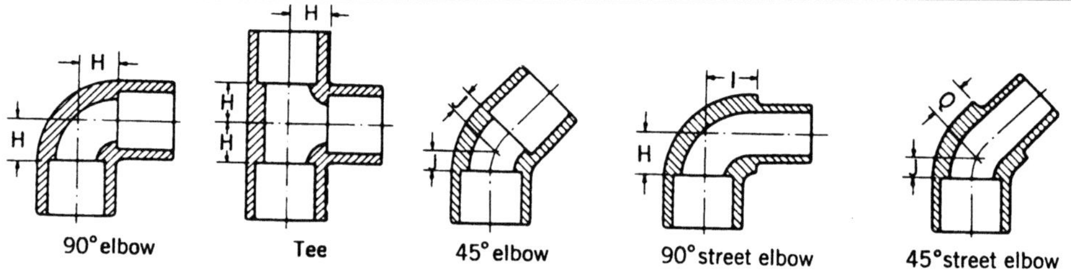

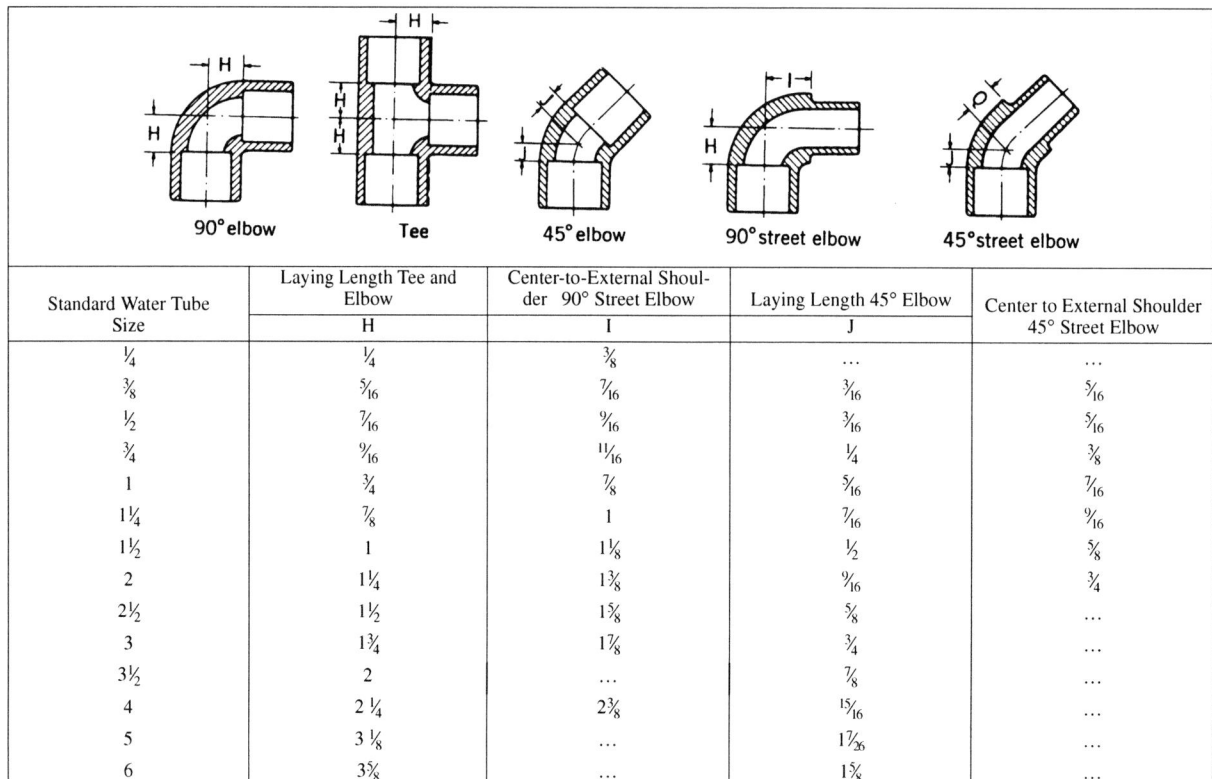

Standard Water Tube Size	Laying Length Tee and Elbow H	Center-to-External Shoulder 90° Street Elbow I	Laying Length 45° Elbow J	Center to External Shoulder 45° Street Elbow
1/4	1/4	3/8	…	…
3/8	5/16	7/16	3/16	5/16
1/2	7/16	9/16	3/16	5/16
3/4	9/16	11/16	1/4	3/8
1	3/4	7/8	5/16	7/16
1 1/4	7/8	1	7/16	9/16
1 1/2	1	1 1/8	1/2	5/8
2	1 1/4	1 3/8	9/16	3/4
2 1/2	1 1/2	1 5/8	5/8	…
3	1 3/4	1 7/8	3/4	…
3 1/2	2	…	7/8	…
4	2 1/4	2 3/8	15/16	…
5	3 1/8	…	1 7/26	…
6	3 5/8	…	1 5/8	…
8	4 7/8	…	2 1/8	…

All dimensions given in inches.

Table 9-99. Brass or Bronze Screwed Fittings

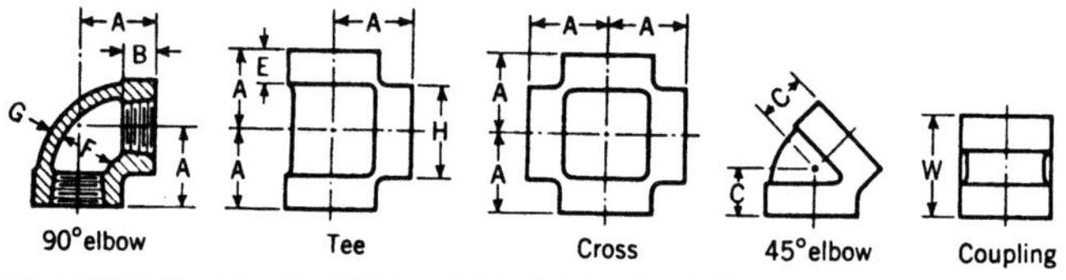

Nominal Pipe Size	Center-to-End Elbows, Tees. and Crosses	Length of Thread, Minimum	Center-to-End 45° Elbows	Width of Band Minimum	Inside Diameter of Fitting Minimum	Inside Diameter of Fitting Maximum	Metal Thickness Minimum	Outside Diameter of Band Minimum	End to End Coupling
	A	B	C	E	F		G	H	W
1/4	0.81	0.32	0.73	0.38	0.54	0.58	0.11	0.93	1.06
3/8	0.95	0.36	0.80	0.44	0.68	0.72	0.12	1.12	1.16
1/2	1.12	0.43	0.88	0.50	0.84	0.90	0.13	1.34	1.34
3/4	1.31	0.50	0.98	0.56	1.05	1.11	0.16	1.63	1.52
1	1.50	0.58	1.12	0.62	1.32	1.38	0.17	1.95	1.67
1 1/4	1.75	0.67	1.29	0.69	1.56	1.73	0.19	2.39	1.93
1 1/2	1.94	0.70	1.43	0.75	1.90	1.97	0.20	2.68	2.15
2	2.25	0.75	1.68	0.84	2.38	2.45	0.22	3.28	2.53
2 1/2	2.70	0.92	1.95	0.94	2.88	2.98	0.24	3.86	2.88
3	3.08	0.98	2.17	1.00	3.50	3.60	0.26	4.62	3.18
4	3.79	1.08	2.61	1.12	4.50	4.60	0.31	5.79	3.69

All dimensions given in inches.

Table 9-100. Brass or Bronze Screwed Fittings

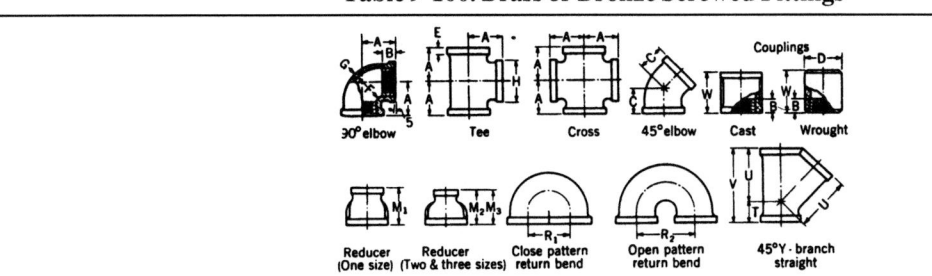

30° elbow · Tee · Cross · 45° elbow · Cast · Wrought · Couplings

Reducer (One size) · Reducer (Two & three sizes) · Close pattern return bend · Open pattern return bend · 45° Y - branch straight

Nominal Pipe Size	Center-to-End Elbows, Tees, Crosses	Length of Thread Minimum	Center-to-End 45° Elbows	Band Length Minimum	Inside Diameter of Cast Fitting		Metal Thickness Minimum	Band Diameter Minimum	End-to-End Straight Couplings	
	A	B	C	E	Minimum	Maximum	G	H	Cast	Wrought
									W	W
⅛	0.54	0.25	0.42	0.14	0.41	0.44	0.08	0.67	0.80	0.83
¼	0.71	0.32	0.56	0.16	0.54	0.58	0.08	0.81	0.97	1.03
⅜	0.82	0.36	0.63	0.17	0.68	0.72	0.09	1.00	1.05	1.11
½	1.01	0.43	0.78	0.19	0.84	0.90	0.09	1.17	1.29	1.36
¾	1.18	0.50	0.89	0.23	1.05	1.11	0.10	1.42	1.43	1.50
1	1.43	0.58	1.06	0.27	1.32	1.39	0.11	1.72	1.68	…
1¼	1.69	0.67	1.22	0.31	1.66	1.73	0.12	2.1	1.86	…
1½	1.84	0.70	1.30	0.34	1.90	1.97	0.13	2.38	1.92	…
2	2.12	0.75	1.45	0.41	2.38	2.45	0.15	2.92	2.2	…
2½	2.70	0.92	1.95	0.48	2.88	2.98	0.17	3.49	2.88	…
3	3.08	0.98	2.17	0.55	3.50	3.60	0.19	4.20	3.18	…
4	3.79	1.08	2.61	0.66	4.50	4.60	0.22	5.31	3.69	…

Nominal Pipe Size	Return Reducers End-to-End Reducing			Return Bends Center-to-Center		45°-Y-Branch			Diameter Wrought Coupling
	One Size	Two Sizes	Three Sizes	Close Pattern	Open Pattern	Center-to-End Inlet	Center-to-End Outlet	End-to-End	
	M₁	M₂	M₃	R₁	R₂	T	U	V	D
¼	0.88	…	…	…	…	…	…	…	9⁄16
⅜	1.01	0.92	…	…	…	0.50	1.28	1.78	11⁄16
½	1.17	1.13	…	1.00	1.50	0.61	1.58	2.19	27⁄32
¾	1.36	1.24	1.24	1.25	2.00	0.72	1.9	2.62	1 1⁄16
1	1.56	1.49	…	1.50	2.50	0.85	2.33	3.18	1 5⁄16
1¼	1.77	1.65	…	…	3.00	1.02	2.83	3.85	…
1½	1.89	1.80	1.80	…	3.50	1.10	3.14	4.24	…
2	2.06	2.03	2.03	…	4.00	1.24	3.76	5.00	…
2½	3.25	…	…	…	…	…	…	…	…
3	3.69	3.69	…	…	…	…	…	…	…
4	4.38	…	…	…	…	…	…	…	…

Table 9-101. Solder Used in Joints

Fluid[a] and Size	50-50 Tin-Lead				95-5 Tin-Antimony or Lead-Tin				Solders Melting at or Above 1100°
	Service Temperatures, °F								
	100	150	200	250	100	150	200	250	350
	Max Service Pressure, psi								
⅛ to 1	200	150	100	85	500	400	300	200	270
1¼ to 2	175	125	90	75	400	350	250	175	190
2½ to 4	150	100	75	50	300	275	200	150	155
Steam, all	…	…	…	15	…	…	…	15	120

[a] Fluid is water except in last line.

All dimensions given in inches.

Table 9-102. Brass or Bronze Flanges

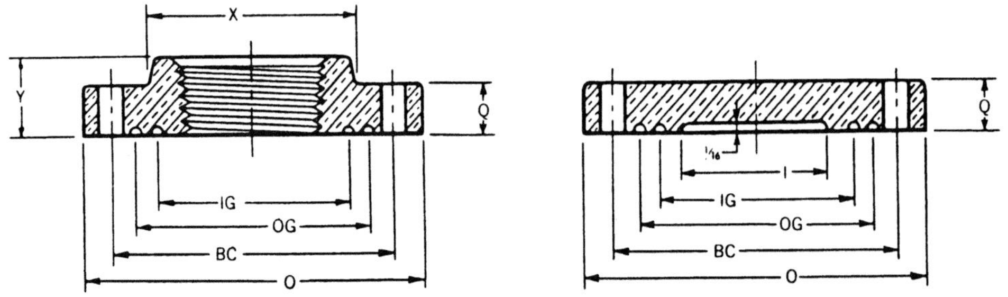

Nominal Pipe Size I	Diameter of Flange O	Thickness of Flange Minimum Q	Bolt Circle BC	Diameter of Outer Groove OG	Diameter of Inner Groove IG	Number of Bolts	Diameter of Bolt	Diameter Bolt Hole	Diameter of Hub, Minimum X	Length Overall, Minimum Y
150 lb Screwed Companion and Blind Flanges										
1/2	3 1/2	5/16	2 3/8	1 3/8	1 1/16	4	1/2	5/8	1 3/16	19/32
3/4	3 7/8	11/32	2 3/4	1 3/4	1 1/4	4	1/2	5/8	1 1/2	5/8
1	4 1/4	3/8	3 1/8	2 1/8	1 5/8	4	1/2	5/8	1 15/16	11/16
1 1/4	4 5/8	13/32	3 1/2	2 1/2	2	4	1/2	5/8	2 5/16	13/16
1 1/2	5	7/16	3 7/8	2 7/8	2 3/8	4	1/2	5/8	2 9/16	7/8
2	6	1/2	4 3/4	3 1/2	2 7/8	4	5/8	3/4	3 9/16	1
2 1/2	7	9/16	5 1/2	4 1/4	3 5/8	4	5/8	3/4	3	1 1/8
3	7 1/2	5/8	6	4 3/4	4 1/8	4	5/8	3/4	4 1/4	1 3/16
3 1/2	8 1/2	11/16	7	5 3/4	5 1/8	8	5/8	3/4	4 13/16	1 1/4
4	9	11/16	7 1/2	6 1/4	5 5/8	8	5/8	3/4	5 5/16	1 5/16
5	10	3/4	8 1/2	7	6 1/4	8	3/4	7/8	6 7/16	1 7/16
6	11	13/16	9 1/2	8	7 1/4	8	3/4	7/8	7 9/16	1 9/16
8	13 1/2	15/16	11 3/4	10 1/4	9 1/2	8	3/4	7/8	9 11/16	1 3/4
10	16	1	14 1/4	12 1/2	11 1/2	12	7/8	1	12	1 15/16
12	19	1 1/16	17	15 1/4	14 1/4	12	7/8	1	14 3/8	2 3/16
300 lb Screwed Companion and Blind Flanges										
1/2	3 3/4	1/2	2 5/8	1 5/8	1 1/8	4	1/2	5/8	1 3/16	19/32
3/4	4 5/8	17/32	3 1/4	2	1 3/8	4	5/8	3/4	1 1/2	5/8
1	4 7/8	19/32	3 1/2	2 1/4	1 5/8	4	1 5/8	3/4	1 15/16	11/16
1 1/4	5 1/4	5/8	3 7/8	2 5/8	2	4	1 5/8	3/4	2 5/16	13/16
1 1/2	6 1/8	11/16	4 1/2	3	2 1/4	4	3/4	7/8	2 9/16	7/8
2	6 1/2	3/4	5	3 3/4	3 1/8	8	5/8	3/4	3 1/16	1
2 1/2	7 1/2	13/16	5 7/8	4 3/8	3 5/8	8	3/4	7/8	3 9/16	1 1/8
3	8 1/4	29/32	6 5/8	5 1/8	4 3/8	8	3/4	7/8	4 1/4	1 3/16
3 1/2	9	31/32	7 1/4	5 3/4	5	8	3/4	7/8	4 13/16	1 1/4
4	10	1 1/16	7 7/8	6 3/8	5 5/8	8	3/4	7/8	5 5/16	1 5/16
5	11	1 1/8	9 1/4	7 3/4	7	8	3/4	7/8	6 7/16	1 7/16
6	12 1/2	1 3/16	10 5/8	9 1/8	8 3/8	12	3/4	7/8	7 9/16	1 9/16
8	15	1 3/8	13	11 1/4	10 1/4	12	7/8	1	9 11/16	1 3/4

All dimensions given in inches.

Table 9-103. Brass or Bronze Flanged Fittings

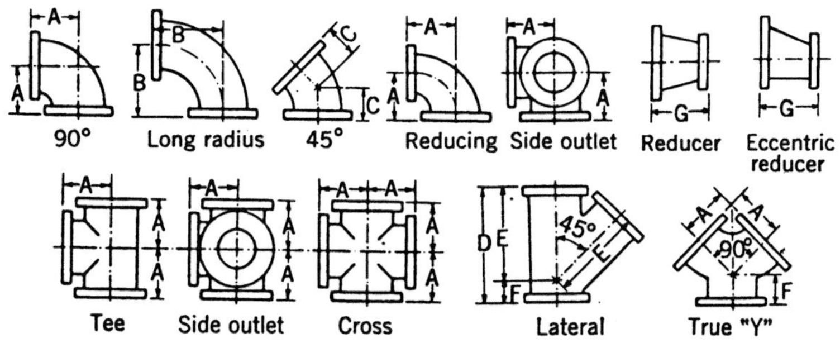

90° Long radius 45° Reducing Side outlet Reducer Eccentric reducer

Tee Side outlet Cross Lateral True "Y"

Nominal Pipe Size	Center-to-Face	Face-to-Face	Center-to-Face	Center-to-Face	Face-to-Face	Center-to-Face	Center-to-Face	Face-to-Face	Wall Thickness
	A	AA	B	C	D	E	F	G	
150 lb									
½	3	6	…	1⅝	…	…	…	…	3/32
¾	3¼	6½	…	1¾	…	…	…	…	7/64
1	3½	7	5	1¾	7½	5¾	1¾	…	⅛
1¼	3¾	7½	5½	2	8	6¼	1¾	…	9/64
1½	4	8	6	2¼	9	7	2	…	5/32
2	4½	9	6½	2½	10½	8	2½	5	3/16
2½	5	10	7	3	12	9½	2½	5½	13/64
3	5½	11	7¾	3	13	10	3	6	
3½	6	12	8½	3½	14½	11½	3	6½	¼
4	6½	13	9	4	15	12	3	7	17/64
5	7½	15	10¼	4½	17	13½	3½	8	19/64
6	8	16	11½	5	18	14½	3½	9	21/64
8	9	18	14	5½	22	17½	4½	11	13/32
10	11	22	16½	6½	25½	20½	5	12	31/64
12	12	24	19	7½	30	24½	5½	14	9/16
300 lb									
½	3	6	…	1¾	…	…	…	…	⅛
¾	3½	7	…	2¼	…	…	…	…	5/32
1	4	8	5	2¼	8½	6½	2	…	11/64
1¼	4¼	8½	5½	2½	9½	7¼	2¼	…	3/16
1½	4½	9	6	2¾	11	8½	2½	…	13/64
2	5	10	6½	3	11½	9	2½	5	¼
2½	5½	11	7	3½	13	10½	2½	5½	9/32
3	6	12	7¾	3½	14	11	3	6	21/64
3½	6½	13	8½	4	15½	12½	3	6½	23/64
4	7	14	9	4½	16½	13½	3	7	13/32
5	8	16	10¼	5	18½	15	3½	8	31/64
6	8½	17	11½	5½	21½	17½	4	9	9/16
8	10	20	14	6	25½	20½	5	11	23/32

All dimensions given in inches.

Table 9-104. Cast Iron Soil Pipe Hub and Spigot Dimensions

Size	Inside Diameter of Hub	Outside Diameter of Spigot	Outside Diameter of Barrel	Telescoping Length	Thickness of Barrel		Width of Spigot Bead
	A	M	J	Y	T (Nominal)	T (minimum)	N
2	2.94	2.62	2.25	2.50	0.18	0.10	0.69
3	3.94	3.62	3.25	2.75	0.18	0.12	0.75
4	4.94	4.62	4.25	3.00	0.18	0.12	0.81
5	5.94	5.62	5.25	3.00	0.19	0.12	0.81
6	6.94	6.62	6.25	3.00	0.20	0.12	0.81
8	9.25	8.75	8.38	3.50	0.22	0.17	1.12
10	11.38	10.88	10.5	3.50	0.26	0.21	1.12
12	13.5	12.88	12.5	4.25	0.28	0.22	1.38
15	16.75	16.00	15.62	4.25	0.30	0.25	1.38

Size	Thickness of Hub		Width of Hub Bead	Distance from Lead Groove to End, Pipe and Fittings		Weight per Length of Pipe, lbs	
	Hub Body	Over Bead					
	S (Minimum)	R (Minimum)	F	P (Minimum)	P (Maximum)	Single Hub	Double Hub
2	0.13	0.34	0.75	0.25	0.38	20	21
3	0.16	0.37	0.81	0.25	0.38	30	31
4	0.16	0.37	0.88	0.25	0.38	40	42
5	0.16	0.37	0.88	0.25	0.38	52	54
6	0.18	0.37	0.88	0.25	0.38	65	68
8	0.19	0.44	1.19	0.25	0.38	100	105
10	0.27	0.53	1.19	0.31	0.50	145	150
12	0.27	0.53	1.44	0.38	0.62	190	200
15	0.30	0.58	1.44	0.38	0.62	255	270

All dimensions given in inches.

Table 9-105. Cast Iron Soil Pipe Y Branches

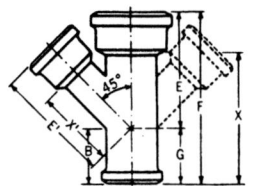

Single and double Y branches

Size	B (min)	Dimensions							Weight, single, Pounds	Weight, double, Pounds
		E	E'	F	G	X	X'			
Y Branches, Single and Double										
2	3½	6 ½	6 ½	10½	4	8	4	6½	9
3	4	8 ¼	8 ¼	13¼	5	10½	5 ½	12½	16
4	4	9 ¾	9 ¾	15	5 ¼	12	6 ¾	17	23
5	4	11	11	16½	5 ½	13½	8	22	28
6	4	12¼	12¼	18	5 ¾	15	9 ¼	28	36
8	5½	15⁵⁄₁₆	15⁵⁄₁₆	23	7 ¹¹⁄₁₆	19½	11¹³⁄₁₆	55	73
10	5½	18	18	26	8	22½	14 ½	94	120
12	7	21⅛	21⅛	31¼	8⅛	27	16 ⅞	135	173
15	7	25	25	35¾	10 ¾	31½	20 ¾	204	262
3 by 2	4	7 ⁹⁄₁₆	7 ½	11¾	4 ³⁄₁₆	9	5	10	13
4 by 2	4	8 ⅜	8 ¼	12	3 ⅝	9	5 ¾	12	15
4 by 3	4	9 ¹⁄₁₆	9	13½	4 ⁷⁄₁₆	10½	6 ¼	14	19
5 by 2	4	8 ⅞	9	12	3 ⅛	9	6 ½	14	17
5 by 3	4	9 ⅝	9 ¾	13½	3 ⅞	10½	7	16½	21
5 by 4	4	10 ⁵⁄₁₆	10 ½	15	4 ¹¹⁄₁₆	12	7 ½	19	24
6 by 2	4	9 ⁷⁄₁₆	9 ¾	12	2 ⁹⁄₁₆	9	7 ¼	16½	20
6 by 3	4	10⅛	19 ½	13½	3 ⅜	10½	7 ¾	19	23
6 by 4	4	10³⁄₁₆	11¼	15	4 ³⁄₁₆	12	8 ¼	22	28
6 by 5	4	11 ⁹⁄₁₆	11¾	16½	4 ¹⁵⁄₁₆	13½	8 ¾	24	31
8 by 2	5½	10 ⅞	11	14	3 ⅛	10½	8 ½	29	32
8 by 3	5½	11⁹⁄₁₆	11¾	15½	3 ¹⁵⁄₁₆	12	9	32	37
8 by 4	5½	12 ¼	12 ½	17	4 ¾	13½	9 ½	36	42
8 by 5	5½	13	13	18½	5 ½	16	10	39	45
8 by 6	5½	13¹¹⁄₁₆	13½	20	6 ⁵⁄₁₆	16½	10 ½	44	51
10 by 4	5½	13 ⁷⁄₁₆	14 ⅛	17	3 ⁹⁄₁₆	13½	11 ⅛	53	59
10 by 5	5½	14³⁄₁₆	14 ⅝	18½	4 ¹⁵⁄₁₆	15	12	57	63
10 by 6	5½	14 ⅞	15 ⅛	20	5 ⅛	16½	12 ⅛	61	70
10 by 8	5½	16 ½	16¹⁵⁄₁₆	23	6 ½	19½	13 ⁷⁄₁₆	77	94
12 by 4	7	15 ⅛	15 ⁷⁄₁₆	19¼	4 ⅛	15	12 ⁷⁄₁₆	70	76
12 by 5	7	15 ⅞	15¹⁵⁄₁₆	20¾	4 ⅞	16½	12¹⁵⁄₁₆	74	81
12 by 6	7	16 ⁹⁄₁₆	16 ⁷⁄₁₆	22¼	5¹¹⁄₁₆	18	13 ⁷⁄₁₆	80	88
12 by 8	7	18 ³⁄₁₆	18 ¼	25¼	7 ¹⁄₁₆	21	14 ¾	96	113
12 by 10	7	19 ¹¹⁄₁₆	19 ⁵⁄₁₆	18¼	8 ⁹⁄₁₆	24	15³⁄₁₆	115	142
15 by 6	7	18 ¼	18 ¾	22¼	4	18	15 ¾	109	117
15 by 8	7	19 ⅞	20 ⁹⁄₁₆	25¼	5 ⅜	21	17 ¹⁄₁₆	127	146
15 by 10	7	21 ⅜	21 ⅝	28¼	6 ⅞	24	18 ⅛	152	176
15 by 12	7	22¹³⁄₁₆	23 ⁷⁄₁₆	31¼	8 ⁷⁄₁₆	27	19 ³⁄₁₆	170	210

All dimensions given in inches.

Table 9-106. Cast Iron Soil Pipe Quarter Bends

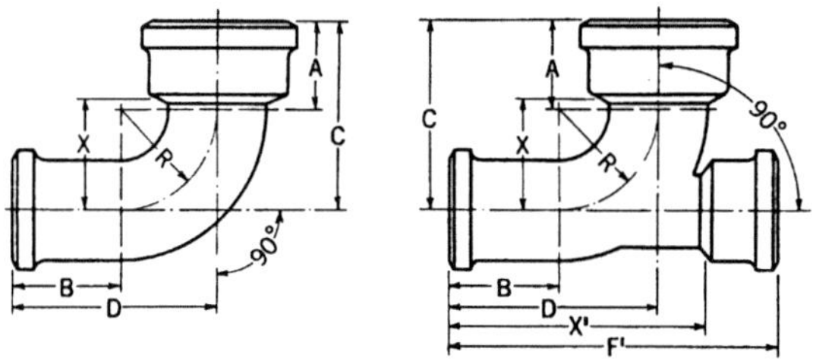

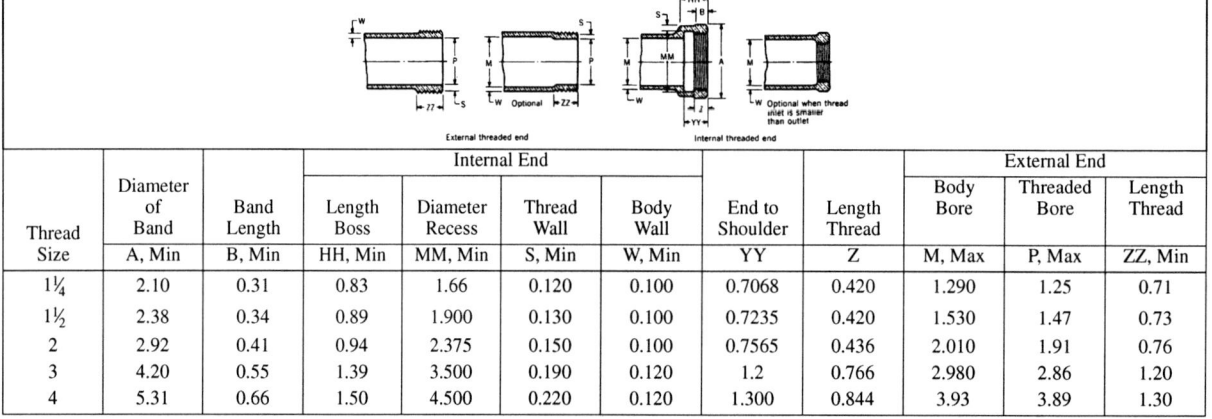

Quarter bend   Quarter bend with heel inlet

Quarter Bends

Size	A	B	C	D	R	X	Weight, lb
2	2 ¾	3	5¾	6	3	3¼	5
3	3 ¼	3½	6¾	7	3½	4	10
4	3 ½	4	7½	8	4	4½	15
5	3 ½	4	8	8½	4½	5	19
6	3 ½	4	8½	9	5	5½	24
8	4 ⅛	5½	10⅛	11½	6	6 ⅝	51
10	4 ⅛	5½	11 ⅛	12½	7	7 ⅝	78
12	5	7	13	15	8	8 ¾	111
15	5	7	14 ½	16 ½	9 ½	10¼	169

Quarter Bends with Heel Inlets

Size	A	B	C	D	F	R	X	X′	Weight, lb
3× 2	3 ¼	3 ½	6 ¾	7	11 ½	3 ½	4	9	13
4 × 2	3 ½	4	7 ½	8	13	4	4 ½	10 ½	18
4 × 3	3 ½	4	7 ½	8	13 ¼	4	4 ½	10 ½	19
5 × 2	3 ½	4	8	8 ½	14 ¼	4 ½	5	11 ¾	22
5 × 3	3 ½	4	8	8 ½	14 ¼	4 ½	5	11 ¾	24
5 × 4	3 ½	4	8	8 ½	14 ¾	4 ½	5	11 ¾	25
6 × 2	3 ½	4	8 ½	9	15	5	5 ½	12 ½	27
6 × 3	3 ½	4	8 ½	9	15 ¼	5	5 ½	12 ½	29
6 × 4	3 ½	4	8 ½	9	15 ½	5	5 ½	12 ½	30

All dimensions given are in inches.

Table 9-107. Dimensions of Screwed Ends

			Internal End						External End		
Thread Size	Diameter of Band	Band Length	Length Boss	Diameter Recess	Thread Wall	Body Wall	End to Shoulder	Length Thread	Body Bore	Threaded Bore	Length Thread
	A, Min	B, Min	HH, Min	MM, Min	S, Min	W, Min	YY	Z	M, Max	P, Max	ZZ, Min
1¼	2.10	0.31	0.83	1.66	0.120	0.100	0.7068	0.420	1.290	1.25	0.71
1½	2.38	0.34	0.89	1.900	0.130	0.100	0.7235	0.420	1.530	1.47	0.73
2	2.92	0.41	0.94	2.375	0.150	0.100	0.7565	0.436	2.010	1.91	0.76
3	4.20	0.55	1.39	3.500	0.190	0.120	1.2	0.766	2.980	2.86	1.20
4	5.31	0.66	1.50	4.500	0.220	0.120	1.300	0.844	3.93	3.89	1.30

All dimensions given are in inches.

Table 9-108. Cast Iron Soil Pipe Sweeps ⅛ and 1/16 Bends

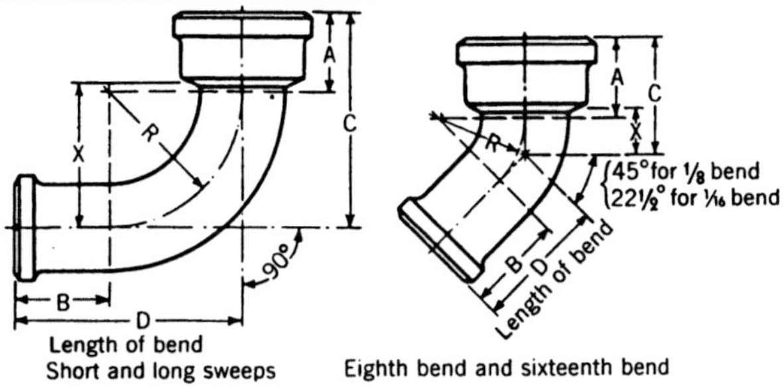
A
C
X
R
B
D
90°
Length of bend
Short and long sweeps
45° for ⅛ bend
22½° for 1/16 bend
Length of bend
Eighth bend and sixteenth bend

Size	Dimensions						Weight, lbs
	A	B	C	D	R	X	
Short Sweeps, Quarter Bend							
2	2¾	3	7¾	8	5	5¼	5
3	3¼	3½	8¾	9	5½	6	9
4	3½	4	9½	10	6	6½	12½
5	3½	4	10	10½	6½	7	16
6	3½	4	10½	11	7	7½	20
8	4⅛	5½	12⅛	13½	8	8⅝	38
10	4⅛	5½	13⅛	14½	9	9⅝	62
12	5	7	15	17	10	10¾	89
15	5	7	16½	18½	11½	12¼	130
Long Sweeps, Quarter Bend							
2	2¾	3	10¾	11	8	8¼	6½
3	3¼	3½	11¾	12	8½	9	11
4	3½	4	12½	13	9	9½	15
5	3½	4	13	13½	9½	10	19½
6	3½	4	13½	14	10	10½	24
8	4⅛	5½	15⅛	16½	11	11⅝	45
10	4⅛	5½	16⅛	17½	12	12⅝	72
12	5	7	18	20	13	13¾	101
15	5	7	19½	21½	14½	15¼	147
Eighth Bends							
2	2¾	3	4	4¼	3	1½	3¼
3	3¼	3½	4 11/16	4 15/16	3½	1 15/16	5½
4	3½	4	5 3/16	5 11/16	4	2 3/16	8½
5	3½	4	5⅜	5⅞	4½	2⅜	10½
6	3½	4	5 9/16	6 1/16	5	2 9/16	13
8	4⅛	5½	6⅝	8	6	3⅛	28
10	4⅛	5½	7	8⅜	7	3½	44
12	5	7	8 5/16	10 5/16	8	4 1/16	64
15	5	7	8 15/16	10 15/16	9½	4 11/16	92
Sixteenth Bends							
2	2¾	3	3⅜	3⅝	3	⅞	3¼
3	3¼	3½	3 15/16	4 3/16	3½	1 3/16	5½
4	3½	4	4 5/16	4 13/16	4	1 5/16	7½
5	3½	4	4⅜	4⅞	4½	1⅜	9
6	3½	4	4½	5	5	1½	11½
8	4⅛	5½	5 5/16	6 11/16	6	1 13/16	25
10	4⅛	5½	5½	6⅞	7	2	38
12	5	7	6⅜	8⅝	8	2⅜	56
15	5	7	6⅞	8⅞	9½	2⅝	78

All dimensions given in inches.

Table 9-109. Cast Iron Screwed Drainage Fittings

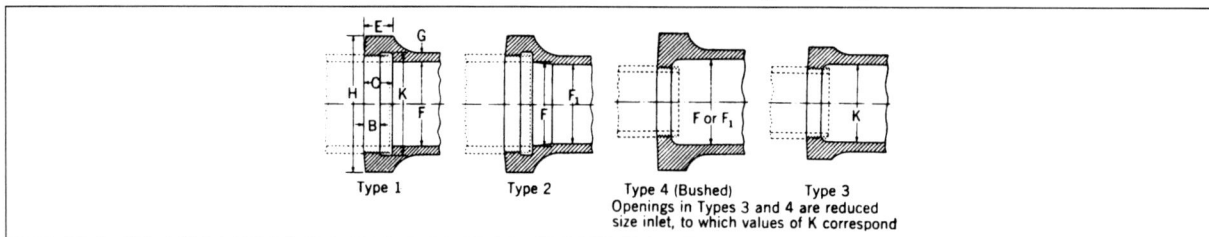

Type 1 Type 2 Type 4 (Bushed) Type 3
Openings in Types 3 and 4 are reduced
size inlet, to which values of K correspond

Dimension of Threaded Ends

Nominal Pipe Size	Lengths of Threads	Total Length of Thread Chamber to Shoulder	Width of Band	Inside Diameter of Fitting		Metal Thickness	Outside Diameter of Band	Recess Diameter	
	B	C	E	F	F_1	G	H	Maximum K	Minimum K
$1\frac{1}{4}$	0.420	0.7068	0.71	1.380	1.25	0.185	2.39	1.730	1.660
$1\frac{1}{2}$	0.420	0.7235	0.72	1.610	1.50	0.200	2.68	1.970	1.900
2	0.436	0.7565	0.76	2.067	2.00	0.220	3.28	2.445	2.375
$2\frac{1}{2}$	0.682	1.1375	1.14	2.469	2.50	0.240	3.86	2.975	2.875
3	0.766	1.2000	1.20	3.068	3.00	0.260	4.62	3.600	3.500
4	0.844	1.3000	1.30	4.026	4.00	0.310	5.79	4.600	4.500
5	0.937	1.4063	1.41	5.047	5.00	0.380	7.05	5.663	5.563
6	0.958	1.5125	1.51	6.065	6.00	0.430	8.28	6.725	6.625
8	1.063	1.7125	1.71	7.981	8.00	0.550	10.63	8.625	8.725

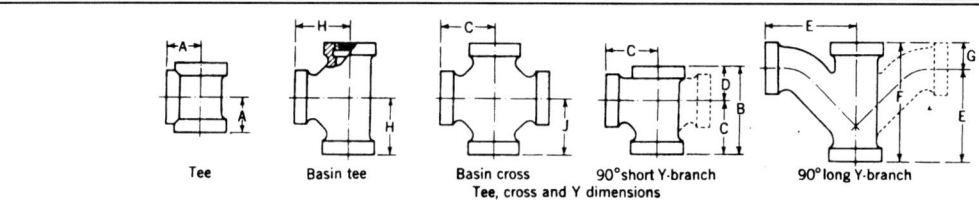

Tee Basin tee Basin cross 90° short Y-branch 90° long Y-branch
Tee, cross and Y dimensions

Dimensions of Tees, Crosses and Y Branches

Nominal Pipe Size	Center-to-End of Tee	90° Short Y-Branch			90° Long Y-Branch			Center-to-End of Basin Tee	Center-to-End of Basin Cross
	A	End-to-End B	Center-to-End C	Center-to-End D	Center-to-End E	End-to-End F	Center-to-End G	H	J
$1\frac{1}{4}$	$1\frac{3}{4}$	$3\frac{3}{4}$	$2\frac{1}{4}$	$1\frac{1}{2}$	$3\frac{5}{8}$	$4\frac{3}{4}$	$1\frac{1}{8}$	$2\frac{5}{16}$	$2\frac{5}{16}$
$1\frac{1}{2}$	$1\frac{15}{16}$	$4\frac{1}{4}$	$2\frac{1}{2}$	$1\frac{3}{4}$	$4\frac{1}{8}$	$5\frac{3}{8}$	$1\frac{1}{4}$	$2\frac{11}{16}$	$2\frac{5}{16}$
2	$2\frac{1}{4}$	$5\frac{3}{16}$	$3\frac{1}{16}$	$2\frac{1}{8}$	$5\frac{1}{4}$	7	$1\frac{3}{4}$	$3\frac{1}{2}$	$3\frac{1}{2}$
$2\frac{1}{2}$	$2\frac{11}{16}$	$6\frac{5}{16}$	$3\frac{11}{16}$	$2\frac{5}{8}$	$6\frac{1}{4}$	$8\frac{1}{4}$	2	$4\frac{1}{4}$	...
3	$3\frac{1}{16}$	$7\frac{1}{4}$	$4\frac{1}{4}$	3	$7\frac{1}{2}$	$9\frac{7}{8}$	$2\frac{3}{8}$	...	...
4	$3\frac{13}{16}$	$8\frac{3}{4}$	$5\frac{3}{16}$	$3\frac{9}{16}$	$9\frac{7}{8}$	13	$3\frac{1}{8}$	...	...
5	$4\frac{1}{2}$	$10\frac{5}{16}$	$6\frac{1}{8}$	$4\frac{3}{16}$	$12\frac{1}{4}$	$15\frac{3}{4}$	$3\frac{1}{2}$	...	...
6	$5\frac{1}{8}$	$11\frac{15}{16}$	$7\frac{1}{8}$	$4\frac{14}{16}$	$14\frac{5}{8}$	$18\frac{3}{4}$	$4\frac{1}{8}$	...	...

Table 9-110. Cast Iron Screwed Drainage Fittings

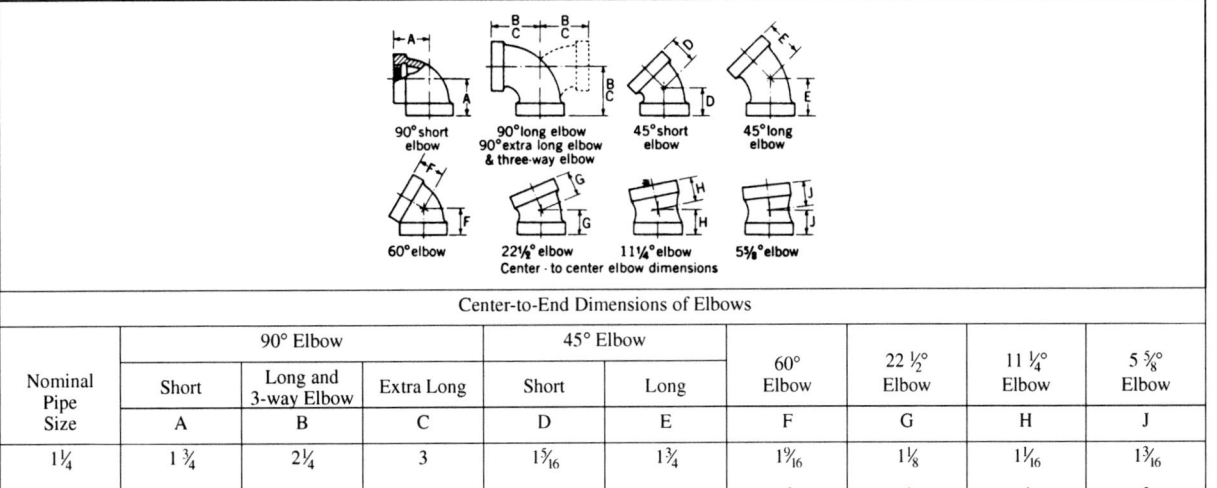

	Center-to-End Dimensions of Elbows								
Nominal Pipe Size	90° Elbow			45° Elbow		60° Elbow	22 ½° Elbow	11 ¼° Elbow	5 ⅝° Elbow
	Short	Long and 3-way Elbow	Extra Long	Short	Long				
	A	B	C	D	E	F	G	H	J
1¼	1 ¾	2¼	3	1⁵⁄₁₆	1¾	1⁹⁄₁₆	1⅛	1¹⁄₁₆	1³⁄₁₆
1½	1¹⁵⁄₁₆	2½	3½	1⁷⁄₁₆	1⅞	1¾	1¼	1¼	1⁵⁄₁₆
2	2¼	3¹⁄₁₆	4	1¹¹⁄₁₆	2¼	2¹⁄₁₆	1⁷⁄₁₆	1⅜	1½
2½	2¹¹⁄₁₆	3¹¹⁄₁₆	4½	1¹⁵⁄₁₆	2⅝	2½	1¾	1⅝	1⅝
3	3 ¹³⁄₁₆	4¼	5¼	2³⁄₁₆	2¹⁵⁄₁₆	2⅞	2	1¹³⁄₁₆	1¾
4	3¹³⁄₁₆	5³⁄₁₆	6¼	2⅝	3½	3⅜	2 ⁵⁄₁₆	2	1⅞
5	4 ½	6⅛	…	3¹⁄₁₆	4⅛	3⅞	2 ⅝	2¼	2
6	5 ⅛	7 ⅛	…	3⁷⁄₁₆	4⅞	4¼	2 ¹⁵⁄₁₆	2⅜	2¼
8	6 ⁹⁄₁₆	9	…	4¼	…	…	…	…	…

All dimensions given in inches.

Table 9-111. Cast Brass Solder Joint Drainage Fittings

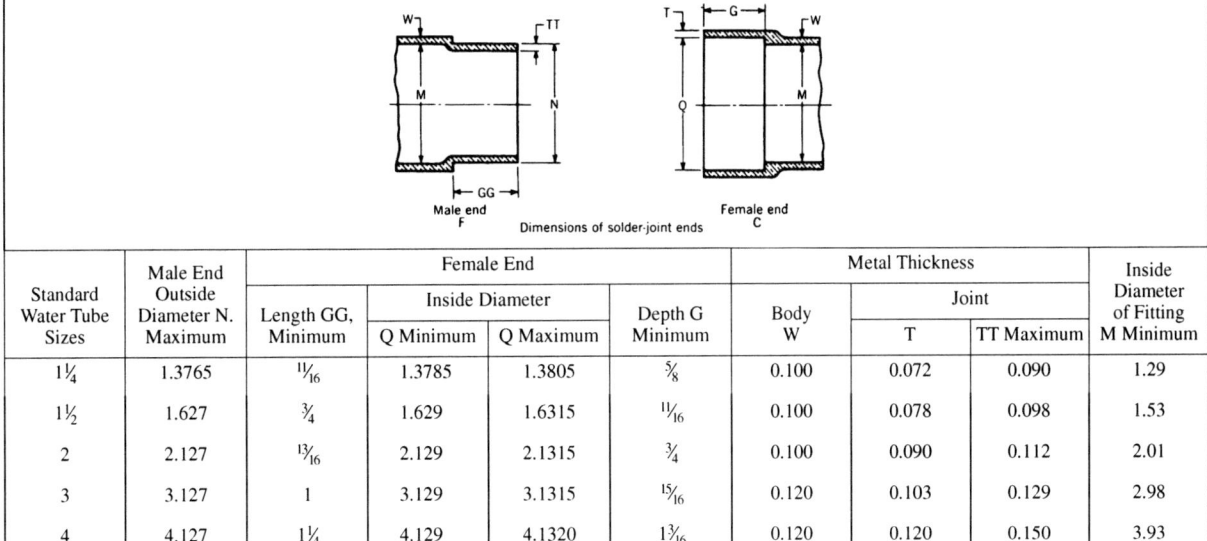

Dimensions of solder-joint ends

Standard Water Tube Sizes	Male End Outside Diameter N. Maximum	Female End				Metal Thickness			Inside Diameter of Fitting M Minimum
		Length GG, Minimum	Inside Diameter		Depth G Minimum	Body W	Joint		
			Q Minimum	Q Maximum			T	TT Maximum	
1¼	1.3765	¹¹⁄₁₆	1.3785	1.3805	⅝	0.100	0.072	0.090	1.29
1½	1.627	¾	1.629	1.6315	¹¹⁄₁₆	0.100	0.078	0.098	1.53
2	2.127	¹³⁄₁₆	2.129	2.1315	¾	0.100	0.090	0.112	2.01
3	3.127	1	3.129	3.1315	¹⁵⁄₁₆	0.120	0.103	0.129	2.98
4	4.127	1¼	4.129	4.1320	1³⁄₁₆	0.120	0.120	0.150	3.93

All dimensions given in inches.

Table 9-112. Surface Area of Flanged Fittings

Nominal Diameter, in.	90° Elbow		Long Radius Ell		Tee		Flanged Coupling		Cross	
	Area, ft²	Feet of Pipe	Area, ft²	Feet of Pipe	Area, ft²	Feet of Pipe	Area, ft²	Feet of Pipe	Area, ft²	Feet of Pipe
Standard Flanged Fittings Plus Accompanying Flanges										
1	0.80	2.31	0.89	2.59	1.24	3.59	0.32	0.93	1.62	4.72
1¼	0.96	2.20	1. 08	2.49	1.48	3.40	0.38	0.88	1.94	4.47
1½	1.17	2.35	1.34	2.68	1.82	3.64	0.48	0.95	2.38	4.78
2	1.65	2.65	1.84	2.96	2.54	4.08	0.67	1.08	3.32	5.34
2½	2.00	2.78	2.32	3.08	3.21	4.26	0.84	1.12	4.19	5.56
3	2.38	2.6	2.68	2.93	3.66	3.99	0.95	1.03	4.77	5.70
3½	2.98	2.85	3.28	3.13	4.48	4.28	1.12	1.07	5.83	5.56
4	3.53	2.9	3.96	3.36	5.41	4.59	1.34	1.14	7.03	5.97
4½	3.95	3.01	4.43	3.38	6.07	4.63	1.47	1.13	7.87	6.01
5	4.44	3.05	5.00	3.43	6.81	4.67	1.62	1.11	8.82	6.06
6	5.13	2.95	5.99	3.45	7.84	4.53	1.82	1.05	10.08	5.81
7	6.17	3.09	7.38	3.70	9.37	4.69	2.17	1.10	12.00	6.01
8	6.98	3.09	8.56	3.79	10.55	4.67	2.41	1.07	13.44	5.96
9	8.71	3.46	10.57	4.2	13.18	5.23	3.00	1.19	16.78	6.66
10	10.18	3.61	12.35	4.38	15.41	4.47	3.43	1.22	19.58	6.95
12	13.08	3.92	16.35	4.9	19.67	5.89	4.41	1.32	24.87	7.45
14	16.38	4.47	20.17	5.47	24.81	6.78	5.39	1.47	31.48	8.6
15	18.50	4.72	22.92	5.83	27.91	7.10	6.18	1.57	35.48	9.04
16	20.17	4.82	25.41	6.07	30.32	7.23	6.69	1.6	38.34	9.15
Extra Heavy Flanged Fittings Plus Accompanying Flanges										
1	1.02	2.95	1.08	3.15	1.58	4.58	0.44	1.27	2.07	6.02
1¼	1.10	2.52	1.34	3.08	1.93	4.43	0.51	1.17	2.53	5.82
1½	1.33	2.67	1.87	3.76	2.68	5.38	0.73	1.46	3.54	7.11
2	2.01	3.23	2.0	3.47	3.09	4.97	0.85	1.36	4.06	6.53
2½	2.57	3.41	2.76	3.67	4.05	5.38	1.11	1.46	5.17	6.87
3	3.49	3.81	3.74	4.08	5.33	5.82	1.48	1.62	6.95	7.58
3½	3.96	3.78	4.28	4.09	6.04	5.77	1.64	1.57	7.89	7.54
4	4.64	3.94	4.99	4.24	7.07	6.00	1.91	1.62	9.24	7.84
4½	5.02	3.83	5.46	4.17	7.72	5.90	2.04	1.56	10.07	7.69
5	5.47	3.76	6.02	4.13	8.52	5.85	2.18	1.50	10.97	7.53
6	6.99	4.03	7.76	4.48	10.64	6.14	2.78	1.6	13.75	7.93
7	8.62	4.32	9.73	4.87	12.33	6.18	3.46	1.73	16.83	8.43
8	9.76	4.32	11.09	4.91	14.74	6.53	3.77	1.67	18.97	8.41
9	11.44	4.54	13.17	5.23	17.23	6.84	4.44	1.76	22.10	8.77
10	13.58	4.82	15.6	5.54	20.41	7.25	5.20	1.85	26.26	9.32
12	17.73	5.31	18.76	5.62	26.65	7.99	6.71	2.01	34.11	10.22
14	22.31	6.08	25.70	7.02	33.63	9.18	8.30	2.26	43.15	11.75
15	25.28	6.43	29.34	7.47	38.04	9.68	9.52	2.43	48.79	12.4
16	27.18	6.48	31.73	7.58	40.94	9.78	10.05	2.40	52.35	12.50

All dimensions given in inches.

Table 9-113. Surface Area of Butt Welded Fittings

Pipe Diameter, in.	Long Radius 90° Elbow		Short Radius 90° Elbow		Long Radius 45° Elbow		Cap	
	Area, ft²	Feet of Pipe	Area, ft²	Feet of Pipe	Area, ft²	Feet of Pipe	Area, ft²	Feet of Pipe
½	0.04	0.18	...	...	0.02	0.09	...	...
¾	0.04	0.15	...	...	0.02	0.07	0.01	0.04
1	0.07	0.20	0.05	0.15	0.03	0.09	0.02	0.06
1¼	0.11	0.25	0.07	0.20	0.05	0.12	0.02	0.05
1½	0.15	0.30	0.10	0.20	0.07	0.14	0.02	0.04
2	0.24	0.39	0.27	0.26	0.12	0.19	0.03	0.05
2½	0.37	0.49	0.25	0.33	0.19	0.25	0.04	0.05
3	0.54	0.59	0.36	0.39	0.27	0.29	0.06	0.07
3½	0.72	0.69	0.48	0.46	0.36	0.34	0.09	0.09
4	0.93	0.79	0.62	0.53	0.46	0.39	0.10	0.08
5	1.43	0.98	0.95	0.65	0.72	0.49	0.16	0.11
6	2.04	1.18	1.36	0.78	1.02	0.59	0.22	0.13
8	3.55	1.57	2.37	1.05	1.77	0.78	0.34	0.15
10	5.53	1.96	3.69	1.31	2.26	0.8	0.52	0.18
12	7.87	2.35	5.25	1.57	3.93	1.18	0.74	0.22
14	10.08	2.52	6.72	1.68	5.04	1.26	0.89	0.22
16	13.00	2.90	8.79	1.93	6.58	1.45	1.21	0.26
18	16.66	3.50	11.11	2.33	8.33	1.75	1.42	0.30
20	20.56	3.91	13.72	2.61	10.28	1.95	1.77	0.34

Pipe Diameter, Inches	Long Radius 180° Elbow		Short Radius 180° Elbow		Cross		Tee	
	Area, ft²	Feet of Pipe	Area, ft²	Feet of Pipe	Area, ft²	Feet of Pipe	Area, ft²	Feet of Pipe
½	0.09	0.41	...	...	...	...	0.04	0.18
¾	0.08	0.29	...	...	...	...	0.06	0.22
1	0.14	0.41	0.09	0.26	...	...	0.10	0.29
1¼	0.21	0.48	0.14	0.32	0.18	0.41	0.16	0.37
1½	0.29	0.47	0.20	0.32	0.26	0.42	0.22	0.35
2	0.49	0.65	0.33	0.44	0.33	0.44	0.30	0.40
2½	0.74	0.81	0.49	0.53	0.50	0.55	0.43	0.47
3	1.08	1.03	0.72	0.69	0.63	0.60	0.57	0.54
3½	1.44	1.22	0.96	0.91	0.79	0.67	0.72	0.61
4	1.85	1.57	1.23	1.04	0.96	0.81	0.88	0.75
5	2.86	1.96	1.91	1.31	1.36	0.93	1.27	0.87
6	4.09	2.36	2.72	1.57	1.82	1.05	1.72	0.99
8	7.09	3.14	4.73	2.10	2.84	1.26	2.74	1.21
10	11.05	3.92	7.37	2.62	4.20	1.49	4.09	1.45
12	15.73	4.70	10.49	3.14	5.81	1.74	5.69	1.70
14	20.15	5.04	13.42	3.36	7.04	1.76	6.88	1.72
16	26.32	5.79	17.56	3.86	8.39	1.85	8.38	1.84
18	33.31	7.00	22.22	4.67	10.62	2.23	10.61	2.23
20	41.13	7.81	27.43	5.21	13.11	2.49	13.1	2.49

Laying Lengths of Pipe with Screwed Fittings.—

The accompanying data for determining the length of pipe between screwed fittings of malleable iron eliminate guesswork to a great extent in determining allowances. The data apply to banded as well as plain fittings. Due to variations in manufacturer, lubricant used, torque on the wrench, and other factors, the figures are to be considered as close approximations.

Each value in Table 9-114 represents the distance from the centerline of the fitting to the end of the pipe screwed into the fitting. To determine the pipe length, this distance must be subtracted from the measured distance between the two centerlines for both ends of the pipe.

Example 10: The centerline distance between a tee and a 90° elbow in a 2 in. line is 8 ft 6 in. According to dimension A in Table 9-114 the distance to subtract for the elbow is $1\frac{1}{2}$ in. and the same for the tee. The total distance to subtract is the sum of the two fitting allowances, 3 in., leaving an actual pipe length of 8 ft 3 in.

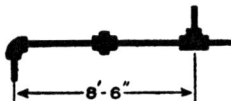

Fig 9-41. Pressure drop per 100 ft, psi

Dimensions G and H in Table 9-114 show the distance to subtract from pipe length where couplings or unions are inserted in the line.

Example 11: Suppose it is necessary to use a union in the line in the previous example. The pipe length between the elbow and the tee must still be 8 ft 3 in. with the union added. To take an 8 ft 3 in. length of pipe, cut it, and insert the union would result in a length greater than 8 ft 3 inches. Additional shortening of the length is necessary. According to dimension G in Table 9-114 the necessary allowance for the 2 in. union is $1\frac{13}{16}$ inches. Subtracting this from 8 ft 3 in. gives us a total length of 8 ft $1\frac{3}{16}$ in. for the two pieces of pipe between the elbow and the tee.

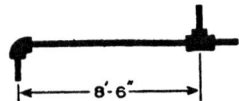

Fig 9-42. Pressure drop per 100 ft, psi

When distances between fittings are short, standard nipples can be used. Nipples are available in lengths up to 12 in., with graduations at $\frac{1}{2}$ inch intervals for shorter pieces and at 1 in. intervals for longer pieces. (When no nipple is available in the exact length calculated, frequently the distance between fittings can be changed slightly to accumulate the closest available standard nipple size.)

Each pipe diameter has a *close* nipple, lengths of which are given in Table 9-115. Shortest *long* nipple lengths for each pipe diameter range from $\frac{3}{8}$ in. longer than the close nipple for the smaller pipe diameters to $1\frac{1}{2}$ in. longer for the larger pipe diameters.

Dimensions L and M in Table 9-114 indicate the amount of offset to allow between center-lines when using street elbows, 90° or 45°. Center-to-center distance on a 45° diagonal is 1.412 times the leg distance. If the vertical or horizontal distance between centerlines of fittings is known, the length of the 45° measurement between fittings can be calculated. From this must be subtracted fitting allowances taken from Table 9-114.

Example 12: A vertical $1\frac{1}{2}$ inch pipe line is to be offset 43 °, using two 45° elbows. The horizontal distance (a) between the centerlines must be 2 ft 8 in. The diagonal distance (b) between the two centerlines will be 2 ft 8 in. × 1.412 or 3 ft $9\frac{1}{4}$ in. From Table 9-114, dimension B, the fitting allowance to subtract for each 45° elbow is $\frac{3}{4}$ in., a total of $1\frac{1}{2}$ in. The actual length of the pipe between the elbows will be 3 ft $9\frac{1}{4}$ in. less $1\frac{1}{2}$ in., or 3 ft $7\frac{3}{4}$ in.

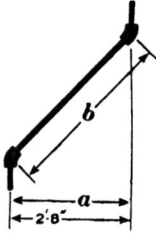

Fig 9-43. Pressure drop per 100 ft, psi

Example 13: A slight change in the above example makes use of a Y-bend. The fitting allowance for Y bend, from Table 9-114, dimension E, is $2\frac{5}{8}$ in., which is greater than the 45° elbow allowance. The sum of the two fitting allowances is $3\frac{3}{8}$ in., which makes the actual pipe length 3 ft $5\frac{7}{8}$ in.

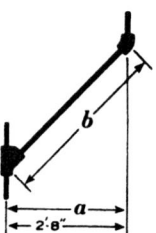

Fig 9-44. Pressure drop per 100 ft, psi

Example: A third example, somewhat more complicated, is shown here. A 45° street elbow is screwed into a cross. This shortens a, according to dimension L, Table 9-114, by $3\frac{1}{8}$ in. Distance *a* is now 2 ft 8 in. less $3\frac{1}{8}$ in., or 2 ft $4\frac{7}{8}$ in. Distance *b* is 2 ft $4\frac{7}{8}$ in. × 1.412 or 3 ft $4\frac{3}{4}$ in. Fitting allowances from Table 9-114 are $^{11}/_{16}$ in. for the 45° street elbow (dimension C) and $^{3}/_{4}$ in. for the regular 45° elbow (dimension B), a total of $1^{7}/_{16}$ in. Pipe length is 3 ft $4^{3}/_{4}$ in. less $1^{7}/_{16}$ in., or 3 ft $3^{5}/_{16}$ in.

Where valves are concerned, or where fittings not included in the tables are used, the table of standard thread engagements may be of help. The thread engagement distance subtracted from the end-to-centerline dimension of the fitting or valve (obtained by measurement) will give the amount to subtract from the pipe-line measurement in order to determine actual pipe length.

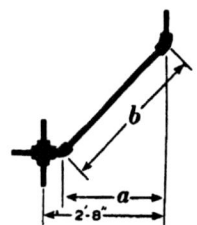

Fig 9-45. Pressure drop per 100 ft/psi

Table 9-114. Laying Length Data, Malleable Iron Screwed Fittings

Dimen-sion	Nominal Pipe Diameter, in.											
	$^{1}/_{4}$	$^{3}/_{8}$	$^{1}/_{2}$	$^{3}/_{4}$	1	$1^{1}/_{4}$	$1^{1}/_{2}$	2	$2^{1}/_{2}$	3	$3^{1}/_{2}$	4
	Dimension, in.											
A	$^{7}/_{16}$	$^{9}/_{16}$	$^{5}/_{8}$	$^{3}/_{4}$	$^{3}/_{16}$	$1^{1}/_{16}$	$1^{1}/_{4}$	$1^{1}/_{2}$	$1^{3}/_{4}$	$2^{1}/_{8}$	$2^{3}/_{8}$	$2^{5}/_{8}$
B	$^{3}/_{8}$	$^{7}/_{16}$	$^{3}/_{8}$	$^{7}/_{16}$	$^{7}/_{16}$	$^{5}/_{8}$	$^{3}/_{4}$	$^{15}/_{16}$	1	$1^{3}/_{16}$	$1^{5}/_{16}$	$1^{1}/_{2}$
C	$^{1}/_{4}$	$^{5}/_{16}$	$^{5}/_{16}$	$^{3}/_{8}$	$^{3}/_{8}$	$^{9}/_{16}$	$^{11}/_{16}$	$^{15}/_{16}$	…	…	…	…
D	$1^{5}/_{16}$	$1^{1}/_{2}$	$1^{5}/_{8}$	$1^{7}/_{8}$	$2^{3}/_{16}$	$2^{1}/_{2}$	$2^{11}/_{16}$	$3^{1}/_{8}$	…	…	…	…
E	…	$1^{1}/_{16}$	$1^{3}/_{16}$	$1^{1}/_{2}$	$1^{3}/_{4}$	$2^{1}/_{4}$	$2^{5}/_{8}$	$3^{1}/_{4}$	$3^{3}/_{4}$	$4^{9}/_{16}$	…	$5^{3}/_{16}$
F	…	$^{5}/_{16}$	$^{1}/_{4}$	$^{3}/_{16}$	$^{1}/_{4}$	$^{7}/_{16}$	$^{1}/_{2}$	$^{11}/_{16}$	$^{5}/_{8}$	$^{11}/_{16}$	…	$^{3}/_{16}$
G	1	$1^{1}/_{8}$	$1^{3}/_{16}$	$1^{5}/_{16}$	$1^{9}/_{16}$	$1^{5}/_{8}$	$1^{11}/_{16}$	$1^{13}/_{16}$	$2^{5}/_{16}$	$2^{9}/_{16}$	…	
H	$^{5}/_{16}$	$^{7}/_{16}$	$^{5}/_{16}$	$^{3}/_{8}$	$^{5}/_{16}$	$^{9}/_{16}$	$^{3}/_{4}$	1	1	$1^{3}/_{16}$	…	$1^{7}/_{16}$
L	$1^{3}/_{8}$	$1^{5}/_{8}$	$1^{13}/_{16}$	$2^{1}/_{16}$	$2^{5}/_{16}$	$2^{3}/_{4}$	$3^{1}/_{8}$	$3^{3}/_{4}$	…	…	…	
M	$1^{5}/_{8}$	2	$2^{1}/_{4}$	$2^{5}/_{8}$	$2^{15}/_{16}$	$3^{1}/_{2}$	$3^{15}/_{16}$	$4^{3}/_{4}$	$5^{9}/_{16}$	$6^{5}/_{8}$	…	$8^{5}/_{16}$

Table 9-115. Thread Engagement of Close Nipples

Nominal Pipe Diameter, in.												
$^{1}/_{4}$	$^{3}/_{8}$	$^{1}/_{2}$	$^{3}/_{4}$	1	$1^{1}/_{4}$	$1^{1}/_{2}$	2	$2^{1}/_{2}$	3	$3^{1}/_{2}$	4	5
Nipple Length, in.												
$^{7}/_{8}$	1	$1^{1}/_{8}$	$1^{3}/_{8}$	$1^{1}/_{2}$	$1^{5}/_{8}$	$1^{3}/_{4}$	2	$2^{1}/_{2}$	$2^{5}/_{8}$	$2^{3}/_{4}$	$2^{7}/_{8}$	3
Thread Engagement, in.												
$^{3}/_{8}$	$^{3}/_{8}$	$^{1}/_{2}$	$^{9}/_{16}$	$^{11}/_{16}$	$^{11}/_{16}$	$^{11}/_{16}$	$^{3}/_{4}$	$^{15}/_{16}$	1	$1^{1}/_{16}$	$1^{1}/_{8}$	$1^{1}/_{4}$
Laying Length (Nipple Length - 2 Thread Engagements)												
$^{1}/_{8}$	$^{1}/_{4}$	$^{1}/_{8}$	$^{1}/_{4}$	$^{1}/_{8}$	$^{1}/_{4}$	$^{3}/_{8}$	$^{1}/_{2}$	$^{5}/_{8}$	$^{5}/_{8}$	$^{5}/_{8}$	$^{5}/_{8}$	$^{1}/_{2}$

Allowable Spaces for Pipes.—Table 9-116 gives the allowable minimum distances between (1) two pipes, (2) pipe and wall, and (3) pipe and furring, for two pipes with standard malleable or cast iron screwed fittings in the same elevation.

The table was developed on the basis of the following analysis: Between two pipes of different diameters, there will be two values for the minimum distance that will allow free turning of an elbow or tee. The value used will depend on which pipe is installed first.

In order that there be no confusion in the field as to which pipe should be installed first, the condition giving the greater distance between pipes will be considered. It is fairly obvious that turning the fitting on the larger pipe will require the larger space between pipes for clearance.

Therefore, less space will be required if the larger pipe is installed first.

It is evident that the minimum distance from the wall will be that distance which will allow turning of a fitting on the pipe. This will be the distance K shown in the left column of the table.

The minimum distance from furring (dimension F in the table) will not be less than $\frac{1}{4}$ in. larger than the radius of insulated pipe because furring is constructed after pipes have been installed.

It should be noted that for pipes smaller than 1 in., the distance allowed for insulation is larger than that required for turning fittings. Therefore, on such small pipes only the allowance for insulation has been considered in the table.

Table 9-116. Minimum Distances Allowable Between Centerlines, Screwed Fittings

Min Distance from Wall (K) in.	Nominal Pipe Size in.	Minimum Distance from Furring (F), in.											
		1½	1⅝	1⅞	2	2⅛	2½	2¾	3⅛	3¾	4½	5	6
		Nominal Pipe Size, in.											
		½	¾	1	1¼	1½	2	2½	3	4	5	6	8
		Distance Between Pipes, in.											
8½	8	9⅛	9⅜	9½	9¾	9⅞	10⅛	10½	10⅞	11⅜	12	12⅝	14
6⅝	6	7⅜	7½	7⅝	7⅞	8	8¼	8⅝	9	9½	10¼	10¾	...
5¾	5	6½	6⅝	6¾	7	7⅛	7⅜	7¾	8⅛	8⅝	9¼	...	...
4⅞	4	5½	5⅝	5¾	6	6⅛	6½	6¾	7⅛	7¾	...	...	...
3⅞	3	4⅝	4¾	4⅞	5⅛	5¼	5½	5⅞	6¼	...	...	...	...
3⅜	2½	4	4¼	4⅜	4⅝	4¾	5	5¼	...	...	...	...	...
2⅞	2	3⅝	3¾	3⅞	4	4¼	4½	...	...	...	...	...	...
2⅜	1½	3⅛	3¼	3⅜	3⅝	3¾	...	...	...	...	...	...	...
2⅛	1¼	3	3⅛	3¼	3½	...	...	...	...	...	...	...	...
1⅞	1	2⅞	3	3⅛	...	...	...	...	...	...	...	...	...
1⅝	¾	2¾	2⅞	...	...	...	...	...	...	...	...	...	...
1½	½	2⅝	...	...	...	...	...	...	...	...	...	...	...

Example 14: Find the minimum space required for 1¼- and 4-in. risers if the smaller riser is located near the wall.

Solution: Table 9-116 shows, under 1¼ in. and opposite 4 in. pipes, that 6 in. is the minimum distance between 4 in. and 1¼ in. pipes.

To the left of 1¼ in. in the second column of the Table 9-116 find 2⅛ in. as the minimum distance from the wall of the small riser.

The distance from the furring of the larger riser is found (above 4 in.) to be 3¾ in.

The total space is thus $6 + 2⅛ + 3¾ = 11⅞$ in.

In the same manner it can be shown that the total space would be $6 + 4⅞ + 2 = 12⅞$ in. Therefore it is advisable to locate the smaller pipe near the wall or column.

Expansion of Pipe.—Expansion of pipe in ordinary temperatures (in fact, up to at least 1500°F) can be calculated according to the formula:

$$L_t = L_o\left[1 + a\left(\frac{T-32}{1000}\right) + b\left(\frac{T-32}{1000}\right)^2\right]$$

where L_t = length in feet at °F

L_o = length in feet at 32°F

T = final temperature, °F

a and b = constants as follows: steel, *a*, 0.006212, *b*, 0.00163; wrought iron, *a*, 0.006503, *b*, 0.001622; copper, *a*, −0.009278, *b*, 0.001244; cast iron, *a*, 0.005441, *b*, 0.001747.

Example 15: A 740-ft steel pipeline was installed during 60°F weather. What is the computed expansion of the line when 420°F steam is turned on in the line?

Solution: Under **Steel** opposite 420°F, find 3.423; opposite 60°F, find 0.449. Subtracting gives 2.974 in. expansion per 100 ft. For 740 ft the expansion is 7.4 × 2.974 = 22.01 in.

Table 9-117. Expansion of Pipe

Temp, °F	Materials			Temp, °F	Materials		
	Steel	Wrought Iron	Copper		Steel	Wrought Iron	Copper
0	0	0	0	390	3.156	3.291	4.532
10	0.075	0.078	0.111	400	3.245	3.383	4.653
20	0.149	0.156	0.222	410	3.334	3.476	4.777
30	0.224	0.235	0.333	420	3.423	3.569	4.899
40	0.299	0.313	0.444	430	3.513	3.662	5.023
50	0.374	0.391	0.556	440	3.603	3.756	5.145
60	0.449	0.470	0.668	450	3.695	3.850	5.269
70	0.525	0.549	0.78	460	3.785	3.945	5.394
80	0.601	0.629	0.893	470	3.874	4.040	5.519
90	0.678	0.709	1.006	480	3.962	4.135	5.643
100	0.755	0.791	1.119	490	4.055	4.231	5.767
110	0.831	0.871	1.233	500	4.148	4.327	5.892
120	0.909	0.952	1.346	520	4.334	4.524	6.144
130	0.987	1.003	1.46	540	4.524	4.715	6.396
140	1.066	1.115	1.575	560	4.714	4.911	6.650
150	1.145	1.198	1.69	580	4.903	5.109	6.905
160	1.224	1.281	1.805	600	5.096	5.309	7.160
170	1.304	1.364	1.919	620	5.291	5.510	7.417
180	1.384	1.447	2.035	640	5.486	5.713	7.677
190	1.464	1.532	2.152	660	5.583	5.917	7.938
200	1.545	1.616	2.268	680	5.882	6.122	8.197
210	1.626	1.701	2.384	700	6.083	6.351	8.460
220	1.708	1.786	2.501	720	6.284	6.539	8.722
230	1.791	1.871	2.618	740	6.488	6.749	8.988
240	1.872	1.957	2.736	760	6.692	6.961	9.252
250	1.955	2.044	2.854	780	6.899	7.175	9.519
260	2.038	2.130	2.971	800	7.102	7.384	9.783
270	2.132	2.218	3.089	820	7.318	7.607	10.056
280	2.207	2.305	3.208	840	7.529	7.825	10.327
290	2.291	2.393	3.327	860	7.741	8.045	10.598
300	2.376	2.481	3.446	880	7.956	8.266	1 0.872
310	2.46	2.570	3.565	900	8.172	8.489	11.144
320	2.547	2.659	3.685	920	8.389	8.713	11.420
330	2.632	2.748	3.805	940	8.608	8.939	11.696
340	2.718	2.838	3.926	960	8.830	9.167	11.973
350	2.805	2.927	4.050	980	9.052	9.396	12.253
360	2.892	3.017	4.167	1000	9.275	9.627	12.532
370	2.980	3.108	4.289	1100	10.042	10.804	13.95
380	3.069	3.199	4.411	1200	11.598	12.020	15.397

Corrosion Resistance.—Corrosion is the destruction of a metal by chemical or electrochemical reaction with its environment. In the corrosion process, the reaction products formed may be soluble or insoluble in the attacking environment. Insoluble corrosion products may deposit at or near the attacked area, in which case purely chemical corrosion, although starting rapidly, reduces its rate of attack due to the obstructive layer. Insoluble products of corrosion may also be carried a considerable distance from the point of attack before being deposited. However, rapid destruction of a material may be expected when the corrosion product is soluble in any liquid present.

Underwater Corrosion: Dissolved oxygen, acid gases, and chloride salts are the corrosion accelerators most frequently encountered in water. The corrosion potential of the solution increases in proportion to the amount of the harmful substances present, the temperature, and the rate of flow of the solution over the metal surface. The accompanying table summarizes the relative ability of metal pipes to resist corrosion by harmful substances.

The actual rate at which oxygen reaches the surface is believed to determine the rate of corrosion of ferrous metals. In water, the oxygen penetration to a surface is often restricted by films and scale, which form on the surface, and consequently the corrosion rate differs from that of a surface exposed to the atmosphere or to alternately wet and dry conditions. Neutral and slightly alkaline waters saturated with air corrode iron at a rate about triple that for the same water free of air. Hot water containing oxygen will corrode iron three to four times faster than the same water when cold.

Corrosion of iron decreases as the pH of water solutions increases, and practically ceases at a pH of 11.

Steam Condensate Systems: Corrosion in steam condensate systems may be minimized through use of four practical means. These are: (1) mechanical or chemical elimination of oxygen from boiler feed water and, therefore, from the steam developed; (2) design of condensing equipment to minimize assimilation in the condensate of non-condensable gases; (3) chemical treatment of the steam or condensate; and (4) use of corrosion-resistant metals.

Cathodic Protection: In addition to the use of special materials and protective coatings for buried pipelines, another form of protection is obtained by rendering the line cathodic to the surrounding soil or water by means of a controlled difference of potential. Protective coatings that insulate a large portion of the metal surface will greatly reduce the total amount of protective current that must be impressed on bare anodic areas to check corrosion.

It is extremely important to know the analysis of the soil before burying pipelines. Soils containing organic matter or high levels of carbon are extremely corrosive. Where high corrosion rates are anticipated, buried piping is usually protected by bitumastic coatings. For extreme conditions, the coating is reinforced by wrappings of impregnated woven fabric. For exceptionally severe corrosion conditions the coated pipes can then be encased in concrete. The concrete must be moisture-proofed with waterproofing membranes.

Where cast iron piping is used to transport corrosive waters such as mine drainage or seawater, a commercially available cement-lined cast iron is commonly utilized.

Pipe Support Spacing.—When a horizontal pipeline is supported at intermediate points, sagging of the pipe occurs between the supports, the amount of sag being dependent upon the weight of the pipe, water, insulation, and valves or fittings which may be included in the line. If the pipeline is installed with no pitch, pockets will be formed in each span, in which case condensation may collect if the line is transporting steam. In order to eliminate these pockets, the line must be pitched downward so that the outlet of each span is lower than the maximum sag.

Tests determined the deflection of horizontal standard pipelines filled with water. Results indicated that for pipes larger than 2 in. and with supports more than 10 feet center to center, the resultant deflection is less than that determined by the use of the formula for a uniformly loaded pipe fixed at both ends. For pipe sizes 2 in. and smaller, the test deflection was in excess of that determined by the formula for pipe having fixed ends and approached, for the shorter spans, the deflection for pipelines having unrestrained ends.

Fig. 9-46 gives the deflection of horizontal Schedule 40 pipelines filled with water, for varying spans, based upon the results obtained from tests for sizes 2 in. and smaller, and upon the formula for fixed ends for the larger sizes of pipe. The deflection values are twice those obtained from tests or calculated, to compensate for any variables including weight of insulation, valves, etc.

The chart can be used (a) to determine the deflection for a given spacing or (b) to determine the slope in the pipe necessary to overcome the deflection. In the former use, for example, the chart shows that the deflection in a 6-inch pipe at a hanger spacing of 20 feet is 0.061 in.

A more useful application of the chart is where it is desired to know what hanger spacing is necessary with a given slope and pipe size. For example, if a slope of 1 inch in 30 feet is practicable in a 4 in. pipe line, what hanger spacing is necessary? To find this answer, locate the intersection of the 4 in. pipe size curve with the 1 inch in 30 feet slope curve and find, on the bottom scale, the spacing to be 22 feet.

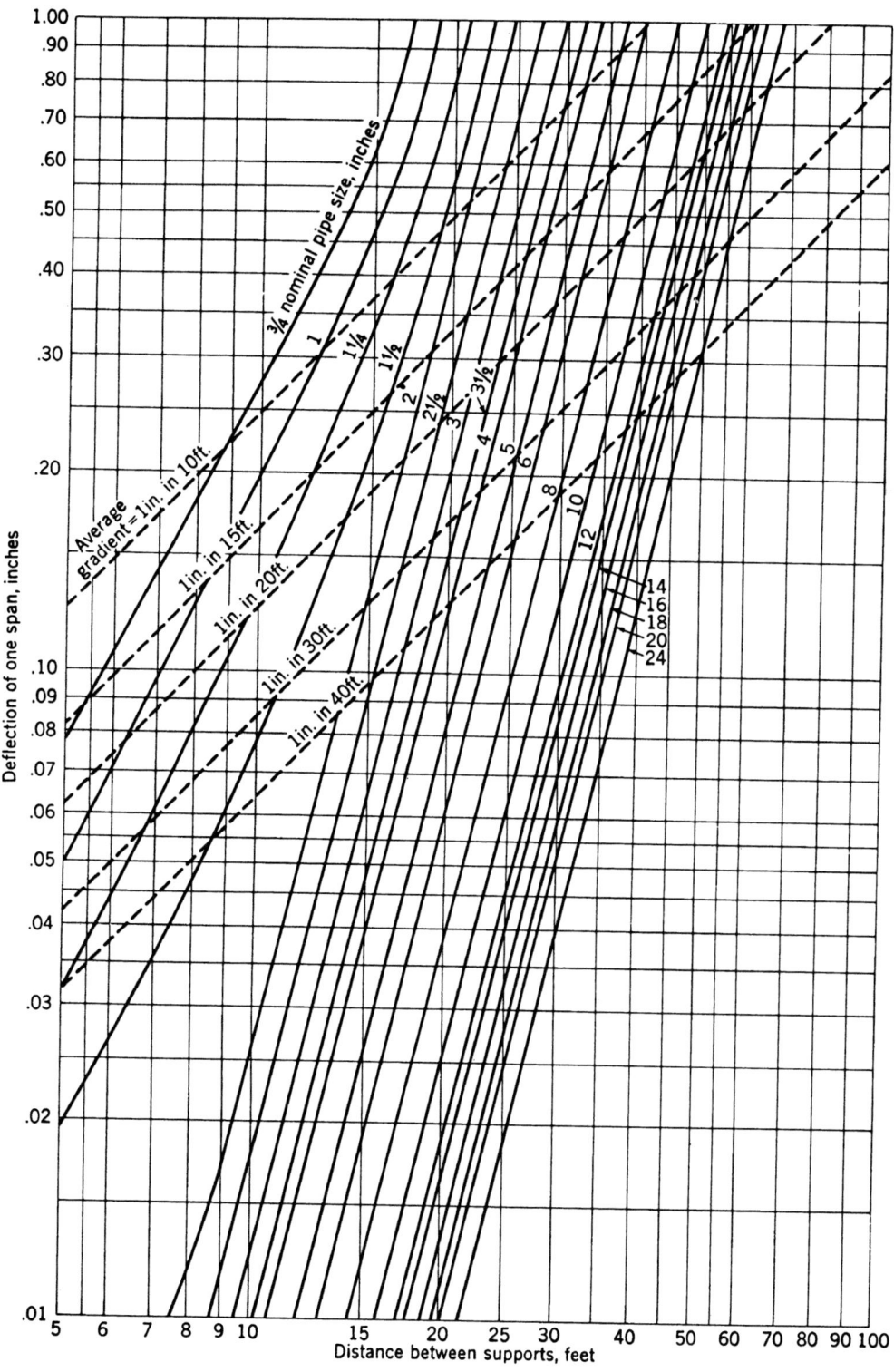

Fig 9-46. Pipe support distances

Table 9-118. Corrosion Resistance of Metal Pipes to Various Fluids
Data apply to fluid temperatures up to 140°F. *S* indicates satisfactory, *L* limited, and *U* unsatisfactory

Fluid	Low Carbon Steel	Stainless Steel 302 303 304	316	410 416 430	Cast Iron	Aluminum	Copper	Red Brass	Lead	Monel	Inconel
Acetic acid, 10%	U	S	S	L	U	S	U	...	...	S	S
Acetic acid, glacial	U	S	S	U	U	S	U	U	...	...	S
Acetone	S	S	S	U	S	S	S	S	S	S	S
Alcohol, methyl	S	S	S	S	S	L	S	...	S	S	S
Ammonium chloride	L	L	S	L	U	U	L	...	S	S	S
Ammonium sulfate	S	S	S	L	S	L	L	L	...	S	S
Aniline	U	S	S	S	L	U	...	...	...	...	S
Benzene	L	S	S	...	S	S	S	...	...	S	S
Benthic acid	...	S	S	S	...	S	...	...	...	...	...
Boric acid	U	S	S	L	L	S	S	...	...	S	S
Butyric acid	...	S	S	...	...	S	...	...	...	S	S
Calcium chloride	S	S	L	L	...	U	L	L	...	S	S
Calcium hydroxide	S	S	S	S	S	L	...	L	...	S	S
Carbon tetrachloride	L	S	S	S	L	L	S	S	L	S	S
Chlorine, dry	L	S	S	S	...	U	S	S	...	S	...
Chlorine, wet	U	U	L	U	U	U	L	U	...	L	U
Chloroform	...	S	S	S	...	U	...	...	...	S	S
Chromic acid, 10%	...	L	S	U	U	L	U	U	...	S	U
Chromic acid, 50%	...	U	L		U		U	U	...	...	...
Citric acid	U	S	S	L	L	S	S	L	...	S	...
Copper chloride		S	L	L		U	L	...	S	L	L
Copper sulfate	U	S	S	S	L	U	L	...	...	U	S
Ethyl acetate	L	S	S	S	S	L	...	...	...	S	S
Ethyl chloride	S	S	S	S	U	...	S	...	...	S	S
Fatty acids		S	S	S	...	S	...	...	...	S	S
Ferric chloride	U	U	U	U	U	U	U	U	...	U	U
Ferric sulfate	U	S	S	S	U	U	U	U	...	L	S
Formaldehyde	L	S	S	S	...	S	S	S	...	S	S
Formic acid	U	S	S	U	...	U	S	U	...	S	...
Hydroponic acid		U	U	U	...	U	L	...	L	U	U
Hydrochloric acid	U	U	U	U	U	U	...	U	...	...	...
Hydrofluoric acid	U	U	U	U	U	U	L	L	S	S	S
Hydrocyanic acid	L	S	S	S	S	S	L	...	...	S	...
Nickel chloride	U	L	S	U	...	U	L	U	...	S	S
Nickel sulfate	U	S	S	L	...	U	U	U	...	S	S
Nitric acid, 20%	...	...	...	...	U	U	U	U	U	L	U
Nitric acid, 40%	...	...	...	...	U	U	U	U	U	U	L
Nitric acid, 68%	...	...	...	...	U	L	U	U	U	U	L
Oleic acid	...	...	S	S		L	S	...	...	S	S
Oxalic acid	U	S	S	L	U	S	S	L	...	S	S
Phosphoric acid, 25%	U	L	S	U	U	U	S	U	S	S	S
Phosphoric acid, 85%	U	U	S	U	U	U	S	U	S	S	S
Picric acid	...	S	S	S	...	...	U	U	...	U	U
Potassium chloride	...	S	S	S	...	L	S	L	...	S	S
Potassium sulfate	L	S	S	S	S	S	S	S	S	S	S
Sodium carbonate	S	S	S	S	S	U	S	L	...	S	S
Sodium chloride	L	S	S	L	S	L	S	...	...	S	S
Sodium sulfate	L	S	S	S	S	S	S	S	S	S	S
Stearic acid	L	S	S	S	L	S	S	L	...	S	S
Sulfur dioxide, dry	S	S	S	S	S	...	S	L	...	S	S
Sulfur dioxide, wet	...	S	S	U	...	...	S	U	...	U	U
Sulfuric acid, 10%	U	U	S	U	U	L	U	U	S	L	...
Sulfuric acid, 75%	U	U	U	U	U	U	U	U	S	S	...
Sulfuric acid, 90%	L	L	S	L	L	U	U	U	S	U	...
Trichloroethylene	L	S	S	S	L	S	S	L	...	S	S
Trisodium phosphate	S	S	S	S	...	U	U	U	S	S	S
Water, fresh	L	S	S	S	...	S	S	S	S	S	S
Water, salt	L	S	S	L	S	S	...	L	S	S	S

For slopes not given on the chart, the following formula can be used:

$$y = \frac{L}{4G}$$

where y = deflection in inch;

L = distance between supports ft; and

G = gradient of pipe expressed in number of ft in which there is a rise of 1 inch

Another example: A slope of 1 inch in 25 feet is desired. What hanger spacing is required for 4 in. pipe?

Solve the formula for two values, say $L = 10$ ft and $L = 60$ ft, and obtain

$$y = \frac{10}{4 \times 25} = 0.10$$

$$y = \frac{60}{4 \times 25} = 0.60$$

Plot these points on the graph, and draw a line through them. The intersection of this line with the 4-in. pipe curve is at $y = 0.24$ and a hanger spacing of 24 feet.

The formula can also be used for exact interpolation of the slope required to overcome deflection of pipe at a given spacing.

For example: the chart shows that a 4-in. pipe supported at 30-ft intervals will have a deflection of 0.62 in. at each span. How much slope must be given the pipe to properly drain the deflection?

The chart shows the slope to be between 10 and 15 feet per inch of fall. Applying the formula:

$$0.62 = \frac{30}{4G}$$

$$G = \frac{30}{4 \times 0.62} = 12.1$$

Therefore, a slope of 1 inch in 12.1 feet will overcome the deflection.

If this slope is too steep for the space available, note that following the 4-in. pipe curve down the chart permits selection of a permissible pitch and corresponding support interval.

If an unusual installation situation should limit the span to, say, 15 ft between supports and at the same time limit the pitch to, say, 1 inch in 30 feet, the chart shows that a 2-in. pipe is the smallest diameter that can be installed to drain properly. The deflection of any smaller pipe will be too great to be overcome by this pitch. Obviously, any pipe can be pitched at any gradient steeper than the minimum gradients determined from the chart. That is, any pipe larger than 2-inches can be pitched at 1 inch in 30 feet or steeper with supports at 15-ft intervals. The values read from the chart are minimum for complete drainage.

Gate, Globe, and Check Valves

Description.—*Gate Valves:* The working parts of gate valves include a wedge or gate, which fits into the open passageway of the valve between machined seats; a threaded stem or spindle; a hand wheel, and packing.

The bonnet may be of one-piece construction screwed directly to the valve body or consist of a union connection screwed to the body. The bonnet also may be bolted to the body or be constructed as a yoke, exposing the stem or spindle.

Packing fits around the stem in a recess in the top of the bonnet and is held in place by a packing nut that screws to the bonnet, or by a packing gland, which is bolted to the bonnet. A packing gland bushing, or follower, installed between the gland or nut and the packing, transmits the force exerted by the packing gland or nut to the packing.

Larger gate valves are the outside screw and yoke (OS&Y) type, with a bolted bonnet, bolted gland, and rising stem. Smaller gate valves are of the inside screw, rising stem, screwed bonnet, or screwed packing nut type. Larger valves are flanged on the ends; smaller valves are screwed or solder end valves.

Globe Valves: The working parts of globe valves consist of a disc that fits over a circular horizontal opening in the valve passageway into which a *seat* has been fitted or machined; a stem or spindle; a hand wheel; and packing.

The same variations that apply to the construction of bonnets, packing glands, or nuts and the type of end connections of gate valves also apply to globe valves.

Check Valves: The working parts of check valves consist of a hinged disc or clapper, which is free to swing upon a hinge pin in only one direction. There are no exterior working parts whatever on a check valve.

Operation.—*Gate Valves:* Gate valves are installed in the pipeline, and the passageway of the pipe continues straight through the valve. A wedge (gate) is moved up or down, out of or into the passageway, to permit or prevent flow through the valve. As the hand wheel is turned counterclockwise, the threads on the stem or spindle engage the threads in the bonnet and the stem, and the attached wedge is raised out of the passageway. When the hand wheel is turned clockwise, the stem screws down through the bonnet and the attached wedge is lowered into the valve passageway, thus preventing flow through the valve. The packing, which is held in place by the packing gland or nut, prevents the fluid within from escaping around the stem, through the bonnet.

Globe Valves: Globe valves operate in the same way as gate valves, except that the disc in the globe valves is horizontal and seats against a horizontal opening. When the hand wheel is turned counterclockwise, the stem threads through the bonnet and the disc is lifted off the horizontal valve passageway. When the hand wheel is turned clockwise, the stem screws down into the bonnet and the disc is lowered onto the valve passageway, thus preventing flow.

Check Valves: Check valves are automatically operated by the fluid flowing through the valve. The clapper is free to swing only in the direction of the flow of the liquid in the pipeline. The pressure exerted by the liquid flowing through the valve lifts the clapper and holds it in an open position. When the flow stops in that direction, the clapper falls back to its original position by gravity, thus preventing back flow.

Recommendations.—A valve must never be forced closed. Although strainers are installed in the pipeline to protect valves and other equipment, pipe scale and other foreign material may be present in the liquid in the pipeline and may become lodged in the valve seat, preventing the valve from closing. To dislodge the foreign material, the valve is partially opened and closed several times. If the valve does not seat properly after this *washing* the supply to the valve is closed off, the bonnet assembly removed, and the seating surfaces wiped with a clean cloth. The valve is then reassembled and the seating action tested to make sure that the trouble is only dirt.

Note: The *washing* process described is useful only where liquid in the pipe is flowing. It is of no value where the line is flooded and fluid is static or where the line has been drained.

All gate valves are to be either tightly closed or fully opened, as required. When left in a partially opened position, the wedge and seats become grooved and damaged, or *wiredrawn.*

The attached piping must be properly supported or hung so that the valve is not subjected to undue strain resulting from pipe movement.

A gate valve must never be used for throttling or regulating flow; it must be either opened fully or closed completely.

When installing flanged valves, the flanges must be properly aligned. The bolts must not be inserted haphazardly or screwed up on the flange nuts until the flanges are forced into contact. Special care must be taken not to mar gasket faces of flanges by tightening while foreign matter is between faces or by accidentally striking with tools.

The piping must not be *sprung* in order to remove or replace a valve. It is better maintenance procedure to cut the pipe about 6 inches from the downstream end of the valve, remove the valve, and install a union in the pipe line before making the valve replacement.

Definitions of Terms.—*Body:* The part of the valve that attaches to the pipeline or equipment, either with screwed ends, flanged ends or solder joint ends, and encloses the working parts of the valves.

Bonnet: The top part of the valve housing, through which the stem extends. It provides support and protec-

tion to the stem and houses the stem packing. It may be screwed or bolted to the body.

Cap: The top part of the housing of a check valve (equivalent to the bonnet of a gate or globe valve) which may be either screwed or bolted onto the main body.

Check Valve: An automatic, self closing valve that permits flow in only one direction. It automatically closes by gravity when liquid ceases to flow in that direction.

Clapper: A common term which is used to describe the disc of a swing type check valve.

Disc: The disc-shaped device attached to the bottom of the stem and which is brought into contact with, or lifted off of, the seating surfaces to close or open a globe valve.

Flanged Bonnet: A type of bonnet so constructed that it attaches to the body by means of a flanged, bolted connection. The whole bonnet assembly, including the hand wheel, stem and disc, may be quickly removed by unscrewing the nuts the bonnet stud bolts.

Gate Valve: A valve which is used to open or close off the flow of fluid through a pipe. It is so named because of the wedge (gate) which is either raised out of or lowered into a double seated sluice, to permit full flow or completely shut off flow. The passageway through a gate valve is straight through, uninterrupted, and is the full size of the pipeline into which the valve is installed.

Gland Bushing: A metal bushing installed between the packing nut and the packing to transmit the force exerted by the packing nut against the packing.

Globe Valve: A valve used for throttling or regulating the flow through a pipe. It is so named because of the globular shape of the body. The disc is raised off a horizontal seating surface to permit flow, or lowered against the horizontal seating surface to shut off flow. The disc may be lifted completely to permit full flow or may be lifted only slightly in order to throttle or regulate flow. The flow through a globe valve has to make two 90° turns.

Handwheel: The wheel-shaped turning device by which the stem is rotated, thus lifting or lowering the disc or wedge.

Hingepin: The pin upon which the disc or clapper of a check valve swings.

Outside Screw and Yoke: A type of bonnet so constructed that the operating threads of the stem are outside the valve housing, where they may be easily lubricated and do not come into contact with the fluid flowing through the valve.

Packing: A general term describing any yielding material used to effect a tight joint. Valve packing is generally *jam packing*; it is pushed into a stuffing box and adjusted from time to time by tightening down on a packing gland or packing nut.

Packing Gland: A device that holds and compresses the packing, and provides for additional compression by manual adjustment of the gland as wear of the packing occurs. A packing gland may be screwed or bolted in place.

Packing Nut: A nut that is screwed into place and presses down upon a gland bushing, which transmits the force exerted by the packing nut to the packing. It serves the same purpose as a packing gland.

Rising Stem: A threaded stem that is unscrewed or screwed through the bonnet to open or close the valve. The handwheel may rise with the stem, or the stem may rise through the handwheel.

Screwed Bonnet: A type of bonnet so constructed that it attaches to the body by means of a screwed joint. It may screw over the body, or inside the body, or may be attached to the body by means of a union-type screwed connection.

Solid Wedge: A wedge consisting of one solid piece.

Split Wedge: A wedge consisting of two pieces into which the valve stem is screwed to expand the two pieces against the valve seating surfaces to assure a tight seal when the valve is closed.

Stem: The usually threaded shaft to which is attached the handwheel at the top and the disc or wedge at the lower end. The stem may also be called the *spindle.*

Stop Plug: An adjusting screw, extending through the body of a check valve, which adjusts and controls the extent of movement of the disc or clapper.

Swing Check Valve: A check valve which uses a hinged disc or clapper to limit the direction of flow. The pressure exerted by the fluid flowing through the valve forces the disc away from the seating surface. When the flow ceases, the clapper falls to its original position, preventing flow in the opposite direction.

Union: A coupling fitting, consisting of three parts (a shoulder piece, a thread piece, and a ring) used for coupling the ends of pipe sections. Adjoining faces of shoulder and thread pieces are lapped together to form a tight joint. Unions permit easy disconnection for repair and replacement of piping and fittings.

Union Bonnet: Type of bonnet which is so constructed that the whole bonnet assembly, including the handwheel, stem and disc assembly, may be quickly removed by unscrewing the bonnet union ring from the valve body.

Union Ring: The large nut-like ring which secures the union thread piece and the union shoulder piece together. It slips over and against the shoulder piece and screws onto the union thread piece.

Union Shoulder Piece: That part of the union which is fastened to the pipe and retains the union ring.

Union Threaded Piece: That part of the union which is fastened to the pipe and has external threads over which the union ring is screwed to effect a coupling.

Wedge: (See also *Disc*) The wedge-shaped device that fits into the seating surfaces of a gate valve and which is drawn out of contact with the seating surfaces to permit flow, or is pushed down into contact with the seating surfaces to close off flow through the valve.

Maintenance Methods.—Maintenance personnel in their normal round are to remain alert to detect evidence of leakage and or valve failure. When evidence of leakage and/or valve failure is detected, the inspection procedures described below are to be followed.

Table 9-119. Trouble-Shooting Methods

Trouble	Cause	Remedy
Gate Valves		
Leakage around stem	Loose packing gland or nut	Tighten packing gland or nut
	Packing worn out	Replace packing
	Bent or scored stem	Replace stem
Leakage around gasketed, screwed or soldered connections	Loose connections	Tighten flange bolts or screwed connections, or resolder joints
	Gasket failure	Replace gasket
Handwheel turns without stopping at extremes	Broken stem	Replace stem
Valve does not close tightly	Wedge damaged	Replace wedge
	Seat damaged	Replace valve
	Wedge-stem joint damaged	Replace stem and/or wedge
	Deposits under wedge	*Wash* or clean
Globe Valves		
Leakage around stem	Loose packing gland or nut	Tighten packing gland or nut
	Packing worn out	Replace packing
	Bent or scored stem	Replace stem
Leakage around gasketed, screwed or soldered connections	Loose connection	Tighten flange bolts
		Tighten screwed, connections or resolder joints
	Gasket failure	Replace gasket
Valve does not close tightly	Disc damaged	Replace disc
	Seat damaged	Replace valve
	Disc-stem joint damaged	Replace disc or stem
	Deposits under disc	*Wash* or clean
Check Valves		
Leakage around gasketed, screwed, or soldered connections	Loose connection	Tighten flange nuts or screwed connections or resolder joints
	Gasket failure	Replace gasket

Gate Valves: 1) Inspect the area around the top of the bonnet and stem for leakage.

2) Inspect the bolted or screwed bonnet body connection for leakage.

3) Inspect flanged or screwed connections for leakage.

4) Check the action of the valve by turning the handwheel counterclockwise to open, and/or clockwise to close. Open and/or close each valve several times to make sure it is not corroded or jammed.

Make sure that the valve is returned to its original operating setting.

Globe valves: 1) Follow the procedure described for the inspection of gate valves.

Check Valves: Inspect the gasketed or screwed connections around the cap and both ends of the body for leakage.

Failure of the internal parts of check valves can not be determined by inspection, except by disassembling the valve. Do not disassemble any gasketed connection unless such disassembly is necessary for repair.

Formulas for Sizing Control Valves

The valve flow coefficient C_v is the standard measure of valve flow capacity, defined as the number of U. S. gallons of water per minute that will flow through the valve in a wide open position with a pressure drop of 1 psi. The C_v rating is determined by flow tests.

While present valve sizing procedures are based on incomplete assumptions and theory, without its use sizing of valves, especially control valves, would be highly complicated. For most engineering purposes, the following procedures are justified:

To Determine Valve Size.—*Given:* All flowing conditions.

Solve: For C_v and select valve size for the type of valve under consideration from manufacturers table of C_v rating vs. valve size.

To Determine Valve Capacity.—*Given:* C_v and flowing conditions.

Solve : For capacity,

V in U. S. gpm of liquid, Q in ft³/hr gas at 14.7 psia and 60°F, W in lb steam per hr.

For liquid:

$$C_v = V\sqrt{\frac{G}{\Delta P}}$$

$$V = C_v\sqrt{\frac{\Delta P}{G}}$$

where V = flow, gpm (U. S.);

P = pressure drop at maximum flow, psi;

G = specific gravity (water = 1.0); and

C_v = valve flow coefficient

When flowing temperature is above 200°F, use specific gravity and quantity at flowing condition.

For gas:

$$C_v = \frac{Q\sqrt{GT_a}\sqrt{(\Delta P)P_2}}{1360}$$

$$Q = \frac{1360 C_v\sqrt{(\Delta P)P_2}}{\sqrt{GT_a}}$$

where Q = ft³/hr at 14.7 psia and 60°F

ΔP = pressure drop $(P_1 - P_2)$ at maximum flow, psi

P_1 = inlet pressure at maximum flow, psia

P_2 = outlet pressure at maximum flow, psia

G = specific gravity (air = 1.0)

T_a = flowing temperature, absolute (460 + °F)

C_v = valve flow coefficient

When P_2 is less than ½ P_1, use the value of $P_1/2$ in place of $\sqrt{(\Delta P)P_2}$.

For steam.—

$$Cv = \frac{WK}{3\sqrt{(\Delta P)P_2}}$$

$$W = \frac{3C_v\sqrt{(\Delta P)P_2}}{K}$$

where W = lb steam per hr;

ΔP = pressure drop at maximum flow, psi;

P_1 = inlet pressure at maximum flow, psia;

P_2 = outlet pressure at maximum flow, psia;

$K = 1 + (0.0007 \times$ °F superheat); and

C_v = valve flow coefficient

When P_2 is less than ½ P_1, use the value of $P_1/2$ in place of $\sqrt{(\Delta P)P_2}$.

The steam formula has been set up using $1/0.00225 P_2$ in place of the specific volume to eliminate the need for steam tables.

Note: Flow of compressible fluids through a restriction reaches a saturation velocity when the differential pressure is increased to approximately 50% of the inlet pressure. This critical pressure ratio varies with the composition of the fluid. The average value of one-half the absolute inlet pressure is well within the tolerance established by the formulas.

For Vapors Other Than Steam.—General formula weight basis

$$C_v = \frac{W}{63.4}\sqrt{\frac{v_2}{\Delta P}}$$

$$W = 63.4 C_v\sqrt{\frac{\Delta P}{v_2}}$$

where W = lb steam per hr;

ΔP = pressure drop at maximum flow, psi;

P_1 = inlet pressure at maximum flow, psia;

P_2 = outlet pressure at maximum flow, psia;

v_2 = specific volume (ft³/lb) at outlet pressure P_2; and

C_v = valve flow coefficient

When P_2 is less than $\frac{1}{2}P_1$, use the value of $P_1/2$ in place of ΔP and use P_2 corresponding to $P_1/2$.

Identification of Piping Systems

Schemes for the identification of piping systems have been developed in the past by a large number of industrial plants and organizations. The schemes arrived at perhaps completely satisfied those who used them, but they suffered from a lack of uniformity. Considerable confusion and accidents occurred to those who changed employment from one plant to another and to outside agencies.

In order to promote greater safety and lessen the chances of error, confusion, or inaction, especially in times of emergency, a uniform code for identification of piping has been established by the American National Standards Institute ANSI-A13.1, and published by The American Society of Mechanical Engineers. The standard is based on primary identification of the contents of a piping system by stenciled legend and secondary identification through the use of color. It is urged that industry and organizations not use color as a means of specifying the type of material contained in a piping system unless its use is in conformity with provisions of the standard and supplementary to the use of legends.

Any material transported in a piping system will fall into one of four main classifications:

Dangerous Materials.—This group includes materials hazardous to life or property because they are easily ignited, corrosive at high temperatures and pressures, productive of poisonous gases, or are themselves poisonous.

Fire Protection Materials and Equipment.— This classification includes sprinkler systems and other fire fighting or fire protection equipment. The identification for this group may also be used to locate such equipment as alarm boxes, extinguishers, fire doors, hose connections, and hydrants.

Table 9-120. Color Identification of Piping System Classifications

Classification	Predominant Color of System	Color of Letters for Legends
F- Fire protection material and equipment	Red	White
D-Dangerous materials	Yellow (or orange)	Black
S- Safe material	Green (or the achromatic colors; white, black, gray, or aluminium)	Black
P-Protective materials	Bright blue	White

Table 9-121. Identifying Colors of Typical Materials Transported in Piping Systems

Material	Color	Material	Color	Material	Color
Acetic acid	Yellow	Distilled water	Green	Muriatic acid	Yellow
Acetone	Yellow	Drain oil	Yellow	Naphtha	Yellow
Acetylene gas	Yellow	Drain water	Green	Natural gas	Yellow
Acid	Yellow	Drinking water	Green	Nitric acid	Yellow
Air	Green	Dye	Yellow	Nitrogen	Green
Alcohol	Yellow	Ethane dye	Yellow	Nitrogen oxide	Yellow
Alum	Green	Exhaust air	Green	Oil	Blue
Ammonia	Yellow	Exhaust gas	Yellow	Oil, lubricating	Blue
Ammonium nitrate	Yellow	Exhaust system	Yellow	Oil, soluble	Blue
Amyl acetate	Yellow	Filtered water	Blue	Oxygen	Yellow
Antidote gas	Blue	Fire protection water	Red	Paint	Yellow
Argon	Green	Flue gas	Blue	Peanut oil	Yellow
Benzol	Yellow	Formite	Red	Phenol	Yellow
Bisulphite liquor	Yellow	Formalin	Yellow	Process gas	Yellow
Blau gas	Yellow	Freon	Green	Producer gas	Yellow
Bleach liquor	Yellow	Fresh water	Green	Propane gas	Yellow
Blow-off water	Yellow	Fuel gas	Yellow	Raw water	Green
Boiler feed water	Yellow	Fuel oil	Blue	Refrigerated water	Green
Brine	Green	Gas	Yellow	River water	Green
Burner gas	Yellow	Gasoline	Yellow	Salt water	Green
Butane	Yellow	Glycerine	Green	Sanitary sewer	Green
Butyl alcohol	Yellow	Heating returns	Red	Soda ash	Green
Calcium chloride	Blue	Heating steam	Red	Solvent	Yellow
Carbon bisulphide	Yellow	Helium	Green	Soybean oil	Yellow
Carbon dioxide	Yellow	Hot water	Red	Sprinkler, water	Red
Carbon monoxide	Yellow	Hydrochloric acid	Yellow	Steam	Grey
Carbonated water	Green	Hydrogen	Yellow	Storm sewer	Green
Caustic soda	Yellow	Hydrogen peroxide	Yellow	Sugar juice	Green

Material	Color	Material	Color	Material	Color
Chlorine	Yellow	Hydrogen sulphide	Yellow	Sulphur chloride	Yellow
Chlorine gas	Yellow	Industrial water	Green	Sulphur dioxide	Yellow
Chloroform	Yellow	Instrument air	Green	Sulphuric acid	Yellow
Circulating water	Green	Kerosene	Yellow	Tar	Yellow
City gas	Yellow	Lacquer	Yellow	Toluene	Yellow
City water	Green	Lactic acid	Yellow	Toluol	Yellow
Coal gas	Yellow	Linseed oil	Yellow	Trichloroethylene	Yellow
Cold water	Green	Lubricating oil	Yellow	Turpentine	Yellow
Compressed air	Green	Make-up water	Green	Vapor	Yellow
Condensate	Yellow	Mercury	Yellow	Varnish	Yellow
Cooling water	Green	Methyl chloride	Yellow	Vegetable oil	Yellow
Cottonseed oil	Yellow	Mixed acid	Yellow	Waste water	Green
Cutting oil	Green	Mixed gas	Yellow	Water	Green
Diesel oil	Yellow	Monoethanolamine	Green	Water gas	Yellow

Safe Materials.—This group includes materials involving little or no hazard to life or property in their handling. Classification embraces materials at low pressures and temperatures that are not poisonous and will not produce fire or explosion.

Protective Materials.—This group includes materials piped through plants for the express purpose of being available to prevent or minimize the hazard of the dangerous materials previously mentioned.

Method of Identification.— Positive identification of contents of a piping system shall be by lettered legend giving the name of the material in full or abbreviated form. Arrows may be used to indicate the direction of flow. Where it is desirable or necessary to give supplementary information such as hazard or use of the piping system contents, this may be done by additional legend or by color applied to the entire piping system or as colored bands. Color identification for the four classifications are shown in Table 9-120.

Table 9-122. Size of Color Bands and Legend Letters

Outside Diameter of Pipe or Covering in.	Width of Color Bands, in.	Height of Legend Letters, in.
$\frac{3}{4}$ to $\frac{1}{4}$	8	$\frac{1}{2}$
$1\frac{1}{2}$ to 2	8	$\frac{3}{4}$
$2\frac{1}{2}$ to 6	12	$1\frac{1}{4}$
8 to 10	24	$2\frac{1}{2}$
Over 10	32	$3\frac{1}{2}$

Table 9-121 presents a list of typical materials transported in piping systems and their identifying colors. Recommended width of color bands and height of legend letters for various sizes of pipe are given in Table 9-122.

Heat Losses in Piping

Heat Losses from Bare Pipe.—Heat is lost from pipes by both radiation and convection. The former can be estimated by the Stefan-Boltzmann formula:

$$\frac{q_r}{A} = 0.174e\left[\left(\frac{T_1}{100}\right)^4 - \left(\frac{T_2}{100}\right)^4\right]$$

where q_r/A = heat transferred by radiation Btu/hr-ft^2 of pipe surface;

e = emissivity of the pipe;

T_1 = absolute temperature of pipe, °F + 460; and

T_2 = absolute temperature of surroundings, °F + 460.

Heat transferred by convection can be determined by the Rice-Heilman formula, which resulted from work done at Mellon Institute, as follows:

$$\frac{q_c}{A} = C\left(\frac{1}{d}\right)^{0.2}\left(\frac{1}{T_{av}}\right)^{0.181}(T_1 - T_2)^{1.266}$$

where q_c/A = heat transferred by radiation btu/hr-ft^2 of pipe surface;

C = a constant with a value of 1.016 for horizontal pipe and 1.394 for vertical plates;

d = outside diameter of pipe, in.;

T_{av} = absolute average temperature of hot body and surrounding air, °F + 460;

T_1 = temperature of pipe, °F; and

T_2 = air temperature, °F.

The emissivity in the radiation formula is the effective emissivity, taking into account the absorptivity of the bodies receiving the radiation. An emissivity of 0.94 was used in the accompanying table on (oxidized) steel pipe; a value of 0.44 is used for tarnished copper tube and 0.08 for new bright copper.

For vertical pipes the emission can be assumed to be closely approximating that of a steel plate. In this connection, note that C becomes 1.394. In the case of vertical pipes, d in the convection formula is not the diameter of the pipe but the height of the plate (pipe) in inches, in which the value of $(1/d)^{0.2}$ becomes constant when $d = 24$ inches. Therefore, the convection formula for vertical pipe or vertical surfaces becomes

$$\frac{q_c}{A} = 1.39 \times 0.53\left(\frac{1}{T_{av}}\right)^{0.181}(T_1 - T_2)^{1.266}$$

where the terms are as defined previously.

For vertical pipe, the radiation is the same as for horizontal pipe.

The tables in the following pages are based on the assumption that the outside surface of the pipe is the same as that of the fluid flowing in the pipe; this is not strictly true, but is close enough for all practical estimating purposes.

Also, the tables assume an air temperature of 70°F and, in the case of radiation, a temperature of 70°F for the surrounding walls, machinery, etc. It can be seen, then, that if the surroundings are at temperatures appreciably above or below 70°F, the heat transferred by both radiation and convection would be appreciably lower than or above, respectively, the values given in the tables. Consequently, the tables should not be used for cases where the air temperatures and surrounding bodies temperatures are lower than 60°F or higher than 80°F.

The convection formulas are both based on free convection with no appreciable air motion from fans or open doors; in other words, the tables apply to still air conditions.

In the formula for radiation, values for e other than those given for steel and iron pipe and copper tube are:

Surface	Emissivity e
Aluminum, polished	0.08
Aluminum paint	0.40
Brass	0.05
Cast iron	0.20
Lead	0.08
Nickel	0.06
Paint	0.94
Tin	0.08
Non-metallic surfaces	0.90

Small iron pipes of ½ inch size, frequently left uninsulated, can be profitably painted with aluminum paint, which, with little effort, serves to reduce the emissivity of the pipe and, consequently, the loss by radiation.

Although the emissivity of copper pipe is substantially lower than that for steel pipe, so that coppers radiation loss is less, the convection loss is the same for copper as for iron where the conditions are the same. Therefore, it is not true that there is no reason to insulate hot lines because they are made of copper.

Many tables are available on heat losses from bare pipe; most of them, however, are on the basis of either Btu/ft^2-hr of pipe surface or Btu/lineal ft-°F-hr of pipe (between pipe surface and air). Note, then, that the accompanying tables are in Btu/lineal ft-hr, with no additional calculation necessary.

Heat Losses from Steam Piping.—The accompanying table shows the heat loss (in Btu or in pounds of steam) from bare steam pipes, provided the following are known:

1) pipe size and length;

2) steam pressure;

3) whether steam is saturated or superheated and, if the latter, degree of superheat;

4) temperature of air surrounding pipe; and

5) insulation efficiency factor if loss is desired when pipe is covered.

Saturated Steam: Example 16: 100 ft of 1 in. bare piping is carrying dry saturated steam at 90 lb of pressure, absolute. The surrounding still air temperature is 70°F. What are the losses Btu/hr expressed in lbs of steam?

Solution: Consult Table 9-126, column C and proceed downward until 90 lb absolute pressure is reached, thence read across to the right to the 1 in. pipe size column and read 28.40 lb of steam as the bare piping losses per 100 ft/hr.

If this pipe were insulated with 80% efficiency pipe covering the losses would be (1.00 −0.80) × 28.40 = 5.68 lb of steam per 100 ft per hr.

Superheated Steam: In case the steam is superheated, proceed as follows:

Example 17: If 100 ft of 2 in. bare piping is passing steam at 33 lb pressure (absolute) and 25°F superheat, surrounding still air temperature is 70°F, and insulated pipe covering rated at 85% efficiency is used, what are the losses before and after the covering is applied?

Solution: In column C, locate 33 lb pressure absolute and in column B, find the corresponding steam temperature at 255°F. With 25°F superheat the steam temperature will be 255 + 25 = 280°F. Follow down column B to 280 °F and note that the corresponding absolute steam pressure is 49 lb. Continue to the right and under 2 in. diameter find the uncorrected bare piping losses as 38.61 lbs of steam per hour per 100 ft. In column D the latent heat of vaporization for 49 lbs absolute pressure is 924.2 Btu/lb while for 33 lb absolute pressure the latent heat is 941.2 Btu /hr. The ratio is therefore 924.2/941.2 = 0.982. The corrected bare piping loss is therefore 0.982 × 38.61 = 37.02 pounds of steam per hour per 100 ft for the superheated line. The losses after covering with 85% efficiency insulation will be (1.00−0.85) × 37.92 = 5.69 pounds of steam per hour.

Example 18: What would be the heat losses from 172 ft^2 of virtually flat surface with 90 lb (absolute) steam pressure on one side and 70°F air on the other?

Solution: Continue down column C to 90 lb absolute pressure; follow to the right and under column E, find the heat loss to be 937.80 Btu/ft^2-hr. For 172 ft^2, the heat loss would be 172 × 737.8 = 126,902 Btu/hr.

Steam losses could be found by continuing over to column F, where the loss is found to be 0.8249 lb of steam per ft^2; for the whole surface, 172 × 0.8249 = 141.9 lb of steam.

Table 9-123. Heat Losses from Bare Steel Pipe

Horizontal Pipes											
Temperature of Pipe, °F											
Diameter of Pipe, in.	100	120	150	180	210	240	270	300	330	360	390
Temperature Difference, Pipe to Air, °F											
	30	50	180	110	140	170	200	230	260	290	320
Heat Loss per Lineal ft of Pipe, Btu/hr											
½	13	22	40	60	82	106	133	162	193	227	265
¾	15	27	50	74	100	131	163	199	238	280	325
1	19	34	61	90	123	160	199	243	292	343	399
1¼	23	42	75	111	152	198	248	302	362	427	496
1½	27	48	85	126	173	224	280	343	410	483	563
2	33	59	104	154	212	275	344	420	503	594	692
2½	39	70	123	184	252	327	410	502	600	709	827
3	46	84	148	221	303	393	493	601	721	852	994
3½	52	95	168	250	342	444	556	680	816	964	1125
4	59	106	187	278	381	496	621	759	911	1076	1257
5	71	129	227	339	464	603	755	924	1109	1311	1532
6	84	151	267	398	546	709	890	1088	1306	1544	1806
8	107	194	341	509	697	906	1137	1391	1671	1977	2312
10	132	238	420	626	857	1114	1399	1714	2060	2437	2852
12	154	279	491	732	1003	1305	1640	2009	2415	2860	3346
14	181	326	575	856	1173	1527	1918	2350	2826	3347	3918
16	203	366	644	960	1314	1711	2149	2634	3308	3753	4395
18	214	385	678	1011	1355	1802	2266	2777	3339	3958	4635
20	236	426	748	1115	1529	1990	2501	3066	3690	4373	5123
Vertical pipes											
Temperature of Pipe, °F											
Diameter of Pipe, in.	100	120	150	180	210	240	270	300	330	360	390
Temperature Difference, Pipe to Air, °F											
	30	50	180	110	140	170	200	230	260	290	320
Heat Loss per Lineal ft of Pipe, Btu/hr											
½	11	20	35	52	71	93	116	142	170	201	235
¾	14	25	44	65	89	116	145	177	213	252	294
1	17	31	55	81	111	145	181	222	266	315	368
1¼	22	39	69	103	141	183	230	281	337	398	465
1½	25	45	79	118	161	210	263	321	386	456	532
2	31	56	99	147	201	262	328	401	481	569	665
2½	37	68	120	178	244	317	397	486	583	687	805
3	46	83	146	217	297	386	484	592	710	839	980
3½	52	94	166	248	339	440	552	676	810	958	1119
4	59	106	187	279	382	496	622	760	912	1078	1259
5	72	131	231	344	472	612	768	939	1126	1331	1555
6	86	156	275	410	562	729	915	1119	1342	1587	1853
8	112	203	358	534	731	950	1191	1456	1747	2065	2412
10	140	254	447	667	913	1186	1487	1818	2181	2578	3012
12	166	301	530	790	1081	1404	1761	2154	2584	3054	3567
14	195	354	624	930	1273	1653	2073	2536	3042	3596	4200
16	221	400	705	1051	1438	1868	2343	2865	3437	4063	4745
18	234	425	748	1115	1526	1982	2486	3040	3648	4311	5036
20	260	472	831	1239	1696	2203	2763	3378	4053	4791	5596

Table 9-124. Heat Losses from Bare Bright Copper Tube

	Horizontal Tubes										
	Temperature of Pipe, °F										
	100	120	150	180	210	240	270	300	330	360	390
Nominal diameter of Tube, in.	Temperature Difference, Tube to Air, °F										
			80	110	140	170	200	230	260	290	320
	Heat Loss per Lineal ft of Pipe, Btu/hr										
¼	3	6	11	16	22	28	34	40	47	54	61
⅜	4	8	13	20	27	35	43	51	60	69	78
½	5	9	16	24	33	42	51	61	72	82	94
⅝	6	10	19	28	38	49	60	71	83	95	108
¾	7	12	21	32	43	55	68	79	95	109	123
1	8	15	26	39	53	67	83	98	115	133	151
1¼	9	17	31	46	63	80	99	117	137	158	179
1½	10	20	36	53	72	92	113	135	158	181	206
2	13	25	44	66	90	115	141	168	196	226	257
2½	15	29	52	78	107	136	167	200	233	268	305
3	18	34	61	90	123	157	192	229	268	309	352
3½	20	38	68	102	139	178	218	260	305	351	400
4	23	43	77	113	154	198	243	289	339	391	445
5	27	51	91	137	185	237	292	347	407	469	533
6	31	59	106	157	213	270	336	400	464	541	60
8	40	75	134	198	271	347	426	507	594	686	790
10	47	89	159	239	323	413	509	607	710	822	935
12	54	104	184	276	377	482	593	707	827	957	1090
	Vertical Tubes										
	Temperature of Tube, °F										
	100	120	150	180	210	240	270	300	330	360	390
Nominal diameter of Tube, Inches	Temperature Difference, Tube to Air, °F										
	30	50	80	110	140	170	200	230	260	290	320
	Heat Loss per Lineal ft of Tube, Btu/ft										
¼	2	4	7	10	14	17	21	25	30	34	39
⅜	3	5	9	13	18	23	28	34	40	46	52
½	3	6	11	17	23	29	36	43	50	57	65
⅝	4	7	13	20	27	35	43	51	60	69	78
¾	5	9	16	23	32	40	50	59	70	80	91
1	6	11	20	30	41	52	64	76	89	103	117
1¼	7	14	25	37	50	64	78	93	110	126	143
1½	9	16	29	43	59	75	92	110	129	149	169
2	11	21	38	57	77	98	121	144	169	198	221
2½	14	26	47	70	95	121	150	178	209	241	274
3	17	31	56	84	113	144	178	212	249	286	325
3½	19	36	65	97	131	167	206	246	289	332	377
4	22	41	74	110	149	191	235	280	329	378	429
5	27	51	92	137	185	237	291	348	408	469	533
6	32	61	110	163	221	282	348	415	487	560	636
8	43	81	146	217	294	376	463	553	648	746	847
10	54	101	182	271	366	468	576	687	806	928	1054
12	66	121	217	324	438	560	689	822	965	1110	1260

Table 9-125. Heat Losses from Bare Tarnished Copper Tube

Nominal diameter of Tube, in.	Temperature of Tube, °F										
	100	120	150	180	210	240	270	300	330	360	390
	Temperature Difference, Tube to Air, °F										
	30	50	80	110	140	170	200	230	260	290	320
	Heat Loss per Lineal ft of Pipe, Btu/hr										
¼	4	8	14	21	29	37	46	56	66	77	88
⅜	6	10	18	28	37	48	60	72	85	99	114
½	7	13	22	33	45	59	72	88	104	121	139
⅝	8	15	26	39	53	68	85	102	121	141	163
¾	9	17	30	45	61	79	97	117	139	162	187
1	11	21	37	55	75	97	120	146	173	201	232
1¼	14	25	45	66	90	117	145	175	207	242	279
1½	16	29	52	77	105	135	167	203	241	281	324
2	20	37	66	97	132	171	212	257	305	356	411
2½	24	44	78	117	160	206	255	310	367	429	496
3	28	51	92	136	186	240	297	360	428	501	578
3½	32	59	104	156	212	274	340	412	490	573	662
4	36	66	118	174	238	307	381	462	550	644	744
5	43	80	142	212	288	373	464	561	669	783	905
6	51	93	166	246	336	432	541	656	776	915	1059
8	66	120	215	317	435	562	699	848	1010	1184	1372
10	80	146	260	387	527	681	848	1031	1227	1442	1670
12	94	172	304	447	621	802	999	124	1446	1699	1969

Vertical Tubes											
Nominal diameter of Tube, in.	Temperature of Tube, °F										
	100	120	150	180	210	240	270	300	330	360	390
	Temperature Difference, Tube to Air, °F										
	30	50	80	110	140	170	200	230	260	290	320
	Heat Loss per Lineal ft of Tube, Btu/hr										
¼	3	6	10	15	21	27	34	41	49	57	66
⅜	4	8	14	21	28	36	45	55	65	77	88
½	5	10	17	26	35	46	57	69	82	96	111
⅝	6	12	21	31	42	54	68	82	98	114	132
¾	7	14	24	36	49	64	79	96	114	134	155
1	10	18	31	46	63	82	102	123	147	172	198
1¼	12	21	38	57	77	100	125	151	180	210	243
1½	14	25	45	67	91	118	147	178	212	248	287
2	18	33	59	88	120	155	192	233	277	325	375
2½	22	41	73	109	148	191	238	288	343	402	464
3	27	49	87	129	176	227	283	343	408	478	552
3½	31	57	101	150	204	264	328	398	474	554	641
4	35	64	114	171	232	300	374	453	539	631	729
5	43	80	142	212	288	373	464	561	669	783	905
6	52	96	170	253	344	445	554	670	798	934	1080
8	69	127	226	337	458	592	737	892	1063	1244	1438
10	86	158	281	419	570	737	917	1110	1322	1548	1789
12	103	189	336	501	682	881	1097	1328	1582	1851	2140

Table 9-126. Steam Losses from Steel Piping – ½ to 2 Inch Pipe

A	B	C	D	E	F	Nominal Pipe Diameter, in.					
						½	¾	1	1¼	1½	2
	Saturated Steam Temp. (Col. A+ 70°F)	Abs. Steam Pressure for Temp. Col. B	Latent Heat of Vapor-ization, Btu/lb	Heat loss Btu/ft²-hr	Heat loss Btu/ft²-hr	Outside Surface Area, ft²/100 Lineal ft					
						21.99	27.49	34.43	43.46	49.74	62.18
Temp. Diff, °F						Steam Lost lbs/hr-100 Lineal ft					
50	120	1.692	1025.1	97.50	0.0951	2.09	2.61	3.27	4.13	4.73	5.91
55	125	1.941	1022.2	109.27	0.1069	2.35	2.94	3.68	4.65	5.32	6.65
60	130	2.221	1019.4	121.04	0. 1187	2.61	3.26	4.09	5.16	5.90	7.38
65	135	2.536	1016.5	132.81	0.1307	2.87	3.59	4.50	5.68	6.50	8.13
70	140	2.887	1013.6	144.58	0.1426	3.14	3.92	4.91	6.20	7.09	8.87
75	145	3.28	1010.6	156.35	0.1547	3.40	4.25	5.33	6.72	7.69	9.62
80	150	3.70	1007.7	168.12	0. 1668	3.67	4.59	5.74	7.25	8.30	10.37
85	155	4.201	1004.7	179.89	0.1790	3.94	4.92	6.16	7.78	8.9	11.13
90	160	4.739	1001.8	191.66	0.1913	4.21	5.26	6.59	8.31	9.52	11.9
95	165	5.334	998.8	203.43	0.2037	4.48	5.60	7.01	8.85	10.13	12.67
100	170	5.990	995.8	215.20	0.201	4.75	5.94	7.44	9.39	10.57	13.44
105	175	6.70	992.8	229.68	0.2313	5.09	6.36	7.96	10.05	11.50	14.38
110	180	7.510	989.8	244.0	0.2467	5.42	6.78	8.49	10.72	12.27	15.34
115	185	8.382	986.8	258.64	0.2621	5.76	7.21	9.02	11.39	13.04	16.30
120	190	9.336	983.8	273.12	0.2776	6.1	7.63	9.56	12.06	13.81	17.26
125	195	10.385	980.8	287.6	0.2932	6.43	8.06	10.09	12.74	14.58	18.23
130	200	11.525	977.7	302.08	0.3090	6.79	8.49	10.64	13.43	15.37	19.21
135	205	12.772	974.6	316.56	0.3248	7.14	8.93	11.18	14.12	16.2	20.20
140	210	14.123	971.5	331.04	0.3408	7.49	9.37	11.73	14.81	16.95	21.19
145	215	16	968.3	345.52	0.3568	7.85	9.81	12.28	15.51	17.75	22.19
150	220	17	965.1	360.00	0.3730	8.20	10.25	12.84	16.21	18.55	23.19
155	225	19	961.7	377.30	0.3923	8.63	10.78	13.51	17.05	19.51	24.39
160	230	21	958.6	394.6	0.4116	9.05	11.31	14.17	17.89	20.47	25.59
165	235	23	955.0	411.90	0.4313	9.48	11.86	14.85	18.74	21.45	26.82
170	240	25	952.0	429.20	0.4508	9.91	12.39	15.52	19.59	22.42	28.03
175	245	27	949.0	446.50	0.4705	10.35	12.93	16.20	20.45	23.40	29.26
180	250	30	945.2	463.80	0.4907	10.79	13.49	16.89	21.33	24.41	30.51
185	255	33	941.2	481.10	0.5112	11.24	14.05.	17.60	22.22	25.43	31.79
190	260	35	938.4	498.40	0.5311	11.68	14.6	18.29	23.08	26.42	33.02
195	265	39	934.4	515.7	0.5519	12.14	15.17	19.00	23.99	27.45	34.3
200	270	42	931.4	533.0	0.5723	12.58	15.73	19.7	24.87	28.47	35.59
205	275	45	928.2	553.48	0.5963	13.11	16.39	20.53	25.92	29.66	37.08
210	280	49	924.2	573.96	0.621	13.66	17.07	21.38	26.99	30.89	38.61
215	285	53	920.9	594.44	0.6455	14.19	17.74	22.22	28.05	32.11	40.14
220	290	58	917.0	614.92	0.6706	14.75	18.43	23.09	29.14	33.36	41.70
225	295	62	913.4	635.40	0.6956	15.30	19.12	13.95	30.23	34.6	43.25
230	300	67	909.6	655.88	0.7211	15.86	19.82	24.83	31.34	35.87	44.84
235	305	72	906.0	676.36	0.7465	16.42	20.52	25.70	32.44	37.13	46.41
240	310	78	902.1	696.84	0.7725	16.99	21.24	26.60	33.57	38.42	48.03
245	315	84	898.3	717.32	0.7985	17.56	21.95	27.49	34.7	39.72	49.65
250	320	90	894.4	737.8	0.8249	18.14	22.68	28.40	35.85	41.03	51.29
255	325	96	890.6	761.82	0.8554	18.81	23.51	29.45	37.18	42.55	53.19
260	330	103	886.5	785.84	0.8865	19.49	24.37	30.52	38.53	44.09	55.12
265	335	110	882.7	809.86	0.9175	20.18	25.22	31.59	39.87	45.64	57.05
270	340	118	878.5	833.88	0.9492	20.87	26.09	32.68	41.25	47.21	59.02
275	345	126	874.4	857.9	0.9811	21.57	26.97	33.78	42.64	48.80	61.00

Table 9-126. *(Continued)* **Steam Losses from Steel Piping – ½ to 2 Inch Pipe**

A	B	C	D	E	F	Nominal Pipe Diameter, in.					
	Saturated Steam Temp. (Col. A+ 70°F)	Abs. Steam Pressure for Temp. Col. B	Latent Heat of Vapor- ization, Btu/lb	Heat loss Btu/ft²-hr	Heat loss Btu/ft²-hr	½	¾	1	1¼	1½	2
						Outside Surface Area, ft²/100 Lineal ft					
						21.99	27.49	34.43	43.46	49.74	62.18
Temp. Diff, °F						Steam Lost lbs/hr-100 Lineal ft					
280	350	135	870.2	881.92	1.0135	22.29	27.86	34.89	44.04	50.41	63.02
285	355	144	865.8	905.94	1.0464	23.01	28.77	36.03	45.48	52.05	65.07
290	360	153	861.7	929.96	1.0792	23.73	29.67	37.16	46.9	53.68	67.10
295	365	163	857.4	953.98	1.1126	24.47	30.59	38.31	48.35	55.34	69.18
300	370	173	853	978.00	1.1465	25.21	31 52	39.47	49.83	57.03	71.29
305	375	184	848.6	1007.40	1.1868	26.10	32.63	40.86	51.58	59.03	73.80
310	380	196	844.1	1036.28	1.2277	27.00	33.75	42.27	53.36	61.07	76.34
315	385	208	839.5	1065.42	1.2691	27.91	34.89	43.70	55.16	63.13	78.91
320	390	220	834.9	1094.56	1.3110	28.83	36.04	45.14	56.98	65.21	81.52
325	395	233	830.3	1123.70	1.3534	29.76	37.20	46.60	58.82	67.32	84.15
330	400	248	825.5	1152.84	1.3965	30.71	38.39	48.08	60.69	69.46	86.83
335	405	262	820.6	1181.98	1.4404	31.67	39.60	49.59	62.60	71.65	89.56
340	410	277	815.8	1211.12	1.4846	32.65	40.81	51.11	64.52	73.84	92.31
345	415	292	810.8	1240.26	1.5297	33.64	42.05	52.67	66.48	76.09	95.12
350	420	309	805.8	1269.40	1.5753	34.64	43.3	54.24	68.46	78.36	97.95
355	425	326	800.7	1303.86	1.6284	35.81	44.76	56.07	70.77	81.00	101.25
360	430	344	795.5	1338.32	1.6824	37.00	46.25	57.93	73.12	83.68	104.61
365	435	362	790.2	1372.78	1.7373	38.20	47.76	59.82	75.50	86.41	108.03
370	440	382	784.9	1407.24	1.7929	39.43	49.29	61.73	77.92	89.18	111.48
375	445	402	779.4	1441.7	1.8498	40.68	50.85	63.69	80.39	92.01	115.02
380	450	423	773.8	1476.16	1.9077	41.95	52.44	65.68	82.91	94.89	118.62
385	455	444	768.1	1510.62	1.9667	43.25	54.06	67.71	85.47	97.82	122.29
390	460	467	762.3	1545.08	2.0269	44.57	55.72	69.79	88.09	100.82	126.03
395	465	490	756.4	1579.54	2.0882	45.92	57.40	71.90	90.75	103.87	129.84
400	470	515	750.3	1614.00	2.1511	47.30	59.13	74.06	93.49	107.00	133.76
405	475	540	744.1	1657.66	2.2277	48.99	61.24	76.70	96.82	110.81	138.52
410	480	566	737.80	1701.32	2.3059	50.71	63.39	79.39	100.21	114.70	143.38
415	485	593	731.30	1744.98	2.3861	52.47	65.59	82.15	103.70	118.68	148.37
420	490	622	724.7	1788.64	2.4681	54.27	67.85	84.98	107.26	123.00	153.47
425	495	651	718.0	1832.30	2.5519	56.12	70.15	87.86	110.91	126.93	158.68
430	500	681	711.1	1875.96	2.6381	58.01	72.52	90.83	114.65	131.22	164.04
435	505	712	704.1	1919.62	2.7263	59.95	74.95	93.87	118.48	135.61	169.52
440	510	745	696.9	1963.28	2.8172	61.95	77.44	97-00	122.44	140.13	175.17
445	515	778	689.6	2006.94	2.9103	64.00	80.00	100.20	126.48	144.76	180.96
450	520	813	682.1	2050.60	3.0063	66.11	82.64	103.51	130.65	149.53	186.93
455	525	848	674.6	2104.54	3.1197	68.6	85.76	109.41	135.58	155.17	193.98
460	530	885	666.8	2158.48	3.2371	71.18	88.99	111.45	140.68	161.01	201.28
465	535	923	659.0	2212.42	3.3572	73.82	92.29	115.59	145.90	166.99	208.75
470	540	963	651.0	2266.36	3.4814	76.56	95.70	119.86	151.30	173.16	216.470
475	545	1003	642.8	2320.30	3.6097	79.38	99.23	124.28	156.88	179.55	224.45
480	550	1045	634.5	2374.24	3.7419	82.28	102.86	128.83	162.62	186.12	232.67
485	555	1089	626.1	2428.18	3.8783	85.28	106.61	133.53	168.55	192.91	241.15
490	560	1133	617.5	2482.12	4.0196	88.39	110.5	138.39	174.69	199.93	249.94
495	565	1180	608.7	2536.06	4.1664	91.62	114.53	143.45	181.07	207.24	259.07
500	570	1228	599.7	2590.00	4.3188	94.97	118.72	148.70	189.70	214.82	268.54

Table 9-127. Steam Losses from Steel Piping – 2 ½ to 6 Inch Pipe

A	B	C	D	E	F	Nominal Pipe Diameter, in.				
						2 ½	3	4	5	6
	Saturated Steam Temp. (Col. A+ 70°F)	Abs. Steam Pressure for Temp. Col. B	Latent Heat of Vaporization, Btu/lb	Heat loss Btu/ft²-hr	Heat loss Btu/ft²-hr	Outside Surface Area, ft²/100 Lineal ft				
						75.27	91.63	117.81	145.64	173.44
Temp. Diff, °F						Steam Lost lbs/hr-100 Lineal ft				
50	120	1.692	1025.1	97.50	0.0951	7.16	8.71	11.2	13.85	16.4
55	125	1.941	1022.2	109.27	0.1069	8.05	9.80	12.59	15.57	18.54
60	130	2.221	1019.4	121.04	0. 1187	8.93	10.88	13.98	17.29	20.59
65	135	2.536	1016.5	132.81	0.1307	9.84	11.98	15.40	19.04	22.67
70	140	2.887	1013.6	144.58	0.1426	10.73	13.07	16.80	20.77	24.73
75	145	3.280	1010.6	156.35	0.1547	11.64	14.18	15. 23	22.53	26.83
80	150	3.716	1007.7	168.12	0.1668	12.56	15.28	19.65	24.29	28.93
85	155	4.201	1004.7	179.89	0.179	13.47	16.4	21.09	26.07	31.05
90	160	4.739	1001.8	191.66	0.1913	14.40	17.53	22.54	27.86	33.18
95	165	5.334	998.8	203.43	0.2037	15.33	18.67	24.00	29.67	35.33
100	170	5.990	995.8	215. 20	0.2161	16.27	19.8	25.46	31.47	37.48
105	175	6.716	992.8	229.68	0.2313	17.41	21.19	27.25	33.69	40.12
110	180	7.510	989.8	244.16	0.2467	18.57	22.61	29.06	35.93	42.79
115	185	8.382	986.8	258.64	0.2621	19.73	24.02	30.88	38.17	45.46
120	190	9.336	983.8	273.12	0.2776	20.89	25.44	32.70	40.43	48.15
125	195	10.385	980.8	287.6	0.2932	22.07	26.87	34.54	42.7	50.85
130	200	11.525	977.7	302.08	0.309	23.26	28.31	36.40	45.0	53.59
135	205	12.772	974.6	316.56	0.3248	24.45	29.76	38.26	47.3	56.33
140	210	14.123	971.5	331.04	0.3408	25.65	31.23	40.15	49.63	59.11
145	215	16	968.3	345.52	0.3568	26.86	32.69	42.03	51.96	61.88
150	220	17	965.1	360.00	0.373	28.08	34.18	43.94	54.32	64.69
155	225	19	961.7	377.3	0.3923	29.53	35.95	46.22	57.13	68.04
160	230	21	958.6	394.6	0.4116	30.98	37.71	48.49	59.95	71.39
165	235	23	955.0	411.9	0.4313	32.46	39.52	50.81	62.81	74.8
170	240	25	952.0	429.2	0.4508	33.93	41.31	53.1	65.65	78.19
175	245	27	949.0	446.5	0.4705	35.41	43.11	55.43	68.52	81.6
180	250	30	945.2	463.8	0.4907	36.93	44.96	57.81	71.47	85.11
185	255	33	941.2	481.1	0.5112	38.48	46.84	60.22	74.45	88.66
190	260	35	938.4	498.4	0.5311	39.98	48.66	62.57	77.35	92.11
195	265	39	934.4	515.7	0.5519	41.54	50.57	65.02	80.38	95.72
200	270	42	931.4	533.0	0.5723	43.08	52.44	67.42	83.35	99.26
205	275	45	928.2	553.48	0.5963	44.88	54.64	70.25	86.85	103.42
210	280	49	924.2	573.96	0.621	46.74	56.9	73.16	90.44	107.71
215	285	53	920.9	594.44	0.6455	48.59	59.15	76.05	94.401	111.96
220	290	58	917.0	614.92	0.6706	50.48	61.45	79.00	97.67	116.31
225	295	62	913.4	635.4	0.6956	52.36	63.74	81.95	101.31	120.64
230	300	67	909.6	655.88	0.7211	54.28	66.07	84.95	105.02	125.07
235	305	72	906.0	676.36	0.7465	56.19	68.4	87.95	108.72	129.47
240	310	78	902.1	696.84	0.7725	58.15	70.78	91.01	112.51	133.98
245	315	84	898.3	717.32	0.7985	60.10	73.17	94.07	116.29	138.49
250	320	90	894.4	737.8	0.8249	62.09	75.59	97.18	120.14	143.07
255	325	96	890.6	761.82	0.8554	64.39	78.38	100.77	124.58	148.36
260	330	103	886.5	785.84	0.8865	66.73	81.23	104.44	129.11	153.75
265	335	110	882.7	809.86	0.9175	69.06	84.07	108.09	133.62	159.13
270	340	118	878.5	833.88	0.9492	71.45	96.98	111.83	138.24	164.63
275	345	126	874.4	857.90	0. 9811	73.85	89.90	115.58	142.89	170.16

Table 9-127. *(Continued)* Steam Losses from Steel Piping – 2 ½ to 6 Inch Pipe

A	B	C	D	E	F	2 ½	3	4	5	6
	Saturated Steam Temp. (Col. A+ 70°F)	Abs. Steam Pressure for Temp. Col. B	Latent Heat of Vaporization, Btu/lb	Heat loss Btu/ft²-hr	Heat loss Btu/ft²-hr	\multicolumn 5 Nominal Pipe Diameter, in.				
Temp. Diff, °F						Outside Surface Area, ft²/100 Lineal ft				
						75.27	91.63	117.81	145.64	173.44
						Steam Lost lbs/hr-100 Lineal ft				
280	350	135	870.2	881.92	1.0135	76.29	92.87	119.40	147.61	175.78
285	355	144	865.8	905.94	1.0464	78.76	95.88	123.28	152.40	181.49
290	360	153	861.7	929.96	1.0792	81.23	98.89	127.14	157.17	187. 18
295	365	163	857.4	953.98	1.1126	·83.75	101.95	131.08	162.04	192.97
300	370	173	853.0	978.00	1.1465	86.30	105.05	135.07	166.98	199.85
305	375	184	848.6	1007.14	1.1868	89.33	108.75	139.82	172.85	205.84
310	380	196	844.1	1036.28	1.2277	92.41	112.49	144.64	178.8	212.93
315	385	208	839.5	1065.42	1. 2691	95.53	116.29	149.51	184.83	220.11
320	390	220	834.9	1094.56	1.3110	98.68	120.13	154.45	190.93	227.38
325	395	233	830.3	1123.7	1.3534	101.87	124.01	159.44	197.11	234.73
330	400	248	825.5	1152.84	1.3965	105.11	127.96	164. 82	203.39	242.21
335	405	262	820.6	1181.98	1.4404	108.42	131.98	169.69	209.78	249.82
340	410	277	815.8	1211.12	1.4846	111.75	136.03	174.90	216.22	257.49
345	415	292	810.8	1240. 26	1.5297	115.14	140.17	180.21	222.79	265.31
350	420	309	805.8	1269.4	1.5753	118.57	144.34	185.59	229.43	273.22
355	425	326	800.7	1303.86	1.6284	122.57	149.21	191.84	237.16	282.43
360	430	344	795.5	1338.32	1.6824	126.63	154.16	198.20	245.02	291.80
365	435	362	790.2	1372.78	1.7373	130.77	159.19	204.67	253.02	301.32
370	440	382	784.9	1407.24	1.7929	134.95	164.28	211.22	261.12	310.96
375	445	402	779.4	1441.70	1.8498	139.23	169.50	217.92	269.40	320.83
380	450	423	773.8	1476.16	1.9077	143.59	174.8	224.75	277.84	330.87
385	455	444	768.1	1510.62	1.9667	148.03	180.21	231.70	286.43	341.1
390	460	467	762.3	1545.08	2.0269	152.56	185.72	238.79	295.20	351.55
395	465	490	756.4	1579.54	2.0882	157.18	191.34	246.01	304.13	362.10
400	470	515	750.3	1614.00	2.1511	161.91	197.11	253.42	313.29	373.09
405	475	540	744.1	1657.66	2.2277	167.68	204.12	262.45	324.44	386.37
410	480	566	737.8	1701.32	2.3059	173.57	211.29	271.66	335.83	399.94
415	485	593	731.3	1744.98	2.3861	179.60	218.64	281.11	347.51	413.85
420	490	622	724.7	1788.64	2.4681	185.77	226.15	290.77	359.45	428.07
425	495	651	718.0	1832.3	2.5519	192.08	233.83	300.64	371.66	442.60
430	500	681	711.1	1875.96	2.6381	198.57	241.73	310.79	384.21	457.55
435	505	712	704.1	1919.62	2.7263	205.21	249.81	321.19	397.06	472.85
440	510	745	696.9	1963.28	2.8172	212.05	258.14	331.89	410.30	488.62
445	515	778	689.6	2006.94	2.9103	219.06	266.67	342.86	423.86	504.76
450	520	813	682.1	2050.60	3.0063	226.28	275.47	354.17	437.84	521.41
455	525	848	674.6	2104.54	3.1197	234.82	285.86	367.53	454.34	541.08
460	530	885	666.8	2158.48	3.2371	243.66	296.62	381.36	471.45	561.44
465	535	923	659.0	2212.42	3.3572	252.7	307.62	395.51	488.94	582.27
470	540	963	651.0	2266.36	3.4814	262.04	319.00	410.14	507.03	603.81
475	545	1003	642.8	2320.30	3.6097	271.70	330.76	425.26	525.2	626.07
480	550	1045	634.5	2374.24	3.7419	281.65	342.87	440.83	544.97	649.00
485	555	1089	626.1	2428.18	3.8783	291.92	355.37	456.9	564.84	672.65
490	560	1133	617.5	2482.12	4.0196	302.56	368.32	473.55	585.41	697.16
495	565	1180	608.7	2536.06	4.1664	313.60	381.77	490.84	606.70	722.62
500	570	1228	599.7	2590.00	4.3188	325.08	395.73	508.80	628.99	749.05

Table 9-128. Steam Losses from Steel Piping – 7 to 12 Inch Pipe

A	B	C	D	E	F	Nominal Pipe Diameter, in.				
						7	8	9	10	12
	Saturated Steam Temp. (Col. A+ 70°F)	Abs. Steam Pressure for Temp. Col. B	Latent Heat of Vaporiza-tion, Btu/lb	Heat loss Btu/ft²-hr	Heat loss Btu/ft²-hr	Outside Surface Area, ft²/100 Lineal ft				
						199.62	1225.80	251.98	281.43	333.8
Temp. Diff, °F						Steam Lost lbs/hr-100 Lineal ft				
50	120	1.692	1025.1	97.50	0.0951	18.98	21.47	23.96	26.76	31.74
55	125	1.941	1022.2	109.27	0.1069	21.34	24.14	26.94	30.08	35.68
60	130	2.221	1019.4	121.04	0.1187	23.69	26.8	29.91	33.41	39.62
65	135	2.536	1016.5	132.81	0.1307	26.09	29.51	32.93	36.78	43.63
70	140	2.887	1013.6	144.58	0.1426	28.47	32.20	35.93	40.13	47.60
75	145	3.28	1010.6	156.35	0.1547	30.88	34.93	38.98	43.54	51.64
80	150	3.70	1007.7	168.12	0.1668	33.3	37.66	42.03	46.94	55.68
85	155	4.201	1004.7	179.89	0.1790	35.73	40.42	45.10	50.38	59.75
90	160	4.739	1001.8	191.66	0.1913	38.19	43.2	48.20	53.84	63.86
95	165	5.334	998.8	203.43	0.2037	40.66	46.00	51.33	57.33	68.00
100	170	5.990	995.8	215.20	0.2161	43.14	48.80	54.45	60.82	72.13
105	175	6.70	992.8	229.68	0.2313	46.17	52.23	58.28	65.09	77.21
110	180	7.510	989.8	244.00	0.2467	49.25	55.7	62.0	69.43	82.35
115	185	8.382	986.8	258.64	0.2621	52.32	59.18	66.04	73.76	87.49
120	190	9.336	983.8	273.12	0.2776	55.41	62.68	69.95	78.12	92.66
125	195	10.385	980.8	287.60	0.2932	58.53	66.20	73.88	82.52	97.87
130	200	11.525	977.7	302.08	0.3090	61.68	69.77	77.86	86.96	103.14
135	205	12.772	974.6	305.56	0.3248	64.84	73.34	81.84	91.41	108.42
140	210	14.123	971.15	331.04	0.3408	68.03	76.95	85.87	95.91	113.76
145	215	16	968.3	345.52	0.3568	71.22	80.57	89.91	100.41	119.1
150	220	17	965.1	360.00	0.3730	74.46	84.22	93.99	104.97	124.51
155	225	19	961.7	377.30	0.3923	78.31	88.58	98.85	110.40	130.95
160	230	21	958.6	394.6	0.4116	82.16	92.94	103.71	115.84	137.39
165	235	23	955	411.90	0.4313	86.1	97.39	108.68	121.38	143.97
170	240	25	952.0	429.20	0.4508	89.99	101.79	113.59	126.87	150.48
175	245	27	949	446.50	0.4705	93.92	106.24	118.56	132.41	157.05
180	250	30	945.2	463.80	0.4907	97.95	110.8	123.65	138.1	163.8
185	255	33	941.2	481.1	0.5112	102.05	115.43	128.81	143.87	170.64
190	260	35	938.4	498.40	0.5311	106.02	119.92	133.83	149.47	177.28
195	265	39	934.4	515.7	0.5519	110.17	124.62	139.07	155.32	184.22
200	270	42	931.4	533.00	0.5723	114.24	129.23	144.21	161.06	191.03
205	275	45	928.2	553.48	0.5963	119.03	134.64	150.26	167.82	199.04
210	280	49	924.2	573.96	0.621	123.96	140.22	156.48	174.77	207.29
215	285	53	920.9	594.44	0.6455	128.85	145.75	162.65	181.66	215.47
220	200	58	917.0	614.92	0.6706	133.87	151.42	168.98	188.93	223.85
225	295	62	913.4	635.40	0.6956	138.86	157.07	175.28	195.76	232.19
230	300	67	909.6	655.88	0.7211	143.95	162.82	181.70	202.94	240.70
235	305	72	906.00	676.36	0.7465	149.02	168.56	188.10	210.09	249.18
240	310	78	902.1	696.84	0.7725	154.21	174.43	194.45	217.40	257.86
245	315	84	898.3	717.32	0.7985	159.4	180.30	201.21	224.72	266.54
250	320	90	894.4	737.8	0.8249	164.67	186.26	207.86	232.15	275.35
255	325	96	890.6	761.82	0.8554	170.75	193.15	215.54	240.75	285.53
260	330	103	886.5	785.84	0.8865	176.96	200.17	223.38	249.49	295.91
265	335	110	882.7	890.86	0.9175	183.15	207.17	231.19	258.21	306.26
270	340	118	878.5	833.88	0.9492	189.48	214.33	239.18	267.13	316.84
275	345	126	874.4	857.90	0.9811	195.85	221.53	247.22	276.11	327.49

Table 9-128. *(Continued)* Steam Losses from Steel Piping – 7 to 12 Inch Pipe

A	B	C	D	E	F	7	8	9	10	12
	Saturated Steam Temp. (Col. A+ 70°F)	Abs. Steam Pressure for Temp. Col. B	Latent Heat of Vaporiza-tion, Btu/lb	Heat loss Btu/ft²-hr	Heat loss Btu/ft²-hr	Nominal Pipe Diameter, in.				
						Outside Surface Area, ft²/100 Lineal ft				
Temp. Diff, °F						199.62	1225.80	251.98	281.43	333.8
						Steam Lost lbs/hr-100 Lineal ft				
280	350	135	870.2	881.92	1.0135	202.31	228.85	255.38	285.23	338.31
285	355	144	865.8	905.94	1.0464	208.88	236.28	263.67	294.49	349.29
290	360	153	861.7	929.96	1.0792	215.43	243.68	271.94	303.72	360.24
295	365	163	857.4	953.98	1.1126	222.10	251.23	280.35	313.12	371.39
300	370	173	853.0	978	1.1465	228.86	258.88	288.90	322.66	382.70
305	375	184	848.6	1007.14	1.1868	236.91	267.98	299.05	334.00	396.15
310	380	196	844.1	1036.28	1.2277	245.07	277.21	309.36	345.51	409.81
315	385	208	839.5	1065.42	1.2691	253.34	286.56	319.79	357.15	425.63
320	390	220	834.9	1094.56	1.311	261.70	296.02	330.35	368.95	437.61
325	395	233	830.3	1123.70	1.3534	270.17	305.60	341.03	380.89	451.76
330	400	248	825.5	1152.84	1.3965	278.77	315.33	351.89	393.02	466.15
335	405	262	820.6	1181.98	1.4404	287.53	325.24	362.95	405.37	480.81
340	410	277	815.8	1211.12	1.4846	296.36	335.22	374.09	417.81	495.56
345	415	292	810.8	1240.26	1.5297	305.36	345.41	385.45	430.50	510.61
350	420	309	805.8	1269.4	1.5753	314.46	355.7	396.94	443.34	525.84
355	425	326	800.7	1303.86	1.6284	325.06	367.69	410.32	458.28	543.56
360	430	344	795.5	1338.32	1.6824	335.84	379.89	423.93	473.48	561.59
365	435	362	790.2	1372.78	1.7373	346.80	392.28	437.76	488.93	579.91
370	440	382	784.9	1407.24	1.7929	357.9	404.84	451.77	504.58	598.47
375	445	402	779.4	1441.70	1.8498	369.26	417.68	466.11	520.59	617.46
380	450	423	773.8	1476. 16	1.9077	380.82	430.76	480.70	536.88	636.79
385	455	444	768.1	1510.62	1.9667	392.59	444.08	495.57	553.49	656.48
390	460	467	762.3	1545.08	2.0269	404.61	457.67	510.74	570.43	676.58
395	465	490	756.4	1579.54	2.0882	40.85	471.52	526.18	587.68	697.04
400	470	515	750.3	1614.00	2.1511	429.40	485.72	542.03	605.38	718.04
405	475	540	744.1	1657.66	2.2277	444.69	503.01	561.34	626.94	743.61
410	480	566	737.8	1701.32	2.3059	460.3	520.67	581.04	648.95	769.71
415	485	593	731.3	1744.98	2.3861	476.31	538.78	601.25	671.52	796.48
420	490	622	724.7	1788.64	2.4681	492.68	557.3	621.91	694.6	823.85
425	495	651	718	1832.30	2.5519	509.41	576.22	643.03	718.18	851.82
430	500	681	711.1	1875.96	2.6381	526.62	595.68	664.75	742.44	880.6
435	505	712	704.1	1919.62	2.7263	544.22	615.6	686.97	767.26	910.04
440	510	745	696.9	1963.28	2.8172	562.37	636.12	709.88	792.84	940.38
445	515	778	689.6	2006.94	2.9103	580.95	657.15	733.34	819.05	971.46
450	520	813	682.1	2050.60	3.0063	600.12	678.82	757.53	846.06	1003.5
455	525	848	674.6	2104.54	3.1197	622.75	704.43	786.1	877.98	1041.4
460	530	885	666.8	2158.48	3.2371	646.19	730.94	815.68	911.02	1080.5
465	535	923	659	2212.42	3.3572	670.16	758.06	845.95	944.82	1120.6
470	540	963	651.0	2266.36	3.4814	694.96	786.1	877.24	979.77	1162.1
475	545	1003	642.8	2320.30	3.6097	720.57	815.07	909.57	1015.9	1204.9
480	550	1045	634.5	2374.24	3.7419	746.96	844.92	942.88	1053.1	1249.0
485	555	1089	626.1	2428.18	3.8783	774.19	875.72	977.25	1091.5	1294.6
490	560	1133	617.5	2482.12	4.0196	802.39	907.63	1012.9	1131.2	1341.7
495	565	1180	608.7	2536.06	4.1664	831.70	940.77	1049.8	1172.5	1390.7
500	570	1228	599.7	2590.00	4.3188	862.12	975.19	1088.3	1215.4	1441.6

Table 9-129. Steam Losses from Steel Piping – 14 to 24 Inch Pipe

A	B	C	D	E	F	Nominal Pipe Diameter, in.				
	Saturated Steam Temp. (Col. A+70°F)	Abs. Steam Pressure for Temp. Col. B	Latent Heat of Vaporization, Btu/lb	Heat loss Btu/ft²-hr	Heat loss Btu/ft²-hr	14	16	18	20	24
						Outside Surface Area, ft²/100 Lineal ft				
Temp. Diff, °F						366.52	418.88	471.24	523.6	628.32
						Steam Lost lbs/hr-100 Lineal ft				
50	120	1.692	1025.1	97.5	0.0951	34.86	39.84	44.81	49.79	59.75
55	125	1.941	1022.2	109.27	0.1069	39.18	44.78	50.38	55.97	67.17
60	130	2.221	1019.4	121.04	0.1187	43.51	49.72	55.94	62.15	74.58
65	138	2.536	1016.5	132.81	0.1307	47.9	54.75	61.59	68.43	82.12
70	140	2.887	1013.6	144.58	0.1426	52.27	59.73	67.20	74.67	89.6
75	145	3.28	1010.6	156.35	0.1547	56.70	64.80	72.00	81.00	97.20
80	150	3.716	1007.7	168.12	0.1668	61.14	69.87	78.60	87.34	104.80
85	155	4.201	1004.7	179.89	0.1790	65.61	74.98	84.35	93.72	112.47
90	160	4.739	1001.8	191.66	0.1913	70.12	80.13	90.15	100.16	120.20
95	165	5.334	998.8	203.43	0.2037	74.66	85.33	95.99	106.66	127.99
100	170	5.990	995.8	215.20	0.2161	79.20	90.52	101.83	113.15	135.78
105	175	6.716	992.8	229.68	0.2313	84.78	96.89	109.00	121.11	145.33
110	180	7.510	989.8	244.16	0.2467	90.42	103.34	116.25	129.17	155.01
115	185	8.382	986.8	258.64	0.2621	96.06	109.79	123.51	137.24	164.68
120	190	9.336	983.8	273.12	0.2776	101.75	116.28	130.82	145.35	174.42
125	195	10.385	980.8	287.6	0.2932	107.46	122.82	138.17	153.52	184.22
130	200	11.525	977.7	302.08	0.3090	113.25	129.43	145.61	161.79	194.15
135	205	12.772	974.6	305.60	0.3248	119.05	136.05	153.06	170.07	204.08
140	210	14.123	971.5	331.04	0.3408	124.91	142.75	160.6	178.44	214.13
145	215	16	968.3	345.52	0.3568	130.77	149.46	168.14	186.82	224.18
150	220	17	965.1	360.00	0.3730	136.71	156.24	175.77	195.3	234.36
155	225	19	961.7	377.3	0.3923	143.79	164.33	184.87	205.41	246.49
160	230	21	958.6	394.6	0.4116	150.86	172.41	193.96	215.51	258.62
165	235	23	955.0	411.90	0.4313	158.08	180.66	203.25	225.83	270.99
170	240	25	952	429.20	0.4508	165.23	188.83	212.43	236.04	283.25
175	245	27	949.0	446.50	0.4705	172.45	197.08	221.72	246.35	295.62
180	250	30	945.2	463.80	0.4907	179.85	205.54	231.24	256.93	308.32
185	255	33	941.2	481.1	0.5112	187.37	214.13	240.90	267.66	321.20
190	260	35	938.4	498.40	0.5311	194.66	222.47	250.28	278.08	333.7
195	265	39	934.4	515.7	0.5519	202.28	231.18	260.08	288.97	346.77
200	270	42	931.4	553.48	0.5753	209.76	239.73	269.69	299.66	359.59
205	275	45	928.2	553.48	0.5963	218.56	249.78	281.00	312.22	374.67
210	280	49	924.2	573.96	0.621	227.61	260.12	292.64	325.0	390.19
215	285	53	920.9	594.44	0.6455	236.59	270.39	304.19	337.98	405.58
220	290	58	917.0	614.92	0.6706	245.79	280.9	316.01	351.13	421.35
225	295	62	913.4	635.4	0.6956	254.95	291.37	327.79	364.22	437.06
230	300	67	909.0	655.88	0.7211	264.30	302.05	339.81	377.57	453.08
235	305	72	906.0	676.36	0.7465	273.61	312.69	351.78	390.87	469.04
240	310	78	902.1	696.84	0.7725	283.14	323.58	364.03	404.48	485.38
245	315	84	898.3	717.32	0.7985	292.67	334.48	376.29	418.09	501.71
250	320	90	894.4	737.8	0.8249	302.34	345.53	388.73	431.92	518.3
255	325	96	890.6	761.82	0.8554	313.52	358.31	403.1	447.89	537.46
260	330	103	886.5	785.84	0.8865	324.92	371.34	417.75	464.17	557.01
265	335	110	882.7	809.86	0.9175	336.28	384.32	432.36	480.40	576.48
270	340	118	878.5	833.88	0.9492	347.9	397.6	447.3	497	596.40
275	345	126	874.4	857.90	0.9811	359.59	410.96	462.33	513.7	616.44
280	350	135	870.2	881.92	1.0135	371.47	424.53	477.60	530.67	636.80

Table 9-129. *(Continued)* Steam Losses from Steel Piping – 14 to 24 Inch Pipe

A	B	C	D	E	F	Nominal Pipe Diameter, in.				
	Saturated Steam Temp. (Col. A+ 70°F)	Abs. Steam Pressure for Temp. Col. B	Latent Heat of Vaporiza-tion, Btu/lb	Heat loss Btu/ft²-hr	Heat loss Btu/ft²-hr	14	16	18	20	24
						Outside Surface Area, ft²/100 Lineal ft				
Temp. Diff, °F						366.52	418.88	471.24	523.6	628.32
						Steam Lost lbs/hr-100 Lineal ft				
285	355	144	865.8	905.94	1.0464	383.53	438.32	493.11	547.9	657.47
290	360	153	861.7	929.96	1.0792	395.55	452.06	508.6	565.07	678.08
295	365	163	857.4	953.98	1.1126	407.79	466.05	524.30	532.56	699.07
300	370	173	853.0	978.00	1.1465	420.22	480.25	540.28	600.31	720.37
305	375	184	848.6	1007.14	1.1868	434.99	497.13	559.27	621.41	745.69
310	380	196	844.1	1036.28	1.2277	449.98	514.26	578.54	642.82	771.39
315	385	208	839.5	1065.42	1.2691	465.15	531.5	598.05	664.50	797.40
320	390	220	834.9	1094.56	1.3110	480.51	549.15	617.8	686.44	823.73
325	395	233	830.3	1123.7	1.3534	496.05	566.91	637.78	708.64	850.37
330	400	248	825.5	1152.84	1.3965	511.85	584.97	658.09	731.21	877.45
335	405	262	820.6	1181.98	1.4404	527.94	603.35	678.77	754.19	905.03
340	410	277	815.8	1211.12	1.4846	544.14	621.87	699.60	777.34	932.8
345	415	292	810.8	1240.26	1.5297	560.67	640.76	720.86	800.95	961.14
350	420	309	805.8	1269.4	1.5753	577.38	659.86	742.34	824.83	989.79
355	425	326	800.7	1303.86	1.6284	596.84	682.10	767.37	852.63	1023.2
360	430	344	795.5	1338.32	1.6824	606.30	704.72	792.81	880.9	1057.1
365	435	362	790.2	1372.78	1.7373	636.76	727.72	818.69	909.65	1091.6
370	440	382	784.9	1407.24	1.7929	657.13	751.01	844.89	938.76	1126.5
375	445	402	779.4	1441.7	1.8498	677.99	774.84	871.70	968.56	1162.3
380	450	423	773.8	1476. 16	1.9077	699.21	799.1	898.98	998.87	1198.6
385	455	444	768.1	1510.62	1.9667	720.83	823.81	926.79	1029.8	1235.7
390	460	467	762.3	1545.08	2.0269	742.90	849.03	955.16	1061.3	1273.5
395	465	490	756.4	1579.54	2.0882	765.37	874.71	984.04	1093.4	1312.1
400	470	515	750.3	1614.00	2.1511	788.42	901.05	1013.7	1126.3	1351.6
405	475	540	744.1	1657.66	2.2277	805.00	933.14	1049.8	1166.4	1399.7
410	480	566	737.8	1701.32	2.3059	845.16	965.9	1086.6	1207.4	1448.8
415	485	593	731.1	1744.98	2 3861	874.55	999.49	1124.4	1249.4	1499.2
420	490	622	724.7	1788.64	2.4681	904.61	1033.8	1163.1	1292.3	1550.8
425	495	681	718.0	1832.30	2.5519	935.32	1068.9	1202.6	1336.2	1603.4
430	500	681	711.1	1875.96	2.6381	966.92	1108.0	1243.2	1381.3	1657.6
435	505	712	704.1	1919.62	2.7263	999.24	1142.0	1284.7	1427.8	1713.0
440	510	745	696.9	1963.28	2.8172	1032.6	1 180.1	1327.6	1475.1	1770.1
445	515	778	689.6	2006.94	2.9103	1066.7	1219.1	1371.4	1523.8	1828.6
450	520	813	682.1	2050.6	3.0063	1101.9	1259.3	1407.0	1574.1	1888.9
455	525	848	674.6	2104.54	3.1197	1143.4	1306.8	1470.1	1633.5	1960.2
460	530	885	666.8	2158.48	3.2371	1186.5	1356	1525.5	1694.9	2033.9
465	535	923	659.0	2212.42	3.3572	1230.5	1406.3	1582.0	1757.8	2109.4
470	540	963	651.0	2266.36	3.4814	1276	1458.3	1 640.6	1822.9	2187.4
475	545	1003	642.8	2320.30	3.6097	1323.0	1512.0	1701.0	1890.0	2268.0
480	550	1045	634.5	2374.24	3.7419	1371.5	1567.4	1763.3	1959.3	2351.1
485	555	1089	626.1	2428.18	3.8783	1421.5	1624.5	1927.6	2030.7	2436.8
490	560	1133	617.5	2482.12	4.0196	1473.3	1683.7	1894.2	2104.7	2525.6
495	565	1180	608.7	2536.06	4.1664	1527.1	1745.2	1963.4	2181.5	2617.8
500	570	1228	599.7	2590.00	4.3188	1582.9	1809.1	2035.2	2261.3	2713.6

Heat Loss from Insulated Pipe.—For pipe covering in single thickness, the heat loss from hot pipes can be expressed as

$$q_1 = \frac{K(T_i - T_o)}{r_2 \ln\left(\dfrac{r_2}{r_1}\right)} \qquad (24)$$

where q_1 = heat loss Btu/ft^2-hr outer surface of insulation;

K = conductivity of insulation, Btu/ft^2-hr-°F-inch thickness;

T_i = temperature of inner surface of insulation, °F;

T_o = temperature of outer surface of insulation, °F;

r_2 = radius of outer surface of insulation, in.; and

r_1 = radius of inner surface of insulation or outer surface of pipes, in.

The objection to the practical application of this formula is that the temperature of the outer surface of the insulation must be known. A more useful formula is

$$q_2 = \frac{(T_p - T_a)}{\dfrac{r_2 \ln\left(\dfrac{r_2}{r_1}\right)}{K} + \dfrac{1}{f_o}} \qquad (25)$$

where q_2 = heat loss Btu/ft^2-hr outer surface of insulation;

T_p = temperature of pipe surface, °F;

T_a = temperature of ambient air, °F;

r_2 = radius of outer surface of insulation, in.;

r_1 = radius of outer surfaces of pipe, in.;

k = conductivity of insulation, Btu/ft^2-hr-°F-in. thickness; and

f_o = surface conductance of outer surface of insulation, Btu/ft^2-hr-°F.

Since in most cases the user knows or can assume the temperature of the ambient air, Equation (25) is more readily applicable than Equation (24).

For very low air movements and low rates of heat transmission the value of $1/f_o$ can be taken at 0.6.

The heat loss figure is usually, in actual problems, desired in Btu/lineal ft of pipe rather than in terms of Btu/ft^2 of outer surface of radiation. The outer surface of insulation per lineal foot of pipe is $\dfrac{2\pi r_2}{12}$ so that the formula becomes

$$q_2 = \frac{0.523\, r_2 (T_p - T_a)}{\dfrac{r_2 \ln\left(\dfrac{r_2}{r_1}\right)}{K} + 0.60} \qquad (26)$$

where q_2 = heat loss, Btu/hr-lineal foot of pipe;

r_2 = outer radius of insulation, in.;

r_1 = outer radius of pipe, in.;

T_p = temperature of pipe, °F; and

T_a = temperature of ambient air, °F.

Equation (26) was used to calculate the tables that follow, which show the heat loss for a range of values of K and a range of values for $(T_p - T_a)$.

The problem becomes more complicated when two or more separate layers of pipe insulation are applied. The equation for this condition is

$$q_2 = \frac{(T_p - T_a)}{\dfrac{r_n \ln\dfrac{r_1}{r_p}}{k_1} + \dfrac{r_n \ln\dfrac{r_2}{r_1}}{k_2} + \ldots + \dfrac{r_n \ln\left(\dfrac{r_n}{r_{n-1}}\right)}{k_n} + \dfrac{1}{f_o}}$$

where q_2, T_p, T_a and f_o are as given for Equation (26) and r_1, $r_2 \ldots r_n$ = outer radius, in inches, of first, second, and nth layer of insulation, respectively; r_p= outer radius of pipe, inches; k_1, $k_2 \ldots k_n$ = conductivity of first, second, and nth layer of insulation, respectively.

The problem of two or more layers of insulation occurs more frequently in high temperature work where, for example, the temperature may be too high for 85% magnesia, so that the first layer may be of calcium silicate or diatomaceous silica.

Values of K.—The thermal conductivity K for specific insulations is available from manufacturers and it is suggested that calculations be based on data that apply to the material and brand name of the insulation to be used. In the absence of such data, Table 9-131 is included as a rough guide. Mean temperatures in Table 9-131 are arithmetic means between the inside surface and outside surface of insulation.

Effect of Air Velocity: The accompanying tables of heat transmitted through insulated pipe were calculated on the basis of still air with a value of $1/f_o = 0.60$. Actually the surface resistance decreases as the air movement increases and as the rate of heat transfer is increased. The effect of air movement on surface resistance is given in Table 9-130.

**Table 9-130. Effect of Air Velocity
on Surface Resistance.**

Heat Transmitted Btu /ft²-hr	Velocity of Air, ft/min			
	0	100	200	400
	Value of $1/f_o$			
0	…	0.56	0.50	0.41
50	0.60	0.52	0.45	0.39
100	0.55	0.48	0.41	0.36
150	0.50	0.45	0.39	0.34
200	0.48	0.42	0.37	0.32
300	0.43	0.38	0.33	0.29
500	0.36	0.33	0.28	0.25

Cold Surface Temperature.—If insulated piping is located where people or animals may come in contact with it, the criterion of economical heat loss in selecting insulation may be outweighed by the need to maintain outside insulation surface temperature at a safe level. The equation

$$T_o = T_i - \left[\frac{\frac{x}{K}}{\frac{x}{K}+\frac{l}{f_o}}\right](T_i - T_a) \qquad (27)$$

gives the temperature of the outside surface of insulation, T_o, or cold surface temperature in terms of T_i, T_a, K, f_o, as already defined, and x, the thickness of insulation in inches.

Example 19: 4-in. pipe, carrying water at 300°F is to be insulated with 2 in. of 85% magnesia whose density is 12 lb/ft³. What will be the cold surface temperature of the insulation?

Solution:

$T_i = 300$

$T_a = 70$ (assumed)

$x = 2$

$K = 0.38$ from Table 135 and assuming a mean temperature of 200 deg

$\frac{l}{f_o} = 0.60$

Substituting in Equation (27)

$$T_o = 300 - \left[\frac{\frac{2}{0.38}}{\frac{2}{0.38}+0.6}\right](300-70)$$

$$= (300 - 206)$$

$$= 94°F$$

Since the assumption of a mean temperature of 200°F was based on the assumption of a cold surface temperature on the order of 100°F, it can be further assumed that the result of 94°F for the cold surface temperature is accurate enough for the purpose of gaging whether humans or animals would be endangered by contact. Should the assumption and the result be very different, one would take the first result as a better approximation in assuming a mean temperature for purposes of selecting a value for K in Equation (27).

**Table 9-131. Heat Conductivity of Pipe Insulating Materials
(values to be used in the absence of specific data for the exact material and brand name used)**

Insulation	Approx. Use Range, °F	Approx. Density lb/ft³	Mean Temperature, °F							
			100	200	300	400	500	600	700	800
			Conductivity, K, Btu/ft²-hr-°F-inch thickness							
85% Magnesia	600	11	0.35	0.38	0.42	0.46	…	…	…	…
Laminated asbestos	700	30	0.40	0.45	0.50	0.55	…	…	…	…
4 Ply corrugated asbestos	300	12	0.57	0.62	…	…	…	…	…	…
Molded asbestos	1000	16	0.33	0.43	0.48	0.53	0.58	…	…	…
Mineral fiber, wire reinforced	1000	10	0.29	0.35	0.42	0.49	0.56	0.63	…	…
Diatomaceous silica	1600	22	…	…	…	0.64	0.66	0.68	0.70	0.72
Calcium silicate	1200	11	0.32	0.37	0.42	0.46	0.51	0.56	…	…
Mineral fiber, molded	350	9	0.26	0.31	0.39	…	…	…	…	…
Mineral fiber, fine fiber, molded	350	3	0.23	0.27	0.31	…	…	…	…	…
Wool felt	225	20	0.33	0.37	…	…	…	…	…	…

Table 9-132. Heat Loss Through Pipe Insulation – ¾ Inch Steel Pipe

Insulation Conduc tivity K	Temperature Difference, Pipe to Air, °F										
	30	50	80	110	140	170	200	230	260	290	320
	Heat Loss per Lineal Foot of Bare Pipe, Btu/hr										
	15	27	50	74	100	131	163	199	238	280	325
	Heat Loss per Lineal Foot of Insulated Pipe, Btu/hr										
1 Inch Thick Insulation – ¾ Inch Pipe											
0.20	2	6	7	10	13	16	18	21	24	27	29
0.25	3	6	9	12	16	19	23	26	29	33	36
0.30	4	7	11	15	19	23	27	31	35	39	43
0.35	5	8	12	17	21	26	30	35	40	44	49
0.40	5	9	14	19	24	29	34	39	44	50	55
0.45	6	10	15	21	27	32	38	44	49	55	61
0.50	6	10	17	23	29	35	42	48	54	60	67
0.55	7	11	18	25	32	38	45	52	59	65	72
0.60	7	12	19	27	34	41	48	56	63	70	77
1½ Inch Thick Insulation – ¾ Inch Pipe											
0.20	2	4	6	8	10	12	14	16	19	21	23
0.25	3	5	7	10	13	16	18	21	24	27	29
0.30	3	5	9	12	15	19	22	25	28	32	35
0.35	4	6	10	14	18	21	25	29	33	37	40
0.40	4	7	11	16	20	24	29	33	37	41	46
0.45	5	8	13	17	22	27	32	37	41	46	51
0.50	5	9	14	19	25	30	35	40	46	51	56
0.55	6	10	15	21	27	32	38	44	49	55	61
0.60	6	10	16	23	29	35	41	47	53	59	66
2 Inch Thick Insulation – ¾ Inch Pipe											
0.20	2	3	5	7	9	11	13	15	17	19	21
0.25	2	4	6	9	11	14	16	18	21	23	26
0.30	3	5	8	11	13	16	19	22	25	28	31
0.35	3	6	9	12	16	19	22	26	29	32	36
0.40	4	6	10	14	18	21	25	29	33	37	40
0.45	4	7	11	16	20	24	28	32	37	41	45
0.50	5	8	12	17	22	26	31	36	40	45	50
0.55	5	8	14	19	24	29	34	39	44	49	54
0.60	5	9	15	20	26	31	37	42	48	53	59
2½ Inch Thick Insulation – ¾ Inch Pipe											
0.20	2	3	5	6	8	10	12	13	15	17	19
0.25	2	3	5	7	9	11	13	15	17	19	21
0.30	3	4	7	10	12	15	17	20	23	25	28
0.35	3	5	8	11	14	17	20	23	26	29	32
0.40	3	6	9	13	16	20	23	26	30	33	37
0.45	3	6	10	14	18	22	26	29	33	37	41
0.50	4	7	11	16	20	24	28	33	37	41	45
0.55	5	8	12	17	22	26	31	36	40	45	50
0.60	5	8	13	18	24	29	34	10	44	49	54

Table 9-133. Heat Loss Through Pipe Insulation – 1 Inch Steel Pipe

Insulation Conductivity K	Temperature Difference, Pipe to Air, °F										
	30	50	80	110	140	170	200	230	260	290	320
	Heat Loss per Lineal Foot of Bare Pipe, Btu/hr										
	19	34	61	90	123	160	199	243	292	343	399
	Heat Loss per Lineal Foot of Insulated Pipe, Btu/hr										
1 Inch Thick Insulation – 1 Inch Pipe											
0.20	3	5	8	12	15	18	21	24	27	30	34
0.25	4	6	10	14	18	23	26	30	34	37	41
0.30	5	8	12	17	21	26	30	35	40	44	49
0.35	5	9	14	19	24	30	35	40	45	50	56
0.40	6	10	16	22	27	33	39	45	51	57	63
0.45	7	11	17	24	30	37	43	50	56	63	69
0.50	7	12	19	26	33	40	47	55	62	69	76
0.55	8	13	20	28	36	44	51	59	67	74	82
0.60	8	14	22	30	39	47	55	63	72	80	88
1½ Inch Thick Insulation – 1 Inch Pipe											
0.20	2	4	7	9	12	14	17	19	22	24	27
0.25	3	5	8	11	15	18	21	24	27	30	33
0.30	4	6	10	14	17	21	25	29	32	36	40
0.35	4	7	11	16	20	24	29	33	37	41	46
0.40	5	8	13	18	23	27	32	37	42	47	52
0.45	5	9	14	20	25	31	36	41	47	52	58
0.50	6	10	16	22	28	33	39	45	51	57	63
0.55	6	11	17	24	30	37	43	49	56	62	69
0.60	7	12	19	26	32	39	46	53	60	67	74
2 Inch Thick Insulation – 1 Inch Pipe											
0.20	2	4	6	8	10	13	15	17	19	21	24
0.25	3	5	7	10	13	15	18	21	23	26	29
0.30	3	5	9	12	15	18	21	25	28	31	34
0.35	4	6	10	14	17	21	25	29	32	36	40
0.40	4	7	11	15	20	24	28	32	37	41	45
0.45	5	8	13	17	22	27	31	36	41	46	50
0.50	5	9	14	19	24	29	35	40	45	50	55
0.55	6	9	15	21	26	32	38	43	49	55	60
0.60	6	10	16	23	29	35	41	47	53	59	66
2½ Inch Thick Insulation – 1 Inch Pipe											
0.20	2	3	5	7	9	11	13	15	17	19	21
0.25	3	4	7	10	12	15	17	20	23	25	28
0.30	3	5	8	11	14	16	19	22	25	28	31
0.35	3	6	9	12	0	19	22	26	29	32	36
0.40	4	6	10	14	18	22	26	29	33	37	41
0.45	4	7	11	16	20	24	29	33	37	41	46
0.50	5	8	13	17	22	27	32	36	41	46	51
0.55	5	9	14	19	24	29	34	40	45	50	55
0.60	6	9	15	21	26	32	37	43	49	54	60

Table 9-134. Heat Loss Through Pipe Insulation – 1¼ Inch Steel Pipe

Insulation Conductivity K	Temperature Difference, Pipe to Air, °F										
	30	50	80	110	140	170	200	230	260	290	320
	Heat Loss per Lineal Foot of Bare Pipe, Btu/hr										
	23	42	75	111	152	198	248	302	362	427	496
	Heat Loss per Lineal Foot of Insulated Pipe, Btu/hr										
1 Inch Thick Insulation – 1¼ Inch Pipe											
0.20	4	6	10	14	17	21	25	28	32	36	39
0.25	5	8	12	17	21	26	30	35	39	44	48
0.30	5	9	14	19	25	30	35	41	46	51	57
0.35	6	10	16	22	28	35	41	47	53	59	65
0.40	7	11	18	25	32	39	46	52	59	66	73
0.45	8	13	20	28	35	43	50	58	66	73	81
0.50	8	14	22	30	39	47	55	63	72	80	88
0.55	9	15	24	33	42	50	59	68	77	86	95
0.60	10	16	26	35	45	54	64	73	83	92	102
1½ Inch Thick Insulation – 1¼ Inch Pipe											
0.20	3	5	8	11	14	16	19	22	25	28	31
0.25	4	6	10	13	17	20	24	27	31	35	38
0.30	4	7	11	16	20	24	28	32	37	41	45
0.35	5	8	13	18	23	28	33	37	42	47	52
0.40	6	9	15	20	26	31	37	42	48	53	59
0.45	6	10	16	23	29	35	41	47	53	59	66
0.50	7	11	18	25	32	38	45	52	59	65	72
0.55	7	12	20	27	34	42	49	56	64	71	78
0.60	8	13	21	29	37	45	53	61	69	77	84
2 Inch Thick Insulation – 1¼ Inch Pipe											
0.20	2	4	7	9	12	4	17	19	21	24	26
0.25	3	5	8	11	14	17	20	23	27	30	33
0.30	4	6	10	13	17	21	24	28	32	35	39
0.35	4	7	11	16	19	24	28	32	37	41	45
0.40	5	8	13	18	22	27	32	37	42	47	51
0.45	5	9	14	20	25	30	36	41	46	52	57
0.50	6	10	16	22	27	33	39	45	51	57	63
0.55	6	11	17	24	30	36	43	49	56	62	68
0.60	7	12	19	26	32	39	46	53	60	67	74
2½ Inch Thick Insulation – 1¼ Inch Pipe											
0.20	2	4	6	8	10	12	15	17	19	21	23
0.25	3	5	7	10	13	16	18	21	24	26	29
0.30	3	5	9	12	15	19	22	25	28	32	35
0.35	4	6	10	14	18	21	25	29	33	37	40
0.40	4	7	11	16	20	24	29	33	37	41	46
0.45	5	8	13	18	22	27	32	37	42	46	51
0.50	5	9	14	19	25	30	35	41	46	51	57
0.55	6	10	15	21	27	33	39	44	50	56	62
0.60	6	11	17	23	29	36	42	48	55	61	67

Table 9-135. Heat Loss Through Pipe Insulation – 1½ Inch Steel Pipe

Insulation Conductivity K	Temperature Difference, Pipe to Air, °F										
	30	50	80	110	140	170	200	230	260	290	320
	Heat Loss per Lineal Foot of Bare Pipe, Btu/hr										
	27	48	185	126	173	224	280	343	410	483	563
	Heat Loss per Lineal ft of Insulated Pipe, Btu/hr										
1 Inch Thick Insulation – 1½ Inch Pipe											
0.20	4	7	11	15	19	23	27	31	35	39	43
0.25	5	8	13	18	23	28	32	37	42	47	52
0.30	6	10	16	21	27	33	39	45	50	56	62
0.35	7	11	18	24	31	38	44	51	58	64	71
0.40	7	12	20	27	35	42	50	57	65	72	80
0.45	8	14	22	30	39	47	55	63	72	80	88
0.50	9	15	24	33	42	51	60	69	78	87	96
0.55	10	16	2.6	36	46	55	65	75	85	94	104
0.60	10	17	28	38	49	59	70	80	90	100	111
1½ Inch Thick Insulation – 1½ Inch Pipe											
0.20	3	5	8	12	15	18	21	24	27	30	34
0.25	4	7	10	14	18	22	26	30	34	38	42
0.30	5	8	12	17	22	26	31	35	40	45	49
0.35	5	9	14	19	25	30	35	41	46	51	57
0.40	6	10	16	22	28	34	40	46	52	58	64
0.45	7	11	18	25	31	38	45	51	58	65	71
0.50	7	12	20	27	34	41	49	56	63	71	78
0.55	8	13	21	29	37	45	53	61	69	77	85
0.60	9	14	23	32	40	49	57	66	75	83	92
2 Inch Thick Insulation – 1½ Inch Pipe											
0.20	3	4	7	10	12	15	18	20	23	25	28
0.25	3	6	9	12	15	19	22	25	29	32	35
0.30	4	7	10	14	18	22	26	30	34	38	42
0.35	5	8	12	17	21	26	30	35	44	49	53
0.40	5	9	14	19	24	29	34	40	45	50	55
0.45	6	10	15	21	27	33	38	44	50	56	61
0.50	6	11	17	23	30	36	43	49	55	62	68
0.55	7	12	18	25	32	39	46	53	60	67	74
0.60	8	13	20	28	35	43	50	58	65	73	80
2½ Inch Thick Insulation – 1½ Inch Pipe											
0.20	2	4	6	9	11	13	16	18	21	23	25
0.25	3	5	8	11	14	17	20	23	25	28	31
0.30	4	6	9	13	16	20	23	27	30	34	37
0.35	4	7	11	15	19	23	27	31	35	39	44
0.40	5	8	12	17	22	26	31	35	40	45	49
0.45	5	9	14	19	24	29	34	40	45	50	55
0.50	6	10	15	21	27	32	38	44	40	55	61
0.55	6	10	17	23	29	35	42	48	54	60	72
0.60	7	11	18	25	32	38	45	52	59	65	72

Table 9-136. Heat Loss Through Pipe Insulation – 2 Inch Steel Pipe

Insulation Conductivity K	Temperature Difference, Pipe to Air, °F										
	30	50	80	110	140	170	200	230	260	290	320
	Heat Loss per Lineal Foot of Bare Pipe, Btu/hr										
	33	59	104	154	212	275	344	420	503	594	692
	Heat Loss per Lineal Foot of Insulated Pipe, Btu/hr										
1 Inch Thick Insulation – 2 Inch Pipe											
0.20	5	8	13	17	22	27	32	36	41	46	51
0.25	6	10	15	21	27	32	39	44	50	56	62
0.30	7	11	18	25	32	39	45	52	59	66	73
0.35	8	13	21	29	36	44	52	60	68	75	83
0.40	9	15	23	32	41	49	58	67	76	84	93
0.45	10	16	26	35	45	55	64	74	83	93	103
0.50	10	18	28	39	49	60	70	81	91	102	112
0.55	11	19	30	42	53	64	76	87	99	110	121
0.60	12	20	32	45	57	69	81	93	106	118	130
1½ Inch Thick Insulation – 2 Inch Pipe											
0.20	4	6	10	13	17	21	24	28	32	35	39
0.25	5	8	12	17	21	26	30	35	39	44	48
0.30	5	9	14	20	25	30	36	41	46	52	57
0.35	6	10	16	23	29	35	41	47	53	59	66
0.40	7	12	18	25	32	39	46	53	60	67	74
0.45	8	13	21	28	36	44	51	59	67	75	82
0.50	9	15	23	32	41	49	58	67	75	84	93
0.55	9	15	25	34	43	52	61	71	80	89	98
0.60	10	17	26	36	46	55	66	76	83	96	106
2 Inch Thick Insulation – 2 Inch Pipe											
0.20	3	5	8	11	14	17	20	23	27	30	33
0.25	4	6	10	14	18	22	25	29	33	37	41
0.30	4	8	12	17	21	26	30	35	39	44	48
0.35	5	9	14	19	24	30	35	40	45	50	56
0.40	6	10	16	22	28	33	39	45	51	57	63
0.45	7	11	18	24	31	37	44	51	57	64	70
0.50	7	12	19	27	34	41	48	56	63	70	77
0.55	8	13	21	29	37	45	53	61	69	77	84
0.60	9	14	23	31	40	49	57	66	74	83	92
2½ Inch Thick Insulation – 2 Inch Pipe											
0.20	3	5	7	10	13	15	18	21	23	26	29
0.25	3	6	9	12	16	19	22	26	29	32	36
0.30	4	7	11	15	19	23	27	31	35	39	43
0.35	5	8	12	17	22	26	31	35	40	45	49
0.40	5	9	14	19	25	30	35	40	46	51	56
0.45	6	10	16	22	27	33	39	45	51	57	63
0.50	6	11	17	24	30	37	43	50	56	63	69
0.55	7	12	19	26	33	40	48	54	61	68	76
0.60	8	13	21	29	37	45	53	61	69	77	85

Table 9-137. Heat Loss Through Pipe Insulation – 2½ Inch Steel Pipe

Insulation Conduc tivity K	Temperature Difference, Pipe to Air, °F										
	30	50	8o	110	140	170	200	230	260	290	320
	Heat Loss per Lineal Foot of Bare Pipe, Btu/hr										
	39	70	123	184	252	327	410	502	600	709	827
	Heat Loss per Lineal Foot of Insulated Pipe, Btu/hr										
1 Inch Thick Insulation – 2½ Inch Pipe											
0.20	5	9	14	20	25	31	36	42	47	52	58
0.25	7	11	18	24	31	38	44	51	57	64	71
0.30	8	13	21	29	36	44	52	60	68	75	83
0.35	9	15	24	33	42	50	59	68	77	86	95
0.40	10	17	27	37	47	57	67	77	87	97	107
0.45	11	18	29	40	52	63	74	85	96	107	118
0.50	12	21	33	45	57	70	82	94	107	119	131
0.55	13	22	35	48	61	74	87	100	113	126	139
0.60	14	23	37	51	65	79	93	106	120	134	148
1½ Inch Thick Insulation – 2½ Inch Pipe											
0.20	4	7	11	15	19	24	28	32	36	40	44
0.25	5	9	14	19	24	29	34	39	44	50	55
0.30	6	10	16	22	28	35	41	47	53	59	65
0.35	7	12	19	26	33	40	47	54	61	68	75
0.40	8	13	21	29	37	45	53	61	69	77	84
0.45	9	15	23	32	41	50	59	67	76	85	94
0.50	10	16	26	35	45	55	64	74	83	93	103
0.55	10	17	28	38	49	59	70	80	91	101	112
0.60	11	19	30	41	53	64	75	86	98	109	120
2 Inch Thick Insulation – 2½ Inch Pipe											
0.20	3	6	9	13	16	20	23	26	30	33	37
0.25	4	7	11	16	20	24	29	33	37	41	46
0.30	5	9	14	19	24	29	34	39	44	49	54
0.35	6	10	16	22	27	33	39	45	51	57	63
0.40	7	11	18	24	31	38	44	51	58	64	71
0.45	7	12	20	27	35	42	50	57	64	72	79
0.50	8	14	22	30	38	46	58	63	71	79	87
0.55	9	15	24	33	42	50	59	68	77	86	95
0.60	10	16	26	35	45	55	64	74	84	93	103
2½ Inch Thick Insulation – 2½ Inch Pipe											
0.20	3	5	8	11	14	17	20	23	26	29	32
0.25	4	6	10	14	18	21	25	29	33	36	40
0.30	4	7	12	16	21	25	30	34	39	43	48
0.35	5	9	14	19	24	29	35	40	45	50	55
0.40	6	10	16	22	27	33	39	45	51	57	63
0.45	7	11	18	24	31	37	44	50	57	64	70
0.50	7	12	19	27	34	41	48	55	63	70	77
0.55	8	13	21	29	37	45	53	61	69	77	84
0.60	9	14	23	31	40	49	57	66	74	83	92

Table 9-138. Heat Loss Through Pipe Insulation – 3 Inch Steel Pipe

Insulation Conductivity K	Temperature Difference, Pipe to Air,°F										
	30	50	80	110	140	170	200	230	260	290	320
	Heat Loss per Lineal Foot of Bare Pipe, Btu/hr										
	46	84	148	221	303	393	493	601	721	852	994
	Heat Loss per Lineal ft of Insulated Pipe, Btu/hr										
1 Inch Thick Insulation – 3 Inch Pipe											
0.20	6	11	17	23	30	36	42	49	55	61	68
0.25	8	13	21	28	36	44	52	60	67	75	83
0.30	9	15	24	33	43	52	61	70	79	88	97
0.35	10	17	28	38	49	59	69	80	90	101	111
0.40	12	19	31	43	54	66	78	89	101	113	124
0.45	13	21	34	47	60	73	86	99	111	124	137
0.50	14	23	37	51	65	79	93	107	121	135	149
0.55	15	25	40	55	71	86	101	116	131	146	161
0.60	16	27	43	59	76	92	108	124	140	156	173
1½ Inch Thick Insulation – 3 Inch Pipe											
0.20	5	8	13	18	22	27	32	37	41	46	51
0.25	6	10	16	22	27	33	39	45	51	57	63
0.30	7	12	19	26	33	39	46	53	60	67	74
0.35	8	13	22	30	39	46	54	62	70	78	86
0.40	9	15	24	33	42	51	60	69	78	87	96
0.45	10	17	27	37	47	57	67	77	87	97	107
0.50	11	18	29	40	51	62	73	84	95	106	117
0.55	12	20	32	44	56	68	80	92	104	116	128
0.60	13	21	34	47	60	73	86	99	112	124	137
2 Inch Thick Insulation – 3 Inch Pipe											
0.20	4	7	11	15	18	22	26	30	34	38	42
0.25	5	8	13	18	23	28	33	38	43	47	52
0.30	6	10	15	21	27	33	39	45	51	56	62
0.35	7	11	18	25	31	38	45	52	58	65	72
0.40	8	13	20	28	36	43	51	58	66	74	81
0.45	8	14	23	31	40	48	57	65	74	82	91
0.50	9	15	25	34	44	53	62	72	81	90	100
0.55	10	17	27	37	48	58	68	78	88	98	109
0.60	11	18	29	40	51	62	73	84	95	106	117
2½ Inch Thick Insulation – 3 Inch Pipe											
0.20	3	6	9	12	16	19	23	26	29	33	36
0.25	4	7	11	0	20	24	28	33	37	41	45
0.30	5	8	13	19	24	29	34	39	44	49	54
0.35	6	10	16	22	27	33	39	45	51	57	63
0.40	7	11	18	24	31	38	44	51	58	64	71
0.45	7	12	20	27	35	42	50	57	64	72	79
0.50	8	14	22	30	38	46	55	63	71	79	87
0.55	9	15	24	33	42	51	60	69	78	87	96
0.60	10	16	26	36	45	55	65	74	84	94	103

Table 9-139. Heat Loss Through Pipe Insulation – 3½ Inch Steel Pipe

Insulation Conduc tivity K	Temperature Difference, Pipe to Air, °F										
	30	50	180	110	140	170	200	230	260	290	320
	Heat Loss per Lineal Foot of Bare Pipe, Btu per Hour										
	52	195	168	250	342	444	556	680	816	964	1125
	Heat Loss per Lineal ft of Insulated Pipe, Btu/hr										
1 Inch Thick Insulation – 3½ Inch Pipe											
0.20	7	12	19	26	33	40	47	54	61	68	75
0.25	9	14	23	32	40	49	57	66	75	83	92
0.30	10	17	27	37	47	57	67	78	88	98	108
0.35	12	19	31	42	54	65	77	89	100	112	123
0.40	13	22	34	47	60	73	86	99	112	125	138
0.45	14	24	38	52	67	81	95	109	124	138	152
0.50	16	26	41	57	72	88	104	119	135	150	166
0.55	17	28	45	61	78	95	112	128	145	162	179
0.60	18	30	48	66	84	102	119	137	155	173	191
1½ Inch Thick Insulation – 3½ Inch Pipe											
0.20	5	9	14	19	25	30	35	41	46	51	56
0.25	7	11	17	24	30	37	43	50	56	63	70
0.30	8	13	21	28	36	44	51	59	67	75	82
0.35	9	15	24	33	41	50	59	68	77	86	95
0.40	10	17	27	37	47	57	67	77	87	97	107
0.45	11	19	30	41	52	63	74	85	96	107	118
0.50	12	20	32	45	57	69	81	93	105	118	130
0.55	13	22	35	48	62	75	88	101	114	128	141
0.60	14	24	38	52	66	81	95	109	123	138	152
2 Inch Thick Insulation – 3½ Inch Pipe											
0.20	4	7	12	16	20	25	29	33	38	42	46
0.25	5	9	14	20	25	30	36	41	47	52	57
0.30	6	11	17	23	30	36	43	49	55	62	68
0.35	7	12	20	27	34	42	49	56	64	71	79
0.40	8	14	22	31	39	47	56	64	72	81	89
0.45	9	15	25	34	43	53	62	71	80	90	99
0.50	10	17	27	37	48	58	68	78	89	99	109
0.55	11	19	30	41	52	63	74	85	96	108	119
0.60	12	20	32	44	56	68	80	92	104	116	128
2½ Inch Thick Insulation – 3½ Inch Pipe											
0.20	4	6	10	14	18	21	25	29	33	36	40
0.25	5	8	12	17	22	26	31	36	40	45	50
0.30	6	9	15	20	26	31	37	43	48	54	59
0.35	6	11	17	24	30	36	43	49	56	62	68
0.40	7	12	19	27	34	41	49	56	63	70	78
0.45	8	14	22	30	38	46	54	62	70	79	87
0.50	9	15	24	33	42	51	60	69	78	87	96
0.55	10	16	26	36	46	55	65	75	85	95	104
0.60	11	18	28	39	49	60	71	81	92	102	113

Table 9-140. Heat Loss Through Pipe Insulation – 4 Inch Steel Pipe

Insulation Conductivity K	Temperature Difference, Pipe to Air,°F										
	30	50	80	110	140	170	200	230	270	300	320
	Heat Loss per Lineal Foot of Bare Pipe, Btu/hr										
	59	106	187	278	381	496	621	759	911	1076	1257
	Heat Loss per Lineal Foot of Insulated Pipe, Btu/hr										
1 Inch Thick Insulation – 4 Inch Pipe											
0.20	8	13	20	28	33	43	51	59	66	74	82
0.25	10	16	25	35	44	54	63	73	82	92	101
0.30	11	19	30	41	52	63	74	86	97	108	119
0.35	13	21	34	47	59	72	85	98	110	123	136
0.40	14	24	38	52	66	81	95	109	123	137	152
0.45	16	26	42	58	73	89	105	121	136	182	168
0.50	17	28	45	62	80	97	114	131	148	165	182
0.55	18	31	49	67	86	104	123	141	159	178	196
0.6	20	33	53	72	92	112	132	151	171	191	211
1½ Inch Thick Insulation – 4 Inch Pipe											
0.20	6	10	15	21	27	33	38	44	50	56	61
0.25	7	12	19	26	33	40	47	55	62	69	76
0.30	8	14	22	28	39	48	56	64	73	81	90
0.35	10	16	26	36	45	55	65	74	84	94	103
0.4	11	18	29	40	51	62	73	84	95	106	116
0.45	12	20	32	44	56	69	81	93	105	117	129
0.5	13	22	35	49	62	75	88	101	115	128	141
0.55	14	24	38	53	67	81	96	110	124	139	153
0.6	15	26	41	57	72	88	103	118	134	149	165
2 Inch Thick Insulation – 4 Inch Pipe											
0.20	5	8	13	17	22	27	31	36	41	46	50
0.25	6	10	16	21	27	33	39	45	51	57	62
0.30	7	12	19	26	32	39	46	53	60	67	74
0.35	8	13	21	29	37	45	53	61	69	77	85
0.40	9	15	24	33	42	51	60	69	79	88	97
0.45	10	17	27	37	47	57	67	78	88	98	108
0.50	11	19	30	41	52	63	74	85	96	107	118
0.55	12	20	32	44	56	69	81	93	105	117	129
0.60	13	22	35	48	61	74	87	101	114	127	140
2½ Inch Thick Insulation – 4 Inch Pipe											
0.20	4	7	11	15	19	23	27	31	35	39	44
0.25	5	8	13	18	24	29	34	39	44	49	54
0.30	6	10	16	22	28	34	40	46	52	58	64
0.35	7	12	19	26	32	39	46	53	60	67	74
0.40	8	13	21	29	37	45	52	60	68	76	84
0.45	9	15	24	32	41	50	59	68	76	85	94
0.50	10	16	26	36	45	55	65	75	84	94	104
0.55	11	18	28	39	49	60	71	81	92	102	113
0.60	11	19	31	42	53	65	76	88	99	111	122

Table 9-141. Heat Loss Through Pipe Insulation – 5 Inch Steel Pipe

Insulation Conductivity K	Temperature Difference, Pipe to Air, °F										
	30	50	80	110	140	170	200	230	260	1290	320
	Heat Loss per Lineal Foot of Bare Pipe, Btu/hr										
	71	129	1227	339	464	603	755	924	1109	1311	1532
	Heat Loss per Lineal Foot of Insulated Pipe, Btu/hr										
1 Inch Thick Insulation – 5 Inch Pipe											
0.20	8	14	23	31	40	48	57	65	74	82	90
0.25	10	17	28	38	48	59	69	79	90	100	110
0.30	12	20	32	45	57	69	81	93	105	117	130
0.35	14	23	37	51	65	79	93	106	120	134	148
0.40	15	26	41	57	73	88	104	119	135	150	166
0.45	17	29	46	63	80	97	114	131	148	165	182
0.50	16	31	50	68	87	106	124	143	180	199	217
0.55	20	34	54	74	94	114	134	154	174	194	214
0.60	21	36	57	79	100	122	143	165	186	208	229
1½ Inch Thick Insulation – 5 Inch Pipe											
0.20	6	11	17	23	30	36	42	49	55	61	68
0.25	8	13	21	29	37	44	52	60	68	76	84
0.30	9	15	25	34	43	53	62	71	80	90	99
0.35	11	18	28	39	50	60	71	82	92	103	114
0.40	12	20	32	44	56	68	80	92	104	116	128
0.45	13	22	36	49	62	75	89	102	115	129	142
0.50	15	24	39	53	68	83	97	112	126	141	156
0.55	16	26	42	58	74	90	106	121	137	153	169
0.60	17	28	45	62	80	97	114	131	148	165	182
2 Inch Thick Insulation – 5 Inch Pipe											
0.20	5	9	14	19	24	29	34	40	45	50	55
0.25	6	11	17	23	30	36	43	49	55	62	68
0.30	8	13	20	28	35	43	51	58	66	73	81
0.35	9	15	23	32	41	50	58	67	76	85	93
0.40	10	17	26	36	46	56	66	76	86	96	106
0.45	11	18	29	40	51	62	73	84	95	106	117
0.50	12	20	32	44	56	68	80	92	105	117	129
0.55	13	22	35	48	61	75	88	101	114	128	141
0.60	14	24	38	52	67	81	95	119	124	138	152
2½ Inch Thick Insulation – 5 Inch Pipe											
0.20	4	7	12	16	21	25	29	34	38	43	47
0.25	5	9	15	20	25	31	36	42	47	53	58
0.30	7	11	17	24	30	37	43	50	56	63	69
0.35	8	13	20	28	35	43	50	58	65	73	80
0.40	9	14	23	31	40	48	57	66	74	83	91
0.45	10	16	25	35	45	54	64	73	83	92	102
0.50	11	18	28	39	49	60	70	81	91	102	112
0.55	11	19	31	42	53	65	76	88	99	111	122
0.60	12	21	33	45	59	70	83	95	107	120	132

Table 9-142. Heat Loss Through Pipe Insulation – 6 Inch Steel Pipe

Insulation Conductivity K	Temperature Difference, Pipe to Air, °F										
	30	50	80	110	140	170	200	230	260	290	320
	Heat Loss per Lineal Foot of Bare Pipe, Btu/hr										
	84	151	267	398	546	709	890	1088	1306	1544	1806
	Heat Loss per Lineal Foot of Insulated Pipe, Btu/hr										
1 Inch Thick Insulation – 6 inch pipe											
0.20	11	18	29	40	51	61	72	83	94	105	115
0.25	13	22	35	48	62	75	88	101	114	128	141
0.30	15	26	41	57	72	88	103	119	134	150	165
0.35	18	29	47	65	82	100	118	135	153	171	188
0.40	20	33	53	72	92	112	132	151	171	191	211
0.45	22	36	58	80	102	123	145	167	189	210	232
0.50	24	39	63	87	110	134	158	181	205	229	252
0.55	25	42	68	93	119	144	170	195	221	246	272
0.6	27	45	73	100	127	154	182	209	236	263	291
1½ Inch Thick Insulation – 6 inch pipe											
0.20	8	13	21	29	37	45	53	61	69	77	85
0.25	10	16	26	36	45	55	65	75	84	94	104
0.30	12	19	31	42	54	65	77	88	100	111	123
0.35	13	22	35	49	62	75	88	101	115	128	141
0.40	15	25	40	55	70	84	99	114	129	144	159
0.45	17	28	44	61	77	94	110	127	143	160	176
0.50	18	30	48	66	84	103	121	139	157	175	193
0.55	20	33	52	72	92	111	131	151	170	190	209
0.60	21	35	56	77	99	120	141	162	183	204	225
2 Inch Thick Insulation – 6 inch pipe											
0.20	6	11	17	23	30	36	43	49	55	62	68
0.25	8	13	21	29	37	45	53	60	68	76	84
0.30	9	16	25	34	44	53	62	72	81	90	100
0.35	11	18	29	40	50	61	72	83	94	104	115
0.40	12	20	33	45	57	69	81	94	106	118	130
0.45	14	23	36	50	63	77	91	104	118	131	145
0.50	15	25	40	55	70	85	100	114	129	144	159
0.55	16	27	43	60	76	92	108	125	141	157	173
0,60	18	29	47	64	82	99	117	134	152	170	187
2½ Inch Thick Insulation – 6 inch pipe											
0.20	5	9	14	20	25	31	36	41	47	52	58
0.25	7	11	18	25	31	38	45	51	58	65	72
0.30	8	13	21	29	37	45	53	61	69	77	85
0.35	9	15	25	34	43	52	62	71	80	89	98
0.40	10	17	28	38	49	59	70	80	91	101	111
0.45	12	19	31	43	54	66	78	89	101	113	124
0.50	13	21	34	47	60	73	86	99	111	124	137
0.55	14	23	37	51	65	79	93	107	121	135	149
0.60	15	25	40	56	71	86	101	116	131	147	162

Table 9-143. Heat Loss Through Pipe Insulation – 8 Inch Steel Pipe

Insulation Conductivity *K*	Temperature Difference, Pipe to Air, °F										
	30	50	80	110	140	170	200	230	260	290	320
	Heat Loss per Lineal Foot of Bare Pipe, Btu/hr										
	107	194	341	509	1697	906	1137	1391	1671	1977	2312
	Heat Loss per Lineal ft of Insulated Pipe, Btu/hr										
1 Inch Thick Insulation – 8 Inch Pipe											
0.20	14	23	36	50	64	78	91	105	119	132	146
0.25	17	28	44	61	78	95	111	128	145	161	178
0.30	20	33	52	72	91	111	130	150	9	189	209
0.35	22	37	59	82	104	126	149	171	193	215	238
0.40	25	42	66	91	116	141	166	191	20	241	266
0.45	27	46	73	101	128	155	183	210	238	265	293
0.50	30	50	79	109	139	169	199	228	258	288	318
0.55	32	53	86	118	150	182	214	246	278	310	342
0.60	34	57	91	126	160	194	229	263	297	331	366
1½ Inch Thick Insulation – 8 Inch Pipe											
0.20	10	16	26	36	46	56	65	75	85	95	105
0.25	12	20	32	44	56	68	80	92	104	117	129
0.30	14	24	38	52	66	81	95	109	123	138	152
0.35	16	27	44	60	76	93	109	125	142	158	174
0.40	18	31	49	68	86	104	123	141	160	178	196
0.45	20	34	54	75	95	116	136	156	177	197	218
0.50	22	37	60	82	104	127	149	171	194	216	238
0.55	24	40	65	89	113	137	161	186	210	234	258
0.60	26	43	69	95	122	148	174	200	226	252	278
2 Inch Thick Insulation – 8 Inch Pipe											
0.20	8	13	21	29	37	45	53	61	68	76	84
0.25	10	16	26	36	46	55	65	75	85	94	104
0.30	12	19	31	42	54	66	77	89	100	112	124
0.35	13	22	36	49	62	76	89	102	116	129	142
0.40	15	25	40	55	70	85	101	116	131	146	161
0.45	17	28	45	62	78	95	112	129	145	162	179
0.50	18	31	49	68	86	104	123	141	160	178	197
0.55	20	33	53	74	94	114	134	154	174	194	214
0.60	22	36	58	79	101	123	144	166	187	209	231
2½ Inch Thick Insulation – 8 Inch Pipe											
0.20	7	11	18	24	31	37	44	51	57	64	71
0.25	8	14	22	30	38	46	55	63	71	79	87
0.30	10	16	26	36	45	55	65	75	84	94	104
0.35	11	19	30	41	53	64	75	86	98	109	120
0.40	13	21	34	47	60	72	85	98	111	123	136
0.45	14	24	38	52	66	81	95	109	123	138	152
0.50	15	26	42	57	73	89	104	120	136	151	167
0.55	17	28	46	63	80	97	114	131	148	165	182
0.60	18	31	49	68	86	105	123	142	160	179	197

Table 9-144. Heat Loss Through Pipe Insulation – 10 Inch Steel Pipe

Insulation Conductivity K	Temperature Difference, Pipe to Air, °F										
	30	50	80	110	140	170	200	230	260	290	320
	Heat Loss per Lineal Foot of Bare Pipe, Btu/hr										
	132	238	420	626	857	1114	1399	1714	2060	2437	2852
	Heat Loss per Lineal Foot of Insulated Pipe, Btu/hr										
1 Inch Thick Insulation – 10 inch pipe											
0.20	16	27	43	60	76	92	109	125	141	158	174
0.25	20	33	53	73	93	113	133	152	172	192	212
0.30	23	39	62	85	109	132	155	179	202	225	249
0.35	27	44	71	97	124	151	177	204	230	257	283
0.40	30	49	79	109	138	168	198	227	257	287	317
0.45	33	54	87	120	152	185	218	250	283	316	348
0.50	36	59	95	130	166	201	237	272	308	343	379
0.55	38	64	102	140	179	217	255	293	332	370	408
0.60	41	68	109	50	191	232	273	313	354	395	436
1½ inch thick Insulation – 10 Inch pipe											
0.20	12	20	32	44	55	67	79	91	103	115	127
0.25	15	24	39	54	68	83	97	112	127	141	156
0.30	17	29	46	63	81	98	115	132	150	167	184
0.35	20	33	53	73	93	112	132	152	172	192	211
0.40	22	37	59	82	104	126	149	171	193	216	238
0.45	25	41	66	91	115	140	165	189	214	239	264
0.50	27	45	72	99	126	153	180	207	234	261	288
0.55	29	49	78	107	137	166	195	225	254	283	313
0.60	32	53	84	116	147	179	210	242	273	305	336
2 inch thick 1nsulation – 10 inch pipe											
0.20	9	16	25	35	44	54	63	73	82	92	101
0.25	12	20	31	43	55	66	78	90	102	113	125
0.30	14	23	37	51	65	79	93	107	120	134	148
0.35	16	27	43	59	75	91	107	123	139	155	171
0.40	18	30	48	66	84	103	121	139	157	175	193
0.45	20	34	54	74	94	174	134	154	174	195	215
0.50	22	37	59	81	103	125	147	169	192	124	236
0.55	24	40	64	88	112	136	,60	184	208	232	256
0.60	26	43	69	95	121	147	173	199	225	251	277
2½ Inch Thick Insulation – 10 inch pipe											
0.20	8	13	21	29	37	44	52	60	68	76	84
0.25	10	16	26	36	45	55	65	74	84	94	104
0.30	12	19	31	42	54	65	77	89	100	112	123
0.35	13	22	36	49	62	76	89	102	116	129	142
0.40	15	25	40	55	71	86	101	116	131	146	161
0.45	17	28	45	62	79	96	112	129	146	163	180
0.50	19	31	49	68	87	105	124	142	161	179	198
0.55	20	34	54	74	94	115	135	155	175	196	216
0.60	22	36	58	80	102	124	146	168	190	211	233

Table 9-145. Heat Loss Through Pipe Insulation – 12 Inch Steel Pipe

Insulation Conductivity *K*	Temperature Difference, Pipe to Air, °F										
	30	50	80	110	140	170	200	230	1260	290	320
	Heat Loss per Lineal Foot of Bare Pipe, Btu/hr										
	154	279	491	732	1003	1305	1640	2009	2415	2860	3346
	Heat Loss per Lineal Foot of Insulated Pipe, Btu/hr										
1 Inch Thick Insulation – 12 inch pipe											
0.20	19	32	51	70	89	108	127	146	165	184	204
0.25	23	39	62	85	109	132	155	179	202	225	248
0.30	27	45	73	100	127	155	182	209	237	264	291
0.35	31	52	83	114	145	176	207	239	270	301	332
0.40	35	58	93	127	162	197	232	266	301	336	371
0.45	38	64	102	140	178	217	255	293	331	369	408
0.50	42	69	111	152	194	235	277	319	360	402	443
0.55	45	75	119	164	209	254	298	343	388	433	477
0.60	48	80	127	175	223	271	319	366	414	462	510
1½ Inch Thick Insulation – 12 inch pipe											
0.20	14	23	36	50	64	77	91	105	118	132	146
0.25	17	28	45	61	78	95	112	129	145	162	179
0.30	20	33	53	73	92	112	132	152	172	191	211
0.35	23	38	61	83	106	129	152	174	197	220	243
0.40	26	43	68	94	119	145	171	196	222	247	273
0.43	28	47	76	104	132	161	189	217	246	274	302
0.50	31	52	83	114	145	176	207	238	269	300	331
0.55	34	56	90	123	157	191	224	258	291	325	359
0.60	36	60	96	132	169	205	241	277	313	349	385
2 Inch Thick Insulation – 12 inch pipe											
0.20	11	18	29	41	52	63	74	85	96	107	118
0.25	14	23	36	50	64	77	91	105	118	132	146
0.30	16	27	43	59	75	92	108	124	140	156	173
0.35	19	31	50	68	87	106	124	143	161	180	199
0.40	21	35	56	77	98	119	140	161	182	203	224
0.45	23	39	62	86	109	133	156	179	203	226	250
0.50	26	43	68	94	120	146	171	197	223	248	274
0.55	28	47	74	102	130	158	186	214	242	270	298
0.60	31	52	83	114	145	176	207	238	269	300	332
2½ Inch Thick Insulation – 12 inch pipe											
0.20	9	15	24	34	43	52	61	70	79	89	98
0.25	11	19	30	42	53	64	76	87	98	110	121
0.30	13	22	36	49	63	76	90	103	117	130	144
0.35	16	26	42	57	73	88	104	119	135	151	166
0.40	18	29	47	65	82	100	118	135	153	170	188
0.45	20	33	52	72	92	111	131	151	170	190	210
0.50	22	36	58	79	101	123	144	166	187	209	231
0.55	24	39	63	86	110	134	157	181	204	228	251
0.60	25	42	68	93	119	144	170	195	221	246	272

Table 9-146. Heat Loss Through Pipe Insulation – 14 Inch Steel Pipe

Insulation Conduc tivity K	Temperature Difference, Pipe to Air, °F										
	30			110	140	170	200	230	1 26o	290	320
	Heat Loss per Lineal Foot of Bare Pipe, Btu/hr										
	181	326	1575	856	1173	1527	1918	2350	2826	3347	3918
	Heat Loss per Lineal Foot of Insulated Pipe, Btu/hr										
1 inch thick 1nsolution – 14 inch pipe											
0.20	22	36	57	79	100	122	143	165	187	208	230
0.25	26	44	70	96	122	149	175	201	227	253	280
0.30	31	51	82	113	143	174	205	235	266	297	327
0.35	35	58	93	128	163	198	233	268	303	338	373
0.40	39	65	104	143	182	221	260	299	338	377	416
0.45	43	72	114	157	200	243	286	329	372	415	458
0.50	47	78	124	171	218	264	311	357	404	451	497
0.55	50	84	134	184	234	284	335	385	435	485	535
0.60	54	89	143	196	250	303	357	303	411	518	571
1½ Inch Thick Insulation – 14 inch pipe											
0.20	15	26	41	56	72	87	102	118	133	148	164
0.25	19	31	50	69	88	107	126	145	163	182	201
0.30	22	37	59	822	104	126	148	171	193	215	237
0.35	26	43	68	194	119	145	170	196	221	247	272
0.40	29	48	77	105	134	163	191	220	249	278	306
0.45	32	53	85	117	148	180	212	244	276	307	339
0.50	35	58	93	127	162	197	232	267	301	336	371
0.55	38	63	100	138	176	213	251	289	326	364	402
0.60	40	67	108	148	189	229	270	310	350	391	431
2 inch thick insulations – 14 inch pipe											
0.20	12	20	31	43	55	66	78	90	102	113	125
0.25	14	24	39	53	68	82	97	111	125	140	154
0.30	17	29	46	63	80	97	114	132	149	166	183
0.35	20	33	53	73	92	112	132	152	171	191	211
0.40	22	37	60	82	104	127	149	171	194	20	238
0.45	25	41	66	91	116	141	166	190	215	240	265
0.50	27	45	73	100	127	155	182	209	236	264	291
0.55	30	49	79	109	138	168	198	227	257	287	317
0.60	32	53	85	117	149	181	213	245	277	309	341
2½ Inch Thick Insulation – 14 inch pipe											
0.20	10	16	26	36	46	56	65	75	85	95	105
0.25	12	20	32	45	57	69	81	93	105	117	130
0.3	14	24	38	53	67	82	96	111	125	140	154
0.35	17	28	44	61	78	95	111	128	145	161	178
0.40	19	31	50	69	88	107	126	145	164	182	201
0.45	21	35	56	77	98	119	140	161	182	203	225
0.50	23	39	62	85	108	131	154	178	201	224	247
0.55	25	42	67	93	118	143	168	194	219	244	269
0.60	27	45	73	100	127	155	189	209	237	264	291

Table 9-147. Heat Loss Through Pipe Insulation – 16 Inch Steel Pipe

Insulation Conductivity K	Temperature Difference, Pipe to Air, °F										
	30	50	80	110	140	170	200	230	260	290	320
	Heat Loss per Lineal Foot of Bare Pipe, Btu/hr										
	203	366	644	960	1314	1711	2149	2634	3080	3753	4395
	Heat Loss per Lineal Foot of Insulated Pipe, Btu/hr										
1 Inch Thick Insulation – 16 inch pipe											
0.20	23	39	62	85	108	131	154	178	201	224	247
0.25	28	47	75	104	132	160	189	217	245	273	302
0.30	33	55	88	122	155	180	188	221	254	287	320
0.35	38	63	101	139	177	215	253	291	329	367	405
0.40	42	70	113	155	197	239	281	324	266	408	450
0.45	46	77	124	170	217	263	310	356	402	449	495
0.50	50	84	135	185	236	286	337	387	438	488	539
0.55	54	91	145	199	254	308	363	417	471	526	580
0.60	58	97	155	213	271	329	387	445	503	561	620
1½ Inch Thick Insulation – 16 inch pipe											
0.20	17	28	45	62	79	95	112	129	146	163	180
0.25	21	34	55	76	97	117	138	159	179	200	231
0.30	24	41	65	90	114	138	163	187	212	236	261
0.35	28	47	75	103	131	159	187	215	243	271	329
0.40	32	53	84	116	147	179	210	242	273	305	336
0.45	35	58	96	128	163	198	333	268	303	338	372
0.50	38	64	102	140	178	217	255	293	331	369	408
0.55	41	69	110	152	193	235	276	317	359	400	442
0.60	44	74	119	163	207	252	296	341	385	430	474
2 Inch Thick Insulation – 16 inch pipe											
0.20	13	22	36	49	62	76	89	102	116	129	143
0.25	16	27	44	60	77	93	110	126	143	159	176
0.30	20	33	52	72	91	111	130	180	169	189	208
0.35	23	38	60	83	105	128	150	173	195	218	240
0.40	25	42	68	93	119	144	170	195	220	246	271
0.45	28	47	75	104	132	160	189	217	245	273	302
0.50	31	52	83	114	145	176	207	238	269	300	331
0.55	34	56	90	124	157	191	225	259	292	326	360
0.60	36	61	97	133	170	206	242	278	315	351	388
2½ Inch Thick Insulation – 16 inch pipe											
0.20	11	19	30	41	52	63	74	86	97	108	119
0.25	14	23	37	5,	64	78	92	106	120	134	147
0.30	16	28	44	60	77	93	109	256	142	159	175
0.35	19	32	51	69	88	107	126	145	164	183	202
0.40	21	36	57	79	100	122	143	165	186	207	229
0.45	24	40	64	88	112	135	159	183	207	231	255
0.50	26	44	70	96	123	149	175	202	228	254	280
0.55	29	48	76	105	134	162	191	220	248	277	306
0.60	31	52	83	114	144	175	206	237	268	299	330

Table 9-148. Heat Loss Through Pipe Insulation – 18 Inch Steel Pipe

Insulation Conductivity K	Temperature Difference, Pipe to Air, °F										
	30	50	80	110	140	170	200	230	260	290	320
	Heat Loss per Lineal Foot of Bare Pipe, Btu/hr										
	214	385	678	1011	1385	1802	2266	2777	3339	3958	4635
	Heat Loss per Lineal Foot of Insulated Pipe, Btu/hr										
1 Inch Thick Insulation – 18 Inch Pipe											
0.20	27	45	72	99	126	153	180	207	234	261	288
0.25	33	55	88	121	153	186	219	252	285	318	351
0.30	38	64	103	141	180	218	257	295	334	372	411
0.35	44	73	117	161	205	248	292	336	380	424	468
0.40	49	82	130	179	228	277	326	375	424	473	522
0.45	54	90	143	197	251	305	359	412	466	520	574
0.50	58	97	156	214	273	331	390	448	506	565	623
0.55	63	105	168	231	293	356	419	452	545	608	671
0.60	67	112	179	246	313	380	448	515	582	649	716
1½ Inch Thick Insulation – 18 inch pipe											
0.20	19	31	50	69	88	106	125	144	163	181	200
0.25	23	38	61	84	107	130	153	176	199	222	244
0.30	27	45	72	99	126	153	180	207	234	261	289
0.35	31	52	83	114	145	176	207	238	269	300	331
0.40	35	58	93	128	163	198	233	269	303	338	372
0.45	39	64	103	142	180	219	258	296	335	374	412
0.50	42	71	113	155	197	240	282	324	367	409	451
0.55	46	76	122	168	214	260	306	351	397	443	489
0.60	49	82	131	181	230	279	328	378	427	476	525
2 inch Thick insulation – 18 inch Pipe											
0.20	15	25	40	55	70	85	100	115	130	145	160
0.25	18	31	49	68	86	105	123	142	160	178	197
0.30	22	36	58	80	102	124	146	168	190	212	234
0.35	25	42	67	93	118	143	168	193	219	244	269
0.40	28	47	76	104	133	161	190	218	247	275	304
0.45	32	53	84	116	148	179	211	243	274	306	338
0.50	35	58	93	127	162	197	232	266	301	336	371
0.55	38	63	101	138	176	24	252	290	327	365	403
0.60	41	68	109	149	190	231	271	312	553	394	434
2½ Inch Thick Insulation – 18 inch pipe											
0.20	12	20	33	45	57	69	81	94	106	118	130
0.25	15	25	40	55	70	86	101	116	131	146	161
0.30	18	30	48	66	84	102	120	138	156	174	191
0.35	21	35	55	76	97	117	138	159	180	200	221
0.40	23	39	62	85	108	131	154	177	200	224	247
0.45	26	44	70	96	122	148	174	201	227	253	279
0.50	29	48	77	106	134	161	192	221	250	278	307
0.55	31	52	84	115	146	178	209	240	272	303	334
0.60	34	56	90	124	158	192	226	260	294	327	361

Table 9-149. Heat Loss Through Pipe Insulation – 20 Inch Steel Pipe

Insulation Conductivity K	Temperature Difference, Pipe to Air, °F										
	30	50	80	110	140	170	200	230	260	290	320
	Heat Loss per Lineal ft of Bare Pipe, Btu/hr										
	236	426	748	1115	1529	1990	2501	3066	3690	4373	5123
	Heat Loss per Lineal ft of Insulated Pipe, Btu/hr										
1 Inch Thick Insulation – 20 inch pipe											
0.20	30	49	79	108	138	168	198	227	256	286	316
0.25	36	60	96	132	168	204	240	276	313	349	385
0.30	42	69	111	153	194	236	278	319	361	403	444
0.35	48	80	128	176	224	273	321	369	418	465	513
0.40	54	89	143	197	250	304	358	411	465	519	572
0.45	59	98	157	216	275	334	393	452	511	570	629
0.50	64	107	171	235	299	363	427	491	556	620	683
0.55	69	115	184	253	322	391	460	529	598	667	737
0.60	74	123	196	270	344	417	491	565	638	712	786
1½ Inch Thick Insulation – 20 inch pipe											
0.20	21	35	56	77	98	118	139	160	181	202	223
0.25	26	43	69	95	121	146	172	198	224	250	276
0.30	30	51	81	111	141	172	202	232	263	293	323
0.35	35	58	93	127	162	197	232	267	301	336	371
0.40	39	65	104	143	182	222	261	300	339	378	417
0.45	43	72	115	159	202	245	289	332	375	418	462
0.50	47	79	126	174	221	268	30	363	410	458	505
0.55	51	85	137	188	239	291	342	393	444	496	547
0.60	55	92	147	202	257	312	367	422	477	532	587
2 Inch Thick Insulation – 20 inch pipe											
0.20	16	27	44	60	76	93	109	125	142	158	174
0.25	20	34	54	74	94	114	134	154	175	195	215
0.30	24	40	64	88	111	135	159	183	207	231	255
0.35	27	46	73	101	128	156	183	211	238	266	293
0.40	31	52	83	114	145	176	207	238	269	300	331
0.45	35	58	92	127	161	196	230	265	299	334	368
0.50	38	63	101	139	177	215	252	290	328	366	404
0.55	41	69	110	151	192	233	274	316	357	398	439
0.60	44	74	118	163	207	251	296	340	385	429	473
2½ Inch Thick Insulation – 20 inch pipe											
0.20	14	23	36	50	63	77	90	104	117	131	144
0.25	17	28	45	61	78	95	112	128	145	162	178
0.30	20	33	53	73	93	112	132	152	172	192	212
0.35	23	38	61	84	107	130	153	176	199	222	244
0.40	26	43	69	95	121	147	173	199	225	251	277
0.45	29	48	77	106	135	164	193	221	250	279	308
0.50	32	53	85	116	148	180	212	244	275	307	339
0.55	35	58	92	127	162	196	231	265	300	335	369
0.60	37	62	100	137	175	212	249	287	324	362	399

Table 9-150. Insulation to Prevent Sweating on Cold Pipes

Liquid Temperature, °F	Pipe Size, in.	Thermal Conductivity k, Btu/ft²-hr (ft thickness)	Air Temperature, °F														
			60			70			80			90			100		
			Relative Humidity,%														
			50	70	90	50	70	90	50	70	90	50	70	90	50	70	90
			Minimum Thickness of Insulation, in.														
0	½	0.024	0.65	1.26	3.55	0.73	1.41	3.87	0.83	1.51	4.17	0.89	1.64	4.5	0.95	1.72	4.71
		0.029	0.74	1.43	4.03	0.84	1.59	4.35	0.94	1.72	4.75	1.00	1.85	5.08	1.10	1.93	5.13
		0.034	0.82	1.63	4.62	0.95	1.81	4.96	1.06	1.96	5.38	1.15	2.09	5.76	1.22	2.20	6.01
	¾	0.024	0.69	1.33	3.8	0.79	1.44	4.08	0.87	1.60	4.43	0.94	1.73	4.78	1.01	1.82	4.94
		0.029	0.78	1.51	4.27	0.89	1.68	4.58	0.98	1.8	5.00	1.06	1.95	5.37	1.14	2.06	5.57
		0.034	0.89	1.71	4.84	1.01	1.90	5.21	1.11	2.04	5.68	1.21	2.21	6.10	1.28	2.33	6.3
	1	0.024	0.71	1.40	3.98	0.82	1.56	4.29	0.92	1.67	4.68	0.98	1.80	4.99	1.05	1.90	5.28
		0.029	0.81	1.57	4.50	0.92	1.74	4.83	1.02	1.88	5.24	1.11	2.04	5.61	1.18	2.16	5.82
		0.034	0.94	1.79	5.09	1.05	2.01	5.47	1.16	2.14	5.99	1.26	2.32	6.37	1.36	2.44	6.64
	1¼	0.024	0.73	1.47	4.21	0.85	1.64	4.52	0.95	1.77	4.89	1.03	1.90	5.26	1.11	2.01	5.47
		0.029	0.84	1.69	4.74	0.97	1.84	5.10	1.10	1.98	5.54	1.16	2.13	5.93	1.25	2.27	7.17
		0.034	0.97	1.88	5.38	1.11	2.10	5.78	1.21	2.26	6.27	1.32	2.43	6.71	1.42	2.57	6.97
	1½	0.024	0.75	1.52	4.35	0.87	1.68	4.67	0.96	1.81	4.86	1.06	1.97	5.43	1.13	2.08	5.67
		0.029	0.86	1.70	4.90	0.99	1.91	5.27	1.09	2.06	5.70	1.19	2.22	6.11	1.28	2.33	6.36
		0.034	0.98	1.96	5.55	1.12	2.18	5.97	1.27	2.33	6.48	1.38	2.5	6.95	1.50	2.65	7.21
	2	0.024	0.77	1.59	4.56	0.89	1.77	4.90	0.99	1.91	5.32	1.09	2.05	5.72	1.17	2.17	5.93
		0.029	0.89	1.79	5.13	1.00	1.99	5.51	1.13	2.14	5.98	1.22	2.32	6.43	1.33	2.44	6.68
		0.034	1.00	2.03	5.82	1.16	2.26	6.26	1.30	2.45	6.78	1.41	2.63	7.29	1.51	2.78	7.57
	3	0.024	0.82	1.68	4.95	0.96	1.89	5.31	1.05	2.05	5.79	1.14	2.21	6.2	1.23	2.36	6.44
		0.029	0.96	1.85	5.61	1.11	2.17	6.04	1.22	2.36	6.55	1.31	2.53	7.04	1.43	2.67	7.30
		0.034	1.08	2.20	6.33	1.24	2.48	6.82	1.97	2.68	7.41	1.49	2.85	7.97	1.61	3.03	8.25
	4	0.024	0.84	1.73	5.24	0.97	1.96	5.6	1.08	2.09	6.12	1.24	2.31	6.57	1.26	2.43	6.76
		0.029	0.97	1.95	5.91	1.13	2.23	6.31	1.26	2.43	6.90	1.35	2.65	7.45	1.46	2.79	7.69
		0.034	1.12	2.27	6.68	1.30	2.56	7.22	1.40	2.81	7.84	1.58	3.03	8.40	1.66	3.22	8.66
	5	0.024	0.85	1.81	5.51	1.03	2.00	5.91	1.17	2.2	6.43	1.25	2.59	6.90	1.33	2.53	7.15
		0.029	1.00	2.06	6.23	1.14	2.31	6.67	1.28	2.48	7.23	1.39	3.06	7.87	1.50	2.87	8.07
		0.034	1.17	2.36	7.03	1.33	2.67	7.57	1.48	2.89	8.22	1.61	3.12	8.82	1.73	3.31	9.18
20	½	0.024	0.38	0.86	2.58	0.50	1.02	2.94	0.61	1.17	3.32	0.69	1.29	3.66	0.75	1.47	3.91
		0.029	0.43	0.97	2.91	0.58	1.12	3.31	0.67	1.32	3.73	0.77	1.46	4.12	0.86	1.60	4.38
		0.034	0.50	1.09	3.3	0.64	1.32	3.75	0.77	1.49	4.24	0.88	1.66	4.71	0.87	1.81	5.00
	¾	0.024	0.39	0.90	2.72	0.53	1.09	3.07	0.63	1.23	3.51	0.73	1.37	3.88	0.8	1.49	4.12
		0.029	0.44	1.03	3.07	0.60	1.23	3.59	0.72	1.40	4.04	0.81	1.54	4.46	0.91	1.68	4.62
		0.034	0.53	1.16	3.49	0.67	1.40	3.96	0.81	1.57	4.47	0.93	1.75	4.94	1.03	1.91	5.26
	1	0.024	0.41	0.95	2.86	0.54	1.13	3.24	0.65	1.29	3.68	0.75	1.44	4.07	0.83	1.56	4.33
		0.029	0.46	1.06	3.23	0.6	1.29	3.66	0.75	1.45	4.15	0.84	1.61	4.60	0.95	1.76	4.87
		0.034	0.55	1.21	3.65	0.69	1.45	4.15	0.84	1.66	4.71	0.97	1.82	5.20	1.06	2.00	5.52
	1¼	0.024	0.43	0.98	3.01	0.57	1.19	3.42	0.66	1.36	3.89	0.77	1.49	4.29	0.86	1.65	4.58
		0.029	0.47	1.12	3.40	0.62	1.34	3.87	0.76	1.54	4.36	0.87	1.71	4.85	0.99	1.85	5.16
		0.034	0.56	1.27	3.85	0.72	1.52	4.38	0.87	1.74	4.96	1.00	1.92	5.45	1.12	2.10	5.84
	1½	0.024	0.43	1.00	3.10	0.57	1.21	3.53	0.67	1.39	4.00	0.79	1.53	4.43	0.88	1.73	4.71
		0.029	0.49	1.14	3.50	0.66	1.39	3.98	0.77	1.57	4.51	0.88	1.74	4.99	1.00	1.92	5.31
		0.034	0.56	1.32	3.97	0.73	1.58	4.52	0.89	1.79	5.14	1.03	1.99	5.65	1.16	2.18	6.04
	2	0.024	0.44	1.03	3.26	0.58	1.33	3.70	0.70	1.46	4.2	0.83	1.60	4.65	0.91	1.79	4.95
		0.029	0.49	1.17	3.65	0.66	1.43	4.19	0.80	1.66	4.74	0.92	1.85	5.24	1.03	2.01	5.59
		0.034	0.57	1.35	4.17	0.74	1.66	4.74	0.91	1.87	5.37	1.06	2.07	5.94	1.18	2.28	6.32
	3	0.024	0.44	1.09	3.55	0.58	1.35	4.02	0.71	1.52	4.55	0.84	1.69	5.04	0.96	1.89	5.37
		0.029	0.49	1.24	4.01	0.66	1.52	4.55	0.84	1.75	5.35	0.98	1.96	5.74	1.09	2.17	6.10
		0.034	0.60	1.45	4.55	0.74	1.73	5.15	0.98	1.99	5.85	1.10	2.24	6.47	1.26	2.50	6.91
	4	0.024	0.45	1.13	3.71	0.58	1.39	4.25	0.71	1.58	4.84	0.88	1.78	5.37	0.99	1.96	5.67
		0.029	0.52	1.29	4.23	0.68	1.6	4.84	0.85	1.85	5.47	1.01	2.05	6.03	1.19	2.23	6.46
		0.034	0.60	1.51	4.79	0.83	1.85	5.45	1.01	2.07	6.18	1.17	2.32	6.84	1.29	2.57	7.31
	5	0.024	0.47	1.17	3.92	0.58	1.44	4.48	0.72	1.59	5.08	0.88	1.87	5.62	1.03	2.00	6.01
		0.029	0.56	1.33	4.45	0.70	1.64	5.03	0.86	1.89	5.73	1.06	2.08	6.33	1.17	2.33	6.72
		0.034	0.60	1.55	5.03	0.84	1.89	5.72	1.03	2.14	6.42	1.20	2.42	7.16	1.36	2.7	7.72

Table 9-150. *(Continued)* **Insulation to Prevent Sweating on Cold Pipes**

Liquid Temperature, °F	Pipe Size, in.	Thermal Conductivity k, Btu/ft²-hr (ft thickness)	Air Temperature, °F														
			60			70			80			90			100		
			Relative Humidity,%														
			50	70	90	50	70	90	50	70	90	50	70	90	50	70	90
			Minimum Thickness of Insulation, in.														
35	½	0.024	0.12	0.50	1.72	0.28	0.71	2.18	0.4	0.88	2.62	0.51	1.04	3.02	0.6	1.16	3.3
		0.029	0.15	0.56	1.94	0.32	0.8	2.46	0.46	0.99	2.96	0.58	1.17	3.40	0.67	1.32	3.71
		0.034	0.18	0.65	2.21	0.37	0.91	2.80	0.53	1.08	3.35	0.66	1.33	3.87	0.77	1.50	4.22
	¾	0.024	0.12	0.52	1.82	0.29	0.75	2.31	0.42	0.93	2.77	0.52	1.10	3.19	0.62	1.23	3.49
		0.029	0.15	0.59	2.06	0.34	0.85	2.6	0.48	1.06	3.12	0.60	1.23	3.59	0.72	1.39	3.93
		0.034	0.18	0.67	2.32	0.38	0.96	2.95	0.55	1.19	3.54	0.69	1.41	4.08	0.82	1.58	4.45
	1	0.024	0.12	0.52	1.91	0.29	0.77	2.41	0.42	1.95	2.9	0.54	1.14	3.34	0.63	1.29	3.8
		0.029	0.15	0.59	2.15	0.35	0.88	2.71	0.48	1.09	3.27	0.62	1.29	3.91	0.73	1.45	4.26
		0.034	0.18	0.69	2.44	0.40	1.01	3.1	0.56	1.24	3.85	0.7	1.46	4.42	0.84	1.66	4.82
	1¼	0.024	0.13	0.54	2.01	0.31	0.81	2.54	0.44	1.01	3.05	0.57	1.21	3.52	0.66	1.35	3.85
		0.029	0.16	0.62	2.27	0.35	0.92	2.86	0.51	1.15	3.45	0.63	1.36	3.97	0.76	1.53	4.35
		0.034	0.18	0.71	2.56	0.43	1.05	3.26	0.58	1.30	3.92	0.74	1.53	4.49	0.87	1.74	4.92
	1½	0.024	0.13	0.56	2.10	0.31	0.81	2.61	0.46	1.05	3.16	0.57	1.25	3.65	0.68	1.40	3.96
		0.029	0.16	0.64	3.35	0.35	0.93	2.95	0.51	1.18	3.55	0.66	1.4	4.09	0.78	1.59	4.48
		0.034	0.18	0.73	2.65	0.43	1.08	3.36	0.59	1.36	4.04	0.74	1.6	4.65	0.9	1.80	5.11
	2	0.024	0.14	0.57	2.16	0.31	0.84	2.75	0.47	1.06	3.32	0.59	1.27	3.82	0.7	1.45	4.16
		0.029	0.16	0.66	2.45	0.35	0.96	3.11	0.53	1.22	3.74	0.67	1.46	4.29	0.79	1.67	4.71
		0.034	0.19	0.74	2.79	0.44	1.09	3.51	0.61	1.39	4.23	0.77	1.67	4.88	0.91	1.87	5.35
	3	0.024	0.14	0.58	2.36	0.33	0.91	2.99	0.47	1.08	3.61	0.61	1.33	4.15	0.7	1.56	4.54
		0.029	0.18	0.7	2.66	0.37	1.03	3.38	0.53	1.30	3.73	0.7	1.56	4.69	0.84	1.77	5.13
		0.034	0.19	0.77	3.02	0.44	1.17	3.85	0.62	1.47	4.61	0.82	1.77	5.31	0.98	2.00	5.81
	4	0.024	0.14	0.59	3.47	0.33	0.95	3.12	0.47	1.15	3.81	0.62	1.39	4.41	0.7	1.6	4.84
		0.029	0.20	0.68	2.79	0.38	1.06	3.55	0.56	1.33	4.3	0.71	1.58	4.96	0.84	1.82	5.42
		0.034	0.2	0.8	3.21	0.45	1.23	4.04	0.63	1.55	4.88	0.82	1.84	5.53	1.01	2.09	6.12
	5	0.024	0.14	0.59	2.53	0.34	0.97	3.25	0.5	1.23	3.97	0.64	1.47	4.58	0.72	1.67	5.03
		0.029	0.2	0.7	2.87	0.38	1.06	3.76	0.56	1.39	4.53	0.72	1.64	5.2	0.85	1.92	5.71
		0.034	0.22	0.8	3.34	0.45	1.25	4.26	0.64	1.61	5.08	0.84	1.92	5.9	1.02	2.17	6.45
50	½	0.024	0	0.01	0.70	0.01	0.33	1.33	0.16	0.56	1.86	0.31	0.74	2.32	0.42	0.9	2.66
		0.029	0	0.01	0.80	0.02	0.37	1.50	0.21	0.63	2.10	0.35	0.85	2.60	0.48	1.02	3.00
		0.034	0	0.01	0.92	0.02	0.43	1.70	0.24	0.72	2.38	0.41	0.96	2.97	0.55	1.16	3.40
	¾	0.024	0	0.01	0.76	0.01	0.35	1.41	0.17	0.59	1.96	0.33	0.79	2.54	0.44	0.95	2.81
		0.029	0	0.01	0.85	0.02	0.4	1.59	0.21	0.65	2.22	0.37	0.9	2.76	0.5	1.08	3.17
		0.034	0	0.01	0.97	0.02	0.45	1.8	0.24	0.77	2.52	0.43	1.02	3.13	0.58	1.18	3.60
	1	0.024	0	0.01	0.79	0.01	0.34	1.46	0.18	0.6	2.05	0.33	0.82	2.57	0.46	0.99	2.94
		0.029	0	0.01	0.88	0.02	0.40	1.65	0.21	0.68	2.31	0.38	0.94	2.88	0.50	1.12	3.31
		0.034	0	0.01	1.01	0.02	0.46	1.88	0.24	0.78	2.63	0.44	1.06	3.28	0.58	1.28	5.90
	1¼	0.024	0	0.01	0.81	0.02	0.37	1.55	0.19	0.62	2.13	0.34	0.86	2.70	0.47	1.04	3.10
		0.029	0	0.01	0.91	0.02	0.42	1.75	0.22	0.71	2.43	0.39	0.98	3.05	0.53	1.18	3.50
		0.034	0	0.01	1.06	0.03	0.47	1.99	0.24	0.82	2.77	0.46	1.10	3.46	0.6	1.35	3.97
	1½	0.024	0	0.01	0.83	0.03	0.41	1.60	0.19	0.64	2.23	0.35	0.87	2.79	0.48	1.07	3.20
		0.029	0	0.01	0.93	0.03	0.43	1.80	0.22	0.72	2.51	0.39	0.98	3.14	0.53	1.22	3.60
		0.034	0	0.01	1.07	0.03	0.5	2.05	0.25	0.82	2.86	0.46	1.14	3.57	0.62	1.39	4.10
	2	0.024	0	0.01	0.84	0.03	0.34	1.67	0.19	0.66	2.35	0.35	0.89	2.93	0.48	1.13	3.36
		0.029	0	0.01	0.97	0.03	0.44	1.87	0.23	0.74	2.63	0.4	1.03	3.3	0.55	1.24	3.77
		0.034	0	0.01	1.12	0.04	0.5	2.13	0.25	0.85	2.98	0.47	1.17	3.75	0.63	1.42	4.28
	3	0.024	0	0.01	0.91	0.03	0.36	1.75	0.19	0.68	2.56	0.35	0.96	3.15	0.49	1.17	3.66
		0.029	0	0.01	1.05	0.03	0.44	2.05	0.23	0.79	2.87	0.4	1.09	3.58	0.56	1.31	4.13
		0.034	0	0.01	1.19	0.04	0.49	2.32	0.26	0.91	3.28	0.47	1.24	3.94	0.67	1.52	4.68
	4	0.024	0	0.01	0.95	0.03	0.36	1.87	0.20	0.68	2.65	0.36	0.97	3.37	0.49	1.24	3.87
		0.029	0	0.01	1.09	0.03	0.44	2.12	0.23	0.79	3.04	0.43	1.12	3.80	0.56	1.40	4.34
		0.034	0	0.01	1.24	0.04	0.52	2.43	0.27	0.95	3.44	0.47	1.30	4.30	0.68	1.02	4.95
	5	0.024	0	0.01	0.97	0.04	0.36	1.92	0.22	0.70	2.73	0.36	1.03	3.47	0.50	1.25	4.04
		0.029	0	0.01	1.11	0.04	0.44	2.17	0.25	0.80	3.14	0.45	1.14	3.98	0.58	1.45	4.56
		0.034	0	0.01	1.25	0.04	0.56	2.50	0.28	0.97	3.64	0.50	1.33	4.51	0.70	1.67	5.23

HYDRONIC HEATING AND COOLING SYSTEM

Basic System

Hot water heating systems (hydronic heating) are conveniently being used in many types of buildings and facilities, especially for single family houses and low rise multiple dwelling buildings. Also many HVAC systems are using hot water systems as the primary source for heating the distribution air. The chilled water cooling systems (hydronic cooling) are popular in certain large residential buildings, hospitals, and office buildings. The main components of a hydronic system are:

1) boiler (heating source) or chiller (cooling source)

2) circulating pump(s)

3) expansion tank(s)

4) Heating load (radiators, convectors, HVAC units, etc.) or Cooling load (terminal units, fan-coil units, HVAC units, etc.)

5) air separator

6) connected piping system

7) make-up and fill water system

8) control system.

The hydronic system can be classified by combination of:

1) operating temperature; 2) pumping and piping arrangement; and 3) operating pressure.

Depending on the particular application and the type of the facility, the proper selection of the boiler(s) or chiller(s), pumping systems, piping arrangement, and control system are essential for an effective and economical hydronic system. Schematic piping drawings of some heating and cooling systems are given in Figs. 10-1 to 10-5.

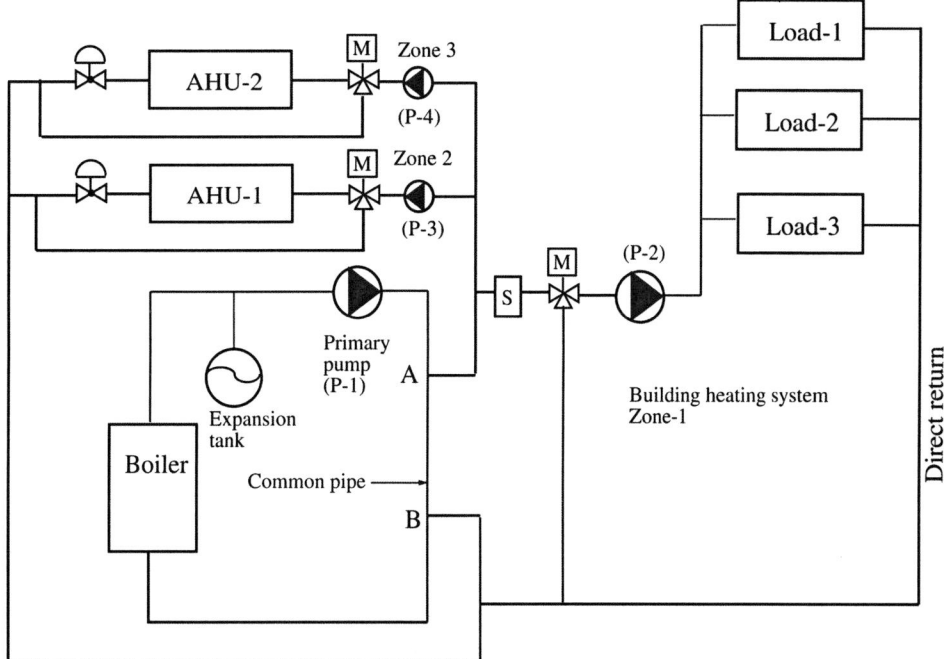

Fig 10-1. Heating system for multiple dwelling building with direct return piping system

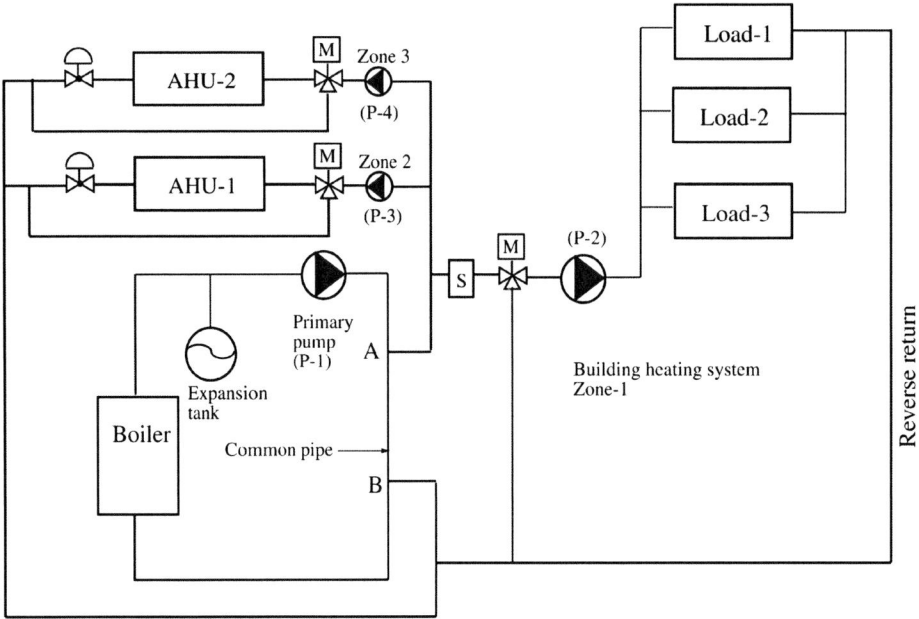

Fig 10-2. Heating system for multiple dwelling building with reverse return system

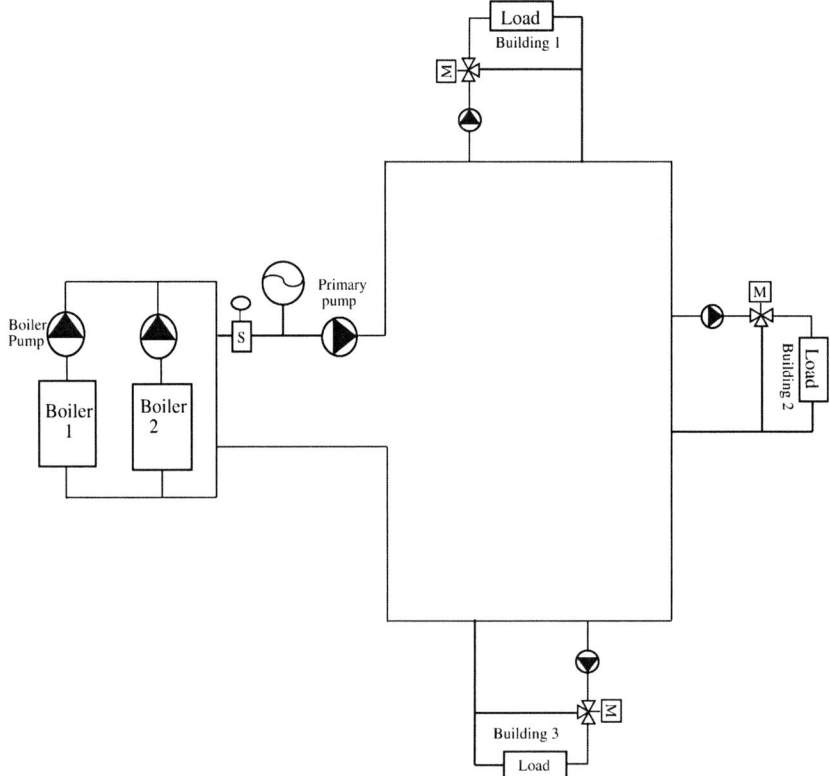

Fig 10-3. Primary system with constant speed heating system pump for multiple buildings

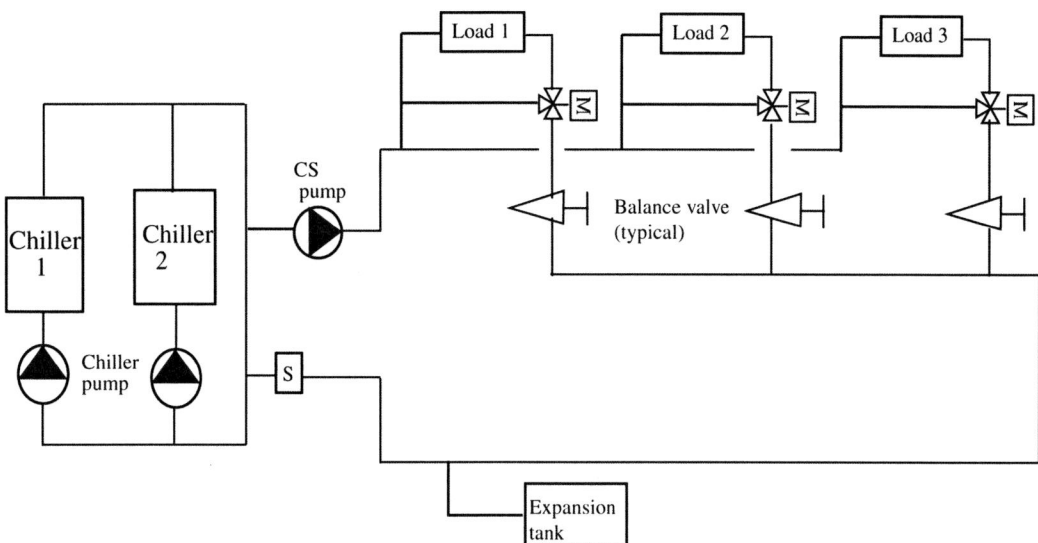

Fig 10-4. Closed chilled water system with constant speed chilled water supply pump and mixing valve

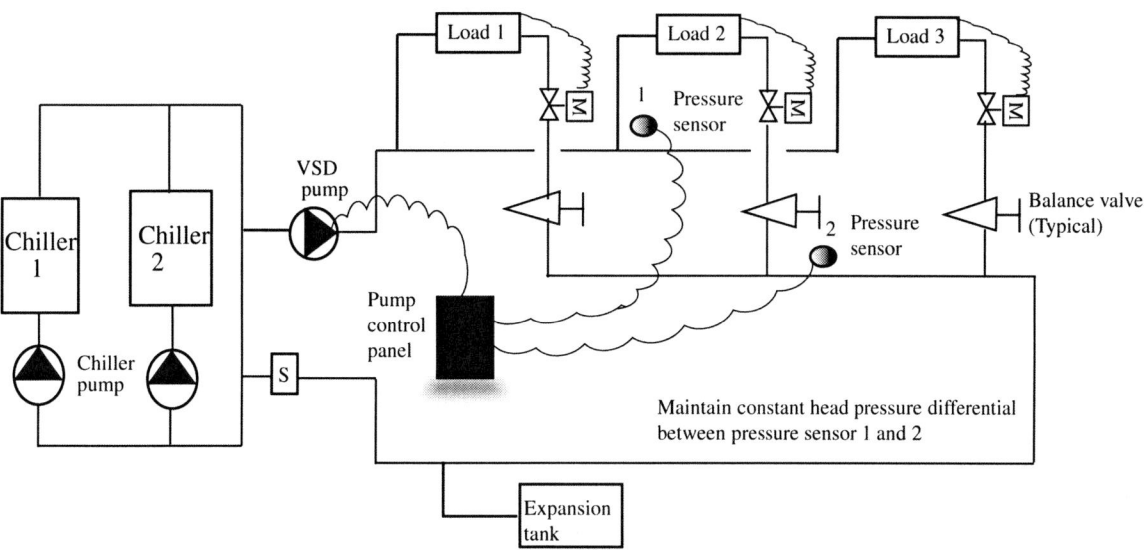

Fig 10-5. Closed chilled water system with variable speed chilled water supply pump

Temperature Classifications.—The temperature classifications of the hydronic systems can be categorized as:

1) Low temperature water (LTW) system
2) Medium temperature water (MTW) system
3) High temperature water (HTW) system
4) Chilled water (CW) system
5) Dual temperature water (DTW) system.

Low Temperature Water (LWT) System: The maximum temperature limitation in this case is 250°F, The maximum allowable working pressure is 160 psig. The maximum working pressure depends on the static head of the building (height of the building) and the location of the system pump(s). It is recommended for working pressure of higher than 60 psi to use steam to water or water to water heat exchanger(s) so that the heating boiler and its closed piping loop can be separated and to operate at lower operating pressure without being affected by the high system working pressure. Separating the boiler by using heat exchanger(s) from the rest of the system minimizes boiler leaks and prolong the life of the boiler.

Medium Temperature Water (MTW) System: In this case, the working temperature is ranged between 250°F and 350°F with an operating pressure of 300 psig. The maximum temperature is 400°F.

Chilled Water (CW) System: In this case the chiller(s) operates to provide supply water temperature of 40 to 55° F, and a pressure of up to 120 psig. For supply temperature below 40°F, mostly in process applications, antifreeze of brine solution may be used.

Dual Temperature Water (DTW) System: In this case, both boiler(s) and chiller(s) are used with common piping system to provide hot water heating and chilled water cooling. The maximum operating temperature of the heating water is limited to 180°F and minimum 40°F for the chilled water.

Closed Hydronic System Components Design

The closed system is a system with only one expansion tank. The main components of the heating and cooling hydronic systems are (1) the heating or cooling source (such as boiler and chiller), (2) system load (convectors, baseboards, fan coil units, and terminal units, etc.), (3) expansion tank, (4) system pump(s), air separator, mechanical fill system; and (5) piping distribution system.

Convectors or Terminal Units.—The convector(s) for each room or space must be sized to be equal or greater than the calculated designed heating load for that particular room or space. The sum of the total convectors and other terminal units load in the building is called the actual connected load. The flow rate through each convector or terminal unit can be calculated from the following equation:

$$gpm = \frac{\dot{q}}{8.02 \times \Delta T \times C_P \times \rho} \quad (1)$$

where q = heat capacity of the terminal unit, Btu/h
gpm = water flow rate, gallon/min
ρ = density of water, lb/ft³
C_p = specific heat of water, Btu/lb ·°F
ΔT = temperature drop across the convector or terminal unit, °F

For standard conditions in which the density of the water is 62.4 lb/ft³ and the specific heat is 1 Btu/lb-°F, Equation (1) can be written as

$$gpm = \frac{\dot{q}}{500 \times \Delta T} \quad (2)$$

In many design applications the ΔT of 20°F is recommended for small simple hydronic systems, in this case the above equation can be written as

$$gpm = \frac{\dot{q}}{10000} \quad (3)$$

Boiler.—For new construction boiler(s) must be sizes based on the actual connected load and piping and pick up losses. The actual connected load must be equal or greater that the calculated design heating load. The piping and pickup losses for the hydronic (hot water) boiler(s) is 15 to 25% of the actual connected load and for steam boilers is 25 to 35%. In design application for which only the boiler needs to be replaced, the boiler(s) must be sized to match the actual installed connected load plus the piping and pickup loss as mentioned above for proper operation of the boiler(s) specially on very cold days.

Air Eliminations Methods.—Air in the hydronic system can cause water hammer and shock waves in the hydronic system when the dissolved air in the water can be separated at the low pressure point of the system.

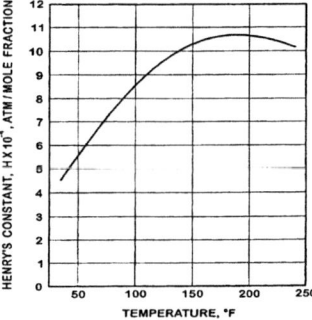

Fig 10-6. Henry's constant versus temperature for air and water

The solubility of air in the water can be described by *Henry's equation* as follow:

$$x = \frac{p}{H} \quad (4)$$

where x = solubility of air in water (% by volume)

   p = absolute pressure

   H = Henry's constant

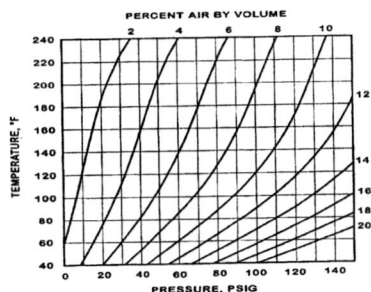

Fig 10-7. Solubility versus temperature and pressure
for air/water solution

Henry's constant is a function temperature as shown in Figure 6. Taking into account the temperature dependency of Henry's constant and combining withEquation (4), the percentage of the solubility of air in water can be determined as shown in Fig. 10-7. Fig. 10-7 clearly shows what percent of air volume would exist in the different parts of the hydronic system when the pressure and temperature are known. For example at 10 psia and 120°F, the percent air volume if 2.5% from Fig. 10-7. Basically the dissolved air in the water at the higher pressure point of the system can be separated at other parts of the system where the pressure is lower. That is the reason air vents are installed (1) at the top of the supply and return risers (highest point) where the pressure is the lowest and (2) at the return side of the terminal units (baseboard loop, convectors, etc.). Air can get into the hydronic system as follow:

1) During the initial fill of the system with city water, which contains dissolved air. In order to minimize the dissolved air during the initial fill, an inline separator is recommended to be installed in the piping system, as shown in Fig. 10-8.

2) Entrain air at the air water interface of the open expansion tank and closed steel expansion tank where the air is being used as compressible fluid. A diaphragm type expansion tank is preferred to be installed since no direct contact exists between the compressible gas and water, since they are separated by a flexible membrane.

3) Through the fittings in the part of the piping system where the system pressure is below atmospheric pressure. Design must ensure that at no point in the system the system pressure is lower than atmospheric pressure.

4) Other considerations are to ensure that (1) pressure at no point in the system will ever becomes lower than saturation temperature of the operating temperature and (2) the calculated (theoretical) net positive head (NPSHA) at the pump inlet is always exceeds the required net positive head given by the pump manufacturer.

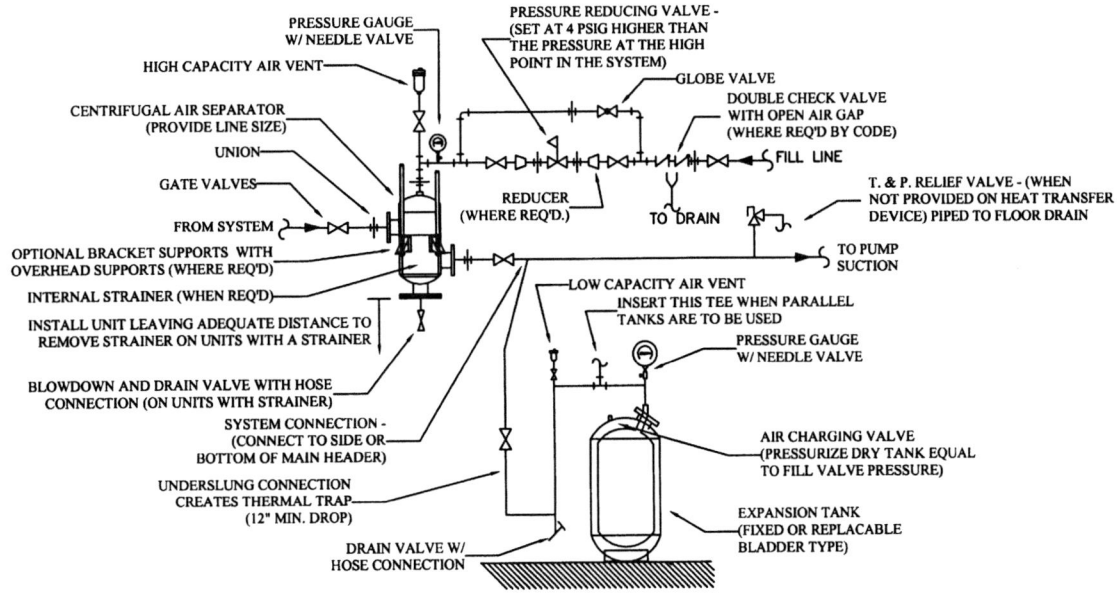

Fig 10-8. Air separator and expansion tank detail

Pressure Increase Due to Change in Temperature.— One should know of how much pressure will increase due to temperature increase; this is especially important for the sizing of the expansion tank. The relationship between pressure change due to temperature change in a piping system is given by the following equations:

$$\Delta P = \frac{(\beta - 3\alpha)\Delta t}{\left(\frac{5}{4}\right)\left(\frac{D}{E\Delta r}\right) + \gamma} \qquad (5)$$

where P = pressure increase, psi;

     β = volumetric coefficient of thermal expansion of water, $1/°F$;

     α = linear coefficient of thermal expansion for piping material, $1/°F$;

     Δt = water temperature increase, °F;

     D = pipe diameter, in.;

     E = modulus of elasticity of piping material, psi;

     γ = volumetric compressibility of water, in^2/lb; and

     Δr = thickness of pipe wall, in.

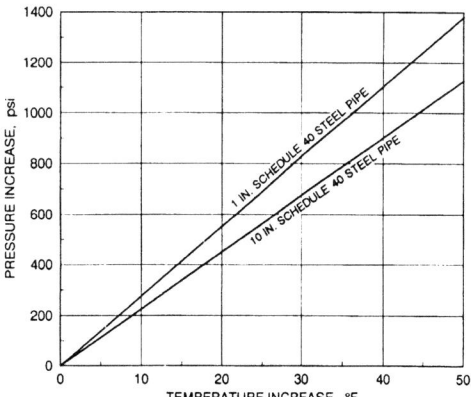

Fig 10-9. Pressure increase resulting from thermal expansion as function of temperature increase

Based on Equation (5), figures can be developed to show the change in pressure due to temperature change for specific pipe sizes and pipe material as shown in Fig. 10-9 which provides pressure increase vs. pressure increase for 1″ and 10″ schedule 40 steel pipes. For example for a 5°F temperature increase for a 10″ schedule 40 steel pipe, the pressure increase is 100 psi.

Expansion Tank.—The connected piping in hydronic systems is subject to expansion and contraction due to changes in system temperature especially during initial system fill. Expansion tanks (or compression tanks) are required to protect against thermal expansion of the piping system due to temperature rise. During initial fill the piping system could experience the largest thermal expansion which is why the size of expansion tank must be based on temperature changes during initial system fill. For example, in low temperature hydronic heating system when boiler and piping system need to be initially filled during winter time, the city water temperature could be as low as 40°F, which must be heated to 200°F. In this case, the piping system will experience a large temperature difference and the system expansion tank must be sized to handle this large temperature increase. Another option is that to heat the city water initially by means of electric heat to reduce the size of the system expansion tank, but same procedure must be followed for the future system fill to avoid drastic damage to the piping system due to excessive expansion. It should be noted that the expansion tanks besides serving a thermal function serves a hydraulic function as well. As a hydraulic device, the expansion tank provides a reference system pressure point analogous to the ground point in an electrical circuit.

Expansion tanks are of three basic configurations: (1) a closed tank, which contains a captured volume of compressed air and water, with an air water interface (sometimes called a plain steel tank) as shown in Fig. 10-12; (2) an open tank (i.e., a tank open to the atmosphere) as shown in Fig. 10-10; and (3) a diaphragm tank, in which a flexible membrane is inserted between the air and the water (another configuration of a diaphragm tank is the bladder tank) as shown in Fig. 10-11.

Equations for sizing the three common configurations of expansion tanks are as follow:

Open tanks with air/water interface:

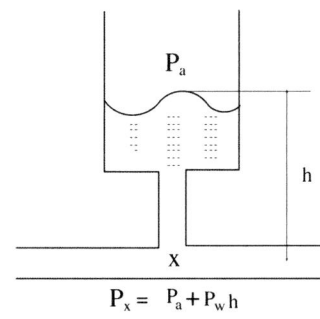

$$P_x = P_a + P_w h$$

Fig 10-10. Open tank

For diaphragm tanks:

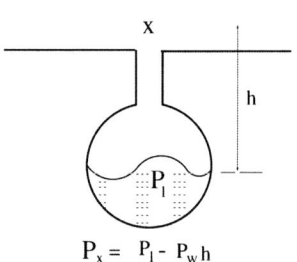

$$P_x = P_1 - P_w h$$

Fig 10-11. Diaphragm tank

For closed tanks with air/water interface:

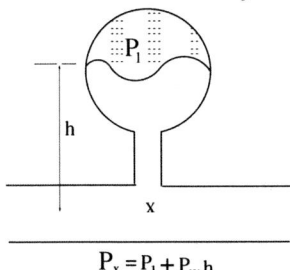

$$P_x = P_1 + P_w h$$

Fig 10-12. Closed tank air water interact

Expansion Tank Sizing .—Equations for sizing the three common configurations of expansion tanks follow:

For closed tanks with air/water interface,

$$V_t = V_s \frac{\left(\left[\left(\frac{V_2}{V_1}\right) - 1\right] - 3\alpha\Delta T\right)}{\left(\frac{P_a}{P_1} - \frac{P_a}{P_2}\right)} \qquad (6)$$

For open tanks with air/water interface,

$$V_t = 2V_s\left(\left[\left(\frac{V_2}{V_1}\right) - 1\right] - 3\alpha\Delta T\right) \qquad (7)$$

For diaphragm tanks,

$$V_t = V_s \frac{\left(\left[\left(\frac{V_2}{V_1}\right) - 1\right] - 3\alpha\Delta T\right)}{\left(1 - \frac{P_1}{P_2}\right)} \qquad (8)$$

where V_t = volume of expansion tank, gal
 V_s = volume of water in system, gal
 T_1 = lower temperature, °F
 T_2 = higher temperature, °F
 P_a = atmospheric pressure, psia
 P_1 = pressure at lower temperature, psia
 P_2 = pressure at higher temperature, psia
 V_1 = specific volume of water at lower temperature, ft³/lb
 V_2 = specific volume of water at higher temperature, ft³/lb
 α = linear coefficient of thermal expansion, in/in-°F
    = 6.5×10^{-6} in/in-°F for steel
    = 9.5×10^{-6} in/in-°F for copper
 $\Delta T = (T_2 - T_1)$, °F

The higher pressure is normally set by the maximum pressure allowable at the location of the safety relief valve(s) without opening them. A tank open to the atmo-

sphere must be located above the highest point in the system. A tank with an air/water interface is generally used with an air control system that continually revents the air into the tank. For this reason, it should be connected at a point where air can best be released.

Example 1: Size an expansion tank for dual temperature system that will be operated at a design temperature range of 40°F to 200°F. The minimum pressure at the tank is 62.3 psig (47.6 psia) and the maximum pressure is 117.3 psig (102.6 psia). (Atmospheric pressure is 14.7 psia.) The volume of water is 2500 gal. The piping is steel.

1. Calculate the required size for a closed tank with an air/water interface.

Solution: From Table 2-3:

$$V_1(\text{ at } 40°\text{F}) = 0.01602$$

$$V_2(\text{ at } 200 °\text{F}) = 0.01663$$

$$V_t = V_s \frac{\left(\left[\frac{V_2}{V_1} - 1\right] - 3\alpha\Delta T\right)}{\left(\frac{P_a}{P_1} - \frac{P_a}{P_1}\right)}$$

$$= 2500 \times \frac{\left(\left[\frac{0.01663}{0.01602} - 1\right] - 3 \times 6.5 \times 10^{-6} \times 160\right)}{\left(\frac{14.7}{62.3} - \frac{14.7}{117.3}\right)}$$

$$= 787 \text{ gal}$$

2. If a diaphragm tank were to be used in lieu of the plain steel tank, what tank size would be required?

Solution: Using Equation (8),

$$V_t = V_s \frac{\left(\left[\frac{V_2}{V_1} - 1\right] - 3\alpha\Delta T\right)}{\left(1 - \frac{P_1}{P_2}\right)}$$

$$= 2500 \times \frac{\left(\left(\frac{0.01663}{0.01602} - 1\right) - 3 \times 6.5 \times 10^{-6} \times 160\right)}{\left(1 - \frac{62.3}{117.3}\right)}$$

$$= 186 \text{ gal}$$

Expansion Tank Location: It should be noted that the location of the tank has no effect on the system pressure before and after the pump as shown in Figs. 10-13 to 10-16. Notice that, when the pump is on, the pressure at the pump inlet decreases equal to the amount of pump head and it increases at the pump discharge equal to the pump head. In good design practice, in order to reduce the size of the expansion tank, it is preferred to install the tank before the system pump. The size of the tank can also be reduced when the tank is installed at the highest point of the piping system where the pressure is the lowest.

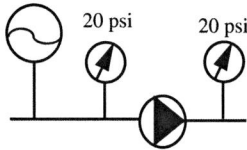

Pump off

Fig 10-13. Effect of expansion tank location with respect to pump pressure

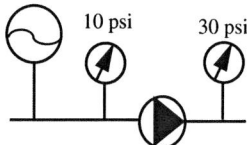

Fig 10-14. Effect of expansion tank location with respect to pump pressure

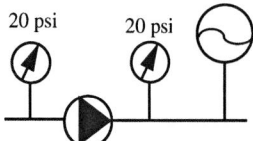

Pump Off

Fig 10-15. Effect of expansion tank location with respect to pump pressure

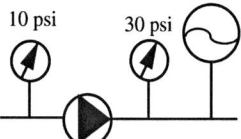

Pump On

Fig 10-16. Effect of expansion tank location with respect to pump pressure

Characteristics of Centrifugal Pumps

There are two distinct types of centrifugal pumps: (1) the turbine type pump, which uses diffusers or guide vanes in the casing for the conversion of velocity to pressure energy, and (2) the volute-type centrifugal pump, most commonly used.

Mechanically, a volute type centrifugal pump consists of an impeller or runner having curved vanes revolving on a shaft and housed in a shell or casing. Liquid enters the impeller axially to the shaft and it has energy imparted to it by rotating vanes of the impeller. The fluid leaves the periphery of the impeller at a relatively high velocity and is collected in the casing or shell. This casing is so designed that the velocity of the liquid is gradually reduced before it is discharged. Here the velocity of the liquid is converted into pressure by reduction of velocity according to Bernoulli's theorem.

The quantity of liquid discharged by the pump is almost always measured in gpm, although sometimes the measure is cubic feet per second. In this discussion gallons per minute is used as the unit.

Pressure developed by a centrifugal pump is specified as head in feet of liquid.

$$h = \frac{2.31P}{s}$$

where s = specific gravity of the liquid compared to water (water at 60/60°F = 1.00);

h = head in feet; and

P = pressure in psi.

The head developed by a centrifugal pump is a function of the impeller diameter and the speed of rotation (rpm). Maximum head that can be developed by a centrifugal pump is when the discharge valve is tightly closed and the pump is discharging zero capacity into the system. This is known as the *shut-off* head of the pump. Since there is a predetermined maximum pressure that the pump can develop and this pressure is taken into account by the designer, centrifugal pumps do not require relief valves or other unloading mechanizers that are otherwise necessary for the positive displacement type pumps. The maximum or *shut-off* head h of any centrifugal pump can be very closely calculated by the formula:

$$h_x = \left(\frac{D \times N}{1840}\right)^2$$

where D = outside diameter of the impeller in. and;

N = rpm.

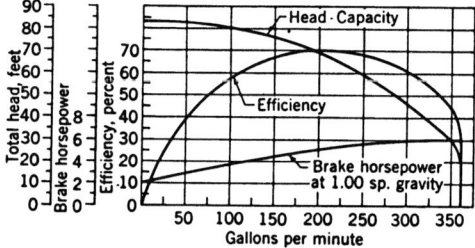

Fig 10-17. Performance curves for a typical centrifugal pump one with 9.5 in. impeller diameter and 1750 rpm constant speed

Operating Characteristics.—Hydraulic operating characteristics of a typical centrifugal pump, or performance curve, is shown in Fig. 10-17. The pressure (or head in feet of liquid) developed by the pump at a specified impeller diameter and at a constant rpm is plotted against the discharge of the pump in gallons per minute (gpm.)

Note that the maximum head developed by the pump is at zero capacity or shut-off as previously mentioned.

The head-capacity curve extends from shut-off to maximum or wide-open capacity. In other words, as the pump discharges more liquid, its pressure decreases. The slope of the head-capacity curve is due to (1) the curve or shape and the number of vanes in the impeller; (2) friction or head loss within the pump. As the pump discharges more liquid, there is increased internal friction, and this friction loss is actually a loss in pressure or head at the discharge of the pump hence, the slope in head capacity curve. The pump designer can control to a certain degree the slope of the head-capacity curve by the shape or warp of the impeller vanes and also by the number of vanes. The internal friction, however, is a factor over which the pump designer has very little control.

The efficiency curve rises to a maximum within certain capacity limits and then falls off toward the maximum capacity of the pump. The brake horsepower curve is usually as shown; that is, brake horsepower gradually increases in value as capacity increases. Maximum efficiency of a centrifugal pump lies within the design range. A pump designer has a definite capacity and head upon which all calculations are based, and the calculations are such that the maximum efficiency of the pump will be at or very near design capacity.

Pump Laws.—The efficiency of a centrifugal pump, as for any machine, is horsepower output divided by the horsepower input. When efficiency is known the horsepower requirement of the pump is determined by the formula:

$$HP = \frac{gpm \times DH \times s}{3960 \times E}$$

where DH = dynamic head in feet;

s = specific gravity; and

E = efficiency expressed as a decimal.

This formula holds for any liquid since the specific gravity of liquid as compared with water may be inserted in the formula.

Change of Performance.—The so-called laws of affinity relating to centrifugal pumps are theoretical rules that apply to the change in performance of a centrifugal pump by a change in the speed of rotation or a change in the impeller diameter of a particular pump. It should always be remembered in using these laws of affinity that they are theoretical and do not always give exact results as compared with tests. However, they are a good guide for predicting the hydraulic performance characteristic of a pump from a known characteristic caused by either altering the speed of rotation or the outside diameter of the impeller. The laws of affinity may be stated as follows:

At a constant impeller diameter,

1. capacity varies directly as the speed:

2. head varies directly as the square of the speed; and

3. horsepower varies directly as the cube of the speed.

In equation form, the foregoing are expressed as

$$\frac{gpm_y}{gpm_x} = \frac{rpm_y}{rpm_x}$$

$$\frac{head_y}{head_x} = \frac{rpm_y^2}{rpm_x^2}$$

$$\frac{bhp_y}{bhp_x} = \frac{rpm_y^3}{rpm_x^3}$$

At constant speed:

1. capacity varies directly as the cube of the impeller diameter;

2. head varies directly as the square of the impeller diameter; and

3. horsepower varies directly as the fifth power of the impeller diameter.

Or, in equation form,

$$\frac{gpm_y}{gpm_x} = \frac{d_y}{d_x}$$

$$\frac{head_y}{head_x} = \frac{d_y^3}{d_x^3}$$

$$\frac{bhp_y}{bhp_x} = \frac{d_y^5}{d_x^5}$$

Example: In Table 10-1 are tabulated actual characteristics of a centrifugal pump at a certain impeller diameter at a constant speed of 1150 rpm. Predict the performance of this particular pump at the increased speed of 1750 rpm by the affinity laws.

Table 10-1. Performance of a Certain Pump at 1150 rpm

GPM	Total Head, ft	BHP	Efficiency,%
0	43.2	6.0	...
200	42.9	7.2	30
400	42.0	8.15	52
800	38.0	10.1	76
1200	29.0	10.7	82.3
1400	21.5	11.0	69

Using the subscript x for the unknown performance at 1750 rpm and y for the performance at 1150 rpm, we have, using the first group of formulas, at 400 fpm for 1150 rpm:

$$gpm_x = \frac{gpm_y \times rpm_x}{rpm_y} = \frac{400 \times 1750}{1150} = 610 \text{ gpm}$$

When the pump operates at 1750 rpm and

$$head_x = \frac{head_y \times rpm_x^2}{rpm_y^2} = \frac{42 \times 1750^2}{1150^2} = 97 \text{ ft}$$

and

$$bhp = \frac{bhp_y \times rpm_x^3}{rpm_x^3} = \frac{8.15 \times 1750^3}{1150^3} = 28.7 \text{ hp}$$

Table 10-2. Performance of Pump in Table 10-1 when Speed is 1750 rpm

GPM	Total Head, ft	BHP	Efficiency%
0	100	21.1	...
304	99	25.3	30
610	97	28.7	52
1220	88	35.6	76
1825	67	37.7	82
2130	50	38.7	69

The 610 gpm, 97 ft, and 28.7 hp are the capacity, head and horsepower of the pump when operating at 1750 rpm. Carrying through the same calculations for other capacities, the data arrived at in Table 10-2 are found.

Centrifugal Pump Selection.—In the following, the calculations will be on the basis of handling clear, cold water having a specific gravity of 1.00. Assume that the desired capacity or discharge of the pump (in gpm) has already been established.

Total Dynamic Head.—In order to select a centrifugal pump for any installation, particular care must be taken in determining the *total dynamic head* of the system. Careful calculation of the total dynamic head is the most important element of centrifugal pump selection. This fact cannot be stressed too strongly. The total dynamic head (TDH) consists of the following factors all added together:

1. *Static suction lift* (h_L) or *suction head* (h_v): The vertical distance in feet from the free level of the source of supply to the horizontal centerline of the pump.

2. *Static discharge head* (h_d): The vertical distance in feet from the centerline of the pump to point of free discharge; or, the level of free surface of the discharged liquid, or, in the case of discharging under pressure, the equivalent level of free discharge in feet of liquid.

3. *Friction head* (h_f): The head in feet of liquid required to overcome the frictional resistance of the piping and fittings of both the suction and discharge lines.

When the pump is above the source of supply and a static suction lift condition prevails,

$$TDH = h_l + h_d + h_f$$

If, however, the source of supply is above the pump, the liquid then flows to the pump by gravity, a static suction head condition exists

$$TDH = h_d - h_p + h_f$$

In determining the total dynamic head of a pumping system, the friction head and static head should be calculated at the maximum or extreme conditions of operation. In other words, the static head should be the maximum capacity required by the system. The drawing of a system head or service curve is recommended practice.

Example 2: Determine the total dynamic head of the following water system: maximum capacity, 200 gpm; maximum static suction lift, 5 ft: maximum static discharge head, 30 ft: suction piping consisting of 10 ft of 4-in pipe and one 90° 4-in. elbow; discharge piping consisting of 115 ft or 3-in. pipe, five 90° 3-in. elbows and one gate valve fully opened.

Solution: The total static elevation is 35 ft (composed of 5 ft static suction lift and 30 ft static discharge). The next step is to plot the friction head at various capacities. From water friction tables secure the following information based on the pipe having a friction coefficient or smoothness factor of 15 year old pipe; one 4-in. 90° elbow is equivalent to 11 ft of straight pipe; five 3-in. 90° elbows are equivalent to 8 × 5 or 40 ft of straight pipe, one 3 in. gate valve fully open is equivalent to 1.5 ft of straight pipe. Therefore, on the suction of the pump there is an equivalent total of 21 ft of 4-in. pipe and on the discharge an equivalent total of 156.5 ft of 3-in. pipe. Friction for the various capacities in the suction and discharge piping is calculated and tabulated in Table 10-3.

Table 10-3. Friction Heads for Illustrative Problem

gpm	Suction Pipe Friction	Discharge Pipe Friction	Total Friction
50	0.07	2.16	2.23
100	0.26	7.80	8.06
150	0.55	16.6	17.15
200	0.91	28.2	29.11
250	1.32	42.2	43.52

Plot the friction head data from Table 10-3 on graph paper and find that at a capacity of 200 gpm a pump is required that can reach 64 ft total dynamic head.

To carry the function of the service curve still further, on the service curve can be plotted the hydraulic performance curve of a pump that will develop 200 gpm at 64 ft total dynamic head. This pump cannot pump more than the predetermined maximum capacity of 200 gpm since if 200 gpm is exceeded, the total head exceeds the head capabilities of this particular pump at 200 gpm. In other words, the friction head of the system throttles the pump to a maximum capacity of 200 gpm providing the maximum conditions of static head prevail. If, for example, the static suction lift might at times be zero or the water level at the suction source is level with the pump horizontal centerline, the total static head reduces itself from 35 to 30 ft, but, since the piping arrangement has not been changed the friction head remains unchanged. A second service curve can therefore be plotted based on the minimum static suction condition. Therefore, when this suction condition exists, the pump capacity would be 212 gpm with a varying discharge condition from 200 to 212 gpm depending upon the static suction lift.

Net Positive Suction Head (*NPSH*).—In addition to selecting a centrifugal pump to perform based on the total dynamic head of the system and the capacity required, it is necessary to check the *net positive suction head* (*NPSH*) characteristic of the pump against the *NPSH* supplied by the system. Pump *NPSH* is determined by test and computation, it is the energy needed to keep the suction of the pump flooded and completely under liquid. Required *NPSH* varies with pump type and design, pump size, operating fluid, and conditions. Its values are normally supplied by the pump manufacturer in the form of a curve covering the entire operating range. Calculation for *NPSH* at the suction side of the pump is:

$$NPSH = Z - \frac{V_s^2}{2g} - h_{fs} + \frac{2.31 P}{s} - \frac{2.31 P_{sat}}{s}$$

where Z = vertical distance of free level of source of supply to horizontal centerline of pump, ft;

V_s = velocity of liquid in suction line;

h_{fs} = friction head in suction line only, ft;

P = pressure on liquid surface, psia;

P_{sat} = saturation pressure at surface of supply source depending on the liquid and its vapor conditions, psia; and

s = liquid specific gravity

The system *NPSH* must be higher than the *NPSH* required by the pump at all operating conditions. When the *NPSH* in the suction line falls below the value required, vapor bubbles form and are carried into the impeller. There the vapor bubbles collapse due to the high pressure level maintained by the pump. This will cause excessive noise and vibration, or *cavitation*. If this condition persists, excessive impeller erosion, bearing failure, shaft breakage, and other evidences of fatigue and wear failure can appear.

Pumping System

Centrifugal pumps are the type most commonly used in hydronic systems. Circulating pumps used in water systems can vary in size and type. Horizontal and vertical in-line centrifugal pumps are mostly used for smaller systems and end suction pumps are being used for larger systems. The pumps should be selected to provide maximum efficiency usually more than 60% is desirable. The piping connections and pump curves for the series 60 and 80 Bell & Gossett centrifugal in-line pumps are given in Figs. 10-18 to 10-20.

The piping connection and pump curves for the series 1510 Bell & Gossett centrifugal end suction pumps are given in Figs. 10-21 to 10-23.

Unlike open systems in which pumps must overcome the net static head and the losses due to friction, in closed hydronic systems the pump must overcome only friction losses in the piping system. The characteristic curve (or system curve) of a closed hydronic system has a half parabola shape and can be described with the following equation shown in Fig. 10-24:

$$\Delta P = C \times gpm^2 \qquad (9)$$

where ΔP = system pressure drop, psi or ft

C = system characteristics coefficient

gpm = flow rate, gallon/min.

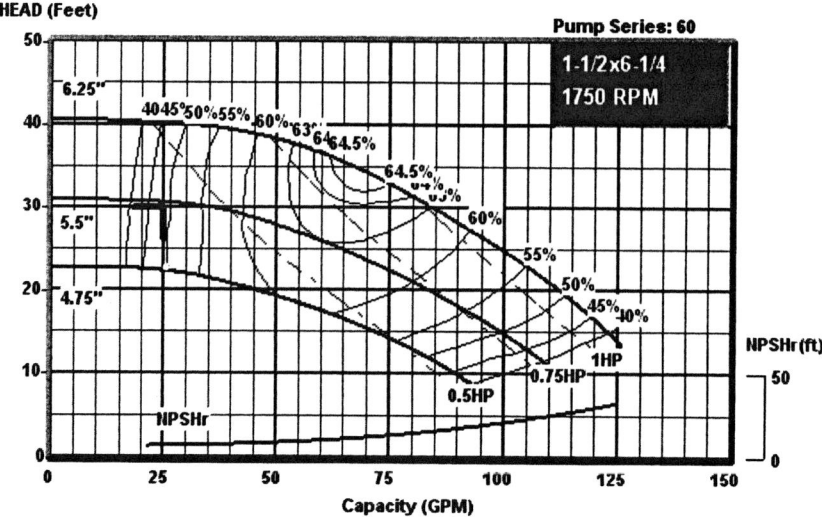

Fig 10-18. Pump curve for Series 60 B&G inline pump

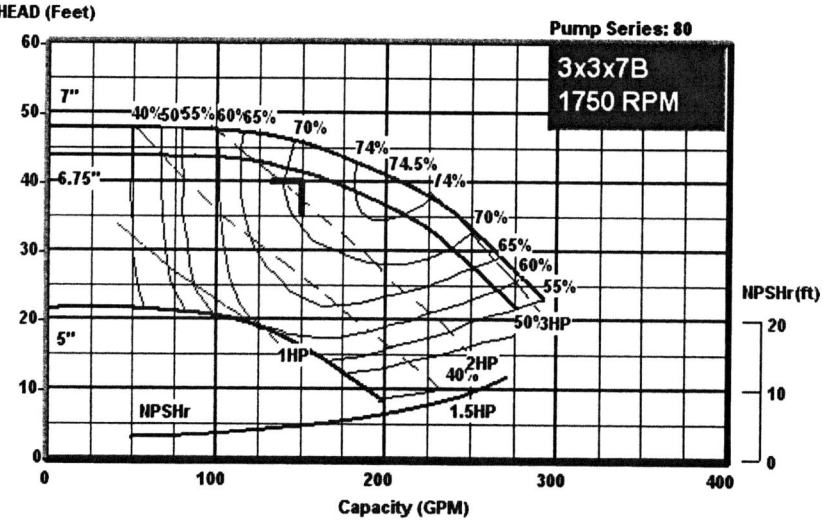

Fig 10-19. Pump curve for Series 80 B&G inline pump

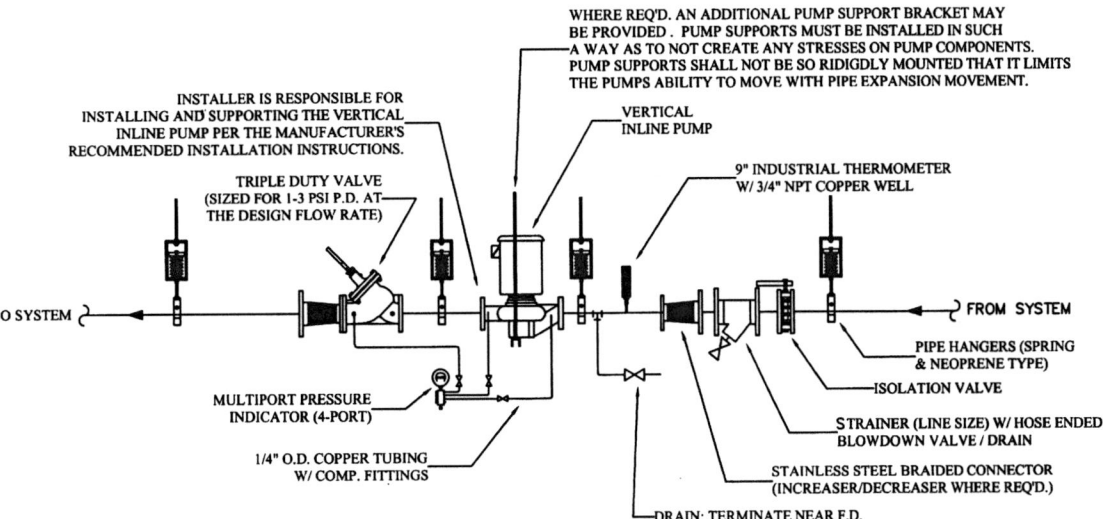

Fig 10-20. Vertical inline pump detail

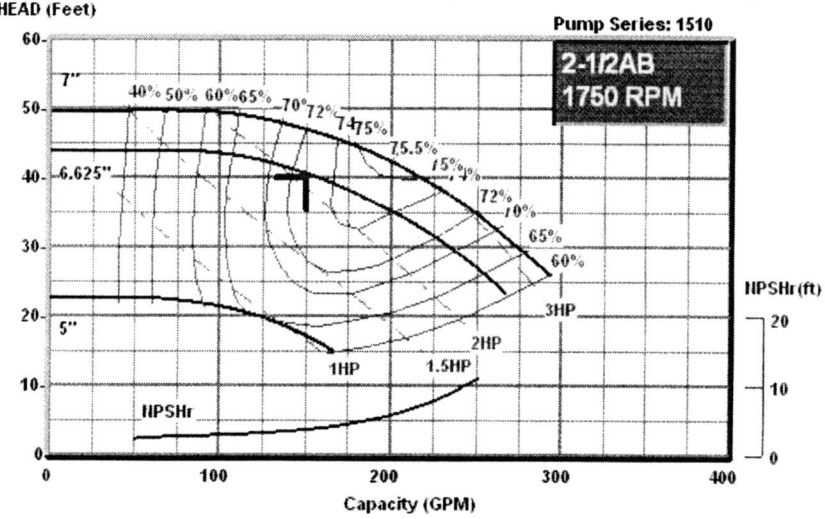

Fig 10-21. Pump curve for Series 1510 B&G end suction pump

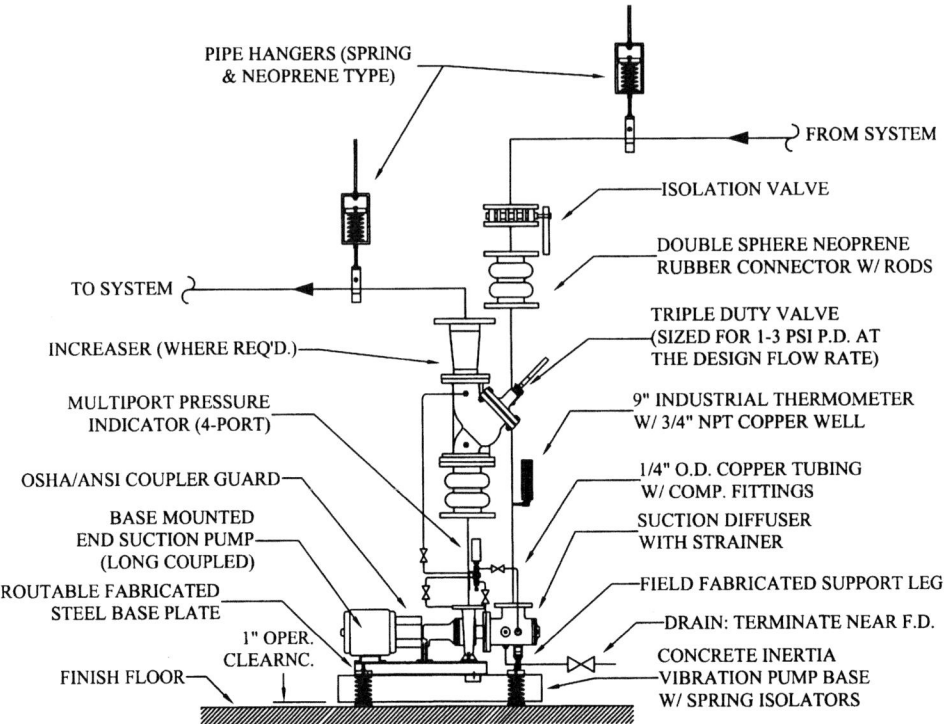

PIPE HANGERS (SPRING & NEOPRENE TYPE)

FROM SYSTEM

ISOLATION VALVE

DOUBLE SPHERE NEOPRENE RUBBER CONNECTOR W/ RODS

TRIPLE DUTY VALVE (SIZED FOR 1-3 PSI P.D. AT THE DESIGN FLOW RATE)

TO SYSTEM

INCREASER (WHERE REQ'D.)

9" INDUSTRIAL THERMOMETER W/ 3/4" NPT COPPER WELL

MULTIPORT PRESSURE INDICATOR (4-PORT)

1/4" O.D. COPPER TUBING W/ COMP. FITTINGS

OSHA/ANSI COUPLER GUARD

SUCTION DIFFUSER WITH STRAINER

BASE MOUNTED END SUCTION PUMP (LONG COUPLED)

GROUTABLE FABRICATED STEEL BASE PLATE

FIELD FABRICATED SUPPORT LEG

1" OPER. CLEARNC.

DRAIN: TERMINATE NEAR F.D.

CONCRETE INERTIA VIBRATION PUMP BASE W/ SPRING ISOLATORS

FINISH FLOOR

Fig 10-22. End suction pump detail

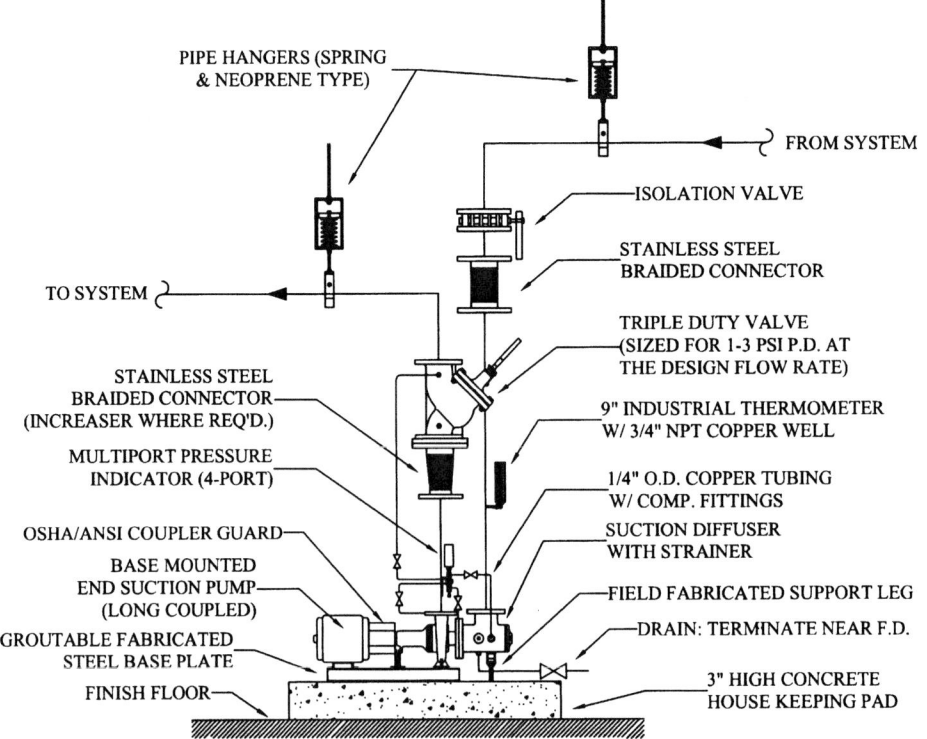

PIPE HANGERS (SPRING & NEOPRENE TYPE)

FROM SYSTEM

ISOLATION VALVE

STAINLESS STEEL BRAIDED CONNECTOR

TRIPLE DUTY VALVE (SIZED FOR 1-3 PSI P.D. AT THE DESIGN FLOW RATE)

TO SYSTEM

STAINLESS STEEL BRAIDED CONNECTOR (INCREASER WHERE REQ'D.)

9" INDUSTRIAL THERMOMETER W/ 3/4" NPT COPPER WELL

MULTIPORT PRESSURE INDICATOR (4-PORT)

1/4" O.D. COPPER TUBING W/ COMP. FITTINGS

OSHA/ANSI COUPLER GUARD

SUCTION DIFFUSER WITH STRAINER

BASE MOUNTED END SUCTION PUMP (LONG COUPLED)

FIELD FABRICATED SUPPORT LEG

GROUTABLE FABRICATED STEEL BASE PLATE

DRAIN: TERMINATE NEAR F.D.

FINISH FLOOR

3" HIGH CONCRETE HOUSE KEEPING PAD

Fig 10-23. End suction pump detail

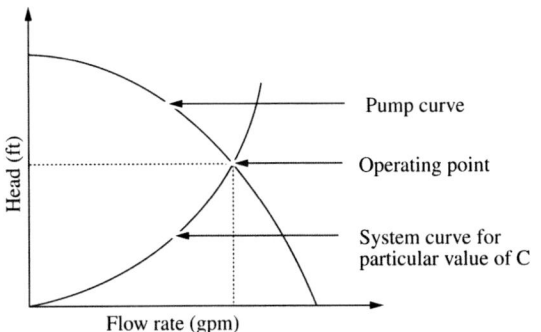

Fig 10-24. System characteristic curves

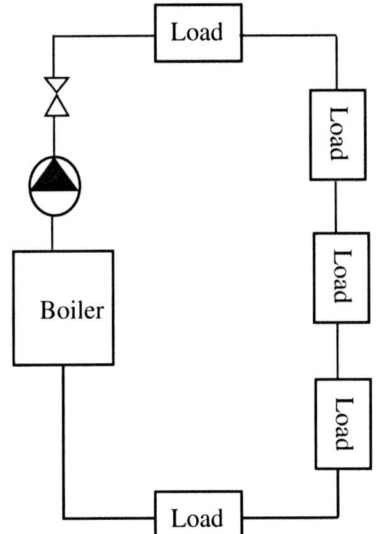

Fig 10-25. Simple hydronic series system

The value of C changes when system friction loss changes. The change in value of C will then result in a change in characteristic curve of the system. For example, for the simple hydronic system shown in Fig. 10-25, the series 60 B&G inline pump must provide 25 gpm and 30 feet of head (discharge pressure) to satisfy the flow rate requirement of the system and overcome the piping system friction losses when the valve is fully open. In this case when the valve is fully open the value of C is determined as follow:

$$C = \frac{\Delta P}{gpm^2} = \frac{30}{25^2} = 0.048$$

$$\Delta P = 0.048 gpm^2$$

The characteristic curve for fully open valve condition based on above equation are shown in Fig. 10-26. However when the valve is partially closed, the friction loss in the system increases to a value more than 30 feet and as a result, system flow rate (gpm) will decreases to a value less than 25 gpm as shown in Fig. 10-26.

The point A where the system characteristic curve (for fully open valve condition) crosses pump curve is called system operating point which in this case is 30 feet of head and 25 gpm. Operating points may be highly variable, depending on(1) load conditions, (2) the types of control valves used, and (3) the piping circuitry and heat transfer elements. In general, the best selection will be

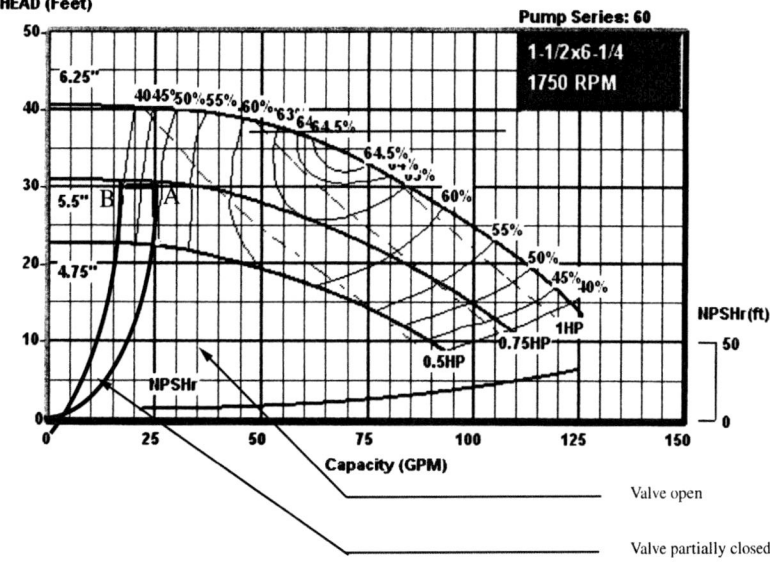

Fig 10-26. Pump curve for Series 60 B&G inline pump

1) For design flow rates calculated using pressure drop charts that illustrate actual closed loop hydronic system piping pressure drops.

2) To the left of the maximum efficiency point of the Pump curve to allow shifts to the right caused by system circuit imbalance, direct return circuitry applications, and modulating three-way valve applications.

3) A pump with a flat curve to compensate for unbalanced circuitry and to provide a minimum pressure differential increase across two-way control valves.

Parallel Pumping.—Now, we apply this system curve knowledge to parallel and series pumping. Fig. 10-27 shows a typical installation consisting of two pumps in parallel with shut off and check valves to allow one-pump operation and to prevent recirculation during one-pump operation. With two pumps in parallel, each pump handles half the total desired flow at the full head required. Fig. 10-28 shows this. The initial single pump selection is made on that basis.

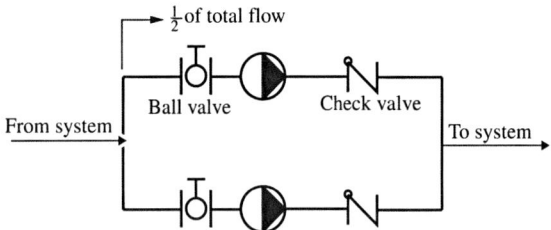

Fig 10-27. Typical installation of two pumps in parallel, with check valve

To construct the combined impeller curve for the two pumps in parallel, the flow produced by the single pump at any given head is doubled. See Fig. 10-29. The actual point of system operation is then as shown in Fig. 10-30.

Assume that a total of 200 gpm at 30 ft is desired when both pumps are running. Again, we calculate the plot points for the system curve as shown in Fig. 10-31.

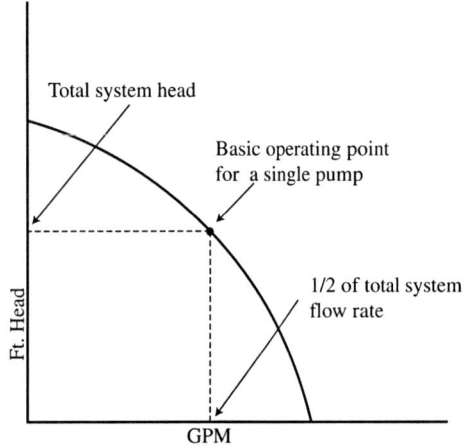

Fig 10-28. Basic pump operating point

When this system curve is plotted over single and combined pump impeller curves, some very important information becomes available. Referring to Fig. 10-32, Point 2, where system and combined impeller curves intersect, is the point of system operation with both pumps running. Point 1, which is the intersection of the operating head line and the single-pump impeller curve, is the point at which each pump operates when both pumps are running. This point represents one half the flow at Point 2 and at the same head as Point 2. This point is also where the power usage of each pump is calculated when they are running together.

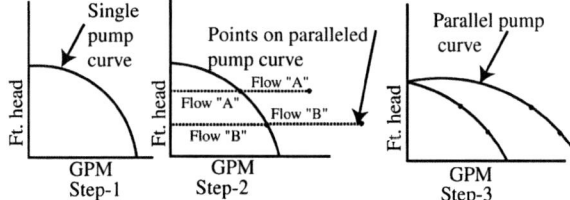

Fig 10-29. Paralleled pump curve construction

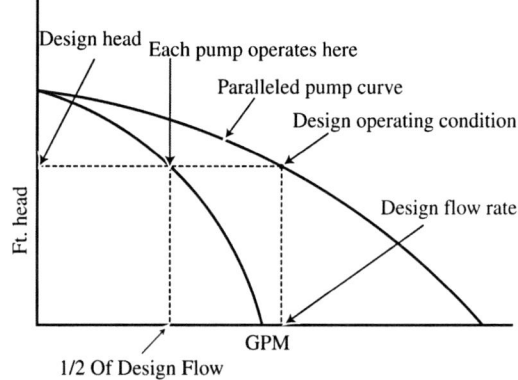

Fig 10-30. Actual point of system operation and the constructed combined parallel curve

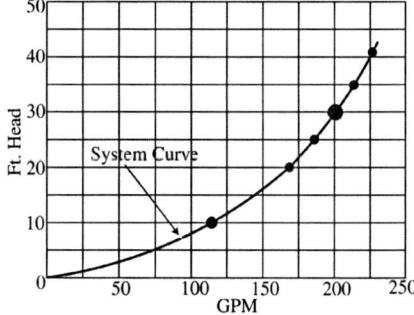

Fig 10-31. Paralleled pump system curve

When one pump is cut off, the point of operation for the system becomes Point 3, Fig. 10-33. Note that the individual operating point of the pump has moved out and down the single-pump impeller curve to the intersection with the system curve. Always remember that, for whatever combination of pumps is running, the operating point has to be on the system curve. With the move from Point 2 to Point 3, it can be seen that more water at less head is being delivered by the one pump running alone than it was delivering as half its share when it was running with the other pump. This means more power is required under this condition and therefore this point must be examined to be sure the motor size is sufficient to take care of this condition.

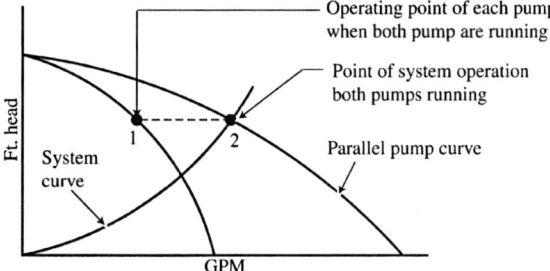

Fig 10-32. System curve plotted over single pump and combined impeller curves

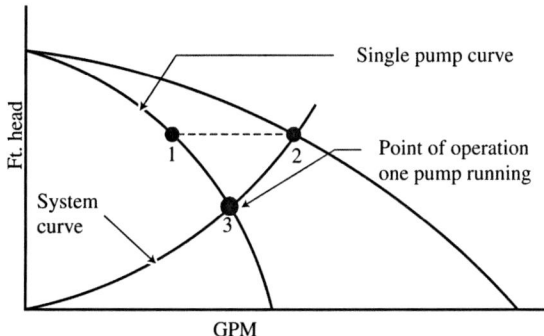

Fig 10-33. Point of system operation, single pump operation, parallel installation

Also note that the system flow is now less than at Point 2 but more than at Point 1. How much less the flow is at Point 3 than at Point 2, of course, determined by the particular pumps and system curve; but, usually, the one-pump point is 80% to 85% of total design flow. This provides a very comfortable stand-by capability if one pump should have to be shut down for repairs.

This also demonstrates why adding a second, equal pump in parallel to an existing system does not double flow, as so many seem to think, but adds only the difference between Points 3 and 2, which could be as much as 20% or as small as 5%.

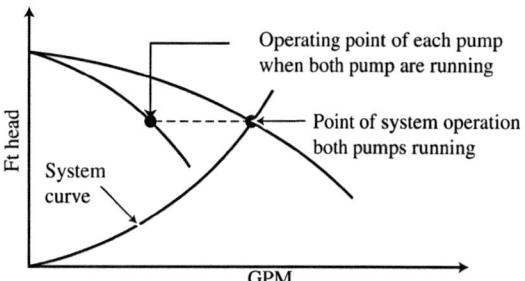

Fig 10-34. Point of system operation, parallel pumps, end point curve

There is another important item that must be checked at Point 3. Refer to Fig. 10-34 here a situation is shown in which the one-pump curve does not intersect with the system curve. This means the pumps selected were too small and, if one pump operation were to take place with this combination, the lone pump would be required to operate beyond its curve, at an unstable point. The result would be unsatisfactory performance and probable damage to the pump itself.

Series Pumping.—Fig. 10-35 shows a basic series pumping arrangement. Fig. 10-36 is a more practical set-up, allowing one pump to operate when the other is down for service. With two pumps in series, each pump delivers 100% of the flow at half of the desired system head. The selection of each pump is made on that basis. See Fig. 10-37.

Fig 10-35. Basic series pump installation

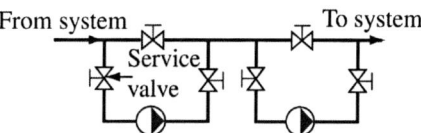

Fig 10-36. Practical series pump installation

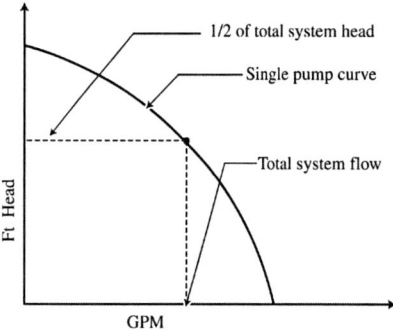

Fig 10-37. Basic series operation single pump curve

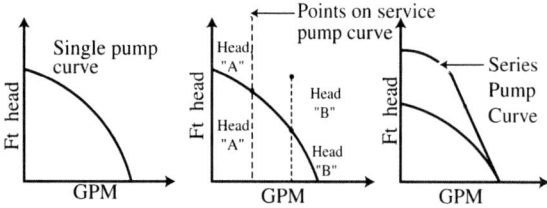

Fig 10-38. Series pump curve construction

To construct the combined impeller curve for the two pumps in series, the head produced by the single pump at any given flow is doubled. See Fig. 10-38. The actual point of system operation, Point 1 is as shown in Fig. 10-39 where the system curve (which was determined by solving Fanning's equation based on full flow and full head at known points) intersects the combined series impeller curve.

Point 2, the intersection of the one-pump curve at design or full flow, is the point at which each pump operates when both are running. Each pump is delivering full flow at half the total head. Power usage of each pump under these conditions is determined at this point.

Fig. 10-40 shows Point 3, the point of one-pump operation, the intersection of the one-pump impeller curve, and the system curve. Note that the individual pump operating Point (2) has moved back and up the impeller curve to Point 3. Thus, the case is just the opposite of the case with parallel one-pump operation. Instead of requiring more, actually less power is required.

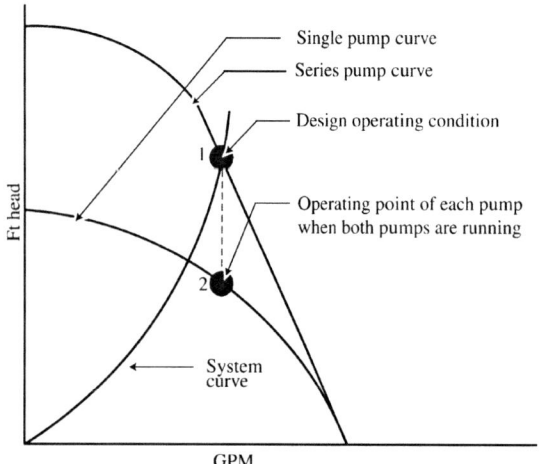

Fig 10-39. Series pump system operation

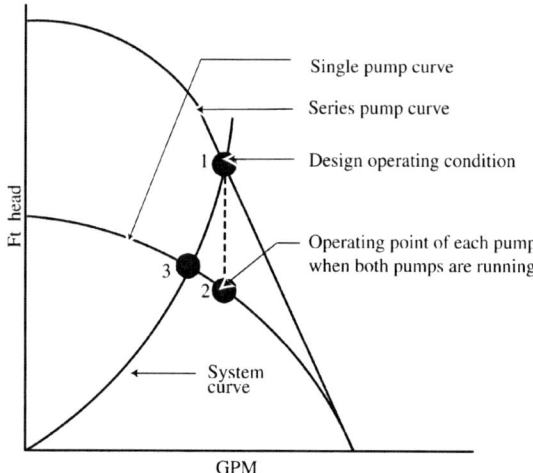

Fig 10-40. Single pump operation series installation

However, as in parallel pumping, single-pump flow is a considerable portion of total flow, as high as 85% to 95%, depending on the particular pumps and system curve. Therefore, considerable standby capacity is available if one pump needs to be serviced. Again, this demonstrates why adding a second, equal pump in series with an existing system does not double the head, as so many seem to think. The actual increase would be from Point 3 to Point 1. The percentage increase of head is greater than the percentage increase of flow, which is from Point 3 to Point 1, but will not be double.

Design Procedures

Preliminary Equipment Layout.—*Flows in Mains and Laterals :* Regardless of the method used to determine the flow through each item of terminal equipment, the desired result should be listed in terms of mass flow on the preliminary plans or in a schedule of flow rates for the piping system. (In the design of small systems and chilled water systems, the determination may be made in terms of volumetric flow). In an equipment schedule or on the plans, starting from the most remote terminal and working toward the pump, progressively list the cumulative flow in each of the mains and branch circuits in the distribution system.

Preliminary Pipe Sizing: For each portion of the piping circuit, select a tentative pipe size from the unified flow chart, using a value of pipe friction loss ranging from 0.75 to 4 ft per 100 ft (approximately 0.1 to 0.5 in/ft). Residential piping size is often based on pump preselection using pipe sizing tables, which are available from the Hydronics Institute or from manufacturers.

Preliminary Pressure Drop: Using the preliminary pipe sizing indicated above, determine the pressure drop through each portion of the piping. The total pressure drop in the longest circuits determines the maximum pressure drop through the piping, including the terminals and control valves, that must be available in the form of pump pressure.

Preliminary Pump Selection: The preliminary selection should be based on the pump's ability to fulfill the determined capacity requirements. It should be selected at a point left of center on the pump curve and should not overload the motor. Because pressure drop in a flow system varies as the square of the flow rate, the flow variation between the nearest size of stock pump and an exact point selection will be relatively minor.

Final Pipe Sizing and Pressure Drop Determination.—*Final Piping Layout:* Examine the overall piping layout to determine whether pipe sizes in some areas need to be readjusted. Several principal circuits should have approximately equal pressure drops so that excessive pressures are not needed to serve a small portion of the building.

Consider both the initial cost of the pump and piping system and the pump's operating cost when determining final system friction loss. Generally, lower heads and larger piping are more economical when longer amortization periods are considered, especially in larger systems. However, in small systems such as in residences, it may be most economical to select the pump first and design the piping system to meet the available pressure. In all cases, adjust the piping system design and pump selection until the optimum design is found.

Final Pressure Drop.— When the final piping layout has been established determine the friction loss for each section of the piping system from the pressure drop charts (Chapter 9) for the mass flow rate in each portion of the piping system. After calculating the friction loss at design flow for all sections of the piping system and all fittings, terminal units, and control valves, sum them for several of the longest piping circuits to determine the pressure against which the pump must operate at design flow.

Final Pump Selection.— After completing the final pressure drop calculations, select the pump by plotting a system curve and pump curve and selecting the pump or pump assembly that operates closest to the calculated design point.

Freeze Prevention.—All circulating water systems require precautions to prevent freezing, particularly in makeup air applications in temperate climates where (1) coils are exposed to outdoor air at below-freezing temperatures, (2) undrained chilled water coils are in the winter airstream, or (3) piping passes through unheated spaces. Freezing will not occur as long as flow is maintained and the water is at least warm. Unfortunately, during

extremely cold weather or in the event of a power failure, water flow and temperature cannot be guaranteed. Additionally, continuous pumping can be energy-intensive and cause system wear. Designers should take following precautions to prevent flow stoppage or damage from freezing:

1. Select all load devices (such as preheat coils) that are subjected to outdoor air temperatures for constant flow, variable control.

2. Position the coil valves of all cooling coils with valve controls that are dormant in winter months to the full-open position at those times.

3. If intermittent pump operation is used as an economy measure, use an automatic override to operate both chilled water and heating water pumps in below-freezing weather.

4. Select pump starters that automatically restart after power failure (i.e., maintain-contact control).

5. Select non overloading pumps.

6. Instruct operating personnel never to shut down pumps in subfreezing weather.

7. Do not use aquastats, which can stop a pump, in boiler circuits.

8. Avoid sluggish circulation, which may cause air binding or dirt deposit. Properly balance and clean systems. Provide proper air control or means to eliminate air.

9. Install low temperature detection thermostats that have phase change capillaries wound in a serpentine pattern across the leaving face of the upstream coil.

When designing fan equipment that handles outdoor air, take precautions to avoid stratification of air entering the coil. The best methods for proper mixing of indoor and outdoor air are the following:

1. Select dampers for pressure drops adequate to provide stable control of mixing, preferably with dampers installed several equivalent diameters upstream of the air-handling unit.

2. Design intake and approach duct systems to promote natural mixing.

3. Select coils with circuiting that allows parallel flow of air and water.

Freeze-up may still occur with any of these precautions. If an antifreeze solution is not used, water should circulate at all times. Valve controlled elements should have low-limit thermostats, and sensing elements should be located to ensure accurate air temperature readings. Primary and secondary pumping of coils with three-way valve injection is advantageous. Use outdoor reset of water temperature wherever possible.

ENERGY ESTIMATING FUNDAMENTALS

ENERGY CALCULATION

The Degree Day

Experience has shown that, for buildings requiring an inside air temperature of approximately 70°F, the amount of fuel or heat used per day is proportional to the number of degrees the average outside temperature falls below about 65°F. The degree day is based upon this principle. Thus the number of degree days (65°F base) per day is the difference between 65°F and the daily mean temperature when the latter is less than 65°F.

The number of degree days for a given day is thus: (65°F − daily mean temperature for that day) × 1 (day), and the number of degree-days for any longer period is the sum of all such products for as many days as the period covers.

No attention is given to those days when the outside temperature averages above 65°F.

Example: The highest temperature recorded in Baltimore on December 12, 1931, was 70°F and the minimum was 52°F. The daily mean temperature was therefore (70 + 52) ÷ 2 or 61°F. The number of degree days for that day in Baltimore was thus (65 − 61) × 1 = 4. Carrying through this operation for each of the 31 days for December 1931, it is found that the number of degree-days in Baltimore for that month was 601.

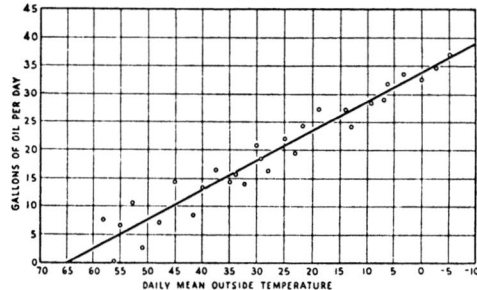

Fig 11-1. Fuel consumption per day plotted against mean daily temperature

The degree-day thus defined is now so widely used that when the unit is mentioned in the United States it is understood that the 65°F base is referred to unless some other base or some other descriptive word is used with it.

The gas consumption of house heating plants in that city varied with the number of degrees difference in outside temperature and 64°F. Later studies indicated that when the figure was 65°F the relationship was improved. As a result the 65°F figure was put into use and the name of "degree-day" was given to the unit related to this base temperature. Thus, from the inception of the unit, field study supported the conclusion that the proportionality between fuel consumption and temperature difference begins at a temperature of 65°F in heating residential buildings.

65°F as the Base.—Perhaps the earliest attempt to gather field data to confirm or reject the validity of the 65°F value of the inside daily temperature took the form of noting in the field if there was any relation between the outside temperature and the time of starting up residential heating plants in the fall. It was found that when the mean daily outside temperature fell to about 65°F, there was a considerable tendency to start the heating plant. Such observations tended to confirm the general idea that the base of proportionality was in the vicinity of 65°F.

The general method of investigating the relationship by direct field studies is illustrated in Fig. 11-1 where observed fuel consumption data are plotted against daily mean outside temperature. In order to make such a study the fuel should be one that is easily measured, so that the exact quantity burned can be recorded without too much work, and the plant should be one in which the fuel measured is all used for the heating of the building and none for cooking or service water heating. In the example shown in Fig. 11-1, on a day when the mean temperature outside was 35°F the plant required 14½ gallons of oil; when it was 40°F, 13½ gallons; 0°F, 32¼ gallons, and so on. These points were plotted and a straight line drawn through them so that the points on either side of the line numbered about the same. In this case the line crosses the zero fuel consumption axis at 65°F. In any particular plant the straight line will cross at or a few degrees above or below 65°F. If the variation is more than a few degrees some special conditions apply which must be taken into consideration. The point at which the axis is crossed fixes the value of the outside temperature at which fuel consumption starts, or the base of the relation between fuel consumption and temperature difference. Evidently, if a large number of separate plant operations could be studied the results would show whether or not the base line was generally at 65°F or whether it was only coincidental. Many such studies have now been made.

Table 11-1. Base Temperature for Different Buildings as determined by Field Tests

Type of Buildings	Base°F	Type of Buildings	Base °F
Office	66.2	Apartments	68.8
Office and banks	65.8	Residences	66.9
Banks	66.2	Clubs	65.5
Telephone exchanges	65.5	Theaters	67.6
Office and stores	67.4	Warehouses and lofts	65.2
Stores	64.0	Manufacturing	65.4
Department stores	64.3	Average for 175 buildings of all types	66.0
Hotels	66.5		

It might be supposed that since the relationship of heat required and temperature was determined from an analysis of the performance of the heating plants in residences, a base temperature of other than 65°F would apply to buildings with a different character of occupancy such as office buildings and stores. When the inside temperature maintained is sharply different from 65°F as in certain industrial buildings, such a conclusion is correct. But buildings heated to 70°F or about 70°F show a relationship to the 65°F base, even though their usage and character of occupancy may differ from that of the ordinary residence. A study made by the National District Heating Association of a number of buildings showed that the heat requirements of the buildings reached zero at the bases listed in Table 11-1. It will be noted that in most cases the base temperature indicated by these studies is at or near 65 °F.

Table 11-2. Variations in Monthly Degree Days in Six Cities for September through June

Month	Normal	Average Warmest	Average Coldest	Compared with Normal Warmest	Coldest
September	92	27	193	–65	+ 101
October	346	176	555	–170	+ 209
November	652	454	852	–198	+ 200
December	1014	785	1319	–229	+305
January	1119	774	1447	–345	+328
February	1016	804	1411	–212	+395
March	859	544	1106	–315	+247
April	519	334	687	–185	+168
May	212	102	413	–110	+101
June	42	7	132	–35	+90
Total	5871	4007	8115	–1864	+2244

From an analysis by Anthracite Institute.

While most types of building are operated with inside air temperatures approximating 70°F during the heating season, there are important cases where the maintained temperature departs considerably from 70°F. Prominent among such cases are industrial buildings of various kinds. But little authentic information is in existence to show at what temperature the proportionality between fuel and temperature difference begins in such plants.

There are two types of degree-day figures for any locality. One is the number of degree-days that have accrued for that locality during a specific period, such as a month, or the whole heating season. These can be termed **actual degree-days**. The other is the normal, or average, number of degree-days for that locality, on a monthly or yearly basis; the normal is the average for similar periods over many years.

The number of degree-days accumulated in a given locality for any period, such as in a month or a year, necessarily varies from month to month and year to year. The analysis by Anthracite Institute presented in Table 11-2 illustrates this fluctuation clearly.

Analysis of Weather Bureau records back to the turn of the century produced the lowest and highest degree-day totals for each month average for the cities of Boston, New York, Philadelphia, Scranton, Syracuse, and Toronto. The years of warmest and coldest months among cities did not coincide in many instances. For example, the coldest Januaries were in 1918 in New York, Philadelphia and Scranton, 1920 in Boston and Syracuse and 1912 in Toronto. On the other hand, 1917 marked the coldest December in each city, while the warmest December everywhere was in 1923.

Table 11-2 shows the average normals in these six cities the average degree days in the warmest and coldest months and deviations from normals. The warmest months constituted a season 31.7% warmer than normal, the coldest 38.2% colder than normal. At the coldest, the heat demand would be more than double that in the warmest of record.

An opinion sometimes expressed is that the degree-day is inaccurate because wind is not taken into account. This is not altogether true. The effect of wind on the heating of a building depends on (1) the velocity and (2) the temperature of the wind. Both are considered for maximum conditions in the design of the heating plant and reflected in its size. The degree-day in turn, by indicating the temperature of the wind, takes care of this variable through the heating season. Not accounted for is the fluctuation of wind velocity through the season. Use of the degree-day implies that the effect of the wind varies inversely as its temperature and that the velocity varies with degree-days. The former is true, the latter true at times, not true at others.

Application of Degree-Day.—There are two principal uses of the degree-day: (1) as a means of eliminating the outside temperature variable in comparing fuel consumption data; and (2) for predicting fuel consumption. The first use is one with wide application for comparison of data for the same building. If a building uses a given amount of fuel for a certain period during which there is a known number of degree-days, simple division gives the amount used per degree-day If, in a subsequent period, this unit figure sharply increases, then some reason must be sought as accounting for the indicated drop in operational efficiency.

The Degree-Day as a Guide in Operation.—The degree-day has been found increasingly useful as time goes on as a means of securing efficient operation of heating plants for it provides a means of checking results while eliminating the weather variable from comparisons. Another wide use of the unit is closely akin to this one and consists of good use of fuel or heat the ultimate consumer.

One example is sufficient to indicate this application of the degree-day, although there are a wide variety of applications and variations in use. The method described is particularly applicable to commercial and institutional buildings where the primary use of fuel or steam is used for the heating of buildings.

Based on past experience for a given building a standard is set up of so many pounds of steam, pounds of coal, gallons of oil or therms of gas that are generally used for that building per degree-day. If a number of buildings are to be considered, this constant can be reduced further to amount of fuel or steam per degree-day per 1000 ft^3 of building volume or square feet of floor space so that it would be possible to compare one building with another.

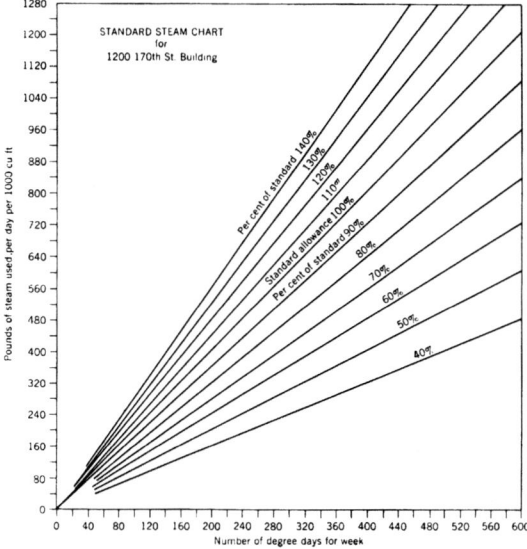

Fig 11-2. Example of chart prepared for a specific building to check operating efficiency

A record of degree-days is kept each day and from this the standard based on previous experience is indicated in amount of fuel or steam per degree-day. The figure for the week, for example, is then compared with the standard and if approximately the same unit figure is arrived at, the plant is being operated as efficiently as during the previous period. If the figure is lower than the standard, then it has been operated more efficiently than formerly and consideration should be given to taking this when setting a new standard. On the other hand, if the unit figure is higher than the standard, then something has happened to affect the operating efficiency and steps should be taken to improve the operation.

Naturally, in such a system the standard should be one that represents really good operating practice with clean boilers, good fuels, and careful efficient operation.

It often happens that when such a standard is set up, the unit figure in fuel used per degree-day gradually increases from week to week rather than show a sharp increase in any one week. This is due to the fact that, as the boilers become dirty or the operator becomes more careless, the lessening efficiency is reflected in a gradual change in the unit figure.

Logical developments in connection with the use of the degree-day can also be considered. For example, since schools are open only five days a week, a record can be kept only of the degree-days on school days so that a com-

parison may be made on a more logical basis for this type of building.

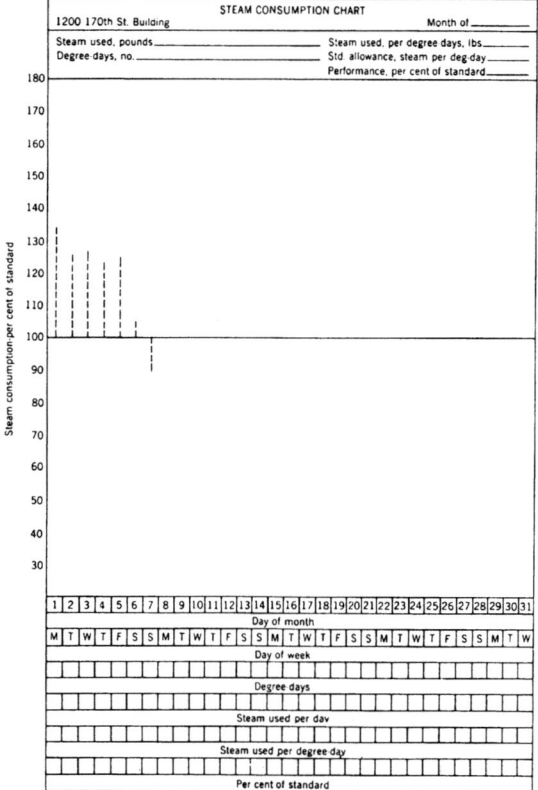

Fig 11-3. Example of chart to record, on a monthly basis, operating results for a specific building

Other uses of the degree-day include to show utility company record customers why their fuel bills are higher in one period than another. For example, gas companies are frequently faced with this problem in explaining to customers why their gas bill goes up so sharply from November to December or from October to November. The consumer is aware, of course, that the weather is getting colder, but ordinarily the precise degree-day figures make more of an impression than the consumer's own awareness of low temperature. Such methods are used not only by gas companies, but by fuel oil dealers and district steam utilities as well. For example, a utility company may even print the number of degree-days on its bills. In this case, the number of degree-days shown is for the period covered by the bill.

As an example of the use of the degree-day as a guide to operating efficiency the following is presented, not as an actual case, but as a composite of several actual uses. The figures used in examples are made up, intended only to demonstrate that the method is workable. Actually, the forms used and details of working out such a method depend on the particular problem, number of buildings under one management, and the individual ideas of the person inaugurating the system.

Based on past records, a chart such as shown in Fig. 11-2 is prepared. In this example a day is used as the time unit. As the ordinate, the quantity of steam or fuel used per day per 1000 cubic feet of building volume is used. If only one building is under consideration the ordinate could omit the per 1000 cubic feet. Where a number of buildings are being compared, however, the cubic feet basis enables comparisons among different buildings of varying sizes.

After study of past records, a standard, or 100% measure of performance is set up. From this, lines representing 90% of standard performance, 110%, 80%, 120%, and so on are plotted as shown. This graph is drawn only once; daily records are subsequently compared against the chart. Obviously, if the standard has been properly set readings over 100% represent substandard operation, readings under 100% good operation. Consistently substandard results should be investigated and operating procedures improved if possible. A wide variety of reasons can exist for below-standard or above standard performance, and every attempt should be made to determine what these are.

A second chart can be employed, as shown in Fig. 11-3, for recording the monthly performance of any building. Whereas Fig. 11-2 is drawn up once for each building, Fig. 11-3 is a blank chart, one is filled in for each building each month.

For each day of the month, only the two top rows, indicating day of month and the day of the week are filled in at the bottom of the blank sheet as shown; the weekday is necessary since it will show any variation from what is normal on certain days of the week. For example, commercial buildings, such as offices, can be expected to show lower fuel or steam consumption on weekends when the building is only partly, if at all, occupied. The other rows are self-explanatory; the extreme bottom row is filled in by referring to Fig. 11-2.

The performance is then plotted by days by the drawing bars, as shown in the dashed lines for the first seven days. The purpose of this graphical portion of the chart is to better show up extreme or repetitive variations from what is normal.

Finally, the steam used for the whole month is obtained by totaling the daily figures, and this is also done for the degree-days. The monthly figures can then be inserted in the spaces at the top of the chart.

It can readily be seen that such a system or a similar one can easily be set up for almost any building where the necessary data can be obtained. Although steam or gas figures can be determined from meters every day, it is not too difficult to set up a system for weighing coal (very rare today) or measuring oil tank depletion.

Once the system is in operation, it can be kept in operation with ease and at very low cost. This cost may be far

more than recovered as the system calls to management's attention an increasing fuel or steam consumption due to faulty operation or equipment failure which otherwise might have gone unnoticed.

The method shown here is a composite and can be varied widely. It may be that a weekly basis rather than a daily one would be more practicable. The system can even be a more simple one, such as the simple plotting on a graph weekly energy consumption per degree-day. The details of the system depend on the size of the building and many other variables. The exact form and type of the system depends entirely on the enthusiasm and ingenuity of the person adopting the system.

Predicting Fuel Consumption.—There are two uses of the degree-day unit in predicting fuel consumption: (1) predicting what the fuel consumption will be in an existing building for which performance data on fuel consumption during past periods are known; and (2) predicting fuel consumption for a new or proposed building or one with a new heating plant for which no previous comparable fuel data are available.

One of the best examples of the use of the degree-day for predicting fuel consumption for an existing building is that used in the fuel oil delivery business where, by use of the degree-day, fuel deliveries are simplified and the fuel oil dealer knows from company records exactly when to deliver fuel oil that time will be just prior to the time when the oil in the tank becomes dangerously low.

As near as can be determined, the first use of the degree-day for this purpose was by Aetna Oil Service Co. Louisville, Kentucky, the system having been devised by W. R. Abbott of that company and reported by him in a talk before the American Society of Mechanical Engineers in 1928. The method used was somewhat as follows: A separate card was maintained for each customer and a constant K determined by dividing the gallons of oil used by that customer for a given period for which the number of degree-days was known. This K then represented the gallons used per degree-day for that customer. Another constant K was also kept, this being the gallons per degree-day per unit load, the unit load being assumed as 1000 square feet of equivalent steam radiation. Also on the customers card was entered the load on the boiler together with this equivalent load which was designated as C. K was then determined by dividing K by the equivalent unit load C.

The constant K was not necessary in connection with fuel deliveries, but was kept as an index of the overall efficiency of the plant and for comparing fuel consumption of that plant with other plants in the same city. It was of interest in evaluating the various types of building construction, insulation, and weather-stripping.

Since a record was kept each day of the number of degree-days, it was possible at short intervals for the supplier to go through the cards and determine how much oil was used by each customer during that period and then subtract that from the previous known amount of fuel in the customers tank. Consequently, it was quite easy for the supplier to determine precisely when the customer's tank would become empty and anticipate this by a delivery of oil.

By adding the fuel consumption on all cards the supply company could arrive at the number of gallons of oil it would need for its customers per degree-day so as to determine its own stocks. Obviously, too, truck schedules could be made up from information obtained from the cards so that the most efficient method of truck operation was possible.

Predicting Future Needs.—An entirely different use of the degree-day unit is the predicting of future fuel (or steam or electrical energy) requirements in a building yet to be built, or in an existing building where, perhaps, a change in fuel or energy is contemplated. It is this particular use of the degree-day that originally led to the development of the degree-day years ago.

If the heat loss calculations for a building were accurate for the design conditions, and if the heat loss at any other outside temperature were proportional to that at design conditions, then the heat lost from the building for a whole heating season could be expressed by the equation

$$H = \frac{24hd(T_i - T_a)}{(T_i - T_o)} \tag{1}$$

where H = seasonal heat loss Btu;

h = hourly heat loss from the building for the design conditions, Btu;

T_i = inside design temperature, °F;

T_o = outside design temperature, °F;

24 = hours per day;

d = number of days in the heating season; and

T_a = average outside temperature for the heating season °F.

For buildings where the inside design temperature is 70 °F the formula becomes

$$H = \frac{24hd(70 - T_a)}{(70 - T_o)} \tag{2}$$

This formula is rational and workable if figures for d (number of days in the heating season) and T_a (average heating season temperature) are available. While some reference books state that the heating season in the United States extends from October 1 to May 1, and that the average outside temperature for the period from October 1 to April 30 can be used for T_a, this assumption is incorrect the length of heating season varies widely throughout the United States and, unfortunately, such a simple assumption is not applicable over the whole country.

However, the degree-day makes it possible to determine the number of days in a normal, or average, heating season for any locality for which sufficient weather data are available, as well as the average outside temperature during the period comprising the months of the heating season.

If the daily mean temperatures for any city are plotted for each day in a given year, the result appears something like Fig. 11-4. As the fall season approaches, the trend is for the temperature is to get colder and colder until the middle of winter is reached, following which it gets warmer and warmer until the summer, when the cycle begins again. This is true in all parts of the United States, the only difference being that the swing is not so pronounced in some parts of the country as in others.

Although the trend in the fall is for the weather to get colder, the temperature does not get colder uniformly but fluctuates more or less drastically, being relatively warm one day and cooler the next. If, however, one were to similarly plot for a city the normal daily mean temperature for all the years that records exist (that is, if one were to average all of the April firsts, then all the April seconds, then all the April thirds, and so on) the result would be a smooth curve as shown in Fig. 11-5. This curve shows graphically the normal daily mean temperature for a typical city.

This normal daily temperature curve will, for most United States cities, cross the 65°F line as shown, except in the extreme south, where the normal curve at all times is above the 65°F line, and in the far north and west, where, in many localities, it is always below the 65°F line.

The *premise* of the degree-day is that heating is required on days having degree-days, and heating is not required on days having no degree-days. Therefore, the heating season in a normal year begins on the date when the normal daily mean temperature crosses downward over the 65°F line, and ends where it crosses upward over the same line. The length of the heating season is the number of days between the two crossings, and thus d (number of days in the heating season) in Equations (1) and (2) can be determined for any city for which normal daily temperatures are available.

The degree-day is a product of time (in days) and temperature, and when a graph such as Fig. 11-5 is plotted in days on the horizontal scale and daily mean temperature is on the vertical scale, the number of degree-days D in the heating season is indicated graphically by the shaded area in Fig. 11-6.

Referring to Fig. 11-6, if the shaded area represents the number of degree-days, then this area D is equal to the base of the area d times the average altitude of the irregular area T_x or

$$D = dT_x \tag{3}$$

As shown on the graph,

$$T_x = 65 - T_a \tag{4}$$

so that

$$T_a = 65 - \frac{D}{d} \tag{5}$$

Consequently, the average outside temperature t_a can be found by Equation (5).

Once d and T_a are available for any city the heat required can be calculated by Equation (2). For example, what would be the heat required for a residence in New York where the design heat loss is 70,000 Btu/hr, $d = 241$, $T_a = 44.0°F$ and $T_o = 0°F$?

Substituting in Equation (2)

$$H = \frac{24 \times 70000 \times 241 \times (70 - 44)}{(70 - 0)}$$

$$= 150384000 \text{ Btu}$$

This can be converted into fuel units by dividing by the heat value per fuel unit and by the utilization efficiency. For example, assuming 1040 Btu per cubic foot of gas at 80% efficiency, the gas consumption per season would be

$$H = \frac{150384000}{1040 \times 0.80}$$

$$= 180750 \text{ cu ft of gas}$$

However, Equation (2) can be further simplified. Substituting Equation (5) into Equation (2) for t_a,

$$H = \frac{24hd}{(70 - T_o)}\left[70 - \left(65 - \frac{D}{d}\right)\right] \tag{6}$$

which reduces to

$$H = \frac{24(5d + D)h}{(70 - T_o)} \tag{7}$$

Since t_o is constant for a given city, as are d and D, the unit heat required per degree-day per Btu heat loss at design conditions is

$$\frac{H}{D} = \frac{24(5d + D)h}{(70 - T_o)D} \tag{8}$$

and since it is desirable to express the unit figure in terms of thousands of Btu heat loss, arrange Equation (8) as

$$\frac{1000H}{D} = \frac{24(5d + D)1000h}{(70 - T_o)D} \tag{9}$$

The whole term $\frac{24(5d + D)1000}{(70 - T_o)D}$ can be calculated for any given city. Expressed in words, this term which can be called K, is the unit heat requirement for that locality, in Btu per degree-day per 1000 Btu per hour heat loss at the design condition. The working formula is thus:

$$H = KD\frac{h}{1000} \tag{10}$$

where H = heat to be supplied, Btu per normal heating season;

$h/1000$ = heat loss in thousands of Btu per hour at design conditions;

D = normal number of degree-days per year; and

K = heat to be supplied, Btu per degree-day per 1000 Btu/hr heat loss at design conditions, for the city in question. Note that K is a constant only for a given city or small locality.

Values of K and D for a large number of United States cities are given in the Tables 11-3, and 11-4.

Example 1: The New York residence previously cited had a calculated heat loss of 90,000 Btu per hour in month. From the Tables 11-3, and 11-4, K for New York City is 424.7 and D is 5050, so that, using Equation (10),

$$H = 424.7 \times 5050 \times 70$$

$$= 150131450 \text{ Btu}$$

Burning 1040 Btu/ft^3 gas at 80% efficiency,

$$\text{cu ft of gas required} = \frac{150131450}{1040 \times 0.75}$$

$$= 180446$$

In cases involving gas or steam, or in any cases where monthly figures are necessary, Tables 11-3, and 11-4 can be used to determine K; then for D the number of degree-days in that locality for the given month is used and entered in Equation (10). In this case, the answer will be in Btu to be supplied for that month.

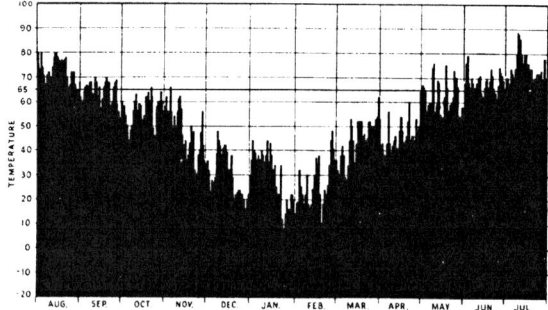

Fig 11-4. Daily mean temperatures for a given year for a specific city

Example 2: For the same residence what would be the gas required for December and for 1040 Btu gas at 80% efficiency?

Solution: The number of degree-days in a normal December is in New York is 908. Using Equation (10):

$$H_{dec} = 424.7 \times 908 \times 24$$

$$= 26993932 \text{ Btu}$$

Burning 1040 Btu/ft^3 gas at 80% efficiency,

$$\text{cu ft of gas required} = \frac{26993932}{1040 \times 0.80}$$

$$= 32445 \text{ ft}^3$$

Empirical Constants.—The term K in Equation (10) is Btu required per degree-day per 1000 Btu heat loss at design conditions. Constants of this general type, in different units, are widely used and, in fact, their use dates back to the earliest applications of the degree-day. Among such units that have been used are "cubic feet of gas per square foot of steam radiator per degree-day," "gallons of oil per square foot of steam radiator per degree-day" "pounds of steam per 1000 cubic feet of building volume" and a great many others.

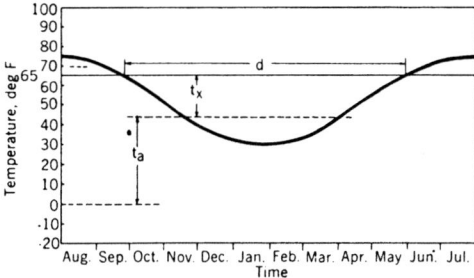

Fig 11-5. Normal daily mean temperatures plotted in a smooth curve

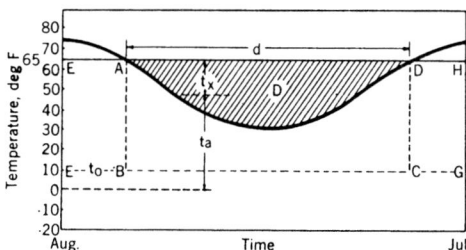

Fig 11-6. Normal daily mean temperature curve showing graphically the number of degree-days

These units were determined empirically and are quite useful in the locality where they were first used. However, in the early days of the degree-day, it was found that fuel constants used in the Northeast were highly inaccurate for the South and Southwest. The reason for this is that the term K is not a constant but varies widely throughout the country, as has been shown, due to the variation in d, D, and T_o.

The advantage of using K in terms of hourly heat loss at design conditions is that the Btu is the basic unit and the result is easily converted to other units (such as square foot of radiator).

Load Factor and Operating Hours.—Refer to Fig. 11-5 which shows design temperature, T_o (which in this graph is at +10°F), the average altitude of the shaded area, T_x and $T_a = 65 - T_x$.

The Seasonal Load Factor (SLF) of a winter heating plant can be defined as the percent of time during the heating season that the heating plant operates. Graphically, in Fig. 11-5, it is the ratio expressed in percent of the shaded area to the area of the rectangle ABCD. Since the shaded area has already been shown to be equal to D, the number of degree-days during the heating season, and since AB = $65 - T_o$ and BC = d, then

$$SLF = \frac{D}{d(65 - T_o)} \times 100 \qquad (11)$$

But $D = dT_x$ so that

$$SLF = \frac{T_x}{(65 - T_o)} \times 100$$

Annual load factor (ALF) of the heating plant is the percent of total time over the year that the heating plant operates. Graphically, it is the ratio of the shaded area in Fig. 11-5 to the area of the rectangle EFGH. Therefore, it can be shown that

$$ALF = \frac{D}{365(65 - T_o)} = \frac{dT_x}{365(65 - T_o)} \qquad (12)$$

A subsequent table gives values of the load factor for a wide range of cities.

The number of operating hours, or OH, that an intermittent or on-off heating plant operates during a normal year is thus

$$OH = ALF \times 24 \times 365 \qquad (13)$$

It is useful to know the number of hours of operation of a heating plant to determine the electrical consumption of burner motors, pumps, and similar equipment.

Limitations.—The foregoing method of predicting fuel consumption and the supplementary data derived from this method are subject to limitations as follows:

1) By definition, the method applies to spaces heated to 70°F during daytime and evening hours, and will not apply to spaces heated to temperatures differing sharply from 70°F, such as industrial buildings.

2) The data apply to a normal year and are subject to variations from year to year as the number of degree-days varies.

3) As H in Equation (10) depends upon design heat loss, the results in terms of fuel can be no more accurate than the heat loss calculation. If the heat losses are figured liberally, then heat loss is on the conservative side, the fuel figure will likewise be too liberal and give too high values of fuel consumption.

4) Since heat gains are not ordinarily calculated in winter heat loss, fuel estimates indicated by the degree-day method will be too high by the amount of heat gain. Heat gains in winter include those from the chimney, cooking and bathing, body heat loss, appliances, and perhaps most important, solar heat. These added together can amount to

as much as 25% of the heat loss and, if they are ignored, the fuel consumption will be estimated too liberally by a corresponding amount.

5) The method is based on an outside design temperature T_o. If any other design temperature is used, refigure K by using Equation (9). This is important because of increasing use of less severe design temperatures.

6) The calculated fuel consumption, since it is based on space heating only, does not include the fuel for service hot water.

7) Note that Equation (10) does not include heating plant efficiency; this must be allowed for separately, as shown in the examples.

Degree-Days Abroad.—Since considerably lower inside temperatures are maintained in European as compared to U.S. buildings, the 65°F base used for the degree-day is not applicable in countries abroad. In many of these countries a base of 60°F is used in calculating degree-days.

Normal Yearly Total Degree-Days for 877 U. S. Cities.—The data in Table 11-4 which follow give the seasonal total number of degree days for the heating season for 877 towns, villages, and cities not covered in Table 11-3 in which the data are given by months.

Figures in this table were compiled by using normal monthly mean temperatures for each station and are based on these monthly normal figures for periods as long as 50 years and at least 20 years. They are not official figures of the US Weather Bureau, with certain exceptions, but were calculated from official publications of the Weather Bureau.

The method used in calculating these figures was to subtract the mean monthly temperature from 65°F and multiply by the number of days in that month.

Consequently, to arrive at the seasonal totals given the monthly figures had to be calculated. The only reason these monthly figures are not presented here is due to lack of space. The exceptions are those stations marked with a dagger for which the figures are those calculated by the US Weather Bureau.

When you use this table, first check to see whether the city is covered in the more complete tabulation of Table 11-3 which precedes Table 11-4 and in which the figures are given for each month.

Table 11-3. Degree-Days to Several Bases (in °F) for Various U.S. Locations

Location	Heating Base 65	55	45	Cooling Base 65	55	45
Alabama						
Birmingham	2844	1333	488	1928	4073	6877
Huntsville	3302	1670	686	1808	3828	6492
Mobile	1684	619	148	2577	5162	8342
Montgomery	2269	945	232	2238	4568	7551
Alaska						
Anchorage AP	10911	7492	4896	0	224	1279
Annette AP	7053	3773	1543	14	386	1803
Barrow AP	20265	16615	13009	0	0	44
Barter Island AP	19994	16344	12733	0	0	44
Bethel AP	13203	9695	6835	0	142	938
Settles AP	15925	12548	9718	17	289	1110
Big Delta AP	13698	10410	7735	34	395	1370
Cold Bay AP	9865	6230	3095	0	16	533
Fairbanks AP	14345	11115	8451	52	467	1468
Gulkana	13938	10507	7648	9	228	1027
Homer	10364	6745	3840	0	24	777
Juneau AP	9007	5557	2925	0	197	1219
King Salmon AP	11582	8047	5304	0	112	1023
Kodiak	8860	5327	2593	0	117	1032
Kotzebue AP	16039	12491	9337	0	102	598
McGrath AP	14487	11107	8348	14	284	1184
Nome AP	14325	10721	7528	0	46	503
St. Paul Island AP	11119	7469	4021	0	0	199
Shemya AP	9735	6085	2693	0	0	254
Summit FAA AP	14368	10790	7640	0	71	578
Talkeetna	11708	8306	5609	6	254	1207
Unalakleet	14027	10515	7565	0	138	842
Yakutat AP	9533	5941	3181	0	56	947
Arizona						
Flagstaff	7322	4421	2299	140	894	2418
Phoenix	1552	431	45	3508	6039	9297
Prescott FAA AP	4456	2321	883	882	2400	4612
Tucson	1752	541	65	2314	5253	8431
Winslow	4733	2683	1249	1203	2802	5018
Yuma	1005	211	8	4195	7045	10498
Arkansas						
Fort Smith	3336	1687	613	2022	4015	6595
Little Rock	3354	1687	624	1925	3908	6496
California						
Bakersfield	2185	760	147	2179	4400	7437
Bishop	4313	2230	848	1037	2603	4875
Blue Canyon	5704	3037	1206	302	1283	3106
Daggett FAA AP	2203	824	166	2729	5004	7996
Eureka	4679	1494	194	0	460	2816
Fresno	2650	995	205	1671	3667	6525

Location	Heating Base 65	55	45	Cooling Base 65	55	45
Long Beach	1606	292	8	985	3325	6696
Los Angeles Intl	1819	295	7	615	2755	6115
Los Angeles Civic Ctr	1245	158	0	1185	3747	7244
Mount Shasta	5890	3215	1338	286	1263	3035
Oakland	2909	714	61	128	1598	4587
Red Bluff	2688	1018	208	1904	3895	6727
Sacramento	2843	1043	186	1159	3011	5812
Sacramento City	2587	893	148	1291	3249	6151
Sandberg	4427	2107	622	800	2123	4293
San Diego	1507	213	9	722	3084	6532
San Francisco	3042	769	67	108	1496	4438
San Francisco Fed Bldg.	3080	608	25	39	1230	4298
Santa Maria	3053	690	42	84	1377	4380
Stockton	2806	1072	219	1259	3167	5968
Colorado						
Alamosa	8609	5654	3457	88	780	2227
Colorado Springs	6473	3954	2089	461	1592	3383
Denver - Stapleton	6016	3601	1852	625	1857	3759
Denver - City	5505	3175	1533	742	2071	4074
Eagle AP	8426	5505	3317	117	845	2313
Grand Junction	5605	3425	1814	1140	2619	4653
Pueblo	5394	3220	1628	981	2456	4514
Connecticut						
Bridgeport	5461	3216	1583	735	2140	4152
Hartford	6350	3971	2173	584	1855	3706
Washington DC						
Wash DC-Reagan Apt	5005	2898	1380	940	2474	4616
Wash DC-Natl Apt	4211	2293	984	1415	3152	5489
Delaware						
Wilmington Ncastle	4940	2839	1330	992	2537	4675
Florida						
Apalachicola	1361	426	67	2663	5377	8669
Daytona Beach	897	215	25	2919	5881	9341
Fort Myers	457	56	0	3711	6958	10553
Jacksonville	1327	429	70	2596	5349	8641
Key West	59	0	0	4888	8474	12124
Lakeland	678	128	7	3298	6398	9927
Miami	206	8	0	4038	7494	11131
Orlando	733	151	9	3226	6291	9806
Pensacola	1578	575	135	2695	5341	8551
Tallahassee	1563	550	116	2563	5200	8415
Tampa	718	151	14	3366	6447	9963
West Palm Beach	299	27	0	3786	7159	10785
Georgia						
Athena	2975	1370	462	1722	3767	6508
Atlanta	3095	1461	524	1589	3604	6316

Table 11-3. *(Continued)* **Degree-Days to Several Bases (in °F) for Various U.S. Locations**

Location	Heating Base 65	Heating Base 55	Heating Base 45	Cooling Base 65	Cooling Base 55	Cooling Base 45	Location	Heating Base 65	Heating Base 55	Heating Base 45	Cooling Base 65	Cooling Base 55	Cooling Base 45
Augusta	2547	1106	348	1995	4204	7094	Shreveport	2167	883	233	2538	4906	7903
Macon	2240	934	271	2294	4643	7626	Maine						
Rome	3342	1653	637	1615	3576	6210	Bangor	7950	5222	3122	268	1194	2740
Savannah	1952	751	185	2317	4766	7851	Caribou	9632	6634	4319	128	784	2118
Hawaii							Old Town FAA AP	8648	5800	3589	209	1016	2454
Hilo	0	0	0	3066	6712	10362	Portland	7498	4764	2705	252	1169	2798
Honolulu	0	0	0	4221	7871	11521	Maryland						
Kahului	0	0	0	3732	7380	11030	Baltimore	4729	2682	1236	1108	2708	4918
Lihue AP	0	0	0	3719	7360	11010	Massachusetts						
Idaho							Blue Hill	6335	3885	2071	457	1659	3498
Boise	5833	3399	1626	714	1929	3811	Boston	5621	3313	1659	661	2000	4000
Lewiston	5464	3050	1366	657	1886	3856	Nantucket AP	5929	3323	1513	284	1332	3170
Pocatello	7063	4454	2504	437	1477	3177	Worcester	6848	4326	2421	387	1514	3259
Illinois							Michigan						
Cairo	3833	2090	925	1806	3710	6197	Alpena	8518	5635	3464	208	981	2459
Chicago Midway AP	6127	3912	219	925	2361	4317	Detroit	6419	4072	2280	654	1961	3815
Chicaao O'Hare AP	6497	4163	2404	664	1986	3872	Flint	7041	4540	2640	438	1586	3335
Molin	6395	4170	2462	893	2324	4262	Grand Rapids	6801	4383	2524	575	1807	3598
Pearl	6098	3910	2239	968	2431	4412	Houghton Lake	8347	5579	3486	250	1132	2689
Rockford	6845	4507	2713	714	2032	3833	Lansing	6904	4464	2595	535	1747	3528
Springfield	5558	3468	1913	1116	2670	4772	Marquette	8351	5517	3378	216	1031	2549
Indiana							Muskegon	6890	4390	2482	469	1620	3360
Evansville	4624	2685	1327	1364	3064	5367	Sault Ste Marie	9193	6215	3971	139	816	2217
Fort Wayne	6209	3930	2193	748	2117	4030	Traverse City AP	7698	5035	3013	376	1362	2989
Indianaoolis	5577	3431	1856	974	2478	4554	Minnesota						
South Bend	6462	4118	2333	695	2002	3867	Duluth	9756	6793	4540	176	864	2259
Iowa							Intnl Falls	10547	7623	5348	176	908	2283
Burlington Radio	6149	3970	2308	994	2466	4447	Minn. - St. Paul	8159	5677	3765	585	17518	3491
Des Moines	6710	4470	2728	928	2335	4243	Rochester	8227	5682	3733	474	1579	3280
Dubuque	7277	4871	3028	606	1850	3657	St. Cloud	8868	6255	4241	426	1468	3098
Mason City AP	7901	5430	3529	580	1763	3508	Mississippi						
Sioux City	6953	4674	2898	932	2298	4177	Jackson	2300	988	319	2316	4664	7639
Spencer	7770	5329	3448	641	1857	3620	Meridian	2388	1042	339	2231	4538	7483
Waterloo	7415	5040	3199	675	1950	3760	Missouri						
Kansas							Columbia Region	5078	3064	1605	1269	2901	5089
Concordia	5623	3509	1912	1302	2832	4886	Kansas City	5161	3157	1694	1421	3061	5249
Dodge City	5046	3011	1512	1411	3022	5176	St Louis	4750	2798	1419	1475	3174	5445
Godland	6119	3804	2041	925	2253	4139	St Joseph	5435	3378	1847	1334	2925	5046
Russell FAA AP	5312	3259	1735	1485	3081	5210	Springfield	4570	2611	1235	1382	3068	5342
Topeka	5243	3203	1700	1361	2974	5112							
Louisiana							Montana						
Alexandria	2200	880	234	2193	4525	7531	Billings	7265	4697	2766	498	1581	3298
Baton Rouge	1670	582	120	2585	5150	8340	Butte	9719	6557	4078	58	545	1718
Lake Charles	1498	500	91	2739	5391	8638	Cut Bank AP	9033	6096	3886	140	856	2299
New Orleans, Park	1383	439	82	2876	5622	8916	Dillon AP	8354	5457	3237	199	953	2382
New Orleans, NO	1465	492	96	2706	5383	8638	Glasgow	8969	6329	4302	438	1449	3074

Table 11-3. *(Continued)* **Degree-Days to Several Bases (in °F) for Various U.S. Locations**

Location	Heating Base 65	55	45	Cooling Base 65	55	45	Location	Heating Base 65	55	45	Cooling Base 65	55	45
Glasgow	8969	6329	4302	438	1449	3074	Binghamton	7285	4714	2767	369	1452	3151
Great Falls	7652	5022	3074	339	1365	3066	Buffalo	6927	4429	2508	437	1590	3319
Havre	8687	6073	4104	395	1432	3113	Massena FAA	8237	5596	3552	343	1352	2958
Helena	8190	5389	3258	256	1105	2629	New York Cntrl Park	4848	2771	1299	1068	2636	4814
Kalispell	8554	5542	3233	117	755	2096	New York JFK INTL AP	5184	2994	1422	861	2321	4395
Lewistown FAA AP	8586	5676	3467	192	933	2379	New York LaGuardia	4909	2806	1311	1048	2587	4740
Miles City AP	7889	5392	3479	752	1905	3641	Oswego East	6792	4274	2376	435	1570	3319
Missoula	7931	5066	2876	188	970	2428	Rochester	6719	4285	2434	531	1750	3549
Nebraska							Syracuse	6678	4250	2429	551	1778	3607
Grand Island	6420	4166	2434	1036	2428	4345	North Carolina						
Lincoln AP	6218	4040	2362	1148	2611	4585	Asheville	4237	2224	937	872	2508	4868
Lincoln	6012	3870	2234	1187	2685	4701	Caoe Hatteras	2731	1166	380	1550	3635	6500
Norfolk	6981	4663	2863	925	2263	4118	Charlotte	3218	1552	585	1596	3579	6263
North Platte	6743	4345	2509	802	2060	3874	Greensboro	3325	1984	825	1341	3149	5640
Omaha - Eppley	6049	3911	2290	1173	2691	4715	Raleigh-Durham	3514	1744	670	1394	3273	5850
Omaha - North	6601	4349	2624	949	2346	4270	Wilmington	2433	1028	321	1964	4225	7162
Scottsbluff	6774	4304	2415	666	1845	3605	Bismarck	9044	6425	4374	487	1518	3116
Valentine	7300	4859	2956	736	1945	3692	Fargo	9271	6663	4615	473	1515	3122
Nevada							Minot FAA	9407	6685	4573	370	1299	2837
Elko	7483	4714	2625	342	1228	2785	Williston	9161	6504	4450	422	1415	3011
Ely	7814	5004	2829	207	1052	2526	Ohio						
Las Vegas	2601	1120	306	2946	5114	7950	Akron-Canton	6224	3883	2129	634	1943	3839
Lovelock FAA	5990	3550	1747	684	1894	3740	Cincinnati Abbe Obs	4844	2830	1412	1188	2819	5060
Reno	6022	3387	1534	329	1344	3140	Cincinnati AP	5070	3001	1527	1080	2654	4834
Tonopah	5900	3492	1723	631	1869	3753	Cleveland	6154	3819	2079	613	1926	3836
Winnemucca	6629	3994	2015	407	1423	3096	Columbus	5702	3480	1846	809	2244	4257
New Hampshire							Dayton	5641	3468	1866	936	2414	4460
Concord	7360	4757	2762	349	1394	3051	Mansfield	5818	3573	1917	818	2225	4219
Mount Washington	13878	10253	6960	0	25	379	Toledo Express	6381	4049	2274	685	2001	3877
New Jersey							Youngstown	6426	4032	2232	518	1774	3623
Atlantic City	4946	2784	1267	864	2349	4485	Oklahoma						
Atlantic City Marina	4693	2530	1076	835	2317	4517	Oklahoma City	3695	1962	809	1876	3788	6289
Newark	5034	2920	1391	1024	2543	4677	Tulsa	3680	1950	778	1949	3865	6347
Trenton	4947	2832	1323	968	2493	4634	Oregon						
New Mexico							Astoria	5295	2233	570	13	596	2598
Albuquerque	4292	2330	963	1316	2996	5288	Burns	7212	4436	2343	289	1168	2724
Clayton	5207	2966	1374	167	2176	4231	Eugene	4739	2141	607	239	1286	3417
Roswell	3697	1898	706	1560	3412	5872	Meacham	7863	4817	2495	103	712	2034
Truth or Consequences	3392	1636	542	1558	3447	6008	Medford	4930	2496	882	562	1779	3813
Tucumcari FAA	4047	2135	858	1357	3096	5467	North Bend AP	4688	1642	292	0	597	2913
Zuni FAA	5815	3381	1648	473	1685	3605	Pendleton	5240	2868	1264	656	1935	3982
New York							Portland	4792	2234	708	300	1378	3520
Albany	6888	4451	2595	574	1787	3583	Redmond AP	6643	3767	1680	170	943	2512

Table 11-3. *(Continued)* **Degree-Days to Several Bases (in °F) for Various U.S. Locations**

Location	Heating Base 65	55	45	Cooling Base 65	55	45
Salem	4852	2246	667	232	1272	3355
Sexton Summit	6430	3477	1374	137	837	2386
Pacific Region						
Guam	0	0	0	5011	8661	12311
Johnston AP	0	0	0	5086	8736	12386
Koror	0	0	0	6008	9658	13308
Kwajalein AP	0	0	0	6164	9814	13464
Majuro AP	0	0	0	5904	9554	13204
Pago Pago AP	0	0	0	5325	8975	12625
Ponape	0	0	0	5652	9302	12952
Truk. Moeni, Ae	0	0	0	5888	9536	13188
Wake	0	0	0	5455	9105	12755
Yap AP	0	0	0	5916	9566	13216
Pennsylvania						
Allentown	5827	3550	1843	772	2150	4088
Bradford AP	7804	5006	2931	170	1022	2596
Harrisburg	5224	3097	1541	1025	2545	4644
Erie	6851	4304	2411	373	1482	3235
Philadelphia	4865	2788	1312	1104	2671	4849
Pittsburgh City	5278	3138	1603	948	2456	4573
Pittsburgh AP	5930	3637	1938	647	2004	3961
W-Barre-Scranton	6277	3928	2149	608	1909	3783
Williamsport	5981	3695	1971	698	2059	3986
Rhode Island						
Block Island	5771	3289	1517	359	1523	3409
Providence	5972	3565	1803	532	1774	3662
South Carolina						
Charleston AP	2146	864	240	2078	4454	7478
Charleston City	1904	741	188	2354	4839	7937
Columbia	2598	1154	374	2087	4292	7159
Florence	2566	1127	374	1952	4171	7060
Grnvle-Spartenburg	3163	1493	519	1573	3552	6229
South Dakota						
Aberdeen	8617	6078	4087	566	1678	3337
Huron	8055	5600	3678	711	1912	3641
Pierre AP	7677	5271	3409	858	2102	3889
Rapid City	7324	4799	2868	661	1786	3511
Sioux Falls	7838	5401	3498	719	1933	3681
Tennessee						
Bristol	4306	2373	1093	1107	2823	5197
Chattanooga	3505	1785	737	1636	3566	6169
Knoxville	3478	1775	744	1569	3518	6135
Memphis	3227	1624	640	2029	4077	6744
Nashville	3696	1964	852	1694	3613	6151
Oak Ridge	3944	2119	933	1367	3187	5856

Location	Heating Base 65	55	45	Cooling Base 65	55	45
Texas						
Abilene	2610	1162	342	2466	4670	7498
Amarillo	4183	2278	976	1433	3177	5527
Austin	1737	620	127	2903	5443	8600
Brownsville	650	146	19	3874	7020	10543
Corpus Christi	930	243	28	3474	6438	9872
Dallas	2290	949	250	2755	5073	8016
Del Rio	1523	494	80	3363	5986	9222
El Paso	2678	1149	326	2098	4229	7048
Fort Worth	2382	1007	274	2587	4862	7775
Galveston	1224	369	54	3004	5800	9139
Houston	1434	471	81	2889	5576	8835
Laredo	876	230	32	4137	7143	10593
Lubbock	3545	1807	666	1647	3559	6068
Lufkin AP	1940	731	163	2592	5033	8114
Midland	2621	1159	333	2245	4434	7258
Port Arthur	1518	504	86	2798	5431	8669
San Angelo	2240	918	227	2702	5031	7993
San Antonio	1570	518	92	2994	5594	8818
Victoria	1227	364	51	3140	5925	9262
Waco	2058	807	195	2863	5271	8303
Wichita Falls	2904	1384	451	2611	4741	7458
Utah						
Blanding	6163	3732	1912	600	1827	3646
Bryce Canyon AP	9133	5949	3480	41	505	1686
Cedar City AP	6137	3690	1897	615	1813	3678
Milford	6412	3957	2121	688	1885	3704
Salt Lake City	5983	3633	1864	927	2221	4108
Wendover	5760	3511	1870	1137	2538	4547
Vermont						
Burlington	7876	5270	3246	396	1440	3066
Virginia						
Lynchburg	4233	2269	966	1100	2783	5128
Norfolk	3488	1710	663	1441	3315	5918
Richmond	3939	2061	866	1353	3127	5580
Roanoke	4307	2326	1011	1030	2690	5029
Wallops Island	4240	2268	978	1107	2788	5149
Washington						
Olympia	5530	2653	854	101	880	2731
Omak	6858	4253	2355	522	1573	3324
Quillayute	5951	2750O	813	8	458	2172
Seattle-Tacoma	5185	2386	731	129	984	2981
Seattle (Urban)	4727	2091	602	183	1197	3358
Spokane	6835	4173	2188	388	1377	3040
Stampede Pass	9400	6006	3256	16	274	1176
Walla Walla	4835	2600	1126	862	2279	4457

Table 11-3. *(Continued)* **Degree-Days to Several Bases (in °F) for Various U.S. Locations**

Location	Heating Base			Cooling Base			Location	Heating Base			Cooling Base		
	65	55	45	65	55	45		65	55	45	65	55	45
Yakima	6009	3483	1688	479	1604	3455	Wisconsin						
Puerto Rico							Eau Claire AP	8388	5832	3860	459	1554	3231
San Juan	0	0	0	4982	8632	12282	Green Bay	8098	5473	3478	386	1411	3066
West Indies							La Crosse AP	7417	5050	3219	695	1978	3798
Swan Island	0	0	0	5809	9459	13109	Madison	7730	5188	3250	460	1572	3279
West Virginia							Milwaukee	7444	4898	2946	450	1554	3252
Beckley	5615	3279	1652	490	1809	3833	Wyoming						
Charleston	4590	2590	1216	1055	2699	4981	Casper	7555	4914	2857	458	1468	3061
Elkins	5975	3533	1834	389	1601	3555	Cheyenne	7255	4562	2512	327	1288	2886
Huntington	4624	2624	1249	1098	2746	5020	Lander	7869	5207	3140	383	1376	2965
Parkersburg	4817	2786	1363	1045	2657	4888	Rock Springs AP	8410	5592	3393	227	1059	2515
							Sheridan	7708	5024	3000	446	1411	3037

Table 11-4. Normal Monthly and Annual Degree-Days Below 65°F for Cities in the United States

Station	Avg. Winter Temp °F	July	Aug	Sept	Oct	Nov	Dec	Jan	Feb	Mar	Apr	May	June	Yearly Total
Alabama														
Birmingham A	54.2	0	0	6	93	363	555	592	462	363	108	9	0	2551
Huntsville A	51.3	0	0	12	127	426	663	694	557	434	138	19	0	3070
Mobile A	59.9	0	0	0	22	213	357	415	300	211	42	0	0	1560
Montgomery A	55.4	0	0	0	68	330	527	543	417	316	90	0	0	2291
Alaska														
Anchorage A	23.0	245	291	516	930	1284	1572	1631	1316	1293	879	592	315	10864
Fairbanks A	6.7	171	332	642	1203	1833	2254	2359	1901	1739	1068	555	222	14279
Juneau A	32.1	301	338	483	725	921	1135	1237	1070	1073	810	601	381	9075
Nome A	13.1	481	496	693	1094	1455	1820	1879	1666	1770	1314	930	573	14171
Arizona														
Flagstaff A	35.6	46	68	201	558	867	1073	1169	991	911	651	437	180	7152
Phoenix A	58.5	0	0	0	22	234	415	474	328	217	75	0	0	1765
Tucson A	58.1	0	0	0	25	231	406	471	344	242	75	6	0	1800
Winslow A	43.0	0	0	6	245	711	1008	1054	770	601	291	96	0	4782
Arakansas														
Yuma A	64.2	0	0	0	0	108	264	307	190	90	15	0	0	974
Fort Smith A	50.3	0	0	12	127	450	704	781	596	456	144	22	0	3292
Little Rock A	50.5	0	0	9	127	465	716	756	577	434	126	9	0	3219
Texarkana A	54.2	0	0	0	78	345	561	626	468	350	105	0	0	2533
California														
Bakersfield A	55.4.	0	0	0	37	282	502	546	364	267	105	19	0	2122
Bishop A	46.0	0	0	48	260	576	797	874	680	555	306	143	36	4275
Blue Canyon A	42.2	28	37	108	347	594	781	896	795	806	597	412	195	5596
Burbank A	58.6	0	0	6	43	177	301	366	277	239	138	81	18	1646
Eureka C	49.9	270	257	258	329	414	499	546	470	505	438	372	285	4643
Fresno A	53.3	0	0	0	84	354	577	605	426	335	162	62	6	2611
Long Beach A	57.8	0	0	9	47	171	316	397	311	264	171	93	24	1803
Los Angeles A	57.4	28	28	42	78	180	291	372	302	288	219	158	81	2061
Los Angeles C	60.3	0	0	6	31	132	229	310	230	202	123	68	18	1349
Mt. Shasta C	41.2	25	34	123	406	696	902	983	784	738	525	347	159	5722
Oakland A	53.5	53	50	45	127	309	481	527	400	353	255	180	90	2870
Red Bluff A	53.8	0	0	0	53	318	555	605	428	341	168	47	0	2515
Sacramento A	53.9	0	0	0	56	321	546	583	414	332	178	72	0	2502
Sacramento C	54.4	0	0	0	62	312	533	561	392	310	173	76	0	2419
Sandberg C	46.8	0	0	30	202	480	691	778	661	620	426	264	57	4209
San Diego A	59.5	9	0	21	43	135	236	298	235	214	135	90	42	1458
San Francisco A	53.4	81	78	60	143	306	462	508	395	363	279	214	126	3015
San Francisco C	55.1	192	174	102	118	231	388	443	336	319	279	239	180	3001
Santa Maria A	54.3	99	93	96	146	270	391	459	370	363	282	233	165	2967
Colorado														
Alamosa A	29.7	65	99	279	639	1065	1420	1476	1162	1020	696	440	168	8529
Colorado Springs A	37.3	9	25	132	456	825	1032	1128	938	893	582	319	84	6423
Denver A	37.6	6	9	117	428	819	1035	1132	938	887	558	288	66	6283
Denver C	40.8	0	0	90	366	714	905	1004	851	800	492	254	48	5524
Grand Junction A	39.3	0	0	30	313	786	1113	1209	907	729	387	146	21	5641
Pueblo A	40.4	0	0	54	326	750	986	1085	871	772	429	174	15	5462

Table 11-4. *(Continued)* **Normal Monthly and Annual Degree-Days Below 65°F for Cities in the United States**

Station	Avg. Winter Temp °F	July	Aug	Sept	Oct	Nov	Dec	Jan	Feb	Mar	Apr	May	June	Yearly Total
					Connecticut									
Bridgeport A	39.9	0	0	66	307	615	986	1079	966	853	510	208	27	5617
Hartford A	37.3	0	12	117	394	714	1101	1190	1042	908	519	205	33	6235
New Haven A	39.0	0	12	87	347	648	1011	1097	991	871	543	245	45	5897
					Delware									
Wilmington A	42.5	0	0	51	270	588	927	980	874	735	387	112	6	4930
					Washington D.C.									
Washington A	45.7	0	0	33	217	519	834	871	762	626	288	74	0	4224
Apalachicola C	61.2	0	0	0	16	153	319	347	260	180	33	0	0	1308
					Florida									
Daytona Beach A	64.5	0	0	0	0	75	211	248	190	140	15	0	0	879
Fort Myers A	68.6	0	0	0	0	24	109	146	101	62	0	0	0	442
Jacksonville A	61.9	0	0	0	12	144	310	332	246	174	21	0	0	1239
Key West A	73.1	0	0	0	0	0	28	40	31	9	0	0	0	108
Lakeland C	66.7	0	0	0	0	57	164	195	146	99	0	0	0	661
Miami A	71.1	0	0	0	0	0	65	74	56	19	0	0	0	214
Miami Beach C	72.5	0	0	0	0	0	40	56	36	9	0	0	0	141
Orlando A	65.7	0	0	0	0	72	198	220	165	105	6	0	0	766
Pensacola A	60.4	0	0	0	19	195	353	400	277	183	36	0	0	1463
Tallahassee A	60.1	0	0	0	28	198	360	375	286	202	36	0	0	1485
Tampa A	66.4	0	0	0	0	60	171	202	148	102	0	0	0	683
West Palm Beach A	68.4	0	0	0	0	6	65	87	64	31	0	0	0	253
					Georgia									
Athens A	51.8	0	0	12	115	405	632	642	529	431	141	22	0	2929
Atlanta A	51.7	0	0	18	124	417	648	636	518	428	147	25	0	2961
Augusta A	54.5	0	0	0	78	333	552	549	445	350	90	0	0	2397
Columbus A	54.8	0	0	0	87	333	543	552	434	338	96	0	0	2383
Macon A	56.2	0	0	0	71	297	502	505	403	295	63	0	0	2136
Rome A	49.9	0	0	24	161	474	701	710	577	468	177	34	0	3326
Savannah A	57.8	0	0	0	47	246	437	437	353	254	45	0	0	1819
Thomasville C	60.0	0	0	0	25	198	366	394	305	208	33	0	0	1529
					Hawaii									
Lihue A	72.7	0	0	0	0	0	0	0	0	0	0	0	0	0
Honolulu A	74.2	0	0	0	0	0	0	0	0	0	0	0	0	0
Hilo A	71.9	0	0	0	0	0	0	0	0	0	0	0	0	0
					Idaho									
Boise A	39.7	0	0	132	415	792	1017	1113	854	722	438	245	81	5809
Lewiston A	41.0	0	0	123	403	756	933	1063	815	694	426	239	90	5542
Pocatello A	34.8	0	0	172	493	900	1166	1324	1058	905	555	319	141	7033
					Illnios									
Cairo C	47.9	0	0	36	164	513	791	856	680	539	195	47	0	3821
Chicago (O'Hare) A	35.8	0	12	117	381	807	1166	1265	1086	939	534	260	72	6639
Chicago (Midway) A	37.5	0	0	81	326	753	1113	1209	1044	890	480	211	48	6155
Chicago C	38.9	0	0	66	279	705	1051	1150	1000	868	489	226	48	5882
Moline A	36.4	0	9	99	335	774	1181	1314	1100	918	450	189	39	6408
Peoria A	38.1	0	6	87	326	759	1113	1218	1025	849	426	183	33	6025
Rockford A	34.8	6	9	114	400	837	1221	1333	1137	-961	516	236	60	6830
Springfield A	40.6	0	0	72	291	696	1023	1135	935	769	354	136	18	5429
					Indiana									
Evansville A	45.0	0	0	66	220	606	896	955	767	620	237	68	0	4435
Fort Wayne A	37.3	0	9	105	378	783	1135	1178	1028	890	471	189	39	6205
Indianapolis A	39.6	0	0	90	316	723	1051	1113	949	809	432	177	39	5699

Table 11-4. *(Continued)* **Normal Monthly and Annual Degree-Days Below 65°F for Cities in the United States**

Station	Avg. Winter Temp °F	July	Aug	Sept	Oct	Nov	Dec	Jan	Feb	Mar	Apr	May	June	Yearly Total
South Bend A	36.6	0	6	111	372	777	1125	1221	1070	933	525	239	60	6439
Iowa														
Burlington A	37.6	0	0	93	322	768	1135	1259	1042	859	426	177	33	6114
Des Moines A	35.5	0	6	96	363	828	1225	1370	1137	915	438	180	30	6588
Dubuque A	32.7	12	31	156	450	906	1287	1420	1204	1026	546	260	78	7376
Sioux City A	34.0	0	9	108	369	867	1240	1435	1198	989	483	214	39	6951
Waterloo A	32.6	12	19	138	428	909	1296	1460	1221	1023	531	229	54	7320
Kansas														
Concordia A	40.4	0	0	57	276	705	1023	1163	935	781	372	149	18	5479
Dodge City A	42.5	0	0	33	251	666	939	1051	849	719	354	124	9	4986
Goodland A	37.8	0	6	81	381	810	1073	1166	955	884	507	236	42	6141
Topeka A	41.7	0	0	57	270	672	980	1122	893	722	330	124	12	5182
Wichita A	44.2	0	0	33	229	618	905	1023	804	645	270	87	6	4620
Kentucky														
Covington A	41.4	0	0	75	291	669	983	1035	893	756	390	149	24	5265
Lexington A	43.8	0	0	54	239	609	902	946	818	685	325	105	0	4683
Louisville A	44.0	0	0	54	248	609	890	930	818	682	315	105	9	4660
Louisiana														
Alexandria A	57.5	0	0	0	56	273	431	471	361	260	69	0	0	1921
Baton Rouge A	59.8	0	0	0	31	216	369	409	294	208	33	0	0	1560
Lake Charles A	60.5	0	0	0	19	210	341	381	274	195	39	0	0	1459
New Orleans A	61.0	0	0	0	19	192	322	363	258	192	39	0	0	1385
New Orleans C	61.8	0	0	0	12	165	291	344	241	177	24	0	0	1254
Shreveport A	56.2	0	0	0	47	297	477	552	426	304	81	0	0	2184
Maine														
Caribou A	24.4	78	115	336	682	1044	1535	1690	1470	1308	858	468	183	9767
Portland A	33.0	12	53	195	508	807	1215	1339	1182	1042	675	372	111	7511
Maryland														
Baltimore A	43.7	0	0	48	264	585	905	936	820	679	327	90	0	4654
Baltimore C	46.2	0	0	27	189	486	806	859	762	629	288	65	0	4111
Frederich A	42.0	0	0	66	307	624	955	995	876	741	384	127	12	5087
Massachusetts														
Boston A	40.0	0	9	60	316	603	983	1088	972	846	513	208	36	5634
Nantucket A	40.2	12	22	93	332	573	896	992	941	896	621	384	129	5891
Pittsfield A	32.6	25	59	219	524	831	1231	1339	1196	1063	660	326	105	7578
Worcester A	34.7	6	34	147	450	774	1172	1271	1123	998	612	304	78	6969
Michigan														
Alpena A	29.7	68	105	273	580	912	1268	1404	1299	1218	777	446	156	8506
Detroit (City) A	37.2	0	0	87	360	738	1088	1181	1058	936	522	220	42	6232
Detroit (Wayne) A	37.1	0	0	96	353	738	1088	1194	1061	933	534	239	57	6293
Detroit (Willow Run) A	37.2	0	0	90	357	750	1104	1190	1053	921	519	229	45	6258
Escanaba C	29.6	59	87	243	539	924	1293	1445	1296	1203	777	456	159	8481
Flint A	33.1	16	40	159	465	843	1212	1330	1198	1066	639	319	90	7377
Grand Rapids A	34.9	9	28	135	434	804	1147	1259	1134	1011	579	279	75	6894
Lansing A	34.8	6	22	138	431	813	1163	1262	1142	1011	579	273	69	6909
Marquette C	30.2	59	81	240	527	936	1268	1411	1268	1187	771	468	177	8393
Muskegon A	36.0	12	28	120	400	762	1088	1209	1100	995	594	310	78	6696
Sault Ste. Marie A	27.7	96	105	279	580	951	1367	1525	1380	1277	810	477	201	9048
Minnesota														
Duluth A	23.4	71	109	330	632	1131	1581	1745	1518	1355	840	490	198	10000
Minneapolis A	28.3	22	31	189	505	1014	1454	1631	1380	1166	621	288	81	8382
Rochester A	28.8	25	34	186	474	1005	1438	1593	1366	1150	630	301	93	8295

Table 11-4. *(Continued)* **Normal Monthly and Annual Degree-Days Below 65°F for Cities in the United States**

Station	Avg. Winter Temp °F	July	Aug	Sept	Oct	Nov	Dec	Jan	Feb	Mar	Apr	May	June	Yearly Total
Mississippi														
Jackson A	55.7	0	0	0	65	315	502	546	414	310	87	0	0	2239
Meridian A	55.4	0	0	0	81	339	518	543	417	310	81	0	0	2289
Vicksburg C	56.9	0	0	0	53	279	462	512	384	282	69	0	0	2041
Missouri														
Columbia A	42.3	0	0	54	251	651	967	1076	874	716	324	121	12	500
Kansas City A	43.9	0	0	39	220	612	905	1032	818	682	294	109	0	4711
St. Joseph A	40.3	0	6	60	285	708	1039	1172	949	769	348	133	15	
St. Louis A	43.1	0	0	60	251	627	936	1026	848	704	312	121	15	4900
St. Louis C	44.8	0	0	36	202	576	884	977	801	651	270	87	0	4484
Springfield A	44.5	0	0	45	223	600	877	973	781	660	291	105	6	4900
Montana														
Billings A	34.5	6	15	186	487	897	1135	1296	1100	970	570	285	102	7049
Glasgow A	26.4	31	47	270	608	1104	1466	1711	1439	1187	648	335	150	8996
Great Falls A	32.8	28	53	258	543	921	1169	1349	1154	1063	642	384	186	7750
Havre A	28.1	28	53	306	595	1065	1367	1584	1364	1181	657	338	162	8700
Havre C	29.8	19	37	252	539	1014	1321	1528	1305	1116	612	304	135	8182
Helena A	31.1	31	59	294	601	1002	1265	1438	1170	1042	651	381	195	8129
Kalispell A	31.4	50	99	321	654	1020	1240	1401	1134	1029	639	397	207	8191
Miles City A	31.2	6	6	174	502	972	1296	1504	1252	1057	579	276	99	7723
Missoula A	31.5	34	74	303	651	1035	1287	1420	1120	970	621	391	219	8125
Nebraska														
Grand Island A	36.0	0	6	108	381	834	1172	1314	1089	908	462	211	45	6530
Lincoln C	38.8	0	6	75	301	726	1066	1237	1016	834	402	171	30	5864
Norfolk A	34.0	9	0	111	397	873	1234	1414	1179	983	498	233	48	6979
North Platte A	35.5	0	6	123	440	885	1166	1271	1039	930	519	248	57	6684
Omaha A	35.6	0	12	105	357	828	1175	1355	1126	939	465	208	42	6612
Scottsbluff A	35.9	0	0	138	459	876	1128	1231	1008	921	552	285	75	6673
Valentine A	32.6	9	12	165	493	942	1237	1395	1176	1045	579	288	84	7425
Nevada														
Elko A	34.0	9	34	225	561	924	1197	1314	1036	911	621	409	192	7433
Ely A	33.1	28	43	234	592	939	1184	1308	1075	977	672	456	225	7733
Las Vegas A	53.5	0	0	0	78	387	617	688	487	335	111	6	0	2709
Reno A	39.3	43	87	204	490	801	1026	1073	823	729	510	357	189	6332
Winnemucca A	36.7	0	34	210	536	876	1091	1172	916	837	573	363	153	6761
New Hampshire														
Concord A	33.0	6	50	177	505	822	1240	1358	1184	1032	636	298	75	7383
Mt. Washington Obsv	15.2	493	536	720	1057	1341	1742	1820	1663	1652	1260	930	603	13817
New Jersey														
Atlantic City A	43.2	0	0	39	251	549	880	936	848	741	420	133	15	4812
Newark A	42.8	0	0	30	248	573	921	983	876	729	381	118	0	4589
Trenton C	42.4	0	0	57	264	576	924	989	885	753	399	121	12	4980
New Mexico														
Albuquerque A	45.0	0	0	12	229	642	868	930	703	595	288	81	0	4348
Clayton A	42.0	0	6	66	310	699	899	986	812	747	429	183	21	5158
Raton A	38.1	9	28	126	431	825	1048	1116	904	834	543	301	63	6228
Roswell A	47.5	0	0	18	202	573	806	840	641	481	201	31	0	3793
Silver City A	48.0	0	0	6	183	525	729	791	605	518	261	87	0	3705
New York														
Albany A	34.6	0	19	138	440	777	1194	1311	1156	992	564	239	45	6875
Albany C	37.2	0	9	102	375	699	1104	1218	1072	908	498	186	30	6201
Binghamton A	33.9	22	65	201	471	810	1184	1277	1154	1045	645	313	99	7286

ENERGY ESTIMATING FUNDAMENTALS

Table 11-4. *(Continued)* **Normal Monthly and Annual Degree-Days Below 65°F for Cities in the United States**

Station	Avg. Winter Temp °F	July	Aug	Sept	Oct	Nov	Dec	Jan	Feb	Mar	Apr	May	June	Yearly Total
Binghamton C	36.6	0	28	141	406	732	1107	1190	1081	949	543	229	45	6451
Buffalo A	34.5	19	37	141	440	777	1156	1256	1145	1039	645	329	78	7062
New York (Cent. Park) C	42.8	0	0	30	233	540	902	986	885	760	408	118	9	4871
New York (La Guardia) A	43.1	0	0	27	223	528	887	973	879	750	414	124	6	4811
New York (Kennedy) A	41.4	0	0	36	248	564	933	1029	935	815	480	167	12	5219
Rochester A	35.4	9	31	126	415	747	1125	1234	1123	1014	597	279	48	6748
Schenectady C	35.4	0	22	123	422	756	1159	1283	1131	970	543	211	30	6650
Syracuse A	35.2	6	28	132	415	744	1153	1271	1140	1004	570	248	45	6756
North Carolina														
Asheville C	46.7	0	0	48	245	555	775	784	683	592	273	87	0	4042
Cape Hatteras	53.3	0	0	0	78	273	521	580	518	440	177	25	0	2612
Charlotte A	50.4	0	0	6	124	438	691	691	582	481	156	22	0	3191
Greensboro A	47.5	0	0	33	192	513	778	784	672	552	234	47	0	3805
Raleigh A	49.4	0	0	21	164	450	716	725	616	487	180	34	0	3393
Wilmington A	54.6	0	0	0	74	291	521	546	462	357	96	0	0	2347
Winston-Salem A	48.4	0	0	21	171	483	747	753	652	524	207	37	0	3595
North Dakota														
Bismarck A	26.6	34	28	222	577	1083	1463	1708	1442	1203	645	329	117	8851
Devils Lake C	22.4	40	53	273	642	1191	1634	1872	1579	1345	753	381	138	9901
Fargo A	24.8	28	37	219	574	1107	1569	1789	1520	1262	690	332	99	9226
Williston A	25.2	31	43	261	601	1122	1513	1758	1473	1262	681	357	141	9243
Ohio														
Akron-Canton A	38.1	0	9	96	381	726	1070	1138	1016	871	489	202	39	6037
Cincinnati C	45.1	0	0	39	208	558	862	915	790	642	294	96	6	4410
Cleveland A	37.2	9	25	105	384	738	1088	1159	1047	918	552	260	66	6351
Columbus A	39.7	0	6	84	347	714	1039	1088	949	809	426	171	27	5660
Columbus C	41.5	0	0	57	285	651	977	1032	902	760	396	136	15	5211
Dayton A	39.8	0	6	78	310	696	1045	1097	955	809	429	167	30	5622
Mansfield A	36.9	9	22	114	397	768	1110	1169	1042	924	543	245	60	6403
Sandusky C	39.1	0	6	66	313	684	1032	1107	991	868	495	198	36	5796
Toledo A	36.4	0	16	117	406	792	1138	1200	1056	924	543	242	60	6494
Youngstown A	36.8	6	19	120	412	771	1104	1169	1047	921	540	248	60	6417
Oklahoma														
Oklahoma City A	48.3	0	0	15	164	498	766	868	664	527	189	34	0	3725
Tulsa A	47.7	0	0	18	158	522	787	893	683	539	213	47	0	3860
Oregon														
Astoria A	45.6	146	130	210	375	561	679	753	622	636	480	363	231	5186
Burns C	35.9	12	37	210	515	867	1113	1246	988	856	570	366	177	6957
Eugene A	45.6	34	34	129	366	585	719	803	627	589	426	279	135	4726
Meacham A	34.2	84	124	288	580	918	1091	1209	1005	983	726	527	339	7874
Medford A	43.2	0	0	78	372	678	871	918	697	642	432	242	78	5008
Pendleton A	42.6	0	0	111	350	711	884	1017	773	617	396	205	63	5127
Portland A	45.6	25	28	114	335	597	735	825	644	586	396	245	105	4635
Portland C	47.4	12	16	75	267	534	679	769	594	536	351	198	78	4109
Roseburg A	46.3	22	16	105	329	567	713	766	608	570	405	267	123	4491
Salem A	45.4	37	31	111	338	594	729	822	647	611	417	273	144	4754
Pennsylvania														
Allentown A	38.9	0	0	90	353	693	1045	1116	1002	849	471	167	24	5810
Erie A	36.8	0	25	102	391	714	1063	1169	1081	973	585	288	60	6451
Harrisburg A	41.2	0	0	63	298	648	992	1045	907	766	396	124	12	5251
Philadelphia A	41.8	0	0	60	297	620	965	1016	889	747	392	118	40	5144
Philadelphia C	44.5	0	0	30	205	513	856	924	823	691	351	93	0	4486

Table 11-4. *(Continued)* **Normal Monthly and Annual Degree-Days Below 65°F for Cities in the United States**

Station	Avg. Winter Temp °F	July	Aug	Sept	Oct	Nov	Dec	Jan	Feb	Mar	Apr	May	June	Yearly Total
Pittsburgh A	38.4	0	9	105	375	726	1063	1119	1002	874	480	195	39	5987
Pittsburgh C	42.2	0	0	60	291	615	930	983	885	763	390	124	12	5053
Reading C	42.4	0	0	54	257	597	939	1001	885	735	372	105	0	4945
Scranton A	37.2	0	19	132	434	762	1104	1156	1028	893	498	195	33	6254
Williamsport A	38.5	0	9	111	375	717	1073	1122	1002	856	468	177	24	5934
Rhode Island														
Block Island A	40.1	0	16	78	307	594	902	1020	955	877	612	344	99	5804
Providence A	38.8	0	16	96	372	660	1023	1110	988	868	534	236	51	5954
South Carolina														
Charleston A	56.4	0	0	0	59	282	471	487	389	291	54	0	0	2033
Charleston C	57.9	0	0	0	34	210	425	443	367	273	42	0	0	1794
Columbia A	54.0	0	0	0	84	345	577	570	470	357	81	0	0	2484
Florence A	54.5	0	0	0	78	315	552	552	459	347	84	0	0	2387
Greenville-Spartenburg A	51.6	0	0	6	121	399	651	660	546	446	132	19	0	2980
South Dakota														
Huron A	28.8	9	12	165	508	1014	1432	1628	1355	1125	600	288	87	8223
Rapid City A	33.4	22	12	165	481	897	1172	1333	1145	1051	615	326	126	7345
Sioux Falls A	30.6	19	25	168	462	972	1361	1544	1285	1082	573	270	78	7839
Tennessee														
Bristol A	46.2	0	0	51	236	573	828	828	700	598	261	68	0	4143
Chattanooga A	50.3	0	0	18	143	468	698	722	577	453	150	25	0	3254
Knoxville A	49.2	0	0	30	171	489	725	732	613	493	198	43	0	3494
Memphis A	50.5	0	0	18	130	447	698	729	585	456	147	22	0	3232
Memphis C	51.6	0	0	12	102	396	648	710	568	434	129	16	0	3015
Nashville A	48.9	0	0	30	158	495	732	778	644	512	189	40	0	3578
Oak Ridge C	47.7	0	0	39	192	531	772	778	669	552	228	56	0	3817
Texas														
Abilene A	53.9	0	0	0	99	366	586	642	470	347	114	0	0	2624
Amarillo A	47.0	0	0	18	205	570	797	877	664	546	252	56	0	3985
Austin A	59.1	0	0	0	31	225	388	468	325	223	51	0	0	1711
Brownsville A	67.7	0	0	0	0	66	149	205	106	74	0	0	0	600
Corpus Christi A	64.6	0	0	0	0	120	220	291	174	109	0	0	0	914
Dallas A	55.3	0	0	0	62	321	524	601	440	319	90	6	0	2363
El Paso A	52.9	0	0	0	84	414	648	685	445	319	105	0	0	2700
Fort Worth A	55.1	0	0	0	65	324	536	614	448	319	99	0	0	2405
Galveston A	62.2	0	0	0	6	147	276	360	263	189	33	0	0	1274
Galveston C	62.0	0	0	0	0	138	270	350	258	189	30	0	0	1235
Houston A	61.0	0	0	0	6	183	307	384	288	192	36	0	0	1396
Houston C	62.0	0	0	0	0	165	288	363	258	174	30	0	0	1278
Laredo A	66.0	0	0	0	0	105	217	267	134	74	0	0	0	797
Lubbock A	48.8	0	0	18	174	513	744	800	613	484	201	31	0	3578
Midland A	53.8	0	0	0	87	381	592	651	468	322	90	0	0	2591
Port Arthur A	60.5	0	0	0	22	207	329	384	274	192	39	0	0	1447
San Angelo A	56.0	0	0	0	68	318	536	567	412	288	66	0	0	2255
San Antonio A	60.1	0	0	0	31	204	363	428	286	195	39	0	0	1546
Victoria A	62.7	0	0	0	6	150	270	344	230	152	21	0	0	1173
Waco A	57.2	0	0	0	43	270	456	536	389	270	66	0	0	2030
Wichita Falls A	53.0	0	0	0	99	381	632	698	518	378	120	6	0	2832
Utah														
Milford A	36.5	0	0	99	443	867	1141	1252	988	822	519	279	87	6497
Salt Lake City A	38.4	0	0	81	419	849	1082	1172	910	763	459	233	84	6052
Wendover A	39.1	0	0	48	372	822	1091	1178	902	729	408	177	51	5778

Table 11-4. *(Continued)* **Normal Monthly and Annual Degree-Days Below 65°F for Cities in the United States**

Station	Avg. Winter Temp °F	July	Aug	Sept	Oct	Nov	Dec	Jan	Feb	Mar	Apr	May	June	Yearly Total
Vermont														
Burlington A	29.4	28	65	207	539	891	1349	1513	1333	1187	714	353	90	8269
Virginia														
Cape Henry C	50.0	0	0	0	112	360	645	694	633	536	246	53	0	3279
Lynchburg A	46.0	0	0	51	223	540	822	849	731	605	267	78	0	4166
Norfolk A	49.2	0	0	0	136	408	698	738	655	533	216	37	0	3421
Richmond A	47.3	0	0	36	214	495	784	815	703	546	219	53	0	3865
Roanoke A	46.1	0	0	51	229	549	825	834	722	614	261	65	0	4150
Washington														
Olympia A	44.2	68	71	198	422	636	753	834	675	645	450	307	177	5236
Seattle-Tacoma A	44.2	56	62	162	391	633	750	828	678	657	474	295	159	5145
Seattle C	46.9	50	47	129	329	543	657	738	599	577	396	242	117	4424
Spokane A	36.5	9	25	168	493	879	1082	1231	980	834	531	288	135	6655
Walla Walla C	43.8	0	0	87	310	681	843	986	745	589	342	177	45	4805
Yakima A	39.1	0	12	144	450	828	1039	1163	868	713	435	220	69	5941
West Virginia														
Charleston A	44.8	0	0	63	254	591	865	880	770	648	300	96	9	4476
Elkins A	40.1	9	25	135	400	729	992	1008	896	791	444	198	48	5675
Huntington A	45.0	0	0	63	257	585	856	880	764	636	294	99	12	4446
Parkersburg C	43.5	0	0	60	264	606	905	942	826	691	339	115	6	4754
Wisconsin														
Green Bay A	30.3	28	50	174	484	924	1333	1494	1313	1141	654	335	99	8029
La Crosse A	31.5	12	19	153	437	924	1339	1504	1277	1070	540	245	69	7589
Madison A	30.9	25	40	174	474	930	1330	1473	1274	1113	618	310	102	7863
Milwaukee A	32.6	43	47	174	471	876	1252	1376	1193	1054	642	372	135	7635
Wyoming														
Casper A	33.4	6	16	192	524	942	1169	1290	1084	1020	657	381	129	7410
Cheyenne A	34.2	28	37	219	543	909	1085	1212	1042	1026	702	428	150	7381
Lander A	31.4	6	19	204	555	1020	1299	1417	1145	1017	654	381	153	7870
Sheridan A	32.5	25	31	219	539	948	1200	1355	1154	1051	642	366	150	7680

COMBUSTION

In light of the continued rise in fuel costs, a good understanding of basic combustion theory is increasingly important. In addition, increasingly stringent environmental regulations and concerns make selection, design and maintenance of combustion control systems of paramount importance.

The following pages contain a brief overview of the combustion process, a discussion of factors that determine the efficiency of a boiler or furnace, and some of the traditional strategies used to accomplish combustion control.

Combustion Basics

Combustion, in its most basic sense, is the process where primarily the hydrogen and carbon in fuels combines with oxygen from the air to release heat. By products include carbon dioxide, water vapor, left over nitrogen from the air, other products of combustion, and possibly unreacted oxygen and/or fuel components.

Combustion control, in its most basic sense, is the maintenance of the proper fuel and air flows into this process to produce the amount of heat energy required by a system as it consumes the least possible fuel, ensuring complete combustion, and generates the fewest possible undesirable by products such as particulate matter and compounds that are detrimental to the environment and health.

Basics.—In general, common fuels may be classified as *hydrocarbons*. This means that they are predominantly composed of carbon and hydrogen. Table 12-1 lists some common fuels and gives typical values for the hydrogen and carbon contents as percentages by weight. All fuels contain other components besides hydrogen and carbon, albeit some in trace quantities. Some, such as sulfur, are combustible and will contribute to the heat released by the fuel. Other components are not combustible and contribute no positive energy to the combustion process. Table 12-2 presents the standard composition of air.

Table 12-1. Fuel Composition (%)

Components	Symbol	Molecular Weight	No 2	No 4 Light	No 4 Heavy	No Light	No 5 Heavy	No 6	Coal	Wood (dry)
Hydrogen	H	2.02	11.8 to 13.9	10.6 to 13.0	10.6 to 13.0	10.5 to 12.0	10.5 to 12.0	9.5 to 12	5.0	5.7
Carbon	C	12.01	86.1 to 88.2	86.5 to 89.2	86.5 to 89.2	86.5 to 89.2	86.5 to 89.2	86.5 to 89.2	75.0	54.9
Nitrogen	N_2	28.01	0.0 to 0.1	...	...	...	...	0.0 to 0.5	1.5	25.3
Oxygen	O_2	32.00	...	...	...	...	...	0.0 to 1.5	6.7	13.1
Sulfur	S	32.06	0.05 to 1.0	0.2 to 2.0	0.2 to 2.0	0.5 to 3.0	0.5 to 3.0	0.7 to 3.5	2.3	trace
Ash	...	...	...	0.0 to 0.1	0.0 to 0.1	0.0 to 0.1	0.0 to 0.1	0.0 to 0.5	7.0	2.0

The Chemistry: Table 12-3 reviews the basic chemical equations, which represent the most common combustion reactions. Note that nitrogen (N_2) is shown on both sides of the equations. This is because the air that provides the oxygen for combustion is composed mainly of nitrogen which must go through the burner and boiler.

Table 12-2. Composition of Air

Gas	Symbol	Molecular Mass	% by Volume	% by Weight
Nitrogen	N_2	28.016	78.09	75.47
Oxygen	O_2	32.000	20.90	23.20
Argon	Ar	39.94	0.933	1.28
Carbon dioxide	CO_2	44.01	0.033	0.046
Neon	Ne	20.18	0.0018	0.0012
Helium	He	4.003	0.0005	0.00007
Krypton	Kr	83.80	0.0001	0.0003
Xenon	Xe	131.29	9×10^{-5}	0.0004

Table 12-3. Common Combustion Reactions

Air	Fuel	Flue Gases
$4N_2 + O_2$	$2H_2$ hydrogen	$2H_2O + 4N_2 + $ HEAT water + nitrogen
$4N_2 + O_2$	C Carbon	$CO_2 + 4N_2 + $ HEAT Carbon dioxide + nitrogen
$4N_2 + O_2$	S sulfur	$SO_2 + 4N_2 + $ HEAT sulfur dioxide + nitrogen

	Rules of Thumb
1	Standard air @ sea level and 70°F has density of 0.07495 lb/ft^3
2	1 lb of standard air @ sea level and 70°F has a volume of 13.34 ft^3
	Required Air for Combustion
3	lb air/lb natural gas =17.5
4	lb air/lb oil = 14.0
5	lb air/lb coal =12.0
6	lb air/MMBtu oil= 750
7	lb air/MMBtu natural gas = 720
8	Required air for combustion increases 4.0% for every 1000 ft above sea level
9	lb/hr air = (ft^3/min) x 4.5 @70°F
10	Required air for combustion in ft^3/min increases 1.9% for every 10° above 70°F

Each atom of carbon in the fuel will combine with two atoms of oxygen (or one molecule of O_2) from the atmosphere to form one molecule of CO_2. On a weight basis, each pound of carbon requires 2.66 lb of oxygen for complete combustion, resulting in the production of 3.66 lb carbon dioxide.

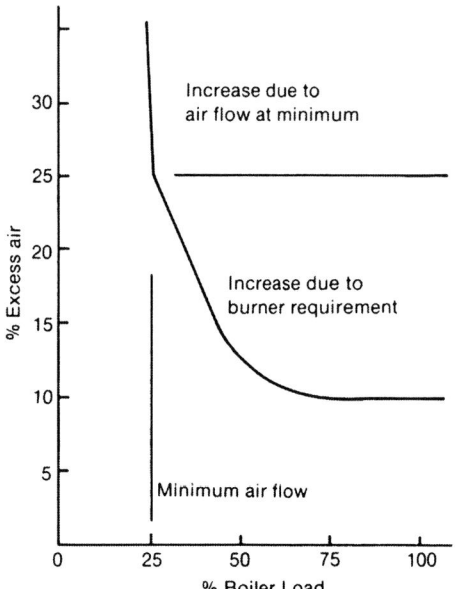

Fig 12-1. Typical curve for excess air versus boiler load

Each pair of hydrogen atoms (or each molecule of H_2) will combine with one atom of oxygen (or one half molecule of O_2) to form one molecule of H_2O, (water). On a weight basis, each pound of hydrogen requires 7.94 pounds of oxygen for complete combustion resulting in the production of 8.94 pounds of water.

By the Numbers: The air we breathe is only about 21% oxygen by volume. For all practical purposes, the remaining 79% is nitrogen. Since oxygen is a little heavier than nitrogen, the percentages by weight are somewhat different. The percentage oxygen by weight is 23%, and the remaining 77% is nitrogen. Thus, it requires about 4.35 pounds of air to deliver one pound of oxygen.

A typical gallon of No. 6 fuel oil weighs 8 pounds and is 87% carbon and 12% hydrogen (the missing percent would be sulfur, ash, water and sediment). This gallon would contain 6.95 pounds of carbon and 0.96 pound of hydrogen. From the data presented earlier it can be computed that 18.49 pounds of oxygen are needed to burn the carbon and 7.62 pounds of oxygen must be provided to burn the hydrogen in this gallon of fuel oil. This represents a total requirement of 26.11 pounds of oxygen. Since air is only 23% oxygen by weight, it will take 113.5 pounds of air (26.1 ÷ 0.23) for the complete and perfect (0% excess air) combustion of this gallon of fuel.

Assuming that there are 13 cubic feet of air to the pound, 1476 ft^3 of air are required to burn each gallon of fuel. A 50 gallon per hour burner (about 200 Boiler HP) would need nearly 74,000 ft^3 of air per hour (or 1230 ft^3/min) to fire without any allowance for excess air.

Real World Considerations: In the real world however, there must always be more air supplied to the combustion

process than the theoretical or stoichiometric air requirement. This is because no burner made is this perfect. This "extra" air is referred to as *excess air.* If 20% more than the theoretical air requirement is supplied, is said to be the burner operating at 20% excess air. Another way of stating the same thing is to say that the burner is operating with 120% total air.

Complete combustion of one gallon of No. 6 fuel oil with 20% excess air would require 136 pounds of air. The 50 gallon per hour burner would actually require about 90,000 cubic feet of air per hour.

For any particular burner-boiler combination there is an ideal minimum excess air level for each firing rate over the turn-down range. Greater air flows would waste fuel because of the increased mass flow of hot gases leaving the stack. Lesser amounts of air would cause fuel waste because the fuel would not be burned completely. Typically, burners require much higher levels of excess air when operating near their minimum firing rates than they do at high fire. Fig. 12-1 shows a typical relationship between percent firing rate and the excess air required to ensure complete combustion of the fuel. In many cases, even though stack temperature might decrease at low fire, efficiency suffers because so much of the fuel energy is lost to heat this excess air.

Varying Oxygen Content of Air: There are many factors which can influence the actual mass flow of oxygen into a burner for any given air control damper setting. Of course, dirty fan wheels and dampers will reduce the volumetric air flow, but changing ambient air conditions also have an effect on the actual input of oxygen into the combustion process.

Starting with normal air at a barometric pressure of 30 in. Hg, a temperature of 60°F, and 45% relative humidity, the actual mass oxygen flow for a constant volumetric air flow can vary by quite a bit with normal seasonal variations. Mass oxygen flow would drop by nearly 20% on a hot humid summer day when the combustion air is 120°F, with a barometric pressure of 29.5 in. Hg and 95% relative humidity. This is why it seems so hard to breathe on a really hot, humid day: There just isn't as much oxygen in each breath as we are used to. Burners have the same problem, except that they smoke, soot, and make noxious emissions if allowances aren't made for this oxygen-lean air.

The oxygen mass flow for a constant volumetric air flow would increase by 10% on a cold dry winter day at 32° F, barometric pressures of 30.5 in. Hg, and 0% relative humidity. It is relatively oxygen rich.

Variations in Fuel Flow: There are also many factors that can influence the actual mass flow of fuel into the burner for a given setting of the fuel control valve. Pressure drop across the metering valve and fluid viscosity have the greatest effect on fuel flow. With residual fuels, this is especially important. Viscosity of the fuel at a given, fixed temperature can vary from delivery to delivery, and temperature variations above this fixed point can cause the viscosity at the fuel valve to vary even more.

Having thick oil in the burner supply line can reduce the pressure at the metering valve while having thick oil in the return line can increase the pressure at the valve. With No. 6 fuel oil, the flow rate through a simple metering valve can vary by as much as +50% as a result of a build-up of typical variations in base viscosity, oil temperature, supply pressure and return line pressure.

Safe Burner Set-Up: In order to operate cleanly and safely, a burner must be adjusted so that, under the worst case fuel and air conditions, sufficient combustion air is supplied for the fuel to be burned. This means that if the burner is set up on a standard day with 60° air, a 30 inch barometric pressure, and 45% relative humidity, an additional 20% excess air must be provided if the burner is to operate cleanly on a hot, muggy summer day with the same ft³/min air flow, but with less oxygen per ambient cubic foot of air. Additionally, any possibility of the burner fuel delivery to increase at a given control setting must be taken into account by further increasing the excess air.

Cost of Excess Air: Since the total amount of air flow in a typical system is so great, it is easy to see why excess air is so costly. This air must be heated by the fire in the burner, yet the heat is not recovered completely. It is wasted up the stack. In the example of a 50 GPH burner, which must be set up with an extra 30% excess air to allow for variations in fuel and air conditions, the net result is an extra ton of air per hour which is heated and then goes up the stack.

At this point, it is sufficient it to say that adding air to the combustion process beyond what is absolutely necessary for complete and clean combustion causes a sizable drop in efficiency. Decreasing air flow can result in incomplete combustion, soot, smoking or carbon monoxide generation. This results in an even greater loss in efficiency because the chemical energy in the fuel is not totally extracted. Fig. 12-2 shows the effect of excess air on fuel loss for a typical burner. Figs. 12-3a and 12-3b show effect of excess air on temperatures.

Efficiency Calculations.—The efficiency of a burner-boiler combination is simply the amount of useful energy leaving the system expressed as a percentage of the chemical energy in the fuel entering the system. The efficiency calculation method based on measuring the fuel input and the steam (or hot water) output is called the *input-output efficiency method*. This method is not used frequently because of the difficulty in obtaining fuel flow, steam flow and steam quality measurements with the required degree of accuracy.

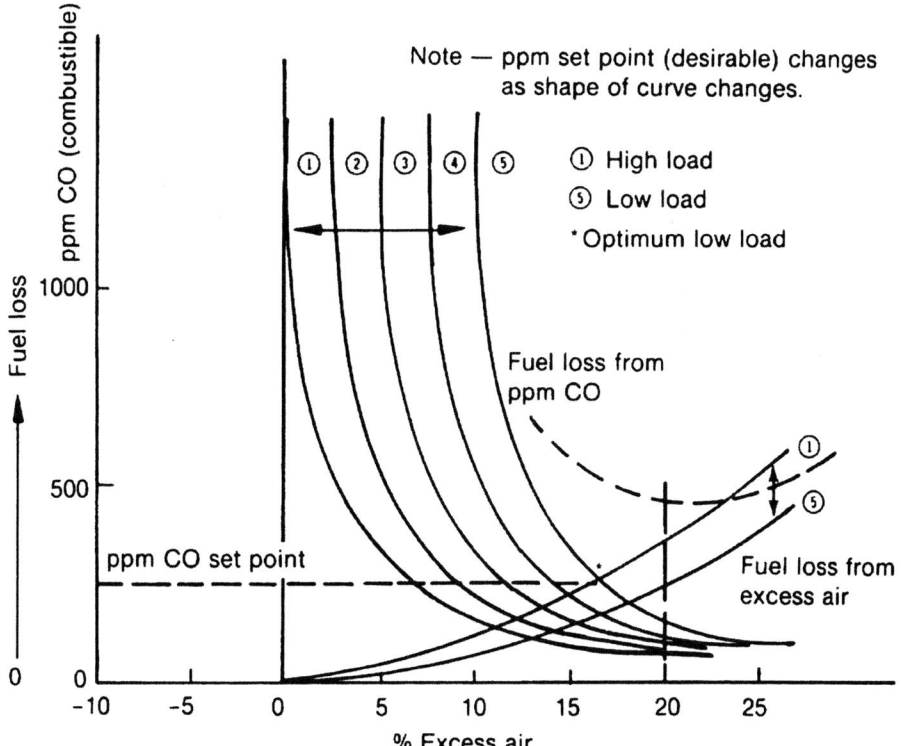

Fig 12-2. Excess air combustible gas relationship

Since the efficiency value will typically be around 80% and a change in efficiency of 5% can have a major impact on the operation expense of a facility, the flow measurements used in the calculations would have to have errors significantly less than 5% for these calculations to be useful. This is beyond the capability of the steam and fuel flow metering devices normally found in the boiler room except possibly at maximum boiler output.

Another less obvious but more accurate way of calculating boiler efficiency is the ASME by-losses method. Here, the boiler burner is assumed to be a black box. Energy enters the black box in the form of chemical energy in the fuel and sensible heat in the combustion air. Energy leaves the black box in the form of steam and as sensible and latent heat in the flue gases and in radiation from the boiler surfaces and in the blowdown water. Fig. 12-4 shows a simple block diagram with various energy flows into and out of the boiler.

Since energy cannot be created or destroyed, and since energy is not stored in the boiler (when operating in the steady state), the amount of energy leaving the system by all available paths must be equal to the amount of energy entering the system by all available paths. By calculating all of the various energy flows out of the system which represent losses, and expressing them as a percentage of the fuel energy entering the system, the total losses may be calculated. If there were no losses the efficiency would be 100%. This results is an accurate estimate of unit efficiency, which can be used to obtain (by direct measurement) the fuel energy into the burner and the steam energy out of the boiler.

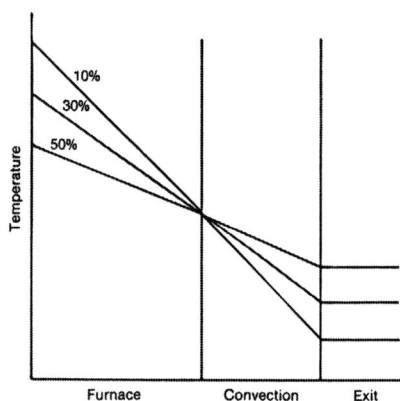

- Reduced excess air improves heat transfer.
- Reduced excess air reduces mass of flue gases.

Fig 12-3b. Effect of excess air on temperatures

Temperature and Barometric Effect on Excess Air: For a burner originally adjusted to 15% excess air when the barometric pressure was 29 in. Hg and air temperature was 80°F, the following table shows excess air changes resulting from changes in air pressure and temperature.

Air Temperature °F	Barometric Pressure in. Hg	Resulting% Excess Air
40	29	25.5
60	29	20.2
80	29	15.0
100	29	9.6
120	29	1.1
80	27	7.7
80	28	11.0
80	29	15.0
80	30	19.0
40	31	34.5
60	30	25.0
80	29	15.0
100	28	5.0
120	27	5.5

Efficiency Losses: The two largest energy losses are stack losses and radiation losses. Taken together, the steam leaving the boiler and stack and radiation losses account for all but a percent or two of the energy entering the boiler in the form of fuel. Stack losses represent the energy that could be reclaimed from the gases leaving the boiler if these gases were cooled to the temperature of the combustion air entering the system. The lower the stack temperature (all other things being equal) the lower the stack losses. The lower the stack losses, the higher the efficiency.

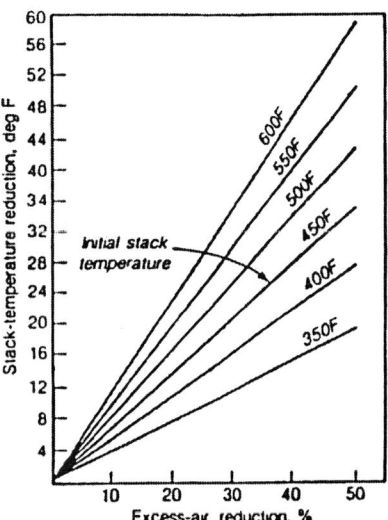

Fig 12-3a. Effect of excess air on temperatures

The stack losses account for nearly all of the wasted energy leaving the boiler. For this reason, the term "combustion efficiency" is often used in place of "efficiency". Combustion efficiency is the number that results when the stack losses are deducted from 100%. This number neglects radiation and miscellaneous losses, so it is generally 3% to 5% higher than the actual efficiency.

Radiation Losses: Radiation losses represent the heat that escapes from the surface of the boiler into the surroundings via the mechanism of radiation heat transfer. The better the boiler is insulated, the lower the radiation losses will be. Radiation losses generally represent a fixed amount of energy lost per unit time since the surface of the boiler is generally at the saturation temperature of the steam being generated. For field erected water tube boilers, with significant amounts of refractory furnace wall surface not covered with water tubes, the total quantity of heat lost to radiation might increase with firing rate since the furnace walls would become hotter at higher inputs.

With water-cooled boiler surfaces (especially fire tube units), since total amount of heat lost from the surface per hour is a constant (dependent on the temperature of the surrounding air), the heat loss to radiation is not dependent on firing rate. When expressed as a percentage of the fuel energy input, however, the radiation loss will be higher at reduced firing rates. If a boiler has a 3% radiation loss at high fire (100% input), it will have a 6% radiation loss at half fire because the constant heat flow by radiation is now twice as large compared with the fuel input.

Radiation losses are not affected by changes in combustion and combustion control. Short of insulating the boiler, there is no real way to control this loss. Stack losses, however, may be controlled.

Stack Losses: Stack losses are composed of sensible and latent components. The latent heat component represents the heat of vaporization of the water (steam) that was formed when the hydrogen in the fuel was burned. This component is a function of the percent hydrogen in the fuel and may be treated as a constant for any given fuel analysis. For typical fuel oils, the efficiency lost due to latent heat in the stack (steam in stack) is roughly 5%. For natural gas, which contains a higher percentage of hydrogen, the efficiency lost due to latent heat in the stack gases is roughly 9%.

The sensible heat component of the stack loss is a function of the amount of gas leaving the boiler and the difference in temperature between the stack gases and the combustion air entering the burner. The higher this temperature difference, the higher the stack loss. The greater the mass flow of gas through the boiler, the higher the stack loss. More excess air, then, results in lowered efficiency.

The temperature of the gases leaving the boiler is effected by boiler design, the cleanliness of the boiler, firing rate, and amount of excess air. The higher the relative air flow, the shorter the residence time of gases in the boiler will be. The gases will have less time to give up heat to the boiler tubes, and the stack temperature will increase, driving the efficiency down. The dirtier the heat transfer surfaces on both fire and water sides, the higher will be the temperature of the gases leaving the boiler, and the efficiency will suffer. Typically, a 40°F increase in stack temperature will result in a 1% decrease in efficiency. Of course, high pressure steam boilers will have higher stack temperatures than low pressure steam boilers because the temperature of the water in the boiler is higher for the higher pressures. The combustion gases are cooled by hotter tube surfaces, and they end up hotter. This is why large high pressure boilers are often equipped with feedwater economizers. Here, the relatively cool boiler feedwater is used to cool the stack gases further after they leave the boiler steam generating section.

Conservation of Energy		Rules of Thumb (approximate Operating Cost)
Fuel energy "in" equals heat energy "out"	1	Cost of fuel = $6.25 per 1000 lb of steam/hr (based on gas @$5.00/1000 ft³)
Energy leaves in steam or in losses	2	Normal firing hr/yr = 8500
Efficiency = 100% minus all losses	3	10% reduction in excess air =1% reduction in fuel input
Typical Boiler Efficiency is 80% to 85%	4	On a packaged water tube boiler, each on-off cycle costs an additional $0.50 per 1000 lb of maximum boiler rating (based on heat losses during purge and increased maintenance)
The remaining 15% to 20% is lost		
Largest loss is a typical 15% "stack loss"		
Radiation loss may be 3% at full input	5	Horsepower cost = $333.00 per/hp-yr (based on electricity cost of $0.05/kw hr)
Miscellaneous losses might be 1 to 2%		

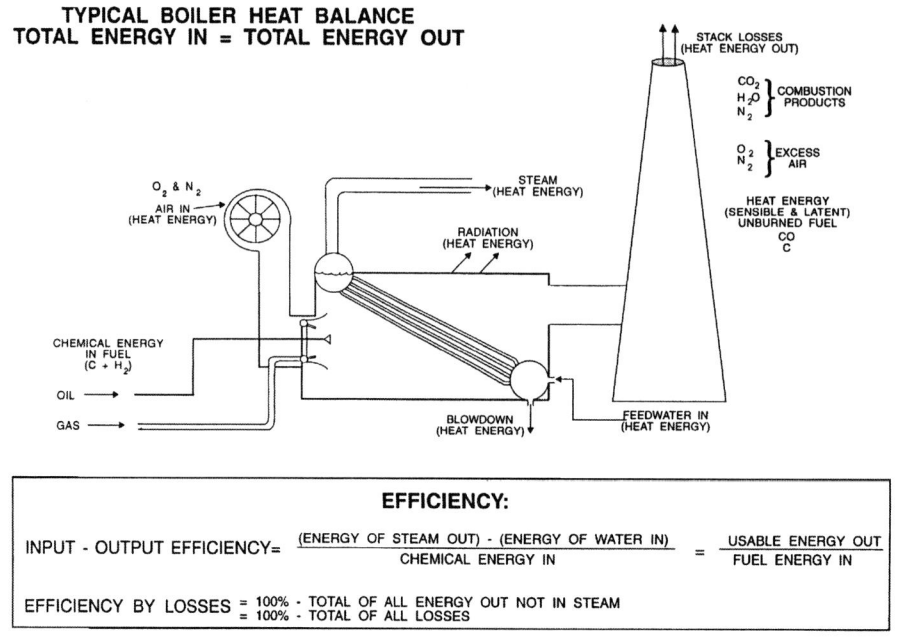

Fig 12-4. Typical boiler heat balance

Measuring Excess Air: The mass flow of air through the boiler is a function of the amount and composition of the fuel being fired and the amount of excess air provided. For theoretical (stoichiometric) combustion with no excess air (0% O_2 in the flue gas), the amount of air required for each unit of fuel may be determined from the analyses of the fuel and air composition as discussed earlier. It is also possible to calculate the maximum CO_2 content of the stack gases based on the percent of carbon in the fuel. By taking a reading of the CO_2 or O_2 content of the stack gases, the amount of excess air may be calculated as well. The efficiency charts on Figs. 12-5 to 12-7 correlate oxygen, carbon dioxide, and excess air levels for various "typical" fuels.

Remember that the flue gases contain a substantial amount of water vapor. If this water vapor is allowed to condense, the remaining gases will take up less volume. If the concentration of oxygen or carbon dioxide in a "dry" sample is measured, the percent by volume will be higher than if the water were still present as a vapor.

This is why there are two sets of values for oxygen on the efficiency charts we use. One is for dry samples. The other is for wet samples with the water vapor still present. In-situ zirconium oxide analyzers operate at a high temperature and provide a "wet" reading because the measured oxygen is part of the entire stack gas sample, water vapor and all. "Wet" reading will always be lower than "dry" readings, and it is important to note the method used when taking combustion data or the wrong excess air levels will be inferred.

Calculating Flue Gas Composition: The amount of water vapor and carbon dioxide formed per unit of fuel is fixed by the amount of hydrogen and carbon in the fuel as determined by the fuel analysis. The amount of nitrogen leaving the boiler is a function of the amount of theoretical air required for each unit of fuel plus the amount of excess air in the combustion products. For each fuel composition, the measurement of excess air in the stack will uniquely determine the composition of the stack gases. Given the composition of these gases, it is possible to determine the amount of latent and sensible heat energy contained in the gases leaving the boiler for any given temperature reading.

In this way it is possible to prepare charts for typical fuels relating the stack losses to the excess air levels and to the temperature rise (difference between stack temperature and combustion air temperature). By using temperature rise instead of absolute stack temperature, the energy in the combustion air entering the burner is accounted for. It is also possible to write computer programs, and to configure microprocessor based controllers to calculate the combustion efficiency based on typical fuel analysis, stack temperature, air temperature, and stack oxygen.

The charts on Figs. 12-5 to 12-7 for the calculation of combustion efficiency were developed in this way. Figs. 12-5, 12-6, and 12-7 were developed for calculating the combustion efficiency of boilers firing natural gas, No. 2 oil, and No. 6 oil respectively.

It is important to realize that it does not matter in the efficiency calculation where the excess air comes from. It might be supplied to the burner intentionally or it might be "tramp air" which has entered the boiler because of leaks in the setting and/or excessively high draft in the furnace. This is why a tight setting and good draft control is very important in maximizing the efficiency of a boiler.

Other Energy Losses: There is a potential third major loss representing unburned fuel. This can be significant when firing solid fuels as the ash leaving the boiler may contain unburned carbon in the several percentage point range. Since focus here is mainly gas and oil firing, and since unburned fuel results in smoke, soot, and carbon monoxide, the assumption is made that this condition cannot be allowed to exist regardless of its effects on efficiency. For this reason unburned fuel losses will be ignored in this chapter.

For high pressure boilers operating with regular or continuous blowdown in order to control dissolved solids, there can be significant energy wasted in the blowdown water. Continuous blowdown controls can minimize this loss by keeping the blowdown rate from exceeding that needed to keep the boiler water conductivity below a predetermined level. On large units it may be economical to install a heat exchanger to transfer this heat to the feedwater.

In general, radiation loss, stack loss, any blowdown loss, and a wild card "miscellaneous loss" account for practically all of the energy lost from the system. Often the radiation loss at high fire and the miscellaneous loss are given in the boiler manufacturer data. If measures the stack temperature, and excess air (via CO_2 or O_2 measurement), a very accurate estimate of total unit efficiency can be obtained if radiation losses and miscellaneous losses are taken into account. Remember that the radiation loss is inversely proportional to the firing rate when taken as a percent figure.

Example 1: Suppose a 600 HP boiler is firing No. 6 oil. The boiler manufacturer gives the high fire radiation loss as 2% and the miscellaneous loss as 1%. Measurement of the stack gases using a Bacharach Fyrite gives a CO_2 reading of 12% and the stack temperature is 580°F. Further, the temperature of the combustion air is 80°F, so the net stack temperature or ΔT is 500°F.

For the sake of argument assume that the burner is operating at 75% of the maximum rating of the boiler. This means that the actual radiation loss would be the high fire rating of 2% divided by 0.75, or 2.67%.

The CO_2 reading is a dry reading because the Bacharach, by its nature, condenses the water out of the stack gases in the process of absorbing the CO_2. From the combustion efficiency chart on Fig. 12-7, note that the 12% CO_2 reading corresponds to 33% excess air. By drawing a line up to the 500°F net stack temperature or Δ-T line, the combustion efficiency is estimated at 82%.

Note that this is just combustion efficiency. From this in Fig. 12-7, the 2.67% radiation loss and the 1% miscellaneous loss must be deducted. The resulting unit efficiency as determined by the ASME by-losses method is 78.33%. This number should agree with an efficiency calculation based on fuel in and steam out if all measurements are accurate to within a tenth of a percent or so.

Saving Fuel with Combustion Controls.—Since the burner must be set up to operate cleanly under worst case conditions, enough excess air must be provided to burn any additional fuel that the metering device at the burner may introduce, as well as to ensure that there will be sufficient excess air available on a hot muggy summer day. There is no way to prevent hot muggy summer days, but fuel flow can be closely controlled with the appropriate hardware.

To compensate for changes in air quality a burner will operate part of the year (assuming that there is no seasonal tuning) with more excess air than at other times of the year. If the air flow must be increased by 20% to accommodate a hot day, then during periods with cooler drier air and most boiler load, the burner will waste fuel. On large units of 600 HP or more, oxygen trim can provide a payback by compensating for these changes in air flow. On smaller units, seasonal tuning can be a solution. On residential size burners, the best practice is to live with the excess air because a burner that runs short of air and builds soot or produces CO is not safe or efficient.

Assume that a particular burner firing No. 6 fuel oil can be adjusted to operate at 20% excess air on a normal day with "normal" fuel metering. Further, assume that this boiler will then show a stack temperature of 460°F. Fig. 12-7 shows that the technician would measure 3.2% O_2 (wet) or 13.4% CO_2 (dry) since the excess air level is 20%. The net stack temperature rise would be 400°F if the ambient air entering the burner was at 60°F. The combustion efficiency would be 85.6%.

Assuming that the air is increased just to cover expected changes in air quality, at least 20% more excess air would have to be added on a "normal" day to compensate for an abnormal day. Looking again at Fig. 12-7, the efficiency loss due to an additional 20% increase in excess air is about 1.6%. For a 750 HP boiler operating at an average load of 65%, this could represent an actual cost of $18,800 per year using a fuel cost of $0.90 per gallon.

If the metering system for the oil had a possible variance of ±20%, then an additional 20% excess air would have to be provided to ensure complete combustion when the oil flow was at a high extreme. Fig. 12-7 indicates that this would result in a decrease to 82.8% efficiency. The additional cost of this excess air would be $14,400 with the same assumptions as before.

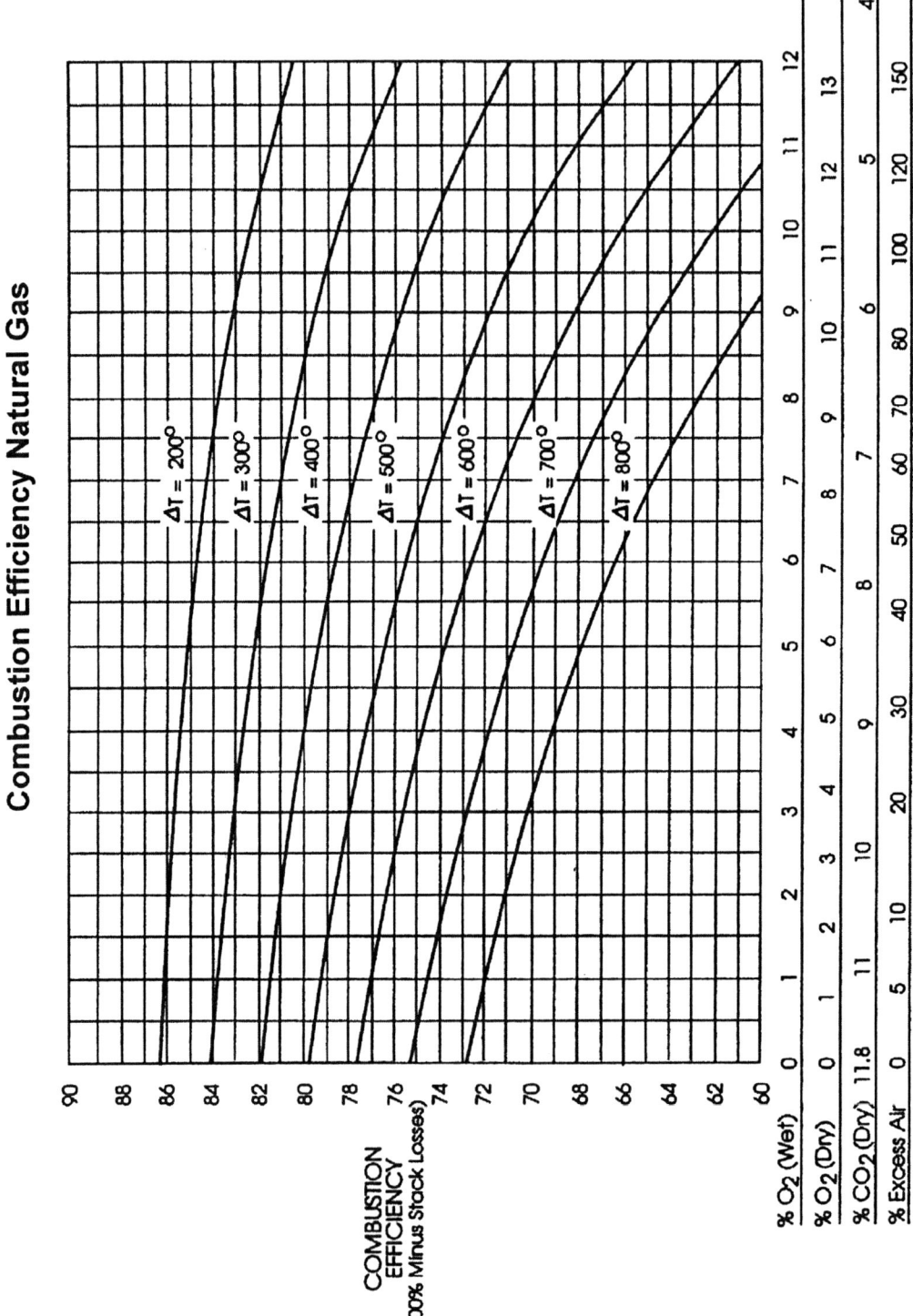

Fig 12-5. Combustion efficiency of natural gas

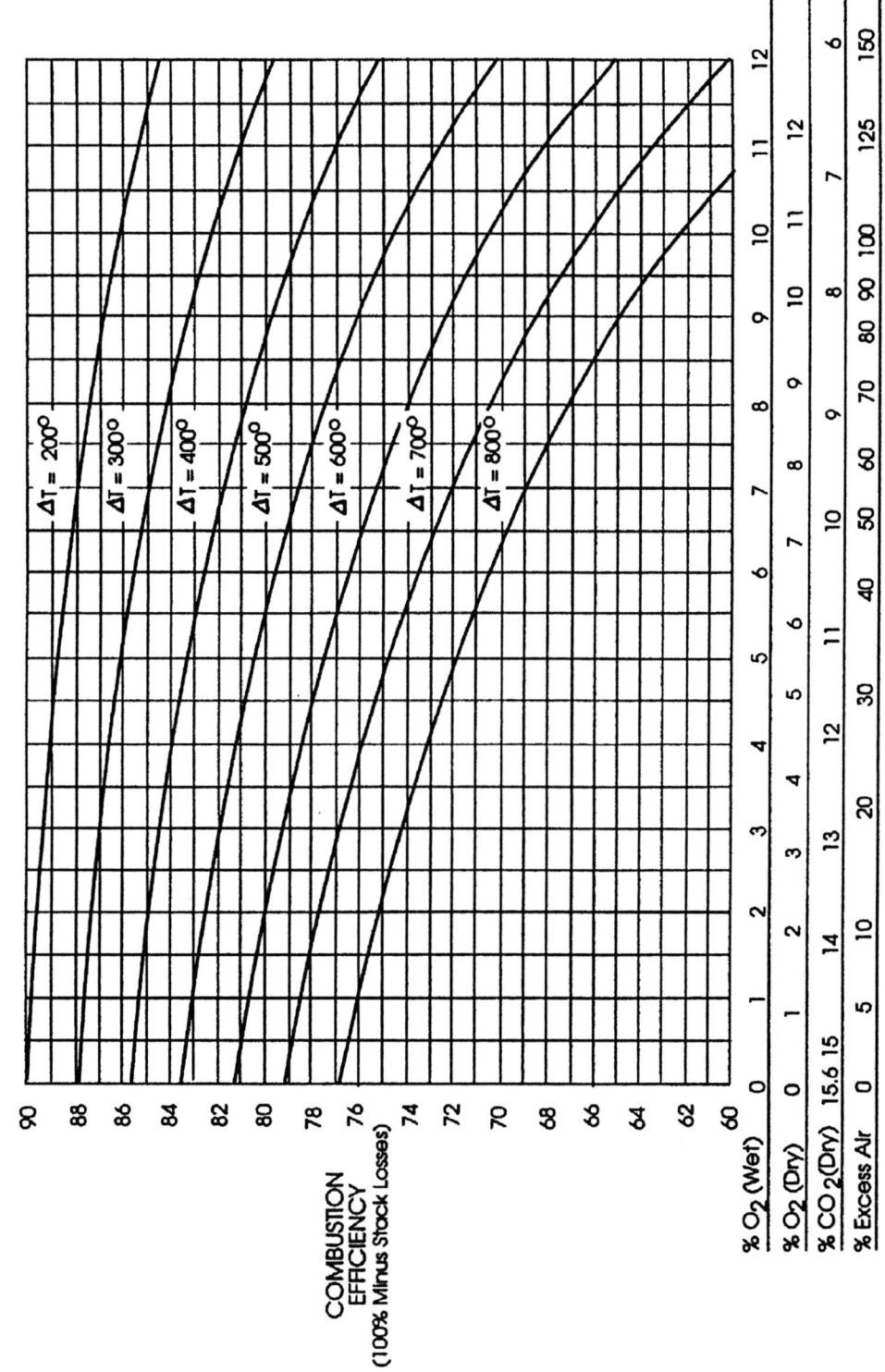

Fig 12-6. Combustion efficiency of No. 2 oil

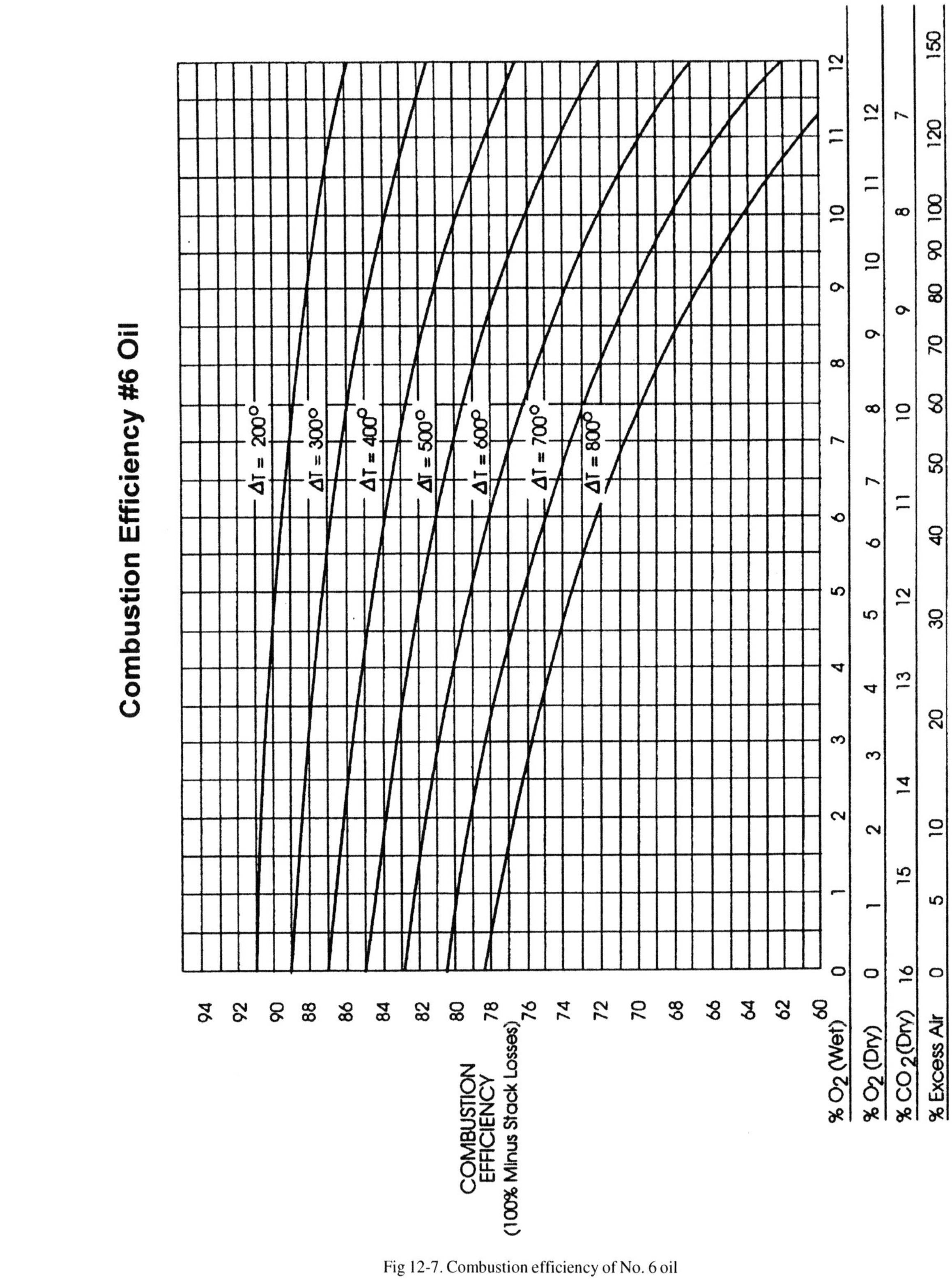

Fig 12-7. Combustion efficiency of No. 6 oil

Typically, the efficiency would drop to around 81.5% with an extra 40% excess air because of a corresponding increase in stack temperature. As excess air increases, the residence time of the gases in the boiler decreases, causing a reduced heat transfer. If a "perfect" control system with oxygen trim and metering fuel flow control could hold this boiler to the ideal 20% excess air at all times, the owner could potentially save $24,000 per year (at 2005 prices, taking the change in flue gas temperature into account).

It is these potential savings that justify the installation of sophisticated control systems on larger units, and burners with sophisticated fuel metering systems on smaller units.

Combustion Considerations – General.— It is the burner's responsibility to accept the input of at least two dissimilar fluids, mix them, ignite them, oxidize all of the combustible material with the least amount of excess air and the least possible emissions, all over the widest range of firing rates without instability and with a flame envelope that does not impinge on heat transfer surfaces. Reduced electrical energy consumption, low fuel and atomizing media supply pressure requirements and reduced atomizing media consumption are other desirable features. To accomplish all of this not only requires that the burner's mechanical design be optimal but that the control and fuel handling systems responsible for the flow control and the conditioning of those inputs be optimal, as well.

Observation: Under the exact same conditions it is not possible to achieve a burner performance level over the full range of firing rates while in the automatic mode which exceeds what is possible when the burner is operated in manual at each firing rate.

Observation: A burner is a system of fixed orifices. Without proper fuel handling and preparation systems, a proper control strategy/system and a means by which to monitor performance, it is not possible to achieve and maintain a level of automation that provides repeatable, efficient and safe operation.

Nothing is this easy, but regardless it raises perplexing questions in the field that may have multiple reasons:

For example, why was the O_2 at 2.5% if the unit was set up at 1.5% at the same firing rate the other day? The reason could be that the air temperature has dropped 50°F since the other day and that the control system is without O_2 trim.

Another reason could be that the regulated gas pressure at the inlet to the piping train is now 10 psig while it was 12 psig the other day. Or that there is a single pressure regulator for all three boilers in the plant where the set up was performed on a day when two boilers were in operative (the load has now increased and all three units are now online).

The above example and the follow up issues are presented to convey that the performance of a burner is not a "snapshot" taken at the time of commissioning, rather it is an ongoing issue that depends on providing control, fuel handling, and monitoring systems that make appropriate adjustments for varying conditions and also provide a means by which to identify and then correct any deficiencies.

Example: The NO_x guarantee on an application is 30 ppmc. The current "indicated" NO_x level is 32 ppm with a corresponding excess O_2 of 2.5% (dry). Correcting the "indicated" value to 3% O_2 (dry) yields

$$32 \times \frac{17.9}{(20.9 - 2.5)} = 31.13 \text{ ppmc}$$

If the O_2 is reduced to 1.5% ("dry"), the "indicated" NO_x remains 32 ppm and the CO does not increase above 100 ppmc:

$$32 \times \frac{17.9}{(20.9 - 1.5)} = 29.53 \text{ ppmc}$$

Pressure and Flow Basic Principles.—Most of these have to do with the resistance to a fluid's flow (i.e. pressure drop) imposed by not only the burner, but by piping, ducting, breeching, etc. and the influence of fluid properties on that resistance. The general equation (developed by Darcy) for calculating pressure drop (DP) across any system element and for any fluid is:

$$DP = K\rho\left(\frac{Q/A}{1096.7}\right)^2 CF_p CF_t CF_e \quad (1)$$

Where DP = pressure drop, inches water column (divide by 27.8 for pressure drop in psi)

$K = f \times L/D_h$

f = friction Factor which depends on the Reynolds Number (Re), the hydraulic diameter (D_h) and the flow conduit roughness (e); Re in turn depends on the fluid mass flow rate, its actual flowing viscosity (μ) and (D_h)

L = length of pipe, or the equivalent length of an elbow, a piping, etc.

D_h = hydraulic diameter (4 × flow cross-sectional area /wetted perimeter) (Note:D_h for any item of around cross-section is equal to its diameter)

ρ = fluid's standard density at 60°F, atmospheric pressure and at sea level, lb/ft³

Q = fluid's flow rate referenced to standard conditions, ft³/min

A = cross-sectional flow area, ft²

CF_p (*pressure correction factor*) = $14.7/(P_{in}+14.7)$

P = pressure in psig

CF$_t$ (temperature correction factor) = $(T_{in}+460)/520$;
where *T* is in °F.

CF$_e$(elevation correction factor) = less than 1 for any
elevation below sea level

Alternatively the above equation can be rearranged to solve for flow:

$$Q = 1096.7A \times \sqrt{\left(\frac{DP}{KpCF_pCF_tCF_e}\right)} \qquad (2)$$

There is no need to remember these equations or know how to use them. One should remember the following for a fixed DP:

1) If the site elevation increases, the flow rate in ft^3/min or lb/hr decreases. (Note: This can occur if the burner is on a rental boiler.)

2) If the inlet temperature of the fluid increases, the flow rate in ft^3/min or lb/hr decreases. (Note: Seasonal change in ambient air temperature).

3) If the inlet pressure of the fluid increases, the flow rate in ft^3/min or lb/hr increases. (Note: Change in pressure regulator set point).

4) If the standard density of the fluid decreases, the flow rate in ft^3/min or lb/hr increases. (Note: This could occur if there were a change in fuel oil grade from No. 6 to No. #2)

5) If the cross-sectional flow area of the item increases, the flow rate in ft^3/min or lb/hr increases. (Note: This could occur if there was an increase in the number of holes or the hole drill size of the gas injectors or sprayer plate).

6) If the viscosity of the fluid increases, the *Re* decreases and the *f* increases where upon the flow rate in ft^3/min or lb/hr decreases. (Note: A change from #2 to No. 6 fuel oil).

Note: The term *K* is used to reflect a given device's resistance to flow. The term C_v used by most control valve manufacturers includes an area allowance, while orifice plate calculations use the terms *C* (orifice coefficient) and *Y* (expansion factor). Nonetheless, the conditions affecting the pressure drop across all of these devices is accounted for identically.

Note: In the guaranteed operating excess oxygen range (1.5–2.5% dry O$_2$ from 50 to 100% firing rate), a change in fuel or combustion air flow by only 5% would produce an approximate 1% excess O$_2$ change.

Atomizing Media Considerations.—The primary purpose of the atomizing media is to shear higher viscosity liquid into fine droplets, which can then be thoroughly burned in a short duration. Simply put, it is the role of the atomizing media to alter the liquid fuel's characteristics so that they approximate that of a gaseous fuel. The two most common atomizing media are compressed air and steam, though any high pressure gas can be used. If applied properly, either is equally effective. Steam, if available, is generally preferred because it is usually

already at a high pressure and the operating cost to differentially produce this steam is lower than that to compress air. The primary considerations applicable to these two atomizing media alternatives are as follows:

Similarities-Moisture: It is well understood that steam must be trapped to remove any condensed moisture. People forget or are simply unaware that there is considerable moisture in atmospheric air, a lot of which is removed with air compressor intercoolers and after coolers. This plant air, which is generally used for atomizing media is interestingly unsuitable as instrument air because it still contains too much moisture. Moisture of any kind adversely affects the shearing process and is very erosive, causing premature wear of all parts that come in contact with the atomizing media alone or the mixture of it with the liquid fuel. The importance of providing a suitable number of traps and applying ample insulation to piping cannot be understated.

Dissimilarities-Change of State: The biggest difference between steam and compressed air is that compressed air does not undergo a change of state while some steam vapor does condense within the atomizer, either by direct or indirect contact with the relatively lower temperature liquid fuel.

Note that some of this condensed steam can actually flash back into vapor when it exits the sprayer plate due to the expansion that occurs as the stream exits a high pressure area and discharges into atmosphere. The benefits of this condensing and flashing on atomization quality is not the subject of this discussion, rather it is the heat exchange process that influences the selection of the correct atomizer. The internal mix design applies the shearing at the distributor and the resulting atomizing media/liquid fuel mixture then passes through some number of mixers before exiting the sprayer plate. In addition to the heat exchange that takes place between the oil tube and steam barrel section of the atomizer, there is the subsequent and more significant heat exchange that results because of the direct contact between the two fluids. With the external mix design, the shearing process takes place within the sprayer plate and the amount of direct contact between the two fluids is limited to the short distance of exposure in the sprayer plate exit hole. For all of these reasons, application of the internal mix will generally be limited to heavy fuel oil with steam atomization or light oil with air atomization applications, while the external mix would generally be used otherwise. This may not always be the case, as emissions and/or flame shaping issues may dominate as the more important criteria on specific applications.

Combustion Air Considerations.—The largest single input to the fired equipment is the combustion air. Under ideal mixing conditions there is an absolute minimum quantity of combustion air required to incinerate all of the combustible material in any given fuel, and any additional amount above this minimum is termed excess air. Usually some excess air is inputted because mixing is not perfect, and to serve as a cushion during firing rate changes. Many burners operate with excess air levels of 15–25% (2.5–4% excess O_2), while low excess air burners operate with 5–10% excess air (1–2% excess O_2). It is advantageous to operate with as little excess air as possible because operation with lower excess air levels generally results in the formation of less NO_x and because fired equipment efficiency increases when the equipment is operated with lower excess air (less heated mass flow exiting the unit). Of course, the difficulty in operating with less excess air is the potential that some portion of the fuel will not be totally incinerated, resulting in CO and hydrocarbon emissions.

The lowest excess air with which the burner is capable of operating (at each firing rate) can be determined during commissioning when the burner is being operated in the manual mode. If the complete set-up is performed within a short period on a given day, it can be presumed that factors affecting combustion air flow are fairly constant. Over the course of time the following conditions bear attention:

Elevation: For a given site this is not an issue. If the burner is on a rental boiler, a change in location could result in a change in job site elevation. At an elevation of 3000 feet above sea level, the density of air is about 10% less than it is at sea level. Therefore, there will be an approximate 10% increase in DP for the same flow, Q, in ft³/min or lb/hr. Alternatively, for the same DP there will be an approximate 5% reduction in ft³/min or lb/hr. Moving a burner from a lower elevation to a higher one generally results in deriding its capacity unless a means is provided to compensate.

Temperature: This is the one condition that is subject to the greatest variation. If the burner is "set-up" with 50°F combustion air and due to seasonal changes the air temperature can vary by ±50°F, then there is the potential for the combustion air flow to vary ±5% from the original set-up value. Oxygen trim would provide the needed compensation.

Draft: See the following section, "Flue Gas Considerations".

Flue Gas Considerations.—Flue gases are of course the products of combustion, and they exit the fired equipment at elevated temperatures. Besides CO_2, N_2 and excess O_2 and the emissions of particulate, VOCs, hydrocarbons, NO_x, SO_x and CO, flue gases contain considerable moisture which at the elevated temperatures are in the form of vapor.

Draft: The furnace of fired equipment is either operated at a positive pressure or a negative pressure usually termed draft. Regardless, flue gases are ultimately discharged from a stack. The height of the stack is important,

because the taller it is, the greater the developed natural draft. If multiple pieces of fired equipment are breeched to a single common stack, the natural draft will be impacted by the number of units in operation and their individual firing rates.

In some cases, even if there is a tall stack, it is necessary to provide an induced draft (ID) fan to overcome resistances imposed downstream of the fired equipment and to assure that a negative furnace pressure is maintained regardless of conditions.

The equation for calculating "natural draft" is as follows:

$$\text{Stack draft} = 7.57 \times L \times \left(\frac{1}{T_a} - \frac{1}{T_g} \right) \times \frac{B}{30} \qquad (3)$$

where L = stack height, feet
T_a = ambient temperature, °R
T_g = flue gas temperature, °R
B = barometric pressure, in Hg

Even on pressurized firing applications, it is possible to have a negative draft in the furnace at reduced firing rates, when the elevated temperature necessary to produce a natural draft exists, while the pressure drop experienced by the flue gas as they pass through the fired equipment is negligible.

There are two potentially serious problems attributable to the existence of draft: The draft is not repeatable (i.e., the draft is not controlled); and/or it results in uncontrolled air infiltration into the fired equipment, causing it to lead to misleading information regarding the presumed combustion air flow through the burner(s). As to the lack of draft repeatability, consider the following:

A) As should be apparent from the above equation, natural draft is dependent on the stack height and the temperature of the flue gases and the environment. For 500°F flue gases, the natural draft is 50% higher on a 20°F day than it is on a 100°F day. Though this unto itself may only represent itself in a few tenths of an inch water column, consider that on the same cold day that the draft is higher, more combustion air is capable of passing through the system. The combination may or may not warrant the use of draft control (unless tramp air is an overruling issue) but the addition of O_2 trim would be justified.

B) Anytime more than one piece of fired equipment is connected to one stack, draft controls should be provided for each unit. This is because the net natural draft depends not only on the conditions described above but also on the resistance imposed by the stack on the flow of flue gases through it. Therefore the number of units in operation and their combined firing rate influences the "net natural draft."

C) Draft control should be provided anytime the expected natural draft is greater than 2.5% of the burner draft loss (i.e. if the BDL is 10 in. water column then draft control should be included if the natural draft will be greater than or equal to 0.25 in. water column). This because the influence of "natural draft" (which is essentially constant throughout the firing rate range) has a pronounced affect on air flow at firing rates less than 50%.

D) Draft control should be provided whenever an induced FGR NO$_x$ reduction strategy is provided. The FGR take-off be upstream of the draft control damper to minimize tramp air infiltration.

E) Flue gas excess O$_2$ measurements should also be taken upstream of the draft control damper to minimize "tramp air" bias of the sample.

FGR (Flue Gas Recirculation): FGR is effective in reducing NO$_x$ emissions despite elevated temperature, because the additional mass flow inputted to the combustion zone reduces the flame temperature and because it is oxygen deficient. If FGR is withdrawn from a location which is at a negative draft, it is possible, depending on the tightness of the setting, that tramp air has infiltrated into the flue gas. FGR should always be withdrawn from the area that has the lowest potential for tramp air infiltration and where the flue gases are at their lowest temperature.

Moisture: The amount of moisture in the products of combustion (resulting from the burning of hydrogen) is considerable (about 10% by volume when burning fuel oils and approaching 20% by volume when burning natural gas). This moisture, if allowed to collect can result in misleading indications of draft, beginning with those specific to the measurement of furnace pressure.

Gas Fuel Firing Considerations.—For a fuel such as Natural gas, one's contract usually stipulates a very narrow range of higher heating value (HHV in Btu/ft^3 or btu/lb) and specific gravity (sg). In the case of chemical process off gases, these conditions are like wise fairly constant when the process is being operated normally, but under start-up, shutdown or operational upsets these could change dramatically. A term often times used to compare one gas to another is called the Wobbe Index:

$$\text{Wobbe index} = \frac{\text{Gas HHV}}{\sqrt{\text{Gas SG}}} \qquad (4)$$

where *HHV* = higher heating value Btu/ft^3.

The reason for creating this index is that it combines conditions that impact the gas flow rate and its density, which in turn affects the pressure drop.Gas heating value and specific gravity variations are not encountered too often but one should be aware of it.

Elevation: Refer to "*Combustion Considerations – General*". At a given site this is not an issue.

Temperature: Like combustion air, variations in temperature are very possible, though generally not to the same extent.

Pressure: There is no reason for pressure variations at the inlet of a burner's piping train, unless the fuel is a by-product of some process. Regardless, every burner piping train should be equipped with a pressure or differential pressure regulator at its inlet. Referencing the Darcy Equation (1), an uncontrolled increase in inlet pressure will result in an increase in flow and vice versa. Note that this effect applies to every component in the piping train, so application of a flow meter does not by itself compensate for pressure fluctuations unless the meter is a thermal mass type or the reading of an alternative meter is pressure compensated.

Fuel Oil Firing Considerations.—Liquids are incompressible fluids, so their density is not influenced by pressure variations, but a liquid's density is affected by temperature, though not to the same extent as gases (water's density reduces by about 20% for a temperature change 100°F to 500°F, while any gas will undergo a 40% reduction in density). There are simply significantly more variables to be concerned about when burning liquid fuels. These primarily have to deal with its composition, which influences emissions and other physical characteristics, and which impact on storage, pumping, preparation, and atomization considerations. Some of the more important fuel oil characteristics are:

Viscosity: Viscosity is a measure of a fluid's resistance to flow. It is probably one of the most important properties of the fuel to be fired since it relates to its ability to flow through the lines and be properly atomized at the burner nozzle.

A high viscosity fuel like No. 6 oil will thicken considerably at normal room temperatures and requires constant heating and circulation in order to flow and be atomized properly. A low viscosity fuel like No. 2 oil will flow and atomize easily at room temperature.

In the combustion industry, viscosity is generally expressed in "SSU" or saybolt seconds universal. This quantity is determined in a lab and is the length of time in seconds required for the oil, heated to a specified temperature, to flow through a standard orifice. To assure good fuel oil combustion, the maximum value is generally between 100 and 200 ssu for most applications.

Temperature vs. viscosity information is critical in determining the required oil temperature at the burner to achieve the correct ssu for atomization. These data can be obtained from standard viscosity tables. However, some fuels, particularly blends may require that an analysis be provided by the supplier. Regardless, it is always sensible for the user to draw a sample monthly and have it tested by an independent lab.

Problems with fuel viscosity control can lead to burner performance problems. High viscosity can decrease the ability of the atomizer to properly atomize the fuel and result in incomplete combustion, high CO, smoking, and sooty deposits. Viscosity that is below the recommended levels can cause flashing at the sprayer tip and erratic burning. The viscosity must be carefully controlled because of its potential effect on stack opacity, NO_x, CO and particulate emissions.

Pour Point: The fuel oil pour point is the lowest temperature at which fuel can be stored and still remain fluid or be pumped.

Cloud Point: Normally determined for No. 2 oil, it is the temperature at which the wax crystals (paraffin) suspended in the fuel first begin to appear and drop out as a slight haze in the sample.

Flash Point: The flash point of the fuel oil is the lowest temperature at which a flash flame can be produced. It is an indication of the maximum temperature at which the fuel can be safely stored or handled without causing a serious fire hazard. Oil should not be preheated to a temperature greater than its flash point.

Sulfur Content: Fuel oil loads containing 1% sulfur or more can be troublesome in terms of corrosion to the fired equipment. During the combustion process, free sulfur will combine with oxygen to form sulfur dioxide that, in the presence of water molecules, will combine to form sulfurous acid. Although relatively weak, it can over time cause severe corrosion to exposed parts and components. Sulfur dioxide or SO_2 is also considered a major atmospheric pollutant and contributes to smog and acid rain.

Nitrogen Content: Fuel oils with high nitrogen content can contribute significantly to the formation of nitrogen oxides or NO_x during the combustion process. Nitrogen atoms located in bonds within the fuel molecule are released into the total nitrogen pool and oxidized leading to an increase in NO_x levels. This is commonly referred to as "fuel NO_x" and can greatly affect burner emission performance. 0.2 to 2.0% N in fuel can potentially yield 60 to 2100 ppm NO.

Summary: It is important that operators understand the different fuel oil characteristics and how they relate to burner and fired equipment performance. It is especially critical that these factors be taken into consideration any time a change in the type or grade of fuel is made.

Problem	Cause
Atomization poor	Oil viscosity too high; improper preheat temperature; atomizing media or oil pressure too low.
Boiler corrosion	Ash contains corrosive elements; oil sulfur and/or salt content is too high; soot has absorbed sulfuric acid.
Burner erosion	High oil sediment or salt content; velocities in eroded areas (liquid or flue gas side) too high.
Burner tip blocked	High oil sludge or lint content; no strainer or strainer mesh not fine enough; carbonization of sprayer plate.
Carbon dioxide low	Too much excess air; poor air and/or fuel cross-sectional distribution.
Carbon on furnace walls	Flame impingement; oil too viscous or too light; atomizing media/oil injection velocity too high.
Carbon in preheater	Too high preheating temperature; oil contains sludge and/or asphaltic compounds.

Problem	Cause
Carbonization of sprayer plate	Carbon residue in oils; high viscosity oil, poor atomization; insufficient, excessive or varying pre heat temperature; inadequate guide pipe purge air.
Discoloration of ceramics	High sulfur, sediment, or iron in the oil.
Sprayer plate dripping oil	Oil viscosity too high; incorrect pre heat temperature, partially plugged sprayer plate; sprayer plate assembly gaskets missing or damaged.
Flame pulses	Water, sediment or sludge in oil; oil viscosity too high; non uniform combustion air or oil flow; air infiltration into oil; atomizing media flow irregular or too high; atomizer internal leak of atomizing media into oil.
Flame leaves sprayer plate	Too much atomization, oil too thin.
Flashback	Flash point is too low resulting in pre-ignition;, water and sludge in oil; fluctuation of atomizing media flow; oil pressure too high.
Foaming of oil	Water or extremely light material in oil.
Heat loss (poor heat transfer)	Sediment and/or water in oil; deficient or excessive combustion air flow; poor combustion; oil temperature too high.
Plugged lines	Sludge in oil; congealed oil; wax in oil; high viscosity oil; foreign materials in oil.
Odor is bad	Preheat temperature too high; high oil sulfur content; contamination by other foreign material.
Oil consumption is excessive	Oil too light, oil of low heat value, excessive combustion air; holes in sprayer plate too large (eroded), water in fuel oil.
Unable to pump oil	Oil too cold or too high in viscosity; restricted or blocked passages; strainers plugged.
Smoke	Not enough or too much combustion air; poor atomization; oil viscosity too high; flame impingement, excessive furnace draft.
Soot excessive	High ash content in oil; poor combustion; heavy compounds in oil.
Spitting, sputtering or sparkling	Water or sediment in oil; oil viscosity too high; high atomizing media flow; leakage of air into oil; atomizer internal leak of atomizing media into oil; wet atomizing media.
Stack temperature too high	Boiler tubes need cleaning; damaged baffles; too much draft; over firing of unit.
Ignition difficulty	No oil; sludge and/or water in lines; viscosity of oil too high; too much atomizing media flow; preheat temperature too high, too much combustion air.
Strainer screens blocked	Sludge; wax or lint in the oil; oil viscosity too high; oil temperature too cold; heavy precipitated compounds in oil; tank scale or rust.
Suction loss	Oil too heavy and/or cold; leak in oil suction line, slippage of oil pump; pump not primed; oil too hot.
Water	Water in oil as delivered; condensation from natural sources (atmospheric humidity) and/or from high temperature heating; leaking heating coils; leaking tank or accesses.

Operational Rules of Thumb.—*Natural Gas and Fuel Oils:* True excess air (O_2) levels in the flame zone that are less than the design level tend to lower NO_x, increase CO, increase flame length and cross section and increase opacity (black).

Fuel Oils: Deficient atomizing media flow or higher than design oil viscosities (low oil temperature) tend to lower NO_x, increase CO, increase flame length and cross-section, increase the visible level of droplets or fire flies or sparklers, increase opacity and increase liquid splatter on furnace surfaces.

Natural Gas and Fuel Oils: True excess air O_2 levels in the flame zone that are significantly high (greater than 10–11% O_2) tend to increase CO, increase opacity (brownish or white) and potentially create instability due to flame blow off.

Common Application-Specific Problems.—The section deals with the combustion theory as it relates to the problems of:

tramp air; feed the grate, starve the burner; short circuiting; regenerative air heater combustion air by passing; location of O_2 sensor; oversized FD and/or ID fans; moisture in draft measurements; air infiltration into fuel oil piping on below grade; storage applications; water in the fuel oil; heating or cooling of fuel oil in atomizers; heavy oil viscosity increases at reduced firing rates; wet atomizing steam or plant air, and; and single pressure regulator but multiple users.

Tramp Air: Tramp air can be defined as any air that enters the fired equipment unintentionally at a location other than the burner. Tramp air can derive from any of the following known inputs: observation port; or tramp air may come from an input that is known, that is "unaccounted for" tramp air. Unaccounted for tramp air is most common on applications where the furnace is operated at a negative pressure. There is, of course, the negative heat transfer aspect of an undesirable level of cool air being drawn through the fired equipment. But in addition, there can be the more serious effect resulting from the operation of a burner at an excess air level based on an O_2 measurement that is gathered downstream of, and whose reading is then biased by, the tramp air infiltration. The problems that will arise are defined in the last section *Operational Rules of Thumb* for less than design levels of excess air.

The corrective actions are as follows:

1) Check the location of the O_2 sensor. Make the necessary arrangements to relocate the sensor if its position is less than optimal.

2) Place the burner in the manual control mode. Attach a manometer to the burner's high air pressure and furnace pressure connections and measure the BDL (burner draft loss). Compare this value to the one the manual for the same burner firing rate.

3) Increase the combustion air flow to the burner until the BDL equals that listed in the manual for the firing rate. CO, opacity, flame appearance, etc. should all be directionally improved. Note the new operating O_2 level indicated by the sensor.

4) Slowly change the furnace pressure setpoint on the furnace pressure controller to a value that brings the furnace pressure to a slightly positive condition (0.00 to + 0.01 in. water column).

Caution: Flue gas infiltration into the operating area can be harmful to personnel. Note the reduction in operating O_2 as indicated by the sensor. This difference in excess O_2 represents the amount of tramp air infiltration. Return the furnace pressure setpoint to its normal operating level.

5) Note and/or correct all unnecessary tramp air infiltration points. Those that cannot be corrected while the unit is operating should be documented for correction during the next scheduled outage.

6) Make the necessary control configuration changes and explain to all operating personnel the new excess oxygen, Air flow to burner and/or furnace pressure operating parameters.

7) Correct any remaining tramp air infiltration points during the next fired equipment outage.

Feed the Grate, Starve the Burner: On grate over firing applications it is common for the combustion air supply to the over-fire burners to be from the same FD fan that supplies combustion air to the grate. Under these circumstances, since the grate fuel (wood, coal, etc.) is the primary fuel, it is common for the majority of the air to be directed to the grate while the over-fire burner(s) are starved for air. In effect, the problem is exactly the same as that encountered with an excess of tramp air high CO, opacity, larger/longer fires and once again a composite flue gas excess O_2 reading can be deceiving. Because two fuels are being fired simultaneously it is not possible to offer a step by step procedure as was offered for the tramp air problem. In this case one should again check the BDL of each individual burner, compare it to that in its manufacturer's manual for the actual burner firing rate and then adjust over fire burner and grate combustion air flow control points until both the over fire burner's and grate's performance is optimal. Since grate firing furnaces are typically operated at negative draft conditions tramp air should be considered in any tuning efforts.

Short-Circuiting: Short-circuiting is defined as the premature exiting of combustion products from the fired equipment's furnace to its convection section or exit. Since combustion requires time (as well as temperature and turbulence) to be completed, this short-circuiting of combustion products is characterized by high levels of CO (greater than 500 ppm) and/or hydrocarbons at operating O_2 levels which should produce less than 100 ppm. This problem is not a progressive one, but rather it will occur immediately upon initial burner start-up. Short circuiting results because of leak paths through the furnace sidewall separating the furnace and the convection section. Sidewall constructions of either the tangent tube or studded tube type are notorious for short-circuiting. On the other hand short-circuiting is unlikely when furnace side wall construction is either of the welded tangent tube or membrane wall type. Regardless, combustion products must travel the entire furnace length to assure complete oxidation of the combustible material; any leak path, no matter how small, should be scrutinized. If the leak is fairly easy to correct, such as by replacing a refractory plug that has fallen out of a tube inspection port, then proceed with the change. On the other hand if gaps between tubes need to be filled, the boiler manufacturer must be contacted for recommendations. Burner changes are not warranted unless the high CO is the result of flame impingement. Operating at higher excess air levels (where the preceding burner likely operated) is a short-term fix to minimize the exiting CO level. However, this will adversely impact on the ability to meet the performance requirements.

Regenerative Air Heater Combustion Air Bypassing: A regenerative air heater consists of a rotor containing heat transfer baskets. This rotor rotates from the combustion air side of the air heater to the flue gas side. While in the flue gas area, the baskets heat and then this heat is subsequently transferred to the combustion air when it has rotated to that side of the air heater. Metal seals (when new) reduce the amount of air leakage to the flue gas side to about 5% of the maximum design combustion air flow. After the seals wear, this leakage rate will increase. Because of this air leakage, one should never sample the O_2 level or locate a continuous O_2 sensor downstream of a regenerative air heater. If an alternate location upstream of the air heater is not available for continuous online sensing, one must at a minimum perform periodic spot checks of the O_2 level on the upstream side (using a portable analyzer) to confirm the level of air leakage and update the operating O_2 parameters based on the downstream sensor.

Location of the O_2 Sensor: Referencing the discussions of tramp air and air heater air bypassing, it should be apparent that the location of the O_2 sensor with respect to any intentional or unintentional air infiltration points is critical for establishing the burner's true performance. The normal operating excess O_2 levels from 30 to 100% of capacity is from 1 to 3%. This excess O_2 difference represents itself in an excess combustion air difference of about 10% (recall that new regenerative air heater air bypassing is about 5%). For these reasons O_2 sensors should be located as follows:

1) Locate O_2 sensors upstream of regenerative air heaters.

2) Locate O_2 sensors upstream of any purging or cooling air sources (i.e., soot blowers, observation ports).

3) The O_2 sensor should protrude into the flue to about 50% of its width. It should also be centered relative to the flue's height.

4) Ideally, the O_2 sensor should be installed in along straight section of the flue. If the sensor must be installed downstream of an elbow, then the flue gas will tend to hug the flue face on the long side of the elbow.

5) If at all possible establish an O_2 cross section of the flue using a portable analyzer before installing the permanent sensor.

Oversized FD and ID Fans: Many burner retrofit applications involve replacing burners whose design excess air levels are considerably higher or replacing solid fuel firing equipment which most assuredly operated with considerably higher excess air. In addition, at the time the original combustion equipment was installed, it is quite possible that the facility did not require this equipment to have high turndown capabilities. The combination of high air delivery capabilities and a lack of a prior need for high turndown will most often result in the existing FD and ID Fans being considerably oversized for the new retrofit burner. This oversizing can have a considerable adverse influence on combustion air flow control, particularly at reduced firing rates. The possible corrective measures are as follows:

1) "Short-stroke" the inlet and/or discharge damper(s) travel (via linkage adjustments) to limit the amount of damper opening at the higher firing grates. Note: This will only improve high firing rate air flow control.

2) Add some form of restriction (such as perforated sheet) at the discharge of the fan(s). The addition of this restriction will likely eliminate the need for short-stroking.
Note: This will only improve high firing rate air flow control.

3) Add closure plates (i.e. strips of metal) to open areas of the fan damper or vanes when they are in the closed position. This will minimize air leakage at lower firing rates.
Note: This will only improve low firing rate air flow control.

4) A combination of either 1) and 3) or 2) and 3). Note: This will improve both low and high firing rate air flow control.

5) Depending on the level of fan derating, replace the existing motor with a lower speed model. This is the most practical alternative but also the most time consuming. Note: This will improve both low and high firing rate air flow control and electrical energy consumption.

6) Install a variable speed drive (VSD). This is the most desirable alternative and will most often prove to be the most expeditious one unless the motor has to be upgraded for application to the VSD.
Note: This will improve both low and high firing rate air flow control and electrical energy consumption.

Moisture in Draft Measurements: Combustion products contain considerable moisture (and humid air can as well). When these gases cool, the moisture condenses.

Since the vast majority of combustion air, flue gas pressure and differential pressure measurements will be in inches water column, if the condensed moisture is allowed to collect about the gauge or transmitter diaphragm, the measurement will be faulty. This can have a significant effect on the control of combustion air to the burner and/or the control of furnace draft. Ideally all sensing tubing should slope downwards from the transmitter connection to the duct, flue, burner, or fired equipment pressure connection to promote drainage back towards the process connection. Regardless, in close proximity to the transmitter, the tubing from the transmitter connection should run vertically downward with a tee connection on the side for connecting to the process and a continuation of the vertical run for at least 6 inches. This will assure that there is a vertical leg for collecting any moisture. This leg should be equipped with a valving arrangement to allow draining the moisture without disrupting control while the fired equipment is online.

Air Infiltration into Fuel Oil Piping on Below Grade Storage Applications: When the oil storage tank (or simply the oil level) is below the centerline of the fuel oil pumps, the suction pipe will be at a negative pressure. Any leak in that suction piping will reflect itself as air infiltration into the pipe (i.e., the leak is not visible). Evidence of this problem will be represented by the pump sounding as if it is pumping gravel while both the pump suction and discharge pressure gauge needles will exhibit considerable pressure or vacuum fluctuations. Burner performance will be noticeably impacted because there will be actual fuel oil supply irregularities to it. Depending on the level of air infiltration the fire may have a visible pulse and there will be excess oxygen fluctuations as well. The only cure for this situation is to locate and repair the leak.

Water in the Fuel Oil: There have been known situations in which fuel oil storage facilities have become intentional receptacles for contaminated water (or other products). Besides these situations, it is not uncommon for leaks to develop on in-tank heating coils over time, resulting in the leakage of steam condensate or hot water into the oil. This water absorbs heat from the combustion process and converts to steam that heat which is never recovered (on noncondensing applications), thereby adversely affecting the fired equipment's efficiency. The water in the oil problem may reflect itself in a visual increase in sparklers or fireflies (as seen in high viscosity or poor atomization) but will definitely be evidenced by an increase in oil flow input for the same heat output, excess air level and flue gas outlet temperature. The problem can be identified by drawing a sample of oil from the supply line to the burner(s) and having a local lab check that sample for water content. For No. 5 or No. 6 fuel oils this percentage should be 1 to 2% or less, while for other grades this percentage should be no greater than 0.5%. For situations involving intentionally contaminated oil,

the problem will resolve itself with close monitoring and time for the contaminated oil to be burned. In tank heating coil leakage can be established by disconnecting the coils from the steam/condensate or hot water sources and checking to see if oil appears on the steam or hot water side of the coil. Note: The higher the oil level the quicker the leak will appear. Be sure to have a means of isolation to prevent spillage.

Heating or Cooling of Fuel Oil in Atomizers: Heavy oil requires heating to lower its viscosity to a level desirable for burning. In most cases heavy oil is atomized with steam. If however during start-up, an atomizing steam source did not exist, and one elected to try using compressed air instead, the atomizer's design would promote cooling of the oil. This would be reflected by a significant increase in sparklers and liquid splatter on heating surfaces (just as would be the case with too low an oil temperature). The only way to compensate for this condition is to raise the temperature of the oil entering the atomizer. Conversely, light oil (No. # 2) requires no heating for viscosity control. However, if atomizing steam is used and oil temperatures climb to levels above this point, overheating can occur within the atomizer and unstable pulses can appear in the combustion zone.

Heavy Oil Viscosity Increases at Reduced Firing Rates:

Heavy fuel oil systems with a single common pumping and heating set, which is located some distance from combustion equipment, are prone to this problem. Piping systems which are not designed with a return loop or a pressure regulator at the connection point to the return line aggravate the problem. Piping with a given amount of insulation transfers heat to the space about it at a fixed rate depending on the fluid's temperature (and that of the space), but essentially independent of the fluid's velocity. Therefore, the same amount of heat is given up to the surroundings whether oil is flowing through the pipe at a rate corresponding to the burner's maximum or its minimum firing rate. However, because the amount of heat transferred is constant, the affect on the fuel oil's temperature is significantly different. On fuel oil systems of the sort described, it is not uncommon for the oil temperature at the burner to be 20 to 40 degrees lower at minimum firing rate (10 to 15% of maximum rate) relative to that at maximum. All of the aforementioned problems attributable to unacceptably high oil burning viscosities will result. Changing the piping system, installation of a back pressure regulator, relocation of the pump and heater set temperature sensing element or installation of a local trim heater are the corrective alternatives.

Wet Atomizing Steam or Plant Air: Moisture in either the steam or compressed air atomizing media will be evidenced by sparklers. The more significant problem is that liquid carried by any gas stream is very erosive and can result in "water hammer." Both the atomizer and the atomizing media piping components will undergo premature failure if subjected to these conditions. Orifices on the atomizer sprayer plate will "oval" due to erosion and obviously oil burning performance will suffer. Well insulated atomizing media piping should connect to the top of well trapped main headers and then run vertically downward to a mud leg complete with drain and trap assembly. The connection to the burner piping train should be off the side of the vertical run approximately 12 in. from the bottom of the mud leg.

Single Pressure Regulator but Multiple Users: A properly designed fuel or atomizing media main piping system should assure that the pressure and temperature (see *Heavy Oil Viscosity Increases at Reduced Firing Rates* above) supplied at the inlet to the burner piping trains are a constant regardless of the firing rate combinations of all of the fired equipment in the facility. Unfortunately due to plant expansions or other reasons, it is common to encounter pressure drops in the fuel pressures at the burner piping train inlets which vary depending on the operating states of all the fired equipment. This results from the existence of only a single pressure regulator which is responsible for controlling the entire header pressure. Pressure variations at the burner piping train inlet is an unacceptable condition and is particularly unsafe when this occurs with gaseous fuels. This is because the actual flow rate and/or the measured flow rate (via flow meters) are both affected by pressure (due to compressibility), so variations can lead to both real and measured errors which can be both inconsistent and dangerous. The solution is to install a pressure regulator in the local piping for the combustion system served.

The most commonly referenced emissions on boiler or HTHW generator applications are NO_x, SO_x, THC, CO, Particulates and VOC. VOC or volatile organic compound is a group of chemicals that react in the atmosphere with nitrogen oxides in the presence of heat and sunlight to form ozone; does not include methane and other compounds determined by EPA to have negligible photochemical reactivity. Examples of VOCs include fumes from gasoline, solvents and oil-based paints. Since there is effectively no unburned carbon resulting from the combustion of natural gas or fuel oils, particulate emissions can be calculated by knowing the percentage of ash in the fuel. Likewise SO_x emissions can be calculated given the percentage of sulfur in the fuel.

THC or total hydrocarbons are rare and effectively negligible but one should be aware of the following when considering both THC and CO emissions; assuming a suitable level of mixing, hydrocarbons will be thoroughly oxidized (i.e., incinerated) if maintained at a temperature of 1460°F for a "residence time" of at least 0.25 sec. while CO will be thoroughly oxidized if maintained at a temperature of 1600°F for a residence time of at least 0.33 sec. The residence time (calculated by knowing the actual temperature-corrected volumetric flow rate of combustion products and the fired equipment furnace volume) in industrial fired equipment furnaces generally exceeds the

requirements, and, at the normal levels of operating excess air, the combustion temperatures well exceed the above guidelines.

NO_x emissions are maximized when combustion temperatures are at their peak. This peak temperature is achieved theoretically when there is absolutely perfect mixing and only the exact requirement of combustion air is inputted (no less or no more) to thoroughly oxidize the combustible matter in the fuel. NO_x is significantly reduced if there is either an excess of combustion air which reduces the combustion temperature by dilution or a deficiency of combustion air which also lowers combustion temperatures by depriving a portion of the fuel of the air necessary to burn it. Regardless, meeting NO_x and CO emissions requirements, as well as furnace flame fit and turndown expectations oftentimes leads to the NO_x/CO box a condition in which the needed reduction in one emission is prevented by the fact that the corrective measure leads to the increase in the other emission.

"Indicated" versus "dry" versus "corrected" emissions values are reviewed here. Indicated emissions values are, as the term implies, simply those displayed by the analyzer. One should never presume that these displayed values are either dry or corrected (some analyzers do have an option for performing the needed mathematics to "correct" the measured values). To obtain dry values it is necessary to remove all of the moisture from the flue gas sample (recall that the moisture in the products of combustion can be from 10 to 20% depending on the fuel being fired). This can be accomplished by directing the sample to an ice-cooled sample bottle before directing it to the analyzer. A corrected emissions value is one that has been adjusted for an EPA established excess oxygen level, which varies depending on the fired equipment application. The value for industrial boilers and HTHW generators is 3% dry O_2 (for duct burner or direct-fired air heaters the value is 15% dry O_2).

As an example, a "corrected" NO_x emissions level for industrial boilers or HTHW generators is calculated as follows:

$$\text{Corr. NOx, ppmc} = \text{Dry NOx ppm} \times \frac{(20.9 - 3)}{(20.9 - O_2\ \%)}$$

For a displayed "wet" emissions level of 50 ppm of CO at an O_2 level of 11% when firing natural gas, the actual emissions will increase to about 60 ppm when the sample is "dry" and will further increase to over 100 ppmc when corrected to 3% O_2.

Note: To effectively enact "staged combustion" requires that there be a combustion zone that has an excess of combustion air and one that has a deficiency of combustion air, which are then subsequently mixed without residual CO or THC emissions and at a composite excess O_2 level that is as low as possible; and what is optimal at higher burner firing rates is not necessarily optimal at lower burner firing rates.

Rules of Thumb: In the design region of operating excess air levels, the corrected NO_x will decrease with reductions in excess air while the corrected CO will increase.

When excess O_2 levels increase above 12% CO emissions increase. This is because combustion temperatures approach the minimum level required for complete oxidation at this value.

At higher firing rates, fuel and combustion air velocities at the point of mixing are at their most optimal (with the appropriate allowance for staging). At reduced firing rates, mixing degrades as the fuel and air velocities decrease. To compensate, either the combustion air input, therefore its velocity, can be increased, or forced mixing via swirl can be imparted. Though increases in O_2 (up to 12%) and swirl help reduce CO, such increases tend to increase NO_x.

Summary: There is for each specific firing rate a low and most efficient excess air level that gives the lowest corrected NO_x for an acceptable corrected CO level (less than 100 ppmc). As the firing rate decreases, this excess air level increases because of the decrease in velocity promoted mixing.

Combustion Control Strategies

Objective.—With an emphasis on safety, maintain fuel Btu flow rate and oxygen mass flow rate in the correct ratio at all times

1) Burners cannot perfectly mix the fuel and oxygen. Therefore, excess oxygen (excess air) is required to completely burn all of the fuel.

2) Burners require more excess air at low firing rates, and less excess air at high firing rates. Therefore, the fuel/air (oxygen) ratio must be variable and characterize the firing rate.

3) Combustion control systems cannot perfectly regulate fuel and oxygen flows. Therefore, extra excess air must be supplied to the burner to account for control system errors.

4) The extra excess air due to control error causes higher operating costs.

5) When selecting a combustion control system, consider safety first, then control system cost vs. operating cost trade-offs.

Control System Errors.—1) Boiler draft changes caused by the number of units firing and/or their combined firing rate when they discharge to a common stack, wind effects, etc. change the boiler system's resistance

and therefore change the amount of air flow and cause extra excess air.

2) Hysteresis (non-repeatability) due to sloppy linkage, worn damper mechanism, and poor actuator positioning.

3) Flow transmitters cannot measure fuel Btu flow rate (Btu/hr) or oxygen mass flow rate (lb/hr). These rates are inferred from assumptions about fuel and air properties.

4) The oxygen content per cubic foot of air changes with humidity. A constant air mass flow rate will yield a variable oxygen flow rate.

5) Air temperature and atmospheric pressure change air density. A constant volumetric flow rate produces a varying air mass flow rate.

6) A constant fuel valve position will yield a fuel flow that varies as fuel supply pressure and viscosity vary.

Combustion Control Strategies.—1) Single point positioning (Jackshaft):
  a) Simple, low cost, safe, requires extra excess air, and
  b) Fuel and air are tied together mechanically.
2) Parallel positioning:
    a) Fuel valve and air damper are positioned separately, and
    b) Allows oxygen trim of air flow.
3) Fully metered:
a) Fuel and air flow (not valve position) are controlled.

Major single point positioning combustion control features are listed below and shown in the Fig. 12-8 diagram:

Fuel control valves and air control dampers are mechanically linked through a jackshaft and linkage arms. One actuator simultaneously moves both fuel and air in order to maintain the desired system pressure. For every particular firing rate demand, there is one and only one position for the fuel valves and a corresponding position for the air damper. The fuel/air ratio is "tuned" by adjusting the fuel valve vs. air device linkage during initial commissioning.

The fuel/air jackshaft actuator is interlocked with flame safeguard to cause the air/fuel jackshaft and therefore the interconnected fuel valve and damper to go to the purge and light-off positions when appropriate during the start sequence.

Advantages: Simplicity provides large turndown; inexpensive; oxygen trim may be added using the preferred instruments' link trim actuator.

All control errors affect this system. Typically, 20–50% extra excess air must be supplied to the burner to account for control inaccuracies. Oxygen trim systems can reduce the extra excess air by 15%. Suitable for smaller fire tube boilers and large fire tube/small water tube boilers that operate at low capacity factors. Typically, the annual fuel expense is too small to justify a more elaborate control system.

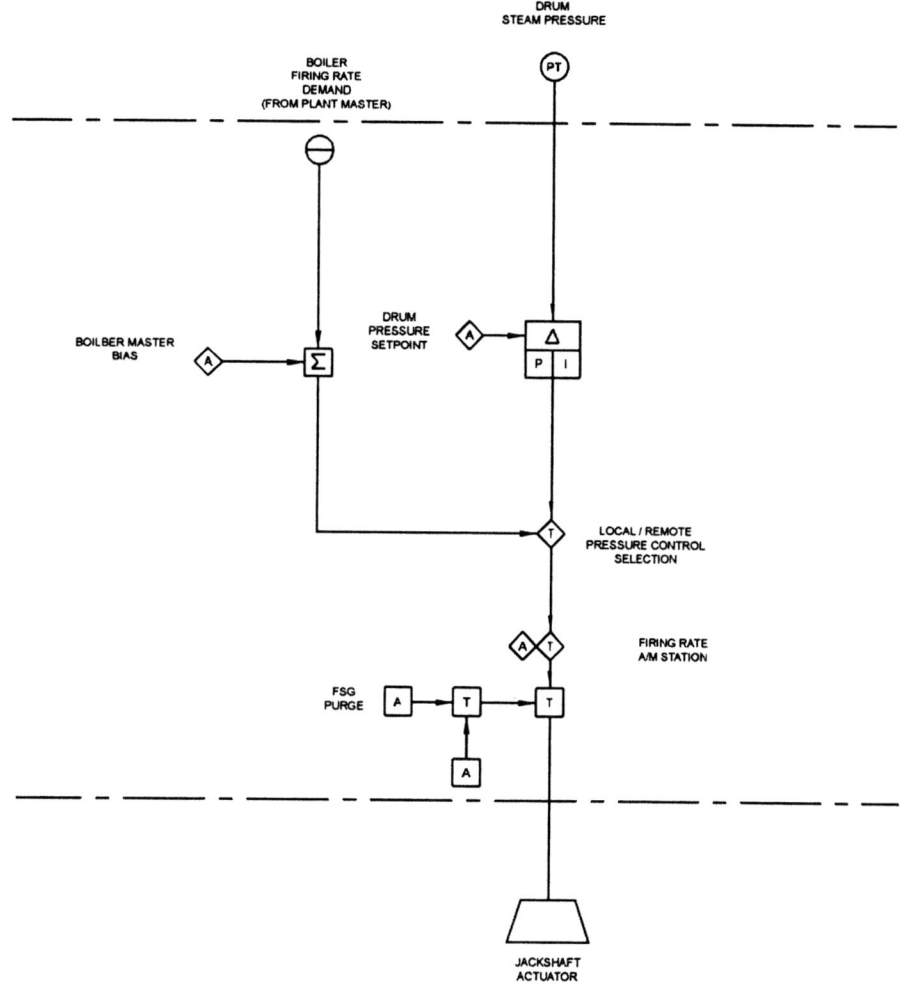

Fig 12-8. Single point positioning shown with local pressure control

This system may be suitable for larger boilers with low stack temperatures resulting from the installation of feedwater economizers or air preheaters. In this situation, much of the heat normally lost up the stack due to extra excess air is reclaimed by the economizer or preheater.

Disadvantages: 20 - 50% extra excess air required; fuel valves and fan damper must be physically close together; changes in fuel or air pressure, temperature, is costly, density, humidity affect fuel/air ratio; only one fuel may be burned at a time; not applicable to multiple burners; not applicable to variable speed fan drives.

Parallel Positioning Systems.—Parallel positioning systems offer key design benefits over single point positioning systems while retaining the benefits of those systems. Major features are listed below and shown in Fig. 12-9.

One actuator positions the fuel control valve(s) while a second actuator positions the air control damper. Each actuator is equipped with a position retransmitter. For every particular firing rate demand, there is one and only one position for the fuel valves and a corresponding position for the air damper. Tuning a soft function curve of fuel position vs. air position varies the fuel/air ratio.

A parallel positioning combustion control strategy includes cross limiting of fuel valve and air damper positions. This position cross limiting is employed for safety and to prevent fuel rich conditions during load changes. Cross limiting requires an accurate and repeatable position feedback signal from each actuator. The controller constantly monitors the positions of the two actuators. A failure of either actuator or feedback pot will force the air damper to an appropriate position while the fuel valve is directed to minimum position. During load changes, the air leads the fuel on a load increase and the fuel leads the air on a load decrease.

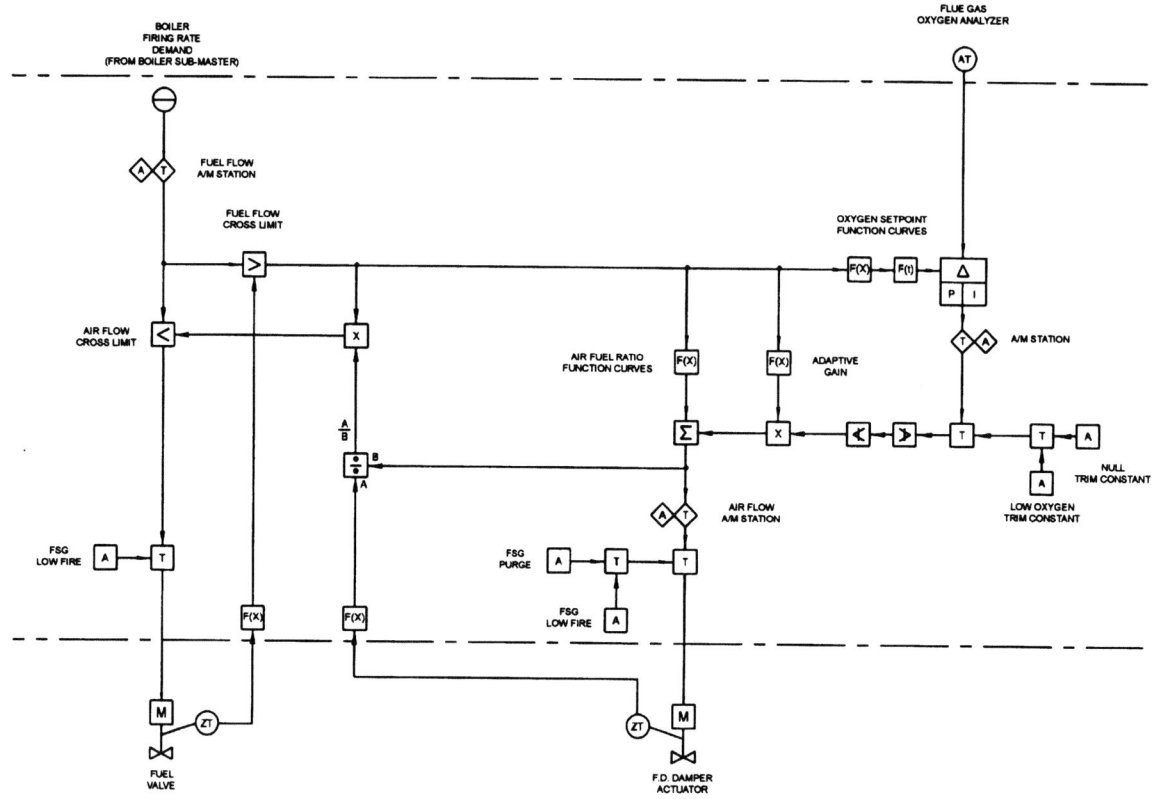

Fig 12-9. Parallel positioning control diagram shown with flue gas oxygen trim

The air and fuel control outputs are interlocked with the flame safeguard to cause the air and fuel control drives to go to the purge and light-off positions when appropriate during the start sequence.

Many of the same applications, limitations and improvements described for single point positioning apply to parallel positioning.

Advantages: Allows electronic characterization of fuel/air ratio; adapts to boilers with remote F.D. fans and/or variable; allows low fire changeover between fuels; and oxygen trim is easy to accomplish..

Disadvantages: 20–50% extra excess air required;

changes in fuel or air pressure, temperature, viscosity; density, humidity affect fuel/air ratio; only one fuel may be burned at a time; not applicable to multiple burners; position feedback is expensive for pneumatic actuators; and a failure of either actuator or feedback pot will force the air damper open and the fuel valve to minimum position.

Fully Metered Control.—The fully metered combustion control system offers key design features that help firing systems meet emissions goals. Major features are listed below and shown in the Fig. 12-10.

Both the fuel flow and the combustion air flow are measured. Separate PID controllers are used for both fuel and air flow control. Demand from a boiler sub-master is used to develop both a fuel flow and air flow setpoint.

Fully metered combustion control strategy includes differential cross limiting of fuel and air flows. This feature adds an additional level of protection to the conventional air flow and fuel flow cross limiting combustion control scheme by preventing the air fuel ratio from becoming too air rich as well as too fuel rich.

The air and fuel control outputs are interlocked with the flame safeguard system to cause the air and fuel control drives to go to the purge and light-off positions when appropriate during the start sequence.

Mass flow meters are available that accurately measure lb/hr mass flow rates for oil, gas, and air flows. This minimizes errors due to pressure, density, temperature, and viscosity variations. Lower cost velocity based flow meters can be adequately compensated with additional sensors by digital controllers. This system has the least control error. Full metering control is suitable for all boiler sizes up through and including electric utility boilers.

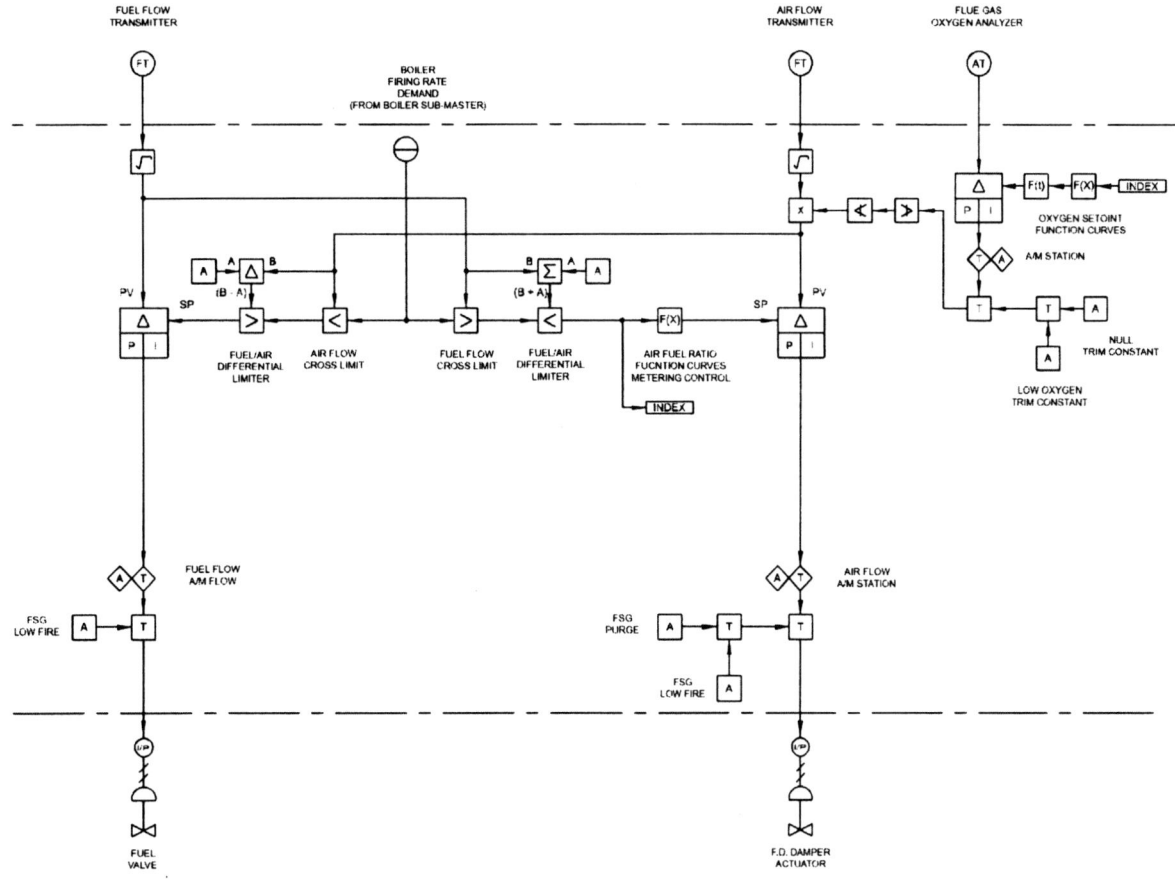

Fig 12-10. Fully metered control diagram shown with flue gas oxygen trim

Advantages: Provides extremely accurate control;

compensates for flow variations; applicable to multiple burners; allows simultaneous firing of oil and gas;

and flow transmitters have no moving parts and require less periodic calibration than position feedback pots.

Disadvantages: Typically, turndown is limited by flow transmitter turn down capability; For all types of flow meters, the fuel Btu value and air Oxygen content must be assumed; and Installation is more costly.

Feedwater Control Systems.—A feedwater control system that is operating properly has no effect on combustion efficiency. A feedwater valve that is constantly swinging from closed to open will cause the steam header pressure to swing up and down, even when the plant load is absolutely constant. This will in turn cause the burner firing rate to swing up and down. Burner load swings cause combustion control cross limiting systems and oxygen trim systems to operate the burner with extra excess air, thus lowering efficiency. The objective is to keep the water in the steam drum at an approximately constant level. Never so low as to trip the low water cutoff (this shuts down the burner), and never so high as to cause

water carry-over into the steam system. Level changes during load swings are expected and unavoidable.

Drum level is subject to shrink and swell during load changes. Following an increase in steam flow, the drum level will increase (swell) for a period of time. The drum level will decrease after the swell subsides. Load decreases cause a level decrease (shrink). Firetube boilers have a proportionally larger volume of water than a corresponding watertube boiler. Firetube boilers exhibit much less shrink and swell than watertube boilers. When the drum level rises, a simple feedwater control system will decrease the flow of water. This is the wrong response during a swell induced by a load increase.

There are four types of feedwater control systems:

On-Off: A water level switch starts and stops the feedwater pump to maintain the drum water level. A water level switch starts and stops the feedwater pump to maintain the drum water level. Suitable only for firetube boilers with slowly changing loads.

Single Element: A drum level sensor causes the feedwater valve to open or close in proportion to the deviation from desired drum level. Suitable for firetube boilers with moderate load swings and watertube boilers with slowly changing loads. Variations in the feedwater supply pressure will cause the drum level to change when the load is steady. Does not respond well to shrink and swell. See Fig. 12-11.

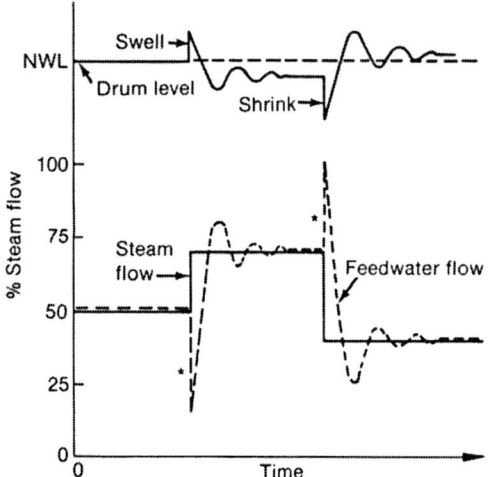

Fig 12-11. Control action of mechanical single element feedwater regulator

Two Element: A drum level sensor is the primary controller input, a steam flow sensor is a feed forward controller input. The steam flow signal allows the controller to respond properly during shrink and swell. Feedwater pressure variations also upset the drum level. Suitable for watertube boilers with substantial load swings if the feedwater pressure is repeatable. See Figs. 12-12 and 12-13.

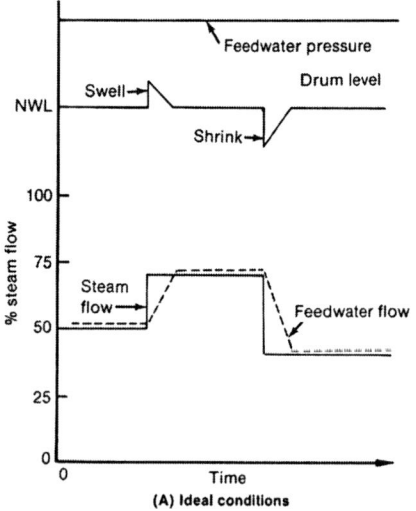

Fig 12-12. Performance of two element feedwater control (ideal conditions)

Three Element: A feedwater flow sensor is added to allow the controller to compensate for variations in feedwater supply pressure. Suitable for watertube boilers with the most severe shrink and swell. See Fig. 12-14.

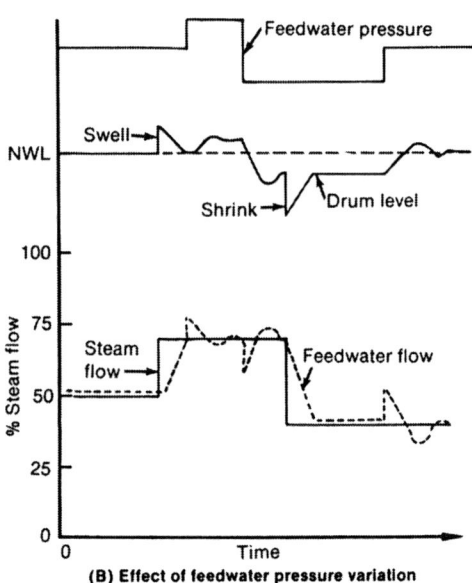

Fig 12-13. Performance of two element feedwater control (effect of feedwater pressure variations)

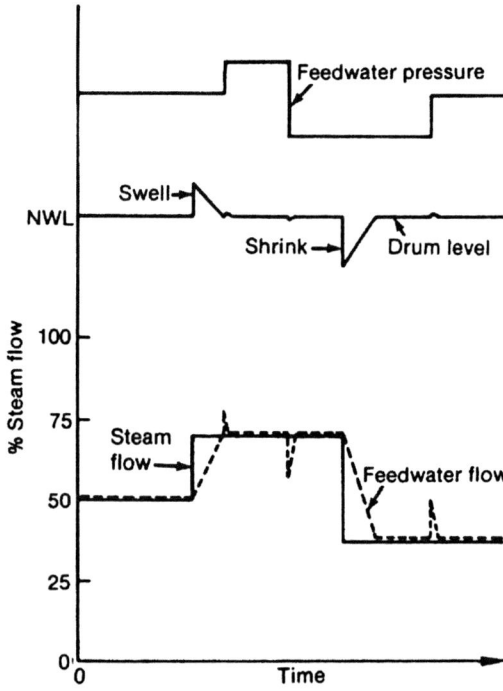

Fig 12-14. Performance of three element feedwater control (effect of feedwater pressure variations)

Draft Control.—Draft controllers modulate the boiler outlet damper in order to maintain a constant pressure in the combustion chamber. Any furnace that will be operated at a negative draft should have a draft control system. Draft control is generally not applied to boilers/furnaces with stub stacks that are designed to be fired at an extremely high furnace pressure. However; if that same boiler is going to be fired into an ID fan or at all stack, then draft controls should be applied in order to keep the pressure drop across the burner constant. Draft controls lowers operating costs in two ways:

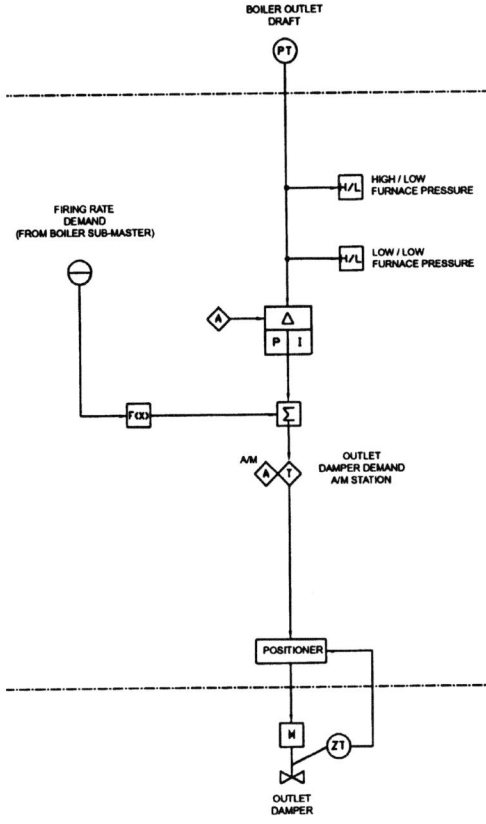

Fig 12-15. Draft system diagram

Reducing the air infiltrating into the furnace reduces heat lost up the stack. Uncontrolled furnace draft would result in a more negative furnace pressure, and more cold air would be sucked into the furnace.

Positioning burner control systems can operate with less extra excess air if the furnace pressure is constant. At a given FD fan inlet damper position, the air flow through a burner will increase when the furnace draft goes more.

Draft controllers generally incorporate logic to close the damper when the burner is off and to open the damper 100% for pre-purge and post purge cycles. Energy is saved while the damper is closed by preventing warm

boiler room air from traveling up the stack. See Fig. 12-14. Draft system diagram in Fig. 12-15.

Low draft (high furnace pressure) and proof of purge interlocks should always be incorporated into the burner flame safety system when draft control systems are utilized.

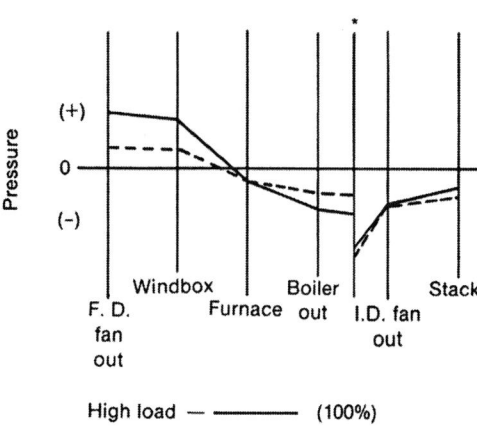

High load ———————— (100%)

Reduced load — — — — — (70%)

*Fan wheel inlet — Control damper inlet

Fig 12-16. Measurement of furnace draft

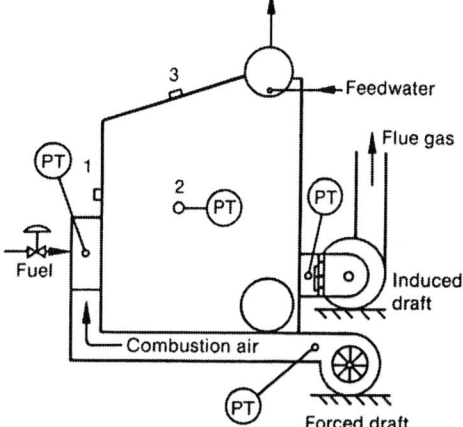

Notes:
1, 2, 3 — alternate furnace draft pressure connections. Reading changes approx. 0.01 in. of H_2O per ft elevation.

Fig 12-17. Profile of pressure and draft of balanced draft boiler

Fig. 12-16 shows typical draft pressure in a furnace and Fig. 12-17 presents a schematic of a balanced draft boiler. Typical response of a draft control strategies are presented in Figs. 12-18 and 12-19.

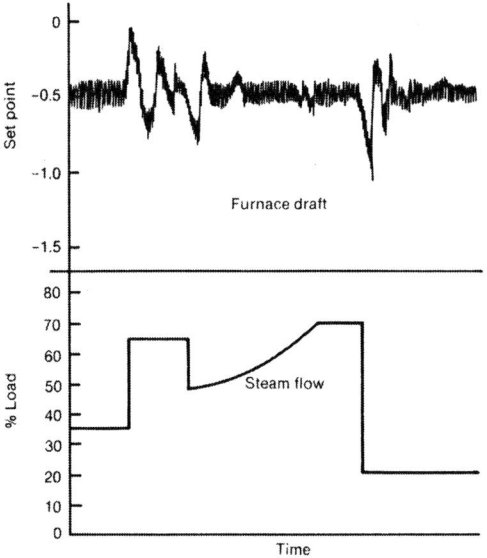

Fig 12-18. Furnace draft control
(single element control of induced draft fan)

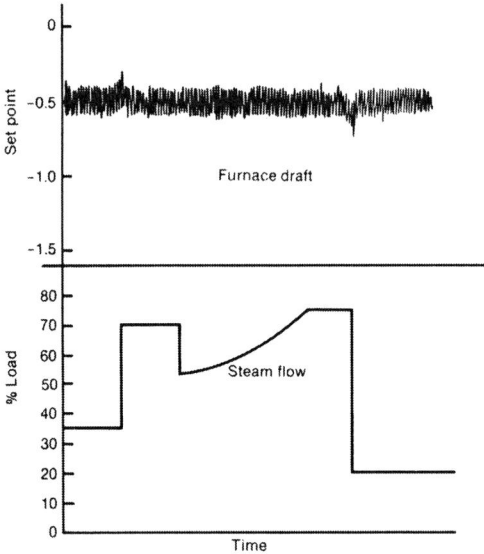

Fig 12-19. Furnace draft control
(feed forward and feedback control of induced draft fan)

Oxygen Trim.—In addition to the jackshaft control shown above, fuel trim (Fig. 12-20) or air trim (Fig. 12-21) can also be applied to parallel positioning or fully metered combustion control strategies. Fuel trim systems use changes in the fuel pressure regulator setpoint to change the fuel/air ratio and air trim systems use changes in the air damper position to change the fuel/air ratio.

Oxygen level increase to the desired oxygen level. The air (or fuel) flow is trimmed by the controller until the

oxygen level is corrected. The desired oxygen level for each firing rate must be entered into a characterized setpoint curve generator. For dual fuel burners independent curves are entered. The control strategy must include variable gain (ratio trimming) and setpoint lead/lag logic to prevent control oscillation.

To ensure safe operation, control action must be limited to no more than ±15% excess air trimming.

Oxygen may be applied to any type of control system; single point positioning, parallel positioning, or full metering.

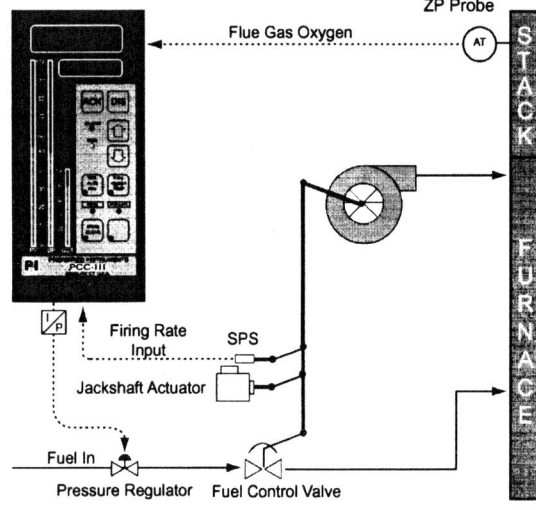

Fuel Trim System Diagram

Fig 12-20. Fuel trim system diagram

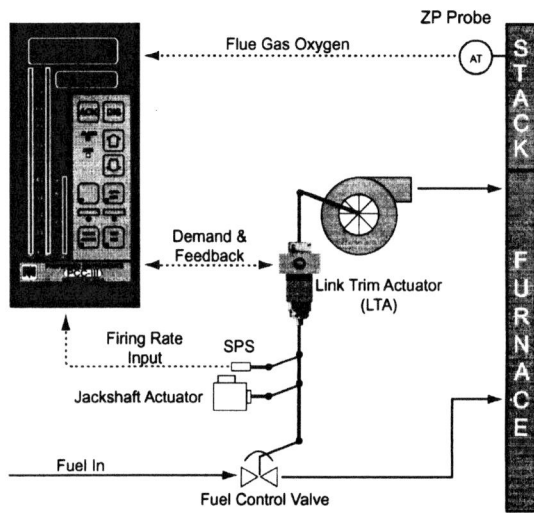

Air Trim with LTA System Diagram

Fig 12-21. Air trim with LTA system diagram

Advantages: Compensates for fuel Btu variations;

compensates for air oxygen content variations; permits a reduction in normal excess air levels; lowers operating costs; and allows real time boiler efficiency measurement and display using the ASME by losses method when flue gas temperature is also measured.

Disadvantages: Cannot be applied to furnaces with significant air infiltration; 3-5 year analyzer cell life; not a cure all for a poorly performing control system; and

constant rapid load changes diminish performance.

Combustion Air Flow Control Techniques.—*Parallel Blade Dampers:* Combustion air flow is controlled by increasing system resistance (pressure).

Variable Speed Drives VSD: Combustion air flow is controlled by varying fan speed. VSD fan control minimizes fan damper pressure drop which significantly reduces motor energy (kWh's). Variable speed fan control is a proven electrical energy savings technique that has been applied to thousands of HVAC installations. VSD basic relationships.

$$HP = \frac{0.0001573 \times cfm \times \text{inch of WC}}{\text{efficiency}} \qquad (5)$$

Efficiency: 45% – 85%, depends on fan type

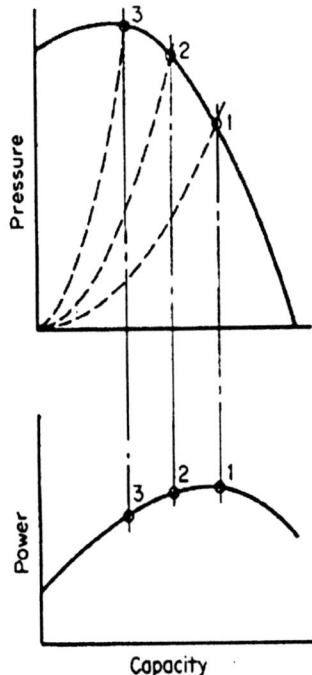

Fig 12-22. Non vortex damper

Vortex Dampers: Combustion air flow is controlled by increasing system resistance (pressure). Vortex dampers spin the air as it enters the rotating fan wheel. These

dampers help reduce motor energy (Kw-hr). See Figs. 12-22 to 12-24.

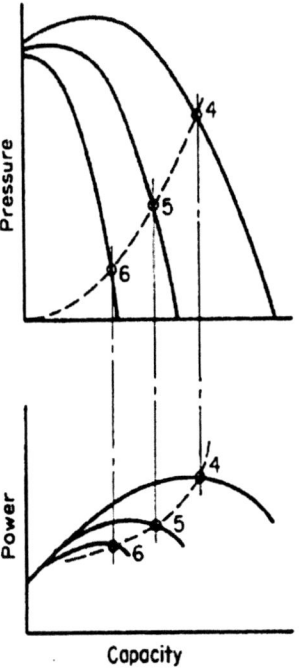

Fig 12-23. Vortex Damper

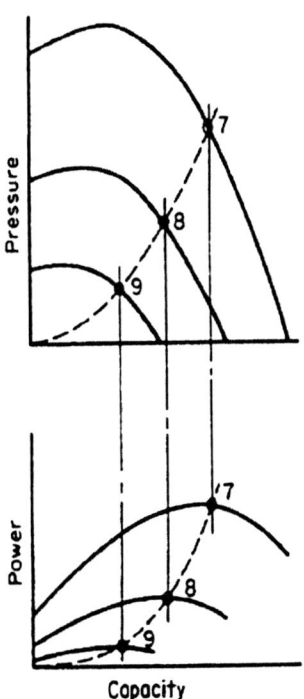

Fig 12-24. Speed control

Affinity Laws

Flow $\propto$ Speed	Pressure $\propto$ Speed^2	HP $\propto$ Speed^3	HP $\propto$ Flow^3	HP $\propto$ Pressure$^{1.5}$

Flue Gas Recirculation (FGR).—FGR is used very effectively to reduce NO_x emissions. Recall that NO_x can be lowered by reducing flame temperatures. By injecting FGR into the flame zone, the additional mass flow lowers the maximum achievable flame temperature and therefore the NO_x. The fact that the FGR is low in O_2 also helps because the availability of O_2 in a given volume is lower (Note: As mentioned in the burner operating principles section, increased excess air also lowers NO_x but not as effectively as the same quantity of FGR because the O_2 content is higher). Currently there are four means by which to inject FGR:

Forced Combustion Air/FGR Mixture: An additional fan is provided to direct FGR to a point of mixing with the combustion air upstream of the burner or plenum.

Induced Combustion Air/FGR Mixture: An additional breeching section is installed from an appropriate point in the flue to the FD fan inlet. In effect the fan draws in both FGR and combustion air, mixes them and delivers them to the burner wind box or plenum. The advantages are that a mixing device is not required (FD fan serves that purpose) and the additional FGR fan is not required, though the FD fan must be sized to handle both streams at the temperature of the mixture. Further draft control becomes an issue, otherwise variations in the flue pressure affect how much FGR is actually induced. Fig. 12-25 shows electrical costs as a function of heat input.

Localized FGR Injection: FGR is directed to a separate burner injection assembly via an FGR fan. The injection assembly is designed to direct FGR at those areas of the flame where temperatures are the highest. There are many operational benefits resulting from keeping the streams separate and the application of selective injection, including a notable savings in overall electrical horsepower consumption.

Forced Gaseous Fuel/FGR Mixture: This of course follows the same general philosophy as that of the air/FGR mixture strategy, but involves the use of a compressor or blower to direct the FGR to a point of mixing with the gaseous fuel. Less FGR is necessary because only an amount necessary to effectively change the fuel into a low Btu gas is required (blower/compressor horsepower is higher due to the higher pressure of the fuel that needs to be overcome).

All of these approaches are effective in reducing NO_x. System complexity and electrical power consumption are the key differences and the best alternative depends on the specifics of the application and customer preferences.

Lead/Lag Control: Multiple boiler "on/off" operation is automatically established to satisfy the overall plant hot water or steam demand. Automatic sequencing ensures that the number of boilers in service meets hot water or steam demand. Tripped equipment is automatically replaced with a standby unit.

Modulating Lead/Lag Control: Multiple boiler firing rates and on/off operation are automatically adjusted to satisfy the overall plant hot water or steam demand. Either unison (parallel) or series modulation is used.

Table 12-4. Multiple Boiler Header Pressure or Temperature Control Recommendation

Boilers Type	Boiler Horsepower	Steam lb/hr	Control Arrangement
ON/OFF	1	0.033	
	5	0.167	Lead/Lag control
	10	0.335	
Cast iron fintube fire box fire tube	20	0.670	
	50	1.674	
	100	3.348	
	200	6.696	
	300	10.044	Modulating Lead/Lag control
	500	16.739	
	600	20.087	
	800	26.783	
	1000	33.479	
	1500	50.218	
Watertube	2000	66.958	
	4000	133.915	
	6000	200.873	
	8000	267.830	Plant master control
	10000	334.788	
	20000	669.576	

Plant Master Control: Multiple boiler firing rates are automatically adjusted to satisfy the overall plant hot water or steam demand. Either unison (parallel) or series modulation is used.

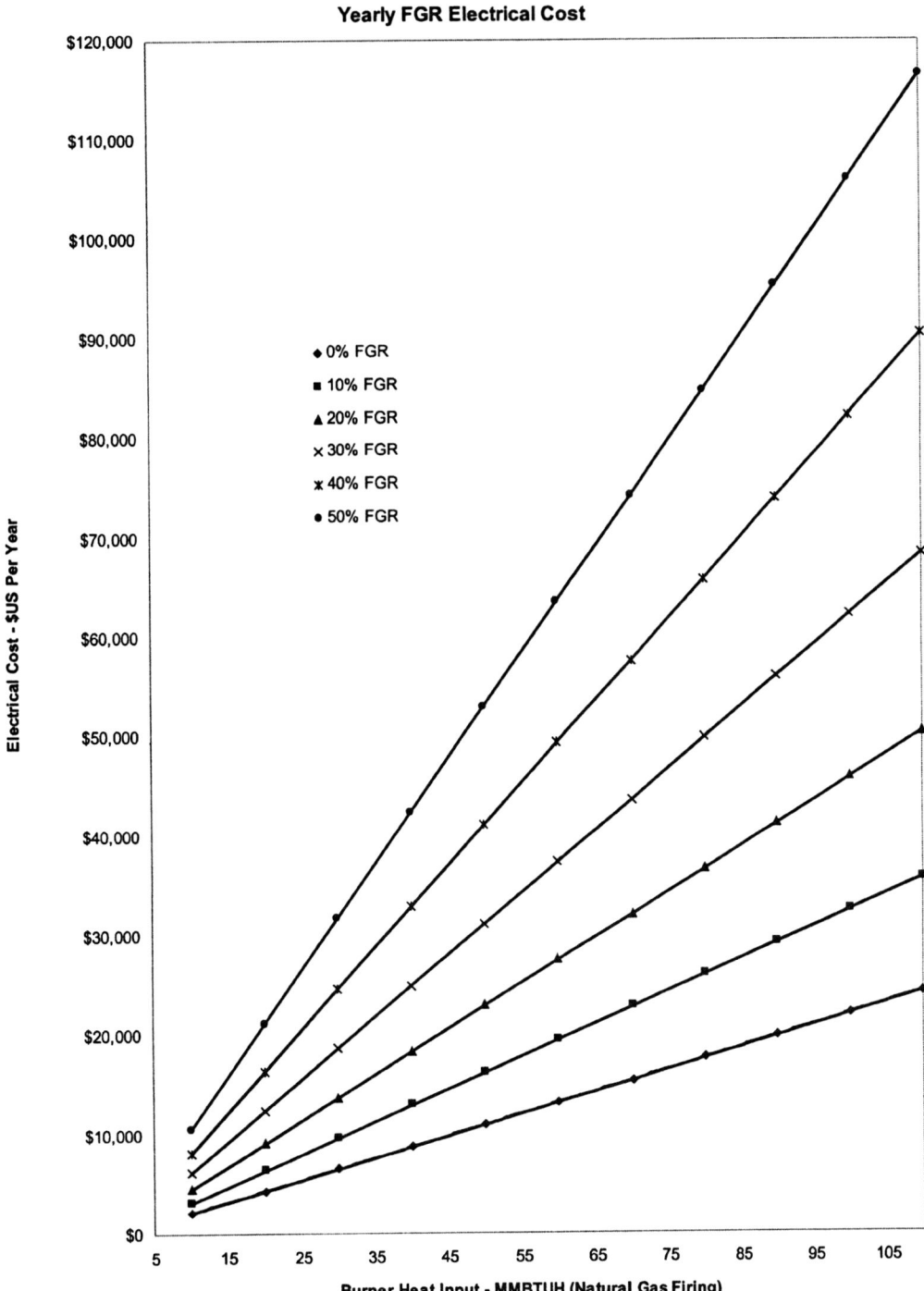

Fig 12-25. Induced combustion Air/FGR mixture electrical cost

The chart is based on $0.07/kw-hr and 24 hour/365 day operation and 7.5" burner draft loss (BDL); 4.5" furnace pressure; 15% excess combustion air at 70° F; 450° F "induced" FGR

Table 12-5. Multiple Boiler Header Pressure or Temperature Control Recommendation

Application Specifics	Jackshaft Positioning	Parallel Positioning	Fully Metered
Dual Fuel Firing			
Low-fire changeover only	Option	Option	Option
Full load simultaneous firing	NR	NR	Option
Single and Multiple Burners			
Single burner	Option	Option	Option
Multiple burners	NR	NR	Option
Furnace Conditions			
Pressurized	Option	Option	Option
Balanced draft (FD & ID Fans are used)	NR	NR	Option
Air Heater Type			
Lungstrom (rotary)	NR	NR	Option
Tubular	Option	Option	Option
Stack Options			
Independent	Option	Option	Option
Common & slight effect on furnace pressure	Option	Option	Option
Common & significant effect on furnace pressure	NR	NR	Option
FD Fan Location			
Integral with windbox	Option	Option	Option
Remote	NR	Option	Option
Air Composition			
Constant	Option	Option	Option
Variable but slight	Option	Option	Option
Variable & significant	NR	NR	Option
Fuel Composition			
Clean	Option	Option	Option
Variations	NR	NR	Option

NR: not recommended

Jackshaft positioning type systems are a good choice for boilers smaller than 200 Bhp (boiler horsepower). When there is difficulty installing jackshaft linkage or a FD fan variable speed drive (VSD) or oxygen trim is included, a parallel positioning system should be selected.

Fully metered type systems are a good choice for boilers larger than 600 Bhp (20 kbps). Fully metered systems with oxygen trim measure and control air flow, fuel flow and flue gas oxygen to minimize extra excess air.

When selecting a combustion control system, consider safety first, then control system cost vs. operating cost trade-offs.

Table 12-6. Multiple Boiler Header Pressure or Temperature Control Recommendation

Boilers Type	Boiler Horsepower	Steam lb/hr	Variable Speed Drive	Oxygen Trim	Combustion Control Jackshaft Positioning	Parallel Positioning	Fully Metered
On/ Off	1	0.033	Yes	...	...	...	...
	5	0.167	Yes	...	...	...	...
	10	0.335	Yes	...	...	...	...
Cast iron, fintube, fire box, fire tube	20	0.670	Yes	...	Yes	Yes	...
	50	1.674	Yes	...	Yes	Yes	...
	100	3.348	Yes	...	Yes	Yes	...
	200	6.696	Yes	Yes	Yes	Yes	...
	300	10.044	Yes	Yes	Yes	Yes	...
	500	16.739	Yes	Yes	Yes	Yes	...
	600	20.087	Yes	Yes	Yes	Yes	...
	800	26.783	Yes	Yes	Yes	Yes	Yes
	1000	33.479	Yes	Yes	...	Yes	Yes
	1500	50.218	Yes	Yes	...	Yes	Yes
Water- tube	2000	66.958	Yes	Yes	...	Yes	Yes
	4000	133.915	Yes	Yes	...	Yes	Yes
	6000	200.873	Yes	Yes	...	Yes	Yes
	8000	267.830	Yes	Yes	...	...	Yes
	10000	334.788	Yes	Yes	...	...	Yes
	20000	669.576	Yes	Yes	...	...	Yes

Table 12-7. Boiler Size Terminology

Boiler Horsepower (Bhp) (output)	Heat MBtu/hr (output)	Steam lb/hr (output)	Electrical Power (MW) (output)	Natural Gas ft³/hr (input)	#2 Fuel Oil gal/hr (Input)
1	0.033	34.5	...	39.86	0.28
5	0.167	172.5	...	199.28	1.42
10	0.335	345.0	...	398.56	2.85
20	0.670	690.0	...	797.11	5.69
50	1.674	1725.0	...	1992.79	14.23
100	3.348	3450.0	0	3985.57	28.47
200	6.696	6900.0	1	7971.14	56.94
300	10.044	10350.0	1	11956.71	85.41
400	13.392	13800.0	1	15,942.29	113.87
500	16.739	17250.0	2	19927.86	142.34
600	20.087	20700.0	2	23913.43	170.81
700	23.435	24150.0	2	27899.00	199.28
800	26.783	27600.0	3	31884.57	227.75
900	30.131	31050.0	3	35870.14	256.22
1000	33.479	34500.0	3	39855.71	284.68
1100	36.827	37950.0	4	43841.29	313.15
1200	40.175	41400.0	4	47826.86	341.62
1300	43.522	44850.0	4	51812.43	370.09
1400	46.870	48300.0	5	55798.00	398.56

Chart data is based on a steam enthalpy of 970.4 Btu/lb and boiler efficiency of 80% when firing natural gas and 84% when firing oil.

Boiler Horsepower: A boiler horsepower (Bhp) is the evaporation of 34.5 lbs of water per hour at a temperature of 212°F and a pressure of 14.7 psia, into dry saturated steam at the same temperature and pressure. The term boiler horsepower started because early boilers were used to drive engines with one engine horsepower.

Rules of Thumb

Boiler Horsepower		
10000 lb/hr steam output	=	300 boiler hp developed
Developed HP ÷ 200	=	*gpm* fuel oil burned
Developed HP × 45	=	*cfh* natural gas burned
Developed HP × 9	=	*cfm* combustion air required (20% excess air)
Developed HP × 20	=	*cfm* hot flue gases (580 °F) used for sizing ID fan (20% EA)

Table 12-8. Flow Meter Piping Requirements

Diameter (D) = Nominal Pipe Size			Fully Open Gate Valve (Unless Another Upstream Fitting Needs More)	Fully Open Globe or Non-Return Valve (Unless Another Upstream Fitting Needs More)	Partially Open Valve
Example: 13 diameters of 6" pipe = 78" 13 diameters of 10" pipe = 130" Beta = (Bore ID/Pipe ID) Bore is the smallest diameter of an orifice or nozzle Up = Upstream diameters Down = downstream diameters					
Orifice/ Nozzle	Beta = 0.5	Up	6	11	26
		Down	3	3	3
	Beta = 0.7	Up	10	15	38
		Down	4	4	4
Venturi	Beta = 0.5	Up	5	7	7
		Down	2	2	2
	Beta = 0.7	Up	9	26	26
		Down	4	4	4
Vortex		Up	25	30	30
		Down	5	5	5
Thermal		Up	15	15	40
		Down	5	5	5
Turbine		Up	10	10	10
		Down	5	5	5
Annubar		Up	8	9	24
		Down	3	3	4

The straight runs shown above are conservative minimums. Longer upstream straight pipe lengths provide better accuracy.

Positive displacement and coriolis effect meters are not influenced by upstream and downstream fittings.

Table 12-9. Flow Meter Piping Requirements

Diameter (D) = Nominal Pipe Size. Example: 13 diameters of 6" pipe = 78"; 13 diameters of 10" pipe = 130". Beta = (Bore ID/Pipe ID). Bore is the smallest diameter of an orifice or nozzle. Up = upstream diameters. Down = downstream diameters						
Orifice/ Nozzle	Beta = 0.5	Up	16	20	9	8
		Down	3	3	3	3
	Beta = 0.7	Up	23	30	12	9
		Down	4	4	4	4
Venturi	Beta = 0.5	Up	21	21	5 (reducer), 2 (expander)	…
		Down	2	2	2	…
	Beta = 0.7	Up	21	21	8 (reducer), 4 (expander)	…
		Down	2	2	4	…
Vortex		Up	30	45	25	…
		Down	5	5	5	…
Thermal		Up	15	40	15 (reducer), 30 (expander)	…
		Down	5	10	5 (reducer), 10 (expander)	…
Turbine		Up	10	10	10	…
		Down	5	5	5	…
Annubar		Up	9	19	8	…
		Down	3	4	3	…

The straight runs shown above are conservative minimums. Longer upstream straight pipe lengths provide better accuracy.

Positive displacement and coriolis effect meters are not influenced by upstream and downstream fittings.

Table 12-10. Flow Meter Piping Requirements

Diameter (D) = Nominal Pipe Size. Example: 13 diameters of 6" pipe = 78"; 13 diameters of 10" pipe = 130". Beta = (Bore ID/Pipe ID). Bore is the smallest diameter of an orifice or nozzle. Up = upstream diameters. Down = downstream diameters					
Orifice/ Nozzle	Beta = 0.5	Up	7	10	8
		Down	3	3	3
	Beta = 0.7	Up	13	18	16
		Down	4	4	4
Venturi	Beta = 0.5	Up	4	4	4
		Down	2	2	2
	Beta = 0.7	Up	4	4	8
		Down	2	2	4
Vortex		Up	30	30	30
		Down	5	5	5
Thermal		Up	15	20	20
		Down	5	5	5
Turbine		Up	10	10	10
		Down	5	5	5
Annubar		Up	7	9	…
		Down	3	3	…

The straight runs shown above are conservative minimums. Longer upstream straight pipe lengths provide better accuracy.

Positive displacement and coriolis effect meters are not influenced by upstream and downstream fittings.

Fuel Oil Handling System Design

Introduction.—This section is intended to provide insight into the design of fuel oil pumping systems. It is intended to provide only introductory and generic information.

This section deals primarily with light fuel oils such as diesel and No. 2 fuel oil, although many of the topics covered are applicable to heavier oils. The design of a light fuel oil transfer system may be broken down into five steps:

1. Determination of required flow rate
2. Determination of maximum inlet suction
3. Determination of required discharge pressure
4. Design of fuel oil piping system
5. Selection of proper control strategy

All of these design tasks are interrelated to some extent, and they all depend on the nature of the application.

General flow meter piping recommendations are detailed in Tables 12-8 to 12-10.

Determination of Required Flow Rate.—The determination of required maximum pumping rate is dependent on the application and the overall piping system, but must be determined as the first step in the design of the entire fuel system. This section treats both day tank systems and burner loops systems, which are different enough to warrant separate discussion.

Rules of Thumb: As a rule of thumb for sizing generator fuel oil systems, each 100 kw of generator capacity will consume about 7 gallons per hour. Any oil that is pumped to the engine but is not returned to the day tank would add to the generator capacity based requirement.

Day Tank and Stand-By E-Generator Applications:

Day tanks are used for any application where a small gravity head is desirable at the inlet to the generator or burner, and/or it is desirable to have a supply of fuel sufficient for some period of operation without the availability of the remote fuel transfer pumps. Day tanks are used with oil burners, for example, when burners are on the upper floors of a building and the main oil tank is underground. The fuel oil transfer set draws oil from the underground tank and pumps it to the day tank at the burner elevation. The burner mounted pump draws oil from the day tank and returns oil to the day tank. It would not be possible for the burner-mounted pumps in this example to draw oil directly from the underground tank because of the high lift. The use of a vented day tank also ensures that the pressure at the inlet to the burners will not become excessive.

Emergency diesel generators are supplied with day tanks to provide a period of operation without being dependent on the electric pumps in the transfer set to deliver fuel to the engines. In some cases, the injector bypass is piped back to the day tank. In other cases this oil

is heated by the engine and must be cooled before it is returned to the day tank. Alternatively, the heated oil is returned to the main tank where it is diluted with cool oil. The recommendations of the engine manufacturer should always be followed with respect to fuel piping and cooling.

If all oil returned by the burner or engine is returned to the day tank, the fuel oil transfer system need only replace the fuel that is burned. The pumps will be sized based on the actual fuel consumption, the desired pump duty cycle, and some safety factor to allow for pump wear and unforeseen contingences. For example, assume that a generator will consume 25 gallons per hour at full rated load and it is desired that the pumps run only 25 percent of the time. The transfer set should then be equipped with 120 gallon per hour pumps to provide a 20% safety factor on top of the 25% duty factor.

If oil returned by the burner or engine is returned to the main tank, the fuel oil transfer system must be sized to replace all of the oil directed to the engine (or burner) whether it is burned or not. The capacity of the day tank must be increased if the same period of operation must be maintained without depending on the operation of the transfer set. If the amount of fuel returned to the main tank is considerable, the installation of an oil cooler in the engine return should be considered. The addition of a cooler will permit the return of oil to the day tank allowing the day tank volume and transfer set capacity to be smaller.

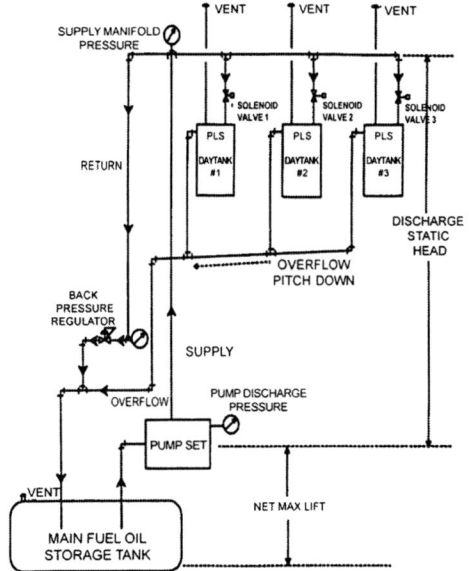

PUMP DISCHARGE PRESSURE - SUPPLY MANIFOLD PRESSURE REQUIRED
- DISCHARGE STATIC HEAD
- FRICTION LOSS IN SUPPLY PIPE AT MAX FLOW

PUMP SUCTION - NET MAX LIFT
- FRICTION LOSS IN SUCTION PIPING
- PRESSURE DROP THROUGH STRAINER

Fig 12-26. Multiple day tanks

For multiple day tank systems piped as shown in Fig. 12-26, the transfer set would be sized to meet the total requirements of the individual generators as outlined above. Of course, the transfer set would only have to be capable of supplying those pieces of equipment that might operate together in a worst case scenario. The level control system would assume the task of starting a pump and opening the appropriate solenoid valve when any day tank level dropped below the pump start setting of the level probe.

Stand by Generator Loop Systems.—It is also possible to design the system shown in Fig. 12-26 with pumps that operate continuously. The pump control portion of the control system would provide for the starting of a back-up pump in the event that flow in the loop was lost. It might also alternate the operation of the pumps on a time-clock basis.

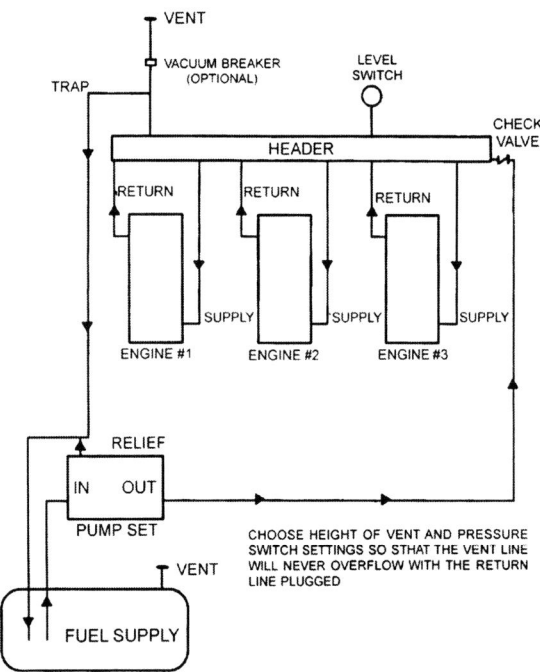

Fig 12-27. Emergency generator "Loop System"

Notes on Header Systems:

1. A back pressure regulating valve is added to keep the header full and to prevent oil siphoning out of the header.

2. The level switch is used for pump control. On pressurized header systems a pressure switch can replace the level switch.

3. A check valve prevents oil from flowing back down the fill line.

A back pressure regulating valve in the loop would provide a constant inlet pressure at the solenoid valves. The tank level control portion of the control system would open and close the appropriate solenoid valves to keep the fuel levels in the individual tanks between the desired limits. It would be good practice to provide a back-up solenoid valve at each tank. This valve would shut off fuel

flow into the tank in the event that high level in the day tank or leakage into the rupture basin was detected.

Sometimes it is desirable to allow for the operation of multiple emergency generators without the installation of the day tanks. One strategy that has been applied is to pump the fuel oil to an oversized pipe header above the generators as shown in Fig. 12-27. A vent pipe extends to a height equivalent to the gravity head that would exist if the return line was shut off. This vent also serves to allow air to enter the header to compensate for the withdrawal of fuel without replacement by the transfer set. The generators are then able to operate without depending on the operation of the transfer set for some time. Optionally, a vacuum breaker is added to prevent oil from being siphoned out of the header.

The larger the pipe size used for the header, the longer the period the generators can operate without power to the transfer set. In effect, the header becomes the day tank. The pressure switch and vent ensure that the pressure in the header does not rise above the safe working pressure of the engine's fuel handling system.

Multiple Pumps.—When two pumps are used to form a duplex pump set, each pump is selected to provide 100% capacity so that there is complete redundancy. When three or more pumps are used, there are more possible options. Very large pump sets often have three 50% pumps so that any two pumps will provide 100% of the maximum required flow. If the load is reduced, say in a boiler plant in spring or fall, one pump may be adequate and the electrical demand of the system will be reduced. Another strategy for triplex pump sets is to use two 100% pumps and one smaller unit for periods of low flow requirements.

In extremely critical applications, pump sets have been constructed with up to four 100% pumps. Here, the control system must reliably sequence through the available pumps if a loss of flow is detected. Microprocessor-based or programmable logic controller based operating systems may be used to provide the degree of control sophistication and reliability required by such pumping systems.

Burner Loop Systems.—Generally, the pump set runs continuously so that the entire piping system is continuously primed, and air is kept out of the burners. Any air entering the system is returned to the tank where it can settle out harmlessly.

The pump set serves to pull oil from the main tank and supply oil to the burners when the burner pumps themselves may be inadequate. This would include cases where the burners are too high above the bottom of the tank or too far away to pull directly. In multiple burner installations, the use of a common fuel oil pump in conjunction with a burner loop system eliminates the need for each burner to be piped individually back to the main tank. To increase reliability, fuel oil pressure or flow switches may be incorporated into the system. Then, an impending loss of oil supply to the burners can be alarmed and corrected before a shutdown occurs. The use of a pump lead/lag control will fulfill the requirements if automatic back up pump operation is specifically required.

In the case of a single oil burner, the selection of the required pumping rate is relatively simple. The pump set must be capable of supplying a greater oil flow into the loop than the maximum oil flow drawn out of the loop by the burner pump. Fig. 12-28 shows a simplified system with a pump set supplying oil to a single burner. Note that the burner draws from the loop and any extra oil flowing through the loop simply bypasses the burner on its way back to the tank.

The important piece of information required for sizing the pumps is not the actual firing rate of the burner, but the pumping rate of the burner-mounted pump. It is relatively common for small burners (say 5 gallons per hour maximum firing rate) to have comparatively high pumping rates (up to 70 gallons per hour).

In this case, the pump set would be quite undersized if it was designed based on the traditional "rule of thumb" of "twice the burner-firing rate."

In the example presented in Fig. 12-28, an undersized pump set would result in oil flowing backwards in the section of the loop between the supply and return connections on the burner. Any air leaking into the burner-mounted pump would be directed back to the burner supply rather than back to the tank where it would separate from the oil. Good practice dictates that the flow of oil in the loop should be continuous and one directional from tank suction to tank return.

Fig. 12-29 shows three burners connected to one loop system. In this case, the absolute minimum flow rate leaving the pump set would be equal to the firing rate of the first and second burners plus the pumping rate of the third burner.

Assume that each burner has a maximum firing rate of 100 gallons per hour, and a pumping rate of 250 gallons per hour. The required minimum pump set capacity would be 100 + 100 + 250 gallons per hour. With all burners operating at maximum rate, the flow up to the supply line of the first burner would be 450 gallons per hour. The first burner would pull its pumping rate of 250 gallons per hour from the loop, leaving 200 gph of oil to flow to the second burner. The first burner would burn 100 gph of the 250 gph drawn from the loop and return 150 gph to the loop. This would join with the 200 gph that had bypassed the burner. A total flow of 350 gph would be present just upstream of the supply connection for the second burner. Again, 250 gph would be drawn into the burner and 100 gph would flow past the burner. Of the 250 gph flowing into the burner, 100 gph would be burned and 150 gph would be returned to join the 100 gph that had bypassed the burner. A total of 250 gph would be available at the supply connection of the third burner. The entire 250 gph would enter the burner, there would be no flow bypassing the burner, and 150 gph would be returned to the tank from the third burner.

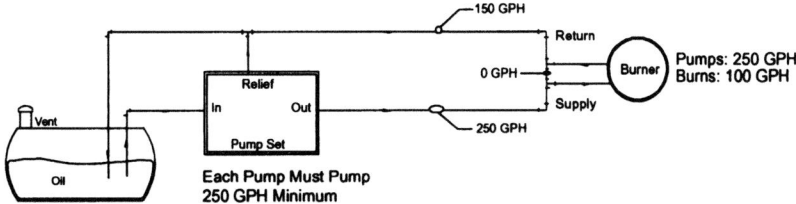

Fig 12-28. Single burner

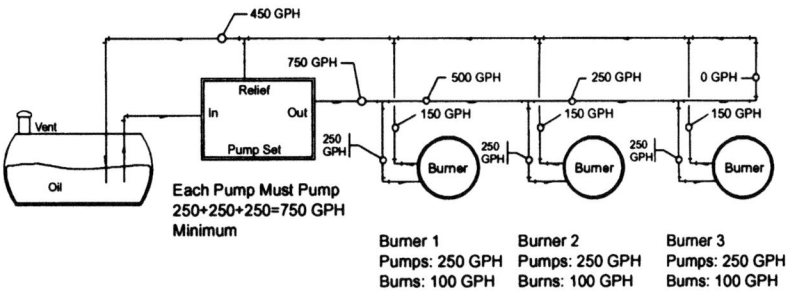

Fig 12-29. Burners piped in parallel

Notes on Series vs. Parallel Piped Systems:
1. Traditional series loops have lower flow rates and operate at very low pressures.
2. If oil is heated, heaters are smaller in Series Loops.
3. Parallel loops may operate at high pressure.
4. Parallel loops are used for pressure atomizing applications without burner-mounted pumps.

Of course the pump set, as designed, would have some reserve capacity because the pumps would be selected to have a design capacity exceeding the minimum requirement.

Fig. 12-29 shows three burners piped in parallel. In this case, the minimum pump set capacity would be equal to the total pumping rate of the three burners. For the burners described above, the pump set would have a minimum capacity of 750 gph. Note: The series system requires a substantially lower pump set capacity than the parallel arrangement.

Actual Pump Capacity vs. Required Minimum Capacity: Once the theoretical minimum capacity of the pump set has been determined, the actual pump capacity must be chosen. An allowance should be made for pump wear especially with high discharge pressure and/or light fuel grade applications where slippage through a worn pump would pose more of a problem. A safety factor should also be applied to cover design approximations. The resultant number would then be compared to the available capacities of various pump and motor combinations. That combination with a capacity just greater than that determined above would be selected.

Determination of Maximum Inlet Suction.—While quality fuel oil pumps are often capable of pulling 20 in. (mercury) suction, it is good practice to keep the suction at the inlet to the pumps below 15 in. Hg. At higher vacuums (lower absolute pressures) the pumps can cavitate as a result of fuel vaporization and/or the expansion of any air that has been entrained in the fuel. The problem of entrained air will be dealt with later on in this section.

The pressure available to the inlets of the pumps then must be kept above 15 in. Hg. in absolute terms. This pressure consists of the available atmospheric pressure (30 in. Hg. At sea level on an average day) less the gravity head that must be overcome to get the oil to the pump inlet from the lowest point in the tank and less the friction losses in the pipe, valves and fittings between the tank and the pump. It is important, of course, to keep all the pressure drop figures in the same units of measure.

Gravity Head: A multiplier may be developed to convert inches of oil to inches of mercury by dividing the specific gravity of the oil by the specific gravity of mercury (13.6). For fuel oil with a gravity of 0.85, a multiplier of 0.0625 would result. To lift this oil 12 feet, the available pump inlet pressure would be reduced by 9.0 in. of mercury (12 feet times 12 in. per foot time 0.0625).

In some cases, priming the system can require higher suctions (or present lower absolute inlet pressures) than normal operation. If the high point of the system is not at the pump inlet, it is imperative that provisions be made to fill the system at the high point. Check and foot valves should also be installed to keep the system primed.

For very large diameter tanks, or tanks buried deeply, it may not be possible to locate the pump set at grade with-

out risking cavitation when the tank is nearly empty. In these instances, the pump set may be placed below grade in a pit. Precautions should be taken to prevent the pit from filling with oil or with ground water in the event of a leak. Drainage from the pit should be piped to a settling tank where oil and water can be separated and disposed of properly.

Line Losses: Once the flow rate of the pump set has been determined, the suction line may be sized to keep the friction or line losses in the piping to an acceptable level. Bear in mind that pump sizes and motor speeds are not available in continuous spectrum. Usually, the next larger pump and motor combination above the minimum flow requirement will be used. Also, it is good practice in estimating friction losses to use the flow rate produced by the pump set with the minimum expected back pressure at the pump discharge. With thin fluids, the pumps will produce a higher flow at low discharge pressures because slippage diminishes. If a pump is rated 300 gph at 100 psig discharge pressure when pumping No. 2 fuel oil, it may pump 350 gph or more with little back pressure. Using the 100 psig flow rating when the actual pressure would be only 25 psig or so would result in underestimating the suction line friction losses.

Total line losses are comprised of frictional losses in the foot valve, the pipe itself, in fittings such as elbows and tees, in valves and in the suction strainer. These losses may be estimated using line loss tables available from your pump manufacturers.

To use any of these methods, it is necessary to know the specific gravity of the fuel as well as the viscosity. Since both the specific gravity and the viscosity of petroleum oils are a function of temperature, it is necessary to correct the values referenced to standard temperatures to those under actual expected flowing temperatures.

Once the flow rates, specific gravity and viscosity are known the pressure drop of the piping system may be determined using appropriate charts or the referenced program.

Strainer Drop: The pressure drop through the suction strainer may be approximated by using the chart found on manufacturer's catalogue. Note that the pressure drops that will be obtained will be for clean strainer baskets. As the strainer becomes clogged with foreign matter, the drop will increase. It is wise to use a 100% safety factor when estimating the strainer loss.

Often the main tank will be far enough away from the pump set such that the friction losses in the suction line are significantly larger than the loss through a strainer of the same pipe size. In these cases, it is common to use a suction strainer that is smaller than the suction piping.

Summary of Suction Line Losses: The net positive pressure available to the inlet of the pump is determined by starting with atmospheric pressure, deducting the static lift from the bottom of the tank to the pump inlet, deducting the line losses at the actual flow rate and viscosity, and deducting the estimated loss through the suction strainer. The result should be comfortably less than 15 inches Hg.

With heated oil it is important to use the worst case viscosity in any evaluations. This will be a function of the actual fuel purchased as well as the lowest temperature to which the piping will be exposed. For heavy oils and above ground piping, it may be necessary to provide heat tracing or impedance heating of the suction and return piping. In extreme cases, the piping can get so cool that the oil will not flow at all.

Pump Discharge Pressure Requirements.—The pressure required at the discharge of the pump set will be the pressure required at the point of use plus the friction losses in the intervening piping, plus any additional gravity head that might need to be overcome. The same methods used for estimating the suction line friction losses and static head equivalents may be used.

In many cases, the gravity head to be overcome presents the largest single component of the pressure requirement. This is especially true when oil-consuming equipment is located near the top of a high-rise building while the pump set is in the basement.

The actual regulation of pressure is best accomplished at or near the point of use with the installation of a back pressure regulating valve. Fig. 12-26 illustrates the application of a back pressure-regulating valve to a multiple daytank system. This valve serves to maintain header pressure independent of the amount of returning oil.

Pressure, air, and steam atomizing burners may require that relatively high pressures be provided by the pump set if there is no pump on the burner itself. It is important that the proper pressure be provided in the loop and that this pressure be closely regulated with a back pressure regulating valve or pressure regulating valve at the burner. The valve should be sized so that the pressure buildup (in the case of a back-pressure valve) or drop (in the case of a pressure regulator) is small.

Day tank systems require that the pressure at the inlet of the level control solenoid valve be sufficient to insure the necessary flow. As an example, assume that a system is to operate with a valve open duty cycle of 25%. The pressure and valve C_v combination should be chosen to provide a flow through the solenoid valve of four times the design flow rate of fuel from the tank.

Piping System Design Considerations.—In laying out the entire fuel piping system, key issues deserve specific attention. Namely, the possibility of entraining air in the fuel should be eliminated; loss of system prime should be prevented; re-establishment of prime should be quick and easy; backflows and overflows should be prevented; and tanks should be properly vented.

Entrained Air: This is a significant problem when dealing with distillate fuels. The best design approach is to insure that all the fuel piping stays full of fuel at all times. This will involve keeping all returns to tanks submerged, putting back-pressure regulating valves at the bottom of vertical runs rather than at the top whenever feasible, and guarding against any suction leaks. Air that has become entrained in distillate fuel takes quite a long time to settle out and can stay in a poorly designed system on a permanent basis. This will cause noisy operation and poor performance of pumps and regulators, short equipment life, and poor performance of the equipment being supplied with the air filled fuel.

Provision for Tank Overflow and Tank Venting: These topics go hand in hand. Day tanks should always be equipped with overflow lines that will take excess fuel to a safe location in the event of a component failure. Note that the vent line must be high enough so that the overflowing oil from the day tank does not just run out the vent. Conversely, an extremely high vent pipe could result in the development of a static pressure within the tank itself that exceeds the design rating. If the day tank is elevated sufficiently above the main tank, it may be necessary to provide an overflow holding tank. This tank would contain any oil spilling from an over filled day tank or from the rupture basin of a leaking day tank. This fuel would be held until the situation is corrected and a return to the main tank could be safely monitored.

Pump Set Control System Strategies.—One of the most difficult tasks in designing a completely integrated fuel oil handling system is selecting the control strategy. The control system must integrate the operation of the pump motors, any automatic valves, warning devices, and operator interfaces such as switches and lights.

The purpose of this section is to review the important considerations involved, not to present a complete design manual for control systems. The selection of the most appropriate control strategy for any given fuel oil pumping system involves answering the following questions:

1. Will the pumps be in operation continuously or intermittently?

2. If the pumps are started automatically, what signal will be used to direct the start?

3. Is automatic alternation of pump operation desirable?

4. Should the back-up pump be brought on line automatically if needed?

5. Are there automatic valves to be operated by the control system?

6. What conditions should result in the generation of an alarm signal?

7. What conditions should cause a shutdown of the pumping system?

Unless these questions are answered it is impossible to design a control system that will optimize the performance, safety, and reliability of the fuel handling system. A brief discussion of each of these major topics follows.

Continuous vs. Intermittent Operation: If the pumps are to be run continuously, automatic start-stop signals are not required. In normal operation, one pump is manually started and remains in operation until manually stopped. This does not eliminate the requirements for safety shut-down interlocks and automatic back-up pump operation. Examples of such systems would include burner loop systems where the fuel oil is continuously circulated through the loop and past all the burners. The circulation is generally maintained regardless of burner operation. Similarly, some day tank level control systems rely on the opening and closing of multiple solenoid valves to keep the individual day tanks at the desired fuel levels. It might be desirable to keep oil circulating in a pressurized loop past all the day tanks to make certain that the suction piping cannot lose its prime during long idle periods.

Often, it is desirable to have the pumps start and stop based on some automatic signal. This should be done only when there is no danger of the suction piping losing its prime during off periods. Many day tank level control systems are designed so that the pumps only operate when one of the tanks requires the addition of fuel. This intermittent operation will minimize wear and tear on the pumps and motors, as well as reduce the average electric energy usage for the facility.

Automatic Start-Stop Signals: In some cases the automatic pump start-stop signals are generated within the fuel handling system, and in other cases they are generated externally. An example of an external start-stop signal is a set of contacts from an emergency generator management system. When a generator is required to operate, these contacts would close, and would be used to start the pump(s). This system could be used in a tankless loop system such as that depicted in Fig. 12-27.

Day tank level control systems are examples of instances when pump start-stop signals are generated within the system. In most cases, level switches in the day tank are used to start and stop the pumps. By using separate switches for pump on and pump off, it is possible to minimize the on and off cycling of the pumps. When the level in the tank drops below the "pump on" setting, the pump will start. When the fuel level in the tank rises past the "pump on" switch, the pump continues to run. It does not shut off until the level reaches the setting of the "pump off" switch. A four switch assembly can be used to provide a high alarm level above the "pump off" switch and a low alarm level below the "pump on" switch.

Multiple day tank level control systems may be designed with a constantly pressurized header feeding the individual solenoid-operated fill valves at each tank. The automatic signal to operate the pumps would come from a pressure switch (with dead band) at the top of the header. This system is similar to a domestic well water based system. An accumulator tank is used to provide an air cush-

ion. Then the pumps will only have to start after a certain volume of fuel (the draw-down) has been drawn out of the accumulator tank.

Automatic Pump Alternation: When pumps are started and stopped remotely it is desirable to alternate the operation of the pumps. This way, run time is spread equally between the available units. Also, if one unit should fail to operate, the pump that handled the last call for operation would be available as a back-up. If only one pump is run routinely, the back-up pump could freeze up, develop a leak, or be manually taken out of service and would not be available when required. With duplex pump sets, a selector switch is used to select Pump 1, Pump 2, or automatic alternation. With more than two pumps, relay or microprocessor logic can be used to sequence the pumps whenever a start signal is received.

Back-Up Pump Operation: The back-up pump(s) may be brought on line either manually or automatically as required. Generally it is desirable for this to happen automatically, and this function is often handled by the same logic that alternates the operation of the lead pump. This logic is referred to as "lead/lag logic", and the pump that is normally in operation is referred to as the "lead pump". The pump that would normally be the back-up pump is called the "lag pump". When there are more than two pumps, the lag pumps are referred to as "first lag", "second lag", etc. The first lag pump is the back-up pump that will start first if the lead pump does not function properly.

The signal to start the back-up pump generally comes from within the fuel system since it must respond to a failure of the primary pump. It is important to select a device that will reliably discriminate between the proper operation and a failure of the lead pump. If the oil is being circulated in a loop without any back-pressure device, there might not be sufficient pressure at the pump discharge to indicate whether or not a pump is operating properly. If the pumps are being used to circulate oil within a loop, a flow switch might be used to detect loss of flow in the system. When the level in a tank is being controlled, the low level switch in the tank would indicate whether or not the lead pump is performing properly. For a system maintaining a pressurized header, a pressure sensor could be used to control the operation of a back-up pump.

When required, additional logic can be provided so that only one pump at a time is allowed to operate. When a lead pump failure is detected, the lead pump is de-energized and the first lag pump is then energized, and so on. When the pumps have to be operated from emergency power, this sort of sequencing can be useful for minimizing the instantaneous total connected motor horsepower on the emergency circuit.

Automatic Valves: When one fuel oil pump set is used to maintain the level in multiple day tanks, automatic valves are required to isolate the tanks from one another. This assures that when the pumps operate, only those tanks that require fuel receive fuel. The control system is designed so that the level switch in the tank operates the fill valve. If the pumps were to run intermittently, the opening of any fill valve would trigger the starting of a pump. A second valve might be installed in the fill line to each tank, and controlled by the high level switch in the tank. If the main fill valve were to leak fuel into the tank, the back-up valve would then be closed preventing an overflow condition.

Another application of automatic valves in fuel oil handling systems is for main storage tank selection. Control logic can be provided that senses a nearly empty main tank, and opens the supply and return valves for the next tank in sequence. When these valves are proven open, the supply and return valves for the emptied tank close, isolating it from service.

Alarm Signals: A properly designed control system will provide sufficient information to the operating personnel to make intelligent decisions regarding the operation and maintenance of the fuel oil handling system. Some of the more common malfunction alarms are discussed here.

The control system should alert the operator if the lag pump is needed. Usually, a memory circuit is required so that this alarm does not clear itself when the lag pump starts. For example, if the lag pump is started because the pump set flow is interrupted, this flow would be re-established once the lag pump is operating. The memory circuit keeps the alarm light on until it is manually cleared so that the operators are made aware that a problem has occurred. Similarly, high level in a tank would correct itself as the fuel is used. A manual reset memory circuit would be used to retain the information that a high level condition had existed.

Other alarm conditions might include high discharge pressure (indication of a restriction in the piping system, or a valve inadvertently closed) or low discharge pressure. Flow through an overflow pipe might indicate a failure of the pump off and high level alarm circuitry, or a manual bypass valve left open or leaking. Build up of fuel in the day tank rupture basin would indicate a leak in the tank or connecting piping. By including a tank gauging system for the main storage tanks in the control system, the entire fuel system can be controlled from a central location and monitored for high and low levels, leaks and losses.

Pump System Safety Shutdown: Some of the alarm conditions listed above might be reason to shut down the fuel system. The detection of leaking tanks or piping is generally used as an automatic safety shutdown signal. When tank overflow must be collected in an overflow catch basin or tank, the system should be shut down when that tank or basin nears capacity. Depending on the nature of the installation, the detection of high level in a day tank might be cause to shut the system down. This is especially true when a pump set serves only one tank. Each system is unique, and the control strategy will be different from one job to another. The need for reliability, safety, and automatic operation must be evaluated on a job by job basis.

Conclusion: Many variables impact the design of a fuel pumping system and associated control logic. While the foregoing discussion is an attempt to highlight many of the major topics, it is not possible in this short chapter to touch on all of the unique problems and solutions that one may encounter.

AIR CONDITIONING SYSTEMS

A unitary air conditioner is an apparatus consisting of one or more factory made assemblies that normally include an evaporator, a blower, a compressor, and a condenser, designed to be used together. The unit often performs heating as well as cooling functions.

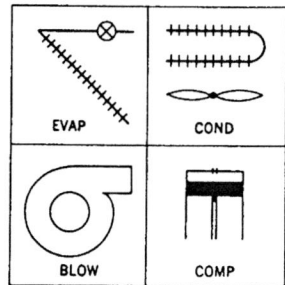

Fig 13-1. Self contained air conditioner

Air Conditioning Systems

Single Package Units.—The single package, or so-called *self-contained* air conditioner, is shown symbolically in Fig. 13-1. All four basic components of the refrigeration cycle are placed in a single *package* or housing. Vertical single-package equipment is usually designed for inside-the-building application. Units often are equipped with line voltage controls, including integral thermostat, all factory prewired. Return air filter and grille are standard with supply air duct flanges usually located at the top of the unit. Most AC units have water-cooled condensers, which can be used with either city water or cooling tower water. Fig. 13-2 is a typical unit of this type. When it is necessary to install a unit without ductwork, a plenum and grille may be fitted to the unit for free air delivery.

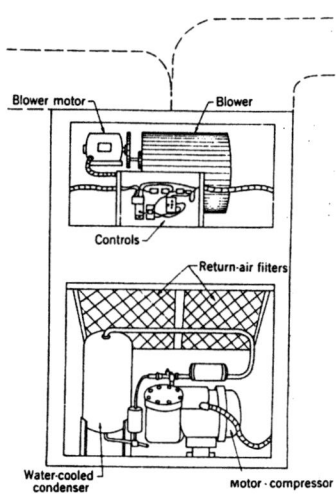

Fig 13-2. Vertical self contained air conditioned unit

Vertical units are available for installation in the space (the traditional *store cooler*) or with more utilitarian cabinets (sometimes designated *commercial*) for remote location; especially where space and noise factors assume extra importance. Commercial units are available in capacities to 50 tons and higher.

Horizontal single package units (Fig. 13-3) are designed for both indoor and outdoor installation, with the majority of units incorporating air cooled or evaporative-cooled condensers. The most common design has supply and return air connections located in the same face with horizontal air flow. Since horizontal units are designed for remote location, they are usually equipped with low voltage thermostat control. Filters are not usually supplied with the unit.

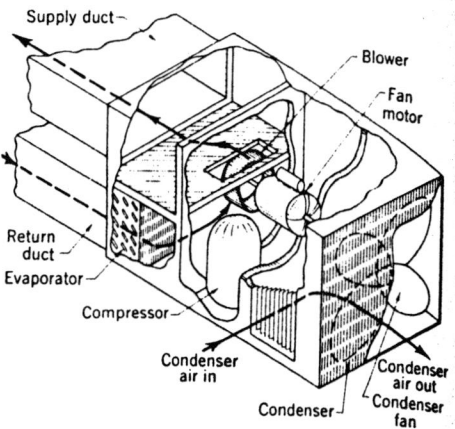

Fig 13-3. Horizontal self contained air conditioned unit

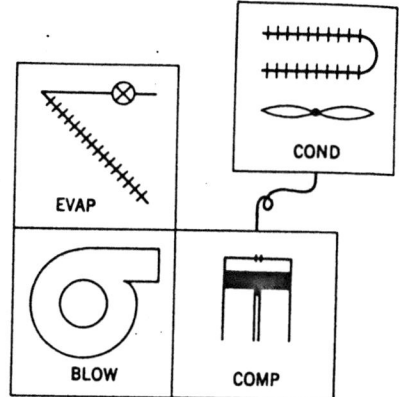

Fig 13-4. Vertical self contained air conditioned unit

Horizontal units are manufactured in capacities from 2 to 20 tons with many modifications for use in residential and light commercial applications. Their outstanding virtue is flexibility, as they can be installed, with ducted air for condensing; outdoors with ducted conditioned air supply and return; and through the wall. Indoors, they can be floor, wall, or ceiling-mounted, and placed in the attic, basement, or in the conditioned space.

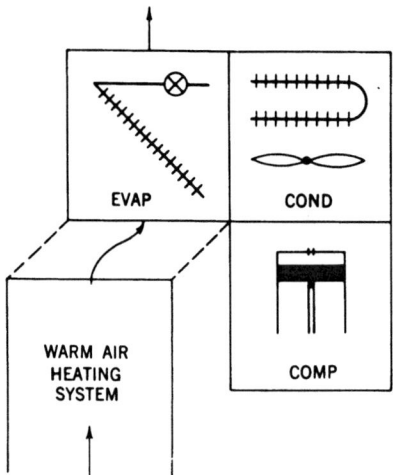

Fig 13-5. Warm air heating system

Units with Remote Condensers: Unitary air conditioners with remote condenser, piped and charged in the field, are basically the same as store coolers but with remote air cooled condensing substituted for integral water cooled condenser.

Refrigeration Chassis: Units in this category are designed to be used with a warm air heating system whose blower supplies the air for the units cooling coil (see Fig. 13-5).

In one version, the compressor-condenser is connected to the evaporator only by several feet of precharged refrigerant line for not too remote location, (see Figs. 13-6 and 13-7). These units are somewhat of a cross between single-package and split systems. Refrigeration chassis are available, also, with (truly) remote air-cooled condensers.

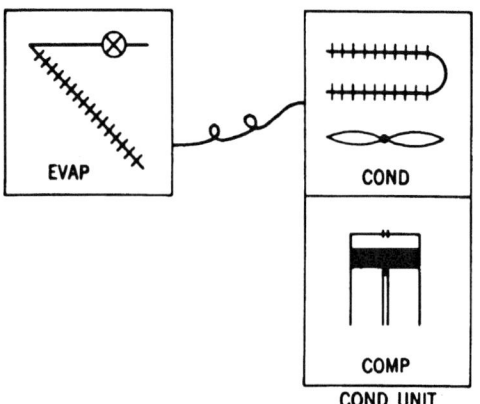

Fig 13-6. Split condenser and evaporator unit

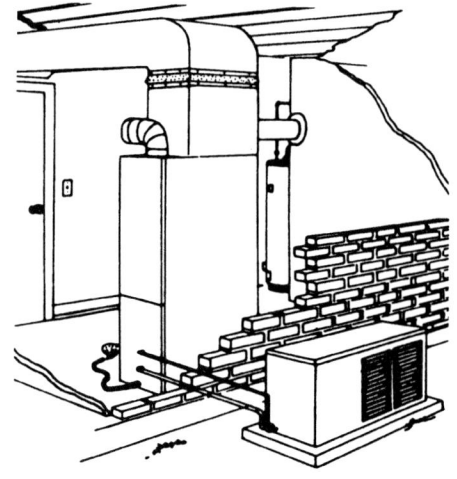

Fig 13-7. Warm air heating system

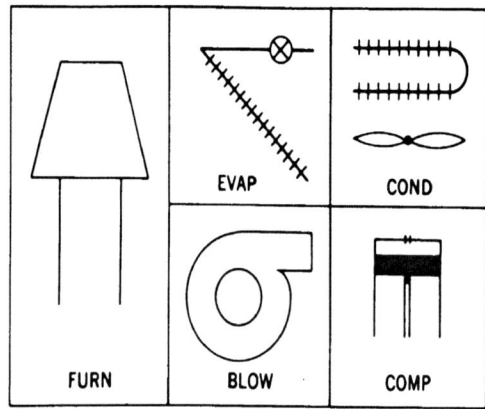

Fig 13-8. Single package year round unit

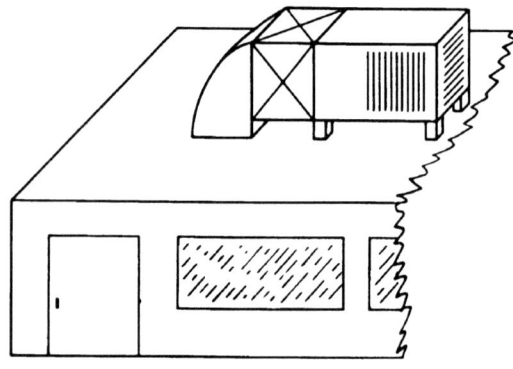

Fig 13-9. Roof mounted A-C unit

Single-Package Year-Round Units: Operated by a factory-wired, interconnected control system through a single heating-cooling thermostat, these units contain a fuel-fired heat exchanger and a factory-sealed and charged refrigeration cycle, (see Fig. 13-8). There are water cooled models designed for installation indoors, but by far the majority are designed for roof mounting with air condensing (see Fig. 13-9). Units are available with natural gas engine compressor drive.

Year-Round Remote Units: These units are the single-package and single package with remote condenser units with heating units attached (see Fig. 13-10).

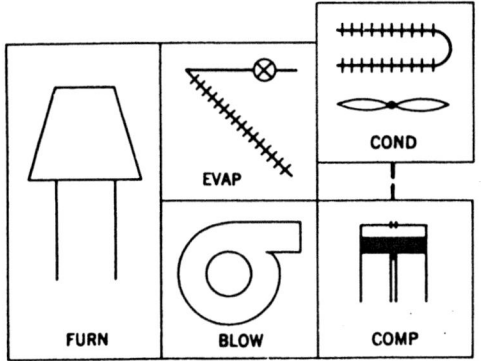

Fig 13-10. Year round air conditioner with remote air cooled conjurers

The round air unit, year-round air conditioner with remote condensing unit (Fig. 13-11) makes the real jump to the *split system.* In the case of both units, interconnecting refrigerant piping is usually field-supplied.

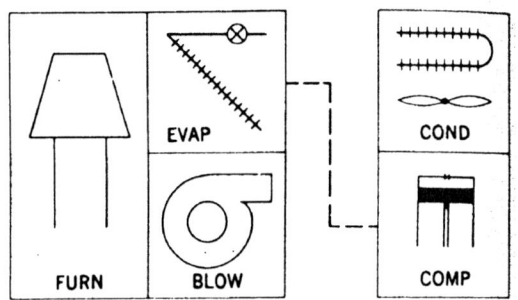

Fig 13-11. Split system year round air conditioner

Remote Condensing Units: A split system air conditioner is a unitary conditioner whose components are assembled in more than one factory made enclosure. The cooling coil is remote from the condensing unit. Because of its similarity to the single package air conditioner units whose condensers only are remote, and refrigeration chassis with or without remote condenser, have already been discussed in conjunction with single-package air conditioners, although they are not truly single package.

Split system components include electric and engine-driven condensing units, remote gas-fired water chillers, cooling coils (evaporators without blowers), and cooling coils with blowers. There is more split-system equipment available than any other type.

Condensing units contain compressor, condenser, and electrical controls. Air cooled and evaporative-cooled

condenser models also contain a fan and fan motor. Units are normally designed for outdoor installation, but some models are designed for indoor or through the wall installations (Figs. 13-12 and 13-13).

Evaporator coils (Fig. 13-14) come in a multitude of sizes and designs. Coils for use with warm air heating systems are available for upflow, downflow, and horizontal air patterns, that is, in bonnet units, under the furnace units, and duct units, respectively.

Fig 13-12. Remote condensing unit application

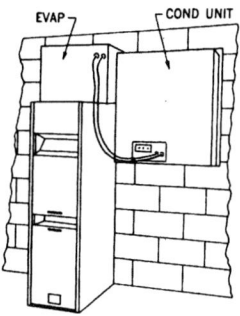

Fig 13-13. Split system, flush wall condensing unit

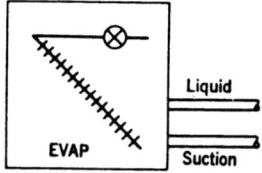

Fig 13-14. Evaporator coils in conjunction with warm air furnace

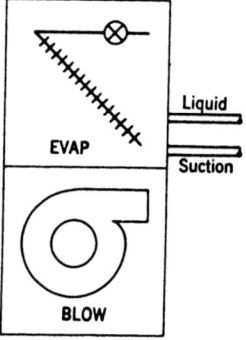

Fig 13-15. Coil with blower units

Condensing units in the unitary category are available in capacities from about 2 to 15 tons. Of course, units in much larger capacities are manufactured and are used to supply multiple cooling coils. However, the engineering of such split systems is more complicated and requires a degree of sophistication on the part of the installer that puts the whole system in the engineered systems category. The essence of the unitary approach is prematched components that can be installed with a minimum of technical skills, quickly and economically. Where total requirements are large, the unitary approach calls for multiple installations of complete unitary systems.

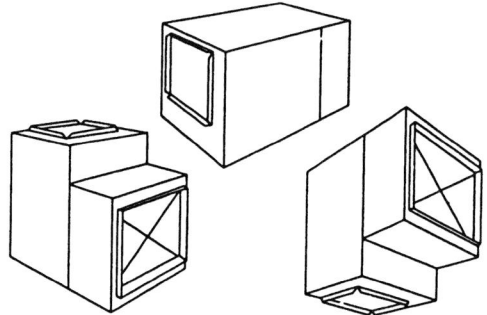

Fig 13-16. Coil with blower units with ductwork

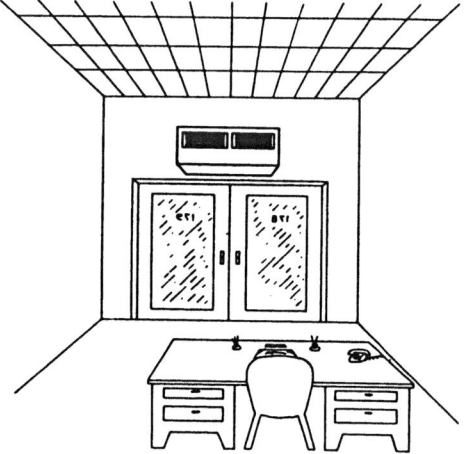

Fig 13-17. Horizontal coil with blower units

Coils with blowers (Fig. 13-15) for applications requiring separate cooling supply air systems are available for horizontal, vertical, or downflow air discharge. Some manufacturer's offer models in building block design for increased flexibility (Fig. 13-16). Both horizontal and vertical coil with blower units are available with decorative grilles for free air delivery.

Absorption Split Systems: Gas fired water chillers are available for use with cooling coils in connection with winter air conditioning and with coil with blower units for summer air conditioning only. The absorption chiller complete with controls and circulating water pump is located outside the building and is air cooled. With polyethylene plastic water connections between chiller and cooling coil the units are said to be unaffected by freezing, hence never require draining. Fig. 13-18 shows the chiller.

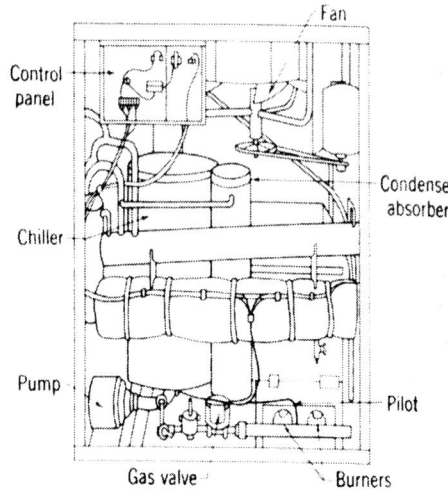

Fig 13-18. Gas fired water chiller

Multizone Units: A relatively recent addition to available unitary equipment is the package multizone air conditioner. It consists of an otherwise conventional self contained combination in which the fan is located so as to blow through the coil or a bypass around the coil. The face of the coil is divided into compartments extending into the bypass area, with a damper located in the bypass where by the proportion of air that is passed may be controlled.

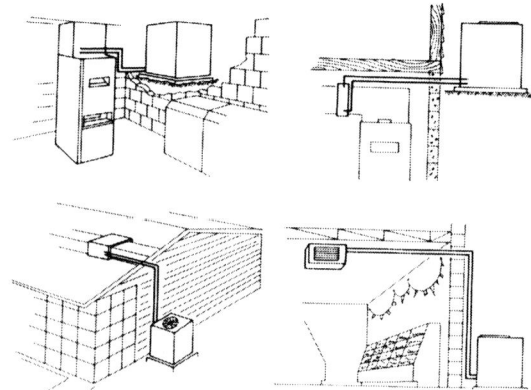

Fig 13-19. Gas fired water chiller with cooling coil

The multizone unitary air conditioner makes possible, from a single unit, the simultaneous individual control of conditions in many zones. However, while they provide all the advantages of unitary equipment, multizone units do require an appreciable amount of engineering in the determination of the zoning and design of the duct system supplied by the unit.

Unitary air conditioners may be located almost any where in a building. This is because they are available in such variety, with many air outlet patterns, and because they are relatively so compact. It is fair to say that their chief virtue is flexibility of location. If an available niche within the building is available, then the unitary equipment may be located in an outside wall.

Single Package Installations.—*Within the Space:* For small areas with no obstructions or partitions, installation within the conditioned space of units arranged for free delivery will often prove to be the most economical installation. For free delivery applications an accessory discharge plenum and grille can be added to self contained units.

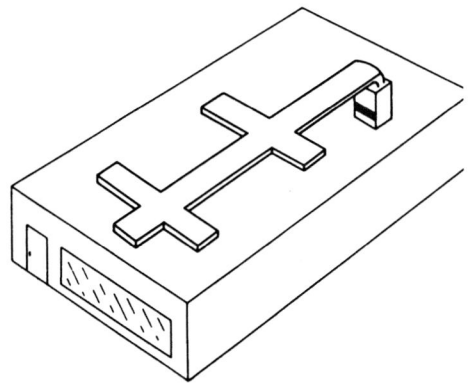

Fig 13-20. Vertical self contained unit

A system of ductwork must be designed for applications involving partitioned or obstructed areas, installation outside the conditioned space, or any other situation that cannot be handled properly with discharge plenums. Fig. 13-20 illustrates a typical duct system for a vertical self-contained unit.

Attic or Crawl Space: Location of self-contained units in an attic or crawl space has been a popular method of installing air conditioning in small homes and in some smaller commercial buildings. However, because of service problems and some restrictive codes, this type of installation appears to be declining in popularity, although the amount of ductwork required is minimal and the unit is completely out of sight, or visible only as a screened and louvered opening.

Because attic and crawl spaces are relatively inaccessible, some method for remote reset is required when the pressure switch kicks out in the event that head pressure exceeds its maximum safe limit. (Underwriters Laboratories requires a manual reset to prevent rapid cycling of the compressor that would occur should the condenser fan fail.)

Because of the constricted space in most attics and crawl spaces, these installations are frequently difficult to service, and they do need service from time to time, particularly since drains should be checked periodically; when they become plugged the first indication will be water dripping through the ceiling, and the cost of water damage in such a situation can run high. Because of this, some city codes require a secondary drain. That is, in addition to the primary drain pan at the bottom of the unit, a second pan, about 2 inches deep and slightly wider and deeper than the unit, is set underneath the unit to collect any overflow from the primary drain or any condensation on the outside of the unit that drips down. Both drains must be independently piped down to the sewer. While the secondary drain is often part of the unit, the double piping is an expense.

Also to be considered is that condenser air may be restricted or hot attic air may be the only cooling source for the condenser, resulting in high head pressures, high operating costs, and increased need for service. More or less satisfactory solutions include: mounting of unit on outside wall of attic, mounting unit through attic wall, installing booster fan or blower in condenser air ductwork to increase air flow through the condenser, and ducting in of air at one end of attic, discharging at the other end.

Finally, noise and vibration from the compressor and fan will be transmitted to the conditioned space unless extreme care is used in mounting the unit and running the ductwork. Spring mounts are effective if proper springs are used. Rubber shock mounts have been applied successfully.

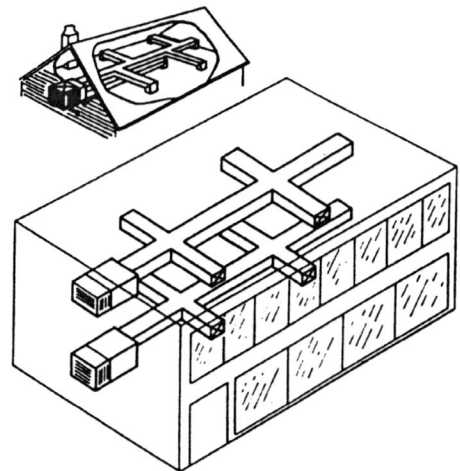

Fig 13-21. Through the wall self contained unit

Through the Wall: Small commercial and some residential buildings without forced air heating are the most likely applications of through the wall installations (Fig. 13-21). Through the wall units may be used on any or all floors of a multistory building. With their weight borne by a solid, load bearing wall, no footings or other special supports are required.

Units may be placed high enough in the wall so that there can be no damage from traffic of passersby. Location of moving parts outside the space tends to reduce noise level inside, although noise and vibration may be transmitted to all parts of the structure unless it is properly installed and mounted.

An important factor in favor of through the wall installation is that units are available for service from the outside, which can be an advantage if units are not too high off the ground, while some are available that can be serviced from the inside, where outside service is not feasible. One must consider whether a replacement unit will be available to fit the wall sleeve in future years.

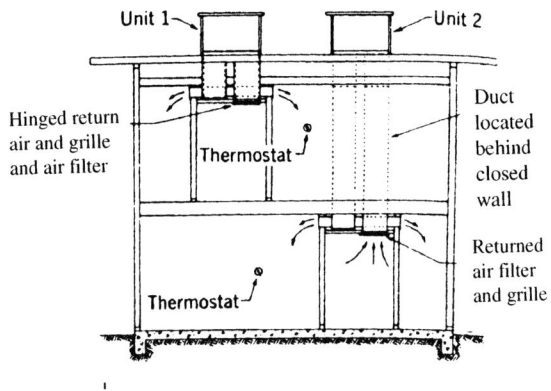

Fig 13-22. Unitary packages on roof ducted to first and second floor

Roof top: Frequently rooftop units are the most economical way to air condition single story commercial and factory buildings (Figs. 13-22- 13-24).

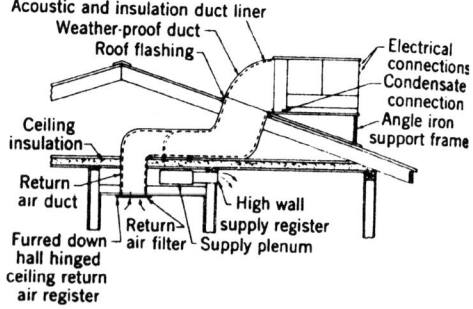

Fig 13-23. Self-contained unit mounted on gabled roof may not be visible from front

In commercial installations it has been found that a number of rooftop units may be used (as in shopping centers) with a minimum of ductwork in addition to excellent zone control. In most cases the equipment is completely hidden from the view of persons on the ground. Another

advantage is to be found in the fact that all noise producing components are outside the conditioned space (although here, again, vibration may cause noise unless unit is properly installed and mounted, and objection to noise by neighboring tenants must be considered, especially if the neighboring building is higher). There is usually no need to run a condensate drain, as condensate can be dumped on the roof or a short line run to a gutter.

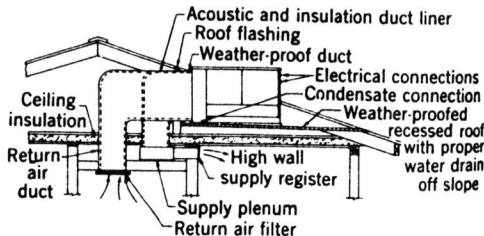

Fig 13-24. Dormer recess installation is less obtrusive

In installing this type of unit, it is well to remember that the roof of an existing building may require reinforcement. New buildings designed for this equipment may have roofs constructed to be of adequate strength during construction, and that a relatively large hole in the roof must be made for ductwork, which, if not properly sealed, will cause trouble.

Here, again, the possibility of inconvenience of servicing should be considered, as well as the fact that condenser air rejection may be adversely affected by wind.

Slab or Ground Level: Mounting of packaged units at ground level outside the conditioned space has become a standard method of installation in many areas, particularly where the heat pump has gained acceptance (Figs. 13-25- 13-27).

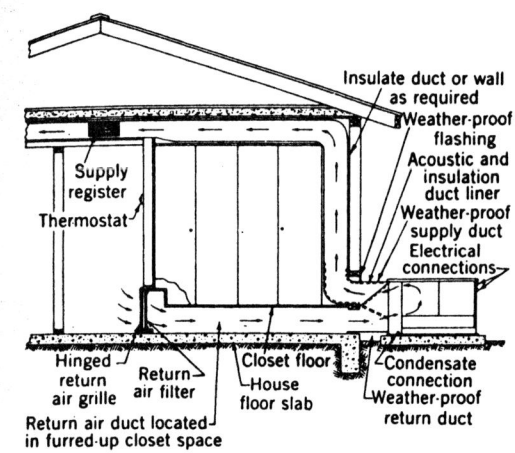

Fig 13-25. Self-contained unit mounted on slab

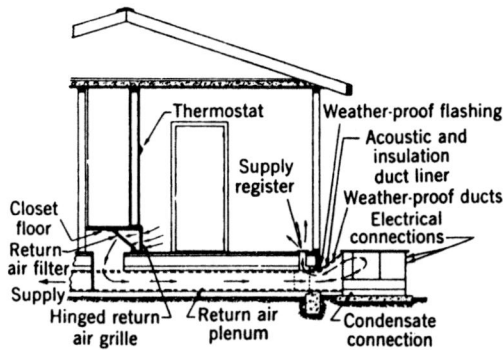

Fig 13-26. Ducts run through crawl space

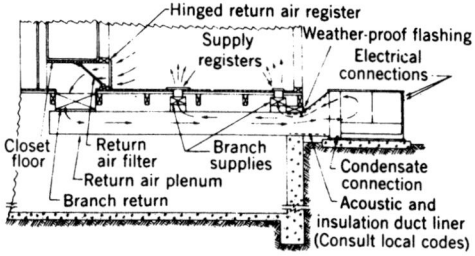

Fig 13-27. Unit in slab where building has basement

The reasons for this are fairly obvious:

1) The only connection between the conditioned space and the unit itself are the supply/return ducts, which virtually eliminates transmission of vibrations and reduce noise to a minimum; 2) the unit is very accessible for servicing, thus tending to reduce service cost and start-up time; 3) ground level installation requires no hoist or crane; and 4) if the condensate drain plugs no damage is done; in fact, in some areas a condensate drain line is not even required. Sometimes, a small rock-filled dry well is constructed next to the unit to take care of condensate.

Furnace Mounting: One finds self contained units mounted directly on warm air furnaces, usually in buildings where first cost is the prime consideration. Many manufacturer's have designed units to match specific heating equipment (Fig. 13-28). Others have modified existing packaged equipment by removing the evaporator blower and adding sheet metal parts so that the furnace blower may be used for both heating and cooling distribution.

Installation of this type is limited almost entirely to new construction, as this equipment usually requires an outside utility room and fairly large holes in the outside wall. A few are installed in a central utility room or basement, with ducted condenser air.

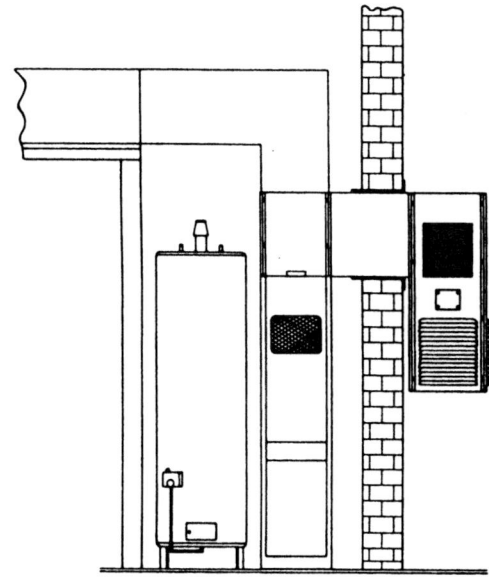

Fig 13-28. Warm air furnaces

Installation of Split Systems.—*Slab or Ground Level:* Slab or ground level installations of split systems are the most common for residential and small commercial and apartment buildings with only one or two floors. Fig. 13-29 is typical. While such installations place the major noise producing components outside the conditioned space, which is good from a sound level standpoint, the condenser becomes subject to possible damage from passersby, trucks, cars, etc., and here again, as with single-package units, the condenser blower tends to pick up dirt and requires more frequent cleaning. Also, condenser air flow may be obstructed by surrounding shrubbery, or trash placed near the air intake or discharge openings.

However, these installations are convenient to install, service or replace, and they add no load to any part of the building roof or walls. An added advantage is that they are generally protected by the building itself from strong winds that might affect air flow through the condenser.

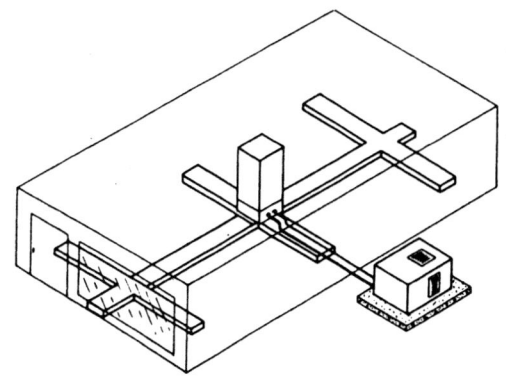

Fig 13-29. Through the wall self contained unit

To prevent flashing of hot liquid refrigerant, the evaporator should not be installed more than 20 feet higher than the condensing unit, which restricts the application to one and two-story buildings, unless extensive ductwork is used.

Through the Roof: Rooftop split system installations are becoming increasingly popular in commercial buildings (Fig. 13-30), as well as apartments and industrial (factory) buildings even though they usually require a crane for installation and may call for reinforcement of the roof in some cases.

However, the reasons for their application include that they require a minimum of connecting tubing (particularly if the evaporator is located directly below the condensing unit), and frequently a minimum of ductwork. Also they have the advantage that the condensing unit is out of the way of street or yard traffic.

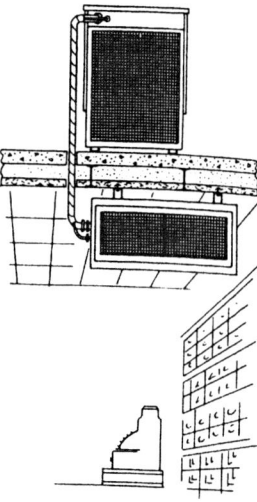

Fig 13-30. Split system with condensing unit on roof

Through-the-Wall Condensing Units: Split systems with condensing units through the wall are particularly well suited for individual cooling and heating in high rise apartments. When installed flush with outside walls, they do not mar the appearance of the building.

Zoning Unitary Installations.—*Single-Zone:* There are two basic ways to apply the unitary approach to air conditioning a large single zone. A decision has to be made whether to employ a large single unit or smaller multiple units. First to be settled is whether the area under consideration is truly a single zone. A single zone has uniform type and periods of occupancy, uniform exposure, and uniform lighting load. Seasonal variations in one compartment could create zones within an area generally considered homogeneous. Conversely, areas that are actually physically separated may be similarly enough exposed and insulated to be considered single zone.

If a building is new a designer may ask whether exposed ductwork will be aesthetically acceptable, and, if not, if it can be hidden. If it is old, one may ask is it easier to run multiple condenser piping or use the ductwork required with a single unit.

Many states require that units over a certain size or containing a maximum refrigerant charge must have an operating engineer. Obviously, this requirement would be obviated by utilizing multiple smaller units.

Loss of refrigerant can be costly. Use of multiple circuits or multiple units can minimize this loss, and further, will reduce the inconvenience and cost resulting from such loss.

Multiple units offer greater standby capacity than a single large unit with one compressor, but a single large unit with multiple compressors is even better in this respect than multiple units. The entire zone will still be covered in the event of failure of one compressor, although at reduced capacity.

Once a decision for multiple units has been made, the engineer must consider thermostat locations carefully. The thermostat for one unit should not be placed where it might be affected by the air delivery of another unit. It should only be within the lineal confines of the distribution pattern of the air delivered by the unit it controls.

Multiple Zones: Here again we find the option of single unit versus multiple units within the unitary approach. The single unit would be considered a central unit in this case, but it is still *unitary* in every sense of the definition (Figs. 13-31- 13-33).

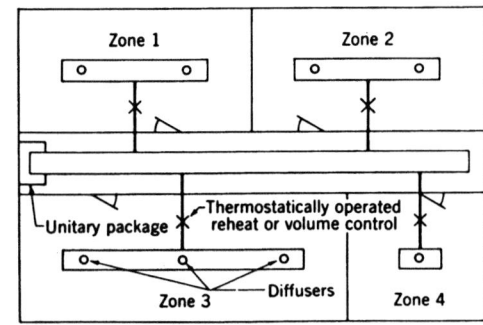

Fig 13-31. Single unit serves in multizone

Many of the factors listed previously also apply in the case of multiple zones, and these should be considered: new or old construction and the structural and aesthetic factors they imply; desirability of a specifying operating engineer, if unit size makes one necessary; and operating economy and standby capacity.

If the decision is made to use a central unitary system, a further choice has to be made between two possible methods:

1) A large unit with single or multiple compressors, connected to a duct system for proper air distribution. Zoning

in this instance will be accomplished either by applying conventional reheat or (less desirable) some means of throttling air in the individual zones for temperature control (Fig. 13-31).

2) A direct expansion multizone unit incorporating steam or hot water heating coils. Here hot and cold air may be blended according to each zone's needs by face and bypass dampers within the unit and delivered in individual ducts to the zones (Fig. 13-32), or hot and cold air can be distributed through a double duct system and blended at the zone in accordance with temperature requirements (Fig. 13-33).

Reheat or Volume Control: The reheat device, whether steam hot water or electric, should be installed in the duct take-off to a zone and should be thermostatically controlled from the zone.

If air volume control is to be used instead, this can be done at the diffuser outlet if there is only one diffuser serving a zone. If, however, the zone is covered by more than one outlet, air delivery should be throttled by a thermostatically operated dampering system installed in the duct take-off to the zone, as seen in Fig. 13-31.

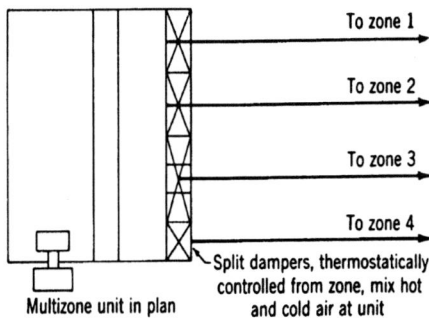

Fig 13-32. Multizone package can serve multiple zones

In certain applications, such as sporadically occupied conference rooms, it will be most economical to use a manual volume control for comfort regulation. And in other applications, such as a split office within one zone, manual volume control provides some measure of independent control at minimum expense.

Multizone or Double Duct: In a multizone air conditioning unit, the heating and cooling coils are placed in parallel with respect to air flow. With the individual duct method of zone control (Fig. 13-32), face and bypass dampers divide the flow of air over the two coil surfaces in the right proportion to control the temperature and humidity of the air delivered to the zone. For year round humidity control a humidifier should be included for winter operation.

If an application should be critical so far as noise is concerned (and system resistance is low due to short ducts and large diffusers), fluctuations in air delivery could cause noise problems and static pressure regulation would be in order.

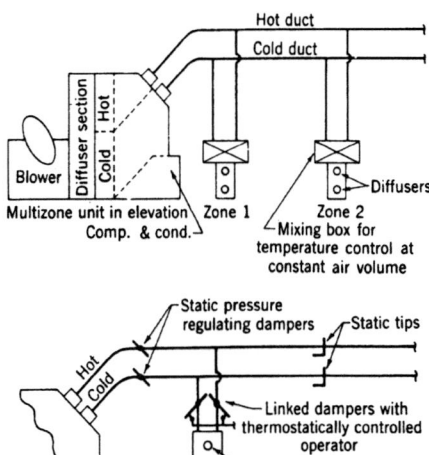

Fig 13-33. Multizone package serves in dual duct system

This contrasts with the double duct method, where some form of static pressure regulation is mandatory. Two variations of this system are shown in Fig. 13-33.

Controls: Multiple unitary air conditioner installations are often advantageously provided with a central control panel. This panel should include controls for starting and stopping unit fans (preferably by time clock with manual override), fresh air damper adjustments, manual summer-winter switches, and fan speed control switches, if fans are used. Optional features that may be included on the panel are: remote adjustment of thermostat set points; remote space temperature reading; pilot light indication of fan, refrigeration, or burner operation, and alarms for fan failure, burner failure or reset lockout, refrigeration overload or failure, condenser fan failure, or dirty filters.

The key to control centralization is simplicity. Only functions that are actually necessary working tools for the particular situation should be on the panel. For example, if unitary systems are roof mounted and thus not easily accessible, more panel indication is needed than for units mounted in an equipment room. Again, if the client employs regular maintenance personnel, fewer indicators and alarms are required than for clients depending on outside help. In such a case a centralized control panel to help a nontechnical building manager diagnose the trouble and decide whom to call will pay for itself in a short time.

Locating the Panel: Location of the centralized panel is important. In a store or other commercial establishment the manager's office is generally the best place. In a factory, the maintenance office may be best. The area should be well lighted and accessible, yet closed to unauthorized persons.

Ventilation Air: Because of varying ventilation codes and individual customer requirements, outside and return air plenums are generally fabricated in the field in situations where the manufacturer's standard provisions for ventilation will not meet the need. The most simple configuration of a ventilation system (Fig. 13-34) has a spring-return motor on the outside air damper. Whenever the fan is started, the outside air damper opens to admit a fixed percentage of outside air. When the fan stops, the outside air damper closes.

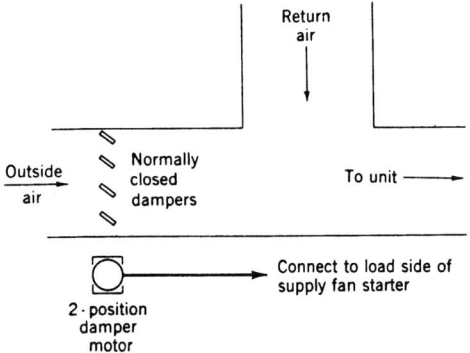

Fig 13-34. Simplest ventilation system

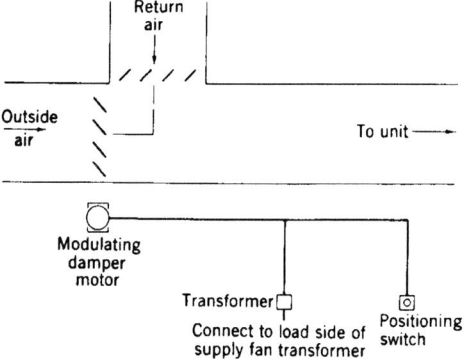

Fig 13-35. Most complex ventilation system with modulating damper motor

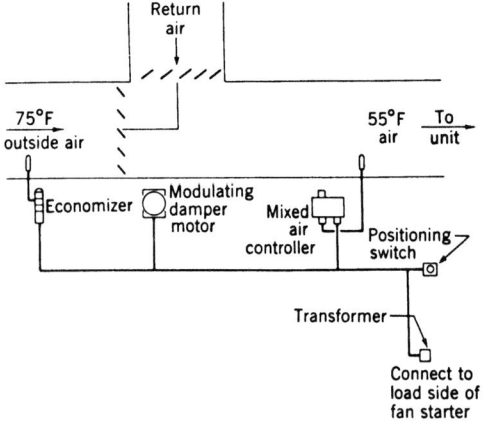

Fig 13-36. Outside air controlled from mixed air temperature

A more complex system (Fig. 13-35) replaces the two-position damper motor with a modulating motor. The per-

centage of outside air is varied by a positioning switch on the control panel. While the operator can open the outside air damper to 100% the modulating motor automatically closes the outside air damper whenever the fan is stopped.

An automatic system of ventilation control (Fig. 13-36) uses a mixed air controller to operate the damper motor, modulating fresh and return air dampers to maintain a constant temperature input to the unitary air conditioner.

Economical cooling operation is assured by an outside thermostat, which overrides the mixed air thermostat in the cooling season. The dampers are controlled by the centrally located minimum position switch. In the heating season this switch provides minimum ventilation required by code or extra ventilation if required for any other reason.

Locating the Thermostat: Nothing works better than a room thermostat properly mounted in the air conditioned space. However, in large spaces with no columns, or where store shelves cover all the wall space, the return-air thermostat is best. A return air thermostat should offer high sensitivity, fast response, low mass, and excellent repeatability.

An added bonus with electronic control is remote temperature reset. In the case of rooftop units, the problem of resetting return air thermostats can be thorny. A central panel with remote temperature reset can solve this problem handily.

Humidity Control: From a control point of view, a slightly undersized unit is preferable to an oversized unit. The undersized unit will keep the cold evaporator running, which is necessary for good latent heat removal. An oversized unit, cycling even in the hottest weather, will re-evaporate moisture into the air and increase the already high humidity. No direct humidity control should be attempted unless summer reheat is available.

Selection Procedure.—Recommended selection procedures vary somewhat with different makes and models of the self contained unit, but all procedures are basically similar. The following discussion and selection of a vertical, self contained unit will illustrate the method.

Before actual selection begins a job survey and cooling load estimate must be made and these seven basic items of necessary data compiled:
  1) outdoor design temperatures;
  2) indoor design temperatures;
  3) ventilation requirement;
  4) total cooling load;
  5) condensing medium and temperature;
  6) air delivery requirements; and
  7) external static pressure.

Once these data are available, the self-contained unit is selected as follows:
1) First a tentative unit selection based on the total cooling load is made. This selection is made from the manu-

facturer's catalogued nominal unit capacities (Fig. 13-36).

2) Next, the rated cfm delivery for the tentative unit is determined from a table of unit specifications and compared to the air delivery requirement. If the rated cfm delivery is considerably larger or smaller than the required cfm but still within 20% either way, the selection should proceed on the basis of the required cfm. If the two cfm values differ by more than 20%, a special built-up system probably should be considered.

3) Temperatures of the air entering the unit are then determined. Entering dry bulb and wet bulb temperatures can be calculated directly or they be obtained from a prepared table. In either outdoor and indoor design, temperature and ventilation air requirement must be known.

4) For units with water cooled condensers, condensing temperature must be determined. A tentative condensing temperature is established as approximately 30°F higher than the entering water temperature.

5) Next, total unit capacity and sensible heat capacity at the given conditions are determined for the selected unit. This information is obtained from the manufacturer's capacity table for the appropriate type of unit (Fig. 13-40).

a) For water cooled condenser models, the evaporator entering the air dry bulb and wet bulb temperatures and the tentative condensing water temperature are necessary (Fig. 13-40).

b) For air cooled condenser models the outdoor design dry bulb temperature and the dry bulb and wet bulb temperatures of the air entering the evaporator are needed. The smaller of the two recommended condensers should be used at this stage in the selection.

6) For evaporative condenser models, the average maximum wet bulb temperature of the air entering the condenser, together with the dry bulb and wet bulb temperatures of the air entering the evaporator, are required.

7) In each case, total unit capacity and percent sensible heat are read directly from the tables. It will be necessary to interpolate to get the exact capacities if any of the given conditions fall between the values listed on the capacity table. The capacities given in these tables are for rated (standard) air delivery only. If quantities other than standard are being used, correction factors will have to be applied to the tabulated capacities. These correction factors are given in a table such as the one shown in Fig. 13-37.

8) The final total unit capacity should not be less than the total cooling load unless a compromise in design temperatures can be accepted. If additional capacity is required, a new selection will have to be made.

a) For units with water cooled condensers, the tentative condensing temperature should be lowered 5 or 10°F and new capacities determined before a larger unit is considered. If the load still cannot be met, the next size larger unit will have to be used.

b) If the capacity is insufficient with the initial air-cooled condenser selection, the larger of the two recommended condensers should be tried. If capacity is still short, the next size larger air conditioning unit will have to be selected.

c) Since the condensing temperature and condenser size are more or less fixed with evaporative condenser models, the next size larger unit will have to be selected unless minor adjustments in conditioned air fan speed will provide for the increase in capacity.

9) After actual unit capacity has finally been established, sensible heat capacity is compared to sensible heat load. If sensible capacity is not equal to or greater than the load, a new system will have to be selected.

10) For water cooled condenser units, water flow and pressure drop through the condenser must be determined. Using the condensing temperature finally established and the total cooling load in tons, the gpm requirement is obtained from a condenser water requirement table (Fig. 13-41). When gpm through the condenser is known, the pressure drop can be read directly from a condenser water pressure drop table (Fig. 13-39).

11) The next items to be determined are fan speed and fan motor horsepower necessary to deliver the required air quantity against the calculated external static pressure. These values are read directly from the fan performance table. If the fan motor horsepower exceeds the recommended limits, a larger motor should be substituted.

Because vertical self contained units are available only in fairly large increments of capacity, many situations arise in which the actual load falls between two available capacities. For example, suppose the cooling load estimate sheet indicates a $1\frac{1}{2}$ ton load. The units which most nearly match this load have either 10 or 15 tons of capacity. However, a $7\frac{1}{2}$ ton unit plus a 5 ton unit can be installed to meet the load exactly, but the cost will be higher for the two unit installation. With an eye on possible future expansion of the area, the single 15 ton unit may be preferable. Or, if first cost is the major criterion, it may be best to tolerate a few warm days and accept the undersized 10 ton unit.

Whatever the case, it is always wise to check actual sensible and latent heat capacities of the unit against the estimated load. From a comfort standpoint it is often most important that the unit be capable of handling the entire sensible load.

If the ratio of sensible heat gains to latent heat gains (sensible heat percentage) is unusually high or low, a more detailed check should be made. This detailed check can be accomplished by use of the manufacturer's published capacity table.

To illustrate the application of the ten-point selection procedure outlined above, a hypothetical example is given below. Estimation of the cooling load is omitted from the discussion, it being assumed that ARI's convenient form or equivalent has been used.

Example 1: Select a vertical self-contained unit with water-cooled condenser for use in a general office in Dallas, Texas. Condensing water will be supplied from a cooling tower, and a free discharge plenum will be added in place of ductwork. No air delivery requirements are specified.

Solution: Data from cooling load estimate:

Outdoor design temperatures: 100°F db; 78°F wb

Indoor design temperatures: 78°F db; 65°F wb

Ventilation requirement: 300 *cfm.*
Total cooling load: 6.97 tons

Condensing medium and temperature: cooling tower water @ 85°F

Air delivery requirements: 400 *cfm* /ton = 400 × 6.97 = 2788 *cfm*

External static pressure: none.

Selection:

1) From Fig. 13-40 tentatively select a Model VW7 unit to meet the 6.97 ton load.

2) From Fig. 13-38 determine a rated cfm delivery of 3000 cfm for a Model VW7 unit. This is close enough to the required cfm.

3) Calculate the dry bulb and wet bulb temperatures of the air entering the self contained unit:

$$\frac{\text{Vent requirement}}{\text{Standard cfm delivery}} = \frac{300 \;\; \text{cfm}}{3000 \;\; \text{cfm}}$$

$$= \frac{1}{10}$$

$$T_m = 0.10 \times 100 + 0.90 \times 78$$

$$= 80.2°\text{F}$$

Wet bulb temperature at 80.2°F db with given mixture is 66.4°F (from Fig. 2-5).

4) Select a tentative condensing temperature: 85°F + 30°F =115°F condensing temperature.

5) From Fig. 13-40 determine total unit capacity and the sensible heat percentage. In this case, sufficient accuracy can be obtained by using 80°F entering db and 67°F entering wb for a VW7 unit at 115°F condensing temperature. Using the above figures, total unit capacity is 6.59 tons and the sensible heat percentage is 75%.

6) This final total unit capacity is less than the calculated total cooling load by 0.38 ton. By reducing the condensing temperature to 105°F and reselecting, a capacity of 7.00 tons can be obtained.

7) Since there is no specified latent heat load, sensible heat percentage need not be considered for this selection.

8) Determine water flow requirement and pressure drop through the condenser.

a) By interpolating between 6.5 and 7.5 in the *Load, Tons* column for a Model VW7 unit, determine a gpm water flow rate at 105°F condensing 85°F entering water temperature of 18.9 gpm.

b) From the *Condenser Water Pressure Drop,* Fig. 13-39, determine a water pressure drop through the condenser of 17.6 feet of water for 18.9 gpm. Next, size the cooling tower pump from the pump manufacturer's literature.

9) Finally, from the *Fan Performance Water and Air-Cooled Models,* Fig. 13-42, determine a fan speed of 800 rpm and a fan horsepower of 1.25 hp for a Model VW7 unit at 3000 *cfm* with ³⁄₁₆ inch external static pressure corresponding to use of a free discharge plenum. Since this is the rated cfm and there is no unusually high external static pressure, it will not be necessary to check the required fan horsepower against an *Electrical Characteristics* table.

CAPACITY CORRECTION FACTORS
To Be Applied to Cooling and Heating Capacities

Cfm*Compared to Rated Quantity	−40%	−30%	−20%	−10%	Std.	+10%	+20%
Cooling Capacity Multiplier	.88	.93	.96	.98	1.00	1.02	1.03
Sensible Capacity Multiplier	.80	.85	.90	.95	1.00	1.05	1.10
Heating Capacity Multiplier	.78	.83	.89	.94	1.00	1.06	1.12

Fig 13-37. For use where *cfm* per ton is not 400

SPECIFICATIONS AND GENERAL INFORMATION

Unit Model	Compressor				Evaporator Fan					
	Type	Qty	Hp	Rpm	No.	DWDI Size	Cfm	Hp	Motor	Rp
VW3 VA3	Herm	1	3	3450	1	10"	1200	½		34
VW5 VA5	Herm	1	5	3450	1	12"	2000	¾		34
VW7 VA7	Herm	1	7½	3450	1	15"	3000	1½		34
VW10	Herm	2	5	3450	2	12"	4000	2		34

Fig 13-38. Use in step 2 of hypothetical example to find *cfm* of model air conditioner tentatively selected

CONDENSER WATER PRESSURE DROP

Unit Model		Flow Rate, Gpm, and Pressure Drop (PD), Ft of Water								
VW3	GPM	3	4	5	6	7	8	9	10	11
	P.D.	1.7	2.9	4.5	6.3	8.4	10.8	13.0	16.5	19.3
VW5	GPM	5	6	7	8	10	12	14	16	18
	P.D.	1.8	2.6	3.3	4.1	6.1	8.6	11.3	14.3	17.9
VW7	GPM	6	8	10	12	15	18	21	24	27
	P.D.	2.2	3.9	5.5	7.8	11.5	16.0	21.2	27.6	33.5
VW10	GPM	10	12	14	16	20	24	28	32	36
	P.D.	1.8	2.6	3.3	4.1	6.1	8.6	11.3	14.3	17.9

Fig 13-39. Pressure drop water through condenser can be read directly from manufacturer's tables like this one

COOLING CAPACITIES—WATER-COOLED MODELS

Unit Model	Entering Air DB, Deg F	Refrigeration, Tons		Condensing Temperature, Deg F											
				95				105				115			
				Entering Air WB, Deg F											
				64	67	70	73	64	67	70	73	64	67	70	73
VW3	75	Total		3.22	3.40	3.60	3.78	2.98	3.18	3.38	3.56	2.73	2.93	3.14	3.32
		% Sens		71	58	46	35	73	60	47	35	75	61	48	35
	80	Total		3.22	3.40	3.60	3.78	2.98	3.18	3.38	3.56	2.73	2.93	3.14	3.32
		% Sens		81	71	61	49	83	73	63	50	85	75	65	51
	85	Total		3.22	3.40	3.60	3.78	2.98	3.18	3.38	3.56	2.73	2.93	3.14	3.32
		% Sens		90	82	75	63	93	84	77	65	95	86	79	67
VW7	75	Total		6.93	7.43	7.98	8.60	6.53	7.00	7.54	8.13	6.10	6.59	7.13	7.72
		% Sens		71	58	46	35	73	60	47	35	75	61	48	35
	80	Total		6.93	7.43	7.98	8.60	6.53	7.00	7.54	8.13	6.10	6.59	7.13	7.72
		% Sens		81	71	61	49	83	73	63	50	85	75	65	51
	85	Total		6.93	7.43	7.98	8.60	6.53	7.00	7.54	8.13	6.10	6.59	7.13	7.72
		% Sens		90	82	75	63	93	84	77	65	95	86	79	67
	90	Total		7.20	7.43	7.98	8.60	6.80	7.00	7.54	8.13	6.35	6.59	7.13	7.72
		% Sens		100	93	84	75	100	96	87	77	100	98	89	79

Fig 13-40. Use this type first table for tentative selection

CONDENSER WATER REQUIREMENTS, GPM

Unit Model	Load, Tons	Condensing Temperature, Deg F											
		95				105				115			
		Entering Water Temperature, Deg F											
		65	70	75	80	70	75	80	85	80	85	90	95
VW3	2.5	3.5	4.6	6.8	10.6	2.9	3.5	4.6	6.8	2.9	3.9	4.6	6.8
	3.0	4.2	5.5	8.1	12.7	3.5	4.2	5.5	8.1	3.5	4.2	5.5	8.1
	3.5	4.9	6.5	9.5	14.9	4.1	4.9	6.5	9.5	4.1	4.9	65	9.5
VW5	4.0	5.6	7.4	10.8	17.0	4.6	5.6	7.4	10.8	4.6	5.6	7.4	10.8
	5.0	7.0	9.2	13.5	21.2	5.8	7.0	9.2	13.5	5.8	7.0	9.2	13.5
	6.0	8.4	11.1	16.2	25.4	6.9	8.4	11.1	16.2	6.9	8.4	11.1	16.2
VW7	6.5	9.1	12.0	17.6	27.3	7.5	9.1	12.0	17.6	7.5	9.1	12.0	17.6
	7.5	10.5	13.9	20.3	31.8	8.7	10.5	13.9	20.3	8.7	10.5	13.9	20.3
	8.5	11.9	15.7	23.0	36.0	9.8	11.9	15.7	23.0	9.8	11.9	15.7	23.0

Fig 13-41. Use after condensing temperature is finally established and total cooling load, in tons, is fixed

FAN PERFORMANCE—WATER & AIR-COOLED UNITS

Unit Model	Standard Fan Speed Range, Rpm	Cfm	External Pressure, Inches of Water						
			3/16		1/4		5/16		3/8
			Rpm	Bhp	Rpm	Bhp	Rpm	Bhp	Rpm
VW3	728– 1113	1000	790	.24	740	.20	840	.28	920
		1100	845	.29	800	.26	890	.33	970
		1200	890	.35	850	.32	930	39	1020
		1300	950	.44		.41			1040
VW7 VA7	628– 904	2400	655	.61	640	.60	670	.63	700
		2700	700	.80	715	.91	740	.96	770
		3000	800	1.25	785	1.21	810	1.28	833
		3300	870	1.62	860	1.57	880	1.67	905
		3600	945	2.10	935	2.05	955	2.14	975
VW10	753–	3200	735	.76	705	.70	770	.82	810
		3600	805	1.01	785	.94	825	1.08	880

Fig 13-42. Example to find fan speed and fan motor horsepower for unit selected

Evaporative Air Conditioning

Refrigeration provides the best type of cooling, serving well where people are in close space in well constructed or relatively insulated structures. However, its first and operating costs bar it from the hottest commercial, industrial, and residential buildings.

Evaporative cooling is an economical substitute in many regions. It is 60% to 80% cheaper to buy and operate. Thus, it is practical for lower income groups in locations and where summers are short. Moreover, it cheaply cools hot, thinly constructed mills, factories, workshops, foundries, powerhouses, farm buildings, canneries, etc. where refrigerated cooling is prohibitively expensive.

Evaporative air conditioning includes air cooling by evaporation of water. When water evaporates into the air being cooled, it creates direct evaporative cooling, the oldest and most common form. When evaporation occurs separately, and the air is cooled without humidity gain, the process is indirect evaporative cooling.

Permissible Air Motion.—The more closely entering air temperatures approximate room conditions the higher the induced air velocities can be. When temperature differences are negligible, as with fan circulation, or outdoors, velocities of 880 fpm (a 10 mph breeze) are acceptable. Thus, since evaporative cooling usually provides air only 3°F to 6°F below room temperature, permissible room velocities are higher than is the case with refrigerated air conditioning.

Evaporative cooled air inherently creates few draft problems. When it enters, although it is 3°F to 6°F cooler, its humidity exceeds that of the room air and it cools skin by evaporation, proportionately less for equal velocity. Hence, its stray currents create fewer chill sensations, and higher velocities become permissible. Of course, full outlet velocity should not strike people directly, not rustle or blow papers in offices, etc. Thus, velocities under 200 fpm are recommended for sedentary workers, with higher ones used where necessary for manual and physical workers.

The designer of an evaporative cooling system can take advantage of the cooling effect of higher air velocities. However, it is difficult to predict how much the sensible temperature and relative humidity can be raised above those values considered comfortable at 15–25 fpm for a given increase in air motion. Table 13-1 attempts to define this relationship in terms of effective temperature. One degree ET is approximately equal to a unit of the *Temperature Humidity Index*, defined by the equation

$$THI = 0.40(T_d + T_w) + 15$$

where *THI* = temperature-humidity index;

T_d = dry bulb temperature; and

T_w = wet bulb temperature.

At 70 or 71 ET (or THI) most people are comfortable; at 75, at least half will be uncomfortably warm; and at so, almost all will certainly be very uncomfortable.

Table 13-1 indicates, for instance, that if a maximum THI of 72 is required, and if air velocity can be 300 fpm, one can design as if for THI = 75, choosing any suitable combination of wet and dry bulb temperatures that will satisfy the equation. The designer is cautioned, however, that the effective temperature and temperature humidity indexes are not always true indices of comfort. In the case of persons at rest or seated and performing light work, there is practically no difference in the sensation of comfort, at moderate temperatures between 30% and 70% relative humidity. Above 80°F, however, increasing relative humidities produce discomfort at an accelerating pace.

Table 13-1. Effect of Air Velocity on Effective Temperature at 50% relative humidity

Air Velocity, fpm	Room ET °F	ET Reduction Due to Velocity	Room ET °F	ET Reduction Due to Velocity
15-25	65	...	70	...
50	64.2	0.80	69.4	0.60
100	63.3	1.70	68.7	1.30
150	62.2	2.80	68.0	2.0
200	61.1	3.90	67.0	3.0
250	60.4	4.60	66.5	3.50
300	59.7	5.30	66.0	4.0
Air Velocity, fpm	Room ET °F	ET Reduction Due to Velocity	Room ET °F	ET Reduction Due to Velocity
15-25	75	...	80	...
50	74.7	0.30	79.7	0.30
100	74.0	1.00	79.0	1.0
150	73.3	1.60	78.5	1.50
200	72.8	2.20	78.2	1.80
250	72.2	2.80	77.7	2.30
300	71.9	3.10	77.2	2.80

Permissible Outdoor Conditions: Evaporative cooling performs well only in places where summer provides adequately dry air. The minimum humidity required differs with the type. Unstaged indirect systems usually require the lowest humidity, while textile mill evaporative cooling and animal cooling and *spot* cooling for factories tolerate the highest. Between these extremes, lie thousands of conventional direct systems.

Comfort cooling in all cases requires a minimum wet bulb depression difference between dry bulb and wet bulb temperatures of 22°F and a maximum wet bulb temperature which depends upon the effective temperature considered comfortable by the people in a given area of the country. A comfort cooling system is here defined as one that will produce comfort over 80–90% of all hot hours.

Relief cooling occurs whenever evaporative coolers maintain air and surroundings cooler than skin temperature (87–94°F) and circulate it rapidly regardless of drafts or humidity. It requires a minimum permissible outdoor wet bulb depression of 13°F.

Table 13-2 gives the geographic performance of direct evaporative cooling, tells whether a particular city is suitable for comfort or relief cooling by evaporative techniques and is based on available weather data for these locations.

Table 13-2. Performance of Direct Evaporative Cooling

City	Evaluation	City	Evaluation	City	Evaluation	City	Evaluation
ALABAMA		ILLINOIS		Valdosta	NR	Jackson	Possible
Anniston	Possible	Belleville	Possible	Warner-Robins	Possible	Gulfport	NR
Birmingham	NR	Cairo	Relief	IDAHO	Comfort	Meridian	Possible
Mobile	NR	Chicago	Possible	Vicksburg	NR	OKLAHOMA	
Montgomery	NR	Moline	Relief	MISSOURI		Ardmore	Relief
ARIZONA	Comfort	O'Hare	Possible	Columbia	Relief	Enid	Relief
ARKANSAS		Peoria	Relief	Kansas City	Relief	Muskogee	Possible
Fort Smith	Possible	Rantoul	NR	Kirksville	Relief	Oklahoma City	Relief
Little Rock	Relief	Springfield	Relief	Springfield	Possible	Tulsa	Relief
Texarkana	Possible	INDIANA		St. Joseph	Possible	Waynoka	Comfort
CALIFORNIA		Columbus	Possible	St. Louis	Relief	OREGON	
Bakersfield	Comfort	Evansville	Relief	MONTANA	Comfort	Arlington	Comfort
Blythe	Comfort	Fort Wayne	Relief	NEBRASKA		Baker	Relief
Burbank	Comfort	Helmer	NR	Grand Island	Relief	Eugene	Relief
Culver City	Relief	Indianapolis	Possible	Lincoln	Relief	Klamath Falls	Relief
Daggett	Comfort	South Bend	Possible	North Platte	Relief	Medford	Comfort
El Centro	Comfort	Terre Haute	Relief	Omaha	Relief	Pendleton	Comfort
El Toro	Comfort	IOWA		Scottsbluff	Comfort	Portland	Possible
Eureka	Comfort	Burlington	Possible	Valentine	Relief	Roseburg	Relief
Fairfield	NR	Davenport	Relief	NEVADA	Comfort	Salem	Possible
Fresno	Comfort	Des Moines	Relief	NEW HAMPSHIRE		PENNSYLVANIA	
Laguna	NR	Dubuque	Possible	Concord	Possible	Allentown	Relief
Livermore	Comfort	Keokuck	Relief	Manchester	NR	Curwensville	NR
Long Beach	NR	Sioux City	Relief	Portsmouth		Erie	NR
Los Angeles	Relief	KANSAS		NEW JERSEY		Harrisburg	Possible
Madera	Comfort	Dodge City	Comfort	Atlantic city	NR	Philadelphia	Possible
Marysville	Comfort	Goodland	Comfort	Camden	NR	Pittsburgh	Possible
Maywood	Relief	Topeka	Relief	Fort dix	NR	Reading	Relief
Merced	Comfort	Wichita	Comfort	Navesink	NR	Scranton	Relief
Muroc	Comfort	KENTUCKY		Newark	NR	Sunbury	NR
Needles	Comfort	Lexington	Relief	Trenton	Possible	Williamsport	Relief
Oakland	Possible	Louisville	Possible	NEW MEXICO	Comfort	RHODE ISLAND	NR
Oxnard	Possible	LOUISIANA		NEW YORK		SOUTH CAROLINA	
Palmdale	Comfort	Alexandria	NR	Albany	Possible	Charleston	NR
Pasadena	Comfort	Baton Rouge	NR	Binghamton	NR	Columbia	NR
Pleasanton	Comfort	Lake Charles	NR	Buffalo	NR	Greenville	Relief
Pomona	Comfort	New Orleans	NR	Canton	NR	Myrtle Beach	NR
Red Bluff	Comfort	Shreveport	Possible	Elmira	Possible	Sumter	Possible
Redding	Comfort	MAINE	NR	Hempstead	NR	SOUTH DAKOTA	
Riverside	Comfort	MARYLAND	NR	Newburgh	NR	Gettysburg	Relief
Sacramento	Comfort	MASSACHUSETTS		New York City	NR	Huron	Relief
San Bernardino	Comfort	Bedford	NR	Niagara Falls	NR	Rapid City	Comfort
Sandberg	Comfort	Boston	NR	Rochester	NR	Sioux Falls	Relief
San Diego	NR	Chicopee Falls	Possible	Svracuse	Possible	TENNESSEE	
San Francisco	NR	East Lynn	NR	Watertown	NR	Bristol	Possible
San Jose	Comfort	Falmouth	NR	White Plains	NR	Chattanooga	Relief
San Rafael	Possible	Nantucket	NR	NORTH CAROLINA		Knoxville	Possible
Santa Ana	Comfort	Springfield	Possible	Asheville	NR	Memphis	Possible
Santa Barbara	Possible	West Lynn	NR	Charlotte	Relief	Nashville	Relief
Santa Maria	Relief	MICHIGAN		Greensboro	NR	TEXAS	
Santa Monica	NR	Alpena	NR	Raleigh	NR	Abilene	Comfort
Thermal	Comfort	Detroit	Possible	Wilmington	NR	Amarillo	Comfort
Victorville	Comfort	Grand Rapids	Relief	Winston-Salem	NR	Austin	Relief
Williams	Comfort	Lansing	Possible	NORTH DAKOTA		Big Spring	Comfort
COLORADO	Comfort	Marquette	NR	Bismarck	Comfort	Brownsville	NR
CONNECTICUT	NR	Sault Ste Marie	NR	Devil's Lake	Relief	Bryan	Possible
DELAWARE	NR	MINNESOTA		Dickinson	Relief	Corpus Christi	NR
FLORIDA	NR	Duluth	NR	Fargo	Relief	Dallas	Relief
GEORGIA		Minneapolis	Possible	Grand Forks	Relief	Del Rio	Relief
Albany	Possible	Rochester	Possible	Pembina	Relief	El Paso	Comfort
Atlanta	Possible	St. Cloud	Possible	Williston	Comfort	Fort Worth	Relief
Augusta	Relief	St. Paul	Possible	OHIO		Galveston	NR
Macon	Possible	MISSISSIPPI		Akron	NR	Harlingen	NR

Table 13-2. Performance of Direct Evaporative Cooling *(Continued)*

City	Evaluation	City	Evaluation	City	Evaluation	City	Evaluation
Marietta	Possible	Biloxi	NR	Canton	NR	Houston	NR
Savannah	NR	Greenville	Possible	Cincinnati	Possible	Killeen	Relief
Columbus	Possible	Waco	Relief	Lubbock	Comfort	Spokane	Comfort
Dayton	Possible	Wichita Falls	Relief	Midland	Comfort	Tacoma	NR
Sandusky	Possible	Wink	Comfort	Mineral Wells	Relief	Vancouver	Possible
Toledo	Possible	UTAH	Comfort	Monahans	Comfort	Yakima	Comfort
Youngstown	NR	VERMONT		New Braunfels	Relief	WEST VIRGINIA	
Palestine	Possible	Burlington	Possible	Richmond	NR	Charleston	Possible
Port Arthur	NR	VIRGINIA		Roanoke	Possible	Elkins	NR
Randolph Field	Relief	Cape Henry	NR	WASH., D.C.	NR	Parkersburg	Possible
San Angelo	Comfort	Fort Eustis	NR	WASHINGTON		WISCONSIN	
San Antonio	Relief	Hampton	NR	Ellensburg	Comfort	Green Bay	NR
San Marcos	Relief	Lynchburg	Relief	Everett	NR	La Crosse	NR
Sherman	Relief	Norfolk	NR	Moses Lake	Comfort	Madison	Possible
Sweetwater	Comfort	Petersburg	NR	North Bend	NR	Milwaukee	NR
Victoria	NR	Quantico	NR	Seattle	NR	WYOMING	Comfort

Comfort: Climate is suitable for maintaining comfort conditions with direct evaporative cooling.

Relief: Climate is suitable for maintaining indoor conditions in the relief cooling range (no more than 2 ET above comfort range)

Possible: Climate data for area only slightly unfavorable or, if favorable, relief is judged doubtful because of proximity to coast.

NR (not recommended): Area unsuited to direct evaporative cooling techniques, but note, indirect evaporative cooling might be feasible.

Variable Volume AC System

Central air distribution systems for air conditioning are either constant or variable volume. In constant volume systems the volumetric rate of flow of air to a conditioned space remains the same, while air temperature is varied to maintain space conditions. In variable volume systems (sometimes called "variable air volume" VAV), air temperature may be held constant over a range of room requirements while the amount of air is changed to satisfy conditioning needs.

The variable volume system is truly an energy conservation system. Within certain limitations only the actual amount of air required to do the heating or cooling is circulated through the system. Savings in system initial cost and operating cost are evident. When air volume reduction occurs as a function of system control, good system design dictates equipment selection based on system diversity. Present day load calculation methods using computers permit fairly accurate determination of system diversity and therefore equipment selection. When equipment is selected on this basis the initial size reduction can be as much as 20 to 30% compared with constant volume systems. Initial equipment size reduction is reflected in initial dollars saved and in lower operation costs. In an all-air system, initial cost savings are almost directly proportional to system size reduction.

High lighting levels designed into todays buildings dictate requirements for cooling even in very cold weather. Solar and lighting loads may require full cooling, at a particular exposure, at any time of year. The variable volume concept handles this type of control problem very well. Where dual duct or reheat terminals are used for perimeter areas, supply air volume is reduced as the solar load diminishes. At the preset minimum volume some form of heat is added. Minimum volume is usually determined by heating requirements, although ventilation codes or air movement standards may take precedence.

For properly designed interior spaces, lighting loads automatically set the minimum volume. Except for space warm-up, a source of heat for interior spaces is not necessary. As lights are usually turned on while a building is occupied, interior space load fluctuations are caused simply by people migration. Volume reduction will generally suffice to offset people load changes.

Here we aim to calculate energy savings by applying variable volume, considering the effect of reducing flow on the operating characteristics of a system as applied to a specific building. A load profile for the southern exposure of this building is shown in Fig. 13-43. Maximum cooling load occurs at 2 pm and is 33 Btu/hr-ft² of space. Maximum heating load is 30 Btu/hr-ft² with building unoccupied and lights off.

Assume that designs are being made of a dual duct system and a reheat system for perimeter areas, and that a comparison is to be made between a constant volume and a variable volume design for both systems. Following are the design requirements for this building:

Room Temp. 75°F	Outside Temp.	Summer	Winter
		95°F db 78°F wb	0°F db
Supply air temp.	cold air	50°F	60°F
Supply air volume	*cfm*/ft²	1.2	0.6
Supply air temp.	warm air	80°F	95°F

Lighting load: 6 watts/ft² (30% of this load is picked up through light troffers and doesn't enter the space).

People: 1 person/100 ft².

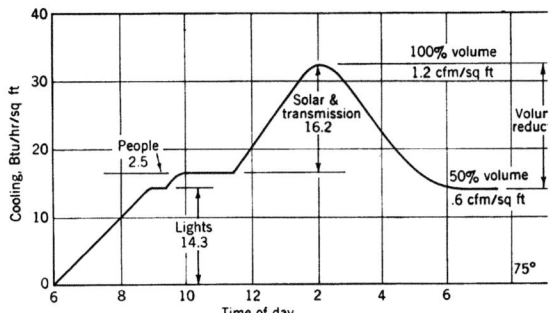

Fig 13-43. Load profile

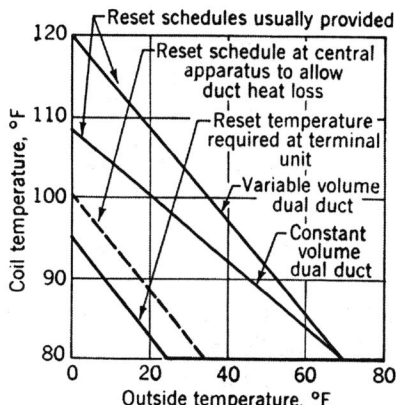

Fig 13-44. Load profile

From an energy standpoint a temperature reset schedule for central apparatus is important. It is general practice to neglect occupied operating conditions and the reset schedule is determined with maximum temperature selected for unoccupied conditions. This means that for dual duct system design, the temperature of the warm air pumped to the space is higher than necessary, causing the mixing unit to provide an increased amount of cold air to offset this higher temperature. Energy is wasted when refrigeration is in operation. Duct transmission losses are higher particularly if warm air ducts are uninsulated and heat losses due to mixing unit damper leakage are increased.

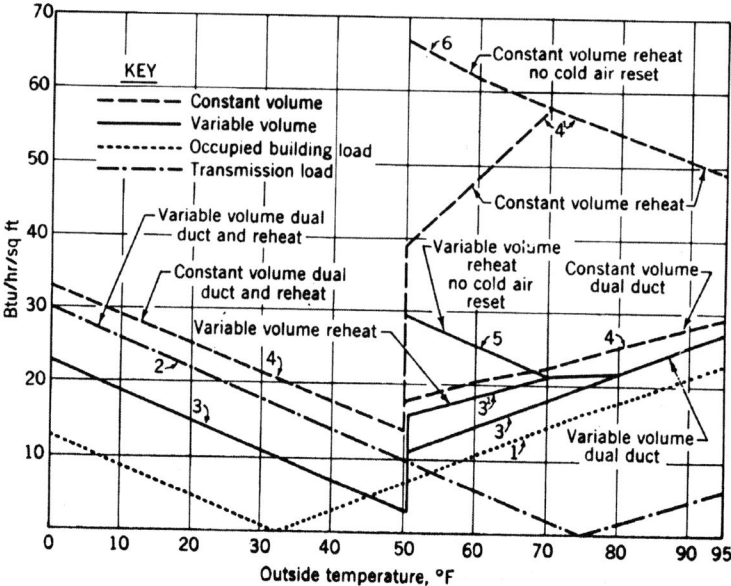

Fig 13-45. Energy requirements in Btu conditions - no sunload, southern exposure

A better procedure is to select the maximum warm air temperature with occupied conditions as the basis for selection. For example: the maximum unoccupied load is 30 Btu/hr-ft². Occupied load due to lights and people is 16.8 Btu/hr-ft². Subtracting 16.8 from 30 leaves 13.2 Btu/hr-ft² as the maximum heat loss, when the building is occupied. See Fig. 13-44 for a comparison of reset schedules. The reset schedule for an occupied building begins at 0°F outside and 95°F warm temperature and reduces to 80°F at 25°F outside. At 25°F outside, the transmission loss is −20 Btu/hr-ft² when the building is occupied, or − 3.2 Btu/hr-ft² when the building is unoccupied. For the variable volume dual duct system the supply air temperature required is:

$$\Delta T = \frac{3.2}{0.60 \times 1.1} = 4.85°F$$

$$T_s = 4.85° + 75° = 79.85°F$$

To be practical we should allow some duct heat loss, mixing damper leakage, plus possible unpredictable building leakage conditions. A slightly higher reset schedule would probably be provided (Fig. 13-44). Warm-up conditions require higher temperatures. The heating coil should be selected for unoccupied load plus any leakage of outside air through dampers, plus infiltration, plus cold mixing unit leakage. Maximum coil temperature could be made available by manual or automatic control for the warm up period only. For intermediate weather operation (50°F to 70°F) an unnecessarily high warm air temperature will require additional energy. For example, if the reset schedule usually provided for variable volume systems was applied, the warm air temperature, as indicated in Fig. 13-44, would be 92°F at 50°F outside. After refrigeration is on, the increased energy required, when compared to 80°F warm air temperature, would be 1.8/Btu/hr-ft², or an increase of approximately 16% in cooling and heating energy.

Initial Costs.—A comparison of energy in Btu required by the two systems (constant and variable volume) to satisfy the load profile of Fig. 13-43 is shown in Fig. 13-45. It is assumed that exterior and interior areas are handled by the same apparatus. This is generally done, particularly in small buildings, in order to keep the initial cost as low as possible. To keep energy costs down the cold air temperature is reset from 0°F to 60°F as the outside temperature falls from 77°F to 0°F. Fig. 13-45 shows energy in Btu/hr-ft² required to maintain 77°F in the space while the building is occupied and as the outside temperature changes from 0°F to 95°F. Where heating and cooling occur simultaneously, they are added in Fig. 13-45. Line 1 is the occupied building load plus transmission loss or gain. Line 2 is unoccupied transmission loss or gain. Line 3 gives Btu requirements for variable volume systems, dual duct and reheat. Line 1 indicates Btu requirements for constant volume systems, dual duct and reheat. Included in Lines 3 and 4 is the energy required to heat or cool ventilation air. The increase in energy from Line 3 to Line 4 below 50°F may be accounted for in the increased outside air volume required to maintain 60°F cold supply temperature for the constant volume system. If ventilation codes required a minimum outside air volume greater than the volume required to produce 60°F cold air, then the variable volume system energy requirements would increase by that amount. The reheat system deviates from dual duct both for constant and variable air volume after refrigeration is applied and outside dampers are closed to the minimum position. The comparison demonstrates the high energy requirements of the constant volume systems, particularly the reheat system (Line 4). The reason for increased energy requirements of the constant volume reheat system is the heat applied to maintain dry bulb conditions at reduced load. Notice the reduction in energy requirements below and above 70°F on Line 4. Above 70°F less heat is needed to offset the above mentioned supply air temperature of 50°F. Energy for the constant volume reheat system drops off below 70°F due to resetting of cold air temperature from; 0 to 60°F. If the cold air temperature is not reset, energy requirements would increase to 66.8 Btu/hr-ft² at 50°F with the refrigeration system running. This is 0.7 times the energy required by transmission losses. The constant volume dual duct system captures space heat for control purposes and is therefore considerably more economical above 0°F. Variable volume systems generally follow space load conditions. For the dual duct variable volume system additional energy required over and above load conditions is simply ventilation load requirements. At some point below 80°F the load is reduced sufficiently so that the volume of air supplied to the space reaches minimum. At this point heat is added to the variable volume reheat unit while the mixing unit for the dual duct system begins to mix warm air from the space to offset load changes. The additional heat required by the reheat unit below 80°F is indicated by Line 3. Line 6 indicate additional heat required by the reheat systems if cold air temperature is not reset to 0°F. Total energy requirements for the various systems are shown in Table 13-3.

Table 13-3. Energy Requirements at Outside Temperatures Indicated

Outside Temp. °F	Constant Volume Dual Duct			Variable Volume Dual Duct			Constant Volume Reheat			Variable Volume Reheat		
	Heating	Cooling	Total	Heating	Cooling	Total	Heating	Cooling	Total	Heating	Cooling	Total
0	...	...	33.0	...	...	23.0	...	...	33.0	...	...	23.0
10	...	...	29.0	...	...	19.0	...	...	29.0	...	...	19.0
20	...	...	25.2	...	...	15.2	...	...	25.2	...	...	15.2
30	...	...	21.2	...	...	11.2	...	...	21.2	...	...	11.2
40	...	...	17.2	...	...	7.2	...	...	17.2	...	...	7.2
[a]50	14.0	...	14.0	3.1	...	3.1	14.0	...	14.0	3.1	...	3.1
[b]50	9.4	12.4	21.8	5.0	10.1	15.1	14.0	26.4	40.4	3.1	13.2	16.3
60	6.6	17.6	24.2	2.6	14.1	16.7	15.6	33.0	48.6	2.4	16.5	18.9
70	2.0	21.4	23.4	1.0	18.1	19.1	18.2	39.6	57.8	1.7	19.8	21.5
80	...	...	25.1	...	...	22.0	14.5	39.6	54.1	...	...	22.0
90	...	...	27.5	...	...	25.7	11.2	39.6	50.8	...	...	25.7
95	...	...	29.6	...	...	27.5	10.0	39.6	49.6	...	...	27.5

[a] Refrigeration off.
[b] Refrigeration on.

The calculation procedure for obtaining energy usage for a condition of 0°F with refrigeration on and no sun load on this exposure is shown in Table 13-4. At 50°F transmission load is −10 Btu/hr. This, subtracted from occupied building load of +16.8, is +6.8 Btu/hr-ft². For the variable volume systems a supply air temperature of 64.7°F is required, and for the constant volume systems it is 69.88°F.

Table 13-4. Heating and Cooling Calculations 50°F to Refrigeration on No Sun for Southern Exposure Only

			Btu/hr. ft²		
			Heat	Cool	Total
CV Dual Duct	$\Delta T = \dfrac{6.8}{1.2 \times 1.1}$ $= 5.12°$	75–5.12	69.88		
		Heating	$(0.5 \times 1.2) \times 7.5 \times 1.1$	5.0	
		Cooling	$(0.5 \times 1.2) \times 20 \times 1.1$		13.2	18.2
VV Dual Duct	$\Delta T = \dfrac{6.8}{0.60 \times 1.1}$ $= 10.3°$	75–10.3	64.7		
		Heating	$(0.235 \times 0.60) \times 7.5 \times 1.1$	1.2	
		Cooling	$(0.765 \times 0.60) \times 20 \times 1.1$		10.1	11.3
CV Reheat	$\Delta T = \dfrac{6.8}{1.2 \times 1.1}$ $= 5.12°$	75–5.12	69.88		
		Heating	$1.2 \times (69.88 - 60) \times 1.1$	13.5	
		Cooling	$1.2 \times 20 \times 1.1$		26.4	39.4
VV Reheat	$\Delta T = \dfrac{6.8}{0.60 \times 1.1}$ $= 10.3°$	75–10.3	64.7		
		Heating	$0.60 \times (64.7 - 60 \times 1.1)$	3.1	
		Cooling	$0.60 \times 20 \times 1.1$		13.2	16.3

The $7\frac{1}{2}$°F heating rise required for dual duct systems is the result of return air mixing with minimum outside air (25% minimum and assuming perfect mixing conditions). Neglecting supply fan temperature rise, 72°F is the temperature of the air entering the heating coil. The variable volume dual duct system supplies one-half the volume of air required by the constant volume system at this condition. Approximately 75% less air is heated and 25% less air is cooled. As the reheat system is unable to take advantage of building heat (unless heat recovery cycles are used), this system requires 2% of the heating energy of the constant volume dual duct system and twice the cooling energy. Even the variable volume reheat system does not compare favorably with the variable volume dual duct system. The variable volume reheat system uses one-half the air volume and one-half the temperature rise for heating compared with constant volume reheat, reducing heating energy approximately 4 times. One-half the air volume is cooled and cooling energy usage is reduced 100%.

Although the analysis applies to only one zone, energy usage should be similar around the perimeter of the building when sun load is discounted. Winter energy needs are reduced from Fig. 13-45 loading as sun load increases for all systems. After refrigeration is turned on energy requirements increase for all but the constant volume reheat system. As the solar load increases less reheat is required, and therefore less total energy is needed. Fig. 13-46 shows energy used with full sun load on the exposure. The variable volume dual duct and reheat systems, Line 7 follow the same energy line at full sun load, as no volume reduction takes place under this condition. Lines 8 and 9 show constant volume systems energy requirements at full sun load: reheat system Line 9 and dual duct system Line 8. Conditions of Fig. 13-45 are superimposed on Fig. 13-46 in light lines to permit comparison.

Cooling Considerations.—Energy requirements in the building interior are purely cooling considerations. Cooling energy usage stops when the refrigeration system is off and outside air is provided. Depending on system design, this occurs between 50°F and 60°F outside temperature. When the building is occupied heat available within the building is sufficient to raise the outside air temperature to the design cold air temperature of 60°F. A mixture of 25% outside air and 15% return will produce 60°F. No additional heating for outside air is needed and free cooling is provided for the interior.

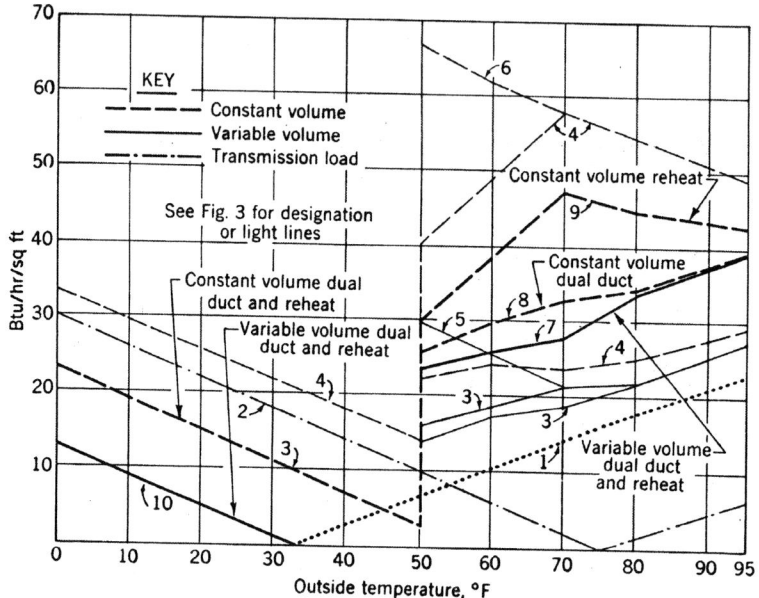

Fig 13-46. Energy requirement in Btu conditions-full sun load southern exposure

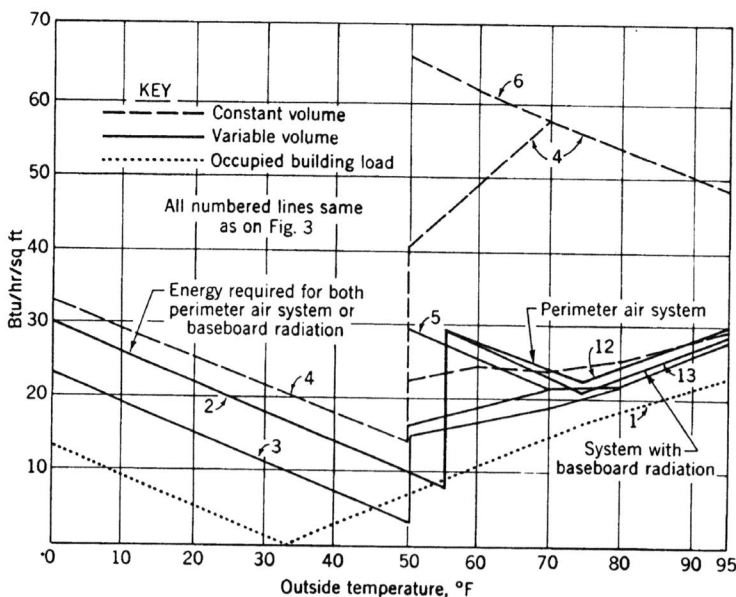

Fig 13-47. Energy requirement in Btu conditions-no sun load southern exposure

Some care must be exercised in equipment layout to prevent stratification of the two air streams at the central apparatus. Where stratification is anticipated and the design is for cold climates, some additional energy in the form of outside air preheat may be required. 25% outside air is generally enough for ventilation purposes, provided, of course, that this volume is sufficient to meet ventilation codes. If necessary a means of insuring minimum volumes at reduced flow may be applied at the central apparatus. Energy cost to provide interior cooling in winter is limited to the cost of pumping the air to the space.

Load fluctuations in interior spaces are principally caused by people moving from place to place. Interior load changes seldom exceed 20% of the total interior space load. Variable volume units can handle this load change with no difficulty and will produce some energy savings as the volume is reduced. Variable volume terminal units for the interior may be dual duct, reheat, or shutoff type. Since the development of variable volume regulating devices, dual duct or reheat types are seldom installed for interior spaces. While the system is operating on outside air, no cooling energy is required for the shutoff type. Volume reduction takes care of load fluctuations. Cooling energy is required after refrigeration is on and then only that energy which is required to exactly offset the load.

When the building is unoccupied, outside dampers should be closed and system fans cycled to maintain a predetermined minimum temperature. For winter, energy requirements will be lower than Lines 3 or 4, depending upon the amount of outside air leaking through closed dampers. The system is not generally cycled during summer operation.

Consider first the system using radiation at the perimeter. The usual procedure for most economical operation is to zone the radiation by exposure and control from outside dry bulb temperature. Two types of terminals are available for the air system. One type shuts off air flow completely and the other permits a minimum flow setting. Where the shut-off terminal is installed, radiation is sized to offset transmission loss while the lighting load is considered sufficient to keep the shut-off terminal open.

Some variable volume system designs provide either a separate source of heating at the perimeter in the form of radiation or a separate air heating and cooling system at the perimeter. The perimeter system is usually designed to handle transmission loads only. Solar loads are handled by the interior system terminals sized to offset solar loads when they occur, thereby providing a minimum volume at the perimeter. Fig. 13-47 indicates energy requirements for this design approach, and once again is superimposed over previous figures. As this is principally an interior zone system it is economical to continue the outside air cycle as long as possible, and eliminate resetting of cold air temperature. 55°F is selected as the changeover point. Heating requirements follow Line 2 (*transmission loss line*) up to 55°F. Heat required above the variable volume system (either dual duct or reheat) is the amount necessary to keep the interior terminals *open*. This difference could be minimized by balancing. This, however, is sel-dom done, as it is normally desired to heat the building perimeter with the perimeter system during unoccupied hours, thereby permitting shutdown of the interior system. Line 13, Fig. 13-47, shows energy required for the system using perimeter radiation and an interior variable volume system. The increase in energy below 75°F occurs only at the perimeter terminals and is the overlap caused by radiation in operation below 75°F. When the building is unoccupied energy requirements are at a minimum as fan systems are off and radiation handles the heating requirements.

The design with a separate perimeter air system will perform in a similar manner except that minimum flow may be provided in the perimeter system permitting interior terminals to cut off if the loads so dictate. With cooling capacity available at the perimeter, interior terminal size may be reduced. Since perimeter design is to offset transmission loads only, no zoning of the perimeter supply temperature is usually provided. The perimeter system is generally a constant volume system and temperature is programmed using the constant volume reset schedule shown in Fig. 13-44. Line 2 of Fig. 13-47 indicates winter energy requirement and Line 12 shows the energy required above 55°F for this approach.

Overlapping.—There is some overlapping of energy requirements unless the perimeter system is zoned by exposure. When the perimeter system is controlled by outside temperature and not zoned, the system is unable to take advantage of sun load shifting and tends to overheat areas exposed to the sun. Actually, no overheating takes place as an additional volume of cold air enters the space from the interior terminal. From a control standpoint the system works quite well. The increase in energy, Line 1 2 over 13, is the increased volume of air handled by the perimeter air system and the energy required to cool the additional heat in the return air supplied to the perimeter air system.

This discussion is somewhat theoretical. The analysis is for only one load profile at one set of varying temperatures, however energy requirements will be similar around the building at no sun load. To go beyond this by manual calculation is an endless task. Only proven calculation procedures and the computer will simplify the task.

As previously stated, many factors affect an analysis of this type. Comfort and economy of operation are not always compatible. In fact, some overlapping of heating may be desirable to insure comfort at perimeter areas. Capturing building heat and distributing it to areas where required will pay dividends in improved comfort and reduced costs. Large glass areas and/or poor building construction tend to defeat attempts to capture space heat and will add to operating costs.

To reach the conclusion that Btu savings are proportional to energy savings would be incorrect. Type of energy used, cost of energy, equipment performance under varying load conditions, etc., must be taken into account to obtain cost savings.

Varying volume permits operating cost savings as described herein. The most uneconomical point of operation occurs when refrigeration is first required. The dual duct variable volume system in combination with single duct variable volume for interior control is the most economical to operate of the systems discussed. The reheat system for comfort applications is extremely uneconomical to operate unless the variable volume concept is applied. With the exception of special applications such as hospitals or laboratories, constant volume is unnecessary for average comfort applications.

A single terminal providing heating and cooling as needed has the capability to provide the energy required, and only that energy to compensate for changing conditions at that particular zone or room. A split system (perimeter heating and/or cooling, with cooling system only for areas just inside of the perimeter) must overlap energy requirements for proper performance. There are several reasons for the overlap:

1) It is not possible to exactly offset transmission losses and, to be safe, a perimeter system is usually oversized.

2) It is desired that inside terminals be open.

3) Exposure zoning is expensive as solar compensators must be used, therefore systems are seldom controlled by exposure.

Perimeter systems, however, provide greater comfort and are mandatory in severe climates. The ultimate solution for comfort and operating economy is a single terminal installation at the perimeter either a mixing unit or reheat unit controlled from the space being served, with cooling only variable volume terminals for interior spaces.

The variable volume concept is a very simple energy conservation approach. It can be used with conventional heating systems or heat recovery refrigeration systems. The engineer must weight the cost of heating outside air from 55°F, 60°F to approximately 95°F, 100°F (including warm up costs) against energy required for the refrigeration machine plus the heating for ventilation air. A question to consider is wheather, if it is economical to run a refrigeration machine to cool a building interior and areas exposed to the sun when the same work can be done with outside air. An exception to this would be warmer climates, with high wet bulb temperatures, where refrigeration demand time is quite high, and/or special considerations where outside air might not be desirable.

Heat Recovery

Integrated Lighting Heating Cooling Systems.—

The following material on integrated systems and heat recovery has been excerpted, with permission, from the Electric Heating and Cooling Handbook, Edison Electric Institute.

Due to the evolution of environment control the ceiling has made an especially functional element of the structure. As shown in Fig. 13-48, it has become the principal distribution point for the elements of a controlled environment: lighting, cleaned air supply, air motion, comfortable temperature and humidity, and noise control. Thus, it provides the opportunity for integration of the lighting, heating, and cooling systems for optimal design.

A properly designed system will prevent much of the heat from the lighting fixtures from entering the occupied space and thereby reduce the cooling load and air handling requirements for the space. If this control over the lighting heat results in cooling the lamps and fixtures, the lamps will operate at higher efficiency, the ballast life will be lengthened, and infrared radiation into the space will be reduced. In addition, lighting heat can be used to supply some portion of the space heating requirement. The magnitude of the portion that the lighting system can supply will depend on the lighting density and the climatic design parameters.

Many systems have been designed for environmental control using integrated lighting-heating-cooling systems. Basically, they are divided into air systems and air-water systems.

Fig 13-48. Modern office environment computer, lighting, temperature, humidity, and air movement

Air Systems.—A typical fluorescent lamp emits 19% of its energy input as light and 31% as radiant heat. The balance, or 50% is converted or conducted heat. The energy represented in the visible light itself also is converted to heat. Fig. 13-49 shows the energy distributed from one type of fixture. In the air system, most of the heat generated is carried away from the occupied space by air induced to flow from the room through the fixture and into the ventilating system for heat recovery, if warranted, or for exhaust, if desired Fig. 13-52 shows a number of typical fixtures and the air flow patterns they employ to prevent most of the heat from entering the room.

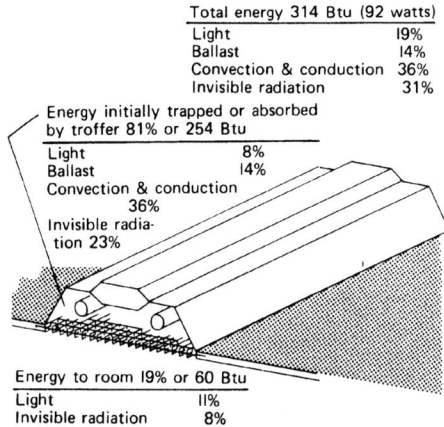

Total energy 314 Btu (92 watts)

Light	19%
Ballast	14%
Convection & conduction	36%
Invisible radiation	31%

Energy initially trapped or absorbed by troffer 81% or 254 Btu

Light	8%
Ballast	14%
Convection & conduction	36%
Invisible radiation	23%

Energy to room 19% or 60 Btu

Light	11%
Invisible radiation	8%

Fig 13-49. Theoretical dissipation of heat with two 40-watt fluorescent lamps and ballast (assumed 60% luminaire efficiency)

Typically, the 75°F room air drawn from the room through these fixtures will be heated to about 85 to 95°F, depending on air flow rate. Under many circumstances the heat in this air can be used elsewhere in the building. If the heat thus absorbed in the air can be confined to a minimum volume of air giving a relatively high temperature, heat recovery may be relatively economical and simple. On the other hand, if the heat is diffused in a large volume of low temperature air, heat recovery may not be justified.

Two basic air systems are currently used, with many variations. One general method supplies conditioned air to the office module and removes room air through the troffer and, thence, to the air handling and conditioning unit for recirculation or exhaust. Another method, the bleed-off system, wastes the return air if no heat is needed, or extracts the heat with a heat pump or other means if heat is needed for perimeter offices. Figs. 13-50, 13-51, and Fig. 13-53 show basic ceiling variations with these systems.

Fig. 13-50 shows an arrangement in which air admission and return air are separate from the luminaires.

The dual duct one hot, one cold supply hot and cold air to a mixing box above the ceiling. A room thermostat con-trols the proportions of hot and cold air supplied to provide the desired room temperature.

If the luminaire is suspended from the ceiling, 100% of the energy from the lights enters the room as heat.

If the luminaire is recessed in the ceiling, and the ceiling space serves as a return plenum, then only about 35% of the heat from the light enters the room. The exact amount of heat entering or removed will depend on air flow rate and fixture design.

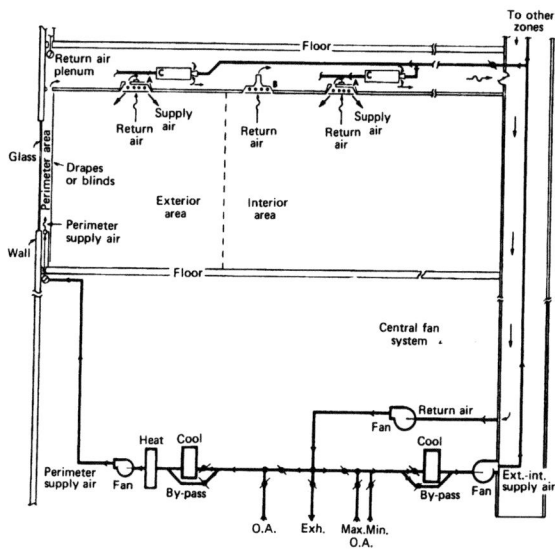

Fig. 13-50. Proportionate heat distribution from ceiling arrangement using air diffusers separate from lighting fixture

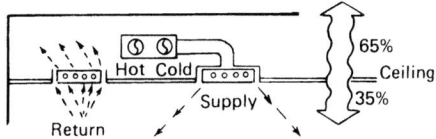

a. Separate fixtures for supply and return (35 % energy enters room)

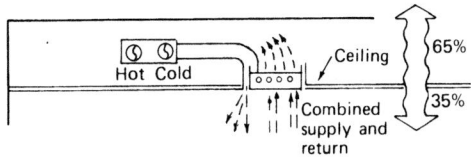

b. Combined fixture for both supply and return (35 % energy enters room)

Fig 13-51. Proportionate heat distribution from ceiling arrangement using luminaires for conditioned air supply distributions and return air removal in same ceiling system

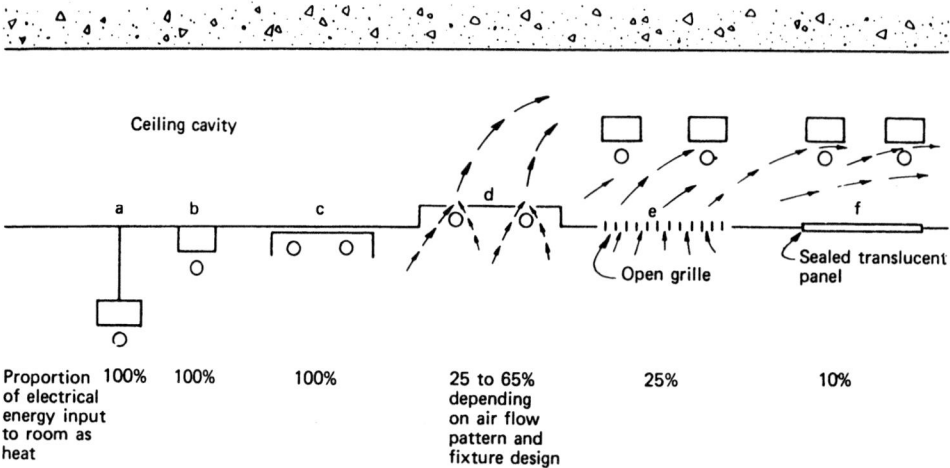

Fig 13-52. Proportionate heat distribution through luminous or louvered ceiling

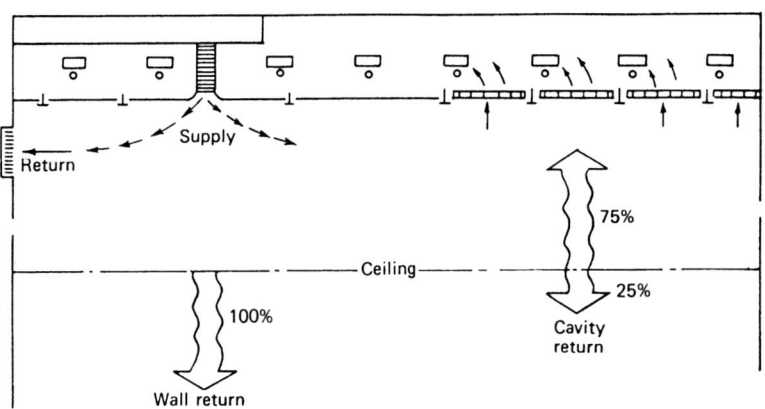

IES Lighting Handbook, 4th ed.

Fig 13-53. Proportionate heat distribution through luminous or louvered ceiling

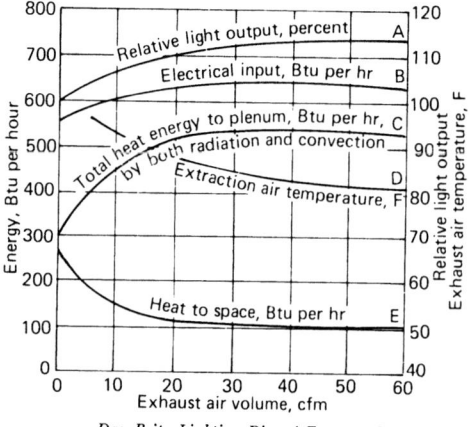

Day-Brite Lighting Div. of Emerson Electric Co.

Fig 13-54. Manufacturer's data on heat distribution
for a typical four lamp troffer

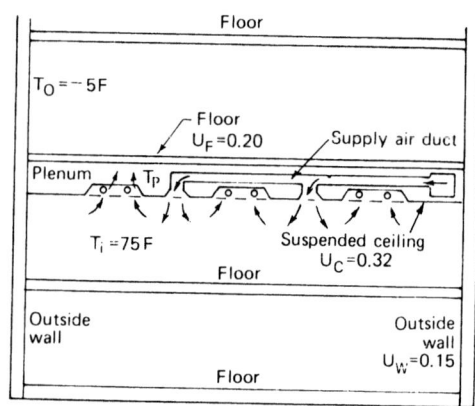

Fig 13-55. Typical plenum arrangement

If the return is through the wall, then about 45% of the heat will enter the room from a recessed luminaire. In Fig. 13-51 mixed air at a controlled temperature is supplied from the hot and cold air ducts to the recessed luminaire, which serves as the point of air distribution. Other luminaires in the room can serve as return outlets or return can be through a wall outlet. Most of the heat from a supply luminaire will enter the room. Less will enter from the ventilated luminaire used as a return. In Fig. 13-53, the light source is in the cavity above either a louvered or translucent luminous ceiling; all of the heat of the lights enters the room. But if the air enters from a diffuser and returns by way of the cavity, then only about 25 percent of the light heat reaches the room.

Manufacturer's of luminaires provide data on the air handling capacity of each of their products. The proportion of input energy withdrawn by the return air before it has an opportunity to enter the room is also provided by manufacturer's. Fig. 13-54 shows the heat distribution for a typical fixture at various return air flow rates.

Calculation of Air Flow Required in a Typical Office Building.—Selection of operating conditions for a combined lighting-heating-cooling system is illustrated in the following example:

In a multistory office building, each floor is to be provided with an illumination level of 150 foot candles. This will require a lighting input of 63.3 kw to each floor. To remove as much of this heat from the fixtures as possible so that heat load in the room is not increased unnecessarily, return air from the room must be drawn into the fixture. Thus, after the illumination level of 150 footcandles, and the fixture type and arrangement required to achieve that level satisfactorily are decided, the supply air rates can be determined.

The supply air enters through separate diffusers in the ceiling supplied by insulated ducts. Return air enters through the lighting troffers to the return air plenum above the suspended ceiling.

Assume outdoor design temperatures of:
Summer: 95°F
Winter: −5°F
Indoor design temperature: 75°F
Area per floor: 11500 ft^2
Perimeter of building: 500 ft
Electrical lighting load per floor: 63.3 kw
Other heat gains (human, solar, motors): 190000 Btu /hr
Return air rate per troffer: to be calculated.
Ratio of return air through troffers to bypass air: 4:1
(Bypass air is air that flows upward into the return air plenum without passing through the troffers.)
Return air volume for four separate floating panel luminaires per floor: 2.30 *cfm*. (This is to be added to Volume of air assumed for troffer return.)
Ventilation exhaust rate through toilet rooms: 1500 *cfm*.
(Not included as troffer exhaust but included in total air

supply).Fig. 13-55 shows a typical plenum arrangement.

The required air volume to remove as much of the heat from the lights as practicable to prevent its passing from the plenum into the occupied space is calculated as follows:

Assume a return air rate through each light troffer as 40 cfm. Thus: A_f = area of floor

A_w = area of wall

F_p = fraction of lighting heat into plenum (a function of troffer flow rate, from manufacturer's data)

D_f = duct heat loss factor

$\dot{q}_{rs}$ = sensible cooling load

cfm_r = quantity of return air (cfm)

T_i = indoor temperature

T_p = plenum temperature

T_o = outdoor temperature

$\dot{q}_l$ = energy input to lighting, watts

U_f, U_c, U_w = heat transfer coefficients, Btu/ft^2-hr-°F

Troffer Return	40×295 troffers	11800 cfm
Bypass (4:1)		2950
Floating panel return		2530
Return air volume		17280
Vent exhaust from toilet rooms		1500
Supply air volume, CFMs (estimated)		18780

The resulting heat balance equation is:

Heat gain by plenum = Heat loss from plenum

$$\dot{q}_1 + \dot{q}_2 = \dot{q}_3 + \dot{q}_4 + \dot{q}_5 + \dot{q}_6$$

The objective of this calculation is to determine the rate of flow of return air required to enable the heat removed from the plenum to just equal the heat input to the plenum:

Heat gain by plenum:

Heat gain from lighting $= 3.415 \times \dot{q}_l \times F_p$

Heat gain from wall $= U_w \times A_w \times (T_o - T_p)$

Heat loss by plenum: the sum of

Heat loss in floor $= U_f \times A_f \times (T_p - 75)$

Heat loss in suspended ceiling $= U_c \times A_c \times (T_p - 75)$

Heat loss through wall $= U_w \times A_w \times (T_p - T_o)$

Heat loss through return air $= 1.10 \times cfm_r \times (T_p - 75)$

Heat gain by plenum = Heat loss from plenum

$$\dot{q}_1 + \dot{q}_2 = \dot{q}_3 + \dot{q}_4 + \dot{q}_5 + \dot{q}_6$$

$$3.415 \times \dot{q}_l \times F_p + U_w \times A_w \times (T_o - T_p)$$

$$= U_f \times A_f \times (T_p - 75) + U_c \times A_c \times (T_p - 75)$$

$$+ U_w \times A_w \times (T_p - T_o) + 1.10 \times cfm_r \times (T_p - 75)$$

$$3.415 \times 63300 \times 0.67 + 0.28 \times 1500 \times (95 - T_p)$$

$$= 0.20 \times 11500 \times (T_p - 75) + 0.32 \times 9140 \times (T_p - 75)$$

$$+ 1.10 \times 17280 \times (T_p - 75)$$

$$145000 + 40000 - 420 T_p$$

$$= (T_p - 75)(2300 + 2920 + 18660)$$

$$185000 - 420 T_p = (T_p - 75)23880$$

$$185000 - 420 T_p = 23880 T_p - 1790000$$

$$24300 T_p = 1975000$$

$$T_p = 81.2°F$$

The corresponding amount of heat to the return air is:

$$\dot{q}_{ra} = 1.10 \times cfm_r \times (T_p - 75)$$

$$= 1.10 \times 17280 \times 6.2$$

$$= 116000 \ Btu/hr$$

But the total heat from the light is:

$$\dot{q}_l = 3.415 \times \dot{q}_l$$

$$= 3.415 \times 63300$$

$$= 216000 \ Btu/hr$$

Hence, the heat into the occupied space from the lights is the total heat liberated less the amount removed by the return air, as follows:

$$216000 - 116000 = 100000 \ Btu/hr$$

Other heat gains (human, solar, motors)=190000 Btu/hr.

Sensible heat gain to occupied space = 290000 Btu/hr. The supply air quantity to remove this is:

$$cfm_s = \frac{\dot{q}_s}{1.10 \times \Delta T} = \frac{290000}{1.10(95 - 75)} = 13400$$

However, this value for cfm_s is considerably less than the 18780 cfm estimated at the start of this calculation.

A second calculation was then made assuming only 25 cfm per troffer instead of the 40 cfm first assumed. This turned out to give too high a supply air quantity (cfm_s) compared to that assumed, hence a third and then a fourth calculation were made. This fourth calculation gave good agreement based on a troffer air rate of 28 cfm per troffer. The corresponding supply air rate, cfm_s of 14300 cfm, is

the amount required by this particular floor of the building. The sum of the air supplies needed for each of the floors, determined similarly, establishes the size of the air-handling equipment needed for summer design conditions for the building. For large, complex building requirements, the above calculation is best carried out with the aid of a computer.

Under winter design conditions, it will often be found that offices at exterior walls will require some additional heat even at the minimum air ventilation rate.

Controls.—Control systems used can be composed of a wide variety of available components and can vary considerably in complexity, degree of control, and in flexibility to meet the desires of individual occupants. Through control of air mixing dampers the individual room thermostats can control the proportionate air flow to and from each room and, thus, control the heat extraction rate from each room. The disposition of recovered heat, whether to reuse, to store, or to waste, can be controlled from appropriate sensors and controls at the mechanical equipment room.

Evaluation of the degree and the frequency of need for heat by the exterior offices under various weather conditions and of the cost of various methods is most readily made by means of a computer study conducted by or under the direction of the consulting engineer.

Integrated Lighting-Heating-Cooling Systems Using Water and Air for Control of Heat Distribution: As with the use of air alone, there are also many possible variations of systems using air and water. The advantages of using water are these:

1) Heat transfer to water tubes or channels near or attached to the metallic luminaire surfaces is very effective.
2) The heat absorbed in water is readily available to:
   a) be utilized at some other location in the building;
   b) serve as a heat source for a heat pump;
   c) simply be dissipated in a cooling tower.
3) Space requirements for heat removal systems are less.
4) The plenum space is cooler, hence less heat is dissipated to the floor above.

With water system there is still the need for air motion in the office space, hence some minimal ventilation air must be supplied.

Examples of Integrated Systems using Air Alone: One system, using air alone, which has been successfully applied to many office buildings, is shown diagrammatically in Fig. 13-58. Essential to its operation is the induction-type mixing box shown in Fig. 13-59. The single duct system supplies cold air, either filtered outdoor air or refrigerated air, to the air flow induction unit. This flow inducing unit, which is also the luminaire, induces the flow of warm air into the cool air by the jet action of the accelerated jet of cool air passing through the unit. The resulting mixture of tempered air is then distributed through the ceiling to the room.

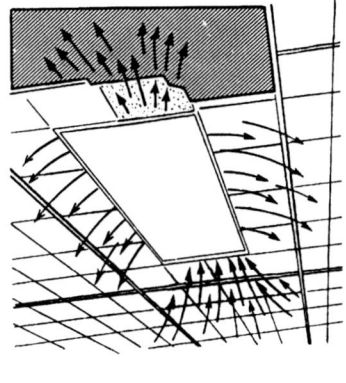

Fig 13-56. Combination of supply and return air and lighting luminaire

Fig. 13-56 illustrates the action, viewed from the room, of the air leaving and entering the room under the action of the air induction unit. Where full cooling is needed in the space, all of the warm room air is returned to the main ventilating fan, carrying with it most of the heat from the lights. When needed, this warm air can be circulated to the perimeter offices to supply the heat lost through the walls and windows.

Air Water Systems.—The use of non-refrigerated water to cool luminaires designed for that method enables reduction of conditioned air flow to that quantity needed for removal of the heat released by occupants, office machines, solar load, and the reduced heat from the lamps and fixtures.

Fig. 13-60 shows simplified diagrams of a typical air-water system. On cold days the warmed water can be raised in temperature by an electric resistance heater, or in a heat pump from which the hot water can be circulated to the perimeter for heating. On warm days, the heat in water from the luminaires and thermal louvers can be dissipated from the evaporative cooler.

The conditioned ventilating air can be introduced to the offices through separate diffusers or through water-cooled luminaires. This air can also be used to induce mixing with recirculated room air as shown in Fig. 13-57.

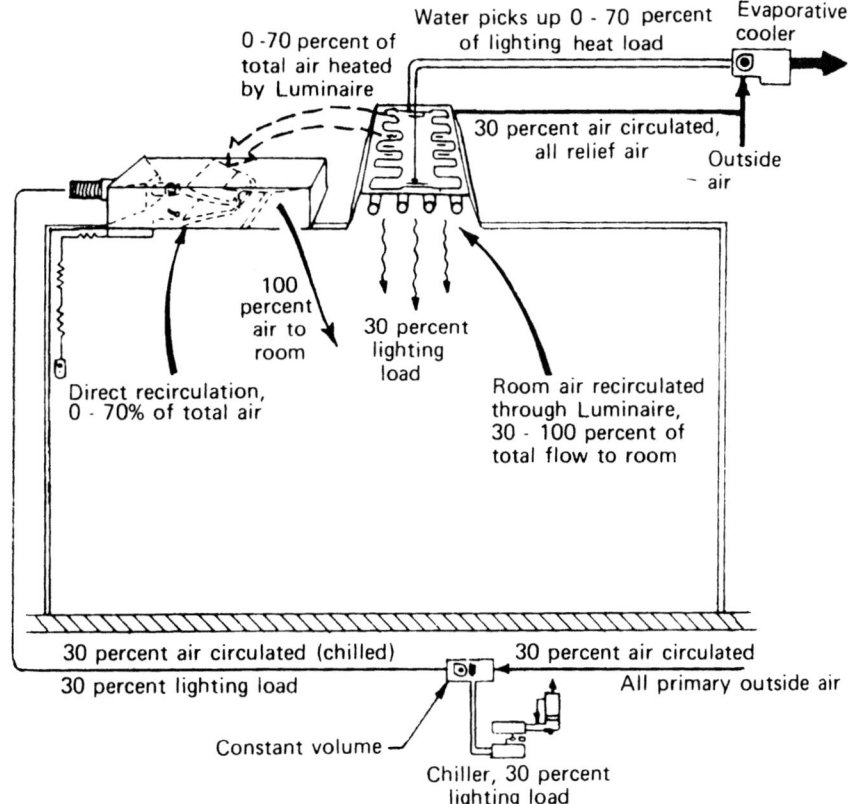

Fig 13-57. Patterns of heat flow and water flow for system

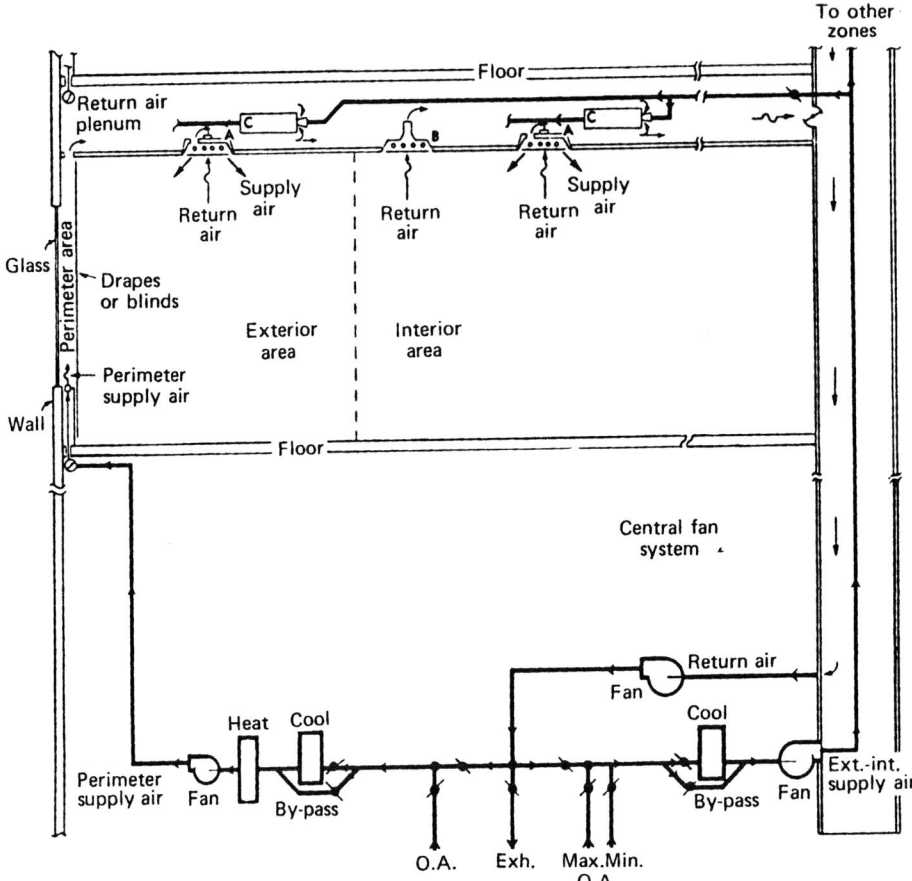

Fig 13-58. Typical air system using induction type mixing units

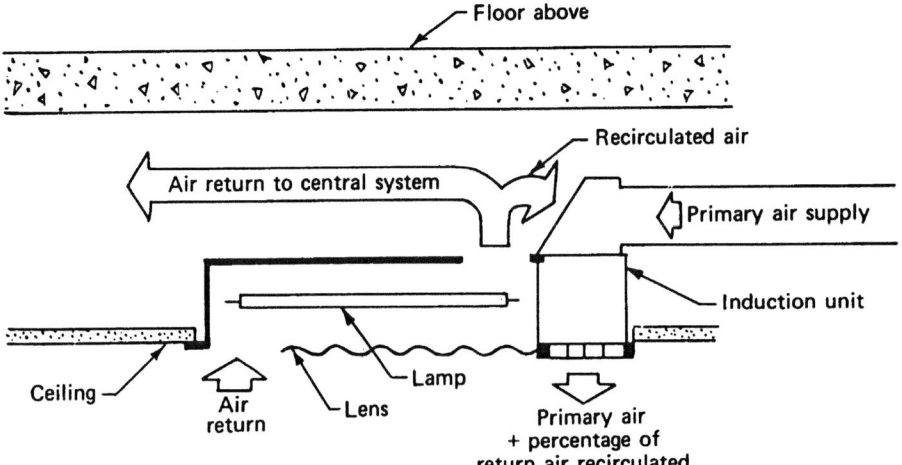

Fig 13-59. Air cooled luminaire application

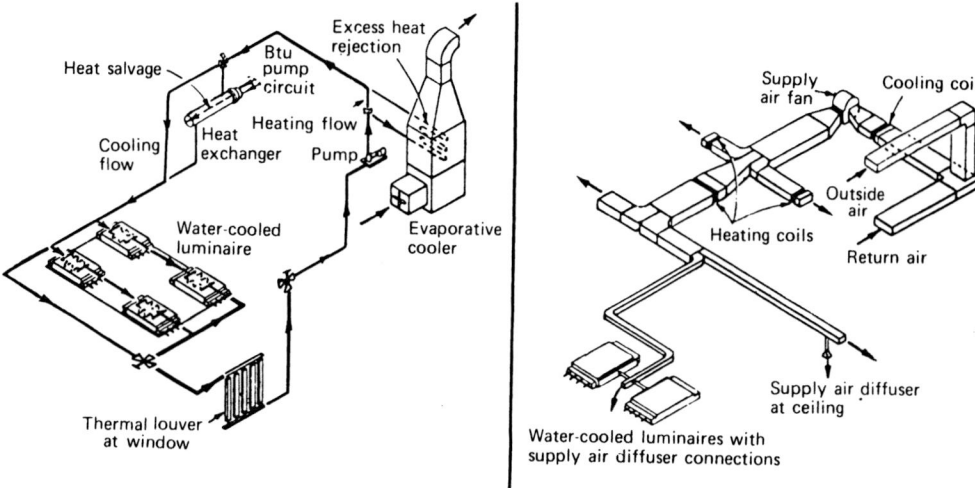

Fig 13-60. Integrated system operation

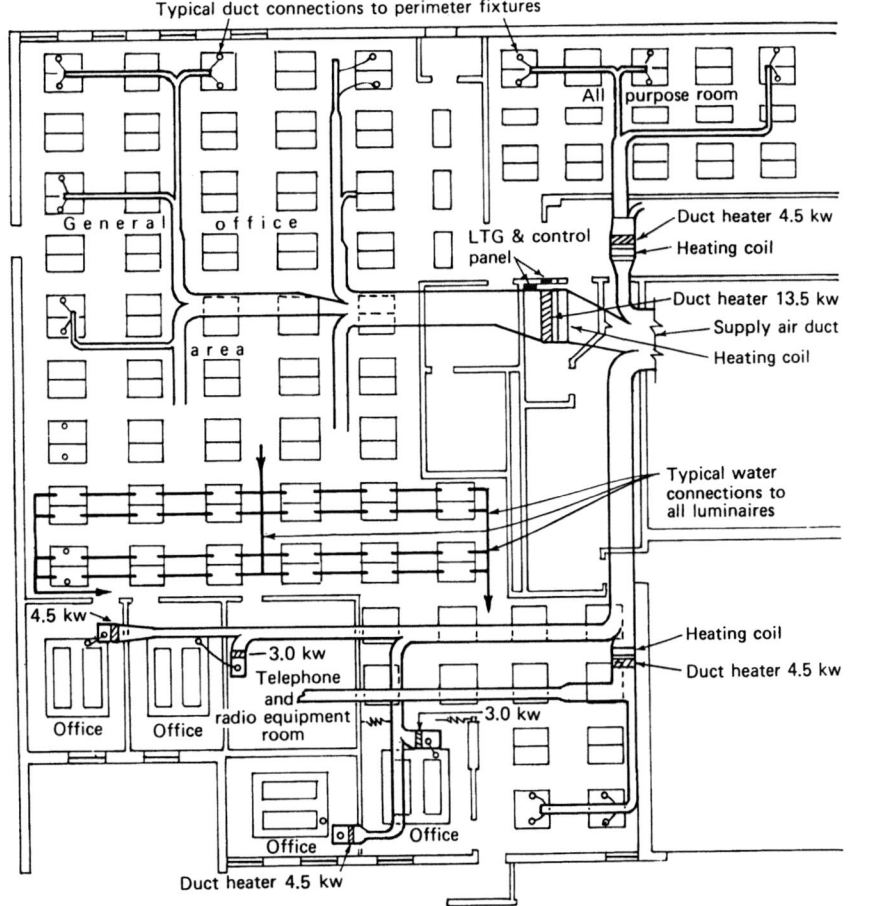

Fig 13-61. Integrated heat by light application

Sources of Internal Heat

Some of the heat energy released by lights, appliances, and production machinery, or heat energy otherwise made available in buildings, can often be recovered or redistributed for reuse at points in the building that need additional heat. Thus, the heat released from lighting fixtures, as described previously, is frequently used to provide the energy for heating the perimeter areas of the building. Also, the heat in the exhaust air from ventilating systems can be recovered by various methods for return to the building at points where heat is needed.

The principal sources of internal heat in modern buildings are lights, office and production machines, and occupants. In addition, windows exposed to sunlight act as heat traps because the solar radiation passes inward through the glass much more readily than incoming heat can be reradiated outward. If this solar heat, and/or internally generated heat, results in an excess of heat in the affected rooms, cooling must be provided to maintain comfort conditions and the heat which is thus removed may then be stored or utilized elsewhere in the building. Table 7-2 provides typical heat release rates from various sources of internal heat gain.

The internal heat gains within buildings are usually absorbed by circulating air, circulating water or, in some cases of small buildings, by direct-expansion refrigeration.

After the internal heat has been absorbed in circulating air, water, or refrigerant, it must be utilized, stored, or discharged. A wide variety of systems is available for handling these alternatives. In some cases, the heat may be recovered by a simple regenerative air heater or stored in enclosed reservoirs of water. However, the heat collected from the internal heat sources by means of circulating air, water, or refrigerant cannot be directly utilized for comfort heating because its temperature usually is too low. For example, the air leaving luminaires is usually heated to the range of 85 to 95°F. In some winter climates this temperature range is too low for use in comfort heating directly. However, the temperature of the air or water can be increased by means of a refrigeration system acting on the heat pump principle.

Thus, wherever a building requires refrigeration for summer cooling, and hence must have refrigeration equipment installed, by appropriate design the central refrigeration system can be used during the winter to raise the temperature of water or air carrying the recovered heat. Furthermore, where a building requires simultaneous heating and cooling because of intense solar heating on the south side of the building on clear winter days, the central refrigeration system can simultaneously serve both the heating and cooling needs of the building without requiring any additional energy beyond that required to drive the refrigeration equipment.

Example of Heat Recovery Using Air or Water to Absorb the Internal Heat Gains: Fig. 13-62 is a schematic diagram of the system installed in an office building in which the heat from the internal heat gains is first absorbed in air, then is transferred to water by means of a duct coil for return to the refrigeration condenser to be heated to a useful temperature level. The heated water is then circulated to heating coils serving the perimeter areas of the building.

If some of the internal heat in the structure is absorbed by water, such as in water cooled lighting fixtures or in water cooled machinery, the warmed water can be pumped directly to the condenser for further heating. From the condenser the heated water can be distributed to points in the perimeter zone needing heat.

Under intermediate or summer weather conditions where the building requires heating only part of the 24-hour day, the internal heat collected can be circulated in water to a cooling tower or pond to be dissipated outdoors or to a water storage tank to be stored for later use for night time or weekend heating of the building.

Fig. 13-64 is a diagram of the heat recovery system for a two-story, 95000 ft² office laboratory building. The heat from the central core is collected by return air passing through the ceiling luminaires. Water coils in the return duct system extract this heat and the warmed water then conveys the recovered heat to either of two refrigeration condensers where it is heated to as high as 130°F. The heated water is then pumped to the peripheral zones for heating, or to the 150,000-gallon storage tank to be held available for later use.

The operating temperature range for the storage tank is considered to be from a high of 125°F down to 45°F. This 80°F range represents a total heat storage capacity of 100 million Btu. The designer arranges to utilize the first 25 million Btu of this stored heat directly, by circulating the stored water to the peripheral zone until the storage tank water temperature is reduced to 105°F. Below that temperature water is first passed through the refrigeration condenser to be heated to at least 105°F before being used for comfort heating.

This use of the refrigeration system to lift the temperature level of water from the storage tank to a point suitable for comfort heating is sometimes referred to as *operating the refrigeration system with a false load.* In effect, in the system described, this false loading technique not only makes available the full 100 million Btu held in the storage tank, but adds to it the heat of compression, making additional heat available for off-peak night time and weekend heating, when most of the unoccupied buildings lighting system may be off.

Heat from Service Refrigeration.—Supermarkets and similar enterprises using large amounts of refrigeration supplied from central condensing units are uniquely fitted for space heating by means of the heat discharged from the condensers. This heat can be absorbed in circulating water for distribution to unit heaters, convectors, duct coils, or baseboard radiation for comfort heating. Fig. 13-67 shows a diagram for a heat recovery installation in a supermarket. In some cases the recovery is through a single central condensing unit. In other cases, where the refrigeration load is handled by a series of condensing units, the condenser of each unit is connected to the heat recovery water loop.

In some cases the recovered heat is sufficient to supply all the comfort heating needs; in others, supplementary heat must be provided. Fig. 13-66 shows the approximate percentage of the heating load that can be supplied by recovered heat for supermarkets in various zones.

Exhaust Air Heat Recovery Systems.—If the exhaust air from a building is discharged from only a few concentrated points, the heat ordinarily lost in such a discharge can largely be recovered by the use of an air-to-air heater to heat the incoming ventilating air. Or in the summer, the same exchanger can be used to partially cool the incoming ventilating air. The heat exchanger can be a static or rotating air-to air type, or it can consist of two liquid-air heat exchangers, one in each air stream with liquid circulating between them.

Fig. 13-63 indicates the principle of the rotary air-to-air heat exchanger. The slowly rotating wheel is packed with corrosion-resistant metallic fabric or fibers through which the air is forced by ventilating tans. As the warm exhaust air leaves the building in the winter through one-half of the packing in the wheel, it gives up most of its heat to the metal fibers. Then, as these fibers are carried by the rotation of the wheel into the duct through which the incoming outdoor air is flowing, the fibers release their heat to raise the temperature of that incoming air. Heat-reclaiming efficiencies up to 80% can be attained by these devices. By means of closely fitting flexible seals separating the two air passages, the air leakage between them can be held to less than 2%. Experience has shown that such equipment can be safely applied to heat recovery from hospital exhaust air without risk of significant air contamination.

Fig. 13-65 shows schematically the application of a rotary regenerative exchanger. In the winter, outdoor air is taken in at 10°F and heated by the rotating wheel to 62°F. In the summer, 95°F intake air is cooled by the same wheel to 79°F. Further cooling and the necessary dehumidification then occurs in the conventional duct coil.

The following tabulation shows the estimated design load saving that can be achieved through the application of the recovery system shown in Fig. 13-65.

Ventilation Air Heating, Winter	Temperature rise	Heat Required Btu/hr per 1000 cfm
Without regenerator	65°F	70,200
With regenerator	13°F	14,000
Saving in design heating load		56,200 Btu/hr per 1000 cfm

Ventilation Air Cooling, Summer	Temperature rise	Heat Required Btu/hr per 1000 cfm
Without regenerator	20°F	21,600
With regenerator	4°F	4,320
Saving in design heating load		1.44 tons per 1000 cfm of outdoor ventilating air

The above calculation is based on saving insensible heat only. The use of a regenerator having a chemical moisture adsorbent coating on its surfaces will increase the potential saving by transferring moisture between the two air streams, resulting in retaining moisture within the system in the winter and reducing the incoming air moisture in the summer.

An important requirement in the economic application of rotary regenerators to heat recovery for occupied buildings is that the intake and exhaust ports must be near to each other so that extensive special ductwork is not needed to bring the two air streams to the wheel. However, a closed system that avoids this limitation is known as the *run around* system. In this arrangement the heat is extracted from one air stream by means of an air-to-liquid heat exchanger. Then, by means of a pump, the heat exchange liquid is passed to a similar coil located in the other air stream. By the use of heavy thermal insulation on the connecting piping and pump, the loss of recovered heat is minimal. To permit operation during freezing conditions, the run around system is filled with antifreeze solution.

Although the run around system permits a more flexible air-duct arrangement, the introduction of two air-to-liquid heat transfer units in the heat recovery path may require a large heat transfer surface to provide sufficient heating or cooling of the ventilating air. Thus, in applying the run around principle for heat recovery, the data of the coil manufacturer should be considered regarding air-to-liquid heat transfer and pressure loss characteristics to assure that ample coil and air blower capacities are selected.

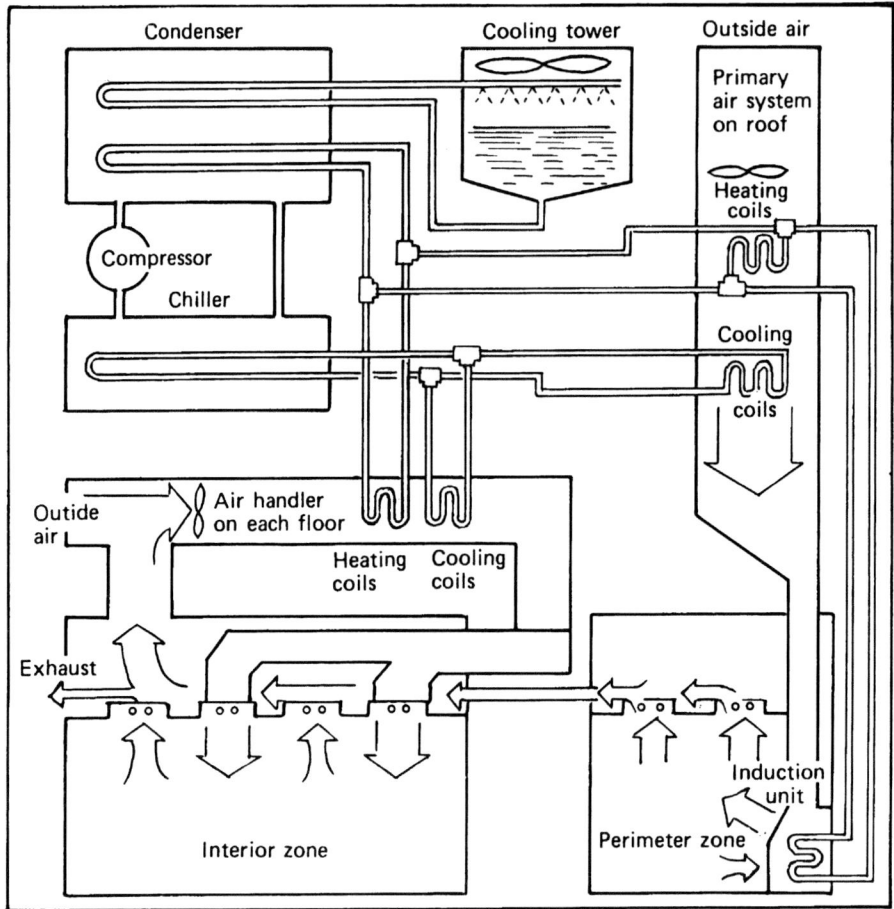

Fig 13-62. Schematic diagram of heat recovery system using split condenser as installed in an office building

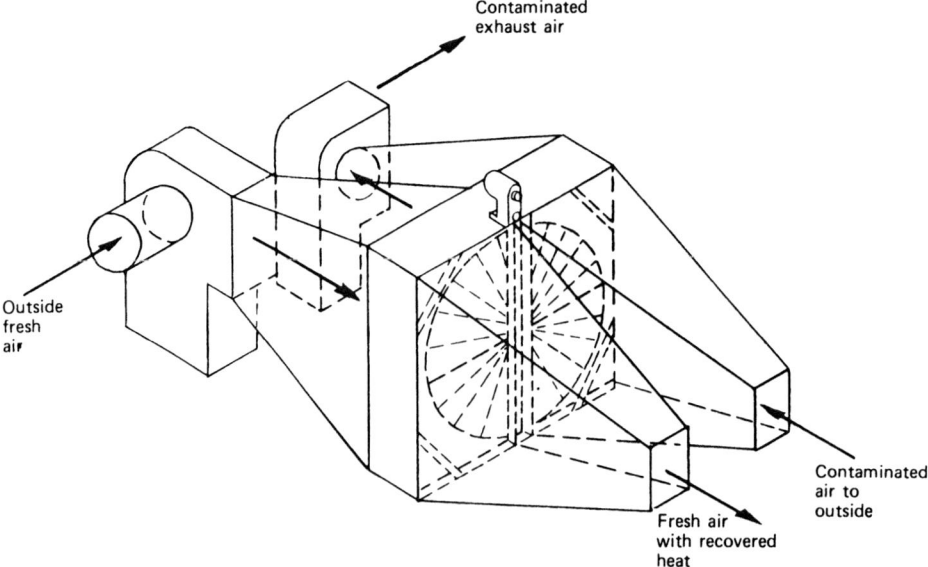

Fig 13-63. Diagram of regenerative heat recovery system

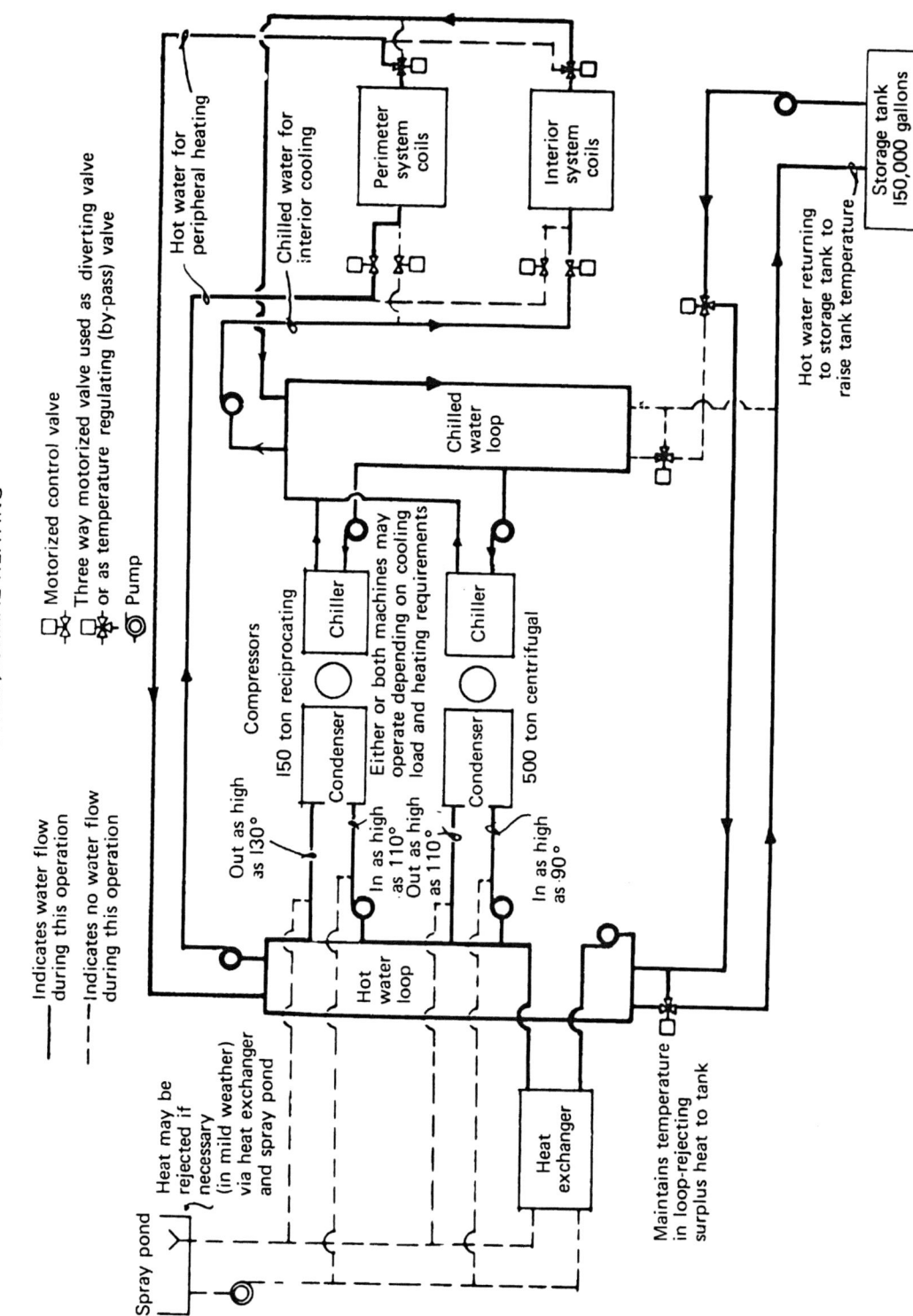

Fig 13-64. Piping system for heat recovery and storage system

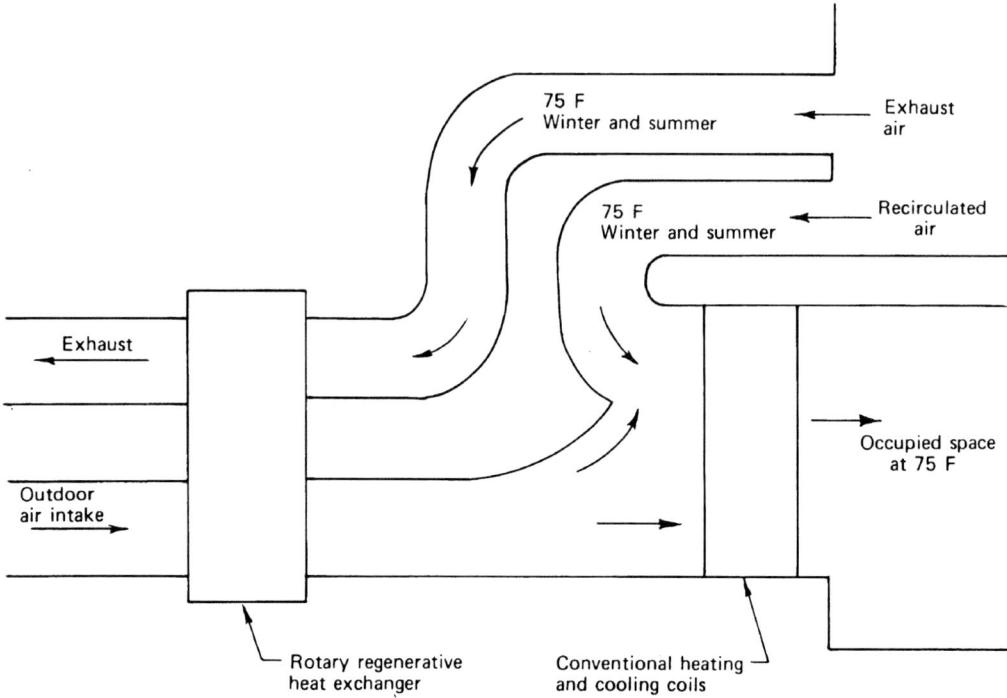

Fig 13-65. Diagram of heat recovery system using rotary heat exchanger

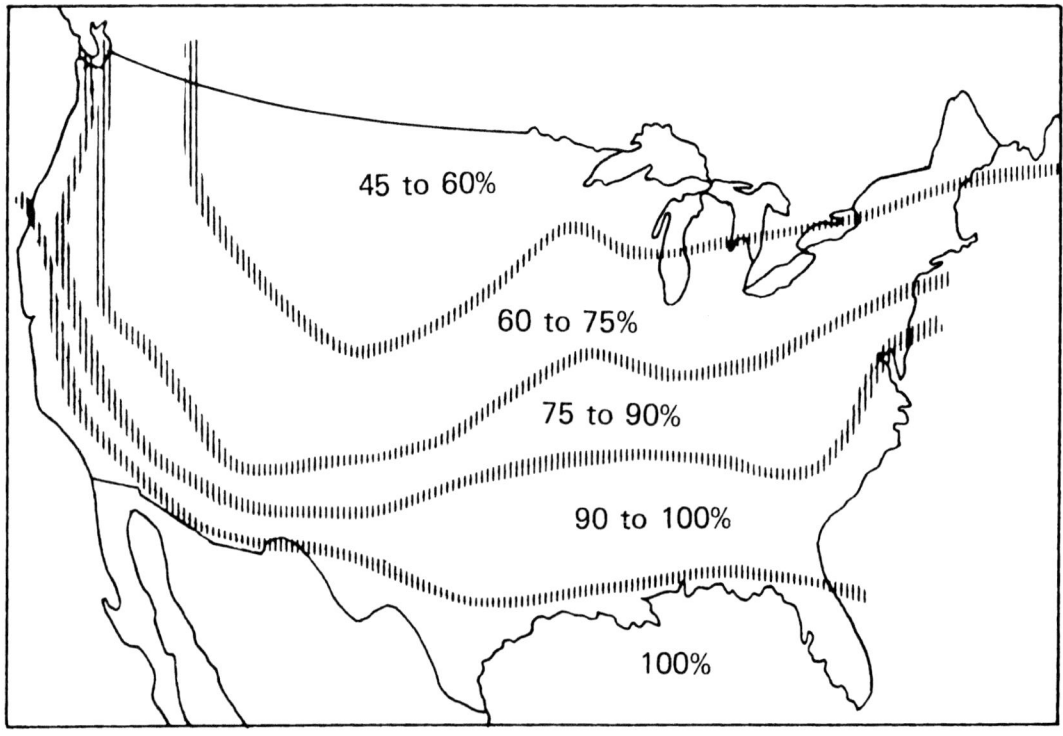

Fig 13-66. Diagram of heat recovery system using rotary heat exchanger

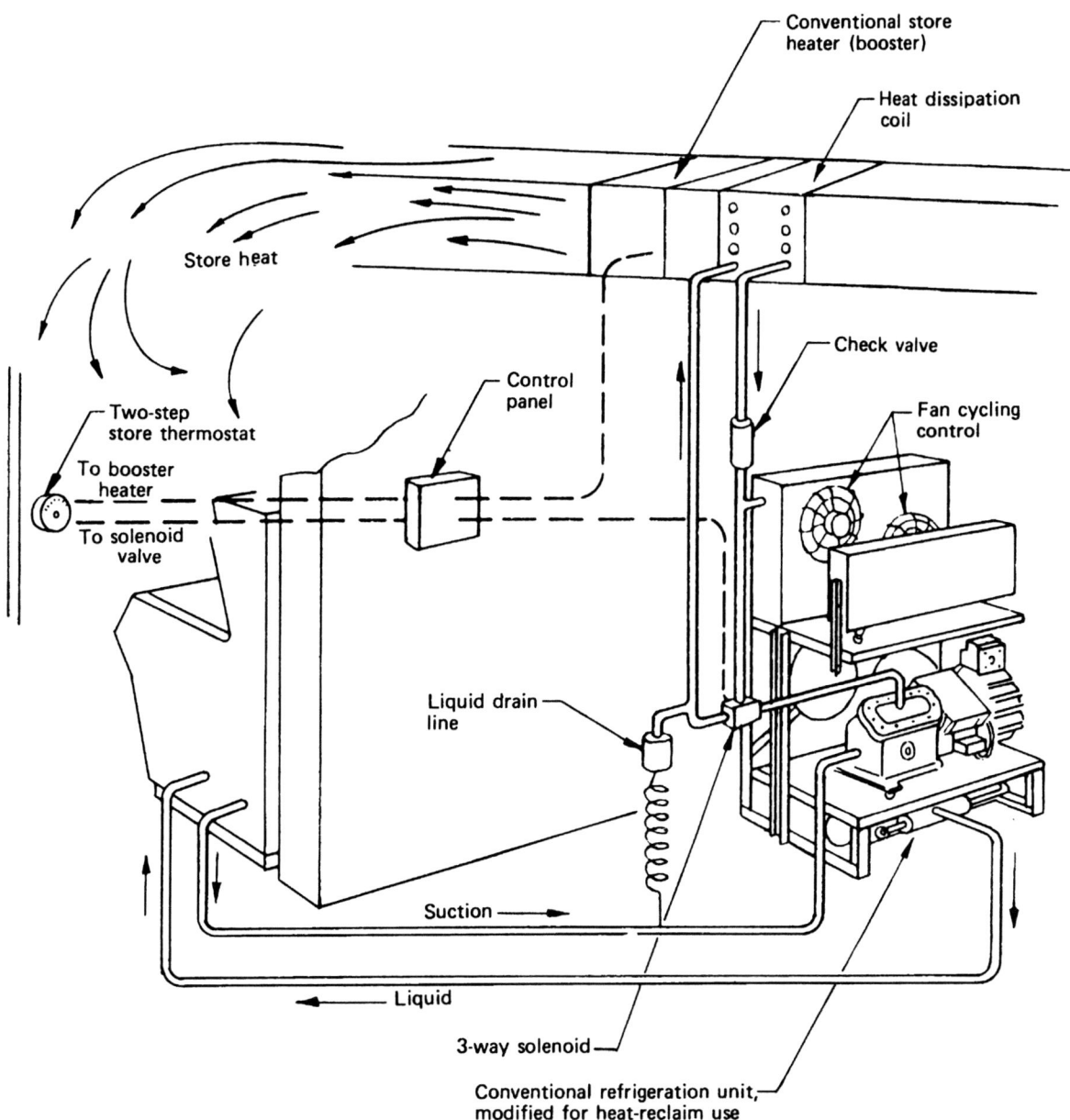

Fig 13-67. Diagram of heat recovery system using rotary heat exchanger

Heat Pumps

A heat pump consists of the same basic components as a refrigerating machine:

1) An element that extracts heat from or rejects heat to a medium outside a conditioned space.

2) An indoor element that adds heat to or extracts heat from a conditioned space.

3) A compressor for pumping the refrigerant containing sensible and/or latent heat in the desired direction so that the heat may be rejected for cooling or used for heating.

4) Controls and other items as required for satisfactory operation.

Reverse-Cycle Principle.—For many years engineers have known that the functions of the evaporator and condenser could be interchanged by reversing the direction of flow of the refrigerant from the compressor. When customer need and economics justified the addition of components in a refrigeration system so that it performed as a heating or a cooling device, the public began to hear about reverse-cycle units and heat pumps. Both terms have been used to identify the same system. Today, most people refer to a heating-and-cooling refrigeration system as a heat pump.

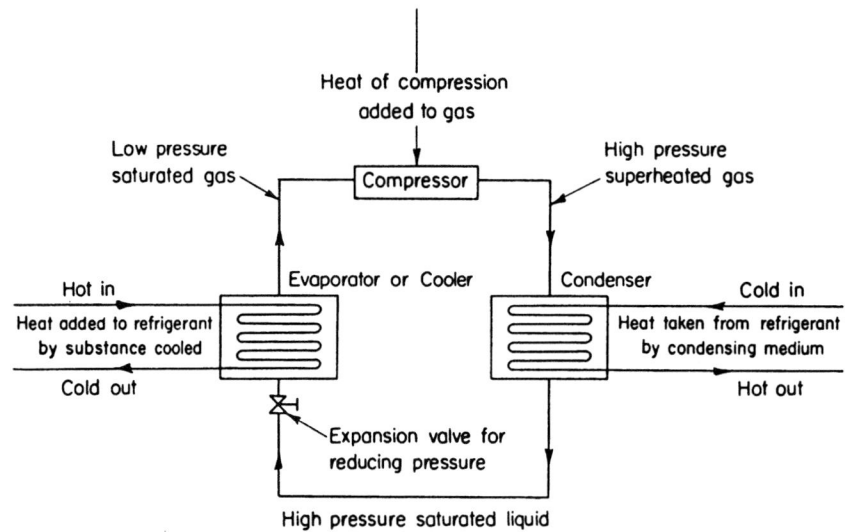

Fig 13-68. Schematic of refrigerant flow in a heat pump system for heating and cooling

Many heat pump systems are assembled with a refrigerant changeover valve or valves, depending upon the capacity and operation of the installation. The changeover valve (or valves) is installed in the refrigerant circuit at or near the compressor. When the structure calls for cooling, the valve directs the flow of the refrigerant so that the indoor coil functions as the evaporator, thereby absorbing heat from the interior. When heating is required, the valve changes the direction of flow of the refrigerant so the indoor coil acts as a condenser, thereby releasing heat to the interior. The internal positioning of the changeover valve (or valves) is automatically controlled by the indoor thermostat or temperature control system. Fig. 13-68 is a schematic sketch of refrigerant flow in a heat pump system for heating and cooling. In addition to a refrigerant changeover heat pump system, there are air change over and water changeover systems. In these units the refrigerant flow is not changed, and heating or cooling is obtained by controlling the flow of air or water. In air changeover systems, ductwork is installed to direct air across the condenser for heating or across the evaporator for cooling before passing to the air

conditioned space. This system requires rather complicated ductwork and dampers.

In water changeover systems the direction of flow of water leaving the condenser and chiller (evaporator section) is controlled by valves to provide heating or cooling in the conditioned area as required.

Water changeover and air changeover systems can be installed to provide heating and cooling for different areas at the same time. This can also be accomplished with extra heat exchangers in the refrigerant-changeover system.

Coefficient of Performance and Performance Factor.—When operating as a cooling unit, electric heat pumps remove more heat energy from the structure than the electrical energy required to run the equipment. Likewise, when operating as a heating unit, electric heat pumps usually provide more heat to the structure than they use or consume in performing the function.

The ratio of the useful heat delivered (in Btu/hr or kw) to the equivalent heat (in Btu/hr or kw) used to operate the entire system at a fixed operating condition is known as the *coefficient of performance* (COP). The COP may also be specified with respect to the compressor only or to any given portion of the system. The following examples are typical for air-to-air pumps.

Example 2:-Cooling Cycle: A 5-ton air-to-air heat pump, delivering 60000 Btu/hr, with a total input of 8 kw. Find the cooling COP? (ARI rating with outdoor air at 95°F dry bulb and 78°F wet bulb and indoor return air at 80°F.)

Solution: Cooling COP $= \dfrac{60000}{8 \times 3413} = 2.20$

Example 3:-Heating Cycle: Operating in an outdoor temperature of 45°F, the same heat pump has a heating capacity of 55800 Btuh, with a total of 6.28 kw. At this rating the indoor-return-air temperature is 70°F at the unit. Find the heating COP?

Solution: Heating COP $= \dfrac{55800}{6.28 \times 3413} = 2.6$

When COP figures are used to compare various types of heat pump systems and/or make of equipment, care must be exercised to insure proper evaluations. The COPs should be based on the same operating conditions, i.e., outdoor indoor temperatures, complete systems or equal portions thereof, etc.

The COP of a heat pump varies with the temperature difference between the heat source and heat sink; the larger this difference, the lower the COP will be.

Fig. 13-69 shows how the COP of an air-to-air heat pump varies with outdoor temperatures during the heating season.

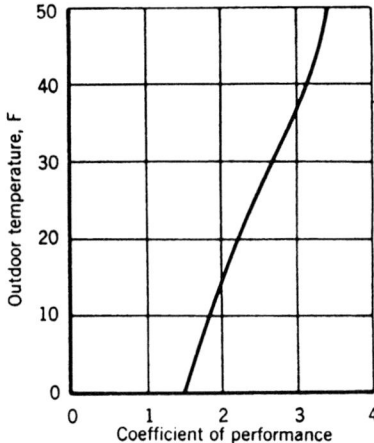

Fig 13-69. COP of air to air heat pumps for heating

Because the COP varies with operating conditions, it cannot be used to compare systems operating over a period of time, such as a day, week, month, or season.

The ratio of the total heating or cooling energy (heat) delivered during a given period to the total equivalent energy used by the system in the same period is indicative of the overall operating conditions. This ratio is known as the *performance factor* (PF). It is expressed as a function of time and operating conditions, such as heating season performance factor or cooling season performance factor. Its usage is associated with the heating characteristics of heat pump systems more often than with cooling operations of mechanical refrigeration systems. The following example shows how a typical heating season performance factor was determined.

Heating Season Performance Factor.—During the 1962–63 heating season, an air-to-air pump system consumed 14000 kw-hr while heating a building requiring 115000000 Btu. The 14000 kw-hr includes power used to drive all components and supplementary resistance heaters as needed. The heat pump system operated with a heating season performance factor of 2.4.

$$PF = \frac{115000000}{14000 \times 3413} = 2.4$$

Performance factor values vary with seasonal climatic conditions, heat pump systems, application, and sizing of equipment, as well as with the specific characteristics of the structures and their internal loads.

Because of a higher temperature heat source, residential heat pump installations in southern regions operate with higher seasonal performance factors than like installations in northern regions.

Because of more efficient motors and compressors, commercial and industrial installations may operate with higher seasonal performance factors than residential installations in the same area.

When performance factors are used to compare heat pump systems, care must be exercised to insure that all components or the same proportion of components are included.

Types of Heat Pumps.—Heat pump systems are designated by the heat source or sink and the type of distribution system in the building, for example, air-to-air, water-to-air, air-to-water, water-to-water, etc., systems. The medium designated first is the external heat source and/or sink. The medium identified second is that which comes in contact with the indoor refrigerant coil. Some larger heat-pump systems are installed with more than one heat source and with both water and air distribution systems.

An air-to-air system uses outdoor air as the heat source and/or sink. Heated or cooled air is supplied through a duct system or air-distribution system within the building.

An air-to-water system uses air as the heat source and/or sink. Heating and cooling is provided within the structure by a water distribution system and appropriate convectors to transfer the heat between water and the air.

From the standpoint of temperature, groundwater is an excellent heat source and heat sink, but it is not readily available in all areas and is in limited supply in many regions during some periods. Air is used predominantly as the heat source and/or sink in residential and small commercial installations. It is becoming popular for larger installations.

Heat pump systems may also use the earth as a heat source and/or sink. This has not proved to be too practical, and few, if any, ground source units are currently considered for use.

Besides air and water, a few other sources have been utilized as the heat source for a heat pump. These are waste heat from various industrial processes, ventilating air exhausts, solar energy, and heat extracted from refrigerated spaces. These sources are generally used in addition to rather than as replacements of the basic heat source.

Air-to-Air Heat Pumps.—Atmospheric air is the most universally available heat source and heat sink; hence, it is the one most commonly utilized. Air-to-air heat pumps use outdoor air as a heat sink or heat source with the heat being delivered to or removed from the indoor air through the use of a direct refrigerant.

The air-to-air-type heat pump is generally the smaller tonnage unit in integral-packaged form for residential and commercial application up to 30 tons. However, built-up systems of any size may be constructed. The models that are presently being marketed of the air-to-air type are either self-contained in one unit or split into two sections. Both types offer definite advantages, depending mainly on the type of application.

An advantage with using air as the heat source is that as temperatures moderate, efficiency improves, thus allowing the heat pump to operate in its more efficient range for most of heating use.

The same economic limitations on size of low velocity duct systems that apply to cooling systems usually limit air-to-air heat pumps to approximately 50 tons per low-velocity duct system.

Generally, a heat pump is selected for the design cooling load. If the design heating load exceeds the heating capacity of the selected heat pump, the necessary supplementary heat is generally supplied by auxiliary electric resistance heaters, which may be required to operate during the infrequent periods of maximum requirements.

The annual kilowatt-hour consumption of supplementary heaters depends upon the application, the capacity of the heat pump in relation to the heat loss of the structure, the climatic conditions, and the control system. In residential applications, supplementary heaters seldom account for more than 10 to 15% of total heating season kilowatt-hours used by the system. In southern regions, use of electricity by supplemental heaters may be negligible. In commercial and industrial installations, lighting loads, body loads, etc. reduce the need for and/or use of supplementary heaters; therefore, they may account for a

very small percentage of total heating season kilowatt-hours.

Various methods have been conceived to get the system through the periods of peak heat demand; however, none of these have yet approached the resistance heating method for practicability and minimum investment.

Another item that requires consideration on this type of heat pump is the outdoor air coil defrosting system. Continuous operation of an air source heat pump with outdoor temperature below 45°F may cause frost accumulation on outdoor air coils. This frost must be periodically removed; otherwise, the coil will become completely blocked with frost, permitting no air flow through it, and the heat pump system will then be ineffective.

Depending upon a number of variables, the frequency of defrost is most severe at outside temperatures between approximately 28°F and 40°F and when high relative humidities are experienced. At lower outside-air temperatures, the ability of the air to hold moisture is limited and fewer defrosts are required. At higher temperatures, the refrigerant temperature in the evaporator will be above the point where frost will form on the coil, and water condensing on the coil surface is easily drained from the unit.

Most air-to-air heat pumps are equipped with automatic defrosting controls. These controls may be timers or devices that measure the difference in temperature between the outdoor air and refrigerant or devices that react to differences in air pressure drop across the outdoor coil. Since the defrosting operation accounts for relatively few kilowatt-hours, how defrost is accomplished is unimportant as long as the device is reliable in performing the operation.

In most air source heat pump systems the outdoor coil is defrosted by reversing the refrigerant cycle so that the system uses the building as a source of heat for defrosting. Supplementary electric heaters located in the air stream may be energized to provide a source of heat to prevent chilling of inside air below comfort levels.

Under special circumstances and in some older systems, heat for defrosting can be provided by resistance elements in the outdoor coil or by water sprays. These systems are most widely used in commercial refrigeration applications for defrosting evaporators in systems without reversing valves.

With electric resistance heating, probes are inserted in the outdoor coil in spaces provided between the refrigerant tubes. To defrost the coil the compressor is shut down and with electricity, the coil is heated directly to melt the frost. This provides a slight improvement over the first method since the compressor is idle, and no compressor and motor losses are encountered.

General considerations in design and use of air-to-air units may be summarized as follows:

1) Since air source units do not use water, problems of piping, corrosion, condenser water disposal, etc. do not exist.

2) Air-to-air units may operate as in-space units to supply filtered warm and cool air, as needed, at a nominal cost.

3) Air-to-air systems are available as packaged integral or remote (split) systems. They are also available as custom-built systems.

4) Air-to-air units are generally installed with an interior distribution system (ductwork) supplying filtered warm and cool air as needed.

5) The cooling capacity drops off a slight amount and the input to the compressor motor increases slightly as the outdoor temperature increases above rated conditions.

6) The heating capacity, as well as the input to the compressor motor, decreases with lowering outdoor temperature. Because of this characteristic, air-to-air systems are generally supplemented with resistance heaters that supply the additional heating requirements under extreme weather conditions. They are controlled via indoor and outdoor thermostats, or other means, to limit their usage to actual need.

7) Frost will form on the outdoor coil during certain outdoor temperature and humidity conditions, necessitating the use of defrosting means and controls.

Water-to-Water Heat Pumps.—The heat pump that uses water from wells, lakes, or other heat sources, with the heat being delivered to the indoor area through the use of a secondary refrigerant in this case, water is generally referred to as a water-to-water type heat pump.

The growth of water-to-water heat pump system has been relatively slow and has been surpassed by the air-to-water type, which had its infancy, except on an experimental basis only, in the years following World War II.

The reason for the slower growth of water source heat pumps compared to air source units is simple. There are few populated areas with generous supplies of clean water. Well water provides an excellent source of heat. Water from this source is occasionally returned to the ground in order not to deplete underground water supplies. Disposal of water also becomes a problem, with many communities charging high sewer rates.

Well water has an advantage over air as a heat source in that it exists at a more nearly constant temperature than air and is a more efficient heat transfer medium than air. This is particularly advantageous when peak heating load occurs, since its temperature is considerably higher than the temperature of outdoor air at this peak condition. This temperature difference also permits water source heat pump to have a higher COP than a comparable air source type.

Another problem is water quality. Soluble minerals such as calcium salts, magnesium salts, and iron will deposit themselves on heat exchanger surfaces and retard

heat transfer. On the other hand, water without mineral content (soft water) can be corrosive. A neutral water supply with a pH-value of 7.0 is seldom found.

Water-to-water heat pumps may operate with either refrigerant or water-reversing valves. With water-reversing systems water flow through the heat exchangers is reversed by automatically operated valves. Therefore, whenever the system operation is reversed from heating to cooling, or vice versa, the indoor conditioned water circuit becomes contaminated with water supplied, whether it is well, lake, or even sea water in more southerly climates. This condition aggravates the water-treating problem of the conditioned-water circuit which is exposed to each air handling unit coil throughout the building. For this reason, units with refrigerant reversing valves are preferred except where near perfect water conditions prevail.

Treatment of the supply water from the heat sink is impractical because of the large quantities involved. Therefore, use of unsuitable water will result in excessive maintenance of heat-exchange surfaces and components.

Where design requires a water changeover system in the face of undesirable water, the problem may be eliminated or minimized by one or more of the following means:

1) Use of admiralty metal or cupro-nickel heat exchangers in all system components.

2) Use of a large heat exchanger to separate well water from condenser-chiller water.

3) Provision of means to positively drain the condenser when changing from cooling to heating and the chiller when changing from heating to cooling. In this way, contamination of the indoor circuit is eliminated and the loss of interior circulating-system water is limited to the volume of the condenser and piping common to both circuits. This allows for proper treatment of the conditioned water.

In some areas the sand content in the well water, if not completely separated from water supplied to the system, can greatly shorten the life of the pumps, heat exchangers, and valves. Increased maintenance of the equipment of the system is also required.

The water-to-water heat pump has several advantages. The yearly electrical operating costs are frequently substantially lower than for any of the fossil fuels commonly used in industrial and commercial establishments. The electricity required will usually be less than that for the air source heat pump for year-round operation, due to the more efficient refrigeration cycle. A further advantage is that the first cost of the system generally will be lower than a conventional heating system provided with a second system for summer cooling.

In brief, water-to-water heat pump can be justified in first cost and operating cost if an abundant supply of approximately 50°F, or warmer, water is available, free from foreign matter and not prone to causing excessive corrosion or scale buildup on heat transfer surfaces. Water- to-water systems are available as packaged or custom built systems. They offer considerable flexibility in commercial and industrial applications.

There is a renewed interest in water-to-water heat pumps used in conjunction with (closed circuit) flat plate solar collectors as a heat source and a water storage tank as the heat sink. This application is discussed later in more detail.

Water-to-Air Heat Pumps.—A heat pump that uses well or lake water or any other available water source as a heat sink or source, with the heat being delivered to the indoor area through the use of a direct refrigerant, is commonly referred to as a water-to-air type. The market for this type of unit is similar to the air-to-air type in the 2- to 50-ton range.

The water-to-air type heat pump has some of the same basic problems as a water-to-water type in regard to availability, quality, and disposal means for water.

In water-to-air heat pumps the refrigerant cycle is reversed to change between summer and winter cycles. This eliminates all conditioned water problems, which can occur in water-to-water units.

General considerations in use and design of water-to-air heat pumps may be summarized as follows:

1) They operate generally with a higher seasonal performance factor than air source units. This advantage is dependent upon the availability of an ample amount of water above 50°F during the entire heating season and upon the amount of power required to supply water.

2) Integral water-to-air units have greater application flexibility than integral air-to-air units in that they are not tied down to the need for an outdoor air supply.

3) They may be operated as free standing in space units.

4) Water-to-air units are available as packaged units and as custom built units.

5) Water-to-air units may be operated with a duct system supplying warmed or cooled filtered air as needed.

6) An ample volume of water must be available to assure sufficient flow in the evaporator section to avoid freezing on the heating cycle.

7) Water availability and disposal may become a problem at some future date.

8) Corrosion problems may create serious maintenance costs unless equipment selected has ability to use available water.

Air-to-Water Heat Pumps.—A heat pump that uses the outdoor air as a heat source or sink, and which delivers the heat to the indoor area to be conditioned through the use of a secondary medium, in this case, water is referred to as an air-to-water type.

This type is marketed in sizes of 3 tons and up. No upper limit is anticipated as jobs are designed to compete with conventional heating cooling systems of all sizes.

If the design heat load exceeds the heating capacity of the selected heat pump, the necessary supplementary heat is generally supplied by auxiliary electric resistance heaters, which may be required to operate during the infrequent periods of maximum requirements. The resistance heaters may be installed in the individual air handling units. This may be preferable, since it permits higher heat pump efficiencies and provides heat to colder spaces before system changeover to heating.

With additional first costs the efficiency of a heat pump can be high at low temperatures by providing compound compression when the pumping differential pressure across the compressors becomes high (patented). Compound compression is a means of pumping gas through several stages of compression to limit the pressure differential and compression ratio across each stage. Two-stage compression reduces the average pumping differential across each compressor by approximately 50% and decreases the compression ratio by approximately 67%.

When one uses compound compression, two things are accomplished toward improving system efficiency. First, the theoretical refrigeration cycle is greatly improved, since only about 75% of the total refrigerant flow need be pumped by the low-stage compressor, with the remaining 25% pumped by only the high stage. This is made possible by the use of an intercooler, which expands some of the refrigerant to intermediate pressure while subcooling the liquid refrigerant flowing to the evaporator. Secondly, the volumetric efficiency of the reciprocating type compressor varies inversely with the compression ratio; when the compression ratio is reduced 67%, a sizable gain in compressor volumetric efficiency results.

Typical figures indicate that two-stage compression can produce about 65% more heat at −20°F evaporator temperature than the same displacement compressors operating as single-stage. Furthermore, the electrical requirement for the single-stage compressors would be approximately 65% greater than for the two-stage for each unit of heat output.

Systems can be arranged to operate single-stage with gas flow in parallel for summer cooling and can be converted to compound compression with series gas flow to improve the operating efficiency at lower outside air temperatures. This is accomplished by providing a single, automatically operated gas valve plus two check valves.

Thus, if the ratio of heating load to cooling load is favorable, the same compressors used for summer cooling may provide sufficient capacity when compounded for outdoor air temperatures of even −10°F without the use of supplementary electric heaters.

Air-to-water systems have the following advantages and limitations:

1) They present the same advantages and limitations as air-to-air units insofar as the heat source and sink are concerned.

2) Warm and cold water are piped throughout the building, thereby eliminating the need for large supply and return duct systems.

3) In large central system installations, rooms and areas may be thermostatically controlled more easily than with large supply and return air distribution systems.

Ground Source Heat Pumps.—The ground coil method for a heat source is mentioned here for general information. The problems arising from this type of heat pump as well as recent developments in other types of heat pumps have practically eliminated the desirability of any further developments of this type.

The availability of heat in the earth for a heat pump system on peak demand days will be better than atmospheric air but poorer than well water at the same location. If ground coils are used, either a direct expansion or a secondary refrigerant system may be used. The problems that arise if leaks develop in the underground coil are very serious and expensive.

Uncertainties arise in designing the underground coil. These stem from the variation of ground temperatures in a relatively small area. Even if test borings that give accurate temperatures are made, the fact that these temperatures will vary somewhat with changes in ground moisture content makes design difficult and uncertain.

Difficulties with moisture content in the soil, chemical content and makeup of the earth (clay, gravel, sand, etc.), plus expansion and contraction of the buried piping, discourage heat pump installers from using the earth as a heat source and/or sink.

Special Heat Sources.—A few other sources besides air and water have been utilized as heat sources for heat pumps. These sources are generally used as additions rather than replacements of the basic heat source. These additional sources supply heat from operations or processes that exist in areas close enough to the desired conditioned area to be used to economic advantage.

On most large commercial and industrial buildings, a positive means of exhausting air from the building is mandatory to obtaining good air distribution. Exhausting this air at one or more central points may be advantageous from the standpoint that heat may be extracted from it. One economical method of removing this heat and returning it to the portions of the building requiring heat is by the use of a direct expansion coil located in the exhaust air stream.

Another method of extracting this heat for beneficial use is by means of the *run around* system. Coils are located in both the ventilation supply and exhaust air ducts, with an antifreeze solution such as ethylene glycol circulating between the two coils. Heat is removed from the exhaust air and absorbed by incoming ventilation air to provide a reduction in heating requirements of the mechanical equipment. Care should be exercised in the design of the run around system to prevent excessive frost formation on the coil in the exhaust air stream. A bypass valve, thermostatically controlled, can be located in the antifreeze solution piping circuit to maintain solution temperatures not lower than approximately 28°F to the exhaust air coil as a means of preventing the formation of frost.

A third method of extracting this heat, for useful heating as well as for reducing the compressor motor electrical consumption, is to locate a refrigerant liquid subcooling coil in the ventilation air plenum chamber, providing preheat to the incoming fresh air while subcooling the liquid refrigerant as it flows to the evaporator. On single stage systems, this arrangement also provides an increase in heating capacity for a given displacement compressor. In effect, useful subcooling of the refrigerant liquid increases the refrigerant effect of each pound circulated to the evaporator, thereby reducing the quantity of refrigerant that the compressor must handle to absorb a given amount of heat. The horsepower is also reduced for each unit of useful work in the same proportion that the flow rate may be decreased. This coil must be bypassed for summer operation.

Other means of subcooling the liquid refrigerant, such as disposing of the heat to the outdoor air or preheating the air circulated to the outdoor evaporator, would actually result in a net loss over a conventional system without sub cooling and should therefore not be used. Rejecting this heat to the outside air would be wasteful. Preheating air at the outdoor evaporator coil increases the air temperature a small amount in proportion to the quantity of heat given up by the system.

The use of subcooling coils is limited in application to buildings where a large portion of the ventilation supply air is introduced to the building at a central point near the compressor room It becomes impractical to run long refrigerant lines to scattered coils located throughout the building because of the first cost (including insulation), the leak hazard with expensive refrigerants, the increased maintenance, and the design problems brought about by increased pressure drop in the refrigerant circuit. Also, it should be kept in mind that a system provided with liquid subcooling means will only be beneficial when the normal supply of fresh air is furnished to the building. When the fresh air supply is shut down during the unoccupied periods, the single-stage system must operate without benefit of the extra capacity. On the two-stage systems, this disadvantage can be offset by locating an intercooler in parallel with the subcooling coil, and no reduction in system capacity will be experienced.

Numerous other building functions and system applications offer means of economically capturing heat from within by a heat pump system. Telephone exchanges, calculating and tabulating machine rooms, and other business machines generate considerable quantities of heat which must be removed to maintain expensive equipment at the necessary temperature level as well as to provide a comfortable temperature for the occupants. Another source is in industrial plants where heat is removed from process work, friction generating equipment, transformer vaults, and exhaust fumes. Still another source is the recovery of heat from refrigeration condensing units or packaged air coolers.

An example of available condensing units is found in supermarkets where many units are used for the various refrigerated cabinets in the market. Heat from this source is generally discarded to the atmosphere but may be economically captured by a heat pump system and made available where heating is necessary.

Operating and Installation Factors.—Residential heat pump installations and commercial industrial heat pump installations must be examined on the basis of application considerations and operating cost factors applicable to the area and type of installation. Like other heating and cooling systems, they do have some common considerations such as:

1) Rule of thumb applications sometimes result in uneconomical and/or unsatisfactory installations.

2) The sizing of the complete system is dependent upon reliable heat gain and heat loss calculations. Design conditions recommended in this handbook or in the current *ASHRAE Handbook* should be followed.

3) Operating cost estimates should be reviewed with the local electric utility. This is especially important with respect to commercial and industrial jobs.

4) Care should be exercised not to oversell the heat pump. The heat pump is not necessarily a panacea for all air conditioning problems.

5) Proper installation of insulation, double glass, ductwork, and other components is most important.

When a heat pump system fails to meet owner ideas and/or requirements, he generally blames the heat pump. The owner seldom appreciates the fact that other considerations, such as lack of insulation or poor ductwork, may have created a problem.

Heat pump manufacturer's usually provide the following helpful information on units:

1) Instructions recommending the manner in which their equipment should be installed.

2) Heating and cooling capacities and kilowatt input at various heat source and heat sink temperatures.

3) Service requirements with respect to installation and location of the equipment.

Outdoor Temperature Effects.—The operation of air-to-air heat pumps is influenced by outdoor temperatures, and their effects are best explained by means of a graph. Fig. 13-70 presents typical heating characteristics of an air-to-air unit.

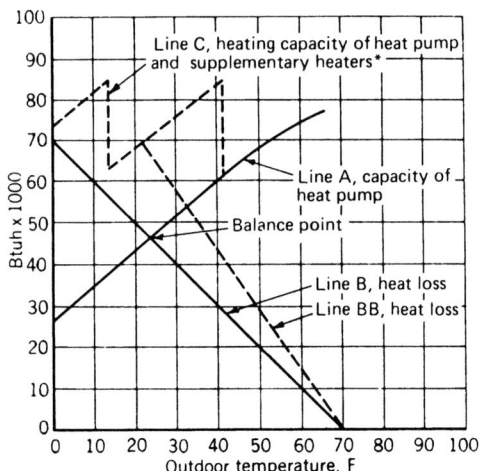

Fig 13-70. Typical air to air heat pump operation with various outdoor temperatures

With decreasing outdoor temperature the heating capacity decreases, as shown by Line A, while the heat loss (heating load) increases, as shown by Line B. The balance point is the temperature at which the heat loss is equal to the heating capacity of the pump. This is the point where Lines A and B cross and, for the example shown, this point is 23°F.

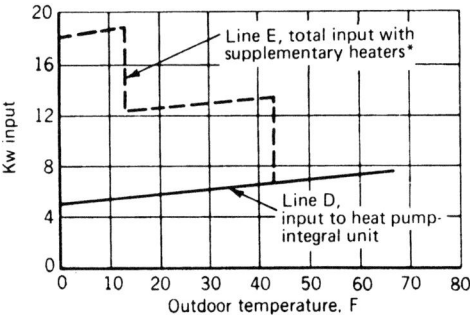

Fig 13-71. Electrical input for various outdoor temperatures

The balance point varies with the application and is a function of capacity of the unit in relationship to the heat loss of the structure. For example, for a heat pump with the capacity as shown in Fig. 13-70 in a home with a heat loss of 10,000 Btuh at 20°F (Line BB), the balance point would be 32°F.

Supplementary resistance heaters are generally used to augment the capacity of the unit when temperatures fall below the balance point. These are available in fixed amounts (such as 5 kw banks) and are installed in the supply plenum. Line C in Fig. 13-70 represents a typical application of resistance heaters.

Line D in Fig. 13-71 represents the instantaneous input in kilowatts versus outdoor temperatures. This value varies, since the load on the compressor motor changes with outdoor temperatures. Line D includes the total input to the compressor motor, the outdoor fan motor, the indoor fan motor, and the controls. Line E shows how the input to the heaters adds to that of the unit.

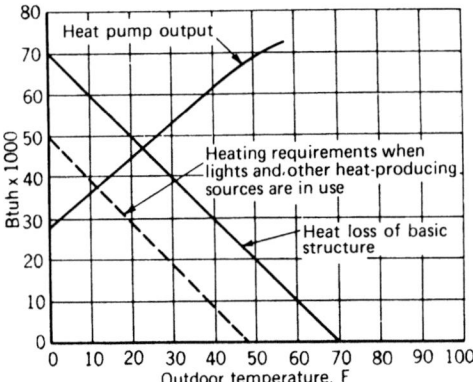

Fig 13-72. Effect of interior heat sources on the heating load and balance point

Fig. 13-72 shows how lighting loads, body loads, etc. shift the balance point in commercial and industrial buildings. With internal heat sources the balance point would be 12°F, compared with 23°F for the basic structure with no internal heat sources.

Thermostats.—Heat pumps operate automatically to provide controlled air conditioning under varying conditions of weather, internal heat sources, and demands of the occupants. Thermostats and other control components are so set up that the electric power consumption of the heat pump and electric resistance heaters is held to a minimum Fig. 13-73 shows a typical control circuit for a residential heat pump with two banks of electric resistance heaters.

Contacts 1 and 2 control the heating functions of the system. Contact 2 is in series with outdoor thermostats. These function to block unneeded use of the supplementary heaters. When Contact 1 closes, the heat pump operates as a heating device.

Contact 2 is mechanically locked to Contact 1. It will close when the indoor temperature drops about $1\frac{1}{2}$°F below the setting of Contact 1. When Contact 2 closes, it energizes the supplementary heater control circuit up to the outdoor thermostats. If the outdoor thermostats are closed the supplementary heaters are energized.

The setting of the outdoor thermostats depends upon the heat loss of the building, the design temperature conditions, and the capacity of the heat pump. Most manufacturer's include outdoor thermostat settings in their installation manuals for applications of their units.

Contact 3 on the indoor thermostat controls the cooling operations of the heat pump. In most thermostats the heating and cooling settings are mechanically blocked from coming within 4 to 5°F of each other. For example, when

Contact 1 (heating) is set for 70°F, then Contact 3 (cooling) cannot be set below 74°F.

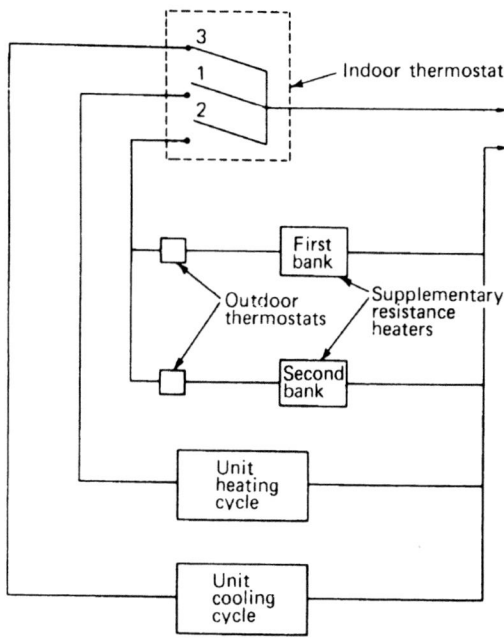

Fig 13-73. Control circuit for residential heat pump

In commercial and industrial installations, various thermostat control arrangements may be used. They may be interconnected with the lighting to block the use of the supplementary heaters when certain amounts of lighting are in use. In multiple unit installations where units are located throughout the building, each unit may be controlled by its own thermostat.

As with any heating and cooling system, the location of the thermostat or thermostats is most important in assuring good comfort control. There are many do's and don'ts in locating the thermostat. With respect to the don'ts. thermostats should not be mounted:

1) where heated or cooled air will blow on them;

2) behind an inside door that is usually open;

3) in front of a hot or cold pipe within the wall;

4) on an exterior wall.

In general, thermostats should be located in the space most often used by occupants. This, frequently, is the space having the greatest heat gain or heat loss per unit volume.

Heat Anticipators.—Heating anticipators used for heat pumps should be designed for the lower thermal storage of heat pump systems. Proper anticipation will prevent excessive cycling of the compressor above the balance point. The moderate anticipation of the two stage heat pump thermostat should not cause cycling of the compressor below the balance point.

Equipment Arrangement.—In residential installations, the heat pump should be located so all supply duct and return duct runs are as short as possible. This will minimize duct losses and help to assure good rated air flows. To avoid transmission of noise and vibration by the duct system, nonmetallic, flexible connections should be installed between the unit and ductwork. In some installations, acoustical treatment may be required in the return and/or supply duct to reduce the noise level.

The situation may arise where an integral air-to-air unit may require outdoor air circuit ductwork. This section handles more air than the indoor section. Large ducts are required in order to provide proper air flow with the available fan power. This ductwork must be insulated and vapor sealed in the conditioned space to prevent condensation in the winter and to minimize increased heating and cooling requirements in the conditioned space.

In general, it is always best to locate integral air source units adjacent to exterior walls. A foam rubber gasket may be used around the edges of the outdoor air circuit to isolate the unit from the structure and to seal the outdoor air circuits.

Some commercial and industrial installations operate with supply and return air duct systems. Others operate with heating and cooling piped to fan coil units. Still other installations may comprise multiple units operating in free space with less piping and ductwork.

In examining any application the designer should consider integral units versus remote (split) units with respect to simplification of indoor supply and return air ductwork. Remote units eliminate the need for outdoor ductwork when integral applications are needed. They do, however, require refrigerant piping which, if improperly installed, may be a noise problem. manufacturer instructions should be carefully followed regarding the use of mufflers in the refrigerant circuit and the method of supporting the refrigerant lines between the outdoor and indoor sections.

Manufacturer application and equipment data sheets should be consulted in locating equipment within a home or structure. All types of heating and cooling equipment require preventive maintenance as well as annual service. The heat pump is no exception. Consideration should be given to the fact that fans, fan motors, water pumps if used, and other equipment must be lubricated, and that filters must be cleaned or changed periodically. Integral, remote, and custom built heat pumps are designed with definite space requirements for servicing. These cannot be ignored in locating the equipment.

Good indoor air distribution contributes as much or more to the success of a heat pump system as any other factor. Therefore, care should be used to assure ample air distribution throughout the structure and to assure operation with a reasonable noise level. Conformance to good duct sizing practice is imperative to accomplish this.

The heating coefficient of performance (COP) and the heating season performance factor (PF) decrease when the indoor air flow is much below rated conditions. Therefore, it is important to maintain approximate rated indoor air flow during the heating season to avoid increases in the estimated operating cost. Registers and ducts should be sized for maximum air flow to the area.

Heating efficiency and comfort are improved if the winter air return is at or near floor level.

Electrohydronic Heat Recovery

Some air conditioning systems used regularly in low rise apartments or hotels are impractical or uneconomical in high rise buildings, while other systems on the contrary, are very practical with high rise structures. The electrohydronic system utilizing water-to-air heat pumps, with a common heat sink, is used in both high and low rise buildings. Generally, the installed cost, in $/ft^2, is less with high rise structures.

In virtually all apartments and hotels, the need for each occupant to control the temperature in his own area is basic. The most critical period of maintaining uniform comfort control may not occur at design summer or winter conditions, but rather at outdoor temperatures of 40 to 70°F. Under such conditions, the traditional central system chiller and boiler can be running simultaneously.

Some building areas, particularly of hotels, are subjected to varying heat gains and losses to a much greater extent than other interior areas. Therefore, they require a system with greater flexibility and quicker response than does a typical interior zone.

The electrohydronic system has only four major components: a device for rejecting excess heat, a water heater, circulating pumps, and air conditioners. Although these components are very familiar, there are important differences in the way they function in this system.

The system (see Fig. 13-74) uses unitary water-to-air, reverse cycle air conditioners. These contain the same components as traditional air conditioners with one important addition: A reversing valve diverts hot refrigerant gas to the water coil when the air conditioner is cooling, or to the air coil for heating. Note, however, that the direction of refrigerant flow through the compressor is not reversed.

The air conditioner is connected to a closed circuit, non refrigerated water loop. Water is recirculated in this loop as a heat reservoir, providing a closed loop water-to-air heat pump.

Cooling Cycle.—On demand of the thermostat for cooling, the reversing valve guides the hot gas from the compressor to the water coil, which serves during the cooling cycle as a condenser, removing heat from it and condensing it into a liquid. The heat picked up is circulated in the closed water loop. The liquid refrigerant then flows through an expansion device to the air coil, which acts as an evaporator. The boiler refrigerant absorbs heat from the room air passing across the evaporator coil. Refrigerant vapor then flows through the reversing valve and into the compressor, thus completing the cooling cycle.

When the thermostat calls for heat, the reversing valve reverses the flow of refrigerant so that hot gas from the compressor flows through the tubes of the air coil which now serves as a condenser.

Air to be heated passes over the tubes, absorbing heat from the refrigerant gas and causing it to condense. This warm air heats the room. Liquid refrigerant then flows through the expansion device to the water coil, which now functions as a water cooler or chiller. As the refrigerant vaporizes, it absorbs heat from the closed water loop, which is a heat reservoir. The refrigerant gas is conducted back through the reversing valve to the compressor, completing the heating cycle.

Maintenance of Loop Temperature Limits.—Note that cooling or heating of room air is done by transfer with the *refrigerant, not water* in the closed loop. This water, ordinarily between 60°F and 90°F, accepts heat on the cooling cycle and provides heat on the heating cycle.

When enough units are on cooling to raise water temperature above 90°F, the excess heat must be rejected from the water loop. This is done most frequently by a closed circuit evaporative cooler, a small factory designed and assembled package with a coil through which the warm system water flows. This system water is cooled by the evaporation of spray water which is recirculated over the outside of the coil (Fig. 13-75).

A small water heater is included to maintain the loop water temperature at 60°F when almost all the units are on heating. This heater can be about two-thirds the capacity required by conventional systems.

On moderate days, units serving the side of the building exposed to the sun may be cooling, while those on the shady side may be heating simultaneously. This situation, which occurs during much of the year, greatly reduces the hours of operation and costs for the water heater and the heat rejector. Even on cold days, interior zones with high heat gain from people, lights, and equipment, requiring cooling, often provide sufficient heat to water loop for the

units warming the perimeter zones so that it is not necessary to operate the supplementary heater.

In addition to effective recovery and utilization of heat where simultaneous heating and cooling is required, the system takes advantage of the *fly wheel effect* in many buildings where net cooling is required during the day and net heating at night. It is possible to calculate building heat requirements throughout any given day as outdoor temperatures and building usage vary. It is also possible to determine the internal heat gains within the building during that same period of time.

If these heat gains and losses are superimposed, it is possible to see how this system can transfer heat within the building and also store excess heat from day-time hours for utilization at night when it would otherwise be necessary to add supplementary heat. During a 24-hour period, the system water temperature may never drop low enough to require supplementary heat, nor reach a high enough temperature to reject excess heat.

Controls are so arranged that, if loop water temperature falls to 50°F the heater automatically operates. If it rises to 90°F the cooler operates. If the temperature is between 60°F and 90°F degrees, neither device is required. At no time do cooler and heater operate simultaneously.

Among the factors that may influence design and installation are the following:

1) If a unit requires service, it can be quickly removed and replaced without affecting other apartments or the rest of the system.

2) Less ductwork may mean less overall building height for the same number of stories, which, of course, reduces building costs.

3) Non insulated pipes reduce material and labor costs. Water in the closed loop is not hot enough for heat loss or cold enough to cause condensation on the pipes. Plastic pipe is being used with increasing frequency.

4) The central water core can be installed and then individual conditioners furnished later as apartments are sold or leased. This is also particularly applicable to modernization projects because conditioners can be added one floor at a time.

5) Conditioners can be individually metered. This is very desirable for rental and leasing situations or condominiums.

6) No complex control system is required. The services of an operating engineer normally are not needed. A simple panel to indicate extreme operating temperatures or lack of flow in the closed water loop is all that is necessary.

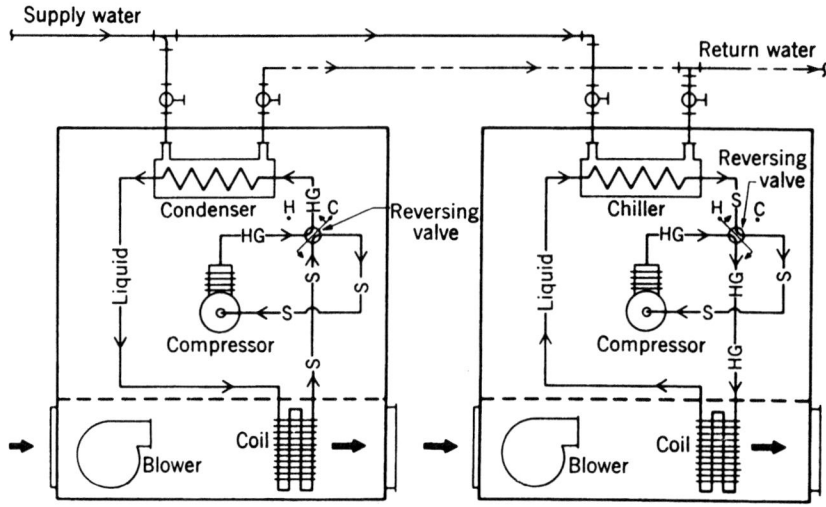

Fig 13-74. Water is recirculated in a loop as a heat reservoir

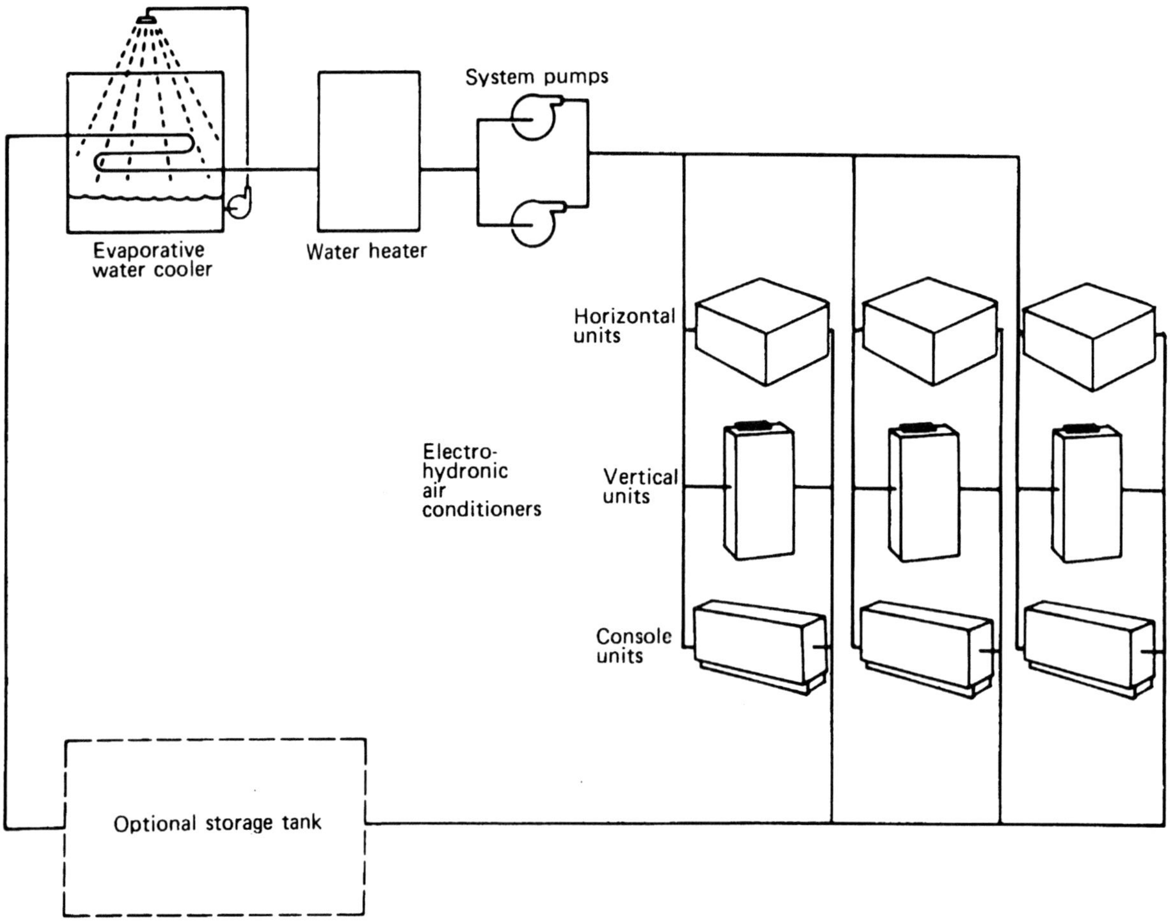

Fig 13-75. System water is cooled by evaporation of spray water, which is recirculated over the outside of the coil

System Design.—Building heat gains and heat losses should be calculated in accordance with normal procedures. Water piping for the system should provide a balanced two-pipe reverse return arrangement wherever possible. Since system water flows continuously to provide either cooling or heating, two pumps should be installed, one on standby.

Supply and return water connections to each air conditioner should include a shut-off valve and a means of disconnecting piping at the air conditioner to facilitate removal should servicing be required. These connections may be made with a good quality hose. The hose will simplify installation and servicing as well as minimize any possible vibration transmission through the piping.

Polyvinyl chloride (PVC) hose may be used as a condensate drain line. It requires no insulation and can be installed very economically.

It is essential that the piping system be thoroughly flushed of foreign material. The recommended means of doing this is to loop over the roughed in piping from supply to return at each unit. It is especially convenient to do this when hose connections are being used. The pump can then be operated to flush the system prior to installation of any air conditioners.

Excess heat may be rejected from water loop through a heat exchanger into a cooling tower, a well, river water, a lake or any other readily available source of coolant suitable to prevent the system water from exceeding the maximum desired temperature.

In order to keep the water system clean and to maintain peak performance, the water loop must be a closed system. The heat exchanger selected for rejection of excess heat may be a water-to-water exchanger, or, when a cooling tower is to be used, a closed circuit evaporative cooler.

The building's peak heat rejection load will be less than the sum of rated heat rejection for all the air conditioning units plus any additional heat from other sources. That portion (diversity factor) of maximum load which can actually be required at any given time must be determined for each job, but it will generally be less than unity. This is based on the premise that not all rooms in an entire building will simultaneously need maximum cooling (room fully occupied, lights and other heat sources all operating, sun shining brightly through windows, etc.). Although it will vary with different applications, the use of a diversity factor of 0.8 for comfort air conditioning will generally be reasonably accurate.

Should a closed circuit evaporative cooler or cooling tower be installed where it may be exposed to freezing temperatures, provision must be made to avoid damage from freezing. If the entire tower cannot be located inside where temperatures can be maintained above 10°F, perhaps the tower sump and makeup water line can. Otherwise, they can be equipped with an immersion heater in the sump and electric heating tape around the makeup

water line. The heaters should be controlled to prevent water temperature from dropping below about 40°F.

It is recommended that full system water flow be maintained through the cooling coil of an evaporative cooler during the entire year. To minimize heat loss in cold climates, any exposed piping to the cooler should be insulated and a positive closure damper installed at the evaporative cooler air discharge. Buildings having an exhaust system that can conveniently be directed into the cooler will benefit during all seasons. The exhaust air will improve warm weather performance of the cooler and will reduce heat loss during cold weather.

Supplementary Heat.—A source of supplementary heat must be provided for any extended cold weather periods when there is inadequate heat for the system to recover. This heat source must add whatever heat is removed from the water loop by the air conditioners once water temperature has dropped to its minimum temperature of about 60°F. Since the air conditioner's heat of compression adds about 30% of the total unit's heat output, the capacity of the supplementary heat source need be only 70% of the heat loss from the area served by the system. To this must be added any additional heat that may be required for other areas or purposes.

Fuel-fired boilers, electric boilers or immersion elements, steam converters, or other heat sources are suitable as supplementary heat sources. They are sized and controlled to add whatever heat is required to prevent system water from dropping below its minimum allowable temperature.

Optimized Data for Heat Pump Systems

While there are substantial operating economies with heat pump systems, often a misconception arise that the first costs of such systems are determined by the capacity of the chiller only. However, the following shows that first costs can be optimized with the proper choice of other operating parameters.

Certain factors, including those of supply and return water temperatures and total water flow, which have some influence on chiller selection at least on its heating condenser have a major influence on the heating system itself.

The heating capacity of any heating unit's air heating coil, fan coil unit, induction unit or radiator is directly proportional to supply water temperature and to the rate of flow of water passing through it. In the case of the heating system, the solution is usually routine: Water is supplied at 190°F or 200°F and flow is fixed by selection of a 20°F temperature drop across the unit. In the case of heat pump systems, however, available supply temperatures are much lower and temperature drop is also limited. The reason is that maximum condenser temperature and, thus, the temperature of water leaving the condenser, cannot be higher than the temperature corresponding to the surge point of the refrigerant.

Optimum conditions occur at that temperature and flow which results in the lowest first costs for the heat distributing system (not including chiller or auxiliary boiler).

Table 13-5. Fan Coil Unit Data

GPM	Unit Capacity MBH	No. Units to Serve 1000 MBH Load
1	35.4	28.2
2	52.9	18.9
4	70.4	14.2
6	79.2	12.6
7	82.2	12.16
8	84.5	11.8
9	86.4	11.57
10	88.0	11.26

The following approach is based on the assumption that a required heating capacity for a building will be provided by the necessary number of identical heating units with identical capacities and operating under identical conditions (this will result in fractional numbers as shown in Table 13-5, Column 3).

The capacity of a unit with heating coil and fan at a given air flow rate and supplied with 190°F water varies with the rate of flow of water through it, as indicated in Table 13-5. At water temperatures T other than 190°F, the number of units required for a 1000 MBh load as given in Table 13-5, Column 3, can be corrected by multiplying the figure by the reciprocal of $(1-0.008)(190-T)$.

The amount of water flowing through the system and the chiller's heating bundle is the product of the number of heating units and the appropriate water flow through each unit.

Piping cost can also be estimated easily. Water flow is taken at 50% of maximum flow on each system (every floor with a separate horizontal distribution system or every riser with a vertical distribution shall be treated as a separate system). Average pipe size is selected to produce a friction of more than 3.5 ft per 100 ft of piping.

Development of Equations.—Let $\dot{q}_h$ be the total heating load in 1000 Btu/hr (MBH); $\dot{q}_c$ minimum cooling capacity required during the heating season; *gpm*, total water flow through the system in gallons per minute; T_1 supply water temperature (the temperature at which water is discharged from the auxiliary boiler); and T_2 return water temperature entering the heating bundle of the condenser.

Total heating capacity equals total flow (taken at 50% of maximum flow) multiplied by total temperature rise and the specific heat of water.

$$\dot{q}_h = 0.5 gpm(T_1 - T_2) \qquad (1)$$

Heat transferred to water in the condenser equals approximately $1.3\dot{q}_c$. This amount of heat shall not raise the temperature of water from T_2 above the temperature corresponding to the refrigerant surge point, which we assume to be 105°F. Then,

$$1.3\dot{q}_c = 0.5 gpm(105 - T_2) \qquad (2)$$

It has been found that total water flow is linear function of unit water flow, gpm_0 a supply water temperature of 190°F, as follows:

$$gpm = \left[\frac{\dot{q}_h}{1000}\right](9.5 gpm_0 + 18.7) \qquad (3)$$

At supply water temperatures T different from 190°F, total water flow is:

$$gpm = \left[\frac{\dot{q}_h}{1000}\right]\left(\frac{9.5 gpm_0 + 18.7}{1 - 0.008(190 - T_1)}\right) \qquad (4)$$

Combining Equations (1), (2) and (4),

$$\frac{\left(1 - 1.3\dfrac{\dot{q}_c}{\dot{q}_h}\right) \times 1000}{0.50(9.5 gpm_0 + 18.7)} = \frac{(T_1 - 105)}{1 - 0.008(190 - T_1)} \qquad (5)$$

which will provide, for any selected ratio $\dot{q}_c/\dot{q}_h$ and any selected supply temperature T_1, a single possible value of gpm_0; and provide the only possible total water flow *gpm* from Equation (3).

Development of Tables.—With the help of Equation (5), Table 13-6 has been established showing the possible unitary water flow values for different $\dot{q}_c/\dot{q}_h$ ratios and T_1 temperatures. From Table 13-6 and Table 13-5, the number of units required for a heating load of 1000 MBh and their cost can be figured. The results are shown in Table 13-7. For heating loads $\dot{q}_h$ different from 1000 MBh, the values should be multiplied by $\dot{q}_h/1000$. Table 13-6 and Equation (3) will provide total water flow data for any combination of $\dot{q}_c/\dot{q}_h$ and T_1 values and, with the help of Fig. 13-74, cost of piping can be established.

Table 13-6. Possible Water Flow Unit GPM at Different $\dot{q}_c/\dot{q}_h$ Values and Supply Temperatures

$\dfrac{\dot{q}_c}{\dot{q}_h}$	Supply Water Temperature, °F						
	108	110	112.5	115	117.5	120	125
0.20	15.89	9.26	5.92	4.18	3.26	2.60	1.77
0.25	14.33	8.27	5.23	3.63	2.72	2.20	1.44
0.30	12.76	7.28	4.54	3.08	2.34	1.79	1.11
0.35	11.19	6.30	3.85	2.54	1.75	1.39	0.78
0.40	9.62	5.31	3.15	1.99	1.42	0.99	0.46
0.45	8.05	4.33	2.46	1.44	0.875	0.59	0.13
0.50	6.48	3.34	1.77	0.89	0.505	0.19	…
0.60	3.24	1.37	0.38	…	…	…	…
0.70	0.20	…	…	…	…	…	…

Table 13-7. Number of Units for Possible Conditions and for 1000 Mbh Heating Load

$\dfrac{\dot{q}_c}{\dot{q}_h}$	Supply Water Temperature, °F						
	108	110	112.5	115	117.5	120	125
0.20	…	32.3	33.27	35.82	37.94	39.62	43.76
0.25	…	32.85	34.82	37.78	40.97	41.74	50.16
0.30	…	33.86	36.17	40.93	43.10	47.23	56.57
0.35	…	34.97	38.22	44.11	49.64	55.73	71.90
0.40	33.57	36.85	42.57	47.07	57.82	64.65	91.10
0.45	34.27	39.06	46.85	60.29	75.23	90.25	110.90
0.50	36.06	44.12	55.34	78.20	99.27	116.65	…
0.60	46.48	69.34	93.10	…	…	…	…
0.70	154.00	…	…	…	…	…	…

Selecting Air Handling Units

The data that follow can be used in a simple fashion for the quick and accurate selection of air handling units without resorting to manufacturer literature. All data are based on a survey of equipment that is commercially available and will be helpful for schematic, preliminary, and final layouts:

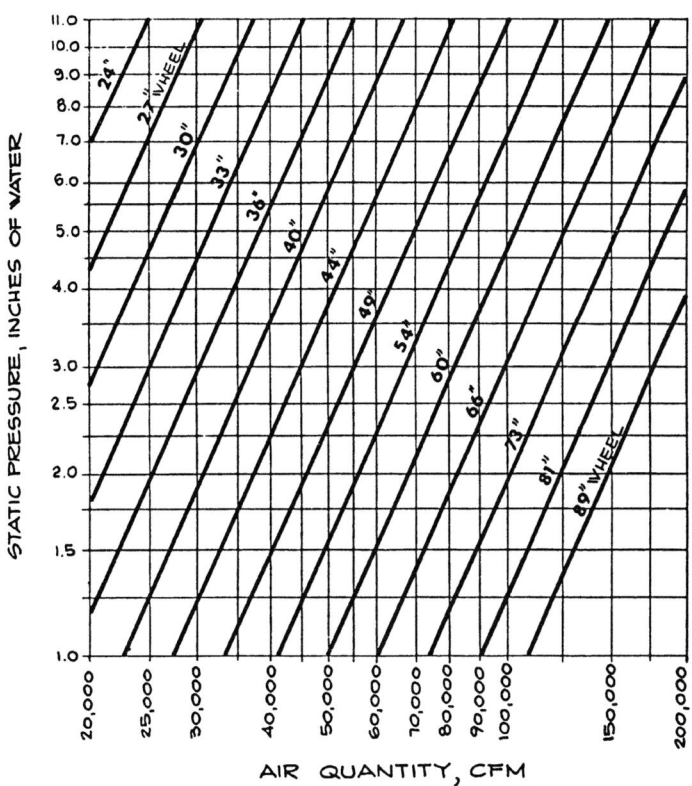

Fig 13-76. Double width fan selection

This chart is applicable to all double width centrifugal fans built in accordance with AMCA Standard.

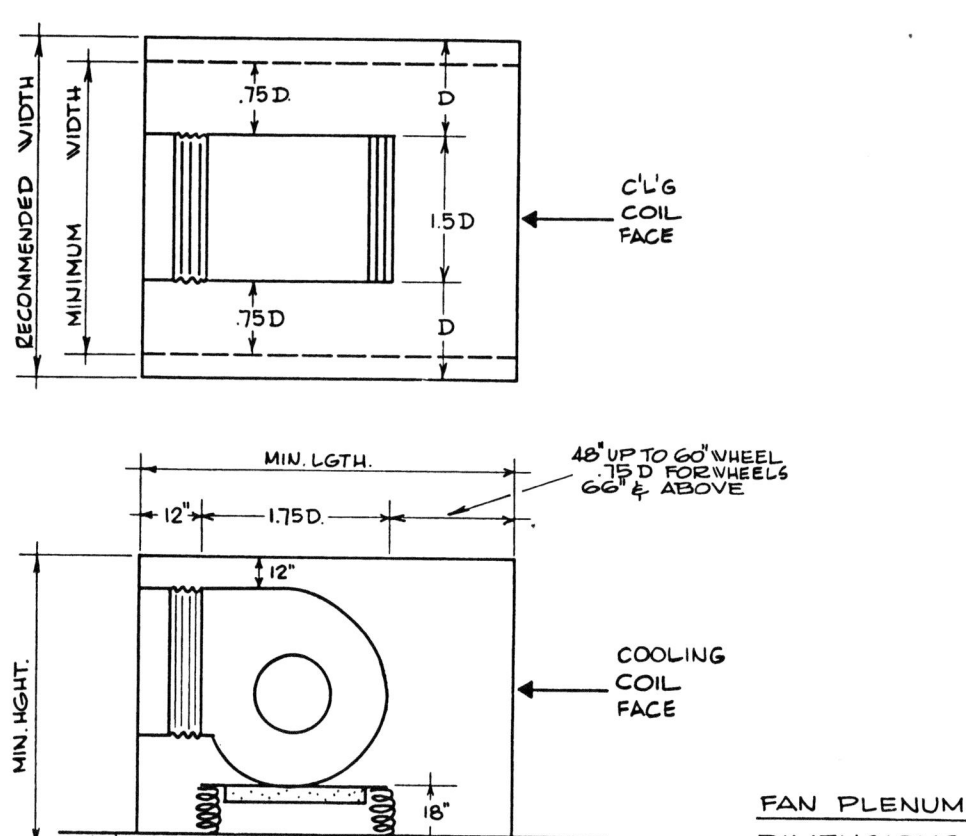

FAN PLENUM
DIMENSIONS

Wheel Diameter D, in.	Casing Width				Minimum Height, ft-in.	Minimum Length, ft-in.
	Minimum (3D)		Rec. Min. (3.5D)			
	in.	ft-in.	in.	ft-in.		
27	81	6-9	95	8-0	7-0	9-0
30	90	7-6	105	8-9	7-6	9-6
33	99	8-3	116	9-8	8-0	9-10
36	108	9-0	126	10-6	8-6	10 -3
40	120	10-0	140	11-9	9-3	10-10
44	132	11-0	154	12-10	9-10	11-6
49	147	12-3	171	14-2	10-8	12-2
54	162	13-6	189	15-9	11-6	13-0
60	180	15-0	210	17-6	12-6	13-9
66	198	16-0	231	19-3	13-6	14-9
73	219	18-4	256	21-3	14-6	16-3
81	243	20-3	284	23-3	16-0	17-10
89	267	22-3	312	26-0	17-6	19-8

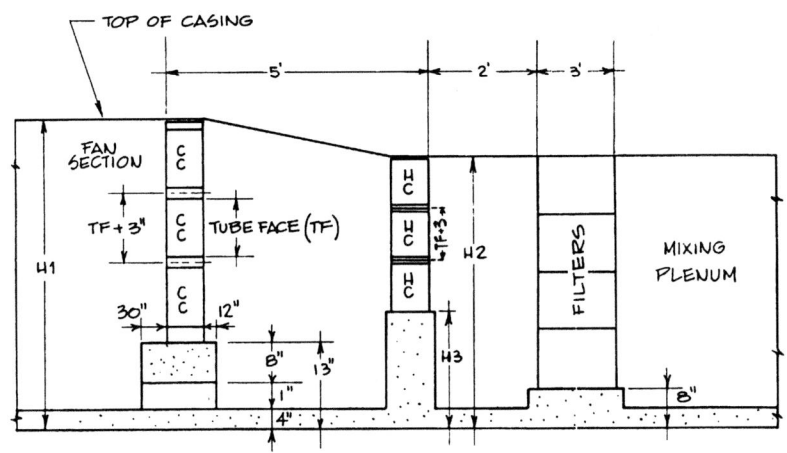

Casing Height H_1, ft-in. ($H_1 = N(TF+3)+1_3$)						
9'-4"	10'-10"	12'-4"	14'-1"	15'-11"	16'-1"	17'-4"
Number of Cooling Coils (N) and TF Dimension, in.						
(3) 30	(3) 36	(3) 42	(4) 36	(4) 39	(4) 42	(5) 36
Number of Heating Coils (N) and TF Dimension, in.						
(2) 30	(2) 36	(2) 42	(3) 33	(3) 36	(3) 39	(3) 42
Height of Heating Coils (N) and TF Dimension, in. (N(TF+3))						
66	78	90	108	117	126	135
Height of Bottom of Heating Coils H_3, in.						
38	52	40	44	35	50	41
Casing Height, $H_2= N(TF+3)+H_3$, in.						
104	130	130	152	152	176	176
Number of (24 in.) Filter High						
4	5	5	6	6	7	7

EXAMPLE :

FOR 50,000 CFM @ 4"
FAN : 44" WHEEL DIA.

COOLING COIL CASING - 9'-4" HIGH }
HTG. COIL & FILT. SECT. - 8'-8" HIGH } x 14 FT. WIDE

COOLING COILS :
(3) HIGH x (2) WIDE
30" FINNED FACE x 6'-6" LGTH. (EA.)

HEATING COILS :
(2) HIGH x (2) WIDE
30" FINNED FACE x 6'-6" LGTH.

FILTERS :
24" x 24" EA.
(4) HIGH x (7) WIDE = (28)

8'-8"   FA = 97.5 ∅
├── 14' ──┤

8'-8"   FA = 65 ∅
├── 14' ──┤

8'-8"
├── 14' ──┤

TOTAL SQ. FT. C.C. 97.5
TOTAL SQ. FT. H.C 65.0

L (2) 6'-6" TL
L (2) 6'-6" TL

(3) 30" T.F
(2) 30" T.F

FAN CASING MIN. DIM'S. 11' WIDE x 9'-10" HIGH

MAKE FAN CASING 9'-10" HIGH.
RAISE COOLING COIL 6" TO MATCH

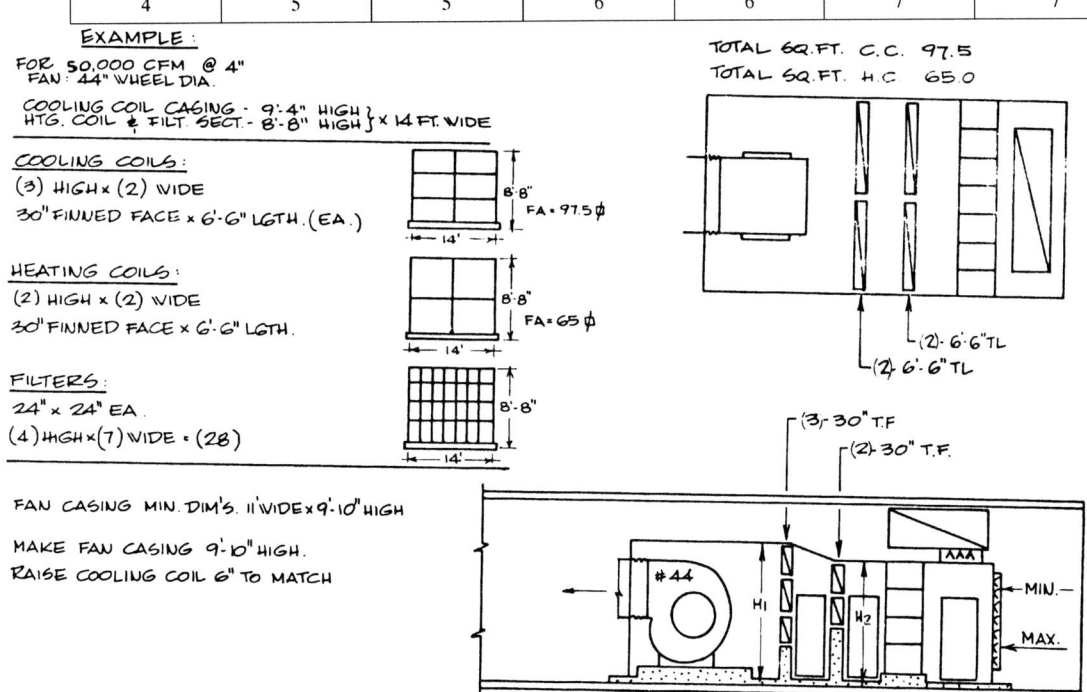

			Two-Coil Wide Units												
			Casing Width ft and Equivalent (in.)												
			14 (168)		16 (192)		18 (216)		20 (240)		22 (264)		24 (288)		25 (300)	
			Finned Tube Length (of each coil) in ft-in.												
Type Coil/ Casing Height Symbol	Casing Height, ft-in.	(No. of coils) and TF in.	6–6		7–6		8–6		9–6		10–6		11–6		12–0	
			Face Area ft²	1000 cfm	Face Area ft²	1000 cfm	Face Area ft²	1000 cfm	Face Area ft²	1000 cfm	Face Area ft²	1000 cfm	Face Area ft²	1000 cfm	Face Area ft²	1000 cfm
CC/H_1	9'-4"	(3) 30	97.5	48.7	112.5	56.2	127.5	64.0	142.5	71.2	157.5	79.0	172.5	86.0	...	...
HC/H_2	8'-8"	(2) 30	65	...	75	...	85	...	95	...	105	...	115	...	...	...
CC/H_1	10'-10"	(3) 36	117	58.5	135	67.5	153	76.5	171	85.5	189	94.5	207	103.5	...	...
HC/H_2	10'-10"	(2) 36	78	...	90	...	102	...	114	...	126	...	138	...	...	...
CC/H_1	12'-4"	(3) 42	136.5	68.2	151.5	80.0	178.5	89.0	199.5	100	220	110.0	242	121.0	...	...
HC/H_2	10'-10"	(2) 42	91	...	105	...	119	...	133	...	147	...	161	...	...	...
CC/H_1	14'-1"	(4) 36	156	78.0	180	90.0	204	102.0	228	114.0	252	126.0	288	144.0	...	...
HC/H_2	12'-8"	(3) 33	107	...	124	...	140	...	157	...	173	...	190	...	...	...
CC/H_1	15'-1"	(4) 38	169	84.5	195	97.5	221	110.0	247	123.5	273	136.5	299	149.5	...	...
HC/H_2	12'-8"	(3)36	117	...	135	...	153	...	171	...	189	...	207	...	...	...
CC/H_1	16'-1"	(4) 42	182	91.0	210	105.0	238	119.0	266	133.0	294	147.0	322	161.0	336	168.0
HC/H_2	14'-8"	(3) 39	127	...	146	...	166	...	135	...	205	...	224	...	117	
CC/H_1	17'-4"	(5) 36	...	...	...	...	...	...	...	...	315	157.0	345	172	360	180.0
HC/H_2	14'-8"	(3) 42	...	...	...	...	...	...	...	...	220	...	242	...	126	
CC/H_1	19'-10"	(5) 42	...	...	...	...	...	...	...	...	368	184.0	402	201	420	210
HC/H_2	16'-8"	(4) 36	...	...	...	...	...	...	...	...	252		276		288	

			One Coil Wide Units								
			Casing Width in ft and Equivalent (in.)								
			9(108)		10(120)		11(132)		12(144)		
			Tube Length (of each coil) in ft-in.								
			8-6		9-6		10-6		11-6		
CC/H_1	8-7	(2) 42	59.5	29.8	86.5	33.2	73.5	36.8	80.5	40.2	
HC/H_2	8-7	(2) 30	42.5	...	47.5	...	52.5	...	57.5	...	
CC/H_1	9-4	(3) 30	63.8	32.0	71.3	35.6	78.8	39.6	86.3	42.1	
HC/H_2	8-8	(2) 30	42.5	...	47.5	...	52.5	...	57.5	...	
CC/H_1	10-10	(3) 36	75.5	38.3	85.5	42.8	94.5	47.3	103.5	51.8	
HC/H_2	10-10	(2) 36	50.5	...	57	...	63	...	69	...	
CC/H_1	12-4	(3) 42	89	44.6	99.6	49.9	110	55.0	121	60.4	
HC/H_2	10-10	(2) 42	59.5	...	66.5	...	73.5	...	80.5	...	
CC/H_1	14-1	(4) 36	104	52.0	114	57.0	126	87	138	69.0	
HC/H_2	12-8	(3) 33	70	...	78.5	...	63.0	...	101	...	

Note: data based on 500 fpm coil face velocity 2200 fpm max. fan outlet velocity
CC

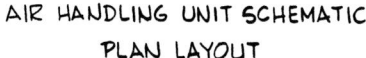

AIR HANDLING UNIT SCHEMATIC
PLAN LAYOUT

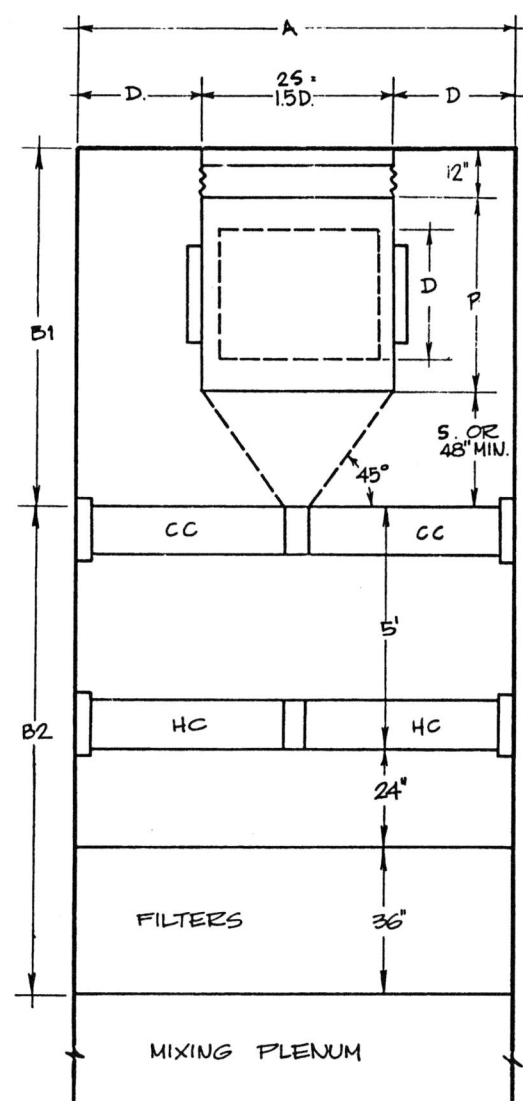

FAN HEIGHT = F
MIN. HEIGHT = F + 3'

MIN. HT.
= F + 3

$B1 = 12" + P + S$ (OR 48")
$A = 2S + 2D$
$S = .75D$
$A = 1.5D + 2D = 3.5D$
$B2 = 10'-0"$

Casing Width, W ft					
24	22	20	18	16	14
Net coil tube length, ft (2 coils wide)					
23	21	19	17	15	13
Tube length of each coil, ft-in.					
11-6″	10-6″	9-6″	8-6″	7′-6″	6′-6″
Number of 24 -in. Filters Wide					
12	11	10	9	8	7

Well Water Air Conditioning

When groundwater is cold enough, a direct supply to cooling coils will eliminate the need for refrigeration in air conditioning systems. Well water is usually a little too warm to accomplish the dehumidification required. In that case, water may be used advantageously for precooling outside air prior to refrigerated cooling and dehumidification, thus reducing the amount of refrigeration needed. In addition, the leaving water from the precooling coil is still cold enough to be an excellent source of condensing water, eliminating the need for and making it thermodynamically superior to a cooling tower or air cooled condenser for the refrigeration system.

Heat Pump/Solar Energy Application

As part of an energy management research and development program, the Georgia Power Company commissioned its demonstration project *Answer House* to illustrate the combined uses of electric heat pump, heat storage, and solar energy systems.

Atlanta Answer House contains 1984 ft^2 of living space. The design is country ranch containing three bedrooms, two baths, great room and fireplace, kitchen, two-car garage, and expandable attic. The structure is 2" × 6" frame construction with wood siding exterior, wood floor over crawl space, and partial basement.

Ceiling construction uses raised trusses, with 6" batt and 8" blown insulation, foil backed sheetrock, giving an *R*-value of 39. The wall construction is 2" × 6" studs, 24" o.c., 1" exterior foam sheeting, 6" friction fit batts, foil backed sheetrock, giving an *R*-value of 24. Floors are constructed using wood and carpet, 6" batt insulation, giving an *R*-value of 22. Windows are double pane with storm windows, representing only 9% of the floor area. Special equipment includes solar heating and water heating with heat pump thermal storage cooling, high efficiency appliances, and fresh air intake type fireplace.

Heat loss for the Atlanta Answer House was 6.1 kw vs. 11.9 kw for a minimum property standard house of this type. Heat gain was 12298 Btu/hr vs. 25,493 Btu/hr for a minimum property standard house. In order to meet these requirements, a special solar heating and off-peak storage cooling system was designed.

Solar Heating and Off-Peak Storage Cooling System.—The system designed for the Atlanta house integrates:

    A) direct solar heat
    B) solar augmented electric heat pump
    C) off-peak electric cooling, and
    D) dehumidification.

The characteristics of the system are:
    A) lower electric heat consumption
    B) load management.
        1) Low winter/summer peak demands, and
        2) off-peak demands,

    C) multipurpose equipment utilization,
    D) pre-engineered package,
    E) simple installation.

The controls involved are a room thermostat, room humidistat, manual heat/cool switch, and manual winter/summer switch. The system was built for ease of installation by integrating the compressor, evaporator, condenser, and all pumps, valves and controls in one package 2' × 2' × 3'.

The solar collector is a low-cost collector with low installation cost and efficiency equivalent to conventional nonselective coated collectors. The concept is simply to flow a nontoxic, nonflammable, transparent fluid with good wetting characteristics and a very low vapor pressure over a black sheet metal pan under a single sheet of fiberglass glazing. The collector is built into the roof rafter structure with the fiberglass glazing serving as the weatherproof covering. There are approximately 700 ft^2 of collectors on the roof.

System Description and Operation.—A schematic of the components of the system is shown in Fig. 13-77. They include:
    1) central energy management package
    2) closed circuit outside water-to-air coil
    3) domestic solar hot water storage tank
    4) air handler with hot and chilled water coils and emergency resistance duct heater
    5) solar collector heat exchanger
    6) solar collector
    7) main water storage tank with immersion heater.

The system operates in nine modes. The proper mode is determined by the input information from:
    1) house thermostat
    2) house humidistat
    3) collector temperature sensor
    4) main storage tank temperature sensor
    5) domestic hot water tank temperature sensor
    6) position of winter/summer switch (changed once a year).

The modes are shown in concept by Figs. 13-79 to 13-87.

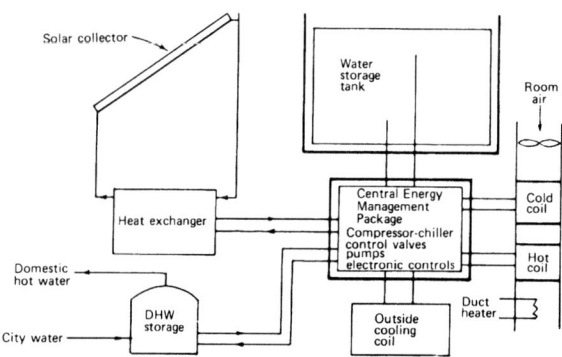

Fig 13-77. Component layout

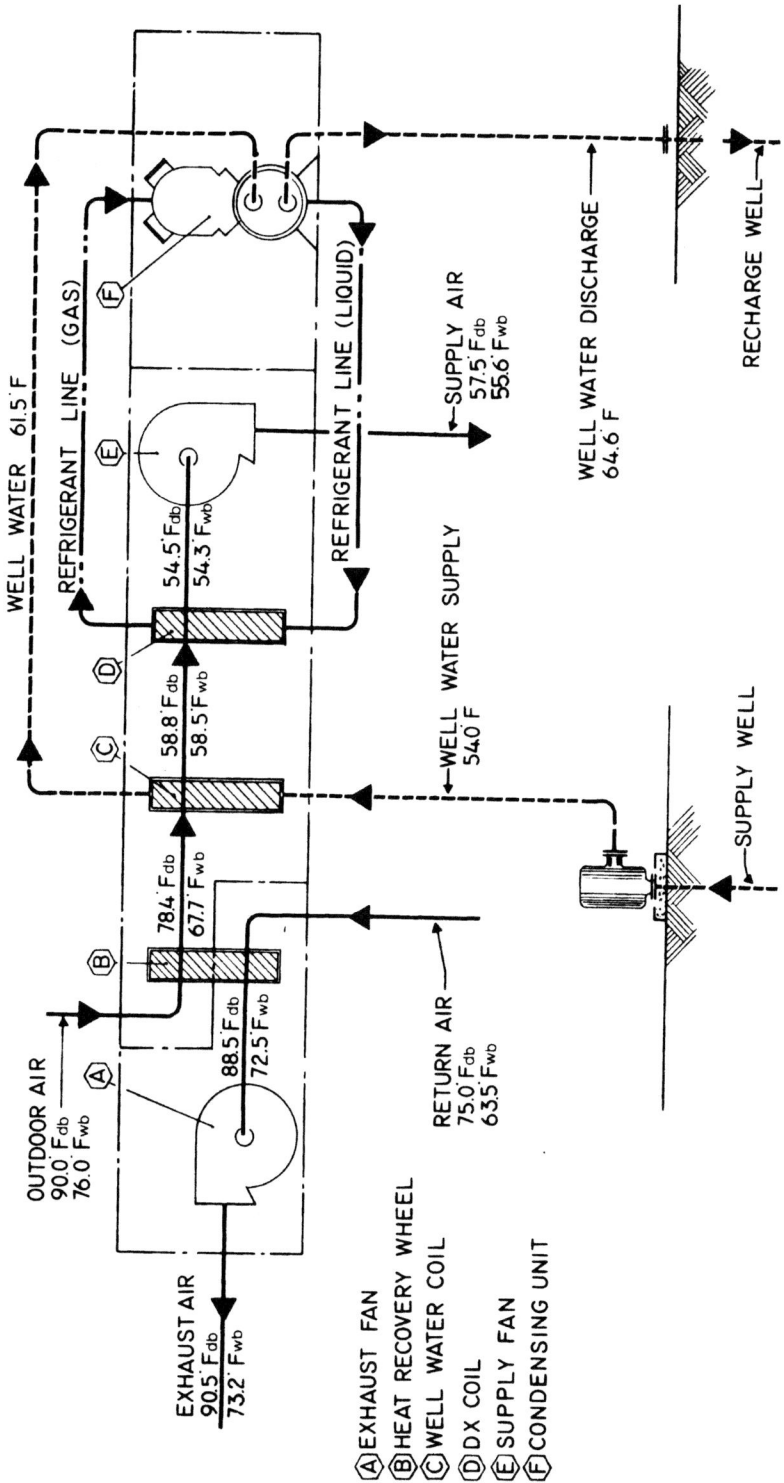

Fig 13-78. Schematic of well water precooling and refrigerant condensing system

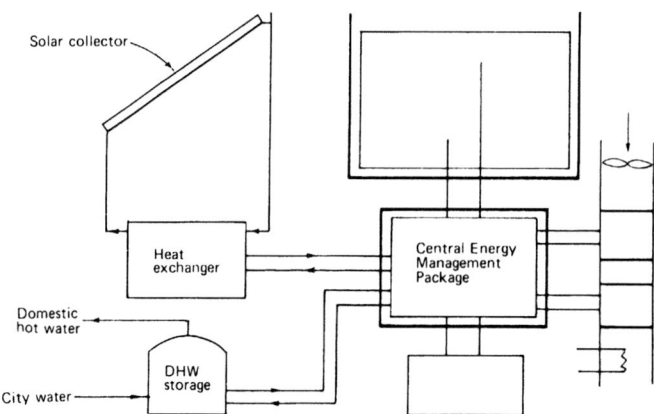

Fig 13-79. Solar heating of domestic hot water

Hot water from the collector heat exchanger is circulated through the coil in the bottom of the domestic hot water storage tank. This modes take priority over the following mode.

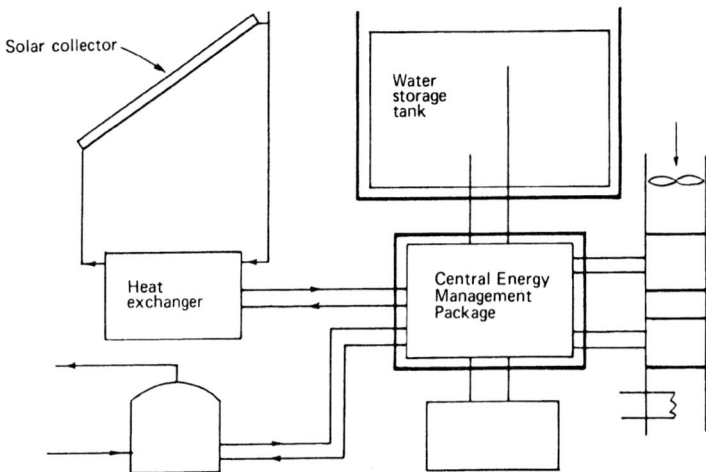

Fig 13-80. Solar heating of main storage tank

This occurs only during the winter and is accomplished by the storage tank water being circulated through the collector heat exchanger

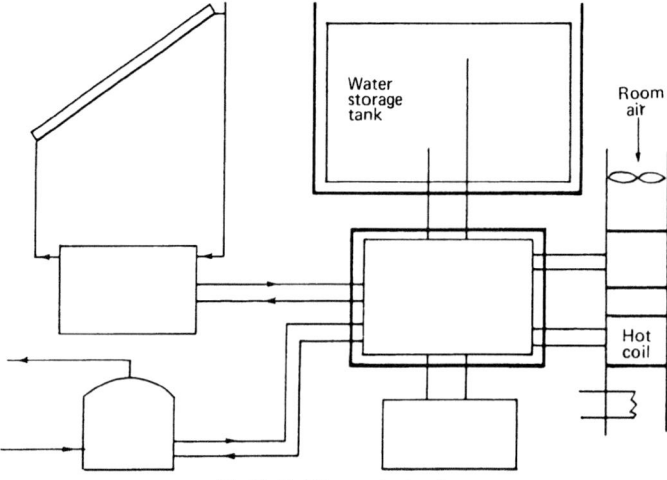

Fig 13-81. Direct solar heating

When the house calls for heating and the tank is above 100°F, hot water from the main storage tank is circulated through the hot water coil in the air handler.

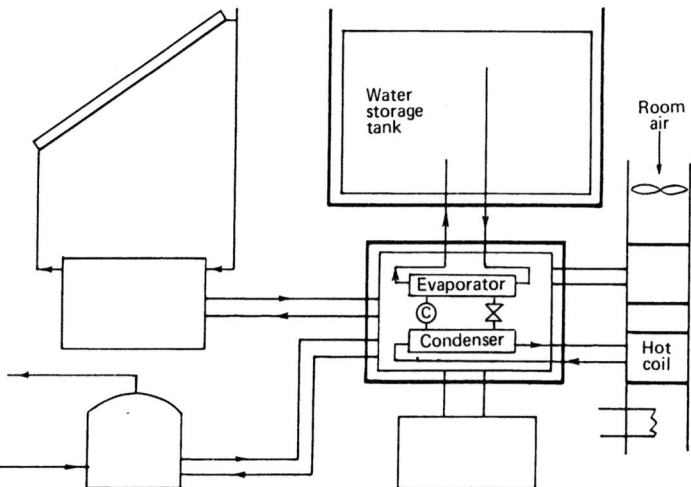

Fig 13-82. Solar augmented heat pump heating

IF the main storage tank temperature is less than 100°F, or if the house thermostat goes to its 2nd stage, indicating inadequate heat is available from the direct solar heating mode, the compressor comes on, which acts as a water to water heat pump, cooling the main storage tank and producing 105°F hot water from the condenser. This hot water is circulated through the hot water coil in the air handler.

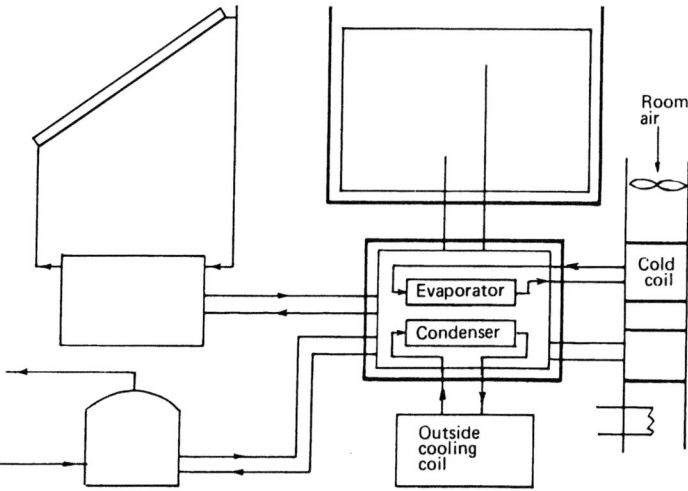

Fig 13-83. Utility off-peak space cooling

During the late fall, winter, and early spring, as well as day off peak summer nights, the house is cooled when necessary by the compressor acting as a conventional air conditioner, circulating chilled water through the cold coil in the air handler while the hot condenser water is cooled by the outside air cooling coil. (This coil is automatically drained to the lower main storage tank when the circulating pump or valve is turned off, to prevent winter freezing.)

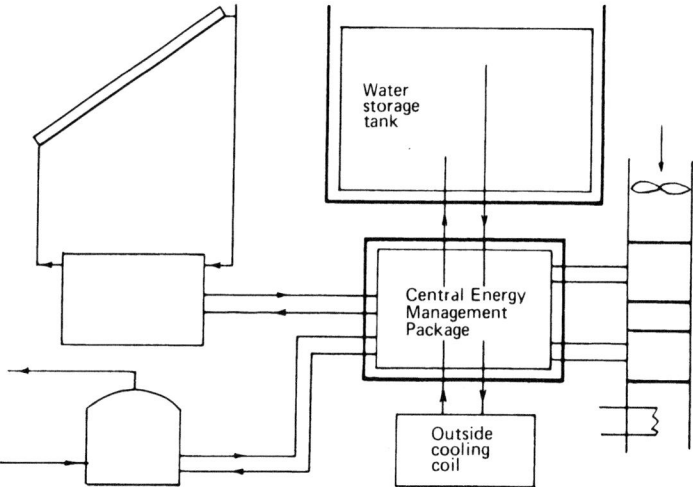

Fig 13-84. Winter to summer tank transition

When the manual winter/summer switch is turned on to the summer position, the tank water is generally be hot and is automatically cooled to outside ambient temperature by circulating water to the outside water-to -air cooling coil.

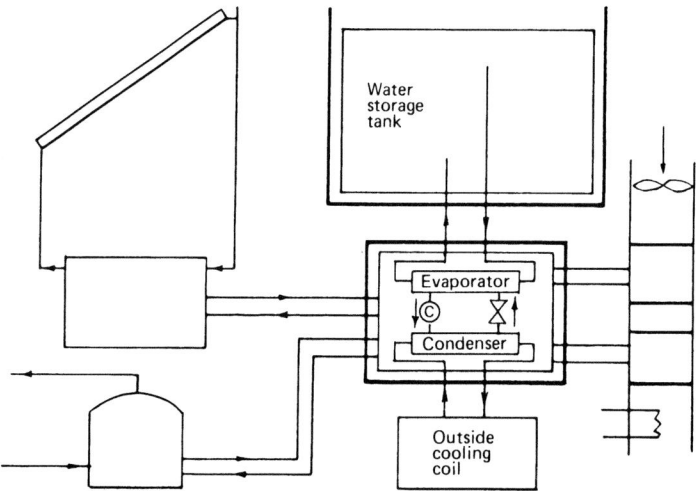

Fig 13-85. Cold storage

During the low electric utility demand periods in the summer (nights), a time clock in the central energy management package allows the compressor to run, to cool the tank. When the tank temperature reaches 40°F, the compressor shut off.

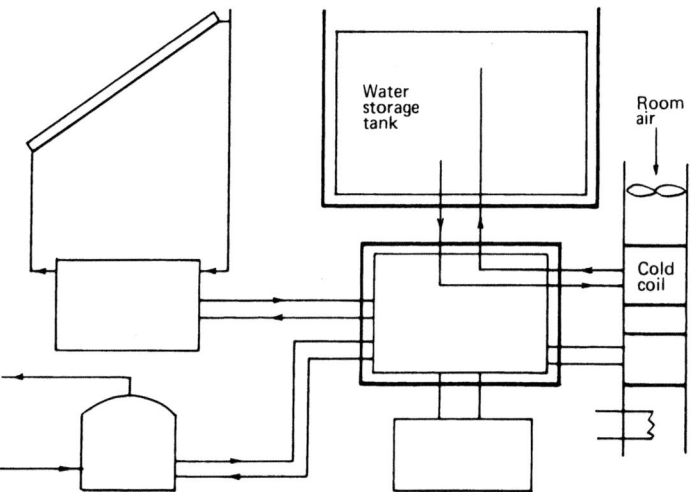

Fig 13-86. Utility off-peak space cooling

During high electrical utility demand periods (hot summer afternoons), the compressor is not allowed to run. When the house thermostat calls for cooling, chilled water from the main tank is circulated through the chilled water coil in the handler.

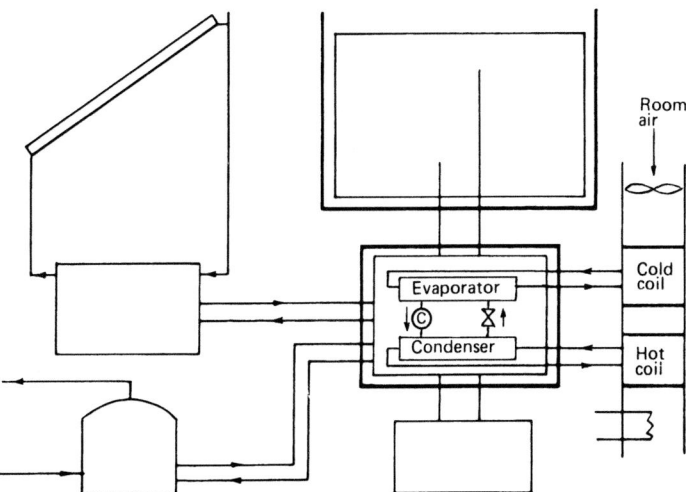

Fig 13-87. Dehumidification

When the house humidistat calls for dehumidification, the compressor comes on, producing chilled water from the evaporator, which is circulated through the chilled water coil to coil and dehumidify the house air. Hot water from the condenser is circulated through the hot water coil to reheat the air before it is returned to the house.

High Velocity Dual Duct Systems

Dual duct systems as referred to in the discussion that follows are air conditioning systems for multizone applications. They employ two parallel ducts, one carrying warm air, the other cold air, thus providing a constant air source for heating and cooling at all times.

In each conditioned space or zone, a mixing valve responsive to a room thermostat mixes the warm and cold air in proper proportions to satisfy the instantaneous heat load of the space. In high and medium pressure systems the volumetric delivery of air is controlled at terminal points in each air mixing unit. In systems with low pressures, the rise in air delivery during partial load operation may sometimes be restricted by controlling air pressures at various points in the duct system.

Advantages and Disadvantages.—The principal advantages of dual duct air conditioning systems are these:

1) all conditioning equipment is centrally located, simplifying maintenance and operation;

2) the system can cool and heat simultaneously without the necessity of central zoning or seasonal changeover;

3) on all-air dual duct systems there is no water-and-steam piping, electrical equipment or wiring in conditioned spaces;

4) the system can utilize outdoor air for cooling purposes in intermediate seasons;

5) the system can be used in combination with direct radiation or other conditioning methods without interference or conflict among the several types of systems. This quality of dual duct system is especially valuable in existing buildings because no change or removal of existing heating system is required;

6) the system has great flexibility to meet specific design or cost objectives on any particular project.

Limitations of dual duct systems in large buildings include these:

1) to make the system mechanically stable, a large number of control points must be inserted in the air stream of the distributing system for control of volumetric delivery;

2) the space limitations and the necessity of running two ducts instead of one requires higher velocities and pressures in the duct system than in conventional systems;

3) the arrangement of two parallel ducts with crossovers to terminal mixing units requires special attention and study on the part of designer and installer;

4) accessibility to terminal mixing devices demands close cooperation between architectural, mechanical, and structural designers.

The necessity of using higher pressures and velocities in dual duct conduits for conditioning large buildings introduces additional problems which are actually inherent to all high pressure systems:

1) dynamic losses in high velocity fittings and take-off are not yet determined with sufficient degree of accuracy;

2) temperature gains and losses in high velocity ducts and flexible tubing also can be determined only approximately, and more, basic research is needed on this subject;

3) high velocities and pressures introduce acoustical problems.

No standard method of presenting acoustical ratings for component parts of high velocity air handling systems has yet been established. Because of this the designer must rely partly on empirical information in achieving desired acoustical results in conditioned spaces.

Dual Duct Cycles.—Basic dual duct cycles applicable to multizone installations are shown by diagram in Figs. 13-88 to 13-92. Modification to the arrangements shown may be dictated by design conditions. These cycles actually represent no new concept in the air conditioning process. Thermodynamically, all dual duct cycles are equivalent to conventional single duct systems, with face and bypass dampers at the cooling coils. Functionally, the cold and warm air duct dampers in dual duct mixing units are the same as the face and bypass dampers in a conventional single duct system, except that the dual duct system automatically possesses flexibility to zone each area independently.

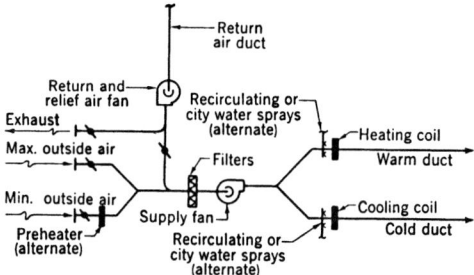

Fig 13-88. Single fan dual duct cycle with blow through dehumidifier

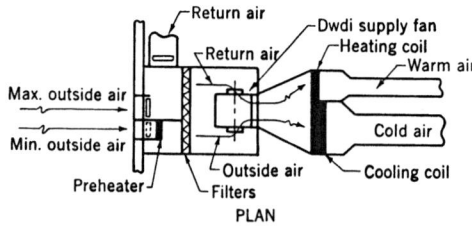

Fig 13-89. Single fan dual duct cycle with stratified air

Since most buildings are not centrally zoned for dual duct systems, consideration must be given to maintenance of conditions in lightly loaded zones or no-load zones. The ability of the system to maintain conditions in no-load zones might be considered a criterion of adequacy of design for a particular installation. Though it is conceivable that on systems with selective temperature controls even more severe loading conditions may occur, experience has shown that when dual duct systems for comfort application are designed to satisfy the conditions of no-load zones, such systems in actual operation will maintain the desired room conditions at all times.

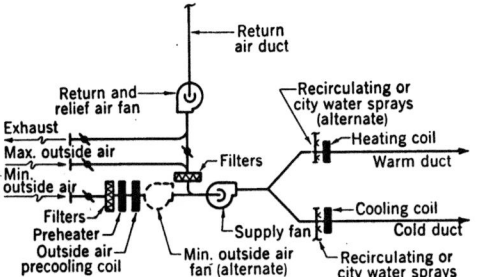

Fig 13-90. Single fan dual duct cycle with additional minimum outside air dehumidifier

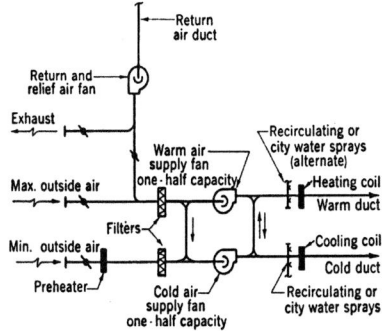

Fig 13-91. Two fan dual duct cycle with blow through dehumidifier

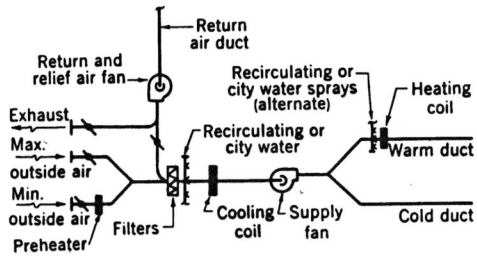

Fig 13-92. Single fan dual duct cycle with push through dehumidifier

The no-load zones are represented on psychrometric charts of Figs. 13-93 and 13-94 by point 2. Thermostats controlling no-load zones will demand a mixture of air from cold and warm air ducts in such proportion as to make the temperature of supply air and room air the same. Practically speaking, provisions for maintenance of conditions in no-load zones will be met if cold air temperatures are kept at a sufficiently low level. The temperature range of 50 to 55°F in the cold air duct is standardized in dual duct systems.

If the volumetric delivery of supply air is controlled and the ceiling outlets are properly selected, temperature differentials (room air temperature minus supply air temperature) as high as 25–30°F can be used. High temperature differentials also can be used if the air from under window type units is discharged through high velocity, high entrainment type outlets or slots.

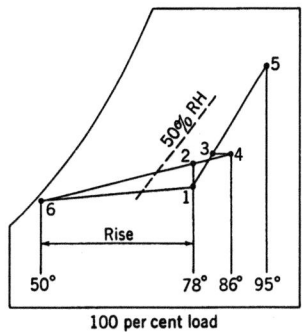

Fig 13-93. Psychrometric chart for dual duct system for Fig. 13-88 full load

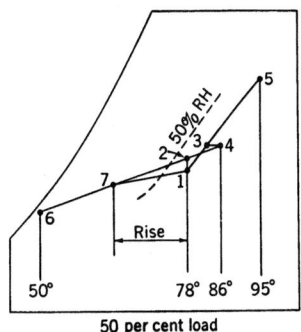

Fig 13-94. Psychrometric chart for dual duct system for Fig. 13-88 50% load

Outdoor air dampers at the central apparatus are usually split into two sections, one for minimum, the other for maximum outdoor air volume. The maximum outdoor air damper is interlocked with the return and relief dampers and used whenever outdoor air is favorable for cooling purposes, In climates where outdoor air is not suitable for cooling, only minimum outdoor air need be provided for ventilating requirements. Return fans shown may be eliminated on small installations if provisions are made to relieve the excess outdoor air from the conditioned spaces. The main function of cold chamber sprays is to effect evaporative cooling during intermediate seasons for operating economy. The cold sprays are arranged to operate prior to the opening of the maximum outdoor dampers, thus decreasing the load on the heating coil in the warm chamber. Warm chamber sprays are only installed when control of humidity is required for winter operation.

In recent years, usage of water sprays on dual duct comfort installations has greatly diminished, especially in large cities, because of operating and maintenance problems associated with sprays.

An important point in the design of dual duct systems is the close relationship between the first cost of the system and the total amount of air handled. The first cost and annual owning and operating cost will always be reduced by using lower temperature in the cold air stream—a wide differential between room temperature and cold air supply temperature.

Cycle of Figs. 13-88, and 13-89: Fig. 13-88 shows the simplest, least costly, and most compact apparatus arrangement for dual duct air conditioning.

Thermostats located in each zone control the dry bulb temperature by mixing warm and cold air to give desired results. Close control of relative humidity is not essential and is never attempted for systems installed to produce comfort conditions. It has been established that humidity variations between 35 and 55, are adequate for summer operation with room dry bulb temperatures between 74 and 78°F.

Cold air stream temperature is normally set at 50°F, with the air nearly saturated. The warm air stream, for summer operation, is maintained at not less than 5°F above the average return air temperature. In winter the warm air temperature varies with that of the outdoor air.

Thermodynamically, this cycle is equivalent to a single duct system having face and bypass dampers at the cooling coil, arranged to bypass a mixture of outdoor and recirculated air in response to a zone thermostat, as internal heat load fluctuates. With falling internal heat load and prevailing high outdoor dew point temperatures, the cycle will produce a rise in room relative humidities unless reheat is added to the warm air.

Psychrometric representations of this cycle for specific design conditions are shown in Figs. 13-93 and 13-94.

In these two figures, the numbers on the psychrometric chart represent:
1) average room air
2) no load zone conditions
3) average mixture of room and 25% outdoor air
4) heat of compression of supply fan
5) warm air
6) outdoor air
7) cold air
8) mixture of cold and warm air entering room at 50% load

Fig. 13-93 shows the state of air when internal heat gain is maximum. Fig. 13-94 shows the conditions when internal heat gain falls to 50% of maximum. Note that both points 1 and 2, representing conditions of average room air and no-load zone, are higher when the system is operating at partial load. If maximum outdoor design conditions, as shown by point 5 in Figs. 13-93 and 13-94 remain constant through the entire range of operation from 0 to 100% of internal heat load. the resulting average room conditions can be shown by curve B in Fig. 13-95. Corresponding conditions of the no-load zone could be represented by the dotted line. Additional curves A, C, D, and E are plotted for arbitrarily warm air temperatures and show average resulting room conditions with different temperatures of the warm air.

To limit the rise of humidity in conditioned spaces to, say, 50% φ, the systems shown would require reheat in the warm air when the internal sensible heat load reduces to 28% of maximum, as shown by point X. If this system were designed with 55°F air in the cold air duct, the conditions of average room air and no-load zone over the whole range of internal sensible heat loads would be as shown in Fig. 13-96. In such a system reheat would be required when the internal sensible load falls to approximately 64% of maximum. Furthermore, it would be impossible to prevent rise of humidities in no-load zones above 50% rh under any condition. Since, in actual operation, internal partial loads coincide with lower outdoor dew point temperatures, the build-up of relative humidities in conditioned spaces can never be as critical as theoretical calculations indicate.

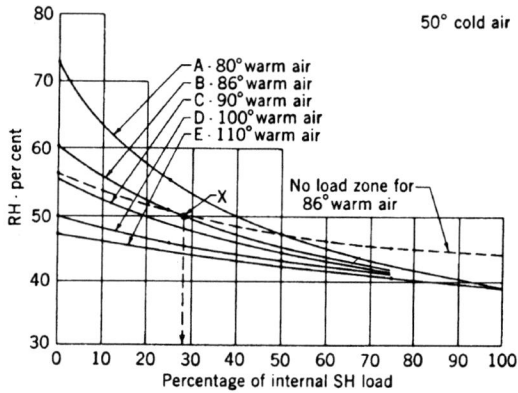

Fig 13-95. Performance over rate of internal sensible heat load; system of Fig. 13-88 and 13-89 for 50°F cold air

The graphs of Figs. 13-95 and 13-96 are based on 25% outside air at 95°F dry bulb, 75°F wet bulb, 99 grains moisture/lb of dry air, and room air temperature of 78°F dry bulb.

This cycle can be used for most multizone comfort installations which are operated during regular hours and located in moderate climates. Because there is direct bypass of outdoor air into the warm air duct, the application of this cycle is usually limited to systems which do not require more than 40% of full fan capacity for ventilation of minimum outside air.

The dual duct cycle in Fig. 13-88 will behave as described only if there is a perfect mixture of air on the leaving side of the supply fan. If the air stratifies, as may happen when double-width, double-inlet fans are used, the performance of the cycle alters. When the apparatus is arranged as shown in Fig. 13-89, the cycle performance resembles the performance of the arrangements shown in Fig. 13-91. In Fig. 13-91 the fan discharges the moist outdoor air to the cooling coil and return air to the warm air duct coil. This arrangement of the cycle is applicable even to structures located in humid climates because only a small part of moist outdoor air will be bypassed in the warm air duct. If the position of return air and minimum outdoor air were reversed, the cycle would be objectionable for all applications. If the apparatus is arranged as shown in Fig. 13-89 the control instruments in the cold chamber should be of averaging type and care should be exercised not to connect separate mains to opposite sides of the cold or warm apparatus chamber.

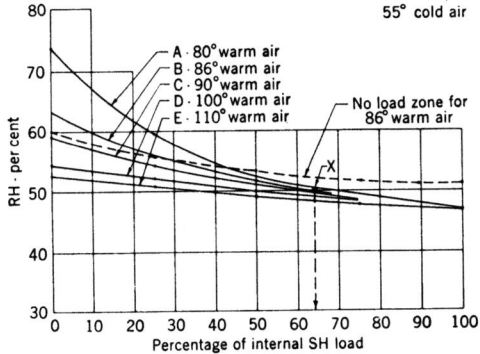

Fig 13-96. Performance over rate of internal sensible heat load; system of Figs. 13-88 and 13-89 for 55°F cold air

It is recommended that a stratified arrangement in the apparatus room be used only on smaller installations in warmer climates. Stratified air in larger plants on installations located in colder climates is inadvisable because of danger of freezeups of cooling coils and because of control and operating difficulties.

Cycle of Fig. 13-90: The arrangement in Fig. 13-90 overcomes the objection of bypassing excessively humid outdoor air to the warm air duct on partial loads. The minimum outdoor air is normally precooled to a point that will not necessitate the application of reheat in the warm air duct on high summer loads. Precooling with well water or with water leaving main cooling coils is ideally suitable for application to this cycle. Otherwise, the performance of this cycle is similar to that of the cycle illustrated in Fig. 13-88 but with reduced rate of humidity built up on partial loads.

Again, care must be exercised so as not to stratify the air in cold and warm apparatus chambers, especially on large installations in colder climates.

This cycle could be applied to all systems that might be called upon to operate at low internal loads while high humidity conditions prevail outdoors. The systems serving hotels, hospitals, or apartment buildings fall into this classification.

Cycle of Fig. 13-91: The two-fan system shown in Fig. 13-91 is the most economical to operate and will permit very close control of room humidities when less than half of total air is handled by the warm air duct. During this time the system will be equivalent to a single duct system with face and bypass dampers at the cooling coils where only return air is bypassed around the cooling coil. On a further drop in the internal load, which will increase the

flow of air in the warm air duct over approximately half of the total system capacity, the performance of this cycle will resemble more and more that of the cycle of Fig. 13-88. The application of reheat to the warm air duct coil will still be necessary to depress the relative humidities in the conditioned spaces during partial load operation when dew point temperature of outdoor air is high.

The general behavior of the system is shown in Fig. 13-97. Note that the rate of build-up of humidity is relatively low, while internal SH (sensible heat) load of the system decreases from 100 to 50%. Actually, in this range the no-load curve and average room condition curve 4 coincide. On further decrease in load, the humidity of both average zone and no-load zone will rise rapidly until it reaches a point where addition of reheat will be necessary. The point of application of reheat is shown at point X, which occurs when internal SH load is 30%. Note also that the curves of Fig. 13-97 are plotted on the assumption that maximum outdoor air design conditions will prevail through the entire range of operation of the system. As pointed out, in actual practice the system will operate under more favorable conditions and the demand for the reheat will not be as critical as indicated in Fig. 13-97. This diagram is based on 25%; outside air at 95°F dry bulb and 75°F wet bulb with 98 grains moisture per pound of dry air and average room temperature is 80°F dry bulb.

Application of this cycle should be limited to smaller installations located in warmer climates. As stated previously, a stratified arrangement of apparatus on larger installations in colder climates may cause cooling coil freeze-ups and will be difficult to control and to operate.

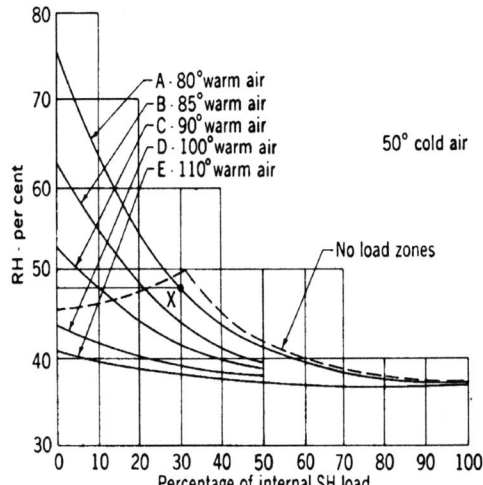

Fig 13-97. Performance over whole range of internal sensible heat load; system of Fig. 13-91 for 50°F cold air

Cycle of Fig. 13-92: Fig. 13-92 shows an arrangement that will permit very close control of relative humidities in the conditioned spaces through the entire range of operation. However, the operating cost of the cycle, because of continuous demand for reheat, is relatively high. Further, additional refrigeration must be provided in most installations to treat the air that will be bypassed to the warm air duct under conditions of maximum loading. For reasons of economy, use of this cycle is not justified for the majority of comfort installations and is restricted only to special applications.

System Design: The design of a dual duct system does not involve any new concepts. All basic principles, procedures, and standards are fully developed and appear in the technical literature. The accepted codes and practices of all recognized groups are equally applicable to the design of a dual duct system. The objective of this discussion is to point out and to discuss only the specific problems and practices associated with handling air in two parallel streams.

Calculating Air Quantities: Air quantities required for a dual duct air handling system are derived from Equations (6) - (12):

$$cfm_c = \frac{\dot{q}_s}{1.10(T_r - T_c)} \quad (6)$$

$$cfm_w = \frac{\dot{q}_w}{1.10(T_w - T_r)} \quad (7)$$

$$cfm_v = \frac{cfm_o}{R_o} \quad (8)$$

$$cfm = cfm_z^1 + cfm_z^2 + cfm_z^3 + \ldots + cfm_z^{n-1} + cfm_z^n \quad (9)$$

$$cfm = cfm_c + cfm_w \quad (10)$$

For summer design conditions,

$$\dot{q}_s + 1.10 cfm_w(T_w - T_r) = 1.10 cfm_c(T_r - T_c) \quad (11)$$

For winter design conditions,

$$\dot{q}_s + 1.10 cfm_c(T_r - T_c) = 1.10 cfm_w(T_w - T_r) \quad (12)$$

where T_r = room air dry bulb temperature, °F

T_c = cold air dry bulb temperature, °F

T_w = warm air dry bulb temperature, °F

$\dot{q}_s$ = total internal sensible heat load system during summer peak, Btu/hr

$\dot{q}_w$ = total internal sensible heat load system during winter peak, Btu/hr

cfm = total air handled by the supply fan

cfm_c = total cold air required by the system during summer or winter peak, cfm

cfm_w = total warm air required by the system during summer or winter peak, cfm

cfm_o = total outdoor air required by the system, cfm

cfm_v = total air required by a particular zone to satisfy ventilating conditions, cfm

cfm_z = total zone air, subscripts refer to auxiliary zone number

R_o = ratio of outside air to total air in the system.

Since all zones of a dual duct system are supplied by a substantial constant volume of air at all times, the air requirements for each zone must be checked for demands of summer and winter peaks and for ventilating requirements. The highest value is used to establish the zone cfm.

Equations (6), (7) and (8) are used to establish these demands. In structures where heating is done by perimeter radiation, only Equations (6) and (8) are used for this purpose.

The total air volume to be supplied by the system must be equal to the sum of the peaks of all zones. Peaks for each zone or room are established by Equations (6), (7) or (8).

Equations (10) and (12) determine the total cold and warm air quantities for summer peak operation. The second term of equation Equation (12) represents heat bypassed in the warm air duct under maximum load conditions. The solution of Equations (5) and (7) will establish the cold and warm air demand for winter peak operation. The second term of Equation (7) will represent the net cooling effect due to bypass of cold air in the cold air duct during the winter peak. The second terms of both Equations (6) and (7) actually do not constitute a *system penalty* but represent part of the ventilating load and heat of compression of the supply fan.

Example 4: The following illustrates how to determine system air quantities by using Equations (6)- (8).

cfm is given as 60000, having been calculated from Equations (6)- (8). Also given are:

$$T_r(\text{summer}) = 78°F$$

$$T_c(\text{summer}) = 50°F$$

$$T_w(\text{summer}) = 86°F$$

$$\dot{q}_s(\text{summer}) = 1400000 \text{ Btu/h}$$

$$T_r(\text{winter}) = 75°F$$

$$T_c(\text{winter}) = 55°F$$

$$T_w(\text{winter}) = 125°F$$

$$\dot{q}_w(\text{winter}) = 2100000 \text{ Btu/h}$$

Solution: Determine cold and warm quantities for peak summer and winter operation:

For summer operation:

$$\dot{q}_s + 1.10cfm_w(T_w - T_r) = 1.10cfm_c(T_r - T_c)$$

$$1400000 + 1.10 \times cfm_w \times (86 - 78)$$

$$= 1.10 \times cfm_c \times (78 - 50)$$

$$1400000 + 8.8cfm_w = 30.8cfm_c$$

$$30.8cfm_c - 8.8cfm_w = 1400000$$

$$cfm = cfm_c + cfm_w = 60000$$

By solving the last two equations;

$$cfm_w = 11300 \text{ cfm}$$

$$cfm_c = 48700 \text{ cfm}$$

Air Quantities: After the air quantities needed for each zone are established by Equations (6) to (8), the exact determination of air flow in the cold and warm air ducts becomes a rather time-consuming process, especially on larger installations. In cold air ducts, for example, it will be necessary to calculate flow at two or three periods of the day to establish the highest rate of flow in different branches. The calculated rate of flow then has to be corrected for the warm air bypass if the design warm air temperatures are higher than the average room design temperatures. During the heating season, actual demand for maximum warm air in each zone has to be calculated and then corrected to compensate for cold air bypass in the cold air duct. At the same time, the flow through the warm air ducts should be analyzed, considering partial load operation during the cooling cycle.

For a system that feeds both exterior and interior zones, a simplified procedure may be used as follows to establish air quantities for sizing cold and warm air ducts. For most comfort installations this procedure, if followed, will introduce a slight safety factor in the design of the duct system as compared to exact calculations. In general, the steps are:

1) Size the cooling coil for the quantity of cold air calculated from Equations (10) and (11).

2) Establish the ratio of total summer cold air to the total system air. In the example given, it will be 49,500/60,000 = 0.83.

3) Using Table 13-8 select a corresponding factor from column B and use this as a multiplier for all zone air quantities as established by Equation (6), (7) or (8). The factor for the example would be 0.90. The air quantities established in this manner can be considered to be simultaneous peak requirements for design of cold air ducts.

4) After the cold air duct sizes are determined, select the corresponding area ratio of warm air duct to cold air duct from columns C or D of Table 13-8 and use this ratio as a multiplier in determining warm air duct sizes. The ratio in the example will either be 0.75×Col C or 0.85×Col D, depending upon the type of the system.

5) Select the dual duct mixing units and size low pressure ducts leaving the unit using the total zone cfm as established by Equations (6) to (8).

As an alternate to the procedure described above, the cold air quantities and cold air duct sizes could be determined by any desired method and warm air ducts then sized by using factors from columns C or D of Table 13-8. The alternate procedure may be, more desirable when the central systems are zoned or when the duct mains supply air to either interior or exterior zones.

The practice of undersizing warm air ducts has been the cause in many cases of serious acoustical problems. A system may be designed to handle a relatively small quantity of warm air. However, there are many sets of operating conditions that may cause much higher air flow in the warm air duct than calculated, thus generating rumbling and other noises in the duct system.

Duct Sizing Technique.—After the general scheme of the ductwork is established, and the air to be supplied to each section of the system is calculated, the actual sizing of the ductwork does not differ greatly from that used for other systems.

In dual duct systems, where volume regulation is accomplished at terminal points, the duct sizing technique is even less critical than for other systems, and extreme precision in duct sizing becomes superfluous. The ducts may be sized by equal friction, static regain or velocity methods, or a combination of all three, if desired. Volume regulators in mixing units will absorb all pressure unbalance caused by the initial design, partial load operation or future unavoidable changes in load distribution and will produce a mechanically stable system under all operating conditions, irrespective of the method or procedure used for duct sizing.

On dual duct multizone installations there will be an infinite set of operating conditions which will create rates of air flow in the cold and warm air ducts entirely different from those used in the original design. For this reason, the possibility of achieving uniformity in duct pressures, for the purpose of volumetric control by some program of duct sizing, is very limited.

Large vs. Small Ducts.—Every effort should be made in designing the ductwork to reduce the total power needed to produce the required rate of flow in the supply system. This will assure a quieter system, reduce duct leakages, and it will approach, in the majority of cases, the point of maximum owning cost economy.

The basic objective in designing a distribution system is to obtain minimum owning cost by balancing the increment cost of power against the increment cost of ductwork, including all associated costs such as insulation, motors, starters, wiring, etc. For most dual duct systems the analysis of cost factors indicates economy of larger ducts if the cost of the building structure is disregarded.

However, the relative economy of a larger duct as compared to power consumption is not of such magnitude as to justify extensive cost calculation in ordinary design work. Economy will be achieved if efforts are made to keep the total resistance of the system to a practical minimum by utilizing most effectively the space available.

Design Velocity.—The chief justification for high duct velocity is space limitation created by past and present architectural and structural practices. By necessity, in a majority of multizone installations, relatively high velocities and high friction rates must be used in some parts of the distribution system. On the other hand, where space is not at a premium, the use of high friction rates is not economically justifiable. In most installations there will always be a point or points of greatest space restriction where the duct velocity must be high. As soon as these points are passed and space becomes less critical, the friction rates should be gradually reduced toward the low end of the duct system.

Example 5: The longest run may be started with a friction rate of 0.75 in. per 100 ft and then gradually reduced toward the end to, say, 0.15 in. per 100 ft, giving an average friction, rate of 0.45 in. per 100 ft. Such a procedure may involve additional work in estimating the total duct friction but will in general satisfy the requirements of economy. The shorter duct branches, if desired, may be equalized in the usual manner by using the equal friction method of sizing. However, in so doing, care should be exercised to avoid excessively high velocities in smaller ducts. Excessively high velocities in duct fittings, tapoffs, and flexible connections may cause noisy operation.

For installations where no space restrictions exist the ductwork may be sized by the equal friction method, using low friction rates of, say, 0.20 to 0.30 in. per 100 ft. The shorter branches again can be equalized as previously described. The straight, long risers may be sized effectively by the static regain method, in this manner making equal static pressures achievable at the takeoffs for each floor under a specified set of operating conditions.

A substantial saving in duct friction is usually achieved by a careful study of the duct mains adjacent to the apparatus room. In order to conserve energy and to prevent regeneration of noise, the connections to the cold and warm plenums should be made as streamlined as possible to reduce the entrance loss to the high velocity duct. In actual layout this is usually accomplished by using a funnel-shaped fitting between the high velocity ductwork and the plenum. In many cases the space conditions in the apparatus room are not critical and a large duct can be used in this area. The duct velocity can then be stepped up gradually when the point of space restriction is reached.

The inefficiency of static and velocity pressure conversions must be carefully evaluated because in high velocity systems it may represent an appreciable part of the total resistance to be imposed on the supply fan.

In the main ductwork it is safe to assume that only 75% of the velocity pressure will be regained. For example, if the highest velocity in the duct is 4000 fpm and the terminal velocity is 2000 fpm, the total loss will be

$$\left[\left(\frac{4000}{4005}\right)^2 - \left(\frac{2000}{4005}\right)^2\right] \times (1 - 0.75) = 0.19 \text{ inch}$$

Velocity pressures in the round connection to the last mixing unit cannot be credited with regain. This pressure must be considered as the part of the total energy required to create the needed rate of flow through the unit. Rating tables for mixing units are normally based on the static pressures at the entrance of the unit, which means that velocity pressures should be added to this value to establish total pressure logs through the unit.

Maximum Velocity.—Maximum velocities recommended for cold and warm air ducts are given in Table 13-9.

Table 13-8. Factors for Duct Design

Column A	Column B	Column C	Column D
Ratio of system summer cold air to system total air = cfm_c/cfm	Ratio of zone cold air to total zone air for purpose of sizing cold air duct	System with supplementary heating at perimeter of building	100% air system
		Ratio of warm air duct area to cold air duct area	
1.0 to 0.9	1.0	0.70	0.80
0.85 to 0.89	0.95	0.70	0.80
0.84 to 0.80	0.90	0.75	0.85
0.79 to 0.75	0.85	0.75	0.85
0.74 and smaller	0.80	0.80	0.90

For duct elbows having velocities less than 2500 fpm, ordinary turning vanes may be used. For higher velocities the vanes should be streamlined, having no sharp edges. It is also recommended that vanes of streamlined construction be used on all sharp offsets and transformers handling high velocity air. In square elbows the turning vanes should be extended at least 5 inches on the downstream side of the vanes. Extreme care should be exercised in designing vanes for fittings placed in series and located close to each other. With high velocity air, two unvaned or poorly vaned fittings in series might create air turbulence and rumble, which may nullify all sound attenuating provisions made in the air handling system.

Table 13-9. Recommended Maximum Velocities in Ducts

Duct Carries, *cfm*	Max Velocity, fpm
60000 to 40000	6000
40000 to 25000	5000
25000 to 15000	4500
15000 to 10000	4000
10000 to 6000	3500
6000 to 3000	3000
3000 to 1000	2500

For better acoustical results in connection with design of high velocity ducts:

1) Avoid the use of dampers for adjustment of distribution. They are practically useless in a dual duct system with its inherently unstable pressure characteristics. In systems with relatively high velocities, they are a source of noise, leakage, and an unnecessary expense.

2) Avoid splitters of any kind. They are a source of noise and can cause distributional troubles.

3) Avoid unvaned rectangular elbows. (All vanes should be of streamline construction.)

4) Avoid undersizing small ducts and take-offs from mains to mixing units.

5) Avoid offsets if possible. When not possible, the transformations and bends should be kept easy; they usually require turning vanes.

6) Avoid undersizing of warm air duct mains under all design conditions. (See Table 13-8.)

7) Never reduce or restrict warm connections to mixing units.

8) Do not use tape for sealing high pressure ductwork. Avoid large 90° tap-offs to risers and mains (say, over 64 in^2). If this is not possible, use straightening vanes at the entrance to avoid air turbulence and regeneration of rumble and other noise.

9) Do not have less than 5 equivalent diameters between two fittings in series. If this is not possible, use straightening vanes.

10) When space conditions permit, use round ductwork.

11) Do not use tap-off fittings that have sharp edges at the entrance. This applies to both rectangular and round ductwork.

The maximum total pressure that may be used in designing a dual duct system will depend chiefly on the characteristics of the mixing units used. Constant volume units are commercially available that will absorb up to 8 inches of static pressure.

Sizing High Pressure Ducts Example.—A system supplying 60,000 *cfm* of cold air is diagrammatically shown in Fig. 13-98. The space conditions are critical at the top of the riser and at the take-off to each floor, as designated by points D and F. The maximum permissible duct sizes are determined at these points and corresponding velocities are plotted on the air friction chart in Fig. 13-99.

The increase in air velocity from point A, in the plenum chamber, to point D is accomplished in two steps. Part of the horizontal main is sized for 2600 fpm and part for 4000 fpm, as indicated by points B and C.

These velocities are again determined from consideration of space conditions. The vertical riser sizes are selected on line DE. This line closely resembles that static regain line, assuming that 75% of the velocity pressure is regained in the riser resulting in 25% loss. The horizontal ducts on each floor are sized on line FG. The Point G is arbitrarily picked for a relatively low friction rate. The velocity in the flexible connections to the mixing units are stepped up to point H, as required by the inlet size of the selected unit. The low pressure ducts leaving the mixing units are sized on equal friction line KL.

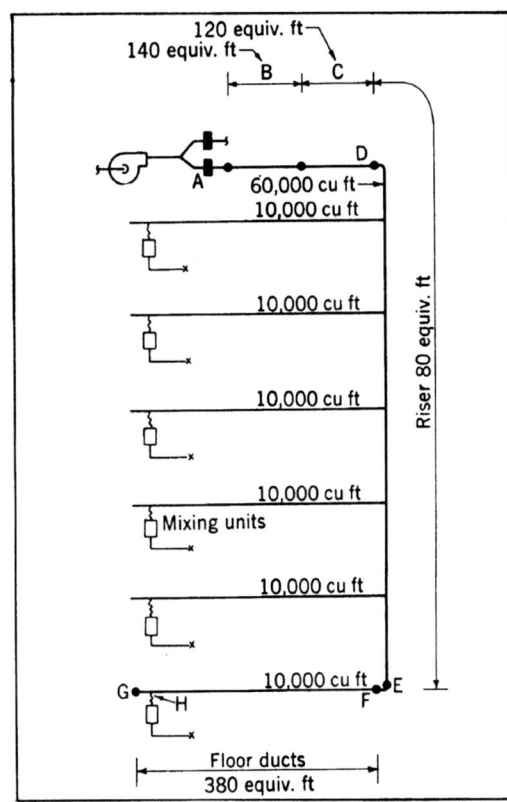

Fig 13-98. Dual duct system showing cold air duct only

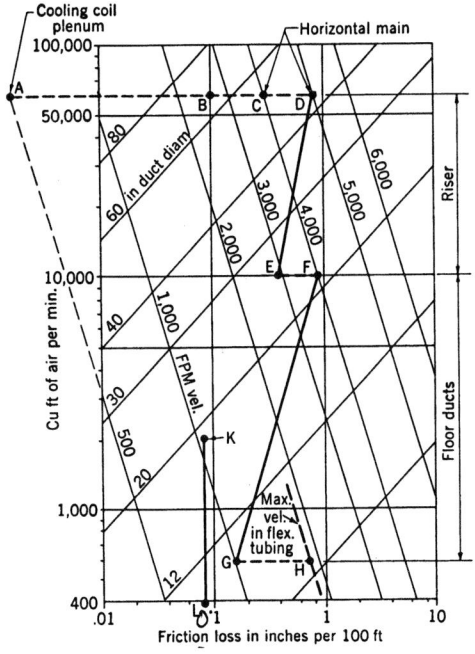

Fig 13-99. Air friction chart

The total resistance of the system is calculated as follows:

Item	Inch of Water
Apparatus	1.25
Horizontal main B	
140 equiv. ft @ 0.10 in. per 100 ft	0.14
Horizontal Main C	
120 equiv. ft @ 0.23 in. per 100 ft	0.28
Riser DE	
80 equiv. ft @ 0.56 in. per 100 ft (aver.)	0.45
Vel. head @ 5000 fpm = 1.56 in.	
Vel. head @ 2800 fpm = 0.49 in.	
1.07 @ 25% loss	0.27
Floor Ducts FH	
380 equiv. ft @ 0.40 in. per 100 ft (aver.)	1.50
Vel. head @ 4000 fpm = 1.00 in.	
Vel. head @ 1000 fpm = 0.25 in.	
0.75 @ 25%	0.19
Loss through flexible conn. and tap-off H	0.25
Last dual duct unit	1.00
Low pressure ductwork and outlet	0.15
Total in. of water	5.46

After the cold air duct sizes are determined, it is more practical to size the warm air duct by using factors from Table 13-8. It is obvious from the example considered that no set procedure can be followed in sizing the duct system. The judgment of the design engineer and space conditions of each project will always be the chief factors in selecting duct sizes.

After the duct sizes are determined by a method like the one described, careful examination of the entire duct system is recommended and further changes in the duct sizes can be made by: (1) eliminating unnecessary transformations, thus keeping the number of duct sizes to a minimum; (2) standardizing the duct sizes in order to have as many duplicate sizes as possible; (3) increasing, by inspection, the end run sizes of longer branches or those branches where load may be expected to increase in the future; (4) eliminating unnecessary fittings, crossovers, and so forth.

This procedure may increase the weight of the metal slightly but it will reduce the actual cost of the installation and assure a more flexible, more quiet, and tighter distributing system.

Return Air Ducts.—Return air ducts are sized at low velocities as in any conventional system. Attempts to pressurize the return duct have not as yet proved to be entirely successful; clogging of high pressure throttling valves by lint and dust still presents a problem. If pressure reducing valves are used in the return air ductwork, easy access should be provided for cleaning. One scheme to simplify the arrangement of the dual duct system is to use hung ceilings or corridors for return plenums and collect all return air at central points on each floor. In some localities there are code restrictions on this method.

Low Pressure Ductwork.—Low pressure ducts leaving the mixing units are sized as any other conventional ductwork. Normally this ductwork is sized for a friction rate of 0.08 in. to 0.10 in. per 100 ft based on ASHRAE duct friction charts, which will give an approximate friction rate of 0.10 in. to 0.12 in. per 100 ft if ductwork is lined. Since, in the majority of cases, the dual duct systems are designed for low cold air supply temperatures, the low pressure ductwork must be either lined or insulated externally. The internal lining is preferable in all cases for acoustical reasons.

Experience has indicated that the least expensive and the safest way to assure a quiet installation is to have some length of lined ductwork on the leaving side of the mixing unit. The lined ductwork, especially when it contains one or two elbows, is a very effective sound attenuator.

The lined ductwork will also provide a necessary safety factor in acoustical design if noise regeneration should occur in the air distributing system because of poorly constructed ducts, fittings, and tap-offs.

Basic Arrangement

Development of the basic scheme of air distribution suitable for a particular structure is the most important function in the design of a dual duct system. The first cost, owning and operating cost, and future flexibility will always reflect the skill with which the basic planning of the system is executed. In every installation, several schemes of air distribution will be feasible and a careful evaluation of all schemes must be made before selecting the one most suitable for the installation.

The cost of the duct system forms a relatively large part of the cost of the total installation. If the system is simple, the weight of metal in the duct system may be, say, 1 lb/ft^2 of conditioned area. If the system is complex, with long runs of low capacity, this weight may rise to 3 or 4 lb. Assuming the cost of erected metal with its associated components to be $4/lb of metal, the penalty for a complicated arrangement becomes obvious.

Special effort should always be made to achieve simplicity in the duct system by utilizing structural and architectural features of the building, judicious location of risers, mains, and apparatus room.

As pointed out previously, over pressurizing of the system should be avoided in all installations. High pressures are always associated with higher owning and operating costs and, in addition, magnify noise and vibration problems. Bear in mind that the actual increment cost of a larger duct is not an average cost of the ductwork but consists mainly of the added cost of the metal and can be assumed to be only 15–20 cents /lb.

Zoning.—The cost of the installation is greatly affected by the general zoning arrangement of the system. If the structure is subdivided into many small zones when larger zones would meet the objectives of the design, the increase in the installed cost of the system represents a very substantial amount of money.

However, on an average comfort installation, little will be gained by using excessively large units (zones). The point of diminishing return will be reached when the size of the unit is increased to, say, 1200 –1400 cfm. Under some design conditions the layout based on large units may be even costlier than the layout where the spaces are served by units of medium capacity.

In existing buildings, it will be more economical to leave the existing perimeter radiation system as it is and to condition all spaces with overhead units.

In some installations only part of the structure must be conditioned, but provisions for treating the remainder must be incorporated in the design. Existing buildings with large numbers of tenants are often treated in this manner. A dual duct system with automatic volume regulation at terminal points is ideally suited for installations of this type. If the central apparatus and duct mains are installed, any part of the building may be provided with

mixing units and the system put into operation prior to its entire completion. When additional units are installed, no rebalancing of the original units will be necessary, as all changes in duct pressures will automatically be compensated for at the terminal points.

Typical Floor Layouts, Existing Office Buildings.—

Floor layouts shown in Figs. 13-100– 13-102 are applicable to existing office buildings or to new office buildings where only a limited amount of glass is used in the facade of the building. The modular arrangement of buildings shown is such that each modulus on the perimeter wall can be subdivided by partitions. This is usually the case when the moduli are 7 ft or larger.

Fig. 13-100 shows a typical floor of an office building arranged for a minimum recommended number of zones. The basic minimum number of zones in a building of rectangular shape should be as follows: (a) four exposure zones; (b) four corner rooms with windows in two walls; (c) interior zones as required by type of loading or occupancy.

In modern buildings, the need for zoning of interior areas with heavy population and business machinery loads is actually greater than in exterior areas of the same exposure. The basic need for zoning exterior areas exists only when one side of the building is partially shaded by the adjacent structures or selective temperature control is needed for each room. The arrangement shown in Fig. 13-100 is supplemented by perimeter radiation for winter operation, which may be controlled independently or in conjunction with the air conditioning system. The system arranged in this manner obviously will be the lowest in first cost and could be applied to both new and existing buildings for conditioning open floors or non-executive areas. Each large zone may consist of a separate mixing unit or of two or more units discharging air into a common duct, as shown on the west side of the building. If the ductwork is arranged in the manner shown, any change in future zoning arrangement can be easily accomplished by installing additional mixing units where required.

In buildings located in warmer climates, exterior wall radiation can be omitted and the entire cooling and heating load can be handled by the air supplied from overhead. The air can be distributed through ceiling and sidewall outlets or through a combination of air diffusers and light troffers. In Europe, especially in Switzerland and Italy, there are very successful dual duct installations with air distribution through perforated ceilings.

Fig. 13-102 illustrates a typical layout with exterior zones supplied by under window air mixing units. The units may be connected to vertical risers, as shown in Figs. 13-103 and 13-104, or to horizontal mains located at the ceiling or on the floor below, as shown in Fig. 13-105. The vertical risers for exterior units are usually collected on one or more floors to form a separate distributing header or loop. The exterior zones might be supplied by a separate air handling system or be a part of the interior system.

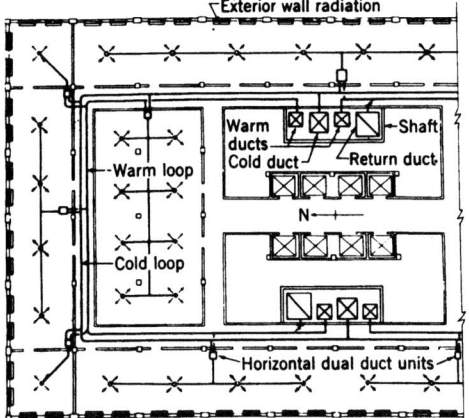

Fig 13-100. Typical office building dual duct layout with supplementary radiation at exterior wall with minimum number of zones

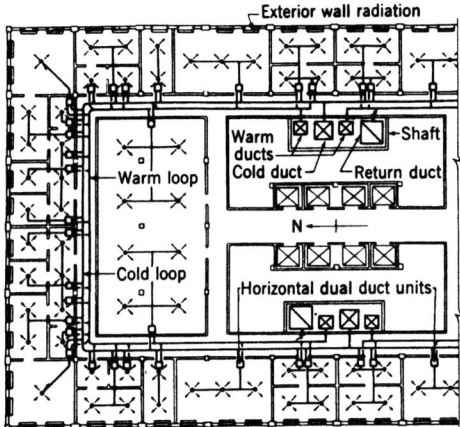

Fig 13-101. Typical office building dual duct layout with supplementary radiation at exterior wall zoned to provide selective temperature control for each enclosure

Fig. 13-101 shows basically the same layout as indicated on Fig. 13-100, with the exception that all spaces are equipped with additional mixing units for selective temperature control. If the horizontal duct mains are properly arranged, future changes in mixing units and zone arrangement are easily made without disturbing the main system. When mixing units are equipped with volume regulators, no rebalancing of units will be required if the pattern of air distribution is changed. In some cases, the mixing units are arranged on a modular basis providing one mixing unit for each exterior modulus. A design executed in this manner has the merit of greater flexibility for future partition changes and should be considered for installations where this is expected.

When space is not available under the windows for the installation of self-contained units or when the exterior wall, for reasons of economy, is subdivided into large

moduli, the exterior can be supplied by horizontal units located at the ceiling or on the floor below, as shown in Fig. 13-106. The air from the unit is discharged into a distributing and sound attenuating header located at the perimeter of the building. The chief objective of the distributing headers, as shown in the layout, is to prevent down drafts during cold weather.

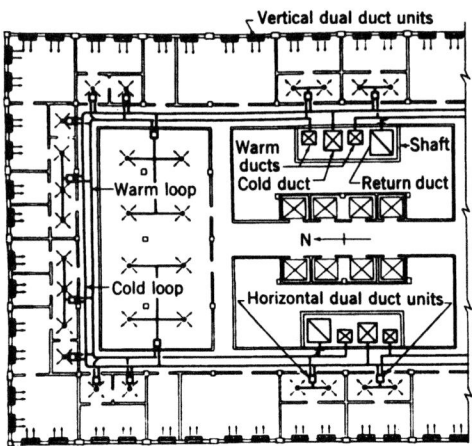

Fig 13-102. Typical office building dual duct layout 100% air stream zoned to provide selective temperature control for each enclosure with vertical duct units at exterior walls

The high pressure horizontal supply ducts feeding individual floors may be arranged in a conventional manner or form a system of loops, as shown in Figs. 13-100– 13-102. The loop system has an obvious advantage when the floors are supplied by more than one central air handling apparatus. If the air flows freely through the ends of the loops from one side of the building to the other to satisfy the sun load, appreciable economy is effected in designing the cold circuits of the central apparatus. With the loop system, the combined coil capacity of all apparatus is sized to take care of the peak of the entire building. If two separate apparatus feed the building, one on the east and another on the west side, each apparatus must be designed to provide for the peak load of its side of the building.

With more than one apparatus supplying a building, combined by looping the supply ducts, each central apparatus can be the same size, thus simplifying the layout work and providing a saving in the first cost of the installation by a duplication of equipment. The looped system also permits partial conditioning of the building by operating only half of the central fans for night, weekend operation, or during a breakdown.

Experience has shown that the best location for high pressure ductwork and mixing units is in corridors or in areas adjacent to the service core of the building. If space for the installation of units is not available in the corridor, the unit can be moved to adjacent spaces.

Ceiling Plenum.—A dual duct layout will be greatly simplified if the return air system is arranged as in Figs.

13-100 to 13-102. If the space above the hung ceiling is used for a return air plenum, all return air may be drawn into the ceiling plenum through conventional grilles and registers or combination light fixtures and return grilles and collected at central points near the risers. In some designs it is sufficient to use as return plenums only the space above corridor ceilings where, normally, high pressure ducts and units are located. Under some design and layout conditions, it is possible to use both the corridors and the hung ceiling spaces for collecting and conveying of return air. However, local codes in some cities prohibit or restrict the use of hung ceilings and corridors for return plenum chambers.

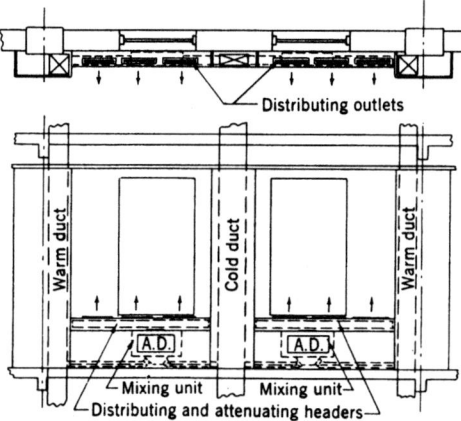

Fig 13-103. Arrangement of vertical, under window, dual duct units connected to risers, one unit per riser

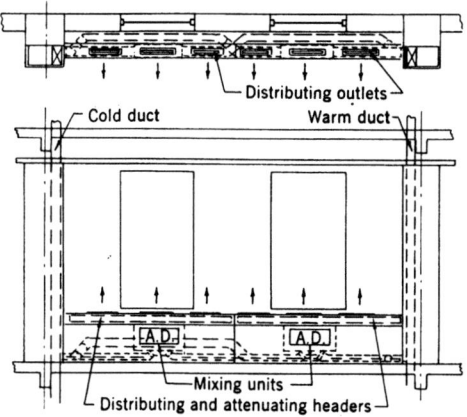

Fig 13-104. Arrangement for vertical under window dual duct units two units per riser

The most critical points in a dual duct system will generally be the areas near the main shaft where the ducts enter a floor and branch off into horizontal mains. A careful study of space conditions must be made in these areas and the ducts sized at the lowest velocity possible. To avoid crossovers of horizontal mains, the risers can be rearranged by dividing the warm riser and placing a cold riser between two warm risers, as shown in Figs. 13-100 to 13-102.

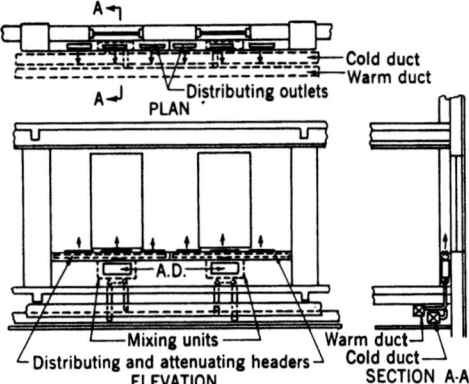

Fig 13-105. Arrangement for vertical under window dual duct units two units per riser

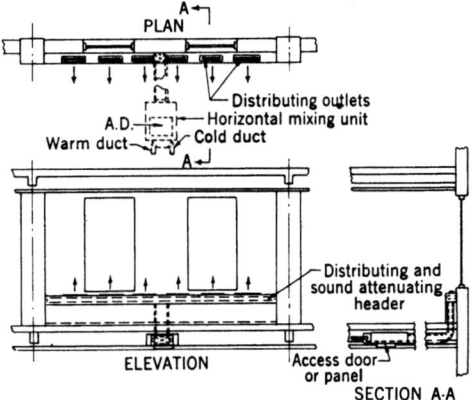

Fig 13-106. Perimeter header feed by horizontal unit

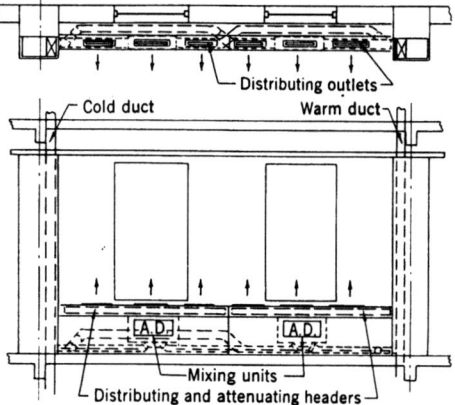

Fig 13-107. Arrangement for vertical under window dual duct units to units per riser

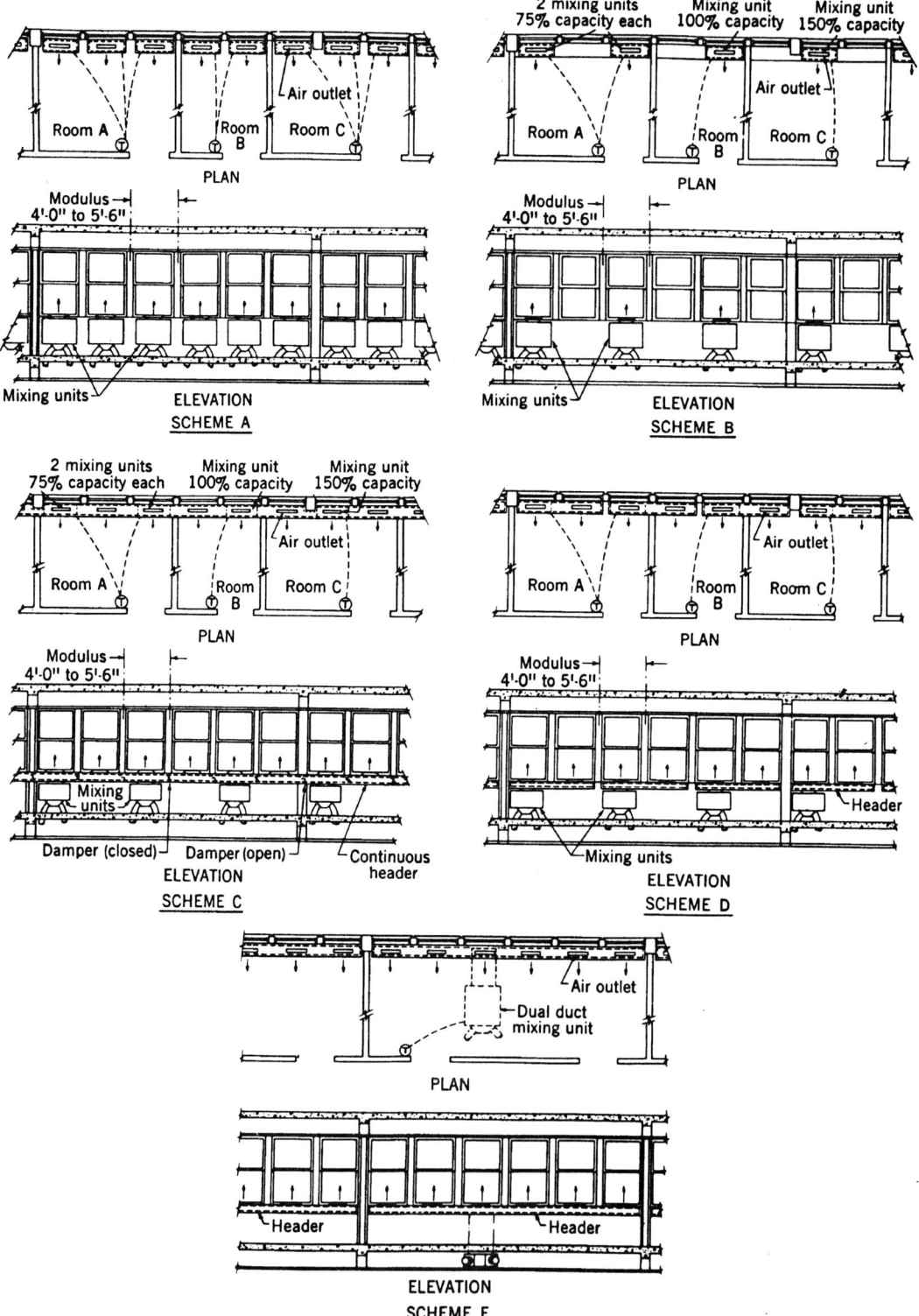

Fig 13-108. Modular arrangement of dual duct mixing units

Modular Type Office Buildings.—When new modular type buildings with large percentages of glass in their facades are conditioned by a perimeter mixing unit. The units can be arranged according, to several alternatives as shown on Schemes A, B C, D, or E in Fig. 13-108.

It is obvious that virtually infinite flexibility for future partition changes could be obtained if one mixing unit is placed in each building modulus, as shown by Scheme A. By discharging a fixed quantity of air upward to blanket the window in each modulus, proper air distribution will be obtained in all conditioned spaces and the possibility of downdrafts during cold weather operation will be eliminated. Since each unit must be sized to take care of the maximum load of the particular modulus it serves, rebalancing of units will not be required with future partition changes. The installed cost of the system based on this scheme will be the highest, another reason it should be used only when the building moduli are large enough to be individually partitioned.

If the building moduli are small (4 –5.5 ft) at no time will less than two moduli be partitioned off, Schemes B, C, or D can be selected. Although almost identical design objectives will be accomplished by Schemes A, B, C, and D, the installed cost of the last three schemes will be lower by approximately 70 cents to $1/ft^2 of exterior area on an average office building.

In warmer climates, or in moderate climates if windows are protected by double glazing, units around the perimeter can be arranged according to Scheme B. All mixing units for this scheme should be sized initially to take care of three moduli. Thus, the units may have to be rebalanced as required by future partition changes. Each unit may be called upon to supply 75, 100, or 150% of air needed for two moduli, as indicated by location of partitions for rooms A, B, and C, respectively. Because of cold downdrafts at unprotected windows, this scheme is not applicable to buildings located in colder climates. If it is desired to eliminate the possibility of cold downdrafts at the perimeter glass in buildings located in colder climates, and at the same time to provide almost infinite flexibility for future partition changes, Scheme C can be selected. With this scheme, the air from the mixing units is discharged into a common header with an air outlet in each building modulus. Complete separation of two adjacent spaces can be obtained by dampers (or friction type baffles) installed in headers as indicated on the elevation drawing. As with Scheme B, the mixing units for Scheme C should be sized initially to provide air for three moduli, if that is required, by partition arrangement.Each perimeter unit may be called upon to supply 75, 100, or 150% of the air required for two moduli. Scheme C is especially suitable for areas where two adjacent spaces may have different load intensities or where the reversal of load in the adjacent spaces is possible. This condition is usually

met when the building is either self-shaded or is shaded by adjacent buildings.

If the character of the internal load for two adjacent spaces on each exposure of the building is subject to only moderate variations, the arrangement of units as indicated in Scheme D will suffice. The headers for this arrangement will extend over two moduli only and future partition changes will not require rebalancing of air mixing units.

For general areas that will not be partitioned, or where selective temperature control in each cubicle is not required by the design criteria, one mixing unit per bay should be provided as shown by Scheme E. Little will be saved by serving more than one bay with one mixing unit.

In all schemes illustrated in Fig. 13-109, it is assumed that exterior spaces are partitioned from the interior areas. In such cases, it is possible to install room thermostats on the back walls, adjacent to doors or return grilles as shown. When the exterior and interior areas are not separated by partitions, room thermostats and thermostatic bulbs should be mounted inside the perimeter type mixing units or in the air distributing headers. One of the methods of mounting and actuating the thermostatic bulb inside the mixing unit using an air sampler is shown in Figs. 13-109 and 13-110.

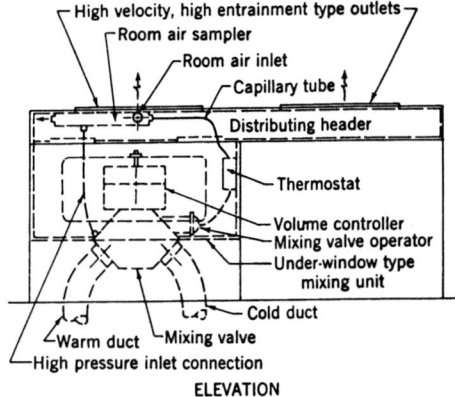

Fig 13-109. Method of mounting air sampler in mixing unit

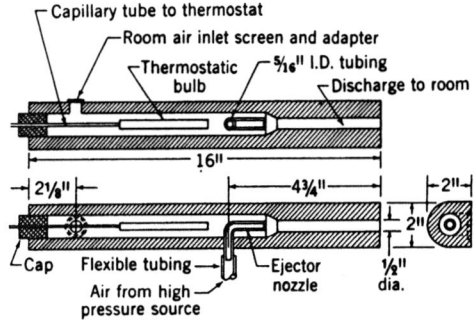

Fig 13-110. Room air sampler tube

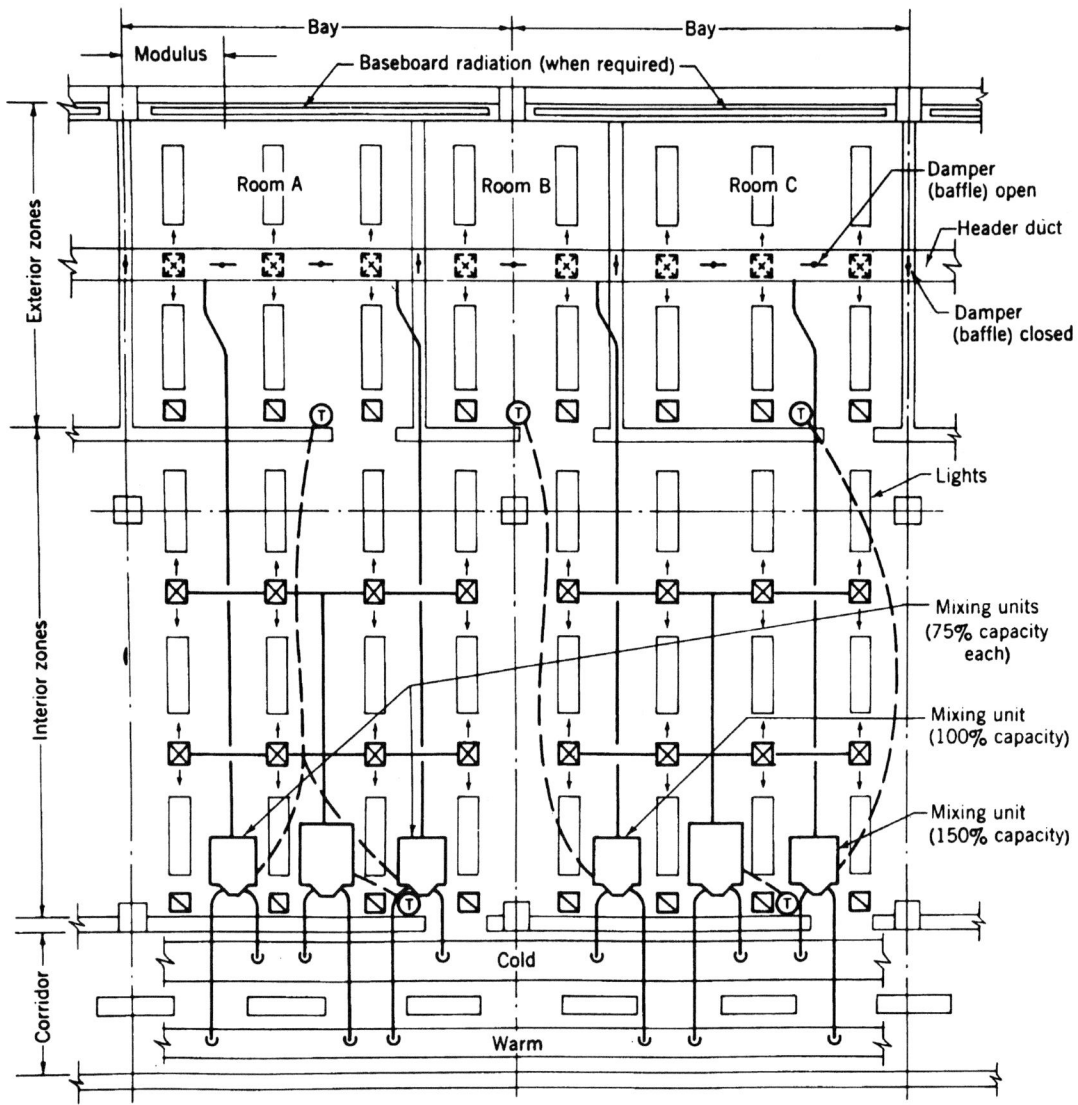

Fig 13-111. Modular arrangement for overhead dual duct system, Scheme C

When room air samplers are used, it is recommended that high velocity high entrainment-type grilles or slots for discharge of air from perimeter mixing units be installed. This will ensure that representative air from the occupied zone is drawn toward the air inlet of the room air sampler. Locating room thermostats on exterior walls or columns should be avoided.

When using Schemes C and D of Fig. 13-108, further savings in installed cost of the system can be achieved by providing only one mixing unit per three or four moduli in all corner rooms.

Schemes A, B, C, D, and E in Fig. 13-108 can be applied also for overhead distribution of air. For example, in Fig. 13-108 and Fig. 13-112, an overhead air distribu-

tion arrangement is shown for Schemes C and D, respectively. The arrangement of outlets shown is schematic and any type of air distributing devices can be adapted with the illustrated schemes.

Many patterns of duct distributing systems are possible with dual duct systems to meet a variety of design objectives for a particular installation. Cost and space requirements for distributing systems can be minimized by properly organizing the element of distribution. The emphasis on organization has resulted in the modern trend toward integrated designs, where structural elements of the building are used for distribution of air, thereby reducing the cost of sheet metal and building space normally occupied by the ductwork.

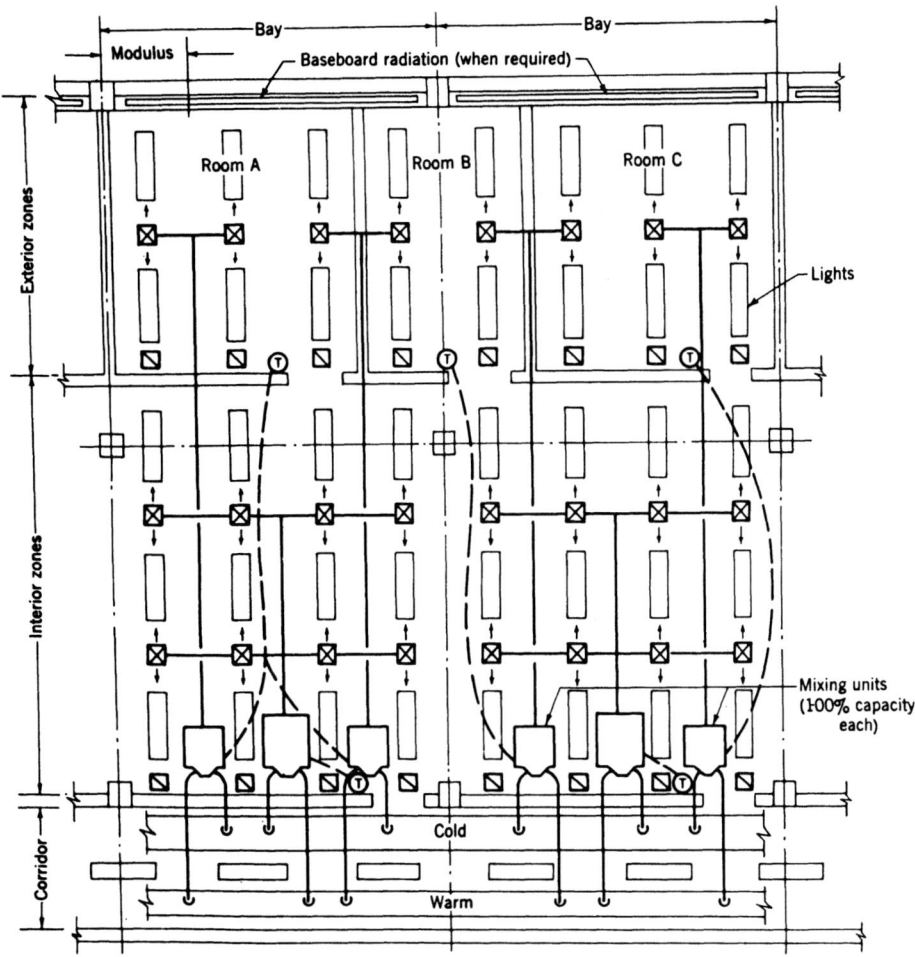

Fig 13-112. Modular arrangement for overhead dual duct system, Scheme D

Guides to Layout: In laying out distribution systems one does not simply follow the technique used in low pressure layouts by running high pressure ductwork over an entire conditioned area. The extent of high pressure mains on each floor should be limited to well defined areas and air distributed to individual rooms by low pressure, internally lined ductwork. The high pressure ductwork is considered a high velocity plenum, which remains intact for the life of the structure. In order to have maximum flexibility and to avoid the danger of obsolescence, all changes due to shifting loads and partition changes should be confined to low pressure ductwork and mixing units.

Layouts consisting of large numbers of small dual duct mixing units should be avoided unless dictated absolutely by the design conditions. A layout made in this manner will be highest in first cost.

In making alternate air distribution schemes for a particular project, do not rule out a scheme consisting of perimeter radiation and overhead air system. On many projects such a scheme will be the least expensive in first cost.

Overhead mixing units of small capacity, unless absolutely necessary for zoning requirements, should be avoided. In order to decrease the cost of installation, use of a larger unit is better with air distributed to individual outlets by low pressure lined ductwork. However, little will be gained by increasing sizes of the units over, say, 1200–1500 cfm.

Mixing units located as close to the high pressure mains as possible will facilitate future changes and servicing.

The high pressure duct system should be designed (and shaped) from consideration of more than present loads only. Internal loads may increase or change in the future and the supply fans will have to be speeded up or a new booster air-handling system connected to the distributing system. With high pressure dual duct systems, the provisions for future adequacy of the installation can be made at a very small additional cost.

Constant Volume Mixing Units.—At the time of this book publication there are several manufacturer's of dual duct air mixing units who offer equipment with automatic control of delivered volume. Arrangement of the mechanical components vary greatly among the manufacturer's, but the basic method of automatic control of volume and temperature falls into only two categories. These two methods are shown in diagrams of Fig. 13-113 and Fig. 13-114.

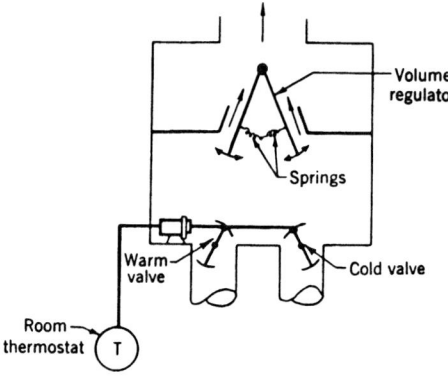

Fig 13-113. Type a duct constant volume unit

For this discussion they will be referred to as Control Method A and Control Method B, respectively.

Method A is a direct control of both temperature and volume. A thermostat controls the mixture of cold and warm air and a self-contained, spring-balanced volume regulator controls the volume at the discharge of a 3-way air mixing valve. With this arrangement, as long as there is sufficient air pressure at both warm and cold inlets of the mixing valve to overcome the resistance interposed by the mixing unit, the volume will remain constant and the thermal quality of the air delivered will be responsive to the requirement of the thermostat.

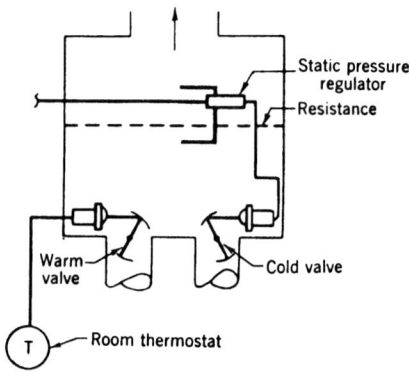

Fig 13-114. Type B duct constant volume unit

If the pressure at either inlet of the valve should fall below the point necessary to overcome unit resistance, the thermostat will throttle or close off the other inlet and the volume delivered by the unit may fall below the specified quantity, but the temperature control of the reduced quantity will not be affected. This is especially important under special design and operating conditions during the heating season, conditions that will be discussed later.

When using Control Method A care should be exercised to avoid creating conditions where air from one duct can be bypassed to the other through the mixing units. If such conditions do exist or may be anticipated, air check valves should be installed in the inlet of the units. Introduction of air check valves may be required:

1) when air mixing dampers are band operated;
2) when room thermostats controlling the units are not properly located or adjusted;
3) when a smooth operation of air mixing dampers is prevented by such mechanical defects as;
   a) folded or leaky diaphragm operator of pneumatic motor;
   b) mixing valve linkages out of adjustment; and
   c) any other mechanical defect which may cause binding of the valve in an intermediate position.
4) When one room thermostat controls mixing units of different sizes and when movement of mixing valves in such units is not properly synchronization is imperative that volume regulators in synchronized.

Method A type units have a positive means to eliminate possible fluttering of the units under conditions of extreme turbulence.

Method B is indirect in controlling both temperature and volume. *Method B* units may be actuated by compressed air or by the air pressure of the system. The results are the same. A space thermostat controls only the warm; repressor regulator controls the flow through the cold air inlet. The pressure drop across a resistance plate is kept constant to give fixed outlet volume.

The thermostat throttles the warm air, the static pressure regulator opens the cold air inlet, maintaining constant volume regardless of the resulting temperature of the mixture. If the warm air pressure is insufficient to overcome the resistance of the mixing unit, the thermostat will open the warm air inlet wide when calling for heat, but low pressure will prevent full flow of warm air and the static pressure regulator will therefore open the cold air inlet until the volume control is satisfied. Thus, insufficient pressure in the warm air duct can produce cooling of the conditioned space when the thermostat is calling for heat.

Several normal design and operating conditions can produce low pressure in some parts of the system. Some typical reasons for insufficient pressure in warm air ducts are these:

1) In starting up after shutdown in cold weather, the warm air ducts are substantially smaller than the cold air ducts.

2) When supply fans are run at low speed for night heating. Normally night and weekend operation does not require maintenance of exact conditions and low speed operation of fans saves power.

3) When one of several fans feeding the same duct system is nonoperative, as during night heating, servicing or breakdowns.

4) When the warm air duct temperature falls substantially below the design temperature due to faulty action of central thermostats, failure of steam pressure, etc.

5) When warm air ducts are sized without due consideration of partial heating loads or intermediate season operation while low temperatures are maintained in the warm air ducts.

6) When an excessive temperature drop occurs in uninsulated warm air ducts.

7) When a partial or complete obstruction occurs in the warm air duct.

8) When the air distributing system is used in conjunction with perimeter radiation there will be an infinite set of operating conditions, which may cause a drop of pressures in the warm air ducts. This may be caused by improper timing in applying radiation or by inadequate temperatures in the warm air ducts or by a combination of both.

9) The type B method may overcool even during the summer cycle under normal operation. For example, when the temperature of outdoor air, warm air duct air. and conditioned spaces are about the same; the internal load in the building is negligible when there is no sun. This condition may be met in summer during partial occupancy of the building. Under this condition of operation, all system air will tend to flow in the warm air duct, producing low or negligible pressures at the end of the warm air duct. Consequently the spaces at the far end of the duct system will be receiving cold air even if room thermostats do not call for it.

It should be kept in mind, also, that *control Method B* may introduce acoustical problems. When the room thermostat calls for all warm air, the volume control function of the unit will be lost completely. During such times, the increased air flow through the unit may generate objectionable noise or low frequency rumble.

Air Handling Apparatus: In a majority of cases the dual duct central apparatus is based on one of the four basic cycles previously described. Minor modifications of the cycles and equipment might be dictated by design conditions. There are no general or special rules that should be followed in the selection of the equipment or shaping of the apparatus casings. The judgment of the design engineer and manufacturer's recommendations will determine the type, size, and quality of the component part, forming the central apparatus. All mechanical equipment

is of standard manufacture as used at present by the industry. However. there are several points that should be given special consideration in designing a push-through, high pressure apparatus of dual duct type. These will now be discussed in detail.

Apparatus Floor Area.— Apparatus floor area constitutes a large part of the total owning and operating cost of any type of air conditioning system. An improperly planned apparatus room may involve waste in floor area which could represent an element of cost greater than the cost of all mechanical equipment in the room.

Table 13-10. Floor Area Required by Air-Handling Equipment

Net Area of Building Served by Equip. Room, ft^2	Total Area Required by Equip. Room, ft^2	Clear Head Room, ft	Preferable Shape of Equipment Room		% of Net Area Served by Equipment Room
			A, ft	B, ft	
50000	1100	8	30	37	2.2
	1000	10	30	33	2.0
	950	12	30	32	1.9
	850	14	30	27	1.7
100000	2100	8	32	66	2.1
	1900	10	32	60	1.9
	1700	12	32	53	1.7
	1500	14	32	47	1.5
150000	2700	10	34	80	1.8
	2400	12	34	70	1.6
	1100	14	34	62	1.4

Net usable area assumed to be 80% of gross building area.

Areas required for refrigeration plant or miscellaneous exhaust systems not included.

Total air handled assumed to be 1.2 cfm/ft^2 of area.

It should be noted that Table 13-10 is compiled on the basis of total air flow, assumed to be 1.2 cfm/ft^2 of net area, and that the net usable area is assumed to be 80% of the gross area.

A well planned dual duct apparatus room can be fitted into a space no more than $1\frac{1}{2}$ to $2\frac{1}{2}$% of the net area it conditions. Such economy in floor area is due to the following factors:

1) Zoning and multiplicity of apparatus systems is not required for dual duct systems and a larger central apparatus may be used, which will always take less space than several small systems of the same total capacity,

2) By supplying the cold air at lower temperatures, the total air supplied is greatly reduced. With 50°F air in the cold air duct, the size of the central apparatus is only 60 to 70% of one using 60°F air.

3) Use of vertically split cold and warm chambers (shown in Fig. 13-115) allows the piping to the cooling coils to be placed in the passage for warm air, saving $2\frac{1}{2}$ to $3\frac{1}{2}$ ft of space on each side of the bank of cooling coils.

4) By using the full height of rooms for banks of coils and filters, floor area is saved.

All air in the dual duct system is conditioned by a central air handling plant. The plant is arranged so that return air can be recirculated or, in suitable climates, 100% of outdoor air can be used for cooling purposes. Additional cooling effect could be achieved by evaporative cooling in the cold chamber.

Fig. 13-115 shows a typical layout of a room containing a plant of large capacity.

The amount of floor space required varies between approximately 1.4% and 2.2% of the net area served by the plant.

While a single plant is very desirable, it may be that in large buildings two plants may prove more practical and economical. These may be arranged on the same floor or one could be in the basement, say, and one on the roof. The latter arrangement could affect economies in shaft sizes for ducts.

Table 13-10 shows the floor area required for the air handling plant related to net areas served by the plant. Dimensions A and B are those of Fig. 13-115.

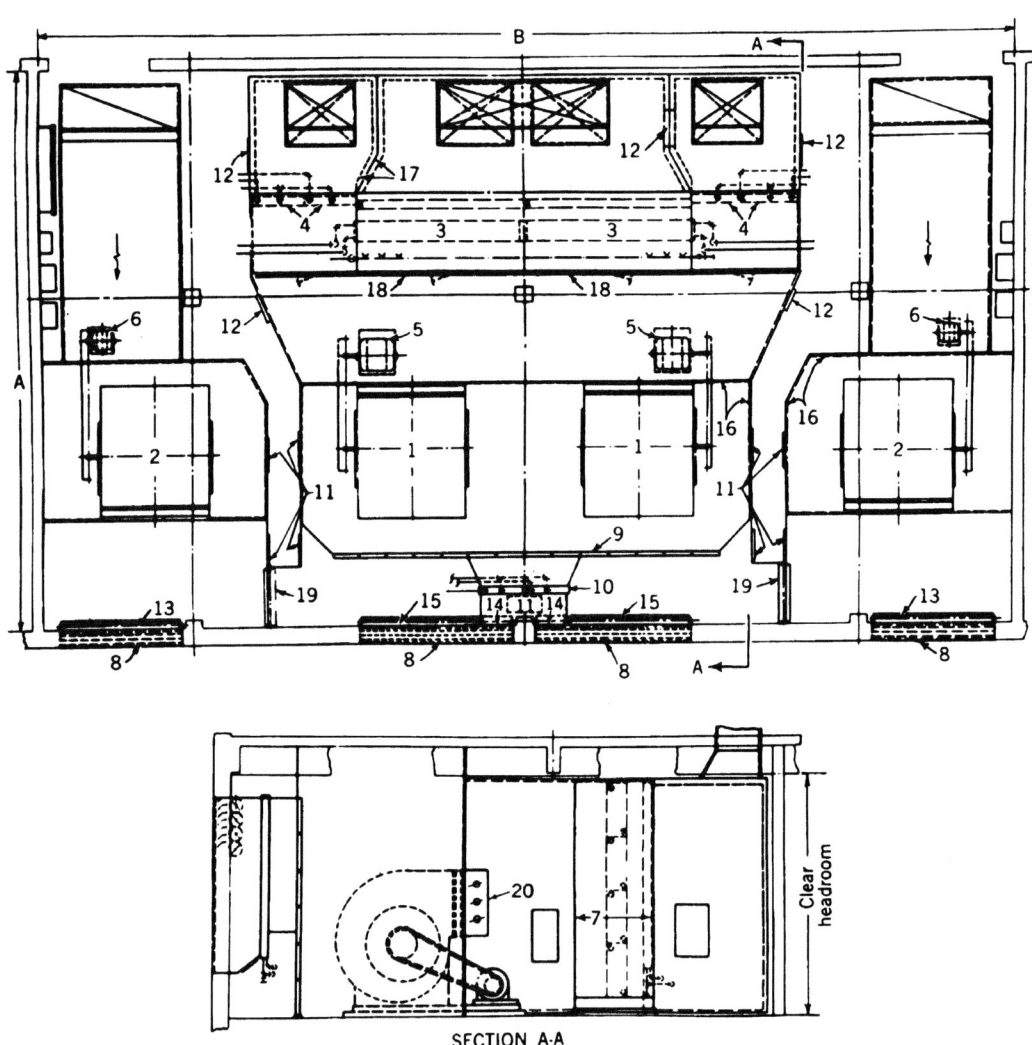

SECTION A-A

Fig 13-115. Type large capacity dual duct system

1. Supply fan	6. Return fan motors	11. Low pressure access doors	16. One inch acoustical lining
2. Return and relief fan	7. High pressure dehumidifier	12. High pressure access doors	17. Four inch acoustical lining
3. Cooling coils	8. Outdoor louvers and screen	13. Relief dampers	18. Perforated distributing plate
4. Heating coils	9. Filters	14. Minimum outside air dampers	19. Return air dampers
5. Supply fan motors	10. Preheaters	15. Maximum outside air dampers	20. Shut off dampers

Backlash and Carryover: Due to unequal distribution of velocity over the face of the cooling coils in the push-through type apparatus, the carryover of moisture in the cold chamber and backlash from the cooling coil represent a serious problem in the design of apparatus rooms. Experience has shown that the most effective way to eliminate carryover and backlash is to install the following: distributing plates over the inlet of both heating and cooling coils. The distributing plate is usually a perforated metal sheet with $\frac{1}{2}$-in. round holes having 40–50% free area. This plate should be amply reinforced, made removable, and provided with access panels to coil chambers and sprays.

In addition, corrosion resistant eliminator plates should be provided on the leaving side of the cooling coils. Three bend eliminators spaced $1\frac{1}{8}$ in. apart have been found to give good results for dual duct installations. If sprays are used in the warm chamber, eliminator plates should also be installed on the leaving side of the warm air duct heating coil.

Apparatus Casing: Utmost care should be exercised in the construction, bracing, and sealing of the high pressure apparatus casing. For practical reasons, it is almost impossible to pressure test the casing chamber before the system is put in actual operation. Consequently, any error in construction, assembly, and sealing is extremely difficult to correct after the system is completed.

Construction standards developed for low pressure apparatus casings are inadequate for large high pressure and medium pressure systems and their application has created serious acoustical problems on many such installations. It is recommended that structural framing for apparatus casings subjected to higher pressures be carefully designed for the imposed loads. In addition, casings should be amply braced and stiffened to prevent vibration and generation of noise. On larger apparatus casings handling over, say, 40000 cfm, one of the following should be considered: double-wall factory-insulated panels, cellular casings, or masonry casings. Masonry casings, internally insulated and made airtight, will provide the optimal construction toward achieving desired acoustical results.

The vertical split of cooling and heating chambers will be more desirable for the following reasons: the heating chamber will be more accessible for inspection and repair; provisions for humidifying devices in the warm air chamber will be more easily made; floor area required for the apparatus will be saved if the pipe space for the cooling coils is utilized for the warm air chamber; in many installations the connections to cold and warm mains are simpler; and less air turbulence and casing vibration will be caused.

Insulation and Sound Lining: It is important that all sound lining installed inside casings be mechanically attached to the casing walls in addition to cementing. The metal clips and washers used for this purpose should not be spaced farther than on 1 ft centers. All joints between insulation sheets should be filled with cement or protected by 1 in. × $\frac{1}{8}$ in. flat bars to prevent air erosion. If lining is installed on the bottom of enclosures, it should be protected by heavy gage screen or perforated metal.

Fans: Careful consideration should be given to the proper selection of fan and motor vibration absorbing bases. In addition to selecting the base for maximum efficiency, it should be adjustable a feature usually incorporated in spring type bases.

In larger air handling plants it might be advisable to have two or more supply fans in parallel discharging air to a common plenum. When such an arrangement is used, the fans are equipped with normally closed inlet vanes or discharge dampers operated by electropneumatic switches.

Noise in High Velocity Systems: Any air conditioning or air handling system is a potential source of noise, which may enter the conditioned area through supply, return, or exhaust ducts, by transmission through the building framework, or by communication from zone to zone through interconnecting ducts. Generally, low velocity conventional systems present relatively few acoustical design problems. Considerable work has been done in acoustical ratings of fans, terminal devices and acoustical treatment of distribution systems by equipment manufacturer's. The design engineer with a knowledge of the noise spectrum generated by the air moving device and the attenuating factors of the low velocity system can with reasonable assurance predict an end environment for the spaces served by the system.

It is not sufficiently understood that high velocity systems cannot be treated in the same manner. Therefore, it is not uncommon to find that a design engineer has provided what might appear to be a conservative acoustical design but that system noise is none the less transmitted to occupied spaces. *The excessive system noise is usually generated by the turbulence of the air stream rather than noise originating at the fan and transmitted through the distribution system. Although there is very little published information regarding this aspect of noise control, it is, by far, the more serious and costly to rectify.*

Various recommendations for acoustical considerations in design and layout of high velocity systems can be found Chapter 16 under the title *Acoustical Problems in High Velocity Air Distribution.*

Installed Costs: Cost data presented here are offered for the design engineer in a form that will allow him or her to establish budget information quickly, without making detailed estimates and partial plans that must be discarded and replaced before final figures are produced. These figures also show the areas in which savings may be found to reduce costs to meet a predetermined budget allowance.

All cost data are based on the net, or usable area of the building. The non-usable areas stairwells, elevators, toilets, main corridors, etc. have little or no effect on the air conditioning cost unless these spaces contribute to the complexity of the distribution system.

Data given were compiled from detailed cost analyses of various high pressure dual duct systems with total refrigeration capacity of over 40000 tons, ranging in size from 50–2500 tons each. Special effort has been made to arrange the information so the design engineer has a tool to guide planning.

Variables Affecting Costs: The main variables that affect the installed cost of dual duct systems are:

1) Initial TD (temperature difference, equal to room temperature minus cold air supply temperature) used in design of the system.
2) Size of individual zones (capacity of mixing units).
3) Size of air handling apparatus rooms.
4) Type of dual duct cycle selected.
5) Basic arrangement of air handling system.
6) Degree of future flexibility required.
7) Number, location, and arrangement of riser shafts.
8) Type of construction of rectangular duct work used.
9) Structural and architectural features of the building.
10) Effect of interior zones on cost of exterior zones.
11) Ratio of floor area of exterior zones to interior zones.
12) Type of terminal units used.

In preliminary design of dual duct systems, the above variables, may be grouped and combined conveniently into four basic items:

1) TD (room–cold air supply temperature).
2) Size of central apparatus (capacity of supply fan).
3) Average size of control zones (capacity of mixing units).
4) Complexity of distribution duct system.

Construction Details.—On many multizone installations due to space limitations, rectangular ducts must be used to make installation feasible. At present the high pressure construction for rectangular ducts is not yet fully standardized and several types of duct construction have been developed by the industry to conform to local practices. The construction shown in Fig. 13-116 and Table 13-11 has been used successfully for15 years and is now extensively used in the United States and abroad. (See, also, details of tap-off fittings for high pressure ductwork under *Acoustical Problems in High Velocity Air Distribution* in Chapter 16.)

Several types of sealing compounds have been developed for making up the joints in high pressure ductwork. They all have a synthetic rubber base with a bonding strength that does not decrease with age and retains good elasticity.

Sealing Duct Joints: Shop procedure for sealing high pressure ducts is as follows:

(1) Before fittings and joints are assembled, sealer is applied to rivets, grooved seams, and tap-off collars on the internal side of the metal. Pittsburgh lock pocket must be flooded with sealer, and the duct assembled; (2) sealer is brushed around reinforcing rod washers, corners, rivets, notches, and tap-off collars after ducts are assembled. A double S-slip is installed on the air-leaving side of the duct and fastened in place with metal screws on 6-in. centers. Sealer is brushed into connecting lap and corner joints of an S-slip; (3) inside of connecting lap of S-slip and duct surface is coated with sealer. Where possible, sealing should be done on inside of the ductwork.

Field Procedure for Sealing Duct Joints is as Follows:

1) Sealer is spread on the inside of the double S-slip and the joints of the duct assembled. Immediately after joints are assembled, holes are drilled through the S-slip and metal screws inserted on 6-in. centers. Sealer is applied over the screw heads and the joint;

2) After 24 hours, a second coat of sealer is spread over the joints and allowed to dry for 24 hours before testing;

3) Where joints are not accessible for proper sealing, hand holes should be cut in the duct and the joints sealed from the inside. Special care should be taken to seal all duct corners;

4) When testing ducts for leaks. leaks should be marked and resealed without pressure in the duct and allowed to dry for 24 hours.

A very similar rectangular duct construction was recently developed by *Sheet Metal and Air Conditioning Contractors National Association, Inc. (SMACNA)* and is illustrated in *SMACNA duct Manual & Sheet Metal Construction for Ventilating and Air Conditioning Systems, Section II-High Velocity Systems.*

Table 13-11. Rectangular High Pressure Duct Data

Duct Sizes, in.	Gage	Joint Length, ft	Slip Class	Tie Rod Reinforcing	Bracing Angle (Top to Bottom)	Tie Angles (Sides)
1-12	24	8	1	None	None	None
13-25	24	8	2	None	$1'' \times 1'' \times 14$-ga angle irons 2 per joint	$1'' \times 1'' \times 14$ ga angle irons 2 per joint
26-30	22	8	2	None	$1'' \times 1'' \times 14$ ga angle irons 2 per joint	$1'' \times 1'' \times 14$ ga angle irons 2 per joint
31-45	22	8	3	$4\frac{1}{4}''$ rods	$1'' \times 1'' \times \frac{1}{8}''$ angle irons 2 per joint	$1'' \times 1'' \times \frac{1}{8}''$ angle irons 2 per joint
46-48	20	8	3	$4\frac{1}{4}''$ rods	$1'' \times 1'' \times \frac{1}{8}''$ angle irons 2 per joint	$1'' \times 1'' \times \frac{1}{8}''$ angle irons 2 per joint
49-60	20	8	3	$6\frac{1}{4}''$ rods	$1'' \times 1'' \times \frac{1}{8}''$ angle irons 2 per joint	$1'' \times 1'' \times \frac{1}{8}''$ angle irons 2 per joint

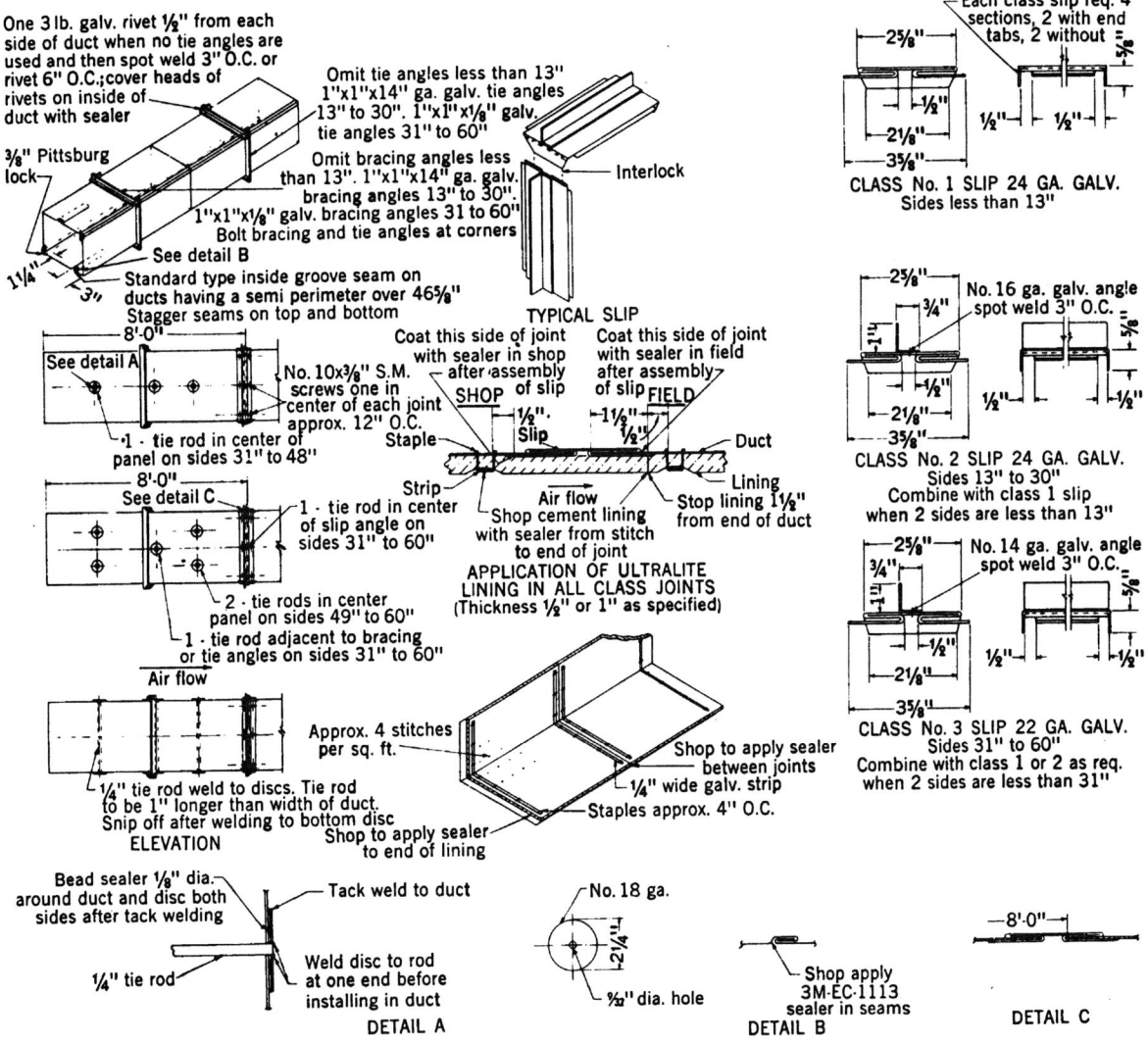

Fig 13-116. Construction of high pressure rectangular ducts

Automatic Control Applications

The following briefly describes applications of commonly used control systems in building air conditioning: rooftop multizone units, multizone units, dampers, unit ventilators, hot water systems, mixing boxes, and rotary air-to-air heat exchangers.

Basic categories of automatic controls include controls for primary equipment such as boilers, chillers, and packaged units, central fan systems, including damper control; valves for steam or hot and chilled water coils and terminal units.

Special applications of control systems are too numerous to be completely discussed. Special cases that are not included can be found in manufacturer's technical bulletins and control manuals. Control manufacturer's offer engineers assistance in control methodology.

Growing interest in rooftop and other packaged units has focused attention on methods to control these units. Their control cycles are more complicated than those of a simple reheat coil, for example. Energy conservation devices, such as air-to-air heat exchanger controls, are also of increasing interest to HVAC engineers.

Rooftop Multizone Units.—The multizone is a constant volume, variable temperature, central system (See Fig 13-117.). Outdoor air and return air are mixed and drawn through the filter section by the blower. Air leaving the blower is divided in parallel paths (the hot and cold decks). After leaving the heating and cooling sections, the two air flows are mixed in proportions necessary to maintain individual zone temperatures.

Most manufacturer's provide eight or more zone dampers on each unit. When fewer zones are required, two or more sets of zone dampers can be linked together to give the required number and size. Rooftop units are equipped with belt driven supply fans for easy adjustment of air flow rates. Linked zone dampers and adjustable air flow rates combine to make rooftop multizones very flexible.

Mixed Air Section: Damper arrangements in multizones vary considerably. Generally, rooftop units are furnished with an outdoor and return air damper linked together. The exhaust damper is controlled in any of three ways:

1) by an additional damper motor;

2) by linkage to the outdoor and return air dampers; and

3) by being opened by exhaust fan static pressure (spring or gravity closed).

Rooftop units often employ the same thermostat for both mixed air and cold deck control. Placed downstream of the DX coil, the thermostat controls the mixed air damper motor and cooling pneumatic-electric switches.

With an economizer cycle, usual with rooftop units, the exhaust fan runs only when the outdoor air damper is open past the minimum setting. The exhaust damper should begin opening slightly before the exhaust fan starts and should not completely close until the fan has stopped.

The exhaust fan, exhaust damper and outside and return air dampers are so sequenced that the building will maintain a positive static pressure. This minimizes the possibility of dust infiltration and non-conditioned air passing into the building.

Fig. 13-119 shows typical cold deck-mixed air control. When outdoor air temperature is below 55°F, T-3 (ther-

mostat No. 3) locks out cooling and T-1 modulates the damper to maintain 55°F cold deck (mixed air) temperature. The exhaust fan starts when the dampers move above minimum position. Between 55°F and 65°F outdoor temperature, the exhaust fan will be on and the outdoor and exhaust dampers will be fully opened.

Cold Deck Control: The cooling coil is found in either of two locations (see Fig. 13-119) in the cold deck, or immediately upstream of the supply fan. The latter is preferred for applications involving high latent loads, as it provides dehumidification of all air passing through the unit.

When the coil is located in the cold deck, air passing through the hot deck will not be dehumidified. In this application, space humidity can be lowered by manually or automatically increasing the hot deck temperature, increasing the volume of dehumidified cool air and decreasing the volume of warm, humid air required to maintain zone dry bulb temperature. Chilled water coils are controlled with either a two- or three way valve.

The compressor will run to keep cold deck temperature at 55°F when one or more zones call for full cooling (via highest pressure R-3 (relay No. 31 and positive relay R-2). Above 65°F outdoor temperature, outdoor and exhaust dampers go to their minimums and the exhaust fan stops. The compressor continues to maintain 55°F cold deck temperature. When the supply fan stops, EP-1 (electro-pneumatic switch No. 1) is de-energized, which stops the compressor and exhaust fan. All dampers then go to normal position.

An alternate control method places T-1 in the mixed air stream (upstream of the cooling coil) and controls PE-2 from a controller mounted in the cold deck.

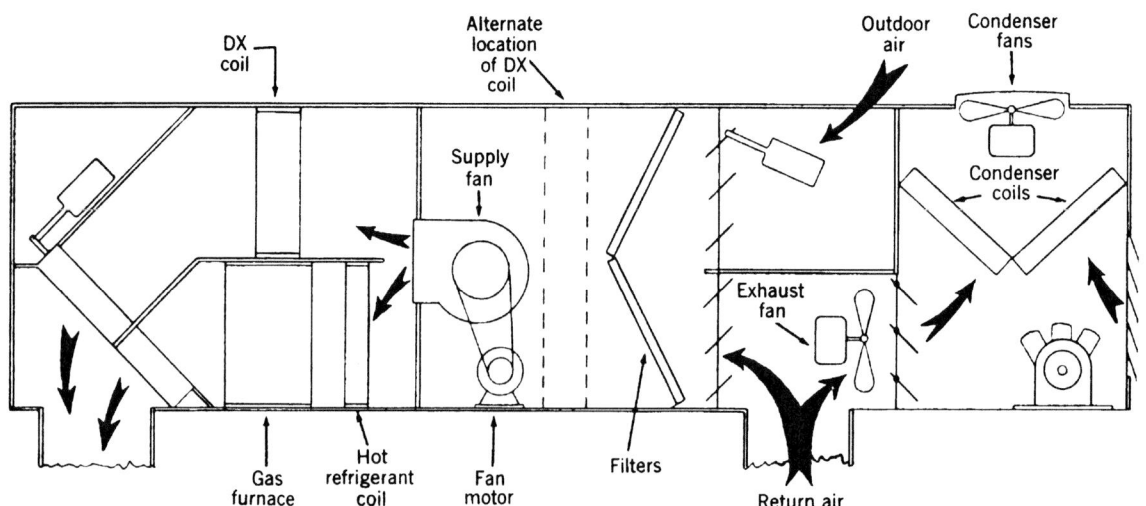

Fig 13-117. Multizone rooftop control

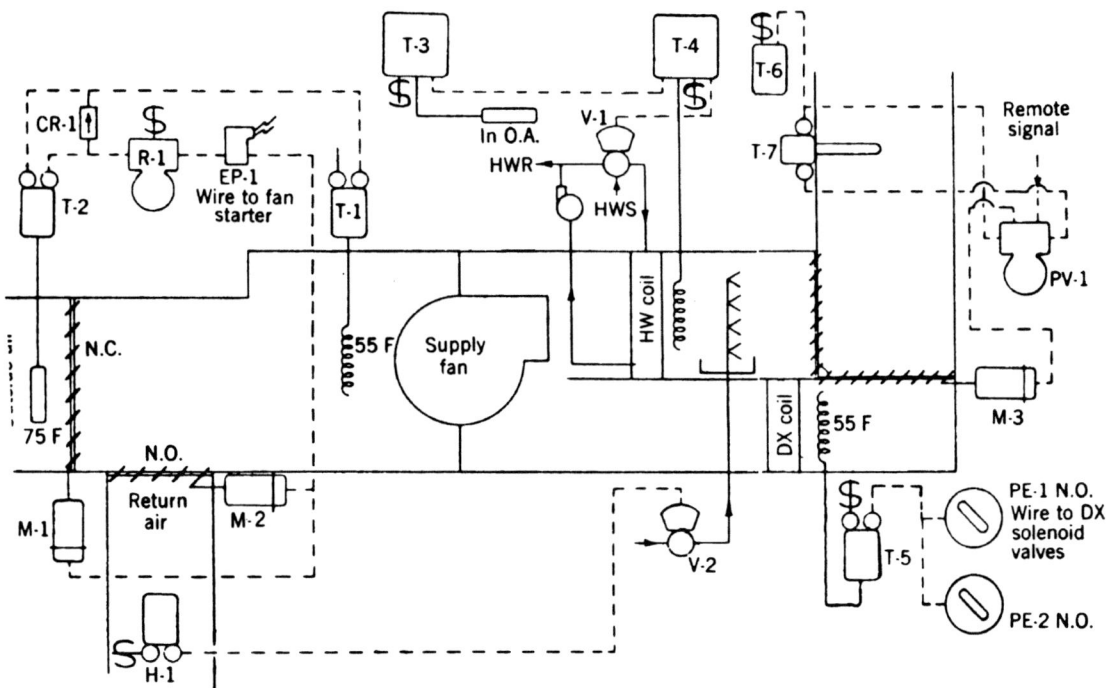

Fig 13-118. Control of typical multizone unit

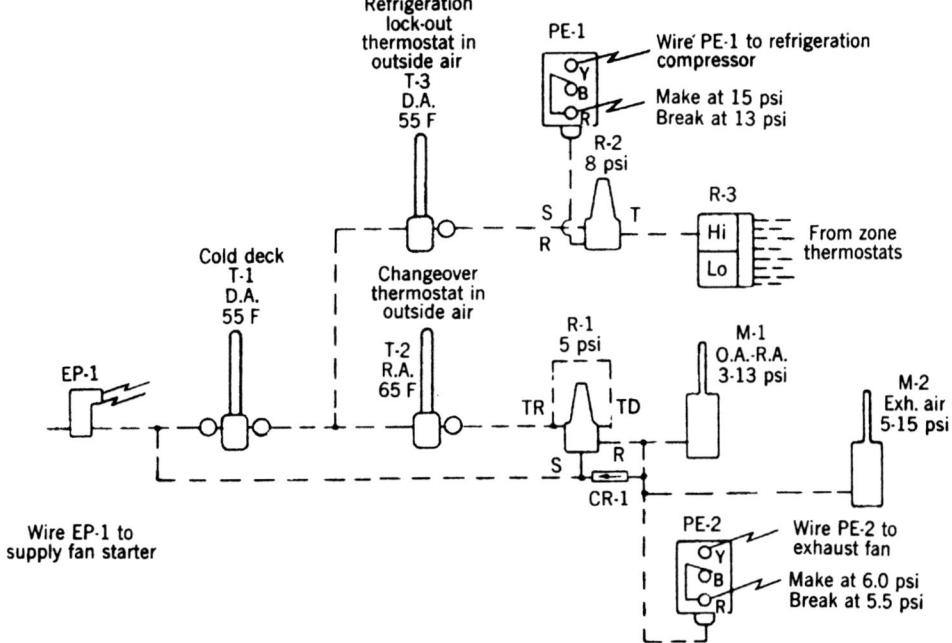

Fig 13-119. Mixed air control

Recommended Cold Deck Control: The compressor is locked out until one or more zones call for full cooling. At that time, the compressor may start if the cold deck temperature is above the thermostat set point. The cold deck thermostat cycles the compressor on and off. Compressor capacity control is achieved through one or two steps of unloading, and a hot gas bypass system (Fig. 13-120).

The refrigeration control circuit is always factory wired with the exception of the cold deck thermostat (or pneumatic electric switches). Each unit should have a low ambient cooling lockout thermostat, and a short cycle time delay relay and compressor interlock with supply fan. The control contractor should make certain these devices are in the refrigeration control circuit.

Hot Deck: The type of heating most widely used for rooftop units, the gas-fired furnace, comes with on-off, two-stage or modulating control. A pneumatic hot deck thermostat and PE switch is used for on-off or two-stage control. Upon a call for heat, the vent motor starts. When this motor is running, a centrifugal switch or air flow switch closes, allowing the prepurge timer to start. After the prepurge period, the pilot solenoid valve opens and the electric igniter lights the pilot. Once the flame is proven, the low-stage solenoid valve opens, and on a further call for heat, the second-stage gas valve opens. Fig. 13-121 shows typical hot-deck control of a gas-fired furnace. It is good practice to prevent the furnace from starting until one or more zones call for full heat.

Gas burner modulating control is similar to the two-stage control described above. Once the first stage is on (approximately 40 to 60% full flame), the modulating valve can increase gas input to 100%.

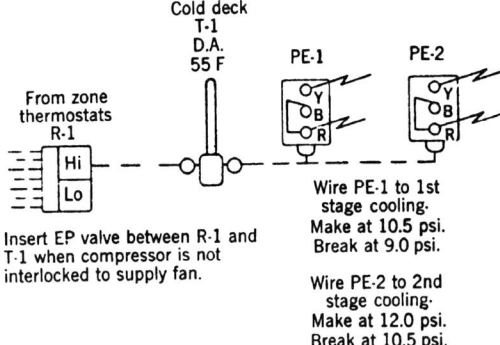

Fig 13-120. Cold deck control

On larger units, where one gas furnace will not span the entire width of the hot deck, two heat exchangers can be placed side-by-side and operated simultaneously.

Several rooftop manufacturer's offer a hot refrigerant coil located in the hot deck. Hot liquid refrigerant leaves the condenser and flows to the hot refrigerant coil, then to the thermal expansion valve, evaporator, and back to the compressor. The hot refrigerant coil warms hot deck air whenever the compressor is running, providing free heat-

ing during mild and warm weather. If more heat is needed than delivered by the coil, the hot deck thermostat energizes the hot gas solenoid. This allows the gas to flow directly from the compressor to the hot-refrigerant coil.

Most rooftop manufacturer's carry a line of roof-mounted hot water or steam boilers which can serve one or more multizone units.

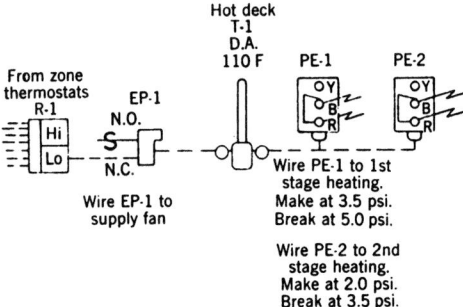

Fig 13-121. Hot deck control

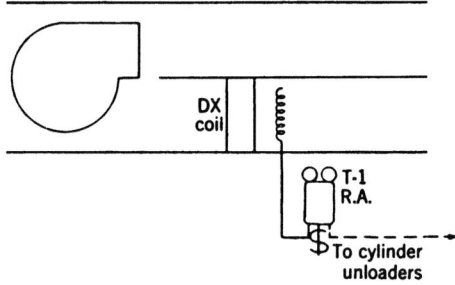

Fig 13-122. Control of cold plenum with cylinder unloader

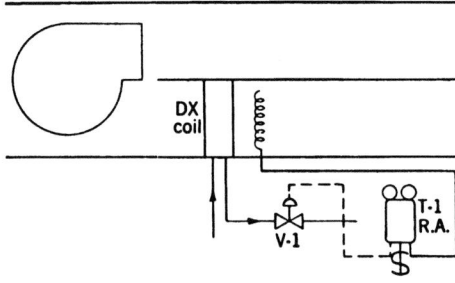

Fig 13-123. Control of cold plenum with cylinder unloader with suction pressure regulator valve

Multizone Unit Control.—As its name implies, the multizone unit is an air conditioning unit that supplies air to a number of zones at varying temperatures. A source of hot and cold air is available at the unit, and, by mixing the two air streams, the unit can easily satisfy the needs of each zone.

Fig. 13-118 illustrates the controls for a typical multizone unit. The controls may vary, depending upon the individual job requirements.

Control of Mixed Air: Thermostat T-1 controls motors M-1 (motor No. 1) and M-2 to maintain 55°F mixed air temperature when the outside air is below 55°F. As outside air rises above 55°F, the outside air damper fully opens, and the return air damper closes. When the outside air rises above 75°F T-2, through the minimum pressure relay R-1, position the outside air damper to its minimum open position. On shutdown, EP-1, which is wired to the fan starter, allows the outside air damper to close and the return air damper to open.

Control of Hot Air Plenum: Control for hot water heating is also shown in Fig. 13-118. The plenum is reset in accordance with outside temperature by master thermostat T-3. The reset range for T-4 will vary, depending upon the job location. Ranges of 110°F to 70°F are typical. These ranges are for outside temperatures of minus 10°F to plus 65°F in northern areas, and 30°F to 70°F in southern areas. Varying the hot plenum temperature, is an attempt to balance the supply air with load. This allows the zone dampers to operate in their mid-positions.

While not shown in Fig. 13-118, a pressure-electric switch, operated by the master thermostat, is often used to stop the circulating pump when the outside temperature rises to a specified value.

A circulating pump is connected to the leaving side of the coil to insure constant circulation through the coil. This pump is necessary because, if one tried to reduce coil output by reducing flow through the coil, one would find that water would take a greater temperature drop and coil output would not be reduced sufficiently.

In areas where it is necessary to protect against coil freeze-up, the averaging bulb of a thermostat is located in the sequence right after the heating coil. The thermostat is set for approximately 40°F at pressure regulator valve. As the temperature rises, the valve opens gradually to reduce the coil suction pressure and, therefore, the temperature.

When humidification is required in all areas, the humidifier is located in the hot air plenum and the humidity controller (H-1) in the return air. H-1 then controls valve V-2 or a step switch for electric immersion heaters. If humidification is needed only in the zone, the humidifier is located in the particular zone duct and controlled from a zone humidistat.

Control of Cold Air Plenum: Fig. 13-118 shows capacity control with liquid line solenoid valves. Thermostat T-5 controls a number of normally open, pressure-electric switches which, when closed, energize the solenoid valves. The pressure-electric switches operate in sequence.

Fig. 13-122 illustrates control with cylinder unloaders. A reverse acting thermostat with averaging bulb controls the cylinder unloaders. On a rise in temperature above the set point of about 50°F to 55°F, the cylinders cut in gradually to give greater capacity.

Fig. 13-123 shows control with a suction (back) connected to the fan starter. Then, whenever the temperature falls below this value, the supply fan stops, and it requires inspection of the unit by maintenance personnel before the freeze detection thermostat is manually reset.

The compressor must have a wide range of capacity reduction in order to handle the varying load conditions. Otherwise, there may be cycling of the zone mixing dampers. Cycling of the dampers is usually caused by varying temperatures across the coil. This occurs when one of the zone dampers changes position. Unless the suction pressure and, hence, coil temperature, is carefully controlled, the variation in air temperature may result in damper cycling. Cylinder unloaders offer very suitable capacity reduction.

To obtain the best humidity control, the coil should be operated as cold as possible during mild weather. During change in seasons, a considerable amount of air bypasses the cooling coil through the hot air plenum. This allows air to enter the zone without being dehumidified. Operating the coil at a low temperature, may allow adequate dehumidification. The bypass air is then used for reheat. If possible the coil should be operated at a colder temperature during mild weather than during peak load. This can be done using master-submaster instruments.

Refrigeration can be started by the zone requiring cooling, as shown in Fig. 13-125. The zone thermostats are connected through check valves to a pressure-electric switch, which is wired to the refrigeration starter. On a call for cooling by any one zone, refrigeration is started.

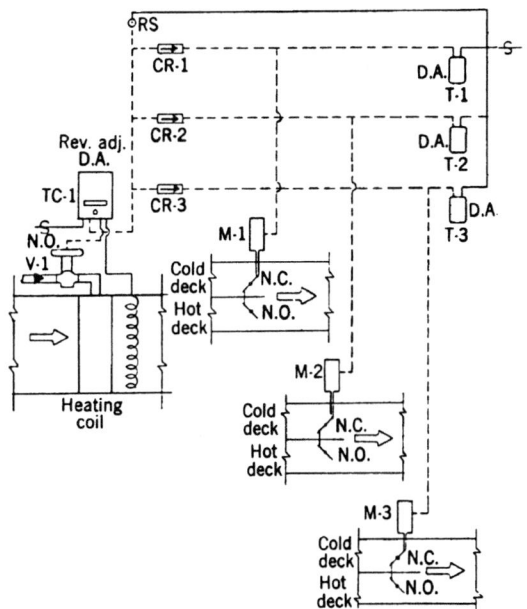

Fig 13-124. Zone mixing damper

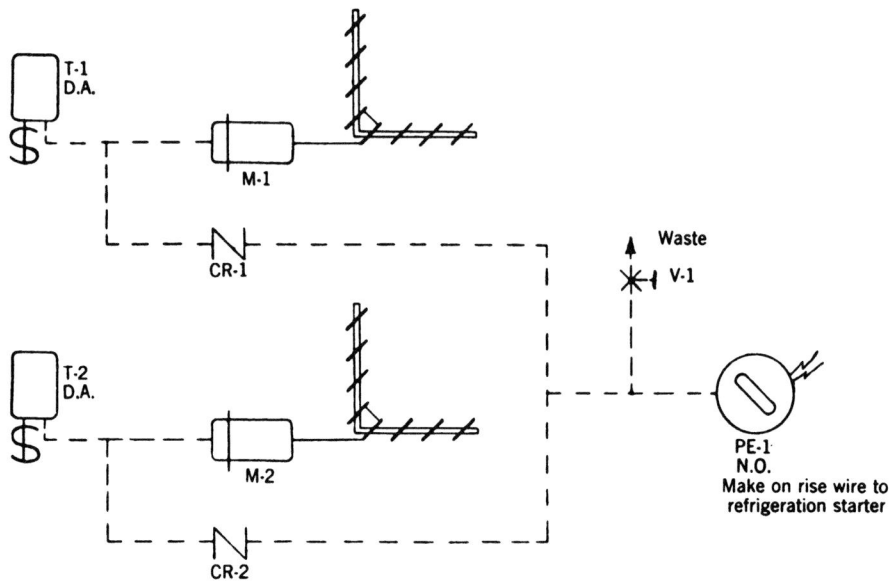

Fig 13-125. Refrigeration starting

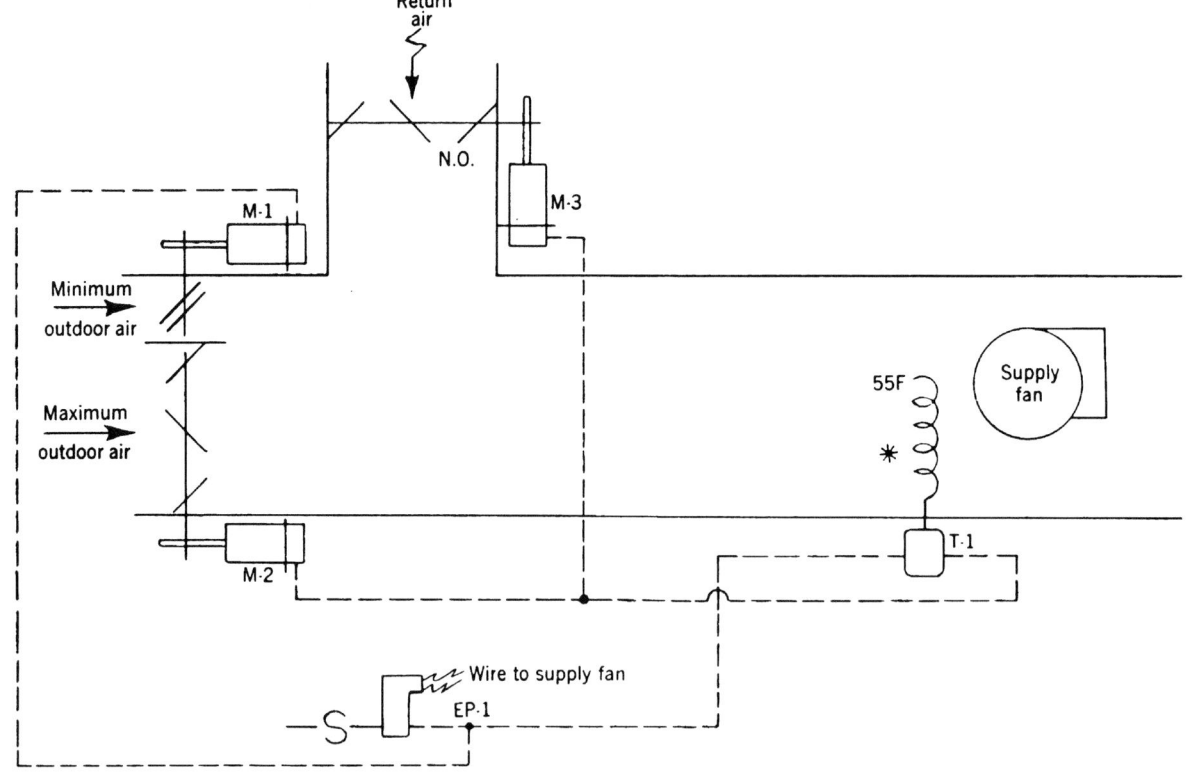

Fig 13-126. Mixed air control with minimum outside air

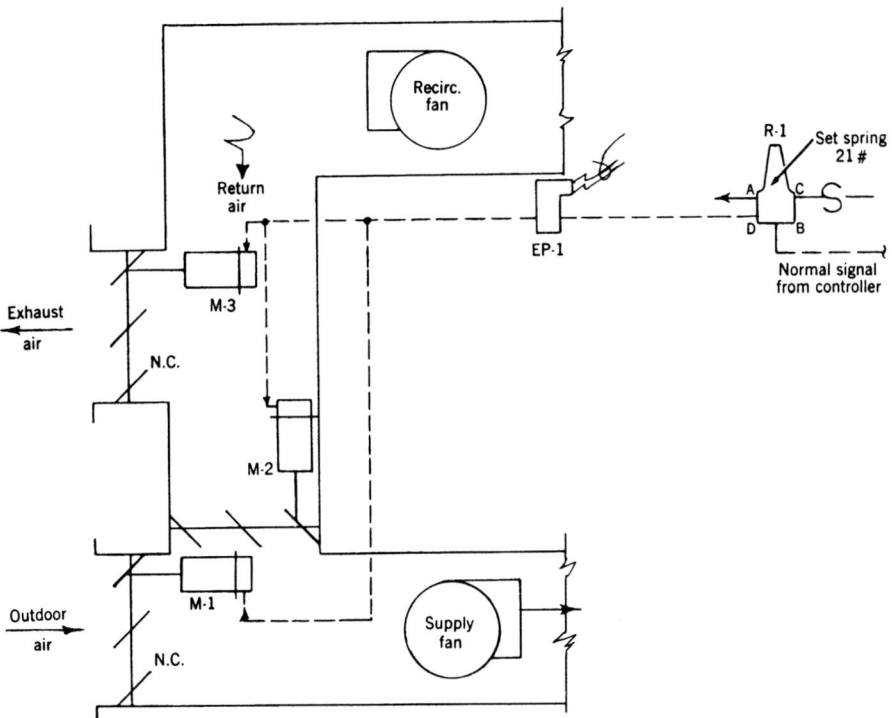

Fig 13-127. Damper operation, day cycle

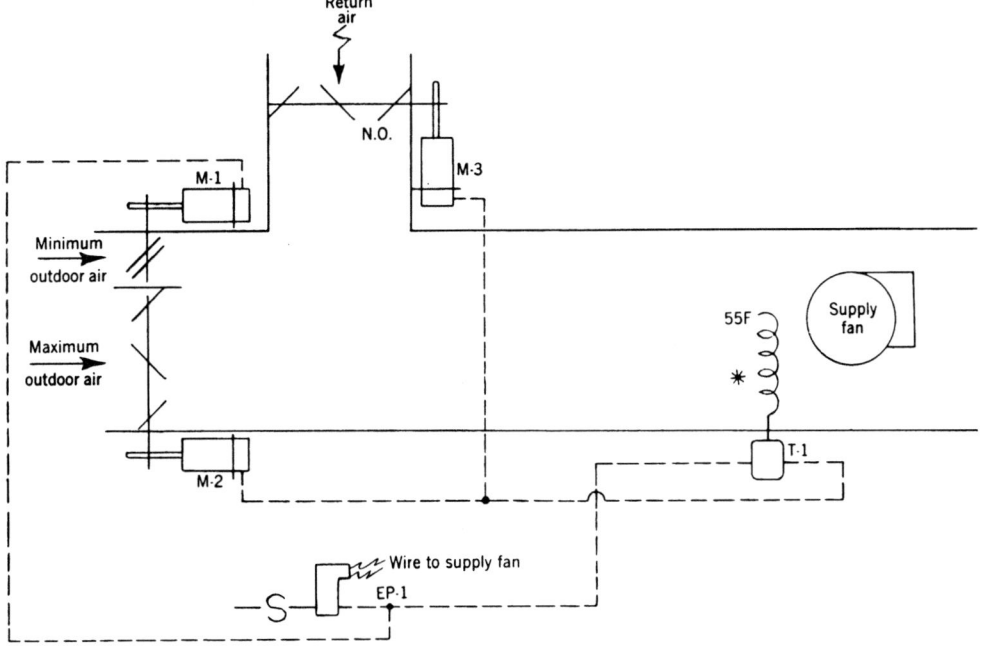

Fig 13-128. Changeover control

Control of Zone Mixing Dampers: Room thermostat T-6 (Fig. 13-122) positions zone mixing dampers to maintain desired zone temperature. With the increase in temperature, the thermostat increases branch pressure to close the hot deck damper and open the cold deck damper. With a decrease in temperature, the thermostat decreases branch pressure to open the hot deck and close the cold deck.

During the heating season in northern climates, it is usually desirable to provide low limit control for certain zones. PV-1 (pilot valve no. 1) is used to place controller T-7 in the control line to the damper motor during heating season and bypass it during cooling season.

Damper Control.—*Zone Mixing Damper Control:* With hot deck reset from coldest zone: As shown in Fig. 13-124, room thermostats T-1, T-2, and T-3 control multizone damper motors M-1, M-2, and M-3, respectively. The lowest control pressure from any room thermostat resets TC-1. TC-1 controls the multizone hot deck discharge temperature through V-1.

As temperature decreases, the zone thermostat will decrease the control pressure to its damper motor. The hot deck zone damper will open and the cold deck will close. The zone thermostat with the lowest control pressure will reset TC-1. As this reset pressure drops, the TC-1 set point will rise. Thus, at direct-acting controller TC-1, control pressure decreases, which opens V-1.

When the temperature in the coldest zone increases, control pressure from the thermostat in that zone increases and resets TC-1 to a lower set point. This increases TC-1 control pressure and closes heating coil valve V-1. The increase in thermostat control pressure gives modulation with the hot deck zone damper closed, and the cold deck damper open.

Mixed Air Control: With minimum fresh-air damper: As shown in Fig. 13-126, the minimum outdoor air-intake damper motor M-1 will open fully at any time the supply fan is operating. Mixed air control T-1 will modulate outdoor air and return air dampers M-2 and M-3 as required to maintain the desired mixed air temperature. Electro-pneumatic valve EP-1 will prevent damper operation unless the supply fan is running.

The system is capable of providing a two-position minimum damper control to open the minimum outdoor air intake damper fully at any time the fan system is operating. The mixed air control modulates the maximum outdoor air damper and return air damper in unison, to maintain a constant 55°F mixed air temperature. When the fan system is not operating, the outdoor air dampers are closed and the return air damper is open.

Damper Operation During Day Cycle Only: This is a positive control system designed for the outdoor return and exhaust air dampers to prevent damper operation during night cycle, or whenever the fan system is not running. The outdoor and exhaust air dampers shall be normally closed and the return air damper shall be normally open (Fig. 13-127).

Day Cycle: During day operation, relay R-1 will connect ports B and D and outdoor, return air, and exhaust damper motors M-1, M-2, and M-3, respectively, will be controlled by the air signal from the controlling device. Electro-pneumatic valve EP-1 will prevent damper operation unless the fan system is running.

Night Cycle: During night operation, relay R-1 will connect ports A and D and the outdoor return and exhaust air dampers will assume their normal position. This allows for night operation of the fan system without opening the outdoor air and exhaust dampers.

Economizer Control Cycle.—*With Changeover and Minimum Damper in Summer Only:* This is a mixed air control to proportion automatically the outdoor and return air dampers as required to maintain the desired mixed air temperature. It provides a changeover controller to reduce outdoor air intake to minimum requirements whenever the outdoor air temperatures rise above a designated temperature (Fig. 13-128).

Winter Cycle: Mixed air controller T-1 will modulate outdoor and return air damper motors M-1 and M-2 to maintain the desired mixed air temperature. Valve EP-1 will prevent damper operation when the fan is not running.

Summer Cycle: Whenever the outdoor air temperature exceeds the setting of changeover control T-2, the outdoor air intake will be limited to the minimum position. Relay R-1 provides field adjustment (panel mounting if desired) of the minimum damper position.

Unit Ventilator Control.—*Large Units:* Generally, the space thermostat is required to modulate in sequence the heating valve and the outdoor and return air dampers to maintain the desired space conditions. Under normal operation, the outdoor and return air damper motors will maintain a minimum fresh air intake and the space thermostat will control temperature by modulating the heating valve or introducing additional outdoor air. However, if the space temperature drops below the thermostat setting, the thermostat should be able to reduce the minimum fresh air intake, as required, in order to maintain space conditions. Discharge low limit control is frequently used to allow reduction of fresh air intake and opening of the heating valves required to maintain a minimum discharge air condition. When the system is not operating, the outdoor air damper should remain fully closed. The heating valve will remain under control of the space thermostat or discharge low limit.

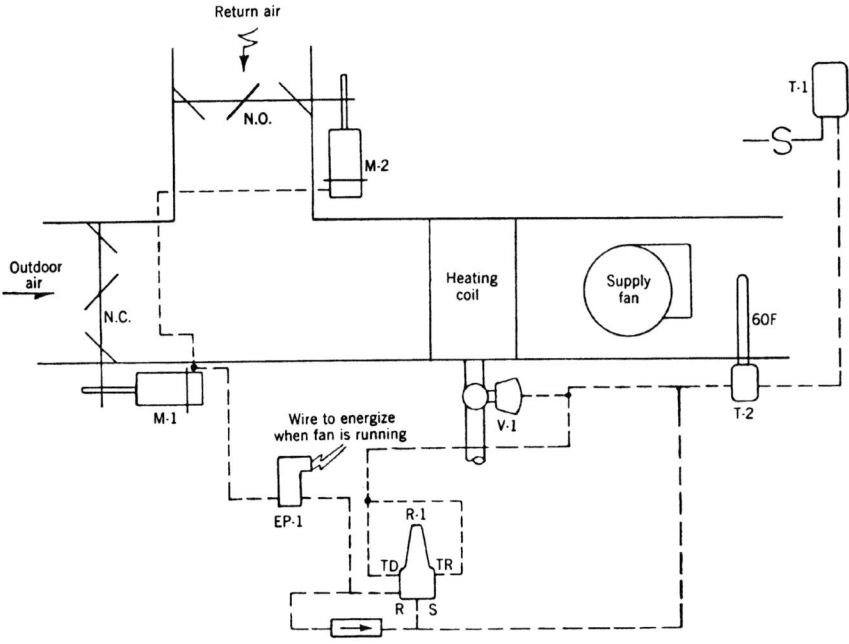

Fig 13-129. Unit ventilator control large unit

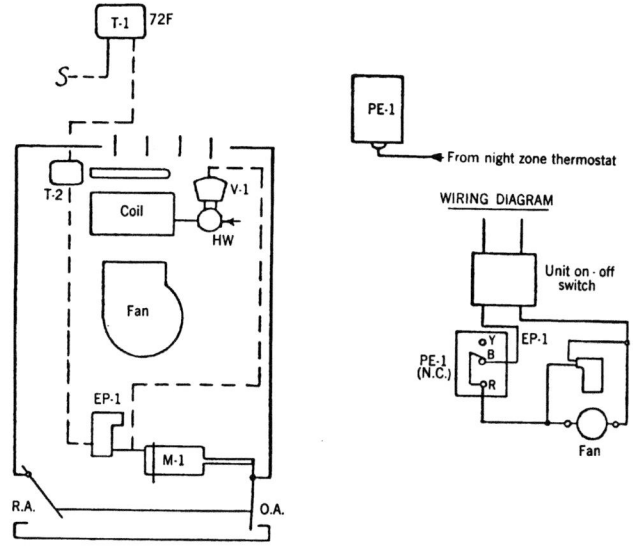

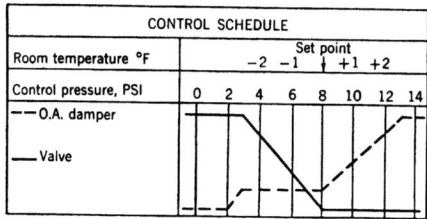

CONTROL SCHEDULE									
Room temperature °F			-2	-1	Set point	+1	+2		
Control pressure, PSI	0	2	4	6	8	10	12	14	
- - - O.A. damper									
—— Valve									

Fig 13-130. One day night operation

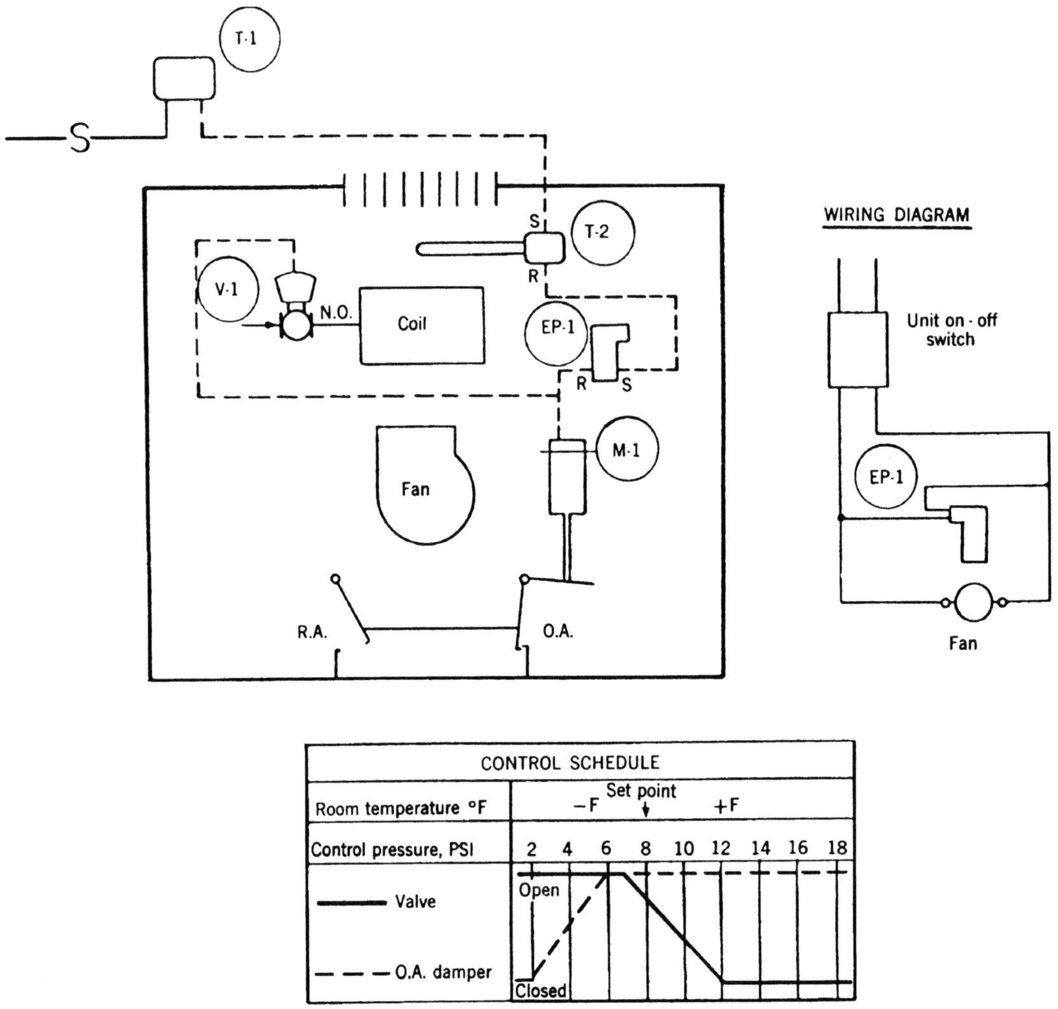

WIRING DIAGRAM

CONTROL SCHEDULE									
Room temperature °F	−F			Set point ↓		+F			
Control pressure, PSI	2	4	6	8	10	12	14	16	18
—— Valve	Open								
- - - O.A. damper									Closed

Fig 13-131. Unit ventilator using hot water

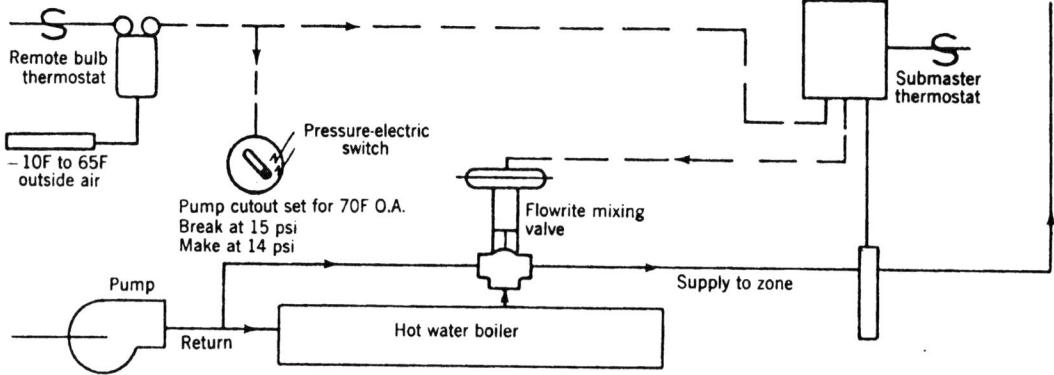

Fig 13-132. Scheduled hot water control

Referring to Fig. 13-129, at any time that space temperature is below the setting of space thermostat, T-1, valve V-1 will remain in the fully open position and the unit will operate on 100% recirculated air for rapid space warm-up. As the space temperature approaches the setting of T-1, outdoor and return air damper motors M-1 and M-2 will modulate to a minimum damper position. A further rise in space temperature will actuate heating valve V-1 into a closed position. A continued rise in space temperature will modulate outdoor and return air dampers M-1 and M-2 for increased outdoor ventilation, as required to maintain space conditions. Low limit control T-2, located in the fan discharge will vary the outdoor air damper to the minimum position and open heating valve V-1 as required to maintain a minimum discharge air temperature. EP-1 will prevent the damper from operating when the fan is not running.

Zone Day-Night Operation: Referring to Fig. 13-130, when room temperature is below setting of thermostat T-1, the valve serving the heating coil is open and the outside air damper is closed. As the temperature approaches the setting of the thermostat, the outside air damper will move to a predetermined minimum open position.

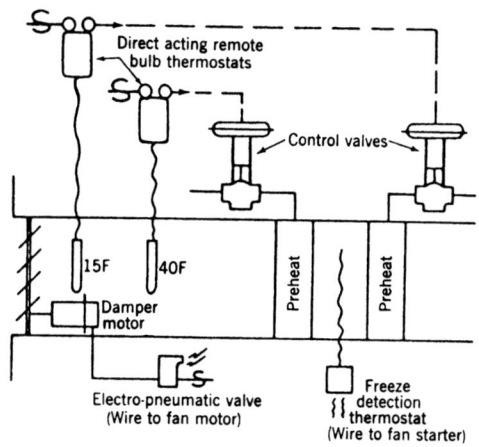

Fig 13-133. Hot water preheat coil control

On a further rise in room temperature, the valve closes. On a still further rise, the outside air damper gradually moves to the fully open position. The airstream thermostat T-2 overrides the room thermostat and repositions the damper and valve in order to maintain a minimum unit discharge temperature of 60°F. An electro-pneumatic valve closes the outside air damper on fan shutdown.

The controls function, as described above, during the occupied cycle of operation. During the unoccupied cycle of operation, a zone thermostat actuates a pressure-electric switch PE-1 to cycle the unit fan. When the fan is de-energized, the electro-pneumatic valve EP-1 opens the

valve (V-1) and closes the outside air damper M-2 to maintain a reduced unoccupied temperature of 60°F.

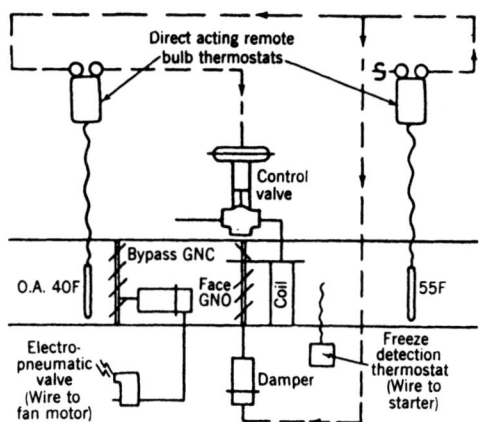

Fig 13-134. Face and bypass control

Hot Water Coil: The simpler unit ventilator control cycle is a day only room thermostat controlled valve and damper. Referring to Fig. 13-131, with fan motor on, electro pneumatic valve EP-1 is energized to open the control line to damper motor M-1 and control valve V-1. Room thermostat T-2 gradually positions M-2 and V-1 to maintain the desired temperature according to the control schedule shown as part of Fig. 13-131. If the discharge temperature drops below 60°F, discharge thermostat T-2 vents pressure from motor M-1 and valve operator V-1 to maintain the minimum discharge temperature.

With fan motor off, valve EP-1 is de-energized, motor M-1 closes, and valve V-2 opens, permitting full water flow for freeze protection.

Hot Water System Control.—Hot water temperature control with outside air reset: For the entire system or zone, an outdoor thermostat resets supply water temperature according to a predetermined reset schedule. Control is maintained when the heat output of the various heat exchange units closely approximates the load, as reflected in the reset schedule.

For the heating unit itself, a three-way water mixing valve provides a variable water temperature by mixing supply water with system return water. Fig. 13-132 shows the general arrangement.

Preheat Control: Fig. 13-133 shows the general arrangement of a preheat control. This layout requires proper sizing of the coil so that freezing can be prevented. A freeze protection thermostat is required. The first coil operates at 40°F and the second coil operates when outdoor temperature drops to 15°F. The damper motor and freeze detection thermostat are all wired to the fan motor for freeze protection.

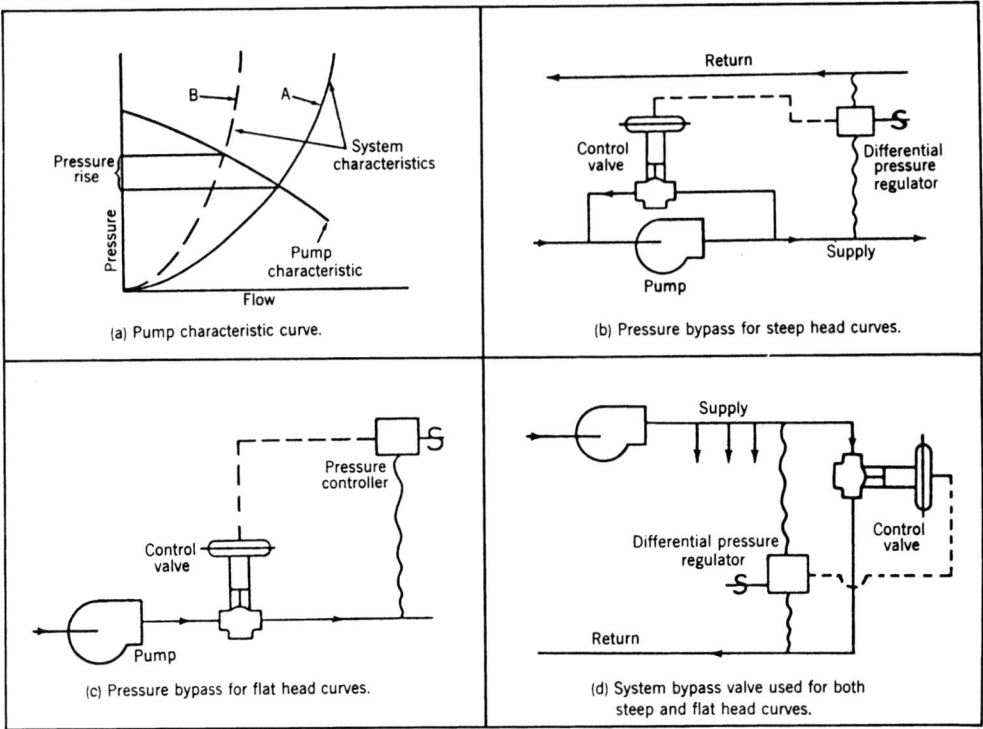

Fig 13-135. Hot water pressure control

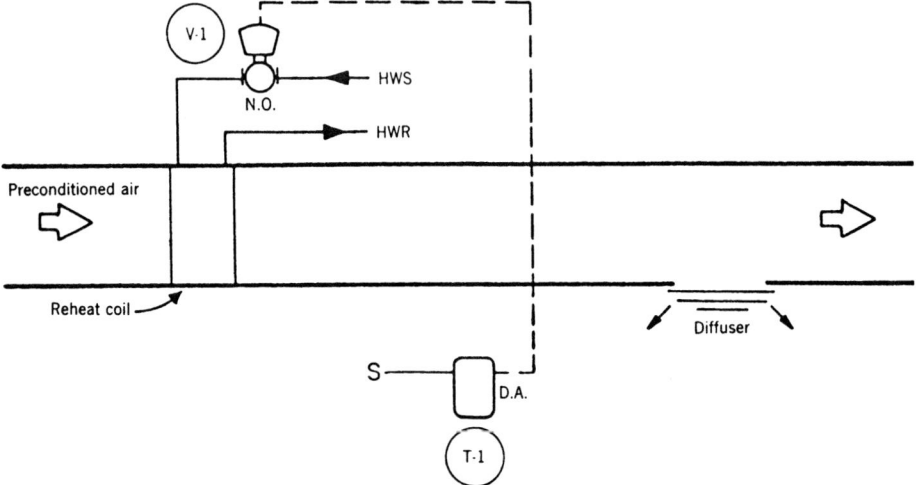

Fig 13-136. Hot water reheat control

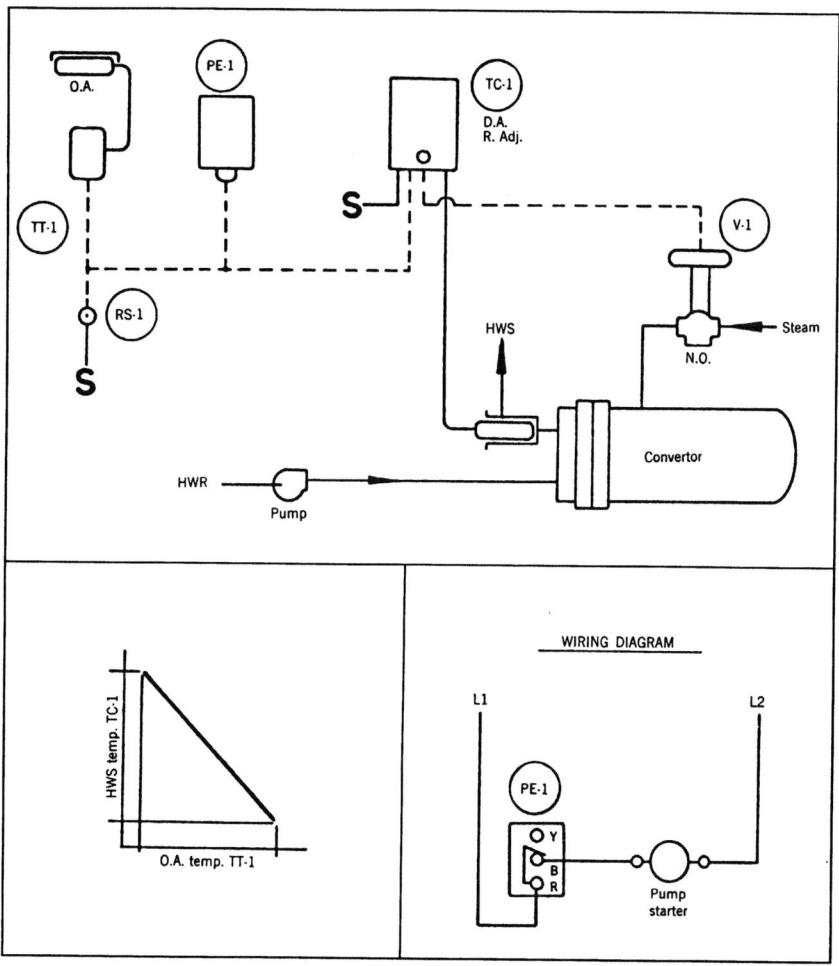

Fig 13-137. Hot water control with reset

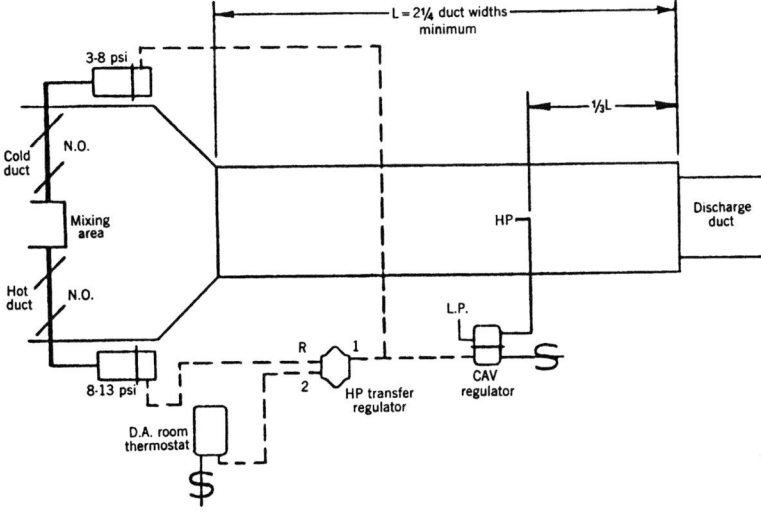

Fig 13-138. Dual duct constant volume mixing box

Face and Bypass Control: Heat transfer to the air stream proportional to the amount of air passing through the coil face is controlled by an automatic face and bypass damper. A control valve stops water flow after the face damper is fully closed. The outside air thermostat will open the coil valve at temperatures below 40°F, while the discharge thermostat will position the face and bypass damper to maintain 55°F for necessary ventilation cooling. Further reheating is added in the air handling unit or zone ducts to satisfy room conditions. A freeze detection thermostat with coiled bulb is recommended on the leaving side of heating coil to insure fan and outside air damper shut down in case of system failure (Fig. 13-134).

Pressure Control: Fig. 13-135(a) illustrates a sloping pump characteristic curve. Without pressure control of the system, pressure will rise when control valves throttle water flow. This causes a shift of system curve from A to B and increases the pressure drop across the valves, adversely affecting control.

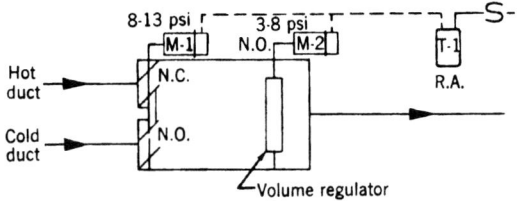

CONTROL SCHEDULE						
Room temperature		+3	+2	+1	SP	−1	−2
Control pressure		2	4	6	8	10	12
Hot duct valve flow	100% Open						
	0% Closed						
Cold duct valve flow	100% Open						
	0% Closed						
Volume regulator flow	100% Open						
	0% Min.						

Fig 13-139. Dual duct variable volume mixing box

It is desirable to maintain a constant system pressure. Most pressure variation is caused by water flow change. A bypass around the pump or piping system is indicated.

1) A pressure bypass can be used around the pump, providing the pump chosen has a steep head curve (Fig. 13-135(b)). To prevent motor overload, caution should be taken in limiting the flow when the valve is fully open.

2) A pressure reducing valve is recommended when the pump curve is flat (Fig. 13-135(c)).

3) A system bypass valve can be employed at the end of a system or zone. Care should be taken in sizing supply and return mains to insure adequate pressure control. This can apply to either flat or steep head pump curves (Fig. 13-135(d)).

Hot Water Reheat: Fig. 13-136 shows a commonly used reheat system with room thermostat T-1 control. Preconditioned air from the fan discharge enters the reheat coil at approximately 55°F. T-1 modulates valve V-1 to maintain desired room temperature.

Hot Water Converter Control: Outside air temperature resets the hot water supply temperature. The signal from the outside air transmitter TT-1 resets submaster controller TC-1 in accordance with a preset schedule. TC-1 positions the normally opened steam valve V-1 to maintain scheduled hot water temperature. Pressure-electric switch PE-1 will shut off the pump when outside air temperature reaches 65°F. The schedule will depend on the load of the system. Fig. 13-137 shows the control diagram.

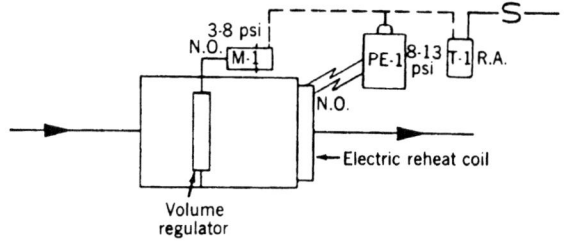

CONTROL SCHEDULE						
Room temperature		+3	+2	+1	SP	−1	−2
Control pressure		2	4	6	8	10	12
P.E. switch	on	Open					
	off						
Volume regulator flow	100%						
	0% Min.						

Fig 13-140. Single duct variable volume mixing box with electric reheat

Mixing Box Control.—Mixing boxes of various designs are generally used for local (room) comfort control. The unit usually has two air dampers for mixing hot and cold air. Damper motors may be mounted inside or outside of the unit. The dampers may be linked together or separately controlled. Following are a few typical control systems for mixing boxes:

Dual Duct Variable Volume: Referring to Fig. 13-139, room thermostat T-1 gradually positions the hot and cold air duct valves through motor M-1 and regulator through motor M-2 to maintain the desired temperature according to the control schedule shown.

Dual Duct Constant Volume-High Velocity: Referring to Fig. 13-138, the constant air volume (CAV) regulator controls the pressure drop across the diffusers at a constant value. Static and velocity pressure will increase or decrease simultaneously as the flow of the unit increases or decreases in the system, whereas resistance downstream from the measuring tip is constant. This allows the use of static or total pressure measurement. The room thermostat controls the mixing ratio of hot and cold air for its load. The CAV regulator keeps the total flow steady.

Single Duct Variable Volume: Referring to Fig. 13-140, thermostat T-1 gradually positions the regulator through motor M-1 and pressure-electric switch or step controller PE-1 to maintain the desired temperature according to the control schedule shown.

Rotary Air-to-Air Heat Exchanger Control.—Since the energy conservation is of paramount interest to this industry, air-to-air heat exchanger control is described:

Face and Bypass Control: Figs. 13-141a, and 13-143a show the control diagram for a rotary air-to-air heat exchanger. The unit runs continuously at maximum speed. Reverse acting thermostat T-1 is set for maximum sensitivity. When outside air temperature is below 73°F, thermostat T-1 allows full control pressure from thermostat T-2 to damper motor M-2. T-2 controls the face and bypass dampers to maintain 55°F incoming air temperature. When the outside air temperature rises above 75°F, T-1 stops control pressure from T-2 and bleeds air from motor M-2 to allow full air flow through the rotary heat exchanger. Electro-pneumatic valve EP-1 is wired to the supply fan to close the outside air and exhaust dampers on fan shutdown.

Variable Speed Control: Referring to Figs. 13-142a, and 13-143b, the reverse acting thermostat T-1 is set for maximum sensitivity. When outside air temperature is below 75°F, T-1 allows full control pressure from T-2 to pressure controller PR-1. T-2 controls the speed of the rotary heat exchanger to maintain 55°F incoming air temperature. When outside air temperature rises above 75°F, T-1 stops control pressure from T-2 and bleeds air from pressure regulator PR-1 to maintain maximum speed of the rotary heat exchanger. Valve EP-1 is wired to the supply fan to close outside air and exhaust dampers on fan shutdown.

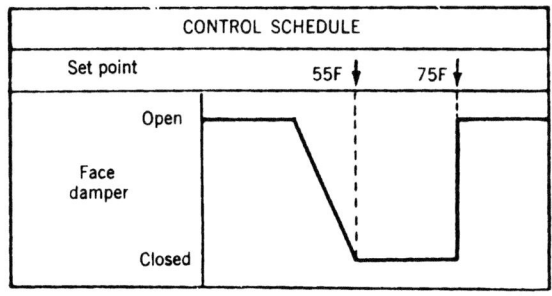

Fig 13-141a. Rotary air to air heat exchanger control, face-bypass

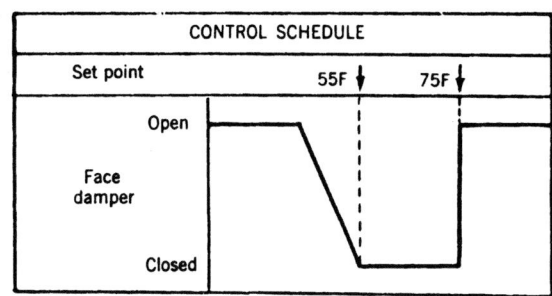

Fig 13-142a. Rotary air to air heat exchanger control, variable speed

Automatic Control for Dual Duct System.—Basic function of automatic controls for dual duct cycle of Figs. 13-88 and 13-89 is shown on Fig. 13-143. The system is assumed to provide for humidity control in winter time and for a preheat coil in the minimum outdoor air duct. Minor modifications in control arrangement would be required for cycles of Figs. 13-90, 13-91 and 13-92.

When the supply fan is started, relay E-1 actuated by the fan motor starter supplies compressed air to all apparatus and room control instruments. Minimum outdoor damper D-1 opens when the supply fan runs. Damper D-1 could be arranged to be closed manually or automatically when ventilation is not required, as during night operation, warm-up, or cool-down periods. Summer-winter switches S-1 and S-2 can be manual or automatic.

Summer Operation: With summer-winter switch S-1 is in summer position, cold air duct thermostat T-1 controls chilled water valve V-3 to maintain desired temperature in the cold deck. The practice of eliminating chilled water control valves or controlling only water temperature leaving the coil is not recommended because of the danger of having excessively low temperatures in the cold air duct on partial loads.

Submaster warm air duct thermostat T-2 is reset through cumulator C-1 by summer humidistat H-1 and controls steam or hot water valves V-4 and V-5. Minimum setting of thermostat T-2 should be approximately 5°F above average room temperature and maximum setting equal to the temperature required for maximum heating load. In order to avoid searching for warm air duct control at low loads, it is recommended two valves, V-4 and V-5, be designed in parallel approximately of one-third and two-thirds capacity respectively. Summer humidistat H-1 adds heat to the warm air duct only when low internal loads occur during humid weather (see Figs. 13-95, 13-96, and 13-97). During high summer load operation control of temperature in warm air duct is not essential and the source of heat might be shut off or the controls made inoperative.

Winter Operation: When refrigeration is not required, the summer-winter switch S-1 is placed in winter position allowing thermostat T-1 to modulate dampers D-2, D-3 and D-4 to maintain cold air duct temperature by drawing cool air from outdoors. For economy, to minimize the amount of reheat in the warm air duct, city water sprays or recirculating pump sprays could be put into operation ahead of dampers D-2, D-3, and D-4 through relay C-2. Evaporative cooling of 8°F to 12°F could be achieved. Contamination of air in industrial cities makes use of recirculating sprays inadvisable for prolonged use. A hand-off automatic switch, if a recirculating pump is used, should be provided to stop sprays during very cold weather. In order to reduce the amount of outdoor air heated during cold weather, thermostat T-1 is usually reset upward in winter for operating economy. Experience indicates proper winter setting of thermostat T-1 can be determined only by actual operation of the particular system.

Warm air duct temperature is controlled by submaster thermostat T-2 as reset by master thermostat T-3. Humidity control can be accomplished by winter humidistat H-2 controlling city water spray valve V-2 or a recirculating spray pump. When a preheater in minimum outdoor air is used, it is controlled by thermostat T-1 to maintain minimum temperature of the air drawn into that system.

On new buildings, where temporary heat is to be provided by a dual duct system, room thermostats T-R should be direct acting with warm air connections in room mixing units normally open. If cold connections in the mixing units are normally open, room thermostats should be reverse acting.

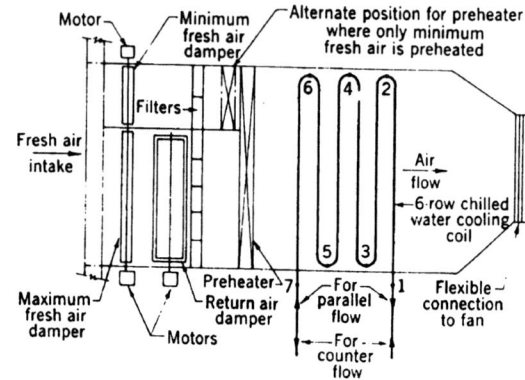

Fig 13-143. Schematic of a large central station air conditioning system

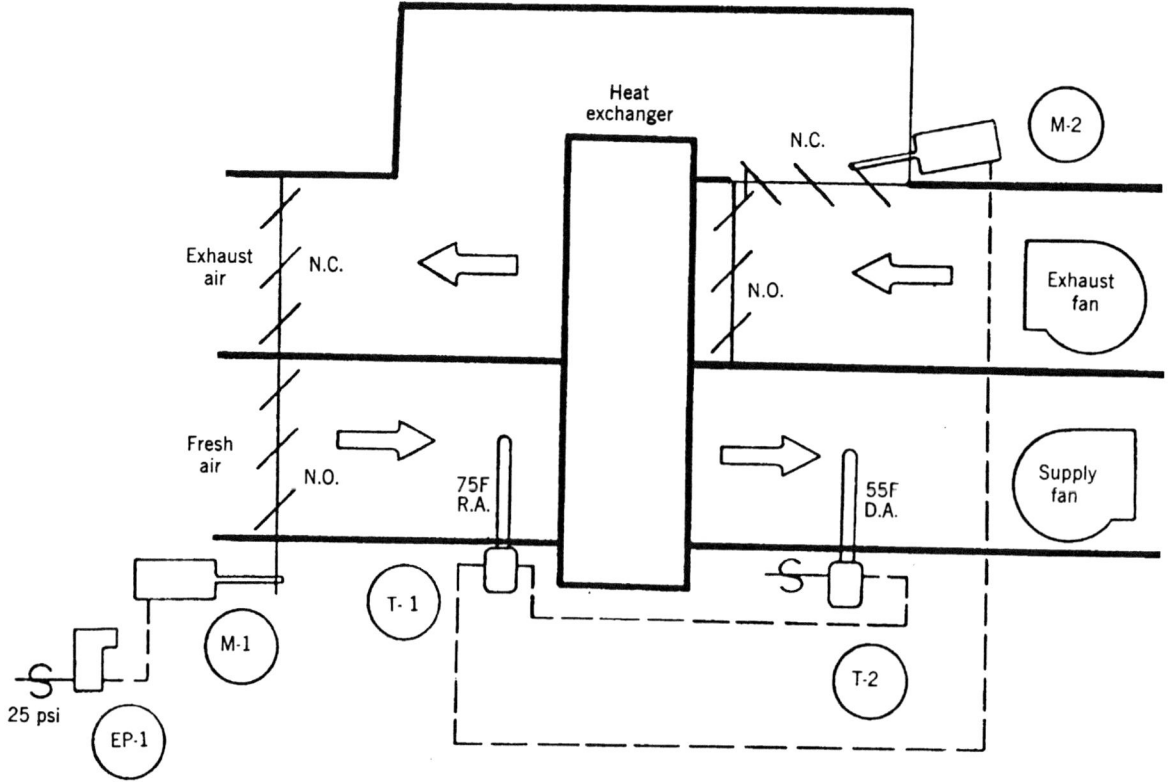

Fig 13-143a. Rotary air-to-air heat exchanger control, face bypass

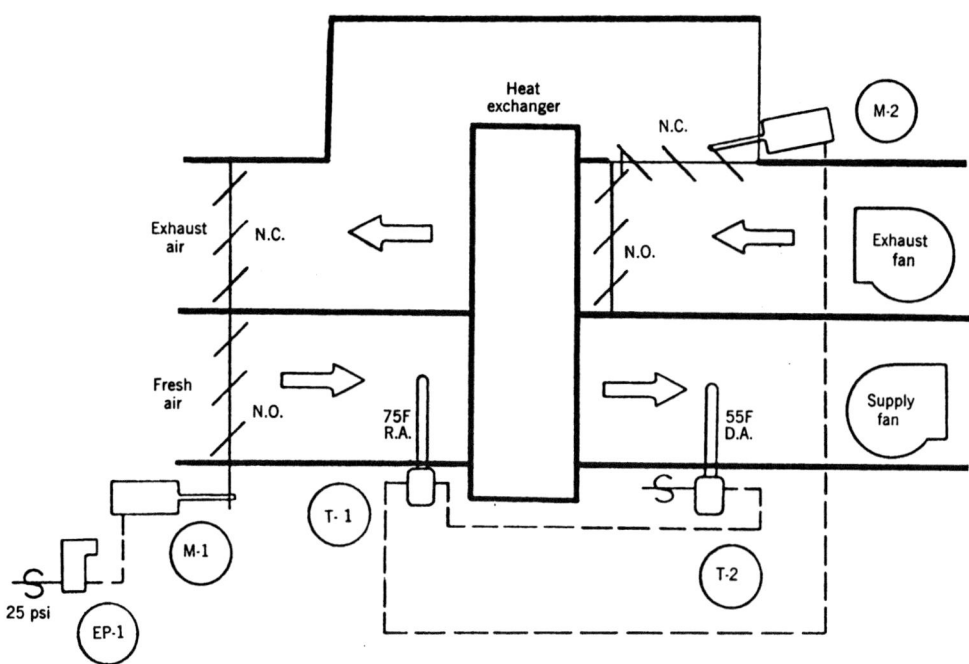

Fig 13-143b. Rotary air-to-air heat exchanger control, variable speed

Winterizing Chilled Water System

During winter operation of year-round air conditioning systems, there is the danger of frozen chilled water coils. A common practice to prevent this hazard is to drain these coils and to circulate antifreeze in them temporarily, or to leave them filled with antifreeze for the winter.

In very large buildings with more than one central station system, the cost of labor and antifreeze can be significant. Also, use of antifreeze entails special precautions to prevent leakage through valve pickings. Finally, most common aqueous solutions with a low freezing point are more viscous than chilled water at low temperatures. As a result, streamline flow might develop in the cooling coils and almost certainly would develop in the secondary water coils of any perimeter units in the system. Streamline flow sharply reduces coil capacity, perhaps better than 50%.

Water Circulation to Prevent Freeze-Up.—Another common method of winterizing chilled water systems lies simply in circulating water in the system when outside temperature drops below 32°F. However, most chilled water coils 4 to 6 rows deep are connected for counterflow operation to obtain good cooling efficiency. In Fig. 13-144 which shows a typical cooling coil counterflow arrangement, chilled water enters the last row downstream at (1) and leaves the first or upstream row at (7). Cold air contacts first the coldest water (at 7), which is an invitation to freeze-up, not a precaution against it.

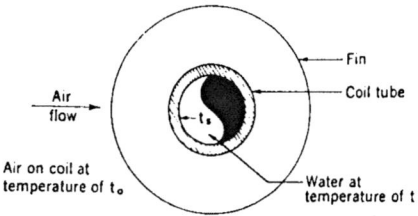

Fig 13-144. Section through a typical chilled water coil tube

What is actually required to prevent freeze-up is that the warmest water first meet the coldest air, that is, parallel flow. In Fig. 13-144 this would be accomplished by water entering at (7) and leaving at (1)

To prevent freeze-up, how warm should water in the coil tubes be? By referring to Fig. 13-144, the following equation gives the heat transferred from water to the air:

$$h_o(T_s - T_o) = h_i(T_i - T_s)$$

where h_o = outside surface film coefficient in respect to inside Btu/hr-ft²-°F;

h_i = inside surface film coefficient Btu/hr-ft²-°F;

T_s = temperature at the inside wall of the coil tube,°F;

T_o = temperature at the air upstream of the coil tube,°F; and

T_i = temperature of water inside of the coil,°F.

Inside tube surface temperature T_s must be 32°F or higher to avert ice formation. The air temperature T_s should generally be taken as the outside design temperature for the winter. The inside film coefficient h_i for water at a specified velocity and estimated temperature is found in most heat transfer books.

The outside film coefficient h_o for the air can be found from the equation:

$$h_o = \left[\frac{(w \times A_f) + A_o}{A_i} \right] h_{out}$$

where h_{out} = outside surface film coefficient Btu/hr-ft²-°F;

   w = finned surface efficiency of coil;

   A_f = surface of coil fins (both sides) per linear foot of coil length, ft²/ft;

   A_o = outside surface of coil tube exposed to air ft²/ft; and

   A_i = inside surface of coil tube exposed to air ft²/ft.

The engineer can obtain w and h_o from the coil manufacturer. Water temperature t_i can now be found from the above equations. If it is greatly different from that used to find h_i, then trial and error solutions should be made until the estimated and calculated values of t_i are in close agreement.

For example, assume that the preheater fails and outside air at 0°F and 500 fpm face velocity should enter over part of the upstream row of the chilled water coil because of air stratification. From the previous equations, a water temperature of approximately 55°F with a velocity of 1 fps would be required under these circumstances to prevent freezeup in a commercial coil with a high finned surface efficiency. Based on a water temperature of 55°F, evaluation of parallel flow vs. counterflow can now be completed with some interesting conclusions.

Counterflow and Parallel Flow: In counterflow, a 6-row coil with air and water conditions as cited would require an inlet water temperature of approximately 180°F to prevent freezing in the upstream row on the air side. Aside from destroying the air conditioning potential of all systems concerned, such a high temperature would make an oven of the building.

Parallel flow winterizing, on the other hand, is feasible with moderate inlet water temperatures, such as 55°F, which will not destroy or even reduce the air conditioning potential in any system in the building.

Steps in Design: There are essentially three steps to design a parallel flow winterizing system.

1) Calculate inlet water temperature required to prevent freeze-up as water proceeds from the first row upstream to that row at which the air temperature is warm enough to prevent freezing water.

2) Design a control system and a warning system that will guarantee that water pumps actually operate during subfreezing weather with water at the temperature calculated in Step 1.

3) Design and lay out the piping and equipment necessary for changing to parallel flow in cold weather.

As for the first step, the engineer should be able to ascertain this water temperature with the heat transfer equations. The coil manufacturer, however, is in a better position to make this check and should do so whenever possible. Step 2 is self-explanatory. The sales engineer for the temperature controls is in the best position to help design a suitable control system for parallel flow winterizing.

Piping Arrangement: The piping arrangement to achieve parallel flow through the coils in cold weather can be accomplished at one of two locations of water system: (1) at each coil, or (2) at the central chilled water pumping station. Under scheme (2) it is necessary to have a manual switch to open the normally closed chilled water control valves. Under neither scheme is it advisable to circulate water through the refrigerating units during winter shutdown because it will unnecessarily pressurize the evaporator. This might cause leakage of the primary refrigerant. Fig. 13-145 shows a typical piping arrangement to effect parallel flow at each coil.

Parallel flow at the central pumping station requires reversing the connections at the pumps with bypass valves. The exact method of piping a system for parallel flow will depend on initial cost and the ease for personnel to make this changeover.

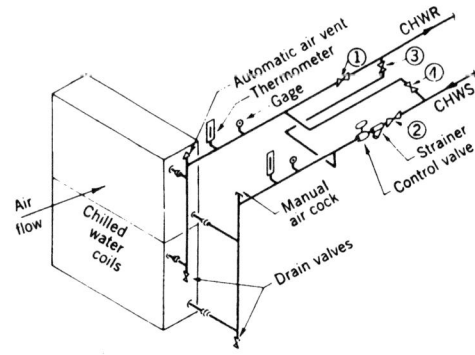

Fig 13-145. Isometric view of chilled water coil for both counterflow and parallel flow

Operating Procedure: Operating procedure for parallel flow when outside air temperature is expected to drop below 32°F usually involves the following steps:

1) All valving are set for parallel flow.

2) Pump or pumps are started when outside air temperature drops to 35°F. Water velocity in coils should be kept at approximately 2 fps for good turbulence and low pumping cost. Since it is of vital importance to keep the pumps in continuous operation in subfreezing weather, some guarantee must be made to ensure this, such as that provided by automatic controls actuated by an outside air thermostat. When plant shutdown occurs, as over weekends when operating personnel are usually reduced to a minimum, continuous operation of the pumps is most advisable, even though the outside temperature may not fall below 32°F most of this time.

3) As the outside air temperature falls to subfreezing, it may become necessary to heat water in order to attain that inlet water temperature calculated to prevent freeze-up. This would require installation of a small converter, if none were already available for this purpose. Fortunately, this is probably not required for most installations, since the vast mass of water will usually come to an equilibrium temperature well above that required to prevent ice formation.

Mechanical Draft Cooling Towers

There are two types of cooling towers in general use: the atmospheric and the mechanical draft. The spray pond and natural draft chimney tower have been largely replaced by those two types of cooling towers. Objection to the spray pond is its limited performance and the nuisance created by the high water loss during certain seasons of the year. Objection to the natural draft tower is the high initial cost and the serious reduction in performance experienced during periods of hot weather.

There are two types of mechanical draft towers: the forced draft and the induced draft. The forced draft tower has its fan mounted at its base and the air is forced in at the bottom and discharged through the top at low velocity. In the induced draft tower, the fan is mounted on the roof of the structure and air is pulled upward and discharged at a high velocity.

Except for fan location, the structural and operational features of the two types of mechanical draft towers are essentially the same. A cross-section of the induced draft tower with the various parts labeled is shown in Figs. 13-146. Entrained moisture is removed from the exhaust air by the drift eliminator just above the spray chamber and below the fan. Water is pumped to the main header at the top of the tower and from there distributed to the various nozzles. This water is sprayed up in a manner similar to

that used in a spray pond and is intimately mixed with the exhaust air before dropping to decks below.

In performance, the up spray distributing system represents the equivalent of adding 8 or 9 ft to the height of the cooling tower over that of the gravity type system. Slat-type grids interrupt water as it flows counter currently to the air. In flowing counter currently, the coldest water contacts the driest air and the warmest water contacts the most humid air. Maximum performance is thus obtained.

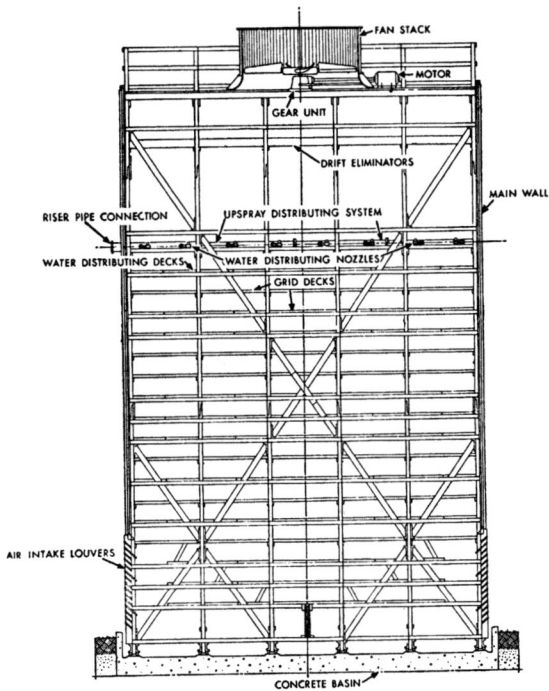

Fig 13-146. Cross section of mechanical draft cooling tower

Performance of a given type of cooling tower is governed by the ratio of weights of air to water and the time of contact between water and air. In commercial practice, variation in the ratio of air to water is first obtained by keeping the air velocity constant at about 350 fpm/ft² of active tower cross section and varying water concentration (gpm/ft²).

Time of contact between water and air is governed largely by varying tower height. Should contact time be insufficient, no amount of increase in the ratio of air to water will produce the desired cooling.

Approach is a term that indicates the difference between the cold water temperature and the wet bulb temperature. *Cooling range* is the difference between the hot water temperature and the cold water temperature.

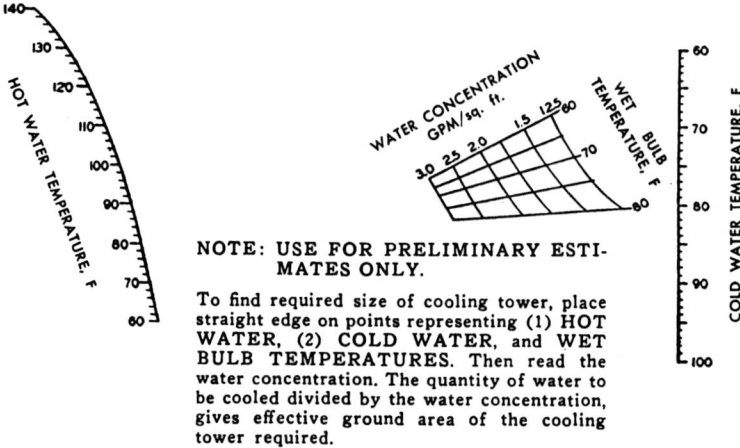

NOTE: USE FOR PRELIMINARY ESTI-
     MATES ONLY.

To find required size of cooling tower, place
straight edge on points representing (1) HOT
WATER, (2) COLD WATER, and WET
BULB TEMPERATURES. Then read the
water concentration. The quantity of water to
be cooled divided by the water concentration,
gives effective ground area of the cooling
tower required.

Fig 13-147. Sizing chart for mechanical draft cooling towers

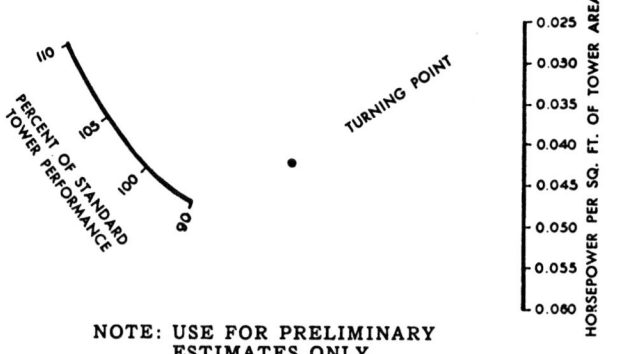

NOTE: USE FOR PRELIMINARY
     ESTIMATES ONLY
To find fan horsepower, place straight edge on
0/0 design tower capacity factor and turning point,
then read fan horsepower per square foot of tower
area at right. Multiply tower area by this factor to
obtain fan horsepower.

Fig 13-148. Fan horsepower curve for mechanical draft cooling towers

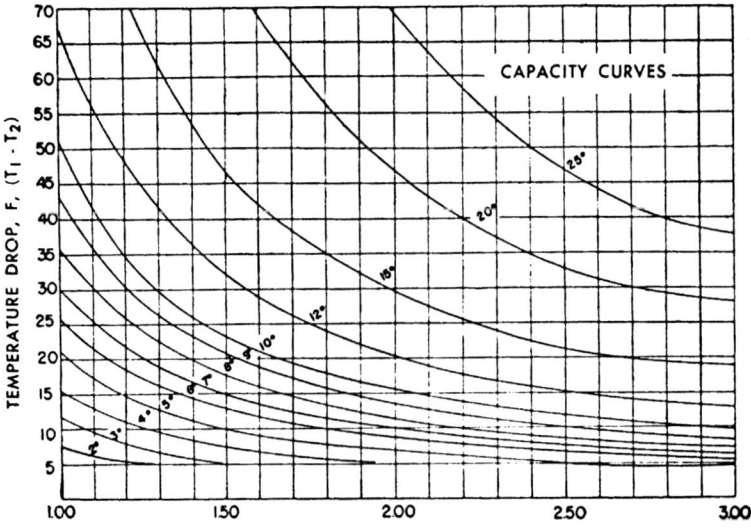

Fig 13-149. Capacity curves for atmospheric cooling towers

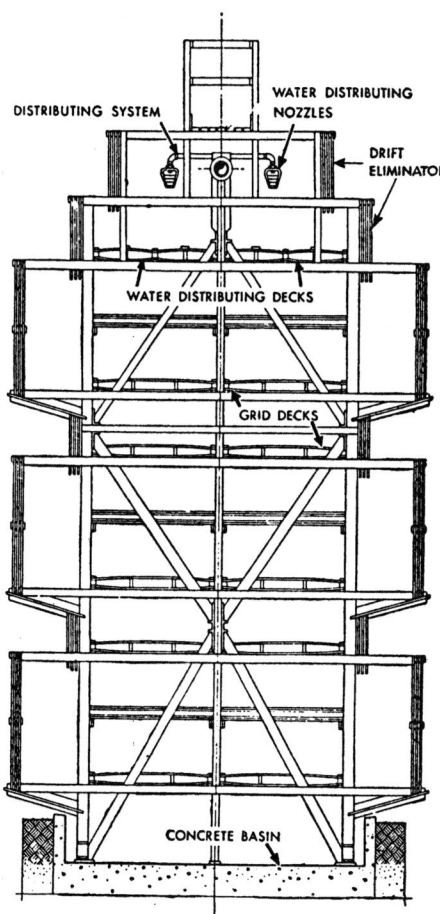

Fig 13-150. Cross section of atmospheric cooling tower

Estimating Data for Mechanical Draft Cooling Towers.—Fig. 13-147 shows the relationship of the hot water, cold water, and wet bulb temperatures to water concentration. From this, the minimum area required for a given performance of a well-designed counterflow induced draft cooling tower can be obtained. The horsepower per square foot of tower area required for a given performance is given in Fig. 13-148. These curves do not apply to parallel or cross-flow cooling; also they do not apply where the approach to the cold water temperature is less than 5°F. They should be considered approximate and for preliminary estimates only. Many factors not shown in the graphs must be included in the computation and hence the manufacturer should be consulted for final design recommendations.

The cooling performance of any tower containing a given depth of filling varies with water concentration. It has been found that the maximum contact and performance are obtained with a tower having a water concentration of 2 to 3 gpm/ft² of ground area. Thus, the problem of calculating the size of a cooling tower becomes one of determining the proper concentration of water required to

obtain the desired results. A higher tower will be required if water concentration falls below 1.6 gal/ft². Should water concentration exceed 3 gal/ft², a cooling tower of less height may be used. Once the necessary water concentration is obtained, the tower area ft² can be calculated by dividing the gpm circulated by water concentration into gal/ft². Required tower size then is a function of the following:

1) cooling range (hot water temperature minus cold water temperature);
2) approach to wet bulb temperature (cold water temperature minus wet bulb temperature);
3) quantity of water to be cooled;
4) wet bulb temperature;
5) air velocity through the cell; and
6) tower height.

To illustrate use of the charts, assume the following cooling conditions:

Hot water temperature	102°F
Cold water temperature	78°F
Wet bulb temperature (T_{wb})	70°F
Water quantity, gpm	2000

Place a straight edge on Fig. 13-147 to connect points representing the design water and wet bulb temperature, and find that a water concentration of 2 gal/ft² is required. Dividing the quantity of water circulated by water concentration, find that the theoretical area of the tower is 1000 ft².

To obtain the theoretical fan horsepower, use Fig. 13-148. Connect points representing the 100% of standard tower performance with the turning point and find that it will require 0.041 hp/ft² of actual effective tower area. Multiplying this by the tower area of 1000 ft², find that 41.0 fan horsepower is required to perform the necessary cooling.

Suppose that the commercial tower size is such that the actual tower area is 910 ft². The cooling equivalent to 1000 ft² of standard tower area can still be obtained by increasing the air velocity through the tower. Within reasonable limits, the actual area shortage can be compensated for by an increase in air velocity through the tower, which, in turn, requires a higher fan horsepower. The problem then becomes one of increasing the performance of the smaller tower by 10%. From Fig. 13-148, by connecting the points representing 110% of standard tower performance and the turning point, the fan horsepower is found to be 0.057 hp/ft² of actual tower area, or 0.057 × 910 = 51.9 hp.

On the other hand, suppose the commercial tower size is such that the actual tower is 1110 ft²; the cooling equivalent to 1000 ft² of standard tower area can be achieved with less air and less fan horsepower. By the use of Fig. 13-148 the theoretical fan horsepower for a tower doing only 90% of standard performance is found to be 0.031 per ft² of actual tower area or 34.5 hp.

This illustrates how sensitive the fan horsepower is to small changes in tower area. The importance of designing a tower that is slightly oversized in ground area becomes immediately apparent.

Assume the same cooling range and approach as used in the first example, except that the wet bulb temperature is lower. The design conditions would then be: gpm, 2000; range 24°F; approach 8°F; T_1 92°F; T_2 68°F; wet bulb temperature T_{wb} 60°F.

From Fig. 13-147, find water concentration required to perform the cooling is 1.75, giving a theoretical tower area of 1145 ft² as compared with 1000 ft² for a 70°F wet bulb temperature.

This shows that the lower the wet bulb temperature for the same cooling range and approach, the larger the tower area required, and, therefore, the more difficult the cooling job.

Estimating the performance of an existing tower at other than design conditions is often required. For example, assume a tower designed for the following conditions: gpm 1000; range 30°F; approach 10°F; T_1 110°F; T_2 80°F; wet bulb temperature 70°F. What will the cold water temperature T_2 be when the wet bulb temperature T_{wb} drops to 60°F, providing that the heat load and water quantity remain constant?

From Fig. 13-147, find that water concentration is 2.0 gal/ft² at design conditions. This water concentration does not change since the volume of water and the tower area remain constant. With water concentration at 2.0 and the wet bulb temperature at 60°F, by adjusting the angle of the straight edge in Fig. 13-148 until a 30°F differential is obtained between the hot water and cold water temperatures, the hot water temperature is found to be 103°F, and the cold water temperature to be 73°F.

Suppose that the above designed tower had 1500 gpm flowing through it, and the total heat load remained constant. What would the cold water temperature be when the wet bulb temperature is 65°F?

Design heat load was 1000×8.33×33 = 250000 Btu/minute. The new cooling range (heat load remaining constant) when recirculating 1500 gpm over the tower would be

$$\frac{250000}{1500 \times 8.33} = 20°F$$

Theoretically, the design area of the tower from Fig. 13-147 was 500 ft² (1000 gpm/2.0 gal/ft² = 500 ft²). Water concentration when circulating 1500 gpm is

$$\frac{1500}{500} = 3 \text{ gal/ft}^2$$

Now, referring to Fig. 13-147, with a water concentration of 3.0 gal/ft² and 65°F wet bulb temperature, adjust the straight edge, until a difference of 20°F exists between the hot water and cold water temperatures. This shows the hot water temperature to be 100°F and the cold water temperature to be 80°F. This indicates that the possibility of a lower cold water temperature obtained by the lower existing wet bulb temperature was lost due to the adverse effect of the increased water quantity.

Atmospheric (Natural Draft) Cooling Towers.—In atmospheric towers, water is pumped to the top of the tower, where it is discharged through a distributing system. A cross section of a typical atmospheric cooling tower is shown in the drawing. As water begins its downward flow, it is broken up and redistributed by the decks that make up the tower. This continually creates newly exposed cooling surface for air to encounter passing horizontally through the tower. The redistribution insures even concentration of water throughout the tower during its entire fall.

Although the initial cost for an atmospheric cooling tower designed for a 3-mph wind is about the same as that for a mechanical draft tower, there are certain important limitations governing its performance. The tower must be located broadside to the prevailing wind in an exposed area. Any surrounding structures, hills, or other barriers would tend to block the wind.

The cooling capacity of any tower, with a given wet bulb temperature and wind velocity, varies with water concentration. Therefore, the problem of calculating tower size becomes one of obtaining the correct water concentration for a tower of chosen height that will operate with a certain wind velocity and wet bulb temperature. Once this water concentration factor is obtained, the area of a given height tower can easily be calculated by dividing the gallons per minute circulated by the concentration factor. The concentration required to produce desired cooling depends primarily on the following conditions:

(1) temperature range ($T_1 - T_2$)

(2) approach to wet bulb temperature ($T_2 - T_{wb}$)

(3) tower height

(4) wind velocity

(5) wet bulb temperature (T_{wb}).

Variation in items (3), (4), or (5) affects water concentration, as follows:

Wind Velocity: The higher the wind velocity, the greater the amount of air that goes through the tower. This results in greater cooling. Therefore, when the wind velocity is higher, the concentration can be greater and equal cooling can still be obtained.

Bear in mind that there is a period occurring during the day and night in which the prevailing wind shifts. When this occurs there is a short period when there is little or no air movement. At such a time, the tower water temperatures will rise 2 to 5°F, depending on the duration of the calm and the design wind velocity, and so this should be evaluated in determining a design wind velocity. Many atmospheric towers are designed to operate successfully at a zero wind condition.

Tower Height: In general, with atmospheric as well as mechanical draft towers, the greater the cooling range and the closer the approach to the wet bulb temperature, the higher will be the tower required to give sufficient time of contact between water and air to accomplish the desired cooling. In atmospheric towers, the performance is limited by both maximum and minimum water concentrations. Should water concentration fall below 1 gpm /ft² of tower area, it will be necessary to employ the next higher tower size. Should water concentration exceed 3 gpm/ft² of tower area, it will then be necessary to choose the next lower size tower.

Wet Bulb Temperature: Theoretically, a cooling tower cannot cool water to a temperature lower than the prevailing wet bulb temperature. With this limit, one is more interested in an economical approach of the cold water temperature to the wet bulb temperature. Air has a greater capacity for absorbing heat at higher wet bulb temperatures. At lower wet bulb temperatures, air in passing through the tower must have a greater temperature rise to accomplish the same cooling. Therefore, to obtain the same approach at the lower wet bulb temperatures, it is necessary to reduce the concentration.

Estimating Data for Atmospheric Cooling Towers.—To calculate the size of an atmospheric type cooling tower with effective width of 12 ft, the following general formula may be used:

$$L = \frac{gpm \times W}{C \times 12 \times C_w \times C_h} \qquad (13)$$

where L = length of tower, ft;

gpm = quantity of water;

W = wind correction factor;

C = concentration of water gal/ft² of cooling tower area;

C_w = wet bulb correction factor;

C_h = tower height correction factor;

T_1 = inlet temperature;

T_2 = outlet temperature;

$(T_1–T_2)$ = temperature range;

T_{wb} = wet bulb temperature; and

$(T_2–T_{wb})$ = approach to wet bulb temperature.

Fig. 13-149 gives capacity curves for determining water concentration (capacity) C for various temperature drops $T_1–T_2$ (left scale) for various approaches to wet bulb temperature $T_2–T_{wb}$ (curves). The accompanying Table 13-13 shows the values of the correction factors C_w,

W, and C_h for cases where the wet bulb is other than 70°F, the wind other than 3 mph and the height other than 35 ft.

Table 13-12. Correction Factors for Equation (13)

Wet bulb Temperature, °F	50	55	60	65	70	75	80	85	90	
Wet bulb correction factor, C_w	0.56	0.61	0.71	0.86	1.00	1.16	1.30	1.45	1.60	
Tower height, feet	19	24	29	34	35	39	44	49		
Height correction factor C_h	0.55	0.68	0.82	0.98	1.00	1.15	1.36	1.60		
Wind velocity, mph	1	2	3	4	5	6	7	8	9	10
Wind correction factor W		1.28	1.13	1.00	0.90	0.83	0.77	0.72	0.68	0.64	0.61

Example 6: Determine the length of a tower 49 ft high to cool 1500 gpm from 90°F to 95°F with a 70°F wet bulb and a 5 mph wind.

Solution: From these conditions the approach $(T_2–T_{wb})$ = 5°F and the range $(T_1–T_2)$ = 15°F. From Fig. 13-149, the intersection of the 5° curve and the horizontal 15°F line gives, on the bottom scale, a value of C = 1.19. Since the height is 49 ft find in the Table 13-12, C_h = 1.60 and for 70°F wb, C_w = 1.0. Referring to the Table 13-12, a wind of 5 mph has a correction factor of 0.83. Substituting in Equation (13)

$$L = \frac{gpm \times W}{C \times 12 \times C_w \times C_h}$$

$$= \frac{2000 \times 0.90}{107 \times 12 \times 0.71 \times 1.00}$$

$$= 54.5 \text{ ft}$$

Once a tower is installed, the problem often arises of determining what cold water temperature one can expect under conditions differing from those for which the tower was designed. Considered the next example. Assume the tower is 35 ft high, 12 ft wide, and 107 ft long.

Example 7: What cold water temperature T_2 can be expected when the wet bulb temperature is 60°F, wind velocity 4 mph, cooling range 15°F, and water circulation 2000 gpm?

Solution: The wet bulb temperature correction factor C_w from the Table 13-12 for a wet bulb of 60°F is 0.71. The wind velocity correction factor (W) for a 4 mph wind is 0.90. By substituting those values in the general formula and solving for water concentration, find:

$$C = \frac{gpm \times W}{L \times 12 \times C_w \times C_h}$$

$$= \frac{2000 \times 0.90}{107 \times 12 \times 0.71 \times 1.00}$$

$$= 1.97 \text{ gal/ft}^2$$

Referring to Fig. 13-149 find that when the cooling range is 15°F and the water concentration is 1.9, the approach to the wet bulb temperature is 9°F. This means that the cold water temperature will be 60°F + 9°F = 69°F.

Quantity of Cooling Water Required.—As shown in Table 13-13 of compressor heat, elsewhere in this section, for every 200 Btu/minute (1 ton of refrigeration) absorbed by the mechanical refrigeration cycle there are approximately 40 Btu absorbed from work done by the compressor, or a total of 240 Btu/minute-ton to be rejected by the condenser refrigerant. The quantity of condenser (cooling) water required, then, depends on the temperature rise of the cooling water.

Table 13-13. Water Circulation Necessary with Various Rises in Water Temperatures in Cooling Surfaces

Rise in Water Temperature Through Cooling Surface, °F	Required per 1000 Btu/hr of Cooling Load	Required per Ton of Refrigeration
	gpm	
0.5	4.800	57.60
1.0	2.400	28.80
1.5	1.600	19.20
2.0	1.200	14.40
2.5	0.960	11.52
3.0	0.800	9.60
3.5	0.686	8.23
4.0	0.600	7.20
4.5	0.535	6.42
5.0	0.480	5.76
5.5	0.437	5.24
6.0	0.400	4.80
6.5	0.370	4.14
7.0	0.343	4.12
7.5	0.320	3.84
8.0	0.300	3.60
8.5	0.283	3.40
9.0	0.276	3.31
9.5	0.253	3.04
10.0	0.240	2.88
10.5	0.229	2.75
11.0	0.218	2.62
11.5	0.209	2.51
12.0	0.200	2.40
12.5	0.198	2.32
13.0	0.185	2.22
13.5	0.178	2.14
14.0	0.172	2.06
14.5	0.166	2.00
15.0	0.160	1.92

Table 13-13. Water Circulation Necessary with Various Rises in Water Temperatures in Cooling Sur-

Rise in Water Temperature Through Cooling Surface, °F	Required per 1000 Btu/hr of Cooling Load	Required per Ton of Refrigeration
	gpm	
15.5	0.155	1.86
16.0	0.150	1.80
16.5	0.146	1.75
17.0	0.142	1.70
17.5	0.137	1.64
18.0	0.133	1.60
18.5	0.130	1.56
19.0	0.127	1.52
19.5	0.123	1.48
20.0	0.120	1.44
20.5	0.117	1.40
21.0	0.115	1.38
21.5	0.112	1.34
22.0	0.109	1.31
22.5	0.107	1.28
23.0	0.104	1.25
23.5	0.102	1.22
24.0	0.100	1.20
24.5	0.098	1.18
25.0	0.096	1.15
25.5	0.094	1.13

Table 13-13 gives the cooling water requirements for various temperature rises in gpm. Table 13-13 is arranged with columns showing the quantity of water (gpm) necessary to conduct away from the refrigerant the heat quantities represented by the two units commonly used in air cooling practice, namely: the MBH and ton of refrigeration capacity. Table 13-13 indicates these quantities at the increase in temperature which water experiences in passing through the apparatus over the range usually covered in practice.

The following example illustrates the use of the Table 13-13.

Example 8: How much water must be circulated through a water cooled refrigeration condenser of 11 ton capacity rating if the temperature rise of water is 10°F?

Solution: Refer to Table 13-13 at 10 in the first column and move horizontally to column 2 and find the figure 2.88. This is the volume gpm/ton and, consequently, multiplying it by 11 gives 31.68 gpm as the quantity which must be circulated. It should be noted that if the temperature rise were 20°F instead of 10°F, the quantity of water required would be one-half of 31.68 or 15.84 gpm.

Clear distinction should be made between water circulation figures given in Table 13-13 and water consumption of refrigeration condensers, or of the total quantity of water required over a period of time per unit of heat removed. The figures in Table 13-13 are for the quantity of water that must be circulated but they are not necessarily the quantity of water consumed. In other words, there is a definite difference between water quantity that must be circulated and water quantity that may be consumed. This is made obvious by the way equipment is so arranged that water circulating through a refrigerant condenser can be recooled and used time after time; the actual water consumption of the condenser can be zero, even though the amount of water circulated is large. Estimates of water consumption required can be arrived at only by knowing the actual performance of the installed equipment. Generally, for air conditioning applications in many sections of the country, maximum water demands for refrigeration condensers are estimated on the basis of 2 gpm/ton being required of refrigeration effect if there is any recirculation of water.

With well designed evaporative cooling equipment, it is possible to reduce water consumption of refrigerant condensers to from 5 to 10% of the amounts necessary without their use.

The Roof as a Location for Air Conditioning Equipment

At one time the invariable practice of designers was to locate the refrigeration system for the air conditioning installation in a basement or subbasement machine room, irrespective of refrigeration capacity required. With basement installations, foundations for the main pieces of equipment, such as refrigeration compressor and driving motor or turbine, chilled water and condenser water circulating pumps, could rest on bedrock underlying the building foundations. This was a logical location at one time, due, in part, to the available equipment, which was bulky, heavy in weight, and noisy. In the case of slow speed reciprocating compressors, vibration and pounding had to be counteracted. In addition, operation of the equipment was generally manually controlled. Therefore, a basement machine room was convenient for the full attention of the operating engineer.

The development of automatic, compact refrigeration equipment and the evaporative condenser for water conservation has changed this situation with the result that today equipment can be located anywhere in the building, providing adequate means of vibration isolation are installed. Basement machine rooms are not a must in the overall design of a system; economic and space considerations should be determining factors in the final selection of the machinery location.

Both roof and basement locations for the necessary equipment have distinct advantages as well as disadvantages. The capacity in tons of refrigeration for the proposed plant is an important consideration for designates to arrive satisfactory decisions.

Advantages of Roof.—*Use of Evaporative Condensers:* When the refrigeration compressors are located within a machine room on the top floor of a building or a penthouse designed for this purpose, evaporative condensers can be located within a very short distance of the compressors. Since such condensers can be located on the compressor room roof above or alongside of the penthouse, usually there is no problem of air supply and discharge for the equipment. This arrangement eliminates the need for water-cooled condensers, cooling tower and circulating pump, and it also reduces the cost of refrigerant piping. The compressor brake horsepower per ton of refrigeration can be kept to a minimum by the installation of adequate size evaporative condensers, thereby reducing the actual cost of operation.

The physical size of the evaporative condenser is usually smaller than that of an equivalent capacity cooling tower. Maintenance of the evaporative condenser depends on its construction; a well designed condenser should have upkeep similar to a cooling tower. Water treatment for both types is desirable, especially in contaminated air surroundings, to protect condensing coils and condenser tubes. Prime surface condensing coils with corrosion is protected metal such as hot-dip galvanizing or nonferrous tubes and corrosion resistant fans are very desirable.

Evaporative condensers can be enclosed in a louvered shell similar to cooling towers to improve their appearance.

Multiple Units: It is economically feasible to divide the total required refrigeration capacity among several compressors. The evaporative condenser installation can likewise be made with separate coils or a separate unit for each refrigeration compressor. This arrangement provides flexibility in the operation of the plant under varying load requirements and can readily be accomplished with the roof installation due to the close spacing of all equipment.

Automatic Control: The development of automatically operated refrigeration equipment lends itself to roof installation. Refrigeration compressors and evaporative condensers can be readily controlled automatically by a means such as the chilled water temperature. This arrangement provides maximum economy of operation in matching the required load and does not require continual supervision by the operating engineer. Periodic supervision by the operating engineer to check machine operation, oiling, and pressures, can readily be combined with other duties. A bell or light in the operating engineer's office connected to the high pressure cut-out and to the low temperature chilled water thermostatic cut-out will give added protection to the system in case of fault operation.

Size of System: The total capacity of the refrigeration system is a paramount factor in the determination of location. Small and medium tonnage installations that lend themselves to the use of reciprocating compressors, either singly or in multiple, have greater economic advantages when located in roof machinery rooms than do large tonnage installations, which generally require centrifugal or axial-flow compressors. The latter are built with an integral water-cooled condenser, and therefore require a cooling tower. The high weight concentration of the cooling tower over a small area calls for heavier structural framing and supports. Usually this is not the case with the smaller capacity, lighter weight reciprocating compressors. It would be impossible to set up an arbitrary tonnage figure as a boundary between reciprocating and centrifugal compressors, since each installation should be analyzed from a cost standpoint and tonnage decided with respect to the installations.

Ventilation: Adequate ventilation of machinery rooms is often a problem for the designer. It is obvious that the roof installation can be readily ventilated at a minimum cost due to its close proximity to outside air. Ductwork required for the basement location can be eliminated and it is not difficult to locate the fresh air intake and exhaust louvers; in some roof installations, the evaporative condenser can be set at one end of the machinery room with the outside air intake louvers placed at the opposite end. The condenser fans will then augment the machinery room ventilation by drawing air across the compressor area.

Location of Air Conditioning Equipment: The location of the air conditioning equipment can play an important part in arriving at the best location for the refrigeration equipment. When air conditioning equipment is located in the upper floor or penthouse fan rooms of a building, it is obvious that a most economical installation can be made should the refrigeration equipment be located near the air conditioning equipment installations. With the development of primary air conditioning systems used in conjunction with individual room conditioners, a penthouse or top floor fan room has decided advantages and lends itself to such an arrangement. There are other less obvious advantages, such as the lower static water pressure on the chilled water circulating pump casing, a pressure that exists when the pump is located at the top of the closed circulating system. This arrangement minimizes stuffing-box seat maintenance problems.

Machinery Space: The location of equipment presents an economic problem, especially in rental type buildings. For example, in large cities where the building cost per cubic foot is high, the basement area, which is usually reserved for refrigeration equipment, can yield a good return when rented for restaurant or similar use. This basement use for a restaurant is feasible if good air conditioning and ventilation are provided and arrangements made for a ground floor entrance. In some cases, the elimination of costly rock excavation required for a subbasement equipment room can significantly change the construction cost. With the increasing use of district

steam, the basic need for high ceiling boiler rooms is eliminated and this tends to further reduce excavation cost. The exclusion of a high ceiling refrigeration equipment room can again help reduce these costs. It must be remembered that the refrigeration capacity of the installation, as discussed previously, plays an important part in the analysis.

Disadvantages of Roof.—*Supporting Structure:* The roof installation obviously requires both a supporting structure for the dead weight of the equipment and adequate bracing for unbalanced loads. The additional steel requirements in the form of columns, girders, and beams is a function of several variables so no arbitrary standards can be established. For example, the installation of multiple smaller capacity refrigeration compressors and evaporative condensers does not present the structural problem that would be encountered with one or two large capacity units. In the former case, by judicious location of the equipment with reference to the main load supporting columns and beams, the cost of additional framing can be minimized; in the latter case, the supporting structure must be designed to meet the expected loadings that may result in deep section girders and beams.

This situation can increase floor-to-floor heights to maintain proper headroom under the structural supports. The building height directly affects the cost of additional steel for columns. A skyscraper type of building, with multiple setbacks and with high refrigeration requirements, obviously is not as well suited to a roof installation as a building of lower height and with uniform floor areas. The designer should analyze each type of structure on its own merits. In many cases, the floor loading selected by the structural engineer for fan rooms is suited to the loading imposed by small tonnage refrigeration equipment without additional steel framing.

Vibration: Reciprocating compressors located on a building roof present problems of vibration isolation. One must prevent transmission and telegraphing of this motion to the occupied portions of the building. Small multicylinder compressors do not create the same situations as large compressors of slower speed. Several types of vibration-absorbing bases and foundations are available, each engineered to the particular type of installation. Specialists in vibration control should be consulted.

It is not costly to isolate a small compressor, and the same type of isolation would generally be used irrespective of the equipment location. Large units require spring-supported floating structural subbases, which in turn must be properly supported by the building. In some cases, weight must be incorporated in the base to absorb unbalanced forces.

It is desirable to isolate interconnecting piping from the building structure by the use of isolated pipe hangers and flexible seamless tube-type connections at the equipment.

Services to Equipment.—Electric power must be carried from the main service location, usually located in the basement, to the equipment on the roof. The cost of this service will depend on the distance involved and wire size. When the fan room is located nearby, all equipment power requirements can be combined; this is less costly than having a separate service is run to each. Separate metering and switches can be located in a service center.

Since water supply must be brought to the evaporative condenser or cooling tower, irrespective of where the design places the refrigeration equipment, no new situation is established. Water can be taken from the main water supply for water-cooled stuffing-box seals, for make-up water for the chilled water system, and for similar needs.

Installation of Equipment.—The cost of rigging refrigeration equipment to a roof location will usually be greater than for a basement location. Rigging costs should be estimated for each location and this figure used in the cost analysis.

Servicing Cooling Plant for Summer Use

Following are practical suggestions for putting a summer air conditioning system into operation.

Because all air conditioning systems are practically *tailor-made*, it is impossible to give explicit instructions applicable to every installation. Therefore, while the points listed are general points, they are important whether they require the adjustment of 20 valves or one valve to make a system operate properly.

Water System.—1) Check coils in the cooling system. Plugs may have been removed and the system drained for winter. Replace plugs and close valves to the coils. Be certain that all valves to coils are closed before cracking the main water supply valve to allow gradual filling of system. If coils are located in several equipment rooms on different floors, start at the bottom of the system, venting coils in each equipment room from first floor to top of system.

2) If a deep well pump is part of the system, it should be checked for proper lubrication and electrical connections. After all valves are open, trip pump switch for momentary operation of pump. Do this two or three times. If operation is normal, throw switch for regular operation.

3) After the system has operated for two days, recheck coils for air binding.

Air Handling System.—The procedure for preparing air handling equipment for operation is the same whether the system uses water or mechanical refrigeration as the source of cooling. Here again there are a number of important steps in setting the system in operation.

1) Check the motors for proper lubrication and electrical connections.

2) Check the fan, bearings, and belts to see that they are in operating condition.

3) Do not forget the filters. While checking the filters for cleanliness also check the surface of the coil to see that it is clean. In one case a building owner had his serviceman start up the system after a check, but he got no cooling– in fact, he got no air distribution at all. The filters were clogged with dust and dirt to such an extent that air could not be drawn into the system.

If it is possible to manually operate the air handling equipment on the spot, check it for noise and general operating characteristics.

Compressor Oil.—Before proceeding further, check the oil pressure in the crankcase of the compressor. The normal operation of shutting down a refrigeration plant for the season is to leave 2 psi in the system. Before opening any valves, observe this pressure to determine if there was a loss of pressure during the shutdown period. A lower pressure indicates a leak in the system. Remember that both refrigerant and oil will escape through the defective part. How to search out these leaks is described later.

Condenser.—If there is an evaporative condenser in the system, it should be next on the check list. In a good many installations, the evaporative condenser is mounted on the roof. The service suggestions here are simple to accomplish, provided the unit was serviced properly when the system was shut down at the end of the previous season (probably fall).

1) Here again motors, fans, and belts are first on the list for checking and servicing. V-belts should be free from wear and have a live feeling when struck with the hand. They should not be *fiddle-string* tight.

2) For outdoor installations, the next step is to clean out the sump. If there is water in the sump, start looking for trouble. This, very possibly, indicates the unit was not properly drained and lines in the system may have frozen and ruptured. Before going ahead with the check up, inspect the piping that is exposed to the elements or where freeze-up may occur.

3) Close the drain on the sump.

4) Open water supply valve to the unit and at the same time check the operation of the float valve in the sump.

5) Check the operation and check for leaks in pump. First, turn the pump over by band to check freedom of operation. Then with the pump operating electrically, check for leaks. There should be a slight leak at the packing for the pump to be operating at its best. This leak should amount to a rather infrequent drip and not a steady flow from the packing.

6) Examine the coil for corrosion or fouling. If the coil is fouled with scale, it should be cleaned with an inhibited acid. After using the inhibited acid, the coils should be well flushed with clear water to remove the cleaner.

7) If the liquid receiver is mounted near the evaporative condenser, now is the time to open both valves in the liquid receiver.

On some installations, there is a shut-off valve in the hot gas line on the evaporative condenser. This valve should be opened as the last step in getting this unit ready for operation.

If the system uses a shell and tube condenser instead of an evaporative condenser, there are two inspections to make. (1) Open the valve for water supply to the condenser. (2) Use a screwdriver to momentarily open the water regulating valve on the condenser. This will flush the valve mechanism and put it in readiness for operation.

Refrigeration Unit.—All parts of the system are important. But the refrigeration unit is the most vital. Every precaution and check must be made to certify the correct operation of this unit.

1) First of all, make the usual inspections for proper motor lubrication, electrical connections, and condition of belts, if belt-driven. If direct-driven, inspect the coupling for signs of wear.

2) Open all valves on the unit. These include the liquid valve, suction valve, and hot gas discharge valve. Its a good idea to double check this operation. Things can happen very fast if one or more valves remain shut during operation of the compressor.

3) Check electrical connections to the compressor. The main fuse disconnect switch has probably been locked in the open position to guarantee nonoperation of the unit during the seasonal shut-down. This should be unlocked and closed at this time.

4) Next, throw compressor switch in and out two or three times. Allow compressor to run a few seconds each time the switch is thrown in to get oil on the seal. This short periodic operation also helps to separate the refrigerant from the oil.

5) Put the system into operation. This includes starting up the air handling equipment, evaporative condenser (if included in the system), and compressor. If there is a gage on the crankcase, observe the oil pressure. It should be above the pressure in the suction line. Observe the oil in the crankcase. If low, one of two things has happened: Oil may have mixed with the refrigerant and be held in another part of the system, or oil has escaped through a refrigerant leak. To determine which of these malfunctions has occurred, run the compressor intermittently for several seconds to try separating the oil and refrigerant. If, after several tries, the oil level still remains low, there may be leaks in the system. Check refrigerant charge through the sight glass on the liquid line. If it bubbles while the compressor is in operation, the charge is short. This is another signal that troubles are present.

6) Shut down the system and close valves. Leaks may be discovered in two different manners. A halide torch may be used for this purpose. Escaping refrigerant will change the color of the torch flame, for it is extremely sensitive to the presence of refrigerant. The other method is to examine the piping system for oil droplets hanging on the underside of the piping. While the refrigerant escapes into the air, the oil usually clings to the piping in the vicinity of the leak.

Check Oil.—There is another possibility, in case the leak cannot be discovered. A previous leak may have been repaired, refrigerant added, but the oil forgotten. To correct this requires only the addition of compressor oil.

When the system is in shape again add the necessary refrigerant and oil. Always remember to add both refrigerant and oil. When there is a leak in the system, both the lubricating oil and the refrigeration charge will escape.

Compressor Now Ready.—A few final inspections remain before placing the unit in operation for the summer. You are now ready to start the air handling unit and the compressor. Run the compressor for approximately 30 minutes. At the end of this time observe the oil in the crankcase and check the condition of the refrigerant in the sight glass. If everything appears correct, continue to run the equipment while checking the entering and leaving air temperatures in the air handling unit. If these temperatures are in accordance with design conditions, check the operation of the controls and upon completion of this step, the air conditioning system should be in excellent shape for summer-long operation.

It is important that this *spring tune-up* be carried out as comprehensively as possible. The investment in the air conditioning system is well worth the few hours required to get it in top condition for its job during the hot days ahead. While these suggestions are necessarily general, they cover the majority of installations and they lend themselves to easy modification to fit particular installation needs.

Air Conditioning Equipment Maintenance.—Maintenance of air conditioning equipment includes the following:

Air Handling Equipment: Treating water for washers, replacing or cleaning air filters, checking fan belts, lubrication of pumps and fans, coils, electrical repairs, and checking of controls.

Air Distribution Equipment: Cleaning air ducts and grilles, repairing insulation on ducts, painting ducts, and checking dampers.

Water-Using Equipment: Treatment of water, lubrication of pumps and fans, checking of piping and valves, painting, and cleaning.

Cooling Equipment: Recharging refrigerant, lubrication, checking of V-belts, maintenance of compressors, checking of motors and controls, checking of valves and piping.

Air conditioning equipment is designed to perform a particular function in the most efficient manner possible and to give good mechanical performance. But before the expected results can be achieved, it is necessary to (1) install the unit so that there are no conditions that are detrimental to good operation; (2) operate and maintain the unit so that a continuance of satisfactory operation is assured.

The following discussion is concerned with cooling towers, evaporative coolers, and evaporative condensers, and also with air conditioning units.

One point that many engineers discount is that not only must equipment have enough space for installation, but there must be sufficient clearance around the unit to enable proper servicing and operation. There should be sufficient space to permit oiling of bearings, removal of coils, fans and shaft, eliminators and wetted deck surface, servicing the spray water pump and strainer and for the air conditioning unit, enough room for servicing fan and pump motors and belts. Space should be allowed to permit the use of brushes and other equipment to clean the coils in the unit.

It is important that the units be lined up horizontally and vertically so proper slope exists for satisfactory drainage.

Air discharge from water-saving devices should be above the roof line, and well above and as far as possible from the air intake. Since dirt and fumes carried into the unit aggravate the problem of keeping clean the heat transfer surfaces, air entering the apparatus should be kept as free as possible from dirt, fumes, and steam. Simple upward direction of the air discharge is not sufficient, and the backwash effect of air currents flowing over buildings should be taken into consideration. Both the air inlet and outlet should be kept free from obstructions that might impede the free flow of air. Runs of discharge duct inside the building should be insulated to reduce condensation on the inside and the ducts should be made watertight.

Before starting equipment, remove the belts and be sure that fans and pump rotate freely. Fill the oil cups on the fan and motor bearings before the electric wiring is completed. Then check the motor and replace the belts. Belts should be adjusted to prevent slipping when starting. However, too much tension will cause rapid wear on both belts and bearings and an unnecessary load on the motor. It is important to check the motor for correct rotation. Directional arrows serve as a guide.

Fill the pump with water and then check and adjust the float valve to maintain proper water level not more than one inch below the overflow pipe. Place the waste line from the spray header inside the overflow cap. Next, open the waste line valve at the spray header about two turns, and with the aid of a gallon bucket, check the flow rate. Set the waste at about 2 gph/ton of refrigeration or per 15,000 Btu/hr heat rejection, and then adjust as required under operation.

Since the spray water system is designed to maintain a running film of water on all heat transfer surfaces, it is necessary to maintain the spray pumping unit in good operation. As one check, see that pump and motor bearings are properly lubricated, that the stuffing-box is not binding the shaft, and that the fan and pump belts are maintained in proper tension and alignment. It is advisable to waste enough water so that the mineral concentration does not exceed that point at which scale will form. One must remember that in operation about one pound of water is evaporated per 1000 Btu and that the mineral content of this water is left after evaporation takes place.

Some mineral salts are more scale-forming than others, and it may be advisable to treat water with compounds that form soluble and nonscaling types of salts after combining with whatever minerals are present. Where wasting of water does not solve the problem, water treatment by a competent company is recommended.

From the cleaning standpoint it is important that the sump tank should be drained and cleaned often enough to prevent large accumulations of sediment that are carried into the unit through the air stream. Pump suction strainer should be cleaned and the spray nozzles checked to see that each is producing a full spray cone and that all parts of coil or wetted deck surface are flooded. Air intake screens should be kept free of leaves and paper, and a check made that boxes or crates do not obstruct free flow of air into the unit.

It is important to note (1) ingoing and outgoing temperatures of the fluids to be cooled, (2) temperature of the spray water, (3) ingoing and outgoing air temperature, and occasionally (4) volume of the air. Readings that deviate from normal indicate the need for closer inspection of the apparatus and the equipment served by it.

All systems using a direct expansion refrigerant should be thoroughly tested for leaks before and after the system is charged with the refrigerant. Particular attention should be given to the thermal valve packing. Avoid any condition that creates gas in the liquid line but if such a condition is unavoidable, provide adequate subcooling of the liquid with a heat exchanger to prevent gasification.

Water coils, sump pan, and various water lines should be adequately drained and blown out for winter operation to prevent freezing of these components. During winter operation if the unit is shut down for any period, the steam coils should also be drained to prevent freezing. Water and steam coils are circulated and sloped in the unit at the factory for proper drainage. Precautionary methods should be taken at all times during winter operation to prevent freezing in the steam coils. Adequate filters should be placed on water, steam, and humidifier lines to prevent dirt accumulation in the coils.

The pump should be located as close as possible to the unit sump tank and one should always avoid a high suction lift. In no case should the total suction lift, including friction in the pipe, be more than 15 ft. If the pump is to handle hot water, it must be so located that water will flow freely into the suction.

On units with face and bypass dampers make certain that the dampers are properly linked for full opening and closing.

Periodic maintenance and inspections should be enforced to insure long and dependable service. About every 60 days inspect the damper bearings and linkage and check fan and motor bearings. A suitable oil should be added. Fans and scrolls should be free and clean of all foreign matter.

Once a year it is good policy to shut down the unit and thoroughly clean all surfaces, remove all scale and rust deposits, and protect surfaces with a good corrosion-resistant paint where necessary. One should remember that the misuse of strong acids or alkali solutions is dangerous and can result in serious damage to this equipment. Interior parts should be brushed and freed of loose particles. As a safeguard, paint bare metal before using any cleaning solutions. After using any chemical, wash, brush clean all surfaces, and repaint as necessary for further protection. However, do not paint coils on evaporative coolers.

Pumps require attention. Clean, flush, and inspect the pump, checking water passages and impeller clearance; clean and regrease pump bearings. every six months the pump should be greased. All worn or damaged parts should be replaced. In addition, inspect the motor and motor-mounting brackets and at the same time clean and oil the motor. However, keep oil away from fan belts and pulleys. Inspect pulleys for worn or damaged grooves and make such replacements as are necessary.

Maintenance resolves itself into a program of cleaning and inspection. Every 60 days the fan and motor bearings should be checked and the proper type of oil added. Also periodically check the tightness and alignment of belts.

Clean the strainer and the pipe in the spray piping as often as necessary. There is no set rule for the periodic cleaning of spray piping and nozzles, but when any nozzle does not have a full cone spray, it should be cleaned. The constant waste valve and waste line should be checked periodically to insure free flow of waste water to the drain. Examine the float valve for proper function, and replace the valve seat if it is worn.

At regular intervals, inspect water humidifier and steam jet humidifier nozzles, and clean them if necessary. On vapor pan humidifiers check for the proper functioning of the float valve. Because of water evaporation these pans will accumulate salt scale deposits so that it is important to flush the pans at least once a month during the winter season.

All coils should be carefully washed with a hose once a month to remove accumulated lint or foreign matter carried to the unit by the air stream. Fans and scrolls should also be washed or brushed down to remove the accumulated dirt in addition to cleaning or replacing air filters when dirty.

Before a unit is to be shut down for a long period of time, at the end of either the cooling or heating season it should be thoroughly drained, well flushed out and cleaned, belt tension relieved, and the unit given a coat of corrosion-resistant paint, especially in spots where rust might appear.

The sump pump on spray type dehumidifier units should be drained and thoroughly flushed at least once every two weeks. If scale deposits appear on the cooling coils, water should be treated.

Air Conditioning Maintenance Schedule

The schedule that follows is designed to serve as a guide for maintenance inspection for air conditioning equipment. In general, inspection should be divided into daily, monthly, and yearly periods.

Daily inspections are those that have to do with checking water levels, water conditions, heating up of parts, hand-oiling, and whatever may be termed a daily once-over.

Monthly inspections are usually those specified by the manufacturer as routine checks on oil levels in reservoirs, checks for leaks of the refrigerant, oil, and water, cleaning of electrical apparatus, filters, spray nozzles, collection pans; and checking of control devices, belt tensions, scale traps, and purging.

Yearly inspections require the opening up of condensers for examination, dismantling of machines, and any inspections that require the apparatus to be shut down for prolonged periods. The grouping in the checklist has been arranged in what is considered a logical order for efficient work.

It might appear that the schedules outlined are an attempt to reduce inspection to a rigid routine. This is not the intention. On the contrary, the grouping is definitely arranged to permit flexibility for physical reasons unique to any given plant. Most failures of equipment are, without question, preventable: a pulley, for example, causing frequent replacements of belts is being neglected by somebody and the relief valve that fails to open the one time it is required to has been a forgotten for some time. Even in an extreme case it may take a dollar's worth of maintenance to prevent a dollar repair; the maintenance dollar, however, is the wiser one because the failure that necessitated the repair may be accompanied by intangible expanses.

The following list is the air conditioning maintenance schedules and it procedure, relates to what is to be done, and when things are to be done.

The schedule comprises the following subsections: (1) unit air conditioners (2) Central systems (3) Condensing water circuit, (4) Cooling water system, and (5) Filters and ducts.

Unit Air Conditioners.—*Unit Air Conditioners:* Self contained air conditioning systems that are built in compact units.

Daily: Since these units are as near *foolproof* as it is possible to make them, *inspection* becomes incidental with *operation.*

Monthly: The system should be checked for leaks with a standard halide gas leak detector. Belts should be inspected each month for signs of abnormal wear or pulley misalignment. Instructions on purging should be followed. Oil levels are checked each month. Knocks should be investigated.

Yearly: A check should be made on water being used to determine its condition. The service of the small unit does not warrant other than reasonable precautions to see that clean water is at all times supplied to the system. At the annual inspection water in the system should be drained and their various parts examined for corrosion and scale. Safety devices should be removed and checked and their condition noted. An overall *condition* record should be made for the year. In some cases it is recommended that a general check-up or inspection be made of unit systems after a stipulated number of service hours: quite often the number of service hours is much longer than a year. The recommendations based on service hours should always be followed because the maintenance requirements are a function of hours of actual operation, which determines the life of individual parts of the unit.

Central Systems.—*Rotating Apparatus:* Those parts of the air conditioning system, such as pumps, compressors, blowers motors, and the controlling devices that convert or assist in the conversion of electrical energy into refrigeration.

Daily: Motors should be given a daily *once over* with particular attention being given to automatic starters and contactors. Any arcing should be noted. Such equipment properly cared for seldom gives trouble.

Monthly: Note the condition of brushes, protective devices, and oil levels. Belt tensions should be checked and any apparent misalignment or abnormal wear should be fully investigated. Blower bearings should be checked for proper adjustment; pump packings should be inspected monthly for leakage. The casing covers of motors used with induced draft cooling towers should be removed once a month for inspection. Where gears are used on this type fan they should be inspected once a month.

Refrigerant Circuit Controls: The part of the system through which the refrigerant circulates including the compressor, connected piping and valves, condenser receiver, and the evaporator. The controls consist of such devices as the thermostatic expansion valves, switches and regulators with automatic cutouts, and solenoid valves for water and refrigerant.

Daily: System should be inspected for overheating of the moving parts, knocking, excessive pressure in the system of piping and vessels. The proper cutting-in and cutting out points of machines should be noted. Any evidence of sticking of the expansion valves should be noted since such sticking is usually caused by moisture in the system. Any signs of leakage should be traced to their source.

Monthly: On monthly inspections the refrigerant circuit should be checked for leaks of the refrigerant. The standard halide refrigerant gas leak detector is recommended for this purpose. Also look for oil leaks around packings and water leaks throughout the system. Scale traps should be checked. Purge valve should be opened or the system should be purged through the means provided. Check thermostatic gas-filled bulbs for tightness against pipes and moisture between the bulb and the pipe; moisture may freeze under certain conditions and break the contact necessary for good operation of such devices. Remove the covers from all pressure switches and such control mechanisms at least once a month as loose screws, springs, and contacts will cause trouble if not checked in time.

Yearly: Safety devices such as relief valves should be removed and tested unless required more frequently by local ordinances. Valves suspected of leaking should be examined for wear. Packings should be inspected. It is assumed that at the time of the yearly inspection the system is out of service so that parts normally inaccessible can be dismantled to check for wear. A summation of the year's record should be made at this time, including notes made of the yearly inspection.

Condensing Water Circuit.—The part of the system through which the condenser cooling water circulates. It consists of condensers, water piping, floats, and valves. If water is recirculated it may include spray or cooling ponds, cooling towers, settling tanks, and collection pans, or it may include an evaporative type condenser.

Daily: The condition of water should be checked for corrosive tendencies. Temperatures should be taken daily since they often are indications of the cleanliness of the system. Quantity of makeup water should be recorded daily when means are at hand to do so. Float valves should be inspected daily since improper functioning of floats may result in waste of water. Leaks, even though not serious, should be noted.

Monthly: Sumps, tanks, and collection pans should be checked for slime formation and algae growth, and for general cleanliness. Water samples should be taken for chemical analysis. Spray nozzles should be inspected for plugging. Accessible parts of evaporative type condensers should be given a thorough inspection each month for accumulations in the air and water passages.

Yearly: Water should be drained from all parts of the system so that all internal parts can be properly inspected. The circulating system should be checked for clogging and partial stoppages. Any valves suspected of leaking during operation should be dismantled for inspection at this time. All internal surfaces should be carefully scrutinized for corrosive action and scale formation. There should be a general summing up of the yearly record at the time of annual inspections. All items carried over from the other inspections will not become a part of the yearly report.

Cooling Water System.—The circuit through which the refrigerated water passes. Includes storage tanks, evaporators, piping, spray units or washers, and collection pans and heating coils.

Daily: The storage tank should be checked for water level and condition. Floats should be inspected daily. On new systems the spray nozzles in the units should be inspected daily for plugging as small particles of dirt find their way to the nozzles for the first month or so of operation.

Monthly: The storage tank should be drained monthly for inspection; the large amount of dirt washed out of the air may cause plugging if a careful check is not made. After daily inspection of the spray nozzles has been dropped the tank should be inspected. A water sample should be taken for chemical analysis. Drains should be inspected.

Yearly: Water should be drained from the cooling water circuit for the annual inspection. This inspection should include a check of evidence of scale formation and corrosion.

Filters and Ducts.—The part of the system that cleans and carries the air of the system. Because of their structural nature they require less attention than other parts of the system.

Daily: Static pressure drop across filters should be checked.

Monthly: Filters should be inspected for dust accumulations. Sections should be removed at random from sectional filters for checking. Insulated ductwork should be inspected monthly for traces of moisture getting between insulation and duct walls.

Yearly: The general condition of filters should be determined. Ducts are inspected at this time for defects and leakages. Dirt accumulations are noted, and any abnormal conditions investigated.

Air Conditioning Maintenance Procedure for Central Systems

Refrigerant Circuit and Controls.—The part of the system through which the refrigerant circulates including the compressor, connected piping and valves, condensers, receiver, and evaporator. The controls consist of such devices as thermostatic expansion valves, switches and regulators with automatic cutouts, and solenoid valves for water and refrigerant.

Leaking Glands: When repairing compressors, valves and fittings, leaking glands should be tightened only to the point where the leak stops. If it is necessary to replace the packing the system may have to be pumped down.

Pumping Down: If the leaks are on the low side, the liquid line valve is closed and the compressors operated until a Vacuum of 20 to 25 in. is reached. This forces the refrigerant into the receiver. In some cases where the system is to be open only for a short period. It is possible to prevent leakage of air into the system, or leakage of refrigerant out by lowering the pressure to atmospheric pressure before the system is opened. After the repair is completed carbon dioxide may be used for testing for tightness. Where air is allowed to get into the system, the system will have to be purged after operation is resumed. In making a repair to the high side of the system the refrigerant is pumped into the low side. In most cases it is not possible to pump all the refrigerant into the low side and therefore it is necessary to draw some of the refrigerant into drums temporarily. Only drums intended for such storage should be used.

Refrigerant Storage in Drums: The drum is laid on a slant and connected to the refrigerant valve in the receiver with a flexible connection. The refrigerant flows into the drum by gravity. If the drum is kept in an ice bath, refrigerant will be speeded. The drum should be filled only to its stamped capacity. The amount of refrigerant in drum can be checked by placing the drum on a scale and noting the weight increase. After refrigerant is replaced and operation resumed the system should be purged.

Purging System: The best way to purge the refrigerant circuit is to first settle out the system to permit all foreign gases and air to rise to the high, or purging point of the system. With pressure on the system the purge valve is opened until refrigerant shows; it is then closed.

Replacing Refrigerant: When additional refrigerant must be added to the system this is done by connecting a refrigerant drum to the suction side of the system in such a way that no liquid refrigerant can enter into the compressor. When conditions permit a warm bath around the drum will speed up the charging. The amount of refrigerant necessary can be determined by watching the head pressure.

Scale Trap Cleaning: System should be pumped down, if necessary, the scale trap cleaned, and the system put back into normal operation. After a short period of operation, air should be purged.

Expansion Valves: To check the operation of expansion valves, the valve should be removed and connected to a cylinder of the refrigerant with the bulb hanging free. Refrigerant will be passed through the outlet of the valve when refrigerant drum is open. Placing the expansion valve bulb in the refrigerant stream should cause the valve to close.

Moisture: To remove moisture from the refrigerant a dehydrator of activated alumina, silica gel, or similar substance should be installed. Dehydrators should be removed after about two weeks because they serve no purpose after the moisture has been removed.

Safety Devices: The fusible plug in liquid receiver should be renewed at least every two years. Relief valves can be tested by removing them from the system and checking them with compressed air or water. If water is used it must be perfectly clean and free from solid matter, which might injure the valve. It should be noted whether safety devices of all types comply with local ordinances covering such devices. The operator should always be sure that protective devices will pass inspection.

Condensing Water Circuit.—The part of the system through which the condenser cooling water circulates. It consists of condensers, water piping, floats, and valves. If water is recirculated it may include spray or cooling ponds, cooling towers, settling tanks, and collection pans.

Strainers: Devices to catch foreign matter; they are often a protective device. Strainers should be examined for signs of wearing or warping that may result in obstruction.

Valves: Periodical flushing with clean water under pressure is necessary to keep the valves clean, even though strainers are placed ahead of the valves. When valves become pitted they should be ground with a fine abrasive. After repairs valves should be adjusted to close when unit is shut down.

Condenser: Condenser should be cleaned mechanically once a year and thoroughly washed with clean water. Tools that are likely to damage the tubes should not be used, nor should the tubes be bulged. A cleaning *brush* should be used for mechanical cleaning. For prolonged lay-up periods condenser should be left completely dry on water side.

Tanks and Pans: Any tank and pan used in a condensing water system should be kept as clean as conditions will permit. During lay-up periods tanks should be first cleaned, then laid up dry. Where tanks show signs of deterioration or corrosion, a coat of corrosion-resisting paint should be applied.

Evaporative Condensers: If ordinary flushing of the tubes does not completely clean them, other methods may have to be used. A caustic solution forced through a spray gun in which air pressure is used to spray, or in which steam is mixed with the caustic solution, will effectively remove stubborn scale. There are a number of commercial solutions with caustic solution that need no preparation.

Cooling Water System.—The circuit through which the refrigerated water passes. Includes storage tanks, evaporators, piping, spray units or washers, and collection pans and heating coils.

Cooling Water: Water should be changed frequently otherwise it may develop odors that will be carried into the air conditioning spaces. In using deodorants, care should be taken to prevent an overdose. The pH concentration of water should be watched to maintain it at the proper point. Addition of chemicals to water may be necessary to establish the proper pH.

Spray Nozzles: Nozzles must be kept clean. To do this, nozzles or a complete bank of nozzles including the header should be removed and blown out backwards with compressed air.

Filters and Ducts.—The part of the system that cleans and carries the air of the system. Because of their structural nature they require less attention than other parts of the system.

Filters: Oil dipping filters should be cleaned with hot caustic solution; they are then washed with hot water or blown with clean, live steam. After cleaning they must be dried well. The oil dipping should give a thin film over all the surfaces after a period of draining to remove the excess oil. After cleaning, filters should be thoroughly washed with clean water and dried. Then they are ready for dipping in an oil. Filters must be well drained before they are replaced in a filter bank.

Ducts: Ducts can be blown out but vacuum cleaning is preferred because it provides better control of cleaning. Unusually large accumulations of dust and dirt in a particular part of an otherwise clean duct may indicate improper contour at that point. Dirt-laden ducts mean poor filtering and washing.

Dampers: Dampers should operate smoothly, which means that piston drives must be free from air leaks that might cause sluggish operation. Dirty parts of such drives should be washed in a solution such as carbon tetrachloride to clean them. Orifices and parts should not be scraped since they may be changed in size by such treatment.

Rotating Apparatus.—Those parts of the air conditioning system, such as pumps, compressors, blowers, motors, and the controlling devices that convert or assist in the conversion of electrical energy into refrigeration.

Compressors: Only lubricants recommended by manufacturer should be used. Oil taken from separators should not be replaced in the system until it has been properly filtered. Packing glands should be tightened only enough to prevent leakage and only soft packing should be used. Where conditions permit, bearings should be opened once a year and the oil grooves cleaned out. Oil piping also should be cleaned. Cross head and connecting rods should be carefully checked for cracks and for signs of unusual wear. The whitewash test is highly useful for locating cracks. The part to be tested is first soaked in oil and then cleaned dry. Whitewash is applied and left to dry. After complete drying, the part is tapped with a hammer and oil will ooze from any cracks. Repairs should be made by welding.

Belts: During long lay-up periods belts should be removed and wrapped in a protective covering, They should be stored away from the heat and in a dry place. No dressing should be applied unless specifically called for by manufacturer's instruction. Unusual wear of belts means misalignment.

Motors: Cooling air passages through motors should be kept clean. Broken brushes are an indication of high spots on the commutator. Motors should be kept covered when not in use. Starters on motors should have all contacts free from arcing during the starting cycle.

Water Pumps: Small water drips from pump packings should be disregarded. As a matter of fact, many manufacturer's specify this condition for good operation. Pump packing that is too tight may damage the shaft. When pump is to be idle for an extended period, packing on pumps should be eased off and all exposed parts should be covered with grease.

Gears: Gear boxes should be well lubricated with the proper grade of oil. They should be washed out and oil renewed each year unless otherwise specified. Attention should be paid to the drives to see that they are kept in good condition.

Unit Air Conditioners.—Self contained air conditioning systems that are built in compact units.

Piping: Flared joints in the piping or tubing should be protected from moisture formation by a coating of grease such as vaseline. Moisture that freezes will cause cracked nuts or flared ends of tubing and result in leaks.

Motors and Fans: In replacing motor bearing oil, unless otherwise recommended, SAE #10 or #20 should be used on small motors. Cleaning of small motors is of considerable importance. Belt tension should be maintained at the proper point.

Cooling Coil: The cooling coil should be kept clean at all times since dirt will not only reduce efficiency but also may cause odors. Coils may be cleaned by washing with a caustic soda solution and rinsing with clean water.

Condensers: Air cooled condensers should be cleaned frequently by compressed air. Tower type condensers may be cleaned by water under pressure.

Air Filters: Air filters should be replaced when they become dirty and a static pressure gage should be used to determine when filters should be renewed.

Checklist for Air Conditioning Surveys.—In making air conditioning surveys it is important that care be taken so that no items left out. The accompanying checklist has been in use for a number of years and is believed to have all the important items included. This list furnishes a systematic method of checking all the important information needed in making an air conditioning survey.

Since preparation of air conditioning drawings is closely related to the survey, it is suggested that reference also be made to the checklists on drawings appearing elsewhere in this book.

Particular attention is called to the last heading in the checklist, under which is listed items of work that may or may not be performed by, or at the expense of, the air conditioning contractor, and which, consequently, should be clearly understood. In some cases such items may total enough to throw what might otherwise be a profitable contract into a loss proposition.

The use of such a checklist as given does not, however, entirely compensate for a surveyor's lack of observation on a site. Instances which might not be duplicated in a thousand jobs do arise and no checklist can possibly foresee them. The cost of returning to a location once the survey is completed may be prohibitive, or at least costly, and it is highly desirable that all data be collected on one visit.

With respect to this, one point is made in relation to existing motors: Instead of attempting to copy only what seems to be pertinent data from the motor nameplate, the surveyor should make a pencil rubbing on a sheet of paper of the whole nameplate; the advantage is that all the information is then available if needed, eliminating the trouble of copying it with the possibility of error.

Checklist for Air Conditioning Surveys

Hot Water Heating Supply		
Location of boiler Size of boiler Excess boiler capacity	Location of storage tank Capacity of storage tank Possible location of hot water pump	Distance, tank to heating coil Distance, heating coil to tank Temperature of hot water
Electric Power Facilities		
Electric power voltage Electric power phase Electric power cycles	Location of power panel Horsepower connected at present Horsepower to be added	Permissible starting current in rush Electric power cost Name of utility company
Refrigeration Facilities		
Name of compressor manufacturer Model number of compressor Operating condensing pressure	Operating suction pressure Refrigerant used Is 15 lb air available continuously?	Quantity flow of chilled water or brine available if system is indirect Excess refrigeration available
Drain and Sewer Facilities		
Size of present sewer Location of sewer Condition of present sewer Is sewer vented?	Size of present slop sink[a] Location of slop sink Condition of slop sink Head for draining condensate pan	Distance, condenser to slop sink Distance, condensate drip line to sink Is condensate pump necessary? Must condensate drip line be insulated?
Date of survey Name of prospect Location of job Owner	Who must approve job? New building or alteration Length of lease Does owner agree to installation?	Must job conform to local code Must job conform to Under writers code Must job conform to any state code Are other trades union or nonunion?
Space Conditions		
To what use is space put? Is smoking allowed? Any unusual odors generated Loose or tight building construction	Floor area Ceiling height Cubical contents Area of doors and windows to be open	What equipment is hooded? Are hoods effective? Are other hoods desirable? Any unusual dust condition
Cooling and Heating Load Quantities		
Number of occupants Degree of activity of occupants Total light wattage Light wattage on sunny day Are awnings and blinds on exposed windows? Are blinds of venetian type? Is load such as to require zoning?	Horsepower of motors Heat generated by gas burners Any other heat-generating equipment Product load, if any Time phases on component loads Period when spaces are occupied Areas with concentrated loads	Moisture, load Exposed window and wall area Compass rose Winter conditions to be maintained Summer conditions to be maintained Outside winter design conditions Outside summer design conditions
Water Facilities		
Size of city main connection Location of possible tap-in City water temperature City water pressure Size of present water meter Is constant quantity flow assured?	Is well water available? Well water flow, quantity Well water temperature Well water pressure Well water location Corrosion properties of well water	Length of water line to condenser Length of water line to spray nozzles Must water lines to condenser be insulated Cost of water Hardness of water Head available using house tank
Steam Supply Facilities		
Location of steam supply Kind of steam supply available Steam pressure available Is there constant supply year round? Boiler location Boiler capacity Type of existing heating system	Excess capacity of boiler Boiler operating pressure Boiler water level, operating Head available to drain heating coil How is boiler fired? Location of controlling thermostat Type of heating system control	Is return trap or condensate pump needed? Distance, steam source to heating coil Length condensate return run to boiler Location steam main nearest heat coil

Checklist for Air Conditioning Surveys

Air Distribution		
Exhaust duct sizes Exhaust fan data Exhaust fan motor data Exhaust fan foundation data Exhaust fan motor foundation	Air quality, exhaust system Exhaust grille sizes Supply duct sizes Supply fan data Supply fan motor data	Supply fan foundation data Supply fan motor foundation data Air quantity, supply system Supply system grille sizes Grille locations

Locating Equipment		
Does available space for ducts Indicate a central duct system or room units passage space for delivery of equipment? Check for possible changes to partitions between survey and installation Noise considerations	Is elevator available? Check loading and size of elevator Is rigging or special handling needed? Is spring loaded compressor foundation needed due to upper floor mounting? Check outside window area with fire code	Is water-proof equipment floor necessary Visualize equipment set in place and check location for accessibility Check the heating of the proposed equip- ment room in winter to prevent the freeze up of condenser if water cooled

Duct System		
Noise considerations Locate fresh air intake so as to prevent contamina- tion of air supply	Locate exhaust to atmosphere and place on side of building opposite to that on which air intake is located	What duct work is to be insulated Locate fire walls and partitions Possible location of control equipment

Miscellaneous Considerations		
Bonded roof to be cut Economizer to run year round Working hours-straight time in what spaces overtime in what spaces	Is job location such that treatment of air washer water is needed Are other washers operating nearby If so, of what material are they	Length of service of nearby washers Present condition of nearby washers Do nearby washers use treated water Bar corrosion experience with nearby plants

Under the Contract Will Contractor Perform Following?		
Cutting and patching	Makeup water connections	Lay foundations
Install water meter	Make refrigerating connections	Carpentry work
Electric wiring	Make steam connections	Masonry work
Clean existing ducts	Insulate steam piping	Excavating
Finish painting of equipment	Insulate ducts	Plastering
Remove or relocate present wiring	Insulate cold water mains	Structural supports for equipment
Remove existing electric fixtures	Insulate hot water mains	Waterproof floors
Remove existing piping	Install access openings	Build equipment room partitions
Install and connect drain mains	Install grilles and plaques	Cut holes for pipes, ducts, grilles

[a] A slop sink, properly vented and provided with a supply of water to maintain water seal in trap, is required. Sinks used for food washing or provided with a plug receptacle and strainer are not acceptable.

AIR HANDLING AND VENTILATION

AIR HANDLING AND VENTILATION

A fan is a gas flow producing machine which operates on the same basic principles as a centrifugal pump or compressor. Each of these devices, including fan, converts rotational mechanical energy, applied to the shaft, to total pressure increase of the moving gas. This conversion is accomplished by changing the momentum of the fluid.

The American Society of Mechanical Engineers power test codes limit fan definition to machines that increase the density of the gas by no more than 7% as it travels from inlet to outlet. This is a rise of about 30 inches of water pressure based on standard air. For pressure higher than 30 in water gauge, the air-moving device is a compressor, or pressure blower. Fans for heating, ventilating and air conditioning, even on high velocity, high-pressure systems, rarely encounter more than 10–12 inches of water pressure.

Fan Terminology and Definitions

Terminology, Abbreviations, and Definitions.—

Definitions of terms common in fan technology follow.

Standard Air: Air at a temperature of 70° F dry bulb and a barometric pressure of 29.92 inches of mercury with a density of 0.075 lb/ft^3.

Water Gauge (wg) (Fig. 14-1): The measure of pressure above atmospheric expressed as the height of a column of water in inches (as in Fig. 14-1, atmospheric at sea level equals 407.1 inches of water or 33.97 feet of water).

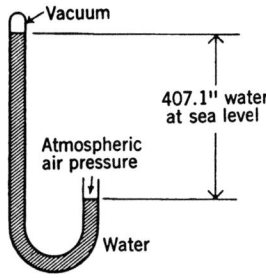

Fig 14-1. Atmospheric pressure

cfm and scfm: The cubic feet per minute (*cfm*) of air produced by a fan in a given system is independent of the air density.

cfm: *cfm* is cubic feet per minute of air handled by a fan at any air density.

scfm: *scfm* is cubic feet per minute of standard air (0.075 lb/ft^3) handled by a fan.

Fan Total Pressure (TP): Fan total pressure is total pressure rise across the fan, or the difference between the total pressure at the fan outlet and the total pressure at the fan inlet. Fan total pressure is the measure of the total mechanical energy added to the air or gas by the fan. How this is measured is illustrated in Fig. 14-2.

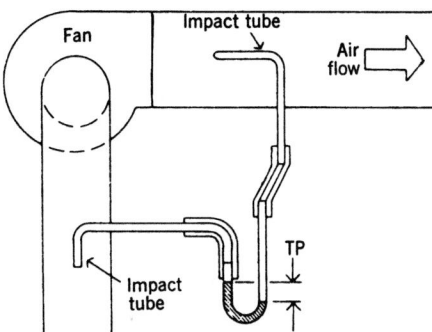

Fig 14-2. Fan total pressure

Fan Static Pressure (SP): Fan static pressure (Fig. 14-3) is the static pressure rise across the fan, i.e., it is the difference between the static pressure at outlet and the static pressure at inlet. The fan static pressure is specified by manufacturers in the form of fan curve (Fig. 14-5) which relates static pressure to *cfm*. In cases where the velocity at the inlet and outlet are identical, static pressure is equal to total pressure (SP = TP) provided that the air density at inlet and outlet is also the same.

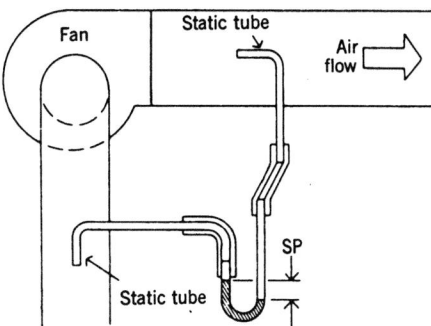

Fig 14-3. Fan static pressure

Fan Velocity Pressure (VP): Fan velocity pressure (Fig. 14-4) is the pressure corresponding to the fan outlet velocity. It is the kinetic energy per unit volume of flowing air.

Air Horsepower (AHP): Assuming 100% efficiency, it is the horsepower required to move a given volume of air against a given pressure.

$$\text{Static } AHP = \frac{cfm \times SP}{6356}$$

$$= \frac{\dfrac{ft^3}{min} \times in.\ wg \times \dfrac{14.7\ lb/in^2}{407.1\ in\ wg} \times \dfrac{144\ in^2}{ft^2}}{33000\ ft\text{-}lb/min/AHP} \quad (1)$$

$$\text{Total } AHP = \frac{cfm \times TP}{6350}$$

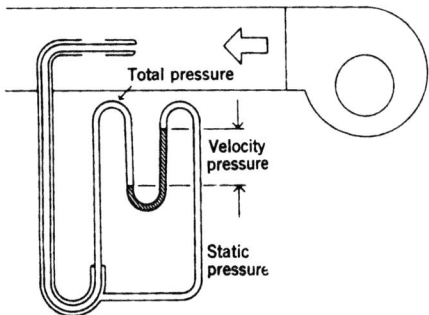

Velocity pressure = total pressure – static pressure

Fig 14-4. Fan velocity pressure

Brake Horsepower (BHP): The actual horsepower a fan requires. It is greater than air horsepower because no fan is actually 100% efficient. It may include power absorbed by V-belt drives, accessories, and any other power requirements, in addition to power input to the fan.

$$BHP = \frac{CFM}{6356} \times \frac{TP}{\text{fan total efficiency}} \qquad (2)$$

Static Efficiency (SE): The static air horsepower divided by the power input to the fan:

$$SE = \frac{\text{power output}}{\text{power input}} = \frac{CFM \times SP}{6350 \times BHP} \qquad (3)$$

Mechanical Efficiency: Also called total efficiency (*TE*). The ratio of power output over power input.

$$ME = \frac{CFM \times TP}{6350 \times BHP} \qquad (4)$$

Application Range (Fig. 14-5): The range of operating volumes and pressures determined by the manufacturer at which a fan will operate satisfactorily (See Fig 14-5.).

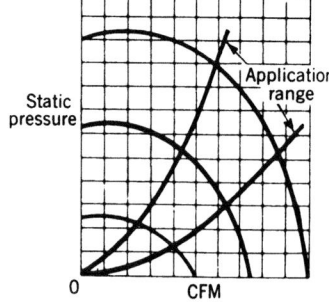

Fig 14-5. Fan curve

Blocked Tight Static Pressure (BTSP): Operating condition when the fan outlet is completely closed, resulting in no air flow (See Fig 14-6.).

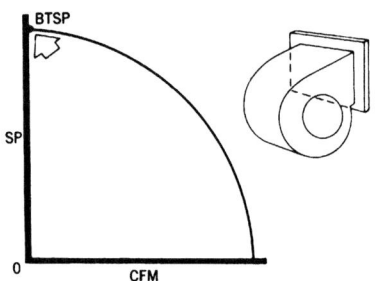

Fig 14-6. Blocked tight static pressure

Free Delivery (Fig. 14-7): Also called *wide open CFM* (WOCFM). At this operating condition, static pressure across the fan is zero (See Fig 14-7.).

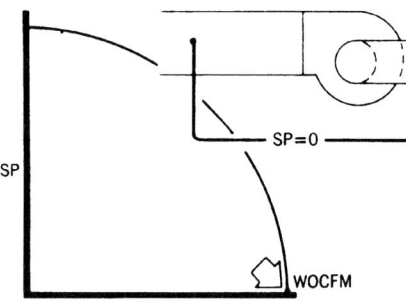

Fig 14-7. Free delivery

Wide Open Brake Horsepower (WOBHP): The horsepower consumed when the fan is operating at free delivery. Frequently, fan characteristics are referred to in terms of the percent of wide open CFM (percent WOCFM) which for a given fan then fixes the corresponding percent blocked tight static pressure (percent BTSP) and percent WOBHP.

Tip Speed (TS): Also called *peripheral velocity,* it equals the circumference of the fan wheel times the RPM of the fan and is expressed in ft/min (See Fig 14-8.).

$$TS = \frac{\pi D \times RPM}{12} \qquad (5)$$

Where *D* is expressed in inches.

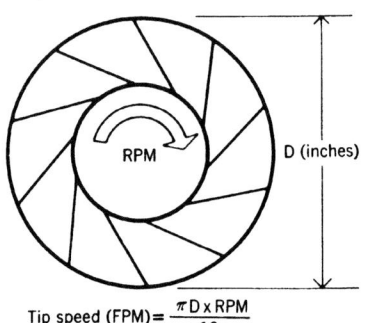

Tip speed (FPM) = $\frac{\pi D \times RPM}{12}$

Fig 14-8. Tip speed

Fan Laws.—The fan laws relate the performance variables for any homologous series of fans and apply to both centrifugal and axial flow types. The variables involved are fan size and related to wheel diameter (D), rotating speed in revolutions per minute (RPM), gas density (d), capacity (cfm), static pressure (SP), brake horsepower (BHP), sound-power level and efficiency. The laws relating to RPM, fan size, and density effects are illustrated below. The fan laws will be accurate for geometrically proportioned fans; however, because tolerances are usually not proportioned, slightly better performance is generally obtained when projecting from a given fan size to a larger one.

Effect of RPM Change: First considered are the fan laws applying to a change only in RPM (constant system) with a given fan and a given system handling air at a given density. Fan law 1 is illustrated in Fig. 14-9.

cfm varies directly as RPM.

$$\frac{cfm_1}{cfm_2} = \frac{RPM_1}{RPM_2} \tag{6}$$

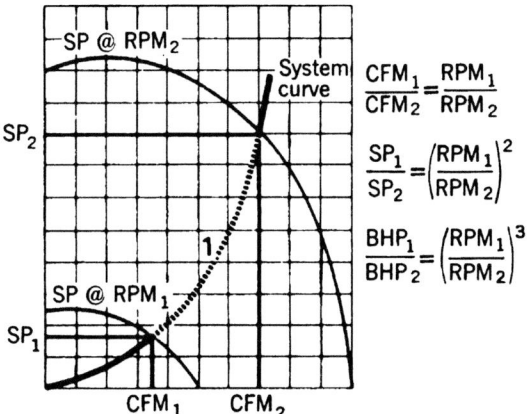

Fig 14-9. Fan law no. 1–RPM change

Static pressure varies directly as the square of the RPM:

$$\frac{SP_1}{SP_2} = \left(\frac{RPM_1}{RPM_2}\right)^2 \tag{7}$$

Horsepower varies directly as the cube of the RPM

$$\frac{BHP_1}{BHP_2} = \left(\frac{RPM_1}{RPM_2}\right)^3 \tag{8}$$

Efficiency does not change.

Point of operation (percent of wide open *CFM*) will not change for a given system. Changing the speed will not change the percent *WOCFM*, static efficiency, etc.

Note that the SP change is greater than the CFM change.

Effect of Fan Size Change: Fan laws no. 2 and no. 3 account for changes in performance due to proportioned changes in fan size. They are based on either constant tip speed or constant RPM.

Fan law no. 2 is illustrated in Fig. 14-10; with constant tip speed, air density, fan proportions, and fixed operating point, fan size is the variable.

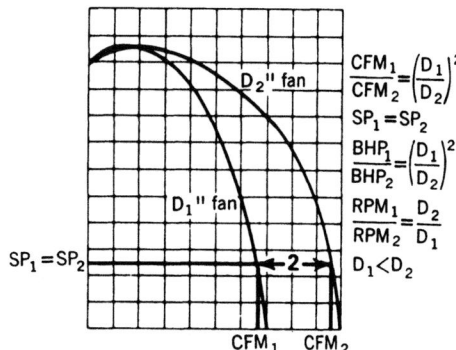

Fig 14-10. Fan law No. 2–change in wheel diameter (constant volume)

CFM and BHP vary as the square of wheel diameter.

$$\frac{CFM_1}{CFM_2} = \frac{BHP_1}{BHP_2} = \left(\frac{D_1}{D_2}\right)^2 \tag{9}$$

Static pressure remains constant: $SP_1 = SP_2$, RPM varies inversely as wheel diameter.

$$\frac{RPM_1}{RPM_2} = \frac{D_2}{D_1} \tag{10}$$

Fan law no. 2 is used mostly by fan designers and rarely has application in the field.

Fan law no. 3 is illustrated in Fig. 14-11; with constant RPM, air density, fan proportions, and fixed operating point.

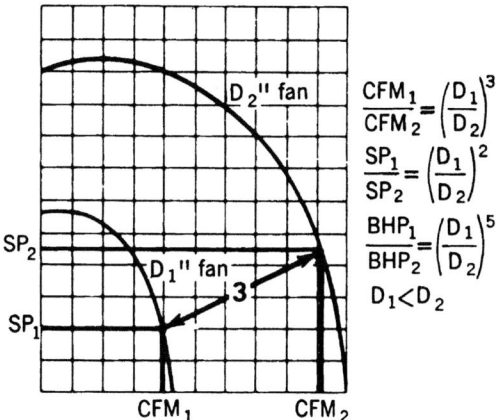

Fig 14-11. Fan law no. 3–change in wheel diameter (constant RPM)

CFM varies inversely as the cube of the fan diameter:

$$\frac{CFM_1}{CFM_2} = \left(\frac{D_1}{D_2}\right)^3 \qquad (11)$$

Static pressure varies directly as the square of wheel diameter:

$$\frac{SP_1}{SP_2} = \left(\frac{D_1}{D_2}\right)^2 \qquad (12)$$

Tip speed varies directly as wheel diameter:

$$\frac{TS_1}{TS_2} = \frac{D_1}{D_2} \qquad (13)$$

Brake horsepower varies directly as the fifth power of wheel diameter.

$$\frac{BHP_1}{BHP_2} = \left(\frac{D_1}{D_2}\right)^5 \qquad (14)$$

Fan law no. 3, with constant RPM and density, is used by fan manufacturers to generate performance data for geometrically proportioned families of fans.

Density Effects: Considered next is the effect of change in air density on fan performance. Three fan laws apply in this situation.

Fan law no. 4 is illustrated in Fig. 14-12 with constant volume (CFM), system, fan size, and RPM.

The fan volume in CFM will not change with density. A fan is a constant volume machine and will produce the same CFM no matter what air density may be:

$$CFM_1 = CFM_2 \qquad (15)$$

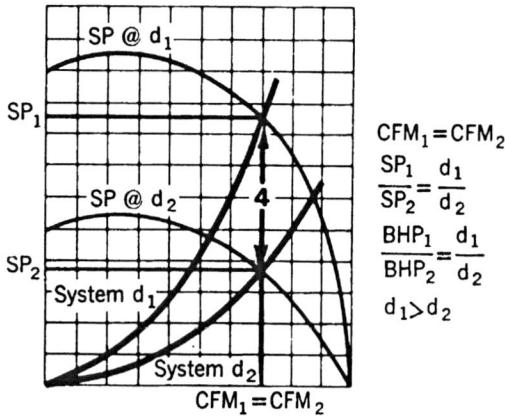

Fig 14-12. Fan law no. 4–effect of density change (constant volume)

The static pressure and BHP developed by the fan will vary in direct proportion to the density. In other words, the heavier the air, the more pressure produced and the more horsepower required.

$$\frac{SP_1}{SP_2} = \frac{BHP_1}{BHP_2} = \frac{D_1}{D_2} \qquad (16)$$

Fan law no. 5 is illustrated in Fig. 14-13 with constant pressure, system, and fan size. Variable RPM, CFM, and brake horsepower vary inversely as the square root of density:

$$\frac{CFM_1}{CFM_2} = \frac{RPM_1}{RPM_2} = \frac{BHP_1}{BHP_2} = \left(\frac{d_2}{d_1}\right)^{\frac{1}{2}} \qquad (17)$$

Static pressure remains constant: $SP_1 = SP_2$

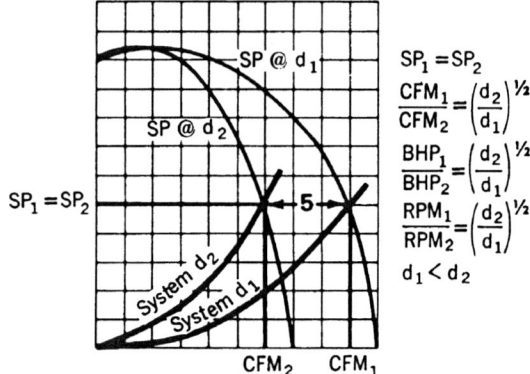

Fig 14-13. Fan law no. 5–density change (constant static pressure)

Fan law no. 6 is illustrated in Fig. 14-14; with constant mass flow rate, constant system, and fixed fan size.

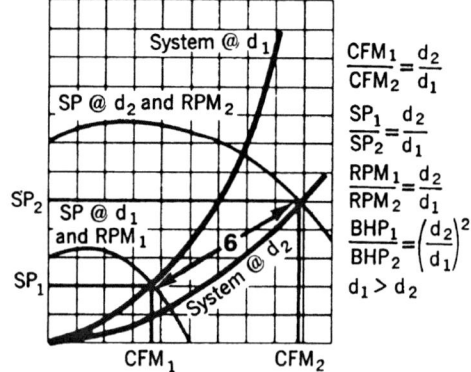

Fig 14-14. Fan law no. 6–density change (constant mass flow)

Variable RPM, CFM, RPM, and static pressure SP vary inversely with density as follows:

$$\frac{CFM_1}{CFM_2} = \frac{RPM_1}{RPM_2} = \frac{SP_1}{SP_2} = \frac{d_2}{d_1} \qquad (18)$$

Brake horsepower varies inversely with square of density:

$$\frac{BHP_1}{BHP_2} = \left(\frac{d_2}{d_1}\right)^2 \qquad (19)$$

Fan laws no. 4 and no. 6 are the basis for selecting fans for other than standard air density using the catalog fan tables which are based on standard air. The following examples illustrate the application of fan laws.

Example 1: An air-conditioning, supply fan is operating at 600 RPM against 2" SP and requiring 6.50 BHP. It is delivering 19000 CFM at standard conditions. In order to handle an air-conditioning load heavier than originally planned, more air is needed. In order to increase the CFM to 21500, what are the new RPM, SP, and BHP?

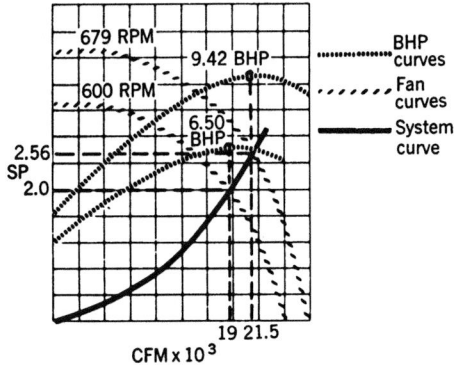

Fig 14-15. Example no. 1–Fan law no. 1 (RPM change)

Solution: The solution to this problem is found by applying *fan law no. 1*, as illustrated in Fig. 14-15.

$$CFM_1 = \left(\frac{RPM_1}{RPM_2}\right)CFM_2$$

Rearranging,

$$RPM_2 = (CFM_2/CFM_1)RPM_1$$

$$RPM_2 = \frac{21500}{19000}(600) = 679$$

$$SP_2 = SP_1\left(\frac{RPM_2}{RPM_1}\right)^2$$

$$= 2\left(\frac{679}{600}\right)^2$$

$$= 2.56 \text{ in}$$

$$BHP_2 = BHP_1\left(\frac{RPM_2}{RPM_1}\right)^3$$

$$= (6.50)\left(\frac{679}{600}\right)^3$$

$$= 9.42 \text{ hp}$$

Example 2: A fan is operating at 2714 RPM on 70 °F air against 3" SP. It is delivering 3560 CFM and requires 2.84 BHP. A 5-hp motor is powering the fan. The system is short capacity but the owner does not want to spend any money to change the motor. What is the maximum capacity from this system with the existing 5 hp motor? What is the allowable speed increase? What will CFM and SP be under the new conditions?

Solution: The solution to this problem is found by applying *fan law no. 1.*

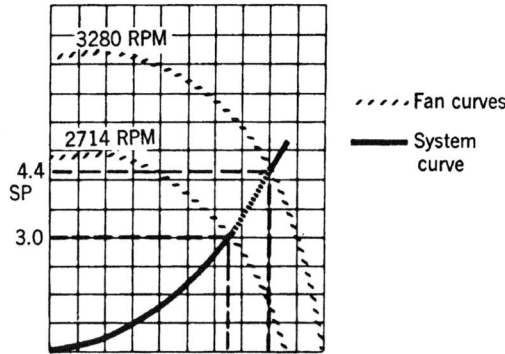

Fig. 14-16. Example no. 2–Fan law no. 1 (RPM Change)

$$RPM_2 = RPM_1\left(\frac{BHP_2}{BHP_1}\right)^{\frac{1}{3}}$$

$$= (2714)\left(\frac{5.00}{2.84}\right)^{\frac{1}{3}}$$

$$= 3280$$

$$CFM_2 = CFM_1\left(\frac{RPM_2}{RPM_1}\right)$$

$$= (3560)\left(\frac{3280}{2714}\right)$$

$$= 4300 \text{ cfm}$$

$$SP_2 = SP_1\left(\frac{RPM_2}{RPM_1}\right)^2$$

$$= 3\left(\frac{3280}{2714}\right)^2$$

$$= 4.4 \text{ in}$$

Example 3: A fan manufacturer wishes to project data obtained for a 30 inch diameter fan to a 60 inch diameter fan. At one operating point the 30 inch fan delivers 7755 CFM of 70°F air against 3 inches SP. This requires 694 RPM (tip speed = 5450 FPM) and 1.77 BHP. What will the projected CFM, SP, BHP, and tip speed (TS) be for a 60 inch fan at the same RPM (Fig. 14-17)?

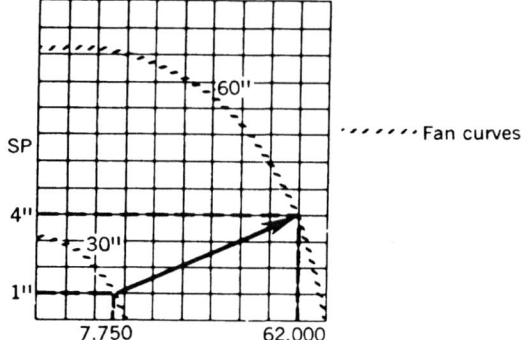

Fig 14-17. Example no. 3–Fan law no. 3 (diameter change)

Solution: The solution to this problem is found by applying Fan law no. 3.

$$CFM_2 = CFM_1\left(\frac{d_2}{d_1}\right)^3$$

$$= (7755)\left(\frac{60}{30}\right)^3$$

$$= 62000 \text{ cfm}$$

$$SP_2 = SP_1\left(\frac{d_2}{d_1}\right)^2$$

$$= 3\left(\frac{60}{30}\right)^2$$

$$= 12 \text{ in.}$$

$$TS_2 = TS_1\left(\frac{d_2}{d_1}\right)$$

$$= 5450\left(\frac{60}{30}\right)$$

$$= 10900 \text{ fpm}$$

This, plus *fan law no. 1*, are the fan laws used to project catalog data for many diameters and speeds from a test on a single fan at one speed.

Example 4 : A fan drawing air from an oven is delivering 18620 CFM of 240°F air against 2½ inches SP. It is operating at 796 RPM and requires 9.90 BHP. Assume the oven loses its heat and the air is at 70°F. What happens to the SP and BHP required (Fig. 14-18)?

Solution: The solution to this problem is found by applying Fan law no. 4.

Density of 70°F air = 0.075 lb/ft³

Density of 240°F air = 0.056 lb/ft³

$$CFM_2 = CFM_1 = 18620$$

$$SP_2 = SP_1\left(\frac{d_2}{d_1}\right)$$

$$= 2.5\left(\frac{0.075}{0.056}\right)$$

$$= 3.35 \text{ inches of water}$$

$$BHP_2 = BHP_1\left(\frac{d_1}{d_2}\right)$$

$$= 9.90\left(\frac{0.075}{0.056}\right)$$

$$= 13.3 \text{ bhp}$$

This example illustrates why the fan motor should always be selected on the BHP at the maximum density, which would be at the lowest air temperature expected.

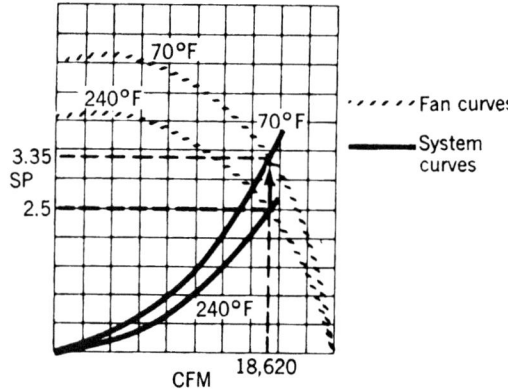

Fig 14-18. Example no. 4–Fan law no. 4 (density change)

Example 5 : An engineer specifies that he wants 15200 CFM at 2 inches SP, 120°F and 1000 feet altitude. Determine the RPM and BHP (Fig. 14-19).

There are two ways to solve this problem. Fan law no. 4 is used in the first solution method.

In order to find data in manufacturer catalog fan tables, which are based on standard air, we must determine the SP that would be required with standard air.

From a chart of air density ratios we would find

$$\frac{d_{actual}}{d_{standard}} = 0.88$$

$$SP_{standard} = SP_{actual}\left(\frac{d_{standard}}{d_{actual}}\right)$$

$$= \frac{2}{0.88}$$

$$= 2.27 \text{ in., say } 2.25$$

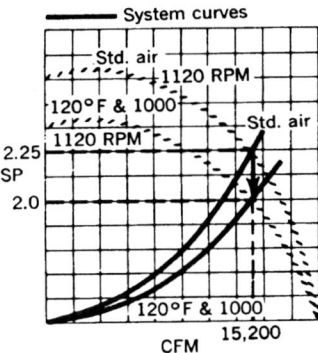

Fig 14-19. Example no. 5–Fan law no. 4 (density change)

From the catalog fan table we find to deliver 15,200 CFM against 2.25 inches will require 1120 RPM. The BHP required is 8.07. The RPM is correct at 1120, but since the fan is handling less dense air, then:

$$BHP_{actual} = BHP_{standard}\left(\frac{d_{actual}}{d_{standard}}\right)^2$$

$$= 8.07 \times (0.88)^2$$

$$= 6.25 hp$$

Note also from this example that the static pressure resistance of the system varies directly with air density.

The other method of solution utilizes *fan law no. 6*, as illustrated in Fig. 14-20. In this case, assume that operating condition is standard to determine an RPM and BHP in the catalog. Then the catalog BHP and SP will be corrected according to *fan law no. 6*.

$$CFM_{actual} = CFM_{standard}\left(\frac{d_{actual}}{d_{standard}}\right)$$

$$= 15200 \times (0.88)$$

$$= 13400$$

$$SP_{actual} = SP_{standard} \times \left(\frac{d_{actual}}{d_{standard}}\right)$$

$$= 2 \times 0.88$$

$$= 1.76 \text{ inches, say } 1.75$$

The fan will deliver 13400 CFM against 1.75" in when operating at 988 RPM. Required BHP = 5.55. Correcting the RPM for density according to *fan law no. 6*, we obtain:

$$RPM_{Standard} = RPM_{actual}\left(\frac{d_{standard}}{d_{actual}}\right)$$

$$= \frac{988}{0.88}$$

$$= 1120$$

$$BHP_{actual} = BHP_{standard}\left(\frac{d_{actual}}{d_{standard}}\right)^2$$

$$= \frac{5.55}{0.88^2}$$

$$= 7.1 hp$$

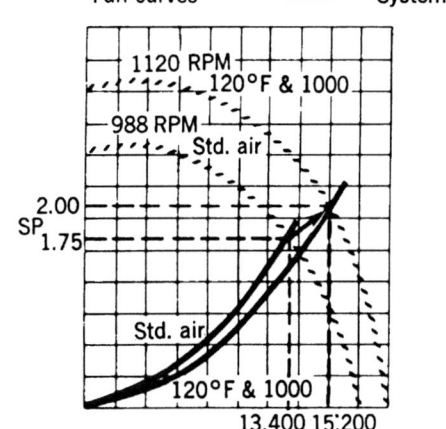

Fig 14-20. Example no.5–Fan law no. 6 (density change)

Example 6 Effect of Changing the Resistance of a Fan System: Assume that a fan is handling 41280 CFM at 1½ inch SP, running at 418 RPM and requiring 14.99 BHP. If the speed remains constant at 418 RPM, but an additional resistance of ½ inch (based on existing velocities) is placed in the system, the static pressure would be 2 inches if the capacity, 41280 CFM, remains the same. From the fan manufacturer's rating table, it is seen that the speed would have to be increased to 454 RPM and would require 18.7 BHP. This new fan rating must be reduced to the predetermined speed of 418 RPM along the new duct resistance curve by use of Fan law no. 1.

$$CFM_1 = CFM_2\left(\frac{RPM_1}{RPM_2}\right)$$

$$= 41280\left(\frac{418}{454}\right) = 38006 \text{ cfm}$$

$$SP_1 = SP_2\left(\frac{RPM_1}{RPM_2}\right)^2$$

$$= 2\left(\frac{418}{454}\right)^2 = 1.70 \text{ inch}$$

$$BHP_1 = BHP_2\left(\frac{RPM_1}{RPM_2}\right)^3$$

$$= 18.7\left(\frac{418}{454}\right)^3 = 14.6 \text{ hp}$$

This example is useful in those cases where added resistance, such as absolute filters, is inserted in the fan system and thereby raises its static pressure beyond the fan manufacturers catalogued ratings.

Air Density Considerations: 1) Standard Density = 0.075 lb/ft³ at 29.92 inches Hg (atmos. press.) and 70°F dry air.

2) Density varies inversely as absolute temperature: i.e., at 120°F:

$$\text{Density} = 0.075 \times \frac{460 + 70}{460 + 120}$$

$$= 0.075 \times \frac{530}{580}$$

$$= 0.0685 \text{ lb/cu ft dry air}$$

3) Density is reduced by elevation: i.e.,

Sea level : 29.92 inches Hg

1000' : 28.85 inches Hg

2000' : 27.80 inches Hg.

See chart for other elevations. So for example at120°F and 2000 feet elevation:

$$\text{Density} = 0.075 \times \frac{460 + 70}{460 + 120} \times \frac{27.80}{29.92}$$

$$= 0.0637 \text{ lb/cu ft dry air}$$

4) Density is reduced when an inlet duct is used, and this reduction may be significant. For a 20 inches H_2O inlet suction (atmospheric pressure is 407 inches H_2O) the density correction is:

$$\frac{407 - 20}{407} = \frac{387}{407} = 0.951$$

For example, at 120°F, 2000 feet elevation and 20 inches suction

$$\text{Density} = 0.0655 \times \frac{27.80}{29.92} \times 0.951$$

$$= 0.0578 \text{ lb/ft}^3$$

For densities of nonsaturated air, refer to psychrometric charts. With wet bulb and dry bulb temperatures, determine air volume ft³/lb. Density = 1 ÷ air volume.

5) Density is reduced when water vapor is added to air, as occurs in wet scrubber exhaust systems. For saturated air, determine density and proceed per Steps 3 and 4, above, as required, i.e., at 120°F saturated (read 0.0655 from Fig. 14-21), 2000 ft elevation and 20 inch suction.

Relation of Air Characteristics and Temperature.—

Table 14-1 shows the effects of temperature on air volume, weight, and pressure, as well as power required to move the air, all based on air at 70°F, for which the ratio is 1.00 in all cases.

Column 2 gives the relative volume of air of the same weight while column 3 shows the relative velocities required to produce the same pressure. Column 4 contains the relative pressures required to pass the same weight of air through the same orifice, and column 5 the relative fan speeds required to move the same weight of air through the same orifice. Column 6 shows the relative power required to move the same weight of air through the same orifice. Column 7 is the relative power needed to move the same volume of air against the same resistance, column 8 the relative power to move the same weight of air against the same resistance, and column 9 the power to move the same volume of air at the same velocity.

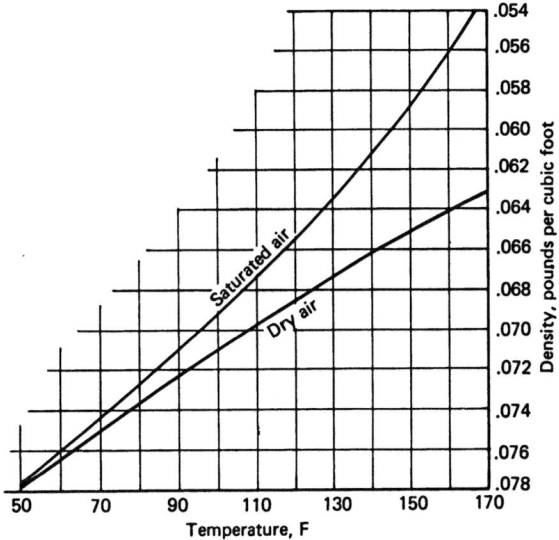

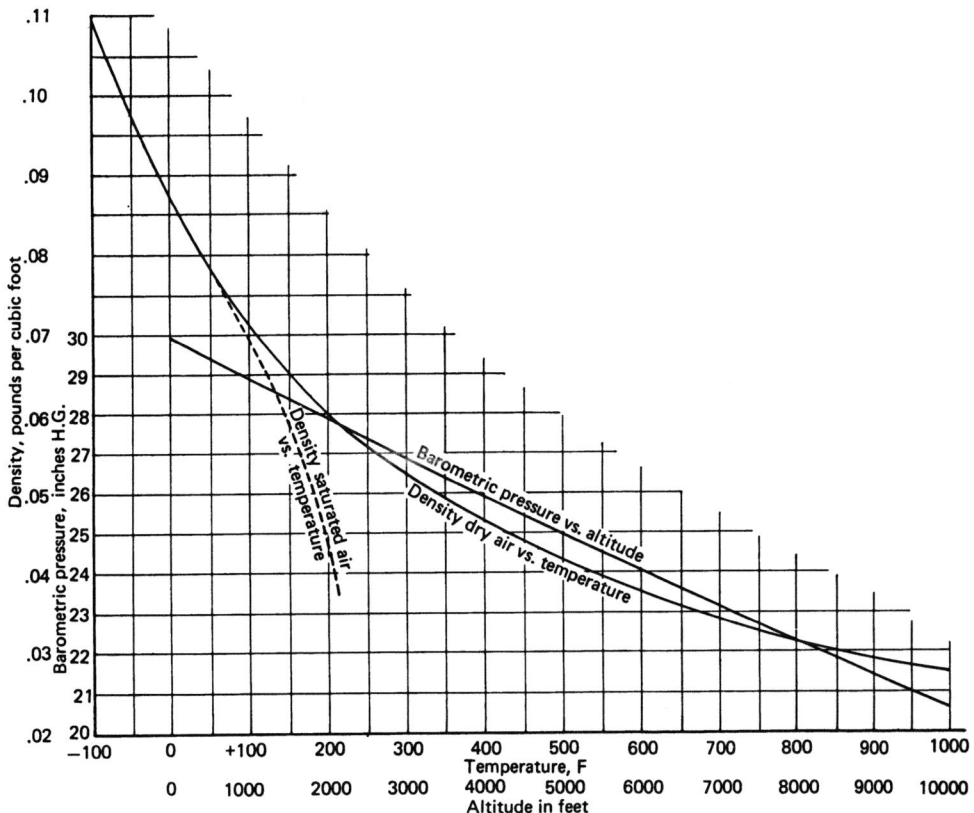

Fig 14-21. Density versus temperature and pressure versus elevation

Table 14-1. Relation of Air Characteristics and Temperature

Temperature, °F	Volume of Same Weight	Velocity to Produce Same Pressure	Pressure to Pass Same Weight	Fan Speed, Same Weight	Power, Same Weight Orifice	Power, Same Volume Resistance	Power, Same Weight Resistance	Power, Same Volume, Velocity
(1)	(2)	(3)	(4)	(5)	(6)	(7)	(8)	(9)
0	0.86	0.932	0.86	0.86	0.74	1.00	0.86	1.15
10	0.88	0.942	0.88	0.88	0.77	1.00	0.88	1.13
20	0.90	0.952	0.90	0.90	0.81	1.00	0.90	1.10
30	0.92	0.961	0.92	0.92	0.85	1.00	0.92	1.08
40	0.94	0.971	0.94	0.94	0.88	1.00	0.94	1.06
50	0.96	0.981	0.96	0.96	0.92	1.00	0.96	1.04
60	0.98	0.990	0.98	0.98	0.96	1.00	0.98	1.02
70	1.00	1.000	1.00	1.00	1.00	1.00	1.00	1.00
80	1.02	1.009	1.02	1.02	1.04	1.00	1.02	0.98
90	1.04	1.018	1.04	1.04	1.08	1.00	1.04	0.96
100	1.06	1.028	1.06	1.06	1.12	1.00	1.06	0.94
125	1.11	1.051	1.11	1.11	1.23	1.00	1.11	0.90
150	1.15	1.073	1.15	1.15	1.34	1.00	1.15	0.87
175	1.20	1.094	1.20	1.20	1.45	1.00	1.20	0.83
200	1.25	1.114	1.25	1.25	1.56	1.00	1.25	0.80
225	1.29	1.135	1.29	1.29	1.67	1.00	1.29	0.77
250	1.34	1.156	1.34	1.34	1.79	1.00	1.34	0.75
275	1.39	1.177	1.39	1.39	1.92	1.00	1.39	0.72
300	1.43	1.197	1.43	1.43	2.06	1.00	1.43	0.70
325	1.48	1.216	1.48	1.48	2.20	1.00	1.48	0.68
350	1.53	1.235	1.53	1.53	2.34	1.00	1.53	0.66
375	1.58	1.254	1.58	1.58	2.48	1.00	1.58	0.64
400	1.62	1.273	1.62	1.62	2.63	1.00	1.62	0.62
425	1.67	1.291	1.67	1.67	2.79	1.00	1.67	0.60
450	1.72	1.309	1.72	1.72	2.95	1.00	1.72	0.58
475	1.77	1.327	1.77	1.77	3.11	1.00	1.77	0.56
500	1.81	1.345	1.81	1.81	3.28	1.00	1.81	0.55
525	1.86	1.362	1.86	1.86	3.46	1.00	1.86	0.54
550	1.91	1.379	1.91	1.91	3.64	1.00	1.91	0.52
575	1.96	1.396	1.96	1.96	3.82	1.00	1.96	0.51
600	2.00	1.414	2.00	2.00	4.00	1.00	2.00	0.50
625	2.05	1.430	2.05	2.05	4.20	1.00	2.05	0.49
650	2.10	1.446	2.10	2.10	4.40	1.00	2.10	0.48
675	2.15	1.462	2.15	2.15	4.46	1.00	2.15	0.47
700	2.19	1.478	2.19	2.19	4.79	1.00	2.19	0.46
800	2.38	1.542	2.38	2.38	5.65	1.00	2.38	0.42
1000	2.76	1.660	2.76	2.76	7.59	1.00	2.76	0.36
1200	3.14	1.770	3.14	3.14	9.85	1.00	3.14	0.32
1500	3.70	1.920	3.70	3.70	13.70	1.00	3.70	0.27
2000	4.65	2.160	4.65	4.65	21.60	1.00	4.65	0.21

Fan Performance Curves.—Since each type and size of fan has different characteristics, fan performance curves must be developed by fan manufacturers. Generally, these curves are determined by laboratory tests, conducted according to an appropriate industry test standard. In the United States and Canada, the test procedures for fan testing have been standardized by the *Air Moving and Conditioning Association (AMCA)*.

It is important to note that the test set-up required by AMCA standards is nearly ideal. For this reason, the performance curves for static pressure and brake horsepower versus CFM are those obtained under ideal conditions, which rarely exist in practice. To make allowances for deviations from the laboratory test set-up, see *Fan Inlet Connections* and *Fan Discharge Conditions* later in this section.

The *Fan Laws* are used to determine the brake horsepower and performance characteristics at other speeds and fan sizes; normally, as mentioned before, only one fan size and speed must be tested to determine the capacity for a given family of fans.

System Resistance Curves: System resistance is the sum total of all pressure losses through filters, coils, dampers, and ductwork. The system resistance curve (illustrated in Fig. 14-22) is simply a plot of the pressure that is required to move air through the system.

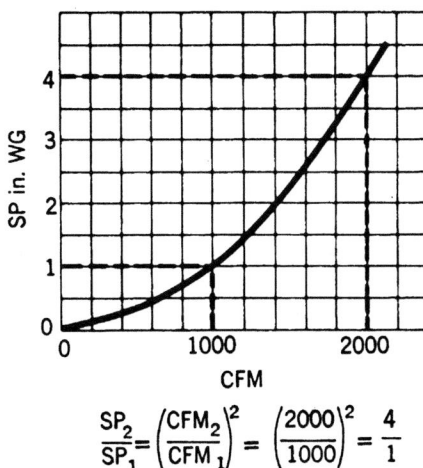

$$\frac{SP_2}{SP_1} = \left(\frac{CFM_2}{CFM_1}\right)^2 = \left(\frac{2000}{1000}\right)^2 = \frac{4}{1}$$

Fig 14-22. System resistance curve

For fixed systems, that is, those with no changes in damper settings, etc., system resistance varies as the square of the air flow (CFM). The resistance curve for any system is represented by a single curve.

For example, consider a system handling 1000 CFM with a total resistance of 1 inch SP. If CFM is doubled, SP resistance will increase to 4 inches, as shown by the squared value of the ratio given in Fig. 14-22. This curve changes, however, as filters load with dirt, coils start con-

densing moisture, or when outlet dampers are changed in position.

Operating Point: The operating point (Fig. 14-23) at which the fan and system will perform is determined by the intersection of the system resistance curve and fan performance curve. Note that every fan operates only along its performance curve. If the system resistance design is not the same as the resistance in the system installed, the operating point will change and the static pressure and volume delivered will not be as calculated.

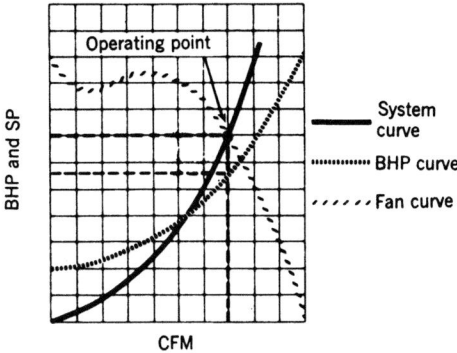

Fig 14-23. Operating point

Note in Fig. 14-24 that the actual system has more pressure drop than predicted in the design. Thus, CFM is reduced and static pressure is increased.

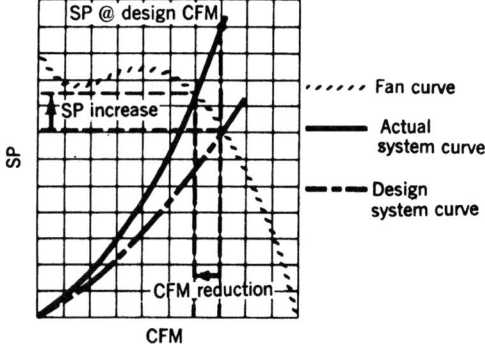

Fig 14-24. Variations from design–air shortage

The shape of the HP curve typically would result in a reduction in BHP. Typically, RPM would then be increased and more BHP would be needed to achieve the desired CFM. In many cases where there is a difference between actual and calculated fan output, it is due to a change in system resistance rather than any shortcomings of the fan or motor. Frequently, the mistake is made of taking the static pressure reading across the fan and concluding that if it is at or above design requirements then the CFM is also at or above design requirements. Fig. 14-24 shows why this assumption is completely invalid.

System Surge, Fan Surge, and Paralleling: The three main reasons for unstable air flow in a fan system are:

(1) system surge

(2) fan surge

(3) paralleling.

System surge (Fig. 14-25), occurs when the system resistance and fan performance curves do not intersect at a distinct point but rather over a range of volumes and pressures. This situation does not occur with backward inclined (BI), airfoil (AF), and radial fans. However, it can occur with a forward curve centrifugal fan when operating, as shown in Fig. 14-25, to the left of the peak of its performance curve.

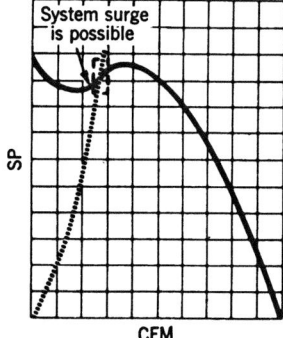

Fig 14-25. System surge

In this situation, because the fan curve and system curve are almost parallel, the operating point can be over a range of CFM and static pressures. This will result in unstable operation known as system surge, pulsation, or pumping.

System surge should not be confused with paralleling, which can only occur when two fans are installed in parallel.

Fan surge (Fig. 14-26), on the other hand, is different than system surge. They may or may not occur at the same time.

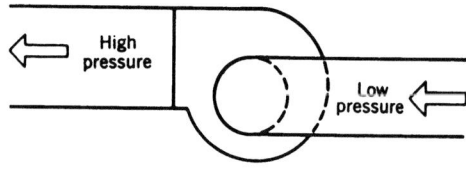

Fig 14-26. Fan surge

For any fan, the point of minimum pressure occurs at the center of rotation of the fan wheel and the maximum pressure occurs just at the discharge side of the wheel. If the wheel were not turning and this pressure differential existed, flow would be from the high pressure point to the low pressure point. This is opposite from the direction air normally flows through the fan. The only thing that keeps

the air moving in the proper direction is the whirling of the blades. Stall occurs unless there is sufficient air entering the fan wheel to completely fill the space between the blades.

This shows up in Fig. 14-27 as fluctuation in CFM and pressure. This surge can be both felt and heard and occurs in nearly all fan types, to varying degrees, as block-tight static pressure is approached. The radial blade is a notable exception. While the magnitude of surge varies for different types of fans (being greatest for airfoil and least for forward curve), the pressure fluctuation close to block-tight may be on the order of 10%. For example, a fan in surge developing about 6 inches of total static pressure might have pressure fluctuation of $\frac{6}{10}$ of an inch. This explains why a large fan in surge is intolerable. Equipment room walls have been cracked from the vibration of ducts serving a fan in surge.

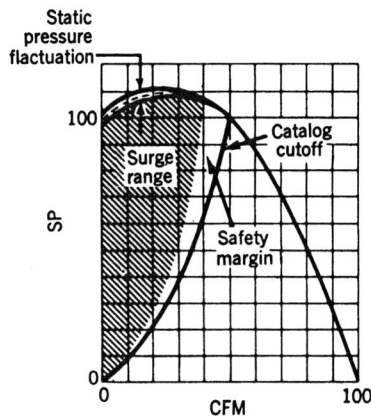

Fig 14-27. Fan surge

Selections should not be made to the left of the surge point on the fan curve. This point, which defines a system curve when all operating speeds of the fan are considered, varies for different fan installations. For instance, stable operation can be obtained much further to the left when the fan is installed in an ideal laboratory type situation. These conditions, of course, are seldom encountered in field applications. Consequently, most manufacturers do not catalog operating ranges all the way to the surge line.

However, since the catalog cut-off point is basically one of engineering judgment, conservative catalog performance data will provide operating ranges that will allow stable operation with any reasonable field ductwork design.

The third cause for unstable operation is paralleling, (Fig. 14-28), which can occur only in a multiple fan installation connected with either a common inlet or common discharge, or both.

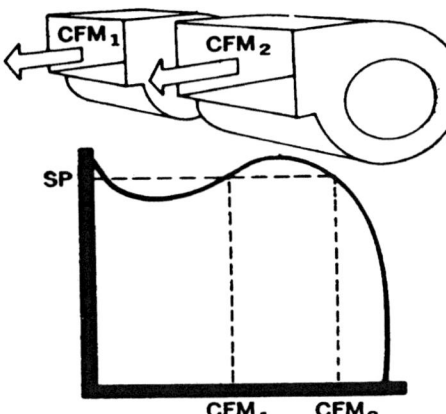

Fig 14-28. Unbalanced parallel operation

In addition, the fan curve must have a characteristic shape where two different CFMs are possible at the same SP. This allows a paralleling situation to exist. It can be theoretically illustrated by drawing a sum of the differences curve or *difference curve* for short (Fig. 14-29).

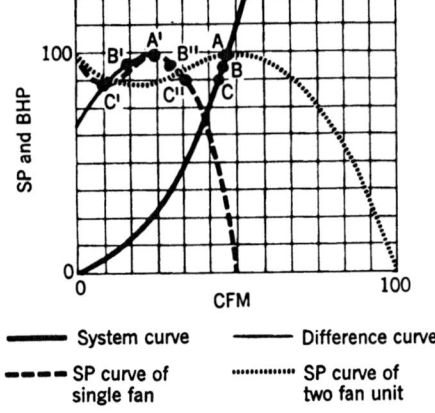

——— System curve   ——— Difference curve

– – – SP curve of   ············ SP curve of
single fan   two fan unit

Fig 14-29. Paralleling

If the curve indicates that the paralleling situation can exist, then corrective measures must be taken to achieve satisfactory performance.

The sum of the differences curve is determined by first plotting the combined two fan curve and the system curve along with the curve of one fan shown alone on the same sheet. Then, the *difference curve* is plotted by taking the CFM difference at constant static pressure between the system curve and the single fan curve.

For example, from Fig. 14-29, the CFM difference between C and C" is plotted as point C' at the same static pressure. Then another point to develop the difference curve is shown by the CFM difference B and B" and is plotted as B'. Finally, A' is exactly half the CFM of A and is the intended operating point for each of the two fans.

Every point where the difference curve intersects the single-fan curve indicates a possible point of operation. Intersection at B' or C' in Fig. 14-29 indicates a parallel-

ing situation. Each of these points then defines a CFM and static pressure falling on the system curve which both fans combined can satisfy: one fan operating on one side of its curve and the other fan operating on the other side.

In this example, the difference curve intersects the single-fan curve at C' and B' in addition to the intended operating point at A'. Thus, the operating point can be not only at the intended point A but also at points B and C. The result is that the fan will not operate at any one of these points, but will bounce between them, causing a fluctuation in static pressure, *cfm*, and noise level.

This requires the installation of scroll volume (outlet volume) dampers (Fig. 14-30). A scroll volume damper serves to change the shape of the fan scroll and thus, for each position of the damper, there is a corresponding different performance curve.

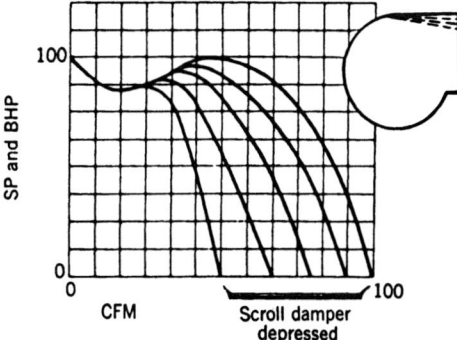

Fig 14-30. Effect of scroll dampers

The effect of scroll, or outlet volume dampers is shown in Fig. 14-31. The fan curve resulting from various positions of the outlet volume dampers is also shown. The purpose, of course, is to change the fan curve sufficiently such that the sum of the differences curve will intersect the single-fan curve at A' and provide stable operation.

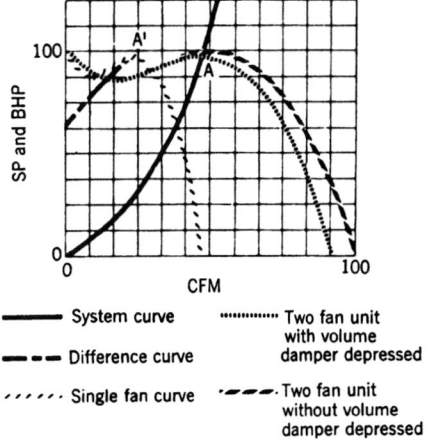

——— System curve   ············ Two fan unit
                                with volume
– – – Difference curve   damper depressed

‚‚‚‚‚‚ Single fan curve   –··–·· Two fan unit
                                without volume
                                damper depressed

Fig 14-31. Elimination of paralleling

The performance may be reduced slightly and a corresponding increase in RPM should be made to achieve the specified conditions. However, this is rarely done since the difference is typically negligible.

To correct, the scroll volume damper is merely pushed down on both fans until the static pressure and noise level pulsation disappear. Generally, they are then left in this position permanently. The curve generated by the damper at this point is so shaped that the sum of the differences curve intersects at only one point.

Fan Types: There are two general types of fans–centrifugal and axial. Flow within the centrifugal fan is substantially radial through the wheel. In an axial fan, flow is parallel to the shaft.

Centrifugal fans are divided into four general classifications: forward curve (FC), backward inclined (BI), radial blade, and tubular centrifugal.

The RPM for a given type centrifugal fan wheel is determined by the tip speed necessary to produce the required absolute particle velocity (Fig. 14-32). This absolute particle velocity vector relative to ground (S) has two components, one radial (r) and the other tangential (t) to the wheel.

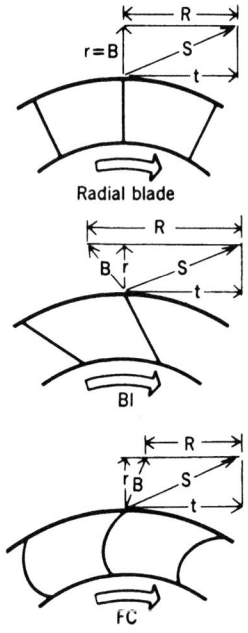

r = Radial component
t = Tangential component
S = Absolute air velocity
B = Air velocity relative to wheel
R = Relative tip speed of wheel

Fig 14-32. Centrifugal fan wheels

The velocity of the air relative to the blade is indicated by the blade vector (B) which is nearly tangential to the blade, though some slip occurs. The length of the tip speed vector (R) as shown in the diagram, indicates the

relative wheel RPM to produce a given capacity. By examining the relative length of the R vector, it can be seen that the FC fan requires the lowest tip speed for a given capacity, while the BI requires the highest tip speed.

Forward Curve Centrifugal Fan: The forward curve centrifugal fan travels at a relatively slow speed and generally is used for producing high volumes at low static pressure.

Typical operating range of this type of fan is from 30% to 80% wide-open volume (Fig. 14-33). The maximum static efficiency of 60–68% generally occurs slightly to the right of peak static pressure. The horsepower curve has an increasing slope and is referred to as an *overloading type.*

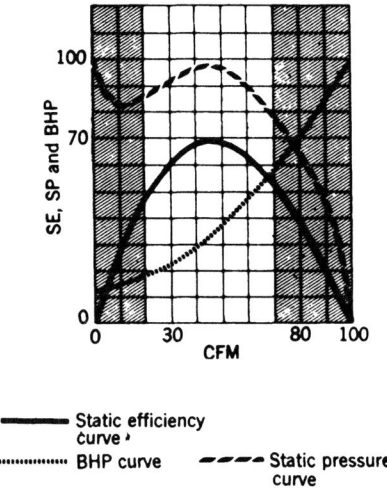

Static efficiency curve

BHP curve

Static pressure curve

Fig 14-33. Characteristic curve for FC fans

The FC fan will surge but the magnitude is typically less than for other types.

Advantages of the FC fan are its low cost, slow speed (which minimizes shaft and bearing size) and wide operating range. The disadvantages are the shape of its performance curve, which allows the possibility of paralleling, and an overloading horsepower curve. Thus, overloading of the motor may occur if system static pressure decreases. Also, it is not suitable for material handling because of its blade configuration. It is inherently weak structurally. Therefore, forward curved fans are generally not capable of the high speeds necessary for developing higher static pressures.

Backward Inclined Fan: Backward inclined fans travel about twice the speed of the forward curved fan, as previously indicated by the velocity vector diagram. The normal selection range of the backward inclined fan is approximately 40–85% of wide open *cfm* (Fig. 14-34). Maximum static efficiency of about 80% generally occurs close to the edge of its normal operating range.

Generally, the larger the fan the more efficient for a given selection.

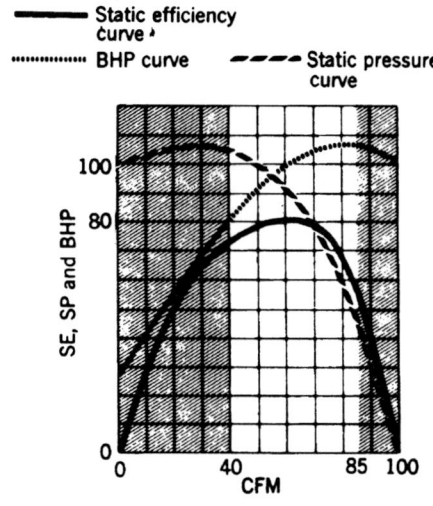

Fig 14-34. Characteristic curve for radial blade fans

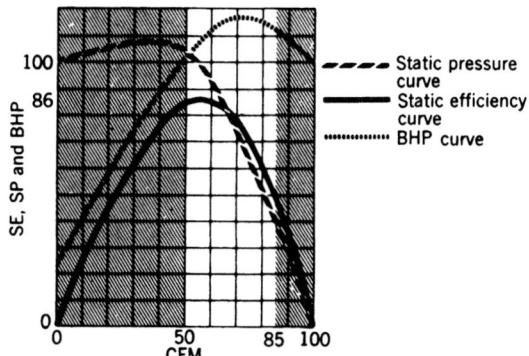

Fig 14-35. Characteristic curve for airfoil fans

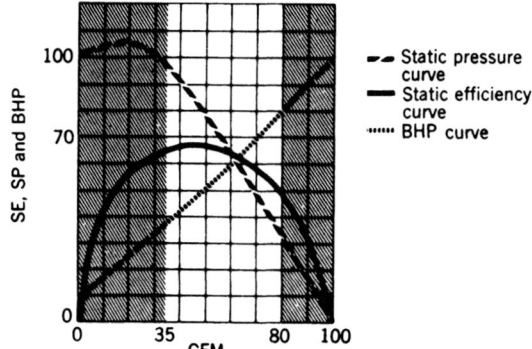

Fig 14-36. Characteristic curves for radial blade fans

The magnitude of surge for a BI fan is greater than for an FC fan.

Advantages of the BI fan are higher efficiency and non overloading horsepower curve. The horsepower curve generally reaches a maximum in the middle of the normal operating range, thus overloading is normally not a problem. Inherently stronger design makes it suitable for higher static pressure operation.

The BI fan's disadvantages include, first the higher speed which requires larger shaft and bearing sizes and places more importance on proper balance, and, second, unstable operation occurs as block-tight static pressure is approached. This fan is also unsuitable for material handling.

A refinement of the flat-blade, backward inclined fan makes use of airfoil shaped blades. This improves the static efficiency to about 86% and reduces noise level slightly. The magnitude of surge also increases with the airfoil blades. Characteristic curves for airfoil fans are shown in Fig. 14-35.

Radial Blade Fans: Radial blade fans (Fig. 14-36) are generally narrower than other types of centrifugal fans. Consequently, they require a larger diameter wheel for a given capacity. This increases the cost and is the main reason why they are not used for air conditioning duty.

The radial blade fan is well suited for handling low volumes at relatively high static pressures and for material handling. Absence of surge and a nearly straight horsepower curve with linear relationship with *cfm* are its other advantages. This proportional relationship allows capacity control to be actuated from motor power input.

Disadvantages of this type of fan are higher cost and lower efficiency.

Tubular Centrifugal Fans: Tubular centrifugal fans, illustrated in Fig. 14-37, generally consist of a single width airfoil wheel arranged in a cylinder to discharge air radially against the inside of the cylinder. Air is then deflected parallel with the fan shaft to provide straight-through flow. Vanes are used to recover static pressure and straighten air flow.

Characteristic curves are shown in Fig. 14-38. The selection range is generally about the same as the scroll type BI or airfoil-blade wheel, 50–85% of wide open volume. However, because there is no housing of the turbulent air flow path through the fan, static efficiency is reduced to a maximum of about 72% and the noise level is increased.

Frequently, the straight-through flow results in significant space savings. This is the main advantage of tubular centrifugal fans.

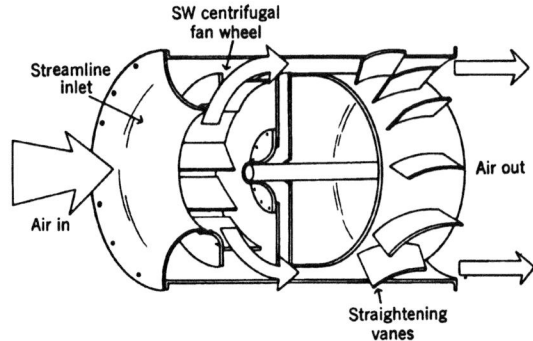

Fig 14-37. Tubular centrifugal fan

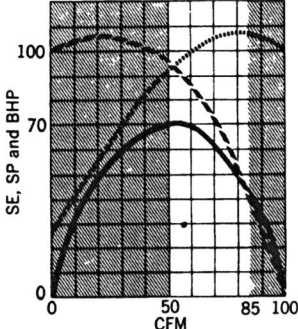

Fig 14-38. Characteristic curves for tubular centrifugal fans

Axial Fans: Axial fans are divided into three groups: *propeller*, *tubeaxial,* and *vaneaxial.*

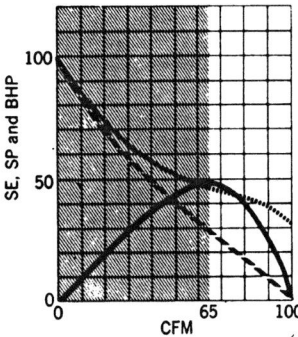

Fig 14-39. Characteristic curves for propeller fans

The propeller fan (Fig. 14-39) is well suited for high volumes of air at little or no static pressure differential. Tubeaxial and vaneaxial fans (Fig. 14-40) are simply propeller fans mounted in a cylinder and are similar to one another except for vane type straighteners on the vaneaxial. These vanes remove much of the swirl from the air and improve efficiency. Thus, a vaneaxial fan is more efficient than a tubeaxial and can reach higher pressures. Note that with axial fans the BHP is maximum at block tight static pressure. With centrifugal fans the BHP is minimum at block tight static pressure.

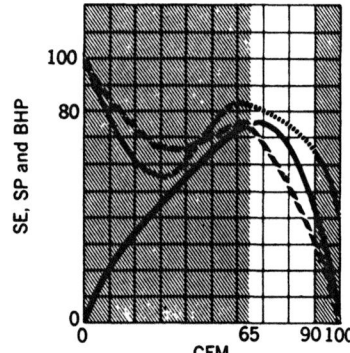

Fig 14-40. Characteristic curves for vaneaxial fans (high performance)

Advantages of tube and vaneaxial flow fans are the reduced size and weight and straight through air flow, which frequently eliminates elbows in the ductwork. The maximum static efficiency of an industrial vaneaxial fan is approximately 85%. The operating range for axial fans is from about 65% to 90%.

The disadvantages of axial fans are high noise level and lower efficiency than centrifugal fans afford.

In recent years, more sophisticated design of vaneaxial fans has made it possible to use these fans at pressures comparable to those developed by the airfoil backward inclined fans, with equal overall efficiency. These fans have variable pitch blades, which can be activated by an external operator. For large size fans requiring motor horse powers above 100 hp, it is comparatively simple to change the fan characteristics by using either a manual or pneumatic controller. The disadvantage of these fans is their high noise level; sound traps are generally required both upstream and downstream. Despite this added acoustical requirement, the initial cost of these fans compares favorably with the airfoil BI fans.

Class Limits for Fans.—The Air Moving and Conditioning Association (AMCA) has adopted a standard that defines operating limits for the various classes of centrifugal fans used in general ventilation applications.

The standard uses limits based on mean brake horsepower per square foot of outlet area, expressed in terms of outlet velocity and static pressure (Figs. 14-41 to 14-43).

When a fan is designated as meeting the requirements of a particular class as defined by the standard it must be physically capable of operating safely at any point inside the *minimum performance* limits for that class.

To assist fan users and consulting engineers, members of AMCA's centrifugal fan division agreed on a standard system of shading multirating tables in catalogs, which should simplify selection of the appropriate fan class for each application. Where the new class limits are used in a catalog, the manufacturer will state that these are *in accordance with revised AMCA Standard 2408-69.*

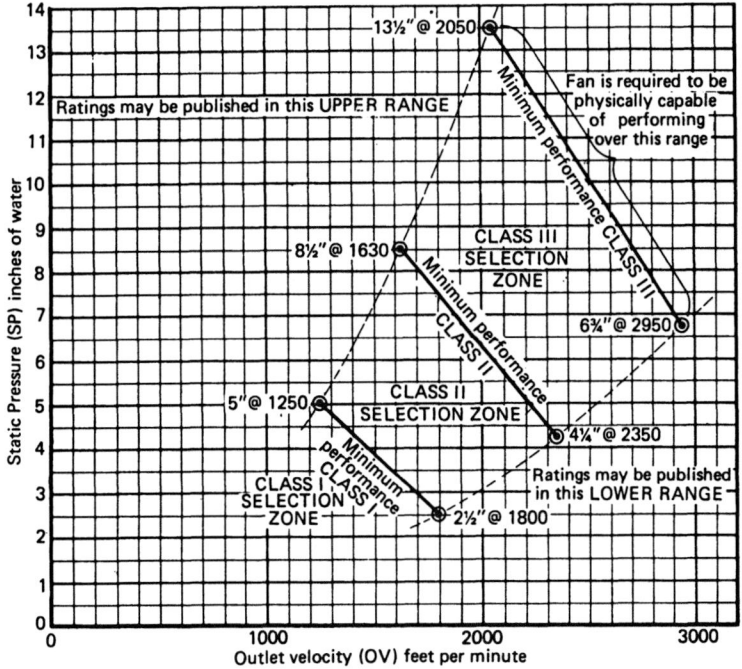

Fig 14-41. Operating limits for centrifugal fans tubular

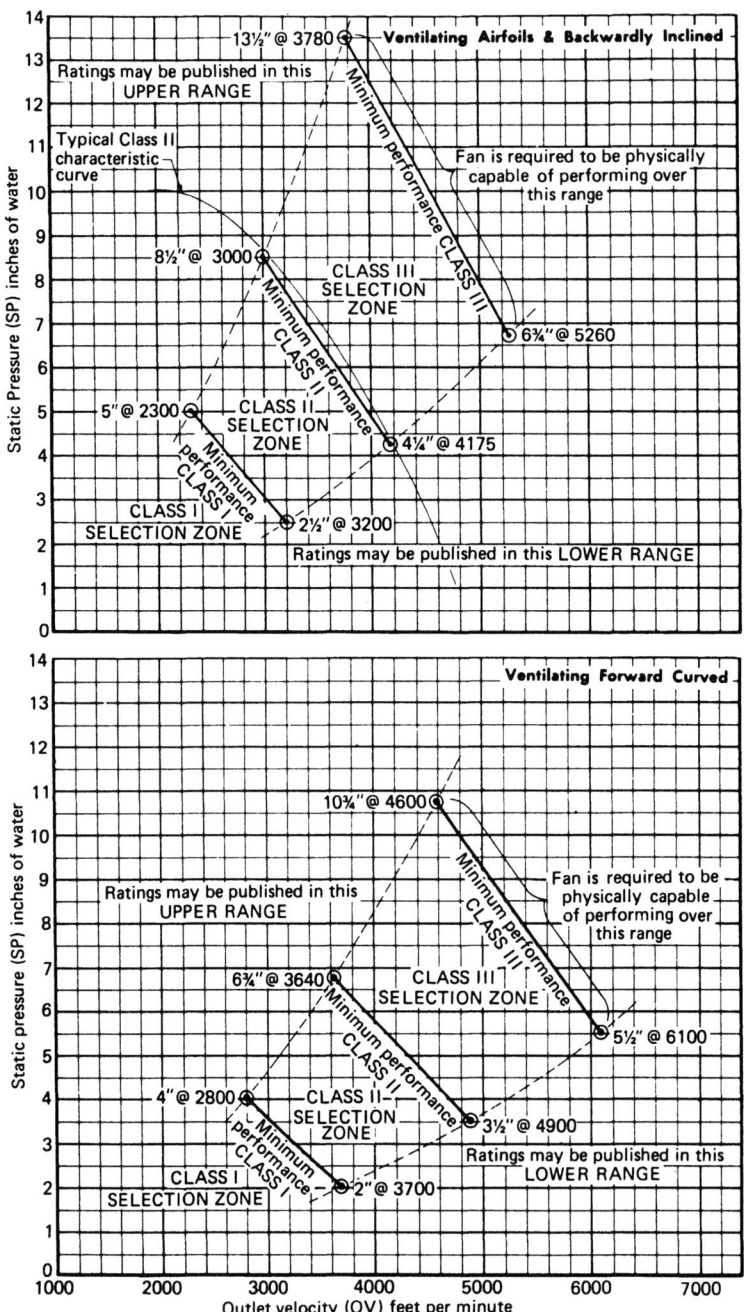

Fig 14-42. Operating limits for single width centrifugal fans

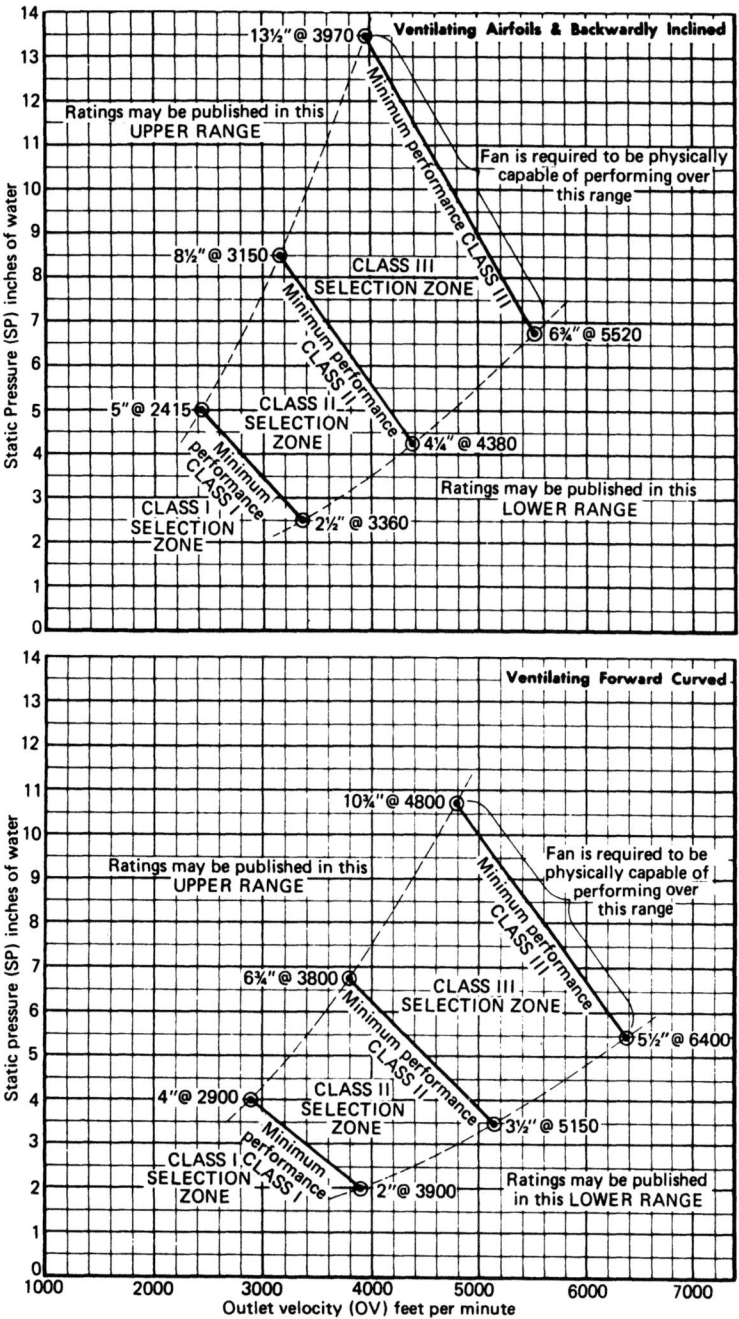

Fig 14-43. Operating limits for double width centrifugal fans

Definitions: Reference line is a horizontal line through the center of the fan shaft. Air entry to the inlet box is determined from drive side of the fan. On single inlet fans the drive side is always considered the side opposite the fan inlet. When drives are on both ends of fan shaft, the drive side is that side having the higher horsepower driving unit and is the same side from which the fan rotation is designated.

Air Entry Position Designation*: 1) top intake; 2) horizontal right intake; 3) (number of degrees) above or below horizontal center line on right; 4) bottom intake;

5) horizontal left intake; and 6) (number of degrees) above or below horizontal centerline on the left.

* It will be found in some cases that this arrangement interferes seriously with the framing of the floor structure by the amount of floor space required.

Designation of Position of Inlet Boxes

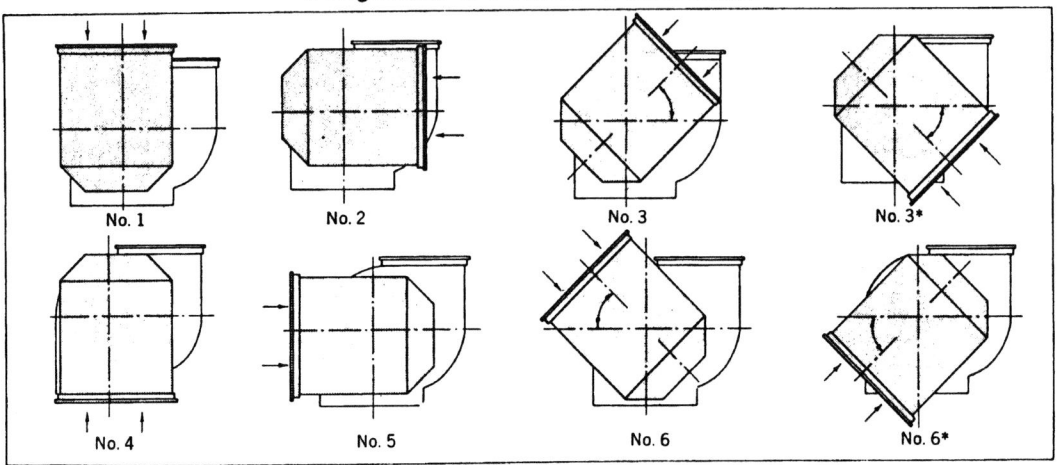

Fig 14-44. Designation of position of inlet boxes

Motor Position, Belt or Chain Drive

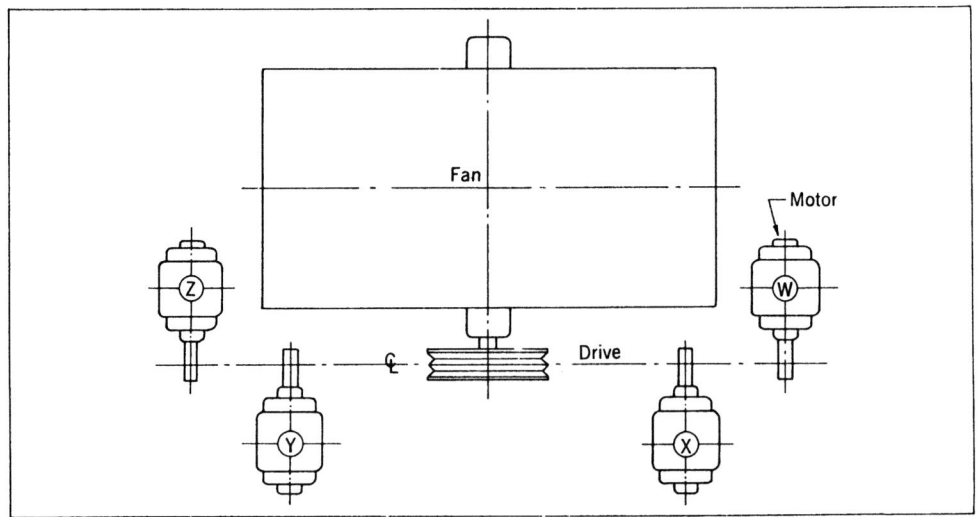

Location of motor is determined by facing the drive side of fan and designating the motor position by letters W, X, Y, or Z as the case may be.

Fig 14-45. Motor position, belt or chain drive

Fan Selection.—As clearly mentioned, in any fan system, two basic parameters are required for fan selection: rate of flow or capacity, generally expressed as cubic feet per minute (*cfm*), and the potential required to move the air through the system, expressed either as static or total pressure (SP or TP).

The *cfm* is determined by the system designer at a specified temperature and barometric pressure at the system inlet. If the system requirement is given in pounds per minute, *cfm* can be found by the following equation:

$$cfm = \frac{\text{lb/min flowing}}{\text{lb/cu ft at inlet (density)}}$$

The fan performance is a function of air density at the fan inlet. This density not only determines the volumetric capacity for a given weight of flow, but the developed pressure of the fan as well. Factors that affect air density are: barometric pressure, temperature, and relative humidity. Whenever these conditions are not specified, the fan supplier usually assumes air at standard conditions (70°F and 29.92 inches Hg barometer).

Definitions of static, velocity, and total fan pressures are given earlier in this section. Fan manufacturers in the United States have customarily catalogued fan static pressure as the single basis for fan selection.

While a fan of almost any size, and either centrifugal or axial, could be selected for a given air flow and system resistance, the realistic possibilities are limited by practical engineering and economic considerations:

1) Space for the fan and its driving mechanism.

2) Application, such as material handling, temperature of air, parallel operation, pressure range, and other factors listed under *Fan Types* section above.

3) Fan first cost versus operating cost (fan horsepower energy and maintenance).

4) Type and loudness of noise produced by fan.

5) Effect of system dampering fan performance.

6) Fan drive mechanism and its reliability, particularly V-belts versus direct drive for large fans.

7) Expected life of fan versus first cost. This is closely tied to the fan construction and class.

While it is possible to select a fan by the *equivalent air method of rating* by using the fan laws, the same results can be more rapidly obtained by resorting to the tables or selection charts published by the fan manufacturer. Multirating tables are the most common type of such data, usually based on standard air. After space requirements, fan application, expected life, and other such considerations have been established, the optimum fan selection is either at, or just to the right of, the peak efficiency point on the performance curve. This results in a slightly undersized fan. However, selection in this range provides a more stable operation than an oversized fan would provide. In fact, oversized fans should be selected only where future increase in capacity is expected, and great care must be exercised not to select one in the unstable range of the curve.

Peak efficiency can be determined from either the fan performance curves or from multirating tables by noting which fan meets the design requirements with minimum BHP. There is only one fan size in any type that will meet these requirements. If the design requirements do not exactly match the catalogued values of *cfm* or SP, linear interpolation of these values will give accurate results. The tabulated value of RPM is the required operating speed. However, the listed value of BHP must be multiplied by the ratio of actual density to standard density to obtain the required operating horsepower.

Multirating charts are also very useful for fan selection; their main advantage is the graphic depiction of the performance for a family of similar fans.

A second method of fan selection is the specific speed method of rating. This method is commonly used to select larger fans with direct drives. Since alternating current electric motors are not available with standard rotating speeds, such as 3600, 1800, 1200 rpm, etc., selection of a motor speed that will produce the most efficient fan selection is a matter of trial assumptions of the standard motor speeds available. From these, the corresponding specific speeds may be calculated and then used with the base performance curves to select fan *cfm* and efficiency for a given SP and air density. This method is generally not recommended for fans with variable speed drives, such as the variable sheave, V-belt drives commonly used for most HVAC systems.

Regardless of the method used to select a fan, there is generally a possible selection of two or more suitable fans. Economics is usually the determining factor in the final selection. The initial cost of each fan, which includes all required accessories, acoustical attenuators, and vibration isolators, must be determined. To these component costs must be added the cost of installation. The first cost can be translated into an annual owning cost, to which is added the annual energy cost for running the fan and the annual maintenance cost. The fan with the lowest annual owning and operating cost would then be the logical selection.

CENTRIFUGAL FAN, DRIVE AND INLET BOX ARRANGEMENTS

Reprinted by permission of Air Moving and Conditioning Association, Inc.

Arrangements of Drive

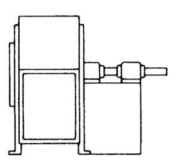 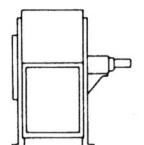 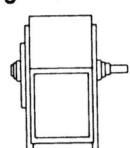 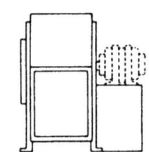 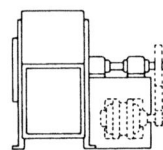

No. 1, SW, SI.
For belt drive or direct connection. Wheel overhung. Two bearings on base.

No. 2, SW, SI.
For belt drive or direct connection. Wheel overhung. Bearings in bracket supported by fan housing.

No. 3, SW, SI.
For belt drive or direct connection. One bearing on each side and supported by fan housing. Not recommended in sizes 27″ diam. and smaller.

No. 4, SW, SI.
For direct drive. Wheel overhung on prime mover shaft. No bearings on fan. Base mounted or an integrally direct connected prime mover.

No. 9, SW, SI.
For belt drive. Arrangement No. 1 designed for mounting prime mover on side of base.

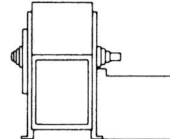 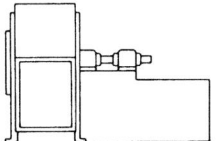 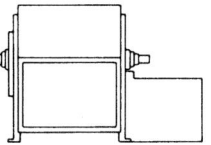 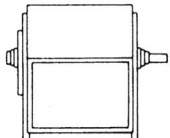

No. 7, SW, SI.
For belt drive on direct connection. Arrangement No. 3 plus base for prime mover. Not recommended in sizes 27″ diameter and smaller.

No. 8, SW, SI.
For belt drive or direct connection. Arrangement No. 1 plus base for prime mover.

No. 7, DW, DI.
For belt drive or direct connection. Arrangement No. 3 plus base for prime mover.

No. 3, DW, DI.
For belt drive or direct connection. One bearing on each side and supported by fan housing.

SW indicates single width, DW double width
SI indicates single inlet, DI double inlet

Designation of Direction of Rotation and Discharge

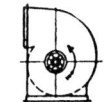 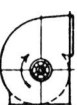  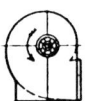

Counter-Clockwise Top Horizontal   **Clockwise Top Horizontal**   **Clockwise Bottom Horizontal**   **Counter-Clockwise Bottom Horizontal**

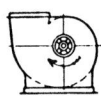 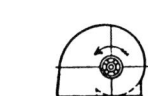 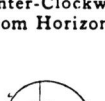

Clockwise Up Blast   **Counter-Clockwise Up Blast**   **Counter-Clockwise Down Blast**   **Clockwise Down Blast**

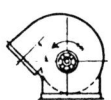 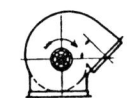  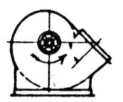

Counter-Clockwise Top Angular Down   **Clockwise Top Angular Down**   **Clockwise Bottom Angular Up**   **Counter-Clockwise Bottom Angular Up**

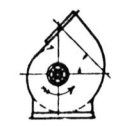 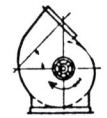

Counter-Clockwise Top Angular Up   **Clockwise Top Angular Up**

Direction of Rotation is determined from drive side for either single or double width, or single or double inlet fans. (The driving side of a single inlet fan is considered to be the side opposite the inlet regardless of actual location of the drive.) For fan inverted for ceiling suspension, Direction of Rotation and Discharge is determined when fan is resting on floor.

Table 14-2. Probable Effects of Various Inlet Connections

Description				% Loss in *cfm* if Not Corrected	% Increase needed in Fan SP to Compensate
	3 pieces elbow	R/D =	0.50	12	30
			1.0	6	13
			2.0	5	11
			6.0	5	11
	4 pieces elbow	R/D =	1.0	6	13
			2.0	4	9
			8.0	4	9
	5 or more pieces elbow	R/D =	1.0	5	11
			2.0	4	9
			8.0	4	9
	Mitered elbow			16	42
Square Ducts with Vane			No vane	17	45
			A	8	18
			B	6	13
			C	5	11
			D	4	9

Table 14-2. Probable Effects of Various Inlet Connections

Description				% Loss in *cfm* if Not Corrected	% Increase needed in Fan SP to Compensate
Round to square to round				8	18
Rectangular elbow without vane	In all cases, use of three long, equally spaced vanes will reduce loss and needed SP increase to ⅓ the values for unvaned elbows				
The maximum included angle of any element of the transition should never exceed 30°. If it does, additional losses will occur. If angle is less than 30° and L is not longer than the fan inlet diameter, the effect of the transition may be ignored. If it is longer, it will be beneficial because elbow will be farther from the fan.	H/W = 0.25	R/W =	0.50	7	15
			1.0	4	9
			2.0	4	9
	H/W = 1.00	R/W =	0.50	12	30
			1.0	5	11
			2.0	4	9
	H/W = 4.00	R/W =	0.50	15	39
			1.0	8	18
			2.0	4	9
	Each 2.5 diameters of straight duct between fan and elbow or inlet box will reduce the adverse effect approximately 20%. For example, if an elbow that would cause a loss of 10% in *cfm* or an increase of 23% in fan SP if on the fan inlet is separated from the fan by straight duct, the effect of the duct may be tabulated thus:				
	No duct		Loss =	10% – SP needed =	23%
	L/D =	2.5	Loss =	8% – SP needed =	19%
		5.0	Loss =	6% – SP needed =	13%
		7.5	Loss =	4% – SP needed =	9%
		10	Loss =	2% – SP needed =	4%

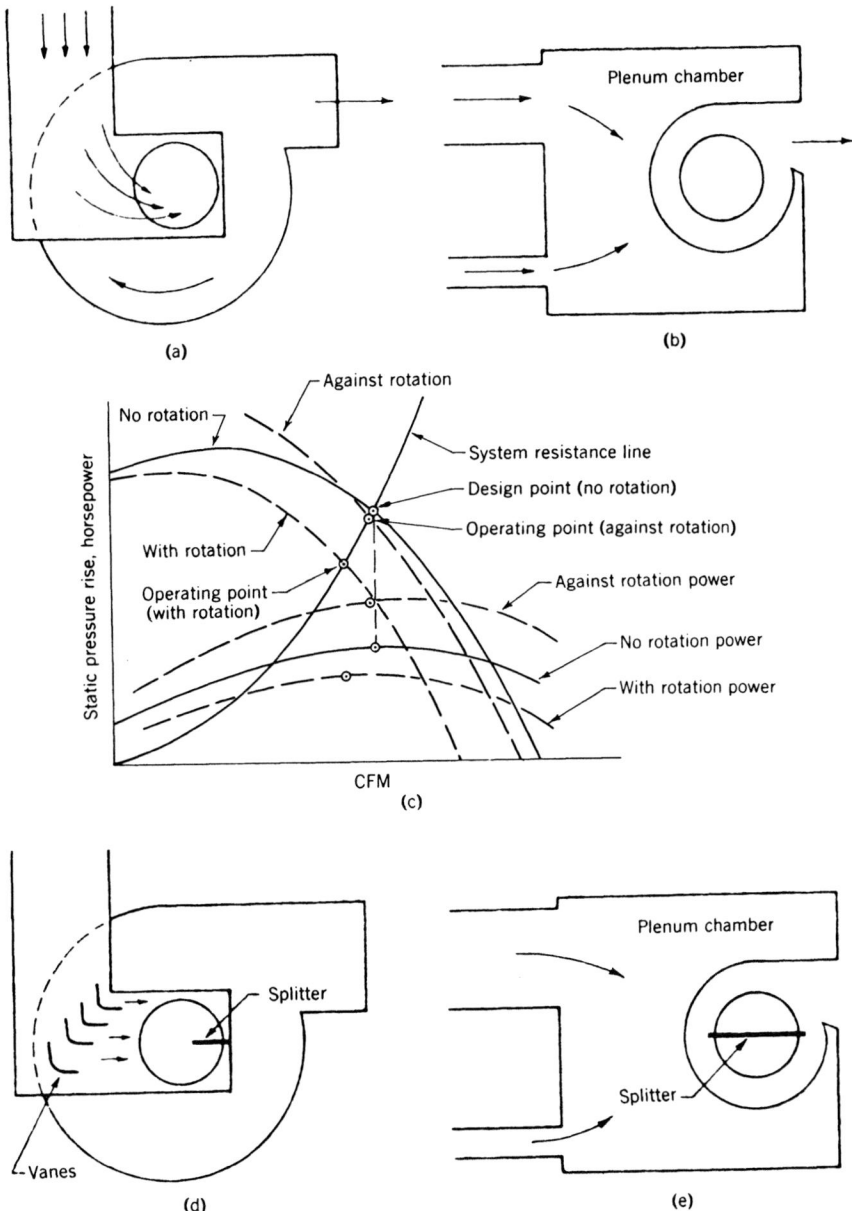

Fig 14-46. Fan inlet swirl (a) inertia of air tends to crowd it to bottom of inlet, setting up swirl. (b) with two unequally sized inlets to plenum chamber, imbalance is set-up, causing swirl at fan inlet. (c) effect of two-inlet swirl on fan performance. (d) vanes and splitter prevent swirl in inlet box. (e) a splitter overcomes the imbalance that is due to unequal inlets.

Fan noise and vibration are important considerations and are influenced by the size and type of fan, its rotating speed, and its efficiency. Generally, axial fans require acoustical treatment on both the suction and discharge sides of the fan, while centrifugal fans usually will need minimal treatment and then only on the discharge. For medium and high pressure fan systems, the advice of an acoustical consultant is recommended. Some manufacturers publish certified sound rating data for their fans, and these should be consulted when available. In addition, the section on *Fan Noise Generation* provides helpful information for estimating the sound power levels of a fan.

Fan Inlet Connections.—Catalogued fan performance is based on lab tests performed under ideal conditions that almost never occur at the fan inlet. This deviation from the ideal produces fan losses that reduce, often seriously, catalogued performance data. There are three basic causes, or various combinations of the three, for fan inlet losses:

1) nonuniform flow into suction of fan
2) swirl or vorticity
3) flow blockage or inlet restrictions.

Due to the infinite variety of inlet conditions at each fan installation, it is difficult to assign specific loss values to these basic causes of fan inlet losses. However, some general guidelines will be useful in reducing them. While bad inlet conditions adversely affect the performance of axial fans, centrifugal fans are extremely susceptible to these conditions. For this reason, most of the ensuing discussion on inlet conditions pertains to centrifugal fans only.

Nonuniform flow into the suction of a fan is typically caused by an elbow installed too close to the fan inlet. The probable effects of various inlet connections are shown in Fig. 14-47.

Inlet swirl, or vorticity, is a frequent cause of reduction in fan performance. If the spin is imparted in the direction of wheel rotation, a situation corresponding to the use of inlet vanes arises: the fan volume, pressure, and horsepower are lower than expected. If the air spin is counter to wheel rotation, the volume and static pressure will be greater than expected and the brake horsepower will also be greater. In either case, spin always reduces efficiency. These conditions are readily overcome by installing vanes and a splitter at the fan inlet, as is graphically shown in Fig. 14-46.

Fan inlet blockage or restrictions may be encountered because of field installation conditions. In these cases, a loss in static pressure will result. This will require an increase in fan speed with a corresponding increase in brake horsepower to correct this situation.

Under some conditions a fan may have a relatively short straight inlet duct starting in a plenum, through a wall, or in a flanged pipe. In some cases, the duct ends abruptly (Fig. 14-47). Where the duct terminates in a ple-

num, through a wall, or flanged pipe, there is a pressure loss of $\frac{1}{2}$ the inlet duct velocity head. Where the duct ends abruptly, the pressure loss is $\frac{9}{10}$ of the inlet duct velocity head. In all these cases, a bell mouth inlet would reduce the inlet loss to $\frac{1}{20}$ of the inlet duct velocity head. In some applications fans are installed in plenum chambers, with open inlets. Occasionally, the wall of the plenum may be close enough to the fan inlet as to restrict its flow. Walls or similar obstructions should be kept at a minimum distance (A) of $\frac{1}{2}$ a fan wheel diameter (Fig. 14-48). A spacing of $\frac{1}{3}$ wheel diameter will reduce pressure and flow about 10%.

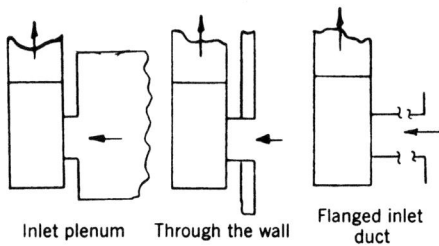

Inlet plenum   Through the wall   Flanged inlet duct

Inlet pressure loss=0.5x inlet duct velocity head

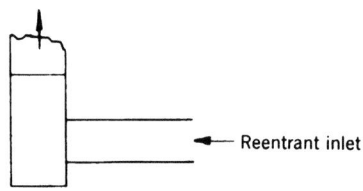

Reentrant inlet

Inlet pressure loss=0.9x inlet duct velocity head

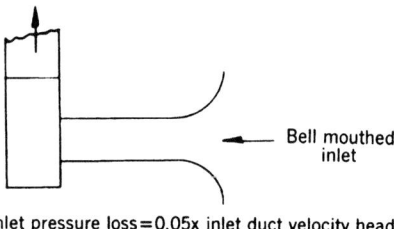

Bell mouthed inlet

Inlet pressure loss=0.05x inlet duct velocity head

Fig 14-47. Straight inlet duct losses

Fan installations employing variable inlet guide vanes frequently result in an additional resistance to flow, which decreases catalogued performance. There is an increasing fan industry trend to mount variable inlet guide vanes in the inlet bell of the fan, as contrasted with the practice of mounting an accessory set of vanes just upstream of the fan inlet in a larger diameter, lower velocity flow field.

The vanes in the inlet bell often have their actuating mechanism at the center, and this partially obstructs the flow, as do the blades themselves. This blockage is percentage wise greater on smaller fans so the performance loss is proportionally greater (Fig. 14-49). For example, a 30 inches diameter fan must run at 4% higher RPM to meet catalog rating with a corresponding increase in HP of about 12%.

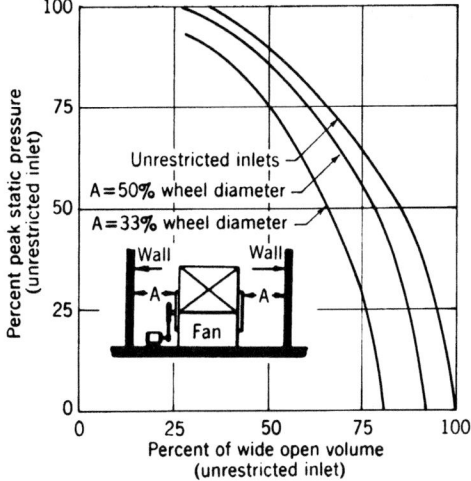

Fig 14-48. Effect of space on fan performance

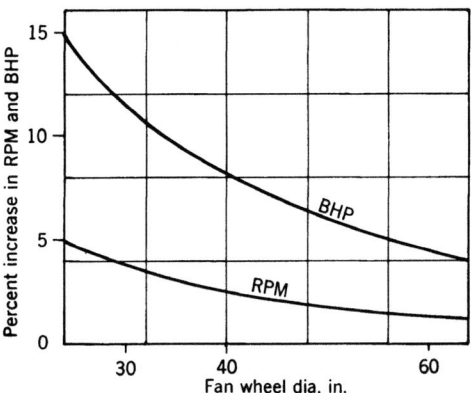

Fig 14-49. Inlet guide vane restriction

Single inlet (SI) fans are often tested for rating purposes in an arrangement without any inlet bearing; hence, the performance of SI fans with an inlet bearing will be slightly less than the catalogued value. The performance reduction will be proportionately greater for smaller fans than for larger fans due to the relatively greater blockage area. The reduction will be greater for higher pressure fans than for low pressure fans due to the larger bearing and bearing support.

Double inlet (DI) fans are often rated using an extension drive shaft. This eliminates the blockage effect of the drive pulley and belts. Catalogued performance is slightly reduced by normal belt drives. This reduction is greater on higher pressure fans due to the wider belts and pulley.

The comment about the effects of bearing support for SI fans applies here as well. Consult a fan supplier for specific correction factors for SI, DI, and drive effects on performance. These effects are usually less than 4% on speed or flow and 12% on HP.

In addition to belt and drive blockage, additional horsepower is required when heavy duty bearings, heavy-duty grease, and belt drives are used. Belt losses are a function of belt tension, number of belts, and type of belts. Typical belt drive losses are from 2 to 6% and can be significantly greater with small fans at slow speeds. When selecting a motor at or near its nameplate rating, this should be taken into account.

Fan Discharge Conditions.—While fan discharge conditions cannot alter the performance characteristics of a fan in the same way that inlet swirl does, fan outlet conditions can be responsible for system losses that are often sizable. Basically, these losses are a result of one or both of the following.

Reduction in Static Pressure Recovery: Air leaving a centrifugal type fan impeller is discharged with a radial velocity component, which results in air discharge vortices. In addition, fan discharge velocity is not uniform across this discharge area, but is peaked from the concentration of air at the outside radius of the scroll. The resulting air flow from a fan outlet is, therefore, one of a nonuniform, spiral nature that does not fill the fan discharge area.

When fans are performance-tested, they typically have many equivalent diameter lengths of constant area duct attached to the fan discharge, including a flow straightener. As a result, there is ample distance for the flow to redistribute itself, and so the spiral flow will disappear partly of its own accord and partly due to the straightener. As a result, at the measuring station the flow will be very uniform, exhibiting a typical, fully turbulent, flow velocity profile. Some of the dynamic energy is converted into static pressure, and the fan manufacturer then tabulates the fan's performance data derived from these ideal discharge conditions. Unfortunately, these outlet conditions are almost never obtained in practice. Either the system design should attempt to use straight ductwork for 3 to 5 equivalent duct diameters downstream of the fan discharge and thereby realize static regain, or, if this is not possible, provide added brake horsepower to accommodate the dynamic losses.

When straight discharge ducts are used, it is not recommended that any sudden transition to larger areas be used. It is recommended that transition to a larger area duct be accomplished with a taper having an included angle of no more than 15° to minimize losses. This is common, good duct design practice (Fig. 14-50).

When fans discharge into a plenum (commonly called *bulkheading*), as they do in many fan systems, a loss occurs due to the sudden enlargement in flow area. Theoretically, if the fan had a uniform velocity over its entire discharge area, the discharge pressure loss would be one velocity head, based on the fan discharge velocity. This is the velocity tabulated in fan catalogs. However, the actual velocity is not at all equal to the tabulated value; actual average discharge velocities are from 120 to 180% of the catalog value. This results in actual discharge pressure losses of 150 to 300% of what one would compute from the catalog outlet velocity. The addition of a short discharge duct of only one or two equivalent diameters in length will significantly reduce this sudden enlargement loss. Even this short distance permits a significant redistribution of the velocity with its corresponding static regain. The discharge loss will then be considerably reduced.

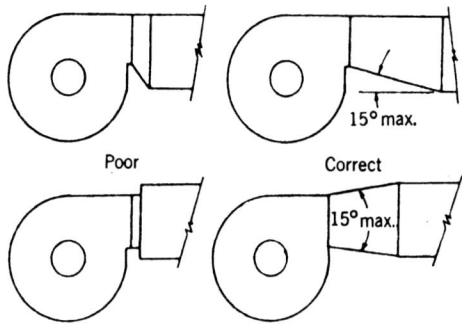

Fig 14-50. Duct transition pieces for centrifugal fan discharge. top: right and wrong transition piece with expansion all on one side of duct. bottom: right and wrong transition piece with expansion in two directions.

It is recommended that the bulkheading loss be obtained from the fan manufacturer, because the magnitude of this loss varies with the type of fan. The Trane Co. has suggested the following approximate increases in fan RPM and BHP to the catalogued values when there is no discharge ductwork:

Fan Type	Percent Increase in RPM	Percent Minimum, BHP
Forward curved	6	20
Backward inclined	4	13
Airfoil	3	9

Fan discharge into an after-filter plenum must, in addition to the bulkheading losses, take into account the damage to filters, especially the bag type, from their being with high velocity air from a short distance. For this reason either 2-inch thick, cleanable metal prefilters or a perforated metal *splash* plate, set in front of the after-filter bank, will protect the after-filters from damage. Unfortunately, this also adds a slight pressure loss for the fan to overcome. The pressure loss for 2-inch thick, cleanable filters would generally not exceed 0.10-inch water gauge, while a perforated metal splash plates resistance depends on the perforation size and free area. This loss can be obtained by referring to air performance data of perforated grilles or small lattice grilles in the catalog of any air grille manufacturer.

Duct Turns: Duct turns, immediately off the fan discharge, create a higher than expected static pressure drop due to turbulence and to the velocity profile existing at the discharge.

When an elbow must be used at the fan discharge, it is not recommended that a short-radius elbow be attached directly to the fan discharge. Preferably, a medium-radius elbow should be used (minimum mean radius 1.5 × equivalent duct diameter); alternately a one diameter length of straight duct followed by a cascade square elbow will give a lower loss but only if the catalog outlet velocity is below 2000 fpm to minimize noise generation problems.

Assuming that a medium-radius elbow of rectangular cross-section is fitted to the fan discharge, the elbow can turn the air in any one of four directions. If the fan discharge velocity were uniform, one could readily calculate the loss in the elbow and whatever direction the elbow faced would be immaterial. With a spiraling nonuniform discharge velocity, one cannot apply any of the normal elbow and duct friction factors. These only apply when the flow is uniform across the duct without any spiral. If the flow were uniform, such an elbow would have a pressure loss of 0.25 × fan outlet velocity.

The flow in a fan discharge elbow differs in each of the four positions for both single-inlet and double-inlet fans (Fig. 14-51 for an illustration of the four positions). For position A the high flow velocity is on the same side of the scroll and the elbow. This will result in the lowest loss of the four positions. It should be used whenever possible. Assume a loss equal to 0.5 × catalogued outlet velocity head for both SI and DI fans. For position B this is the second lowest loss position for an SI fan; the high velocity out of the scroll continues to the outside of the elbow. Assume a loss equal to 0.60 × catalogued outlet velocity head for SI fans and 0.75 catalogued outlet velocity head for DI fans. The DI loss is higher than the SI loss because the peak velocity out of the fan discharge is at the center and it must be diverted to the outside of the elbow. Energy must be expended to shift the flow and, consequently, an additional loss is introduced.

For position *C* assume a loss equal to 1.0 × catalogued outlet velocity for both type fans. In SI and DI fans the peak discharge velocity is on the opposite side of the elbow than is usual. The resulting flow redistribution results in high losses. This position is the most unfavorable of the four.

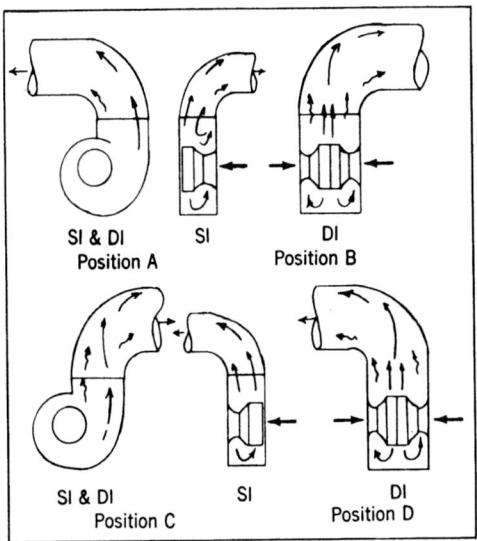

Fig 14-51. Discharge elbow flow patterns

For position *D*, assume 0.90 × catalogued outlet velocity head for SI fans and 0.75 × catalogued outlet velocity for DI fans. The SI fan has its peak discharge velocity from the fan discharge at the opposite side from that which is normal for an elbow. As a result the velocity redistribution in this situation results in a higher loss than for DI fans where the peak discharge velocity is centered as in position *B*. These loss factors are approximate only, but they do establish an approximate level of loss for design purposes.

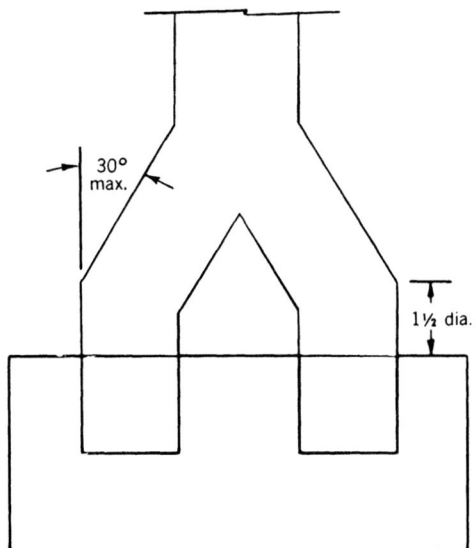

Fig 14-52. Proper construction of a pants connection on a two-fan unit

Fans are frequently installed in factory-fabricated rectangular enclosures called cabinets. Cabinet fans often

have two fans discharging into a common duct by a pants connection. Fig. 14-52 shows the requirements of the pants connection to achieve catalog performance. There should be $1\frac{1}{2}$ equivalent fan diameters of straight duct before the transition, with the convergence angle a maximum of 30° on each side. If these design parameters cannot be met, the fan discharge is treated as though it were a free discharge into a plenum, and bulkheading losses are then used.

Fan Performance Modulation: Some fan systems have changing air requirements during operation, such as variable air volume systems, while others have changing pressure requirements; both air flow and pressure are often altered during operation. To accommodate these changes, some form of fan performance modulation is required. The types of modulation typically used in ducted applications are:

Scroll Volume Control: This is discussed under "System Surge, Fan Surge, and Paralleling" on page 11.

Scroll volume dampers are sometimes used on small, single-fan utility sets as a means of quickly adjusting the air delivery. However, it is not considered as a good means of capacity control. Efficiency is reduced and the very nature of outlet volume control makes it difficult to operate automatically off a static pressure-sensing device. Thus, while the scroll volume damper serves a useful purpose in controlling the paralleling of fans, it is not recommended for capacity modulation.

Inlet Dampers: The primary purpose of inlet dampers, or face dampers, as they are better known in central station units, is for the prevention of backdraft and air circulation when the unit is shut down.

Inlet dampers merely add resistance to the system and cause a corresponding change in static pressure at the fan to vary the *cfm*.

There are two basic drawbacks to inlet dampers. First, they allow little capacity modulation unless the operator forces the fan to operate in an unstable part of its performance range. Second, since they are frequently mounted in front of an outside air opening or in front of a coil bank, they are much larger in size than the fan inlet. Thus, the static pressure differential across the damper is spread over a large area.

Because of this second drawback, care must be taken to make sure that the fan is not capable of producing a static pressure sufficient to warp or cave-in the dampers. Static pressure differential across most face dampers used on central station air-handling units should not exceed 4 inches, total. If the fan is capable of developing more than this static pressure at the operating RPM, care must be taken to insure that face dampers cannot be closed while the fan is operating. If the dampers are used for trimming the system, a manual stop can be put in the damper linkage to prevent them from closing completely. For an on-off shutoff to prevent air circulation, damper motors should be installed to close the dampers only after the fan motor has shut off; conversely, the fan motor should not start until these dampers are at least partly opened. This can be done by an end switch on the dampers, which precludes fan motor operation when the dampers are completely closed and will permit fan operation only when the dampers are sufficiently opened to avert high suction static pressure.

Discharge Dampers: Discharge dampers are a method of varying the *cfm* over a rather narrow performance range.

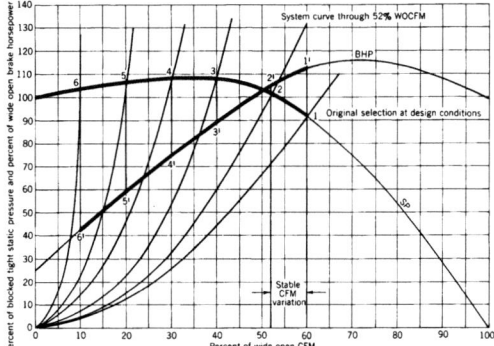

Fig 14-53. Discharge damper performance for air foil fan

Since discharge dampers are typically mounted on the fan discharge, the area of the dampers is relatively small. Thus, there is generally no need to worry about excessive static pressure damaging the dampers. They will operate satisfactorily at block-tight conditions unless fan static pressure exceeds the structural capability of the dampers. Normally, the damper strength should withstand at least 4 inches of static pressure.

Fig. 14-53 shows fan performance with discharge dampers. These dampers increase system static pressure to modulate the *cfm*. Discharge dampers do not change the unstable area of the fan. Thus, they should not be used for *cfm* modulation with AF centrifugal fans below about 50% of wide open *cfm*, as this figure indicates.

Neither discharge dampers nor inlet dampers have much effect on the system noise level in the wide open position on low and medium pressure applications. However, they do increase the noise level as they near a closed position. The magnitude of the increase is a function of the air velocity and static pressure differential.

Inlet Vanes: Inlet vanes are sometimes given the misnomer of vortex dampers. Actually, these vanes are not dampers; their sole purpose is to impart a swirl to the air in the direction of rotation as it enters the fan. The resulting vorticity results in a reduction in *cfm*, static pressure, and brake horsepower. Moreover, for every position of the inlet vanes, separate curves for static pressure and brake horsepower versus *cfm* are generated.

As these vanes are modulated, the brake horsepower curve generated is lower than the brake horsepower curve with the vanes wide open. Therefore, inlet vanes do provide some operating cost savings. The magnitude of these savings is generally about 20 to 30% if the vanes are operated a majority of the time in the range of 60 to 80% of design *cfm*. Since inlet vanes cost two to three times as much as parallel blade discharge dampers, it doesn't pay to use them unless capacity reduction is at least 50% for long periods of time, since its horsepower savings over parallel and opposed blade dampers average about 25% under these conditions.

Quite apart from economics, inlet vanes are useful for capacity reduction on large centrifugal fans requiring BHP of more than 100, fans that are equipped with direct drive. This need results from the difficulty of using V-belt, variable-speed drives on such large fans.

There are three drawbacks in using inlet vanes for capacity modulation: First, the fan can be forced to operate in an unstable range with inlet vanes. This is most likely to occur when the vanes are used to modulate a constant static pressure system. The resultant noise and vibration has been known to shake an entire floor.

Secondly, capacity reduction also occurs when the inlet blades are in the wide-open position, as is shown in Fig. 14-49. Construction of the vanes with the hub and turning mechanism located in the center creates a pressure drop, the magnitude of which is a function of the fan size. For very small fans, the hub is a relatively large percentage of the total inlet area. Thus, the capacity reduction is substantial. On the other hand, with very large fans, the hub area is a very small percentage of the total area and the reduction is negligible. For belt drive applications this does not present any particular problem since the fan speed can be readily increased to compensate for the reduction. However, brake horsepower also goes up with fan speed.

For example, RPM must be increased approximately 3% for a 36-inch diameter wheel to achieve full load capacity with inlet vanes in wide-open position. This increases the BHP approximately 9.3% which could be a problem if the BHP is very close to that printed on the nameplate motor horsepower.

In direct drive units, however, the use of inlet vanes becomes more of a problem. Fairly accurate means must be available for estimating the capacity reduction for various size fans.

Third, inlet vanes will increase the fan's noise level, even at wide-open position. Because test data are limited, a good rule to follow is to assume 5 db is added to the fan noise level when using inlet vanes.

Before using inlet vanes the fan manufacturer should be consulted for information regarding the unstable range of operation, the capacity reduction due to inlet area restriction, and the resultant noise levels.

Speed Modulation: Speed variation in fans can be accomplished in a number of ways, including through the use of multispeed motors, fluid drives, mechanical speed reducers, and solid state devices.

Speed modulation is not generally used in air conditioning applications and will not be discussed in detail. Typically, the cost is greater and requires more elaborate control.

Solid state devices have some merit on fractional horsepower motors and smaller integral horsepower motors. However, the control must be closely matched with the motor for the device to operate properly.

All of these devices affect fan performance in accordance with the following fan laws:

$$\frac{cfm_2}{cfm_1} = \frac{RPM_2}{RPM_1} \tag{20}$$

$$\frac{SP_2}{SP_1} = \left(\frac{RPM_2}{RPM_1}\right)^2 \tag{21}$$

$$\frac{BHP_2}{BHP_1} = \left(\frac{RPM_2}{RPM_1}\right)^3 \tag{22}$$

Care must be exercised in using this type of modulation in systems requiring constant static pressure either at the fan or at remote distribution boxes, as the static pressure at the fan reduces proportionally to the square of the RPM reduction.

Fan Blade Pitch Variation: Vaneaxial fans are available with adjustable pitch blades to permit the varying of the fan's performance. The pitch blades may be used to increase or decrease system capacity on direct drive fans, depending upon the original selection. On belt-driven pitch variations fans, the variation may allow some increase in efficiency if static pressure was grossly overestimated when the original selection was made.

This form of capacity modulation will generally reduce BHP more than any of the previous methods for a given *cfm* and static pressure. It also obviates the V-belt drive problem for larger fans requiring more than 100 BHP since control modulation can be accomplished fairly easily.

One method of fan blade pitch variation allows for a change in pitch while the fan is in operation. This makes the fan very adaptable for such applications as automatic static pressure control for variable air volume systems.

Since the vaneaxial fan generally must have acoustic treatment anyway, noise generation due to change in fan pitch is easily handled. For this reason, the greatest drawback in this type of fan modulation is the added cost of the device. The more sophisticated the modulation and its

controls, the greater the cost premium. These fans may still be cheaper, however, in both initial and operating costs than centrifugal fans with either dampers or inlet vanes.

Useful Fan Formulas.—The first is

$$Q = A \times V \tag{23}$$

where　Q = volume per unit time, usually *cfm*

A = cross-sectional flow area, usually ft^2

V = average air velocity, usually fpm

The next is

$$cfm = \frac{\text{lb/hr (air or gas)}}{60 \times \text{density}} \tag{24}$$

$$Density = 0.075\left(\frac{460° + 70°}{460° + \text{elev. temp}}\right)$$
$$= 0.075 \frac{°R\ \text{Base}}{°R\ \text{Actual}} \tag{25}$$

Air pressure is at 29.92 inch Hg and 70°F at sea level

Atmospheric pressure

　　= 14.7 psig at sea level and 70°F

　　= 407 in H$_2$O at sea level and 70°F

　　= 20.92 in Hg at sea level and 70°F

　　=33.93 ft H$_2$O at sea level and 70°F

$$TP = SP + VP \tag{26}$$

Total pressure = Static pressure + Velocity pressure

The conversion from farenheit to rankine temperature is:

$$°R = 460° + °F$$
$$= \text{Absolute temperature or } °\text{Rankine} \tag{27}$$

$$V = 1096.2 \sqrt{\frac{VP}{\text{Density}}} \tag{28}$$

$$V = 4005 \sqrt{VP} \text{ (at 0.075 lb/ft}^3) \tag{29}$$

Air horsepower:

$$\text{AHP} = \frac{cfm \times \text{TP}}{6350} = \frac{cfm \times \text{TP}}{6350} \tag{30}$$

Brake horsepower:

$$\text{BHP} = \frac{cfm \times \text{TP}}{6350 \times TE} = \frac{cfm \times \text{TP}}{6350 \times \text{Total effic.}} \tag{31}$$

$$\text{BHP} = \frac{cfm \times SP}{6359 \times SE} = \frac{cfm \times \text{SP}}{6350 \times \text{Static effic.}} \tag{32}$$

Outlet velocity:

$$OV = \frac{cfm}{\text{outlet area}} \qquad (33)$$

Conversion from celsius to farenheit temperature is

$$°F = \frac{9 \times °C}{5} + 32 \qquad (34)$$

Torque is

$$T = \frac{W \times D}{55} \qquad (35)$$

Where T = starting torque, in lb-ft

W = weight of wheel plus shaft, in lbs

D = diameter of fan bearings, in inches

The next refers to sleeve bearings. Fly wheel effect (polar moment of inertia:

Flywheel effect (polar moment of inertia):

$$WR^2 \text{(fan wheel)}= \text{wheel wgt} \times \text{radius of gyration}^2 + \qquad (36)$$
$$\text{shaft weight} \times \left(\frac{\text{shaft hub dia}}{3}\right)^2$$

The above is used direct connected fans and motors

$$WR^2 = WR^2 \text{(fan wheel)} \times \left(\frac{\text{fan RPM}}{\text{motor RPM}}\right)^2$$

For V-belt driven fans and motors:

$$SHP = \frac{\text{amps} \times \text{volts} \times \sqrt{3} \times \text{eff.} \times \text{power factor}}{746} \qquad (37)$$

where SHP = shaft horse power

Operating torque in ft-lbs is given by:

$$\text{operating torque} = \frac{SHP \times 33000}{2\pi r \times \text{RPM}}$$
$$= 5250 \times \frac{SHP}{\text{RPM}} \qquad (38)$$

Temperature rise through fan:

$$\text{Air temp. rise through a fan} = \frac{0.00278 \times SP}{SE \times \text{Density}}$$
$$= \frac{42.5 \times \text{BHP}}{\text{lb/min} \times 0.241} \qquad (39)$$

Where SP = static pressure (inches H_2O)

SE = static efficiency

0.241 = specific heat of air

42.5 = constant

0.00278 = constant

Monographs for Fan Horsepower and Actual Capacity.—The monographs that follow are for use in solving problems in air handling (Fig. 14-54, 14-55).

In either nomograph, should a quantity be involved that exceeds the range of any of the scales, it may be divided by any number (10, 100, and 1000 are most convenient) and the reduced number used. Each time a quantity has been reduced by division, the answer must be multiplied by the same number it has been divided by.

The fan horsepower nomograph on this page is a solution of the equation:

$$\text{BHP} = \frac{0.01573 \times P \times cfm}{\text{efficiency}} \qquad (40)$$

Example 7: What BHP is required to drive a 95% efficient blower in order to deliver 150,000 *cfm* at a pressure of 3 inches of water?

Solution: Since 3 inches of water is outside the range of the pressure scale on Fig. 14-54, divide by 10 and use 0.3. Then, align E = 95% with P = 0.3 (dashed line 1), marking its intersection with the pivot line. Since 150,000 *cfm* is outside the range of the *cfm* scale, divide it, also, by 10 and use 15,000. Through the intersection of line 1 and the pivot line, draw a line through *cfm* = 15,000, and read BHP = 0.745 (line 2). Because 2 quantities were divided by 10, the answer must be multiplied 2 by 10. Therefore, the answer is 74.5 BHP.

The second nomograph is based on the following equation:

$$scfm = \frac{acfm \times (68 + 460)(P_g + 14.7)}{14.7(T + 460)} \qquad (41)$$

Example 8: If a dryer can handle 41,000 standard ft^3 of air per minute (*scfm*) at 66 psig and 1940°F, what is the actual cfm (*acfm*) it is handling at those conditions?

Solution: In order to bring the given data within the scales of the nomograph in Fig. 14-55, *scfm* is divided by 1000. Align *scfm* = 41 with P_g = 66 (dashed line). Through the intersection of this line and the pivot line, draw another through T = 1940°F. Read *acfm* = 1000 × 34 = 34,000 *cfm*.

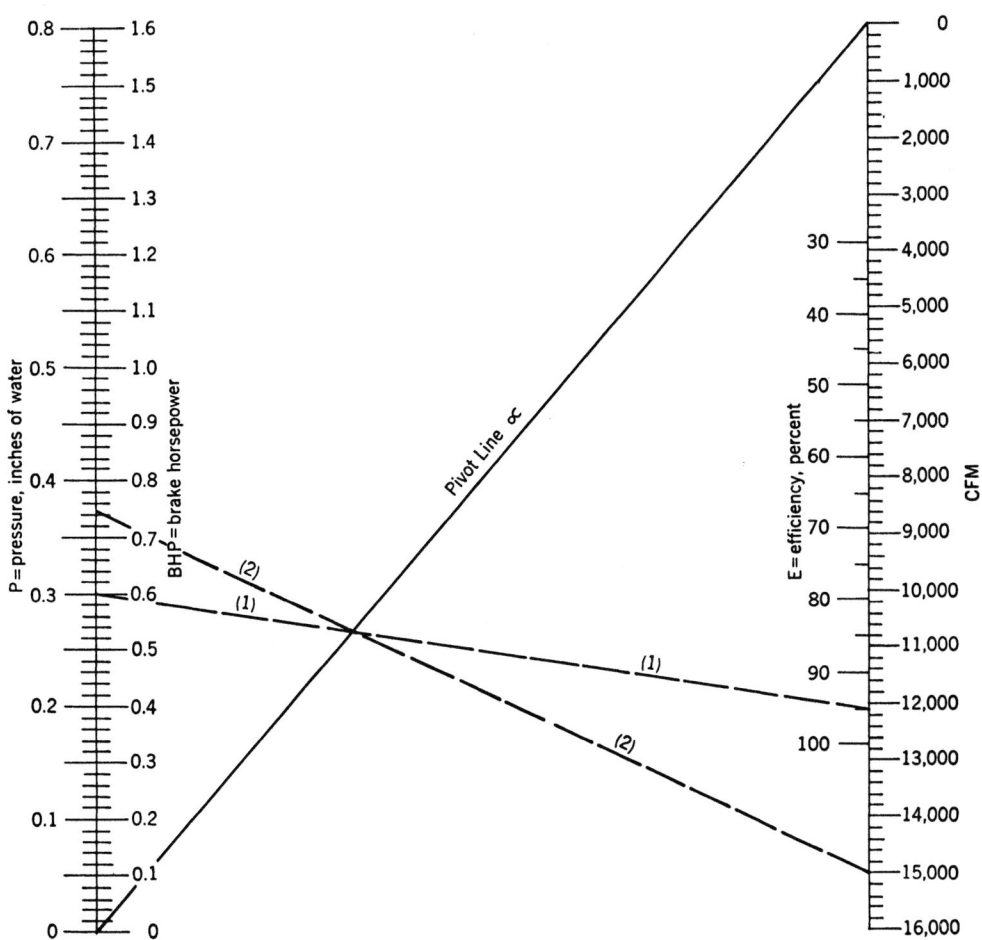

Fig 14-54. Nomograph for fan HP and actual capacity in *cfm*

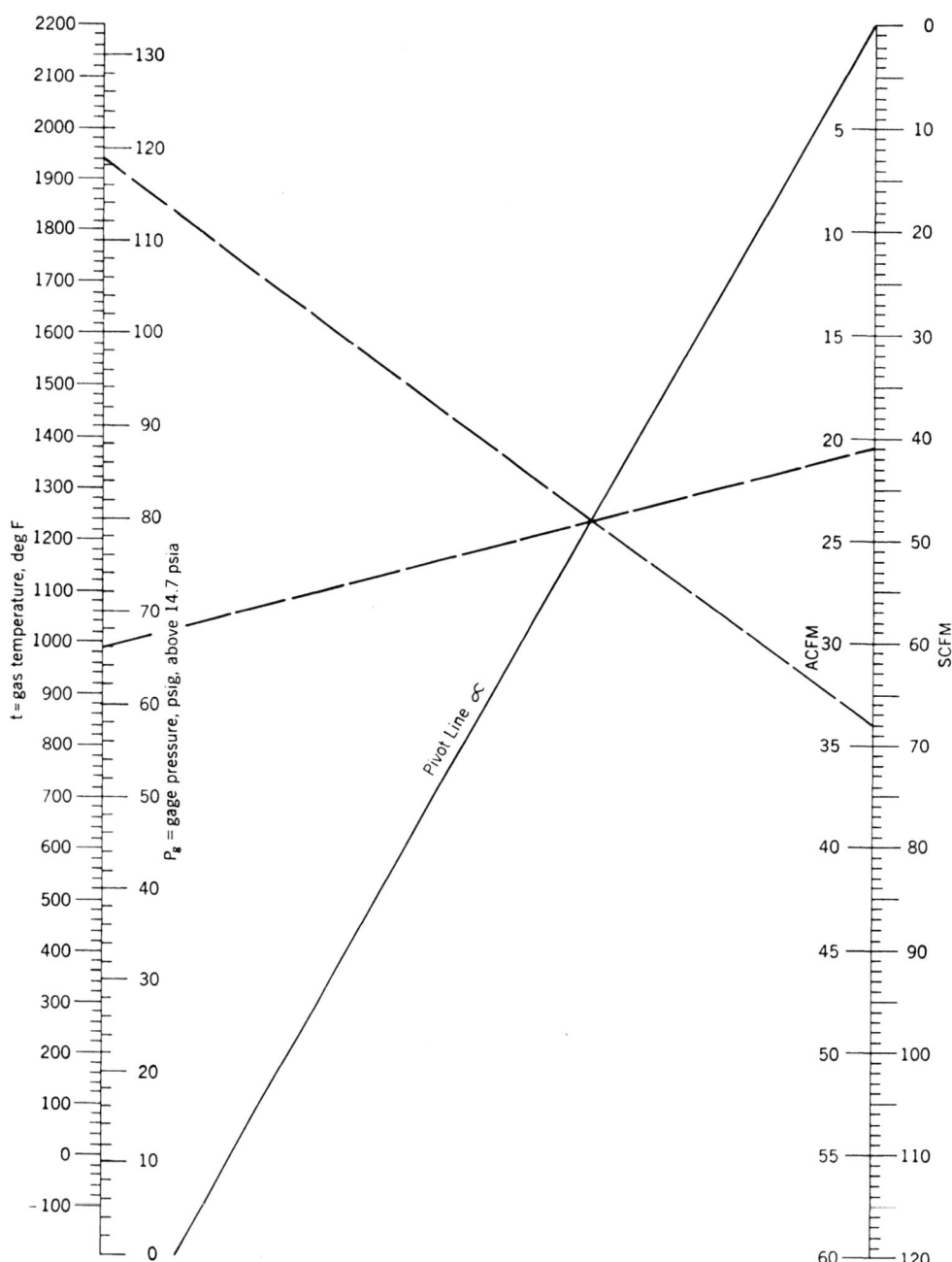

Fig 14-55. Nomograph for pressure and actual capacity in *cfm*

Fan Selection Questionnaire.—To assist the designer in a systematic procedure for selection of the proper fan and drive, a fan selection questionnaire, as given below, lists a logical progression of steps in the choice of fan and drive for a specific application.

Fan Selection

Manufacturer:

Air Temperature density:

Fan *cfm* at design temperature and density:

Fan SP corrected to standard conditions: inch of water gauge

Type of fan: (Centrifugal, roof-top, axial flow, tubular centrifugal)

Fan speed (corrected for inlet and discharge factors):   RPM

Wheel diameter:

Tip speed: FPM

Outlet velocity: FPM

Fan width and inlet: (I, II, III)

Class:

Arrangement:

Discharge:

Rotation:

Fan curve: Is operating point on the negative slope?

Fan efficiency:

Fan Motor

BHP (corrected for inlet and discharge factors)

Motor HP:

Voltage: (Open drip-proof, splash-proof, TE, TE-explosion proof)

NEMA frame no.:

Single speed or 2-speed:

2-Speed RPMs:

Fans polar moment of inertia, WR^2 for acceleration characteristic of motor drive:

Special motor (description):

Fan Drive

V-Belt:

Direct:

Special:

Fan Construction

Type of bearings:

Housing material:

Wheel material:

Birdscreen-mesh and material:

Drain in fan housing:

Adjustable inlet vanes:

Gravity discharge dampers:

Cleanout doors:

If fan is operating in parallel, show curves for single and parallel operation. Also, select motor for non-overloading capability.

Is fan flywheel effect (WR^2) large enough to require special starting? (See Chapter 17 on *MOTORS AND STARTERS* later in this Handbook, for proper motor and starter selection.)

Type of fan performance modulation control:

Example 9 Fan Comparison: The following example is intended to show the factors that are taken into account when a fan selection is made. In this case, the engineer is looking for a fan which will deliver 75000 *cfm* of standard air against a static pressure of 8.0 inches wg. This fan will have a free inlet and bulkheaded discharge into a sound-attenuated plenum. Capacity control is required.

The following fans are considered as feasible.selections:

Fan No.	Type	Arrangement No.	Type of Capacity and Control
1	Airfoil centrifugal DWDI (Double width, double inlet)	4	Inlet vanes
2	Air foil centrifugal DWDI	3	Inlet vanes
3	Inline tubular centrifugal	9	Inlet vanes
4	Vaneaxial	4	Controllable pitch

Note: Fans 1 and 4 have direct drive and fans 2 and 3 are driven by vee-belts. All fans are Class III fans. Fan 4 has a bell mounted inlet and a sound trap on the suction side.

Flywheel Effect: Fan motors and drives for most small fans can be selected on the basis of full-load horsepower and speed alone. However, in larger fans, it is advisable to examine the starting characteristics of the fan-drive combination. Since this involves breakaway torques, speed-torque relations, flywheel effect, acceleration time, temperature effects, etc. It is beyond the scope of this handbook to cover these items. However the fan manufacturer can readily supply all information necessary for fan load characteristics. The engineer can also find several excellent references on this subject.

Since there is a dramatic difference in flywheel effect between the centrifugal fans and the vaneaxial fan in this example, the polar moment of inertia WR^2 for each fan rotor is:

Fan No.	WR^2
1	1910
2	1910
3	8100
4	210

The above flywheel effects are for the fan rotors only, not the drives.

Octave Band cps	Fan 1	Fan 2	Fan 3	Fan 4
	(Certified Sound Power Level Decibels)			
1-63	117	113	120	101
2-125	118	116	113	98
3-250	109	111	111	107
4-500	106	106	107	120
5-1000	103	103	103	116
6-2000	97	98	98	114
7-4000	94	95	93	109
8-8000	92	92	88	105

Note: These are AMCA-certified values without any attenuation. Fans 1, 2, 3 have comparable sound power spectra, with higher values at the low frequencies which the human ear can better tolerate. Fan 4 has somewhat lower values in the low frequencies, but significantly higher values in the higher frequencies, but significantly

higher values in the higher frequencies. This is what gives the vaneaxial fan its shrill sound, akin to a jet engine. For this reason, it is usually necessary to acoustically treat both the inlet and discharge of the vaneaxial fan with sound trapping. Such sound treatment will make the vaneaxial fan as quiet as, or quieter than, Fans 1, 2, or 3.

As can be seen from this example, the retardant effect of the polar moment of inertia is high for the tubular centrifugal fan and very low for the vaneaxial; or conversely, the vaneaxial fan can come to rated speed much faster than can the centrifugal fans.

The comparative cost of each of these four types of fan is a difficult area to evaluate because of the wide range of fan quality. For larger fans (such as those in the example), the tubular centrifugal would probably be about twice the cost of the specified vaneaxial. Fans 1 and 2 would be higher (somewhere around 35 to 50%) in installed cost than the vaneaxial, but considerably lower than the tubular centrifugal.

Table 14-3. Fan Performance Data

Performance Requirement	Fan 1	Fan 2	Fan 3	Fan 4
System resistance, inches wg	8.0	8.0	8.0	8.0
Velocity pressure, including "bulkhead," inches wg	0.375	0.375	0.125	1.10
Added sound attention				
Total pressure, inches wg	8.375	8.375	8.125	9.32
cfm of standard air	75000	75000	75000	75000
RPM for rated conditions	1140	1041	800	1770
BHP for rated conditions and RPM	123	123	126	132
V-belt drive loss on fan RPM, percent		4	4	
RPM required because of V-belts	1140	1081	832	1770
BHP required because of V-belts	123	135	138	132
Inlet vane loss on fan BHP, percent		3	3	
RPM required because of inlet vanes	1140	1113	857	1770
BHP required because of inlet vanes	141	147	150	132
Static efficiency, percent	67.0	64.0	63.0	73.0
Overall total efficiency, percent	70.5	67.5	64.0	83.5

Fan Weights

Fan No.	Weight less Motor, lbs	Installed Weight with Motor Inertia Block and Isolators, lbs
1	3800	13000
2	3800	13000
3	7200	17000
4	970	3000

Installed Cubage

Fan No.	Volume, ft³
1	880
2	1080
3	1152
4	245

For smaller fan sizes, the relative installed cost differential would tend to lessen.

Conclusions:

1) Based on economics alone, the vaneaxial fan (fan no 4) would have an advantage both in operating cost (because of a better overall efficiency) and in first cost.

2) Based on sound data, the vaneaxial fan is the least attractive selection and would certainly require sound attenuation both upstream and downstream. However,

even with the added sound trap, Fan no 4 might still cost less initially.

3) Other considerations such as direction of fan discharge, may dictate the use of fans 1 and 2 over fans 3 and 4.

4) While these fans were selected for a free inlet and a bulkheaded discharge, this is not the most general requirement for HVAC. Usually, there are filters, coils, etc., upstream of the fan, and very often a duct connection on the discharges. This set of parameters may give fans 1, 2, or 3 a decided advantage over fan no 4 because of sound-trapping requirements.

5) For variable volume control, fan no 4 is the best in terms of efficiency, and probably also best in terms of case and range of control. Inlet vane control simply cannot match controlled pitch.

The main theme of this example is that there are many considerations in properly selecting a fan, particularly a large fan. The engineer must evaluate them all for any particular application.

Air Flow in Ducts

Air flowing in ducts or pipes is characterized by three pressures: static pressure, velocity pressure, and total pressure.

Static pressure P_s is the pressure exerted normal to the direction of flow. Atmospheric pressure is usually taken as the zero datum, so static pressures less than atmospheric are negative. Static pressure is analogous to potential energy.

Velocity pressure P_v is the pressure in the direction of flow equivalent to the kinetic energy of motion of the gas. Since velocity pressure is always measured in the direction of flow, numerical values are always positive.

Total pressure P_t is the algebraic sum of P_s and P_v.

The basic equation for the velocity of a gas is

$$V = 1096.5 \sqrt{\frac{P_v}{W}} \qquad (42)$$

where V is the velocity in fpm, P_v is the velocity pressure in inches water gage, and W is the gas density in lbs/ft^3. For standard air at 29.92 inches of mercury and 70 °F, $W = 0.07495$, and Equation (41) becomes

$$V = 4005 \sqrt{P_v} \qquad (43)$$

Air density varies with temperature, pressure, and water vapor content. Velocity equivalents of velocity pressures for non standard air may be found from Equation (41). However, in order to speed computation and eliminate extraction of the square root, a correction factor method has been developed. If CF, the correction factor, is defined as the square root of the ratio, 0.07495 divided by W, Equation (41) becomes

$$V = (4005 \sqrt{P_v})(CF) \qquad (44)$$

P_v values is given in Table 14-4. Values of CF are given in Table 14-5 for various densities. Air densities may be obtained from psychrometric charts and tables for most conditions. For moisture laden air beyond this range, densities may be obtained from Fig. 14-56.

Air Tempera-ture, °F	Constant in Equation (42)	Air Tempera-ture, °F	Constant in Equation (42)
35	3872	75	4025
40	3891	80	4045
45	3910	85	4064
50	3932	90	4081
55	3952	95	4101
65	3987	100	4117
70	4005	150	4268

Dry air density W_d is given by the equation

$$W_d = 0.07495 \left(\frac{530}{°F + 460}\right)\left(\frac{P_{abs}}{29.92}\right) \qquad (45)$$

Where P_{abs} is the absolute pressure in inches of mercury.

The procedures to be followed for nonstandard conditions are as follows:

To Find P_v for a Known Velocity.—Divide known velocity by CF from Table 14-5 to determine equivalent velocity. Determine P_v from equivalent velocity using Table 14-4.

Example 10: What is velocity pressure of air at 560°F, 0.2 lb moisture per lb dry air, if its velocity is 3000 fpm?

Solution: From Fig. 14-56, $W = 0.0355$. From Table 14-5, CF = 1.46 (by interpolation between $W = 0.03$ and $W = 0.04$). Dividing the known velocity 3000 fpm by the correction factor, the equivalent velocity of 2040 fpm is found. From Table 14-4, the velocity pressure is seen to be 0.026 wg.

To Determine V for a Known P_v.—Determine equivalent velocity for P_v from Table 14-4. Multiply equivalent velocity by CF to determine actual velocity.

Example: What is the velocity of saturated air at 180°F if the velocity pressure reading is 1.42?

Solution: From Table 14-4, if $P_v = 1.42$, $V = 4772.5$ fpm for standard air. From Fig. 14-56, $W = 0.050$, and from Table 14-4, CF = 1.22. Dividing V by CF, the velocity is found to be 3912 fpm.

To Determine Average Velocity.—From a number of P_v readings as in a pitot traverse (discussed below), determine the equivalent velocities using Table 14-4, then average the equivalent velocities. Multiply the average equivalent velocity by the correction factor CF from Table 14-5.

Table 14-4. Velocity Equivalents of Velocity Pressures

Pressure P_v in of Water	Velocity V fpm	Pressure P_v in of Water	Velocity V fpm	Pressure P_v in of Water	Velocity V fpm	Pressure P_v in of Water	Velocity V fpm	Pressure P_v in of Water	Velocity V fpm	Pressure P_v in of Water	Velocity V fpm	Pressure P_v in of Water	Velocity V fpm	Pressure P_v in of Water	Velocity V fpm
0.01	400.5	0.43	2626.3	0.85	3692.4	1.27	4513.4	1.69	5206.5	2.11	5817.6	2.53	6370.3	2.95	6878.8
0.02	566.4	0.44	2656.6	0.86	3714.1	1.28	4531.1	1.70	5221.9	2.12	5831.4	2.54	6382.9	2.96	6890.5
0.03	693.7	0.45	2686.6	0.87	3735.6	1.29	4548.8	1.71	5237.2	2.13	5845.1	2.55	6395.5	2.97	6902.1
0.04	801.0	0.46	2716.3	0.88	3757.0	1.30	4566.4	1.72	5252.5	2.14	5858.8	2.56	6408.0	2.98	6913.7
0.05	895.5	0.47	2745.7	0.89	3778.3	1.31	4583.9	1.73	5267.8	2.15	5872.5	2.57	6420.5	2.99	6925.3
0.06	981.0	0.48	2774.7	0.90	3799.5	1.32	4601.4	1.74	5283.0	2.16	5886.1	2.58	6433.0	3.00	6936.9
0.07	1059.6	0.49	2803.5	0.91	3820.5	1.33	4618.8	1.75	5298.1	2.17	5899.7	2.59	6445.4	3.01	6948.4
0.08	1132.8	0.50	2832.0	0.92	3841.5	1.34	4636.1	1.76	5313.2	2.18	5913.3	2.60	6457.9	3.02	6959.9
0.09	1201.5	0.51	2860.1	0.93	3862.4	1.35	4653.4	1.77	5328.3	2.19	5926.9	2.61	6470.3	3.03	6971.5
0.10	1266.5	0.52	2888.0	0.94	3883.0	1.36	4670.6	1.78	5343.3	2.2	5940.4	2.62	6482.7	3.04	6983.0
0.11	1328.3	0.53	2915.7	0.95	3903.6	1.37	4687.7	1.79	5358.3	2.21	5953.9	2.63	6495.0	3.05	6994.4
0.12	1387.4	0.54	2943.1	0.96	3924.1	1.38	4704.8	1.80	5373.3	2.22	5967.3	2.64	6507.4	3.06	7005.9
0.13	1444.0	0.55	2970.2	0.97	3944.5	1.39	4721.8	1.81	5388.2	2.23	5980.7	2.65	6519.7	3.07	7017.3
0.14	1498.5	0.56	2997.1	0.98	3964.7	1.40	4738.8	1.82	5403.0	2.24	5994.1	2.66	6532.0	3.08	7028.7
0.15	1551.1	0.57	3023.7	0.99	3984.9	1.41	4755.7	1.83	5417.9	2.25	6007.5	2.67	6544.2	3.09	7040.1
0.16	1602.0	0.58	3050.1	1.00	4005.0	1.42	4772.5	1.84	5432.6	2.26	6020.8	2.68	6556.5	3.10	7051.5
0.17	1651.3	0.59	3076.3	1.01	4025.0	1.43	4789.3	1.85	5447.4	2.27	6034.1	2.69	6568.7	3.11	7062.9
0.18	1699.2	0.60	3102.3	1.02	4044.9	1.44	4806.0	1.86	5462.1	2.28	6047.4	2.70	6580.9	3.12	7074.2
0.19	1745.7	0.61	3128.0	1.03	4064.6	1.45	4822.7	1.87	5476.8	2.29	6060.7	2.71	6593.1	3.13	7085.6
0.20	1791.1	0.62	3153.5	1.04	4084.3	1.46	4839.3	1.88	5491.4	2.30	6073.9	2.72	6605.2	3.14	7096.9
0.21	1835.3	0.63	3178.9	1.05	4103.9	1.47	4855.8	1.89	5506.0	2.31	6087.1	2.73	6617.3	3.15	7108.2
0.22	1878.5	0.64	3204.0	1.06	4123.4	1.48	4872.3	1.90	5520.5	2.32	6100.2	2.74	6629.5	3.16	7119.4
0.23	1920.7	0.65	3228.9	1.07	4142.8	1.49	4888.7	1.91	5535.0	2.33	6113.4	2.75	6641.5	3.17	7130.7
0.24	1962.0	0.66	3253.7	1.08	4162.1	1.50	4905.1	1.92	5549.5	2.34	6126.5	2.76	6653.6	3.18	7141.9
0.25	2002.5	0.67	3278.2	1.09	4181.3	1.51	4921.4	1.93	5563.9	2.35	6139.5	2.77	6665.6	3.19	7153.2
0.26	2042.2	0.68	3302.6	1.10	4200.5	1.52	4937.7	1.94	5578.3	2.36	6152.6	2.78	6677.7	3.20	7164.4
0.27	2081.1	0.69	3326.8	1.11	4219.5	1.53	4953.9	1.95	5592.7	2.37	6165.6	2.79	6689.7	3.21	7175.5
0.28	2119.2	0.70	3350.8	1.12	4238.5	1.54	4970.1	1.96	5607.0	2.38	6178.6	2.80	6701.6	3.22	7186.7
0.29	2156.8	0.71	3374.7	1.13	4257.4	1.55	4986.2	1.97	5621.3	2.39	6191.6	2.81	6713.6	3.23	7197.9
0.30	2193.6	0.72	3398.4	1.14	4276.2	1.56	5002.2	1.98	5635.5	2.40	6204.5	2.82	6725.5	3.24	7209.0
0.31	2229.9	0.73	3421.9	1.15	4294.9	1.57	5018.3	1.99	5649.7	2.41	6217.4	2.83	6737.5	3.25	7220.1
0.32	2265.6	0.74	3445.2	1.16	4313.5	1.58	5034.2	2.00	5663.9	2.42	6230.3	2.84	6749.3	3.26	7231.2
0.33	2300.7	0.75	3468.4	1.17	4332.1	1.59	5050.1	2.01	5678.1	2.43	6243.2	2.85	6761.2	3.27	7242.3
0.34	2335.3	0.76	3491.5	1.18	4350.5	1.60	5066.0	2.02	5692.2	2.44	6256.0	2.86	6773.1	3.28	7253.4
0.35	2369.4	0.77	3514.4	1.19	4368.9	1.61	5081.8	2.03	5706.2	2.45	6268.8	2.87	6784.9	3.29	7264.4
0.36	2403.0	0.78	3537.1	1.20	4387.3	1.62	5097.5	2.04	5720.3	2.46	6281.6	2.88	6796.7	3.30	7275.4
0.37	2436.1	0.79	3559.7	1.21	4405.5	1.63	5113.2	2.05	5734.3	2.47	6294.4	2.89	6808.5	3.31	7286.5
0.38	2468.8	0.80	3582.2	1.22	4423.7	1.64	5128.9	2.06	5748.3	2.48	6307.1	2.90	6820.3	3.32	7297.5
0.39	2501.1	0.81	3604.5	1.23	4441.8	1.65	5144.5	2.07	5762.2	2.49	6319.8	2.91	6832.0	3.33	7308.4
0.40	2533.0	0.82	3626.7	1.24	4459.8	1.66	5160.1	2.08	5776.1	2.50	6332.5	2.92	6843.7	3.34	7319.4
0.41	2564.5	0.83	3648.7	1.25	4477.7	1.67	5175.6	2.09	5790.0	2.51	6345.1	2.93	6855.5	3.35	7330.4
0.42	2595.5	0.84	3670.6	1.26	4495.6	1.68	5191.1	2.10	5803.8	2.52	6357.7	2.94	6867.1	3.36	7341.3

Table 14-5. Correction factors to be Applied to Table 14-4 for Non-Standard Air

Gas Density lb/ft³	Correction Factor	Gas Density lb/ft³	Correction Factor
0.01	2.74	0.08	0.968
0.02	1.94	0.09	0.913
0.03	1.58	0.10	0.866
0.04	1.37	0.11	0.825
0.05	1.22	0.12	0.790
0.06	1.12	0.13	0.759
0.07	1.03	0.14	0.732
0.075	1.000	0.15	0.707

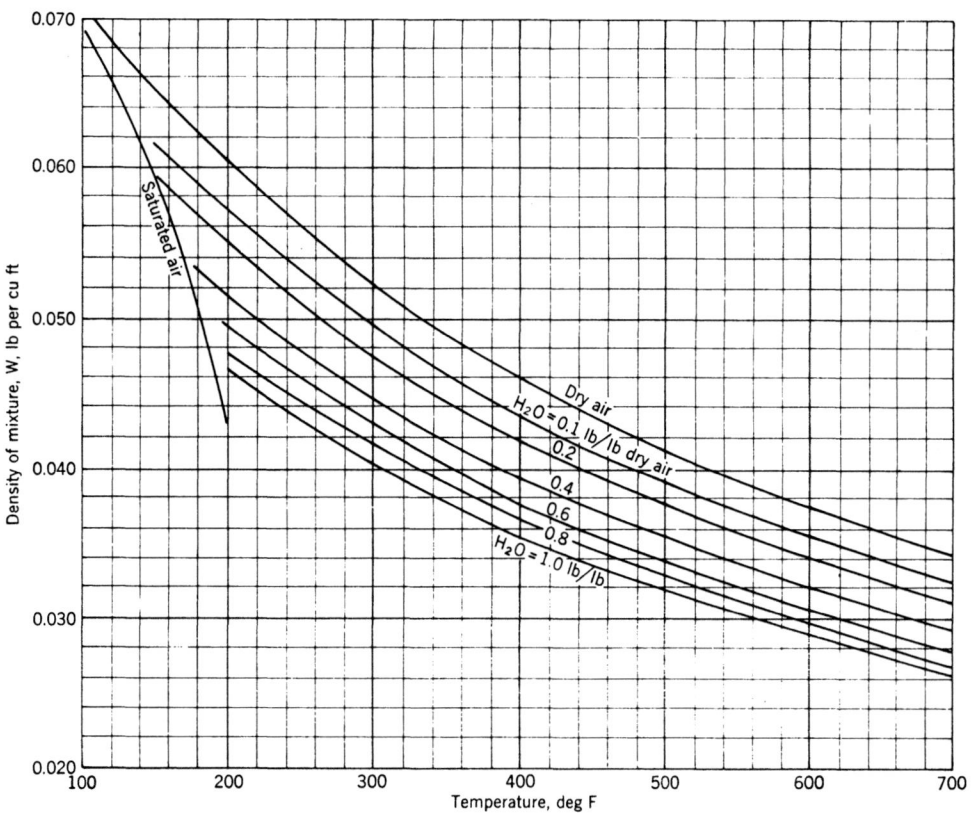

Fig 14-56. Density of air water vapor mixtures lb/ft³ of mixture 100 to 700°F

Table 14-6. Pitot Traverse Points for Round Duct (10-Point Traverse)

		Duct Diameter, in.						
		12	16	20	24	30	36	48
Point	% of Diameter			Distance Inward from Side Wall, in.				
1	1.95	$\frac{1}{4}$	$\frac{5}{16}$	$\frac{3}{8}$	$\frac{7}{16}$	$\frac{9}{19}$	$\frac{11}{16}$	$\frac{15}{16}$
2	8.15	1	$1\frac{5}{16}$	$1\frac{5}{8}$	$1\frac{15}{16}$	$2\frac{7}{16}$	$2\frac{15}{16}$	$3\frac{15}{16}$
3	14.65	$1\frac{3}{4}$	$2\frac{5}{16}$	$2\frac{15}{16}$	$3\frac{1}{2}$	$4\frac{3}{8}$	$5\frac{1}{4}$	$7\frac{1}{16}$
4	22.60	$2\frac{11}{16}$	$3\frac{5}{8}$	$4\frac{1}{2}$	$5\frac{7}{16}$	$6\frac{3}{4}$	$8\frac{1}{8}$	$10\frac{7}{8}$
5	34.20	$4\frac{1}{8}$	$5\frac{1}{2}$	$6\frac{13}{16}$	$8\frac{3}{16}$	$10\frac{1}{4}$	$12\frac{5}{16}$	$16\frac{7}{16}$
6	65.80	$7\frac{7}{8}$	$10\frac{1}{2}$	$13\frac{3}{16}$	$15\frac{13}{16}$	$19\frac{3}{4}$	$23\frac{11}{16}$	$31\frac{9}{16}$
7	77.40	$9\frac{5}{16}$	$12\frac{3}{8}$	$15\frac{1}{2}$	$18\frac{9}{16}$	$23\frac{1}{4}$	$27\frac{7}{8}$	$37\frac{1}{8}$
8	85.35	$10\frac{1}{4}$	$13\frac{11}{16}$	$17\frac{1}{16}$	$21\frac{1}{2}$	$25\frac{5}{8}$	$30\frac{3}{4}$	$41\frac{1}{16}$
9	91.85	11	$14\frac{11}{16}$	$18\frac{3}{8}$	$22\frac{1}{16}$	$27\frac{9}{16}$	$33\frac{1}{16}$	$44\frac{1}{16}$
10	98.05	$11\frac{3}{4}$	$15\frac{11}{16}$	$19\frac{5}{8}$	$23\frac{1}{2}$	$39\frac{7}{16}$	$35\frac{5}{16}$	$47\frac{1}{16}$

Pitot Traverse.—Air volumes flowing in a duct are frequently determined by traversing the duct with a standard Pitot tube. The Pitot tube reads P_v directly in inches of water. A Pitot traverse should be made only at a point where relatively uniform velocities exist, such as seven or more duct diameters downstream from the nearest elbow, branch entry damper, or like flow disturbance. For rectangular duct, the cross-section of the duct should hypothetically divided into 12 or more equal areas and a Pitot reading taken at the center of each area. For round ducts, Table 3 gives the distance inward from the side wall for each traverse point in order that readings be taken at the center of equal annular areas. If readings are taken at such equal area points, the average velocity may be determined from the simple arithmetic average of velocities at each point. Do not average the velocity pressures. For small ducts of 6 inches in diameter or less, average velocities may be estimated by taking 0.81 times the centerline velocity.

Friction Losses.—Duct friction varies directly with duct length, inversely with duct diameter, as the square of the velocity of the gas flowing, and with a friction factor. Because the friction factor varies in a rather complex way with roughness of the duct Reynolds number, and with viscosity of the gas flowing, and because these factors are not constants but are in turn dependent upon other factors, the formulas that describe gas flow are time-consuming in their application. Therefore, the application engineer depends upon friction charts, such as are presented here. Figs. 14-58a, and 14-58b give friction losses in standard round galvanized duct for standard air pressure. Figs. 14-59a gives friction losses in round aluminum ducts. Knowing any two of the three factors (1) duct diameter, (2) air velocity, and (3) air flow rate, the third factor and the friction loss may be determined. Examples of friction chart manipulations are shown in Figs. 14-60a, 14-60b, and 14-60c.

Correction for Roughness.—For duct materials other than galvanized iron or aluminum, roughness correction factors given in Fig. 14-57 should be applied. Table 14-7 may be used as a guide to roughness of various pipes.

Rectangular Duct.—Figs. 14-58a, 14-58b, and 14-59a the friction charts for round duct, may be used for rectangular duct. Table 14-11a, and 14-11b presents the equivalent size of round duct for equal friction at equal volume flow (not equal velocity) for various rectangular duct sizes. It is a solution of the formula,

$$d = 1.3 \frac{(ab)^{0.625}}{(a + b)^{0.25}} \qquad (46)$$

where d = equivalent round duct diameter, in.;

a = one side of rectangular duct, in.; and

b = other side of rectangular duct, in.

Example 11: (Refer to Table 14-11b) A 10-inch (left margin) by 6-inch (top line) rectangular duct has the same friction losses at the same volume flow as an 8.4-inch (body of table) round duct.

Correction for Density: For the normal range of temperature, pressure, and moisture content encountered in air handling, variations in air viscosity are small enough to be neglected. Friction chart values may be corrected for variation in air density from standard by the following methods:

Table 14-7. Degrees of Roughness in Various Ducts

Pipe	Degree of Roughness
Drawn tubing	Very smooth
New steel of wrought iron	Medium smooth
Asphalted cast iron	Medium smooth
Galvanized iron	Average
Wood stave	Average
Average concrete	Medium rough
Riveted steel	Very rough

(A) If actual air volumes or velocities at operating conditions are used in reading the friction chart, then to get the actual friction loss per 100 ft, multiply the friction loss per 100 ft from the chart by either air density divided by 0.075, or by an equivalent ratio, 13.35 divided by actual specific volume.

(B) If standard air volumes are used in reading the friction chart, then the actual friction loss per 100 ft will be the loss from the chart multiplied by the reciprocal of the factor in (A), 0.075.

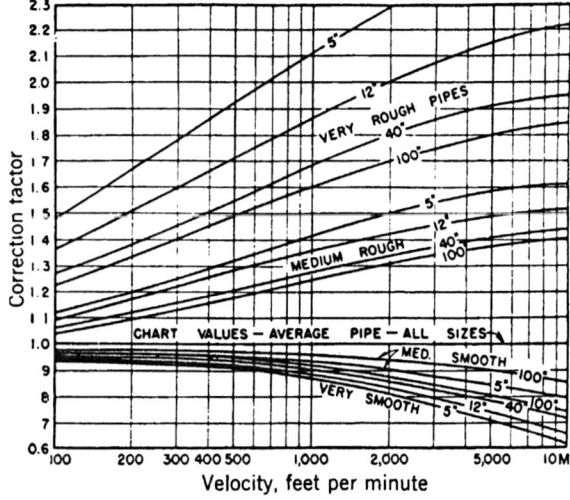

Fig 14-57. Correction factors for pipe roughness, to be applied to values read from Figs. 14-58a, and 14-58b.

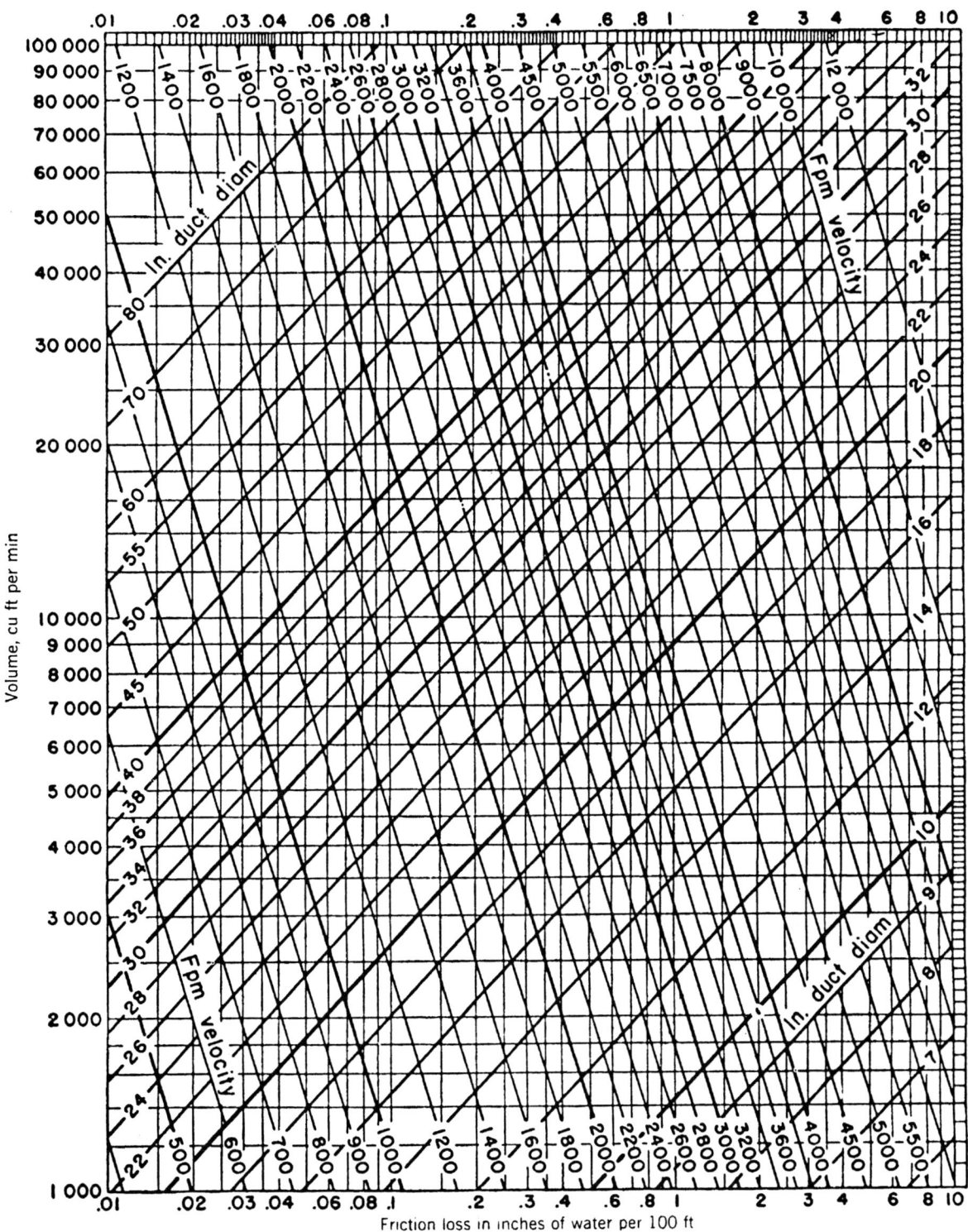

Fig 14-58a. Friction of air in straight galvanized ducts, for volumes 1000 to 100,000 *cfm*. (Same basis and source as Fig. 14-58b)

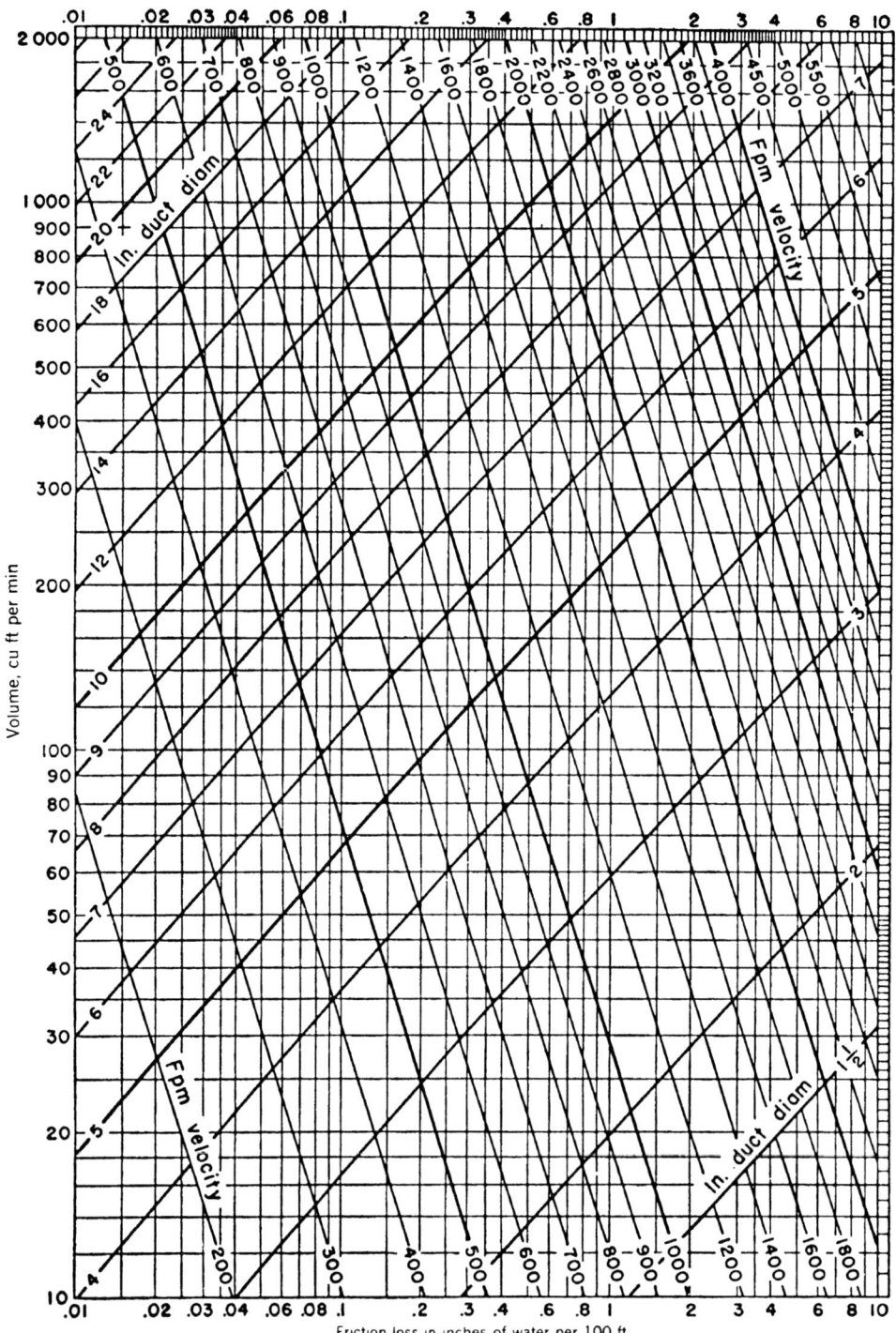

**Friction of air in straight galvanized ducts,
for volumes of 10 to 2000 cfm.**

Fig 14-58b. Friction of air in straight galvanized ducts, for volume of 10 to 2000 *cfm*
(Based on standard air of 0.075 lb/ft^3 density flowing through clean round galvanized ducts having approximately 40 joints per 100 ft)

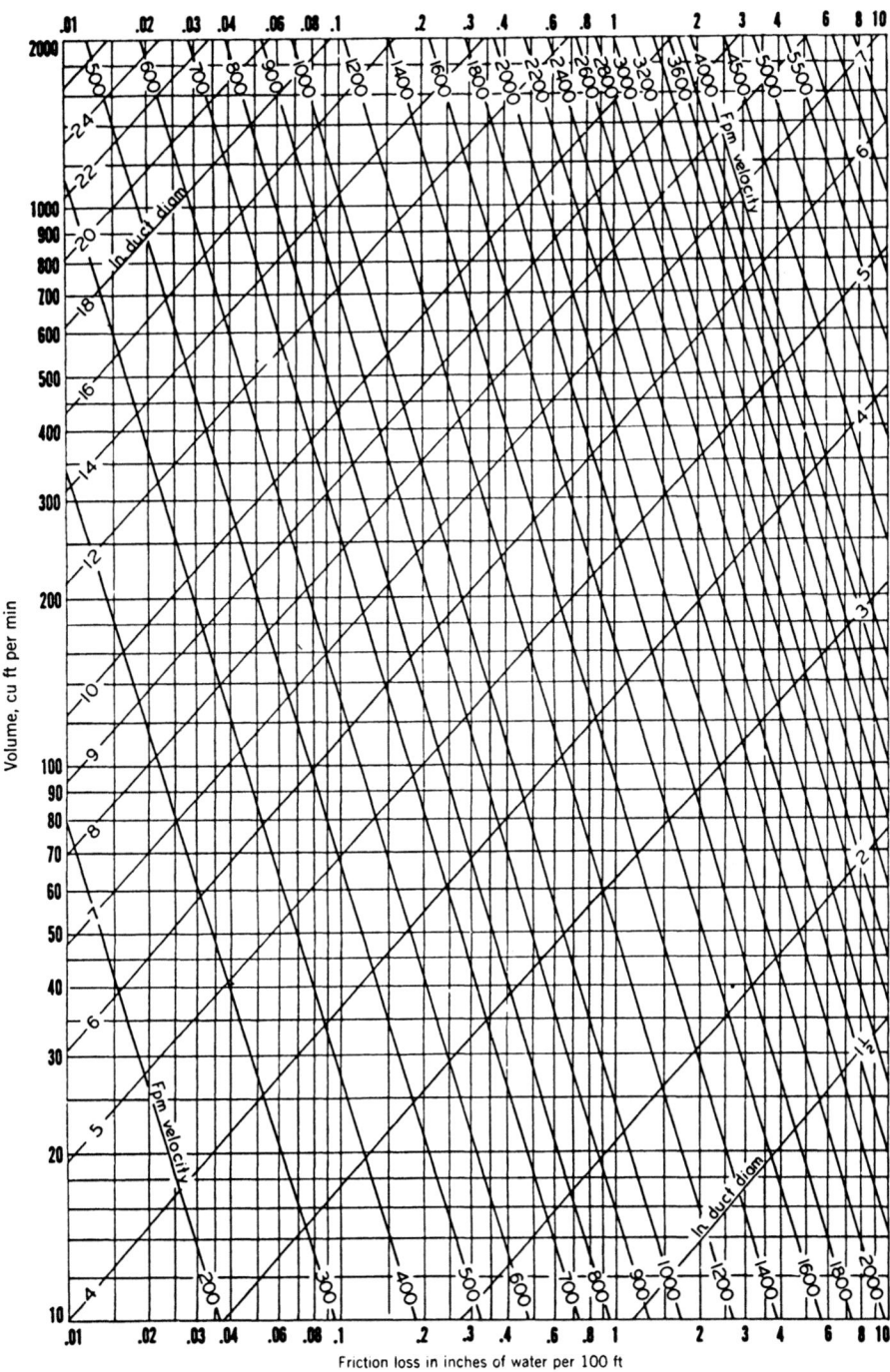

Fig 14-59a. Friction of air in straight aluminum ducts for volume of 10 to 2000 *cfm* (Same basis and source as Fig. 14-59b)

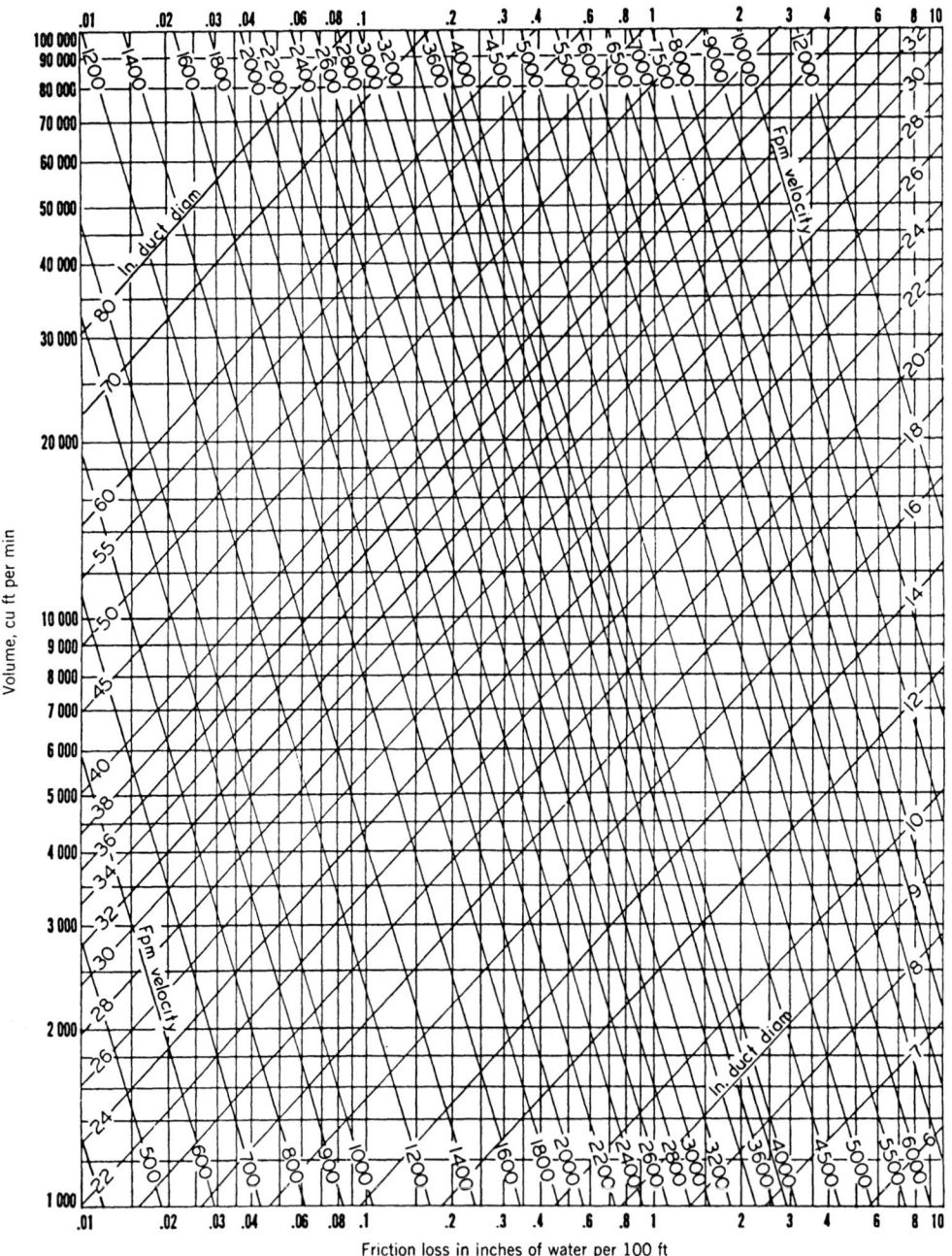

Fig 14-59b. Friction of air in straight aluminum ducts for volume of 1,000 to 100,000 cfm
(Based on standard air of 0.075 lb/ft³ density flowing through clean round galvanized ducts having approximately 40 joints per 100 ft)

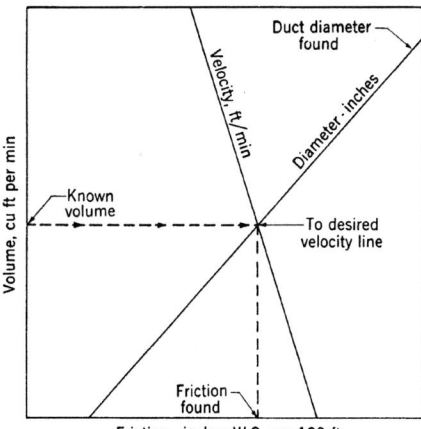

Fig 14-60a. Finding diameter and friction from known volume and velocity

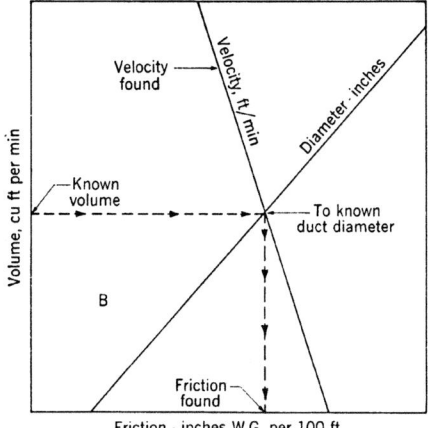

Fig 14-60b. Finding velocity and friction from known volume and diameter

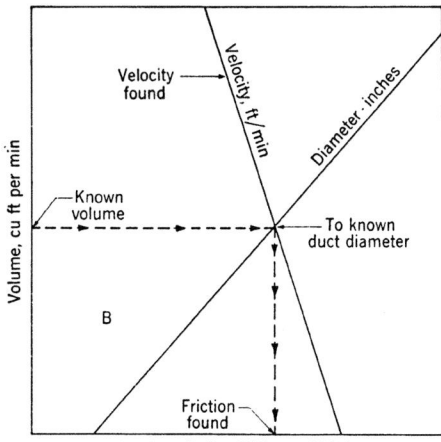

Fig 14-60c. Finding volume and friction from known velocity and diameter

Example 12: Dry air at 300°F is conveyed through 12 inch duct at 2000 *cfm* (actual). From the friction chart, Fig. 14-58a, friction loss per 100 ft is 0.75. From Fig. 14-56, density is 0.052. Then the actual friction loss per 100 ft is 0.75 (0.052/0.075) = 0.52 where it is divided by gas density, or its equivalent, specific volume divided by 13.35.

Example 13: An air flow of 5000 *cfm* (standard air) has been specified, and a duct size of 18 inches diameter has been chosen. Before the air reaches the duct it passes through a spray chamber and emerges at 100 deg, saturated. From Fig. 14-58a, for 5000 *cfm* and an 18-inch duct, friction loss per 100 ft is 0.56. From Fig. 14-56, density is 0.069. Therefore, the actual friction loss in the duct is 0.56 (0.075/ 0.069) = 0.61.

Table 14-8. Loss Fractions in 90° Round Elbows

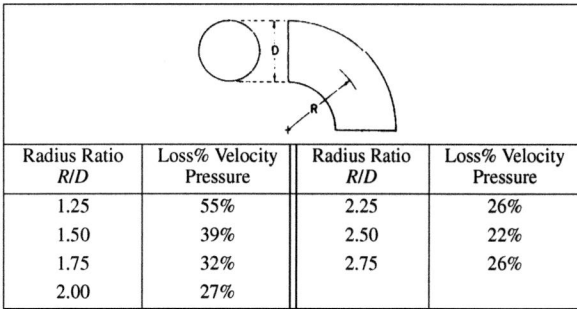

Radius Ratio R/D	Loss% Velocity Pressure	Radius Ratio R/D	Loss% Velocity Pressure
1.25	55%	2.25	26%
1.50	39%	2.50	22%
1.75	32%	2.75	26%
2.00	27%		

Losses in Elbows and Fittings: When an air stream undergoes a change of either direction or velocity, a dynamic loss occurs. Unlike friction losses in straight duct, fitting losses are a clue to internal turbulence rather than skin friction. This turbulence destroys the forward motion of some elements of the air stream and therefore requires energy to reestablish its forward motion. Hence, roughness of material has but slight effect over a wide range of moderately smooth materials.

Fitting losses can be expressed as equivalent length of straight duct; or as a fraction of velocity pressure; or directly in inches water gage.

Losses as a percent of velocity pressure and as equivalent length of round duct in diameters are shown in Tables 14-8, 14-9, and 14-10. The losses for a variety of fittings are shown in equivalent feet of duct in the section on *Chapter 8, and Warm Air Heating in Chapter 15.* Losses are shown in the following section on *Duct System Design* in Chapter 8.

Table 14-9. Percent of 90° Elbow Loss for Various Bends

Bend degrees	Loss% 90° bend	Bend degrees	Loss% 90° bend
30°	33%	120°	127%
45°	52%	135°	140%
60°	67%	150°	150%
75°	85%	165°	158%
90°	100%	180°	165%
105°	115%		

Table 14-10. Loss in Rectangular 90° Elbows, Percent Velocity Pressure

Aspect Ratio	No. of Splitters	0.0 (mitre elbow)	0.50	0.75	1.00	1.50	2.0	3.0	4.0
		Radius Ratio, R/W							
		Friction Loss Percent of Velocity Pressure							
0.25	0	150	136	55	46	28	24	24	28
	1	135	77	22	26	24	26	...	...
	2	120	49	16	22	26	...	...	...
	3	109	31	12	22	...	...	...	...
0.50	0	132	120	48	28	...	15	15	18
	1	119	67	19	16	15	16	...	...
	2	104	43	14	13	16	...	...	...
	3	96	27	10	13	...	...	...	...
1.0	0	115	105	42	21	...	11	11	13
	1	104	59	17	12	11	12	...	...
	2	92	38	12	10	12	...	...	...
	3	84	24	9	10	...	...	...	...
2.0	0	104	95	38	21	...	11	11	13
	1	94	53	15	12	11	12	...	...
	2	83	34	11	10	12	...	...	...
	3	76	22	11	10	...	...	...	...
3.0	0	83	76	30	20	...	11	11	13
	1	75	42	12	12	11	12	...	...
	2	67	27	9	10	12	...	...	...
	3	61	18	9	10	...	...	...	...
4.0	0	61	55	22	19	...	10	10	11
	1	55	31	12	11	10	11	...	...
	2	49	20	9	9	11	...	...	...
	3	45	13	9	9	...	...	...	...

Table 14-11a. Equivalent Round and Rectangular Ducts with Equal Friction

One side Rec. Duct in.	22	24	26	28	30	32	34	36	38	40	42	44	46	48
	Other Side of Rectangular Duct, in.													
	Diameter of Equivalent Circular Duct, in.													
22	24.05	...	...	...	...	...	...	...	...	...	...	...	...	...
24	25.11	26.24	...	...	...	...	...	...	...	...	...	...	...	...
26	26.12	27.30	28.42	...	...	...	...	...	...	...	...	...	...	...
28	27.08	28.32	29.49	30.61	...	...	...	...	...	...	...	...	...	...
30	28.00	29.29	30.51	31.68	32.79	...	...	...	...	...	...	...	...	...
32	28.88	30.22	31.49	32.70	33.87	34.98	...	...	...	...	...	...	...	...
34	29.10	31.11	32.43	33.69	34.90	36.05	37.17	...	...	...	...	...	...	...
36	30.00	31.97	33.33	34.64	35.89	37.09	38.24	39.35	...	...	...	...	...	...
38	31.32	32.80	34.21	35.55	36.85	38.08	39.28	40.43	...	...	...	...	...	...
40	32.07	33.60	35.05	36.44	37.77	39.05	40.28	41.47	42.62	43.73	...	...	...	...
42	32.81	34.37	35.87	37.30	38.67	39.98	41.25	42.48	43.66	44.80	...	...	...	...
44	33.51	35.12	36.66	38.13	39.54	40.89	42.19	43.45	44.67	45.85	46.99	...	...	...
46	34.20	35.85	37.43	38.93	40.38	41.77	43.11	44.40	45.65	46.86	48.04	49.18	50.29	...
48	34.87	36.56	38.17	39.72	41.20	42.63	44.00	45.33	46.61	47.85	49.06	50.23	51.36	...
50	35.52	37.25	38.90	40.48	42.00	43.46	44.86	46.22	47.54	48.81	50.05	51.25	52.41	53.55
52	36.15	37.92	39.61	41.22	42.78	44.27	45.71	47.10	48.45	49.75	51.01	52.24	53.44	54.60
54	36.77	38.57	40.30	41.95	43.53	45.06	46.53	47.95	49.33	50.66	51.96	53.22	54.44	55.63
56	37.37	39.21	40.97	42.65	44.2 7	45.83	47.33	48.79	50.19	51.56	52.88	54.17	55.42	56.63
58	37.96	39.83	41.63	43.34	45.00	46.58	48.12	49.60	51.04	52.43	53.78	55.09	56.37	57.61
60	38.53	40.44	42.27	44.02	45.70	47.32	48.89	50.40	51.86	53.28	54.66	56.00	57.30	58.57
62	39.10	41.04	42.90	44.68	46.39	48.04	49.64	51.18	52.67	54.12	55.52	56.89	58.22	59.51
64	39.65	41.62	43.51	45.32	47.07	48.75	50.37	51.94	53.46	54.93	56.37	57.76	59.11	60.43
66	40.18	42.19	44.11	45.96	47.73	49.44	51.09	52.69	54.23	55.73	57.19	58.61	59.99	61.33

Table 14-11b. Equivalent Round and Rectangular Ducts with Equal Friction

One side Rec. Duct in.	Other Side of Rectangular Duct, in.													
	3	4	5	6	7	8	9	10	11	12	14	16	18	20
	Diameter of Equivalent Circular Duct, in.													
3.5	...	...	...	...	...	5.66	5.97	6.25	6.52	6.77	7.24	7.65	...	...
4	3.78	4.37	4.88	5.32	5.72	6.09	6.43	...	...	...	...	...	...	...
4.5	4.00	4.64	5.18	5.66	6.09	6.49	...	...	...	...	...	...	...	...
5	4.20	4.88	5.47	5.98	6.44	...	...	...	...	...	...	...	...	...
5.5	4.39	5.11	5.73	6.28	6.77	...	...	...	...	...	...	...	...	...
6	4.57	5.33	5.98	6.56	7.08	7.55	...	...	...	...	...	...	...	...
7	4.90	5.73	6.44	7.08	7.65	8.18	8.66	...	...	...	...	...	...	...
8	5.20	6.09	6.87	7.55	8.18	8.75	9.27	9.76	...	...	...	...	...	...
9	5.48	6.43	7.26	7.99	8.66	9.27	9.84	10.37	10.86	...	...	...	...	...
10	5.74	6.74	7.62	8.40	9.11	9.76	10.37	10.93	11.46	11.96	...	...	...	...
11	5.98	7.03	7.95	8.78	9.53	10.22	10.86	11.46	12.02	12.56	13.54	...	...	...
12	6.20	7.31	8.27	9.14	9.93	10.66	11.33	11.96	12.56	13.12	14.16	15.11	...	...
13	6.42	7.57	8.57	9.48	10.31	11.07	11.77	12.44	13.06	13.65	14.75	15.74	16.67	...
14	6.62	7.81	8.86	9.80	10.66	11.46	12.20	12.89	13.54	14.16	15.30	16.35	17.32	18.22
15	6.81	8.05	9.13	10.11	11.00	11.83	12.60	13.32	14.00	14.64	15.84	16.93	17.94	18.89
16	7.00	8.27	9.39	10.41	11.33	12.19	12.98	13.73	14.44	15.11	16.35	17.49	18.54	19.52
17	7.18	8.49	9.64	10.69	11.64	12.53	13.35	14.13	14.86	15.55	16.84	18.03	19.12	20.14
18	7.35	8.69	9.88	10.96	11.95	12.86	13.71	14.51	15.27	15.98	17.32	18.54	19.68	20.73
19	7.51	8.89	10.12	11.22	12.24	13.18	14.05	14.88	15.66	16.40	17.78	19.04	20.21	21.31
20	7.67	9.08	10.34	11.47	12.52	13.48	14.38	15.23	16.04	16.80	18.22	19.52	20.73	21.86
22	7.97	9.45	10.76	11.95	13.05	14.06	15.01	15.91	16.76	17.56	19.06	20.44	21.73	22.92
24	8.26	9.80	11.16	12.41	13.55	14.61	15.61	16.55	17.44	18.28	19.86	21.31	22.66	23.93
26	8.53	10.12	11.54	12.83	14.02	15.13	16.17	17.15	18.08	18.96	20.61	22.13	23.55	24.87
28	8.79	10.43	11.90	13.24	14.47	15.62	16.70	17.72	18.69	19.61	21.33	22.92	24.39	25.78
30	9.03	10.73	12.25	13.63	14.90	16.09	17.21	18.27	19.27	20.22	22.01	23.66	25.20	26.64
32	9.27	11.01	12.57	14.00	15.31	16.54	17.70	18.79	19.82	20.81	22.66	24.37	25.97	27.47
34	9.49	11.28	12.89	14.35	15.71	16.97	18.16	19.29	20.36	21.38	23.29	25.06	26.71	28.26
36	9.71	11.55	13.19	14.69	16.09	17.39	18.61	19.77	20.87	21.92	23.89	25.72	27.42	29.02
38	9.92	11.80	13.48	15.02	16.45	17.78	19.04	20.23	21.36	22.44	24.47	26.35	28.11	29.76
40	10.12	12.04	13.77	15.34	16.80	18.17	19.46	20.68	21.84	22.95	25.03	26.96	28.77	30.47
42	10.31	12.28	14.04	15.65	17.14	18.54	19.86	21.11	22.30	23.43	25.57	27.55	29.41	31.15
44	10.50	12.50	14.30	15.95	17.47	18.90	20.25	21.53	22.74	23.91	26.10	28.13	30.03	31.82
46	10.69	12.73	14.56	16.24	17.79	19.25	20.63	21.93	23.18	24.37	26.60	28.68	30.63	32.47
48	10.86	12.94	14.81	16.52	18.11	19.59	21.00	22.33	23.60	24.81	27.10	29.22	31.22	33.09
50	11.04	13.15	15.05	16.79	18.41	19.92	21.35	22.71	24.01	25.25	27.58	29.75	31.78	33.70
52	11.21	13.36	15.29	17.06	18.70	20.25	21.70	23.09	24.41	25.67	28.05	30.26	32.34	34.30
54	11.37	13.56	15.52	17.32	18.99	20.56	22.04	23.45	24.79	26.08	28.50	30.76	32.88	34.88
56	11.54	13.75	15.74	17.57	19.27	20.87	22.37	23.81	25.17	26.48	28.95	31.25	33.40	35.44
58	11.69	13.94	15.96	17.82	19.55	21.17	22.70	24.15	25.54	26.87	29.38	31.72	33.92	35.99
60	11.85	14.13	16.18	18.06	19.81	21.46	23.01	24.49	25.90	27.25	29.81	32.19	34.42	36.53
62	12.00	14.31	16.39	18.30	20.08	21.74	23.32	24.82	26.26	27.63	30.22	32.64	34.91	37.06
64	12.15	14.49	16.59	18.53	20.33	22.02	23.63	25.15	26.60	28.00	30.63	33.08	35.39	37.57
66	12.29	14.66	16.80	18.76	20.58	22.30	23.92	25.47	26.94	28.35	31.03	33.52	35.86	38.08

Table 14-12. Design Air Velocities for Conventional and High Velocity Systems

Duct Element	Conventional						High Velocity	
	Residences		Public Buildings		Industrial Buildings		Commercial Buildings	
	Normal	Maximum	Normal	Maximum	Normal	Maximum	Normal	Maximum
	Design Velocities, fpm							
Main ducts	700	1200	1000	1600	1500	2200	2500	6000
Branch ducts	600	1000	800	1300	1000	1800	2000	4500
Fan outlets	1000	1700	1500	2200	2000	2800	2500	5000
Suction connections	700	900	800	1100	1000	1400	1700	3300
Outside air intakes	500	800	500	900	500	1200	600	1000
Filters	250	300	300	350	350	350	350	350
Heating coils	450	500	500	600	600	700	600	700
Air washers	500	...	500	...	...	...	500	...
Dehumidifiers	450	...	500	...	...	...	500	...

Table 14-13. Total Pressure Losses in Duct Elements

Element	Figure	Conditions	Loss, Friction of Velocity Pressure	Equivalent Length of Round Duct, Diameters
Weather cap		H/D = 1.00	0.10	6
		= 0.75	0.18	11
		= 0.65	0.30	18
		= 0.55	0.56	38
		= 0.50	0.73	44
		= 0.45	1.00	60
Expansion		a = 5°	0.17	10
		= 10°	0.28	17
		= 20°	0.45	27
		= 30°	0.59	36
		= 40°	0.73	44
Contraction		a = 30°	0.02	1
		= 45°	0.04	2
		= 60°	0.07	4
Transition piece			0.15	9
Abrupt entrance			0.50	30
Abrupt exit			1.0	60
Bell mouth entrance			0.03	2
Bell mouth exit			1.0	60
Reentrant entrance			0.85	51
Sharp edge round orifice exit		A_2/A_1 = 0.00	2.8	170
		= 0.25	2.4	140
		= 0.50	1.9	115
		= 0.75	1.5	90
		= 1.00	1.0	60
Abrupt Contraction		V_1/V_2 = 0.00	0.50	30
		= 0.25	0.45	27
		= 0.50	0.32	19
		= 0.75	0.18	11

Table 14-13. Total Pressure Losses in Duct Elements

Element	Figure	Conditions	Loss, Friction of Velocity Pressure	Equivalent Length of Round Duct, Diameters
Abrupt expansion		$V_1/V_2 = 0.00$	1.0	60
		$= 0.20$	0.64	39
		$= 0.40$	0.36	22
		$= 0.60$	0.16	9
		$= 0.80$	0.04	2
Double elbows		Loss for both elbows		
		$L = 0$	0.43	26
		$L = D$	0.31	19
		Elbows vaned	0.15	9
		$L = 0$	0.43	26
		$L = D$	0.31	19
		Elbows vaned	0.15	9
Branch entry		$a = 10°$	0.06	4
		$= 15°$	0.09	5
		$= 20°$	0.12	7
		$= 25°$	0.15	9
		$= 30°$	0.18	11
		$= 35°$	0.21	13
		$= 40°$	0.25	15
		$= 45°$	0.28	17
		$= 50°$	0.32	19
		$= 60°$	0.44	26
		$= 90°$	1.00	60
Pipe running through duct		$E/D = 0.10$	0.20	12
		$= 0.25$	0.55	33
		$= 0.50$	2.00	120
Bar running through duct		$E/D = 0.10$	0.70	40
		$= 0.25$	1.40	80
		$= 0.50$	4.0	240
Streamlined covering over construction		$E/D = 0.10$	0.07	4
		$= 0.25$	0.23	14
		$= 0.50$	0.90	54

The *equivalent feet of duct method* of determining turbulent losses has great appeal to the designer of small air systems, which predominate in the residential warm air heating industry. For larger commercial and institutional air conditioning systems, the designer is advised to use the fraction of velocity pressure or the tabulated loss readings for various fittings in preference to the equivalent-length method. In high velocity systems (over 2000 fpm air velocity), use of the *equivalent feet of duct method* will often result in errors on the low side because large, high velocity ducts usually have fairly low friction losses against which the equivalent feet for a particular fitting is applied. Even the loss coefficients for elbows (such as those shown in Table 14-10), vary with velocity, but fortunately there is, at most, an 8% difference over the air velocity range of 2000 to 6000 fpm.

Good Duct Turns: Air will not turn of its own volition; it must be turned. Even with a standard elbow (throat radius equals duct width), the air cannot make the turn, and high velocity occurs at the outside with an eddy zone at the throat. This nonuniform condition, as shown in Fig. 14-62a does not permit outlets or branches to be located near the elbow on the throat side. Ductwork can be designed to accommodate this nonuniform condition. Elbows *b* through *g* will cause difficulties in Fig. 14-62, Elbow *f* is fair because the air can expand along the vanes, but this arrangement should be used with care and a good section of straight duct ahead of the vanes. For elbow *g*, the air will jam on the vanes at the top and cause excessive energy loss. Elbow *h* should be used where the depth of the duct changes also. Note that the transition accommodates the air flow as compared to the poor condition in *d*. Elbows *i*, *j*, and *k* are needed when an outlet or branch is located less than six duct widths from an outlet. Even with vanes or splitters, some distance must be allowed for improved uniformity and better performance. For elbow *k*, keep in mind that the splitter should extend beyond the tangency point in the direction of flow to straighten the air stream. As a minimum, *L* should equal *W* and preferably should be 1.5 to 2*W*. If space conditions make it necessary for the throat radius to be eliminated, i.e., $R_1 = 0$, then W_1 should be a minimum of 3 inches, $W_2 = 6$ inches, $W_3 = 12$ inches, etc. The venturi elbow, shown in Fig. 14-64, will also provide a smooth expansion.

Good Aerodynamics for Duct Systems: Since air does not turn by itself, as mentioned previously, it must be guided by fittings and elbows whose configurations should make for a good aerodynamic path. The designer should use those fittings, where possible, which produce the lowest loss friction of velocity pressure. Abrupt transitions and compound elbows should be avoided unless space conditions make them absolutely necessary.

It is beyond the scope of this handbook to discuss theoretical aspects of aerodynamics. However, some practical guidelines can be given to the design of turns and elbows in rectangular ducts, as shown in Fig. 14-62. The two worst cases of duct turns in Fig. 14-62 are shown in *b* and *c*; these can readily be converted to good duct turns by turning vanes *i* and splitters *k*, respectively.

It was previously thought that better aerodynamics resulted from use of double thickness turning vanes in square or rectangular elbows, as against the single-thickness type. This theory has been contradicted in the literature, which indicates that single-thickness vanes result in lower losses than double-thickness vanes. Moreover, the dynamic losses in single-thickness vaned elbows can be reduced even more by extending the trailing edge of each vane. Turning vane loss coefficients are a function of air velocity, vane radius, and vane spacing; the lowest loss coefficient for the several vane types and geometry tested was a constant 0.12, based on the duct velocity range of 500 to 5000 fpm. This particular vane was single-thickness type, 2-inch radius, 1.5-inch space between vanes on the diagonal, trailing edge extended 0.75 inch. This study further showed that the best double thickness vane had a loss coefficient that varied from 0.34 at 500 fpm to 0.16 at 5000 fpm.

One type of elbow, shown in Fig. 14-61, should be avoided; this is the *warped* elbow, which changes in both depth and width at the outlet. It has poor aerodynamics and is expensive to manufacture because of the labor involved.

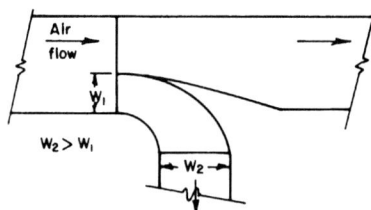

Fig 14-61. Warped elbow (Note: Depth is greater at inlet than at outlet of this elbow; this gives the warped appearance to the elbow.)

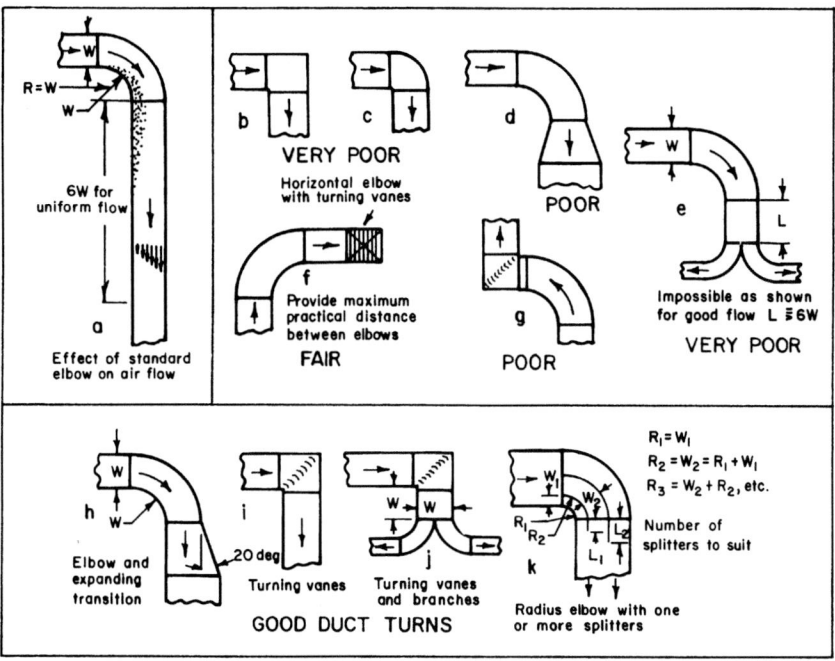

Fig 14-62. Duct turns

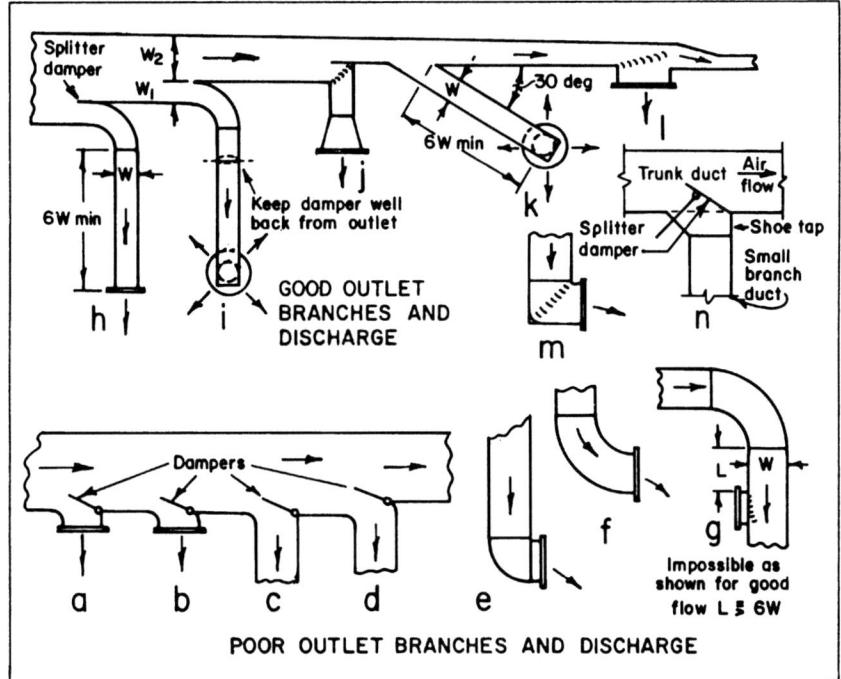

Fig 14-63. Outlet branches and discharge

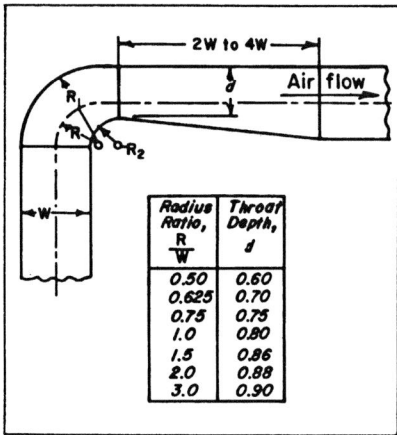

Fig 14-64. Venturi elbow

For branch duct connections to the trunk duct, sonic means must be provided to assure good approach at the outlets. Otherwise, uneven flow will occur from the outlet, which can cause draft or prevent the desired air motion. The throw may be greatly reduced, perhaps to as little as one-third of the catalog value. Poor flow will always result from the outlet connections and branches shown by branches and outlets a through g in Fig. 14-63. Noise, higher friction, and balancing difficulty will also occur if these configurations are used. For arrangement g, inflow is more probable than outflow at the grille.

Full tap branch connections should always have shoe tap connections and splitter dampers.

Cost is always a factor, but savings are of no value if outlets do not perform satisfactorily. Outlets and branches a, b, c, and d in Fig. 14-63 should not be used. Impossible grille performance will result with a and b because the air will discharge through the far end. Recirculation will exist at the upstream end. Branches c and d will produce extremely nonuniform flow, which may cause difficulties with an outlet or branch downstream. All of these dampers will be noisy and because of turbulence downstream will make it more difficult to balance downstream branches and outlets. Outlets e and f will be greatly affected by the non uniformity that occurs with these elbows. The throws may be as little as 35% of catalog values. The outlet in g cannot be expected to perform unless it is intended to aspirate air into the duct. This is unlikely. If an outlet must be near an elbow, the engineer should provide room for flow uniformity to be established, or provide turning vanes as shown in h through m. In all branches keep dampers far enough back from outlets so outlets can perform as intended, with good approach. Branch k is used frequently, particularly where a small branch is taken off a large duct. In industrial areas,

it may be straight, as shown, or if interferences prevent this, the duct may be turned to provide a branch similar to h or i. Splitter dampers should never be less than 4 inches wide, and should generally have a width equal to $1.5W_1$ (where W_1, is small neck size). Note that neck sizes W_1 and W_2 in Fig. 14-63, are in direct proportion to air flow through each neck, except that minimum neck size W in this case. should never be less than 3 inches.

Where air registers in low velocity systems are connected into the side of the trunk duct, an extractor should be used to obtain uniform air flow, as shown in Fig. 14-65. Also, to preclude noise generation, the trunk duct velocities should not exceed those recommended by the register manufacturer.

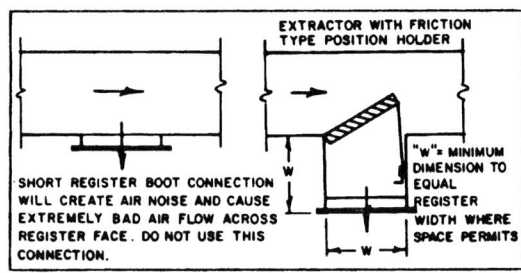

Fig 14-65. Top register connection to trunk duct

Air Balancing and Air Turning Hardware.—For air balancing proper hardware should be provided at branch ducts to divert or throttle air flow. Most air diffusers and registers have their own terminal dampers, usually the opposed blade type, which are key operated, and these alone would seem to be sufficient. Unfortunately, this is not true, because any throttling required to kill excess static pressure, above $\frac{1}{4}$ inch water gauge virtually closes these terminal dampers and will thereby cause either a whistle or a whirring noise. For this reason, local branch dampers are required upstream of the outlet or outlets. These branch dampers are manually operated and for small ducts are of the single blade type; while for larger duct sizes they are the opposed blade type. For high-velocity duct systems, factory fabricated dampers with good aerodynamic design (often called *air pressure reducing valves*) are required to reduce the high pressures encountered in high velocity design to low pressures suitable for conventional low velocity duct construction. If air pressure reducing valves are not used, dampers for high velocity systems should certainly be the *airfoil* type, preferably factory made where close quality control can guarantee against defective damper configuration, burrs, poor leading edges, etc.

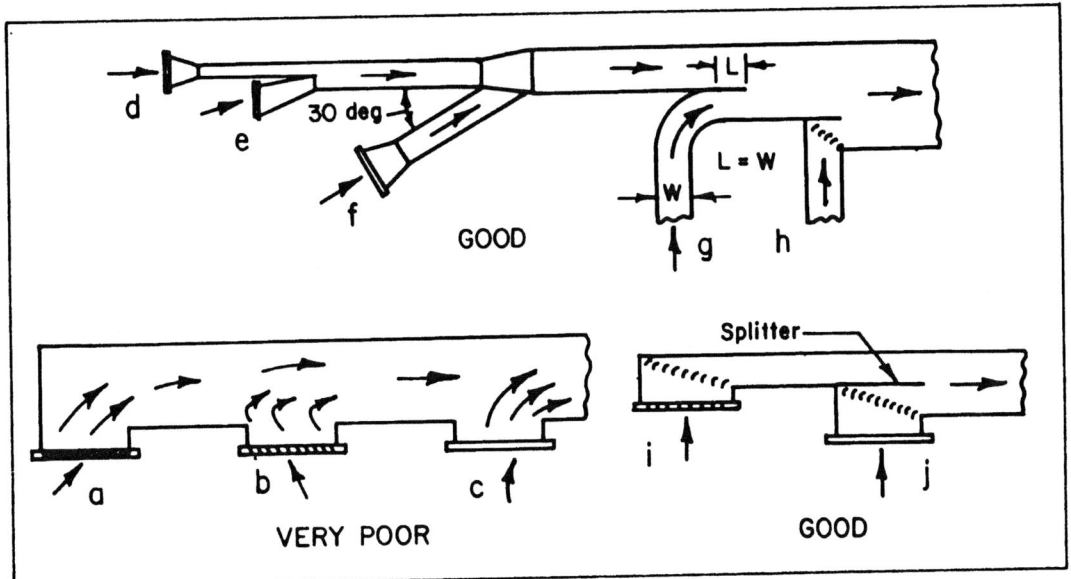

Fig 14-66. Air flow into ducts

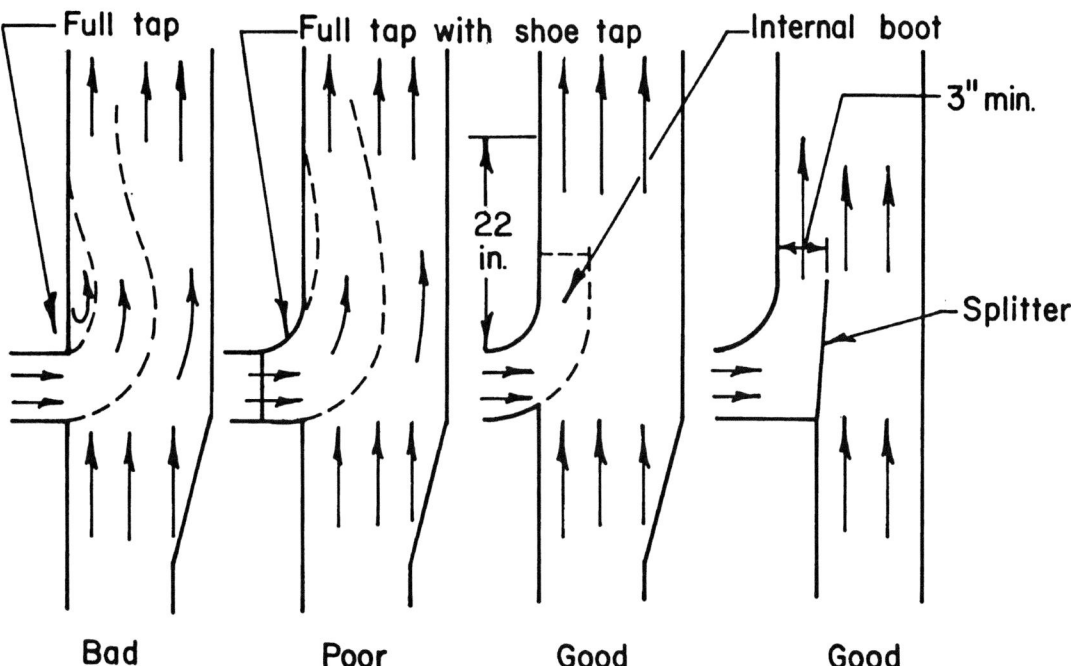

Fig 14-67. Four types of arrangements of return or exhaust air duct branch fittings

Where supply trunk ducts split into branches, splitter dampers are recommended since sizing of the necks does not automatically assure that the air goes through the branches in the designed quantities. In effect, the splitter damper offers a means, of adjusting the neck size. It is true that manual volume dampers will do the same thing, i.e., by they add resistance to the branch that supplies more air than the design flow. However, manual dampers will add resistance to the system, unlike splitter dampers.

Air flow into exhaust or return ducts follows the same rules of fluid flow as it does for supply ducts. The inlets in a, b, and c will cause severe turbulence in the duct and interfere with the flow front upstream inlets the same as if a damper were located about halfway, or more, into the air stream. Full flow will not occur in the length of the grilles, so much of the length is wasted. Tire inlets in d through h will provide good flow. In industrial areas appearance is seldom of great importance, so inlets such as d and e can and should be used. These will provide the best flow. Balancing can be improved by proper sizing of the branches. For better performance the grilles in i and j should have straight vanes as opposed to the 43° setting of the grille blades in a and b. However, if curved or deflected vanes are used to hide the interior of the duct, they should deflect in the direction of air flow.

Exhaust or return ducts and inlets suffer in the same manner and for much the same reasons as do supply ducts. Air is not pulled into ducts; it moves because of a pressure differential, as does supply air. It also has mass and momentum. Air entering an exhaust or return duct perpendicularly at a branch or inlet creates considerable impact and turbulence because it cannot make the turn, as shown by a, b, and c in Fig. 14-66. This acts as a block, or choke, for flow from inlets upstream. For reduced turbulence and friction the air should enter the main stream as close to parallel as is practical and at nearly the same velocity. Straight inlets such as d and c in Fig. 14-66, should be the first choice. Arrangements f, g, i, and j also provide good flow. It should be noted that the branch channel in g is extended into the duct by the length L. The rule here is that at an entrance or elbow turn, the splitter or branch should be extended to avoid serious impingement on the main stream or adjacent streams, and the air should be fully turned to provide good flow. L should at least equal W. Better flow results when L equals 1.5W. Where it is very important that the air stream be turned for particularly good flow conditions, L should equal 2W.

Full taps for small exhaust or return duct branch connections into trunk ducts should not be used unless there is an internal boot, or at least a splitter or a splitter damper. Tests have shown that even a full tap with a *shoe tap* connection to the trunk duct will result in turbulent losses four times those that occur with boots or splitters. This is shown in Fig. 14-67.

A splitter damper may be used in lieu of a fixed splitter; however, its only purpose in a return or exhaust duct is better aerodynamics, not air balancing. For this reason, the added cost of the splitter damper may not justify it over a fixed splitter.

Return Air Plenums: It has long been known that return air plenums, often called mixing boxes, where return air and outside air are brought together, do not really mix the air. Rather, stratification generally results when the return air and outside air have widely different temperatures. Short of using a propeller fan inside the mixing box or a bulky factory-fabricated air blender to achieve a homogeneous mixture, there is really no effective way to mix the two air streams of widely different temperatures. However, some duct arrangements at the mixing box are better than others; these are shown in Figs. 14-68 and 14-69.

Uniform flow and thorough mixing of outside and return air are essential for good equipment operation. In diagram a of Fig. 14-68 air directed by inlet louvers to the top of the casing results in backflow through bottom filters, condensate blow-off from cooling coils, and uneven heating or possibly freezing of heaters. Similarly diagram b of Fig. 14-68 the air cannot make the turn and flows to the top. In *diagram c of Fig. 14-68* the flow depends on the damper setting. With a high percentage of return air, return air flows to the opposite side, causing recirculation on the near side. Only a thin stream of outside air is allowed to enter. With mostly outside air, return air flows to the opposite side, allowing a thin stream of outside air in any damper position. Stratification is extreme for diagram d, and this arrangement should not be used particularly if outside air enters under the return air. Better arrangements for uniform flow and mixing are shown by *diagram e, f, and g*. In *diagram e*, two-position dampers are arranged to act as louver extensions to turn the air. In diagram f, the inlet hood splitters are extended to turn the air. The extension should be at least as long as the channel width. Better flow will occur if the extension is 1.5W, and if it is important that the air be fully turned, the extension should be 2W. This will not provide instant uniform flow, but it will help greatly. Good mixing and flow are encouraged in *diagram g* because the air is an offset pattern, which causes rotation and mixing of the streams.

Outside and return air have been successfully mixed by various added means. In diagram a of Fig. 14 69, outside and return air should not be brought into the casing in parallel; but if this cannot be avoided, alternate baffles as shown will create alternate streams of outside and return air, following the baffles to the opposite side to encourage mixing. In diagram b, similar baffles will cause mixing for air streams entering at right angles. In this case, the dampers do not modulate but where they do, they should be set for opposed operation. Another excellent way of mixing the air stream is by means of a propeller fan in the mixing compartment, as in diagram c. This was used effectively in one large building to eliminate freezing caused by stratification.

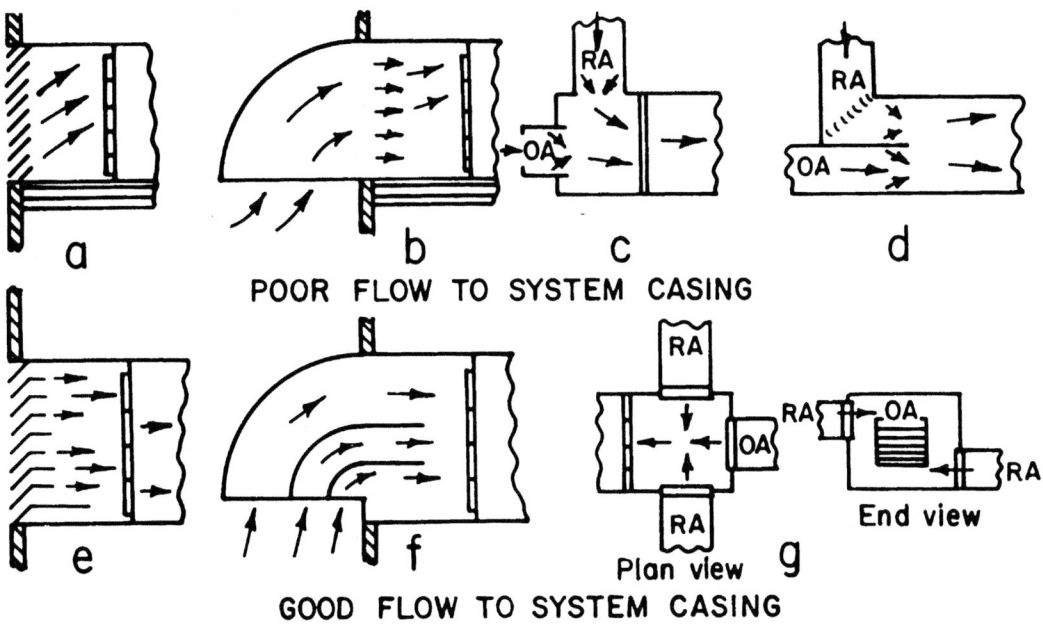

Fig 14-68. Flow to system casing

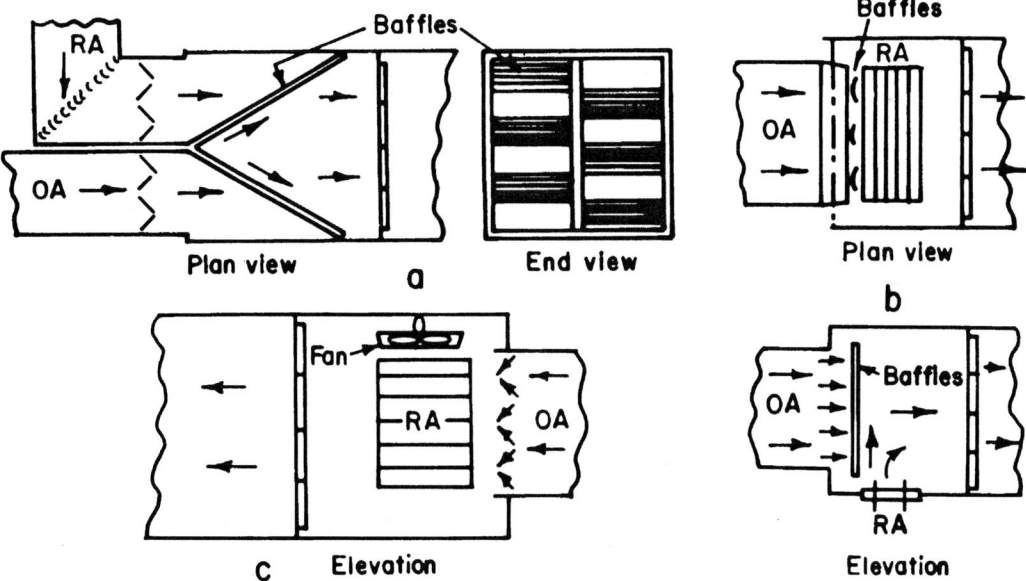

Fig 14-69. Mixing outside and return air

Air Distribution.—At the ends of the air supply duct system, air supply outlets must be selected to provide proper air motion in the occupied spaces. Table 14-14 can be used as a general guide in this respect.

The air distribution system is achieved by use of a valid, single number called the air diffusion performance index (ADPI). This index is based on comfort criteria at which 80% of test occupants felt comfortable and a maximum allowable draft velocity of 70 fpm.

With the increased concern for energy conservation and the use of the variable-air volume system to maximize energy efficiency, the ADPI methodology will assist engineers in designing a draft-free environment.

Outlets vary widely in their throw and performance characteristics. Manufacturers provide a wealth of data on air throws, noise levels, etc., for various types of air supply diffusers, registers, and grilles. The ASHRAE Guides contain detailed recommendations for particular applications; however, a very general guide to air outlet characteristics is indicated in Table 14-15.

Table 14-14. Acceptable Air Motion in the Occupied Zone

Room Air Velocity, fpm	Recommended Application
0–16	Should not be used because of complaints about *stiffness* (stagnant air).
25	Ideal for all commercial air-conditioning applications.
25–50	Acceptable range for commercial air conditioning where occupants are seated.
50–75	Retail and department store air conditioning where people are moving about.
75–300	Factory air conditioning (spot cooling).

Table 14-15. Characteristics of Air Supply Outlets

	Outlet	Characteristic
1	All outlet air steams	Act as jet pumps. Entrain many times their primary volumes. They slow down and approach room temperature slowly
2	Circular (or similar diffusers	Short throw, high entrainment for a flat pattern
3	Round or square (low aspect ratio) outlets	Long throw, moderate entrainment
4	Long slots	Moderate throw, high entrainment
5	Perforated sheet	Short throw, low entrainment

Table 14-16. Applications for Air Supply Outlets

Outlet	Application
Conventional diffusers, grilles	For fully air conditioned spaces or normal ventilation not requiring heat relief or velocity control.
Directional grilles	For general area relief ventilation systems or spot cooling; must provide direction and velocity control.
Directional diffusers	For general area relief ventilation but better suited for aisle ventilation and spot cooling; must provide direction and velocity control.
Nozzles	For spot cooling (large sizes are needed) and high local air velocities; must provide direction and velocity control.
Two way damper sections	For heat recovery and conservation, to permit directing adjustable air supply to ceiling in winter, to work zones in summer; these also prevent volume reduction of supply air for makeup systems.
Slots	For crowded areas or those requiring good mixing and air motion for close environmental control; can release high volume in small space.
Perforated panels	For high air change rates and where very low air motion is required because of hood or process requirements.

Having determined the type of performance required for a specific space, one can now select the outlet types can now be selected with the help of Table 14-16. Care should be taken in laboratories against using conventional diffusers and grilles ordinarily employed in air conditioned spaces. They may undermine the safety of nearby fume hoods. Such outlets are not good selections for laboratories with hoods, particularly if high air change rates are involved.

Fire Dampers and Fire Protection.—Every fire prevention code– Federal, State or Local uses fire-stopping devices at fire walls and partitions, and fire-rated ceilings or floors; these safety devices are called *fire dampers*. NFPA 90A requires the HVAC designer show and specify all fire dampers and fire doors required by this standard. Moreover, these dampers and doors must have an Underwriters Laboratories rating for a give time span, such as one hour, under this standard. This gave rise to the use of factory made fire dampers and doors with the UL level. It also stimulated the greater use of the *shutter* or *guillotine* type of fire damper, over the *butterfly* type. The latter is less compact in size and sustains more pressure loss from air turbulence than the shutter type.

The NFPA standards are replete with information on fire prevention or fire stopping for special exhaust systems, such as kitchen ventilation, hospital operating rooms, labs, etc. The designer should always consult the most current edition of these standards. They are revised annually to meet the increasingly stringent requirements of current fire prevention.

Duct System Design.—*Constant Pressure Drop:* With this method, pressure loss in each foot of duct length is constant. The choice of this constant (in inches of water column per 100 ft of duct) is based largely on noise and economical limitations. Tables 14-17 and 14-18 contain normal and maximum velocities, which will serve as a guide in planning a design. As a first step, the velocity to be assigned to the main duct is chosen from the tables. Then, with the main duct volume known and its velocity assigned, Figs. 14-72 and 14-73 are used to determine pressure loss per 100 ft. This loss is then uniformly assigned to the rest of the duct system except for losses in transition pieces, air inlets and outlets, filters, coils, etc. Because, for a given pressure loss, larger ducts carry proportionately larger air volumes at higher velocities, it follows that velocities automatically diminish as the ducts become smaller.

Table 14-17. Recommend and Maximum Duct Velocities for Low Velocity systems

Designation	Recommended Velocities, fpm		
	Residences	Schools Theaters, Public Buildings	Industrial Buildings
Outdoor air intakes[a]	500	500	500
Filters[a]	250	300	350
Heating coils[a]	450	500	600
Cooling coils[a]	450	500	600
Air washers[a]	500	500	500
Fan outlets	1000–600	1300–2000	1600–2400
Main ducts	700–900	100–1300	1200–1800
Branch risers	500	600-700	800
	Maximum Velocities, fpm		
Outdoor air intakes[a]	800	900	1200
Filters[a]	300	350	350
Heating coils[a]	500	600	700
Cooling coils[a]	450	500	600
Air washers	500	500	500
Fan outlets	1700	1500–2200	1700–2800
Main ducts	800–1200	1100–1600	1300–2200
Branch ducts	700–1000	800–1300	1000–1800
Branch risers	650–800	800–1200	1000–1600

[a] These velocities are for total face area, not net free area; other velocities in table are for net free area

This system is most applicable where the lengths of branch runs are symmetrical and of nearly uniform length. Any differences in pressure at the take-offs are made up by dampers at each branch.

In systems with unequal branches, mains and branches of equal length may be sized by the *constant pressure drop method*. Each unequal branch may then be sized in accordance with the pressure at its take-off. This is a refinement not always followed, but it permits branches near the fan to carry air at a higher pressure drop than the uniform drop used throughout the rest of the system. Care should be taken, however, to make certain that branch velocities do not exceed the maximum velocities shown in Table 14-17.

Table 14-18. Recommended Maximum Duct Velocity Systems

cfm Carried by Duct	Maximum Velocities, fpm
60000 to 40000	6000
40000 to 25000	5000
25000 to 15000	4500
15000 to 10000	4000
10000 to 6000	3500
6000 to 3000	3000
3000 to 1000	2500

An example of the constant pressure drop method is given below for the system shown in Fig. 14-70.

Example 14: Given, a public building in which a total air volume of 3700 *cfm* is moved. The main duct velocity chosen from Table 14-17 is 1300 fpm. From Fig. 14-58a the volume of 3700 *cfm* and the velocity of 1300 fpm intersect at 0.09 inches wg per 100 ft of duct. This loss is used in sizing all ducts from *A*, via *C, D, E,* and *I* to *L*, not including transitions at filters, fan, and coil. Other portions of duct, such as *G* to *M* and *E* to *P*, are often sized on the same uniform pressure drop as the main run; in this case, 0.09 inch per 100 ft. It is possible, however, to design a more economical system, and one more readily balanced, if the pressure drop from *G* to *M* is made the same as from *G* to *L* and the pressure drop from *E* to *P* the same as from *E* to *L*. This must be done with caution, as high velocities may result in branch circuits, causing noisy operation.

Total straight duct work A to L 280 ft	
Pressure loss in ductwork, inches wg (280/100) (.09)	0.25
2 hard bends at 0.02 (Table 14-13: H/W = 0.41; R/W = 1.0)	0.04
2 easy bends at 0.01 (Table 14-13: H/W = 2.4; R/W = 1.5)	0.02
Branch take-off at (Table 14-13. based on I-J)	0.3
Loss thru 6-row coil (approx) 8 fins per inch l at 500 fpm	0.34
Filters assumed dirty	0.25[a]
Loss in supply register	0.05[a]
Loss in return-air grille	0.15[a]
Transitions fan and filters	0.10
Static pressure loss in system, inches wg	1.23

[a] Refer to manufacturers' data

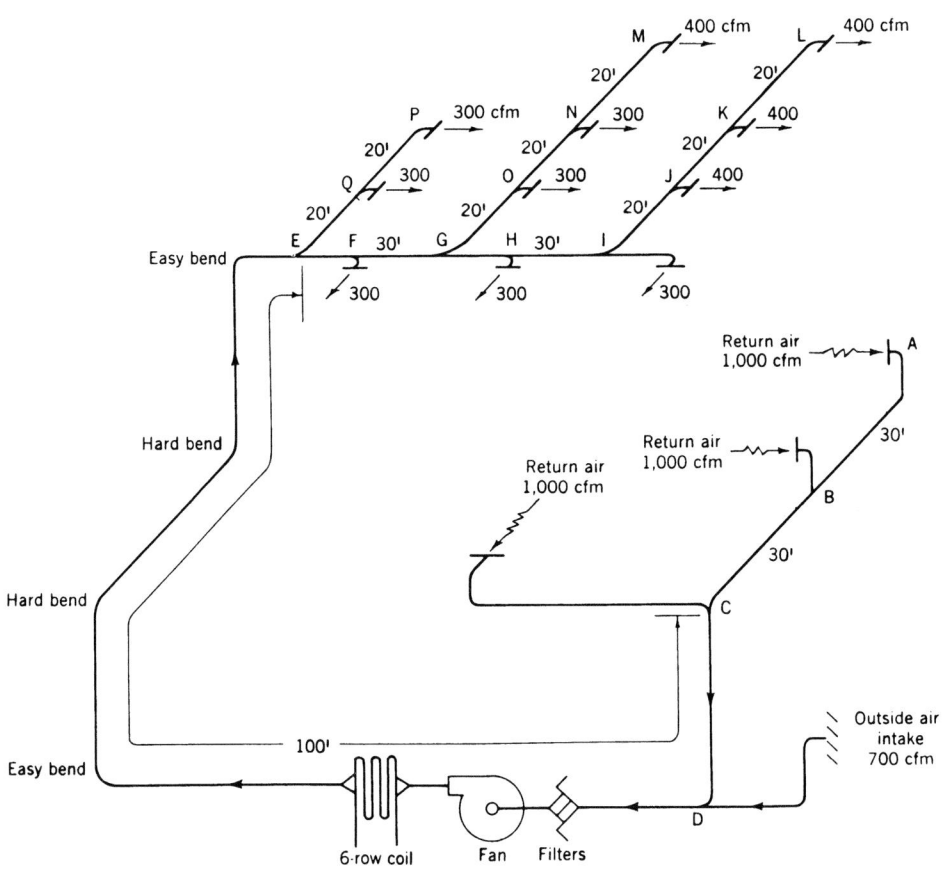

Fig 14-70. Layout of system employing constant pressure drop method

Table 14-19. Calculations for Duct Design Example 14

Duct Section	Air Volume, *cfm*	Pressure Drop, in./100 ft	Round Duct Diameter, in.	Round Duct Velocity, fpm	Equivalent Rectangular Duct, in.	Rectangular Duct Velocity, fpm
A-B	1000	.09	14.2	950	14 × 12	860
B-C	2000	.09	18.5	1100	24 × 12	1000
C-D	3000	.09	21.7	1200	34 × 12	1050
D-E	3700	.09	23.4	1300	34 × 14	1120
E-F	3100	.09	22.0	1200	34 × 12	1090
F-G	2800	.09	21.0	1200	32 × 12	1050
G-H	1800	.09	17.9	1080	22 × 12	980
H-I	1500	.09	16.6	1030	19 × 12	945
I-J	1200	.09	15.3	970	16 × 12	905
K-J	800	.09	13.1	890	12 × 12	820
K-L	400	.09	10.0	750	12 × 8	600
For branch G to M designed for a higher pressure loss of 0.123 inch per 100 ft, we obtain:						
G-O	1000	0.123	13.4	1050	12 × 12	1000
O-N	700	0.123	11.7	960	10 × 12	840
N-B	400	0.123	9.4	850	10 × 8	720
For branch E to P designed for a higher pressure loss of 0.27 inch per 100 ft, we obtain:						
E-Q	600	0.27	9.5	1250	10 × 8	1080
Q-P	300	0.27	7.2	1100	6 × 8	895

Assuming the same register and take-off losses, the duct pressure loss from G to L for the 90-ft length is $(90/100)(.09) = 0.081$. If this drop is applied to the 60 ft length from G to M, the design pressure loss per 100 ft for G to M would be $(.081)(100)/60 = 0.123$ per 100 ft. To size the branch E to P, the 120 ft from FE to L would have a pressure loss of $(120/100)(.09) = 0.108$. If this is applied to the 40 ft length from E to P, the design pressure loss per 100 ft for E to P would be $(0.108)(100)/40 = 0.27$ per 100 ft. If we now apply these pressure losses per 100 ft against the respective air volumes, we obtain for branches G to M and E to P the values shown in the lower part of Table 14-19.

For small branches, such as G-M and E-P, the designer will usually find that it generally does not pay in sheet metal costs to size them by the higher pressure drops, 0.123 and 0.27, as shown in the example. This derives from the fact that most duct work is priced the same per foot up to certain sizes, such as a 36-inch total duct circumference (e.g., 12 in × 6 in cross section); therefore, these branches could more readily be sized at 0.09 in. wg/100 ft with very little additional cost. If this is done, a volume damper would be inserted at the entrance to each branch to handle the pressure difference.

Total pressure loss in the system and, hence, the static pressure developed by the fan is obtained as follows: (table numbers refer to section high velocity system design that follows this sections).

Static Regain: The intent of this method is to maintain the static pressure at practically a constant value throughout the system. The advantage of doing this is that static pressure determines the rate of discharge through outlets; hence, if the static pressure remains constant, the size of outlet for given volume of discharge would also be constant. For installations such as hotels or hospitals, there would be an obvious advantage in having the same size outlet in a series of like rooms.

The static regain method utilizes a velocity reduction at the end of each section of duct, the magnitude of the reduction being sufficient to provide a loss of velocity pressure equal to the loss of total pressure that occurred in the preceding section of duct. Thus, for a given length of duct the method of application would be as follows:

1) Determine the friction loss per 100 ft from friction charts.

2) Calculate the static drop in the given length of duct by multiplying the friction loss (from Step 1) by the duct length divided by 100.

3) For known velocity in the duct section read the upstream velocity pressure VP_u from a table of velocity equivalents.

4) Calculate the velocity pressure in the down stream section from the equation,

$$VP_d = VP_u - 2SP \qquad (47)$$

where SP is the friction loss as determined in Step 2; VP_u is the velocity pressure from Step 3. The coefficient reflects the assumption that the regain occurs at 50% efficiency. VP_d is the necessary velocity in the downstream section of duct to provide complete regain of the static pressure lost in the upstream section.

5) Knowing VP_d go to the velocity equivalent Table 14-13 and read the necessary velocity (thus fixing diameter) in the downstream section of the duct.

The static regain method is likely to be more time-consuming than other duct design procedures, but in many cases it will be found to justify the added effort through more effective air distribution.

Simplified Static Regain: It will generally be found that the constant pressure drop method produces a constant friction drop of roughly 0.15 in. wg/100 ft of duct for large trunk ducts carrying 10,000 to 15,000 *cfm*. By dividing the longest equivalent duct run into approximately three parts, each third can be sized at a descending equal friction rate in the direction of air flow, say 0.15, 0.12, and 0.09 in. wg/100 ft of duct run. These rates can be determined in the same manner as the example above.

By designing with descending equal friction rates, the duct system realizes static regain, which makes the system easier to balance and less wasteful of fan energy, while making the design procedure considerably more simple than pure static regain.

Branch sizing can be done as in Example 14 (Table 14-19); however, it is usually satisfactory for short branches to simply use the same friction rate used for the trunk duct.

Total Pressure Method (High Velocity Method): The following coverage on *High Velocity System Design* includes all the elements for design of large systems at any velocity, as well as the special considerations for design at high velocity. It will serve as an example of a design method that can be modified to suit any situation, whether more or less rigorous.

High Velocity System Design.—High velocity duct design is based on the same basic laws of fluid flow as the design of conventional duct systems. There are a few important differences, however:

1) Smaller ducts are used and, therefore, higher friction and dynamic losses are incurred.

2) More extensive use is made of standardized fittings.

3) At high velocities, static pressure regain due to velocity changes becomes significant.

Therefore, the following observations should be borne in mind:

Selection of High Velocity Units: High velocity units and diffusers are selected from manufacturers catalog ratings according to volume flow rate, permissible sound level, and desired location.

Main Duct: The critical duct run is selected on the basis of the system layout, not necessarily on the basis of length alone. Duct runs with greater air flow rate, with more fit-tings (elbows, transitions, branch take-offs, etc.), and/or with a high velocity terminal having greater minimum resistance, are often more appropriate as a basis for duct design.

Duct Velocity and Friction: An initial main duct veloc-ity of approximately 4000 to 4500 fpm and a constant fric-tion loss of about 1.0 inch wg/100 ft of run are recommended. Note that since round ducts of standard diameter are generally used, it is not always possible to maintain an exactly constant friction loss factor. The rec-ommended duct velocities for high velocity systems were listed earlier in Table 14-18.

Dynamic Losses: Static pressure drop caused by branch take-offs, elbows, and duct fittings depends upon both fit-ting design details and air velocity.

Static Pressure Loss and Regain: Velocity drop in a system can produce regain of static pressure, and, con-versely, a velocity rise will result in a loss of static pres-sure. These changes occur in connection with conversion of velocity into static pressure and vice versa. They are important because their calculation may result in (1) reduction of required fan horsepower; (2) calculation of correct pressure available at a branch take-off; (3) deter-mination of correct friction losses in the branch and hence selection of the proper take-off fitting.

Table 14-20 permits direct reading of static regain, or transition loss by relating downstream velocity to upstream velocity. The values in the table apply equally to reducer transitions with an included angle of 45° to 60°. *Caution: Table 14-20 values do not apply to velocity changes that occur with a change in direction of the air stream, as occurs at an elbow or a branch take-off.*

Primary Equipment Losses: To determine the overall static pressure drop for fan selection, it is essential to con-sider also the losses due to primary equipment, such as coils, filters, fresh air intakes, transitions between fan and plenum, heat exchange apparatus, etc. Return duct losses must also be added unless a separate return air fan is pro-vided. Table 14-23 gives losses or regain in commonly used primary equipment.

Branch Trunk Ducts: Generally, branch ducts are sized on the basis of an equal friction loss of 1.0 inch per 100 ft of run. Take-offs and other fittings are selected according to the static pressure available at take-off, less branch fric-tion and terminal pressure resistance. Thus, excess avail-able pressure may be partly absorbed by choosing fittings with higher resistance. The first branch take-off, and fre-quently the last branch take-off, are considered fittings of the branch trunk duct.

Single Branch Lines: Generally, required air volume flow rate and inlet size of the terminal unit also determine branch duct velocity and diameter. Again, fitting details are selected according to available static pressure at the take-off.

Dual Duct Systems: Dual duct systems are designed in the same manner as single duct systems, with the follow-ing two exceptions:

First, the high velocity units are selected on the basis of sound level ratings corresponding to an inlet static pres-sure of 2.5 inches of water. However, the minimum inlet pressures of the selected units are used for the purpose of duct sizing and fan horsepower determination.

Second, to improve stability throughout the system, branch ducts and fittings are designed for low static pres-sure resistance and excess available static pressure is allowed to be absorbed at the inlet valves of the high velocity unit.

Design air quantities for cold ducts are usually 100% of the required *cfm.* Hot ducts are generally based on 50% to 75% of the cold duct *cfm,* depending on the expected load variations, building heat losses, and the required comfort conditions.

Economy in duct sizing can be realized by taking advantage of the probability that 100% of design air quan-tity will rarely be required, even through cold air ducts. One method for saving on cost is to divide the system into four sections of equal design capacity. Then the cold air ducts of the section farthest from the fan are sized for 100% of design capacity; the preceding quarters are sized for 90%, 80%, and 70%, decreasing towards the fan. The hot air ducts are then designed for 75% of the cold duct capacities.

Combined Duct Systems: Sometimes high velocity ducting ends in a multiple (octopus) or end discharge unit from which rectangular or round ducts carry air to the sup-ply outlets at conventional velocities. Static pressure losses in these downstream portions of the system are determined in the same manner, with certain modifica-tions noted later in this article.

Rectangular Ducts: Use of rectangular ducting in high velocity systems is generally avoided because of its greater weight per volume of air carried, greater cost, lower rigidity, and leakage hazards. However, when space and structural reasons require the use of high veloc-ity rectangular ducts, their dimensions are determined either by the desired air velocity through the duct or by the equivalent diameter tables for round ducts (Tables 14-11a and 14-11b in the preceding section on air flow in ducts). The average air velocity in a rectangular duct can be found by dividing the *cfm* by the ducts cross-sectional area in square feet. Do not use the velocity for the equiva-lent round duct size found in Figs. 14-58a, 14-58b, 14-59a and 14-59b, as it will obviously always be higher than the average air velocity through the equivalent rectangu-lar duct for the same air flow.

When calculating dynamic air losses in rectangular duct fittings, always use the average air velocity, not that of the equivalent round duct, to determine the velocity pressure. On the other hand, with rectangular ducts, the equivalent round duct sizes should be used to obtain friction losses from Figs. 14-58a, 14-58b, 14-59a and 14-59b.

Pressure Losses in Branch Take-offs, Elbows, and Fittings in High Velocity Rectangular Ductwork: As stated in good aerodynamics for duct systems above, some of the preferred elbow types for rectangular ductwork in high velocity systems are venturi elbows, easy-bend radius elbows, and radius elbows with elongated splitters. These are shown in Fig. 14-64, 14-62h, and 14-62k.

Where ample space for installation is available, venturi elbows or radius elbows with very easy bends (aspect ratios of 3.0 and above and radius ratios of 1.5 and above) are preferred. Venturi elbows do not require as much turning space as easy bend radius elbows, and have an excellent loss factor; roughly 0.2 loss friction of velocity pressure.

Turning space frequently is unavailable for either venturi or easy-bend radius elbows, in which case square elbows with double-thickness turning vanes might be considered. However, these are not recommended as they tend to increase resistance and become noise generators in high-velocity systems. Instead, the designer should use radius elbows with splitters elongated to $2W$ as in Fig. 14-62k to be constructed according to the *SMACNA High Velocity Duct Manual* to preclude rattling and fluttering. While a minimum throat radius of 3 inches is desirable for a radius elbow with these splitters, the throat radius (R_1 in Fig. 14-62k) can be *squared off* in extreme cases where tight installation conditions prevail; hence these elbows can be installed in the same space that accommodates a square elbow with turning vanes. Dynamic loss fractions, given as a percent of velocity pressure, are tabulated in Table 8.

For 90° branch take-offs and elbows in rectangular high velocity ducts, the designer is advised to use very easy bends where space conditions permit. The losses for these branch take-offs are found in Tables 4 and 5. The loss fractions for various other high velocity duct fittings, such as transition pieces, are tabulated in Tables 6 and 9.

Care should be taken to allow an absolute minimum of five equivalent diameters of straight duct run between successive 90° turns. If this is not possible, use either 45° elbows or radius elbows with elongated splitters. A good arrangement for close distances between turns is shown in Fig. 14-71.

For duct main shaft take-offs, conical fittings (for circular duct), and prism-shaped shoe fittings (for rectangular duct) should be used; 90° duct main or shaft take-offs should not be tolerated for larger sizes (say, over 8 inches diameter) and high velocities (say, over 2000 fpm). All efforts, where large duct panels are involved at shaft take-

off and main duct branch take-offs should be made to reduce the velocity even further (Fig. 14-72).

Where shaft take-off conditions do not permit adequate space conditions to provide conical or prism-type taps, it is recommended that 10-gage duct be installed to permit the fire damper to be located further downstream of the tap within the 100-gage duct. The shaft wall thickness may then be utilized to permit the installation of conical or prism type tap and thereby provide better aerodynamic take-off and approach conditions to the fire damper. See Fig. 14-73.

When possible, the fire damper should be constructed with blades out of the take-off air stream (shutter type). Under no circumstances should the blades be permitted to extend into the shaft air stream.

Pressure Losses for Divided Flow Fittings in Round, High-Velocity Ductwork: DUCT DESIGN gives the loss data for several additional shapes of these fittings in tabulated format. These are round fittings which are commercially available.

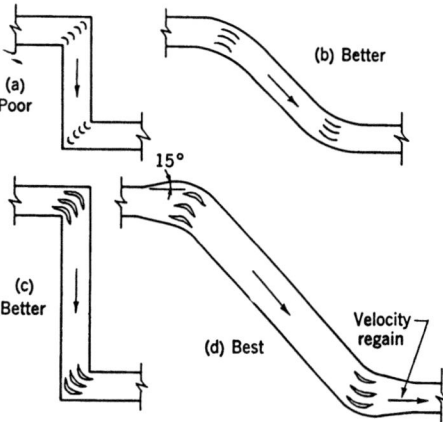

Fig 14-71. Air stream turns between successive fittings

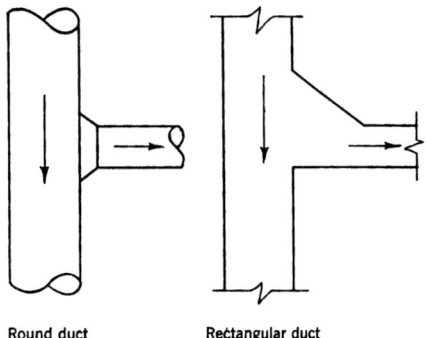

Fig 14-72. Tap off from riser

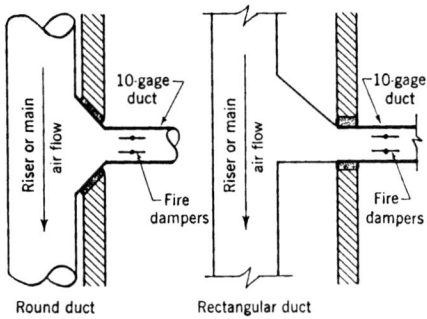

Fig 14-73. Shaft take-off space is inadequate; use extra heavy duct

A modified type of round, high velocity duct is that which has an oval cross-section. The duct is generally called *flat oval*. It is very satisfactory for high velocity systems where limited height is available for installation. However, this ductwork should be factory fabricated, not shop fabricated. Only factory fabricated fittings are recommended for flat oval ducts.

Losses in Tap-Off Fittings in High Velocity Rectangular-Duct Systems: The pressure losses in the tap-off fittings shown in the charts in Fig. 14-74 are experimentally determined for the following set of conditions:

1) The fittings are constructed and installed as discussed in fibrous glass *"Duct Construction"*.

2) The ratio of main duct area to branch duct area is greater than 4.

3) The mains are of rectangular construction.

4) The mains on the upstream side of the tap-off fittings have approximately 8 diameters of straight pipe.

Only static pressure losses through the tap-off fittings are shown in the charts. When the branch ducts from the tap-off connections feed high pressure dual-duct or single duct units, the velocity pressure in the branch duct cannot be credited with regain. This velocity pressure must be considered as a part of the total energy required to create the needed rate of flow through the unit. Rating tables for the high pressure units are normally based on the static pressures at the entrance of the units which means that velocity pressure should be added to these values to establish the total pressure loss through the unit.

To establish the true loss through the tap-off fittings, the velocity pressure in the main duct should be added to,

and the velocity pressure in the branch duct should be deducted from, the values given in the illustrations. In Fig. 14-74, SPM is the static pressure in the main duct and SPB, static pressure in the branch duct.

One should keep in mind that the losses indicated in the chart apply only to well constructed fittings as specified. Fittings with raw edges at the main duct will have losses much greater than those indicated in the chart and will have different acoustical characteristics at higher air velocities.

Flexible Round Ducting for Connections between High-Velocity Ductwork and Terminal Units: Flexible duct is available in aluminum, plastic, and steel can stand pressures within the usual ranges of high velocity duct systems. Manufacturers of flexible duct should be consulted as to the suitability of material and pressure selected for a particular application; flexible metal ducts, for example, may not be sufficiently airtight to meet high-velocity duct specifications. The practice has been to use flexible ducts to connect high velocity ductwork to the terminal units, such as dual duct mixing boxes, in diameters up to 8 inches and in lengths up to 12 feet.

Operating temperature limitations for metallic ducts are:

Aluminum	350°F
Steel	650°F
Stainless steel	1400°F

Single-ply, aluminum flexible duct is good for a maximum working pressure of 3 inches wg, whereas double-ply aluminum can be used for negative or positive pressure as high as 15 to 20 inches wg.

Steel flexible duct is usually galvanized and is stronger than aluminum for the same ply. Single-ply steel is made for negative or positive working pressures as high as given number of inches wg.

It is recommended that flexible duct be UL approved for fire safety; this may be required by some codes and should be checked.

In some areas, the sheet metal trade unions have agreements that limit the length of flexible ducting that can be used in terminal connections. For metallic, flexible, round duct friction losses, consult the manufacturers literature, which will generally be very reliable.

Table 14-20. Static Regain or Loss in Round Transition Pieces

Upstream Velocity V_u, fpm	Downstream Velocity V_d, fpm												
	600	800	1000	1200	1400	1600	1800	2000	2100	2200	2300	2400	2500
	Static Loss or Regain in. wg												
600	0.001	0.020	0.043	...	...	...	...	...	...	...	...	...	...
800	0.015	0.002	0.026	0.055	0.088	...	...	...	...	...	...	...	...
1000	0.035	0.018	0.003	0.032	0.066	0.106	...	...	...	...	...	...	...
1200	0.060	0.043	0.022	0.005	0.038	0.078	0.122	0.172	0.200	...	...	...	...
1400	0.090	0.072	0.051	0.026	0.006	0.046	0.090	0.140	0.167	0.195	0.220	0.260	0.290
1600	0.123	0.116	0.084	0.058	0.030	0.008	0.050	0.102	0.129	0.160	0.185	0.220	0.250
1800	0.161	0.144	0.123	0.096	0.066	0.033	0.010	0.060	0.087	0.115	0.143	0.175	0.210
2000	0.20	0.186	0.165	0.139	0.106	0.073	0.036	0.013	0.040	0.068	0.096	0.128	0.160
2100	0.23	0.21	0.188	0.162	0.132	0.096	0.058	0.016	0.014	0.042	0.070	0.102	0.134
2200	0.25	0.23	0.21	0.18	0.156	0.120	0.081	0.040	0.016	0.015	0.043	0.075	0.107
2300	0.27	0.25	0.23	0.21	0.18	0.144	0.104	0.062	0.043	0.016	0.016	0.048	0.008
2400	0.30	0.28	0.26	0.24	0.21	0.172	0.131	0.089	0.065	0.045	0.017	0.018	0.050
2500	0.33	0.31	0.29	0.26	0.23	0.198	0.158	0.114	0.093	0.068	0.047	0.017	0.020
2600	0.36	0.34	0.32	0.29	0.26	0.230	0.188	0.143	0.119	0.097	0.071	0.049	0.017
2700	0.39	0.37	0.35	0.32	0.29	0.260	0.220	0.172	0.147	0.124	0.100	0.074	0.051
2800	0.42	0.40	0.38	0.35	0.32	0.290	0.250	0.210	0.178	0.152	0.129	0.103	0.077
2900	0.45	0.43	0.41	0.39	0.36	0.32	0.28	0.24	0.20	0.185	0.16	0.134	0.107
3000	0.48	0.47	0.45	0.42	0.39	0.35	0.30	0.27	0.24	0.22	0.19	0.164	0.139
3100	0.52	0.50	0.48	0.45	0.42	0.39	0.35	0.30	0.28	0.25	0.23	0.20	0.17
3200	0.55	0.54	0.52	0.49	0.46	0.42	0.38	0.34	0.31	0.29	0.26	0.23	0.21
3300	0.58	0.57	0.55	0.53	0.50	0.46	0.42	0.37	0.35	0.32	0.30	0.27	0.24
3400	0.63	0.61	0.59	0.56	0.53	0.50	0.46	0.41	0.39	0.36	0.34	0.30	0.28
3500	0.67	0.65	0.63	0.60	0.57	0.54	0.50	0.45	0.43	0.40	0.38	0.35	0.32
3600	0.71	0.69	0.67	0.64	0.61	0.58	0.54	0.49	0.47	0.44	0.42	0.39	0.36
3700	0.75	0.73	0.71	0.68	0.65	0.62	0.58	0.53	0.51	0.48	0.46	0.43	0.40
3800	0.79	0.77	0.75	0.72	0.69	0.66	0.62	0.58	0.55	0.52	0.50	0.47	0.44
3900	0.83	0.81	0.79	0.76	0.73	0.70	0.66	0.62	0.59	0.57	0.54	0.51	0.48
4000	0.88	0.86	0.84	0.81	0.78	0.74	0.70	0.66	0.64	0.61	0.58	0.55	0.52
4100	0.92	0.91	0.88	0.86	0.83	0.79	0.75	0.71	0.68	0.66	0.63	0.60	0.57
4200	0.97	0.95	0.93	0.90	0.87	0.84	0.80	0.76	0.73	0.70	0.68	0.65	0.62
4300	1.02	1.00	0.98	0.95	0.92	0.88	0.84	0.81	0.78	0.75	0.73	0.70	0.67
4400	1.07	1.05	1.03	1.00	0.97	0.93	0.89	0.85	0.83	0.80	0.78	0.75	0.72
4600	1.17	1.15	1.13	1.10	1.07	1.04	1.00	0.95	0.93	0.90	0.88	0.85	0.82
4800	1.27	1.25	1.23	1.20	1.17	1.14	1.00	1.05	0.03	1.00	0.98	0.95	0.92
5000	1.38	1.37	1.34	1.32	1.28	1.25	1.21	1.17	1.14	1.11	1.09	1.06	1.03
5200	1.50	1.48	1.46	1.43	1.40	1.36	1.33	1.28	1.26	1.23	1.20	1.18	1.15
5400	1.61	1.60	1.58	1.55	1.52	1.48	1.44	1.40	1.37	1.35	1.32	1.29	1.27
5600	1.73	1.72	1.70	1.67	1.64	1.61	1.57	1.53	1.50	1.47	1.45	1.42	1.39
5800	1.86	1.85	1.83	1.80	1.77	1.74	1.70	1.66	1.63	1.60	1.57	1.55	1.52
6000	1.99	1.98	1.96	1. 93	1.91	1.87	1.83	1.78	1.76	1.73	1.70	1.68	1.65

Table 14-21. Static Regain or Loss in Round Transition Pieces

Up stream Velocity V_u, fpm	Downstream Velocity V_d, fpm												
	2600	2700	2800	2900	3000	3100	3200	3300	3400	3500	3600	3700	3800
	Static Loss or Regain, in. wg												
1600	0.28	0.32	…	…	…	…	…	…	…	…	…	…	…
1800	0.24	0.27	0.30	0.35	…	…	…	…	…	…	…	…	…
2000	0.194	0.23	0.26	0.30	0.34	0.38	0.42	…	…	…	…	…	…
2100	0.168	0.20	0.24	0.28	0.31	0.35	0.40	0.44	…	…	…	…	…
2200	0.141	0.17	0.21	0.25	0.29	0.33	0.37	0.41	0.46	…	…	…	…
2300	0.114	0.148	0.183	0.22	0.26	0.30	0.34	0.38	0.43	0.47	…	…	…
2400	0.084	0.118	0.153	0.191	0.23	0.27	0.31	0.35	0.40	0.44	0.49	…	…
2500	0.054	0.088	0.123	0.161	0.20	0.24	0.28	0.32	0.37	0.41	0.46	0.51	…
2600	0.021	0.055	0.09	0.128	0.168	0.21	0.25	0.29	0.34	0.38	0.43	0.47	0.52
2700	0.180	0.023	0.058	0.096	0.135	0.175	0.22	0.26	0.30	0.35	0.39	0.44	0.49
2800	0.052	0.018	0.025	0.062	0.102	0.141	0.183	0.23	0.27	0.31	0.36	0.41	0.46
2900	0.080	0.054	0.019	0.026	0.065	0.105	0.147	0.189	0.23	0.28	0.32	0.37	0.42
3000	0.110	0.083	0.056	0.019	0.028	0.068	0.11	0.152	0.196	0.24	0.29	0.34	0.38
3100	0.144	0.114	0.087	0.057	0.02	0.03	0.072	0.114	0.158	0.20	0.25	0.30	0.35
3200	0.176	0.149	0.118	0.09	0.059	0.02	0.032	0.074	0.118	0.163	0.21	0.26	0.31
3300	0.210	0.183	0.153	0.122	0.093	0.06	0.021	0.034	0.078	0.123	0.169	0.22	0.27
3400	0.250	0.22	0.189	0.158	0.126	0.096	0.06	0.021	0.036	0.081	0.127	0.176	0.22
3500	0.290	0.26	0.22	0.194	0.162	0.129	0.099	0.062	0.022	0.038	0.084	0.133	0.182
3600	0.330	0.30	0.26	0.23	0.199	0.166	0.132	0.102	0.063	0.022	0.041	0.087	0.137
3700	0.370	0.34	0.31	0.27	0.24	0.20	0.171	0.136	0.105	0.064	0.023	0.043	0.091
3800	0.410	0.38	0.35	0.31	0.28	0.25	0.21	0.175	0.139	0.108	0.065	0.023	0.045
3900	0.450	0.42	0.39	0.36	0.32	0.29	0.25	0.22	0.18	0.142	0.111	0.066	0.024
4000	0.490	0.46	0.43	0.40	0.36	0.33	0.29	0.26	0.22	0.184	0.146	0.114	0.067
4100	0.540	0.51	0.48	0.45	0.41	0.37	0.34	0.30	0.27	0.23	0.189	0.149	0.117
4200	0.590	0.56	0.53	0.49	0.46	0.42	0.38	0.34	0.31	0.27	0.24	0.193	0.153
4300	0.640	0.61	0.57	0.54	0.50	0.47	0.43	0.39	0.35	0.32	0.28	0.24	0.20
4400	0.690	0.66	0.62	0.59	0.55	0.52	0.48	0.44	0.40	0.36	0.33	0.28	0.25
4600	0.790	0.76	0.72	0.69	0.65	0.62	0.58	0.54	0.50	0.46	0.42	0.38	0.34
4800	0.890	0.86	0.83	0.79	0.75	0.72	0.68	0.65	0.60	0.56	0.52	0.48	0.44
5000	1.000	0.97	0.94	0.90	0.87	0.83	0.79	0.76	0.72	0.68	0.63	0.59	0.55
5200	1.120	1.09	1.05	1.02	0.98	0.95	0.91	0.87	0.83	0.79	0.75	0.71	0.66
5400	1.240	1.20	1.17	1.14	1.10	1.07	1.03	0.99	0.95	0.91	0.87	0.82	0.78
5600	1.360	1.33	1.30	1.26	1.23	1.19	1.15	1.11	1.08	1.03	0.99	0.95	0.91
5800	1.490	1.46	1.43	1.39	1.36	1.31	1.28	1.24	1.20	1.16	1.12	1.08	1.03
6000	1.620	1.59	1.56	1.52	1.49	1.45	1.41	1.37	1.33	1.29	1.25	1.21	1.17

Table 14-22. Static Regain or Loss in Round Transition Pieces

Upstream Velocity V_u, fpm	Downstream Velocity V_d, fpm													
	3900	4000	4100	4200	4300	4400	4600	4800	5000	5200	5400	5600	5800	5900
	Static Loss or Regain, in. wg													
2700	0.54	...	...	...	...	...	...	...	...	...	...	...	...	...
2800	0.51	0.56	0.61	0.67	...	...	...	...	...	...	...	...	...	...
2900	0.47	0.52	0.58	0.63	0.69	...	...	...	...	...	...	...	...	...
3000	0.44	0.48	0.54	0.59	0.65	0.71	...	...	...	...	...	...	...	...
3100	0.40	0.46	0.50	0.56	0.61	0.67	0.79	...	...	...	...	...	...	...
3200	0.36	0.41	0.46	0.52	0.57	0.63	0.75	0.87	...	...	...	...	...	...
3300	0.32	0.37	0.42	0.48	0.53	0.59	0.71	0.83	0.96	...	...	...	...	...
3400	0.28	0.33	0.38	0.43	0.49	0.55	0.67	0.79	0.91	1.05	...	...	...	...
3500	0.23	0.28	0.34	0.39	0.45	0.50	0.62	0.74	0.87	1.00	...	...	...	...
3600	0.19	0.24	0.29	0.35	0.40	0.46	0.58	0.70	0.83	0.96	1.10	...	...	...
3700	0.143	0.194	0.250	0.300	0.360	0.41	0.53	0.65	0.78	0.92	1.05	...	...	...
3800	0.094	0.145	0.200	0.260	0.310	0.37	0.49	0.61	0.74	0.87	1.00	...	...	...
3900	0.048	0.098	0.153	0.210	0.260	0.32	0.44	0.56	0.69	0.82	0.96	1.10	...	...
4000	0.024	0.050	0.102	0.160	0.220	27.00	0.39	0.51	0.64	0.78	0.91	1.06	...	...
4100	0.068	0.025	0.053	0.106	0.162	0.22	0.34	0.46	0.59	0.72	0.86	1.00	1.15	...
4200	0.120	0.068	0.0250	0.055	0.111	0.167	0.290	0.410	0.540	0.660	0.810	0.95	1.10	...
4300	0.159	0.230	0.069	0.026	0.058	0.114	0.230	0.350	0.480	0.620	0.760	0.90	1.05	...
4400	0.200	0.164	0.126	0.070	0.026	0.061	0.179	0.300	0.430	0.560	0.700	0.84	0.99	1.15
4600	0.300	0.250	0.210	0.174	0.129	0.070	0.066	0.188	0.320	0.450	0.590	0.73	0.88	1.04
4800	0.40	0.36	0.31	0.27	0.22	0.180	0.072	0.072	0.200	0.330	0.470	0.62	0.76	0.92
5000	0.50	0.46	0.41	0.37	0.32	0.280	0.186	0.074	0.078	0.210	0.350	0.49	0.64	0.80
5200	0.62	0.57	0.52	0.48	0.43	0.390	0.290	0.192	0.076	0.084	0.220	0.37	0.510	0.67
5400	0.73	0.69	0.64	0.59	0.54	0.490	0.400	0.300	0.200	0.078	0.091	0.23	0.380	0.54
5600	0.86	0.81	0.76	0.72	0.66	0.61	0.52	0.42	0.31	0.21	0.08	0.098	0.250	0.40
5800	0.99	0.94	0.89	0.85	0.79	0.74	0.64	0.54	0.43	0.32	0.22	0.80	0.106	0.26
6000	1.12	1.07	1.02	0.98	0.92	0.87	0.77	0.66	0.55	0.44	0.34	0.22	0.081	1.15

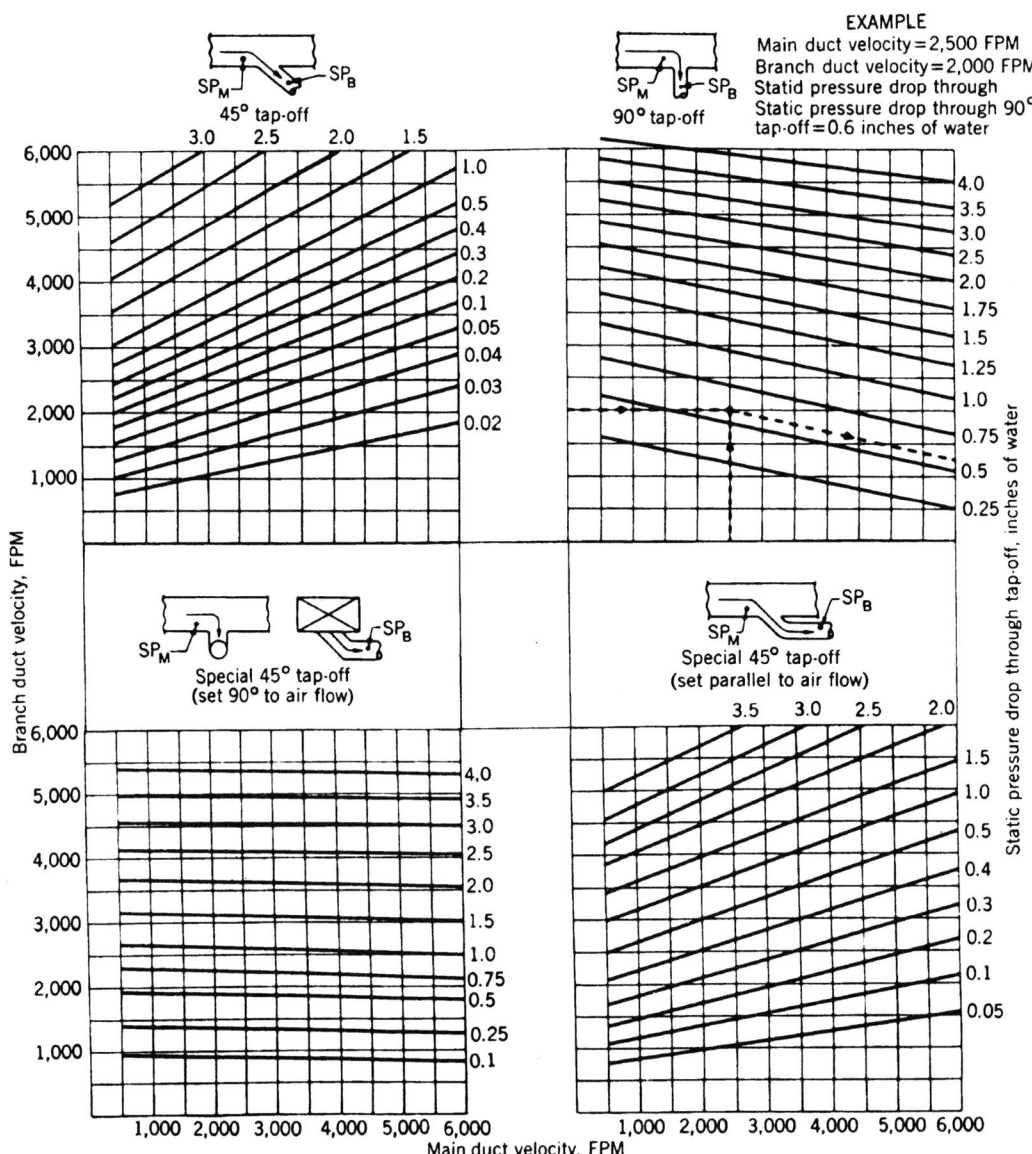

Fig 14-74. Static pressure losses through 4 types of tap off connections in high velocity duct systems

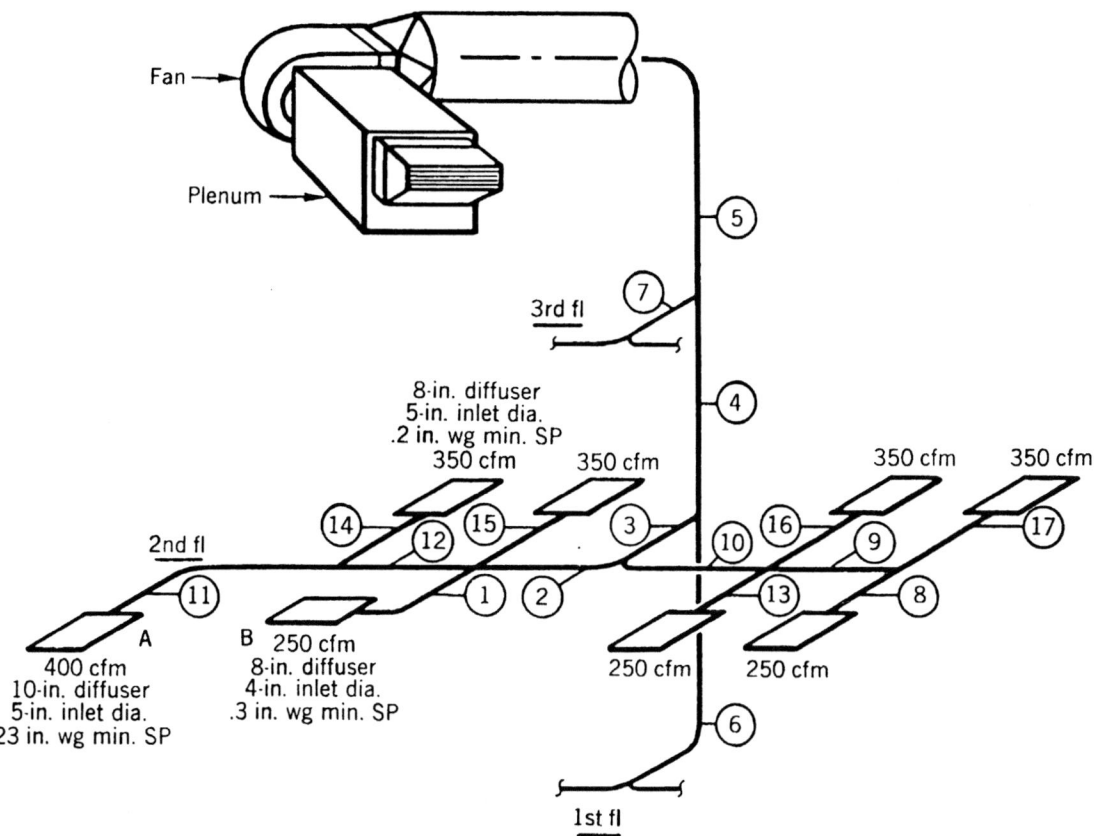

Fan

Plenum

3rd fl ⑦

⑤

8-in. diffuser
5-in. inlet dia.
.2 in. wg min. SP
350 cfm   350 cfm

④

350 cfm   350 cfm

2nd fl   ⑭   ⑫ ⑮   ③ ⑩ ⑯   ⑨

⑪   ① ②   ⑬   ⑧

A
400 cfm   B 250 cfm
10-in. diffuser   8-in. diffuser
5-in. inlet dia.   4-in. inlet dia.
.23 in. wg min. SP   .3 in. wg min. SP   250 cfm   250 cfm

⑥

1st fl

Fig 14-75. Layout and specifications chart for duct system in a 3-story office building

Section	cfm	Length, ft	Section	cfm	Length, ft	Section	cfm	Length, ft
1	250	9	6	2550	18	11	400	12
2	1350	10	7	2550	6	12	750	10
3	2550	6	8	250	6	13	250	6
4	5100	12	9	600	10	14–15	350	6
5	7650	16	10	1200	10	16–17	350	6

Table 14-23. Static Pressure Loss and Regain, Fan Plenum Duct Transitions, Inches WG

Blow Through Fan System	Draw Through Fan System		Heat Exchanger
	Divergent Transition	Convergent Transition	

Blow Through Fan System	Divergent Transition	Convergent Transition	Heat Exchanger
SP loss, inches wg:	SP regain, inches wg:	SP loss, inches wg:	SP loss, inches wg:
$L = VP_2 \times C_2 - VP_1 \times C_1$	$L = (VP_2 - VP_1) \times C_1$	$L = VP_2 \times C_2 - VP_1$	$L = (VP_D - 0.02) \times C_2 - (VP_u - 0.02) \times C_1$

Velocity V, fpm –Velocity Pressure VP, inches wg								C Factor Table		
V	VP	V	VP	V	VP	V	VP	Transition	C_1	C_2
600	0.023	2300	0.33	3300	0.68	4300	1.15	Abrupt enlargement	0.18	
800	0.040	2400	0.36	3400	0.72	4400	1.21	Abrupt contraction		1.47
1000	0.062	2500	0.39	3500	0.77	4600	1.32	Gradual enlargement 30°	0.44	
1200	0.09	2600	0.42	3600	0.81	4800	1.44	Divergent transition 45°	0.33	
1400	0.122	2700	0.46	3700	0.85	5000	1.56	Included angle: 60°	0.26	
1600	0.16	2800	0.49	3800	0.90	5200	1.69	Gradual contraction		
1800	0.20	2900	0.53	3900	0.95	5400	1.82	(convergent transition)		
2000	0.25	3000	0.56	4000	1.00	5600	1.96	30° – 60° included angle		1.07
2100	0.28	3100	0.60	4100	1.05	5800	2.10	Bellmouth		1.05
2200	0.30	3200	0.64	4200	1.10	6000	2.25			

Note: Static pressure losses due to conventional return duct systems are calculated in the customary manner. Static pressure losses due to equipment, such as filters, coils, etc are determined according to manufacturers literature. To determine fan motor hp all pressure losses must be considered.

Example 15: An elbow in a 24 by 8 inch duct with 12 inch center radius handles 2800 *cfm.* Velocity is 2400 (previously calculated). $H/W = 24/8 = 3.0$; $R/W = 12/8 = 1.50$; and static pressure drop = 0.047 inches wg.

Note: Rectangular elbows with radius ratio below 0.50, but not below 0.25 and those above 6.0 should be avoided.

Elbows other than 90° cause a drop in static pressure equal to tabular value times the angle divided by 90. Static pressure losses of rectangular elbows with low radius ratio can be reduced by use of turning vanes. Correction factors are given in table below. Values not shown indicate no static pressure drop reduction due to vanes.

	Number of Turning Vanes		
	1	2	3
R/W	Correction Factor		
0.75	0.43	0.32	0.25
1.00	0.56	0.46	...
1.50	0.85	...	...

Example 16: Blow Through Fan I: Fan outlet velocity, $V_1 = 3000$ fpm; main duct velocity, $V_2 = 4400$ fpm. Both transitions (fan plenum and plenum duct) of 60° included angle; $VP_1 = 0.56$, $VP_2 = 1.21$, $C_1 = 0.26$, $C_2 = 1.07$; static pressure loss = $1.21 \times 1.07 - 0.56 \times 0.26 = 1.15$ inches wg.

Example 17:Draw Through Fan II-a: $V_1 = 3000$ fpm; $V_2 = 4200$ fpm, 45° divergent transition (fan duct) $VP_1 = 1.56$, $VP_2 = 1.10$, $C_1 = 0.33$, regain = $(1.56 - 1.10) \times 0.33 = 0.152$ in. wg.

Example 18:Draw Through Fan II-b: $V_1 = 3000$ fpm; $V_2 = 4200$ fpm, 45° convergent transition (fan duct) $VP_1 = 0.56$, $VP_2 = 1.10$, $C_2 = 1.07$, static pressure loss = $1.10 \times 1.07 - 0.56 = 0.617$ in. wg.

Example 19: Reheater Coil Section III: $VP_U = 3800$ fpm; $V_D = 4600$ fpm. Both transitions at 45° included angles. $VP_U = 0.56$, $VP_D = 1.10$, $C_1 = 0.33$, $C_2 = 1.07$, static pressure loss = $(1.32 - 0.02) \times 1.07 - (0.90 - 0.02) \times 0.33 = 1.10$ in. wg.

Step by Step Design.—A 14-step method for design of high velocity systems is demonstrated by its application to a hypothetical 3-story office building. Schematic layout of the system is shown in Fig. 14-75. The worksheet is Table 14-24. Air requirements and duct layout for each of the three floors are assumed to be identical.

Main Duct.—*Step 1:* Select critical high velocity unit and duct run. Consider capacity and pressure loss characteristics of units and fittings, as well as duct length. Include branch take-off before critical unit.

Referring to the schematic layout, Fig. 14-75, note that Unit A is farthest from riser, but has low minimum static pressure, only one elbow fitting, and may possibly benefit from static regain at upstream transition fittings. Unit B has shorter duct run but higher minimum SP, both an elbow and a take-off fitting, and less potential benefit from static regain. Unit B is, therefore, selected as the critical unit. For similar reasons, the ducting serving the second floor is selected as part of the main duct run.

Table 14-24. Work Sheet for Design Example

1	2	3	4	5	6	7	8	9	10	11	12	13	14	15
							Static Pressure, "WG"					Branch-Off		
								Velocity Conversion						
Duct Section or Fitting Detail	Capacities, cfm	Initial Velocities, fpm	Diameter in.	Section Length, ft	SP 100 ft wg	V_d/V_u	Prelim.	Loss	Regain	Section	Cumulative	At	Avail SP	Remarks
8" Diffuser	250						0.30							
1	250	2800	4	9	3.5		0.315	a						
90°L B = 1.5D, 5 pc	250	2800	4				0.117							
90°T short cone	250	2800				1.12	0.425		1.157	1.157				
2	1350	2500	10	10	.9		.09	a						
45°L R = 1.5D, 3 pc	1350	2500	10				.047							
45°T	1350	2500				.80	.039		.176	1.333				
3	2550	3200	12	6	1.2		.072	a						
90°T Long Cone	2550	3200				.86	.24		.312	1.645				
4	5100	3700	16	12	1.1		.132		.28	.148	1.497			
5	7650	4400	18	16	1.3		.208			.498	1.995			
90°L, R=1.5D, 5Pc.	7650	4400	18				.29			.498	1.995			
Draw-thru fan system,30° incl. angle transition							.154							
	V₁= 5000	fpm	V₂=4400	fpm										
Primary equipment and air intake							.65			.496	2.491			
Static pressure recheck of other branch ducts:														
1st floor	Equal to	Main	Duct Sections 1,2							1.333		3	1.645	
6	2550	3200	12	18	1.2		.216	.171	.198	1.531				
90°T, R =1.5D		3200	12				.153	.171						
3rd floor	Static Pressure Recheck of Other Branch Trunk Ducts:									1.333		4	1.497	
7	2550	3200					.072		.072	1.405				
90°T, Long cone	2550	3200				.725			.072	1.405				
Select fan on basis of 2.491, say 2.5" w.g. overall S.P. resistance														
8" Diffuser	250						.3					2	1.333	
8	250	2800	4	6	3.5		.21	a	.95	.95				
90°T Short cone	250	2800				1.27	(.44)		.95	.95				
9	600	2200	7	10	1.2		.12	.124 =	.004	.946				
10	1200	2700	9	10	1.2		.12		.26	1.206				
45°L, R=1.5D, 3Pc		2700	9				(0.55)							
5°T	1200	2700					(0.85)							
Preliminary					S.P. = 0.75–0.124 = 0.626									
Avaliable for fittings: 1.333–0.626 =0.707				Selected Section 8-90°T			Short Cone =.44		10 45°L R=1,5d,3Pc=0.055		45°T = 0.085			
Excess available S.P. absorbed at terminal inlet valve:							0.707–0.58=1.333–1.206=0.127" wg							
10" Diffuser	400						.23					1	1.015	
11	400	3000	5	12	3.0		.36	.29						
90°L(R =1.5D)	400	3000					(.135		1.015	1.015				
12	750	2200	8	100	.9		.09		.068	.022	1.037			
13	250	Equal to Section 8			1.04	.51+.41		a		.92		9	.946	
8" Diffuser	350						.2							
14	350	2600	5	6	2.25		.135	a		.705		11	1.015	b
90°T, Short cone	350	2600				1.18	.37							
15	350	Equal to Section 14			1.04	.335+	.36	a		.695		1	1.157	b
16	350				.965	.335+	.34			.675		9	.946	
17	350				1.18	.335+	.37	a		.705		8	.95	

[a] When change in velocity is combined with change in direction of flow (elbow or branch take-off)
[b] 90° branch take-off fittings could be used for sections 14 and 15, but short cone type was selected throughout for reasons of uniformity.

Step 2: Starting at the critical high velocity unit and working upstream toward the fan, identify and enter in the worksheet, Table 14-24, columns 1, 2, and 5, the main duct fittings, their *cfm* and section lengths, respectively. (Refer to sections 1 to 5 in the layout, Fig. 14-75.)

Step 3: Starting with the duct section handling the most *cfm*, determine duct velocities, diameters, and SP per 100 ft (columns 3, 4, and 6) by means of a standard air duct friction chart (Figs. 14-58a, 14-58b, 14-59a, or 14-59b).

    For example:

    Main duct, section 5............... 7650 *cfm*;

    Initial velocity (column 3) .... 4400 fpm;

    Duct diameter (column 4).......... 18 in. wg;

    SP per 100 ft (column 6).......... 1.3 in. wg.

Step 4: Determine preliminary SP losses (column 8).

1) Refer to manufacturers literature for high velocity units minimum SP resistance.

2) Multiply duct length by friction SP loss per 100 ft and divide by 100. For example, section 5:

    Length (column 5)................. 0 ft;

    SP per 100 ft (column 6)......... 1.3 in. wg;

    SP loss, (column 8)............... 0.208 in. wg.

3) Refer to Table 14-24 for elbow losses. For example, duct section 1:

    Velocity, (column 3).......... 2800 fpm;

    90°, 5-piece elbow, R/D = 1.5,

    SP loss (column 8) .... 0.117 in. wg.

4) For branch take-off losses (chapter 8).

    For example:

    Duct section 1, branch velocity, V_B ... = 2800 fpm;

    Duct section 2, upstream velocity, V_U .. = 2500 fpm;

    Velocity ratio, V_B / V_U (column 7)... = 1.12;

    Short cone take-off loss (column 8) ... = 0.425 in wg.

5) Refer to manufacturers literature for SP ratings of primary equipment, such as coils and filters, and determine losses due to fresh-air intakes, return ducts, etc., by separate calculation.

Step 5: Determine SP losses (column 9) and regain (column 10) due to velocity conversion.

1) Refer to Table 14-24 for the duct system proper. For example, Duct Section 4:

Upstream velocity (column 3) V_U .... = 4400 fpm;

Downstream velocity (column 3) V_D .... = 3700 fpm;

Regain (column 10).......... = 0.28 in. wg.

2) Refer to Table 14-6 for fan-plenum-duct transitions. For example, fan plenum arrangement 11-a:

Static regain, $R = (VP_1 - VP_2) \times C_1$ in. wg;

    Fan discharge velocity $V_1 = 5000$ fpm;

    From the table, $VP_1 = 1.56$ in. wg;

    Initial duct velocity, $V_2 = 4400$ fpm;

    From the table $VP_2 = 1.21$ in. wg;

    From C-factor table

    C_1 for 30° divergent transition = 0.44;

    Enter static regain (column 10) = 0.154 in. wg.

Step 6: Add up pressure losses (columns 8 and 9) and deduct regain (column 10) for each section to obtain sectional SP losses (column 11).

Step 7: Determine cumulative SP losses (column 12) by adding up sectional losses step by step, starting with Section 1. The highest value obtained represents the tentative SP drop for the entire system, subject to recheck of other branch trunk ducts, as outlined in Step 8 below.

Branch Trunk Ducts.—*Step 8:* Determine the static pressure available for designing the branch duct. It is equal to the pressure in the main duct at the junction and, therefore, also to the sum of pressure losses downstream of the take-off.

From columns 1 and 12 of the main duct calculations, identify and enter in the worksheet the main duct section following the branch take-off (column 13) and available SP at the take-off (column 14).

For example:

(Refer to layout, Fig. 14-75.) Main duct Section 2 follows junction of branch trunk duct, sections 8 to 10.

(Refer to work sheet, Table 14-24.) Available SP at take-off = cumulative SP for duct section 2 = 1.333 inches wg.

Step 9: Branch trunk ducts, resembling a portion of the main duct in layout and capacity, often require rechecking of only one fitting and/or duct section against available SP. Check particularly for:

    (a) Low available SP. Check main duct, column 12;

    (b) High V_b/V_u ratio, Check columns 3 and 7;

    (c) Longest duct run , Check column 5.

For example, referring to layout and worksheet for section 7:

Duct layout and *cfm* for the 3rd floor are equal to previously calculated main duct Sections 1 to 3.

Available SP (column 14) = 1.4497 in. wg. Note that this is a lower value than that for the 2nd floor.

Branch SP losses (column 12) = 1.405 in. wg, due to low V_B/V_u ratio, take-off losses are disregarded.

Available SP exceeds branch duct losses. Therefore, no changes are required. (Should branch duct losses exceed available SP, increase fan SP rating by a corresponding amount or select fittings or high velocity terminal with lower resistance.

Step 10: Design branch trunk ducts with different *cfm* and dimensions as follows: Determine location of take-off and available SP, as before (columns 13 and 14). Enter on worksheet the branch duct sections, fittings, and high velocity unit, their *cfm* and section lengths, as before (columns 1, 2, and 5) but omit fitting details.

Summary of Procedure for Using Worksheet

Step	Description	Ref. or Table	Work Sheet Column
Main Duct			
1	Select "critical" high velocity unit and duct run.	Layout	
2	Enter duct sections and fittings, *cfm* and duct section lengths, starting at velocity unit.	Layout	1,2,5
3	Enter duct fpm, dia. and SP/100 ft, starting at fan.	Friction Chart	3,4,6
4	Enter preliminary SP losses of:		
	a) High velocity unit.	Catalogue	8
	b) Duct sections.	Col. 5,6	8
	c) Fittings (for branch take offs, determine V_b/V_u ratio)	Table 8-24	8
	d) Fan-plenum-duct transitions	ASHRAE	9,10
	e) Primary equipment	Mf's ratings	8
	f) Air intakes and/or return ducts.	Separately calculated	8
5	Enter velocity conversion losses and regain.	Table 8-1	9,10
6	Add up SP losses, deduct regain for each section.	Table 14-22	11
7	Add up sectional SP losses, step by step	Col.11	12
Branch Trunk Duct			
8	Enter main duct section following take off and available cumulative SP.	main duct Col. 1,12	13,14
9	With branch ducts resembling portion of main duct, check take-off fitting losses against available SP.	Col. 14	7,8
10	with branch trunk ducts in general, enter duct sections and fittings, *cfm* and lengths; omit fitting details.	Layout	1,2,5
11	Enter fpm, dia., SP/100 ft, V_b/V_u ratio, friction losses, conversion losses and regain and high velocity unit resistance. Add values in Col. 8 and 9, deduct values in Col. 10, and deduct results from available SP	Col. 14	
12	Difference is SP available for fittings, select fittings and enter their SP losses.	Table 14-24	1,8
	Add up sectional and cumulative losses.	Col. 8,9,10	11,12
Single Branch Line			
13	Proceed as under steps 8 and 9 (or 10)		1,2,5,13,14
	Enter duct fpm, dia., *SP*/100 ft, V_b/V_u ratio		3,4,6,7
14	Enter SP losses and regain as before	Col. 14	8,9,10
	Subtract their sum from available SP and select fitting details accordingly	Table 14-24	1,8,11,12

Step 11: Determine duct velocities, diameters, SP per 100 ft, V_b/V_u ratios, friction losses, conversion losses and regain, and high velocity unit minimum SP resistances, as before, (columns 3, 4, 6, 7, 8, 9, and 10) but omit fitting losses. Add up values, entered in columns 8 and 9 so far, and deduct those in column 10. Subtract the result from the available SP, (column 14) to obtain the pressure available for the fittings.

Step 12: Select fitting details from *Chapter 8.* Enter them and their losses on the worksheet (columns 1 and 8). Add up sectional and cumulative SP losses, as before (columns 11 and 12). As an example, refer to work sheet for duct sections 8 to 10.

Single Branch Lines.—*Step 13:* Enter take-off location and available SP from previously established data (columns 13 and 14); also terminal, duct section, and duct length, according to layout (columns 1, 2, and 5); duct velocity, diameter, SP per 100 ft, and V_b/V_u, according to the high velocity unit selected and an air duct friction chart (columns 3, 4, 6, and 7).

Step 14: Determine duct friction and minimum high velocity SP loss (column 8), also conversion loss or regain wherever applicable (columns 9 and 10). Finally, check fitting details and SP losses (columns 1 and 8) and sectional pressure losses (column 11) against available *SP* (column 14).

Alternate Procedure for High Velocity Duct Design.—The preceding example suggests that trial duct sizes in the longest run can be obtained by finding the equivalent friction loss of the main trunk duct then using this static pressure loss per 100 ft, by going to size each succeeding duct section. This method would result in excessively high fan pressures for larger and more sophisticated systems than the one shown in the example. In preference to the example's method, the designer is advised to take a standard duct friction chart (Figs. 14-58a, 14-58b, 14-59a, or 14-59b).

1) Select a velocity in the trunk duct leaving the fan. Table 2 will be useful for showing the limiting velocities in trunk ducts.

2) After a trunk duct velocity is selected for the maximum *cfm*, it will almost invariably result in a duct friction loss below 1.0 inch wg/100 ft. If so, base all trial trunk duct sizes on the trunk duct velocity selected in Step 1, until the duct velocity line crosses the constant friction line of 1.0 inch wg/100 ft. It will not be possible to base all duct sizes on exactly the velocity selected in Step 1 since round ducts come in standard diameters and rectangular ducts are usually made to the nearest inch; however, the designer should attempt to keep velocity changes in this section to the minimum or lowest range possible because the dynamic losses for each velocity change become significant at higher velocities. Trial sizes for rectangular ducts in this section must be based on the average velocity in the duct cross section, not the velocity of an equivalent round duct.

3) At the point where the constant velocity line from Step 1 crosses the constant friction line of 1.0 in. wg per 100 ft the *cfm* for this duct size and all trial sizes for downstream sections thereafter will be sized on an equal duct friction of 1.0 inch wg/100 ft. When sizing on a constant

friction line, all ducts with rectangular cross sections are sized from the equivalent round-duct size.

The constant pressure drop was arbitrarily set at 1.0 inch wg/100 feet, which should give reasonably conservative trial duct sizes. The designer can use 1.5 inches wg /100 ft for smaller trial sizes, or select trial sizes based on a band between 1.5 inches and 1.0 inch wg. For very conservative trial duct sizes, a constant pressure of 0.75 inch wg per 100 ft is recommended.

After the trial sizes have been selected, the designer can proceed to calculate the duct friction losses, static losses, and static regain, all as shown in the preceding example. Where there are large losses due to friction or static losses (from velocity increase), the designer can change the trial size to a larger size, and so reduce these losses.

In the end, the designer must not come out with static pressures above 6 inches wg if he expects to use high velocity, medium pressure duct construction. Moreover, he must stay below 10 inches wg in the main trunk duct since this is the limiting pressure for high velocity, high pressure duct construction. If the pressure limits for high velocity duct construction are exceeded, the ducts may very well balloon or blow apart at the seams.

The smallest duct sizes recommended for high velocity systems are 4 inches diameter for round ducts and 6 inches square for rectangular ducts.

Duct Design by Computer.—Recently, great strides have been made in the computerization of duct design. This includes programs that design duct systems on the equal friction method, on static regain, or on total pressure methods. It further includes high and low velocity duct design, and both supply and return (or exhaust) systems.

Most programs give the following items on the printout:
1) dimensions of each duct section;
2) velocity in each duct section;
3) static pressure required at fan discharge;
4) pressure drop through each duct section;
5) total pounds of sheet metal required for the whole duct system;
6) air flow rate at each air device;
7) air supply temperature at each air device for cases where duct is bare; and

8) static pressure at each branch take-off.

Some programs are set up to optimize duct design so that the available static pressure is dissipated completely in each run. Others permit the designer to make fitting substitutions so that fan static pressures can be reduced. In general, the computer can do in seconds what a designer may never be able to do in a short time: i.e., determine which run in a system has the greatest pressure drop. While the computer can do marvels in duct design, the major problem is to set the system up so that its input data can be readily fed into the computers program.

For example, one program has been set up in conversational English. It progressively asks the designer all pertinent questions required by the program, such as *What are the air flows for each diffuser? How long are the duct lengths for each section? What type of fitting has been chosen? What is the friction rate to be used for constant friction design? What are the velocity limits, the type of duct construction desired, etc.?* For this program, it is necessary to set up the duct system on an architectural sepia print, in single line. From this, nodes can be numbered, duct section lengths estimated, and input sheets made out. These input data may require many hours for a large, complicated duct system, but the results are rewarding: All answers are in conversational English, and they give a clear picture of the whole system, as designed, by the assumed parameters. The designer has only to transcribe the duct sizes on the single line sepia prints from which the final ductwork drawing can now be made by a draftsman or draftsmen.

There is, however, one word of caution about the use of computer results. They are based on ideal construction of the duct system, which rarely ever happens. For this reason, the static pressure for the system, as calculated by the computer, may be on the light side. To be safe for fan selection, a healthy safety factor should be applied to the calculated static pressure for the duct system, and the fan motor should be able to accommodate a fan static pressure of 30 to 50% more than the calculated static pressure.

There are many companies, technical institutions, and trade organizations that offer ductwork programs for computers, as well as any number of arrangements for renting or buying these programs.

Fibrous Glass Duct Construction.—Fibrous glass duct construction is used for low velocity, low pressure systems and enjoys an increasing popularity, particularly in smaller duct systems for homes, small offices, soundproof areas such as studios, etc. The advantages of this duct material are:

1) It combines the conduit capability of carrying air with thermal insulation and sound absorption. On the other hand, sheet metal ductwork requires two separate materials to accomplish the same result.

2) Because it is taped at the construction joints, air leakage is almost nil and rated air delivery is dependable.

3) Fibrous glass duct systems are approximately 75% lighter in weight than insulated sheetmetal systems of comparable size. This greatly aids both duct delivery to the jobsite and field assembly. For example, duct sections 16 to 20 feet long can be easily assembled, handled, and installed as one unit, whereas sheet metal ducts are limited to 8 foot lengths.

4) Duct condensation is not a problem; the vapor barrier jackets on the preformed sections are excellent for the warm side barriers on air conditioning systems. With properly taped and sealed joints, no condensation will occur.

5) At one time, the interior surfaces of fibrous glass ductwork were rough and required greater fan horsepower to overcome the added skin friction. Advances in fibrous glass duct board technology have resulted in smooth interior surfaces, essentially equal to those of sheet metal.

6) By the use of color-coded hand tools, fibrous glass ductwork can be rapidly grooved and notched in the field or on the shop bench. The mechanic need not possess unusual manual skills to perform these simple operations.

The current SMACNA* standard for fibrous glass duct construction limits this material to positive or negative static pressures in the duct of 2 inches wg and an air velocity of 2000 fpm. There are other limitations on the use of fibrous glass for ductwork:

1) Maximum air temperature inside duct of 250°F and maximum ambient air temperature outside the duct of 150°F.

2) Fibrous glass cannot be used for kitchen or exhaust ducts, or to convey solids or corrosive gases.

3) Ducts of fibrous glass should not be buried below grade or in concrete.

4) These ducts are limited to indoor use, unless weather protection and proper reinforcement are provided.

5) Fibrous glass cannot be used for casings and housings.

6) High temperature heating coils should not be installed immediately adjacent to the fibrous glass material.

7) For other limitations on fibrous glass ductwork, such as flexural rigidity, maximum allowable deflection, board fatigue, moisture, and safety standards.

8) If a fibrous duct system is to be used for air conditioning only, positive closing-type air diffusers and return-air grilles should be used. They must be closed during off-season periods to minimize the entrance of heat and moisture.

While the past market for fibrous glass ductwork has been primarily in the smaller systems, the technology for this material has advanced so rapidly that it is now used on larger installations. In the current SMACNA standard, maximum duct dimensions of 96 inches are indicated. One fibrous glass duct manufacturer shows duct dimensions up to 10 ft using heavy duct board. Sample specifications are available from the SMACNA standard, as well as from the duct board manufacturers.

Duct board is 1-inch thick, but comes in three classifications based on flexural rigidity as determined by ASTM Test D-1037-64: 475EI (light), 800EI (medium), and 1400EI (heavy). These are so marked by the manufacturers. Small duct sizes may be made without reinforcement; however, in larger sizes, steel tee or channel reinforcement is essential for duct strength.

The current SMACNA standard shows all reinforcement requirements condensed on a single page, with color accent to emphasize ranges of reinforcement spacing relative to duct size and to each of the three types of duct board. Reinforcement spacings are listed in four categories: Not required and maximum longitudinal spacings of 48 inches, 24 inches, and 16 inches These spacings are further tabulated on the basis of three static pressure ranges: over 0 inch–½ inch, ½ inch–1 inch, and over 1 inch –2 inch.

To simplify reinforcement construction, the SMACNA standard shows only two alternative shapes (tee or channel) of reinforcement members; they come in only two gages of metal (22 and 18) and four sizes.

SMACNA standard also has the following:

1) Fire damper connections, transverse joints, and ducted electric heater installations. In addition, plates for hangers, access doors, and reinforcements.

2) Thermal conductivity, airflow friction loss, and acoustical absorption data.

3) Ship lap joint assembly methods V-groove methods.

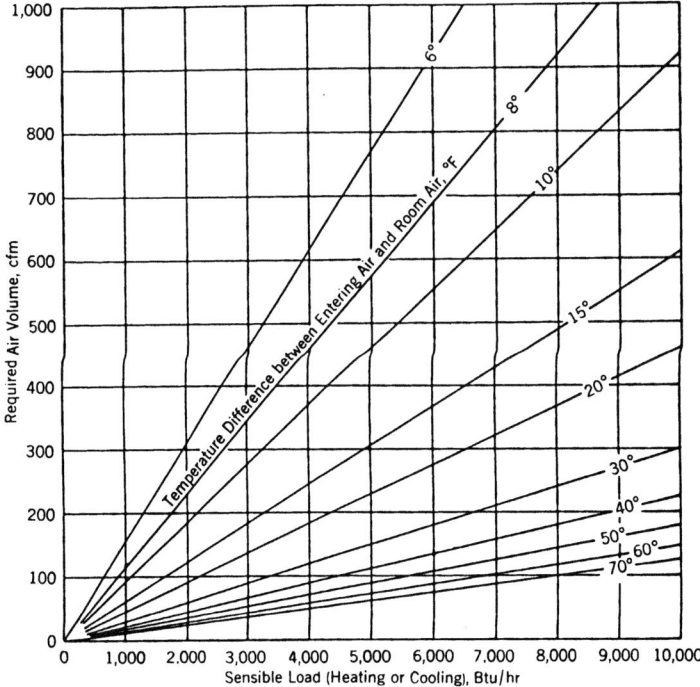

Fig 14-76. Air volume required to handle sensible heating or cooling loads

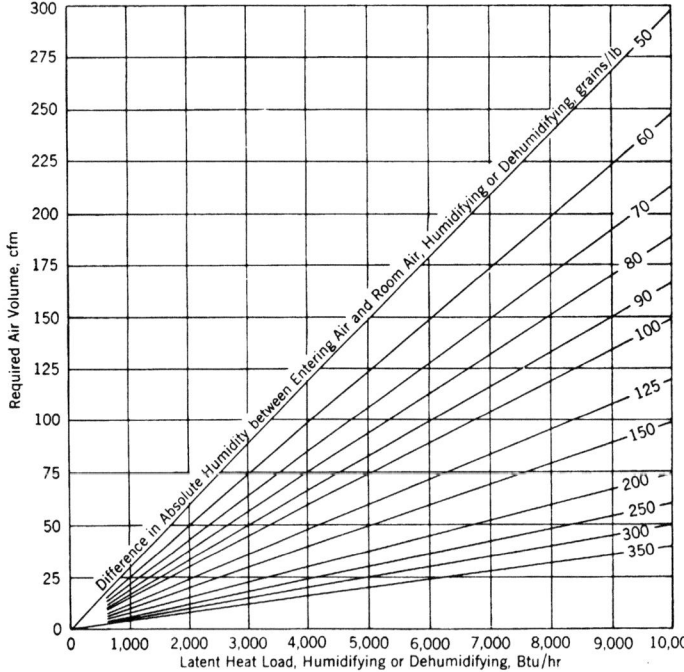

Fig 14-77. Air volume required to handle humidifying or dehumidifying or dehumidifying loads

Determining Required Air Volume.—The first step in the design of a heating or a cooling system is to determine the heat and moisture loads due to transmission and infiltration losses or gains and to internal heat and moisture sources. Once the load has been determined the next step is to calculate the volume of air that must be delivered in order to carry the load. Fig. 14-76 provides a graphical means of evaluating air volume without calculation. Although the sensible heat scale (Fig. 14-76) goes only to 10000 Btu/hr and the volume scale to 1000 *cfm* the figure can be used for larger values by merely multiplying both scale readings by 10 or 100 as may be necessary.

Example 20: The load on a room which is to be heated is 8000 Btu/hr. Room temperature is to be held at 72 °F and air is to be supplied at 92°F.

The temperature difference available for supplying the sensible heat losses amount to 92°F–72°F = 20°F. Enter Fig. 14-76 at 8000 load and rise to intersection with the radial line for a 20°F temperature difference; from this point move horizontally left to read the required air volume as 390 *cfm*.

Example 21: The sensible heat load on a house is 78,000 Btu/hr and warm air is to be supplied with a temperature 70°F greater than room temperature. Enter the graph at 7800 rise to the 70°F line and move left to read 100 *cfm*. But the load is ten times greater than 7800 so the required air volume will be 10×100 or 1000 *cfm*.

Handling Moisture Loads: Fig. 14-77 provides a graphical means of determining air volume for systems that provide either humidification or dehumidification. The latent heat load is first determined by the usual methods, the humidity difference between entering air and room air selected and the required air volume, then it is read from the figure. Note that with Fig. 14-77 as with Fig. 14-76 the graphs can be used beyond their scale range by merely multiplying both scales by 10.

In many heating systems the total lead will include both sensible and latent fractions. In such a case the designer can select either the temperature or the humidity of the supply air and then use Figs. 14-76 and 14-77 as follows:

1) If the humidity of the supply air is known:

a) From Fig. 14-76, for known latent load and known humidity difference, read the required air volume.

b) Enter Fig. 14-77, at known sensible load, then re-enter at the air volume from step (a) and at the intersection of these two lines read the necessary temperature difference.

2) From Fig. 14-76, for known sensible load and known temperature difference, read the required air volume.

3) Enter Fig. 14-77 at known air volume from step (a), then reenter at known latent heat load; the intersection of these two lines will give the required humidity difference.

4) Add (or subtract) the humidity difference to (or from) room humidity to determine the required humidity of the supply air.

Estimating Weight of Metal in Circular Ducts.—

The accompanying table is for use in determining the weight of galvanized steel sheet metal used in fabricating ducts of circular cross section. Also included are data on the surface area of circular ducts for use in estimating insulation areas.

Recommended gages for circular ducts for heating and general ventilating work are:

Diameter, in.	Gage
6 to 19	26
20 to 29	24
30 to 39	22
40 to 49	20
Over 49	18

For industrial exhaust systems referencing the following table of gages and diameters is good practice:

Diameter, in.	Gage
Under 9	24
9 to 14	22
15 to 20	20
20 to 30	18
Over 30	16

The weights given in the table include allowance for seams on the basis that the ducts are cut from sheets 30 inches wide, and that one lap of 1 inch is required for each sheet. Thus, ducts up to 9 inches diameter contain one lap and so on, up to ducts of 72 inches diameter, which contain 8 laps. No allowance is made for waste, bracing, or hanging.

Table 14-25. Weights of Non Ferrous Metal Sheets

American Wire or Brown & Sharpe Gage No.	Thickness, in	SAE Aluminum Alloy No 5. 26 and 27	SAE Aluminum Alloy No. 28	Aluminum Commercially Pure (10 to 99.4 %)	Nickel Silver	Nickel Silver 20%–30 %
0000	0.4600	6.68	6.410	6.490	20.93	21.20
000	0.4096	5.950	5.710	5.780	18.64	18.88
00	0.3645	5.290	5.090	5.140	16.6	16.81
0	0.3249	4.720	4.530	4.58	14.78	14.97
1	0.2893	4.200	4.030	4.080	13.16	13.33
2	0.2576	3.738	3.591	3.632	11.72	11.87
3	0.2294	3.329	3.198	3.234	10.44	10.57
4	0.2043	2.964	2.848	2.88	9.296	9.414
5	0.1819	2.640	2.536	2.565	8.277	8.382
6	0.162	2.351	2.258	2.284	7.372	7.466
7	0.1443	2.094	2.012	2.034	6.566	6.649
8	0.1285	1.865	1.792	1.812	5.847	5.921
9	0.1144	1.66	1.595	1.613	5.206	5.272
10	0.1019	1.479	1.420	1.437	4.637	4.696
11	0.0907	1.316	1.264	1.279	4.127	4.179
12	0.0808	1.172	1.126	1.139	3.677	3.724
13	0.0720	1.045	1.004	1.015	3.276	3.318
14	0.0641	0.930	0.894	0.904	2.917	2.954
15	0.0571	0.829	0.796	0.805	2.598	2.631
16	0.0508	0.737	0.708	0.716	2.312	2.2341
17	0.0453	0.657	0.631	0.639	2.061	2.087
18	0.0403	0.585	0.562	0.568	1.834	1.857
19	0.0359	0.5210	0.5010	0.506	1.634	1.1655
20	0.0320	0.4640	0.4.460	0.4510	1.456	1.474
21	0.0285	0.4140	0.3970	0.4020	1.297	1.313
22	0.0253	0.3671	0.3527	0.3567	1.156	1.171
23	0.0226	0.3280	0.3150	0.3186	1.028	1.041
24	0.0201	0.2917	0.2802	0.2834	0.9146	0.9262
25	0.0179	0.2597	0.2495	0.2524	0.8145	0.8248
26	0.0159	0.2307	0.2216	0.2242	0.7235	0.7327
27	0.0142	0.2060	0.1980	0.2002	0.6462	0.6544
28	0.0126	0.1828	0.1756	0.1776	0.5734	0.5807
29	0.0113	0.164	0.1575	0.1593	0.5142	0.5207
30	0.0100	0.1451	0.1394	0.1410	0.4550	0.4608
31	0.0089	0.1296	0.1245	0.1259	0.4050	0.4101
32	0.008	0.1154	0.1108	0.1121	0.3640	0.3686
33	0.0071	0.1027	0.0987	0.0998	0.3231	0.3272
34	0.0063	0.0914	0.0878	0.0888	0.2867	0.2903
35	0.0056	0.0814	0.0782	0.0791	0.2548	0.2580
36	0.005	0.0726	0.0697	0.0705	0.2275	0.2304
37	0.0045	0.0646	0.0620	0.0627	0.2048	0.2074
38	0.0040	0.0576	0.0553	0.0560	0.1820	0.1843
39	0.0035	0.0512	0.0492	0.0498	0.1593	0.1613
40	0.0031	0.0456	0.0438	0.0443	0.1411	0.1429

Multiply weights in this column by for 10 percent nickel-silver and by 0.9937 for 1.5 percent nickel-silver.

Table 14-26. Estimating Weight of Metal in Ducts

American Wire or Brown & Sharpe Gage No.	Thickness, in	Approximate Weight, lbs/ft^2				
		Copper	Yellow Brass	Tobin Bronze	5% Phosphor Bronze	Everdur 1010
0000	0.4600	21.3300	20.2700	20.1400	21.2000	20.4000
000	0.4096	18.9900	18.0500	17.9300	18.8800	18.1700
00	0.3645	16.9200	16.0700	16.4100	16.8100	16.1800
0	0.3249	15.0600	14.3200	14.2300	14.9800	14.4100
1	0.2593	13.4100	12.7500	12.6700	13.3300	12.8300
2	0.2576	11.9400	11.3500	11.2800	11.8700	11.4300
3	0.2294	10.6400	10.1100	10.0400	10.5700	10.1700
4	0.2043	9.4730	9.0020	8.9430	9.4140	9.0610
5	0.1819	8.4340	8.0150	7.9630	8.3820	8.0680
6	0.162	7.5120	7.1380	7.0920	7.4650	7.1850
7	0.1443	6.6910	6.3580	6.3170	6.6490	6.4000
8	0.1285	5.9580	5.6620	5.6250	5.9210	5.6990
9	0.1144	5.3040	5.0410	5.0080	5.2720	5.0740
10	0.1019	4.7250	4.4900	4.4610	4.6960	4.5190
11	0.0907	4.2060	3.9970	3.9710	4.1800	4.0230
12	0.0808	3.7470	3.5600	3.5370	3.7230	3.5840
13	0.0720	3.3380	3.1730	3.1520	3.3180	3.1930
14	0.0641	2.9720	2.8250	2.8070	2.9540	2.8430
15	0.0571	2.6480	2.5160	2.5000	2.6310	2.5320
16	0.0508	2.3550	2.2380	2.2230	2.3410	2.2530
17	0.0453	2.1000	1.9960	1.9830	2.0870	2.0090
18	0.0403	1.8690	1.7760	1.7640	1.8570	1.7870
19	0.0359	1.6650	1.5820	1.5720	1.6540	1.5920
20	0.0320	1.4840	1.4100	1.4010	1.4750	1.4190
21	0.0285	1.3210	1.2560	1.2480	1.3140	1.2640
22	0.0253	1.1780	1.1190	1.1120	1.1700	1.1270
23	0.0226	1.0480	0.9958	0.9893	1.0410	1.0020
24	0.0201	0.9320	0.8857	0.8799	0.9263	0.8915
25	0.0179	0.8300	0.7887	0.7836	0.8248	0.7939
26	0.0159	0.7373	0.7006	0.6960	0.7327	0.7052
27	0.0142	0.6584	0.6257	0.6216	0.6544	0.6298
28	0.0126	0.5842	0.5552	0.5516	0.5806	0.5588
29	0.0113	0.5240	0.4979	0.4947	0.5207	0.5012
30	0.0100	0.4637	0.4406	0.4377	0.4608	0.4435
31	0.0089	0.4127	0.3922	0.3897	0.4102	0.3947
32	0.008	0.3709	0.3525	0.3502	0.3686	0.3548
33	0.0071	0.3292	0.3129	0.3109	0.3272	0.3149
34	0.0063	0.2921	0.2776	0.2758	0.2903	0.2794
35	0.0056	0.2597	0.2468	0.2452	0.2581	0.2484
36	0.005	0.2318	0.2203	0.2189	0.2304	0.2218
37	0.0045	0.2087	0.1983	0.1970	0.2074	0.1996
38	0.0040	0.1855	0.1763	0.1752	0.1844	0.1774
39	0.0035	0.1623	0.1542	0.1532	0.1613	0.1552
40	0.0031	0.1437	0.1366	0.1357	0.1429	0.1375

Copper sheet can also be obtained in fractional inch thicknesses varying by sixteenths of an inch from $\frac{1}{16}$ to 2 inches.

Apparatus Casing Construction.—Built-up air conditioning units must house the *mixing box*, *air filters*, *heating and cooling coils*, and for medium or high pressure design, the fan or fans. Since most built-up units are for large air systems which cannot be accommodated by factory built units the physical size of these built-up units make their casing construction a very substantial structural problem. An internal positive pressure of 8 inches wg exerts a pressure of 41.5 lb/ft²; this requires that the casing walls and roof be of reinforced metal construction.

Casing construction for low, medium, and high pressure units is specified and illustrated in the SMACNA standards for low and high velocity ductwork. All construction details, such as access doors, insulation, fan, and duct openings are clearly illustrated in these standards. Casing floors are usually poured concrete.

Table 14-27. Typical Design Lateral Loads for Unreinforced Concrete Block Walls

Wall height	Vertical Load from Roof or Ceiling	Type N Mortar, in. wg	Type M or S Mortar in. wg
8 ft – 0 in.	0	2.6	3.7
8 ft – 0 in.	25 lb/ft	3.0	4.4
10 ft – 0 in.	0	1.6	2.3
10 ft – 0 in.	25 lb/ft	2.0	2.9
12 ft – 0 in.	0	1.0	1.5
12 ft – 0 in.	25 lb/ft	1.3	1.9

Note: The above pressure are based on allowable design loads on the wall, as published by the National Concrete Masonry Association (1971)

Attempts to use unreinforced concrete blocks for casing walls have been successful only for low pressure units because concrete block construction cannot tolerate pressures in excess of 3.0 inches wg (8 ft - 0 in. wall height) or 1.3 inches wg 12 ft- 0 in. wall height). Concrete block walls, for this reason, do make an economical fresh air intake plenum since the pressures in such a plenum rarely exceed 1.0 inch wg. Typical design loads for plenum or casing wall construction are listed in Table 14-27, and proper mortar mixes in Table 14-28.

Table 14-28. Mortar Mixes for Concrete Block Walls

Mortar Types	Portland Cement	Masonry Cement	Masonry Sand
Type M	1	1	3
Type S	½	1	3
Type N	…	1	3

When the values in Table 14-27 are compared with the commonly used design pressures of 6 inches, 8 inches, or 10 inches in the fan plenum of buildings, it can readily be seen that an 8 inches unreinforced block wall is not a satisfactory type of construction for these plenums.

Casing construction for low pressures (maximum of 2 inches wg) is adequate for either positive or negative pressures; however, medium and high pressure casings are rated for 6 inches wg and 10 inches wg maximum positive pressures, respectively, in the SMACNA high-velocity-duct standard. They are not rated for negative pressures, but experience shows that they will not tolerate negative pressures nearly as high as the maximum positive pressures.

If the fan is started on either a medium or high pressure system with both the outside air dampers and return air damper in the closed position, it is possible that at the extreme negative pressure will collapse the casing. To preclude this possibility it is recommended that system start-up the outside air damper be opened first to minimum position. An end switch on the open damper will then start the return fan. The supply fan should be interlocked with the return fan so that it starts after the return fan. During system construction and initial start-up, the automatic control system will probably be inoperative. Until the controls are functioning properly, the contractor is well advised to block open the outside air or return air damper.

Condensate Drains for Air Conditioning Units.—

One of the most serious problems with air conditioning casings is the proper drainage of the cold condensate off the cooling coils. First, the drain pan must be large enough to hold the condensate under maximum latent load. If the pan is long, say 10 ft, it is advised that the pan be drained at each end. Also, if the pan is too shallow, the water will tend to *slop* over the downstream edge of the pan because of the air flow across the water surface.

The second problem associated with drainage is failure to design a proper trap for the drain tubing, which carries the cold condensate from the pan to the floor drain. This drain tubing should be type L copper tubing, minimum diameter of 1⅜ inches O.D., with a trap designed as in Fig. 14-78, for a *draw-through* unit.

Determine the design negative static pressure within the fan plenum. Note that this pressure is not the same as the fan total pressure, which includes the pressure losses downstream as well as upstream of the supply fan. Assume the worst conditions, such as having the air filters fully loaded.

Differential (Fig. 14-78a) must be equal to, or larger than, the plenum negative static pressure at design operating conditions.

To store enough water to prevent loss of the trap seal, differential 2 (Fig. 14-78b) must be equal to, or larger than, one-half the plenum maximum negative static pressure.

Differential 3 (Fig. 14-78c) is equal to the maximum negative static pressure in the plenum. This condition probably occurs at start-up, before the air distribution system is brought up to operating pressure. However, tests of actual fan installations indicate that differential 3 is practically the same as differential 1, the plenum negative static pressure at design operating conditions. Evidently, the initial surge of negative pressure at fan start-up is not noticeably greater than the normal negative pressure within the plenum, and can be ignored.

Therefore, once differentials 1 and 2 are determined, a proper condensate trap for draw through air conditioning units can be designed.

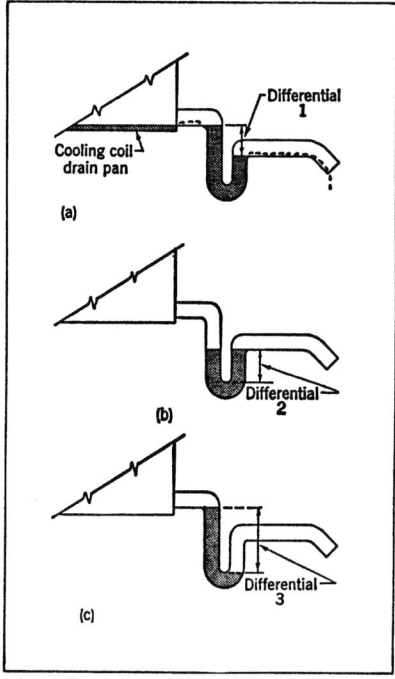

Fig 14-78. Properly designed trap, shown, here does not lose its seal under various fan conditions. (a) Fan running and condensate draining; (b) Fan off; (c) Trap solves the problem)

Air Filters and Dust Collectors

Devices employed to separate solid particulate from a moving air system may be categorized as either (1) air filters or (2) dust collectors.

Generally speaking, air filters are used in conjunction with warm air heating systems, air conditioning, and ventilating systems, and at the intake of process air systems. Applications suitable for air filters are limited usually to contaminant concentrations found to occur naturally in the atmosphere. These concentrations normally will cover a range from as low as 0.03 grain (7000 grains = 1 lb) per 1000 ft^3 of air to a high of 0.20 grain/1000 ft^3 of air. While these numbers appear to have a low order of magnitude it is obvious that a system operating on a continuous basis and bringing in 50,000 *cfm* of air containing a concentration of 0.10 grain/ft^3 will introduce about 30 lbs of airborne dirt per month into the space receiving the air.

Dust collectors are most frequently applied to the exhaust from dust control systems and from processes that result in a contaminant of some form being dispersed into the ambient air surrounding the process. Systems employed primarily to capture dust to provide a satisfactory in plant environment for industrial workers are classified as *dust control systems*, whereas those intended to prevent the escape of contaminants into the atmosphere are defined as *air pollution control systems*. Dust collectors are called upon to entrap contaminant concentrations which vary from a low of 0.05 grain/ft^3 of exhaust air or gas, to as high as 20 grain/ft^3. A simple exercise in arithmetic will show that contaminant concentrations handled by dust collectors are approximately 100,000 times greater than those to which air filters may be successfully applied.

Air Filters .—Three basic types of air filters are in common use today: viscous impingement, dry, and electronic. The principles employed by these filters in removing airborne solids include viscous impingement, interception, impaction, diffusion, and electrostatic precipitation. Some filters utilize only one of these principles; others employ them in combination.

For selected heavy duty applications where high concentrations are present inertial separators merit consideration as first-stage preclearance.

Viscous Impingement Filters: Viscous impingement filters are made up of a relatively loosely arranged medium, usually consisting of spun glass fibers, metal screens, or layers of crimped expanded metal. The surfaces of the medium are coated with a tacky oil generally referred to as an *adhesive*. The arrangement of the filter medium is such that the air stream is forced to change direction frequently as it passes through the filter. Solid particles, because of their momentum, are thrown against, and adhere to, the viscous coated surfaces. Larger airborne particles having greater mass are filtered in this manner, whereas small particles tend to follow the path of the air stream and escape entrapment. Operating characteristics of viscous impingement filters are shown in Table 14-29 as category I.

Dry Filters: Dry air filters constitute the broadest category of air filters in terms of the variety of designs, sizes, and shapes in which they are manufactured. The commonest filter medium is glass fiber. Other materials used are cellulose, paper, cotton, and polyurethane and other synthetics. Glass fiber is used extensively because of its relatively low cost and the unique ability to control the diameter of the fiber in manufacture (in general, the finer the fiber diameter, the higher will be the air cleaning efficiency of the medium).

Dry filters employ the principles of interception, in which particles too large to pass through the filter openings are literally strained from the air stream; impaction, in which particles strike and stick to the surfaces of the glass fibers because of natural adhesive forces (even though the fibers are not coated with a filter adhesive); and diffusion, in which very small particles behave as true gases and move toward a filter fiber to replace those particles in the immediate vicinity of the fiber that have impacted on its surface. Through the process of diffusion a filter is able to separate from the air stream particles much smaller than the openings in the medium itself. Operating characteristics of dry type filters are shown as categories IIa and IIb in Table 14-29.

Electronic Air Cleaners: Used primarily on applications requiring high air cleaning efficiency, these devices operate on the principle of passing the air stream through an ionization field where a 12–14 kV potential imposes a positive charge on all airborne particles. The ionized particles are then passed between aluminum plates, alternately grounded and connected to a 6–8 kV source, and are precipitated onto the grounded plates.

The original design of the electronic air cleaner utilizes a water-soluble adhesive coating on the plates, which holds the dirt deposits until the plates require cleaning. The filter is then deenergized, and the dirt and adhesive film are washed off the plates. Fresh adhesive is applied before the power is turned on again. Newer versions of electronic air cleaners are designed so that the plates serve as agglomerators; the agglomerates of smaller particles are allowed to slough off the plates and to be trapped by viscous impingement or dry type filters downstream of the electronic unit. Operating characteristics of electronic air cleaners are shown as category III in Table 14-29.

Testing and Rating: Filter testing and rating has been recently standardized for the first time on an industry-wide basis with the implementation of ASHRAE Test Standard 52-76. Applicable both to nominal efficiency filters, where efficiency is determined, and to high efficiency filters, where a dust spot efficiency on atmospheric air is established, the ASHRAE procedure requires the reporting of initial (clean) efficiency, dust holding capacity with a standardized test dust, and simultaneous determination of average efficiency and dust holding capacity. To insure the accuracy of published data there must be independent laboratory certification of the manufacturers performance claims. For high efficiency particulate air (HEPA) filters, such as those used in special purpose applications involving protection from radioactive contamination, clean rooms, etc., the dioctylphthalate (DOP)

test is employed. This test uses a specially generated smoke of uniform 0.3-micron particles.

Filter Selection: Unlike other components of mechanical ventilation and air conditioning systems the selection of the proper air filter for a specific application involves judgment beyond reliance on clearly defined parameters. The coordinates of air filtration do not lend themselves to selection charts and tables as do other system components such as fans and heat exchangers. However, there are important guidelines to proper selection. These are efficiency requirements, initial and operating cost factors; maintenance characteristics; effect on system of air friction loss; and equipment space requirements. A generalized analysis of how these guidelines apply to the more commonly used types of air filters is shown in Table 14-30. Since operating cost can be a major variable it is good practice to prepare a detailed cost study for any sizable installation.

Dust Collectors.—Dust collectors may be divided into four major categories:

1) dry mechanical collectors

2) wet collectors and scrubbers

3) fabric collectors

4) electrostatic precipitators.

Industrial dusts emanate from three major sources:

1) abrading

2) combustion

3) materials handling.

A typical industrial process, such as metal grinding, will produce metallic dusts in the range from 10 to 100 microns.

Differences in size and concentration of particulate matter dictate a considerable difference in the performance requirements of dust collectors, as compared with air filters. The family of curves shown in Fig. 14-79 may be used as an unrefined method of arriving at the recommended type of dust collector for a given application.

The usual method of rating dust collectors, even those with a high efficiency characteristic, is on a weight basis. By comparison, only low efficiency air filters are rated on a weight method while high efficiency filters are always rated by the dust spot or DOP methods.

Major differences between rating air filters and dust collectors on the weight method is that an artificial test dust is used for rating air filters, whereas on dust collectors the rating is determined by actual performance against the specific dust to be collected.

Table 14-29. Guide to Air Filter Selection*

			Filter Types	
A	Throwaway (I)	G	Cartridge, 50–55% NBS (IIa)	
B	Cleanable (I)	H	Cartridge, 80–85% NBS (IIa)	
C	Replaceable pad (I)	J	Cartridge, 90–97% NBS (IIa)	
D	Automatically renewable media (I)	K	Electronic agglomerator with automatically renewable media storage (III)	
E	Cartridge, 30% NBS (I or II)	L	Electron agglometer with replaceable cartridge storage section, 93–97% NBS (III)	
F	Cartridge, 40% NBS (I or II)	M	Electronic air cleaner, washable plates (III)	

	Filter Type Rating		
System Selection Factor	Normal Efficiency	Medium Efficiency	High Efficiency
Air Friction Loss			
Constant	D		K, M
Variable	A, B, C	E, F, G	H, J, L
Initial Cost			
Low	A, B, C	E, F, G	
Moderate	D		H, J
High			K, L, M
Operating Costs			
Low	D	F	K, M
Moderate	B, C	E, G	L
High	A		H, J
Maintenance Skills Required			
Minimal	A, B, C		
Average	D	E, F, G	H
trained			J, K, L, M

Table 14-30. Characteristics of Air Filters

Filter Categories	Principles of Operation	Type of Filter Surface	Media Velocity versus Face Velocity fpm	Air Friction Loss	Efficiency Test Methods (see Testing and Rating)	Efficiency%	AFI Dust Holding Capacity Grains /ft²
I. Viscous coated	Straining & impingement	Coarse fiber, loosely spaced, or metal screens	300–600 vs. 300–600	Variable, low, 0.10–0.50	Arrestance (ASHRAE)	Low 70–85	High 75–150
IIa. Dry	Straining & interception	Medium to fine fiber, moderately to closely spaced	20–50 vs. 250–625	Variable moderate 0.20–1.0	Arrestance or dust spot (ASHRAE)	Moderate 85–95 to High 85-95	Moderate 5–15
IIb. HEPA	Interception & diffusion	Ultra fine fiber, very closely spaced	5–6 vs. 250–300	Cariable, high 1.0–2.0	DOP	Ultra High 99.7	Low 1–2
III. Electro-static	Precipitation &/or agglomer-ation	Plates	400–600 vs. 400–600	Constant & low, or variable & moderate, 0.45, or 0.5–1.0	Dust spot (ASHRAE)	High 85–97	

*Filters of various types are rated with respect to election factors of air friction loss, initial cost, operating cost, and maintenance skills required for nominal, medium, and high efficiency applications. The filter category from Table 14-29 is shown in parentheses after each type commonly used.

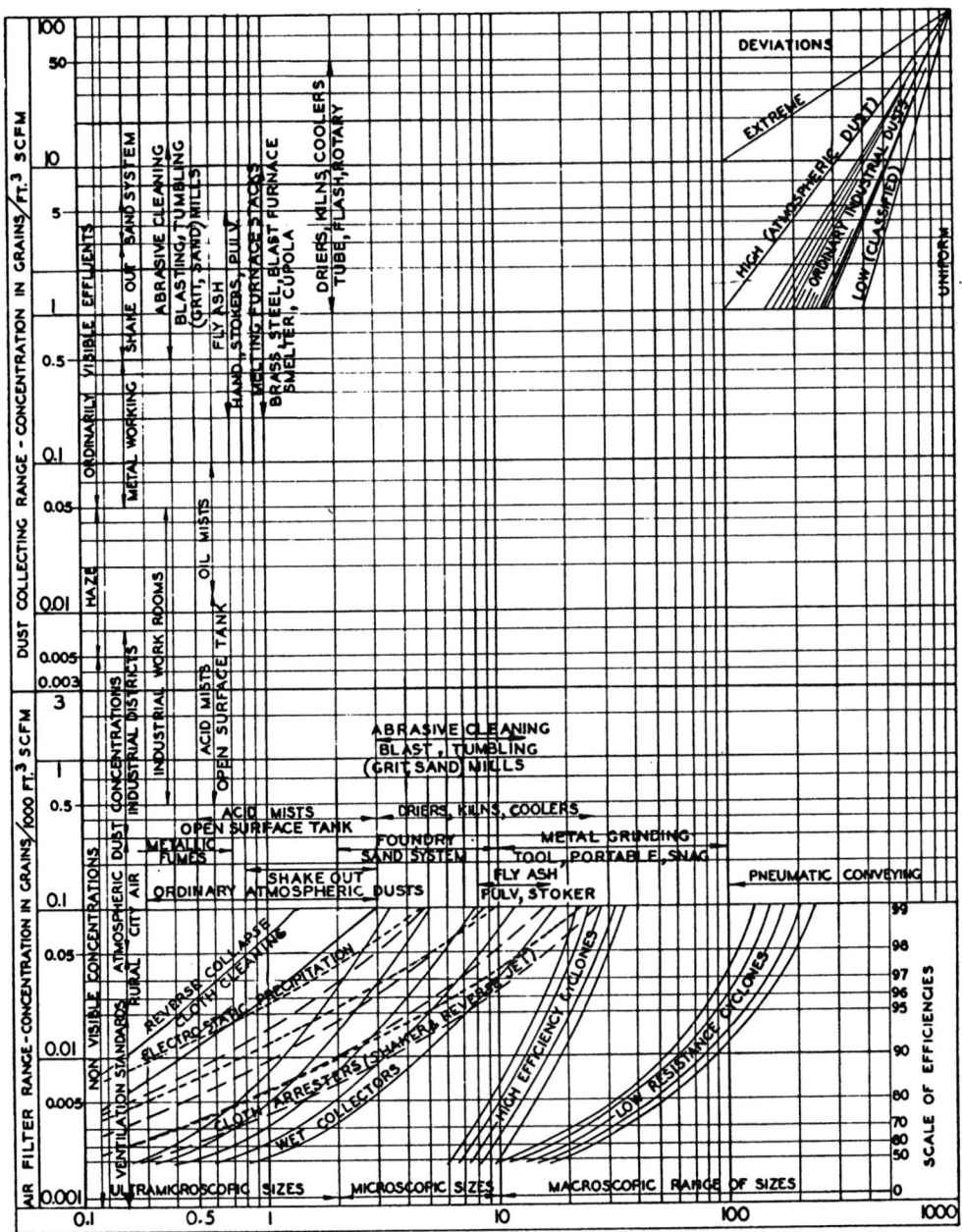

Fig 14-79. Range of particle sizes concentration and collector performance

Dry Centrifugal Collectors.—Dry centrifugal collectors are the least costly and for many years were the most frequently used type of dust collection equipment. They are effective on almost all types of medium to coarse size granular dusts and are commonly used as either primary collectors or as precleaners to more efficient final collectors. They have the advantage of being low in cost, inexpensive to operate and maintain, and relatively small in size.

Because of modern more stringent, emission standards, the use of the dry centrifugal collector is limited almost exclusively to product recovery applications that are upstream of more efficient secondary collectors.

Dry centrifugal collectors are commercially available in a wide variety of designs, but all depend on centrifugal force to separate dust particles from the air stream.

The magnitude of the centrifugal force that can be exerted on a particle is a function of particle mass and angular acceleration. The latter is dependent on air velocities in the collector. As velocities increase, energy losses due to friction and turbulence also increase, and the pressure drop across the collector rises. In general, dust collection efficiency becomes greater as collector pressure-drop increases.

Unfortunately, collection efficiency cannot be limitlessly improved by increasing the energy input and collector pressure drop. Although higher velocities result in a larger centrifugal force vector, which causes the particle path to diverge from that of the air stream, the aerodynamic forces acting to resist path divergence are also increased. This effect is particularly pronounced on smaller particles because they have a greater surface area per unit mass. Every dry centrifugal collector, therefore, has an upper performance limit (which can be expressed conveniently in terms of pressure drop) beyond which its collection efficiency for a given dust cannot, for practical purposes, be increased. Collector sizing and selection is largely a matter of choosing an optimal operating point; the point selected should yield the highest possible return, in terms of collection efficiency, for power input.

Wet Collectors.—Wet dust collectors provide a comparatively simple, moderate-cost solution to many dust control and air pollution problems. Space requirements are generally less than for other collector types. Because equipment size is small in relation to air cleaning capacity, most collectors can be shipped from the manufacturer completely assembled or in major subassemblies, simplifying installation and reducing erection costs.

Capable of cleaning hot, moist gases, which are difficult or even impossible to handle with other collector types, wet collectors also are often able to eliminate or substantially reduce the hazards associated with the collection of explosive or highly flammable materials. In addition, since solids are collected in a wetted form, secondary dust problems during material disposal are avoided. They are commercially available in a wide variety of designs, shapes, and sizes. The collection principles employed are centrifugal force, impaction, and impingement, either separately or in combination.

Independent investigators studying wet collector performance have developed the contact power theory, which states that for well-designed equipment, collection efficiency is a function of the energy consumed in the air-to-water contact process and is independent of the collector design. On this basis, well designed collectors operating at or near the same pressure drop can be expected to exhibit comparable performance.

All wet collectors have a fractional efficiency characteristic; that is, their cleaning efficiency varies directly with the size of the particle being collected. In general, collectors operating at a very low pressure loss will remove only medium to coarse size particles. High efficiency collection of fine particles requires increased energy input, which will be reflected in higher collector pressure loss.

High-efficiency wet collection of submicron particulate, fume, and smoke has been made possible largely by the development of the high energy venturi type collector. Venturi designs are now used on a large number of applications formerly limited to fabric or electrostatic collectors. In accordance with the contact power theory, venturi type collectors require substantial energy input to achieve high collection efficiency on submicron particles. A recent new concept in wet collectors, which appears to present a solution to a long standing problem employs a mobile bed contactor for scrubbing of SO_2 fumes from the products of combustion of power generating and large industrial boilers.

Collector water requirements represent a continuing operating cost, which must be evaluated in selection of specific equipment. Further considerations are necessary when applying wet collectors to certain fume scrubbing processes, since a solution of water and a chemical additive may be required to achieve the desired objective. When required water rates are high, substantial savings can usually be realized by using a recirculating water system. Such systems usually employ a settling tank or pond to separate the collected material by gravity. Since the water returned to the collector will invariably contain some solids, it is advantageous in these applications to choose a collector that does not require spray nozzles or other small water orifices.

Corrosive substances are often present in typical wet collector applications. Modern construction materials are capable of providing satisfactory protection against nearly all corrosive agents, but the chemical compounds present must be correctly anticipated and identified in order to make the proper material selection.

Fabric Collectors.—Fabric collectors represent one of the oldest and most successful methods of dust collection.

They are commonly used when particle size is small and a high degree of cleaning efficiency is required. They also have the added capability of reclaiming maximum quantities of valuable process materials in a dry state. Newly enacted governmental regulations placing limitations on process emissions has created an even stronger demand for the use of fabric collection.

All fabric collectors employ the same method of separating particulate from the air stream. Dust-laden air flows through a cloth tube or envelope, where particles larger than the fabric interstices are deposited by simple sieving action. A mat or cake of dust is quickly formed on the air-entering surface of the fabric. The dust cake acts as a highly efficient filter, capable of removing submicron dusts and fumes, while the fabric serves principally as a supporting structure for the cake.

There are many different fabric collector designs in current use. Basically, the collectors differ in the method used to remove the deposited material from the fabric surface. Common methods include mechanical shaking, reverse-air collapse, and pulse-jet.

Selection of the method of fabric reconditioning (removal of dust accumulation from the fabric surface) is primarily a function of the nature of the dust, (whether the process is of a continuous or intermittent nature), and the choice of fabric. Fiberglass cloth, for example, is often selected for higher temperature applications (up to 500°F). However, it is generally limited to reverse-air equipment since the glass fibers would fail if subjected to the flexing imposed by a shaker mechanism. Shaker collectors are frequently used for intermittent process applications, while the pulse jet type is a more common choice for continuous processes. As with most capital equipment, the final selection generally resolves itself into a matter of economics where there are no other overriding factors.

Fabric options include almost all the organic and synthetic fibers. The choice of fabric is usually a function of the temperature and fume content of the exhaust gases and the chemical composition of the dust being captured.

Electrostatic Precipitators.—These are capable of attaining a dust-collecting efficiency equal to that of a fabric collector. The frequency with which they are used is somewhat limited, however, due to both high initial installed cost, which prohibits their use on small and medium air volumes, and the need for more sophisticated engineering personnel to maintain them properly. The high voltage electrostatic precipitator should not be confused with the low voltage, small dust-holding capacity designs used for filtration in air conditioning systems.

The principle of collection relies on the ability to impart a negative charge to particles in the gas stream causing them to move and adhere to the grounded, or positively charged, collector plates. Most precipitators are made for horizontal air flow with velocities of 100 to 600 fpm. The collecting plates are parallel elements, typically on 9-inch centers, and constructed in various ways including corrugated or perforated plates or rod curtains. The weighted wire or rigid electrodes are centered between the collector plates. Voltage difference between electrode and plate is 60,000 to 75,000 volts in most designs. Collector plates of cylindrical shapes surrounding the electrode rod are provided where water is used to wash off collected material and where the gas stream is under high pressure or vacuum.

Removal of the collected material is obtained by rapping or vibrating the elements, either continuously or at predetermined intervals. Vibration or unloading usually takes place without stopping air flow through the precipitator, although some loss to the effluent air can be expected in most applications during the cleaning cycle.

Pressure drop is negligible. Collection efficiency is high and nearly uniform. regardless of particle size including submicron particles. Space is relatively large and cost is high where small gas volumes (below 50,000 *cfm*) are involved, due to the cost of high-voltage equipment. Efficiency is improved with increased humidity of the air stream as a change takes place in the dielectric properties of the dust. Heavy concentrations, on the other hand, cause a reduction in collection as the space charge on numerous particles blankets the corona effect from the electrodes.

Under these circumstances a precleaner, often of the dry centrifugal type, is introduced for the purpose of reducing the inlet concentration entering the precipitator.

Electrostatic precipitators have been extensively used in high temperature gas cleaning from equipment such as blast furnaces, open hearth furnaces, and central station pulverized fuel boilers. The chemical industry offers many applications, including sulfuric acid plants, carbon black, cement kilns, and soda ash from paper mill black-liquor furnaces. As voltage setting is close to the spark over potential, application is limited to materials that are not explosive or combustible in nature unless the carrier gas stream is an inert gas.

Breeching Design and Construction

Boiler breeching for HVAC installations must handle flue gases at elevated temperatures; for HVAC boilers, these temperatures vary in a range from 400 to 500°F. For the correct flue temperature one should consult the boiler manufacturer. These elevated temperatures affect breeching design as explained in the following.

Expansion.—The sheet steel breeching is erected at room ambient temperatures so that it expands when hot flue gases are carried to the chimney flue. Expansion joints are required to absorb relative movement between fixed sections of breeching or between a section of breeching and the chimney flue.

As a rule-of-thumb for expansion joint location, use the following:

For very short breeching runs of 10 feet or less between fixed points, such as connections to boilers, expansion joints are required for combined axial and lateral movements over $\frac{1}{4}$ inch.

For longer runs of breeching between fixed points, the maximum total relative axial and lateral movement that can be tolerated is $\frac{1}{2}$ inch. If this movement exceeds $\frac{1}{2}$ inch, an expansion joint is required.

To find the total relative axial and lateral movement, multiply the linear coefficient of expansion of steel (0.00000702 inch/inch/°F) by the expected temperature rise (flue gas temperature minus ambient temperature at installation, usually taken at 40°F); this gives the breeching movement per inch of run. Next, multiply the total runs of breeching between fixed points, based on center-line distances (including offsets) in inches, by the movement per inch of run. If this total expansion exceeds $\frac{1}{4}$ inch for very short runs or $\frac{1}{2}$ inch for longer runs, an expansion joint is required in this section.

Individual breechings must have individual expansion joints to take care of the temperature variance of each duct causing different expansions at different times, as shown in Fig. 14-85.

Expansion joint construction is based on either a slip joint, illustrated in Fig. 14-80, or the welded bellows joint (accordion type). The slip joint is easier to fabricate and less expensive, and, though not airtight, will be satisfactory for positive pressures encountered in most HVAC installations. The welded bellows joint is used for large boilers, such as power plant installations.

Aerodynamics.—Good aerodynamic design is essential for breeching to prevent eddy currents, which cause vibrations and pressure losses. There are, however, some special considerations for breeching design:

1) If a boiler uses natural draft, which is not common practice, the maximum attainable flue gas velocity is 1500 fpm. The engineer should check local code requirements, which may not accept velocities that low.

2) If a boiler uses mechanical draft, either forced or induced, a flue gas velocity of 2000 to 3000 fpm in the breeching is recommended to prevent soot or ash dropout; however, flue gas velocities as high as 4000 fpm are permissible, provided the draft is available. Again, the engineer should check local code requirements.

3) In calculating flue gas draft requirements, breeching, and chimney losses can be calculated in the same manner as ductwork losses, except that these losses must be based on the actual flue gas temperature. This affects the gas density, hence the losses. Fig. 14-80 gives the overall efficiency of a steam generating unit vs. leaving flue gas temperature. In the absence of manufacturer data this will assist the designer in selecting the flue gas temperature leaving the boiler.

4) The type of draft arrangement depends on the boiler and burner selected. Some boilers have induced or forced draft only, others have both; and a few use natural draft only. The draft requirements through the boiler are set by the boiler manufacturer; however, those in the breeching and chimney are calculated by the engineer. The forced and/or induced draft head available should be adequate to guarantee maximum flue gas flow requirements. In recent years, air pollution control agencies have demanded that exiting velocity from the chimney be a minimum of 3000 fpm at 60% of the total load. This means a stack exiting velocity of 5000 fpm when all boilers are firing at their maximum rate. To get this high terminal velocity, a tapered cone is installed on the chimney outlet. This flue gas pressure to velocity conversion requires a large increase in the draft pressure, and must be added to the other calculated draft losses for proper fan selection. The height of the reducing cone should be at least two diameters of the stack before the taper starts.

5) Transition pieces in breeching should not be abrupt. For decreasing cross-sectional area of the breeching (converging section), the total angle of transition should not exceed 60°. For increasing cross-sectional area of the breeching (diverging section), the total angle of transition should not exceed 30°.

6) Multiple gas flows from more than one boiler into a common breeching should flow parallel into the breeching without one flow disturbing or even cutting off the flow from the other boiler, as this can lead to explosions during start up. This is shown in Figs. 14-79 and 14-86.

7) Where shoe taps are made into the bottom of the breeching due to tight ceiling heights, splitters must be used in the breeching; otherwise, the upward jet of the boiler's flue gas into the main stream will result in high dynamic losses.

8) Entering a round stack with two opposite breechings requires a partition plate that should be arranged tangentially or diagonally so as to prevent bounce back eddy currents when a breeching discharges at a 90° impact on the partition plate. The available stack draft would then not be reduced, provided that the flow areas are correct. This is illustrated in Fig. 14-82.

9) If directional flow changes are at an angle of more than 30°, they should have vane guidance plates, approximately 12 inches apart so that a person can get through the clearance between the vane blades. These turning vanes must be stiff and connected to the duct sides by continuous strength weld for the full edge length of the vane plate to eliminate the possibility of having them tear off the duct walls. If the vane blades are over 4 ft long, a center support for the vanes (made of flats or pipes) should be provided. The vanes should be made of 16 gage, minimum thickness, with smooth leading and trailing edges. The trailing edge should be extended at least 12 inches on a straight run to obtain better regain (Fig. 14-83).

10) Round breeching cross-section is preferred to rectangular cross section for two reasons:

    a) It is a more efficient cross section for gas flow.

    b) It has rigidity from its shape, whereas the rectangular cross section usually requires external or internal stiffeners.

Unfortunately, tight headroom conditions may preclude round breeching cross-section; in this case, the rectangular cross-section should be as close to square as is possible.

Access.—Access must be provided to all parts of the breeching for the purpose of conducting inspection maintenance and repair. The means of obtaining this access are doors attached to the breeching plate or, in some cases, entry from some other area that is provided with a door. Location and means of access should be carefully considered in order to ensure the following:

1) Convenience: Doors must be located where they may be easily entered from platforms or ladders.

2) Interference: Do not locate doors within 12 inches of corners, expansion joints, or dampers.

3) Code requirements: A minimum clear space of 15 inches must be maintained around breeching for access to its surfaces.

4) Access doors on both sides (certainly one side) of dampers are advisable.

In addition to access doors, 2 inches drain nipples with gate valves should be welded to the bottom of depressed breeching sections, to permit draining condensate during start-up, etc.

Openings in the breeching must be provided for draft gage connections, smoke density sensors, thermometers, and carbon dioxide sampling connections.

Round Breeching Construction.—Round breeching is made of rolled black steel plate (0.15 to 0.25 carbon), all welded longitudinal seams. End joints are either welded or made with companion rolled angle flanges ($2\frac{1}{2} \times \frac{1}{4}$ in) with asbestos gasket.

A schedule of steel gages for round breeching is tabulated below:

Breeching Diameter	Steel Plate Gage
12 in. and below	18
13 to 24 in.	16
25 to 36 in.	14
37 to 60 in.	12
60 in. and above	10

If the fuel has more than $\frac{1}{2}$% sulfur content and flue gas temperatures are expected to drop below the dewpoint (generally below 270°F) at low loads, the breeching steel should be corrosion resistant (COR-TEN or equal). This will be more likely to happen to uninsulated breeching; therefore, breeching inside the boiler plant should be insulated to keep flue gases above the dewpoint and

ensure comfort for operating engineers. In this case, insulation retaining clips should be specified.

Rectangular Breeching Construction.—Rectangular breeching is made of black steel plate (0.15 to 0.25 carbon), all welded construction. End joints for each section are 2-inch flanges with open corners, fully welded all around, as shown in Fig. 14-86.

For small rectangular breeching cross-sections, maximum side-width of 48 inches, the construction shown in Fig. 14-86 is satisfactory, provided the design pressures do not exceed 3 inches wg. While 10 gage steel plate is recommended for this construction, very small breeching sizes (up to 18 inches max. width) can be made with 16 gage steel plate.

A schedule for steel gages for rectangular breeching construction is tabulated in left column for higher pressures and larger cross-sections than those shown in Fig. 14-86.

Welded duct joints are preferred, but removable duct sections may have to be used for access to parts behind the duct. These removable sections should be companion flanged with a composition gasket material to withstand the high temperatures of the flue gases. Bolted flanges of joints should be stiff; 3 inches × 3 inches × $\frac{3}{8}$ inches angles, or larger, may be required. If the long side of the duct is 3 ft, or less, $2\frac{1}{2}$ inches × $2\frac{1}{2}$ inches × $\frac{1}{4}$ inch angles may do. The bolts should not be less than $\frac{1}{2}$ inches and should be $\frac{5}{8}$ inches where static pressures plus or minus of more than 6 inches are encountered. Bolts should be spaced about $2\frac{1}{2}$ inches, or a maximum of 3 inches apart.

Metal selection for rectangular breeching should also consider corrosion and wear; see *Round Breeching Construction* above. Shop painting generally is required and specifications may spell out: "Bare metal before painting; shot or sandblasting; primer and finish coat suitable for the temperatures involved."

Detail for expansion joint (for either round or rectangular cross-section) is shown in Fig. 14-81.

Breeching hanger supports are required to support each section of breeching. Typical hanger detail is shown in Fig. 14-86. Spacing between supports is dictated by the beam strength of the breeching. Usually, the supports are located next to the joints, which are normally strong enough to permit hanging spacing at 6 to 10 ft intervals.

Dampers at flue gas outlet of each boiler in a multiboiler installation are recommended to prevent injury to personnel from back puffs. These dampers must be tied in with the burner controls so that the burner cannot operate unless the dampers are fully open.

Breeching construction, flue gas velocities, flue gas dampers, and breeching access are often subject to legal or code requirements, which may supersede those herein above. Check all pertinent codes before designing the boiler breeching.

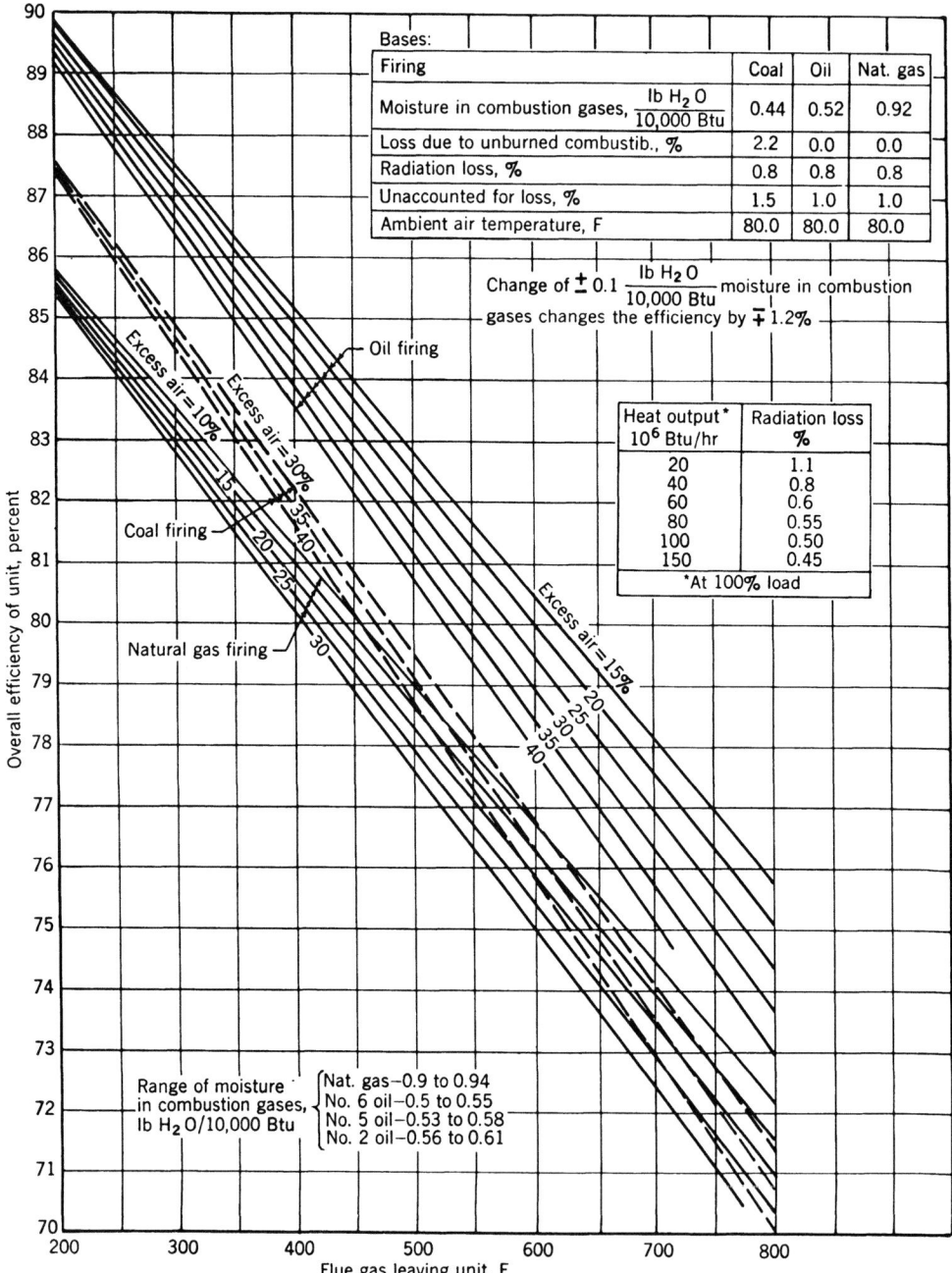

Fig 14-80. Overall efficiency of steam generating unit

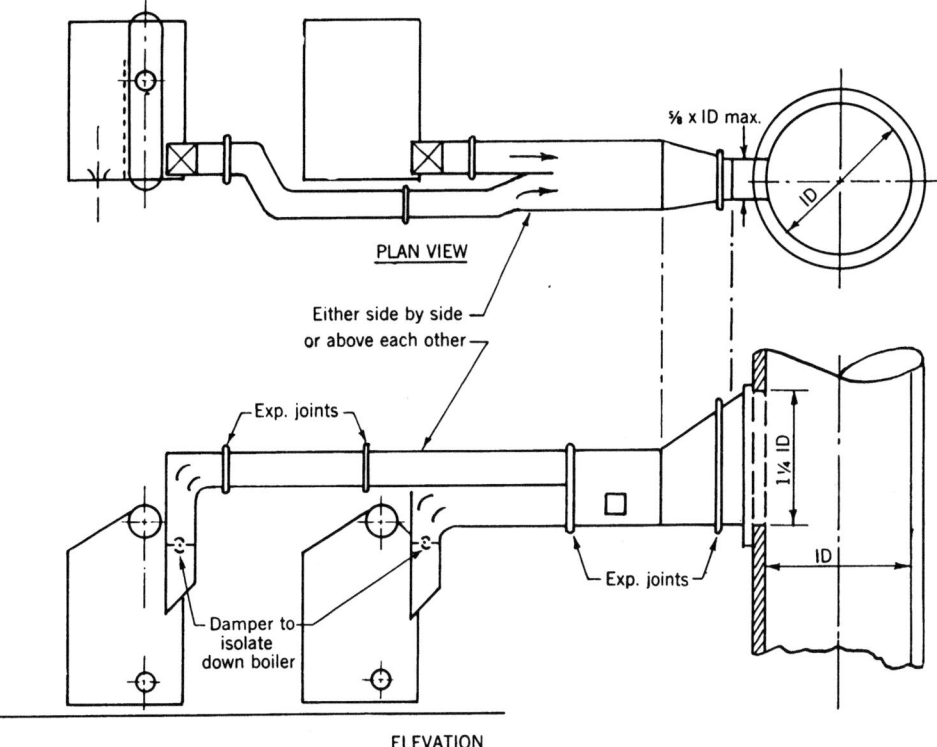

Fig 14-81. Typical breeching flow arrangements and stack entry

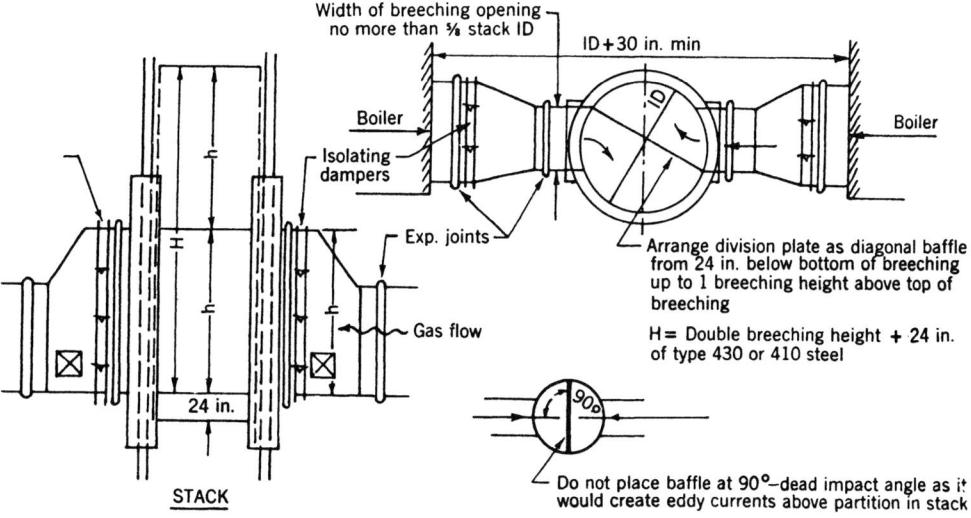

Fig 14-82. Opposite stack entry

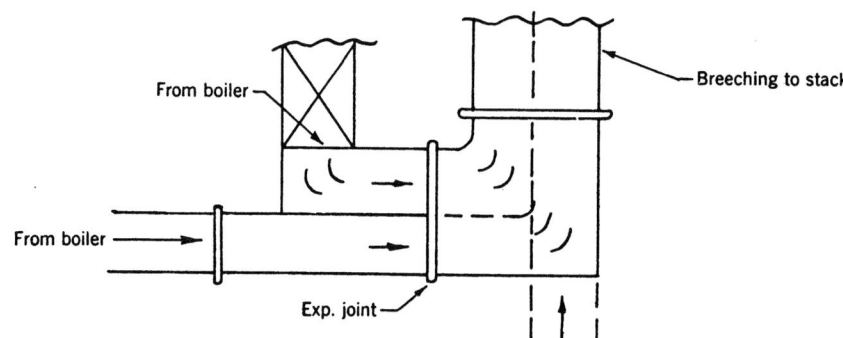

Fig 14-83. Breeching entries for joining gas flows parallel

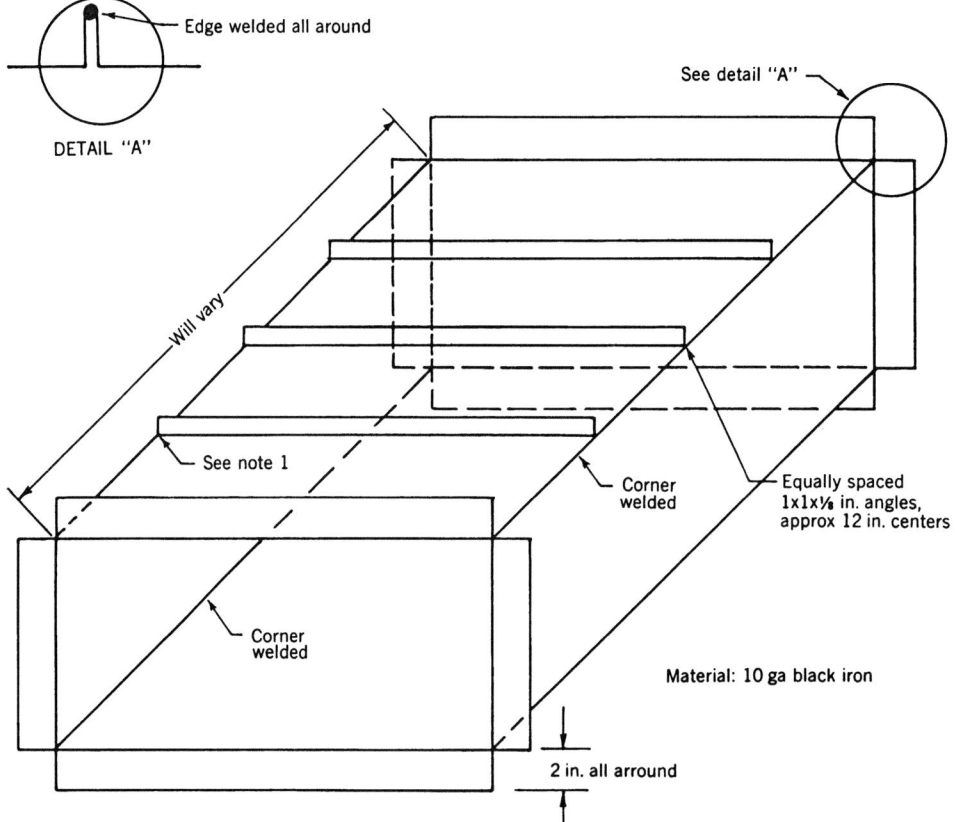

Fig 14-84. Typical rectangular breeching for low pressure

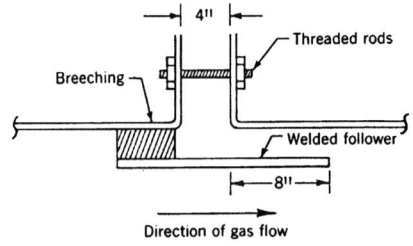

Fig 14-85. Expansion joint

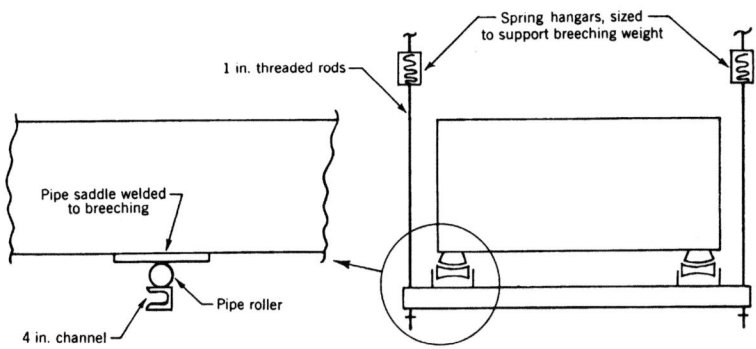

Note: Hangers positioned as shown on plans.

Fig 14-86. Breeching hanger supports

Largest Cross Section Dimension	Design Pressure	
	up to 15 in. wg	16 in. to 27 in. wg
up to 6 ft	10 gage	…
6 ft to 10 ft	$\frac{3}{16}$ in.	$\frac{3}{16}$ in.
over 10 ft	$\frac{1}{4}$ in.	$\frac{1}{4}$ in.

Table 14-31. Reinforcements for Flat Areas of Breechings and Ducts*

Max. Design Pressure H_2O	Max. ft² Reinforced Area	Maximum Stiffener Length				
		5 ft–0 in	7 ft–0 in	9 ft–0 in	11 ft–0 in	13 ft–0 in
0 in. to 6 in.	16 ft²	2 in. × $\frac{3}{8}$ in.	2½ in. × $\frac{3}{8}$ in.	3 in. × $\frac{3}{8}$ in.	4 in. × $\frac{3}{8}$ in.	4 in. × 1$\frac{5}{8}$ in.
6.1 in. to 10 in.	14 ft²	2½ in. × $\frac{3}{8}$ in.	3 in. × $\frac{3}{8}$ in.	4 in. × $\frac{3}{8}$ in.	4 in. × 1$\frac{5}{8}$ in.	4 in. × 2½ in.
10.1 in. to 12 in.	13 ft²	3 in. × $\frac{3}{8}$ in.	4 in. × $\frac{3}{8}$ in.	4 in. × 1$\frac{5}{8}$ in.	4 in. × 2½ in.	6 in. × 2 in. or 6 in. high bent shape
12.1 in. to 18 in.	11 ft²	4 in. × $\frac{3}{8}$ in.	4 in. × 1$\frac{5}{8}$ in.	4 in. × 2½ in.	6 in. × 2 in. or 6 in. high bent shape	6 in. × 2½ in. or 6 in. high bent shape
18.1 in. to 27 in.	8 ft²	4 in. × 1$\frac{5}{8}$ in.	4 in. × 1$\frac{5}{8}$ in.	4 in. × 2½ in.	6 in. × 2½ in. or 6 in. high bent shape	6 in. × 2½ in. or 6 in. high bent shape

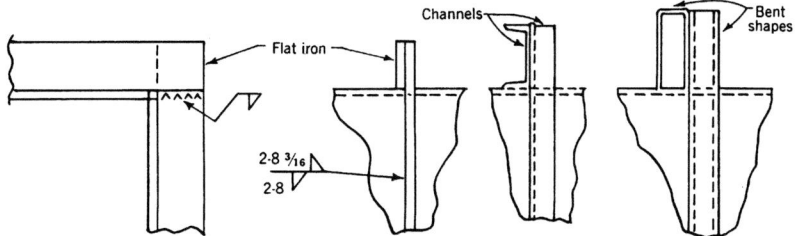

All breeching to be $\frac{3}{16}$ inch minimum thickness. For $\frac{1}{4}$ inch plates increase maximum allowable unreinforced area 25%. Stiffeners to run the shortest spans possible. Joints of ducts or breeching must be stiffened also to suit, as in table above.

*Reinforcements for flat areas of breeching and ducts should be tack welded 2 in. every 9 in. using the tables guidelines.

Chimney Draft and Velocities.—The amount of natural convective draft theoretically available in a chimney is

$$D_r = 2.96BH\left(\frac{W_a}{T_a} - \frac{W_s}{T_s}\right) \qquad (48)$$

where D_r = draft in inches of water;

B = atmospheric pressure in inches of mercury (30 usually taken as normal barometer);

H = height of stack in feet;

W_a = density of the atmosphere sea level pressure, pounds per cubic foot;

W_s = density of stack gas under the same conditions;

T_a = absolute air temperature, °F absolute = 460 + T_a (T_a = air temperature, °F); and

T_s = absolute gas temperature, °F absolute = 460 + T_s (T_s = gas temperature, °F).

When the velocity V is in feet per minute,

$$V = 1890\sqrt{BH\left(\frac{1}{T_a} - \frac{W_s}{W_aT_s}\right)} \qquad (49)$$

and when $T_a = 0$°F and $B = 30$,

$$V = 484\sqrt{H\left(1 - \frac{W_sT_a}{W_aT_s}\right)} \qquad (50)$$

Since gas densities are directly proportional to molecular weight M at the same pressure and temperature and $H_1/12$, (inches) = H we can place Equation (50) in a form which will permit calculations to be made for unconfined convection currents where chimney or convective columns are of lower magnitude:

$$V = 140\sqrt{H_i\left(1 - \frac{M_sT_a}{M_aT_s}\right)} \qquad (51)$$

where M_s = molecular weight of the stack gas; and

M_a = molecular weight of air.

Equation (51) may be used to predict the maximum possible velocity under theoretical conditions for a given instance. For example, what is the maximum velocity that a column of steam will attain in a frictionless chimney at a point 12 inches above a boiling pan or vat in ambient air at 70°F, assuming that the steam temperature is 212°F at this height? (Because of the high latent heat of steam this is a reasonable assumption.) Substituting in (51)

$$V = 140\sqrt{H_i\left(1 - \frac{M_sT_a}{M_aT_s}\right)}$$

$$= 140\sqrt{12\left[1 - \frac{18(460 + 70)}{29(460 + 212)}\right]}$$

$$= 344 \text{ fpm}$$

Equations (48) and (51) assume that no loss has taken place through friction or flow resistance. In the actual case, however, the resistance to flow will reduce the velocity considerably. In the case of confined convection currents this can be evaluated since the resistance loss is subtracted from the theoretical draft. In mathematical form the actual draft in a confined condition is defined by

$$D_r = \text{theoretical draft} - \text{resistance loss} \qquad (52)$$

where in addition to the terms defined in equation (1) we have:

f = friction factor;

D = minimum internal diameter of chimney stack in feet = $0.288\sqrt{\dfrac{WT_s}{BW_sV}}$

where W = weight of gas flowing in pounds per second. Hence, if the friction factor f, gas velocity, and density are known, the loss in theoretical draft can be computed from Equation (53).

For the average chimney f is equal to 0.016. It should be recognized that f depends upon the nature of the chimney surface as well as the viscosity and temperature of the discharging gas. The value of 0.016 corresponds to chimney gases at 500°F. If the stack is to discharge gases only slightly above room temperature or at an appreciably lower density than the ambient air, then the second term of the equation should be replaced by a value of friction loss corresponding to the type of stack construction and the gas density involved. If heavy-gauge galvanized iron pipe is employed, such as that used in industrial exhaust systems, then the ordinary friction factor charts can be used with a correction for gas density. Such a value can also be obtained from Equation (53):

$$\text{Resistance loss} = \frac{L}{CD}\left(\frac{V}{4000}\right)^2 \qquad (53)$$

Where resistance loss is in inches of water for air at 70°F; for other gases multiply by ratio of

$$\frac{\text{density}}{0.075} = \frac{W_a}{0.075}$$

where L = length of pipe, ft;

D = pipe diameter, ft;

V = velocity, feet per minute;

C = 60 for perfectly smooth pipe;

C = 50 for heating and ventilating ducts;

$C = 45$ for smooth tile ducts, brick; and

$C = 40$ for rough tile ducts, concrete.

Direct measurement of the velocity in the stack or chimney can be accomplished by means of the Pitot tube. The static pressure tube when used alone will read the draft pressure. The chief limitation of the Pitot tube is that traverses of equal area must be made for determining average velocity if the discharged quantity is to be calculated. Another limitation is that on velocity. The velocity is determined from the Pitot tube by means of the formula:

$$V = 1098 \sqrt{\frac{h_i}{W_a}} \qquad (54)$$

where V = velocity, feet per minute;

h_i = manometer reading, inches of water;

W_a = air density, pounds per cubic foot.

If the air temperature is 70°F, the formula becomes

$$V = 4000 \sqrt{h_i} \qquad (55)$$

where V = velocity, feet per minute;

h_i = manometer reading inches of water;

W_a = air density, pounds per cubic foot.

The lowest reading that can be made accurately on an inclined draft gage is approximately 0.025 in. of water. That is, on a 1 to 10 inclined gage a reading of 0.25 in. of water is obtained. This corresponds to a velocity of 600 fpm at 70°F. For velocities less than this amount other devices must be used or a micro manometer such as the Wahlen gage, which will read as low as 0.001 in. of water may be employed.

The measurement of convection currents in unconfined instances requires that both qualitative and quantitative indicators be used. The most common direction indicator is smoke, either chemical or that produced by burning tobacco, etc. Small fine threads, candle flames, and fine powders are also used for direction indicators. One handy type of smoke generator is a device that employs tin or titanium tetrachloride, which hydrolyzes on contact with the moisture in air forming a dense white smoke. By means of this smoke tube, the direction of convection currents may be ascertained. The degree of turbulence of the air may also be estimated by the rate at which the smoke dissipates and diffuses as it moves with the air current. Quantitative measurements of low air flows can be made by timing the travel of a puff of smoke over a measured distance.

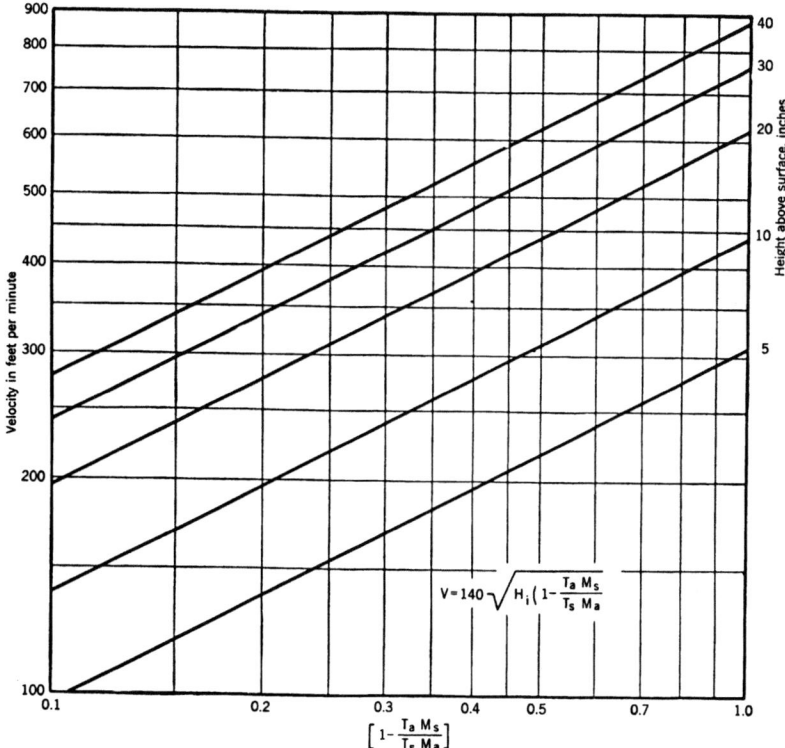

$$V = 140 \sqrt{H_i \left(1 - \frac{T_a M_s}{T_s M_a}\right)}$$

Fig 14-87. Calculation chart for determining theoretical convection velocity

Forced Draft and Draft Control.—Draft in a heating system refers to the pressure difference that causes a current of air or gases to flow through a combustion chamber, flue, or chimney. *Natural draft* is the draft obtained without any mechanical means. It is the heat of the combustion processes that creates the differential pressure causing the draft. *Mechanical draft* is created by fans that either force or pull the air or combustion products through the system. When the combustion products are forced through the system, the system is designated as a *forced draft system.* When the combustion products are pulled through the system, the system is designated as an *induced draft system.*

The overall problem of obtaining proper combustion of fuel includes, in addition to the design and installation of the actual firing equipment, a consideration of the entire path of the gas travel, from the air openings into the boiler room, through the burner, the combustion area, the heating surfaces, the breeching, and the vent or chimney.

To obtain this flow of air and gas, some force is required to provide the movement and to overcome the friction through the burner, boiler, and flue passages. Different firing systems employ one or more of the following means of providing this force:

1. natural draft chimney,

2. forced draft fan,

3. induced draft fan.

Natural draft is used on rotary oil burners in both the air register models and those with air openings in the combustion chamber floor. These units have a primary air fan, but its function is merely to atomize the oil or premix some air with the flue gas, leaving the bulk of the required combustion air to be supplied by natural draft. Natural draft is also used in combination with forced draft on pressure and air atomizing oil burners and combination gas oil burners. In these cases the fan provides the force to move the combustion air through the burner and the chimney pull provides the forces to move the combustion products through the boiler, breeching, and flue.

Forced draft burners are fired with gas, oil, or gas-oil in combination, and the types of oil burners are usually of the pressure or air atomizing type. In forced draft equip-

ment the burner fan has sufficient power to overcome the resistance of the boiler passages. Under certain conditions there is even sufficient power to overcome the resistance of the boiler breeching and a short stub stack. This type of burner equipment is usually found on packaged scaled boilers. The forced draft type burner can be utilized on a natural draft boiler that is not sealed. In this case the natural draft chimney is sufficiently negative in pressure to pull the products of combustion through the boiler and breeching.

Induced draft fans are not usually furnished as an integral part of a burner. However, they can be used as auxiliary equipment with any burner in which the chimney does not provide adequate draft. Some package boilers fired with rotary burners will utilize an induced draft fan to overcome the resistance of the boiler.

Larger heating plants will require draft at the boiler outlet in order to maintain satisfactory combustion. Obviously, equipment of this type cannot be operated with a draft diverter. However, some sort of draft control is necessary, and one of the simplest devices used for draft control is the barometric draft regulator. These are usually sized to have a free opening equal to the breeching to which they are attached. On gas or combination gas-oil fired installations they should be of the double swing type to relieve downdrafts or pressure due to a blocked chimney. A thermal spill switch should also be installed to shut down the burner equipment in the event of spillage.

Where chimneys are especially high-usually over 100 feet otherwise the firing rates must be varied widely in conjunction with large inputs sequence draft control may be required. In a sequence draft control system, the draft is controlled by positioning a damper in the breeching, which automatically maintains a specified draft throughout the firing range of the combustion equipment.

In general, some sort of draft control is required whenever there is a negative pressure in the boiler breeching. Even on so-called forced draft equipment this rule holds true. It must be made clear, however, that a forced draft burner has 100% of the combustion air supplied by the burner fan; this burner does not normally have the capability of overcoming the resistance of the boiler flue passages, breeching, and chimney.

If draft control is not provided there will usually be instability in the main burner or pilot burner on both gas and oil. The result of this will be nuisance shutdowns.

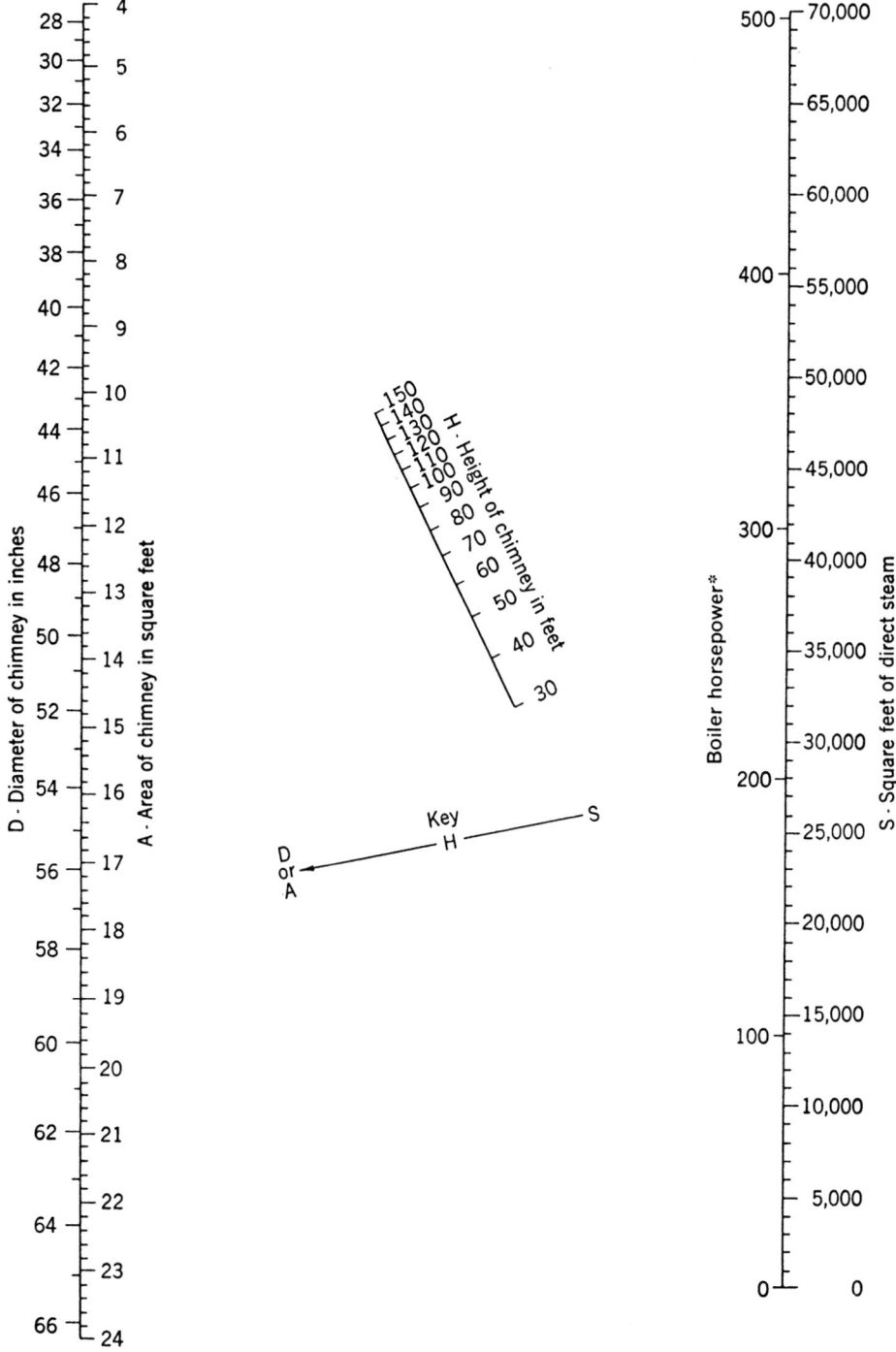

Fig 14-88. Breeching design selection

Sizing of Large Chimneys.—The charts shown Fig. 14-89 are for the determination of chimney sizes when the nominal boiler horsepower or square feet of radiation is known.

For example, assume a 1000 boiler horsepower load and a tentative chimney height of 150 ft. What must be the area of the chimney? Refer to the chart Fig. 14-89. Through the 1000 point mark on the horsepower scale and 150 on the diagonal scale draw a line to intersect the Q-axis. About this point on the Q-axis adjust the straight edge until identical readings are obtained on the two A scales, in this case, 27.5 ft^2 area. The diameter can be read directly opposite the area on the left hand scale; in this case a 71 in. diameter chimney would be required.

To use the chart Fig. 14-89 on this page, assume a chimney 150 ft high for a 55,000 ft^2 load. Through the 55,000 point on the S-scale and 150 on the diagonal scale, draw a straight line until it intersects the A and D scales. Find the diameter, to be 46 inches with an area of 11.5 ft^2.

The chart on this page is a solution of the formula

$$HP = 3.33(A - 0.60\sqrt{A})\sqrt{H}$$

where S = direct steam radiator surface, ft^2

     A = chimney area in, ft^2

     H = chimney height, ft

The chart below is a graphical solution of the formula

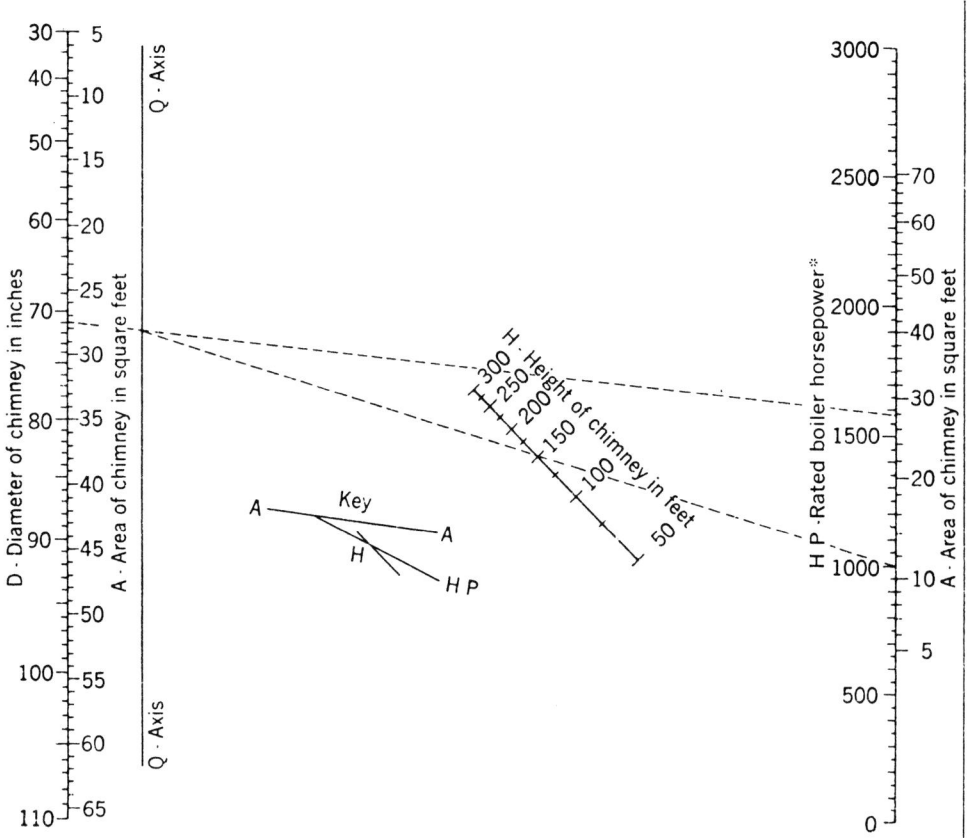

Fig 14-89. Chimney size determination

Chimney Design and Construction.—In connection with chimneys the question of area arises, since this is related to the volume of flue gases.

The cross-sectional area is given by Severns as:

$$A = \frac{Q}{V \times R} \qquad (56)$$

where A = chimney area, ft^2;

Q = flue gas volume, *cfm*;

K = velocity coefficient roughness (from 0.30 to 0.50); and

V = theoretical gas velocity, ft/sec.

The draft required from a chimney varies with the fuel. Table 14-32 gives approximate data for hand fired coal.

The maximum attainable (not theoretical) draft per foot of chimney height is given by Sefing as tabulated in Table 14-33. Note that the draft increases with the flue gas temperature.

Table 14-32. Draft Required for Burning Coal

Fuel	Burning Rate, lbs Coal per ft^2 Grate per hr						
	5	10	15	20	25	30	35
	Draft, in. of wg						
Anthracite No. 3, buckwheat	0.15	0.40	0.75	1.24	...	...	...
Anthracite No. 1, buckwheat	0.10	0.24	0.44	0.68	1.00	...	...
Anthracite, pea	0.06	0. 16	0.30	0.45	0.65	0.90	1.20
Semi-bituminous	0.05	0.10	0.18	0.26	0.35	0.45	0.58
Bituminous	0.04	0.09	0.15	0.22	0.28	0.38	0.45
Bituminous, run of mine	0.04	0.05	0.08	0.10	0.14	0. 16	0.20
Bituminous, on chain grate	0.00	0.12	0.15	0.23	0.31	0.44	0.57

Table 14-33. Maximum Attainable Draft/ft of Chimney

Average Flue Gas Temperature. °F	Outside Air Temperature,°F					
	0	20	40	60	80	100
	Draft/ft of Chimney Height, in. wg					
150	0.00360	0.00283	0.00225	0.00167	0.00113	0.00062
200	0.00460	0.00385	0.00325	0.00267	0.00213	0.00162
250	0.00543	0.00468	0.00408	0.0035	0.00286	0.00245
300	0.00615	0.00540	0.00480	0.00422	0.00368	0.00335
350	0.00679	0.00604	0.00545	0.00466	0.00432	0.00399
400	0.00735	0.00660	0.00600	0.00542	0.00488	0.00455
450	0.00787	0.00712	0.00652	0.00595	0.00540	0.00507
500	0.00831	0.00756	0.00696	0.00638	0.00584	.00551

Tests by the National Bureau of Standards on very short chimneys of 6 inch bare smoke pipe produce results about 80% of those in Table 14-33.

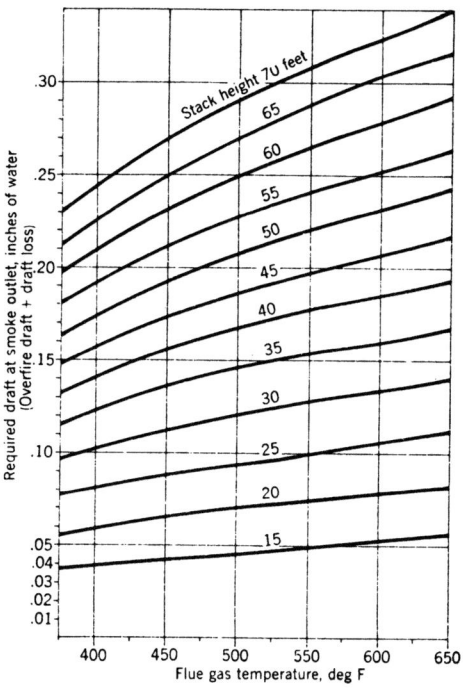

Fig 14-90. Chimney draft versus flue gas temperature for various height chimneys

Draft required for oil burning domestic heating equipment is about as follows: mechanical draft oil burners, 0.03 to 0.06 inch of water: space heaters, 0.04 to 0.08 inch of water.

Table 14-34. Capacities of Chimneys for Gas Appliances with Draft Hoods

Inner Diameter of Flue. in.	Height of Chimney, ft					
	10	15-20	30	40	50	60
	Gas Input, 1000 Btu/hr					
3	24	27	30	32	...	...
4	45	50	57	61	67	...
5	74	82	93	100	110	120
6	110	120	115	145	160	180
7	150	165	200	215	230	250
8	210	230	270	300	325	350
9	260	300	350	380	410	450
10	335	370	440	500	520	600
11	420	470	590	620	650	930
12	500	560	690	940	800	870

Fig. 14-90 shows the draft for oil-fired steel heating boilers at various flue gas temperatures as given by the Steel Boiler Institute in connection with its test code for boilers and boiler burner units.

Allowable gas input to gas appliances for various sizes of circular flues is given in Table 14-34. This table is based on a 150°F flue temperature, 60°F outside air temperature, 100% excess air, and 100% dilution at draft hood, terra cotta flues, and short horizontal breeching. Reduce capacity in table by 3.5% for each 1000 feet above sea level.

The National Board of Fire Underwriters code contains numerous provisions relating to chimneys, including the following:

1) *Flue connections required.* Every heating apparatus or heat producing appliance requiring a flue connection shall be connected with a flue conforming to the provisions of this article. This shall not include electric appliances; gas appliances, except as specifically required in this article; nor oil fired appliances especially designed for use without flue connection

2) *Use of nonconforming Flues.* Flues not conforming to the requirements of this article for chimneys, metal smokestacks or vents for gas appliances shall not he used unless listed by Underwriters' Laboratories, Inc., installed in full compliance with the listing and the manufacturer's instructions. and approved for such use by the building official.

3) *Smoke Pipe Connections.*

a) No flue shall have smoke pipe connections in more than one story of a building. unless provision is made for effectively closing smoke pipe openings with devices made of noncombustible materials whenever their use is discontinued temporarily, and completely closing them with masonry when discontinued permanently.

b) Two or more smoke pipes shall not be joined for a single connection, unless the smoke pipes and flue are of sufficient size to serve all the appliances thus connected.

c) The smoke pipe of a heating appliance shall not be connected into the flue of an incinerator that has the rubbish chute identical with the smoke flue.

4) *Construction of Chimneys.*

a) Chimneys hereafter erected within or attached to a structure shall be constructed in compliance with the provisions of this section.

b) Chimneys shall extend at least 3 ft above the highest point at which they pass through the roof of the building, and at least 2 ft higher than the ridge within 10 ft of each chimney.

c) Chimneys shall be wholly supported on masonry or self-supporting fireproof construction.

d) No chimney shall be corbeled from a wall more than 6 inch, nor shall a chimney be corbeled from wall less than 12 inches in thickness, unless it projects equally on each side of the wall, provided that in the second story of 2-story dwellings corbeling of chimneys on the exterior of the enclosing walls may equal the wall thickness. In every case the corbeling shall not exceed 1 in. projection for each course of brick projected.

Balancing Air Flow in Air Conditioning Systems

The duct system of an air conditioning installation must be properly balanced to insure satisfactory operation. Engineers of York Corporation compiled these easy step-by-step instructions for use in balancing small, medium, or large systems.

Balancing Small Air Conditioning Systems.—To balance small air conditioning systems, proceed as follows:

1) See that all the filters installed as part of the system are clean.

2) Start the fan. With forward curved blade fans and variable pitch pulleys see that the motor is not overloaded by excessive fan speed.

3) Examine all supply and return grilles to see that they are each getting air, and that there are no restrictions.

4) Block the face damper so it is open and the bypass damper closed.

5) By means of velocity measurements on the return and outside air inlets, set these two air quantities so that they are in the same proportion as the job conditions require (for example, 75% return air and 25% outside air) regardless of what their actual values may be. The air velocities may be read by means of anemometer, velometer, or pitot tube, as convenience dictates.

6) Take anemometer readings at the grilles and convert these to *cfm* to get the total air quantity handled by the fan. If this is within 10% of the estimate, adjustment of the fan speed is unnecessary. If the *cfm* differs more than this from the required value, change the fan speed in the proportion of *cfm* required over *cfm* obtained. Note: The *cfm* may be obtained also by pitot tube readings in the fan discharge, if convenient.

7) Select one outlet and take an accurate velocity reading (record for further reference).

8) Open the bypass damper and partially close the face damper.

9) Again take a velocity reading at the selected outlet or grille. If the velocity read is below that observed under step 7, the face damper should be opened until the velocity corresponds within 10% to the value obtained under step 7. If the observed velocity is higher than obtained under step 7, move the face damper toward the closed position. Mark the damper position finally obtained. Note: Instead of observing grille velocities, the above procedure can be followed by using in the same manner, the static pressure in the fan discharge.

10) Adjust the damper motor linkage so that with the damper motor at one end of its travel, the bypass will be closed and the face damper wide open; and at the other end of its travel, the bypass will be wide open and the face damper will be in the position determined under step 9.

11) Set the splitters and dampers so that each grille delivers the required *cfm* by means of anemometer or velometer readings (generally readings within 10% are close enough).

12) Place the system under automatic control.

13) Check the room temperatures for uniformity, and adjust the grilles further if necessary.

14) Mark all damper positions finally obtained so that if a complaint arises later, it can be determined whether the position of the damper (or dampers) has been moved.

Balancing Medium and Large Systems.—*General:*

While these systems may vary considerably in size or in the extent of the duct distribution, the same general procedure for balancing may be followed on all jobs. In any case, it should be done in a systematic manner by keeping a complete set of records of every operation, and the results obtained. Furthermore, the larger the job, the more difficult it is for an engineer to assimilate the details of the installation in a short time. For this reason, it is good practice, as well as economical, to have someone available who is familiar with the location of all dampers and splitters.

As mentioned before, the apparatus should be balanced first. This procedure would be as follows:

1) Examine the entire duct system to make sure all grilles, dampers, and splitters are open for both supply and return.

2) Start the fan. (If it is a forward curved blade fan, see that the fan motor is not overloaded.) Note: If the ducts are dirty, it may be necessary to cover the outlets temporarily with cheesecloth to catch the dirt.

3) Examine the filters to see whether they are dirty or not, as testing should be done with clean filters.

Table 14-35. Record of Data in Making Check of Air Quantity

Item	Est. cfm	Test 1	Test 2	Test 3	Test 4
Bypass damper		Closed	Closed	Open	Open
Return damper		Open	Closed	Closed	Open
Outside dampers, minimum		Open	Open	Open	Open
Outside dampers, maximum		Closed	Open	Open	Closed
Face damper		None	None	None	None
Maximum washer *cfm*	17,800	18,000	18,000		
Fan speed	428		430		
Fan discharge static pressure, inches		0.62	0.63	0.62	0.63
Velocity at eliminator		750	750	400	400
Minimum bypass *cfm*					
Maximum bypass *cfm*	8,300			8,400	8,400
Minimum outside air *cfm*	5,000				5,200
Maximum outside air *cfm*	17,000		18,000		

Setting Outside and Return Air Dampers: The following steps are taken in checking dampers:

1) Open the minimum outside air damper to its approximate setting, and close the maximum outside damper.

2) Close the bypass damper and open the return air dampers. By means of velocity measurements on return and minimum outside air dampers, set these two air quan-

tities so that they are in the same proportion as the job conditions require (such as 75% return air and 25% outside air, for example) regardless of what their actual values may be. The air velocities may be read by means of anemometer, Velometer, or Pitot tube, as convenience dictates.

3) Take a static pressure reading on the fan discharge.

4) Close the bypass, open the maximum outside air damper, and close the return damper.

5) Take a static pressure reading as in step 6. If this static pressure is lower than in step 6 the outside air intake is restricted. If the resistance cannot be removed, block the return air damper partially open so that the fan discharge static pressure is equal to that observed in step 6. Install a permanent stop on the damper. If the fan discharge static pressure is higher than in step 6, block the outside air damper partially closed so that the fan discharge static pressure is equal to that observed in step 6, and install a permanent stop on the damper. Note: By means of this procedure, outside and return air dampers have been set so that the same total air quantity will be handled with the dampers in the positions corresponding to maximum and minimum outside air. The next step is to set the bypasses.

Setting Bypass Dampers: There are two cases, washers with and without face dampers. If face dampers are used, it is possible to set the face and bypass dampers so as to keep the total *cfm* constant for any position of these dampers, and at the same time to give the designed maximum and minimum *cfm* through the washer. The procedure is as follows:

6) With the bypass closed, and face, return, and minimum outside air dampers opened, read and record the fan discharge static pressure.

7) With the bypass, minimum outside air and return air dampers open, move the washer face damper to such a position that the fan discharge static pressure reads the same as in step 9.

8) By means of anemometer, velometer, or pitot tube readings, determine the *cfm* through the bypasses and the washer when the dampers are in the position determined by step 10. If the portion bypassed exceeds the design quantity, add resistance to the bypasses. If the proportion bypassed falls below that required, bypass is restricted and must be relieved.

9) By trial and error, repeat steps 9, 10 and step 11, until the bypass resistance and face damper position are found which give the design proportion of bypassed and washer air when the bypass is wide open and at the same time give the same fan discharge static pressure with the dampers in positions described in steps 9, and 10.

10) Adjust the damper motor linkage so that with the damper motor at one end of its travel, the bypass will be closed and the face damper will be in its minimum open position as determined in step 12; and with the damper motor at the other end of its travel, the bypass is closed and the face damper open. Note: When the washer is not

fitted with face damper, it is not possible to keep the total air quantity constant with the bypass damper in open and closed position, the *cfm* variation depending on the portion of the total system resistance represented by the washer. In such cases, the procedure is as follows:

11) With the bypass closed and return and minimum outside air damper open, observe the fan discharge static pressure.

12) Open the bypass and observe the fan discharge static pressure. If this exceeds the static pressure observed in (14) by more than about 20%, resistance must be added to the bypass until the static pressure increase at the fan discharge falls within 20% of the value in step 14.

13) By velocity readings over the face of the washer and in the bypass, determine the proportion of bypassed to washer air with the bypass open. If the proportion of bypass air exceeds the design value, add resistance to the bypass by trial until the design proportion is reached. If the proportion of bypassed to washed air falls below that required, the bypass is restricted and must be relieved. The limit of relieving the bypass is fixed by step 15 above. If after the limit of static pressure given in step 15 has been reached and there is still insufficient bypassed air, a washer face damper must be used, in which case the adjustment is as described in step 9 to step 13 inclusive.

Setting Total Air Quantity: In establishing the setting for the total air quantity, proceed as follows:

14) Take readings of the fan discharge velocity to determine accurately the *cfm* handled. If this *cfm* differs from the design value. change the fan speed in the proportion of *cfm* required over *cfm* observed.

15) As a final check, read and record fan discharge static pressure and air quantities, and record as tabulated in Table 14-35. If the air quantities are not within 10%, of the design volume, the previously described procedure should be checked through to find errors.

As in balancing the apparatus, the testing of the duct outlets should be done in a careful and systematic manner.

Balancing Duct Distribution.—The simplest procedure is to take the blueprints of the duct layout, and number each grille, splitter, and damper. On the larger jobs, it is good practice to mark also the grilles, dampers, etc. In marking the prints, where the supply duct is divided into two or more branches, each branch should be numbered or lettered as well as the grilles, etc. For example, supply S-1 will have grille S-1-1, S-1-2, etc., and the return will have grill R-1-1, R-1-2, etc.

Tabulation of test results is very important and it will be found that careful recording will save considerable time.

1) When the *cfm* from the fan is correct, for all damper positions determine the amount of air to be handled by each branch.

2) Measure each branch at a suitable point, and from the estimated *cfm* figure the velocity of air in the duct.

3) Convert velocity into pressure in inches of water.

4) Take velocity readings in the branch ducts and set the splitter so that the velocity pressure will be as figured under step 3. Note: It is not necessary to take a complete transverse of the duct, but for this purpose three or four readings are all that is required in large ducts.

5) When the *cfm* to all the branch supplies are approximately correct, select one branch and take reading of all grilles, record and compare these with the estimated velocities.

6) From the tabulations of the grille test, note which ones have higher velocity than estimated, and set the dampers or valves to reduce the air quantity to these grilles. This will automatically increase the *cfm* of the grilles that have low velocity.

7) Repeat the readings as under step 5 and step 6 until all are within 10% of estimate.

8) Proceed in a similar manner on the remaining branches.

9) Make up a tabulation of the return grilles similar to the tabulation for the supply grilles.

10) By means of an anemometer, determine the *cfm* on the return grilles and set the dampers so each handles the correct amount.

11) Take wet and dry bulb readings in various areas to determine the uniformity of temperature and humidity and adjust the supply grilles if necessary.

Balancing Systems Using Booster Fans.—On installations using booster fans, the bypass air is handled at each zone fan, and there is no bypass at the main apparatus. The balancing of such a system is done substantially in the following manner:

Setting of Outside and Return Air Dampers: The next three steps should now be followed:

1) Close the bypass and open the dehumidified air dampers on all the booster fans.

2) Proceed as step 1 to step 6 under Balancing Medium or Large Air Conditioning Systems. Note: Under *Starting the Fan*, the booster fans should also be started.

3) Close the maximum outside air damper and open the return damper on the main supply apparatus.

Setting Total Air Quantities: This is a more extensive procedure and calls for the following steps:

4) Close the dehumidified air and open the bypass dampers on the booster fans.

5) By means of pitot tube readings on the booster fan discharges, determine the actual *cfm* being handled by each fan. If this *cfm* differs front the design value, change the fan speed in the proportion of the *cfm* required over the *cfm* observed.

6) When the *cfm* of each booster is correct, take the static pressure in the booster fan discharge.

7) Open the dehumidified air and close the bypass dampers on the booster fans.

8) Set the splitters in the supply duct from the main fan so that each booster fan receives the correct proportion of the total *cfm* regardless of whether the total is correct or

not. To do this, take the pitot tube readings and determine the total *cfm* from the main fan, and then take readings at each branch duct to the booster fans and set the splitters accordingly.

9) Take a static pressure reading in the booster fan discharge. If this reading is 10% above or below the static pressure taken at step 6, change the speed of the main supply fan by:

$$\text{new rpm} = \text{old rpm} \times \sqrt{\frac{\text{SP taken under step 6}}{\text{SP taken under step 9}}}$$

This procedure will be satisfactory when the *cfm* of the booster fan is equal to the *cfm* of dehumidified air from the main supply fan. When the booster fan *cfm* is greater than the *cfm* of dehumidified air supplied to it, such as when a constant amount of bypass air is handled, use steps step 1 to step 8.

10) With the bypass dampers open and the dehumidified air dampers closed, take a static pressure reading in the bypass air duct near the damper.

11) Open the dehumidified air and close the bypass dampers on all booster fans. If a hand bypass damper is provided, open it slightly to an approximate position to handle the constant bypass; if not, block the automatic dampers partially open.

12) By means of an anemometer, velometer or pitot tube, determine the *cfm* of the constant bypass air and place a stop on the dampers when the correct position is found.

13) Open the dehumidified air dampers and close the bypass dampers to the stop.

14) Take a static pressure reading in the dehumidified air supply duct, as near as possible to the damper. If this static pressure is more than 10% above or below the static pressure taken at step 10, change the main supply fan speed accordingly. Note: While the static pressure taken under item step 10 may not be the same on each fan, the difference between the static pressure taken at step 10 and step 14 should be the same for each fan.

15) With the static pressure taken under step 10 and step 14 equal, the total *cfm* from the main supply fan should be correct. However, take pitot tube readings in the main dehumidified air supply duct to check. If it is not correct, the indication is that either the bypass air dampers were not set correctly or the booster fans were not receiving the correct proportion of air as set under step 8.

16) Take a static pressure reading in the discharge of the main supply fan and set the static regulator to maintain a constant static pressure (if a static pressure regulator is furnished).

17) Open the bypass damper and close the dehumidified air damper to the approximate minimum position.

18) With a pitot tube, check the dehumidified air supply to each booster fan and set the dampers to the correct minimum position, and install stops.

There are two important reasons for checking the performance of air conditioning installations as soon as they are placed in operation. They are:
1) To see that each part is operating correctly.
2) To see that the various parts and their functions are coordinated.

Air Balancing by Balancing and Testing Engineers.—*Basic Design Items:* 1) Supply fan designed for 10% over required air to allow for leakage.

2) Return fan included if system contains *economy cycle* (100% outside air for winter, spring, and fall cooling).

3) Adjustable pressure relief system included (in lieu of 2) to limit building pressurization to 0.05 inch wg if system contains economy cycle.

4) Fan capacities selected with correction factor for elevation above sea level.

5) Fan motor selected to allow for additional static due to field conditions.

6) Fan curve checked to provide safety factor against higher operating static pressures.

7) Ceiling diffusers selected for proper application according to manufacturer recommendations (i.e., high induction type to satisfy high air volume requirements).

8) Select air outlets that have damper mechanisms readily accessible.

Specification Items: 1) Variable-pitch (adjustable) sheaves specified for fan motors supply, return, and exhaust.

2) Provision made for complete change of filters just prior to balancing.

3) Provision for single-blade manual damper with locking quadrant hardware in each zone duct of multizone system near unit.

4) Provision for manual damper at each branch duct take-off from main duct (return or supply air).

5) Provision for manual damper at each duct drop to diffusers from main duct.

6) Provision for opposed blade dampers at each diffuser and register or grille.

7) Provision for manual damper downstream of mixing dampers at each zone of double duct system.

8) Provision for turning vanes in all square elbows (double-wall type or extended edge type) in low velocity systems.

9) Provision for perforated static pressure plates at fan discharge of blow through air handling units.

10) Provision for access holes for tachometer readings in all belt guards.

11) No duct liner at duct connections to high velocity air handlers or multizone units.

12) Provision for $\frac{1}{2}$ mesh screen on intakes to pre clogging.

13) Provision for access doors of adequate size within working distance of all volume dampers, fire dampers, pressure-reducing valves, reheat coils, mixing boxes, blenders, constant volume regulators, etc.

14) Provision of extractors at all 90° boot type branch duct connections to main duct.

15) Provision for all duct seams, duct connections, casing and plenum connections to be sealed to minimize leakage factor to approximately 5%.

16) Provision for pressure testing of high pressure duct runs (i.e., spiral duct) for casing wall leakage.

17) Requirement for mixing box manufacturers to set mechanical volume controllers to plus or minus 5% of design *cfm* by actual air flow test methods rather than measured spring adjustments.

18) Requirement for duct liner in discharge duct after leaving mixing box according to manufacturer's recommendations.

19) Provision for mixing baffles (perforated plate, etc.) at the outlet of all mixing boxes to prevent temperature stratification in supply duct.

20) Requirement for mixing box dampers not leaking more than 3% of design *cfm* when unit is operating at the design static pressure conditions.

21) Provision for round volume dampers to be installed in hot and cold duct take-offs to mixing boxes.

22) Provision for control manufacturer to be responsible for setting and testing all controls in conjunction with air-balance work.

Plan Items: 1) Be absolutely certain that all dampers required in Specification Items Section above are distinctly shown in their proper locations on the plans. If a choice is necessary, the best place to cover dampers is on the plans rather than just in the specs.

2) For purposes of locating duct obstructions that reduce air flow to various outlets or zones, all damper locations, including fire dampers, should be shown.

3) Indicate damper locations at accessible points and, whenever possible, at a distance from a duct transition or fitting.

4) Provide manual, opposed-blade-type dampers in outside and return air ducts at the entrance to the mixed air plenum in addition to the automatic proportioning dampers.

5) Splitter dampers to be used as diverters only and not to control air volume; use only in low velocity systems.

6) Where proportional type take-offs are employed, a splitter blade is also recommended to allow adjustment of proportion in the event of higher or lower duct pressures. This does not eliminate the necessity for volume control dampers in the resulting branch ducts.

7) Prevent short-circulating of discharge air from cooling towers, condensing units, relief exhausts, roof exhausters, etc., to any fan system outside air intake due to close proximity or wind.

8) Connections of outside air or return air ducts should not be made at only one side of a fan inlet plenum.

9) Avoid placement of return air inlet in or adjacent to the return air plenum.

10) Avoid the use of masonry or composition wall vertical shafts for exhaust systems on multistory buildings without interconnecting ductwork. Inherent leakage prohibits the removal of exhaust air from designated locations within the occupied spaces.

11) Avoid locating diffusers, registers, or grilles directly into the bottom or sides of a main duct as no amount of adjustment will decrease the generated noise level.

12) Avoid locating troffer light diffusers on the same duct run or zone with standard type diffusers or registers due to difference in static pressure imposed by each. The higher statics of the troffers will require the standard outlets to be throttled severely and will cause objectionable noise levels at these outlets.

13) Avoid long duct runs containing large volume diffusers on main ducts with small diffusers or registers on branch ducts from the same main duct.

14) Avoid locating ceiling diffusers on the same duct run with registers due to differences in static pressure imposed by each.

15) Provision for extractors (adjustable type) at each boot type branch duct take-off.

16) Length of duct drops to diffusers should be two times the duct diameter and should contain a volume control damper.

17) Avoid the passage of return air from one space or zone through that of another to reach a return air register.

18) Avoid the use of door louvers for passage of return air when supply air system operates at low pressure (i.e., ceiling plenum supply system).

19) Avoid the use of combination supply and return outlets due to inability to determine amount of short circuiting.

20) Avoid short discharge ducts between mixing boxes and supply registers, as they will cause excessive discharge velocities and air noise at face of register.

21) Avoid short, abrupt connections from mixing box outlet to proportional take-offs or branch ducts.

22) Provision of temperature and pressure gages, flow meters, etc.

23) Duct sizing increased at mixing damper and fire-damper locations so as to provide same free area as in adjoining ductwork.

24) For high velocity systems, manual volume dampers should be avoided where possible because they are noise generators. If manual throttling is required in these systems, factory made pressure reducing valves with airfoil-shaped vanes should be used. They are available with either manual or motor operators.

STEAM HEATING SYSTEM DESIGN

STEAM HEATING SYSTEM DESIGN

This chapter is divided into three parts. The first pertains mainly to the design of large commercial, industrial, and institutional steam heating systems. The second is chiefly concerned with design of one pipe systems in residential pipe installations. The third applies to design of two pipe steam heating systems of various types for residential and larger installations.

Large Systems

Vacuum pumps are essential in large steam heating systems to assure quick and uniform distribution of steam to all parts of the system and to obtain prompt return of condensate to the boiler. Basic system components are shown in Figs. 15-1 to 15-4.

Steam supply to the heating units may be upfeed or downfeed, as desired. When downfeed supply of steam is desired, the mains are located above the heating units and supplied by main risers. Steam is distributed by downfeed risers from the mains. When upfeed supply of steam is employed, the mains are located below the heating surfaces and steam is supplied through upfeed risers. A combination of downfeed and upfeed supply may be employed depending on building construction.

Steam mains must pitch down in the direction of steam flow so as to provide concurrent flow of steam and of condensate occurring in the mains. Diagrams in a later section on supply and return piping connections illustrate the basic connections between mains and risers.

Heating units condense the steam, changing it to liquid or condensate. In this change of state, latent heat is given up by steam at the rate required by the heating units and is distributed by the heating units to the space being heated.

Traps permit condensate and air to pass into the return piping of the system, but prevent the passage of steam. It is essential that no connection be made between the supply side and the return side of the system at any point except through a suitable trap.

The return piping conducts the condensate and air back to the pump and must pitch down toward the pump. This piping must provide unrestricted gravity flow of condensate to the pump receiver.

As the condensate and air reach the pump they are separated, the gases are discharged to the atmosphere, and the condensate is returned to the boiler or boiler feed system.

These same basic components may be used in the design of a vacuum or a subatmospheric system. A vacuum heating pump maintains a vacuum in the return piping under all operating conditions, assisting the supply steam in overcoming the resistance of the system piping and assuring rapid and uniform steam distribution. The subatmospheric system permits control of building temperature by variation of steam temperature and output of heating units.

Fig. 15-3 illustrates the six basic components of a system that includes a vacuum heating pump.

When it is necessary to install returns below the level of the pump inlet, a mechanical lift should be installed to handle the low returns, as illustrated in Fig. 15-4.

Equivalent Direct Radiation (*EDR*).—Equivalent direct radiation is a unit measure of heat output from a heating surface amounting to a 240 Btu/hr. This is approximately equal to the latent heat given up when $\frac{1}{4}$ lb steam per hr is condensed. To convert lb of steam to EDR multiply ft^2 EDR by 4.00. To convert EDR to MBH (1000 Btu/hr) multiply ft^2 EDR by 0.24.

Piping Connections to Boilers.—Fundamentals applying to connections of supply and return piping to boilers are illustrated in Figs. 15-1, 15-5, 15-6, 15-7, and 15-8. Piping at the boiler including the Hartford return connection is shown for a single boiler in Fig. 15-1.

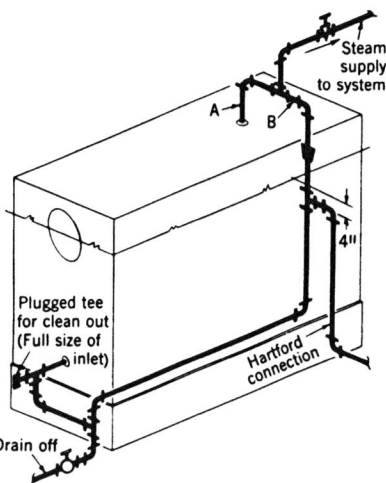

Fig 15-1. Single boiler with Hartford connection

Steam is supplied by the boiler through the boiler nozzle. The size of the uptake A, Fig. 15-1, should never be less than the nozzle opening. The steam supply header B must be at least the same size as the uptake A. The connection between the end of the steam supply header B and the return inlet of the boiler is the equalizer and steam header drip. This connection is reduced in size depending upon the capacity of the boiler but should not be smaller than the size shown in tables (later in this section).

The supply header piping is arranged to direct the flow of steam from the boiler toward the equalizer. This ensures a pressure balance in the piping between the supply and return connections to the boiler.

Note the plugged tee at the connection to the boiler return inlet for cleaning and the drain valve at the bottom of the equalizer. The horizontal piping connection to the boiler inlet should be the same size as the inlet.

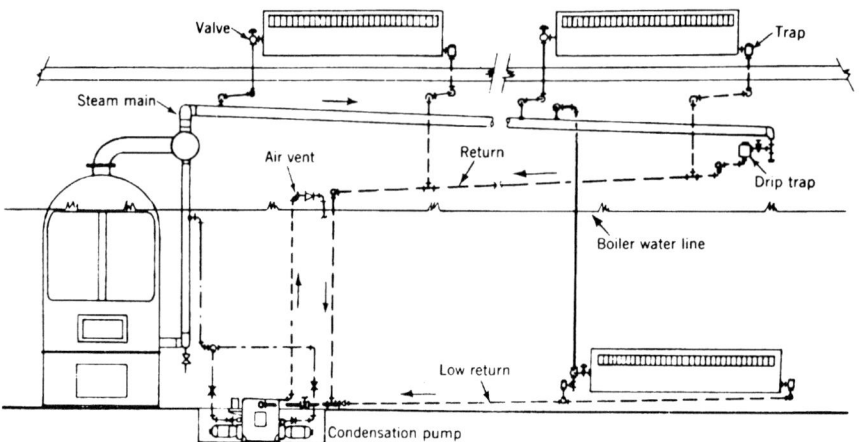

Fig 15-2. Basic components of steam heating system

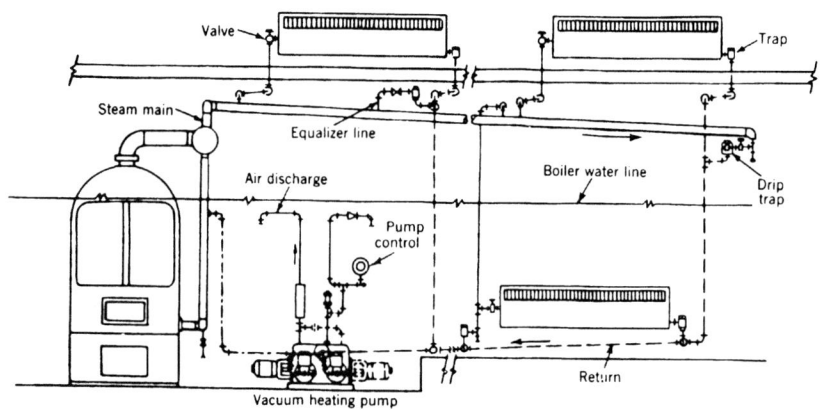

Fig 15-3. Vacuum heating pump maintains a vacuum in the return piping under all operating conditions

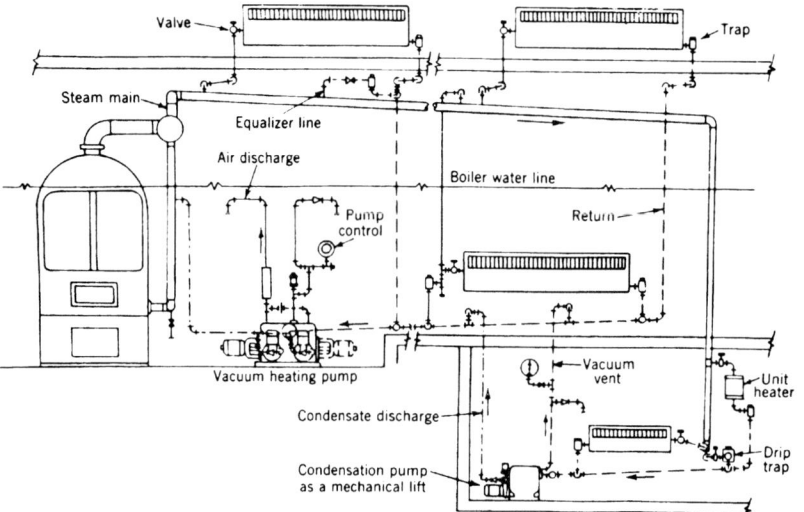

Fig 15-4. Mechanical lift should be installed to handle returns below the level of pump inlets

The condensate return to the boiler is connected to the equalizer at a point 4 inches below the recommended boiler water level. This constitutes the *Hartford connection*. It includes a short nipple to eliminate undesirable vapor accumulation, a cause of water hammer. The vertical rise in the condensate return to the Hartford connection should be the same size as the equalizer line. This ensures low velocity flow of condensate into the equalizer.

When the length of run from the condensate pump or boiler feeder to the boiler exceeds 25 ft, a check valve should be installed close to the base of the vertical rise to the Hartford connection. A check valve is always installed close to the pump discharge. When the pump discharge is overhead, a spring-loaded check valve should be installed at the base of the vertical rise to the Hartford connection.

Pipe Size, in.	Flow, gpm	Pipe Size, in.	Flow, gpm
1	10	2½	60
1¼	18	3	90
1½	25	3½	120
2	42	4	160

The pump discharge pipe should be sized to limit the velocity of flow to the boiler. The above table shows correct pipe sizes in order for velocities not to exceed 4 ft/sec.

When a condensate boiler feed unit is vented to the atmosphere and employed with a vacuum heating system, a check valve should be installed in the vent. Also, an equalizer line with thermostatic trap must be installed between the boiler supply header and the receiver of the boiler feed unit. A check valve is also required in the overflow line from the receiver. This will allow equalization between the receiver of the boiler feed unit and the boiler whenever an induced vacuum or a vacuum caused by vacuum pump operation occurs in the boiler. Omission of these features can cause boiler flooding on shutdown.

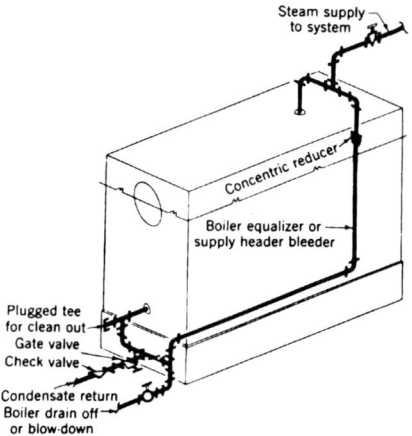

Fig 15-5. Single boiler with direct return connection

Single Boiler with Direct Return Connection.—

When the condensate return is connected directly to the boiler without the use of a Hartford connection, it is connected directly to the return inlet of the boiler (see Fig. 15-5). The connection is made with a check valve, gate valve, and a valved drain off at the boiler inlet.

The direct return of condensate to the return inlet of the boiler has the advantage of delivering condensate to the coolest portion of the boiler. This advantage is important when a building is heated intermittently, for example, in a school or office building with night and weekend shutdown, when the initial condensate returned after a shutdown is relatively cool.

Two Boilers with Common Return Header and Hartford Connection.—In Fig. 15-6 the drop supply provides swing connections from each boiler to the common header. It also ensures the separation of entrained condensate, which flows to the supply header drip without entering the heating system piping with the steam. The common drop supply header may be provided with blank flanges for the addition of future boilers. Supply mains are taken from the top of the header.

The common supply header should be sized for the total connected load of the system based on the total developed length of the longest run.

The drip from the header is taken from the bottom and connected to the common return header. The horizontal run in the drip line must be at least 24 inches above the water line of the boilers to prevent surging of condensate in the line. The size of this line should not be less than the size of the equalizer line on each boiler.

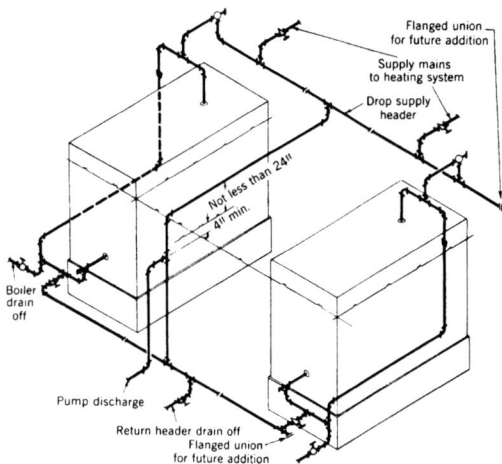

Fig 15-6. Two boilers with common return header and Hartford connection

The common return header should be sized for the total connected load of the entire system based on the total length of the longest return main. The condensate return to the boilers is connected to the drip line at a point 4 inches below the water level of the boilers to constitute a Hartford connection.

The boiler piping arrangement described eliminates the necessity of drip traps or other mechanical devices for dripping the steam headers, and it provides equalization of pressure in all the boiler piping.

Two Boilers with Separate Direct Return Connections from Below.—The drop supply header must be dripped through a float and thermostatic trap to the return main of the heating system since the boilers are not equalized. This arrangement is shown in detail in Fig. 15-7.

The supply outlet of each boiler is equalized with its return inlet. Since the boilers have no common return header, a separate boiler feed is made direct to the return inlet of each boiler. The connection is made with a check valve, gate valve, and a valved drain-off at the inlet.

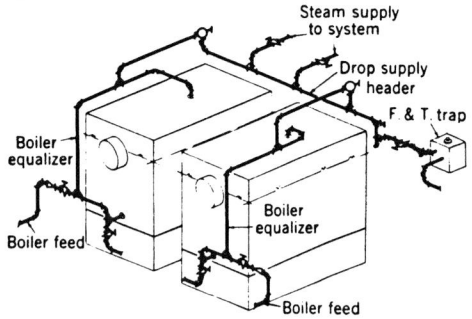

Fig 15-7. Two boilers with separate direct return connections from overhead

Two Boilers with Separate Direct Return Connections from Overhead.— When returns to the boilers are from overhead, as shown in Fig. 15-8, a spring loaded check valve should be installed at each boiler connection to prevent drainage in the overhead lines. This eliminates the possibility of water hammer on future pump operations. Note the discharge line enters the return header at each boiler so that direction of flow is toward the boiler return inlet.

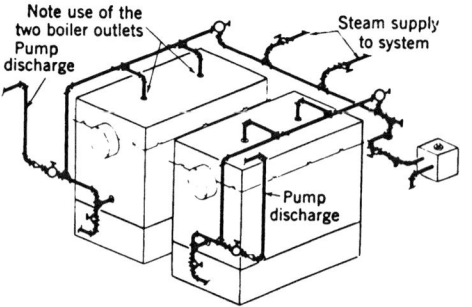

Fig 15-8. Two boilers with separate direct return connections from overhead

Connections to Steam Using Equipment.—Proper methods of connecting piping to steam using equipment, controls, and traps are shown in Figs. 15-9 to 15-15.

Convector Piping Detail: Piping connections for convectors are shown in Fig. 15-9 for both downfeed and upfeed risers.

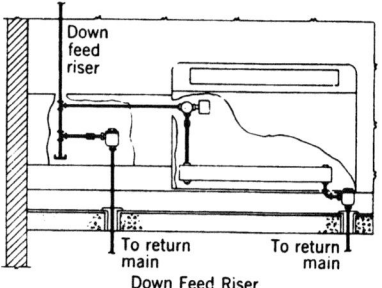

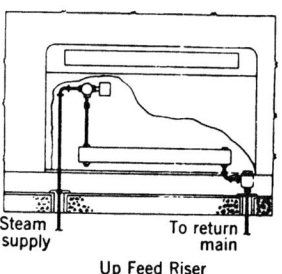

Fig 15-9. Convector piping connection

When an automatic control valve is employed with a heating unit installed below the steam main, it is necessary to drip the downfeed riser to prevent accumulation of condensate in the riser when the valve is closed.

A control valve should be installed above the heating element of a convector to prevent accumulation of condensate in the supply end of the convector.

Fin Tube Piping Detail: Piping details for a fin tube heater are shown in Fig. 15-10.

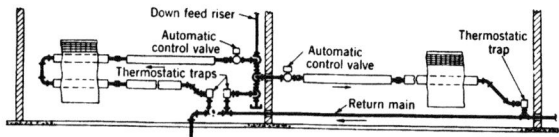

Fig 15-10. Fin tube heater piping connections

Note that the downfeed riser is provided with a drip to prevent the accumulation of condensate in the riser.

The installation of the fin tube heaters requires consideration of the relation between length of element and steam distribution. Note a two tier fin tube heating element with a return bend has a length of run equal to twice the length of the unit. An approximation of the pressure drop through a long run of fin tube can be calculated by utilizing Table 9-34.

Expansion joints are necessary to prevent expansion noises and element distortion.

Unit Heater Piping Details: Installation of a unit heater with propeller fan and large air capacity should be made with careful consideration to support of the unit and to prevention of expansion strains. The unit should be supported separately from the piping, and allowance should be made for expansion of supply piping by use of swing joints. See piping details in Fig. 15-11.

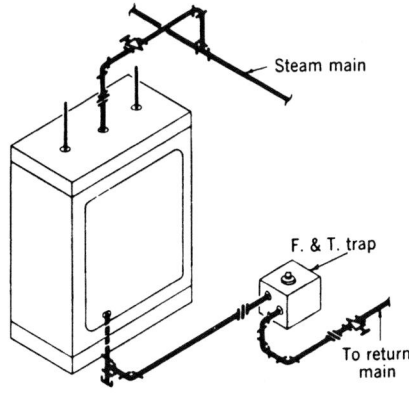

Horizontal Unit Heater

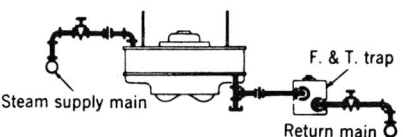

Vertical Delivery Unit Heater

Fig 15-11. Unit heater piping details

Industrial Type Unit Heater Piping Details: This heater, which has centrifugal fans, is capable of delivering air under sufficient pressure for distribution through duct work or with discharge flow directed to selected areas. The unit has capacity for heating large quantities of air relative to the space it occupies. The unit requires the use of a heavy duty float and thermostatic trap. Automatic control of the steam supply is rarely used, but thermostatic control of the fan operation is often employed. Piping details are shown in Fig. 15-12.

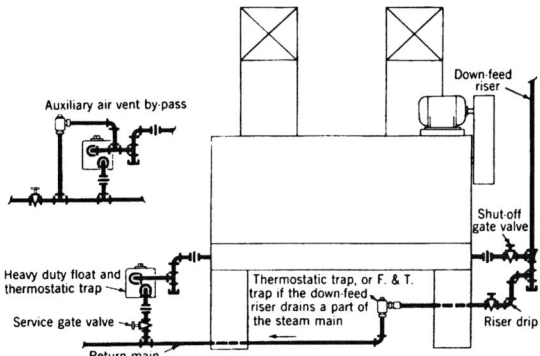

Fig 15-12. Piping connection for industrial type unit heater

When thermostatic control of the steam supply is employed, the supply and return should be arranged the same as shown for an auditorium type unit with equalizer and auxiliary air vent bypass (Fig. 15-14).

Unit Ventilator Piping Details: The steam supply to the heating coils is normally automatic. The capacity range of the coils usually permits the use of a thermostatic trap rather than a float and thermostatic trap. Unit ventilators are usually operated with continuous fan operation during room occupancy. Piping details for unit ventilators are shown in Fig. 15-13.

An equalizing line with check valve is employed by some unit manufacturers, as illustrated, on units that have the heating element near bottom of cabinet. This set up assists coil drainage.

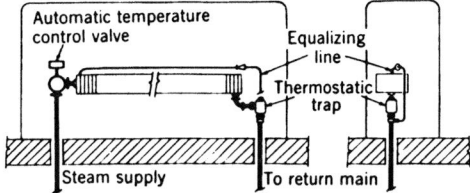

Fig 15-13. Unit ventilator piping details

Auditorium Type Unit Ventilator Piping Details: An auditorium type unit ventilator having large air capacity is used, when ventilation as well as heating is required for large spaces. Ventilation is accomplished by adding either a proportion of outdoor air with recirculated air from the space being heated or 100% outdoor air. Equipped with centrifugal type fans, this ventilator is suitable for delivering air under sufficient pressure for distribution through ductwork. Piping details are shown in Fig. 15-14.

Supply valves for individual units installed on a subatmospheric system should be sized for not more than 1 psi pressure drop at design conditions.

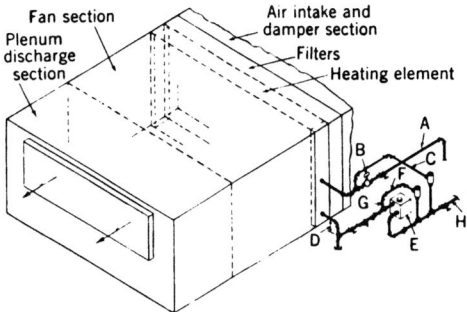

Fig. 15-14. Auditorium ventilator piping connections

A heavy duty float and thermostatic trap is used. The auxiliary air vent bypass in the Fig. 15-14 at F may not be required, if pressure steam is always available to the coils on automatic operation. The bypass should be employed with all subatmospheric systems to provide adequate venting of coils under this condition. This will ensure removal of air in leakage from the supply mains and compensate for reduction of venting and condensate capacity in the float and thermostatic trap at low subatmospheric pressures. The bypass connection should be made as close to the float and thermostatic trap inlet as possible and must be left uncovered to assure a cooling leg for proper thermostatic trap operation.

The equalizer line the Fig. 15-14 at C operates as an induced vacuum breaker for the coils. When the automatic temperature control valve throttles, a high induced vacuum can occur in the coils and retard the drainage of condensate, particularly on conventional low vacuum systems due to frequent supply valve closing.

Hot Water Generator Piping Details: Piping details for a hot water generator are shown in Fig. 15-15. When the steam supply to a hot water generator comes from overhead, it is essential to drip the supply ahead of the control valve. This prevents accumulation of condensate in the supply line when the automatic supply valve is closed. Accumulation of condensate ahead of this valve can cause water hammer. When the run of steam supply piping to the generator is short, a thermostatic trap may be used in place of the float and thermostatic trap shown.

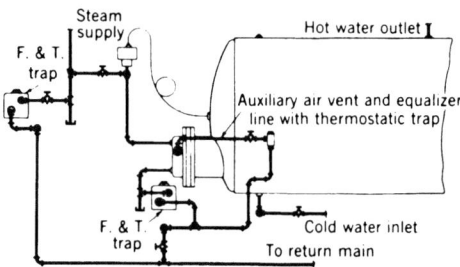

Fig 15-15. Piping connections to hot water generator

The auxiliary air vent with thermostatic trap from the steam coil of the heater to the vacuum return line provides venting of the coils on heating up and relief of the induced vacuum caused by closing of the automatic control valve. This back venting allows complete drainage of the steam coils. The float and thermostatic trap is a heavy duty trap.

When the returns from a hot water generator are close to a vacuum return pump, provision should be made for cooling this condensate. This may be done with a section of fin tube heating element.

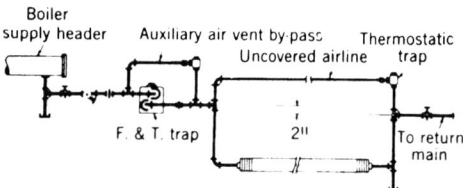

Fig 15-16. Boiler supply header drip

Supply and Return Piping Connections: In laying out piping for a steam system particular attention must be

given to connections and locations of traps for venting of air and removal of condensate. Means must be provided for permitting expansion of piping without incurring a change of alignment that may interfere with flow of condensate. Condensate should flow promptly and smoothly to the return piping. Proper pitch is needed for all mains and branches. Where changes in elevation or direction of mains are required, drips should be used at low points. The methods of making connections that ensure proper system operation are shown in Figs. 15-16 to 15-36.

Boiler Supply Header Drip: Provision should be made for cooling the hot condensate from a boiler supply header when the drip connection is close to a vacuum return pump. This is accomplished as shown in Fig. 15-16 with a section of fin tube radiation beyond the float and thermostatic trap. The $\frac{1}{2}$ inch uncovered air line with thermostatic trap stabilizes the flow of condensate through the cooling coil by separating air and noncondensable gases from the liquid.

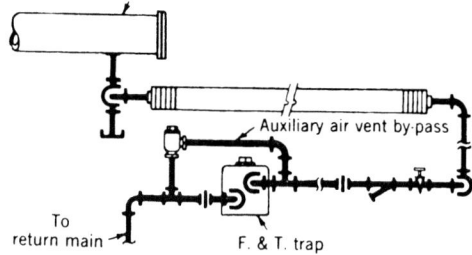

Fig 15-17. Controlled steam header drip

The auxiliary air vent bypass around the float and thermostatic trap is recommended to ensure rapid venting of the supply header. It also prevents vapor binding of the float and thermostatic trap on this relatively severe service.

A priming or foaming boiler can carry boiler water into the header by entrainment with the steam. This can exceed the trap capacity. The excessive hot drips caused by this entrained boiler water can adversely affect the return side of a vacuum heating system.

Controlled Steam Header Drip (Vacuum, Subatmospheric System): The controlled steam header of a subatmospheric system contains superheated steam most of the time. This is due to rapid reduction in steam pressure caused by the throttling of the control valves admitting steam from the boiler supply header. The thermostatic element of the float and thermostatic trap for this controlled steam header must therefore be protected from this superheat, which would cause excessive closing pressure of the thermostatic element. This is accomplished, as shown in Fig. 15-17, by means of a section of fintube radiation inserted ahead of the float and thermostatic trap.

Steam Main Rise and Drip: Whenever it is necessary to reestablish the elevation of a steam main to provide proper pitch in the main, a float and thermostatic trap is employed as shown in Fig. 15-18. The trap provides venting and drainage of the steam main ahead of the rise in the main.

On extended mains that have several reductions in pipe size, a rise and drip should be provided to relieve the end sections of the main from carrying all the condensate that is produced on warm up in the entire length of main.

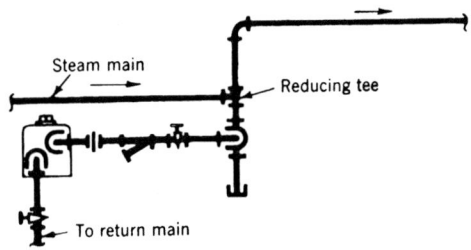

Fig 15-18. Steam main rise and drip connection

On short connections between a trap and the return piping a swing joint is recommended to relieve pipe strain due to expansion of the main.

End of Main Drip: A float and thermostatic trap is used at the end of a steam main to provide venting and drainage of the main. This arrangement, shown in Fig. 15-19 with static head before the trap and a drop leg on the discharge, assists drainage of the trap at all times.

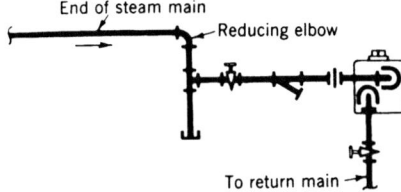

Fig 15-19. Details of end of main drip

End of Main Drip with Minimum Elevation Between Steam Main and Return Main: When the relative elevation between a steam main and return main must be at a minimum, the arrangement in Fig. 15-20 with a float and thermostatic trap may be used for venting and draining the end of the steam main. With this arrangement, however, condensate flow may be periodically retarded because of insufficient differential across the trap. The arrangement shown in Fig. 15-19 above should be used whenever possible.

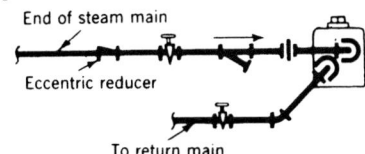

Fig 15-20. End of main drip with minimum elevation between steam main and return main

How to Split a Single Steam Main into Two Mains with a Drip: The arrangement shown in Fig. 15-21 is recommended whenever it is necessary to divide a main into two branches. It may be used at any point and the float and thermostatic trap serves to vent and drain the common section of the supply mains. An additional advantage of the arrangement is that it provides a means for establishing a new elevation for the branches.

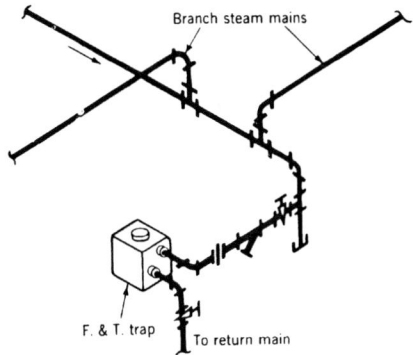

Fig 15-21. Splitting a single steam main into two mains with a drip

Two Methods of Splitting a Single Steam Main into Two Mains without a Drip: The arrangements A and B in Fig. 15-22 are convenient whenever it is necessary to divide a main into two branches. *Method A* should be used when the common section of the main, beyond the last drip, is relatively short or when the main must be split close to the boiler header. This eliminates the necessity of a float and thermostatic trap close to the header where the service would be most severe. With *Method B*, most of the condensate drains into one branch.

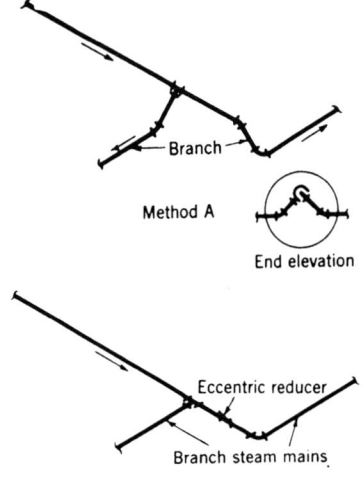

Fig 15-22. Two methods of splitting a single steam main without a drip

Main Supply Riser Drip: A float and thermostatic trap is always used at the base of a main supply riser as shown in Fig. 15-23. This trap provides drainage of the steam main ahead of the riser as well as drainage of the riser itself.

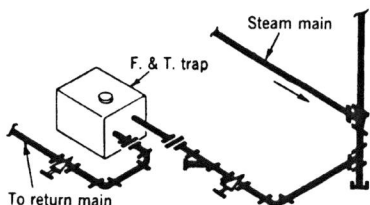

Fig 15-23. Details of main supply riser drip

Connections for Branch Mains: When the branch main is concealed in the ceiling, a 90° connection is preferred due to the ceiling opening. The 90° connection also serves to provide better conditions for expansion of the main (Fig. 15-24).

End of Branch Main Drip with Thermostatic Trap: A float and thermostatic trap should be used at the end of a branch main as shown in Fig. 15-26 the same as shown in Fig. 15-19 for the end of a main. However, a suitable thermostatic trap may be used, when the load on the branch does not exceed 1500 ft^2 EDR and the difference in elevation between the supply and return piping mains is limited. The use of a straightway, or side outlet thermostatic trap, permits the higher return line connection.

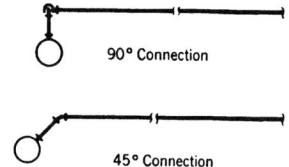

Fig 15-24. Connections for branch mains

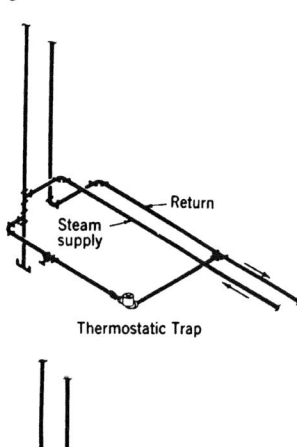

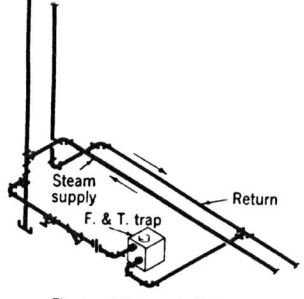

Fig 15-25. Supply riser drip connection

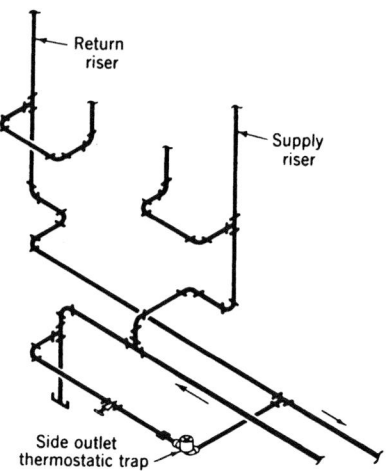

Fig 15-26. End of branch main drip with thermostatic trap

Supply Riser Drips: The arrangements in Fig. 15-25 may be employed whenever both the riser and spring piece are to be drained by the same drip trap. They should be used whenever a spring piece exceeds 16 ft of run. A float and thermostatic trap should be used for heavy loads. A thermostatic trap may be used when the load on the riser does not exceed 1500 ft^2 EDR.

Connections to First Floor Heating Units or Risers: The 45° connection shown in Fig. 15-27 is preferred because, with counterflow of condensate and steam it lessens entrainment of condensate with the steam. Note that the spring piece should be one pipe size larger than the riser due to counterflow.

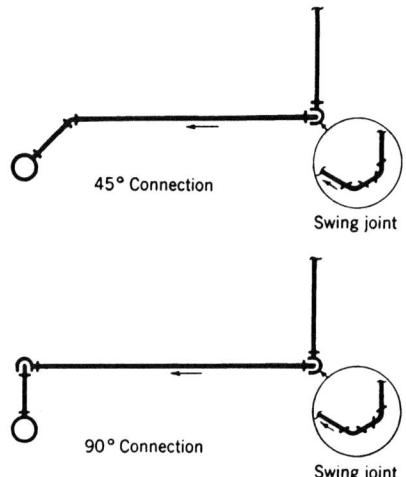

Fig 15-27. Connections to first floor heating units or riser

Connections from Mains to Downfeed Risers: The 45° connection shown in Fig. 15-28 is preferred because it provides better separation of condensate and steam. The concurrent flow does not require an increase in size of spring piece over riser.

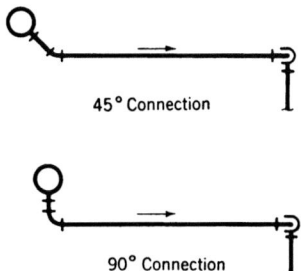

Fig 15-28. Connections from main to down feed riser

Runout Connections from Risers to Heating Units: The runout connections shown in Fig. 15-29 must pitch at least ½ in./foot of length after allowing for the expansion of the riser. This ensures positive drainage of the runout under all conditions of operation.

All runouts from risers must include swing joints.

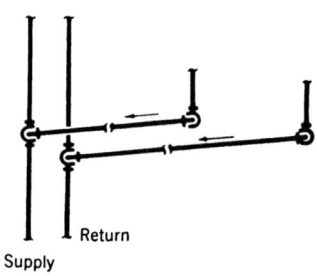

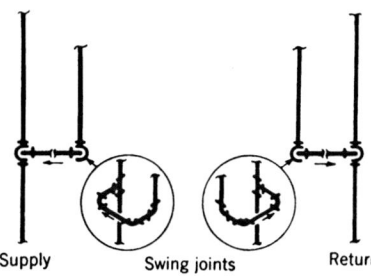

Fig 15-29. Runout connections from main to heating units

Offset Connections in Risers: Offset connections in risers as shown in Fig. 15-30 must pitch at least ½ inch/ft of length after allowing for the expansion of the riser sections.

All offset connections in risers must include swing joints.

Note that the supply offset connection must be one size larger than the largest section of riser.

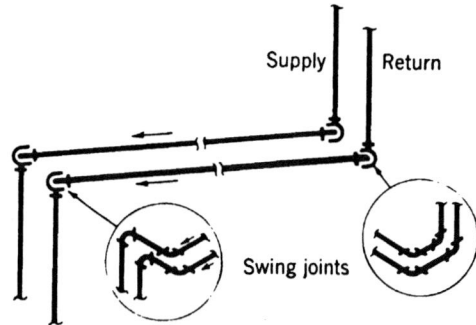

Fig 15-30. Offset connections in riser

Expansion Joints and Loops: The expansion joint and expansion loop shown in Fig. 15-31 are two general methods of allowing for expansion in low pressure steam mains. The expansion joint allows a greater amount of expansion than the loop with less strain.

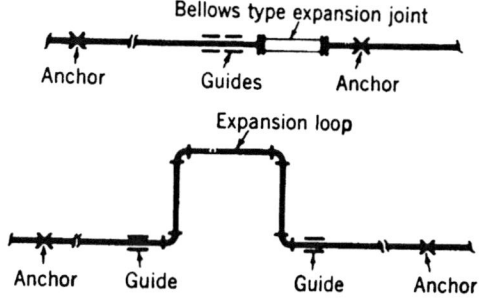

Fig 15-31. Expansion joint detail

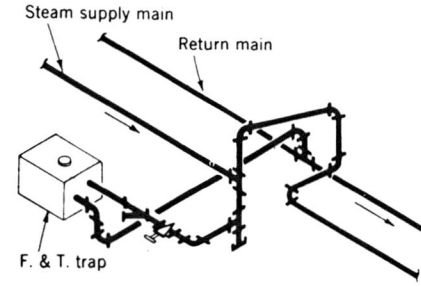

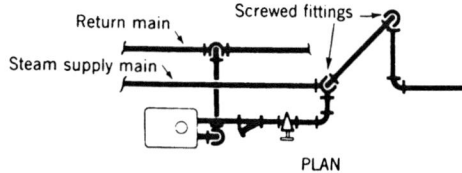

Fig 15-32. Swing type expansion loop combined with main rise and drip

Provision for expansion must be made in any length of steam pipe. Allowance for expansion in risers is important to prevent dislocation of the heating units and to maintain proper grade in the runouts. Provision must also be made for expansion of the main where the riser is joined. See Fig. 15-29.

Swing Type Expansion Loop Combined with Rise and Drip of Main: Whenever it is necessary to reestablish the elevation of a steam main, it is possible to combine the rise and drip with a swing type expansion loop (Fig. 15-32). The swing type expansion loop is less rigid than the expansion loop shown in Fig. 15-31 and allows for greater expansion.

Piping Around a Door or Obstacle: The method of piping around a vertical obstacle is shown in Fig. 15-33.

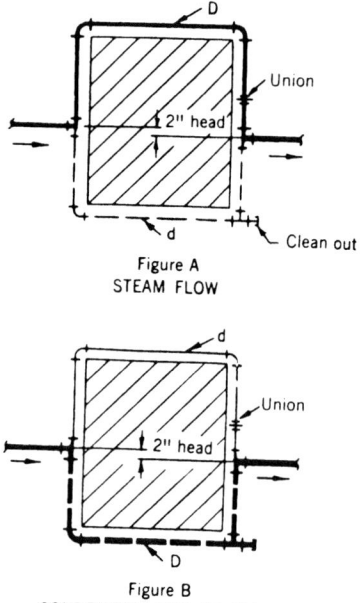

Fig 15-33. Detail of piping around obstacle

Diagram A shows piping for a steam main. The steam will flow through the upper line D. Any condensate flowing with the steam will flow by gravity through the lower line d.

Diagram B shows piping for a return main. The condensate will flow by gravity through the lower line D. Any air and vapor will flow through the upper line d.

In *Diagram A*, line D remains the same size as the steam main. In *Diagram B*, line D remains the same size as the return main. Lines d in *Diagrams* A and B may be reduced.

Pipe Anchor Details: The best method of anchoring steam pipes will depend on the building construction. Two methods are shown in Fig. 15-34.

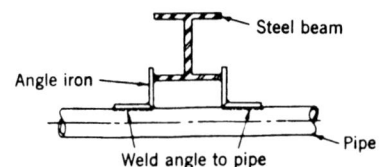

Note: Two angle irons may be used on each side of beam, depending on size of pipe, temperature differential and distance between anchors

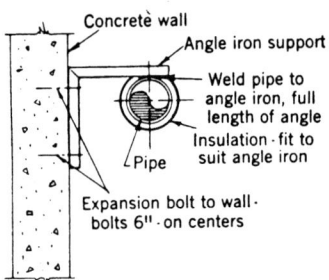

Fig 15-34. Anchoring steam supply piping

Piping Recessed Below Floor: Fig. 15-35 shows a method of supporting pipe in a horizontal recess. In the recess shown the cover plate provides a semi permanent flooring above the recess, permitting access to the piping during the life of the building.

When the elevation of the exterior grade permits, transverse recesses can be arranged with cover plates for access from the outside of the building.

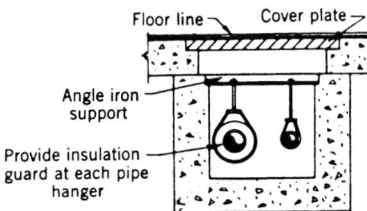

Fig 15-35. Anchoring steam supply piping

Reducing Main or Branch through Eccentric Reducer:

When the load on a steam main or branch main is reduced, and it is possible to reduce the pipe size, an eccentric reducer should be employed. This permits free flow of condensate from the larger to the smaller pipe size as shown in Fig. 15-36. The reducer should be installed a distance from the last outlet in the larger pipe equal to not less than 3 pipe diameters.

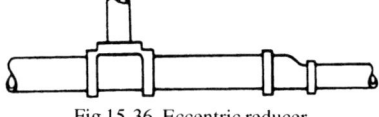

Fig 15-36. Eccentric reducer

Steam Riser: The piping and trap that follow were prepared, with permission, from Piping Design, Carrier System Design Manual, Carrier Corp.

Figs. 15-37 and 15-38 illustrate steam supply risers connected to mains with runouts. The runout in Fig. 15-37 is connected to the bottom portion of the main and is pitched toward the riser to permit condensate to drain from the main. This layout is used only when the riser is dripped. If a dry return is used, the riser is dripped through a steam trap. If a wet return is used, the trap is omitted.

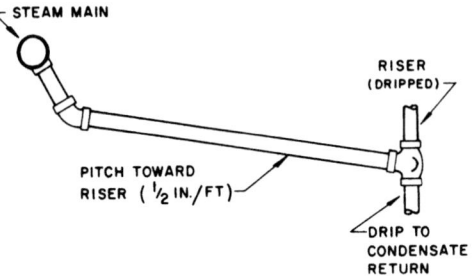

Fig 15-37. Connection to dripped risers

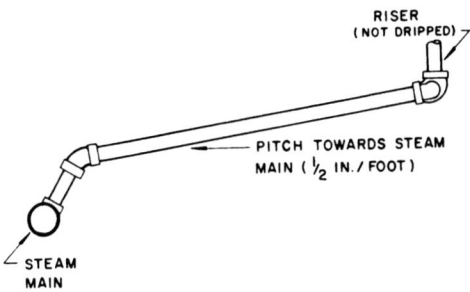

Fig 15-38. Connection to risers

Fig. 15-38 shows a piping diagram when the steam riser is not dripped. In this instance the runout is connected to the upper portion of the steam main and is pitched to carry condensate from the riser to the main.

Prevention of Water Hammer: If the steam main is pitched incorrectly when the riser is not dripped, water hammer may occur as illustrated in Fig. 15-39. Fig. 15-39a shows the runout partially filled with condensate but with enough space for steam to pass. As the amount of condensate increases and the space decreases, a wave motion is started as illustrated in Fig. 15-39b. As the wave or slug of condensate is driven against the turn in the pipe (Fig. 15-39 c), a hammer noise is caused. This pounding may be of sufficient force to split pipe fittings and damage coils in the system.

The following precautions must be taken to prevent water hammer:

1) Pitch pipes properly.

2) Avoid undrained pockets.

3) Choose a pipe size that prevents high steam velocity when condensate flows opposite to the steam.

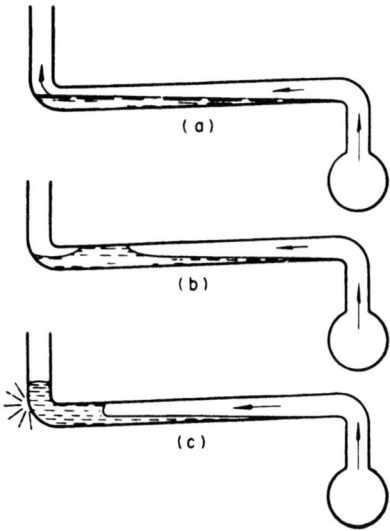

Fig 15-39. Water hammer

Expansion and Contraction: Where a riser is two or more floors in height, it should be connected to the steam main as shown in Fig. 15-40. Point A is subject to a twisting movement as the riser moves up and down.

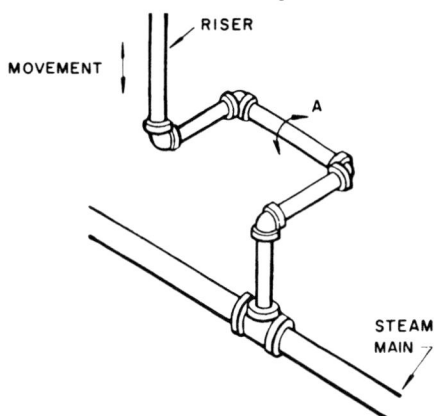

Fig 15-40. Riser connected to allow for expansion

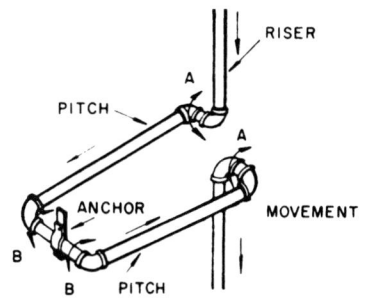

Fig 15-41. Riser anchor

Fig. 15-41 shows a method of anchoring the steam riser to allow for expansion and contraction. Movement occurs at A and B when the riser moves up and down.

Obstructions: Steam supply mains may be looped over obstructions if a small pipe is run below the obstruction to take care of condensate as illustrated in Fig. 15-42. The reverse procedure is followed for condensate return mains as illustrated in Fig. 15-43. The larger pipe is carried under the obstruction.

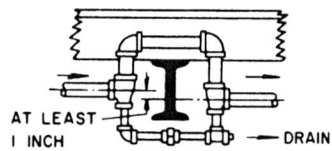

Fig 15-42. Supply main loops

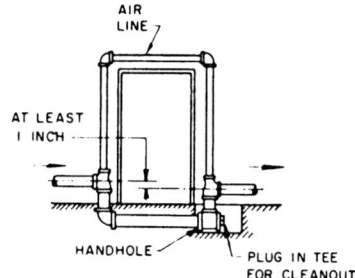

Fig 15-43. Return main loop

Dripping Riser: A steam supply main may be dropped abruptly to a lower level without dripping if the pitch is downward. When the steam main is raised to a higher level, it must be dripped as illustrated in Fig. 15-44. This diagram shows the steam main dripped into a wet return.

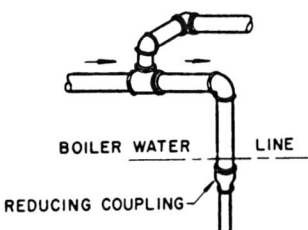

Fig 15-44. Dripping steam main

Fig. 15-45 is one method of dripping a riser through a steam trap to a dry return. The runout to the return main is pitched toward the return main.

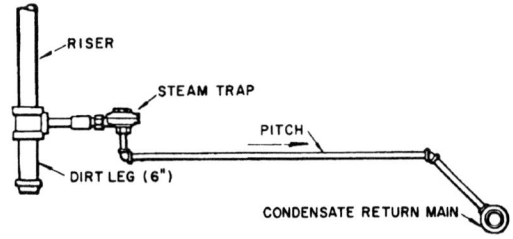

Fig 15-45. Riser dripped to dry return

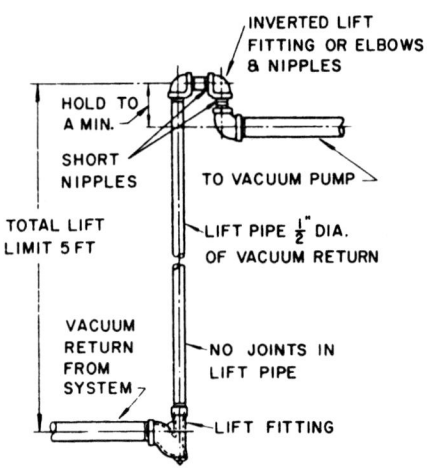

Fig 15-46. One step condensate life

Vacuum Lift: As described under vacuum systems, a lift is sometimes employed to lift the condensate up to the inlet of the vacuum pump. Figs. 15-46 and 15-47 show a one step and two step lift, respectively. The one step lift is used for a maximum lift of 5 ft. For 5 to 8 ft a two step lift is required.

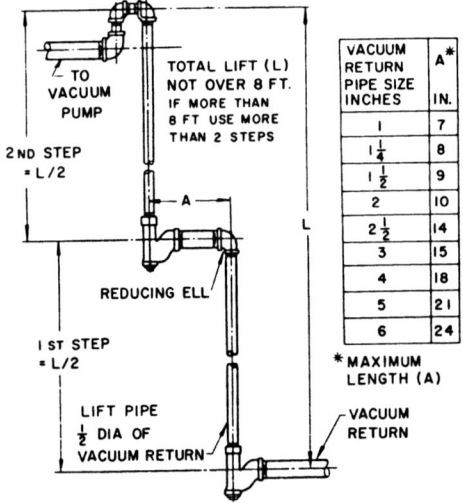

VACUUM RETURN PIPE SIZE INCHES	A* IN.
1	7
1¼	8
1½	9
2	10
2½	14
3	15
4	18
5	21
6	24

*MAXIMUM LENGTH (A)

Fig 15-47. Two step condensate lift

Steam Coils: Fig. 15-48 through 15-57 show methods of piping steam coils in a high or low pressure of vacuum steam piping system. The following general rules are applicable to piping layout for steam coils used in all systems:

1) Use full size coil outlets and return piping to the steam trap.

2) Use thermostatic traps for venting only.

3) Use a 15° check valve only where indicated on the layout.

4) Size the steam control valve for the steam load, not for the supply connection.

5) Provide coils with air vents as required, to eliminate noncondensable gases.

6) Do not drip the steam supply mains into coil sections.

7) Do not pipe tempering coils and reheat coils to a common steam trap.

8) Multiple coils may be piped to a common steam trap, if they have the same capacity and the same pressure drop and if the supply is regulated by a control valve.

Piping Single Coils: Fig. 15-48 illustrates a typical steam piping diagram for coils used in either a high or medium pressure system. If the return line is designed for low pressure or vacuum conditions and for a pressure differential of 3 psi or greater from steam to condensate return, a flash trap may be used.

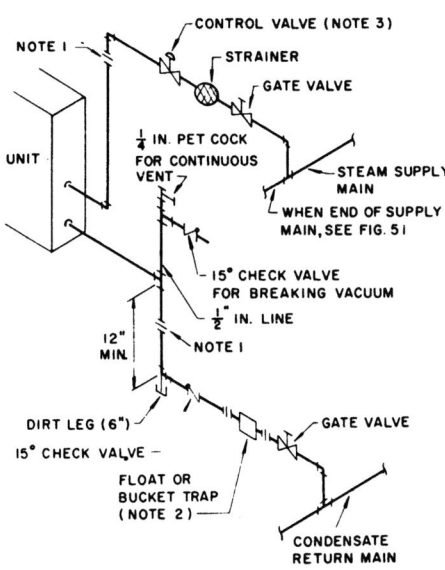

Fig 15-48. High or medium pressure coil piping

1) Flange or union is located to facilitate coil removal.

2) Flash trap may be used, if pressure differential between steam and the condensate return exceeds 5 psi.

3) When a bypass with control is required, see Fig. 15-52.

4) Dirt leg may be replaced with a strainer. If so, tee on drop can be replaced by a reducing elbow.

5) The petcock is not necessary with a bucket trap or any trap that has provision for passing air. The great majority of high or medium pressure returns end in hot wells or deaerators, which vent the air.

Low pressure steam piping for a single coil is illustrated in Fig. 15-49. This diagram shows an open air relief located after the steam trap closes to the unit. This arrangement permits noncondensable gases to vent to the atmosphere.

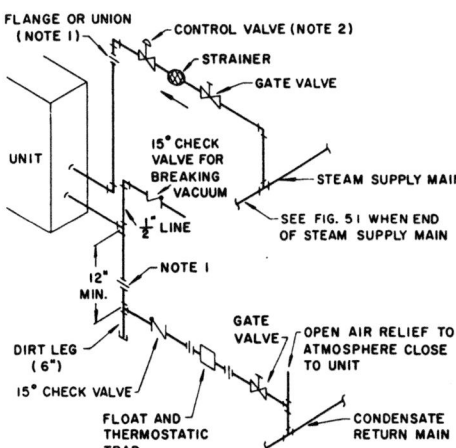

Fig 15-49. Single coil low pressure piping gravity return

1) Flange or union is located to facilitate coil removal.
2) When a bypass with control is required, see Fig. 15-52.
3) Check valve is necessary when more than one unit is connected to the return line.
4) Dirt pocket is the same as unit outlet. If dirt pocket is replaced by a strainer, replace tee with a reducing elbow from unit outlet to trap size.

Fig. 15-50 shows the piping layout for a steam coil in a vacuum system. A 15° check valve is used to equalize the vacuum across the steam trap.

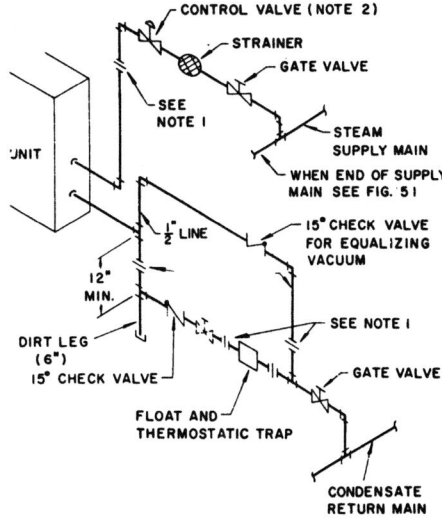

Fig 15-50. Vacuum system steam coil piping

1) Flange or union is located to facilitate coil removal.
2) When a bypass with control is required see Fig. 15-52.
3) Check valve is necessary when more than one unit is connected to the return line.

Dripping Steam Supply Main: A typical method of dripping the steam supply main to the condensate return is shown in Fig. 15-51.

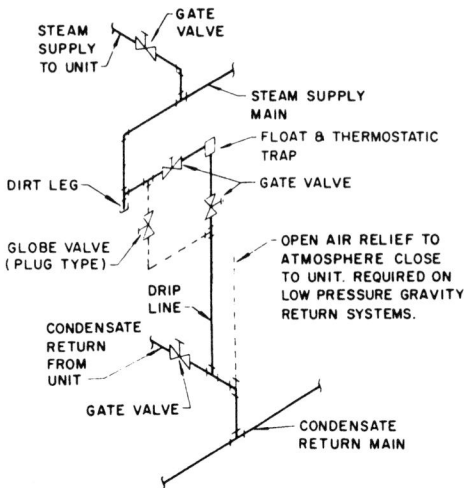

Fig 15-51. Dripping steam supply to condensate return

1) A bypass is necessary around trap and valves when continuous operation is necessary.

2) Bypass to the same size as trap orifice but never less than ½ inch.

Steam Bypass Control: Frequently a bypass with a manual control valve is required on steam coils. The piping layout for a control bypass with a plug type globe valve as the manual control is shown in Fig. 15-52.

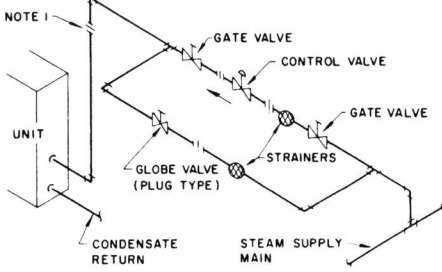

Fig 15-52. Bypass with manual control

1) Flange or union is located to facilitate coil removal.

2) A bypass is necessary around trap and valves when continuous operation is necessary.

3) Bypass to the same size as trap orifice but never less than ½ inch.

Lifting Condensate to Return Main: A typical layout for lifting condensate to an overhead return is described in Fig. 15-53. The amount of lift possible is determined by the pressure differential between the supply and return sides of the system. The amount of lift is not to exceed 1 foot for each pound of pressure differential. The maximum lift should not exceed 8 ft.

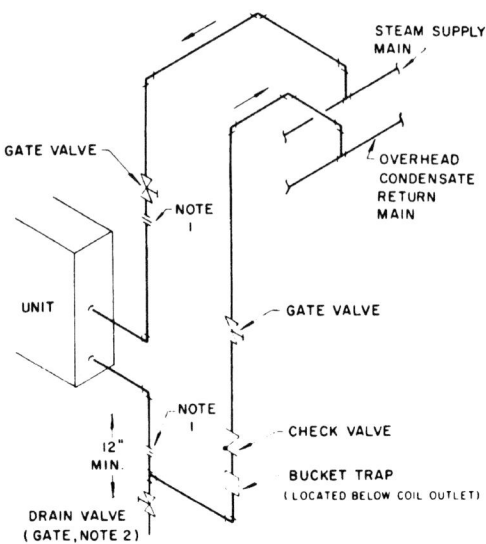

Fig 15-53. Condensate lift to overhead return

1) Flange or union is located to facilitate coil removal.

2) To prevent water hammer, drain coil before admitting steam.

3) Do not exceed 1 foot of lift between trap discharge and return main for each pound of pressure differential.

4) Do not use this arrangement for units handling outside air.

Piping Multiple Coils: Figs. 15-54 through 15-57 show piping layouts for high pressure, low pressure and vacuum systems with multiple coils. If a control valve is not used, each coil must have a separate steam trap as illustrated in Fig. 15-57. This particular layout may be used for a low pressure or vacuum system.

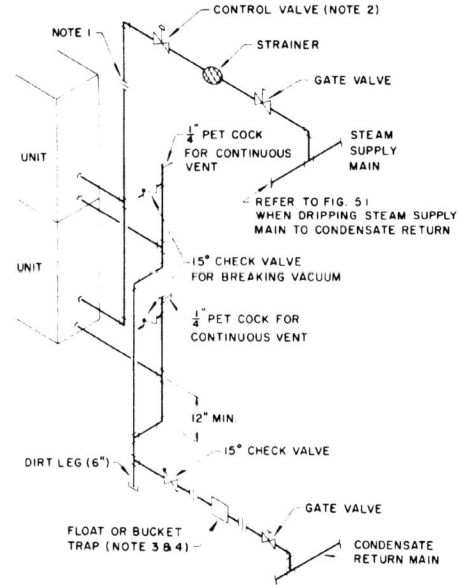

Fig 15-54. Multiple coil high pressure piping

If the coils have different pressure drops or capacities, separate traps are required with or without a control valve in the system.

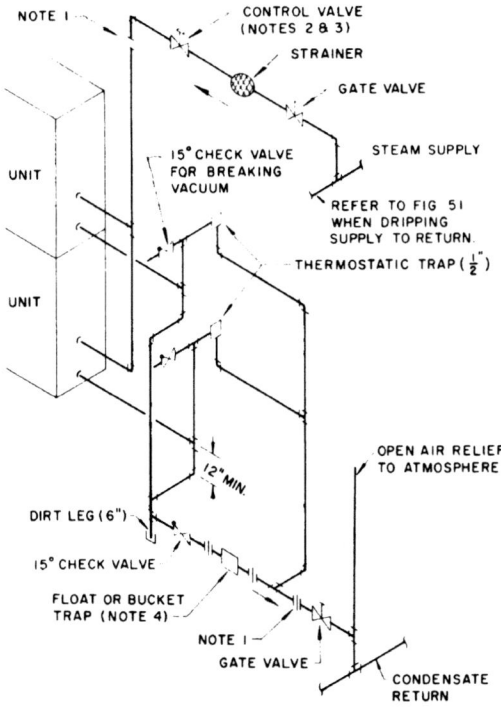

Fig 15-55. Multiple coil low pressure piping gravity return

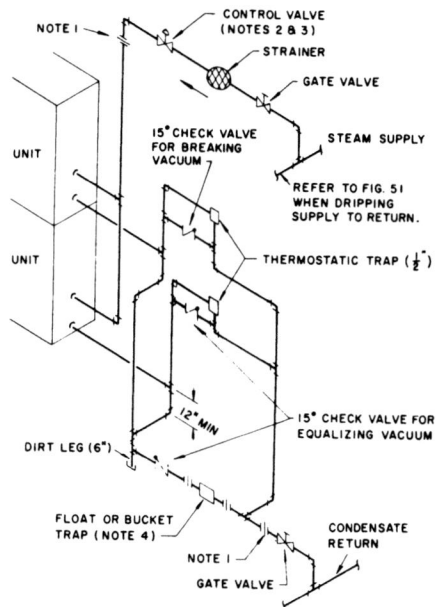

Fig 15-56. Multiple coil low pressure vacuum system piping

1) Flange or union is located to facilitate coil removal.
2) When a bypass with control is required, see Fig. 15-52

3) Flash trap may be used, if pressure differential between steam and the condensate return exceeds 5 psi.

4) Coils with differential pressure drops require individual traps. This is often caused by varying air velocities across the coil bank.

5) Dirt leg may be replaced with a strainer. If so, tee on drop may be replaced by a reducing elbow.

6) The petcock is not necessary with a bucket trap or any trap that has provision for passing air. The great majority of high or medium pressure returns end in hot wells or deaerators that vent the air.

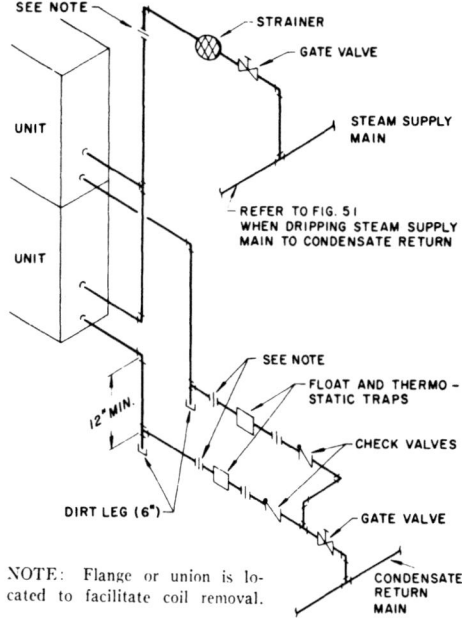

Fig 15-57. Low pressure or vacuum system steam traps

1) Flange or union is located to facilitate coil removal.
2) See Fig. 15-57 when control valve is omitted on multiple coils in parallel air flow.
3) When a bypass with control is required, see Fig. 15-52.
4) Coils with differential pressure drops require individual traps. These drops are often caused by varying air velocities across the coil bank.

Boiler Piping: Fig. 15-58 illustrates a suggested layout for a steam plant. This diagram shows parallel boilers and a single boiler using a *Hartford Return Loop.*

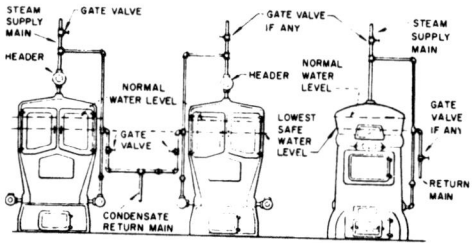

Fig 15-58. Hartford return loop

Freeze up Protection: When steam coils are used for tempering or preheating outdoor air, controls are required to prevent freezing of the coil.

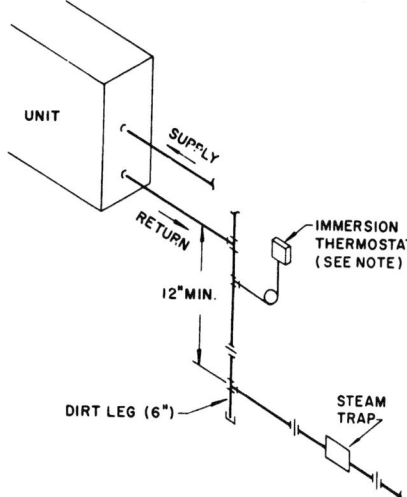

Fig 15-59. Freeze-up protection for high medium, low pressure and vacuum systems

Immersion thermostat is for control of outdoor air dampers and fan motor. Thermostat closes damper and shuts off fan when condensate temperature drops below a predetermined level.

In high, medium, low pressure and vacuum systems, an immersion thermostat is recommended to protect the coil. The protection device controls the fan motor and the outdoor air damper. The immersion thermostat is actuated when the steam supply fails or when the condensate temperature drops below a predetermined level, usually 120°F to 150°F. The thermostat location is shown in Fig. 15-59.

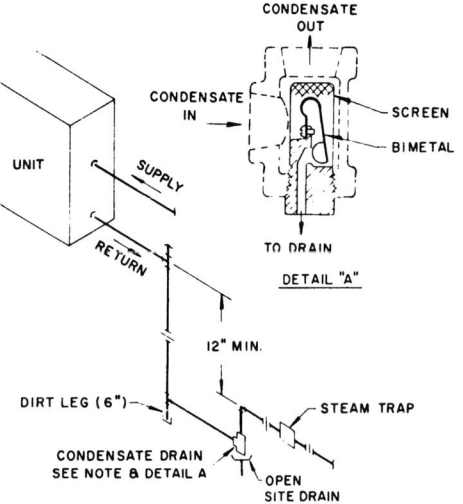

Fig 15-60. Freeze up protection for low pressure and vacuum systems

Condensate drain drains coil when a condensate temperature drops below a predetermined level.

The 15° check valve shown in the various piping diagrams provides a means of equalizing the pressure within the coil when the steam supply shuts off. This check valve is used in addition to the immersion thermostat. The petcock for continuous venting removes non condensable gases from the coil. Non condensable gases can restrict the flow of condensate, causing coil freeze up.

On low pressure and vacuum steam heating system, the immersion thermostat may be replaced by a condensate drain with a thermal element (Fig. 15-60). The thermal element opens and drains the coil when the condensate temperature drops below 165°F. Condensate drains are limited to 5 lb of pressure.

The following are general recommendations in laying out systems handling outdoor air below 35°F:

Codes and Regulations: All applicable codes and regulations should be checked to determine acceptable piping practice for the particular application. These codes usually dictate piping design, limit the steam pressure, or qualify the selection of equipment.

Water Conditioning: The formation of scale and sludge deposits on the boiler heating surfaces creates a problem in generating steam. Scale formation is intensified since scale forming salts increase with an increase in temperature.

Water conditioning in a steam generating system should always be under the supervision of a specialist.

Table 15-1. Recommended Hanger Spacings for Steel Pipe

| Nominal Pipe Size (inch) | Distance Between Supports (ft) | | |
| | Average Gradient | | |
	1 inch in 10 ft	½ inch in 10 ft	¼ inch in 10 ft
¾	9	…	…
1	13	6	…
1¼	16	10	5
1½	19	14	8
2	21	17	13
2½	24	19	15
3	27	22	18
3¼	29	24	19
4	32	26	20
5	37	29	23
6	40	33	25
8	…	38	30
10	…	43	33
12	…	48	37
14	…	50	40
16	…	53	42
18	…	57	44
20	…	50	47
24	…	64	50

Piping Supports: All steam piping is pitched to facilitate the flow of condensate. Table 15-1 contains the recommended support spacing for piping pitched for different gradients. The data are based on Schedule 40 pipe filled with water and having an average amount of valves and fittings.

Piping Design: A steam system operating for air conditioning comfort conditions must distribute steam at all operating loads. These loads can be in excess of design load, such as that occurs during early morning warm up and at extreme partial load, when only a minimum of heat is necessary. The pipe size to transmit the steam for a design load depends on the following:

1) The initial operating pressure and the allowable pressure drop through the system.

2) The total equivalent length of pipe in the longest run.

3) Whether the condensate flows in the same direction as the steam or in the opposite direction.

The major steam piping systems used in air conditioning applications are classified by a combination of piping arrangement and pressure conditions as follows:

1) two pipe high pressure

2) two pipe medium pressure

3) two pipe low pressure

4) two pipe vapor

5) two pipe vacuum

6) one pipe low pressure

One Pipe System: A one pipe gravity system was used primarily on residences and small commercial establishments. Fig. 15-61 shows a one pipe, upfeed gravity system. The steam supply main rises from the boiler to a high point and is pitched downward from this point around the extremities of the basement. It is normally run full size to the last take off and is then reduced in size after it drops down below the boiler water line. This arrangement is called a wet return. If the return main is above the boiler water line, it is called a dry return. Automatic air vents are required at all high points in the system to remove noncondensable gases. In systems that require long mains it is necessary to check the pressure drop and make sure the last heating unit is sufficiently above the water line to prevent water backing up from the boiler and flooding the main. During operation steam and condensate flow in the same direction in the mains and in opposite directions in branches and risers. This system requires larger pipe and valves than any other system.

The one pipe gravity system can also be designed as shown in Fig. 15-62, with each riser dripped separately. This is frequently done on more extensive systems.

Another type of one pipe gravity system is the down feed arrangement shown in Fig. 15-63. Steam flows in the main riser from the boiler to the building attic and is then distributed throughout the building.

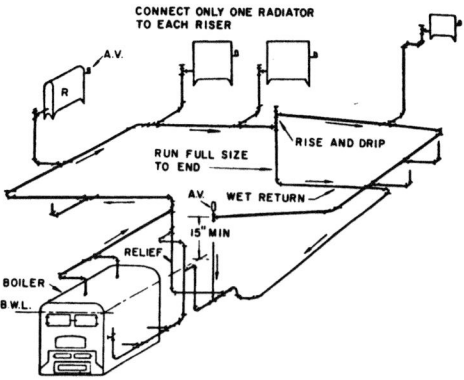

Fig 15-61. One pipe upfeed gravity system

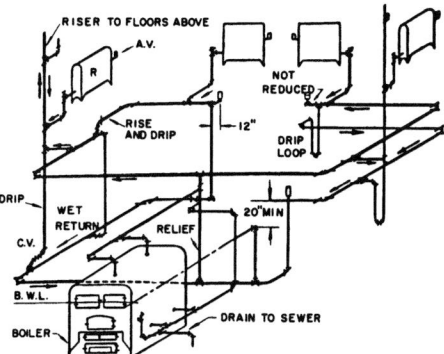

Fig 15-62. One pipe gravity system with dripped risers

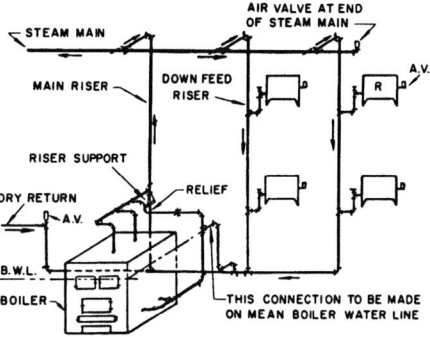

Fig 15-63. One pipe downfeed gravity systems

Two Pipe System: A two pipe gravity system is shown in Fig. 15-64. This system is used with indirect radiation. The addition of a thermostatic valve at each heating unit adapts it to a vapor or a mechanical vacuum system. A gravity system has each radiator separately sealed by drip loops on a dry return or by dropping directly into a wet return main. All drips, reliefs, and return risers from the steam to the return side of the system must be sealed by traps or water loops to insure satisfactory operation.

If the air vent on the heating unit is omitted, and the air is vented through the return line and a vented condensate receiver, a vapor system as illustrated in Fig. 15-65 results.

The addition of a vacuum pump to a vapor system classifies the system as a mechanical vacuum system. This arrangement is shown in Fig. 15-66.

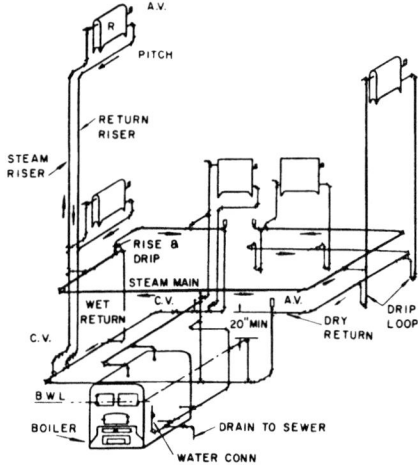

Fig 15-64. Two pipe gravity system

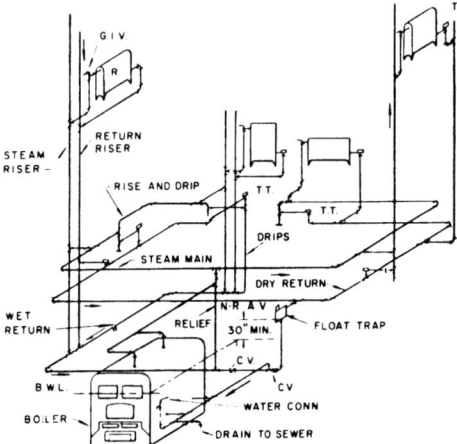

Fig 15-65. Vapor system

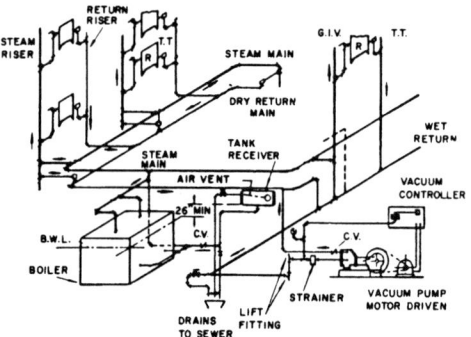

Fig 15-66. Mechanical vacuum system

Pipe Sizing: Tables have been developed to select the proper pipe to carry the required steam rate at various pressures.

Fig. 15-67 is a universal chart for steam pressure of 0 to 200 psig and for a steam rate of from 5 to 100,000 lbs/hr. However, the velocity as read from the chart is based on a steam pressure of 0 psig and must be corrected for the desired pressure from Fig. 15-67. The complete chart is based on the Moody friction factor and is valid where condensate and steam flow in the same direction.

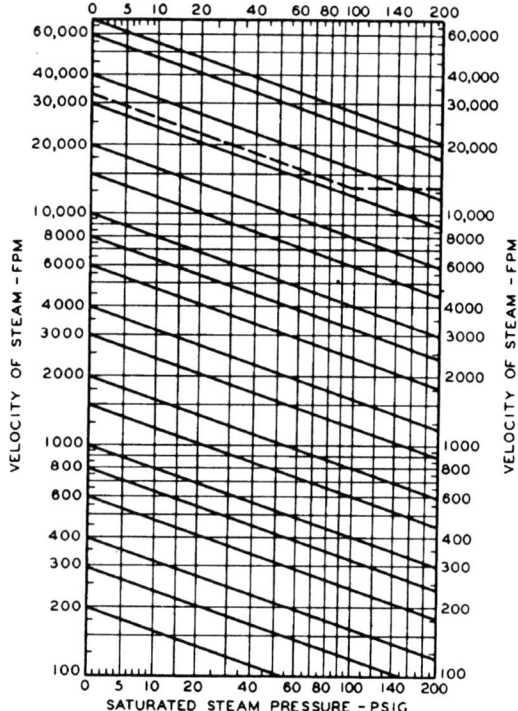

Fig 15-67. Velocity conversion

Tables 15-2 through 15-7 are used for quick selection at specific steam pressures. Fig. 15-68 has been used to tabulate the capacities shown in Tables 15-2 through 15-4. The capacities in Tables 15-5 through 15-7 are the results of tests reported by ASHRAE. Suggested limitations for the use of these tables are shown as notes on each table. In addition, Table 15-7 shows the total pressure drop for two pipe low pressure steam systems.

Recommendations: The following recommendations are for use when sizing pipe for the various systems:

Two Pipe High Pressure System: This system is used mostly in plants and occasionally in commercial installations.

1) Size supply main and riser for a maximum drop of 25 –30 psi.

2) Size supply main and risers for a maximum friction rate of 2–10 psi per 100 ft of equivalent pipe.

3) Size return main and riser for a maximum pressure drop of 20 psi.

4) Size return main and riser for a maximum friction rate of 2 psi/100 ft of equivalent pipe.

5) Pitch supply mains $\frac{1}{4}$ inch /10 ft away from boiler.

6) Pitch return mains $\frac{1}{4}$ inch/10 ft toward the boiler.

7) Size pipe from Table 15-2.

Two Pipe Medium Pressure System: This system is used mostly in plants and occasionally in commercial installations.

1) Size supply main and riser for a maximum pressure drop of 5–10 psi.

2) Size supply mains and risers for a maximum friction rate of 2 psi/100 ft of equivalent pipe.

3) Size return main and riser for a maximum pressure drop of 5 psi.

4) Size return main and riser for a maximum friction rate of 1 psi/100 ft of equivalent pipe.

5) Pitch supply mains $\frac{1}{4}$ inch/10 ft away from the boiler.

6) Pitch return mains $\frac{1}{4}$ inch/10 ft toward the boiler.

7) Size pipe from Table 15-3.

Two Pipe Low Pressure System: This system is used for commercial, air conditioning, heating and ventilating installations.

1) Size supply main and risers for a maximum pressure drop determined from Table 15-7 depending on the initial system pressure.

2) Size supply main and riser for a maximum friction rate of 2 psi/100 ft of equivalent pipe.

3) Size return main and riser for a maximum pressure drop determined from Table 15-7, depending on the initial system pressure.

4) Size return main and riser for a maximum friction rate of $\frac{1}{2}$ psi/100 ft of equivalent pipe.

5) Pitch mains $\frac{1}{4}$ in./10 ft away from the two pipe vapor system boiler.

6) Pitch return mains $\frac{1}{4}$ in./10 ft toward the boiler.

7) Use Tables 15-4 through 15-6 to size pipe.

Two Pipe Low Pressure System: This system is used for commercial, air conditioning, heating, and ventilating installations.

This system is used in commercial and residential installations.

1) Size supply main and riser for a maximum pressure drop of $\frac{1}{16} - \frac{1}{8}$ psi.

2) Size supply main and riser for a maximum friction rate of $\frac{1}{16} - \frac{1}{8}$ psi/100 ft of equivalent pipe.

3) Size return main and supply for a maximum pressure drop of $\frac{1}{16} - \frac{1}{8}$ psi.

4) Size return main and supply for a maximum friction rate of $\frac{1}{16} - \frac{1}{8}$ psi/100 ft of equivalent pipe.

5) Pitch supply $\frac{1}{4}$ in./10 ft away from the boiler.

6) Pitch return mains $\frac{1}{4}$ in./10 ft toward the boiler.

7) Size pipe from Tables 15-4 through 15-6.

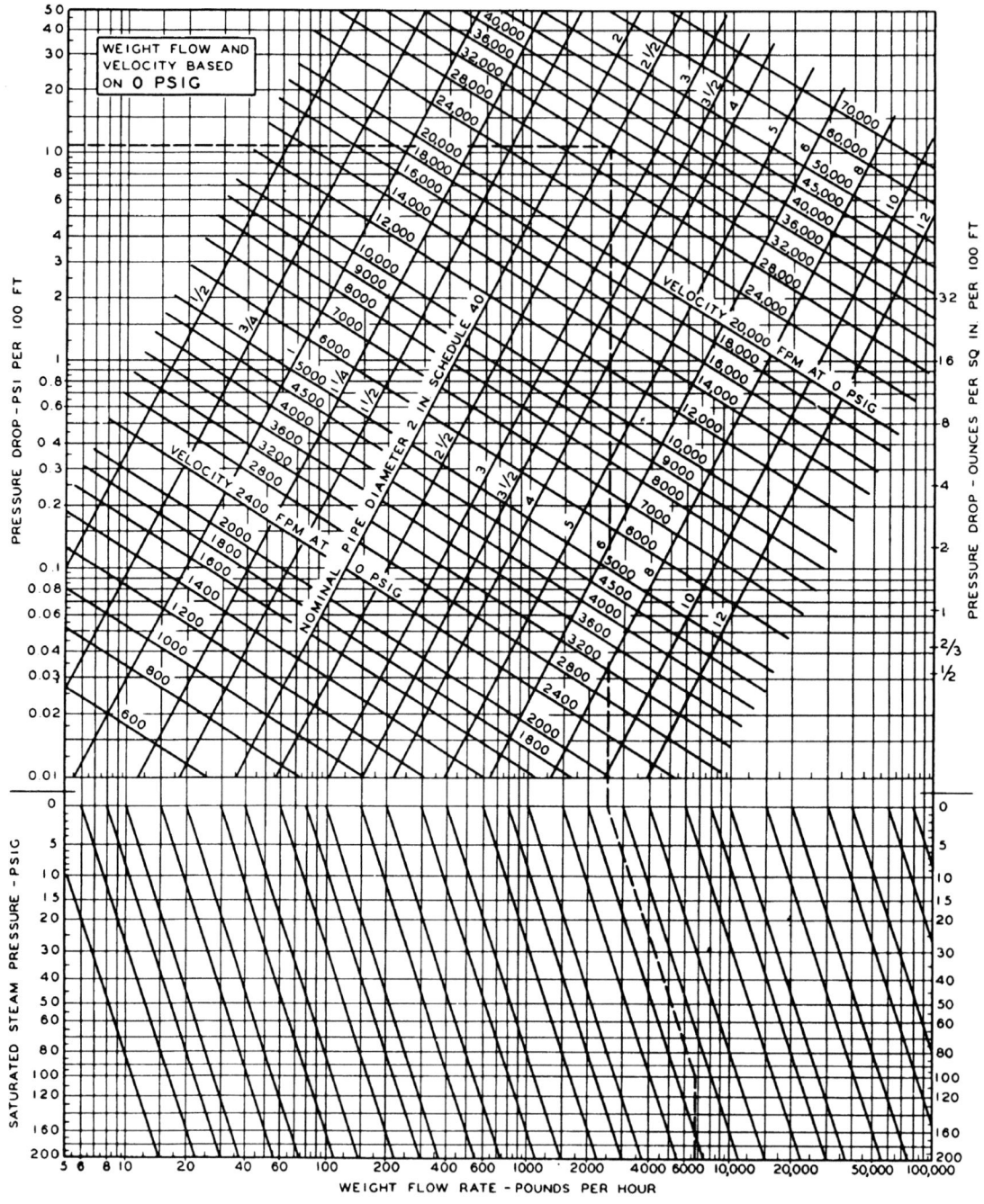

Fig 15-68. Pipe sizing

Table 15-2. High Pressure System Pipe Capacities (150 psig)

Pipe Size (in.)	Pressure Drop per 100 ft							
	⅛ psi (2 oz)	¼ psi (4 oz)	½ psi (8 oz)	¾ psi (12 oz)	1 psi (16 oz)	2 psi (32 oz)	5 psi	10 psi
Supply Mains and Risers 130–180 psig-Max Error 8%								
¾	29	41	58	82	116	184	300	420
1	58	82	117	165	233	369	550	790
1¼	130	185	262	370	523	827	1230	1720
1½	203	287	407	575	813	1230	1730	2600
2	412	583	825	1167	1650	2000	3410	4820
2½	683	959	1359	1920	2430	3300	5200	7600
3	1237	1750	2476	3500	4210	6000	9400	13500
3½	1855	2626	3715	5250	6020	8500	13100	20000
4	2625	3718	5260	7430	8400	12300	19200	28000
5	4858	6875	9725	13750	15000	21200	33100	47500
6	7960	11275	15950	22550	25200	36500	56500	80000
8	16590	23475	33200	46950	50000	70200	120000	170000
10	30820	43430	61700	77250	90000	130000	210000	300000
12	48600	68750	97250	123000	155000	200000	320000	470000
Return Mains and Risers 1–20 psig - Max Return Pressure								
¾	156	232	360	465	560	890	…	…
1	313	462	690	910	1,120	1,780	…	…
1¼	650	960	1,500	1,950	2,330	3,700	…	…
1½	1,070	1,580	2,460	3,160	3,800	6,100	…	…
2	2,160	3,300	4,950	6,400	7,700	12,300	…	…
2½	3,600	5,350	8,200	10,700	12,800	20,400	…	…
3	6,500	9,600	15,000	19,500	23,300	37,200	…	…
3½	9,600	14,400	22,300	28,700	34,500	55,000	…	…
4	13,700	20,500	31,600	40,500	49,200	78,500	…	…
5	25,600	38,100	58,500	76,000	91,500	146,000	…	…
6	42,000	62,500	96,000	125,000	150,000	238,000	…	…

Table 15-3. Medium Pressure System Pipe Capacities (30 psig)

Pipe Size (in.)	Pressure Drop per 100 Ft					
	⅛ psi (2 oz)	¼ psi (4 oz)	½ psi (8 oz)	¾ psi (12 oz)	1 psi (16 oz)	2 psi (32 oz)
Supply Mains and Risers 25–35 psig-Max Error 8%						
¾	15	22	31	38	45	63
1	31	46	63	77	89	125
1¼	69	100	141	172	199	281
1½	107	154	219	267	309	437
2	217	313	444	543	627	886
2½	358	516	730	924	1,033	1,460
3	651	940	1,330	1,628	1,880	2,660
3½	979	1,414	2,000	2,447	2,825	4,000
4	1,386	2,000	2,830	3,464	4,000	5,660
5	2,560	3,642	5,225	6,402	7,390	10,460
6	4,210	6,030	8,590	10,240	12,140	17,180
8	8,750	12,640	17,860	21,865	25,250	35,100
10	16,250	23,450	33,200	40,625	46,900	66,350
12	25,640	36,930	52,320	64,050	74,000	104,500
Return Mains and Risers 1–4 psig - Max Return Pressure						
¾	115	170	245	308	365	…
1	230	340	490	615	730	…
1¼	485	710	1,025	1,285	1,530	…
1½	790	1,155	1,670	2,100	2,500	…
2	1,575	2,355	3,400	4,300	5,050	…
2½	2,650	3,900	5,600	7,100	8,400	…
3	4,850	7,100	10,250	12,850	15,300	…
3½	7,200	10,550	15,250	19,150	22,750	…
4	10,200	15,000	21,600	27,000	32,250	…
5	19,000	27,750	40,250	55,500	60,000	…
6	31,000	45,500	65,500	83,000	98,000	…

Table 15-4. Low Pressure System Pipe Capacities (lb/hr) Condensate flowing with the steam

Pipe Size (in)	Pressure Drop Per 100 ft													
	1/16 psi (1 oz)		1/8 psi (2 oz)		1/4 psi (4 oz)		1/2 psi (8 oz)		3/4 psi (12 oz)		1 psi (16 oz)		2 psi (32 oz)	
	Saturated Pressure (psig)													
	3.5	12	3.5	12	3.5	12	3.5	12	3.5	12	3.5	12	4	12
¾	9	11	14	16	20	24	29	35	36	43	42	50	60	73
1	17	21	26	31	37	46	54	66	68	82	81	95	114	137
1¼	36	45	53	66	78	96	111	138	140	170	162	200	232	280
1½	56	70	84	100	120	147	174	210	218	260	246	304	360	430
2	108	134	162	194	234	285	336	410	420	510	480	590	710	850
2½	174	215	258	310	378	460	540	660	680	820	780	950	1150	1370
3	318	380	465	550	660	810	960	1,160	1,190	1,430	1,380	1,670	1,950	2,400
3½	462	550	670	800	990	1,218	1,410	1,700	1,740	2,100	2,000	2,420	2,950	3,450
4	726	800	950	1,160	1,410	1,690	1,980	2,400	2,450	3,000	2,880	3,460	4,200	4,900
5	1,200	1,430	1,680	2,100	2,440	3,000	3,570	4,250	4,380	5,250	5,100	6,100	7,500	8,600
6	1,920	2,300	2,820	3,350	3,960	4,850	5,700	7,000	7,200	8,600	8,400	10,000	11,900	14,200
8	3,900	4,800	5,570	7,000	8,100	10,000	11,400	14,300	14,500	17,700	16,500	20,500	24,000	29,500
10	7,200	8,800	10,200	12,600	15,000	18,200	21,000	26,000	26,200	32,000	30,000	37,000	42,700	52,000
12	11,400	13,700	16,500	19,500	23,400	28,400	33,000	40,000	41,000	49,500	48,000	57,500	67,800	81,000

Table 15-5. Return Main and Riser Capacities for Low Pressure Steam Systems, lbs/hr

Pipe Size (in.)	Pressure Drop Per 100 ft																	
	1/32 psi (1/2 oz)			1/24 psi (2/3 oz)			1/16 psi (1 oz)			1/8 psi (2 oz)			1/4 psi (12 oz)			1/2 psi (8 oz)		
	Return Mains																	
	Wet	Dry	Vac	Wet	Dry	Vac	Wet	Dry	Vac	Wet	Dry	Vac	Wet	Dry	Vac	Wet	Dry	Vac
¾	...	...	...	...	...	42	...	...	100	...	...	142	...	...	200	...	...	283
1	125	62	...	145	71	143	175	80	175	250	103	249	350	115	350	...	120	494
1¼	213	130	...	248	149	244	300	168	300	425	217	426	600	241	600	...	255	848
1½	338	206	...	393	236	388	475	265	475	675	340	674	950	378	950	...	385	1,340
2	700	470	...	810	535	815	1,000	575	1,000	1,400	740	1,420	2,000	825	2000	...	830	2,830
2½	1,180	760	...	1,580	868	1,360	1,680	950	1,680	2,350	1,230	2,380	3,350	1,360	3,350	...	1410	4,730
3	1,880	1,460	...	2,130	1,560	2,180	2,680	1,750	2,680	3,750	2,250	3,800	5,350	2,500	5,350	...	2,585	7,560
3½	2,750	1,970	...	3,300	2,200	3,250	4,000	2,500	4,000	5,500	3,230	5,680	8,000	3580	8,000	...	3780	11,300
4	3,880	2,930	...	4,580	3,350	4,500	5,500	3,750	5,500	7,750	4,830	7,810	11,000	5,380	11,000	...	5,550	15,500
5	6,090	4,600	...	7,880	5,250	7,880	9,680	5,870	9,680	13,700	7,560	13,700	19,400	8,420	19,400	...	8,880	27,300
6	8,820	6,670	...	12,600	7,620	12,600	15,500	8,540	15,500	22,000	10,990	22,000	31000	12,200	31000	...	12,800	43,800
8	15,200	11,480	...	21,700	13,120	21,700	26,700	14,700	26,700	37,900	18,900	37,900	53,400	22,800	53,400	...	25,500	75,500
10	24000	18,100	...	34,300	20,800	34,300	42,200	23,200	42,200	59,900	29,800	59,900	84,400	33,300	84,400	...	35400	114,400
	Return Risers																	
¾	...	48	...	...	48	113	...	48	175	...	48	249	...	48	350	...	48	494
1	...	113	...	...	113	244	...	113	300	...	113	426	...	113	600	...	113	848
1¼	...	248	...	...	248	388	...	248	475	...	248	674	...	248	950	...	248	1,340
1½	...	375	...	...	375	818	...	375	1000	...	375	1,420	...	375	2,000	...	375	2,830
2	...	750	...	...	750	1,360	...	750	1,680	...	750	2,380	...	750	3,350	...	750	4,730
2½	...	1,230	...	...	1,230	2,180	...	1,230	2,680	...	1,230	3,800	...	1,230	5350	...	1230	7,560
3	...	2,230	...	...	2,250	3,250	...	2,250	4,000	...	2,250	5,680	...	2,250	8,000	...	2250	11,300
3½	...	3,230	...	...	3,230	4,480	...	3,230	5,500	...	3,230	7,810	...	3,230	11,000	...	3230	15,500
4	...	4,830	...	...	4,830	7,880	...	4,830	9,680	...	4,830	13700	...	4830	19400	...	4,830	27,300
5	...	7,560	...	...	7,560	12,600	...	7,560	15,500	...	7,560	22,000	...	7,560	31,000	...	7560	43,800
6	...	10,990	...	...	10990	21,700	...	10,990	26,700	...	10,990	37,900	...	10990	53,400	...	10990	75,500
8	...	18,900	...	...	18,900	34,300	...	18,900	42200	...	18,900	59,900	...	18,900	84,400	...	18900	114,400
10	...	29,800	...	...	29,800	...	...	29,800	...	...	29,800	...	...	29,800	...	...	29800	...

Vac values may be used for wet return mains.

Two Pipe Vacuum System: This system is used in commercial installations.

1) Size supply main and riser for a maximum pressure drop of $\frac{1}{8}$–1 psi.

2) Size supply main and riser for a maximum friction rate of $\frac{1}{16}$ – $\frac{1}{2}$ psi/100 ft of equivalent pipe.

3) Size return main and riser for a maximum pressure drop of $\frac{1}{8}$–1 psi.

4) Size return main and riser for a maximum friction rate of $\frac{1}{8}$–$\frac{1}{2}$ psi/100 ft of equivalent pipe.

5) Pitch supply mains $\frac{1}{4}$ in/10 ft away from the boiler.

6) Pitch return mains $\frac{1}{4}$ in/10 ft toward the boiler.

7) Size pipe from Tables 15-4 through 15-6.

Table 15-6. Low Pressure System Pipe Capacities (lbs/hr) Condensate Flowing against the Steam Flow

Pipe Size (in.)	Two Pipe System		One Pipe System		
	Vertical	Horizontal	Up feed Supply Risers	Vertical Connectors	Riser Runouts
A	B	C	D	E	F
$\frac{3}{4}$	8	…	6	…	7
1	14	9	11	7	7
$1\frac{1}{4}$	31	19	20	16	16
$1\frac{1}{2}$	48	27	38	23	16
2	97	49	72	42	23
$2\frac{1}{2}$	159	99	116	…	42
3	282	175	200	…	65
$3\frac{1}{2}$	387	288	286	…	119
4	511	425	380	…	186
5	1,050	788	…	…	278
6	1,800	1,400	…	…	545
8	3,750	3,000	…	…	…
10	7,000	5,700	…	…	…
12	11,500	19,500	…	…	…

One Pipe Low Pressure System: This system is used on small commercial and residential systems.

1) Size supply main and riser for a maximum pressure drop of $\frac{1}{4}$ psi.

2) Size supply main and risers for a maximum friction rate of $\frac{1}{16}$ psi/ 100 ft of equivalent pipe.

3) Size return main and risers for a maximum pressure drop of $\frac{1}{4}$ psi.

4) Size return main and risers for a maximum friction rate of $\frac{1}{16}$ psi/l00 ft of equivalent pipe.

5) Pitch supply main $\frac{1}{4}$ in./10 ft away from the boiler.

6) Pitch return main $\frac{1}{4}$ in./10 ft toward the boiler.

7) Size supply main and dripped runouts from Table 15-4.

8) Size undripped runouts from Table 15-6, *Column* F.

9) Size upfeed risers from Table 15-6, *Column* D.

10) Size downfeed supply risers from Table 15-4.

11) Pitch supply mains $\frac{1}{4}$ in./10 ft away from boiler.

12) Pitch return mains $\frac{1}{4}$ in./10 ft toward the boiler.

Example 1:Determine pressure drop for sizing supply and return piping:

Given:

Two pipe low pressure steam system.

Initial steam pressure:15 psig.

Approximate supply piping equivalent length: 500 ft.

Approximate return piping equivalent length: 500 ft.

Find:

Pressure drop to size supply piping;

Pressure drop to size return piping.

Table 15-7. Total Pressure Drop for Two Pipe Low Pressure Steam Piping Systems

Initial Steam Pressure, psig	Total Pressure Drop in Supply Piping (psi)	Total Pressure Drop in Return Piping (psi)
2	$\frac{1}{2}$	$\frac{1}{2}$
5	$1\frac{1}{4}$	$1\frac{1}{4}$
10	$2\frac{1}{2}$	$2\frac{1}{2}$
15	$3\frac{3}{4}$	$3\frac{3}{4}$
20	5	5

Solution: 1) Refer to Table 15-7 for an initial steam pressure of 15 psig. The total pressure drop should not exceed 3.75 psi in the supply pipe. Therefore, the supply piping is sized for a total pressure drop of 3.75, or $\frac{3}{4}$ psi/100 ft of equivalent pipe.

2) Although $\frac{3}{4}$ psi is indicated in *Step* 1, *Step* 4 under *Two Pipe Low Pressure System* recommends a maximum of $\frac{1}{2}$ psi for return piping. Therefore, use $\frac{1}{2}$ psi/100 ft of equivalent pipe:

Return main pressure drop: $\frac{1}{2} \times \frac{500}{100} = 2.5$ psi

Friction Rate: Example 2 illustrates the method used to determine the friction rate for sizing pipe when the total system pressure drop recommendation (supply pressure drop plus return pressure drop) is known and the approximate equivalent length is known.

Example 2:Determine friction rate:

Given:

Four systems,

equivalent length of each system 400 ft.

Total pressure drop of system:$\frac{1}{2}$, $\frac{3}{4}$, 1, and 2 psi

Find:

Friction rate for each system.

Solution:

System number	System Equivalent Length, ft	Total system pressure drop, (psi)	Friction rate for pipe sizing/100 ft
1	400	½	$\left(\dfrac{400}{100}\right)x = \dfrac{1}{2}$ $x = \dfrac{1}{8}$
2	400	¾	$\left(\dfrac{400}{100}\right)x = \dfrac{3}{4}$ $x = \dfrac{3}{16}$
3	400	1	$\left(\dfrac{400}{100}\right)x = 1$ $x = \dfrac{1}{4}$
4	400	2	$\left(\dfrac{400}{100}\right)x = 2$ $x = \dfrac{1}{2}$

Example 3: Determine Steam Supply Main and Final Velocity: Given:

Friction rate 2 psi/100 ft of equivalent pipe initial steam pressure 100 psig

Flow rate 6750 lb/hr

Find:

1. Size of largest pipe not exceeding design friction rate.

2. Steam velocity in pipe.

Solution: 1.) Enter bottom of Fig. 15-68 at 6750 lb/hr and proceed vertically to the 100 psig line (dotted line in Fig. 15-68). Then move obliquely to the 0 psig line. From this point proceed vertically up the chart to the smallest pipe size not exceeding 2 psi/ton-ft of equivalent pipe and read 3½ in.

2.) The velocity of steam at 0 psig, as read from Fig. 15-68, is 16,000 fpm. Enter the left side of Fig. 15-67 at 16,000 fpm. Proceed obliquely downward to the 100 psig line and horizontally across to the right side of the chart (dotted line in Fig. 15-67). The velocity at 100 psig is 6100 fpm.

Example 4 illustrates a design problem for sizing pipe on a low pressure, vacuum return system.

Example 4: Sizing Pipe for a Low Pressure, Vacuum Return System: Given:

Six units.

Steam requirement per unit: 72 lb/hr.

Layout as illustrated in Figs. 15-69 through 15-71.

Threaded pipe and fittings.

Low pressure system: 2 psi.

Find:

Size of pipe and total pressure drop.

Note: Total pressure drop in the system should never exceed one half the initial pressure. A reasonably small drop is required for quiet operation.

Solution: Determine the design friction rate by totaling the pipe length and adding 50% of the length for fittings:

$$115 + 11 + 113 = 239$$
$$239 \times 0.50 = 120$$
$$\text{Total} = \overline{359} \text{ ft equiv. length}$$

Check pipe sizing recommendations for maximum friction rate from two pipe vacuum system, Items 2, ⅛, ½ psi. Check Table 15-7 to determine recommended maximum pressure drop for the supply and return mains (½ psi for each).

Design friction rate = 1/3.59 × (½ + ½) = ¼ psi/100 ft. The supply main is sized by starting at the last unit G and adding each additional load from unit G to the boiler; use Table 15-4. The following tabulation results:

Section	Steam Load (lb/hr)	Pipe Size (in.)
F–G	72	1¼
E–F	144	2
D–E	216	2
C–D	288	2½
B–C	360	2½
A–B	432	3

Convert the supply main fittings to equivalent lengths of pipe and add to the actual pipe length

Equivalent Pipe Lengths	Feet
1–1¼ inch side outlet tee	7.0
2–1¼ inch elbow	4.6
1–2 inch reducing tee	4.7
1–2 inch run of tee	3.3
2–2 inch elbow	6.6
1–2½ inch reducing tee	5.6
1–2½ inch run of tee	4.1
1–2½ inch elbow	6.0
2–3 inch elbows	15.0
1–3 inch reducing tee	7.0
Actual pipe length	115.0
Total Equivalent Length	178.9 ft

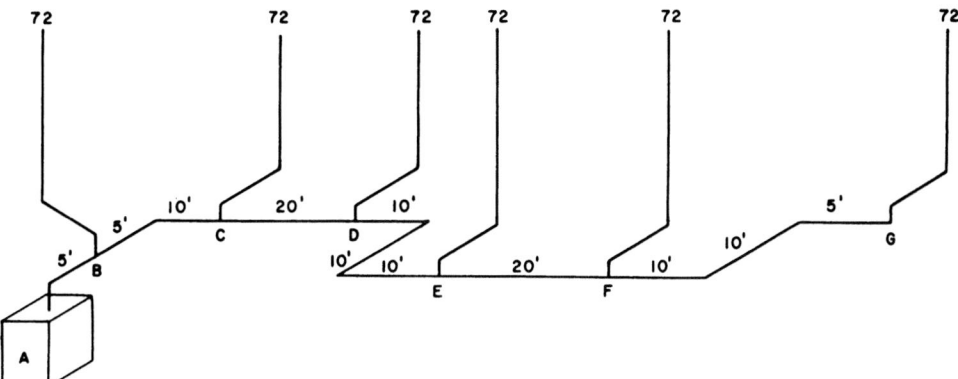

Fig 15-69. Low pressure steam supply main

Pressure drop for the supply main is equal to the equivalent length times pressure drop per 100 ft:

$$178.9 \times \frac{0.25}{100} = 0.447 \text{ psi}$$

This is within the recommended maximum pressure drop (1 psi) for the supply.

The branch connection for Fig. 15-70 is sized in a similar manner at the same friction rate. From Table 15-6 the horizontal run out pipe size for a load of 72 lb is $2\frac{1}{2}$ inch and the vertical riser size is 2 inches.

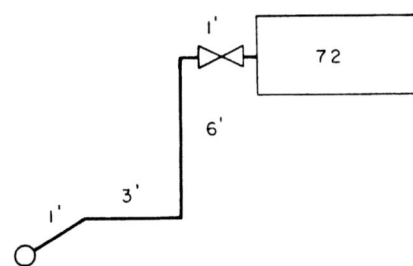

Fig 15-70. Low pressure run out and riser

Convert all the fittings to equivalent pipe lengths, and add to the actual pipe length.

Equivalent Pipe Lengths	Feet
1–1½ inch 45° elbow	3.2
1–2½ inch 90° elbow	4.1
1–2 inch 90° elbow	3.3
1–2 inch gate valve	2.3
Actual pipe length	11
Total Equivalent Length	23.9 ft

Pressure drop for branch out and riser is:

$$23.9 \times \frac{0.25}{100} = 0.060 \text{ psi}$$

The vacuum return main is sized from Table 15-5; by starting at the last unit G and adding each additional load between unit G and the boiler. Each riser-72 lb/hr, $\frac{3}{4}$ in.

Section	Steam Load (lb/hr)	Pipe Size (inch)
F–G	72	¾
E–F	144	¾
D–E	216	1
C–D	288	1
B–C	360	1¼
A–B	432	1¼

Convert the return main fittings to equivalent pipe lengths and add to the actual pipe length.

Equivalent Pipe Lengths	Feet
1–¾ inch run of tee	1.4
5–¾ inch 90° elbow	7.0
1–1 inch reducing tee	2.3
1–2 inch run of tee	1.7
2–1 inch 90° elbow	3.4
1–1¼ inch reducing tee	3.1
1–1¼ inch 90° elbow	6.9
1–1¼ inch run of tee	2.3
Actual pipe length	133.0
Total Equivalent length	161.1 ft

Pressure drop for the return equals

$$161.1 \times \frac{0.25}{100} = 0.403 \text{ psi}$$

Total return pressure drop is satisfactory since it is within the recommended maximum pressure drop ($\frac{1}{8}$ –1 psi) listed in the two-pipe vacuum return system. The total system pressure drop is equal to

$$0.447 + 0.060 + 0.403 = 0.91 \text{ psi}$$

This total system pressure drop is within the maximum 2 psi recommended (1 psi for supply and 1 psi for return).

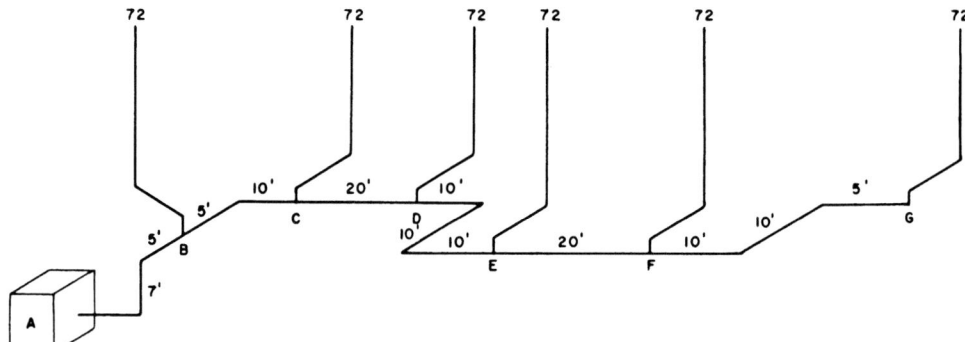

Fig 15-71. Low pressure vacuum return

Piping Application.—The use and selection of steam traps and condensate and vacuum return pumps are presented in this section.

Also, various steam piping diagrams are illustrated to familiarize the engineer with accepted piping practice.

Steam Trap Selection: The primary function of a steam trap is to hold steam in a heating apparatus or piping system and allow condensate and air to pass. The steam remains trapped until it gives up its latent heat and changes to condensate. The steam trap size depends on the following:

1) Amount of condensate to be handled by the trap, lb/hr.

2) Pressure differential between inlet and discharge at the trap.

3) Safety factor used to select the trap.

Amount of Condensate: The amount of condensate depends on whether the trap is used for steam mains or risers, or for the heating apparatus.

The selection of the trap for the steam mains or risers is dependent on the pipe warm up load and the radiation load from the pipe. Warm up load is the condensate formed by heating the pipe surface when the steam is first turned on. For practical purposes the final temperature of the pipe is the steam temperature. Warm up load is determined from the following equation:

$$C_1 = \frac{W \times (T_f - T_i) \times 0.114}{h_l \times t}$$ (1)

where C_1 = warm up condensate, lb/hr;

   W = total weight of pipe, lb;

   T_f = final pipe temperature, °F
      (steam temperature);

   T_i = initial pipe temperature, °F
      (room temperature);

   0.114 = specific heat constant for wrought iron
      or steel pipe (0.092 for copper tubing);

   h_l = latent heat of steam, Btu/lb ($= h_g - h_f$, Table 2-3); and

   t = warm up time, hr.

The radiation load is the condensate formed by unavoidable radiation loss from a bare pipe. This load is determined from the following equation and is based on still air surrounding the steam main and riser:

$$C_2 = \frac{L \times K \times (T_f - T_i)}{h_l}$$ (2)

where C_2 = radiation condensate, lb/hr;

   L = linear length of pipe, ft;

   T_f = final pipe temperature, °F
      (steam temperature);

   T_i = initial pipe temperature, °F
      (room temperature);

   K = heat transmission coefficient Btu/hr-ft-°F;
      and

   h_l = latent heat of steam, Btu/lb ($= h_g - h_f$, Table 2-3)

The radiation load builds up as the warm up load drops off under normal operating conditions. The peak occurs at the midpoint of the warm up cycle. Therefore, one half of the radiation load is added to the warm up load to determine the amount of condensate that the trap handles.

Pressure Differential: The pressure differential across the trap is determined at design conditions. If a vacuum exists on the discharge side of the trap, the vacuum is added to the inlet side pressure to determine the differential.

Safety Factor: Good design practice dictates the use of safety factors in steam trap selection. Safety factors from 2 to 1 to as high as 8 to 1 may be required, and for the following reasons:

1) The steam pressure at the trap inlet or the back pressure at the trap discharge may vary. This changes the steam trap capacity.

2) If the trap is sized for normal operating load, condensate may back up into the steam lines or apparatus during start up or warm up operation.

3) If the steam trap were selected to discharge a full and continuous stream of water, the air could not be vented from the system.

The following guide is used to determine the safety factor:

Design	Safety Factor
Draining steam main	3 to 1
Draining steam riser	3 to 1
Between boiler and end of main	2 to 1
Before reducing valve	3 to 1
Before shut off valve	3 to 1
Draining coils	3 to 1
Draining apparatus	3 to 1

When the steam trap is to be used in a high pressure system, determine whether or not the system is to operate under low pressure conditions at certain intervals such as night time or weekends. If this condition is likely to occur, then an additional safety factor should be considered to account for the lower pressure drop available during night time operation.

Example 5 illustrates the three concepts mentioned previously in trap selection condensate handled, pressure differential, and safety factor.

Example 5:Steam Trap Selection for Dripping Supply Main to Return Line: Given:

Steam main: 10 inch diameter steel pipe, 50 ft long.

Steam pressure: 5 psig (227 °F).

Room temperature: 70°F db (steam main in space).

Warm up time: 15 minutes.

Steam trap to drip main into vacuum return line (2 inch vacuum gage design).

Find:

1) warm up load;
2) radiation load;
3) total condensate load;
4) specifications for steam trap at end of supply main.

Solution: 1) The warm up load is determined from the following equation:

$$C_1 = \frac{W \times (T_f - T_i) \times 0.114}{h_l \times t}$$

$$= \frac{2024 \times (227 - 70) \times 0.114}{960 \times 0.25}$$

$$= 150 \text{ lb/hr of condensate}$$

where $W = 40.48$ lb/ft $\times$ 50 ft
$T_f = 227°F$
$T_i = 70°F$
0.114 = specific heat constant for wrought iron or steel pipe (0.092 for copper tubing)
$h_l = 960$ Btu/lb (from steam tables)
$t = 0.25$ hr

2) The radiation load is calculated by the following formula:

$$C_2 = \frac{L \times K \times (T_f - T_i)}{h_l}$$

$$= \frac{50 \times 6.41 \times (227 - 70)}{960}$$

$$= 52 \text{ lb/hr of condensate}$$

where $L = 50$ ft
$T_f = 227°F$ (steam temperature)
$T_i = 70°F$ (room temperature)
$K = 6.41$ Btu/hr-ft-°F
$h_l = 960$ Btu/lb (from Table 2-3)

3) The total condensate load for steam trap selection is equal to the warm up load plus one half the radiation load:

$$\text{total condensate load} = C_1 + \frac{1}{2}C_2$$

$$= 150 + \frac{1}{2}52$$

$$= 176 \text{ lb/hr}$$

4) Steam trap selection is dependent on three factors: condensate handled; safety factor applied to total condensate load; and pressure differential across the steam trap.

The safety factor for a steam trap at the end of the main is 3 to 1 from the table on this page. Applying the 3 to 1 safety factor to the total condensate load, the steam trap would be specified to handle 3×176 or 528 lb/hr of condensate.

The pressure differential across the steam trap is determined by the pressure at the inlet and discharge of the steam trap.

Inlet to trap = 5 psig.

Discharge of trap = 2 in. vacuum (gage).

When the discharge is under vacuum conditions, the discharge vacuum is added to the inlet pressure for the total pressure differential.

Pressure differential = 6 psi.

Therefore the steam trap is selected for a differential pressure of 6 psi and 528 lb/hr of condensate.

Steam Trap Types: The types of traps commonly used in steam systems are:

1) float; 2) flash; 3) thermostatic; 4) impulse; 5) float and thermostatic; 6) lifting; 7) upright bucket; 8) boiler return; 9) inverted bucket; and 10) alternating receiver.

The description and use of these various traps are presented now.

Float Trap: The discharge from the float trap is generally continuous. This type (Fig. 15-72) is used for draining condensate from steam headers, steam heating coils, and other similar equipment. When a float trap is used for draining a low pressure steam system, it should be equipped with a thermostatic air vent.

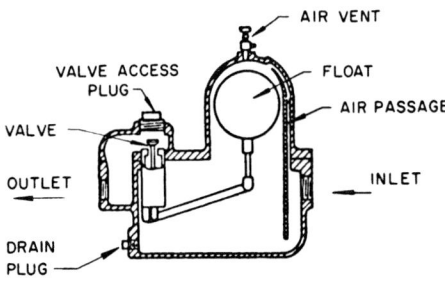

Fig 15-72. Float trap

Thermostatic Trap: The discharge from this type of trap is intermittent. Thermostatic traps are used to drain condensate from radiators, convectors, steam heating coils, unit heaters, and other similar equipment.

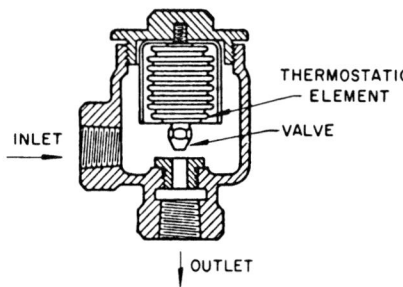

Fig 15-73. Thermostatic trap bellows type

Strainers are normally installed on the inlet side of the steam trap to prevent dirt and pipe scale from entering the trap. On traps used for radiators or convectors, the strainer is usually omitted. Fig. 15-73 shows a typical thermostatic trap of the bellows type, and Fig. 15-74 illustrates a disc type thermostatic trap.

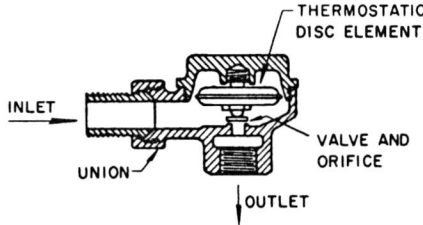

Fig 15-74. Thermostatic trap disc type

When a thermostatic trap is used for a heating apparatus, at least 2 ft of pipe are provided ahead of the trap to cool the condensate. This permits condensate to cool in the pipe rather than in the coil, and thus maintains maximum coil efficiency.

Thermostatic traps are recommended for low pressure systems up to a maximum of 15 psi. When used in medium or high pressure systems, they must be selected for the specific design temperature. In addition, the system must be operated continuously at that design temperature. This means no night setback.

Float and Thermostatic Trap: This type of trap is used to drain condensate from blast heaters, steam heating coils, unit heaters and other apparatus. This combination trap (Fig. 15-75) is used where there is a large volume of condensate that would not permit proper operation of a thermostatic trap. Float and thermostatic traps are used in low pressure heating systems up to a maximum of 15 psi.

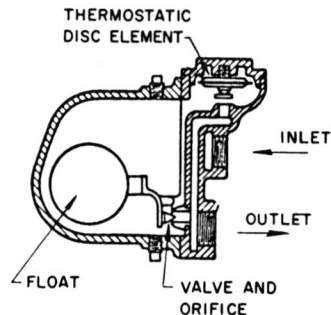

Fig 15-75. Typical float and thermostatic trap

For medium and high pressure systems, the same limitations as outlined for thermostatic traps apply.

Upright Bucket Trap: The discharge of condensate from this trap (Fig. 15-75) is intermittent. A differential pressure of at least 1 psi between the inlet and the outlet of the trap is normally required to lift the condensate from the bucket to the discharge connection. Upright bucket traps are commonly used to drain condensate and air from the blast coils, steam mains, unit heaters, and other equipment. This trap is well suited for systems that have pulsating pressures.

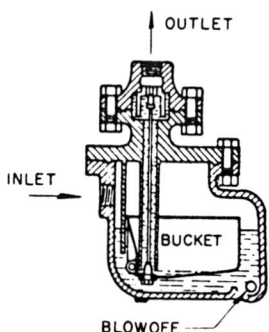

Fig 15-76. Upright bucket trap

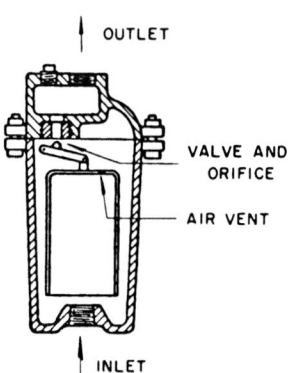

Fig 15-77. Inverted bucket trap

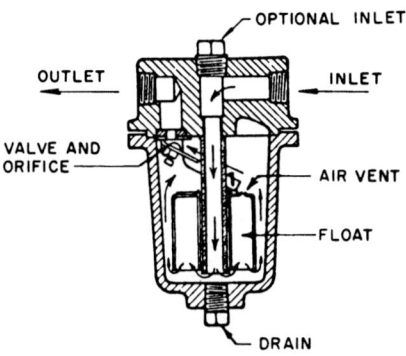

Fig 15-78. Inverted bucket trap with guide

Inverted Bucket Trap: The discharge from the inverted bucket trap (Figs. 15-77 and 15-78) is intermittent and requires a differential pressure between the inlet and discharge of the trap to lift the condensate from the bottom of the trap to the discharge connection. Bucket traps are used for draining condensate and air from blast coils, and unit heaters.

Flash Trap: The discharge from a flash trap (Fig. 15-79) is intermittent. This type of trap is used only if a pressure differential of 5 psi or more exists between the steam supply and condensate return. Flash traps may be used with unit heaters, steam heating coils. steam lines, and other similar equipment.

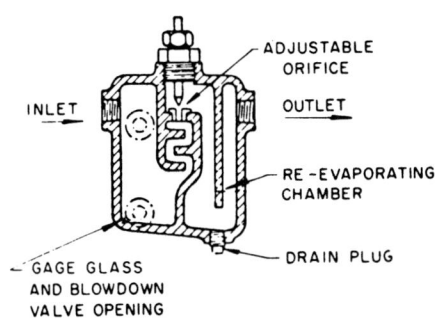

Fig 15-79. Flash type

Impulse Trap: Under normal loads the discharge from this trap (Fig. 15-80) is intermittent. When the load is heavy, however, the discharge is continuous. This type of trap may be used on any equipment where the pressure at the trap outlet does not exceed 25% of the inlet pressure.

Lifting Trap: The lifting trap (Fig. 15-81) is an adaptation of the upright bucket trap. This trap can be used on all steam heating systems up to 150 psig. There is an auxiliary inlet for high pressure steam, as illustrated in the figure, to force the condensate to a point above the trap. This steam is normally at a higher pressure than the steam entering at the regular inlet.

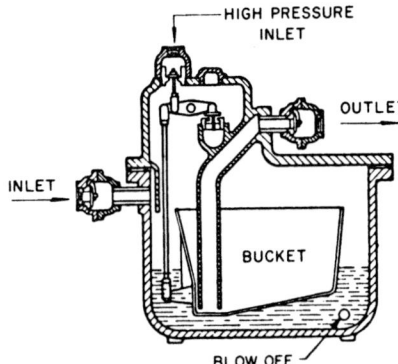

Fig 15-80. Impulse trap

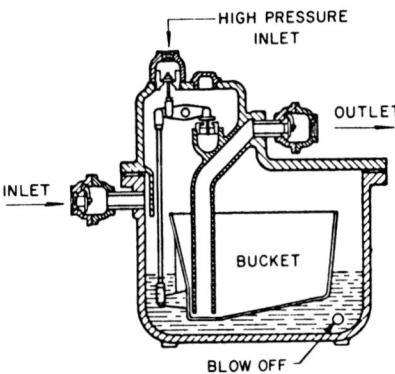

Fig 15-81. Lifting trap

Boiler Return Trap or Alternating Receiver: This type of trap is used to return condensate to a low pressure boiler. The boiler return trap (Fig. 15-82) does not hold steam as do other types, but is an adaptation of the lifting trap. It is used in conjunction with a boiler to prevent flooding return mains when excess pressure prevents condensate from returning to the boiler by gravity. The boiler trap collects condensate and equalizes the boiler and trap pressure, enabling the condensate in the trap to flow back to the boiler by gravity.

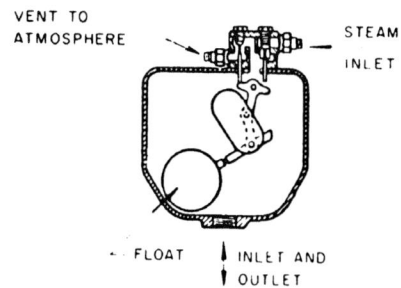

Fig 15-82. Boiler return trap or alternating receiver

Condensate Return Pump: Condensate return pumps are used for low pressure, gravity return heating systems. They are normally of the motor-driven centrifugal type and have a receiver and automatic float control. Other types of condensate return pumps are the rotary, screw, turbine, and reciprocating pump.

The condensate receiver is sized to prevent large fluctuations of the boiler water line. The storage capacity of the receiver is approximately 1.5 times the amount of condensate returned per minute, and the condensate pump has a capacity of 2.5 to 3 times normal flow. The relationship of pump and receiver to the condensate takes peak condensation load into account.

Vacuum Pump: Vacuum pumps are used on a system where the returns are under a vacuum. The assembly consists of a receiver, separating tank, and automatic controls for discharging the condensate to the boiler.

Vacuum pumps are sized in the same manner as condensate pumps for a delivery of 2.5 to 3 times the design condensing rate.

Industrial and Commercial Steam Requirements.—

Following are data from many sources concerning steam requirements for a variety of specific industrial and commercial processes for use in gaging the adequacy of an existing steam plant in the case of a proposed expansion of steam using facilities or for the purpose of sizing the boiler plant for a new facility.

Published Boiler Ratings: Boiler output is specified in a wide variety of systems, including ft^2 of equivalent direct radiation, steam, or hot water, Btu per hr (or Btu/hr), lb per hr of steam and boiler horsepower. Table 15-8 permits conversion from one system to the other.

Boiler horsepower is a theoretical figure, by definition equivalent to generating 34.5 lb/hr of steam at zero psig (212°F) from feedwater at 212°F.

Table 15-8. Conversion of Standard Boiler Ratings

Boiler Horsepower	Lb/hr Steam at 212°F	MBH or 1000 Btu/hr	ft^2 EDR (Steam)	ft^2 EDR (Water)
1	34.5	33.5	139.55	223.30
0.02898	1	0.971	4.044	6.472
0.02985	1.0298	1	4.165	6.665
0.007165	0.2472	0.2400	1	1.600
0.004478	0.1545	0.1502	0.6249	1

In comfort heating, the notion of ft^2 of equivalent direct radiation (EDR) is still in use. When the term was developed, in the days of less efficient gravity systems, a square foot of cast iron radiation was considered capable of radiating 240 Btu/hr when heated with steam or 150 Btu/hr if heated with lower temperature hot water. When modern improvements in heating radiators making the definition generally obsolete, Btu/hr became a more acceptable term.

The basic in boiler output is Btu/hr, the fundamental unit of heat required to raise a pound of water one degree Fahrenheit. A boiler's capacity in Btu/hr is independent of makeup or return temperature or output pressure or temperature. It is the form in which heat losses in buildings

are calculated. It is readily convertible into other more arbitrary rating systems.

Pounds per hour of steam is the most generally accepted method of rating industrial steam using equipment. Steam ratings of boilers as published in lb per hr from and at 212°F are inaccurate for practical application since feedwater is rarely, if ever, admitted as high as 212°F and steam is never utilized at 212°F (zero psig).

Table 15-9. Fraction of Boiler Rating under Operating Conditions

Feed water Temperature, °F	Boiler Operating Pressure Psig						
	10	25	50	100	150	200	250
	% of from at 212°F						
40	84	83	82	82	81	81	81
60	86	85	84	83	83	82	82
80	87	86	85	85	84	84	84
100	89	88	87	86	86	85	85
120	90	89	89	88	88	87	87
140	92	91	90	89	89	89	89
160	94	93	92	91	91	91	91
180	95	95	94	93	93	92	92
200	97	97	96	95	94	94	94

Pressure, Temperature Corrections: As a guide for more accurately estimating steam boiler capacity in lb per hr under specific conditions, Table 15-9 should be consulted. Note that with excessively low feedwater temperature, a boiler generating steam at reasonably high pressure can have an actual output in lb per hr of steam of only 80% or even less than that indicated in published tables, which are from and at 212°F.

Specific Applications: Following, in alphabetical order are steam consumption data for various applications.

Asphalt Plants: Asphalt, for the preparation of road surfacing materials at bituminous central plants, must be kept hot to insure its ability to flow. A 125 psi boiler operating pressure is normally recommended. Steam at 125 psi will heat asphalt to 300°F, while steam at 130 psi will heat asphalt to 311°F. In general 50 MBH is required for each 1000 gal of asphalt to be heated and 170 MBH is required for each 100 ft of 3 inch steam jacketed pipe. A 10,000 gal tank car, therefore, requires 500 MBH for heating plus whatever heat may be dissipated in the steam jacketed piping.

Baths (Steam and Turkish): Turkish bath houses require 5–10 psi steam. The usual inside temperature is 110°F. Allow 33.5 MBH/100 ft^2 of steam radiation. This estimate includes compensation for all losses.

Canning: Retorts, blanchers, steamers, preheaters, cookers, and other vegetable canning machinery requiring steam are widely variable in size, design, and purpose because of the specialized needs and whims of individual canners, equipment manufacturers, and the vegetables themselves.

Because of batch operations, initial steam condensing rates of such equipment are usually high; thus a great deal of judgment is required for even reasonably accurate estimating.

For instance, scalders and blanchers ranging from 6 to 20 ft in length and 4 to 6 ft wide, require 500–840 MBH of steam. Reports for cooking filled cans generally fall in the same range. Some types of preheating and scalding equipment such as the type required to loosen tomato skins for easy removal use considerably less steam.

Cheese Vats: An equipment manufacturer has indicated the ratings in Table 15-10 for jacketed cheese vats. A boiler of 100-psi design pressure is recommended. The usual temperature rise is 60°F to 105°F.

Table 15-10. Conversion of Standard Boiler Ratings

VAT Capacity, Lb	Steam, MBH	VAT Capacity, Lb	Steam, MBH
1,500	107	9,300	486
4,000	211	14,000	704
7,500	402		

Concrete Block: Concrete block, after about a two-hour atmospheric presetting period, is ordinarily cured in kilns with a start up preheat cycle of high steam demand of perhaps three hours duration during which a maximum temperature of 140–155°F is attained using 125 psi steam. This is followed by a three-hour or longer holding period of considerably less steam demand. Frequently, live steam up to 10 psi is injected initially into the kiln in combination with indirect air heating. Good curing practice requires a rate of temperature rise approximating 60°F/hr up to the final 150°F.

Such kilns are operated in batteries and are loaded and started one at a time so that the high start up steam demand of more than one kiln is never imposed on the boiler for more than one kiln at a time. Normally, some kilns will be unloading and some will be at holding temperature. However, it is well to establish the actual operating cycle at each specific concrete block operation.

Steam requirements can be safely estimated on the basis of a production rate of 1.5 standard blocks (8 in. × 8 in. × 16 in.) per MBH.

As an example, a plant with a block making machine turning out 800 blocks/hr probably would have six 2500 block high temperature kilns. On an 8-hr curing cycle, which is standard in the industry, the plant can thus be operated on a two or three shift basis.

A maximum production load might be three kilns operating at one time with the other kilns being loaded and unloaded so that 9500 blocks (3 kilns × 2500 block capacity) might be produced in an 8-hr shift, requiring a 5025 MBH boiler.

Concrete Ready-Mix: Concrete ingredients contain varying amounts of moisture from outdoor storage and must be dried in both summer and winter weather before mixing to keep the amount of moisture in the finished

concrete within proper values required by the mixing formulas. Steam is ordinarily used at high pressure, on the high side of the 100–150 psi range. For average conditions, aggregate is assumed to contain 5% moisture.

Table 15-11. Steam Required to Dry Aggregate

% Moisture	Initial Temperature of Aggregate °F			
	20	30	40	50
	lb/hr Steam per ton of Aggregate			
2	14.4	17.9	21.4	24.9
4	20.6	24.1	27.6	31.1
6	26.6	30.1	33.6	37.1
8	32.7	37.2	39.7	43.2
10	39.0	42.5	46.0	49.5

Table 15-11 gives steam required to dry one ton of aggregate with original moisture content up to 10% and at initial temperatures of 20°F through 50°F. At higher storage temperatures aggregate moisture content is proportionately higher, requiring increasing amounts of steam for adequate drying.

Table 15-12. Mixing Water Temperature for 60°F Concrete

Aggregate Temperature °F	Water Required gal/yd³					
	15	20	25	30	35	40
	lb/hr steam per ton of Aggregate					
35	...	180	155	140	130	120
40	190	155	135	126	115	110

Steam is used to heat water for mixing with cold aggregate in winter climates to provide the required 60°F wet concrete temperature for proper setting. For example, with aggregate at 35°F and using 30 gal of water per cubic yard of concrete, water temperature must be 140°F to produce 60°F concrete. At higher aggregate temperatures and in summer climates heated water is not required.

Table 15-12 presents water temperatures necessary to produce 60°F concrete when the aggregate is at initial temperatures of 35°F or 40°F, using amounts of water varying between 15 and 40 gal/yd³.

Calculations of steam required for heating water are available elsewhere. A convenient rule of thumb is to assume 1 Btu required per degree of temperature rise per pound of water, 8.3 lb of water per gallon.

Cookers, Coil: Submerged coils in open kettles are used widely in chemical and food processing operations. For instance, tomato puree is concentrated to one third for catsup in coil heated open cookers. There are a number of coil arrangements, such as single and double spirals and various combinations of series and parallel connections. Variations in steam requirements for these different designs are inconsequential. Piping used for the coils is normally of 3 inches diameter.

Steam is usually utilized in the 100–150 psi range. A 1000 gal cooker requires about 6700 MBH during the 3 or 4 minutes, when the watery puree is being brought to a boil and about 3400 MBH to maintain evaporation during the remainder of the cycle about 40 minutes in tomato concentration. These cookers range from about 750 gal to 1500 gal capacity. Occasionally, coil cookers down to 250 gal capacities are found. Usually, steam jacketed kettles are used for smaller capacities.

In batteries of cookers, a quarter of the cookers may be starting up, a quarter may be boiling, another quarter may be washing up, while the final quarter may be reloading for another cycle. Therefore, on batch operations of this kind peak load is always considerably less than connected load.

Cookers, Jacketed Kettles: Jacketed kettles are generally used where smaller volumes per batch are processed. For cooking jams, jellies, preserves, and various types of candies and confections, a 60-gal or 70-gal kettle is usually used. These also may be equipped with electrically driven mixers, evacuation devices for vacuum cooking and other accessories. Steam pressure rarely exceeds 70 psi.

A 150 gal to 300 gal jacketed kettle may be figured at 838–1675 MBH, while the smaller 60-gal size will require 335–503 MBH. As with coil cookers, any battery of kettles will consist of about one quarter of them condensing at the maximum startup rate while half may be considered as cooking normally at the minimum load. The remainder would be in the midst of filling, dumping, or cleaning up.

Cookers, Rendering: Rendering cookers are jacketed, horizontal, cylindrical vessels, usually 5 or 6 ft in diameter and about 12 ft long, for recovering fat for soap and chemical manufacturing. Some method of rotation is employed, usually an internal agitator. Pressures are normally in the 60–70 psi range and the units condense at a rate of about 2000 MBH.

One manufacturers cooker has a steam consumption of about ¾ lb steam per pound of raw material. Thus, an 8000 lb capacity cooker requiring a 3-hr cycle would condense approximately 6000 lb of steam at a rate of 2000 lb/hr, corresponding roughly to 2350 MBH.

Distilleries: Distilling equipment is varied and somewhat complicated. In one typical arrangement live steam is bubbled into the product through a perforated sparge pipe. In making complete calculations on a "heat input equals heat output" basis, the constants in Table 15-13 may be used.

Table 15-13. Thermal Data for Water and Alcohol

Liquid	Specific Heat	Specific Gravity	Heat of Vaporization, Btu/lb
Water	1.0	1.0	970
Alcohol	0.60	0.80	363

A good average is about 24 lb of steam required per hr wine gallon, in which distilling capacity is rated. Thus, a still that produce 500 gallons of wine per hour would require 12,000 lb steam per hr.

Dry Cleaning: Because more delicate fabrics are involved drycleaning operations are usually performed at lower steam pressures and temperatures 70 psi than laundry operations 100 psi. Principal operation in dry cleaning is carried out in the solvent still. Cleaning solvents are used over and over and require the use of filters and stills to purify the solvent after each cleaning cycle. Depending on nominal still size, steam requirements range from about 50 to 500 MBH. See Table 15-14.

Table 15-14. Dry Cleaning Still Steam Requirement

Size, Gal	Steam, MBH	Size, Gal	Steam, MBH
25	50	125–150	168
50	67	175–200	200
75	100	250	300
100	134	350–400	470

The small amounts of live steam used in hand spotting operations and some finishing operations generally are inconsequential.

Steam requirements of tumblers and finishing equipment are about the same as for laundries and will be found elsewhere in this section under those specific types of equipment.

Dryers, Double Drum: Double drum dryers are frequently used to dry milk, brewers yeast, various other foods, and chemicals. Steam is usually applied at less than 100 psi. The dryers consist of two cylindrical, steam filled rolls on parallel horizontal axes revolving slowly toward each other. In the center, between the two rolls, the fluid to be dried is sprayed thinly on the two rolls. After about three quarters of a revolution the dried residue is removed by long doctor blades and the powdered product drops down below the rolls, where it is picked up by an integral screw conveyor for continuous removal.

Table 15-15. Drycleaning Steam Requirement

Drum Sizes, in.	Steam, MBH	Drum Sizes, in.	Steam, MBH
24 × 60	1000	36 × 100	3350
28 × 72	1500	36 × 120	4200
36 × 84	2345	...	...

Table 15-15 presents steam requirements of several popular dryer sizes based on the size of one of the twin drying rolls.

Since operation is continuous rather than batched, multiple units in a battery could conceivably all be in service simultaneously. The plant's specific cycle of operation should be explored to arrive at an accurate estimate of steam load.

Dryers, Revolving Steel Tubular: Revolving steel tubular dryers consist of stationary steel piping inside a rotating steel shell. Sloped for continuous feeding and removal of dried product, they are used for drying grain, pigments, and various forms of granular solids. In this way, spent distillery and brewery mash is pressed dry, then dried for high vitamin content stock feed.

A 6 ft diameter by 30 ft long unit, operated at 50 psi, condenses about 3350 MBH. During the startup, the steam requirement is only slightly greater. In batteries, of course, all units may be operating simultaneously if the process is continuous rather than batch.

Dryers, Spray: The convenience to manufacturers of other foods of dried milk and the acceptance of reconstituted dry milk solids as a home beverage have led to tremendous increases in milk drying operations. Several methods are available for recovering the dry solids from milk, which is nearly 90% water. One of the most popular methods is spray drying, in which the milk is sprayed into a steam heated atmosphere, the water thus evaporated, and the white crystalline nutrients recovered by gravity.

Spray dryers for recovering dried milk solids can generally be estimated as requiring about a quarter of the lb per hour milk input capacity in boiler horsepower. Thus, a spray dryer rated to handle 7000 lb of raw milk per hour would require 8375 MBH of steam capacity.

Dyeing: The process of dyeing consists of dipping fabrics or yarns in a dye solution (called liquor) at boiling temperature, rinsing and drying. In the ordinary dye vat, steam jets in the tank bottom heat the liquor to boiling temperature. The turbulence from the jets agitates the liquor and mixes the solution thoroughly.

The following formula provides a practical method of computing the MBH required for a dye vat:

$$(\text{Btu/hr} = (\text{gal capacity})) \times$$
$$(8.33 \text{ lb/gal}) \times (\text{temp. rise to } 212 \text{ F})$$

Assume a vat of 400 gal capacity and water supply temperature of 60°F:

$$\text{Btu/hr} = (400\,\text{gal}) \times (8.33 \text{ lb/gal}) \times (212\text{F} - 60\text{F})$$
$$= 505000 \text{ Btu/hr}$$
$$= 505 \text{ MBH}$$

This formula is based on raising the temperature of the liquor to the boiling point in one hour. If the vat is to be brought up to temperature in 30 minutes, multiply the result by 2, if 20 minutes multiply by 3, etc.

After the cloth has been dyed it must be dried, usually in a heated compartment or cabinet. The load can be determined from the size of the pipe as indicated under the *Kilns (Bare Pipe Radiation)*.

Feed Mills: In pelleting various ground grains with vitamins and other fortifying agents for stock feed, live steam at 10–30 psi (240–295°F) is admitted to the feed, both for heating and as a moistening agent as part of the process of compressing the material into solid lozenges from very small diameters for baby chicks to ¾ inch range cubes for cattle. Frequently, because of production problems, baby chick feed is processed into relatively large diameters and then recrumbled or reground into appropriate sizes for such a small animal.

Steam consumption is normally estimated at about 50 lb of steam per 1000 lb of animal feed at the input. Some feeds, alfalfa for instance, may require as little as 30 lb of steam per 1000 lb of feed. Since there may be about 5–10% loss of fines in the processing, if output figures are used to measure the size of the production machinery, the output capacity is increased by 10% for use in estimating steam requirements.

When a low pressure boiler is used, steam pressure available at the steam controls on the pellet mill usually will be around 8–10 psi due to line losses, even with 13–15 psi boiler pressure. A high pressure boiler, with steam reduced and regulated to 20–30 psi at the pellet mill, is more flexible and will give better control of the processing. Accurate temperature regulation is of primary importance for quality control. Effectiveness of the steam pressure regulation system should be carefully studied to avoid later complaints against the boiler.

In estimating the steam requirements a convenient rule of thumb, therefore, can be 5% of the rated input capacity to the pellet mill. Thus, a pellet mill producing 10 tons (20,000 lb) per hour should be increased by 10% to 22,000 lb/hr to arrive at feed input compensating for loss of fineness in processing and multiplied by 5% to arrive at a steam consumption figure of 1100 lb of steam per hour. Since steam is condensed in the feed and not returned to the boiler, this is a 100% makeup application. Installing a 1350 MBH boiler is better than attempting to squeeze by with a 1000 MBH boiler. Cold makeup would reduce the 1000 MBH boiler steaming capacity under actual operating conditions to a figure well below the required 1100 lb of steam per hour.

Greenhouses and Soil Sterilization: Fresh vegetables are frequently grown under glass, even in the coldest climates, year round. Tomatoes, for instance, may be grown at the rate of three or four crops a year at temperatures of 55–58°F, increased to 62–65°F in milder weather. Greenhouse heating loads may be estimated at about 4200 MBH per acre (43,560 ft²), although greenhouse sources recommend 5000 MBH.

Steam for soil sterilization to kill weeds between crops is usually admitted through buried porous pipes or tiles to maintain a section under treatment at 212–215°F for 4 to 6 hours.

One method of effecting soil sterilization is to put a raw potato under the tarpaulin with which the ground being sterilized is covered to retard the escape of steam. When the potato is cooked, the soil is sterilized.

Sterilizing steam requirements are 4 or 5 times greater than the space heating requirement, and a boiler sized for normal space heating can be used for soil sterilization one section at a time. This is also practicable, since the remainder of the growing area is usually producing plants in various growth stages.

Kilns (Bare Pipe Radiation): For bare pipe radiation as utilized in brick, lumber, veneer, and wallboard dryers and many other similar kiln type applications, a factor of 0.3 lb/hr of steam for each square foot of pipe surface is a fairly accurate approximation.

For instance, assume an installation contains 1500 ft of $\frac{3}{8}$ inch finned copper tubing and 1800 ft of $1\frac{1}{2}$ inch steel pipe in each of five kilns. The radiating area may be calculated from the pipe OD (converted to feet) in each case:

$$\pi\left(\frac{0.675}{12}\right) \times 1500 = 264 \text{ ft}^2$$

$$\pi\left(\frac{1.90}{12}\right) \times 1800 = 864 \text{ ft}^2$$

Total radiating area per kiln = 264 + 894 = 1158 ft^2

Total radiating area = 1158 ft^2/kiln × 5 kilns = 5790 ft^2

Steam requirement for 5 kilns = 5790 ft^2 × 0.30 lb/hr-ft^2 = 1737 lb/hr

Laundries, Commercial: Commercial laundries require substantial quantities of steam for washing, drying and finishing operations. Steam is generally utilized at pressures slightly above 100 psi (338°F) to provide sufficiently high temperatures for finishing operations.

Heating of wash water to 180°F is probably the peak source of boiler load. Drying and finishing operations usually require less steam and are staggered with the actual washing although the individual laundry's operating procedure should be carefully checked in each instance. The number of wash wheels and their dimensions determine hot water load with reasonable accuracy. See Table 15-16.

A double check is based on the poundage of dry, dirty clothes being laundered either by the laundry owner's estimate or rapid calculation based on two rules of thumb:

1) One ft^3 of wash wheel volume contains 4–6 lb of dry dirty clothes. A 36-inch dia × 54-inch wash wheel holds

$$\frac{\pi}{4}\left(\frac{36}{12}\right)^2 \times \left(\frac{54}{12}\right) \times 5 = 160 \text{ lb}$$

About 3 gal of hot water are required per pound of dry dirty clothes washed.

Absorption	0.33 gal/lb ×160 lb	=	53 gal
Suds	4 × 21 gal @ 3 in	=	84 gal
Rinses	5 × 50 gal @ 9 in	=	250 gal
			387 gal

Dry clothes may be assumed to absorb between $\frac{1}{4}$ and $\frac{1}{3}$ gal of water per pound. Individual laundry operators have their preferences as to specific washing cycles but typically one might be 4 gal suds with the wash wheel filled to a 3 in. level (about 21 gal each for a 36 inch × 54 inch unit) and five rinses filled to a 9 inch level (50 gal): 387 gal/160 lb is 2.41 gal hot water/lb laundry; 3 gal/lb of dry dirty clothes is a safely conservative figure to use in estimating.

Table 15-16. Dry Cleaning Still Steam Requirement

Wheel Dia, in.	Hot Water, gal	Wheel Dia, in.	Hot Water, gal
30 × 30	110	42 × 108	810
30 × 36	130	44 × 36	300
30 × 48	190	44 × 54	450
36 × 36	200	44 × 60	495
36 × 48	270	44 × 72	595
36 × 54	300	44 × 84	695
36 × 64	350	44 × 96	790
42 × 36	270	44 × 108	900
42 × 54	405	44 × 120	990
42 × 64	475	54 × 84	870
42 × 72	540	54 × 96	990
42 × 84	630	54 × 108	1110
42 × 96	720	54 × 120	1230

The sum of the individual capacities of the washers will give the maximum gallons of hot water required. In actual practice, a wash round can be completed in less than an hour. However, allowing for loading and unloading the wheels, starching, and the use of low temperature water on certain rounds, the preceding estimate is reasonable.

This is approximately equivalent to a 100-hp boiler requirement.

Some laundries are equipped with reclaimers to preheat incoming water, with otherwise wasted heat in the laundry wash water going to the sewer; thus the temperature differential is reduced.

Another factor that may reduce the amount of boiler capacity required is a hot water storage tank, smoothing peak hot water requirements.

Laundries, Self Service: Hot water load can generally be estimated at 38 gal of 140°F water per hour for each machine on the basis of a 9 lb clothes load, a 30–50 minute washing cycle, and a requirement of 25 gal of 140°F water per cycle.

Laundry and Dry Cleaning Finishing Equipment: Flatwork ironers or mangles are the largest consumers of steam in the area of finishing equipment. They are used for pressing tablecloths, sheets, pillowcases, napkins and other flatwork. These machines have a large production output when properly operated with sufficient temperature. An outcome of wet multiple thickness hems of sheets and pillowcases are usually the first indication of inadequate pressing temperature (and steam pressure at the ironer inlet). Steam requirements per flatwork ironer range from 100 to 670 MBH (Table 15-17).

Large single or dual cylinder (24–48 inch diameter) mangles have largely been replaced by the more modern multiple cylinder steam chest flatwork ironers. Where the old type machines are still in use, a 335 or 500 MBH figure can be used.

Drying rooms or cabinets are used for drying curtains, blankets, and bedspreads. These are usually heated by radiators or pipe coils. An estimate of 2 bhp is usually adequate. In unusual cases of special designs, radiation load can be computed as for comfort heating or as described under Kilns. However, these cabinets are not in frequent use and usually do not increase the maximum load.

Table 15-17. Flatwork Ironer Steam Requirements

Iron Size	Length of Rolls, in.	
	100	120
	MBH Requirements	
2–roll	104	127
4–roll	211	255
6–roll	300	330
8–roll	430	476
12–roll	…	650

Laundry and Drycleaning Tumbler Dryers: Since most garments are pressed in a damp condition, the extractor plays the biggest part in the drying operation of a laundry. The extractor removes excess moisture from clothing by centrifugal action and does not require any steam. Further drying is provided by tumbler dryers for some delicate garments and for fabrics that must be dry before finishing.

The tumbler consists of a cylinder with perforated outer wall mounted inside a steam heated cabinet. The cylinder is rotated while warm air circulates through the cabinet in the same general way that an electric or gas heated home laundry dryer operates. Size of the tumbler dryer is determined by the dimensions of the cylinder. Ratings for the more popular sizes are given in Table 15-18.

Table 15-18. Tumbler Dryer Steam Requirement

Wheel Dia, in.	Hot Water, gal	Wheel Dia, in.	Hot Water, gal
36 × 24	124	42 × 40	218
36 × 30	130	42 × 60	268
30 × 42	150	42 × 90	400
36 × 48	201	44 × 120	536

Because of more delicate fabrics in dry cleaning applications, fewer coils are sometimes used, thus reducing the steam requirements. However, Table 15-18 data are adequate for estimating purposes.

Ovens, Proof Boxes (Bakeries): Specialized requirements for steam in bakeries cover ovens and proof boxes. Other steam uses include jacketed kettles (described elsewhere) for confections, hot water for washing, and space or comfort heating.

Proof boxes are used to speed the process of raising yeast dough before baking in ovens. The proof box is similar to a steam room, since steam is injected directly into the box to obtain a warm, humid atmosphere. The amount of steam released is regulated in accordance with the amount of dough to be raised.

Steam requirements for proof boxes are normally inconsequential in comparison with other larger steam loads. Commercial types of proof boxes are rated by the number of racks they contain on the basis of 10 MBH per rack. The standard proof rack is about 30 inches wide by 6 ft long and holds 8–10 trays of bread. Proofing time varies from 4 to 60 min.

Baking ovens are of three types: the simple hearth oven, the traveling oven, and the revolving oven. In all types, steam is injected into the baking chamber to cure the bread or to glaze the surfaces of certain breads and rolls. The normal baking time for bread is 30 minutes, so that bakeries usually average two bakes per hour. Regardless of type of oven, a practicable rule of thumb is to assume about 67 MBH of steam required per 100 lb of bread baked per hour. Thus, an oven designed to hold 320 one pound loaves could bake 640 lb of bread per hour, requiring about 430 MBH of steam capacity.

Table 15-19. Steam Requirement for Typical Commercial Ovens

Number and Sizes of Trays, in.	Capacity in 1-lb Loaves	MBH Steam	Number and Sizes of Trays, in.	Capacity in 1-lb Loaves	MBH Steam
4, 20 × 54	80	107	10, 24 × 96	320	430
4, 20 × 80	128	170	10, 24 × 108	360	482
6, 20 × 54	120	161	10, 26 × 98	320	430
4, 20 × 80	192	258	10, 26 × 110	400	536
6, 23 × 92	216	291	12, 24 × 96	384	515
6, 23 × 110	264	355	12, 24 × 108	432	580
6, 23 × 128	288	385	12, 24 × 120	480	643
6, 23 × 146	352	450	12, 26 × 98	384	515
6, 23 × 92	384	385	12, 26 × 110	480	643
8, 23 × 110	352	470	12, 24 × 108	540	725
8, 23 × 128	384	515	12, 26 × 98	384	515
8, 23 × 146	448	600	12, 26 × 110	480	643
10, 23 × 110	440	590	15, 24 × 108	540	725
10, 23 × 128	480	643	15, 26 × 110	600	805
10, 23 × 146	560	750	16, 26 × 110	576	775
12, 23 × 128	576	775	20, 24 × 120	800	1070
12, 23 × 146	672	900	22, 24 × 120	880	1180

Hearth-type oven capacities can be calculated from the number and dimensions of trays used.

Revolving ovens may contain from 4 to 12 trays, which revolve on a wheel similar to a ferris wheel.

Traveling ovens are in continuous motion, being loaded with, and discharging, bread simultaneously, at opposite ends of a 100-ft long tunnel oven.

Table 15-19 gives typical commercial oven sizes, indicating the bread capacity and steam requirement of each.

Paper Corrugators: Paper corrugators are integrated machines that take rough paper filler, spray it with steam for softening, and corrugate it over toothed rolls. Following this, heavier liners are glued to one or both sides and the assembled sheet is passed rapidly over steam heated plates. Steamfitter preheating cylinders are frequently used ahead of the corrugating operation. The entire process may run at speeds of 200 to 400 fpm. Steam is used at up to 175 psi. Corrugating machines condense from 224–517 lb/hr steam, although a specific machine can be checked with the manufacturer.

A convenient rule of thumb is to use 40 lb of steam per 1000 ft² of corrugated board produced. About 15% of the steam is directly condensed in softening the filler sheet, although the remainder is easily recovered as condensate. With 60-inch board running at 300 fpm, this comes to 3600 lb/hr of steam.

Additional processing loads and plant and office heating should also be considered in sizing the boiler.

Paper Making: Paper is made from a slurry of ground wood pulp, waste paper, or rags spread out and drained on a wire screen or a felt blanket and finally dried by passing continuously over the surface of steam heated rotating drum dryers.

Steam is ordinarily utilized at relatively low pressures, under 50 psi, although newer machines are being constructed to utilize pressures up to 175 psi. Frequently, two or three successively increasing pressures are used in consecutive banks of drying rolls, which may total anywhere from about 25 to 100 in number. The lower pressure (and temperature) steam is applied first, to heat the new paper slowly. Higher pressure and temperature, if applied first, might case harden the outer surface of the paper sheet. Moisture sealed inside later explodes and wrinkles the finished sheet.

In the absence of flow meter readings, a figure of $3\frac{1}{2}$ or 4 lb steam per pound of paper produced may be used for paper machine dryers. Thus, a mill producing 30 tons of paper per 24-hour day would be producing $1\frac{1}{4}$ tons or 2500 lb of paper per hour, requiring about 10,000 lb per hr of steam.

Occasionally, water for the pulp slurry will be preheated. Other steam process loads and plant and office heating loads should be calculated before selecting the boiler size.

Pasteurization: Conventional pasteurization in the dairy industry consists of raising milk to a predetermined temperature well short of boiling and holding it at that temperature for approximately 30 minutes to kill disease carrying bacteria. The process is also employed in canning and in bottling fruit juices.

Some equipment is sized in terms of gallons of product per minute, other types may be sized in total gallons per 20-minutes or 30-minutes cycle. In the latter case this amount can be converted readily into a gpm figure. A 400 gal pasteurizer for a 30 minutes cycle can be said to be a $13\frac{1}{3}$ gpm size.

A convenient estimate of steam need in boiler horsepower is to use $1\frac{1}{2}$ times the nominal equipment size rating as specified in gpm. Thus, a 400-gal pasteurizer for a 30 minutes cycle would require about 20 bhp of steam.

Platen Presses: Platen presses, used in the production of plastic parts and components, veneer plywood, and other manufactured products, consist of two or more steam filled plates or platens, which are brought together under high mechanical pressure for forming under combined heat and pressure as a part of each manufacturing cycle.

One convenient rule of thumb is to estimate about 30 lb steam/hr or 1 bhp for each 12–15 ft² of exposed platen surface.

Process Heating: There are many variations to the application of heat by steam in the process industries. Frequently, determination of steam requirements must be accomplished by primary heat and steam formulas.

Table 15-20. Specific Heats of Various Materials

Vessel Material	Specific Heat	Substance Material	Specific Heat
Aluminum	0.22	Ammonia (gas)	0.50
Brass	0.09	Acetic acid	0.47
Copper	0.09	Air	0.24
Iron	0.11	Ethyl alcohol	0.58
Lead	0.03	Glycerin	0.57
Monel	0.13	Hydrogen peroxide	0.58
Magnesium alloy	0.25	Olive oil	0.47
Stainless steel	0.11	Paraffin	0.69
...	...	Sugar (solid)	0.28
...	...	Sulfuric acid	0.34
...	...	Turpentine	0.41

In the basic approach to the measurement of steam required for process heating, the following factors must be considered:
1) heat to raise temperature of substance,
2) heat to raise temperature of heating vessel,
3) heat to overcome radiation losses.

The greatest amount of steam is consumed in raising the temperature of the substance and the heating vessel to the operating temperature of the process. This is the maximum load that must be provided by the boiler. Maintenance of operating temperature in batch operations merely requires replacement of losses due to radiation, convection, and conduction. They can be safely ignored in these rough calculations.

The heat required in Btu is equal to the weight of the substance in pounds times its specific heat plus the weight of the vessel in pounds times its specific heat, all multiplied by the temperature rise in degrees Fahrenheit:

$$\text{Btu required} = (W'S' + W''S'') \times \Delta T$$

where W' = weight of substance, lb
$\quad S'$ = specific heat of substance Btu/lb-°F
$\quad W''$ = weight of vessel, lb
$\quad S''$ = specific heat of vessel Btu/lb-°F
$\quad \Delta T$ = temperature rise, °F.

This is the total heat required per batch and must be related to time to get the steam needs. If the cycle is accomplished in one hour, the resulting total Btu requirement can be converted directly into pounds per hour of steam or boiler horsepower. If the cycle is only 30 minutes, or 15 minutes, the Btu figure must be doubled or quadrupled respectively to get an equivalent Btu per hr rate for conversion to lb/ hr or bhp steam need.

Specific heats of some typical vessel materials and substance materials are given in Table 15-20. Other specific heats can be found in standard reference sources.

Obviously, in practical plant situations a great deal of guesswork is necessary in the selection of approximate specific heat figures as well as the weight of the vessel or heat exchanger. Weight of the substance being processed can usually be more accurately estimated from plant production figures. Erring high in estimates of weights and in selection of specific heat figures will give higher than necessary steam load figures and provide adequate safety factors for these rough estimates.

In continuous operations only the rate of heating of the substance really need be considered. Normal load then is the amount of heat added to the substance at its flow rate.

For example, assume a continuous flow of a vegetable oil through a copper tube heat exchanger in a pharmaceutical, food, or cosmetic process at a rate of 30 to 50 gpm, or 400 lb/minute, 24,000 lb/hr. You might estimate the heat exchanger weighs 1000 lb. The temperature rise undoubtedly would be well documented by plant officials, say, from 60°F to 150°F. Thus, maximum start up Btu per hr load becomes:

$$\text{Max. load} = [(1000 \times 0.09) + (24000 \times 0.50)] \times 90$$

$$= (90 + 12000)90$$

$$= 1088100 \text{ Btu/hr}$$

This amounts to about 1100–1200 lb/hr of steam. Note that the weight and the specific heat of the vessel are insignificant in establishing the steam requirement of the process.

Restaurants: Because of lighting, cooking, and body heat, the comfort heating load requirements of a restaurant are on the low side. But, because restaurants are an integral part of an increasing number of office buildings, industrial plants, apartments, hospitals, hotels and motels, and other installations, restaurant process steam load must be considered.

Standard steam requirement may be estimated of about 30 lb steam/hr-ft of length. A bain marie (hot water filled steam table) is considered at half of a steam table heating requirement.

Jacketed holding kettles for stock, ranging from 10–60 gal capacity, require from 15–60 lb steam/hr.

Hot water loads are uniformly high because the sanitary use of hot water is spread over the entire day. Restaurant dishwashers may use 2–8 bhp of steam. Restaurants

serving only two, or even one, meal a day would have relatively higher peak hot water demands over a shorter time period say, only 2 hr consequently, in the selection of equipment; these require greater hot water storage or quicker recovery.

Snow Removal: Snow and ice is removed from sidewalks, driveways, airports, loading ramps, and other paved areas by circulating 140°F water through a piping grid embedded in the pavement. A convenient rule of thumb is to assume a 100-Btu heat requirement to remove a square foot of 1 inch deep snow or 0.1 inch thickness of ice. This works out to about 335 ft^2 of 1 inch deep snow or 0.1 inch thick ice per bhp. Thus, in figuring on removing a 2 inch snowfall from a filling station driveway measuring 100 ft on each side, an additional heating load of 2000 MBH must be considered.

Sterilizers, Autoclaves: Sterilizers are used by the medical profession for surgical dressings and hospital supplies and industrially in various phases of the manufacture of pharmaceuticals, packed food products, textiles, plastics, hair and bristle products, and allied processing operations.

The steam consumption figures in Table 15-21 are based on annunciated sterilizers. If 2-inch magnesia insulation or its equivalent is applied, steam consumption figures can be reduced by 25%.

Table 15-21. Steam Requirements for Sterilizers

Size Sterilizer, in.	Steam Consumption per hr		Size Sterilizer, in.	Steam Consumption per hr	
	Fabric loads	Solution loads		Fabric loads	Solution loads
24 × 24 × 36	55	60	36 × 42 × 84	145	185
24 × 24 × 48	65	70	42 × 48 × 96	210	265
24 × 24 × 60	70	80	48 × 54 × 96	260	340
24 × 36 × 48	80	90	48 × 60 × 96	285	375
24 × 36 × 36	85	100	60 × 66 × 96	395	515
30 × 42 × 84	125	155	60 × 66 × 156	700	900
30 × 48 × 84	135	175	60 × 66 × 228	1000	1200

The operating cycle assumes starting with a cold fully loaded machine operating through a complete cycle in one hour (15 minutes slow heating of jacket to 250°F and 15 psi pressure, 30 minutes exposure of load to 240–250°F, 15 minutes for drying during which jacket is maintained at 15 psi).

In battery operations sterilizers should be put into operation on a staggered schedule. To insure adequate steam pressure within the sterilizer, it is recommended that 25% to 50% be added to the steam load to compensate for line losses and that 40 psi steam pressure be available and reduced at the sterilizer inlet.

Table 15-22. Steam Consumption for Tire Recapping

Size Sterilizer, in.	Steam, MBH
600–16, 650–15, 700–15	33.5
600–20, 700–20, 900–16	50
750–20, 1000–20	67
1200–24, 1400–20	84
Off-road equipment	335

Tire Recapping: Tire recappers are increasingly important users for steam generating and steam handling equipment, both in U.S. and other countries. The best source of steam requirement information is a manufacturer of the tire recapping vulcanizers under consideration. In Table 15-22, are some reasonably accurate estimates of steam requirements based on tire sizes.

Vacuum Pans: Condensed or evaporated milk is produced by evaporating part of the moisture from whole or skim milk. The evaporating or condensing takes place in vacuum pans which are operated under approximately 25 inches of vacuum. The raw milk is usually preheated to about 210°F before it enters the vacuum pan. Depending on the ratio of concentration, Table 15-23 is a guide to the steam requirements for vacuum pans of various diameters.

Table 15-23. Steam Requirements for Vacuum Pans

Vacuum Pan Dia, in.	Pan outlet lb/hr	Steam lb/hr
16	21–265	100–200
26	56–450	250–590
36	131–1050	600–1360
42	248–1980	1170–2450
48	416–3330	1960–4300
60	574–4590	2700–5900
72	979–7830	4600–10000

Washers, Bottle: Many types of bottle washers are in use by dairies, breweries, soft drink bottlers and other industries. The manufacturer of each particular machine normally provides the information regarding steam need which is essential for heating wash water to the required 180°F–200°F in a specified time from an assumed minimum water supply temperature.

Table 15-24. Bottle Washer Steam Consumption

Bottle Capacity	Bottles/ minute	Required Fresh Water, gpm	Steam, MBH	Bottle Capacity	Bottles/ minute	Required Fresh Water, gpm	Steam, MBH
5000	400	72	2000	2000	160	40	1000
4000	320	60	1675	1500	120	32	670
3000	240	50	1350	1000	80	21	500
2500	200	45	1200	500	50	15	335

There is little difference in hot water consumption as related to bottle size (half pint, pint, quart, half gallon, gallon), but the total amount of water required should be determined carefully and the steam load to produce it then added to the steam needs of other specialized plant process and comfort heating equipment to arrive at the total boiler load.

Bottle washers are identified in terms of bottle per minute capacity. If nameplates are obliterated the machine operator or plant management can estimate the operating rate. A consensus of manufacturer data indicates maximum steam need and water supply required as given in Table 15-24, related to the holding capacity and rate of bottle washing.

Flash Steam Calculations

Where high temperature condensate or continuous boiler blowdown is available, there may be opportunities to make controlled use of flash steam. The energy in water at high pressure and near saturation temperature produces flash steam instantaneously when pressure is reduced below saturation. The amount of steam so produced depends on the enthalpy of water and steam at each temperature and pressure.

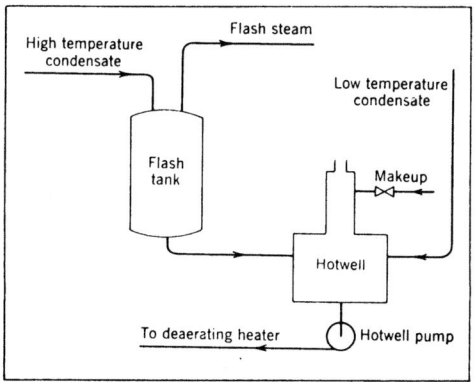

Fig 15-83. Flow diagram for generation of flash steam from high temperature condensate returns

As an example, if saturated water at 70 psia and 303°F with enthalpy of 272.6 Btu/lb is discharged into a tank maintained at 20 psia, it must immediately assume the saturation conditions of the lower pressure, 228°F, and 196.2 Btu/lb. Some of the energy which had formerly held the temperature at 303°F is converted into latent heat of steam at the new temperature. The amount of energy so converted is 272.6 −196.2 = 76.4 Btu/lb. Since the latent heat of steam at 20 psia is 960.1 Btu/lb, this excess heat is enough to produce 76.4/960.1 or 0.08 lb of steam per lb of high temperature condensate; in other words, 80% of the condensate will flash into steam at the lower pressure. A similar 50-lb drop in another range of the pressure scale, say from l00 to 50 psia, would produce only a 5.2% conversion to flash steam because of the nonlinearity of the enthalpy function.

Several tables are presented pertaining to this matter. One, showing the amount of heat given up by condensate to flash steam at various pressure reductions, will save the time and tedium of individual calculations. The second table, converting this heat into percent of condensate flashed to steam, leaves nothing for calculation except interpolation when required. Both tables are based on absolute pressures.

Fortunately, experience has contributed to the design of flash tanks that work. The accompanying table gives flash tank dimensions for various steam capacities. The table is based on tanks provided with tangential inlets, flash pressure of 2 psig, and vent pipe diameters giving

steam velocities leaving on the order of 11000 fpm. Water storage space is one third tank volume.

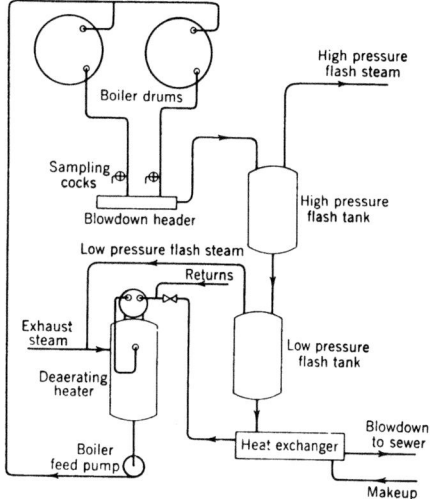

Fig 15-84. Flow diagram for two-stage flash system based on heat in continuous boiler blowdown

Assume a condensate return system returning 2750 lb of condensate per minute at 45 psia and flashing down to the pressure of a heating system at psig or, approximately, 20 psia. From Table 15-28, it is found that 4.9% of condensate flashes at this pressure. The specific volume of steam at 5 psig is 20.4 ft³/lb. Hence, 2750 × 20.4 × 4.9% = 2750 cfm of steam flashed. In order to use the flash tank table for flash steam at 2 psig, difference in specific volumes must be accounted for. The ratio is 23.9/20.4 = 1.17, and 2750/1.17 = 2350 cfm. Tank 4 provides the required dimensions to satisfy this capacity.

Table 15-25. Flash Tank Dimensions for Various Steam Capacities* (Tanks Provided with Tangential Inlet†)

Tank No.	Dia of Tank, ft	Height over Heads, ft	Flash Area, ft²	Volume, ft³	Vent Dia in.	Flashed Steam	
						cfm	lb
1	2.00	4.25	3.1	13	3	627	26
2	2.67	5.50	5.6	28	4	1058	45
3	3.33	6.67	8.7	58	5	1645	70
4	4.00	7.83	12.5	98	6	2390	101
5	4.50	8.16	15.9	116	8	4113	174
6	5.00	8.50	19.6	160	10	6658	281
7	5.50	8.75	23.8	200	12	9400	397
8	6.00	9.00	28.3	222	14	11360	480
9	7.00	10.50	38.5	400	16	15667	662
10	8.00	12.00	50.2	600	18	19192	811
11	9.00	13.50	63.6	830	20	23892	1010
12	10.00	15.00	78.5	1010	24	34858	1474

* Quantities are for 2 lb gage pressure.
† For tanks with top inlet multiply quantity of steam flash by 0.70.

Figs. 15-83 and 15-84 show typical flow diagrams for flash steam systems. Fig. 15-83 is a possible arrangement for generation of flash steam from high temperature condensate returns. Fig. 15-84 is a two stage flash system based on the heat in continuous boiler blowdown.

Sizing of Vertical Flash Tanks.—Following are data for sizing of vertical flash tanks for steam and the float traps that drain them.

To Size Flash Tank.—To obtain the proper size of a vertical flash tank the following steps should be taken:

1) Calculate maximum amount of flash steam from Fig. 15-86.

2) Find, from Fig. 15-88, the size area in which both condensation rate and flash steam quantity lie.

Example 6: A unit maintained at 80 psig condenses 3000 lb/hr of steam. Flash steam from this is to be used in another unit at 5 psig.

From Fig. 15-86 find that condensate at 80 psig produces just over 0.1 lb of flash per lb when dropped to 5 psig. So the total flash is 300 lb/hr.

From Fig. 15-88 we see that 3000 lb of condensate per hour meets the line of 300 lb flash per hour in size 4 area. So a size 4 flash vessel must be chosen for the duty.

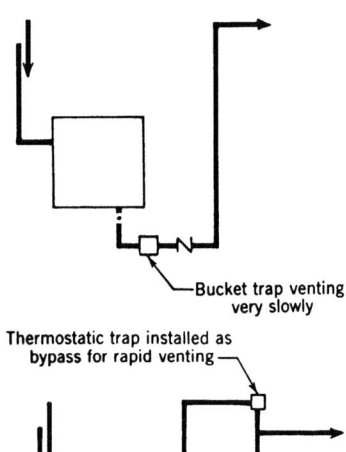

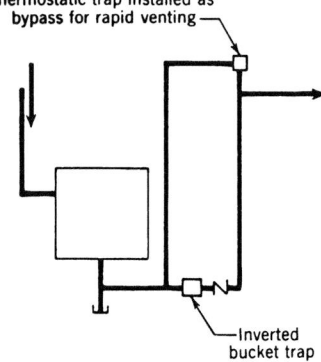

Fig 15-85. Cause and cure of airbinding

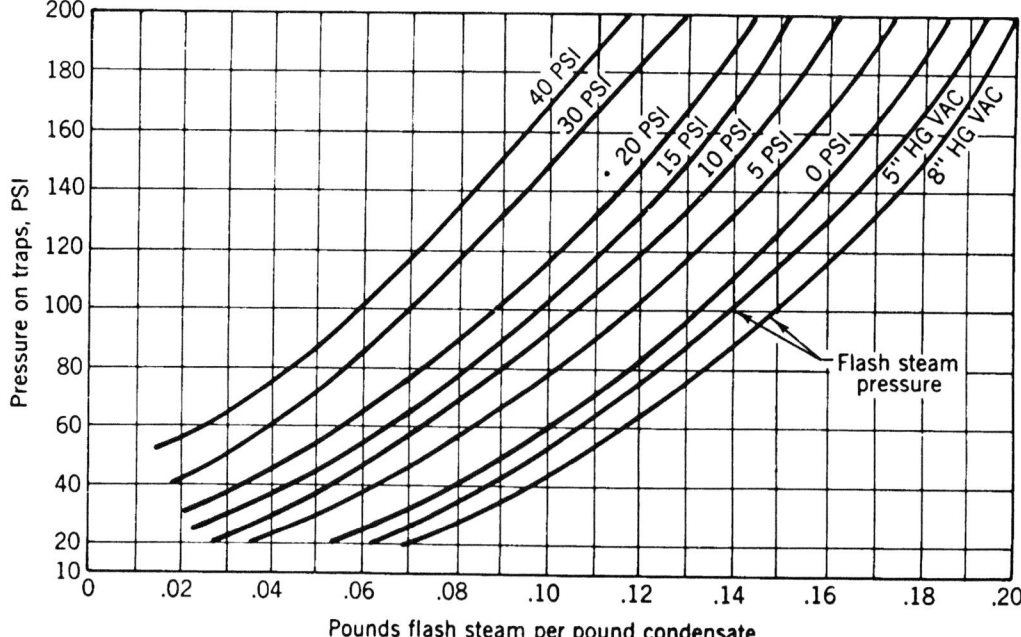

Fig 15-86. Lbs flash steam per lb condensate

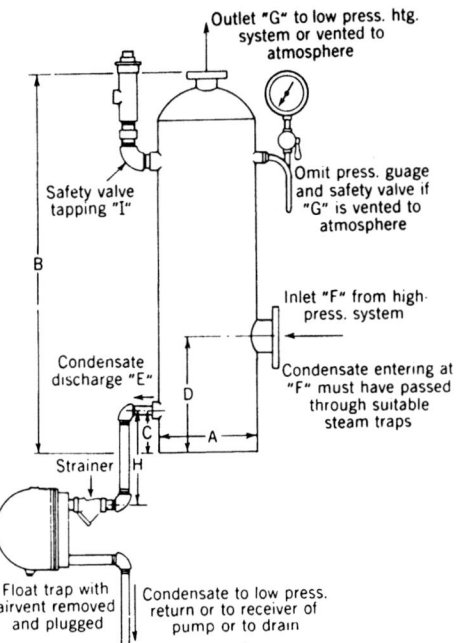

Fig 15-87. Elevation vertical flash tank

See Table 15-25 for full dimensions for each size number of vertical flash tank.

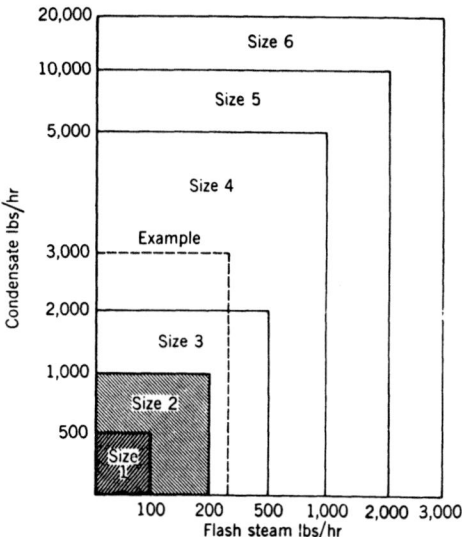

Fig 15-88. Chart for determining size number of tanks

To Size Float Trap.—Select a trap having capacity to discharge given quantity of condensate (pounds per hour) at pressure corresponding to static head H plus pressure differential (if any) between tank and return main (or atmosphere), as the case may be.

Airbinding.—Air entrapped in a steam system retards or even stops the flow of steam. This condition is known as airbinding. Lack of a proper vent in the right place may be one cause; or the trap (usually a bucket trap) may have insufficient venting capacity. A water trap may be the result of locating the trap too far from the appliance being drained. It prevents the air from reaching the point where it can be vented. Fig. 15-85 shows a common cause, and a cure, for air binding.

Table 15-26. Quantity of Heat in Flash Steam

High Pressure System			Pressure in Low Pressure System, Psia										
Saturation Pressure, psia	Saturation Temp., °F	Enthalpy of Sat. Liquid, Btu/lb	1	5	10	14.7	20	25	30	35	40	45	50
			Total Heat in Flash Steam, Btu/lb of High Pressure Condensate										
5	162.2	130.1	60.4	…	…	…	…	…	…	…	…	…	…
10	193.2	161.2	91.5	31.1	…	…	…	…	…	…	…	…	…
14.7	212.0	180.1	110.4	50.0	18.9	…	…	…	…	…	…	…	…
20	228.0	196.2	126.5	66.1	35.0	16.1	…	…	…	…	…	…	…
25	240.1	208.4	138.7	78.3	47.2	28.3	12.2	…	…	…	…	…	…
30	250.3	218.8	149.1	88.7	57.6	38.7	22.6	10.4	…	…	…	…	…
35	259.3	227.9	158.2	97.8	66.7	47.8	31.7	19.5	9.1	…	…	…	…
40	267.3	236.0	166.3	105.9	74.8	55.9	39.8	27.6	17.2	8.1	…	…	…
45	274.4	243.4	173.7	113.3	82.2	63.3	47.2	35.0	24.6	15.5	7.4	…	…
50	281.0	250.1	180.4	120.0	88.9	70.0	53.9	41.7	31.3	22.2	12.9	6.20	
55	287.1	256.3	186.6	126.2	95.1	76.2	60.1	47.9	37.5	28.4	20.3	12.9	6.2
60	292.7	262.1	192.4	132.0	100.9	82.0	65.9	53.7	43.3	34.2	26.1	18.7	12.0
65	298.0	267.5	197.8	137.4	106.3	87.4	71.3	59.1	48.7	39.6	31.5	24.1	17.4
70	302.0	272.6	202.9	142.5	111.4	92.5	76.4	64.2	53.8	44.7	36.6	29.2	22.5
75	307.6	277.4	207.7	147.3	116.2	97.3	81.2	69.0	58.6	49.5	41.4	34.0	27.3
80	312.0	282.0	212.3	151.9	120.8	101.9	85.8	73.6	63.2	54.2	46.0	38.6	31.9
85	316.3	286.4	216.7	156.3	125.2	106.3	90.2	78.0	67.6	58.5	50.4	43.0	36.3
90	320.3	290.6	220.9	160.5	129.4	110.5	94.4	82.2	71.8	62.7	54.6	47.2	40.5
95	324.1	294.6	224.9	164.5	133.4	114.5	98.4	86.2	75.8	66.7	58.6	51.2	44.5
100	327.8	298.4	228.7	168.5	137.2	118.3	102.2	90.0	79.6	70.5	62.4	55.0	48.3
110	334.8	305.7	236.0	175.6	144.5	125.6	109.5	97.3	86.9	77.8	69.7	62.3	55.6
120	341.3	312.4	242.7	182.3	151.2	132.3	116.2	104.0	93.6	84.5	76.4	69.0	62.3
130	347.3	318.8	249.1	188.7	157.6	138.7	122.6	110.4	100.0	90.9	82.8	75.4	68.7
140	353.0	324.8	255.1	194.7	163.6	144.7	128.6	116.4	106.0	96.9	88.8	81.4	74.7
150	358.4	330.5	260.8	200.4	169.3	150.4	134.3	122.1	111.7	102.6	94.5	87.1	80.4
160	363.5	335.9	266.2	205.8	174.7	155.8	139.7	127.5	117.1	108.0	99.9	92.5	85.8
170	368.4	341.1	271.4	211.0	179.8	161.0	144.9	132.7	122.3	113.2	105.1	97.7	91.0
180	373.1	346.0	276.3	215.9	184.8	165.9	149.8	137.6	127.2	118.1	110.0	102.6	95.9
190	377.5	350.8	281.1	220.7	189.6	170.7	154.6	142.4	132.0	122.9	114.8	107.4	100.7
200	381.8	355.4	285.7	225.3	194.2	175.3	159.6	147.0	136.6	127.5	119.4	112.0	105.3
225	391.8	366.1	296.4	236.0	204.9	186.0	169.9	157.7	147.3	138.2	130.1	122.7	116.0
250	401.0	376.0	306.3	245.9	214.8	195.9	179.8	167.6	157.2	148.1	140.0	132.6	125.9
275	409.4	385.2	315.5	255.1	224.0	205.1	189.0	176.8	166.4	157.3	149.2	141.8	135.1
300	417.3	393.8	324.1	263.7	232.6	213.7	197.6	185.4	175.0	165.9	157.8	150.4	143.7
350	431.7	409.7	340.0	279.6	248.5	229.6	213.5	201.3	190.9	181.8	173.7	166.3	159.6
400	444.6	424.0	354.3	293.9	262.8	243.9	227.8	215.6	205.2	196.1	188.0	180.6	173.9
450	456.3	437.2	367.5	307.1	276.0	257.1	241.0	228.8	218.4	209.3	201.2	193.8	187.1
500	467.0	449.4	379.7	319.3	288.1	269.3	253.2	241.0	230.6	221.5	213.4	206.0	199.3
1000	544.6	542.4	472.7	412.3	381.2	362.3	346.2	334.0	323.6	314.5	306.4	299.0	292.3

Table 15-27. Quantity of Heat in Flash Steam

High Pressure System			Pressure in Low Pressure System, psia											
Saturation Pressure psia	Saturation Temp., °F	Enthalpy of Sat. Liquid, Btu/lb	55	60	65	70	75	80	85	90	95	100	110
			Total Heat in Flash Steam, Btu/lb of High Pressure Condensate										
60	292.7	915.8	5.8	...	...	...	...	...	...	...	...	...	...
65	298.0	911.6	11.2	5.4	...	...	...	...	...	...	...	...	...
70	302.9	907.9	16. 3	10.5	5.1	...	...	...	...	...	...	...	...
75	307.6	904.5	21.1	15.3	9.9	4.8	...	...	...	...	...	...	...
80	312.0	901.1	25.7	19.9	14.5	9.4	4.8	...	...	...	...	...	...
85	316.3	897.8	30.1	24.3	18.9	13.8	9.0	4.4	...	...	...	...	...
90	320.3	894.7	34.3	28.5	23.1	18.0	13.2	8.6	4.20	...	...	...	...
95	324.1	891.7	383.0	32.5	27.1	22.0	17.2	12.6	8.20	4.0	...	...	...
100	327.8	888.8	42.1	36.3	30.9	25.8	21.0	16.4	12.0	7.8	3.8	...	...
110	334.8	883.2	49.4	43.6	38.2	33.1	28.3	23.7	19.3	15.1	11.1	7.3	...
120	341.3	877.9	56.1	50.3	44.9	39.8	35.0	30.4	26.0	21.8	17.8	14.0	6.7
130	347.3	872.9	62.5	56.7	51.3	46.2	41.4	36.8	32.4	28.2	24.2	20.4	13.1
140	353.0	868.2	68.5	62.7	57.3	52.2	47.4	42.8	38.4	34.2	30.2	20.4	19.1
150	358.4	863.6	74.2	68.4	63.0	57.9	53.1	48.5	44.1	39.9	35.9	26.4	24.8
160	363.5	859.2	79.6	73.8	68.4	63.3	58.5	53.9	49.5	45.3	41.3	32.1	30.2
170	365.4	854.9	84.8	79.0	73.6	68.5	63.7	59.1	54.7	50.5	46.5	42.7	35.4
180	373.2	850.8	89.7	83.9	78.5	73.4	68.6	64.0	59.6	55.4	51.4	47.6	40.3
190	377.5	846.8	94.5	88.7	83.3	78.2	73.4	68.8	64.4	60. 2	56.2	52.4	44.1
200	381.8	843.0	99.0	93.3	87.9	82.8	78.0	73.4	69.0	64.8	60.8	57.0	49.7
225	391.8	833.8	109.8	104.0	98.6	93.5	88.7	84.1	79.7	75.5	71.5	67.7	60.4
250	401.0	825.1	119.7	113.9	108.5	103.4	98.6	94.0	89.6	85.4	81.4	77.6	70.3
275	409.4	816. 9	128.9	123.1	117.7	112.6	107.8	103.2	98.8	94.6	90.6	86.8	79.5
300	417.3	809.0	137.5	131.7	126.3	121.2	116.4	111.8	107.4	103.2	99.2	95.4	88.1
350	431.7	794.2	153.4	147.6	142.2	137.1	132.3	127.7	123.3	119.1	115.1	111.3	104.0
400	444.6	780.5	167.7	161.9	156.5	151.4	146.6	142.0	137.6	133.4	129.4	125.6	118.3
450	456.3	767.4	180.9	175.1	169.7	164.6	159.8	155.2	150.8	146.6	142.6	138.8	131.5
500	467.0	755.0	193.1	187.3	181.9	176.8	172.0	167.4	163.0	158.8	154.8	151.0	143.7
1000	544.6	649.4	286.1	280.3	274.9	269.8	265.0	260.4	256.0	251.8	247.8	244.0	236.7

Table 15-28. Percent of Condensate Flash to Steam

High Pressure System			Pressure in Low Pressure System, psia										
			1	5	10	14.7	20	25	30	35	40	45	50
			Total Heat in Flash Steam, Btu/lb										
			1036	1001	982.1	970.3	960.1	952.1	945.3	939.2	933.7	928.6	924.0
		Enthalpy of Sat. Liquid, Btu/lb	Volume of Steam, ft³/lb										
			333.6	73.5	38.4	26.8	20.1	16.3	13.7	11.9	10.5	9.4	8.5
Saturation Pressure psia	Saturation Temp., °F		% of High Pressure Condensate Flashed at Low Pressure										
5	162.2	130.1	5.8	...	...	...	...	...	...	...	...	...	...
10	193.2	161.2	8.8	3.1	...	...	...	...	...	...	...	...	...
14.7	212.0	180.1	10.7	5.1	1.9	...	...	...	...	...	...	...	...
20	228.0	196.2	12.2	6.6	3.6	1.7	...	...	...	...	...	...	...
25	240.1	208.4	13.4	7.8	4.8	2.9	1.3	...	...	...	...	...	...
30	250.3	218.8	14.4	8.9	5.9	4.0	2.4	1.1	...	...	...	...	...
35	259.3	227.9	15.2	9.8	6.8	4.9	3.3	2.1	1.0	...	...	...	...
40	267.3	236.0	16.0	10.6	7.6	5.8	4.4	2.9	1.8	0.9	...	...	...
45	274.4	243.4	16.7	11.3	8.4	6.5	4.9	3.7	2.6	1.7	0.8	...	...
50	281.0	250.1	17.4	12.0	9.1	7.2	5.6	4.4	3.3	2.4	1.4	0.7	...
55	287.1	256.3	18.0	12.6	9.7	7.9	6.3	5.0	4.0	3.0	2.2	1.4	0.7
60	292.7	262.1	18.5	13.2	10.3	8.4	6.9	5.6	4.6	3.6	2.6	2.0	1.3
65	298.0	267.5	19.1	13.7	10.8	9.0	7.4	6.2	5.2	4.2	3.4	2.6	1.9
70	302.0	272.6	19.5	14.3	11.3	9.5	8.0	6.7	5.7	4.8	3.8	3.1	2.4
75	307.6	277.4	20.0	14.7	11.8	10.0	8.5	7.3	6.2	5.3	4.4	3.7	3.0
80	312.0	282.0	20.4	15.2	12.3	10.5	8.9	7.7	6.7	5.8	4.9	4.2	3.5
85	316.3	286.4	20.9	15.6	12.8	11.0	9.4	8.2	7.2	6.2	5.4	4.6	3.9
90	320.3	290.6	21.3	16.1	13.2	11.4	9.8	8.6	7.6	6.7	5.8	5.1	4.4
95	324.1	294.6	21.7	16.5	13.6	11.8	10.3	9.1	8.0	7.1	6.3	5.5	4.8
100	327.8	298.4	22.1	16.8	14.0	12.2	10.7	9.5	8.4	7.5	6.7	5.9	5.2
110	334.8	305.7	22.8	17.5	14.7	12.9	11.4	10.2	9.1	8.2	7.4	6.6	6.0
120	341.3	312.4	23.4	18.2	15.4	13.6	12.1	10.9	9.9	9.0	8.2	7.4	6.8
130	347.3	318.8	24.0	18.9	16.0	14.3	12.8	11.6	10.6	9.7	8.9	8.1	7.4
140	353.0	324.8	24.6	19.3	16.6	14.9	13.4	12.2	11.2	10.3	9.5	8.8	8.1
150	358.4	330.5	25.2	20.0	17.2	15.5	14.0	12.8	11.8	10.9	10.2	9.4	8.7
160	363.5	335.9	25.7	20.6	17.8	16.0	14.5	13.4	12.4	11.5	10.7	10.0	9.3
170	368.4	341.1	26.2	21.1	18.3	16.6	15.1	14.0	12.9	12.1	11.3	10.5	9.9
180	373.1	346.0	26.7	21.6	18.8	17.1	15.6	14.5	13.4	12.6	11.8	11.0	10.4
190	377.5	350.8	27.1	22.1	19.3	17.6	16.1	15.0	14.0	13.1	12.3	11.5	10.9
200	381.8	355.4	27.6	22.5	19.7	18.0	16.6	15.5	14.4	13.6	12.8	12.1	11.4
225	391.8	366.1	28.6	23.6	20.8	19.1	17.7	16.6	15.6	14.7	14.0	13.2	12.6
250	401.0	376.0	29.8	24.6	21.8	20.2	18.7	17.6	16.6	15.8	15.0	14.3	13.6
275	409.4	385.2	30.4	25.5	22.8	21.1	19.7	18.6	17.6	16.7	16.0	15.3	14.6
300	417.3	393.8	31.3	26.4	23.6	22.0	20.6	19.5	18.5	17.7	16.9	16.2	15.5
350	431.7	409.7	32.8	28.0	25.1	23.6	22.2	21.1	20.2	19.4	18.6	17.9	17.3
400	444.6	424.0	34.2	29.4	26.1	25.1	23.7	22.6	21.6	20.9	20.1	19.4	18.9
450	456.3	437.2	35.4	30.7	28.0	26.4	25.1	24.0	22.8	22.2	21.5	20.8	20.1
500	467.0	449.4	36.6	31.9	29.3	27.7	26.1	25.3	24.4	23.6	22.8	22.2	21.6
1000	544.6	542.4	45.6	41.2	38.8	37.2	36.0	35.1	34.2	33.5	32.8	32.2	31.7

Table 15-29. Percent of Condensate Flash to Steam

High Pressure System			Pressure in Low Pressure System, psia											
			55	60	65	70	75	80	85	90	95	100	110
			Total Heat in Flash Steam, Btu/lb										
			919.6	915.5	911.6	907.6	904.5	901.1	897.8	894.7	891.7	888.8	883.2
		Enthalpy of Sat. Liquid, Btu/lb	Volume of Steam, ft³/lb										
Saturation Pressure psia	Saturation Temp., °F		7.8	7.2	6.7	6.2	5.8	5.5	5.2	4.9	4.7	4.4	4.05
			% of High Pressure Condensate Flashed at Low Pressure										
60	292.7	1177.6	0.6	...	...	...	...	...	...	...	...	...	...
65	298.0	1179.1	1.2	0.6	...	...	...	...	...	...	...	...	...
70	302.9	1180.6	1.8	1.1	0.6	...	...	...	...	...	...	...	...
75	307.6	1181.9	2.3	1.7	1.1	0.5	...	...	...	...	...	...	...
80	312.0	1183.1	2.8	2.2	1.6	1.0	0.5	...	...	...	...	...	...
85	316.3	1184.2	3.3	2.7	2.1	1.5	1.0	0.5	...	...	...	...	...
90	320.3	1185.3	3.7	3.1	2.5	2.0	1.5	1.0	0.5	...	...	...	...
95	324.1	1186.2	4.2	3.5	3.0	2.4	1.9	1.4	0.9	0.4	...	...	...
100	327.8	1187.2	4.6	4.0	3.1	2.8	2.3	1.8	1.3	0.9	0.4	...	...
110	334.8	1188.9	5.7	4.7	4.2	3.6	3.1	2.6	2.1	1.7	1.2	0.8	
120	341.3	1190.4	6.1	5.5	4.9	4.4	3.9	3.4	2.9	2.4	2.0	1.6	0.8
130	347.3	1191.7	6.8	6.3	5.6	5.1	4.6	4.1	3.6	3.2	2.7	2.3	1.5
140	353.0	1193.0	7.5	6.8	6.3	5.7	5.2	4.7	4.3	3.8	3.4	3.0	2.2
150	358.4	1194.1	8.1	7.5	6.9	6.4	5.9	5.4	4.9	4.5	4.0	3.6	2.8
160	363.5	1195.1	8.7	8.1	7.5	7.0	6.5	6.0	5.5	5.1	4.6	4.2	3.4
170	368.4	1196.0	9.2	8.6	8.1	7.5	7.0	6.6	6.1	5.6	5.2	4.8	4.0
180	373.2	1196.9	9.8	9.2	8.6	8.1	7.6	7.1	6.6	6.2	5.8	5.4	4.6
190	377.5	1197.6	10.3	9.7	9.1	8.6	8.1	7.6	7.2	6.7	6.3	5.9	5.0
200	381.8	1198.4	10.8	10.2	9.6	9.1	8.6	8.1	7.7	7.2	6.8	6.4	5.6
225	391.8	1199.9	11.9	11.4	10.8	10.3	9.8	9.3	8.9	8.4	8.0	7.6	6.8
250	401.0	1201.1	13.0	12.4	11.9	11.4	10.9	10.4	10.0	9.5	9.1	8.7	8.2
275	409.4	1202.1	14.0	13.4	12.9	12.4	11.9	11.5	11.0	10.6	10.2	9.8	9.0
300	417.3	1202.8	15.0	14.4	13.9	13.3	12.9	12.4	12.0	11.5	11.1	10.7	10.0
350	431.7	1203.9	16.7	16.1	15.6	15.1	14.6	14.2	13.8	13.3	12.9	12.5	11.8
400	444.6	1204.5	18.2	17.7	17.2	16.7	16.2	15.8	15.3	14.9	14.5	14.1	13.4
450	456.3	1204.6	19.6	19.1	18.6	18.1	17.7	17.2	16.8	16.4	16.0	15.6	14.9
500	467.0	1204.4	21.0	20.5	20.0	19.5	19.0	18.6	18.2	17.7	17.4	17.0	16.3
1000	544.6	1191.8	31.1	30.6	30.2	29.7	29.3	28.9	28.5	28.1	27.8	27.5	27.0

Table 15-30. Dimensions of Vertical Flash Tanks

Size No.	A	B	C	D	E	F	G	I
1	4	32	5	10	1	1¼	1¼	½
2	5	32	5½	10	1½	2	1½	½
3	8	34	5½	12	1½	2½	2	½
4	10	36	5½	12	1½	3	2½	¾
5	14	36	5½	12	1½	3ᵃ	2½ᵃ	1½
6	16	42	6	14	2	6ᵃ	3ᵃ	2

ᵃ Flanged connection

Estimating Friction in Hot Water Piping.—Friction charts for cold water (*Chapter 9*) were designed using the following formulas:

$$\text{smooth} \qquad h = \frac{0.00682v^{1.75}}{d^{1.25}} \qquad (3)$$

$$\text{fairly smooth} \qquad h = \frac{0.0073v^{1.83}}{d^{1.17}} \qquad (4)$$

$$\text{fairly rough} \qquad h = \frac{0.008v^{1.92}}{d^{1.08}} \qquad (5)$$

$$\text{rough} \qquad h = \frac{0.0101v^{2}}{d} \qquad (6)$$

where h = friction loss, ft of water/ft of pipe;

v = velocity, fps;

d = inside diameter of pipe, in.

Following the same theory as outlined for cold water and using the basic formulas above, but substituting a value for the viscosity of water at 175°F instead of that for 50°F water, the following formulas result:

$$\text{smooth} \qquad h = \frac{60v^{1.75}}{d^{1.25}} \qquad (7)$$

$$\text{fairley smooth} \qquad h = \frac{72v^{1.83}}{d^{1.17}} \qquad (8)$$

$$\text{fairly rough} \qquad h = \frac{84v^{1.92}}{d^{1.08}} \qquad (9)$$

$$\text{rough} \qquad h = \frac{120v^{2}}{d} \qquad (10)$$

where h = friction loss, milinches of water/ft of pipe

v = velocity, ft/sec.

d = inside diameter of pipe, in.

Note that part of the difference between the coefficients in the two sets of formulas is due to a change in units of h.

The hot water friction charts which follow are graphical plots of Equation (7) and (10), the former being used for copper tubing. The fairly rough formula was used for iron and steel pipe so that, as the pipe ages, corrodes and scales, the friction values will be ample.

The hot water friction charts, then, show graphically the friction, as well as the heat carried, in steel pipe and Type L copper tubing when the fluid is water at 175°F temperature and with a 20°F temperature drop. The tem-perature of 175°F was chosen as meeting the requirements of both forced and gravity systems with reasonable accuracy, so that the charts are suitable for all forms of hot water heating.

Use of Charts: Use of the charts in Figs. 15-89 and 15-90 is best illustrated by examples as follows:

Example 7: A 46 ft branch steel pipe must have a loss of 3680 milinches to balance, and based on a 20°F drop, carry 150,000 Btu/hr. What size pipe and velocity are required?

Solution: The friction loss per foot of pipe must be 3680/46 = 80.0 milinches locate on Fig. 15-90 the intersection of 150 on the side scale and 80 on the lower scale, and find that a 2 inch pipe and a velocity of 1.5 ft/sec meet the conditions.

The copper tubing chart in Fig. 15-90 is used in exactly the same manner.

Use of these charts is not, of course, limited to cases where the temperature drop is 20°F, if correction is made. If the temperature drop is other than 20°F, multiply the heat carried as found on the vertical scale by a correction factor of

$$\text{actual temp. drop} \div 20$$

In other words, in the example above, if other conditions were the same but the heat to be carried were 150000 Btu/hr, based on a 15°F temperature drop, the correction factor would be $15 \div 20 = 0.75$. Therefore $150,000 \div 0.75 = 200,000$ Btu, to be found on the vertical scale. Locate the intersection of 200 on the side scale and 20 on the lower scale, and find 2½ in. pipe and velocity of 1.5 ft/sec velocity, which would be somewhat large; however, 2-inch pipe would have been too small.

Fig. 15-89 is based on the formula

$$h = \frac{60v^{1.75}}{d^{1.25}} \qquad (11)$$

where h = friction loss, milinches/ft of tube

v = velocity, ft/sec

d = actual inside diameter of pipe, inches (1 milinches of water= 0.000036 lb/in²).

Fig. 15-90 is based on the formula

$$h = \frac{84v^{1.92}}{d^{1.08}} \qquad (12)$$

where h = friction loss, milinches/ft of tube,

v = velocity in ft/sec, and

d = actual inside diameter of pipe inches (1 milinches of water 0.000036 lb/in²)

HOT WATER FRICTION CHART — TYPE L COPPER TUBING

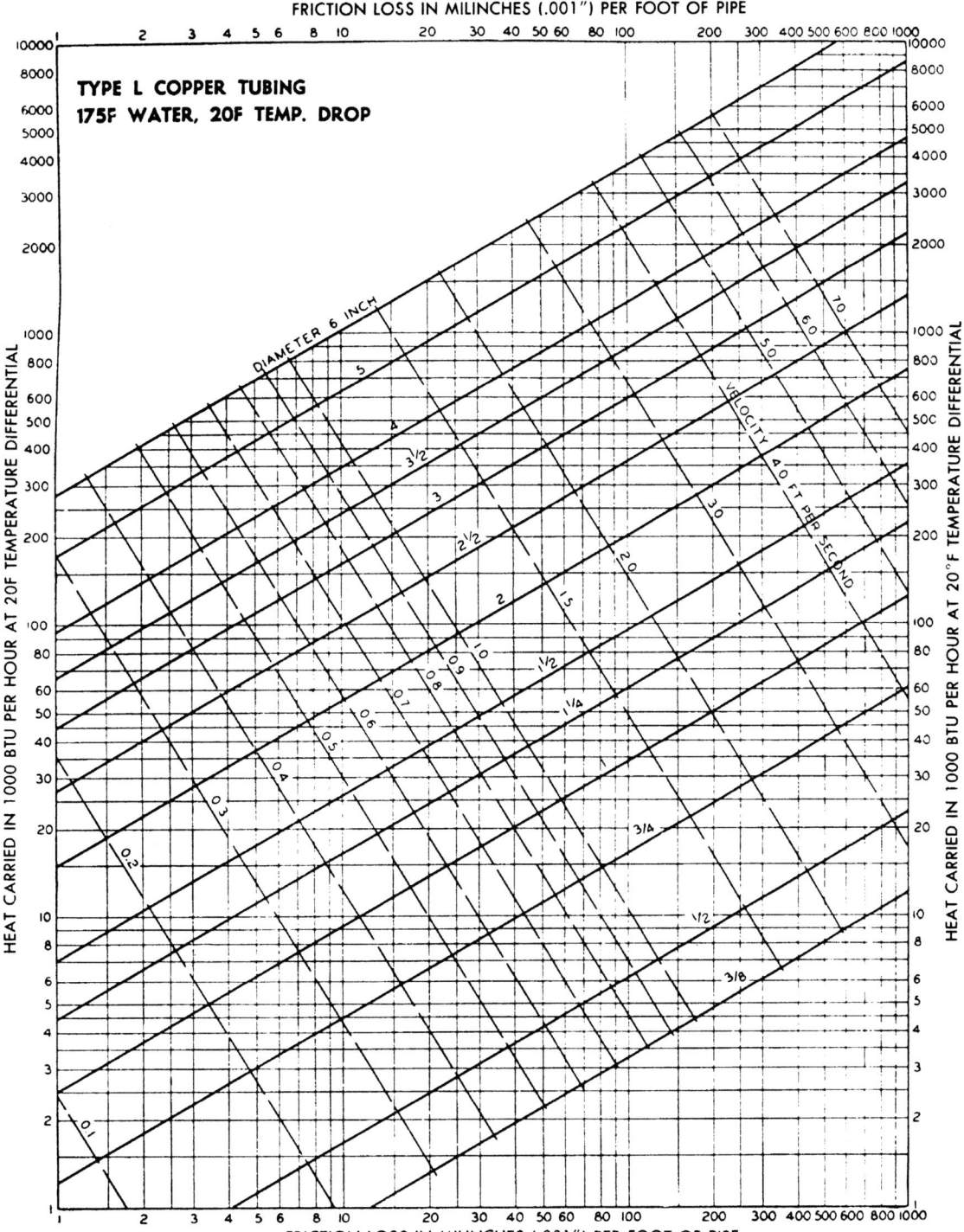

Fig 15-89. Hot water friction chart (for copper tube)

HOT WATER FRICTION CHART — IRON OR STEEL PIPE

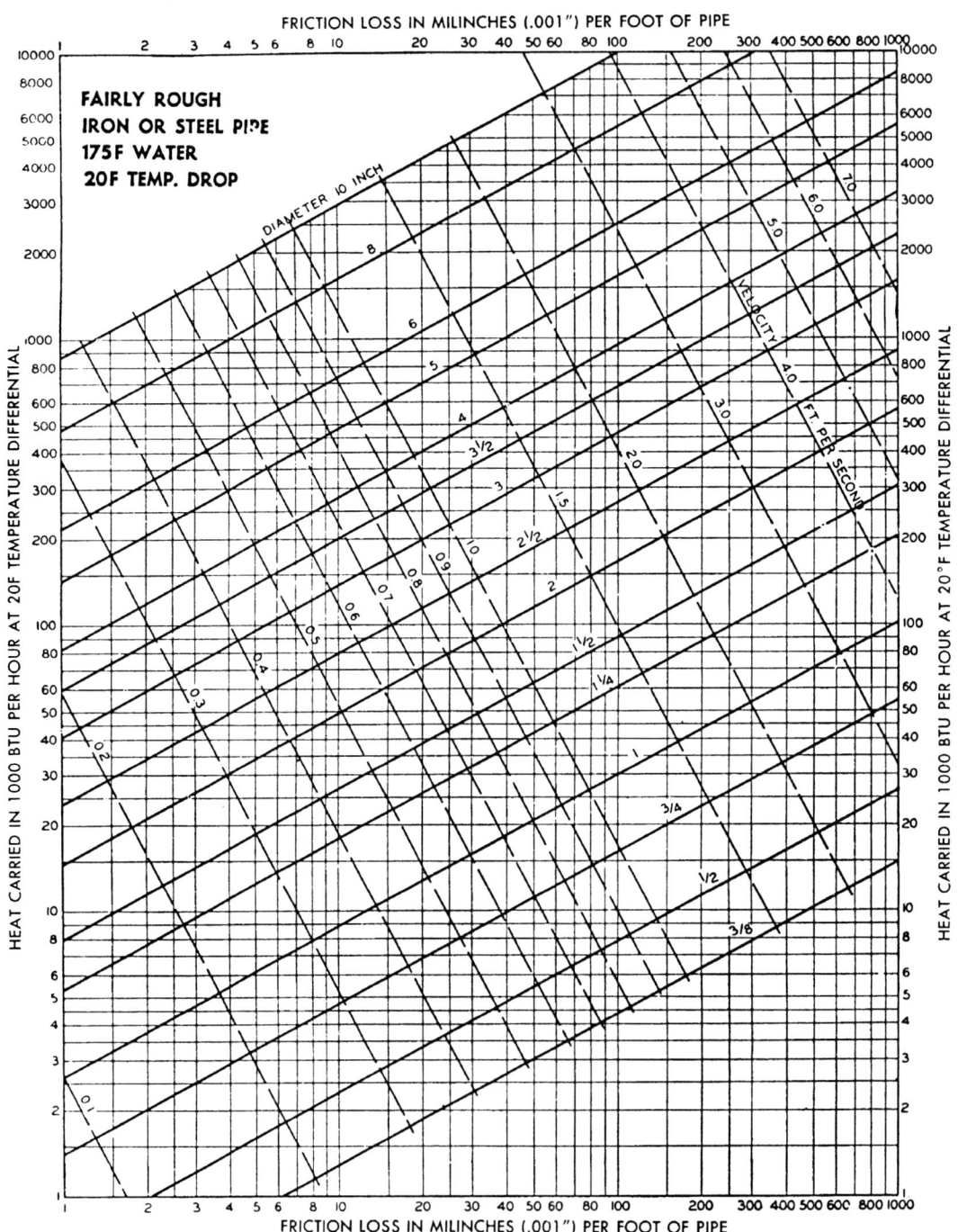

Fig 15-90. Hot water friction chart (for iron or steel tube)

Hot Water Heating Systems

Practically all new hot water heating systems are designed for forced circulation because circulation is positive, good circulation to all parts of the system is assured and system temperatures may be readily varied to suit the load. Pipe sizes may be small, and piping need not be pitched in direction of flow. Another feature of forced circulation systems (particularly valuable in residential and other small systems) is the practicability of obtaining service water from a coil in the boiler.

Although we are here concerned chiefly with forced circulation systems. The principles given can be applied to gravity circulated systems, as explained later.

Service Water Heating.— If a flow control valve is provided at the boiler outlet, boiler water temperature may be maintained continuously, so that a coil inserted in the water can be used to heat service water. The coil may be small, in which case it is used with a storage tank, or the coil may have enough surface so that water is heated to the required service temperature by one passage through the coil. This latter type is advantageous where a storage tank may overheat the basement in places. Year round operation of the system keeps the boiler warm continuously and keeps any soot deposits dry, thereby preventing corrosion of the boiler surfaces or chimney connection pipe.

In residence heating the load imposed by the instantaneous water heater may be disregarded in determining boiler size because it has such short duration. In some cases, however, the water heating load of the instantaneous heater gpm heated 100°F may be larger than the heating load and will therefore determine the boiler or burner capacity required.

Operating Water Temperature.— Systems for heating with hot water are flexible in regard to operating temperature. For instance, if the system is designed for 250°F operating temperature it is easy to use a lower temperature in spring and a setting in fall, setting the boiler thermostat at a temperature that will satisfy the service water heater, say 160°F. This lowered setting at reduced heating loads results in more continuous pump operation and more uniform space temperature than with operation at 250°F. Service water temperature of 140°F is usually satisfactory for residences.

Air Removal from System.—To facilitate movement of air to high points in the piping system for venting, it is common practice to give supply piping a slight upward pitch (¼ inch in 25 ft) in the direction of flow of water. Separation of air from water is greatest where the water is hottest, which is in the top of the boiler.

In a closed heating system, air is admitted only to replace that absorbed from the expansion tank by the water passing in and out of the tank. Absorption of air from the tank occurs mostly during the off cycle when the water cools. This cannot be prevented because water when cool, can absorb more air than when heated. Some of this absorbed air can be returned to the expansion tank if there is space at the top of the boiler (in which the water is heated) where the air released by the water may collect and be returned through a pipe to the tank. Special air release fittings are sometimes used to separate air from the circulating water and return it to the tank. If air carried by the water collects in heating units or other points from which it must be vented there will be a loss of air from the expansion tank that must be replaced either from a source of compressed air or by air admitted to the tank after the tank has been drained.

Water Flow Velocity.— The velocity of flow in any hot water heating system will be that at which the resistance of the system is equal to the head produced by the pump. In other words, when the pump is started the velocity will build up until the friction of flow in the system uses up the head produced by the pump at whatever speed the pump is run by the pump motor. The pump head produced depends on the pump design characteristics as well as speed. Performance curves are available from the pump manufacturer; these should be considered when selecting a pump. If a system is found after installation to be noisy it may be necessary to reduce pump size or size of motor in order to reduce the velocity.

Quiet operation is expected from hot water heating systems. For residential and commercial buildings it is common practice to limit velocities to 4 fps in small piping. In piping above the 2-inch diameter, this velocity may be increased somewhat. In industrial buildings, friction loss in the piping is the limiting factor, rather than noise due to flow. Noises due to expansion can be prevented by designing the piping for necessary movement.

Prevention of Freezing.—When freezing temperatures occur, there should be sufficient circulation of water to prevent lowering of water temperature at any point in the system to the freezing point. Dampers may be necessary to prevent incoming air from striking water coils before they have become heated. Complete drainage of all parts of the system should be provided if there is a shutdown long enough to cause freezing in cold weather.

Water Circulation below Mains.—Circulation of water to units placed below mains is practicable if special fittings are used to divert necessary flow to such units. Some special fittings are proprietary. Whether these fittings are required on both supply and return connections at the main will depend on the fitting design and the distance of the unit below the main. Capacities of diversion fittings and instructions for their use are available from manufacturers.

Limitation of Pressure.— In tall buildings (six stories and higher) it may be advisable to divide the system into vertical zones, not exceeding six stories each, and have each zone supplied with water from a heat exchanger. By this arrangement the pressure in the boiler can be held below the common legal limit of 30 psig for low pressure water boilers. In some states the law demands that a full time licensed engineer operate equipment if pressures are over the legal low limit. An engineer attendant is an expensive employee, and if there must also be a night attendant, the operating cost of the high pressure system may seem excessive. Beyond the hydraulic limit of 30 psig on low pressure classifications boiler prices go up and it may be difficult to obtain convectors and baseboards for the high pressure service.

System Adaptability.— The variety of piping arrangements that can be used is an attractive feature of hot water heating systems.

Commercial and industrial structures frequently require several distinct climates in their various areas. If these various climates can be obtained with heat from a single heat source, the economy of the job generally is promoted. Thus, hot water from a central boiler can be sent to rooms heated by convectors, then sent beyond the partitions of these rooms to unit heaters or to a radiant panel floor or ceiling and, still further, along the hot water main to a fan coil for warming up air for local duct distribution. Each area can be heated with the apparatus that fits it best, with hot water as the basic heat source. Fig. 15-91 illustrates this flexibility.

Use of Waste Steam Heat.—It should be noted that if waste steam is available from some plant process, economic comparisons are likely to favor the waste steam over a hot water system for these installations. However, one point that must be considered is the effect of the source or prior use of the steam on the steam itself. To explain, low pressure steam taken from an engine exhaust header is almost certain to bear traces of oil; consequently, if adequate steam purification is not accomplished before the steam enters the heating system, a gradual fouling of the piping, traps, and other components of the system is rather certain to follow. If waste steam is used in a heat exchanger to heat the circulating water in a hot water system, the troubles due to oil will not occur in the heating system. Arrangements can be made with little difficulty to remove the oil that reaches the exchanger.

Heat from District Steam System.—When district steam is available as a heat source, it may be used with a heat exchanger to transfer heat to the circulating water. Typical steam and water piping and controls between the steam service and the pump circulating hot water are shown in Fig. 15-92. If a condensate meter is used the flow meter orifice and connections are omitted.

Summer Cooling.—Summer cooling is readily incorporated in a hot water installation by providing a water chiller. It is just as easy to pump cold water in summer as it is to pump hot water in winter. This arrangement is the basis of some notably efficient all year designs with fan coil cabinets strategically located.

However, chilled water is of no practical value when it is circulated through convectors, baseboards, or radiant panels. In convectors and baseboard, heat exchange is insignificant unless the ambient air is forced to circulate over the cold surfaces. For the radiant panels, surface condensation is a hazard in most areas of the country, although in some parts of the southwest United States, where relative humidities vary between 1.5 and 25% cool panels probably would be a suitable means of cooling.

In general, some form of auxiliary cooling is necessary whenever fan coil apparatus is not a part of the area heating scheme.

Types of Water Heating Systems.—The designations of the various types of hot water heating systems are based on the piping arrangement. Whether the final heat emitter is a convector, radiant panel, fan coil unit or baseboard, the hot water system that serves it is designated by one of the following:

One Pipe Series System: This is one in which the water flows through each of the heat-emitting units in turn before it returns to the boiler.

Care must be exercised in sizing the successive heat emitting units to compensate for the progressively cooler water. The practice of sizing the whole loop on an average water temperature has given rise to overheating in some areas and under heating in others. For best results, the heating demands on each unit should be determined accurately, and the heating surface apportioned accordingly. Fig. 15-93 illustrates this system.

Because of its simplicity, a series layout can be very appropriate and useful as a branch or zone when incorporated in an installation of multiple requirements.

One-Pipe Diversion System: This system is one in which the water is diverted from the main to the heat-emitting unit, and then returns to the main for eventual reheating in the boiler. Fig. 15-94 illustrates this system.

As in the series system, it is necessary to increase the size of the heating units successively to compensate for lower water temperatures toward the end of the circuit.

Two-Pipe Direct Return: This is an arrangement of the piping that causes each heat emitter to discharge the cooled water back to the boiler by the shortest possible route. To use this system for balanced heating, it is necessary to control the water that flows through each heating unit circuit, otherwise short circuiting takes place and some areas will be overheated, others under heated. The use of balancing cocks is recommended, a cock being placed on the return from each unit and set to permit the proper flow for that unit and no other. This system is illustrated in Fig. 15-95.

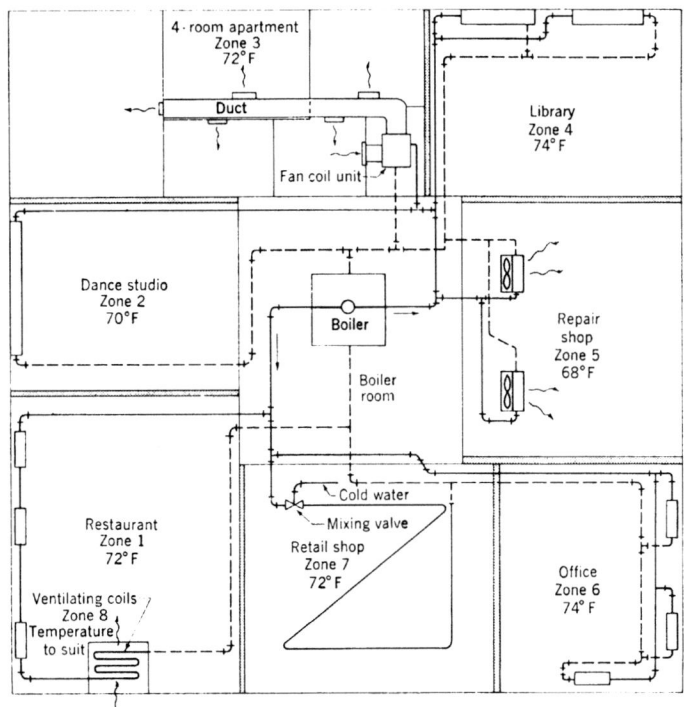

Fig 15-91. Application of hot water system for production of different space requirements: zone 1 convectors, 1 pipe series loop; zone 2 baseboard, single pipe; zone 3 fan coil duct system; zone 4 fan coil room units; zone 5 unit heaters; zone 6 convectors, 2 pipe direct return; zone 7 panel ceiling; zone 8 fan coil, for heating outdoor air for restaurant

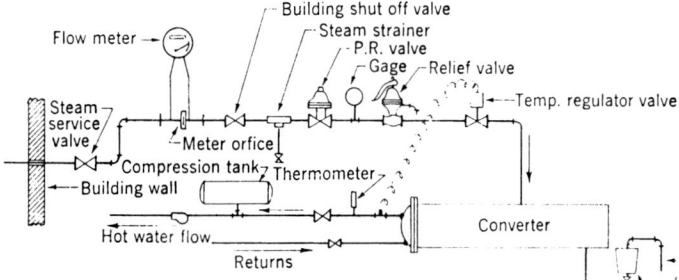

Fig 15-92. Use of district steam as a heat source

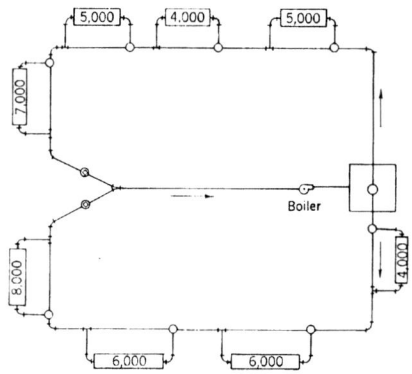

Fig 15-93. One pipe diversion loop system

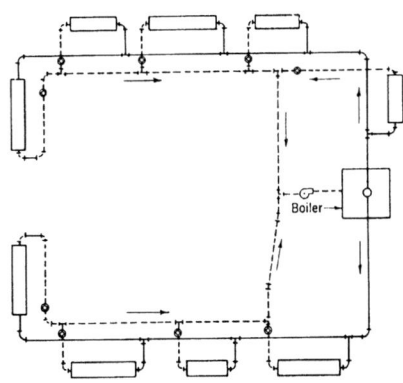

Fig 15-94. Two pipe direct return system

Two pipe reversed return: This design endeavors to make circuits to all heat emitters of equal length, so that the pipe friction to and from each unit is approximately the same. This system is illustrated in Fig. 15-96.

This system is balanced by replacing the cocks of a direct return arrangement with a return main that is calculated to make all of the heat emitter circuits of equal length, and consequently of equal friction. This scheme has the advantage of eliminating the individual balance cocks, and the disadvantage of increasing the amount of pipe that must be used on a job.

For the large installations, as a general rule, either (c) or (d) is common; however in many cases where multiple zoning is involved, individual zones in the form of (a) or (b) may be found to best suit the requirements of a particular zone. In other words, there are four forms of hot water circulation available to be used as circumstances indicate. This is another illustration of the flexibility characteristic of hot water heating.

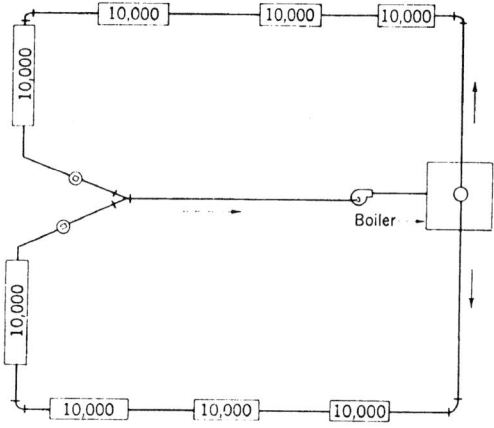

Fig 15-95. Details of main supply riser drip

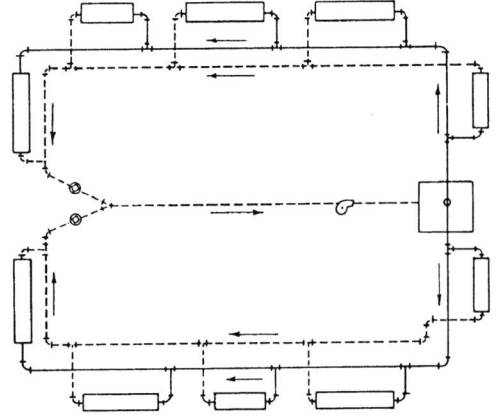

Fig 15-96. Two pipe reversed return system

Design Recommendations for Hot Water Systems

Water Velocity.—Water velocity should be limited in order to prevent noise in piping and to keep friction loss within acceptable limits. Generally accepted limits for velocity are 4 to 10 fps with 4 fps applying to pipe up to 2 inches diameter and 10 fps to pipe of 6 inches and over. The 4 fps limitation should be observed for residences and commercial space such as offices. Friction loss, rather than noise, will be a limiting factor in industrial buildings because it affects the size of pump required and the cost of pumping. Common friction loss design values are 100 to 500 milinches/ft of pipe (0.83 to 4.1 ft of head per 100 ft of pipe).

Pump Location.—Place the pump to draw water from the boiler for large installations, for cases with high pumping heads, and for those cases where the radiation is even with or below the top of the boiler. When the radiation is below the boiler or at the same elevation, and the boiler is on the suction side of the pump, the pressure on the system piping is increased, a condition that helps a great deal in venting. Another benefit is less likelihood of pump cavitation, since the air separates mainly in the boiler, rather than later in the pump.

For high head pumping, and for buildings more than three stories high, pumping out of the boiler becomes practically obligatory to avoid opening of the relief valves on the boiler, and to escape some occurrence of boiling at the high points. Why this is so is made clear in the above discussion of effect of pump location on system performance.

Air Venting.—In designing a system, be careful to prevent air entry and pocketing, and make certain that air is vented. Venting is essential at the high points of the circuit, and is recommended additionally at the boiler outlet. An air separator, Fig. 15-97, is effective since the separation and removal of the air takes place in an area of high water temperature, and where separation probably is easiest.

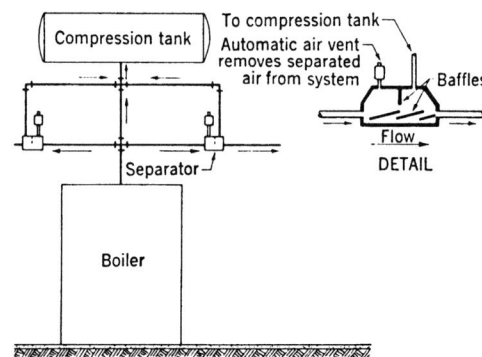

Fig 15-97. Use of air separators for air removal

Two air separators are shown in Fig. 15-97 to suggest a technique for handling two circuits with flow in opposite directions. One separator would usually suffice, if it were placed in the piping at a point before piping is divided into two circuits.

To avoid air pockets, use eccentric reducers wherever the horizontal piping changes size. Fig. 15-98 illustrates this point.

Balancing Circuits.—Use adjustable cocks to balance water flow through circuits of unequal loading whenever these circuits merge into a common main. Otherwise the circuit of lesser resistance will obtain too large a share of the circulating water.

Filling Pressure.—In filling a low pressure system with cold water, the pressure should not exceed 19 psig because the expansion of the water in being heated in the boiler from, for instance, 50 to 200°F would increase the pressure approximately 10 psi, which added to the fill pressure of 19 psig, would almost open the relief valve, set at 30 psig. A slight increase in pressure due to pump operation would open the relief valve.

A commonly used cold fill pressure is 12 psig, but this may not be enough to fill a high system. When pressures exceed 30 psi, the system is no longer low pressure and, consequently, the boiler and equipment must be suitable for the more severe conditions.

Preventing Backflow.—If two or more pumps discharge into a common header, a check valve or flow control valve must be used in each discharge to prevent backflow into nonoperating circuits or to prevent unauthorized operation of any circuit. This is illustrated in Fig. 15-99.

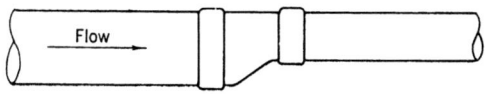

Fig 15-98. Details of main supply riser drip

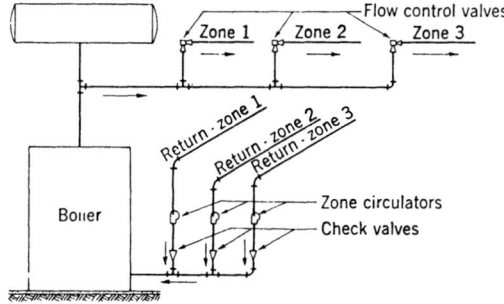

Fig 15-99. Schematic diagram shows proper use of both check valves and flow control valves

Connecting Returns to Boiler.—Satisfactory ways for connecting a return to the boiler are illustrated in Fig. 15-103.

In general, when making boiler connections to both inlet and outlet, the paths of flow through the boiler

should be equalized. Complaints of inadequate capacity sometimes are due to an incorrect arrangement of boiler connections, the trouble being that the water finds a short route to the outlet nozzle and thus leaves the boiler at less than the intended temperature. This situation is aggravated if the water temperature control is mounted in a hot spot that is out of the path of water circulation and can consequently shut down the firing equipment prematurely. When the boiler and system appear to be of adequate capacity but the building occupants are dissatisfied, the trouble may be the water flow pattern in the boiler.

Locating the Circulating Pump.—The place where the compression tank is connected into the system is the one point on the whole circuit where pressure remains the same when the pump begins to operate. When the pump is started, pressure from the pump discharge to the tank rises above system static pressure, and pressure from the pump suction to the tank falls below. The amount of rise and fall is a maximum at the pump and decreases in each direction, finally disappearing at the point of connection to the expansion tank. (The algebraic sum of the rise and fall at the pump is the pump head, which equals total system friction.) Thus, location of pump and tank determines how system pressures will vary through the circuit.

The compression tank is most commonly located above the boiler, connected to the supply piping. Although not critical in small residential systems, it is recommended that it pump out of the boiler. With this arrangement, the entire circuit, from the pump discharge to the boiler, is under positive pressure, reducing the possibility at any point in the circuit, but especially at the highest elevations, that pressure will fall below saturation pressure and cause the hot water to boil. Lack of positive pressure in the system can also prevent proper venting of air. In addition, if pumping into the boiler is desirable for other reasons, other factors should be checked to guarantee that pressures in the boiler will not exceed the setting of the pressure relief valve.

Sizing the Expansion Tank.—The simplest expansion tank is an open tank set sufficiently above the highest point in the system to produce a head of at least 4 ft to ensure adequate venting. Adding a few more feet of head may be desirable to prevent boiling. In addition, if the effect of pump location is to reduce system pressure between tank and pump suction, additional head may be required to offset this drop. Capacity can be calculated from the numerator of the formula below. It allows for the offsetting effect of pipe expansion on excess water volume when system temperature rises.

$$V_t = \frac{(0.00041t - 0.0466)V_s}{\left(\dfrac{P_a}{P_f} - \dfrac{P_a}{P_o}\right)}$$

where V_t = minimum volume of tank, gal

V_s = system volume, gal

t = maximum average operating temperature, °F

P_a = pressure in tank when water first enters, feet of water, absolute (usually atmospheric = 34 ft)

P_f = initial fill or minimum pressure at tank, ft of water, absolute

P_o = maximum operating pressure at tank, ft of water, absolute.

Compression tanks may be sized by the following ASME formula applicable for operating temperatures between 160°F and 280°F.

System volume can be found from water capacities of boilers and heat consuming apparatus in manufacturers catalogs and from tables of dimensional and capacity data for piping elsewhere in this volume.

The higher the compression tank is situated in the system, the smaller is *minimum pressure at the tank P_f*, hence the smaller the tank. For this reason, compression tanks are often located in the attic.

Two graphical methods for sizing compression tanks are given elsewhere in this section.

Compressed Air to Reduce Tank Size.—By injecting air under pressure into the compression tank, it is possible to economize on tank size. This is worthwhile if compressed air is available or if a hand pump can be kept conveniently in the area. Tank must be equipped with an air fill valve, a pressure gage, and a water column to allow an intelligent estimate of conditions within the tank at all times.

To determine tank size using compressed air, the value of P_a in the formula above should reflect the addition of air. Thus, if 5 psig air is used, P_a = 34 + 5(2.31) = 45.55 feet of water, absolute.

Piping Details.— The following suggestions pertain to the layout of piping for a hot water heating system:

1) When a run of piping must cross a beam or other obstruction at a conflicting level, route the piping under the beam, not over it. Fig. 15-100 shows how this idea prevents the formation of an air pocket at this point.

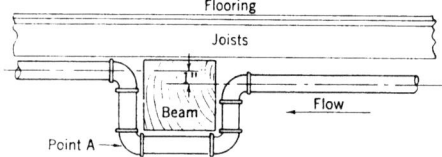

Fig 15-100. Method of crossing a beam

If the pipe crosses over the beam, that point becomes a high point on the run and provides a collecting place for bubbles of air. Trouble will be almost certain to develop eventually unless the over-the-beam arrangement is vented at that point.

2) Do not connect the supply pipe to the upper part of a radiator when the supply originates at or under the floor, because air, accumulating in the top of the radiation, would gradually choke off circulation. Making both supply and return connections low does not stop air from accumulating at the top, but it does keep most of the radiation warm. Fig. 15-101 illustrates this type of installation.

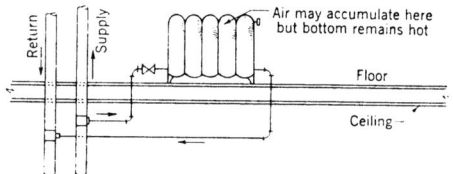

Fig 15-101. Preferred connection when radiation is above supply and return

3) When the radiation is below the main, be careful to connect the supply into the top of the radiation, the return to the bottom. This permits air to escape upwards to the main. This path of flow also allows the gradually cooling water to sink to the bottom of the radiation, doing all the heating possible before returning to the main above. See Fig. 15-102.

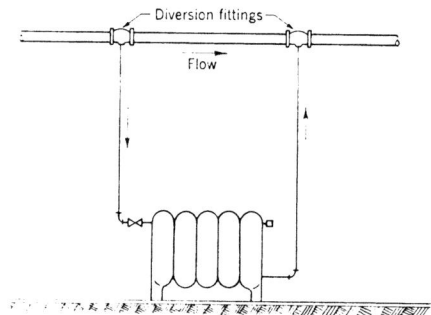

Fig 15-102. Preferred connection when radiation is below supply and return

4) When unit heaters are supplied with hot water from a main below the heaters, each must carry its own automatic vent. Otherwise the heater becomes a natural air pocket.

5) When changing the size of horizontal mains use eccentric reducers as shown in Fig. 15-98 in order to cause the top of the pipe to pitch smoothly to the desired high point. Concentric reducers create air pockets.

6) In making up screwed pipe joints, use pipe compound on the male threads only. This keeps the compound from being pushed into the pipe where it can be picked up by the circulating water and deposited in undesirable locations.

7) Experience indicates that upside down placement of valves is best avoided. A valve in this position develops leaks and needs service earlier than when it is installed upright.

8) A temperature pressure relief valve should be so connected that it is in intimate contact with the hottest water in the boiler. It should not be in a spot where incrustation can form over the relief orifice, A valve mounted several inches above the boiler does not register true temperatures of the boiler water and may not open when it should. Valves that must be so mounted can be obtained with a bulb that extends into the boiler water, and therefore are desirable from a safety viewpoint.

Design of Piping Systems for Hot Water Heating.—

To determine the pipe or tube sizes required in the various sections of a hot water heating system:

1) Calculate hourly heat loss of the structure for the indoor and outdoor design temperatures currently used in the locality.

2) Determine the sizes of heating units required to deliver the calculated heat loss at the selected system water temperature. Supply water temperatures in forced circulation systems are usually within the range of 180°F to 250°F. Temperature drop is usually assumed to be 20°F. Output of heating units are obtained from manufacturer catalogs.

3) Select the best locations for heating units to provide proper heating of the space. Lay out the piping from the boiler to all heating units so that the length of all piping can be measured for both supply and return.

4) Measure total length of the piping circuit that appears to be the longest, from the boiler to the farthest heating unit and back to the boiler. Add 50% as an allowance for fitting friction loss in terms of length. The total will be the length used to determine the friction loss per foot or per 100 ft that will be the basis for preliminary pipe sizes of all sections of the system.

Determine rate of flow in gpm that must be maintained at the pump.

$$gpm = \frac{\text{hourly heat loss of structure, Btu/hr}}{\text{temperature drop} \times 60 \times 8.33}$$

(8.33 lb is the weight of one gallon of water; 60 is the number of minutes per hour.) If a temperature drop of 20°F is chosen, the denominator becomes $20 \times 8.33 \times 60 = 9996$, which may be taken as 10,000. For example, if the structure heat loss is 104,000 Btu/hr, and system temperature drop is selected as 20°F, the required pumping rate is $104,000/10,000 = 10.4$ gpm.

5) Select pump from a manufacturers catalog that will deliver water at the required rate, noting permissible head in feet of water at pump outlet. Divide permissible head by equivalent length of pipe, as found in Step 4, and multiply the result by (a) 100, to obtain permissible loss in feet per 100 ft of pipe, or by (b) 12,000, to obtain permissible loss in milinches per ft of pipe. If the pump selected will deliver 10.4 gpm at a head of 6.6 ft and total equivalent length of pipe is 230 ft, the design friction loss is $(6.6/230)(100) = 2.87$ ft per 100 ft or $(6.6/230)(12,000) = 344$ milinches per foot.

6) Make a table, entering each section of the circuit previously selected as the longest. Then determine pipe size. Two hot water friction charts, for Type L copper tubing and iron or steel pipe, are given in Figs. 15-89 and 15-90. One enters the chart for each section of piping to be sized with the heat carried in that section of piping, in Btu/hr, as determined from the piping layout in Step 3, selecting that commercial pipe size whose friction loss per foot is closest to the permissible drop per foot selected in Step 6. Note velocity. If excessive, choose a larger pipe size. The partially completed table should then show pipe section (with convenient letter designations), heat carried in that section, pipe size, friction loss per foot based on pipe size selected, and velocity.

7) Multiply friction loss per foot for each section by actual length of section in feet and enter friction loss of pipe for that section of table.

8) Determine the exact fittings required for each section of pipe tabulated in Step 7 and find the friction loss for each from Tables 15-31 and 15-34. Table 15-31 gives pressure drops through 90° screwed elbows for various nominal pipe sizes and velocities from 1 to 20 fps. Table 15-34 gives losses through other fittings in terms of the number of 90° elbows. Thus from Table 15-34 pressure drop through a 45° screwed elbow is 0.5 of 90° elbow, and from Table 15-31 the pressure drop for a 1½-inch elbow at 3 fps is 1400 milinches. Therefore, pressure drop through a 1½ inch, 45° screwed elbow is $1400 \times 0.5 = 700$ milinches. These values are very approximate. For pipe fittings below 2 inches diameter, these values may vary above and below the values given by 40%, depending on construction and installation details. Enter fittings losses in their appropriate sections of the table.

9) Total the straight pipe and fittings friction losses to obtain friction loss for each section of piping. Total the friction losses for all sections to obtain total friction loss against which the pump will operate.

If total friction loss for the circuit exceeds the head that the pump can handle, an inspection of the pipe sizes tabulated may show that, by some changes in pipe size, the head can be reduced to an acceptable value. If total friction loss is too small, it may be desirable to reduce the pipe sizes in some sections.

Water velocity limitations as previously given in this chapter should be followed.

Table 15-31. Pressure Drop Through 90° Screwed Elbow

Nominal Pipe Size. in	Water Velocity, fps										
	K	1	2	3	4	5	6	.7	8	9	10
	Pressure Drop Through 90° Elbow, Milinches										
½	182	182	728	1,640	2,910	4,550	6,550	8,920	11,600	14,700	18,200
¾	176	176	704	1,580	2,820	4,400	6,340	8,620	11,300	14,300	17,600
1	170	170	680	1,530	2,720	4,250	6,120	8,330	10,900	13,800	17,000
1¼	162	162	648	1,460	2,590	4,050	5,830	7,940	10,400	13,100	16,200
1½	156	156	624	1,400	2,500	3,900	5,620	7,640	9,980	12,600	15,600
2	147	147	588	1,320	2,350	3,680	5,290	7,203	9,410	11,900	14,700
2½	140	140	560	1,260	2,240	3,500	5,040	6,860	8,960	11,300	14,000
3	132	132	528	1,190	2,110	3,300	4,750	6,470	8,450	10,700	13,200
3½	127	127	508	1,140	2,030	3,180	4,570	6,220	8,130	10,300	12,700
4	120	120	480	1,080	1,920	3,000	4,320	5,880	7,680	9,720	12,000
5	111	111	444	999	1,780	2,780	4,000	5,440	7,100	8,990	11,100
6	103	103	412	927	1,650	2,580	3,710	5,050	6,590	8,340	10,300
8	90	90	360	810	1,440	2,250	3,240	4,410	5,760	7,290	9,000
10	82	82	328	738	1,310	2,050	2,950	4,020	5,250	6,640	8,200
12	78	78	312	702	1,250	1,950	2,810	3,820	4,990	6,320	7,800

Table 15-32. Sizing Circuit to Radiator No. 5, Example 8

1	2	3	4	5	6	7	8	9	10	11	12
Section Designa-tion	Actual Length ft	MBH Carried	Pipe Size	Friction, Milinches per ft	Veloc ity, fps	Loss in Pipe, Milinches (Col. 2 × Col. 5)	Fittings	Equiv-alent Elbows	Loss in one Elbow, milinches	Loss through Fittings, milinches (Col. 9 × Col. 10)	Loss through Section, Milinches (Col. 7 Plus Col. 11)
A–B	15	52	1	300	2	4500	1-90° elbow tee	2	680	1100	5600
B–C	16	44	1	200	2	3200	1-90° elbow tee	2	680	1100	4300
C–D	13	32	¾	350	2	4550	1-tee	1	704	420	4970
D–E	14	20	½	600	2	8400	1-tee	1	728	440	8840
E–F	16	12	½	200	1	3200	1-90° ell, 6-90° ells, 45° ell	1	182	180	3380
F–G	20	12	½	200	1	4000	Radiator valve, tee	16	182	2800	6800
G–L	5	52	1	300	2	1500	90° elbow,1 cock	1	680	680	2180
L–M	12	52	1	300	2	3600	1–Y	1	680	680	4280
M–N	38	104	1¼	275	2	10450	2–90° ells, 2–90° ells	2	648	1300	11750
N–A	4	104	1¼	275	2	1100	2-tees flow valve boiler	21	648	1200	23600
Total	153										65700

Table 15-33. Sizing Circuit to Radiator No. 1, Example 8

1	2	3	4	5	6	7	8	9	10	11	12
Section	Btu/hr	Flow	Pipe size, in.	Velocity fps	Loss, milli-inch/ft	Fittings	Equiva-lent Elbows	Total Fitting Loss	Measured Pipe, ft	Total Equiv. Pipe ft	Total Loss millinches
A–B	52000	5.2	1	1.9	250	1–90° elbow, 1–tee	3	7.2	15	22.2	5550
B–H	8000	0.8	½	0.84	105	1–tee, 1–45° ell, 4–90° ell,1–rad valve, 1–rad	11.7	13.	20	33	3460
H–1	8000	0.8	½	0.84	105	1–90° ell, 1–tee	3	3.3	13	16.3	1710
I–J	20000	2	½	2.05	550	1–tee	2	2.8	14	16.8	9250
J–K	32000	3.2	¾	1.88	330	1–tee	2	3.6	16	19.6	6480
K–G	40000	4	¾	2.4	500	1–90° elbow	1	1.9	16	17.9	8950
G–L	52000	5.2	1	1.9	250	1 –90° elbow	1	2	5	7.4	1850
L–M	52000	5.2	1	1.9	250	1 –cock, 1–Y	1.7	4.1	12	16.1	4020
M–N	104000	10.4	1 ¼	2.3	240	2–90° elbow	2	6.6	38	44.6	10,700
N–A	104000	10.4	1 ¼	2.3	240	2–90° elbow, 2–tees flow valve boiler	29	95	4	99	23,800
Totals								145.3	153	295.9	75770 = 6.3 ft

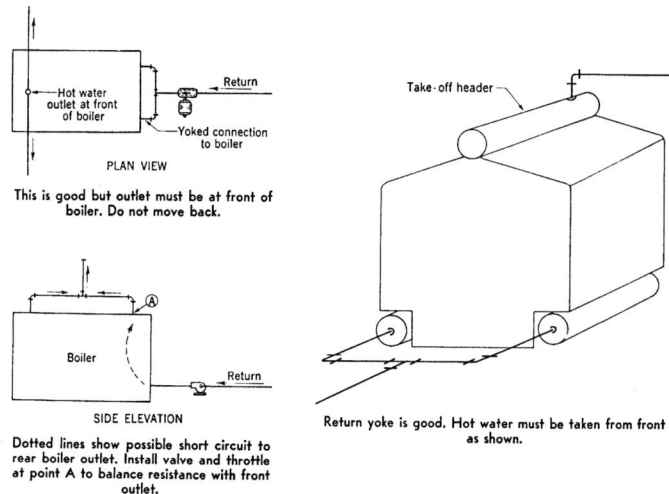

Fig 15-103. Connecting a return line to boiler

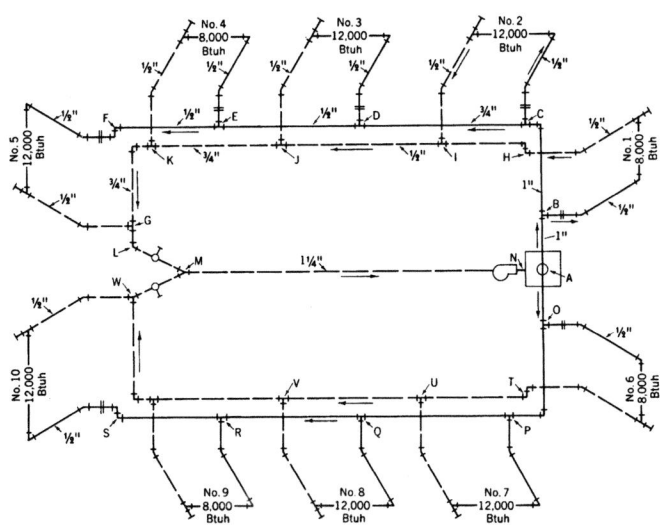

Fig 15-104. Layout for Two-pipe reversed return hot water heating system with forced circulation (For Example 8)

Table 15-34. Pressure Drop Through Fittings

Fitting	Pressure Drop in Equivalent 90° elbows	Fitting	Pressure Drop in Equivalent 90° Elbows
90° elbow, screwed	1	90° welding elbows and smooth bends: (R = bend radius, d = pipe diameter)	0.5
90° elbow, flanged	0.8	R/d = 1½	0.4
45° elbow, screwed	0.5	R/d = 2	0.3
45° elbow, flanged	0.4	R/d = 4	0.3
180° open return bend, screwed	1.0	R/d = 6	0.3
180° close return bend, screwed	2.0	R/d = 8	0.4
180° close return bend, flanged	1.5	Gate valve, full open	0.3
Tee (flow through side), screwed	2.0	Globe valve, full open	11
Tee (flow through side), flanged	1.5	Angle valve, full open	6
Tee (flow through run), screwed	0.6	Angle radiator valve, full open	3
Tee (flow through run), flanged	0.5	Swing check valve, full open	3
		Radiator or convector	4
		Boiler	4

Piping Design for Two Pipe Reversed Return System.—The procedure outlined for determining pipe sizes is illustrated in the following Example 8.

Example 8: Select pipe sizes for two-pipe forced circulation reversed return hot water heating system for a structure having a design heat loss of 104,000 Btu/hr. There are 10 radiators so arranged that the system may be laid out in two symmetrical equal circuits, as shown in Fig. 15-104, each having a total load of 52,000 Btu/hr.

Circuit to Radiator No. 5: The piping to Radiator No. 5 is selected as the longest circuit. Table 15-32 is constructed to facilitate its sizing. Section designations, corresponding to the letter symbols in Fig. 15-104, are listed in Column 1 and their actual lengths in Column 2. The amount of radiation carried by each section, in thousands of Btu, are set down in column 3, having been taken from Fig. 15-104.

Total measured length of the circuit (Column 2) is 153 ft. It is common practice to increase actual length by 50% for preliminary sizing purposes. Therefore, it is assumed that equivalent length is $153 \times 1.5 = 230$ ft.

If a 20°F drop is selected, flow through the pump will be, approximately, $104,000/10,000 = 10.4$ gpm. From catalog data, it is found that a 10.4 gpm capacity will operate against a head of 6.6 ft of water. Since the circuit is 230 ft, permissible friction loss would average $(6.6/230)(12,000) = 344$ milinches per ft.

For each section of pipe, Table 15-32, the friction chart is entered at the MBH value in Column 3 and a pipe size selected as close to 344 milinches per ft pressure drop as possible. In each case actual friction drop for the pipe selected is recorded in Column 5 and the water velocity in feet per second to the nearest integer recorded in Column 6.

Losses in straight pipe sections are calculated by multiplying actual pipe length, column 2, by friction per foot, Column 5, and the product recorded in Column 7.

The entire circuit, Fig. 15-104, is then carefully examined and the fittings in each section recorded in Column 8. The equivalent number of 90° elbows, from Table 15-34, are set down in column 9 and the loss per elbow, from Table 15-31, recorded in Column 10. Loss through fittings is the product of columns 9 and 10, recorded in Column 11.

Total loss in each section is the sum of straight piping loss, Column 7, and loss through fittings, Column 11. Their sum is recorded in column 12. Column 12 is summed up, giving the approximate actual friction loss (in Table 15-34) of 65,700 milinches, which, when divided by 12,000, is 5.5 ft.

The total of 5.5 ft of head compares to 6.6 ft against which the pump selected must work in order to produce the proper flow. The discrepancy reflects the very rough approximations that were made at the beginning of the calculations and the very approximate nature of all the

data, especially for loss through fittings, valves and equipment. An equivalent resistance of 11 elbows was assigned to the flow valve, assumed full open. Closing it partially will bring the resistance of the circuit up to the required amount if, indeed, the system, as installed, has the calculated resistance.

Had the calculated resistance of the circuit been significantly greater than 6.6 ft, it would have been necessary to increase some of the pipe sizes, thereby reducing the friction head to the allowable amount.

Circuit to Radiator No.1: Table 15-33 contains the working data for sizing the circuit to Radiator No. 1 by a slightly different method. Resistance of fittings are recorded in equivalent feet of pipe from data. Equivalent length is added to actual pipe length for each section and the sum multiplied by the friction loss per foot as found in the friction charts, giving friction loss for that section.

Note that the friction loss for the circuit is 6.32 ft. Since the friction loss in the circuit to Radiator No. 5 will be adjusted to approximately 6.6 ft the difference may be eliminated by addition of a square head cock in Section H-1 for achieving balance, or the angle valve at Radiator No.1 can be partially closed. However, such a close balance is not necessary in a system with a reversed return.

Final Check of Pipe Sizes.— The friction losses of all remaining radiator circuits should be obtained and tabulated as for Radiators No.1 and No. 5 so that, if necessary, corrections can be made by changing some pipe sizes or by adding adjustable cocks, orifices, or valves to obtain a balanced flow through all circuits.

Piping Design for Two-Pipe Direct Return System

In a two-pipe direct return system, the procedure for selecting pipe sizes is the same as for a reversed return system. To the measured length of the longest circuit is added 50% of the length to obtain the equivalent length. For a 20°F temperature drop, the water flow through the pump is found by dividing the heat loss of the structure by 10,000. A pump is selected from a manufacturers catalog and the available head is noted. The available head is divided by the equivalent length of the circuit to obtain a design unit friction loss for the system.

Preliminary pipe sizes are found in the friction chart for hot water and listed for all sections of the circuit as was done in Table 15-34 for the reversed return system in Example 8. The actual unit friction loss per foot, the velocity, and the total friction loss for the longest circuit are tabulated. If the total friction loss does not exceed the rated pump head and if the velocities are within limits suggested in the previous chapter section on "Design Recommendations" the selected pipe sizes are satisfactory.

If necessary, corrections are made in the piping of some parts to obtain a balance of the total circuit friction and the available pump head.

The procedure just outlined for the longest circuit is repeated for circuits to all heating units so that the friction losses in all circuits are equal. However, it may not be possible to achieve balance by change in pipe sizes and number of fittings because there may be too much difference in circuit lengths, and therefore it may be necessary to add adjustable cocks or orifices in circuits that have too low friction loss.

Piping for One-Pipe Diversion System

In a one pipe system the same principles apply to design of piping as explained in the example for a two-pipe system. But, since special fittings are generally used to induce or proportion flow from the main through the heating units and back to the main, it is necessary to obtain from the manufacturer the capacities and resistances of these fittings at various rates of flow in the main for different fitting sizes.

Sizing Piping for Main.—After the heat loss of the structure has been determined and the proper heating units have been selected and their location established, a layout should be made showing all piping and fittings.

To the measured length of the main add 50% to obtain the equivalent length of main. If there is more than one main circuit, this applies to one such circuit from boiler to the end of the main at the boiler return connection.

Assume a design temperature drop of 20°F.

Since the water taken from the main to any heating unit returns to the main, the flow through the main is the same throughout the circuit. The main may therefore be uniform in size except in parts, if any, where flow is combined with that from another circuit.

Next, select a pump from a manufacturer catalog that will deliver the gpm required. This flow is found by dividing the heat loss of the structure by 10,000.

Note the head produced by the pump at the rated flow. Divide the pump head by the equivalent main length found to obtain the design unit friction loss for the circuit.

From friction chart, select a pipe size that will have approximately the unit design friction loss at the flow rate required.

Sizing Piping for Branches.—Since the flow required through the piping from a main to a heating unit and back to the main is known (because it is determined from the heat required by the heating unit and the temperature drop) it is convenient to select from the tables provided by the manufacturer of the flow inducing fitting the size of fitting required for a desired flow in gpm for a given equivalent length of branch piping.

As an example, the capacity table for special fittings of one manufacturer shows:

For a $1\frac{1}{4}$-inch fitting in a $1\frac{1}{4}$-inch main, when the branch has an equivalent length of 30 ft the connection to the fitting should be $\frac{3}{4}$-inch and the flow in the main should be 10 gpm if the flow through the branch is to be 1.9 gpm. This manufacturer states that the special fitting should be in the main at the return branch connection and that the tee at the connection of the supply branch should be a regular pipe tee. It is also stated that only one special fitting is required.

For these fittings the manufacturer recommends that the distance along the main between supply and return connections be at least 18 inches.

It should be noted that manufacturers show a reduction in flow inducing or diverting capacities of special fittings if the heating unit is below the level of the main. This reduction is due to the opposition of the gravity head in the branch. This gravity head is greatest when the pump starts because at that time the water in the branch is at room temperature. Opposition decreases as the water in the branch becomes warmer but, nevertheless, continues at a decreased rate as long as the pump is in operation.

The manufacturer of another special fitting that may be used singly or in pairs to divert the proper amount of water from the main to a heating unit circuit and back to the main shows the capacities of fittings having various sizes of outlet to branch for various milli-inch pressure drops for heating units one, two, and three floors above the main, using either one or a pair of the fittings. For circulation to heating units below the main, a pair of these special fittings is always required and, consequently, capacities are shown only for pairs of fittings for this use.

Pipe Size Check.—When finding the actual friction loss of mains and branches after the preliminary pipe sizes have been found, it is necessary to know the friction at the given flow in the main through the special fitting. The manufacturer therefore shows the pressure drop at various rates of flow in single fittings, or for fittings in pairs for fittings of various sizes. The recommendation is given by one manufacturer that only 40% of the given pressure loss should be considered when determining the friction loss in the main due to the special fitting.

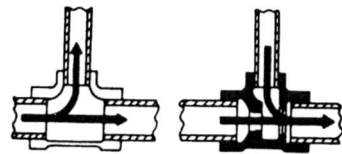

Fig 15-105. Flow through taco venture fitting and standard pipe tee

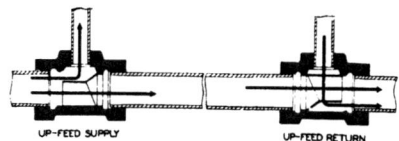

Fig 15-106. Flow through Bell & Gossett monoflow fitting upfeed supply and upfeed return

The operating principles of the special fittings mentioned will be evident from Figs. 15-105 and 15-106.

Part- II Piping for One Pipe Series System

In the one-pipe series system, the same water flows progressively through the heating units in any circuit and consequently the water temperature entering any unit is lower than in the preceding unit. It is therefore common practice to limit the number of heating units in any one circuit so that the water temperature at the last units on the circuit not be so low as to necessitate an increase of heating unit size. A common temperature drop used for these systems is 20°F. A drop of 5°F per heating unit in any circuit is sometimes used. An increase in velocity can be used to lower the temperature drop in the system but will be limited by noise considerations, pump head, or cost of pumping.

In order to size the piping, a layout is made and the total flow rate (in gpm) in the system is obtained by dividing the design heat loss of the structure by 10,000 when a temperature drop of 20°F is used. A preliminary selection of pump may now be made for the flow rate required. The available circulation head of the pump should be noted.

The equivalent length of piping should be the measured length plus 50% of the length, added length for fittings plus the length of the heating units.

The available pump head should be divided by the equivalent pipe length to obtain the design unit friction loss.

The pipe size may now be found from the friction chart for the required flow rate and the design unit friction loss.

The actual friction loss of the system is found by adding to the loss through piping the losses through heating units and fittings (see Tables 15-31 and 15-34) or by adding (1) the actual piping length, (2) the heating unit lengths, and (3) the equivalent length of boiler and pipe fittings, then multiplying this total by the actual unit friction loss.

This total system friction loss should be compared with the available pump head. It may be necessary to change the pump size or pipe size if the two losses are not in balance.

In systems having baseboard units preliminary pipe sizes are sometimes selected equal to the tappings or connection sizes provided by the manufacturer. The actual system friction loss is then determined as outlined above for comparison with the available pump head.

If the system has a large number of baseboard heating units, the system may be designed with more than one loop or circuit. In this case, the piping will be designed for the required flow in each circuit and it will be necessary to equalize the friction of the different circuits.

Combination of Piping Systems

While the different piping systems for hot water heating were discussed separately, it will be found practicable in many a system to use more than one type of piping in different parts of a system. The principles for obtaining proper water circulation, the balancing of friction drop in parallel circuits, the limiting of friction loss to the available pump head, and the limiting of velocities to accepted values, can be applied to assure proper functioning of all parts.

Sizing Hot Water Expansion Tanks (System Water Capacity Known).—Fig. 15-107 is use to size the hot water expansion tanks, when the quantity of water in the system is known. Use of the chart is explained by the following examples.

Example 9: A hot water system has a head of 53 feet and a system water volume (W) of 1000 gallons. What size expansion tank is to be used, what pressure will be developed in it, and what would be the minimum size tank that could be used?

Solution: From the head 53 feet on the horizontal scale move vertically to the optimum reference line, then right and read 0.30 W. Since 0.30 W = 300 gallons, this is the recommended size tank. The intersection of the curve and the 53 line also shows the working pressure to be 50 psig.

The minimum tank size is found to be 0.163 W or 163 gallons, in which case the working pressure would be 100 psig.

If a predetermined working pressure is selected, read to the right. For example, if 60 psig is desired, move up the 53 line to 60, then right and read 0.24 W, or 240 gallons as the tank capacity.

The safety valve pressure should be 10 lbs above the working pressure.

If the system is connected to the water supply by means of a self filling pressure reducing valve, the reducing valve must be adjusted to the system static pressure. If it is not, a higher working pressure will be developed in the system.

Conditions Affecting Design.—The designer of a HTW system is immediately concerned with problems due to the following conditions, some of which introduce complications not found in the design of low temperature water heating systems:

1) Water temperature is high, often 300°F to 400°F. A common temperature is 350°F.

2) Pressures must be high enough to prevent formation of steam in any part of the system.

3) Expansion of pipe and metal parts is greater than with lower temperature systems.

4) Corrosion must be limited to a minimum by special precautions for excluding oxygen. Loss or removal of water should be limited in order to prevent introduction of oxygen when makeup water is added to replace loss of water.

5) Piping, pumps, boilers, heating units, controls, and other equipment must be constructed for operation at the high temperatures and pressures required in the system.

6) Pump characteristics and performance must be carefully considered to assure operation at economical rates for the capacity pumped and the friction loss of the piping.

7) Means for obtaining water at different temperatures for various uses in the equipment attached to the system will require heat exchangers or water mixing devices, and controls for such purpose.

8) A method of producing and maintaining the required pressure must be selected; the usual mediums being steam or nitrogen.

9) Steam formation may occur due to loss of pressure at elevated points in the piping or at the pump suction. Water hammer due to steam formation and its subsequent contact with cooled water must be avoided.

10) Condensation on boiler tubes may occur, causing them to corrode if too cool return water flows through the boiler.

11) Due to the large storage of heat in the system it is not advisable to operate the circulation system intermittently, or to try to make rapid changes in water temperature. A relatively constant temperature in the mains with separate control of heating units will, therefore, be necessary for maintaining or controlling space temperatures.

12) Pumps are always used to produce circulation in HTW systems and consequently the mains need not be pitched in the direction of flow. They may be run at any desired level to follow the contour of the land or to pass obstacles.

13) HTW systems are usually designed for a temperature drop of 100 to 150°F instead of the 20°F drop commonly used for low temperature systems. While the design temperature drop may be as low as 80°F, it is more economical to use a 150°F drop. In some instances it can be shown that a drop of 180°F or even 200°F is practicable and economical.

Many of the conditions mentioned in the preceding thirteen items will be treated more in detail in later text.

Example 10: What will be the working pressure in the given example with a tank size 0.3W if the self filling pressure reducing valve is adjusted to 30 psig?

Solution: The systems effective static head will be:

$$H = \frac{30}{0.434} = 70 \text{ ft}$$

Utilizing Fig. 15-107 with 70 feet of head and 0.3W tank capacity in 71 psig will be developed instead of 50 psig. This is shown by the intersection of vertical 70 feet head with the horizontal 0.3W.

It is well to bear in mind that the pressures given are maximum pressures developed by the expansion of a system filled cold and then heated.

The optimal tank size (volume) reference line is based on the volume of the tank capacity in gallons being equal to kW, where W is the water volume in the system in gallons, and k is 0.1 for a one story building, and 0.13, 0.17 and 0.23 for 2, 3 and 4 story buildings, respectively.

Sizing Hot Water Expansion Tanks (Boiler Output Known).—The application of Fig. 15-108 should be limited to conventional hot water heating systems. It should not be used for multi story buildings, water temperatures above 220°F, or specially designed industrial installations. The selections it indicates are based on standard, commercially available compression tank sizes.

The following steps should be followed in use of the chart:

1) Determine net boiler output and locate on left hand scale.

2) From this point, draw a horizontal line to intersect the appropriate system curve. The choice is made from among flash or conventional boiler source, hot water heating systems utilizing radiant panels or baseboard, convectors, or thin tube cast iron pipe.

3) From this intersection, extend vertical line downward through both maximum and minimum baselines.

4) Select compression tank size as indicated where vertical line intersects dotted, diagonal line. If vertical line does not intersect a dotted line, use next larger tank size indicated to right.

5) Apply correction factor, if necessary, from the accompanying table to the tank size.

Correction Factors: Standard conditions are 12 psig initial pressure, 30 psig final pressure, and 18.5 ft maximum system height above tank. For single pipe systems, deduct 13–20% from tank size given for conventional boilers; 18–22% from tank size given for flash boilers

Initial Pressure, psig	Static Height, ft	Tank Size Multification Factor
12	18.5	1.00
16	27.5	1.43
20	36.5	2.18
24	46.0	3.82

High Temperature Water Systems.—High temperature water (HTW) systems have grown in popularity due to their adaptability for supplying heat at various temperatures for industrial and space heating purposes. The system supply temperature is governed by the heating unit or process requiring the highest temperature, but lower temperatures, if required for other loads in the system, are readily provided by drawing mixed water from supply and return mains, by restricting flow to certain units, or by use of water-to-water heat exchangers. If a process in the system requires steam, this may be generated in a heat exchanger if the saturation temperature of the steam required is sufficiently below the supply water temperature to permit the transfer of heat to produce the steam.

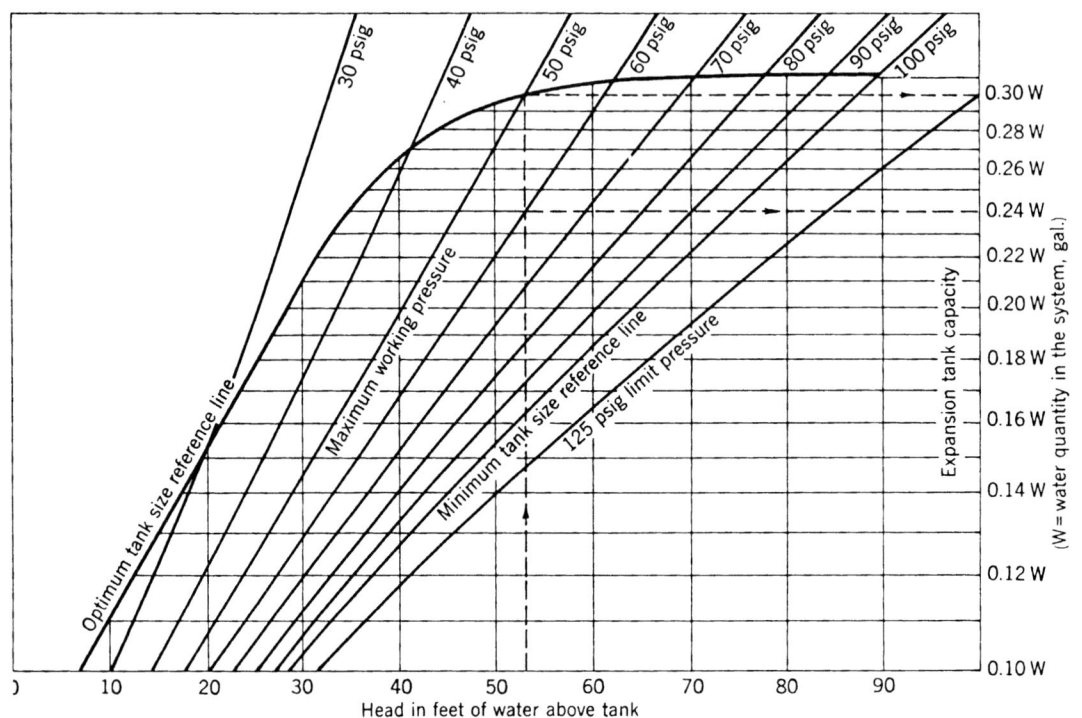

Fig 15-107. Head in feet of water above tank

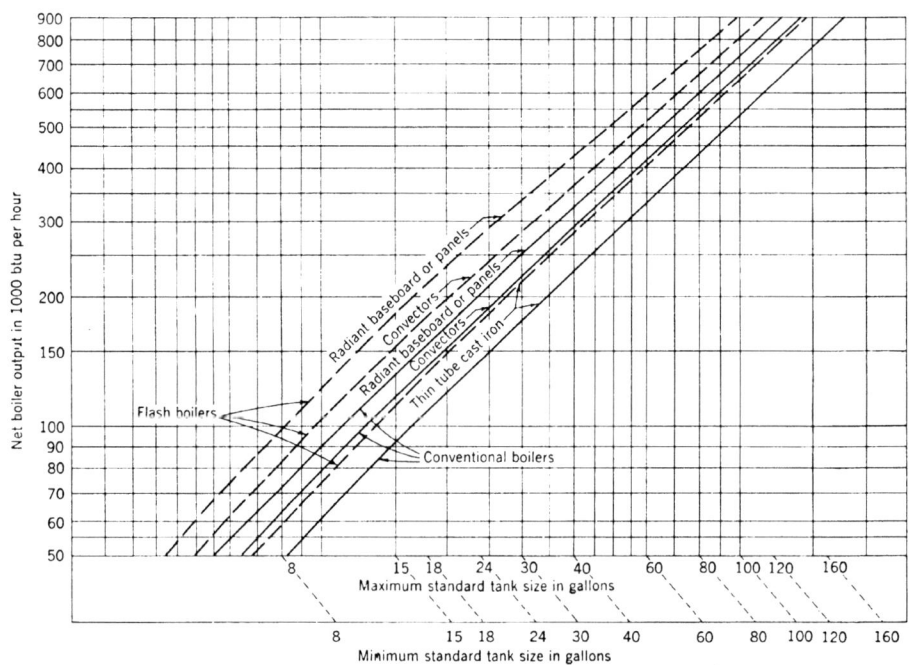

Fig 15-108. Minimum standard tank size in gallons

Purpose of High Temperature Drop.—High temperature drops between supply and return mains are used in HTW systems in order to reduce the flow of water that must be circulated and thereby permit reduction of pipe sizes to a minimum practical limit. For instance, if a pipe line is to transmit 1,000,000 Btu/hr through a mile of pipe at a 50°F temperature drop and a velocity of 4 fps, a 2½ inches pipe will be required. For the same system, if the temperature drop is 120°F, the pipe size may be reduced to 1½ inches. Similarly, if the heat transmitted is to be 10,000,000 Btu/hr, the pipe size required is 6 inches for a 50°F drop or 4 inches for a 120°F drop.

Comparison with Steam.—In heating units or processes the heat available from steam is the latent heat due to condensation only, while the heat available from water is the sensible heat given up by cooling of the water. Condensation of steam at 175 psia will yield 852.8 Btu/lb of steam or 256 Btu/ft³ of steam. One cubic foot of water at the same temperature, if cooled through 100°F (the minimum temperature drop) to 271°F will give up the difference between the fluid heats at 371°F and 271°F, or (18830 –14002) = 4828 Btu. Therefore, water will give up under equivalent design conditions almost 19 times the heat of an equivalent volume of condensing steam.

The high heat content of the water in the HTW distribution system increases the response of the system to demands for heat and facilitates the maintenance of uniform temperatures in the heated space.

Heat Storage.—An HTW system contains a large quantity of stored heat in the circulating water. The stored heat may also be increased during periods of light load by increasing the temperature of the water in the return main. An example of large storage capacity is found in a system having a total length of 20 miles in the supply and return mains, and a storage capacity equal to a 24 hour reserve of heat.

Limitation of Corrosion.—In determining the method of system pressurization or provision of space for the expansion of water as temperature changes, it is of prime importance to limit corrosion within the system. It is therefore necessary to limit addition of oxygen, which is the main cause of corrosion. Oxygen enters as a constituent of air (if air is used for pressurization) or as a gas dissolved with air in the makeup water and released as the water is heated.

It is advisable that water not be drawn from a system for outside purposes because doing so would necessitate additional makeup water, which would introduce oxygen unless the water is given special treatment before being added.

Pressurization of HTW System.—In all water heating systems there must be sufficient pressure on the surface of the water at all points of the system to prevent formation of steam. This pressure must be above the saturation pressure corresponding to the temperature of the water at any point. Some of the most critical points in the system are: (1) the pump suction (where cavitation may occur), (2) the top tubes in the boiler (where the tubes may burn out if not covered by water or filled with water), (3) the expansion tank or other high points in the system, and (4) heat exchangers or converters.

Extensive damage might occur in the system to pumps and other equipment if water hammer results from steam formation.

The medium for pressurizing is mainly steam, air, or an inert gas, usually nitrogen.

Steam Pressurization.—The principle of steam pressurization is shown in Fig. 15-109 in which it will be noted that the expansion tank provides (1) space for expansion of system water, (2) means for pressurization by steam in the upper part of the tank, and (3) storage space for heated water from the boiler. The boilers shown in Fig. 15-109, schematically, are of the water tube type with the expansion tank serving also as the steam drum. Note that the supply water for system circulation is taken from the expansion tank and that a bypass is provided to permit mixing some return water with the heated water in order to reduce water temperature at the pump suction and thereby reduce the possibility of cavitation at the pump.

Steam pressurized system operations are very critical with regard to fluctuations in pressure and therefore require precise control of pressure.

Pressure fluctuation in steam pressurized systems can be prevented by supplying additional steam to the expansion chamber from a separate steam generator. By this means any desirable pressure can be maintained in the system at all times regardless of the load or water temperature. The heat required by the separate generator would be equivalent only to the heat loss from the expansion chamber surface.

When a boiler has a large steam space within its shell (such as a Scotch Marine or other fire tube boiler) this steam space can be used for both pressurization space and for space for water expansion in the system. However, a separate expansion tank placed high above the boiler is generally preferred because it increases net positive suction head and prevents cavitation at the pump.

Expansion tank volume should be equal to the sum of (1) volume required for steam space, (2) volume required for expansion of the water in the system, and (3) volume required or occupied by internal headers and piping and an allowance for sludge and reserve.

Steam space required will be about 20% of the sum of items (2) and (3). Item (2), the space required for expansion of the water in the system, will be the change in volume of the water content from minimum to maximum operating temperature, assuming that water will be drawn off as required after the initial filling of the system to limit the pressure in the expansion tank to the pressure corresponding to the lowest average operating temperature.

Item (3), volume allowance for internal headers, sludge, etc., may be equivalent to 40% of item (2) for small systems and up to 80% of item (2) for large systems.

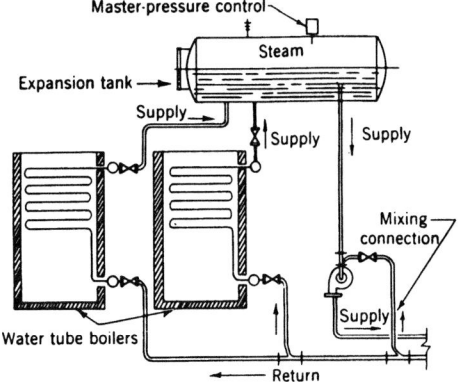

Fig 15-109. HTW system pressurized by steam

Gas Pressurization.—Pressurization of an HTW system by means of gas eliminates the difficulties occurring in steam pressurized systems due to fluctuations of pressure that cause cavitation, water hammer, etc.

Air and nitrogen have been used, but nitrogen is preferred because it is inert, while air introduces oxygen, which is very corrosive, especially where metal surfaces are in a moist condition.

An advantage of gas pressurization is that the pressure in the system can readily be maintained at the desired level and, consequently, the tendency for steam formation is eliminated. The expansion tank can be placed where it will be convenient. Also, since it is considered to be unfired pressure vessel it need only meet the requirements of the ASME Unfired Pressure Vessel Code. Vertical expansion tanks are frequently used to save floor space.

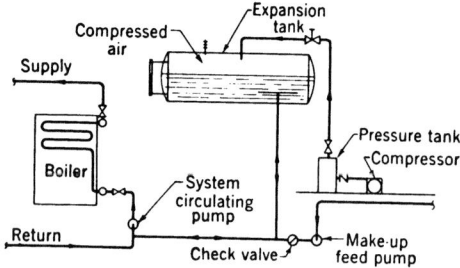

Fig 15-110. Method of pressurizing HTW system by air

Air Pressurization.—Use of air for pressurization is shown schematically in Fig. 15-110. Air escapes through a relief valve to the atmosphere when pressure due to the expansion of the water exceeds the pressure setting of the valve. Air for replacement is supplied by an air compressor and pressure tank and enters the expansion tank under control of a regulating valve when the pressure falls.

Since the interior of the tank is moist, corrosion within the tank may be extensive.

Nitrogen Pressurization.—There are three basic methods of pressurization with nitrogen using (a) an overhead tank, Fig. 15-111, (b) an overflow or spill tank at boiler floor level for expansion and contraction of the system water, with a hot well for make up, Fig. 15-112, and (c) elimination of the hot well. In (a), nitrogen is recycled by a compressor, thereby eliminating gas losses except by absorption, which is small. Note that with this earlier method three drums are necessary: one expansion drum and two nitrogen drums. (In earlier systems nitrogen was released to the atmosphere when excessive pressures were built up, as the pressures would otherwise become the system pressures and could cause damage to equipment.)

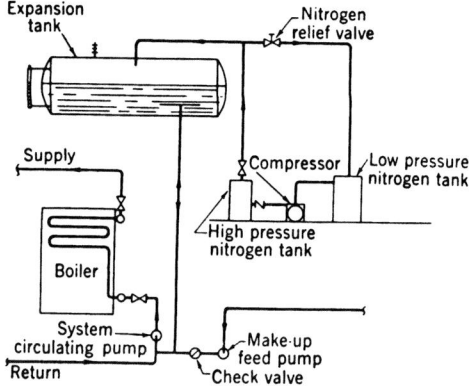

Fig 15-111. Insert gas pressurized htw system using nitrogen

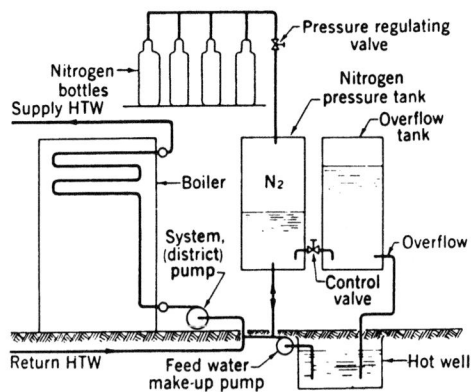

Fig 15-112. Nitrogen pressurization HTW system without overhead tank

The more modern method of pressurizing with an inert gas is to combine the feedwater make-up with the expansion and contraction of the circulating water. (Some of these designs are proprietary, including those of completely packaged pressurization units.) By eliminating the overhead pressure tank, no elaborate and costly structural steel is needed to support it, and, further, the height of the boiler house can be considerably reduced, again reducing capital costs.

Pressurization is accomplished in a tank or tanks of minimum size at the boiler floor level, and the small losses of nitrogen that occur in these systems are more than offset by the considerable capital and other savings effected.

Expansion Tanks

Expansion Conditions.—It is impossible for a boiler to take up the expansion of heated water even within a shell type boiler in large HTW systems. An independent expansion tank is necessary. Further, since this tank serves also as a pressure vessel to maintain the operating pressure on the system, it must be large enough for both duties. By absorbing expansion and contraction, the original water is retained and only a minimum quantity of feedwater makeup is required. This reduces the amount of chemical water treatment necessary. In a good system, daily makeup water should not exceed 1% of the total water in the system.

Initial expansion of water to fill the system as it is heated from fill temperature (assumed to be at 50°F) to the mean temperature of the heated water at 300°F, can be drawn off the system through the blowdown valve so that expansion during operation begins at 300°F. The blowdown valve is closed when the water level at 300°F is at the center of the expansion tank. Further expansion of water to the maximum temperature is then contained in the expansion tank.

The following fittings are needed: safety valves and relief valves constructed according to applicable codes, high and low water level alarms, and controls.

Determining Expansion Tank Size.—The first step in calculating tank size is to establish design pressure. In steam pressurized systems design pressure is the saturation pressure corresponding to the temperature of the water. In gas pressurized systems, gas pressure is usually maintained at about 40 psi above design saturation pressure.

The second step is to determine the total volume of water in the system. It is calculated from the length and size of all piping plus the water content of all heat exchangers, drums, boilers, fittings, etc. It is not a function of rated plant output.

The third step is to calculate the daily mean water temperature change. This is a rather indefinite variable from the design standpoint. Its value is the average of system flow and return temperatures at daily maximum and minimum load conditions. The daily load cycle, however, is a function of the type of load, that is, whether it is strictly a heating load, a process load, or a combination of both. From studies of operating records at various heating installations, actual daily load swings of 25% of rated output are about average and should be expected during most

of the heating season. In a process application, daily load swings of 50% or more of rated output are usual.

To illustrate, assume: system water capacity of 500,000 lb, supply temperature at 350°F, return temperature at 250°F and makeup boiler feed water at 50°F. Values for specific volume, in cubic feet per pound of water, at 50°F, 250°F, 300°F, and 350°F are, respectively 0.01603, 0.01700, 0.01745, and 0.01799. Multiplying each by 500,000 lb gives the system volume at the four temperatures as 8015, 8500, 8725, and 8995 ft³, respectively.

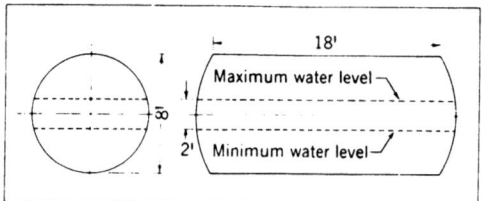

Fig 15-113. Horizontal steam pressurizing tank

For expansion from 300°F to 350°F, the increase in volume is (8995 − 8725) or 270 ft³. If a 24-inch (2-ft) rise of water in the expansion tank is considered, the area of tank required at the water line should be 270/2 = 135 ft². Referring to a cylindrical tank or drum placed horizontally as in Fig. 15-113 the surface area at the center should be satisfactory if the tank is 8 ft in diameter and 18 ft long.

If expansion had been computed from 50°F to 350°F, the expansion would have been (8995 − 8015) or 980 ft³, which is about 3½ times the expansion found for a temperature rise from 300°F to 350°F.

Location of Steam Pressurizing Tank.—The expansion tank for steam pressurization should be placed well above the boiler to allow for expansion loops in the pipe lines between the boiler header and tank. It does not have to be directly above the boiler. For piping design reasons, it is best to locate the tank above the circulating pumps.

Care must be taken when designing inlet and outlet connections from the expansion tank. The supply outlet leading from the tank to the system circulating pumps should be placed so that no vortex can be formed where the velocity is highest and where, consequently, steam can be drawn with the water. If a dip tube is used for hot water supply to the circulating line of the system, its entrance should be well below the surface of the water (where steam bubbles collect) so that the bubbles cannot be drawn into the supply line to cause water hammer and troubles at the pump.

Where two expansion tanks are connected, they must be fitted with steam and water balance pipes to keep the two tanks in equilibrium. These steam and water pipes must be used solely to maintain equilibrium and should not be connected into any other lines.

Nitrogen Pressurizing Tanks.—In nitrogen pressurized systems, gas pressure is usually maintained at about 10% above design saturation pressure. Vertical drums are preferred for nitrogen pressurization. As an example, assume that the drum is to be sized for the same conditions used in the previous illustration for a steam pressurized system. The increase in volume of the water when heated from 300°F to 350°F is the same, 270 ft³. Assume that the tank as illustrated in Fig. 15-114 is 8 ft in diameter, which provides a cross sectional area of approximately 50 ft². The water will then change 5½ ft in level. If a distance of 5½ ft is allowed from the maximum water level to the top and 4 ft from the minimum level to the bottom of the tank, the required tank height will be 12½ ft.

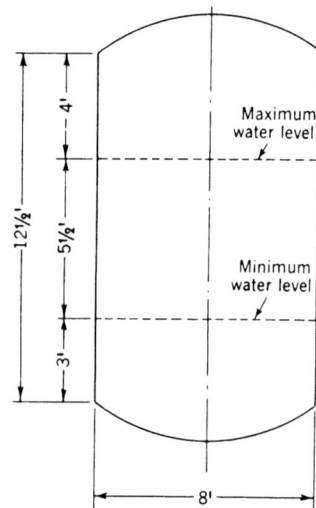

Fig 15-114. Vertical nitrogen pressurizing tank

Application of HTW for Process Steam.—Although HTW has many advantages over steam, it is not a substitute for steam in all cases. There are some processes for which steam is essential because of the type of equipment used or by the nature of the operation. In such cases HTW can always be used as the prime heat source. Instead of piping steam over long distances, with attendant trap and grading problems, the HTW, with its simple circulating system, is brought to the equipment requiring steam. There, either below or adjacent to the unit, dry steam can be made available at a constant pressure and with adequate reserve.

It is not unusual for several pieces of equipment, all requiring steam, to be operated from the same HTW supply line, each steam consuming unit working at a different pressure. If steam were used instead of hot water as the distributing medium from the central boiler house, pressure reducing valves would have to be fitted to every unit,

and, apart from the somewhat complicated condensate return line with receivers and condensate pumps, there would not be the same adequate reserve of steam (as with HTW) without a much larger boiler plant. Further, uniform control of pressure would, to a great extent, be dependent entirely on manual observation and control to make certain that large steam consuming units are not suddenly thrown on the line, as can often happen in a factory. Where each steam consuming unit has its own heat exchanger, not only will the overall efficiency of the plant be higher, but waste can almost be eliminated and the cost of steam considerably reduced.

Heat exchangers that produce steam from HTW are often called *converters*. Steam temperatures range from 320 to 400°F, but more often from 337 to 353°F which correspond to 100 psig and 125 psig, respectively. Typical applications are: steam cooking equipment, sterilizers, calender rolls, radiators, finned coils, and many pieces of hospital equipment such as dressing sterilizers, kitchen and cafeteria equipment, and laundry calenders. Many of these applications require steam at different pressures, but can still be connected to the same supply and return HTW lines that serve the space heating units.

Circulating Pumps.—The circulating pump is the heart of the HTW system. Careful design and selection is of vital importance because all heat distribution depends upon it. It must be selected not only for the quantity of water to be pumped at the head or heads required, but also for the high temperatures at which it will be operating. If a pump is designed to deliver 700 gpm against a 200 ft head, it will deliver a greater gallonage against 160 ft head, and will absorb more power, too. It is, therefore, important for the design engineer and pump manufacturer to determine the point of maximum efficiency and allow for a non overload characteristic, so that if the pressure head drops, the horsepower required will be within the capacity of the driving motor.

In steam pressurized systems proper practice is to install circulating pumps in the supply line because this maintains the pressure above the flash point of the hottest water and prevents steam formation in the system.

Another safeguard against flashing or cavitation at the pump in steam pressurized systems is a mixing connection as shown in Fig. 15-115, which bypasses some of the cooler water from the return into the supply line at the pump suction. This reduces the supply water temperature 5 or 10°F, enough to prevent flashing but without diminishing of system pressure. For example, if the temperature of the water leaving the expansion tank is 350°F at 120 psig (near saturation, an unstable condition) a reduction of 5°F by admixture of cooler return water will result in 345°F, 120 psig water, which will not flash.

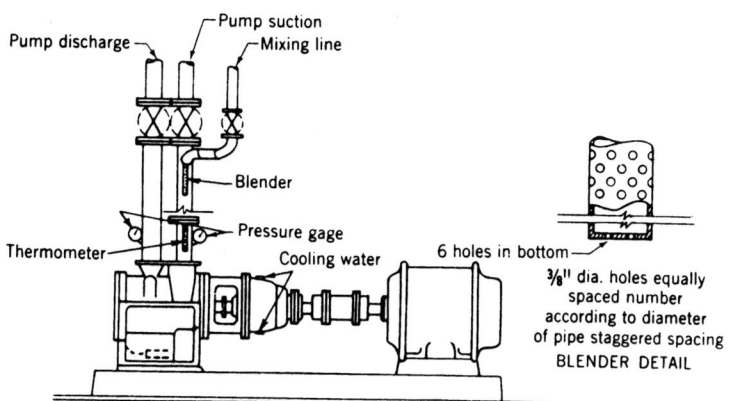

Fig 15-115. Mixing connection for steam pressurized HTW system

Further precautions against flashing include the location of the circulating pumps well below the level of the boiler outlet and the use of a large connecting suction pipe dropping vertically to the pumps. By thus increasing the static head on the pump suction, long suction lines are avoided and the suction piping is arranged so that any sudden acceleration in flow is avoided. The total circulating head equals the sum of the head due to pump pressure and the head due to gravity. It should be noted, however, that in design calculations, the head due to gravity is usually neglected when it is small in comparison with the pumping head.

In HTW systems pressurized with air or inert gas, the system circulating pump can be placed in the return line because the system pressure is always maintained well above the flashpoint of the water. The pumps may also be placed in the supply line if design conditions make this advisable.

Pumps for HTW Systems.—The centrifugal pump is used to circulate water in HTW systems. A description of the characteristics of such pumps their operation, performance and methods of converting performance for changes in speed, head, horsepower, impeller size and also a discussion of pump selection are given in the *Piping and Plumbing* section of Chapter 9. The discussion of pumps here will, therefore, be limited to features and factors relating to pump applications for HTW systems.

Manufacturer's Information.—A typical manufacturers form will contain the following information:

Conditions of Service:	
Capacity (gpm)	Liquid
Total head (feet)	Pumping temperature (°F)
Speed (rpm)	Specific gravity
Efficiency (%)	Viscosity
Brake horsepower	Vapor pressure
Suction pressure	NPSH above vapor pressure required

Materials of Construction:	
Casing and nozzle	Impeller
Casing and nozzle rings	Base plate
Shaft sleeve	Coupling
Brake horsepower	Vapor pressure
Suction pressure	NPSH above vapor pressure required

Stuffing Box Sealing:
Type

Pump Specifications.—When writing a specification or calling for bids for the centrifugal pump, the pump manufacturer needs to have the following information:

1) The number of units required.

2) The temperature, vapor pressure, and specific gravity of the liquid pumped.

3) The required capacity of the pump, including the minimum and maximum amount of liquid the pump will ever be called upon to deliver.

4) The suction conditions. Is there a suction lift or a suction head? What are the length and diameter of the suction pipe?

5) The discharge conditions. The static head. Is it constant or variable? The friction head. The maximum discharge pressure against which the pump must deliver liquid.

6) The total head, which will vary as items (4) and (5) above vary.

7) Whether service is continuous or intermittent.

8) The type of power available to drive the pump and the characteristics of this power.

9) Space weight or transportation limitations involved.

10) The location of the installation, its geographic location, elevation above sea level, whether indoors or outdoors, range of ambient temperatures.

11) Any special requirements or marked preferences with respect to the design, construction, or performance of the pump.

It is not necessary when writing pump specifications to state the required total head as long as the discharge pressure and the prevailing suction conditions are given. As a matter of fact, it is safer to specify the latter two only, rather than the suction pressures and total heads. The reason for this suggestion is that the specification writer generally works in terms of psi and will give more accurate conditions thereby with less effort.

Net Positive Suction Head (NPSH).—In any centrifugal pump, there is a definite friction and velocity head loss that takes place before the liquid enters the impeller vanes to a degree sufficient for it to receive energy from the pump. When water enters the first stage impeller of a centrifugal pump, a certain amount of pressure energy is, therefore, converted into kinetic energy; the exact amount of conversion depends upon various features of the suction passage and impeller inlet design.

In order to prevent flashing of the water before it has a chance to receive additional pressure energy from the impeller, it is necessary to avoid lowering the pressure energy at the impeller vanes below the vapor pressure.

It is somewhat difficult to measure the static pressure at the impeller entrance proper, and therefore pump designers specify the required pressure as measured at the pump suction flange and refer to the pump horizontal centerline. This pressure is determined for a given pump and for a given capacity on the basis of the calculated or predicted friction head losses. This is the NPSH.

In boiler pump terminology, the net positive suction head (NPSH) represents the net suction over the pump suction referred to the pump centerline over and above the vapor pressure of the water. The reason for this definition is that incipient cavitation must be expected to take place as soon as the static pressure at some one point within the pump has dropped to the value of the vapor pressure so that vaporization begins. This definition of suction head renders it automatically independent of any variations in temperature and vapor pressure of the water.

Effect of Cavitation Within Pump.—If the static pressure at the impeller vanes should fall below the vapor pressure corresponding to its temperature, a portion of the water contained in the impeller suction would immediately flash into steam. This flashing will form vapor filled cavities within the body of the flowing water and cause cavitation, the immediate effect of which is to prevent a further increase of the pump capacity because the pumping space normally allotted to the flow of water is occupied by steam.

There are other serious effects of cavitation. As the steam bubbles pass on to regions of the impeller under somewhat higher pressure, they condense in a sudden collapse with all the characteristics of an explosion. This violent collapse produces water hammer pressure of great intensity on small localized areas of the impeller.

Pump Construction for HTW Systems.—Above a temperature of 150°F, the pump casing must always be

steel. Bearings, housing, glands, and stuffing boxes must be water cooled. The suction inlet should be shaped to avoid sudden changes in flow and velocity and to avoid cavitation. The casing and head should be steel or cast iron with a high tensile strength, the impeller should be of chrome steel or high tensile ferrous alloy, the shaft of stainless steel, the sleeves and bushings of chrome steel, and bearings should be of the ball bearing type, oil lubricated and water cooled. Couplings should be designed to permit dismantling of the pump without breaking the suction or discharge piping. Otherwise the entire pump must be dismantled.

Circulating Pump Seals.—One of the most troublesome problems in the handling of HTW is the sealing of the rotating shaft. While packed stuffing boxes are not condemned, the use of mechanical seals for the higher pressures is strongly recommended. The mechanical seal, when installed by the pump manufacturer at the factory and not left to an inexperienced mechanic in the field, has many advantages compared to conventional stuffing boxes.

Mechanical seals are available from several manufacturers. It is of greatest importance that a mechanical seal properly installed never be touched by an inexperienced mechanic except for periodic inspection as directed by the manufacturer.

Since a great number of HTW systems are being installed in remote areas where the maintenance facilities and the ability of the personnel are very limited, the packed box pump could be more suitable to choose than the mechanical seal type in these locations. Most pump mechanics can handle packing gland problems, but only the best and more experienced can handle properly the installation and maintenance of a mechanical seal.

The mechanical seal is highly efficient and very effective for the duty required and has proved to be superior to the conventional asbestos or metallic stuffing box packing. Mechanical seals are especially suitable where pressures and shaft speeds are extremely high, or where corrosive conditions exist. The mechanical seal will reduce leakage to a minimum and will operate over long periods without the deterioration of the conventional packing. Shaft sleeve replacement, a regular repair with packed boxes, is almost eliminated.

The cooled gland is recommended for pumping temperatures of 400°F or over. Whereas cooling piping is standard for all HTW pump bearings, the cooling piping to the mechanical seal gland cooling jacket must be of flexible tubing to prevent piping movement from affecting seal operation by deflecting the gland out of alignment.

In large installations, the outlet or hot line from the pump bearing can be used for many purposes, such as providing domestic or service water requirements.

Boiler Recirculating Pump.—The boiler manufacturer should be consulted to ascertain the minimum flow requirements for the boiler. In some boilers the manufacturer may find 50% of full load flow to be safe while for others the manufacturer may insist that flow not be reduced below 85% of full load flow. Some manufacturers of forced circulation boilers recommend a minimum flow rate of 7000 lb of water per million Btu maximum boiler output. This flow is equivalent in a 50,000,000-Btu boiler to 350,000 lb/hr. Under some conditions, especially during very light (summer) loads, the use of a separate boiler recirculating pump in addition to the system circulating pump might have advantages. But the additional cost of piping, complicated valve circuits, and fittings will increase the initial cost of the system to little advantage. In most cases, it is practicable and efficient to install a separate system pump for summer loads and eliminate the boiler recirculation pump altogether.

However, where the friction head loss or boiler flow resistance is too high for one pump, i.e., combining both boiler and distribution circuits, then a separate boiler recirculating pump must be used. If the boiler flow resistance exceeds 35 ft head loss, one authority would recommend a two-pump system.

Boilers for HTW Systems.—Boilers for HTW systems, in addition to meeting construction requirements suitable for the operating pressure of the system, must be so constructed that proper circulation is assured in all parts of the boiler. To assure such circulation, some boilers are equipped with circulation pumps and distribution means to proportion the water to the heat absorbing capacity of the tube surface, which varies in heat absorption in different parts of the boiler. Boiler bypass connections must not create a condition that reduces circulation of water or supply to any part of the heating surface.

In some boilers (controlled circulation type) water is distributed to the various tubes through screens that practically meter the water to each tube circuit. This feature is of importance also when boilers are operated in parallel because it assists in obtaining equal flow distribution to each boiler.

Water velocity in a controlled circulation boiler is set for a minimum pressure loss that does not exceed 10 psi even for large boilers. A high pressure loss in boilers can easily require an increase of motor size by horsepower. Since some motors may operate through the 24-hr day, it is important to use boilers that have a low pressure drop.

Boiler Emergency Protection.—Many types of emergency valves have been designed to prevent loss of water in case of pipe breakage, but of these, only those controlled by flow have proved to be satisfactory. Such valves must be of a type that does not close too quickly otherwise the shock will produce water hammer.

One valving arrangement for emergency operation that will prevent loss of water in the boilers is shown diagrammatically in Fig. 15-116. If a break should occur in the distribution line, the drop in flow will open the emergency control valve and bypass the water from the pump discharge header to the return water (boiler inlet) header. Thus, the boilers will never be without water.

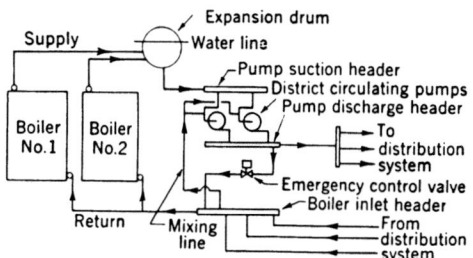

Fig 15-116. Piping arrangement for emergency control valve

Pipe, Valves, and Fittings for HTW Systems.—

HTW systems can be compared to steam systems of equivalent pressure in that valves designed for steam pressures of 150, 200, or 250 psig can be used in most HTW systems. Since the design or test pressure of any valve is always much greater than its operating pressure, a steam valve sold for a nominal 150 psig can be selected for HTW systems operating at 350°F, equivalent to 150–190 psig, depending on the method of pressurization. For HTW systems operating at 400°F, equivalent to 260–300 psig, and where process heating by steam or hot water is required, valves must be of the 300 psig class. All pipe, valves, and fittings for HTW systems should comply with the requirements of the American National Standard for Pressure Piping.

Generally speaking, HTW valves are restricted to the 150 and 300 psig classes, with preference for the former due to cost. This means that unless higher pressures are otherwise required, HTW systems for all forms of space heating should be limited to from 325 to 340°F, or pressures below 150 psig.

The importance of well made, tight-fitting valves cannot be overstressed because most leakage occurs at the valves. Leakage from HTW systems flashes into steam and is, therefore, not detected except by deposits of scale or salt formation on the surface at point of leakage.

Since it is usually not possible to control the difference in pressure between supply and return mains within narrow limits in the distribution system, the pressure available to force the water through the control valve may vary as much as 5 to 40 psi. Therefore, the valve has to be sized to pass the correct amount of hot water at both extremes. To do this the valve must have a large number of positions, a high lift, an equal percentage throttling plug, and an actuator powerful enough to hold the valve in position with the changes in water supply pressure.

Valve Installation.—Valves in HTW service must always be located on the downstream or return side of converters or steam generators and similar equipment to be controlled because this allows the valve to operate at the lower temperature. If installed on the upstream side, a large pressure drop across the valve could occur when the valves starts to close, thereby causing flashing of water into steam and consequent water hammering.

Welded Joints.—To assure tightness of the HTW system, all joints to valves and fittings for sizes above 1¼ inches should be welded, except in the boiler house where flanges should be used to facilitate maintenance or changes in piping to equipment.

Venting of Piping.—Provision for air-collecting chambers at all high points in the piping should be made as shown in Fig. 15-117. These chambers should have vent pipes run to valves conveniently located for manual operation. The accumulation of air is considerable when the system is first put in operation and for the period when the entrained air escapes from the heated circulating water. Thereafter, only periodic opening of the vent valves will be necessary.

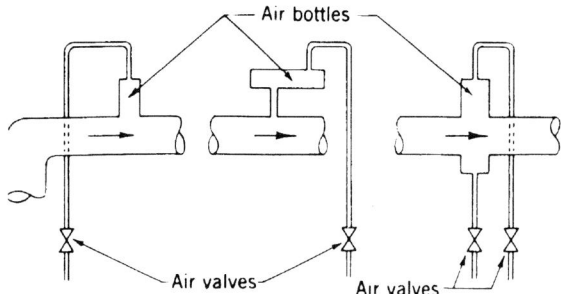

Fig 15-117. Collecting chambers for venting of air

Effect of Load Variation on Operation

Considerable differences occur between design temperatures and pressures as well as between winter and summer design loads. Sometimes in design the extreme conditions for winter are overstressed without taking into account that extremes are usually of short duration and

can be handled readily by either the storage capacity of the system or the ability of the boilers to operate above rating for such periods. In HTW systems, heat is available promptly from the main in which the water is always up to design temperature. For the brief extreme periods, space heating units can be operated as necessary to prevent large drops in space temperature during periods of non occupancy and, consequently, reduce peak demands such as occur when the space is being brought up to occupancy temperature.

It is of greatest importance that the summer low load, usually a night load, be established carefully in order to plan boiler and pump operation that will maintain balanced system conditions. If only one boiler is put on the line, a bypass line will greatly reduce the load on the boiler when the system load is dropping to minimum conditions. Summer low load conditions may be met by having a boiler circulating pump at each boiler to recirculate the boiler water or by having a bypass from the system circulating line to the boiler inlet (see Figs. 15-118 and 15-119).

In the case of one HTW system having three water tube boilers, each of 25,000,000 Btu/hr capacity, it was found necessary with an extremely low summer load, especially at night, to use a bypass from the discharge side of the circulating pump to the return connection of each boiler to obtain a balanced condition at this low load.

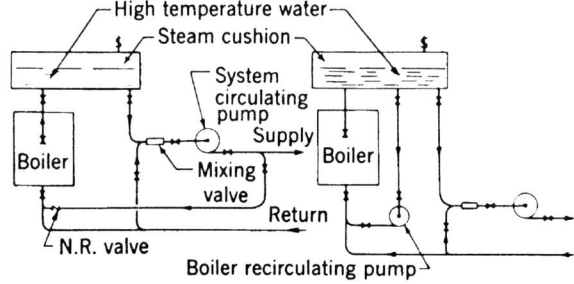

Fig 15-118. HTW system with boiler recirculating

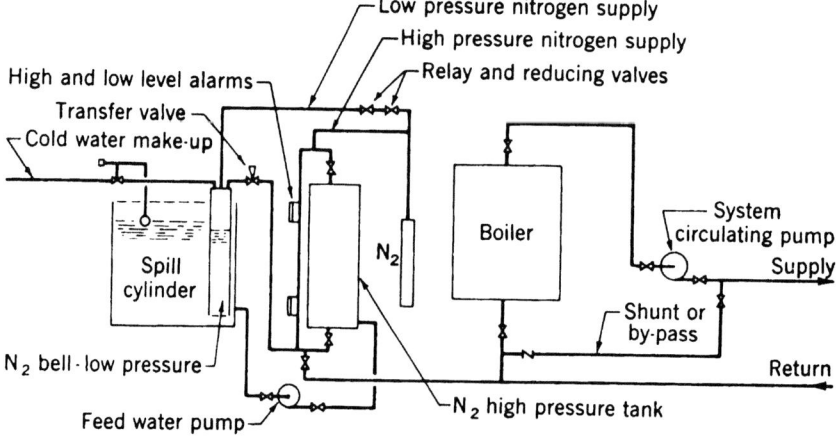

Fig 15-119. HTW system with bypass for light load condition

Pipe Sizing for HTW Systems

Pipe sizes for HTW systems are usually selected from charts or tables, which show for some average temperature such as 200 or 300°F: (1) rate of water flow, (2) size of pipe, (3) water velocity, and (4) the unit friction loss in the piping. The units in which the items (1) to (4) are expressed vary with the preferences of the user. Since friction loss varies with the different water temperatures, the charts or tables are often accompanied by factors for correcting the values obtained from the charts or tables.

Approximate heat carrying capacities of pipe-lines for HTW systems, based on 100°F temperature drop, on 0.1 to 0.2 in. water friction loss per foot of pipe, and velocities of 1.5 to 4.5 fps are shown in Table 15-35. This table is approximate only and should not be substituted for the more precise tables and charts that follow.

Fig. 15-121 is a convenient chart for sizing pipe for HTW systems. In Chapter 9 a complete table of pipe friction losses for 60°F, 180°F and 300°F water in Schedule 40 pipe is provided. Unit friction losses obtained from Fig. 15-121 and from this table for 300°F water may be used, with the help of the correction factors in Fig. 15-120, for temperatures other than 300°F.

For a discussion of calculation of friction loss in piping, including data for losses through valves and fittings, the reader is referred to the text on hot water heating systems in Chapter 9.

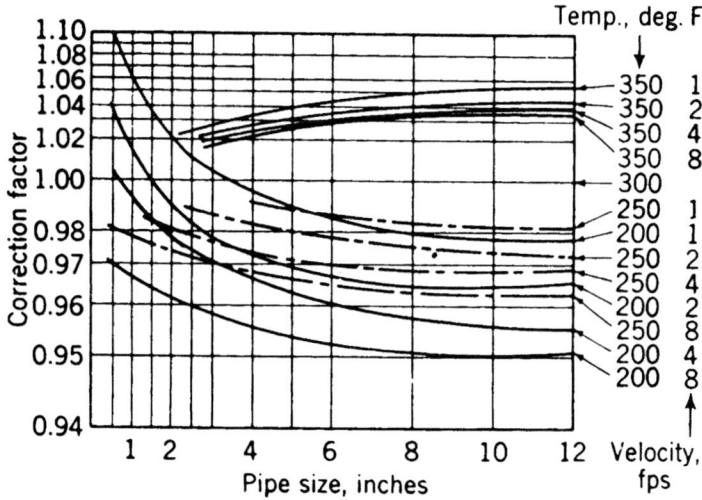

Fig 15-120. Correction factors for friction loss from Fig. 15-121

Table 15-35. Heat Capacity of Pipes

	Pipe Dia, in.	Transmitted Btu/hr	Pipe Dia, in.	Transmitted Btu/hr	Pipe Dia, in.	Transmitted Btu/hr
	¾	100,000	2	1,500,000	4	8,000,000
Data based on 100°F temperature drop and friction loss of 0.10 to 0.20 inch wg/ft. Velocities will vary from 1.5 to 4.5 fps	1	250,000	2½	2,500,000	5	12,000,000
	1¼	400,000	3	4,000,000	6	20,000,000
	1½	700,000	3½	6,500,000		

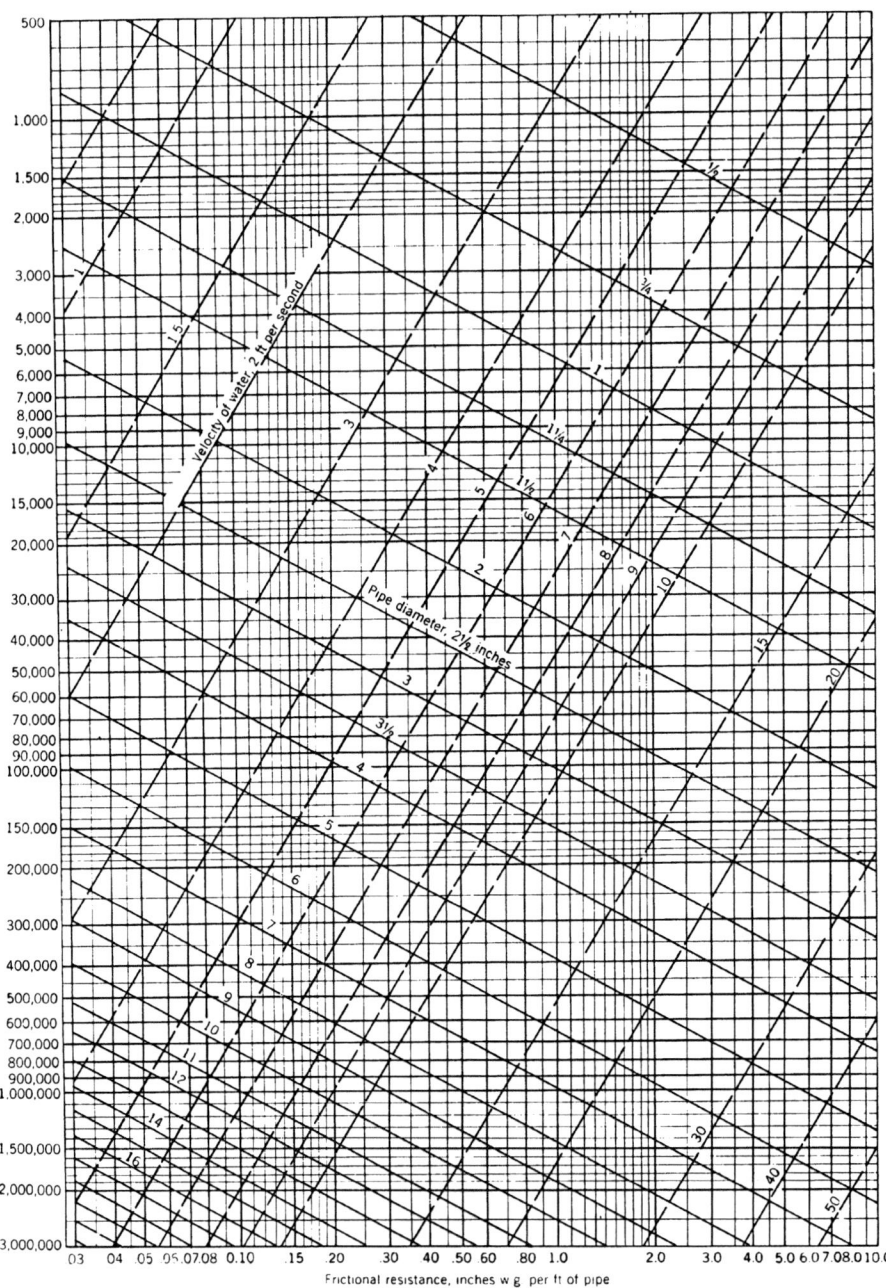

Fig 15-121. Frictional resistance of 300°F water in schedule 40 steel pipe

Ratings of Steel Boilers

Steel heating boiler ratings given on these pages are those of the Steel Boiler Institute (SBI), from whose Rating Code (edition, 1958) the accompanying tables and text are abstracted by permission.

General.—The code applies to all designs of steel boilers designated as Table 15-37. Ratings of Mechanically Fired, and Hand Fired Boilers Table 15-39. Net Rating Data for Steel Boilers and Table 15-41. IBR Ratings for Cast Iron Boilers .

Table 15-37 steel boilers are those containing the heating surfaces shown and the ratings of which have been determined in accordance with the Institute's code.

Table 15-39 steel boilers are those containing not more than 294 ft^2 of heating surface and having catalog SBI net ratings (steam) are not more than 5000 ft^2 mechanically fired and 4120 ft^2 hand fired.

Table 15-39 steel boilers are those with gross outputs and net ratings listed in Table 15-39. Table 15-39 boilers have no limits of minimum heating surface or furnace volume.

Ratings.—One ft^2 of steam radiation shall be considered equal to the emission of 240 Btu/hr, and 1 ft^2 of water radiation shall be considered equal to the emission of 150 Btu/hr.

A boiler horsepower is the evaporation of 34.5 lb of water per hr into dry steam from and at 212°F.

The SBI rating indicates the estimated design load that the boiler will carry as determined by the sum of items A, B and C given below under connected loads.

The SBI net rating indicates the net load the boiler will carry as determined by the sum of items A and B below under connected loads except that, if the heat loss from the piping system exceeds 20% of the installed radiation, the excess shall be considered as additional net load.

The SBI gross output for boiler indicates a heat output at the boiler nozzle of 5040 Btu/hr-ft^2 of catalog heating surface. For Table 15-38 boilers the SBI gross output indicates a heat output of 6120 Btu/hr-ft^2 of catalog heating surface. For Table 15-39 boilers the SBI gross output is the output tabulated in Table 15-39 for a boiler operating within all the limits stipulated in the code. The SBI gross output indicates the load the boiler will carry as determined by the sum of items A, B, C and D below, under connected loads.

Connected Loads: A) The estimated normal heat emission at design temperature of the connected radiation required to heat the building as determined by accepted practice, expressed in ft^2 of radiation or in Btu/hr.

B) The estimated maximum heat required by water heater or other apparatus connected to the boiler, expressed in ft^2 of radiation or in Btu/ hr.

C) The estimated heat emission at design temperature of piping connecting radiation and other apparatus to the boiler, expressed in ft^2 of radiation or in Btu/ hr.

D) The estimated increase in normal load in Btu/ hr due to heating the boiler and contents to operating temperature and heating up cold radiation and piping.

Furnace Volume: The furnace volume for furnaces in which solid fuel is burned is the cubical content of the space between the bottom of the fuel bed and the first plane of entry into or between the tubes or flues.

The furnace volume for furnaces in oil fired Table 15-38 and Table 15-39 steel boilers is the furnace volume used in running SBI rating tests and does not include the volume occupied by refractory material, insulation, or fill used in the construction of the combustion chamber.

The furnace volume for furnaces in which pulverized fuel, liquid or gaseous fuel is burned is the cubical content of the space between the hearth and the first plane of entry into or between the tubes or flues.

Heating Surface: Heating surface is expressed in ft^2 and includes those surfaces in the boiler exposed to the products of combustion on one side and water on the other. The outer surface of tubes is used.

Heating Value of Coal: The ratings for hand fired steel boilers are based on coal having a heating value of 13,000 Btu per pound as fired. When selecting hand fired steel boilers for coal of less heating value, the estimated design load should be multiplied by the proper factor selected from Table 15-36.

Table 15-36. Multiplying Factors for Coal Boilers

Heating Value, Btu/lb	Factor	Heating Value, Btu/lb	Factor
13,000	1.00	10,500	1.24
12,500	1.04	10,000	1.30
12,000	1.08	9,500	1.37
11,500	1.13	9,000	1.44
11,000	1.18		

Grate Area: Grate area is expressed in ft^2 and is measured in the plane of the top surface of the grate. For double grate boilers the grate area is the area of the upper grate plus $\frac{1}{4}$ of the area of the lower grate.

Table 15-37. Ratings of Mechanically Fired, and Hand Fired Boilers

Mechanically Fired Boilers										Hand Fired Boilers							
SBI Rating			SBI Net Rating			SBI Gross Output, 1000 Btu/hr	Minimum Furnace Volume, ft³	Minimum Furnace Height, in.	Minimum Heating Surface, ft²	SBI Rating			SBI Net Rating			Minimum Grate Area, ft²	Minimum Heating Surface, ft²
ft² Steam	ft² Water	1000 Btu/hr	ft² Steam	ft² water	MBH					ft² Steam	ft² Water	MBH	ft² Steam	ft² Water	MBH		
(1)	(2)	(3)	(4)	(5)	(6)	(7)	(8)	(9)	(10)	(11)	(12)	(13)	(14)	(15)	(16)	(17)	(18)
2,190	3500	526	1,800	2,880	432	648	15.7	26	129	1,800	2,880	432	1,500	2,400	360	7.9	129
2,680	4,280	643	2,200	3,520	528	792	19.2	28	158	2,200	3,520	528	1,830	2,930	439	8.9	158
3,160	5,050	758	2,600	4160	624	936	22.6	29 1/4	186	2,600	4,160	624	2,170	3,470	521	9.7	186
3,650	5,840	876	3,000	4,800	720	1,080	26.1	29 1/2	215	3,000	4,800	720	2,500	4,000	600	10.5	215
4,250	6,800	1,020	3,500	5600	840	1,260	30.4	30	250	3,500	5,600	840	2,920	4,670	700	11.4	250
4,860	7,770	1,166	4,000	6400	960	1,440	34.8	30 1/2	286	4,000	6,400	960	3,330	5,330	800	12.2	286
5,470	8,750	1,313	4,500	7,200	1,080	1,620	39.1	31 1/4	322	4,500	7,200	1,080	3,750	6,000	900	13.4	322
6,080	9,720	1,459	5,000	8,000	1,200	1,800	43.5	31 3/4	358	5,000	8,000	1,200	4,170	6,670	1,000	14.5	358
7,290	11,660	1,750	6,000	9,600	1,440	2,160	52.1	32 3/4	429	6,000	9,600	1,440	5,000	8,000	1,200	16.4	429
8,500	13,600	2,040	7,000	11,200	1,680	2,520	60.8	34	500	7,000	11,200	1,680	5,830	9,330	1,400	18.1	500
10,330	16,250	2,479	8,500	13,600	2,040	3,060	73.8	35 1/2	608	8,500	13,600	2,040	7,080	11,330	1,700	20.5	608
12,150	19,440	2,916	10,000	16,000	2,400	3,600	86.8	37 1/2	715	10,000	16,000	2,400	8,330	13,330	2,000	22.5	715
15,180	24,280	3,643	12,500	20,000	3,000	4,500	108.5	40 1/4	893	12,500	20,000	3,000	10,420	16,700	2,500	25.6	893
18,220	29,150	4,373	15,000	24,000	3,600	5,400	130.2	43	1,072	15,000	24,000	3,600	12,500	20,000	3,000	28.4	1,072
21,250	34,000	5,100	17,500	28,000	4,200	6,300	151.8	46	1,250	17,500	28,000	4,200	14,580	23,330	3,500	30.9	1,250
24,290	38,860	5,830	20,000	32,000	4,800	7,200	173.5	48 3/4	1,429	20,000	32,000	4,800	16,670	26,670	4,000	33.2	1,429
30,360	48,750	7,286	25,000	40,000	6,000	9,000	216.9	54 1/2	1,786	25,000	40,000	6,000	20,830	33,330	5,000	37.4	1,786
36,430	58,280	8,743	30,000	48,000	7,200	10,800	260.3	60 1/2	2,143	30,000	48,000	7,200	25,000	40,000	6,000	41.2	2,143
42,500	68 000	10,200	35,000	56,000	8,400	12,600	303.6	66	2,500	35,000	56,000	8,400	29,170	46,670	7,000	44.7	2,500
48,570	77,710	11,657	40,000	64,000	9,600	14,400	346.9	71 3/4	2,857	40,000	64,000	9,600	33,330	53,300	8,000	48.0	2,857
54,640	87,420	13,114	45,000	72,000	10,800	16,200	390.3	77 1/2	3,214	45,000	72,000	10,800	37,500	60,000	9,000	51.0	3,214
60,710	97,140	14,570	50,000	80,000	12,000	18,000	433.6	83 1/2	3,571	50,000	80,000	12,000	41,670	66,700	10,000	54.0	3,571

Table 15-38. Net Rating Data for Table 15-37 Steel Boilers, Oil Fired

SBI Net Rating			SBI Gross Output, MBH	Minimum Furnace Volume, ft³	Minimum Heating Surface, ft²
Steam		Water, MBH			
ft²	MBH				
(1)	(2)	(3)	(4)	(5)	(6)
275	66	74	99	2.5	16
320	77	87	115	2.9	19
400	96	108	144	3.6	24
550	132	149	198	5.0	32
700	168	189	252	6.4	41
900	216	243	324	8.2	53
1,100	264	297	396	10.0	65
1,300	312	351	468	11.8	77
1,500	360	405	540	13.6	88
1,800	432	486	648	16.4	1 06
2,200	528	594	792	20.0	129
2,600	624	702	936	23.6	153
3,000	720	810	1,080	27.3	177
3,500	840	945	1,260	31.8	206
4,000	960	1,080	1,440	36.3	236
4,500	1,080	1,215	1,620	40.9	265
5,000	1,200	1,350	1,800	45.4	294

Table 15-37 Ratings.—The SBI rating of a boiler expressed in ft^2 of steam radiation in which solid fuel hand fired is burned is equal to 14 times the heating surface of the boiler in ft^2.

The SBI rating of a boiler in ft^2 of steam radiation in which solid fuel is mechanically fired or in which oil or gas is burned is equal to 17 times the heating surface of the boiler in ft^2.

Grate Area: The grate area is not less than the values shown in Table 15-37, which have been determined by the following formulae:

For boilers with SBI ratings of 1800 ft^2 to 4000 ft^2 of steam radiation

$$G = \sqrt{\frac{R - 200}{25.5}}$$

For boilers with SBI ratings of 4000 ft^2 of steam radiation and larger

$$G = \sqrt{\frac{R - 1500}{16.8}}$$

where G = grate area in ft^2

R = SBI net rating in ft^2 of steam radiation.

The minimum grate requirement does not apply to Scotch type boilers.

Furnace Volume: The furnace volume for a boiler in which pulverized fuel, oil or gas, or stoker fired bituminous coal is burned is not less than one cubic foot for every 140 ft^2 of steam rating. No minimum furnace volume is specified for mechanically fired boilers burning anthracite.

Furnace Height: Furnace height is the vertical distance from the bottom of the water leg to the crown sheet measured midway between the sidewalls and midway between the front and back (or bridgewall if used) of the furnace.

The minimum furnace height requirement does not apply to Scotch type boilers.

Table 15-38 Ratings.—*Oil Fired Boilers:* The SBI net rating expressed in ft^2 of steam radiation is 17 times the minimum heating surface shown in Column 6, Table 15-38.

The net rating for steel boilers, expressed in Btu/hr, is 270 times the SBI net rating in ft^2 of steam radiation.

In determining Table 15-38 ratings the following factors were applied.

The burner was set to produce 10% CO_2 ($\pm 0.2\%$) in the flue gases, the O_2 in the flue gases was not less than 7%, the flue gas temperature did not exceed 600°F when the boiler operated at the gross output. Further, the overall efficiency of the boiler and burner was not less than 70% when operating at the gross output. Also, the difference between the draft in the breeching and the draft in the fire-box when the boiler is operating at the gross output was not greater than that determined by the formula:

$$DL = \frac{NR}{200} + 4$$

where *DL* is the draft loss in hundredths of an inch of water, and *NR* is the net rating in ft^2 of steam radiation.

This limitation does not apply to integral boiler burner units that are regularly catalogued and marketed complete with boiler burner and refractory designed to operate with higher draft losses, and where means are provided to develop sufficient draft to overcome the high draft losses.

Furnace Volume: The furnace volume is not less than 1 ft^3 for every 110 ft^2 of steam net rating.

This limitation shall not apply to integral boiler burner units regularly catalogued and marketed complete with boiler, burner, and refractory.

Stoker Fired and Gas Fired Boilers: The SBI net rating is not greater than the oil fired gas or fired boiler ratings. If baffles or turbulators are used in determining the oil fired ratings they may be omitted from boilers furnished for stoker firing.

Hand Fired Boilers: The net rating in ft^2 of steam radiation is not greater than 14 times the heating surface.

The grate area is not less than that determined by the formula:

$$G = \sqrt{\frac{NR + 600}{9}} - 8$$

where G = grate area in ft^2

NR = SBI net rating in ft^2 of steam radiation

The firebox volume for the purpose of determining the coal storage capacity of a hand fired boiler is that volume between the grate and the crown sheet. The volume of the uptake, the upper combustion chamber and that beyond the front face of the bridgewall is not included.

The firebox volume is not less than that determined by the formula:

$$FV = \sqrt{\frac{NR + 90}{5}} - 5.5$$

where *FV* = firebox volume in ft^3

NR = SBI net rating in ft^2 of steam radiation

Boiler Nameplate: Minimum data to be shown on a boiler are:
 1) manufacturers name and address
 2) boiler number and type
 3) SBI symbol
 4) heating surface
 5) SBI net rating in Btu/hr for each type of firing recommended
 6) ASME code symbol
 7) whether or not baffles or turbulators or other means of directing or retarding flue gases are used.

Table 15-39 Steel Boilers.—Table 15-39 boilers include boiler burner units defined as integral units, regularly catalogued complete with boiler, burner and combustion chamber.

Oil Fired Boilers: In rating Table 15-39 boilers, the burner is set to produce 10% CO_2($\pm$ 0.2%) in the flue gases. This limit does not apply to boiler burner units but, if the CO_2 produced during the tests of such units exceeds 10.2%, the flue gas temperature and overall efficiency figures determined from the tests are adjusted as follows:

For each 0.1% CO_2, over 10.2% 2.5°F is added to the recorded stack temperature and 0.175% deducted from the calculated test efficiency.

The O_2 percent by volume in the flue gases is not less than calculated according to the following formula:

$$7(3 - 0.2CO_2) = \text{Minimum permissible}$$

where CO_2 is the percent CO_2 recorded in the test.

With certain exceptions the flue gas temperature does not exceed 600°F when the boiler is operating at the gross output. When the CO_2 is over 10.2% the adjusted flue gas temperature shall meet this requirement.

Smoke Test: Smoke density is required to be not more than No. 2 on the Shell Bacharach scale when boiler is operating at 100% of the SBI gross output. One smoke test is made within 15 minutes after start, one after about one hour and one within five minutes of end of recorded test and all three tests must meet this requirement.

Flue Gas Temperature Adjustment: A boiler or a boiler burner unit is allowed an increase of 1°F over the 600°F flue gas temperature limit for each 0.1% increase in test efficiency achieved over 70%. For boiler burner units the allowance is above the calculated adjusted stack temperature limit. The maximum allowance in either case is 30°F.

Table 15-39. Net Rating Data for Steel Boilers

SBI Gross Output, MBH	SBI Net Ratings		
	Water MBH	Steam MBtu	Steam ft²
99	74	66	275
115	87	77	320
144	108	96	400
198	149	132	550
252	189	168	700
324	243	216	900
396	297	264	1100
504	378	336	1400
648	486	432	1800
792	594	528	2200
1008	756	672	2800
1260	945	840	3500
1512	1134	1008	4200
1800	1350	1200	5000

The overall efficiency of the boiler and burner is not less than 70% when operating at the SBI gross output.

There are no furnace volume limitations for Table 15-39 Boilers.

Draft Loss: The difference between the draft in the breeching and the draft in the firebox when the boiler is operating at SBI gross output is not greater than determined by the following formula:

$$DL = \frac{\text{SBI gross output (1000 Btu)}}{75} + 4$$

where DL = draft loss in hundredths inches of water.

This limitation does not apply to boiler burner units that are regularly catalogued and marketed complete with boiler, burner, and combustion chamber, designed to operate with higher draft losses, and where means are provided to develop sufficient draft to overcome the high draft loss.

Minimum stack dimensions for Table 15-39 boilers are given in Table 15-40.

The accompanying table is from the 6th edition of the I-B-R Testing and Rating Code for Low Pressure Cast Iron Boilers, effective June, 1958.

Table 15-40. Minimum Stack Dimensions, Table 15-39 Boilers and Boiler Burner Units

Rectangular Stack		
Firing Rate, GPH, Not Over	Nominal Dimensions, in.	Inside Dimensions of Liner, in.
2.1	8 × 8	6¾ × 8¾
3.5	8 × 12	6½ × 10 ½
5.3	12 × 12	9¾ × 9 ¾
7.7	12 × 16	9½ × 13 ½
11.5	16 × 16	13 ¼ × 13¼
15.0	16 × 20	13 × 17
21.0	20 × 20	16¾ × 16 ¾
26.0	20 × 24	16½ × 20 ½
Round Stack		
Firing Rate, GPH, Not Over		Inside Diameter of Liner, in.
1.3		6
1.8		7
2.5		8
4.7		10
5.6		11
7.0		12
12.0		15
19.0		18

Table 15-41. IBR Ratings for Cast Iron Boilers

Gross I-B-R Output, MBH	Hand-Fired						Automatic-Fired			
	Net I-B-R Rating		Piping and Pickup Factor	Time Available Fuel Will Last, hr	Maximum Stack Height, ft	Minimum Stack Area, in^2	Net I-B-R Rating		Piping, and Pickup Factor	Maximum Allowable Draft Loss
	Steam and Water, MBH	Steam, ft^2					Steam and Water, MBH	Steam, ft^2		
30	...	...	...	...	...	...	22.5	94	1.333	0.043
40	...	...	...	...	...	...	30.0	125	1.333	0.044
50	21.2	88	2.360	7.50	29.0	50.0	37.5	156	1.333	0.046
100	42.4	177	2.36	7.09	31.0	50.0	75.0	313	1.333	0.052
200	87.5	365	2.285	6.41	36.0	50.0	150.0	625	1.333	0.065
300	136.8	570	2.193	5.95	39.5	50.0	225.1	938	1.333	0.078
400	190.1	792	2.104	5.58	43.0	62.5	300.1	1250	1.333	0.090
500	245.9	1025	2.033	5.29	46.0	84.5	375.1	1563	1.333	0.102
600	304.0	1266	1.974	5.02	48.5	106.5	450.1	1875	1.333	0.114
700	363.1	1513	1.928	4.80	51.0	128.0	525.1	2188	1.333	0.126
800	423.3	1764	1.890	4.59	53.5	149.0	600.1	2501	1.333	0.137
900	484.4	2018	1.858	4.42	55.5	169.5	675.2	2813	1.333	0.149
1000	546.7	2278	1.829	4.31	57.5	190.5	750.2	3126	1.333	0.161
1100	611.1	2546	1.800	4.22	59.0	211.5	825.2	3438	1.333	0.172
1200	677.2	2822	1.772	4.14	61.0	232.5	900.2	3751	1.333	0.183
1300	745.4	3106	1.744	4.07	63.0	254.0	978.9	4079	1.328	0.195
1400	815.4	3397	1.717	4.00	64.5	275.0	1061.4	4423	1.319	0.207
1500	886.5	3694	1.692	4.00	66.5	295.5	1145.0	4771	1.310	...
1600	960.4	4002	1.666	4.00	68.0	315.0	1227.9	5116	1.303	...
1700	1036.0	4316	1.641	4.00	69.5	333.3	1311.7	5466	1.296	...
1800	1113.9	4641	1.616	4.00	71.0	350.0	1394.3	5809	1.291	...
1900	1193.5	4973	1.592	4.00	72.5	366.0	1474.0	6142	1.289	...
2000	1274.7	5311	1.569	4.00	73.5	381.0	1552.8	6470	1.288	...
2500	1707.6	7115	1.464	4.00	80.0	450.0	1941.0	8087	1.288	...
3000	2142.9	8929	1.400	4.00	86.5	512.0	2329.2	9705	1.288	...
3500	2500.0	10417	1.400	4.00	92.5	572.0	2717.4	11322	1.288	...
4000	2857.1	11905	1.400	4.00	98.5	630.0	3105.6	12940	1.288	...
4500	3214.3	13393	1.400	4.00	104.0	688.0	3493.8	14557	1.288	...
5000	3571.4	14881	1.400	4.00	109.0	746.0	3882.0	16175	1.288	...
5250	3750.0	15625	1.400	4.00	111.5	775.0	4076.1	16084	1.288	...
5500	3928.6	16369	1.400	4.00	113.5	803.0	4270.2	17792	1.288	...
5750	4107.1	17113	1.400	4.00	115.5	831.0	4464.3	18601	1.288	...
6000	4285.7	17857	1.400	4.00	117.5	858.0	4658.4	19410	1.288	...
6250	4464.3	18601	1.400	4.00	119.0	884.0	4852.5	20219	1.288	...
6500	4642.9	19345	1.400	4.00	120.0	900.0	5046.6	21027	1.288	...
7000	5000.0	20833	1.400	4.00	120.0	900.0	5434.8	22645	1.288	...
7190	5135.7	21399	1.400	4.00	120.0	900.0	5582.3	23260	1.288	...
7300	5214.3	21726	1.400	4.00	120.0	900.0	...	...	...	...

The gross I-B-R output is obtained by test. For hand-fired boilers the minimum efficiency, time available fuel will last, chimney size, and draft are subject to limitations set by the code. For automatically fired boilers, flue gas temperature and analysis, draft loss, and heat output of the combustion chamber are similarly subject to code limitations. Net I-B-R rating is obtained from gross rating by applying piping and pickup factors.

Heat Emission of Cast Iron Radiators: The accompanying data make readily available the information necessary in the field to determine the net heat given off by direct cast iron radiators. The data given are not intended to be used in design but are for surveys of existing plants.

Each of the tables can be used alone, if desired. To determine the combined effect of the different variables affecting the heat given off by radiators, refer to the formula given later.

Table 15-44: Heat emissions in equivalent ft² (1 EDR = 240 Btu/hr) of bare, unenclosed, direct, cast iron radiators standing in still air at 70°F and with 215°F heating medium temperature.

Table 15-45: Relative heat emissions of radiators under varying radiator and room temperatures. In general, it may be assumed that the radiator surface temperature will be the same as the temperature of the heating medium. The table shows that, for example, a radiator with 210°F steam in an 80°F room will use 0.87 as much steam as one standing in 70°F air using 215°F steam. Similarly, a radiator supplied with hot water at 170°F air has a heat output 0.62 as much as a steam radiator in still air at 70°F with a 215°F surface. The factors given in this table when multiplied by the ratings there give the equivalent ft² (EDR) for the room, and heating medium conditions given.

Table 15-42: Painting of a radiator affects its heat output. This table gives the relative effect of commonly used finishes as compared with a bare cast iron radiator.

Table 15-43: Gives the relative effect of some common enclosures on radiators as compared with bare, unenclosed, cast iron direct radiators.

The combined effect of all of these variables can be expressed as

$$R = H \times N \times F \times P \times E$$

where R = net heat given off in EDR (240 Btu/hr)

H = rated EDR as given in Table 15-44

N = number of sections of given radiator

F = factor from Table 15-45 depending on the room and the heating medium temperature

P = multiplier from Table 15-42 for finish

E = multiplier from Table 15-43 depending on type of enclosure used.

Example 11: What is the net heat given off by a 12 section tubular radiator with 5 tubes, 22 inches high, lb/in² steam pressure? The radiator is painted with aluminum bronze, has a shield above it, and is in a room maintained at 80°F.

Solution: Find the net heat given off by substituting in the formula

$$R = H \times N \times F \times P \times E$$

The section on tubular radiators of Table 15-44 shows that

H = rated EDR per section for a 5-tube, 22-inches, bare cast iron radiator is 3.00

N = number of sections, given as 12

F = correction factor for room and surface temperature for an 80°F room temperature and psia steam pressure 0.92 in Table 15-45

P = multiplier (depending on the radiator finish), 0.91 for an aluminum finish from Table 15-42

E = multiplier for the enclosure, found in Table 15-43 to be 0.90 for a shield above a radiator.

Substituting these figures in the formula

$$R = 3.00 \times 12 \times 0.92 \times 0.91 \times 0.90$$
$$= 27.1 \, \text{EDR}$$

Radiators that use hot water for a heating medium frequently have a lower EDR per section because of the lower surface temperatures maintained. Hot water temperatures will range anywhere from 170°F for a gravity installation to 220°F or higher for a forced pressure system. Of course, when surface temperatures of 215°F or over are encountered, the EDR will be equal to or higher than the rating under standard conditions.

Table 15-42. Relative Effect of Radiator Finishes on Heat Emission

Finish	Multiplier (P)
Bare cast iron, foundry finish	1.00
Gold bronze	0.90
Aluminum bronze	0.91
White paint	1.02
Cream paint	1.04
Red lacquer	1.00
Dull green paint	0.96
Brown pain	1.05

Table 15-43. Relative Effect of Enclosures on Radiator Heat Emission

Description of Enclosure	Multiplier (E)
None, bare cast iron radiator	1.00
None, shield above radiator	0.90
Open front and ends at bottom large free area in outlet, front only, upper half	0.90
Solid top, grilled front and ends, with large free area	0.86
Solid top, grilled front and ends, small free area	0.85
Solid top and ends, full grilled front. Factor depends on free area of grille; drops off rapidly as free area decreases	0.70–0.87
Solid top and ends, upper half of grilled front	0.83

Table 15-44. Capacity of Unenclosed Bare Cast Iron Radiators

Height, Floor to Top, in.	Column Type, Number of Columns							Tubular Type, Number of Tubes				
	1	2	3	4	5	6	Solid	3	4	5	6	7
	Heat Emission (H) per Section, ft² EDR											
12	...	...	...	...	...	3.00	...	...	...	...	...	
13	...	...	...	...	3.00	...	...	...	...	...	...	2.50
14	...	...	...	...	...	3.25	...	...	...	...	...	2.50
15	...	1.50	...	...	...	...	...	...	...	...	...	...
16	...	...	...	...	3.50	3.75	...	...	...	...	...	2.50
17	...	...	...	...	...	4.00	...	...	...	2.25	...	3.00
18	...	...	2.25	3.00	4.00	4.33	...	...	...	...	...	3.50
20	1.50	2.00	...	...	5.00	5.25	3.25	1.75	2.25	2.67	3.00	3.67
22	...	...	3.00	4.00	6.00	...	...	2.00	...	3.00	...	4.00
23	1.67	2.33	...	4.67	...	...	4.00	2.00	2.50	3.00	3.50	4.25
26	2.00	2.67	3.75	5.00	7.00	...	4.50	2.33	2.75	3.50	4.00	5.00
28	...	...	...	...	...	...	5.00	...	...	...	...	...
30	...	...	...	...	...	...	...	3.00	3.50	4.00	5.00	5.50
31	...	...	...	...	...	...	...	3.00	...	4.25	...	...
32	2.50	3.33	4.50	6.50	8.50	...	5.75	3300	3.50	4.33	5.00	6.25
36	...	...	...	...	...	...	...	3.50	4.25	5.00	6.00	6.75
37	...	...	...	...	...	...	...	...	4.25	5.00	6.00	...
38	3.00	4.00	5.00	8.00	10.00	...	7.00	3.50	4.25	5.00	6.00	7.50
45	...	5.00	6.00	10.00	...	...	...	...	...	...	...	...

Table 15-45. Relative Heat Emission of Bare Radiators at Various Temperatures

Room Temperature, °F	Surface Temperatures of Radiators °F									
	150	160	170	180	190	200	210	215	250	275
	Multiplier (F) for Bare Cast Iron Radiators									
50	0.62	0.70	0.78	0.87	0.96	1.04	1.15	1.20	1.54	1.82
60	0.54	0.62	0.70	0.78	0.87	0.96	1.04	1.10	1.45	1.69
65	0.50	0.57	0.66	0.74	0.83	0.92	1.00	1.04	1.41	1.64
70	0.46	0.54	0.62	0.70	0.78	0.87	0.96	1.00	1.35	1.59
75	0.42	0.50	0.57	0.66	0.74	0.83	0.92	0.96	1.30	1.54
80	0.39	0.46	0.54	0.62	0.70	0.78	0.87	0.92	1.25	1.49

Typical Ratings for Baseboard Radiation

Hot Water Ratings (65°F entering air)				Steam Ratings (1 psi) Btu/hr-ft	Heating Element Material and Tube Dia, in.	Finned Surface		Overall Height from Floor, in.	Nominal Length of Sections, ft
Average Water Temperature, °F						Material	Size, in.		
170	180	190	200						
Btu/hr-ft at 1 gpm Flow Rate									
500	560	630	700	820	¾ copper	aluminum	2 × 2¾ × 0.010	9	3,4,5,8
350	390	430	480	560	cast iron	cast iron	...	7	...
520	590	660	720	830	cast iron	cast iron	...	9⅞	1½–6
590	660	730	800	990	¾ copper	aluminum	2½ × 3½ × 0.017	9⁹⁄₁₆	4,5,6,8
543	618	702	785	930	1 ips	steel	2¾ × 4	10	6
620	706	802	898	1060	1 copper	aluminum	2¾ ×4	10	18
330	365	430	510	...	⅝ copper	aluminum	1⅝ × 1¾	9½	8
410	455	500	550	...	⅝ copper	aluminum	1⅝ ×1¾	12	8
520	585	640	705	...	⅝ copper	aluminum	1⅝ × 1⅝	9½	8
650	720	795	865	...	⅝ copper	aluminum	1⅝ × 1⅝	12	8

Ultra Slender Tubular

Height, Floor to Top, in.	Number of Tubes		
	3	4	5
	Heat Emission (H) per Section, EDR		
19	1.1	1.4	1.8
22	1.3	1.6	2.1
25	1.5	1.8	2.4

Bathroom Radiators

Short Side, in.	Long Side, in.	
	17	20 ½
	Heat Emission (H) per Section, EDR	
8	…	3.50
9	3.50	…
12	4.25	…

Front Wall Radiators

Number of Tubes	Height, in.		
	17	20	23
	Heat Emission (H) per Section, EDR		
1	1.75	2.00	2.25
2	3.33	…	4.25
3	2.00	2.33	2.67
4	2.67	3.00	3.33
5	3.25	…	4.00

Wall Radiators

Dimension, One side in.	Dimension, Other Side, in.					
	16½	18½	21	22–24	26–29	38
	Heat Emission (H) per Section, EDR					
2½	…	…	1.4	…	1.8	…
12	…	…	…	5.0	7.0	9.0
12½	5.0	…	6.0	7.0	9.0	…
13¼	5.0	7.0	…	7.0	9.0	…

Typical Capacities of Unit Ventilators

Standard Air Rating, cfm	Anemometer Rating, cfm	Heat for Ventilation, MBH	Heating Medium		
			Steam	Hot Water	Electric
			Total Heat, MBH		
500	750	9.45	40.60	32.00	31.60
750	1000	14.20	59.80	48.00	47.60
1000	1260	18.90	76.50	64.00	63.90
1250	1560	23.60	96.60	80.00	79.60
1500	1860	28.30	117.70	96.00	95.50

Adapted from ASHRAE Guide and Data Book.

Based on 218.5°F steam, 0°F entering air, leaving air converted to standard air at 70°F.

Rating specified in some school codes.

Based on 25% outdoor air at 0°F, 70°F room temperature.

Heat for ventilation plus heat available to offset room heat loss. The latter is called surplus heat.

Typical Propeller Unit Heat Capacities
(200°F water, 60°F entering air)

Heat Emission MBH	Final Air, °F	Water Rate, gpm	Water Friction of Head, ft
10°F Water Temperature Drop			
23	107	4.5	0.14
45	110	9.0	0.40
90	110	18.0	0.73
210	107	41.0	1.89
20°F Water Temperature Drop			
20	102	2	0.08
45	104	4.5	0.14
90	98	9.00	0.21
225	98	22.5	0.75

Heat Emission of Pipe Coils (wall mounted, pipe horizontal, 215°F steam, air at 70°F)

Number of Rows	Pipe Sizes, in.		
	1	1¼	1½
	Heat Emission, Btu/hr-ft of Coil (Not Pipe)		
1	132	162	185
2	252	312	348
4	440	545	616
6	567	702	793
8	651	796	907
10	732	907	1020
12	812	1005	1135

Typical Propeller Unit Heat Capacities
(2 psi steam, 60°F entering air)

Heat Emission MBH	Final Air, °F	Air Rate, cfm	Motor HP
Standard 2-Row Coil Units			
18	105	370	$\frac{1}{30}$
50	118	790	$\frac{1}{20}$
100	124	1450	$\frac{1}{8}$
200	128	2700	$\frac{1}{6}$
High Air Capacity Units			
26	101	590	$\frac{1}{30}$
55	101	1230	$\frac{1}{8}$
100	101	2260	$\frac{1}{6}$
130	100	2970	$\frac{1}{6}$

Miscellaneous Heating and Cooling Media

Following are data on heating and cooling media other than water.

Brine.—The introduction of certain salts into water alters the boiling and freezing point of the solution in a specific manner according to the concentration of salt. It is interesting to note that the freezing point of water is gradually lowered as salt is added up to a certain concentration, above which the freezing point rises and may eventually be higher than that of water. The actual boiling and freezing points depend on the nature of the salt as well as the concentration of salt in the solution. Calcium chloride is a salt commonly used in brine solutions for heat transfer purposes.

Table 15-46. Boiling and Freezing Points of Calcium Chloride Solutions

Concentration% Weight	Specific Gravity at 60°F	Freezing Point, °F	Boiling Point, °F
40	1.410	+56	248
30	1.295	−51	237
20	1.186	0	221
10	1.087	+22	214

Table 15-46 shows the boiling and freezing points of calcium chloride solutions.

The characteristics of calcium chloride brine are such as to make it attractive for cooling systems but less attractive for heating systems.

Glycerine.—Glycerine can be readily handled for both heating and cooling applications. In high concentrations it has a high boiling point. Both the boiling point and freezing point are lowered when glycerine is diluted with water, the freezing point reaching a minimum of −51°F when the water content is about a third of the weight of solution. Table 15-47 shows the characteristics of aqueous solutions of glycerine.

Table 15-47. Boiling and Freezing Points of Aqueous Solutions of Glycerine

Concentration% Weight	Specific Gravity at 60°F	Freezing Point, °F	Boiling Point, °F
98.2	1.261	+56	554
95.0	1.253	+46	332
90.0	1.240	+29	281
80.0	1.213	−5	250
70.0	1.185	−38	237
66.7	1.178	−51	234
60.0	1.157	−30	228
50.0	1.129	−9	223
40.0	1.102	+4	219
30.0	1.075	+15	217

Glycol.—Ethylene glycol has some of the characteristics of glycerine. It is heavier than water and has no marked corrosive effect on iron and steel. On some other metals and alloys it has a marked corrosive effect, which can be modified by inhibitors. It should not be used with zinc or galvanized iron. Characteristics of ethylene glycol solutions are shown in Table 15-48.

Table 15-48. Boiling and Freezing Points of Aqueous Solutions of Ethylene Glycol

Concentration% Weight	Specific Gravity at 60°F	Freezing Point, °F	Boiling Point, °F
100	1.113	+10	386
90	1.105	−17	288
80	1.098	−45	260
70	1.088	−47	245
60	1.078	−54	235
50	1.061	−34	229
40	1.045	−13	225
30	1.032	+3.2	221

Other Media.—Oracular is a trade name applied to a group of chlorinated biphenyls. Oracular 1248 has a boiling point of 644°F and a freezing point less than 20°F. Its specific heat at 86°F is 0.29 and increases to 0.44 at 248°F. Viscosity at 86°F is 112 centipoises.

Dowtherm A is a trade name of diphenyl and diphenyl oxide, produced as a heating medium at high temperature. Table 15-49 shows properties.

A heat transfer oil developed specifically for snow melting systems by Socony Vacuum Oil Co. is S/V Sovaloid S. Characteristics of two S/V oils are shown in Table 15-50.

Certain organic silicates are liquids having high boiling and low melting points. By chemical combination and mixing of compounds, liquids of a common generic type but having different physical properties are produced within a liquid range of −60°F to 800°F. Tables 15-51 and 15-52 give some of the properties of aryl and crassly silicates.

Physical properties of mercury are shown in Table 15-53. It is the only metal that liquefies at atmospheric temperatures. It can be used with iron and steel but dissolves brass and other metals.

Table 15-49. Properties of Tetra Crassly Silicate

Boiling point, °F		815
Specific gravity, at:	77°F	1.125
	392°F	0.982
	572°F	0.908
Specific heat, Btu/lb-°F at:	77°F	0.4
	392°F	0.53
	572°F	0.62
Viscosity, centistokes at:	77°F	41
	392°F	1.4
Coefficient of expansion, per °F		.000775 to 0.000977
Density, lb/ft³ at 60°F		69.3
Flash point, °F		325 minimum
Pour point, °F		1

Table 15-50. Physical Properties of Mercury

Boiling point, °F		675
Melting point,°F		−38
Viscosity, centipoises at:	−4°F	1.85
	68°F	1.56
	212°F	1.22
	572°F	0.93
Specific heat, at:	32°F	0.0333
	212°F	0.0326
	392°F	0.0318
Density, lb/ft^3 at:	32°F	845
	212°F	830
	392°F	816
Heat content, Btu/ft^3-°F at:	32°F	28.2
	212°F	27.0
	392°F	25.9

Table 15-51. Physical Properties of Tetra Aryl Silicate

Viscosity, centipoises, at:	0°F	740.00
	50°F	52
	300°F	1.55
	600°F	0.43
Specific heat, at:	50°F	0.37
	300°F	0.48
	600°F	0.74
Density, lb/ft^3, at:	50°F	72.2
	300°F	65
	600°F	56.2
Heat content, Btu/ft^3-°F, at:		
	50°F	26.7
	300°F	31.1
	600°F	41.5

Table 15-52. Physical Properties of Dowtherm A

Boiling point	496°F	
Freezing point	54°F	
Flash point	228°F	
Fire point	246°F	
Auto-ignition temperature exceeds	932°F	
Viscosity, centipoises, at:	60°F	5
	2 50°F	0.86
	450°F	0.4
Specific heat, at	54°F	0.37
	2 50°F	0.47
	450°F	0.6
Density lb/ft^3 at:	54°F	66.9
	250°F	61.1
	450°F	54.8
Heat content, Btu/ft^3-°F at		
	54°F	24.7
	2 50°F	28.6
	450°F	32.8

Table 15-53. Physical Properties of Heat Transfer Oils

Property	S/V Sovaloid S	S/V Heat Transfer Oil
Gravity, API at 60°F/60°F	10	11
Specific gravity, at 60°F/60°F	1.0	0.9930
Flash Point, °F, open cup	260 min.	335
Kinematic Viscosity Centistokes at:		
450°F		0.86
300°F		1.95
175°F	1.7	8.25
100°F	3.9	50.00
50°F	10.00	450.00
0°F	48.0	
−10°F	70.0	
Coefficient of expansion, per °F	0.0035	
Distillation range initial boiling point, °F	500 min.	615
Final boiling point, °F	640 max.	735 (90%)
Specific heat, Btu/lb °F, at:		
450°F		0.966
300°F		0.910
175°F	0.47	0.864
100°F	0.43	0.835
50°F	0.42	0.820
0°F	0.39	

Warm Air Heating

If a warm air furnace is defined as a heat transfer device in which heat is released on one side of the heat exchanger surface and heat is absorbed by circulating air on the other side, a large number of devices can be included in this category, some of which are illustrated in schematic form in Fig. 15-123.

Early Types.— *Stove:* The earliest ancestor of the present day warm air furnace is the parlor stove, sometimes referred to as the pot-bellied stove. Aside from the cheery aspects of the flame that could be viewed through the isinglass openings, the stove was a utility that was tolerated but not aesthetically admired.

Pipeless Furnace: Warmed air rose by gravity action and was delivered into the room above through a large grilled opening in the floor.

Gravity Hot Air Furnace (Pre 1918): These early systems were installed without benefit of engineering knowledge. Air flow was restricted, and the furnaces were aptly described as hot air furnaces, since the air temperatures were in excess of 200°F.

Gravity Warm Air Furnace (Pre 1930): The early experimental work at the University of Illinois by Professors A. C. Willard and A. P. Kratz in the period following 1918 showed that, for example, markedly improved results could be obtained by the use of streamlined, amply sized return air ducts, large warm air stacks, and registers with ample free area. In these improved systems the actual operating register air temperature was much less than the assumed design value of 175°F, even under design weather loads.

Early Forced Air Conversion Models (Pre 1940): Even in the greatly improved gravity warm air furnace system the surfaces had to be extensive and the furnaces were large in size. The obvious step to increase the heat transfer rate was to use some mechanical means for circulating the air. Propeller fans located in the return air boot or in the bonnet were found to be lacking in pressure and capacity. When centrifugal fans were placed in a compartment attached to the casing, it was found that furnace casings had to be made smaller to prevent by passing the heating surface. Later, casings became rectangular and smaller; fans, filters, burners, and controls were integrally built into the casing, and a whole new line of products was introduced. In the trade, the centrifugal fans used for warm air furnaces are referred to as "blowers".

Current Types.—*Forced Air Furnace Types:* The current types of furnaces, some of which are illustrated in Fig. 15-122, show a great diversity of shapes and arrangements. Among the principal types used for residences and small buildings the following arrangements are common:

1) Low boy arrangement with furnace and blower in separate compartments, and with air discharged upwards. Used for basement installation, but also usable with furnace closets located on the first story.

2) High boy arrangement with upflow of air, in which the blower is located at the bottom of the casing and the heat exchanger is located at the top. Used for either basement installation or for first story installation.

3) High boy arrangement with downflow of air, in which the blower is located at the top of the casing and the heat exchanger is located below the blower. Used mainly for first story installation in which warm air is discharged downward.

4) Horizontal arrangement in which the blower and the heat exchanger are located side by side and the warm air is discharged horizontally. Used for basement or attic installations, or crawl space installations.

The current types are integrally designed and coordinated units in which the blower and control equipment are selected and arranged for the specific unit. In fact, in the smaller size of high boy units, the furnace package consists of a factory wired and factory installed assembly of heat exchanger, blower, blower motor, filter, controls, and humidifier.

Special Types; Other Current Types of Equipment.— The dividing line between a warm air furnace and a device which is not a warm air furnace is difficult to define sharply. The following are included here as special types of warm air furnaces (see Fig. 15-124):

Space Heater: This reminder of the early parlor stove still persists. Most space heaters are gravity circulating systems, but some are provided with propeller fans to stir the room air. No ducts are attached. Oil fired and gas fired space heaters are available, some of them with thermostatic control equipment.

Floor Furnace: This device is reminiscent of the early pipeless furnace, but on a much smaller scale and with refinements of automatic firing and controls. The unit is usually attached to the ceiling joists of the basement and is ductless. The circulating air temperature is extremely high with gravity circulating units.

Wall Furnace: This device is a space saving unit that is installed in the wall of a room and is usually a gravity circulation, pipeless unit. Some are tall and some are low enough to be installed just above the baseboard.

Direct Fired Unit Heater: Unit heaters can be direct fired, either with or without a circulating fan behind the heat exchanger surface. Used mainly for industrial or commercial installations.

Direct Fired Floor Model Unit Heaters: Extremely large unit heaters are available either with or without duct connections. Used for commercial and industrial buildings. Capacities in excess of 1,000,000 Btu/hr are available.

Industrial Warm Air Furnaces: Industrial warm air furnaces, or heavy duty furnaces, are available with capacities in excess of 1,000,000 Btu/hr. Used for schools, churches, commercial buildings, and industrial buildings.

Aircraft Air Heaters: Direct fired air heaters of small size but high capacity are available for aircraft heating. These are usually gasoline fired heaters.

The styles, models, and types of warm air furnaces are extremely diverse. Models are available for burning wood, coal, coke, oil fuel, kerosene, natural gas, bottled gas, and manufactured gas. The diversity was the result of demand: the demand of special building types and the demands of both the builder and the public for small, efficient, and economical units.

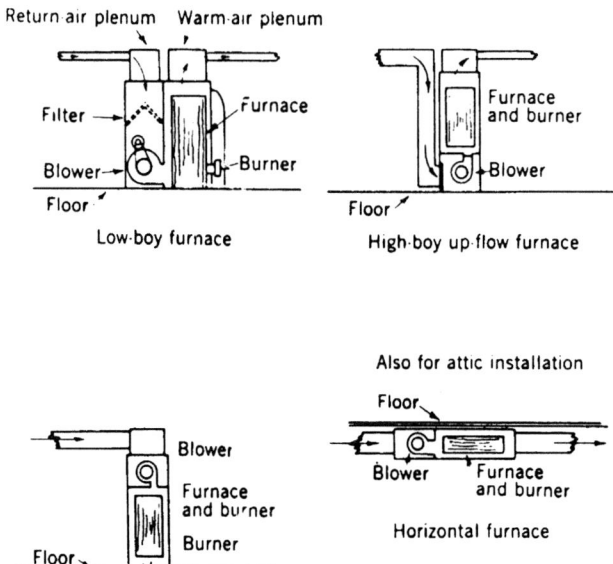

Fig 15-122. Forced air furnaces

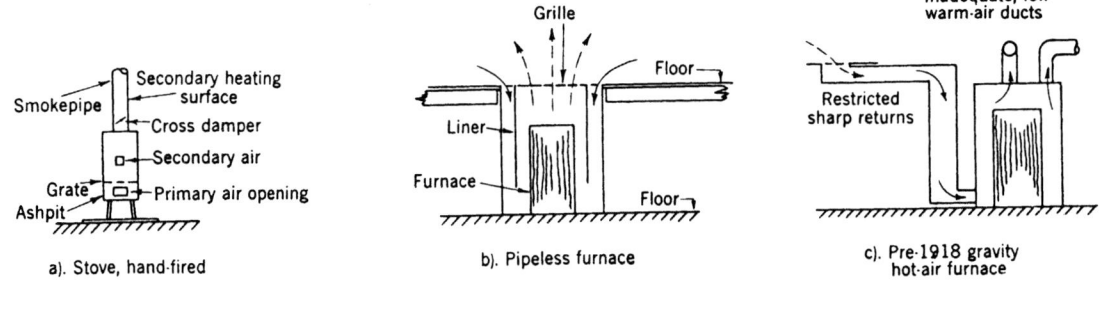

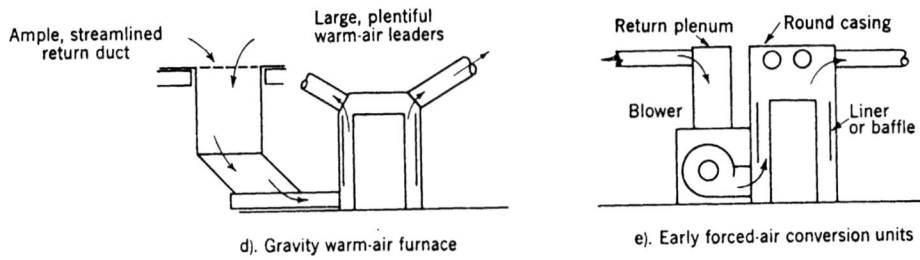

Fig 15-123. Development stages of forced air furnace

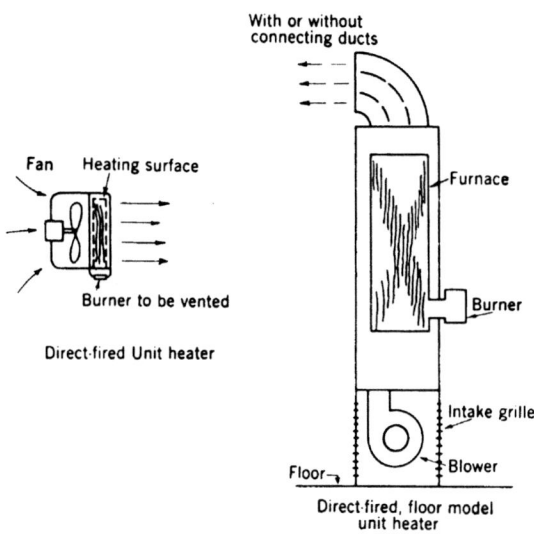

Fig 15-124. Allied version of forced air furnaces

Furnace Performance Terminology.—A few terms appear in catalog description of warm air furnaces which require definition (see also Fig. 15-125):

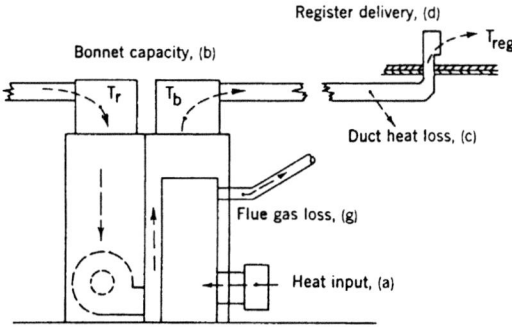

Fig 15-125. Furnace performance terminology

Input, or Heat Input: is the rate at which heat is released inside the furnace and is in units of Btu/ hr.

For Gas: Input, Btu/hr = ft³ gas/hr × heating value Btu/ft³
For Oil: Input, Btu/hr = gal oil/hr × heating value Btu/gal
For Coal: Input, Btu/hr = lb coal/hr × heating value Btu/lb

Capacity, or Bonnet Capacity: The heat available in the air at the furnace bonnet, in units of Btu/hr.

$$\text{Capacity} = (cfm)_b(60)(0.24)(d_b)(t_b - t_r)$$

where $(cfm)_b$ = air flow in cfm as measured at bonnet temperature;

d_b = density of air corresponding to bonnet temperature;

t_b = bonnet air temperature, °F; and

t_r = return air temperature, °F

Duct Heat Loss: The heat loss from the warm air ducts to the space surrounding the ducts, in units of Btu/hr.

Register Delivery: The heat available in the air that is delivered from the registers into the space to be heated, in units of Btu /hr:

$$\text{Delivery} = (cfm)_{reg}(60)(0.24)(d_{reg})(t_{reg} - t_r)$$

where $(cfm)_{reg}$ = air flow, cfm;

d_{reg} = density of air, lb/ft³; and

t_{reg} = register air temperature, °F.

Bonnet Efficiency: The ratio of the capacity to the input.

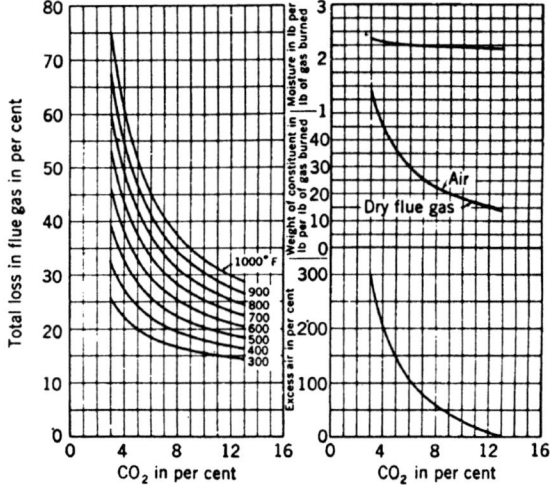

Fig 15-126. Flue gas losses with natural gas as fuel

Duct Transmission Efficiency: The ratio of the register delivery to the capacity.

Flue Gas Loss: The heat loss of the flue gases, expressed as a percentage of the heat input, and includes both sensible and latent heat losses. See Fig. 15-126 for a typical flue gas loss curve.

Combustion Efficiency: 100 minus the flue gas loss, expressed as a percentage.

Testing and Rating of Furnaces.—A given furnace in combination with a given blower can be operated in a number of different ways and provide almost an indefinitely large number of different capacities and efficiencies. For example, the rate of heat input to the furnace could be successively increased with a fixed speed of the blower and a set of performance data taken. After this, the whole set of tests could be repeated with another speed of the blower. From the standpoint of a commercial rating, it becomes necessary, therefore, to hold some of the variables at a constant value and to vary only one item. This is shown by a typical performance curve for a furnace, as shown by Fig. 15-127. For this furnace the rate of fuel input was successively increased after each test, but each time the blower speed was so adjusted that the temperature rise of the circulating air over the furnace was maintained at a constant value of 100°F. The typical curves in Fig. 15-127 show some interesting trends, common to all furnace performance tests:

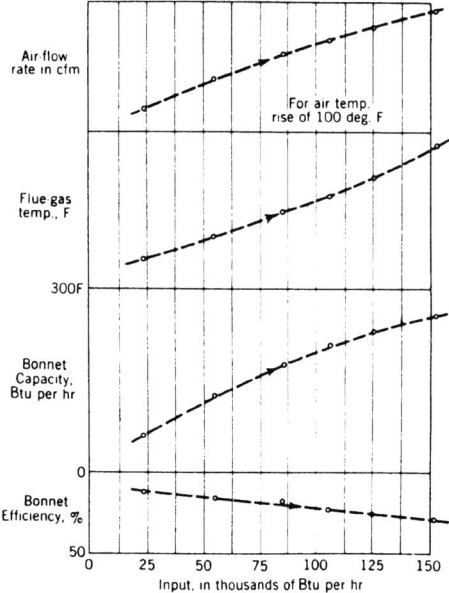

Fig 15-127. Typical trends of furnace performance tests

1) In common with most heat transfer devices, the maximum efficiency occurs at a low value of input. In fact, the efficiency gradually decreases as the input is increased.

2) The capacity increases with the increase in input, but not in linear relationship. Theoretically, if the input could be made large enough the capacity could be extended indefinitely.

3) The flue gas temperatures constantly increase with an increase in input since the heat exchanger surface is fixed in amount.

4) Since the tests were conducted with a constant rise in temperature of the circulating air (100°F) the required air flow rate also increased. Note that it would be possible to conduct tests with a constant flow rate and a constantly increasing air temperature.

From the standpoint of the engineer a complete performance curve of the type shown is much more informative and useful than a single point rating, but a single point rating is the only kind of rating that is acceptable to the trade in general. Every manufacturer is interested in a rating of the single point type. The user is also interested in a single point rating so that he can select a furnace for a given job and have reasonable assurance that it is adequate but not too large.

Acceptable Limits.—Theoretically, the furnace whose performance curves are shown in Fig. 15-127 could be rated at any value between, say, 10,000 Btu/hr up to 160,000 Btu/hr input. As a matter of fact, if no limits of any kind were imposed the furnace could have been tested

with higher and higher inputs until finally the furnace disintegrated. It becomes obvious that in order for a manufacturer to specify a single point rating it is necessary for the testing laboratory to impose some arbitrary limits, or boundaries, as to what is acceptable. The single point rating that is finally chosen would not necessarily be a point of maximum efficiency since the maximum efficiency was obtained at an abnormally low input and capacity. On the other hand, the single point rating would not be one for which the equipment was strained to the last notch. The arbitrary limits that happen to be selected by industry are not important for this discussion.

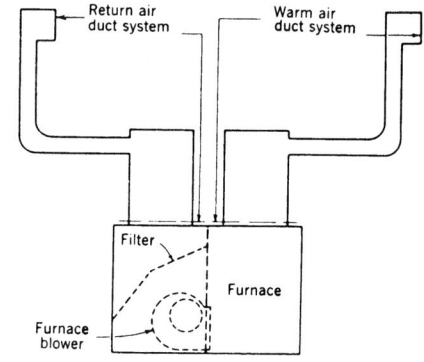

Fig 15-128a. Schematic diagram of a forced air system

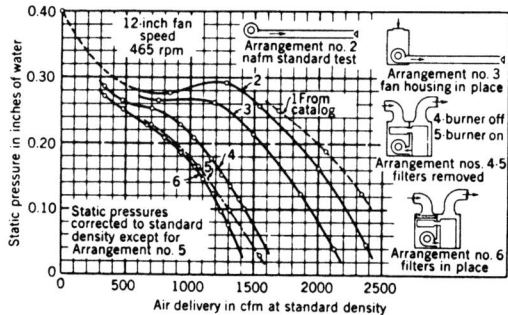

Fig 15-128b. Static pressure characteristics of a blower furnace combination

What is important is that industry have sensibly and wisely agreed upon certain limits, not only for the safeguard of the consumer, but primarily for the protection of the manufacturer who hopes to stay in the business. Industry could mutually agree upon a value of, say, 75% as the minimum bonnet efficiency acceptable, or a flue gas temperature of, say, 800°F could be considered as the maximum, or the surface temperature of the heat exchanger could be limited to, say, 900°F, or the draft could be limited, or all of these limits could be imposed simultaneously. Whatever capacity corresponded with the most stringent limit would then be the capacity for rating purposes. In practice, an extremely stringent set of limits have been imposed by the manufacturer acting through such laboratories as the American Gas Association Testing Laboratory. In general, the single point ratings that are given in catalogs are reasonably attainable values for a well designed installation. A typical single point rating for a small gas fired furnace would show:

Input = 90,000 Btu/hr

Capacity = 72,000 Btu/hr

All gas fired forced air furnaces that bear the approval label of the American Gas Association show a bonnet efficiency of 80%, no more and no less.

Selection of Furnace for Given Installation.—The selection of a furnace for a given installation is simple in principle, since it consists of selecting a furnace whose capacity is adequate to take care of the heat losses for the building under design weather conditions. In practice, a number of minor points arise that require clarification. For example, if the register delivery is to be made equal to the design heat loss, the manufacturers catalog should either state the delivery or give some means of estimating the duct transmission efficiency. In this connection the design manuals of the National Environmental Systems Contractors Association (NESCA) arbitrarily assume that the register delivery will be 0.85 times the bonnet capacity or, in other words, that the duct transmission efficiency will be 85%. This assumption may be greatly in error in large installations. Another question that arises in connection with design heat loss is that of determining what portion of the house should be included in the heat loss calculations. For example, should the basement heat loss be considered? If not, what should be done with basement playrooms and hobby rooms?

Rule for Selection.—For the sake of uniformity and consistency, one set rule is offered for the selection of furnaces, as follows:

Calculate the design heat loss for the entire structure, including the basement space, and select a furnace whose bonnet capacity is equal to this design heat loss.

For example, if the design heat loss for the first story rooms is 48,300 Btu/hr and that for the basement is 14,600

Btu/hr, the total heat loss for the entire structure is 62,900 Btu/hr. The furnace for this building should have a capacity equal to or greater than 62,900 Btu/hr. The suggested rule applies to a furnace that is to be located in the space to be heated. If, however, the furnace is to be located in a separate building, such as an attached garage or in the attic space, the heat loss from the ducts will be lost and will not be available for heating the house. In this case, it will be necessary to add a correction to take into account the heat loss from the ducts and the furnace casing to the design heat loss from the structure.

Blower Characteristics.—The blower is an integral part of the smaller furnace blower combinations used for residential heating, and the air flow characteristics are not for the blower alone, but for the combination. The curves in Figs. 15-128a and 15-128b, for example, one typical performance curves not only for the blower alone but for various arrangements of casing and filter.

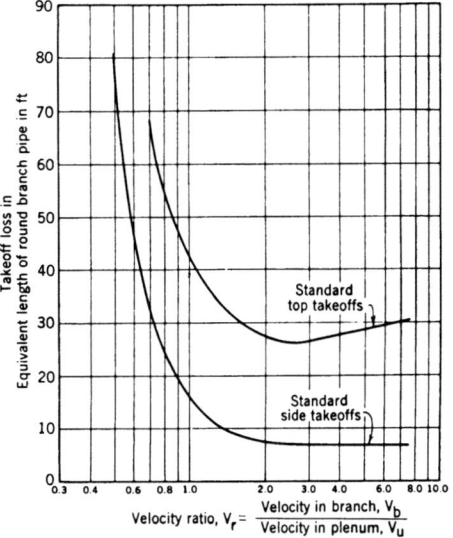

Fig 15-129. Loss of extended plenum fittings, in equivalent length of branch duct

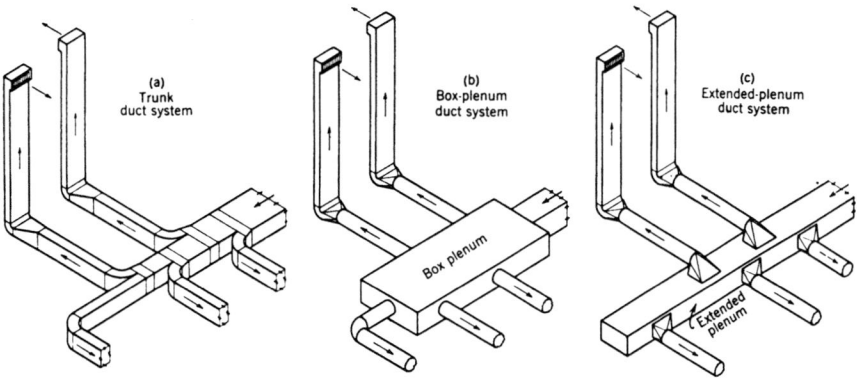

Fig 15-130. Three types of air duct system

The performance curve no. 6 is markedly lower than that labeled as no. 2, which is for the blower without any housing. For smaller furnaces the furnace blower combination should be capable of providing for an air flow corresponding to a 100°F temperature rise through the furnace and against a static pressure of 0.20 inch of water, measured external to the furnace blower combination. In other words, the 0.20 inch of water is for overcoming the frictional losses of the attached duct systems, shown at left in Figs. 15-128a and 15-128b. The internal losses due to frictional effects and expansion losses within the casing and the blower housing have been accounted for by the manufacturer and need not be taken into account by the designer of the duct system.

Blower Sizes.—With larger units of the industrial type, the temperature rise through the furnace is usually lower than 100°F, which corresponds to a larger air flow rate for a given heat input to the furnace than is characteristic of the small units. For example, temperature rises of the order of 50°F to 70°F are commonly specified for industrial type furnaces. Furthermore, the external static pressure is not limited to 0.20 inch of water and is usually considerably larger.

In order to satisfy the long rising trend towards summer cooling, more furnace blower combinations are now provided with more than one size of blower for a given size of furnace. In these arrangements a greater range of air flow rates is possible without over speeding a small blower or over loading the blower motor. Hence, if a given furnace blower combination is to be used in connection with a refrigeration unit, a larger blower can be made available than is normally used for heating purposes alone. This large blower will permit the use of a cooling coil in the air stream without creating a need to resort to an auxiliary fan for overcoming the resistance of the cooling coil.

Duct System Characteristics.—The ducts that connect the furnace blower combination with the registers and return intakes are the only part of the entire system that are not factory planned and factory assembled. It is true that certain portions of the duct system can be prefabricated, but essentially the duct system for each job is a tailor-made affair: no two are exactly alike, except perhaps in a housing project.

The duct system plays an important part in the final cost to the owner since a substantial part of cost and labor is involved in installing the equipment. In Fig. 15-130 are shown several alternate types of duct systems, although in an actual installation a combination of these different arrangements might be used. In any case the basic arrangements consist of:

Trunk Duct System: This has graduated sizes of trunk duct. This duct system, which is practical for large installations involves costly fittings and many changes in duct section. This system has proven costly to install in small jobs, in spite of the use of prefabricated fittings.

Box Plenum Duct System: This has advantages in certain installations where it is possible to construct a box plenum. In this arrangement the air is led to a central box from which a number of individual ducts are tapped off with butt take-off connections. The most common locations of the box plenum are in a central hallway or below the floor of one wing of a large structure.

Extended Plenum Duct System: This is a most practical duct system, especially for small installations. In this arrangement the trunk duct is not reduced in cross sectional area, and a number of branch ducts are connected to the extended plenum with simple branch take-off connections.

Individual Duct System : This system offers the other extreme in duct arrangements. It is easy to install, but in many cases proves fairly expensive if many individual ducts are to be run to a far end of the building. Furthermore, the heat loss from the ducts can be large and the duct transmission efficiency can be low. The system is easy to balance.

The air velocity near the furnace can be high, over 1000 fpm, but as one proceeds downstream the branch ducts divert air away from the plenum and the air velocity in the downstream portions of the plenum become smaller. The reduction in velocity head in the plenum is partially offset by an increase in the static pressure. In fact, the static pressure in an extended plenum duct system tends to be constant throughout the length of the duct. Furthermore, as shown in Fig. 15-129, the larger entry losses into the branch ducts occur at the upstream branches rather than at the downstream branches. The net result is, therefore, that a larger flow rate is obtained for a given size of duct at downstream branches than at upstream branches, which is contrary to the usual experience with the reduced trunk system. In small jobs where the additional cost of sheet metal used is of little consequence compared to the saving in installation labor and fabrication, the extended plenum duct system has proven most practical.

Trends.—Some interesting trends have taken place over the years, some of which conflicted in character. In the first place, as a natural outcome of the successful use of small duct, high velocity systems for aircraft heating, the idea of using small ducts took hold. In fact, duct sizes ranging from 3 inches in diameter to 6 inches in diameter have been tried. As indicated in Fig. 15-131, a reduction in duct diameter causes a sharp increase in air friction. Either smaller air flow rates can be handled through each duct or larger pressure losses can be maintained for the duct system. In fact, as one alternative, some thought has been given to the use of static pressures larger than 0.20 inch of water for the duct system. Such an increase can be handled up to a certain point with commercially available blowers. However, when static pressures much in excess of 0.50 inch of water are contemplated, the usual simple low cost blower is no longer applicable. Hence, increases in static pressure are limited by types of blowers that are commercially available.

The second approach was to decrease the air flow rate handled by the ducts and the entire system.

Diameter, inches	Area, sq in	All values at 600 fpm flow velocity		
		Flow rate, cfm	Friction loss, in. wg. per 100 ft	Temp drop, deg F per ft; 140 F entering
6	28.3	115	0.120	0.72
5½	23.8	98	0.130	0.83
5	19.6	82	0.145	0.96
4½	15.9	66	0.170	1.09
4	12.6	53	0.190	1.22
3½	9.6	40	0.230	1.41
3	7.1	29	0.280	1.67
2½	4.9	20	0.370	2.00
2	3.1	13	0.470	2.45

Fig 15-131. Characteristic of small air ducts

This can be done up to a point. It would be possible to increase the temperature rise through the furnace from the current 100°F to some value such as 150°F or even 200 °F. This increase in temperature rise would result in a markedly lower air flow requirement for a given capacity. Unfortunately, the use of higher bonnet air and register air temperatures brings additional problems. In the first place, the furnaces that are tested for acceptance by laboratories must undergo a 100°F temperature rise. For any other temperature rise, special tests will have to be conducted and perhaps some changes made in the test provisions. These changes are not easy to make since they must be accepted by a large segment of industry, including the public utilities. If such changes are considered to be a lowering of the standards, rather than an uplifting, the changes are not easy to make. In the second place, the higher air temperatures in the ducts will result in larger temperature drops of the air in the ducts. Small ducts lose a proportionally larger part of the initially available heat than do larger ducts handling the same velocity of air. By increasing the duct air temperature the heat loss is accentuated. In the third place the introduction of high temperature register air creates problems of air stratification in the room. Special diffusers are required when a quick diffu-

sion of the high temperature air is needed as it enters the room, so that the heated air does not simply rise and accumulate at the ceiling.

The current trend towards the use of a single system of ducts for both heating and cooling has also affected duct sizes. In general, air flow requirements for summer for a given space are larger than those for winter. If a duct system is to be adapted for year around air conditioning the small duct system, which may be most suitable for winter heating, may not be adequate for summer cooling. It would be possible, of course, to provide additional small ducts for use in summer cooling alone. In any case, the trend to smaller and smaller ducts has been stopped pending an evaluation of year round air conditioning load.

Warm Air Registers.—The flexibility of the forced air heating system is best illustrated by the wide variety of registers that are commercially available and the extremely diverse methods of installation that are possible. In fact, registers can be installed in the floor, the baseboard, above the baseboard, high in the sidewall, in the ceiling, the window ledge, or any other place to which a duct can be run. The more common types of registers consist of:

1) rectangular registers of perforated grille or straight vane type that do not provide for air deflection;

2) rectangular registers with movable or adjustable vanes that permit deflection, up, down, sideways, or both vertically and horizontally;

3) baseboard types that have long narrow openings;

4) diffuser types that attempt to mix the register air and the room air rapidly before the air stream has travelled far into the room;

5) ceiling registers and diffusers of square, round, rectangular, and oval-shaped designs;

6) rectangular slots for use in window ledges, in the floors below windows, or in the ceiling above windows;

7) a multiplicity of special designs for special purposes, such as railroad cars, airplane cabins, etc.

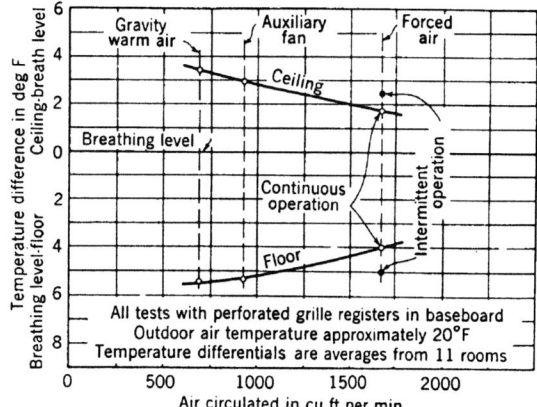

Fig 15-132. Average temperature differentials with gravity, auxiliary fan, and forced air systems

In many respects registers are the most important aspect of the forced air system as far as the occupant is concerned, since it is the visible evidence of the system in the living quarters. When improperly located the registers create drafty conditions and provide poor room temperature conditions. When properly located the registers can do much to improve room air temperature conditions. For example, Fig. 15-132 shows that for a given location of the registers, the indoor temperatures will be much more uniform with a forced air system than with either a gravity or auxiliary fan system. The reduction in temperature difference with the use of the forced air system may be attributed not only to the increase in the quantity of air that was circulated, but also to the decrease in the temperature of the air that was introduced into the rooms.

As will be shown in the next section on duct arrangements, the practical location of a register is governed to some extent by the type of structure in which the system is installed. The use of a baseboard register under a window, for example, may not be practical for a system in which the supply ducts are carried overhead. In general,

1) the register should introduce the air into the room in such a manner that the air does not strike an occupant that is seated and at rest

2) it should tend to overcome the downdrafts that occur below windows and cold walls, and

3) it should not interfere with furniture placement.

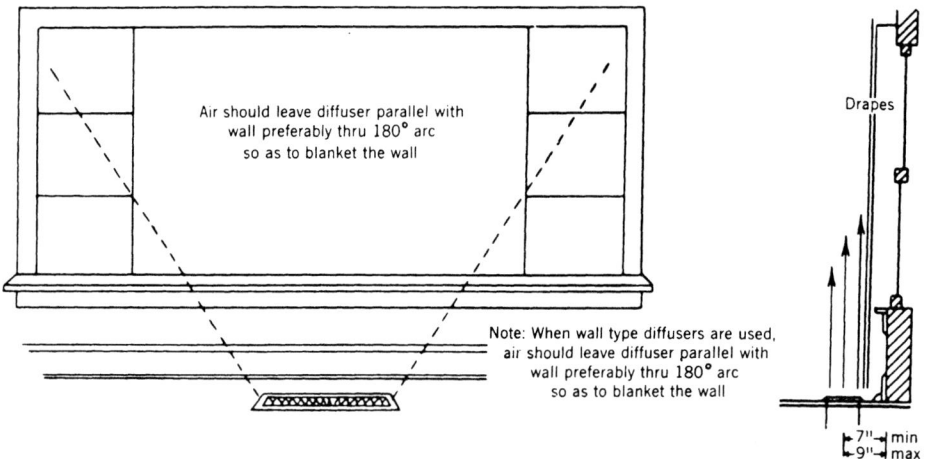

Fig 15-133. Location of floor diffuser below window

Room air velocities in the living zone preferably should not exceed 35 fpm, and the moving air stream should not deviate by more than 1.0°F from the room air temperature. The perimeter warm air system in which the warm air is introduced through floor registers located along the exposed walls of the structure, as shown in Fig. 15-133, has proven most successful, even for structures built over concrete slab floors or over unheated crawl spaces.

Return Air Intakes.—The function of the return air intake or grille is to provide a means for the room air to be returned to the furnace to be reheated and recirculated. In smaller residences the use of one or two return intakes has been found to be as satisfactory as the use of a large number of smaller intakes. As a matter of fact, if the warm air registers are located so that a small difference in temperature exists from floor to ceiling, the location of the return air intake is not too important. Equally satisfactory results have been obtained with the intakes at the ceiling, at the high sidewall, at the low wall, at the baseboard, and at the floor locations. The return air from small bedrooms escapes from the room through the space below the closed door. The only precaution necessary in the location of a relatively large intake is to avoid a place near seated occupants, not only because of air movement but also because of air noise. A hallway location will usually meet the requirements of a central location and of distance from seated occupants.

Contrary to popular belief, room air cannot be pulled towards a return intake. In fact, the pulling action is limited to the immediate vicinity of the intake. Fig. 15-134, for example, shows how the air velocity diminishes rapidly as the distance from the intake increases. Even with 1000 fpm velocity at the opening, at a distance of 12 inches from the opening, the velocity was reduced to 90 fpm, and at a distance of 24 inches from the opening, the velocity was essentially room air velocity or 25 fpm.

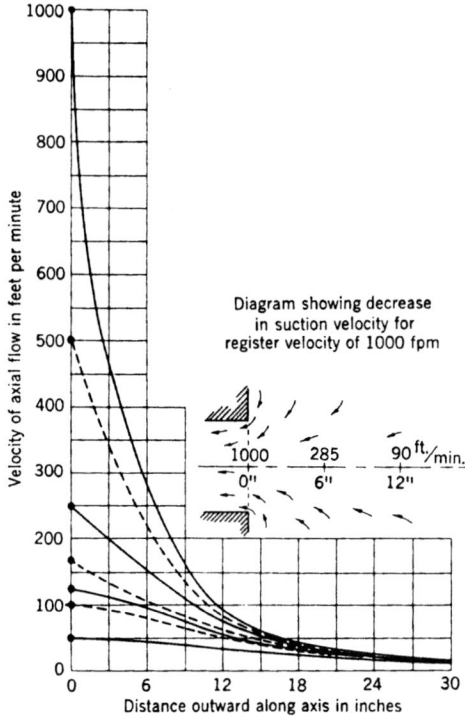

Fig 15-134. Air velocity front of intake

An outdoor air intake can be provided in a forced air system for introducing outdoor ventilation air into the structure. Such provisions are more common in the milder climate regions of the country. This outdoor air should be conveyed through an individual duct leading from the outdoors directly to the return plenum of the furnace and should be provided with a manually operated damper. The introduction of large quantities of outdoor air into a structure will result in large fuel bills and a lower relative humidity in the structure. In general, even with moderately large amounts of outdoor air introduced into a structure it is not possible to build up indoor pressures sufficiently to stop window infiltration. It should be realized that fireplace openings, chimney openings, door crackages, and window crackages permit air to flow readily from the structure to the outdoors.

Arrangement of Furnace and Ducts.—The discussion up to this point has been with the components of the warm air system, and not with the integration of the parts into a whole. The arrangement of the furnaces, ducts, registers, and intakes will be dependent upon the type of structure. Since each system is a hand tailored arrangement for that particular job, no two contractors will agree in all respects on the manner in which the job should be installed. A number of arrangements in common use are:

1) Basement furnace with ductwork at ceiling of basement

2) Utility room location of furnace with ductwork at the ceiling of the rooms. This arrangement is common with individual apartment units in which each tenant operates his own heating unit and pays for the fuel bill.

3) House built over a concrete slab floor. Furnace is located in a utility room and all ducts are embedded in the concrete floor to give a perimeter loop arrangement. See Figs. 15-135a and 15-135b.

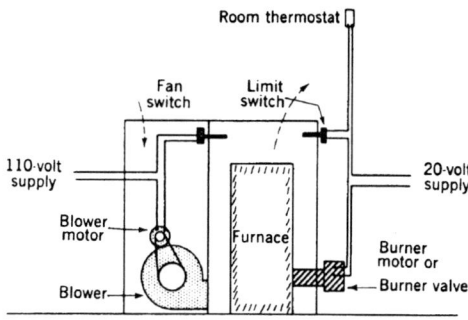

Fig 15-135a. Air velocity front of intake

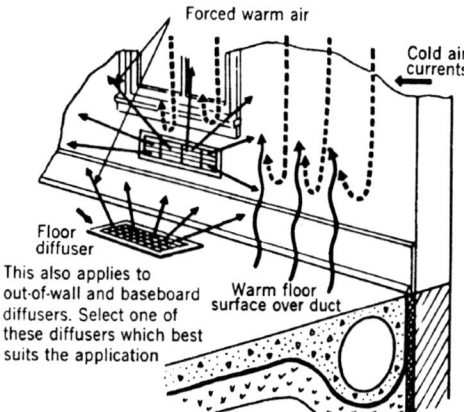

Fig 15-135b. Details of perimeter loop system with floor or baseboard diffuser below window

4) Same as (c), but with a radial feeder arrangement of individual ducts in place of the perimeter loop arrangement. See Fig. 15-135c.

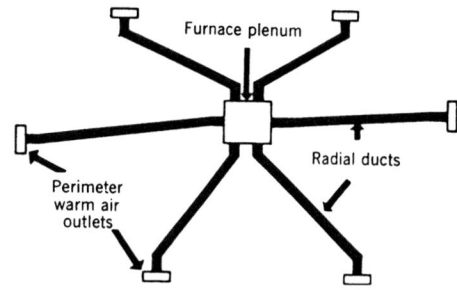

Fig 15-135c. Air velocity front of intake

5) Slab floor with numerous air passages provided below the floor through which warm air can be circulated. This is a warm air floor panel system, one form of which

is shown in Fig. 15-135d. A warm air ceiling panel system is also available.

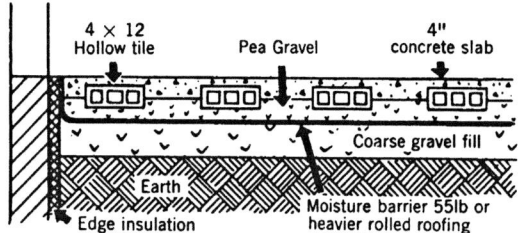

Fig 15-135d. One form of warm air floor panel heating

6) House built over a crawl space. In one arrangement, individual ducts are carried below the floor to the registers in the floor or in the baseboard.

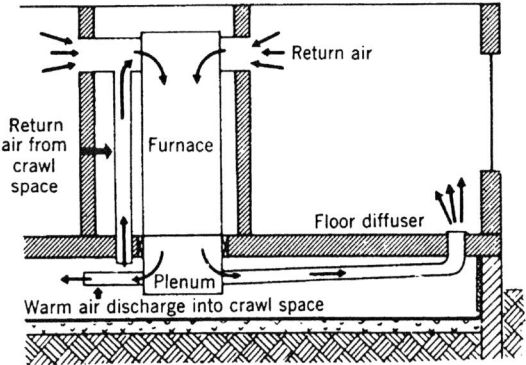

Fig 15-135e. Downflow furnace with crawl space duct system and crawl space plenum system

In another arrangement, warm air is pumped into the crawl space and permitted to enter the rooms through floor registers, as indicated in Fig. 15-135e. With a crawl space plenum system the foundation wall requires special insulation and the ground must be protected against moisture travel from the ground to the crawl space. This arrangement may not be permissible in areas where building codes prohibit ductless systems in combustible areas.

7) Overhead attic installation of furnace. Furnaces are available for attic space installation. All ducts in the attic space should be heavily insulated since the heat loss from the ducts will not be available for heating the building. See Fig. 15-135f.

8) For large buildings the use of multiple furnace units is often possible. Each of several furnaces can be located close to the particular zone to be heated in order to shorten the ductwork. Individual zone temperature control is possible. Multiple furnace systems have been successfully used in the heating of churches, commercial buildings, schools, etc.

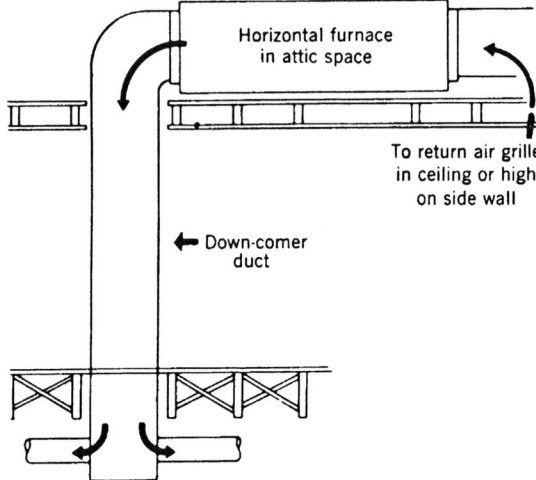

Fig 15-135f. Attic furnace installation leading to duct system in crawl space

The forced air system is a flexible system and one that has few limitations except that of extreme size. The ducts require no pitching and can be carried upward, downward, or sideways; small air leaks in the ducts are of no consequence; the system needs no purging; the system is extremely responsive to temperature changes outdoors; and all that is required to shut down a plant is that the burner be turned off.

A few installation precautions are necessary, as is true of any combustion device. The approval tests for furnaces include specifications for space clearances on the sides and top from combustible construction, and such clearances should be provided in the actual installation. If the furnace is to be located in a small furnace room or closet the diagrams in Figs. 15-136a and 15-136b show the code requirements as far as combustion air supply and closet ventilation are concerned.

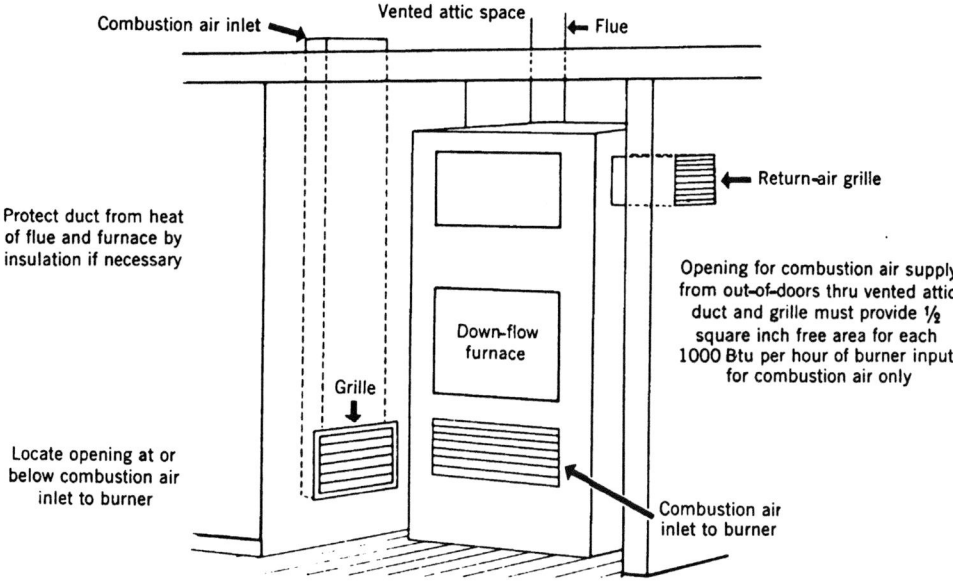

Combustion air inlet ►   Vented attic space   ◄ Flue

Protect duct from heat
of flue and furnace by
insulation if necessary

◄ Return-air grille

Opening for combustion air supply
from out-of-doors thru vented attic.
duct and grille must provide ½
square inch free area for each
1000 Btu per hour of burner input
for combustion air only

Down-flow
furnace

Grille

Locate opening at or
below combustion air
inlet to burner

Combustion air
inlet to burner

Fig 15-136a. Combustion air supply from attic space

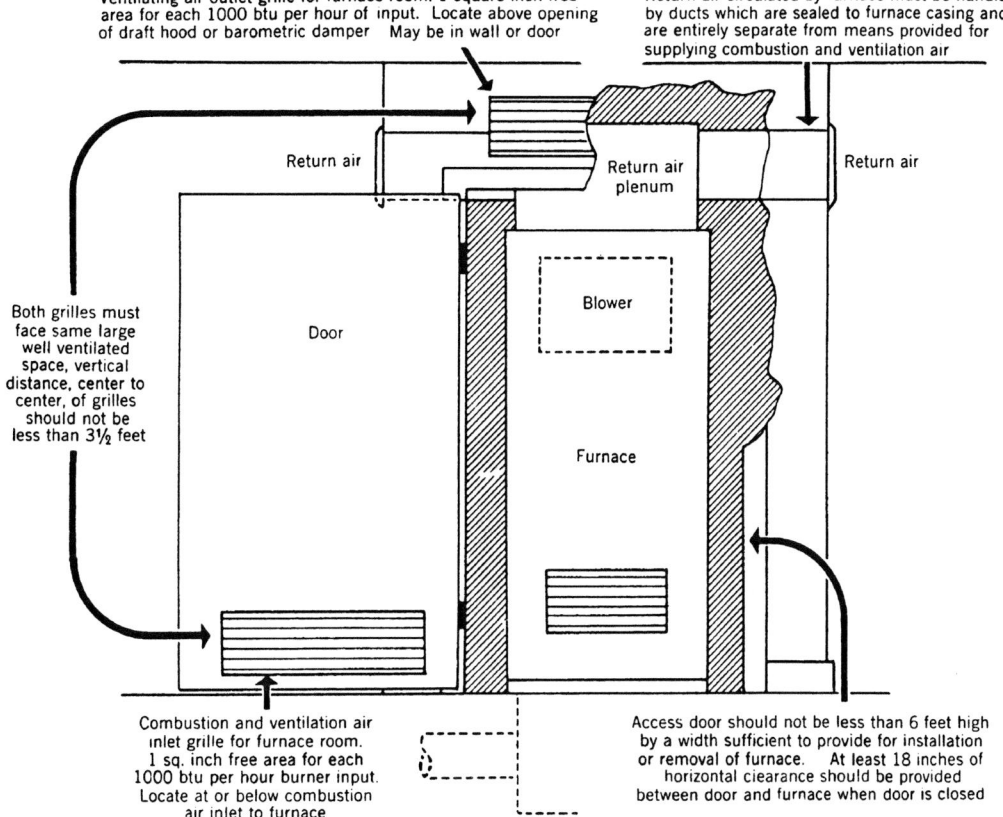

Ventilating air outlet grille for furnace room. 1 square inch free
area for each 1000 btu per hour of input. Locate above opening
of draft hood or barometric damper   May be in wall or door

Return air circulated by furnace must be handled
by ducts which are sealed to furnace casing and
are entirely separate from means provided for
supplying combustion and ventilation air

Return air

Return air
plenum

Return air

Both grilles must
face same large
well ventilated
space, vertical
distance, center to
center, of grilles
should not be
less than 3½ feet

Door

Blower

Furnace

Combustion and ventilation air
inlet grille for furnace room.
1 sq. inch free area for each
1000 btu per hour burner input.
Locate at or below combustion
air inlet to furnace

Access door should not be less than 6 feet high
by a width sufficient to provide for installation
or removal of furnace.   At least 18 inches of
horizontal clearance should be provided
between door and furnace when door is closed

Fig 15-136b. Provisions for combustion and ventilation air for furnace closet

Basic Thermostatic Controls.—An almost endless number of control arrangements is possible, but the simplest and the most practical is that which is shown in diagram form in Fig. 15-137. The components consist of:

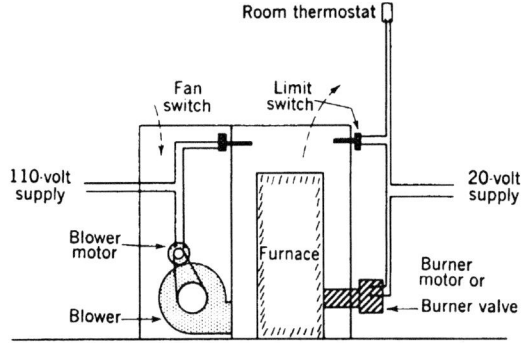

Fig 15-137. Basic arrangement of controls

Room Thermostat: This should be provided with a differential adjustment setting not to exceed about 1.0°F.

Limit Switch: For shutting off the burner whenever the bonnet air temperature becomes excessively high. The recommended setting is between 175°F and 200°F. In the normal sequence of operation the limit switch is not called upon for action, but is available in case of possible overheating of the furnace.

Burner Motor or Burner Valve: This is directly connected to the room thermostat circuit. Obviously, the frequency of operation of the burner is dependent upon the setting and sensitivity of the room thermostat. In a warm air furnace system, unlike a hot water or steam system, there is little lag and at the same time no heat storage. In other words, the heat must be generated only as needed and must be distributed as soon as it is generated. For this reason, the sensitivity of the room thermostat must be acute and the differential settings must be of the order of 0.5 to 1.0°F. The purpose of the small differential setting is to cause frequent and short operations of the burner. The length of each burner cycle should not, however, be less than about 2 minutes for a gas burner nor less than about 4 minutes for an oil burner because shorter operating periods might contribute to large combustion losses due to incomplete burning at the beginning of each burner operation.

Fan Switch: Located in the bonnet is a device that turns on the blower when the air temperature in the bonnet is high and turns off the blower when the bonnet air temperature is low. The recommended setting of the fan switch is about 110°F for the cut-in point and about 85°F for the cut-out point. These settings are of great importance in the successful operation of the entire system.

Continuous Air Circulation Principle (CAC).—In many respects the basic principle of a gravity warm air system of heating is an ideal one and difficult to surpass even with a mechanical system. As shown in Fig. 15-138,

the gravity warm air system provides a 24-hour circulation of air, the temperature of which is modulated in accordance with the demand. Furthermore, the quantity of air flow is small in mild weather and large in cold weather, so that the air flow rate is also modulated. In any case, the system is readily adapted to the changing demands of weather, and such changes occur automatically and without artificial stimulus. If it were possible to operate a forced air system in exactly the same manner and just as simply, the problem of control would be eased.

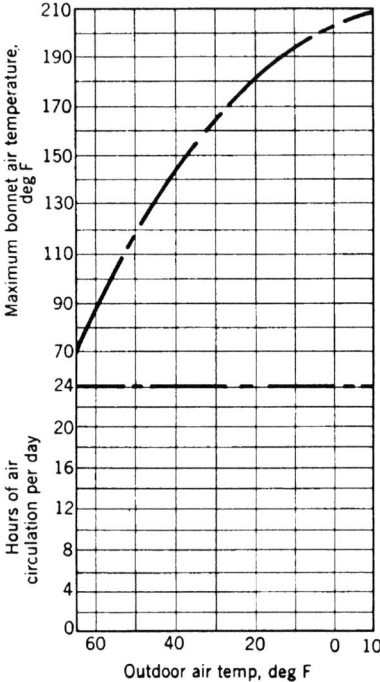

Fig 15-138. Air flow and air temperature for gravity warm air system

With a forced air system, the flow of air is not dependent upon the weather or the heating demands, but is fixed only by the blower speed, the blower size, and the frictional restrictions in the duct system. It is possible with any given duct system to vary the air flow rate over a considerable range.

Furthermore, it is possible to control over a wide range the number of hours that the blower will operate during the day. For example, on a day in which the outdoor air temperature is 30°F the fan switch can be adjusted so that the blower runs continuously during the 24 hour period, or for 16 hours, or for 8 hours, or for as little as 1 hour. This wide range of blower operating periods is dependent mainly upon the settings of the fan switch, and to some extent upon the blower speed. Longer operating periods of the blower are desirable since, when the blower is operating, the control of distribution of heated air is possible; whereas when the blower is not operating, and the system is under the influence of gravity action, no control exists as far as air distribution to the various rooms is concerned.

Continuous Blower Operation.—The argument might be raised that if continuous air circulation is ideal, the system should be operated to give continuous blower operation, as shown in Fig. 15-139. In this case, the fan switch could be eliminated and the blower operated from a manual switch that is turned on at the start of the heating season and left on all during the season. Or, the fan switch could be left in place and the cut in point of the fan switch lowered to about 70°F.

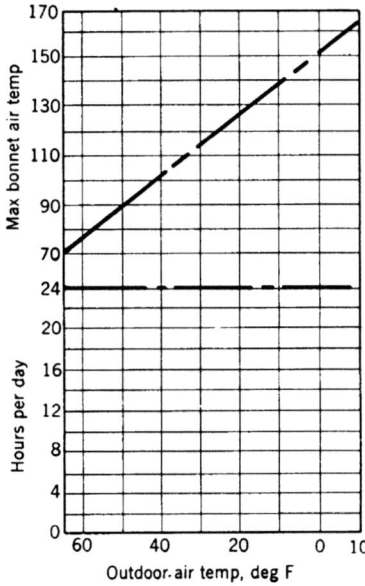

Fig 15-139. Air flow and air temperature for continuous blower operation

The two possible objections to this arrangement are:

A) The blower does not need to be operated in extremely mild weather when little heat demand occurs, and the electrical cost of blower operation could be saved.

B) The temperature of the air issuing from the registers can be as low as room air temperature and might create objectional drafts in front of the registers.

With high sidewall registers, with floor registers, or with baseboard registers that discharge the air sharply upwards towards the ceiling, this draft possibility does not exist. With such register installations the fan switch cut-in settings can be lowered below 110°F, and such a lower setting would prove most advantageous from the standpoint of temperature control and uniform distribution of heated air.

Intermittent Blower Operation.—For a number of reasons heating contractors have not appreciated the necessity of obtaining almost continuous blower opera-

tion in average heating weather. The influence of gravity warm air heating practice undoubtedly persists. For example, in gravity heating it was common practice in overcoming the deficiencies of an inadequate plant to raise the bonnet air temperature, thereby increasing the motive head of circulation, and eventually obtaining a larger air flow rate.

In the earlier days of forced air heating a similar idea persisted. For example, since the design temperature for bonnet air was assumed as 165°F, the contractor assumed that the fan switch cut-in point should be 165°F. Under this setting the operation obtained was as shown by the curves labeled A in Fig. 15-140. The bonnet air temperature would average 165°F in all weather and the blower would operate intermittently in all weather except during design weather. Frequently, in the case of trouble jobs, the contractor raised the cut-in temperature even higher than 165°F and thereby only aggravated troubles, for the system then operated intermittently under all weather conditions. Essentially, a system so controlled is a booster system, which is partly gravity and partly mechanical in its operation. Since the ducts were designed for blower operation only, it is little wonder that air distribution was poor and the rooms at some distance from the furnace were improperly heated. Many complaints arose that the heating was spasmodic and that when the blower turned on, the register air was cold at first. Unfortunately, such poor control operations still exist in many older plants and the potentialities of a good warm air system have not been realized.

As shown by the curves labeled as B in Fig. 15-140, a lowering of the fan switch cut in point causes a reduction in the bonnet air temperature, especially during moderate weather conditions and a marked increase in blower operating times. As a matter of fact, if the cut in point can be lowered below 1°F, the blower begins to operate continuously at much higher outdoor air temperatures. A desirable method of blower operation is considered to be that in which the blower operates continuously as soon as the outdoor temperature drops to about 40°F.

The matter of proper control settings is so important for the satisfactory operation of a forced air system that industry has set up rules of procedure for adjusting the heating system. Essentially, these adjustments consist of:

1) A differential setting of the room thermostat not to exceed 1.0°F and preferably only 0.5 to 0.75°F.

2) Adjustment of the blower speed to give an air temperature rise through the furnace of 100°F.

3) Adjustment of the fan switch to give a cut-in point of about 110°F and a cut-out point of about 85°F. If a lower setting can be maintained without danger of objectionable drafts in the rooms, the settings should be lower.

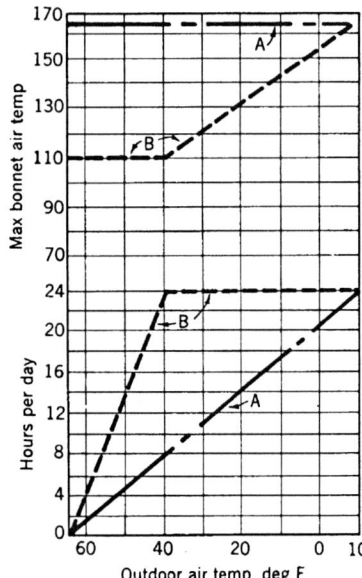

Fig 15-140. Air flow and air temperature for intermittent
blower operation

Basic Factors for Designing Warm Air Systems: Many
different methods exists for use in designing such diverse
types of warm air systems. These include:

   (a) small duct, high velocity systems,

   (b) ceiling warm air panel systems,

   (c) floor warm air panel systems,

   (d) small duct perimeter systems,

   (e) large, commercial systems.

Regardless of the system of design most of them are
based on a few basic concepts, which will be considered
in detail. The assumption will be made that the design
heat loss of the spaces to be heated has been established.

Bonnet Air Temperature: The starting point of any
design consists in selecting a value for bonnet air temperature. As can be seen from the following equation, which
was presented earlier, the bonnet air temperature determines the air flow rate that will be used to maintain a certain capacity:

$$\text{Bonnet capacity} = (60)(0.24)(d_b)(t_b - t_r)cfm$$

For a given capacity the air flow rate increases as the
bonnet air temperature is decreased. For example, for a
bonnet capacity of 100,000 Btu/hr the air flow rate will be
1092 cfm for a bonnet air temperature of 165°F, but 1004
cfm for a temperature of 115°F. As noted before, for small
residential units the temperature rise $(t_b - t_r)$ is arbitrarily
determined to be 100°F. That is, for a return air temperature of 65°F the bonnet air temperature is assumed to be
165°F.

For large furnaces used for industrial and commercial
applications a temperature rise of less than 100°F is usu-

ally selected. This corresponds to bonnet air temperatures
less than 165°F. A suggested method for selecting a bonnet air temperature is by use of Table 15-54 for jobs having a heat loss up to 350,000 Btu/hr, and Table 15-55 for
jobs having a heat loss in excess of 350,000 Btu/hr. Both
the shortest as well as the longest duct lengths, from the
bonnet to the register, should be measured from the building plans for the tables to be useful.

   (a) Using the shortest actual duct length, read downward in the nearest column in Table 15-54 until the lower
heavy diagonal line is reached, but do not cross the line.
Run horizontally to the left to obtain the value of the maximum bonnet temperature in the first column.

For example, for an actual length of duct of 30 ft the
corresponding maximum bonnet air temperature is
160°F.

   (b) Now, using the longest actual duct length, read
downwards in the nearest column in Table 15-54 until the
heavy diagonal line is just crossed. Run horizontally to
the left to obtain the value for the minimum bonnet air
temperature in the first column.

For example, for an actual length of duct of 130 ft the
corresponding minimum bonnet air temperature is 150°F.

   (c) Select as the design bonnet temperature any value
between the maximum and the minimum, preferably one
of the values shown in the first column of Table 15-54.
For the example shown, either 160°F or 150°F could be
selected.

Table 15-55 is used similarly. This method of selecting
the bonnet air temperature merely assures that the final
bonnet temperature selected will be between 150°F and
110°F, corresponding to temperature rises through the
furnace of 85°F and 45°F. Regardless of whether the
design bonnet temperature was selected arbitrarily or by
the preceding method it must be used thereafter for determining the air flow rates.

Temperature Drop of Air in Ducts: The individual
boxes in Tables 15-54 and 15-55 show two values: The
upper value is the estimated register air temperature and
the lower value is the cfm air flow rate for each 1000
Btu/hr heat loss. For example, the box corresponding to a
bonnet air temperature of 110°F and a duct length of 10 ft
gives 108°F as the register air temperature and 23.1 cfm
for each 1000 Btu/hr room heat loss. It is apparent that the
values in Tables 15-54 and 15-55 take into account the
temperature drop of the air as it flows down the duct. The
tabular values also indicate that the temperature drop is
greater when the bonnet air temperature is higher. For
example, for a bonnet air temperature of 110°F the
temperature drop is 2°F in 10 ft of duct, whereas for a bonnet air temperature of 200°F, the temperature drop is 7°F
in 10 ft of duct. A further examination of Tables 15-54 and
15-55 shows that the temperature drop is relatively large
for distances close to the bonnet and is relatively small for

distances away from the bonnet. In other words, the temperature drop of air in the ducts is not a constant value.

The temperature drop data used in setting up Tables 15-54 and 15-55 were obtained from the basic data given in Bulletin 351. The basic curves, shown in Fig. 15-141 for various duct velocities, apply to uninsulated, galvanized iron ducts located in an environment of 70°F. For the purpose of deriving the values in Tables 15-54 and 15-55 it was necessary to assume average values for duct velocity (800 fpm) and duct size (10 inches diameter), since neither were known at this point in the design procedure. Theoretically, a correction in temperature drop could be made later for actual duct velocities and actual duct diameters used, but in actual practice the correction is not warranted. The register air temperatures, shown in the upper part of each box in Tables 15-54 and 15-55, would be slightly high for velocities less than 800 fpm and for ducts smaller than 10 inches in diameter, and hence would give lower values of cfm requirements for 100 Btu/hr loss than if corrected values were used. However, calculations made for a 6-inches duct carrying air at 400 fpm velocity

indicated that the maximum discrepancy was only of the order of 6%. Conversely, the cfm requirements shown in Tables 15-54 and 15-55 would be on the safe side for ducts larger than 10 inches in diameter and for air velocities greater than 800 fpm. Hence, in spite of the fact that the values in Tables 15-54 and 15-55 were based upon a specific diameter and velocity, the results obtained from their use should be well within the accuracy required for ordinary calculations.

Register Air Temperature and Room Air Requirements:

The register air temperature is obtained by subtracting the temperature drop from the bonnet air temperature. This register air temperature in turn establishes the air flow rate necessary at the register face to offset the heat loss from the space to be heated. The equation for air flow rate at the register is:

$$cfm \text{ at register} = \frac{\text{design heat loss, Btu/hr}}{(60)(24)(d_{reg})(T_{reg} - T_r)}$$

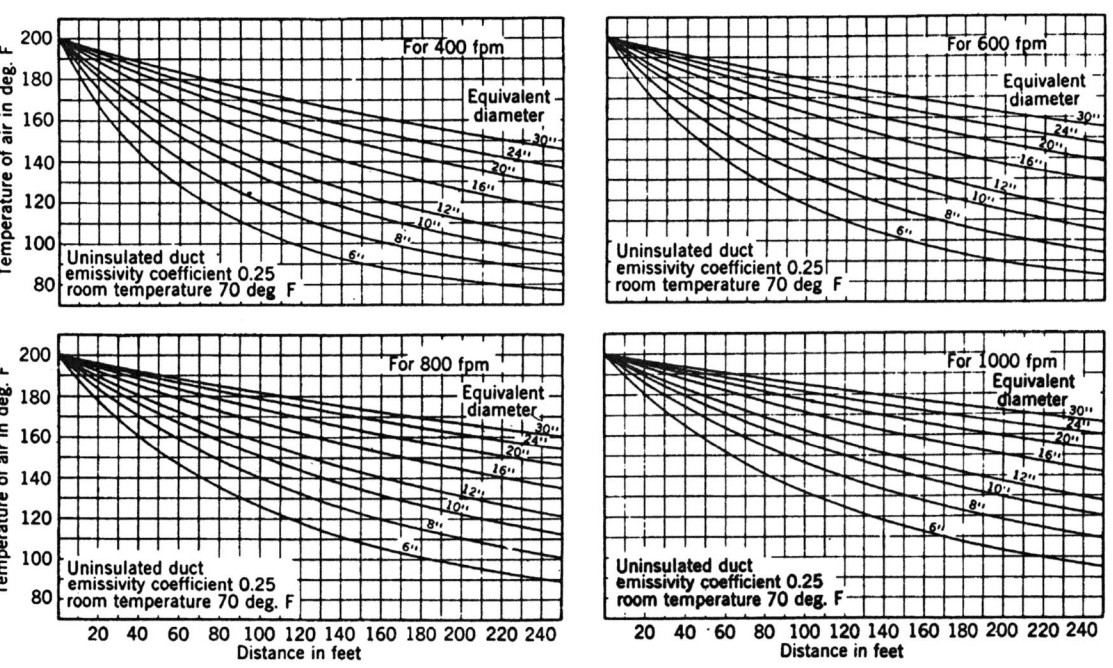

Fig 15-141. Temperature drop in ducts for different air velocity

Table 15-54. Register Temperatures and Air Volume for Buildings with Heat Loss Up to 350,000 Btu/hr
(National Environmental Systems Contractors Associations)

Temperature of Bonnet, °F	Linear Distance from Bonnet to Register, ft											
	10	20	30	40	50	60	70	80	90	100	110	120
	Register temperature, upper figure; and cfm/MBH, lower figure											
110	108	107	106	104	103	102	101	100	99	98	97	96
	23.1	23.60	24.20	25.40	26.00	26.60	27.30	28.00	28.80	29.60	30.50	31.50
120	118	116	114	112	111	109	108	106	105	103	102	101
	19.00	19.60	20.30	21.10	21.60	22.50	23.1	24.20	24.80	26.00	26.60	27.30
130	128	126	123	121	119	117	115	113	111	110	108	107
	16.40	16.90	17.60	18.10	18.70	19.30	20.00	20.70	21.60	22.10	23.10	23.60
140	137	134	131	129	126	124	122	120	118	116	114	112
	14.6	15.1	15.70	16.20	16.90	17.30	17.90	18.40	19.00	19.60	20.30	21.10
150	147	143	140	137	134	131	129	127	124	122	120	118
	12.90	13.50	12.70	14.60	15.10	15.70	16.20	16.60	17.30	17.90	18.50	18.40
160	156	152	149	146	142	139	136	133	130	128	126	123
	11.80	12.30	12.70	13.20	13.70	14.20	14.80	15.30	15.90	16.40	16.90	17.60
170	166	161	157	153	150	146	143	140	137	134	131	128
	10.80	11.3	11.7	12.20	12.60	13.1	13.50	14.00	14.60	15.10	15.70	16.40
180	175	170	166	161	157	153	150	146	143	140	137	135
	10.00	10.5	10.80	11.3	11.7	12.2	12.60	13.1	13.50	14.00	14.60	14.90
190	184	179	174	169	165	160	156	153	149	145	142	139
	9.40	9.80	10.10	10.60	10.9	11.4	11.80	12.20	12.70	13.20	13.70	14.20
200	193	187	182	176	171	167	163	158	154	151.00	147	144
	8.9	9.2	9.6	9.9	10.4	10.7	11.1	11.6	12.1	12.41	12.9	13.4

Temperature of Bonnet, °F	Linear Distance from Bonnet to Register, ft											
	130	140	150	160	170	180	190	200	210	220	230	240
	Register temperature, upper figure; and cfm/MBH, lower figure											
110	95	94	93	92	91	90	90	89	89	88	88	87
	32.30	33.30	34.60	35.90	37.30	38.60	38.60	38.90	39.90	41.30	41.30	42.70
120	100	99	98	97	96	95	94	93	92	91	90	90
	28.00	28.80	29.60	30.50	31.50	32.30	33.30	34.60	35.90	37.30	38.60	38.60
130	105	104	103	102	101	99	98	97	96	95	94	93
	24.80	25.40	26.00	26.60	27.30	28.80	29.60	30.50	31.50	32.30	33.3	34.60
140	110	109	107	106	105	103	102	101	100	99	98	97
	22.10	22.50	23.60	24.20	24.80	26.00	26.60	27.30	28.00	28.80	29.60	30.50
150	116	114	112	110	109	107	106	105	103	102	101	100
	19.60	20.30	21.10	22.10	22.50	23.60	24.20	24.80	26.00	26.60	27.30	28.00
160	121	119	117	115	113	112	110	108	107	106	109	103
	18.10	18.70	19.30	20.00	20.70	21.10	22.1	23.1	23.60	24.20	25.40	26.00
170	126	124	122	120	118	116	114	112	110	109	107	106
	16.90	17.30	17.90	18.40	19.00	19.60	20.30	21.10	22.10	22.50	23.60	24.20
180	131	128	126	124	122	120	118	116	115	113	111	110
	15.70	16.40	16.90	17.30	17.90	18.40	19.00	19.60	20.00	20.70	21.60	22.10

Table 15-55. Register Temperatures and Air Volume for Buildings with Heat Loss Up to 350,000 Btu/hr (National Environmental Systems Contractors Associations)

Tempera-ture of Bonnet, °F	Linear Distance from Bonnet to Register, ft											
	10	20	30	40	50	60	70	80	90	100	110	120
	Register temperature, upper figure; and cfm/MBH, lower figure											
140	138	136	134	132	130	128	127	126	125	124	123	121
	14.40	14.80	15.10	15.70	15.90	16.40	17.00	16.90	17.20	17.30	17.60	18.10
150	148	146	143	141	139	137	135	133	131	129	128	127
	12.80	13.10	13.50	13.90	14.20	14.60	14.90	15.30	15.70	16.20	16.40	16.60
160	158	155	152	150	147	145	143	140	138	136	134	132
	11.60	12.00	12.30	12.60	12.9	13.20	13.50	14.00	14.40	14.80	15.10	15.70
170	167	164	161	158	155	152	150	147	145	143	140	138
	10.70	11.00	11.30	11.60	12	12.30	12.60	12.90	13.20	13.5	14.00	14.40
180	177	173	170	167	164	161	158	155	152	150	147.00	145
	9.90	10.20	10.50	10.70	11.00	11.30	11.60	12.00	12.30	12.60	12.90	13.20
190	186	182	178	175	172	168	165	162	159	156	153	151
	9.30	9.60	9.80	10.00	10.30	10.70	10.90	11.20	11.50	11.80	12.20	12.40
200	196	191	187	183	179	176	172	169	166	163	160	157
	8.80	9.00	9.20	9.50	9.80	9.90	10.30	10.60	10.80	11.10	11.40	11.70

Tempera-ture of Bonnet, °F	Linear Distance from Bonnet to Register, ft											
	130	140	150	160	170	180	190	200	210	220	230	240
	Register temperature, upper figure; and cfm/MBH, lower figure											
140	120	119	118	117	116	115	114	113	112	111	110	109
	18.40	18.70	19.00	19.30	19.60	20.00	20.30	20.70	21.10	21.61	22.10	22.50
150	126	124	123	122	120	119	118	117	116	115	114	113
	16.90	17.30	17.60	17.90	18.40	19	19.00	19.30	19.60	20.00	20.30	20.70
160	130	128	127	126	125	124	123	121	120	119	118	117
	15.9	16.40	16.60	16.90	17.20	17.30	17.60	18.10	18.40	18.70	19.00	19.30
170	136	134	132	130	128	127	126	125	124	123	121	120
	14.8	15.10	15.70	15.90	16.40	16.60	16.90	17.20	17.32	17.60	18.10	18.40
180	143	140	138	136	134	132	130	128	127	126	125	124
	13.5	14.00	14.40	14.80	15	15.70	15.90	16.40	16.6	16.9	17.2	17.30
190	148	146	143	141	139	137	135	133	131	129	128	127
	12.8	13.10	13.50	13.90	14.20	14.60	14.90	15.30	15.7	16.2	16.4	16.60
200	154	151	149	147	144	142	140	138	135	133	131	130
	12.1	12.4	12.70	12.90	13.40	13.70	14.00	14.40	14.90	15.3	15.7	15.90

A study of the data in Tables 15-54 and 15-55 shows that a larger air flow rate is needed for those rooms at some distance from the bonnet. For example, for a bonnet air temperature of 150°F, a register that is 10 ft from the bonnet requires 12.9 cfm for each 1000 Btu/hr room heat loss, whereas a register which is 100 ft from the bonnet requires 17.9 cfm for each 1000 Btu/hr heat loss. This is an increase of 39% to take into account the heat loss from the duct.

With the exception of duct systems installed in small homes, where the branch ducts are about the same length, considerable errors will be introduced if a constant register air temperature is assumed to exist at all registers. Such errors in air flow requirements will necessitate drastic adjustments in balancing after the duct system is installed. After the air flow rates have been determined for each register, the total cfm may be considered the same as that handled by the blower even though a slight density correction is theoretically necessary.

Available Static Pressure at Bonnet: In the case of small furnace systems the available static pressure external to the furnace blower combination is considered to be 0.20 inch wg. This pressure of 0.20 inch wg is available for the losses in both the warm air and return air sides of the system. For large furnaces, such as are used for commercial and industrial buildings, no fixed value of external static pressure is used. In fact, a wide range of values is permissible, and a choice of several blower sizes is possible. Normally, however, the static pressures do not exceed about 1.0 inch of water. Suggested bonnet pressures are given in Table 15-55.

Table 15-56. Suggested Bonnet Pressures

Total Flow Rate through Any One Duct, cfm	Suggested Bonnet Pressure, in. wg
800 to 1000	0.10
1000 to 1200	0.10
1200 to 1800	0.10
1800 to 2400	0.13
2400 to 3500	0.14
3500 to 5000	0.15
5000 to 7500	0.25
7500 to 10,000	0.375
10,000 to 12,000	0.50
12,000 to 14,000	0.75

Before a blower can be selected for the given job, it is necessary to estimate two other items and add them to the bonnet pressure:

(a) The pressure loss for the return duct system

(b) The pressure loss for internal losses through the furnace casing and the blower housing. This item should be available from the furnace manufacturer. In any case, the manufacturer should be able to recommend the blower size and speed to handle loss items for the bonnet and the return system.

Before the static pressure at the bonnet is finally fixed, some consideration should be given to the pressure required for the throw of air from registers. This takes on great importance where the throw is greater than about 30 ft or where the air must be rapidly dispersed outwards.

Throw of Air from Registers: A basic equation (Tuve-Priester) is of the form:

$$V_r = \frac{KQ}{X\sqrt{A_e}} \qquad (13)$$

where V_r = residual maximum velocity, fpm
K = constant to be determined by test
Q = volume of air discharged, cfm
X = throw of air, ft
A_e = effective area of outlet, ft^2
Furthermore,

$$A_e = \frac{A_e}{C} \qquad (14)$$

and

$$V_c = \frac{Q}{A_c} \quad \text{or} \quad V_c = \frac{Q}{V_c} \qquad (15)$$

where A_c = core area of register, ft^2
C = coefficient of discharge
V_c = core velocity, fpm

By rearranging Equations (13), (14), and (15), the following form was derived:

$$V_c = \frac{X^2}{Q}\left(\frac{CV_r^2}{K^2}\right) \qquad (16)$$

Numerical values for V_r = 50 fpm, K = 2.5, and C = 0.61 were inserted in Equation (16) and the relationship was simplified to the form:

$$V_c = \frac{X^2}{Q}(244) \qquad (17)$$

Numerical values for X and Q in Equation (17), values of V_c were obtained, and these in turn were substituted in Equation (15) to give the required core areas, A_c.

Free Areas: In order to obtain free areas, which are commonly given in manufacturer catalogs, the assumption was made following consultation with the register manufacturers that the ratio of free area to core area was 0.78. Hence, by the use of a modified version of the Tuve–Priester equation, relationships between throw, volume, and free areas of registers could be obtained.

A residual velocity of 50 fpm at the wall opposite a register might be considered too large, and an average stream velocity of the order of 15 fpm to 20 fpm might be considered more reasonable. It is possible to modify Equation (17) by inserting a value for the residual velocity on the order of 20 fpm. However, it is questionable whether such an extrapolation to velocities that are practically unmeasurable can be justified. The suggestion has been made that the length of the throw should be considered to be some proportion of the width of the room, say three quarters of the width of the room, and that the values obtained from Equation (17) be applied to this shortened distance. The difficulty is that three quarters of a room that is 20 ft wide is only 15-ft, leaving 5 ft distance between the far wall and the end of the throw; whereas three quarters of the distance of a room that is 60 ft wide is 45 ft, leaving a 15 ft distance from the far wall and the end of the throw. In the small room the air may have sufficient momentum to carry on to the far wall, whereas in the larger room the same velocity air may not extend to the far wall. In any case, these are hypothetical objections that have no proof as yet. Hence, unless better evidence exists that some other equation should apply, the modified version of the Tuve–Priester equation is offered for use.

Pressure Required at Register: For those installations in which relatively long throws of air are required at the register, an available pressure behind the register of 0.10 inch wg or more will be encountered. A search of a number of references, including manufacturer catalogs, indicated the need of a summary table embodying complete performance characteristics of a wide range of register sizes. Wherever such data for a specific model are given in a catalog, they are preferred to any typical results derived for an average register.

In Fig. 15-142 is shown the relation between the free area velocity and the total pressure head of the register, based upon tests of 22 commercial types of widely varying design in which *no air deflection* was used. The total pressure ahead of the register included not only the losses due to friction, turbulence, and expansion, but also the velocity head of the air leaving the register.

In Fig. 15-143 is shown the relation between the deflection angle and pressure loss, based upon tests conducted with eight different commercial types. The pressure loss increased relatively slowly when the deflection angle was increased from 0°F to about 15°F, but increased at a greatly accelerated rate for angles larger than 15°F.

The extensive data given in Bulletin 342, part of which are shown in Figs. 15-142 and 15-143, as well as the data of Tuve and Priester, were incorporated in Tables 15-58 and 15-59. The working values in Table 15-59 are for 22°F deflection of air and are for both register free area as well as total pressure requirements. These values are shown for various flow rates and for varying distances of the register from the opposite wall. The tabular values do not apply to any specific commercial type of register. Hence, where reliable data can be obtained from a manufacturer for a specific register, such data are preferred to the general information contained in Tables 15-58 and

Table 15-59. An example of the use of Table 15-59 follows:

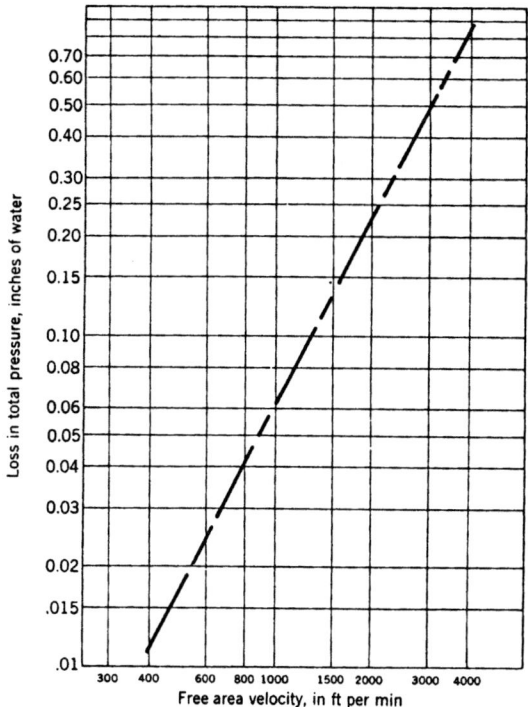

Fig 15-142. Total pressure loss of register as affected by free area velocity

Table 15-57. Capacity and Pressure Loss of Registers

Capacity, cfm	Register, in.	Pressure Loss, in. of Water
Up to 59	10 × 4	0.01
	10 × 6	0.01
60–69	10 × 6	0.01
	12 × 4	0.02
70–99	10 × 6	0.02
	12 × 4	0.02
100–119	12 × 6	0.02
	14 × 4	0.02
120–129	12 × 6	0.02
	14 × 6	0.02
130–169	14 × 6	0.02
170–189	14 × 8	0.02

Pressure loss is based on flat face adjustable bar type and does not include stack head. For other type registers, consult manufacturer, catalogs.

Floor Registers: where a velocity of approximately 300 fpm is used,

$$\text{Free area} = \frac{cfm \times 144}{300} \quad \text{or approximately } cfm/2$$

Assume a pressure loss of 0.01 inch.

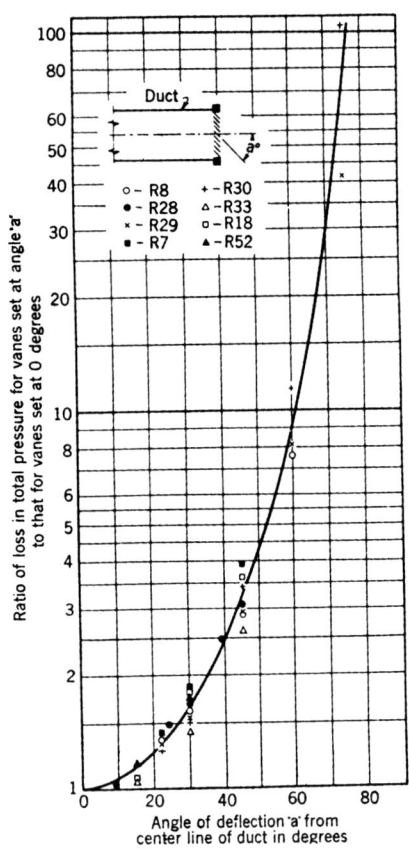

Fig 15-143. Increase in pressure loss with different angles of deflection. symbols represent different experimental use

Example 12: Refer to Fig. 15-144 if the pressure loss for register (a) is 0.12 inch wg, for register (b) is 0.01 inch, and for register (c) is 0.03 inch, then the maximum pressure loss of the registers is 0.12 inch. The required bonnet pressure must be greater than 0.12 inch. If, for example, the bonnet pressure selected is 0.25 inch, then the avail-

able pressure for overcoming resistances in each of the ducts from the bonnet to the register will be for (a) 0.13 inch, for (b) 0.24 inch, and for (c) 0.22 inch.

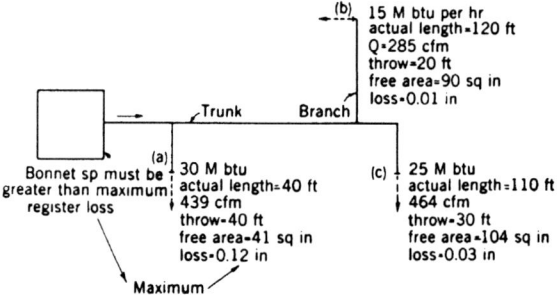

Fig 15-144. Maximum register loss and its relation to duct loss and bonnet static pressure

Given: a room 38 ft wide, one register to handle 300 cfm air flow rate, and a deflection angle of 22° to be used. Find register free area and pressure loss?

Solution: From Tables 15-57, a register having a free area of 37 in^2 and a pressure loss of 0.21 inch will handle the given requirements.

Tables 15-57 shows average free areas of registers for typical commercial types and should be used only when specific manufacturer data are not available.

The heavy dividing lines in Tables 15-58 and 15-59 were included in an attempt to show distinction in sound level. For this purpose the work of Stewart and Drake on sound level was selected from a number of references consulted as the most practical for air conditioning work. The curves of Fig. 15-145 are based upon the results of tests by Stewart and Drake on registers with horizontal and vertical fins, and supersede those published in the original paper.

It is possible to subtract the pressure required at the register from the total available at the bonnet and thereby obtain the pressure available for the duct system alone.

Table 15-58. Register Free Area and Pressure Loss, 22° Deflection of Air
(National Environmental Systems Contractors Association)

Volume, cfm	Up to 18		19–21		22–24		25–27		28–30		31–34		35–39		40–49	
	Free Area	Pressure Loss	Free Area	Pressure Loss	Free Area	Pressure Loss	Free Area	Pressure Loss	Free Area	Pressure Loss	Free Area	Pressure Loss	Free Area	Pressure Loss	Free Area	Pressure Loss
190–209	68	0.02	49	0.03	38	0.05	29	0.08	24	0.11	19	0.16	...	...	...	...
210–229	82	0.02	60	0.03	45	0.04	35	0.06	28	0.10	23	0.13	...	...	...	...
230–249	...	...	71	0.02	54	0.04	42	0.06	34	0.08	28	0.11	22	0.17	...	...
250–269	...	...	84	0.02	63	0.03	49	0.05	40	0.07	52	0.10	25	0.16	...	...
270–299	...	...	100	0.02	76	0.03	60	0.04	48	0.06	38	0.09	30	0.13	...	...
300–339	...	...	...	...	96	0.02	73	0.04	60	0.05	48	0.07	37	0.11	...	...
340–379	...	...	...	...	122	0.02	95	0.03	78	0.04	61	0.06	47	0.09	33	0.18
380–419	...	...	...	...	...	...	117	0.02	94	0.03	75	0.05	58	0.08	39	0.15
420–459	...	...	...	...	...	...	142	0.02	113	0.03	91	0.04	70	0.06	47	0.13
460–499	...	...	...	...	...	...	168	0.02	135	0.03	108	0.04	83	0.06	56	0.11
500–539	...	...	...	...	...	...	...	...	159	0.02	126	0.03	97	0.05	66	0.10
540–579	...	...	...	...	...	...	...	...	185	0.02	147	0.03	113	0.04	77	0.08

Volume, cfm	28–30		31–34		35–39		40–49		50–59		60–69		70–79		80–89	
	Free Area	Pressure Loss	Free Area	Pressure Loss	Free Area	Pressure Loss	Free Area	Pressure Loss	Free Area	Pressure Loss	Free Area	Pressure Loss	Free Area	Pressure Loss	Free Area	Pressure Loss
580–619	212	0.02	169	0.03	130	0.04	88	0.08	51	0.18	...	...	...	...	...	...
620–659	...	...	192	0.02	147	0.03	100	0.07	59	0.15	...	...	...	...	...	...
660–499	...	...	217	0.02	166	0.03	113	0.06	75	0.13	...	...	...	...	...	...
700–739	...	...	243	0.02	186	0.03	127	0.06	85	0.11	...	...	...	...	...	...
740–779	...	...	271	0.02	208	0.03	141	0.05	94	0.10	...	...	...	...	...	...
780–819	...	...	...	...	230	0.02	157	0.05	105	0.09	...	...	...	...	...	...
820–859	...	...	...	...	254	0.02	173	0.04	115	0.08	...	...	...	...	...	...
860–899	...	...	...	...	278	0.02	190	0.04	126	0.08	...	...	...	...	...	...
900–939	...	...	...	...	304	0.02	207	0.04	138	0.07	...	...	...	...	...	...
940–979	...	...	...	...	332	0.02	226	0.04	151	0.07	108	0.12	...	...	...	...
980–1019	...	...	...	...	360	0.02	245	0.04	163	0.06	118	0.11	...	...	...	...
1020–1059	...	...	...	...	390	0.02	265	0.03	177	0.06	127	0.11	...	...	...	...
1060–1099	...	...	...	...	...	...	285	0.03	190	0.06	137	0.10	...	...	...	...
1100–1139	...	...	...	...	...	...	307	0.03	204	0.05	147	0.09	...	...	...	...
1140–1179	...	...	...	...	...	...	330	0.03	220	0.05	158	0.09	...	...	...	...
1180–1219	...	...	...	...	...	...	353	0.03	235	0.04	169	0.08	...	...	...	...
1220–1259	...	...	...	...	...	...	376	0.02	251	0.04	180	0.08	...	...	...	...
1260–1299	...	...	...	...	...	...	401	0.02	167	0.04	192	0.07	136	0.13	...	...
1300–1339	...	...	...	...	...	...	426	0.02	284	0.04	204	0.07	144	0.13	...	...
1340–1379	...	...	...	...	...	...	452	0.02	301	0.04	217	0.06	154	0.12	109	0.22
1380–1419	...	...	...	...	...	...	479	0.02	319	0.04	230	0.06	163	0.12	116	0.21
1420–1459	...	...	...	...	...	...	508	0.02	338	0.03	244	0.06	172	0.11	122	0.20
1460–1500	...	...	...	...	...	...	536	0.02	356	0.03	256	0.06	182	0.10	129	0.19

If register selected based on distance from register to opposite wall is unsatisfactory on account of size or pressure loss, it is permissible to shift one or more spaces left or right in the table to obtain a more suitable register.

If requirements fail in blank space, select two registers in place of one and divide cfm capacity between the two registers.

Values on the right of thick line should not be used in churches, auditoriums, concert halls, and such applications.

Values on the right of double line should not be used in residential work, motion picture theatres, court rooms, schools, and such applications.

Pressure loss is based on flat face adjustable bar type and does not include stack head. For other type registers, consult manufacturer catalogs.

Floor registers: Where a velocity of approximately 300 fpm is used,

$$\text{Free area} = \frac{cfm \times 144}{300} \quad \text{or approximately cfm/2.}$$

Assume a pressure loss of 0.01 inch.

Table 15-59. Register Free Area and Pressure Loss, No Deflection of Air
(National Environmental Systems Contractors Association)

Volume, cfm	Distance from Register to Opposite Wall, ft													
	Up to 21		22–24		25–27		28–30		31–34		35–39		40–49	
	Free Area	Pressure Loss	Free Area	Pressure Loss	Free Area	Pressure Loss	Free Area	Pressure Loss	Free Area	Pressure Loss	Free Area	Pressure Loss	Free Area	Pressure Loss
190–209	62	0.02	47	0.03	37	0.04	30	0.06	24	0.09	18	0.15	...	...
210–229	76	0.02	58	0.02	45	0.04	36	0.05	29	0.08	22	0.12	...	...
230–249	...	...	69	0.02	53	0.03	43	0.04	34	0.07	26	0.11	...	...
250–269	...	...	81	0.02	63	0.03	50	0.04	40	0.06	31	0.09	21	0.18
270–299	...	...	93	0.02	73	0.02	59	0.03	47	0.05	36	0.08	24	0.16
300–339	...	...	...	...	95	0.02	77	0.03	61	0.04	46	0.06	32	0.12
340–379	...	...	...	...	120	0.02	97	0.02	77	0.03	59	0.05	40	0.10
380–419	...	...	...	...	...	...	119	0.02	95	0.03	73	0.04	50	0.08
420–459	...	...	...	...	...	...	149	0.02	114	0.03	88	0.04	60	0.07
460–499	...	...	...	...	...	...	171	0.02	136	0.02	105	0.03	71	0.06
500–539	...	...	...	...	...	...	...	...	160	0.02	123	0.03	84	0.05

Volume, cfm	Distance from Register to Opposite Wall, ft													
	31–34		35–39		40–49		50–59		60–69		70–79		80–89	
	Free Area	Pressure Loss	Free Area	Pressure Loss	Free Area	Pressure Loss	Free Area	Pressure Loss	Free Area	Pressure Loss	Free Area	Pressure Loss	Free Area	Pressure Loss
540–579	186	0.02	143	0.02	97	0.05	65	0.09	47	0.17	...	...	...	...
580–619	213	0.02	164	0.02	111	0.04	74	0.08	54	0.15	...	...	...	...
620–659	...	...	180	0.02	127	0.04	85	0.07	61	0.14	...	...	...	...
660–499	...	...	210	0.02	143	0.03	95	0.07	69	0.12	49	0.22	...	...
700–739	...	...	236	0.02	160	0.03	107	0.06	77	0.11	54	0.21	...	...
740–779	...	...	262	0.02	179	0.03	119	0.06	86	0.10	61	0.18	...	...
780–819	...	...	291	0.02	198	0.03	132	0.05	95	0.09	97	0.17	...	...
820–859	...	...	320	0.02	218	0.03	145	0.05	105	0.08	74	0.15	...	...
860–899	...	...	352	0.02	240	0.02	160	0.04	115	0.08	81	0.14	...	...
900–939	...	...	385	0.01	262	0.02	175	0.04	126	0.07	89	0.13	...	...
940–979	...	...	419	0.01	285	0.02	190	0.04	137	0.07	97	0.12	...	...
980–1019	...	...	455	0.01	309	0.02	206	0.04	148	0.06	105	0.11	...	...
1020–1059	...	...	493	0.01	335	0.02	223	0.03	161	0.06	113	0.11	...	...
1060–1099	...	...	530	0.01	361	0.02	241	0.03	173	0.06	123	0.10	...	...
1100–1139	...	...	571	0.01	388	0.02	258	0.03	186	0.05	132	0.09	93	0.17
1140–1179	...	...	...	...	416	0.02	277	0.03	199	0.05	141	0.08	100	0.16
1180–1219	...	...	...	...	446	0.02	297	0.03	214	0.04	151	0.08	107	0.15
1220–1259	...	...	...	...	476	0.02	317	0.03	228	0.04	161	0.07	116	0.14
1260–1299	...	...	...	...	507	0.01	338	0.02	243	0.04	172	0.07	122	0.13
1300–1339	...	...	...	...	539	0.01	359	0.02	258	0.04	183	0.07	130	0.12
1340–1379	...	...	...	...	...	...	382	0.02	274	0.04	195	0.07	138	0.12
1380–1419	...	...	...	...	...	...	403	0.02	290	0.03	206	0.06	146	0.12
1420–1459	...	...	...	...	...	...	...	...	308	0.03	218	0.06	155	0.10
1460–1500	...	...	...	...	...	...	...	...	324	0.03	230	0.06	163	0.10

If register selected based on distance from register to opposite wall is unsatisfactory on account of size or pressure loss, it is permissible to shift one or more spaces left or right in the table to obtain a more suitable register.

If requirements fail in blank space, select two registers in place of one and divide cfm capacity between the two registers.

Values on the right of thick line should not be used in churches, auditoriums, concert halls, and such application.

Values on the right of double line should not be used in residential work, motion picture theatres, court rooms, schools, and such applications.

Pressure loss is based on flat face adjustable bar type and does not include stack head. For other type registers, consult manufacturer catalogs.

Floor registers: Where a velocity of approximately 300 fpm is used,

$$\text{Free area} = \frac{cfm \times 144}{300} \quad \text{or approximately cfm/2.}$$

Assume a pressure loss of 0.01 inch.

Return Intake Sizes: As indicated previously, the location of the return intake is not as critical as the locations of the warm air registers. The air flow from more than one register can be handled through a single return intake. If uniform room air temperatures are maintained by the proper placement of registers, then the return intakes can be located in the ceiling as well as in the sidewall or in the floor. Usually floor locations are not favored because the intakes will be stepped upon.

Table 15-60. Sizes and Capacities of Return Intakes

Nominal Size, in.	Approx Capacity, cfm	Nominal Sizes, in.	Approx Capacity, cfm
10 × 4	100	24 × 4	260
10 × 5	125	24 × 5	320
10 × 6	125	24 × 6	390
10 × 8	215	24 × 8	490
12 × 4	120	24 × 10	665
12 × 5	155	24 × 12	795
12 × 6	190	30 × 4	300
12 × 8	260	30 × 5	400
12 × 10	325	30 × 6	485
14 × 4	145	30 × 8	660
14 × 5	180	30 × 10	830
14 × 6	220	30 × 12	1015
14 × 8	305	30 × 14	1160
		30 × 16	1355

This table is not complete and does not list all sizes being manufactured. For other sizes and exact free areas refer to register manufacturer catalogs.

Free area requirements of baseboard or floor intakes for any capacity can be determined by the following equation:

$$\text{Free area} = \frac{cfm \times 144}{500} = 0.288 \times cfm$$

Theoretically, the air flow rate in cfm at the register is greater than that at the return intake because of the less dense air at the supply register. In actual practice the difference of 10 to 15% is not considered material. Furthermore, if the flow rate at the registers is considered to be the same as that at the return intakes, the design of the return duct system will be conservative. Hence, the air flow to be handled by any given return intake is obtained by adding the flow rates for all of the registers in that part of the space. For example, suppose that eight warm air registers, each handling 150 cfm, are located in a large space, or a total of 1200 cfm of air. Assume that two return intakes are to be located in the space. Then the air flow requirements of the two return intakes can be any combination that will total 1200 cfm.

A suggested design value for return intakes is 500 fpm through the free area. On this basis the values for Table 15-60 were derived.

Table 15-61. Free Area of Flat Face, Adjustable Bar Type Registers

Nominal Sizes, in.	Approx. Capacity, cfm	Nominal Sizes, in.	Approx. Capacity, cfm
10 × 4	24	14 × 6	54
10 × 5	30	14 × 8	75
10 × 6	38	14 × 10	95
10 × 8	52	24 × 4	60
12 × 4	29	24 × 6	91
12 × 5	37	24 × 8	129
12 × 6	46	24 × 10	163
12 × 8	64	24 × 12	200
12 × 10	82	30 × 6	120
14 × 4	34	30 × 8	167
14 × 5	44	30 × 8	167

This table is not complete and does not list all sizes being manufactured. For other sizes and exact free areas refer to register manufacturer catalogs.

Sizes of Ducts and Equivalent Lengths of Fittings: Once the total loss in pressure for each run has been determined, the selection of the friction loss per 100 ft of duct for each run can be determined by:

$$\frac{\text{Available pressure for each run in inches of water}}{\text{Effective lengths of duct from bonnet to register}}$$

(in units of 100 ft)

Now the effective length of duct is the summation of the straight lengths of duct and the equivalent lengths of fittings in each run. For the purpose of determining the equivalent lengths of fittings commonly used in forced air systems, the values in Figs. 15-146 and 15-147 are shown. The values, which are in equivalent feet of straight duct are only approximate, and are on the low side for extremely large ducts over 18 inches in diameter, or 18 in².

The design procedure from this point forward is no different from that commonly referred to as the equal friction pressure loss method. For each branch duct in the system, both the cfm to be handled as well as the friction loss per 100 ft of duct will be known. By means of the common air friction chart for air flow, the size of the ducts can be determined as well as the duct velocity. By means of tables or charts, the round pipe diameters can be converted to rectangular or square pipe sizes that will have the same friction loss characteristics.

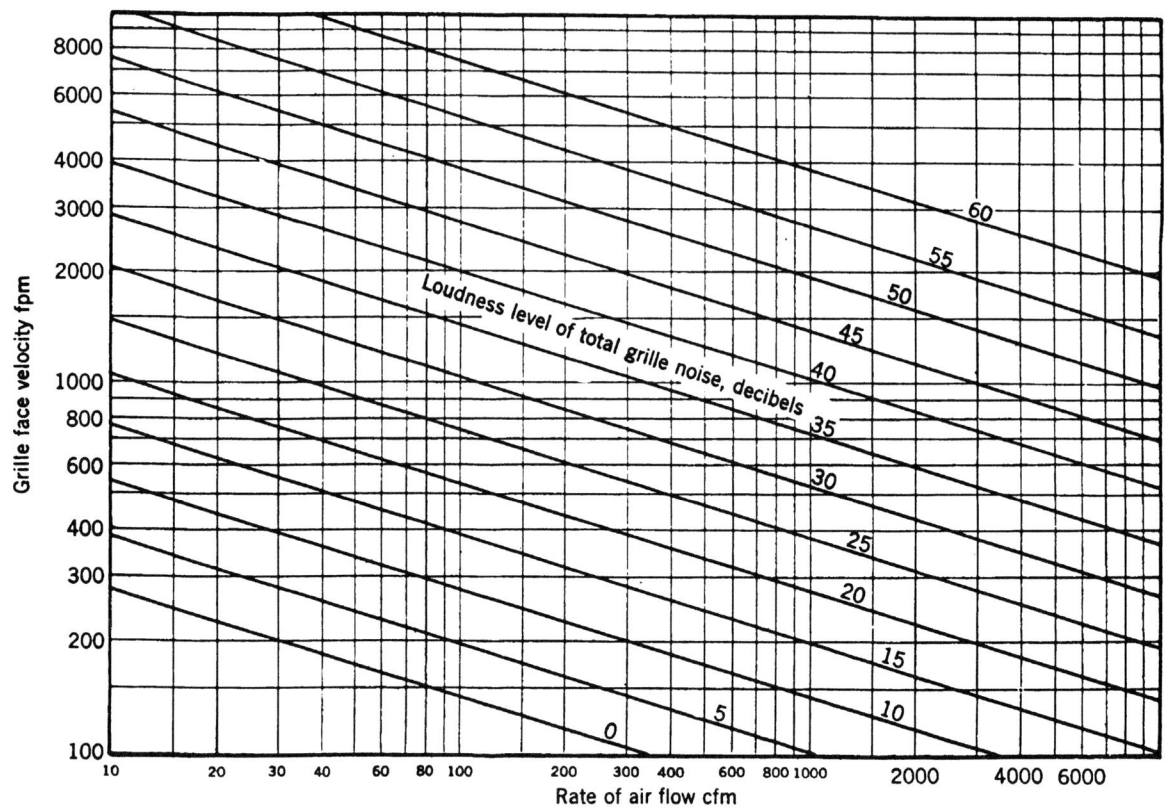

Fig 15-145. Average loudness levels for registers with vertical and horizontal fins

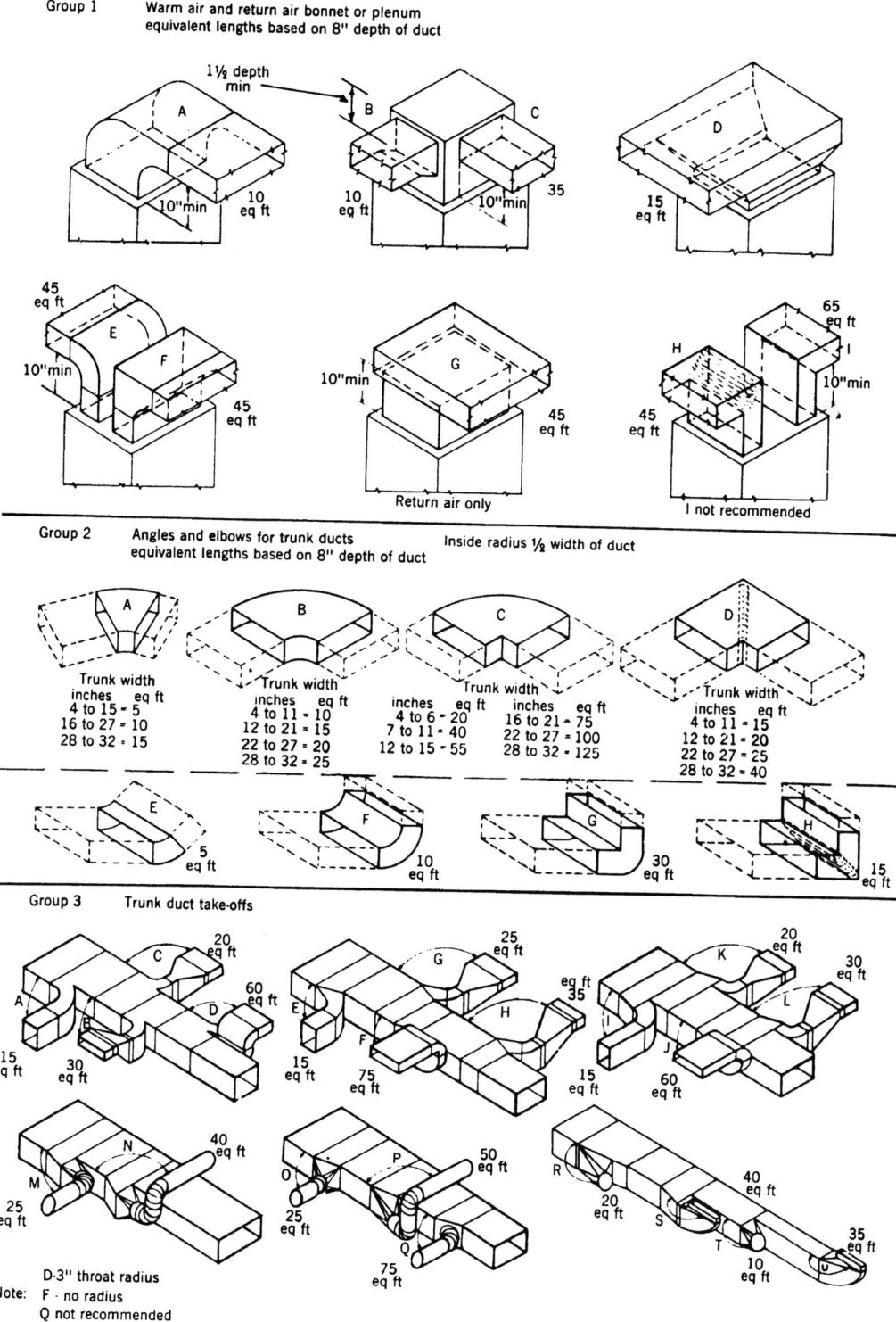

Fig 15-146. Equivalent length of duct fittings (NESCA)

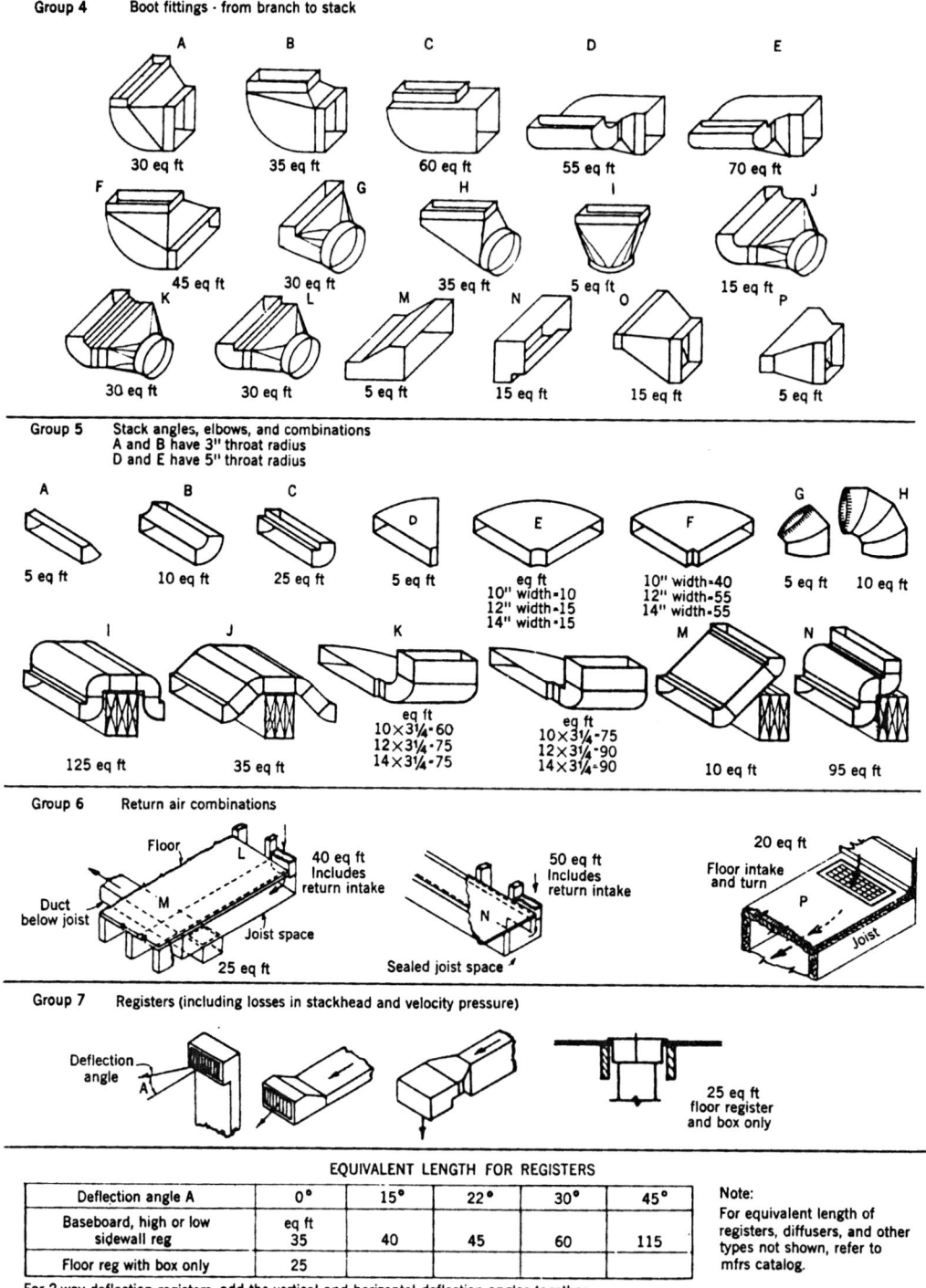

Fig 15-147. Equivalent length of duct fittings (NESCA)

Steam Supplied Unit Heater Performance Factors.—It is accepted practice to rate unit heaters in Btu per hr at an entering air temperature of 60°F and at a given steady steam pressure within the coil at 2 psig, dry and saturated. Furthermore, heater capacity for such constant entering air temperature and constant steam pressure machines increases with increase in steam pressure and decreases with increase in entering air temperature. It is not enough to know capacity change alone to utilize fully and effectively unit heater performance data for space heating. Leaving air temperature is important, too.

Graphs Accurate Enough: The graph on the page following enables one to correct heater capacity and estimate leaving air temperature, given steam pressure and entering air temperature. Results are sufficiently accurate for design use and apply to free delivery conditions with no duct attachments.

Temperature Limits: Tests and actual performance data have proved that leaving air temperature should be from 50°F to 60°F higher than design room temperature. With air entering the steam coil at 60°F, the leaving air temperature should be from 110°F to 120°F; with room air at 70°F, leaving air should be 120°F to 130°F. If these criteria are followed, there should be no real concern for air delivery from the units selected.

Too Buoyant Air: A unit heater with acceptable leaving air characteristics with steam at 2 psig will deliver excessively heated air if fed high pressure steam. This air, if too high above 120°F, becomes so buoyant that it may never reach the floor to do its heating job.

Rules of Thumb: There are several rules of thumb in unit heater selection that may be used to give realistic results. A standard coil unit may be selected for higher steam pressure conditions as per the following:

Stem Pressure, psig	Leaving Air Temperature at Standard Conditions, °F
0 to 25	110 to 120
30 to 125	95 to 105

However, the step graph may be used to obtain the leaving air temperature more easily.

Suspended Heaters: When suspended heaters are used with free delivery, higher entering air temperatures must be used over and above the room temperature at breathing level. Thus, when calculating actual operating capacity when taking air high above the floor, the environmental temperature may vary as much as ½°F for each foot of elevation above the breathing line during maximum design conditions, say 0°F outdoors and 70°F indoors.

Example 13: A heater has catalog performance data as follows: 19,000 Btu/hr and a leaving air temperature of 119°F. It is to be supplied with 20 psig steam and will have a new entering air temperature of 70°F. What is the new capacity and new leaving air temperature?

Solution: Temperature difference from catalog is 119°F– 60°F = 59°F. Start at 20 psig on constant steam pressure scale, Figs. 15-146 extreme right on graph, and move to the left until the entering air temperature line of 70°F is intersected. Read capacity factor 1.18 below. Locate 59°F sloping line belonging to leaving minus entering air line family. By coincidence it happens to fall on the same point. Thus, the air temperature rise is 70°F. New capacity is 19,000 ×1.18 = 22,420 Btu/hr and the leaving air temperature is 70°F + 70°F = 140°F. Heater is acceptable under these conditions.

Example 14: Same heater in previous example is to deliver 160°F air for process use. What is the operating steam pressure under new conditions?

Solution: Air temperature rise must be 160–70 = 90°F. Enter graph at 90°F on air temperature rise scale on extreme left of graph. Move horizontally until striking the 59°F line. Then move vertically up the capacity factor line of 1.52 to the entering design line of 70°F. Now read across to steam pressure of 67.5 psig. New capacity is 19,000 ×1.52 = 28,880 Btu/hr.

Gas Fired Radiant (Infrared) Heaters.—A relatively new method for the space or spot heating of industrial and commercial buildings is by means of overhead gas burning infrared radiant heaters. These are listed under the Room Heater classification of the AGA Directory of Approved Appliances.

Overhead radiant heaters have proved successful for heating of warehouses, garage, industrial plants, shopping centers, showrooms, bus stations and repair shops, airport hangars and auditoriums.

Vented Metallic Radiant Overhead Panels: These units are available with inputs from 62,500 to 125,000 Btu/hr. (Vented heaters tested under ANSI Z21.11 are required to meet a standard thermal efficiency test. Part of this output may be in the form of convected heat.) Metal temperatures are approximately 750°F. Equipment manufacturers claim that heat losses in industrial buildings above the level at which radiant heaters are installed (above 15 ft in high bay buildings) can be neglected unless there is an overhead wet sprinkler system.

Unvented Ceramic or Metallic Overhead Radiant Heaters: These are available up to 50,000 Btu input. Ceramic surfaces reach a temperature of 1600°F to 1650°F. Around the burner assembly is a bright aluminum reflector which may be straight sided or parabolic, and has the purpose of better defining the area receiving radiation. The units may be used single or in multiple assembly. About 50% of the heat is claimed to be radiated downward, the remainder being transferred by convection and undirected low level radiation from warmed sides of the unit. The latent heat (about 10%) is not recovered.

Since these heaters are usually used in high bay buildings and are installed well above breathing level, vents are usually provided in the roof to carry off combustion products, the entire roof area serving as a large vent hood.

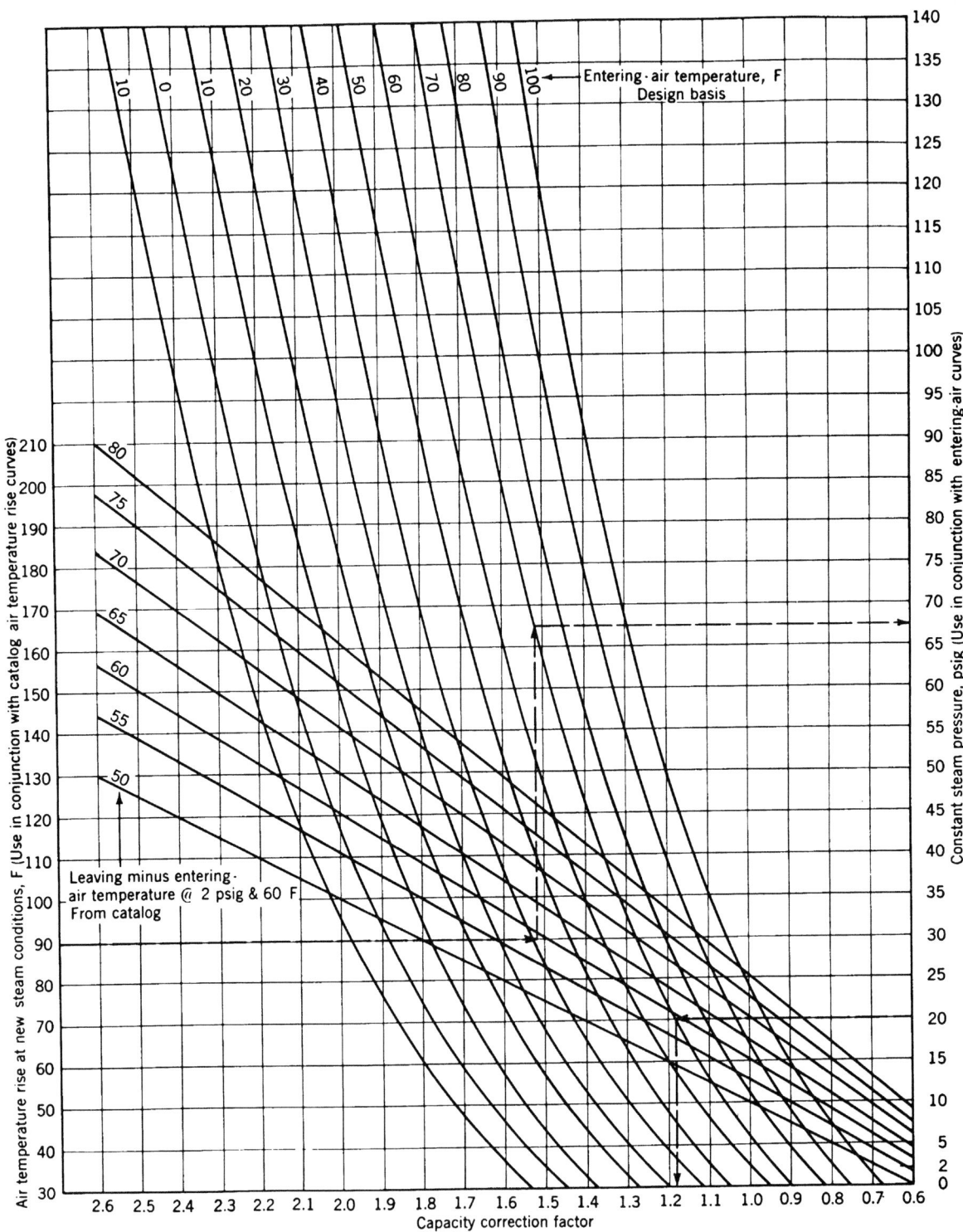

Fig 15-148. Steam supplied unit heater performance factors

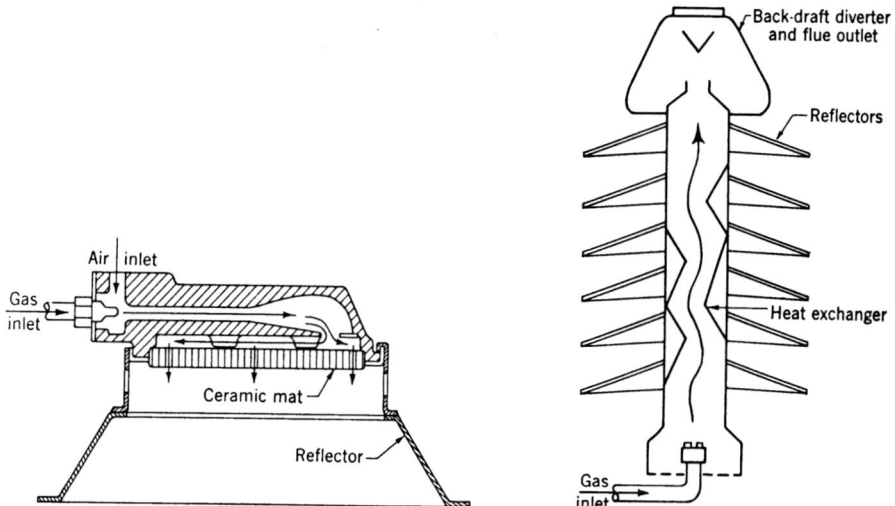

Fig 15-149. Two types of gas fired radiant (infrared) heaters
left is unvented ceramic type, at right vented metallic type. mounted overhead, they can be used in systems designed for partial or full area heating.

A minimum 50 in^2 roof vent opening is generally considered desirable for each 100,000 Btu/hr input. This area may change depending upon local or state codes.

Figure illustrates the principal features of both vented and unvented types of infrared heaters.

Application: When applying gas fired infrared units for comfort heating, manufacturers recommendations as to minimum mounting height and spacing should be followed. These recommendations are based on the pattern of radiant output from the units, and empirical information relating maximum radiation intensity and comfort.

There are basically two ways in which infrared radiant heaters can be employed.

Partial Area Heating or Spot Heating : When only partial areas or spots in a building are heated by overhead radiant panels, the actual ambient temperature in the areas will be lower than when the entire building is heated.

On spot or partial heating jobs, the secondary convection plays a lesser part in the heating and primary radiation becomes the controlling factor. Care must be taken in the placement of the radiant panels to be sure that all persons are seen by the panels and, equally important, that they receive radiation on both sides of their bodies.

Area or spot heating should be approached cautiously. There is an indication that approximately 200 to 250 Btu/hr-ft^2 of area are required. As mentioned previously, manufacturers charts are available to show amount of radiation for various mounting heights. Heat should be provided from two or three directions to the spot being heated. Heaters should be mounted as low as possible to give the spot the greatest infrared intensity.

Full Area Heating : Where the entire building area is heated by overhead radiant panels, the actual comfort that results is due to several factors.

Direct radiation from the panels passes directly through air and is absorbed by the floor and machinery in the building, where it is converted to heat and convection is established.

Following are recommendations of a manufacturer of the Schwank infrared heater:

Each burner has a comparatively low output, so many heaters may be required for a large building, each heating a small floor area. The height at which heaters may be mounted depends on the type of building. Heaters may be located high provided reflectors are used to prevent waste of heat on the upper part of outside walls. Heaters near outer walls should be kept as low as possible, and in some cases should be tilted inward (Fig. 15-150).

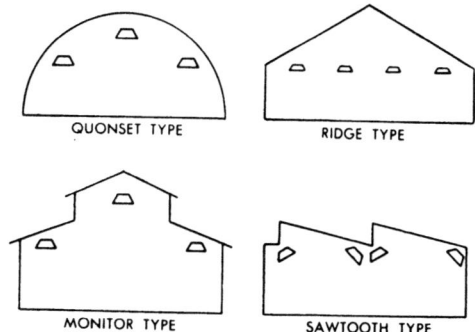

Fig 15-150. Building construction determines mounting arrangement

It is important to avoid high concentration of heat on the heads of occupants, so heaters at low levels should be of smaller size (two or three rayheads), whereas heaters at a 20–40 ft elevation can be larger units (four or more rayheads).

Total installed capacity must be sufficient to compensate for heat losses from the area heated, but since these losses are less than for conventional heating, the input to be installed is correspondingly reduced. In buildings of normal ceiling height, average construction, and for 0°F design outside temperature, one rayhead for each 100 ft² of floor space generally does a good job. This gives 120 Btu/ft² input of floor area. For buildings with high ceilings, leaky walls, no insulation, and similar conditions of high heat loss, the number of heaters to be installed must be greater than this, while for well insulated buildings and higher design temperatures, the number of units can be less.

The highest concentration of heat should be around the periphery of the heated area. For heating spots, or limited areas of large rooms, the capacity installed per square foot must be at least double or triple the amount used when the entire area is heated. In such cases, a number of heaters should be installed around the periphery of the space to be heated. They should have parabolic reflectors and should be inclined toward the center of the area.

While high buildings have higher heat losses per square foot of floor area and require more input than those with lower ceilings, the input required is not increased to the extent it would be with convection heating, and high bay buildings show the greatest savings over convection systems.

Sizing of Steam Traps at Air Heating Coils.—A heating coil is usually equipped with a throttling control valve. In mild weather, or most of the time, the control valve throttles so that, except for the vacuum breakers installed, the coil would frequently be under vacuum and the condensate would not be discharged.

The vacuum breaker equalizes the pressure between coil and return piping (whether the system be a vacuum or an open system, with returns under atmospheric pressure).

When vacuum breakers open and the pressure is equalized, the vertical drop (or static head of water column) between coil outlet and trap inlet supplies the only force available to discharge condensate through the trap. Thus, the criterion for sizing traps that drain coils with throttling control is not the steam pressure in the system ahead of the regulator, but this head of water column.

The four sizing graphs apply to ball float traps with built in thermostatic air bypass. Each curve shows the maximum quantity of condensate recommended (with a safety factor of 2) for a trap of the type and size shown, according to original standard Steam Heating Equipment Manufacturers Association (SHEMA) ratings. There is one graph for each of four pressure drops through the trap: $\frac{1}{2}$, $\frac{1}{4}$, 1, and 2 psi. (Note: inches of water column × 0.03613 = psi.) On each graph, air flow rate through coils is plotted against temperature rise of air through the coil.

Example 15: A 12 inch drop exists between coil outlet and trap inlet, corresponding to 0.435 psi. Which chart to use for sizing? If it is decided to size the trap using the chart for $\frac{1}{4}$ psi with a safety factor of 2, this will give a total safety factor of $(0.435/0.250) \times 2 = 3.5$, which is ample, since the volume of steam is considerably less when valve throttles than when control is fully open. Hence, the $\frac{1}{4}$ psi chart suffices.

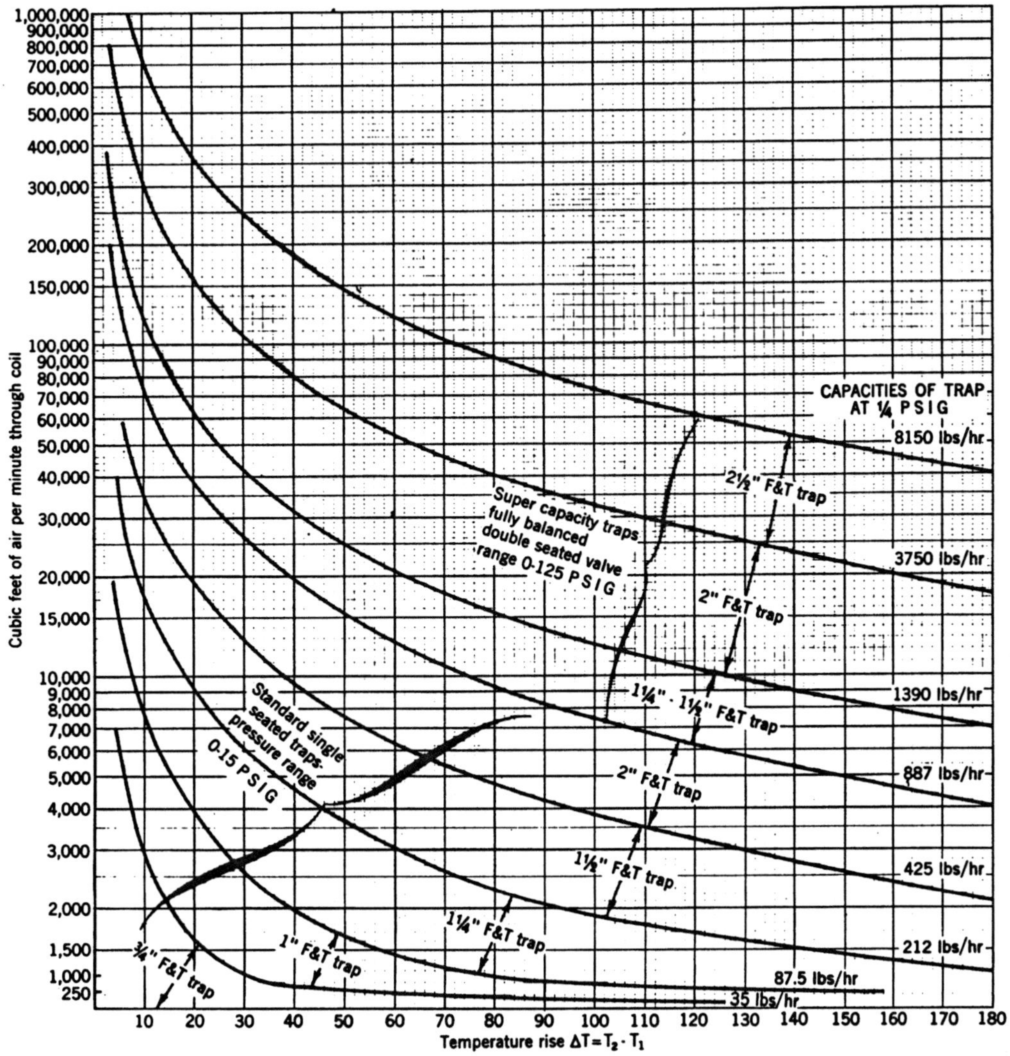

Fig 15-151. Sizing of steam traps

The chart contains the following labels:

- y-axis: Cubic feet of air per minute through coil (1,000,000 / 900,000 / 800,000 / 700,000 / 600,000 / 500,000 / 400,000 / 300,000 / 200,000 / 150,000 / 100,000 / 90,000 / 80,000 / 70,000 / 60,000 / 50,000 / 40,000 / 30,000 / 20,000 / 15,000 / 10,000 / 9,000 / 8,000 / 7,000 / 6,000 / 5,000 / 4,000 / 3,000 / 2,000 / 1,500 / 1,000 / 250)
- x-axis: Temperature rise $\Delta T = T_2 \cdot T_1$ (10 20 30 40 50 60 70 80 90 100 110 120 130 140 150 160 170 180)

CAPACITIES OF TRAP AT ¼ P S I G

- 8150 lbs/hr — 2½" F&T trap
- 3750 lbs/hr — 2" F&T trap
- 1390 lbs/hr — 1¼" · 1½" F&T trap
- 887 lbs/hr — 2" F&T trap
- 425 lbs/hr — 1½" F&T trap
- 212 lbs/hr — 1¼" F&T trap
- 87.5 lbs/hr — 1" F&T trap
- 35 lbs/hr — ¾" F&T trap

Super capacity traps fully balanced double seated valve range 0-125 P S I G

Standard single seated traps pressure range 0-15 P S I G

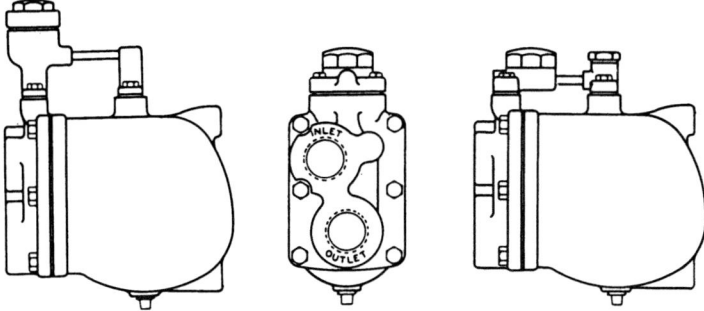

Fig 15-152. Heavy duty double ported float thermostatic steam traps

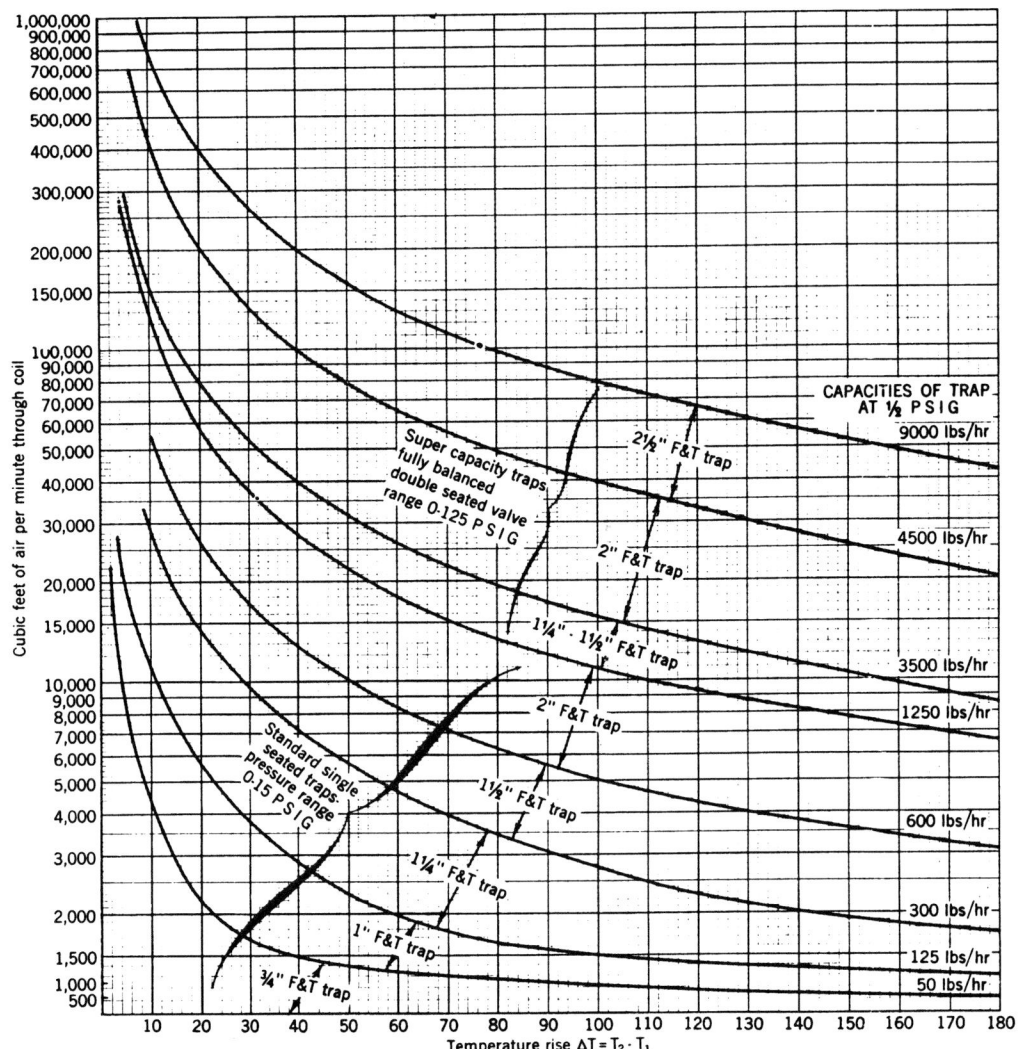

Fig 15-153. Sizing of steam traps

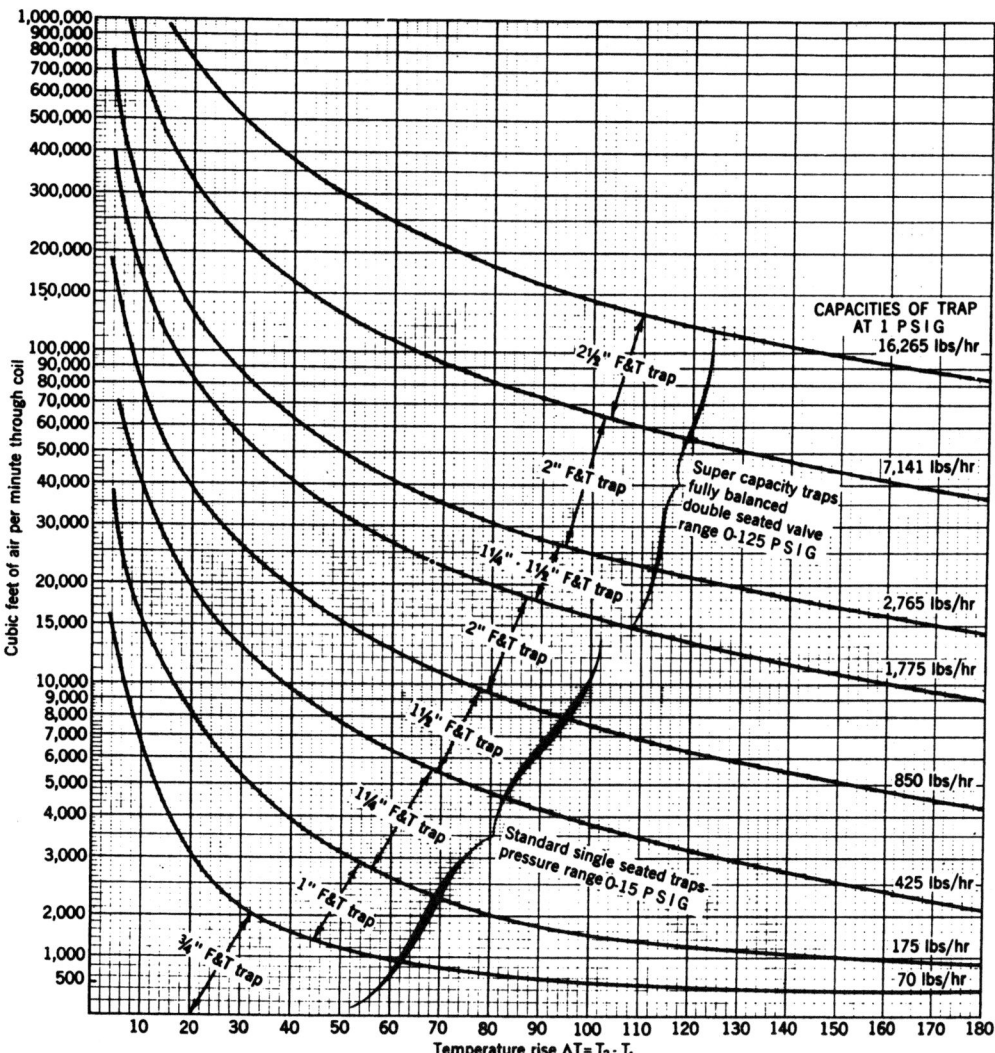

Fig 15-154. Sizing of steam traps

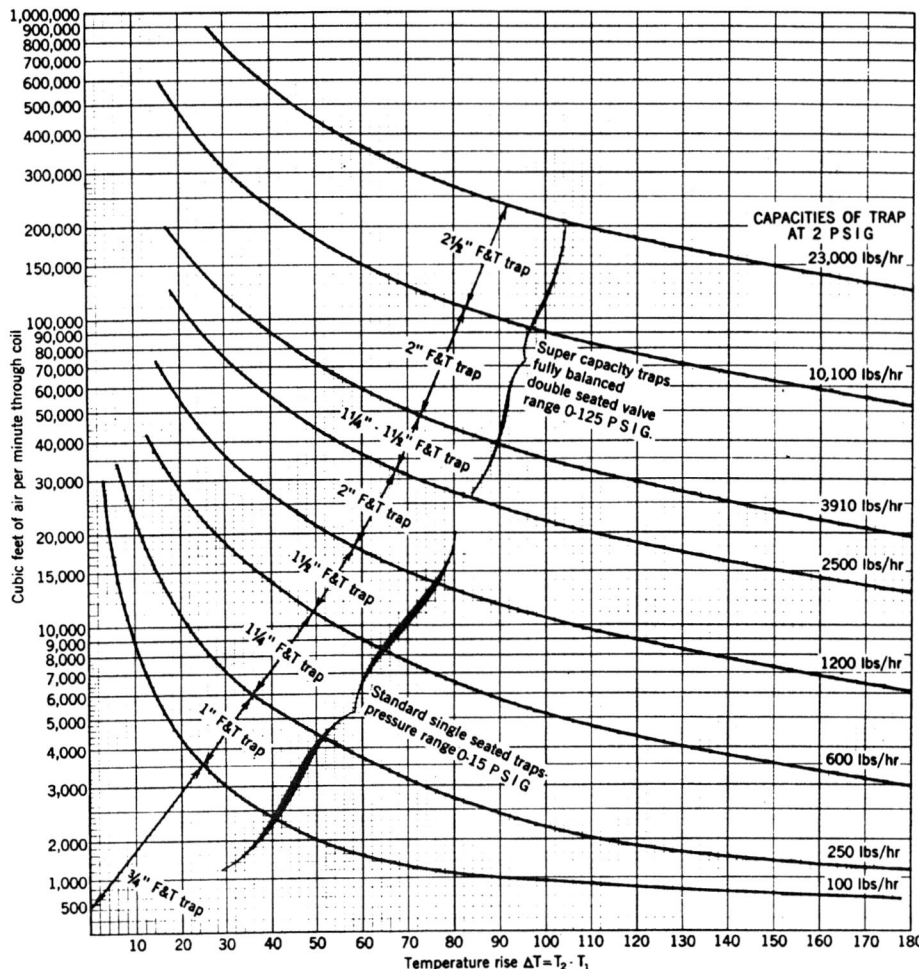

Fig 15-155. Sizing of steam traps

Unit Heaters and Other Gas Fired Air Heaters.—

Unit heaters described here are self contained, automatically controlled, vented, gas burning devices designed for the heating of non residential space. They may be divided into two groups in two ways; first, according to the static pressure against which they will deliver heated air; and second, according to the method of location.

Types of Unit Heaters

Type	Input Range, MBH
Suspended unit heaters	
Propeller fan	25 to 300
Blower type (with or without duct)	25 to 300
Heavy duty suspended blower	250 to 5000
Floor or platform mounted unit heaters	
Vertical blower type	60 to 750
Heavy duty floor mounted blowers	250 to 5000

Propeller Fan Type: Theoretically, the unit heater with the propeller fan should not operate against any static pressure but should have full opening of the unit heater face. When it becomes necessary to use ductwork with a unit heater in order to direct heat at a desired spot location, it is mandatory that the unit heater be equipped with a blower.

Propeller type unit heaters are, in the main, designed for suspended installation.

Placement of units is governed by the individual heating job. Usually, however, units are spotted in one or two ways:

1) they are placed so they circulate the heated air along the outside walls, or

2) they are located on outside walls so as to pick up colder air from outside walls, heat it and force it toward the center of the area or where heat is most needed.

Fig. 15-156 is a typical suspended gas fired propeller type unit heater installation.

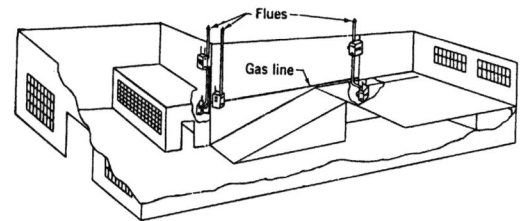

Fig 15-156. Typical installation of suspended propeller type heaters

Suspended Blower Type: Suspended blower type unit heaters are used much the same as propeller units. Because of the blower type fans, however, they handle larger quantities of air and can be used with or without ductwork. As a result, many special problems in plant heating, such as automatic temperature control of large warehouses, door draft tempering, fog elimination, and many others including some low temperature drying, can be easily accomplished with these units.

Blower units are particularly effective for heating buildings, where it is necessary to suspend the units more than 12 ft above the floor. Also, when cold air is to be picked up off the floor to overcome drafty conditions, it is necessary only to install return air supplies to blower type units to accomplish this task. Heat distribution ducts may also be attached to the blower type units and several rooms heated by the one unit (Fig. 15-157).

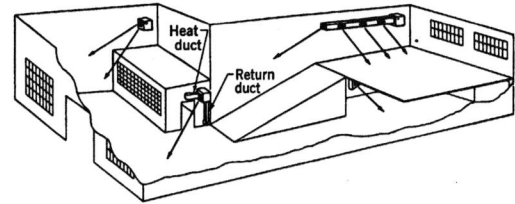

Fig 15-157. The same industrial area could be served by suspended blower type unit heaters shown in this manner. Gas lines and flutes are not shown.

Suspended Heavy Duty Units: For heavy duty work, large blower type units ranging in input capacities from 250,000 Btu/hr to 5,000,000 Btu/hr and over are obtainable. For airplane hangars, mills, foundries, factories, warehouses and other large space installation, where it is necessary to suspend the units because of codes or to save floor space, these units effectively blanket large areas at great distances from the unit with automatically controlled heat. By use of high velocity nozzles and specially designed plenums, heat may be directed down and in any direction so that particular areas may be given more attention than others.

Floor Mounted Vertical Blower Units: Vertical floor type gas heaters have a wide application in the industrial heating field. Another important usage is that of supplying heat to office suites and special enclosures when it is found desirable to have these separate from the main heating system. This type equipment is desirable because of the ease with which the air is filtered. In candy plants, dress factories, and others of the type where great care is exercised in the cleanliness of the product, these units are especially adapted. For larger areas, such as barracks or large assembling rooms, they are usually spotted around the outside walls and deliver the heated air toward the center of the building. Recirculated air is drawn from the floor at the base of the unit. In this manner, effective zone control is obtained.

Floor Mounted Heavy Duty Units: Heavy duty floor mounted unit heaters are available:

1) without connected ductwork but with high velocity nozzles, and

2) for application with ductwork.

In the first application, the units are mounted on the floor and the heated air is delivered around the 8 ft level.

Delivery nozzles are rotatable and usually both horizontal and vertical louvers may be obtained. Placement of the unit is optional, being governed by the heating requirements of the building, as well as by the fundamentals of good heating practice.

As a general rule, units are either placed around the outside walls and discharge toward the center, or wherever possible units are run down the center of the space and discharge in both directions. In this latter method, it is many times possible to cut down on the number of units needed to heat a given space. Effective delivery of heat with high temperature rise air and high velocity nozzles of this kind ranges from approximately 110 to 250 ft, depending upon conditions under which the units are installed. The blowers are usually driven by a single motor, but some designs are sectionalized so as to provide a wide variety of output capacities and combinations.

In the second instance, a duct distribution system is connected directly to the outlet of the unit. Units of this kind are well suited to extremely large space heating, particularly in leaky, drafty industrial buildings where it is desirable to have reasonably high leaving temperatures in order to have sufficient heat at long distances from the duct opening.

Sizing Unit Heaters: Unit heater capacity should be at least 10% greater than the heat loss of the structure to provide a margin of safety during severe weather and some pickup capacity. Allowing an equipment efficiency of 80%, Btu input would be 1.4 times the heat loss. Where temperature is set back at night or for intermittent heating of cold loading areas, a greater allowance should be made for pick up.

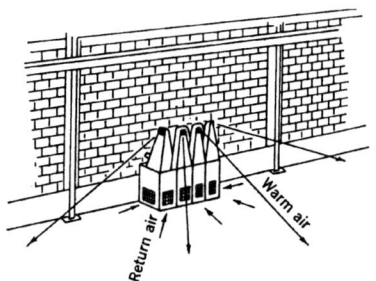 

Fig 15-158. Details of gas fired heater installation

When unit heaters are planned for industrial occupancies, there may be included in the heat loss such items as air for process use, heating cold stock and vehicles entering the building and other such heating requirements not normally encountered in residential and commercial building heating.

In the calculation of heat loss where unit heaters are to be used, consideration should be given to the type of occupancy there will be in the building. For example, where a working temperature of 60°F might be required in a shop, there is no point in designing units to maintain a temperature of 80°F. This would result not only in a lot of unnecessary on-off operation of the units but would not give as steady a heat or circulation as it would if the units were designed for the specific requirements.

Duct Furnace: Normally installed in distribution ducts of air conditioning systems to supply warm air for heating, duct furnaces are tested to insure that temperatures of combustible materials will not be excessive at points 6 inches from the sides and top, and on the floor at clearances of zero or 2 to 6 inches as specified by the manufacturer. Where floor clearance is greater than zero inches, a noncombustible stand or legs must be provided by the manufacturer.

Duct furnaces may be designed and approved only for suspension, in which case both the installation instructions and a permanent plate attached to the unit must state the required floor clearance. Where draft hoods extend above the top of the casing, a 6 inch clearance must be maintained above the top of the draft hood when designed for horizontal connection and above a standard 90° elbow when designed for a vertical outlet.

Circulating air should not be taken from the same enclosure in which the furnace is located.

Duct furnaces, when used in conjunction with a refrigeration system, should not be located downstream from the refrigeration coil unless specifically approved for such installation.

Enclosed Furnaces: These widely used furnaces are designed primarily for use in such places of public assembly as school rooms, churches and auditoriums. They incorporate an integral total enclosure around the furnace and they use only air from outdoors for combustion.

Typical enclosed furnaces provide automatic room ventilation, blending outside air and recirculation. Such furnaces include insulation for prevention of condensation and to insure quiet operation; they can be used against static pressures up to 0.50 inch wc; they normally operate with air temperature rise of 70 to 105°F.

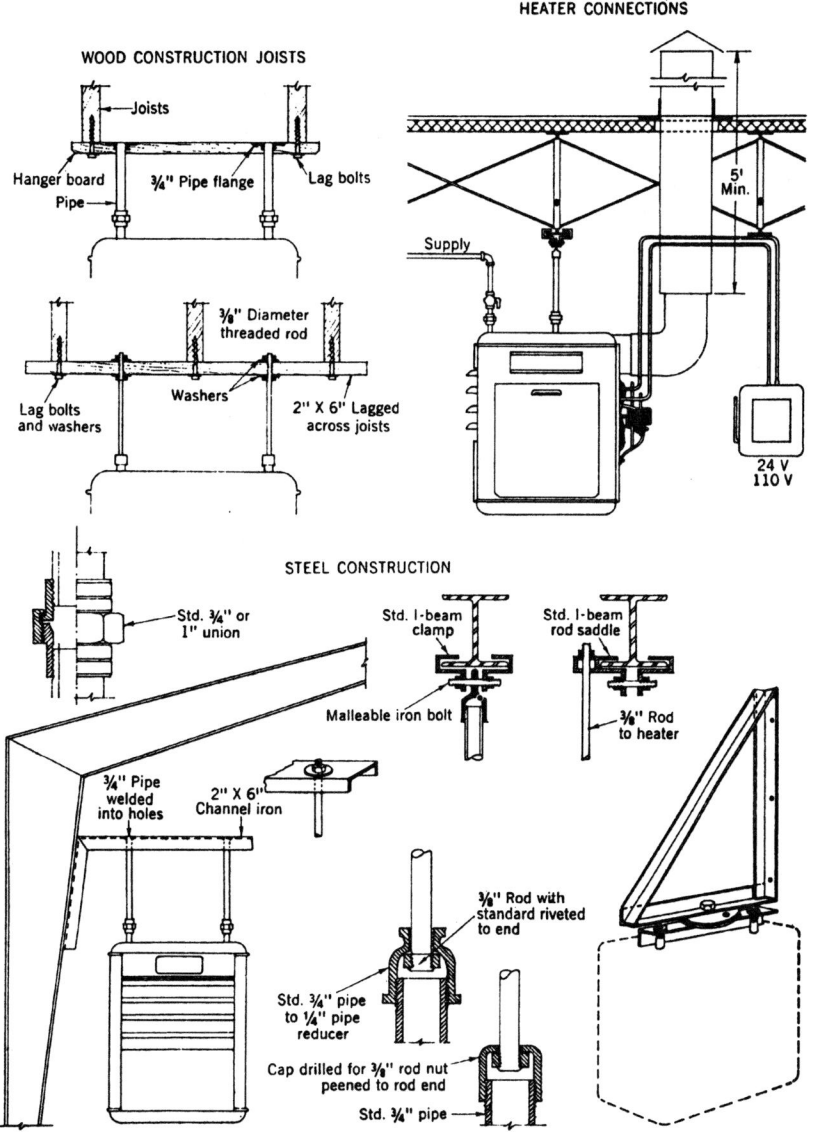

Fig 15-159. Details of gas fired heater installation

Enclosed furnaces are approved for installation with zero inch clearance to combustible materials on the floor and one vertical side and, at the option of the manufacturer, may be approved additionally with zero inch clearance at one or both ends. Surfaces exposed to air in the heated space may not exceed 60°F above room temperature.

Installation of Unit Heaters: Suspended units should be placed as low as permitted by headroom requirements. High mounting increases the difficulty of forcing warm air down to the working plane, and increases the floor ceiling differential.

An exception to this recommendation concerns unit heaters located in garages for more than 3 cars or in airplane hangars these should be installed at least 8 ft above the floor.

Suspended type unit heaters should be safely and adequately supported with due consideration given to their weight and vibration characteristics (Fig. 15-159).

AGA approved gas fired unit heaters should not be located closer to combustible construction than 6 inches above the top when heater has an internal draft hood; not less than 18 inches at the sides, and not less than 12 inches at the bottom, except in cases where the heater is approved for installation with reduced clearances.

Direction of Air Stream: In general, the direction of the air stream leaving a unit heater should be toward the location where the most uniform temperature is desired. This is usually that portion of any space which is most frequently occupied by people at rest or doing work requiring no motion.

Exposed Wall: If unit heaters are directed so that the high temperature air strikes an exposed wall, the temperature on the inside of the wall will be higher than the design temperature along this exposure and will result in greater heat losses to the outside and consequently, increase fuel consumption. This is especially true if the exposed area consists mainly of glass or some other material with a high transmission factor. The air stream from a unit heater should not be directed against any exposed wall or other cold surface close to the unit.

Circulation of Air: The more complete the circulation of air through the entire space being heated, the more uniform will be the temperature throughout. Where more than one unit is installed in a large space, the units may be placed so that the air will be circulated completely around the inside walls of the building. The air discharged from a unit is projected toward the rear of the next unit, which receives the air after it is reduced in temperature and projects the reheated air in the same direction.

To maintain good circulation in small rooms, requiring only one unit heater, it is generally good practice to place the unit heater near an unexposed wall with the air stream from the unit directed toward the exposed wall surfaces, but not playing directly on them.

Obstructions: The direction of the air stream from unit heaters will be materially diverted by any obstruction within the building itself. Location of partition walls not extending to the ceiling, displays, piles of material, or other obstructions should be carefully considered. The direction of the air stream leaving the unit should be such that not too great a quantity of the heated air will be diverted by such obstructions.

Occupants: In many places favorable to unit heater installation, certain portions are set aside for heavy labor workers or office workers. Such spaces are usually located near the windows to obtain the best lighting conditions. Most uniform temperatures should be maintained where such occupants work. Careful consideration, however, should be given to the direction of the air stream from the unit heaters so that occupants are not subjected to a direct blast of heated air from a unit, as this will result in considerable discomfort.

Location of Thermostats: Thermostats to control the operation of gas fired unit heaters should be located on an unexposed wall or column at about eye level. If no unexposed walls, columns or other suitable locations for thermostats are available they may be mounted on exposed walls, provided they are mounted on a bracket, or carefully insulated from the wall.

Thermostats should not be located in a way that causes a blast of warm air from the unit heater to strike them.

Each unit may be operated by an individual thermostat or, by means of electric relays, any number of units may be operated from one thermostat. It is usually advisable to keep the number of units controlled by one thermostat down to a minimum. Sun effect, wind pressure, lights, shifting of persons from one part of a room to another, can all affect temperature changes within a space, and if all the unit heaters in that space are controlled by one thermostat, it is difficult to keep everybody in the space comfortable.

Table 15-62. Check List for Conservation of Fuel

Physical Features of Buildings						
Building Name				Checked by		
Address				Date		
Exterior of Building Structure						
				Side		
			E	W	N	S
Exterior walls	Need insulation					
	Have open cracks					
	Unneeded openings should be closed					
	Fan opening needs louvers					
Exterior doorways	Unneeded					
	Frames need caulking					
	Doors rattle					
	Weatherstripping needed					
	Weatherstripping repairs					
	Door check needed					
	Door check need repairs					
	Storm door needed					
	Storm door needs repair					
	Revolving door could be used					
	Revolving door needs repairs					
Loading Platform	Outer door needed					
	Door needs repair					
	Rear partition needed					
	Rear partition needs repair					
	Swinging partition needed					
Roof	Insulation needed					
	Ceiling needed					
	Has open cracks					
	Unneeded openings					
	Fan opening needs louvers					
Skylight	Glass needed					
	Lower sash needed					

Physical Features of Buildings					
Building Name			Checked by		
Address			Date		
Penthouse	Insulation needed				
	Has open cracks				
	Openings unneeded				
	Frames need caulking				
	Doors rattle				
	Door checks needed				
	Door checks need repairs				
	Windows rattle				
	Weatherstripping needed,				
	Weatherstripping needs repair				
	Door locks needed				
	Door locks need repairs				
	Window lock needed				
	Glass needed				
	Putty needed				

Physical Features of Buildings					
Building Name			Checked by		
Address			Date		
	Interior of Building Structure	E	W	N	S
Windows	Window is unneeded				
	Frame needs caulking				
	Sash is loose				
	Weatherstripping needed				
	Weatherstripping needed repairs				
	Lock needed				
	Lock needs repair				
	Glass needed				
	Putty needed				
	Weights should be changed				
	Shade missing				
	Ventilating fan in place				
Partitions	Door needed				
	Door needs lock				
	Lock needs repair				
	Transom unneeded				
	Transom needs glass				
	Transom lock needs repair				

Suggestions for Operating Economy	
Methods recommended	Prevent the entrance of cold air through, storm sash, windows, doors, ventilating fan openings, transoms, window ventilators etc.
	Clean windows on warm days, during non business hours and with doors from room closed.
	Decrease transmission losses by pulling shades down and closing shutters.
	Keep daily records of fuel use, degree days, wind, rain and difficulties. Make adjustments when possible during non business hours.
Personnel	Instruct and arouse enthusiasm in building employees When in doubt secure advice from: Local steam utility, heating engineer, control contractor, or heating contractor of ability

Table 15-63. Records and Data on Past Operations

Building		Heating System	
Type:		Type:	
Age:		Age:	
Height:			
Height:		Kind of temperature control:	
Ground floor dimensions:			
Major changes:		Major changes:	
Kind of fuel used:		Degree days in normal year:	
District heating service used:			
Fuel or service records furnished by:			

Table 15-64. Fuel Record

Period Included Between (Days)	Total Fuel or Service Used	Amount Fuel or Service Non Heating	Fuel or Service Space Heating	Unit	MBH per Unit	MBtu for Space Heating	Degree Days in period	MBH per D.D.	MBH for Normal Year		
Conditions during period											
Overheating General		Local		When		Where		Est. Temp.		Cause	
Underrating General		Local		When		Where		Est. Temp.		Cause	
Percentage of building occupied						Percentage heated					
Was there any other considerable source of heat?											
Describe:											
Occupancy hours											
Weekdays to		Saturdays	to	Sundays	to	Holidays	to				
Temperature during occupancy						Temperature during non occupancy					
Odd hour occupants											
System difficulties such as leaks											
Tenants opening windows											
Skill, energy and enthusiasm of operators											
Other tenant peculiarities											

Steam Heating Systems Checklist

Basement	
Steam Lines	Unneeded but connected
	Uninsulated
	Flanges uninsulated
	Fittings uninsulated
	Too small
	Improperly sloped
	Sag in pipes
	Pocketed
	Clogged
	Broken
	Leaking
	Special service needed
	Shut off valves not accessible
	Shut off valve broken
	Shut off valve clogged
	Shut off valve leaking
	Relief valves needed

Basement	
Return Lines	Uninsulated
	Too small
	Improperly sloped
	Clogged
	Broken
	Leaking
Traps	Too small
	Faulty leg too short
	Cooling
Air vents	Too small
	Faulty
	Automatic regulation faulty
Radiation	Needed
Control equipment	Motor faulty
	Wiring faulty
	Tubing faulty
	Clock faulty
	Mechanism faulty
Pumping equipment	Motor faulty
	Wiring faulty
	Pump faulty

Basement	
Pressure regulator	Diaphragm faulty
	No pressure gauge
	Improperly installed
	Governor line faulty
Chimney	Repairs needed
	Cleaning needed
Grates	Too small
	Wrong type
	Defective
	Firing methods
Generating equipment	Added heating surface for boiler
	Boiler leaking
	Flues need cleaning
	Boiler needs insulation
	Stoker needs repairs
	Burner needs repairs
	Door and frame settings show leaks
	Air handling equipment needs repairs
	Feedwater regulation faulty
	Water treating equipment needs repairs
	Boiler dirty
	Safety valves defective

Evening Inspection	
Wall, floor and roof openings (encl. pent house)	Shutdown fan
	Close louvers or opening
	Close roof trap door tight
	Close floor openings
	Note difficulties
Radiators	Open valve if under control
	Shut valve in unoccupied rooms
	Note difficulties:
	Valve:
	Air valve:
	Trap:
	Steam inlet
	Condensate outlet

If feasible and permissible
Suggestions for operating economy
Run ventilating fans only when needed and no faster than necessary.
Check and correct meters.
Heat to no higher temperature than necessary.
Turn steam off wherever and whenever not needed, especially in vacant rooms.
Turn steam off at the main or zone valves rather than at the radiators.
Turn valves either entirely off or entirely on.
Check air fuel proportion.

Basement
Carry a low pressure on steam system; a high vacuum on vacuum system.
Carry a protective ash bed on grates.
Prompt move out ash discharged from grate.
Do not heat up the system for a few persons; lend electric heaters.
Carry on a regular schedule of maintenance.
Study damper control for best operation.
Study methods of heat saving, sources of building heat loss, heating and ventilating system operation and peculiarities of tenants.
Instruct and arouse enthusiasm in building employees.
Prepare a valve operation schedule for hand control; for use if there is no automatic control; or for use in case of a failure of control to functions.
Keep daily records of fuel use, degree days, wind, rain and difficulties.
When in doubt secure advice from: local steam utility, heating engineer, control contractor, or heating contractor.

Rooms and halls	
Radiators	Unneeded
	Location bad
	Oversized
	Undersized
	Shield obstructs
	Drapes obstruct
	Cover obstructs
	Water pan obstructs
	Metal radiator reflectors
	Painted with metallic paint
	Space between fins dirty
	Obstructed by furniture
	Air valve faulty
	Trap faulty
	Shut off valve inaccessible
	Shut off valve needs packing
	Radiator control valve inaccessible
	Orifice undersized
	Orifice oversized
Lines	Steam connection undersized
	Steam connection pocketed
	Steam connection broken
	Steam connection leaking
	Steam connection uninsulated
	Return connection undersized
	Return connection pocketed
	Return connection broken
	Return connection leaking

Hot Water Heating Systems

Flow and return mains and branches	Improperly graded
	Trapped
	Improperly sized
	Leaking
	Uninsulated
	Special service needed
Boiler	Improperly sized
	Improper type
	Leaking
	Flues need cleaning
	Insulation needed
	Door and frame leaks
	Ash pit dirty
	Grates need replacing
	Defective parts
	How fired
	Draft and check dampers bind
Chimney	Repairs needed
	Cleaning needed
	Too small in diameter
	Too short
	Obstructed by high trees or surround in buildings
Pressure system	Pressure tank improperly connected
	Pressure tank water logged
	Pressure relief valve improperly installed
	Pressure relief valve faulty
	Damper regulator inoperative
	Damper regulator improperly connected or adjusted
	Pressure gauge faulty
	Thermometer faulty
	Pressure reducing valve faulty
Firing device	Stoker or burner needs repairs
	Proper grade fuel being used?
	Yes
	No
	Combustion:
	Good
	Bad
	Air
	Too much
	Too little
Control equipment	Room thermostat faulty
	Improperly located
	Burner control faulty
	Relay faulty
	Thermostat setting:
	Too high
	Too low

Water circulating pump	Improperly installed
	Improperly sized
	Motor faulty
	Pump leaking
	Improperly lubricated
	Improperly controlled
	Noisy
Radiators	Improperly located
	Improperly sized
	Not needed
	Obstructed by dirty convectors
	Air valve faulty
	Radiator valve faulty
	Circulation through radiators
	Good
	Bad

Evening Inspection		
Inspection Checked by Date		
Wall, floor and roof openings (encl. pent house)	Shutdown fan	
	Close louvres or opening	
	Close roof trap door tight	
	Close floor openings	
	Note difficulties	
Radiators	Open valve if under control	
	Where feasible, shut valve in unoccupied rooms	
	Note difficulties	
	Valve	
	Air valve	

Suggestions for operating economy
Runs fans only when needed and no faster than necessary.
Heat to no higher temperature than necessary.
Turn heat off wherever and whenever not needed: especially in vacant rooms.
Turn radiator valves either entirely off or entirely on.
Check air fuel proportion.
Carry minimum boiler temperature.
Carry a protective ash bed on grates.
Promptly move out ash discharged from grate.
Carry on regular schedule of maintenance.
Study damper control for best operation.
Study methods of heat saving, sources of building heat loss, heating and ventilating system operation and peculiarities of tenants.
Instruct and arouse enthusiasm in building employees.
Keep daily records of fuel use, degree-days, wind, rain and difficulties.
When in doubt secure advice from local heating contractor of ability.

Checklist for Heating System Servicing.—The checklists that follow are for locating the cause of troubles with hot water, steam and vapor, gravity warm air and forced circulation warm air systems. It is not the intention to solve all troubles by checking off items of brief tables such as these, but with their help most problems can either be solved or the cause reduced to only a few possibilities. Such checklists often save time.

Hot Water Systems Checklist

Complaint Slow Heating or Not Enough Heat Throughout Building			
Possible Cause	Check	Details	Remedy
Insufficient heat input to boiler	Time required to raise temperature of water	Average job about 1½°F per minute Underrated job 1¾° to 2°F per minute Overrated job 1 to 1½°F per minute	Increase burner input
Shortage of radiator surface	Amount of radiator surface	Determine heat loss of building and check against actual heat output of surface installed.	Increase burner input and set water temperature control higher. Install a closed system with tank for temperatures over 200°F. Add surface.
Slow or sluggish circulation	Piping	Check pipe sizes against piping tables. Check pitch of mains and connections.	Increase burner input. Balance circulation with orifices. Install circulating pump.
	Air vents	Radiators may be airbound.	Open vents to allow to escape
	Water level	System may not have enough water.	Fill to proper level.
	Boiler insulation	Circulation is slowed up because high heat loss of boiler reduces water temperature.	Cover with good insulation.
	Piping insulation	Circulation is slowed up because high heat loss of piping reduces water temperature.	Insulate all main and reduce infiltration to basemen
Radiator covers	Radiator covers	Covers may interfere with air circulation to radiators.	Change design or remove.
Undersized boilers	Boiler rating against total load	Boiler may be large enough for radiator load but because of shortage of radiator surface it is not large enough for building. Boiler may be overloaded.	Increase burner input or install larger burner. Install copper coils in firepot. Install larger boiler.
Oversized boiler	Boiler rating against total load	Greater volume of water will cause greater standby losses.	Increase burner input.
Loss of water from system	Water relief valve and expansion tank Water level and over-flow line	Closed systems without expansion tanks during firing periods will lose hot water which will be replaced with cold water. Open systems if too full will overflow on firing periods. If no vent is used in over-flow line, system may lose water through siphoning.	Install cushion tank. Fill to proper level. Install vent on overflow lines.
Complaint: slow or insufficient heat in one or more room			
Insufficient radiator surface	Heat loss and radiator surface	Determine heat loss of room and check against actual output of sur-face installed.	Paint bronzed radiators. Set water tem-perature higher and reduce circulation to other radiators. Make more favorable tap-ping of riser on main and increase pitch. Install more surface.
Slow or slug-gish circulation	Piping	Check piping size to radiator; also check pitch and main connec-tion.	Set water temperature higher and reduce circulation to other radiators. Make more favorable tapping of riser on main. Increase pitch. Change pipe size.
	Radiator vents	Air in radiator may interfere with circulation and reduce surface.	Open vents to remove air.
	Water level	System may not be filled with dirt.	Add water.
	Radiator valve	Dirt in valve opening may reduce circulation. Faulty valve may not open properly.	Clean, repair, or replace valve.
	Radiator connections	Water may be bypassed due to improper connections. Inlet arid return may be tapped off same main in two pipe system.	Make more favorable connections to main and return.
Complaint: Noisy System			
Possible Cause	Check	Details	Remedy
Water boiling	Water temperature	Boiling water will cause a noise like a water hammer. Temperature of boiling in open systems will depend upon height of system.	Provide water temperature limit control and set 215°F or lower.
Expansion of piping	Size of pipe holes through floor	Expansion of pipe causes; risers to be forced against sides of holes in floors causing a rubbing action.	Enlarge floor holes.

Steam and Vapor Systems Checklist

		Complaint: Slow Heating or Not Enough Heat Throughout Building	
Possible Cause	Check	Details	Remedy
Insufficient heat input to boiler	Time required to raise 1 lb of steam pressure or to kill vacuum	Atmospheric system with all radiators on average job 20 to 30 minutes. Underrated job 10 to 20 minutes. Overrated job 30 to 40 minutes. Vapor system with all radiators on average job 15 minutes. Underrated job 10 minutes. Overrated job 20 minutes.	Increase burner input to desired steaming rate.
Shortage of radiator surface	Amount of radiator surface	Determine heat loss of building, divide by 240, and check against actual surface installed.	Set pressure control to higher setting and minimum differential and increase burner input. Paint bronzed radiators. Add surface needed.
Slow or sluggish circulation	Piping	Check sizes of all pipes against piping tables for particular system. Check riser connections on mains, pitch of all pipes especially for trapped lines, for possible bypassing.	Correct pipe size, riser connections, pitch and eliminate by passing if necessary.
	Valves	Make sure nipple and valve openings are not clogged. On one-pipe system see that valves are of type with openings equal to full pipe size. Also check other valves to see that they are of proper type.	Clean or replace nipples or valves. Replace improper valves.
	Air vents	Look for clogged air openings on vents. Make sure vents do not pass steam. Vents should be located as low as possible on radiators, on ends of mains and returns, and on dry returns at top of vertical drop to boiler return. Main and return vents should be of return, quick venting type. On two-pipe vapor systems check operation of air eliminators and traps.	Clean vent openings. Replace corroded valves. Install in correct position if necessary. Clean or repair poorly operating eliminates or traps.
Uncovered or poorly insulated boiler	Boiler insulation	An uncovered or poorly insulated boiler will steam poorly because of increased standby loss and condensation in dome	Cover with good insulating material.
Uncovered or poorly insulated piping	Pipe insulation and air infiltration to basement	Uncovered or poorly insulated piping will decrease amount of steam especially when basement temperature is low.	Insulate mains and reduce infiltration to basement.
High water line in boiler	Position of water line	Water line should be in center of gage glass. High water line increases water volume and decreases steam volume, and with burner input set for normal water line, input will not be sufficient and slow steaming will result	Lower water line to normal position. If burner capacity is not sufficient for proper steaming, lower water line a few inches.
Water leaves boiler	Water level and return connections	With a fast steaming boiler, pressure may build up so rapidly that the pressure in boiler will back the water out through returns and low water cut off will shut off burner before radiator gets hot.	Install a Hartford equalizer loop on return.
Foaming boiler	Action of water line	A jumping water line when boiler is operating indicates foaming caused by oil and dirt in boiler water.	Clean boiler with boiler cleaning compound.
Undersized boiler	Boiler rating against load total	Boiler may be large enough for radiator load but because of shortage of radiator surface it is not large enough for building. Or boiler may be overloaded.	Increase burner input or install larger burner to obtain faster steaming. Install copper coils in firepot. Operate with a lowered water line. Install larger boiler.
Vacuum equipment	Return to condensate	On vacuum jobs faulty action of pumps, traps or air eliminators will cause faulty return of condensate to boiler.	Clean and repair all steam specialties.
		Complaint: Slow or Insufficient Heat in One or More Rooms	
Possible Cause	Check	Details	Remedy
Insufficient radiator surface Poor circulation to radiator	Heat loss and radiator surface Piping	Determine heat loss of room, divide by 240 and check against actual surface installed. Check branch and riser sizes, pitch of piping from main to radiator, connections to radiators, branches, mains and returns.	Paint bronzed radiators. Increase radiator size. Correct pipe sizes, pitch and connections.
	Radiator valve	Check valve and nipple opening for possible clogging by rust or scale. Determine if valve seat has become loose and is only partially open.	Clean valves or nipples. Repair or replace faulty valves.
Poor radiator venting	Radiator vents	Check air vent under normal operating conditions to determine the speed of venting, if radiator is hot all over when venting stops, if vent leaks steam, and if vent is too high,	Clean. If radiator vents slowly replace vent with one with larger opening.
Trapped radiator	Slope of radiator	On one pipe system if radiator slopes down from opening too much condensate will remain in radiator. On two pipe systems if radiator return is higher than inlet, condensate will flow back into riser on bottom inlet radiators and will collect in radiator on top inlet jobs.	Pitch radiators slightly in proper direction.

Steam and Vapor Systems Checklist

		Complaint: Slow Heating or Not Enough Heat Throughout Building	
Possible Cause	Check	Details	Remedy
Radiator main flooded	Boiler return connections	If end of main is not elevated sufficiently above water line of boiler on systems not having a Hartford loop, condensate may flood end of main, preventing steam from entering end radiator.	Install a Hartford equalizer loop.
Faulty customer operation	Radiator valves	On one-pipe jobs, radiator valves may not be kept wide open causing condensate to be trapped while steam is on.	Instruct customer to keep valve wide open.
Faulty radiator traps	Radiator traps	Dirt or scale will interfere with trap operation.	Clean or install new traps.
Insufficient input	Bonnet temperature	Bonnet temperature of at least 150°F should be attained.	Increase input of burner.
Undersized furnace	Furnace rating against heat loss	Determine heat loss of building and check against rating of furnace.	Increase burner input. Install larger furnace.
System unbalanced	Room temperature	Too much heat may be supplied to unimportant rooms and too little to important rooms.	Balance system with dampers in supply and returns.
Insufficient air delivery	Air volume	Air circulated may not be adequate to deliver enough heat or provide good heat distribution.	Increase speed of blower. Change blower size.
Dirty filters	Air filters	Dirty filters will decrease the amount of air circulated.	Clean or replace filters.
Poor design	Location of furnace	If furnace is located at one end of a long building, there may be a large temperature drop in the supply duct causing cold air to be delivered to end rooms.	Insulate duct and balance systems. Relocate furnace in center of building,
	Duct sizes	Incorrect size ducts and many bends will cause poor air distribution.	Increase input and air delivery. Balance system.
		Complaint: Slow or Insufficient Heat in One or More Rooms	
System unbalanced	Temperature in all rooms	If some rooms are overheated and some underheated it is necessary to decrease the flow to overheated rooms and increase it to underheated rooms.	Balance the system with dampers in supply and return ducts.
		If a number of rooms have the correct temperature while the rest are underheated, add more heat to the building.	Increase the burner input and balance the system.
Poor air distribution	Register location	If registers are improperly located the air will tend to stratify and cause cold floors. Registers should be on inside walls while return grilles should be on outside walls.	Try increasing air volume. Relocate registers and return grilles.
	Temperature of air from attic trunk line	Sometimes attic trunk lines are used to supply upper floors. If the attic is cold the trunkline will be chilled. Also downward air currents from the attic may cool off riser to trunkline.	Insulate attic trunkline. Seal the shaft in which the riser is installed to prevent cold attic air from reaching the riser. Insulate the riser.

Forced Air Systems Converted From Gravity

		Complaint: Slow Heating or Not Enough Heat Throughout Building	
Possible Cause	Check	Details	Remedy
Insufficient heat input	Bonnet temperature	Bonnet temperatures of a least 150°F should be developed.	Increase input to furnace.
Undersized furnace	Furnace rating against heat loss	Determine heat loss of building and check against rating of furnace.	Increase burner input. Install larger furnace.
System unbalanced	Room temperatures	Too much heat may be supplied to unimportant rooms and little to important rooms.	Balance system by means of dampers in leaders.
Insufficient air volume	Air volume	Blower may not be capable of delivering required amount of air.	Increase speed of blower. Change blower size.
Inadequate return air	Size of grilles and return ducts	Return ducts may be too small or have too much resistance. Grilles may have too small free area.	Increase fan capacity. Install larger ducts or grilles.
Unbalanced return air	Return air volume	It may be possible hat one return is carrying more air than it should.	Balance returns.
Poor return connections	Return connections	Two or more returns should be connected into a manifold to the fan chamber and not enter furnace separately.	Connect all returns to fan chamber.

Forced Air Systems Converted From Gravity

Complaint: Slow Heating or Not Enough Heat Throughout Building			
Possible Cause	Check	Details	Remedy
Poor furnace return connection	Furnace return connection	To even up air distribution in furnace a wide flaring connection with spreaders in it should be used to connect fan chamber to furnace.	Connect fan chamber to furnace with wide flaring connection with spreaders.

Complaint: Slow or Insufficient Heat in One or More Room			
Possible Cause	Check	Details	Remedy
Unbalanced system	Temperature in all rooms	If some rooms are overheated and some underheated it is necessary to reduce air flow to overheated rooms and decrease it to underheated rooms.	Balance system with leader dampers.
		If some rooms have the proper temperature while the rest are underheated, it will be necessary to add more heat.	Increase the burner input and balance the system.
Poor air distribution	Number of registers and location	Registers located on outside walls or an insufficient number of registers will cause poor air distribution.	Increase fan speed and limit air volumes to other rooms. Provide additional registers. Relocate.
	Cold air return	An undersized or poor return will result in poor distribution	Install proper return.
	Leader size	Check leader size against calculated area. Large number of bends will cut down air flow.	Rebalance system. Eliminate on necessary turns.
	Return grille location	Return grilles should be located on exposed walls. If located on inside walls they will cause cold, drafty floors.	Relocate grilles to exposed walls.

Gravity Circulation Air Systems

Possible Cause	Check	Details	Remedy
Insufficient heat input to furnace	Time required to raise register temperature to 140°F	Average job should have living room register air temperature of 140°F within 20 to 30 minutes of time burner starts. Poorly circulating jobs should raise air temperature faster.	Increase input of burner.
Slow or sluggish circulation	Leader pipe sizes against heat loss	Determine heat loss of rooms and divide by 111 for first floor, 167 for second, and 200 for third to obtain leader area in inches. Add 2% to area for each foot over 12 ft of length, 20%, for each elbow over one, 10% for every turn over one.	Balance system with dampers. Increase input of burner.
	Wall riser sizes	Wall risers to second and third floors should have area of at least 70% of leader supplying them.	Balance system. Increase burner input. Add risers.
	Cold air returns	Total return duct area should at least equal total leader area. Drops to furnace should be of two 45° ells and round pipe rather than two 90° ells and rectangular pipe. Free area of grilles at least equal to area of duct. Two returns joining will often cause unbalanced returning and poor air distribution to furnace.	Increasing burner input will overcome defects to some extent. Otherwise changes in returns will be necessary. Connect each return separately to furnace casing and balance return air.
	Cold air shoe connection to furnace casing	High point of cold air shoe should not be above the grate level or burner head level.	If shoe is above, protect top of shoe with deflector in upper part or install a radiation shield between firepot and casing extending down to below grate level.
	Number of returns	If only one return is used poor circulation is practically certain even if return area is equal to leader area.	Increase input or burner. Install additional return.
Furnace too small or too large	Furnace rating against heat loss	On undersized furnace an increased burner input is necessary to supply sufficient heat. On an oversized furnace somewhat greater burner input is necessary to heat up more metal and take care of radiation losses.	Increase burner input. Install correct size furnace.

Gravity Circulation Air Systems

Possible Cause	Check	Details	Remedy
		Complaint Slow or Insufficient Heat in One Room	
Poor circulation	Leader pipes	Note whether leader has dents, is flattened or has air leaks. Check size. Leaders size in square inches should be the heat loss of room divided by 111, 167, or 200 for first, second, or third floor, respectively. Add 27, to area for each foot over 12 ft in length, 20% for each elbow over one, or for each turn over one.	Remove dents and flattening and seal leaks. If leader is long cover with good insulation, install small fan in leader and control by room thermostat.
	Leader pitch and turns	Insufficient pitch and sharp turns will slow circulation.	Increase pitch and burner input. Balance system.
	Wall riser	Riser to second or third floor room may have come loose from register boot allowing warm air to escape in wall.	Reconnect wall stack securely.
	Returns to furnace	Unequal distribution of return air in furnace will cut down on air flow to leaders located at points where small amounts of air are returned. This will often occur where only one return is used and where it is of nonflaring type.	Change return shoe to a flaring type with splitters. Change location of leader.
	Leader connection to furnace	On most furnaces there is little circulation at the front, and leaders connected here will have poor air supply.	Change location of leader to other part of bonnet.
	Register area	Register free area should at least equal area of leader pipe supplying it.	Replace with register having proper free area.
	Leader pipes, boots, and risers	A restriction in either leader, boot or riser will decrease circulation.	Provide full opening throughout run.
	Register location	Register should be on inside wall and direct air towards or along exposed walls.	Change location of register.
	Room location	Rooms on cold side of house may heat poorly even with proper size leaders and returns because of the effect of wind.	Add or increase size of cold air returns.
	Register and return grille location	Registers located too close to return grilles will cause short cutting of air and poor room circulation.	Relocate registers or return grilles.
	Studding space	Where studding space is used to return air from second floor rooms it is necessary to block off space above grille to stop flue action which tends to carry air up to attic.	Block of studding space above grille.
		Complaint Cold Floors	
Possible Cause	Check	Details	Remedy
Air stratification	Remove temperatures at various levels	Air stratification may result when the burner is shut off and air circulation has stopped	Shorten off periods by using thermostat set for minimum differential.
Cold air traveling across floor	Return grille location	If return grilles are located on inside walls, cold air will travel across floor from the cold walls and windows	Locate return grilles at outside walls.

NOISE AND VIBRATION CONTROL

NOISE AND VIBRATION CONTROL

Noise and Vibration

Introduction.—In addition to fulfilling air conditioning requirements, an air handling system must meet acceptable noise and vibration criteria. The purpose of the following section is to provide design engineers of air handling systems with guidelines for selecting the proper criteria for building spaces, and methods for specifying design requirements on system. Common sources of vibrations in buildings are fans, blowers, water chillers, water pumps, and air compressors. Methods for specifying and reducing noise and vibration levels for ducted systems will be given.

Ducted systems treated in this chapter are used to transmit air from a fan or blower to the necessary locations. Air transmission may be for central station air conditioning, industrial ventilating systems, or industrial applications such as process cooling and furnace air supply, among others. Although the fan or blower is usually considered the major source of noise in such systems, the flow of air through duct elements like elbows, turning vanes, and flow control valves can also produce vibration and, therefore, sound.

The design engineer should be aware of noise and vibration principles, since these have become a major concern in the acceptability of air handling systems. While it is not economical to over design a system for noise or vibration control, disastrous results can occur if potential problem areas are not considered in the design stage. Optimal design avoids overdesign but allows for a system that meets accepted criteria for the use of building space.

Definitions and Terminology.—*Attenuation:* The reduction in sound power as sound propagates through a duct or enclosure. Attenuation is expressed in decibels, as the ratio of the sound power at a point upstream to the sound power at a point downstream in the direction of the sound propagation. For a duct, attenuation is expressed in units of decibels per foot (dB/ft), indicating the average reduction of sound power level for each foot of duct length.

Band Pressure Level: The band pressure level of a sound for a specified frequency band is the sound pressure level for the sound contained within the restricted band. The reference pressure must be stated. The band may be specified by its lower and upper cut-off frequencies, or by its geometric center frequency and bandwidth. The width of the band may be indicated by a preceding modifier; e.g., octave band (sound pressure) level, half octave band level, third octave band level, or 50 Hz band level.

Broadband Noise: Noise whose energy is distributed over a broad frequency range (generally speaking, more than one octave).

Continuous Noise: On going noise whose intensity remains at a measurable level, which may vary but is without interruption over an indefinite period or a specified period of time.

Decibel: A mathematical scale that is similar to a logarithmic scale used to describe the level of a physical quantity compared to a reference point. Mathematically, the decibel is ten times the logarithm (base 10) of the ratio of a power or energy quantity with respect to a reference base of the same physical quantity. The scale compresses the quantities into numbers that are convenient for data presentation.

Frequency: For a function periodic in time, is the reciprocal of the period. The unit is cycle per unit time and must be specified. The unit *cycle per second* is commonly called *hertz* (Hz).

Insertion Loss: The difference in sound pressure level at a point after a modification has been made in either the source or the transmission path between the point and the source. It is expressed in decibels as the ratio of sound pressure before modification to sound pressure after modification. Since it is quite possible for sound pressure to increase with modification, the insertion loss can have a negative value.

Microbar: A unit of pressure commonly used in acoustics. One microbar is equal to 1 dyne/cm². The SI metric equivalent is $\frac{1}{10}$ pascal (Pa) or newton per square meter (N/m²).

Octave Band: A range of frequencies such that the highest frequency in the band is double the lowest frequency. Also, for successive octave bands, the center frequency of the higher band is twice the frequency of the next lower center frequency band. In acoustics standard center frequency bands are specified.

Octave Band Center Frequency: A specific frequency used to define a particular octave band.

Pitch: A qualitative term used to describe the frequency makeup of a sound. Thus we say that a low frequency sound has a low pitch. Although pitch depends primarily upon frequency, it also depends upon sound pressure and the waveform of the sound vibration stimulus.

Power Level: Given in decibels, 10 times the logarithm to the base of 10 of the ratio of a given power to a reference power.

Sound Level: A weighted sound pressure level obtained by the use of metering characteristics and the weightings A, B, or C as specified in the American National Standard Specification for Sound Level Meters, ANSI 1.4 1971. The weighting employed must be stated.

Sound Pressure Level: Given in decibels, for a sound, it is 20 times the logarithm to the base 20 of the ratio of the pressure of this sound to the reference pressure. The reference pressure must be stated. *The reference pressure in use for measurements concerned with hearing and with sound in air and liquids:* 2×10^{-5} N/m². Unless otherwise explicitly stated, it is to be understood that sound pressure is the V_N effective (rms) sound pressure.

Noise Criteria.—Noise criteria are necessary during the design stage for specifying permissible maximum sound levels in building spaces. Such criteria serve as a guide to designers, manufacturers, customers, and engineers as an indication of the noise performance of a system. Acceptable criteria for various space usage have been developed from the subjective reactions of humans experiencing acceptable noise levels while engaged in specific activities. One of the most widely used sets of design values is the preferred noise criterion curves (PNC Curves), plotted in Fig. 16-1. The octave band sound pressure levels for specific PNC values are given in Table 16-1. A list of recommended PNC criteria for a variety of indoor spaces is given in Table 16-2. Some building codes specify certain of these criteria (Table 16-3).

Speech Interference Criteria.—Interference with speech communication is the result of a phenomenon known as *masking*. In the masking process, sounds in the speech frequency range are rendered indistinguishable from non speech sources by excessive noise levels. The most common speech interference criterion is the *preferred speech interference level* (PSIL), which is computed from the simple arithmetic average of the background octave band sound pressure levels having center frequencies of 500, 1000, and 2000 Hz.

$$\text{PSIL} = \left[\frac{L_{P500} + L_{P1000} + L_{P2000}}{3} \right] \quad (1)$$
$$(\text{dB re } 2 \times 10^{-5} \text{N/m}^2)$$

where L_{P500} = 500 Hz octave band sound pressure level, re 2×10^{-5} N/m²

L_{P1000} = 1000 Hz octave band sound pressure level, re 2×10^{-5} N/m²

L_{P2000} = 2000 Hz octave band sound pressure level, re 2×10^{-5} N/m².

The relationship between PSIL, voice effort required, and distance between speaker and listener is given in Fig. 16-2. Computation of the preferred speech interference level requires octave band sound pressure levels that are measured or calculated. In some instances, only a weighted sound pressure levels may be available and, in such instances, an approximation to the PSIL value is given by:

$$PSIL = L_P(A) - 7 \quad (\text{dB re } 2 \times 10^{-5} \text{N/m}^2) \quad (2)$$

where $L_P(A)$ = A weighted sound pressure level, dB re 2×10^{-5} N/m².

To illustrate the use of the PSIL criteria, let us assume that the measured octave band sound pressure levels in a mechanical room: L_{P500} = 60, L_{P1000} = 62, L_{P2000} = 58, dB re 2×10^{-5} N/m²; then from Equation (1), PSIL = $\frac{1}{3}$ (60 + 62 + 58) = 60 dB. From Fig. 16-2 for PSIL 60 dB, is the normal voice level for face to face communication between two individuals, 3 ft (1 m) provides satisfactory distance for speech intelligibility. If the two individuals were 6 ft apart, they would need to use raised voices. Note that for good face to face communication at 6 ft at normal voice levels, the PSIL must be reduced to 53 dB.

Sound Levels of Sources.—Noise ratings of air conditioning machinery are preferred in terms of octave band sound power levels. Single figure, overall sound level values were formerly used but are not adequate for proper analysis of building space sound levels. Sound power levels in octave bands are necessary to compute octave band sound pressure levels for comparison to indoor noise criteria. In some instances, a loudness rating in *sones* or *phons*, while not preferred, is used to rate mechanical equipment. The loudness level in *sones* or *phons* is calculated from the loudness index I_i for each band as given in Fig. 16-3. The calculation is as follows:

1) Enter the geometric mean frequency F_i for each band as the abscissa of Fig. 16-3. From the band pressure level (ordinate of Fig. 16-3) obtain the loudness index I_i for each band.

2) Find the total loudness S_t in sones by means of the formula:

$$S_t = \left(I_m + F \left[\left(\sum_{(i=1)}^{(i=n)} I_i \right) - I_m \right] \right) (\text{sones}) \quad (3)$$

where I_m = largest of the loudness indexes
I_i = sum of the indexes for all frequencies
F = a factor dependent on the band width used for the analysis from Table 16-4.

3) The overall loudness level in phons is obtained adjacent to the S_t in the nomograph at the right of Fig. 16-3, or by computation from the equation:

$$P = 40 + 10 \log S_t \quad (\text{phons}) \quad (4)$$

Generally, loudness levels are used to compare one product with another with respect to annoyance caused by noise. While this does not provide an absolute scale, it can be helpful in estimating the loudness of one source as compared to another. By rough approximation, a source having a loudness of two sones is twice as loud as one having a rating of one sone. Loudness levels are not recommended for rating air moving devices and air conditioning equipment. However, manufacturers are urged to provide octave band sound power levels in order for the design engineer to make the necessary computations.

Table 16-1. Octave Band Sound Pressure Levels

Preferred Noise Criterion	Octave Band Center Frequency, Hz								
	31.51	63	125	250	1500	11,000	12,000	14,000	18,000
	Sound Pressure Levels, dB								
PNC – 15	58	43	35	28	21	15	10	8	8
PNC – 20	59	46	39	32	26	20	15	13	13
PNC – 25	60	49	43	37	31	25	20	18	18
PNC – 30	61	52	46	41	35	30	25	23	23
PNC – 35	62	55	50	45	40	35	30	28	28
PNC – 40	64	59	54	50	45	40	36	33	33
PNC – 45	67	63	58	54	50	45	41	38	38
PNC – 50	70	66	62	58	54	50	46	43	43
PNC – 55	73	70	66	62	59	55	51	48	48
PNC – 60	76	73	69	66	63	59	56	53	53
PNC – 65	79	76	73	70	67	64	61	58	58

Table 16-2. Recommended Noise Criteria

Type of Space	NC or PNC curve	Approximate dBA level	Type of Space	NC or PNC Curve	Approximate dBA Level
Residences			Churches and schools		
			Recreation halls, corridors and halls	35 – 50	42 – 56
Private homes (rural and suburban)	20 – 30	30 – 38	Kitchens, washrooms and lavatories	40 – 50	47 – 50
Private homes (urban)	25 – 35	34 – 42	Public buildings		
Apartment houses (2 and 3 family units)	30 – 40	38 – 47	Public libraries, museums, art galleries, court rooms	30 – 40	38 – 47
Hotels			Post offices, banking areas, lobbies	35 – 45	38 – 52
Individual rooms or suites	30 – 40	38 – 47	Washrooms and toilets	40 – 50	47 – 56
Ballrooms, banquet rooms	30 – 40	38 – 47	Restaurants, cafeterias		
Halls, corridors, lobbies	35 – 45	42 – 52	Restaurants	35 – 45	42 – 52
Garages	40 – 50	47 – 56	Cocktail Lounges	35 – 45	42 – 56
Kitchens and laundries	40 – 50	47 – 56	Night Clubs	35 – 45	42 – 52
Hospitals and clinics			Cafeterias	40 – 50	47 – 56
Private rooms	25 – 35	34 – 42	Stores		
Operating rooms, wards	30 – 40	38 – 47	Clothing stores, department stores (upper floors)	35 – 45	42 – 52
Laboratories, halls corridors lobbies, waiting rooms	35 – 45	42 – 52	Department stores (main floor) small retail stores, supermarkets	40 – 50	47 – 56
Washrooms, toilets	40 – 50	47 – 56	Sports facilities		
Offices			Coliseums	30 – 40	38 – 47
Board rooms	20 – 30	30 – 38	Bowling alleys, gymnasiums	35 – 45	42 – 52
Conference rooms, meeting rooms (for 50)	25 – 30	34 – 38	Swimming pools	40 – 50	47 – 56
Executive office, meeting rooms (for 20)	30 – 35	38 – 42	Transportation (rail, bus, plane)		
Supervisor office, reception room	30 – 45	38 – 52	Ticket areas	30 – 40	38 – 47
General open offices, drafting rooms	35 – 50	42 – 56	Lounges, waiting rooms	35 – 50	42 – 56
Halls, corridors	35 – 55	42 – 61	Baggage areas	40 – 50	47 – 56
Tabulation and computation rooms	40 – 60	47 – 66	Manufacturing areas		
Auditoriums and music halls			Supervisors offices	30 – 45	38 – 52
Concert and opera halls studios for sound repro-duction	20 – 25	30 – 34	Laboratories, engineering rooms, drafting rooms, general office areas	40 – 50	47 – 56
Legitimate theaters, multi – purpose halls	25 – 30	34 – 38	Maintenance shops, office equipment rooms, computer rooms, washrooms and toilets	45 – 55	52 – 61
Movie theaters, tv audience studios semi – outdoor amphitheaters, lecture halls, planetarium	30 – 35	38 – 42	Control rooms, electrical equipment rooms	50 – 60	56 – 66
Lobbies	35 – 45	42 – 52	Foreman's office, tool crib, areas where speech communication is required	Not to exceed 60	Not to exceed 66
Broadcast studios			Manufacturing areas, assembly lines, machinery areas, packing and shipping areas	Use Speech Inter-ference Level or OSHA Criteria	
Distant microphone pickup	10 – 20	21 – 30			
Churches and schools					
Sanctuaries, music rooms	20 – 30	30 – 38			
Libraries, classrooms	25 – 35	34 – 42			
Teaching laboratories	35 – 45	42 – 52			

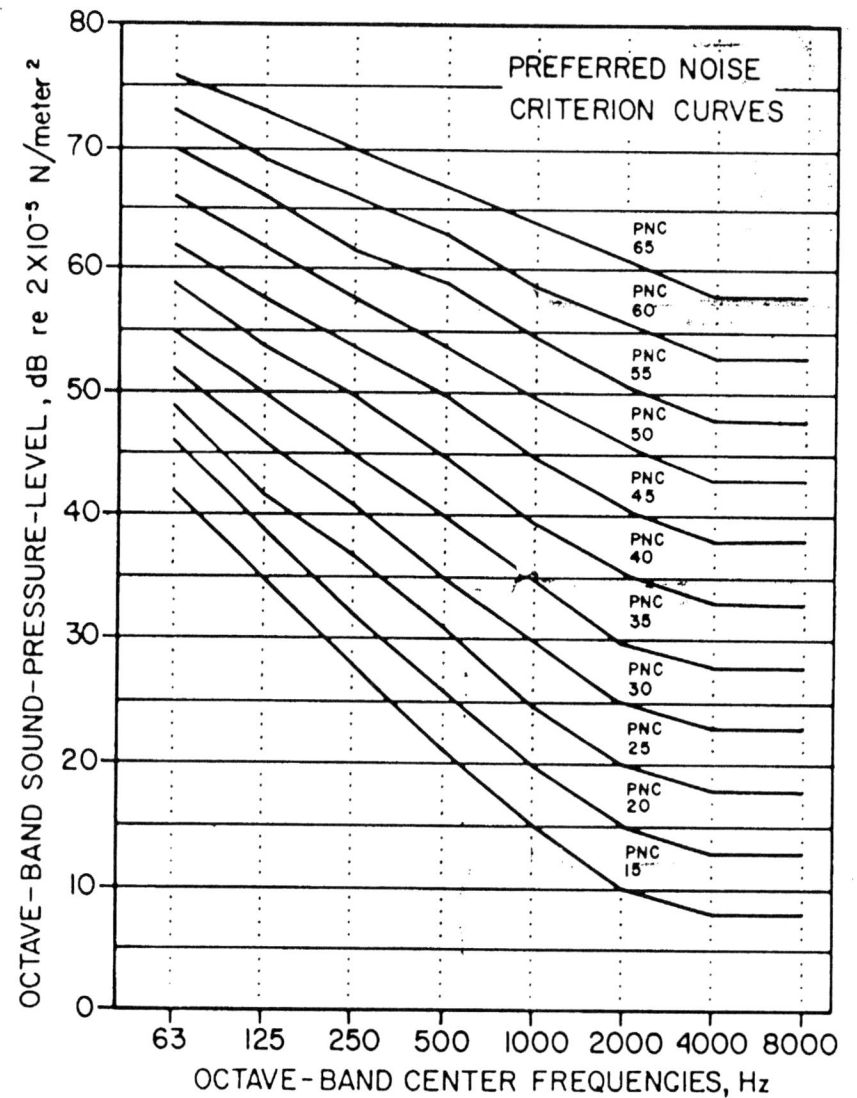

Fig 16-1. Preferred Noise Criteria Curves for determination of Permissible Broad Band background Sound Levels for indoor spaces

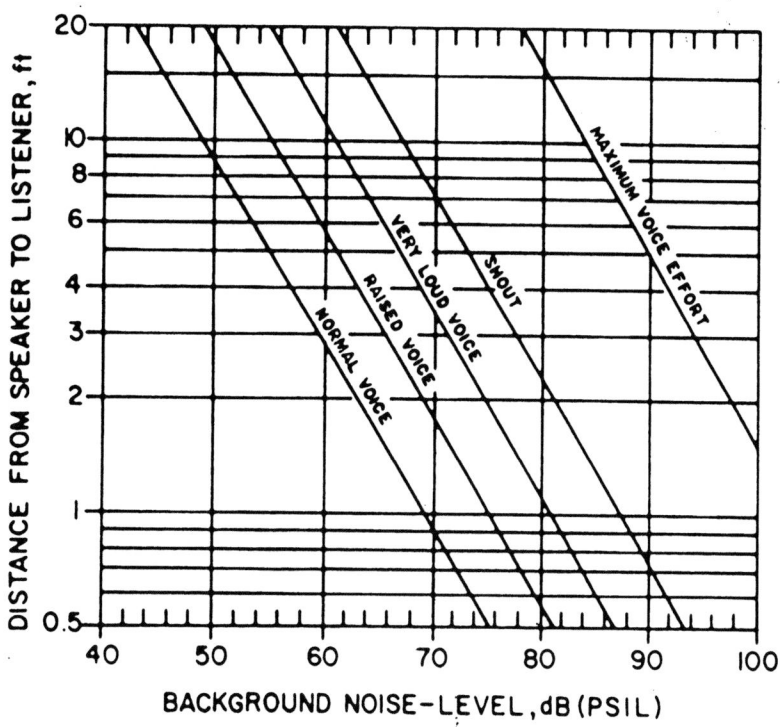

Fig 16-2. Relation of required Voice Effort for Communication in terms of PSIL and distance between Speaker and Listener

Table 16-3. Standards Pertaining to Heating, Ventilating, and Air Conditioning Systems

Organization [a]	Standard Designation	Title
ASTM	E413 – 73	Classification for determination of sound transmission class
ASTM	E477 – 73	Testing duct liner materials and prefabricated silencers for acoustical and air flow performance
SAE	Standard J952B (1969)	Sound levels for engine powered equipment
IEEE	85 (1965)	Test procedure for airborne noise measurements on rotating electrical machinery
ASHRAE	36 – 62	Measurement of sound power radiated from heating, refrigerating, and air – conditioning equipment
ASHRAE	36A – 63	Method of determining sound power of room air conditioners
ASHRAE	36B – 63	Method of testing for rating the acoustic performance of air control and terminal devices and similar equipment
ANSI	S1.2 – 1962 (Rev. 1971)	American National Standard method for the physical measurement of sound
ANSI	S1.6 – 1967 (Rev. 1971)	American National Standard preferred frequencies and band numbers for acoustical measurements
ARI	443 (1970)	Standard for sound rating of room fan coil air conditioners
AMCA	300 – 67	Standard test code for sound rating air moving devices
ADC	AD – 63	Measurement of room to room sound transmission through plenum systems
CAGI	Test Code (1969)	Cagi – pneurop test code for measurement of sound from pneumatic equipment
ISO	Recommendation R140 (1960)	Field and laboratory measurements of airborne and impact sound transmission
ISO	Recommendation R1680 (1970)	Test code for the measurement of airborne noise emitted by rotating electrical machinery

[a] ANSI: American National Standards Institute; STEM: American Society of Testing and Materials, SAE: Society of Automobile Engineers; IEEE: Institute of Electrical and Electronics Engineers; ASHRAE: American Society of Heating, Refrigerating and Air Conditioning Engineers; ARI: Air conditioning and Refrigerating Engineers; AMCA: Air Moving and Conditioning Engineers; ADC: Air Diffusion Council; CAGI: Compressed Air and Gas Institute; ISO: International Organization for Standardization

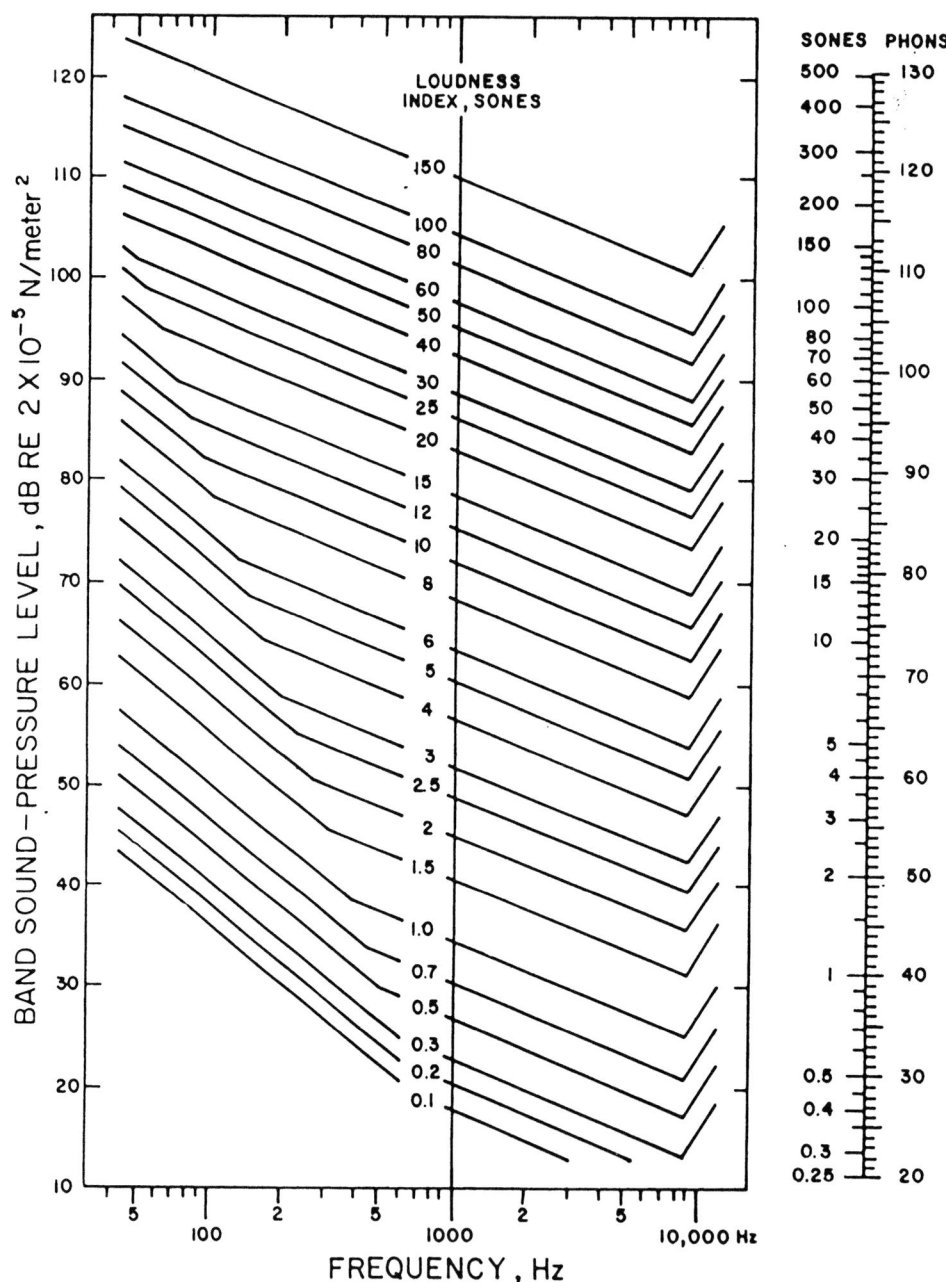

Fig 16-3. Contours of equal loudness index to compare noise source

Table 16-4. Band Width Correction Factor

Band Width	F value
One third – octave	0.15
One half – octave	0.20
Octave	0.30

Ratings and Standards.—The end purpose of noise ratings is to achieve an installed system which, while acceptable, will not disrupt building space usage or be a source of annoyance to occupants. Measurement standards are necessary to insure comparative acoustical quantities, such as sound power levels of equipment by various manufacturers. Other standards pertain to sound measurements in buildings. A listing of standards related to heating, ventilating and air conditioning systems is given in Table 16-3.

Airborne Sound Transmission.—When mechanical equipment rooms containing fans, pumps, compressors, or other noisy air conditioning equipment are located in areas adjoining critical occupancy areas such as bedrooms, conference rooms, and offices, a very severe problem arises. In so far as the mechanical equipment room may contain equipment with noise output as great as 90 or 100 decibels and the adjoining critical room must have a sound pressure level not exceeding 25 - 30 decibels, the construction of the sound barrier separating the two must of necessity take up a great deal of space, be very heavy, become completely airtight from floor to slab above and, in all probability, must be quite expensive. For these reasons and the very important consideration that small mistakes in the design of the partition, construction of the partition, or vibration isolation of the equipment may result in something less than the estimated degree of isolation, it is exceedingly advisable to avoid placing mechanical equipment adjacent to very critical areas. Experience indicates that in most cases it is practical to place the equipment room elsewhere than adjoining critical room areas. However, it sometimes becomes uneconomical to move equipment rooms to such parts of the building where adjoining spaces are not extremely critical, such as general offices, public corridors, stenographic offices, or cafeterias.

When the mechanical equipment room is located next to a moderately critical space of the type noted above, airborne sound isolation becomes possible with reasonable reliability and without tremendous expense.

Fig. 16-4 shows typical constructions of floor, wall, and ceiling structures that will provide adequate acoustical isolation between rooms containing either fans or pumps and spaces that will be satisfactory with moderately noisy acoustical environments.

In those critical situations where a noisy mechanical equipment room may be on a floor above a space requiring relatively quiet surroundings, such as executive offices, libraries, and board rooms, the use of floating floor systems has been successful. Shown in Figs. 16-6A and 16-6B, are two such structural methods for reducing the noise to a floor below mechanical equipment.

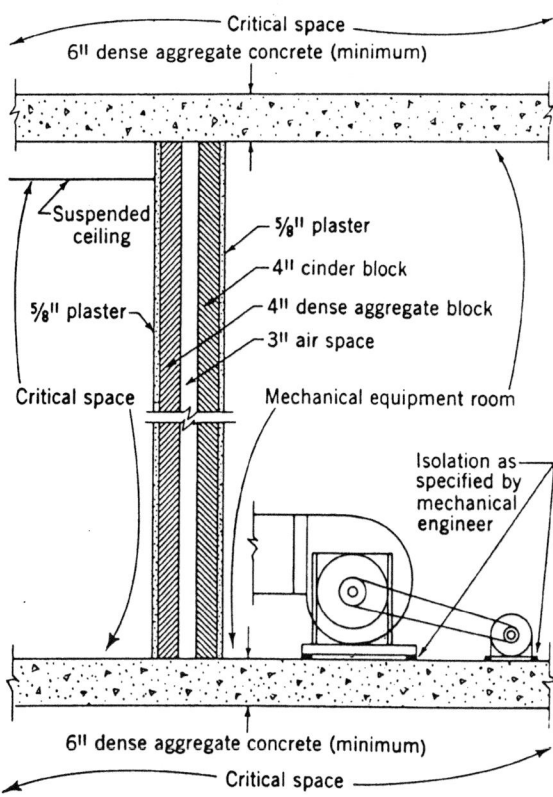

Fig 16-4. Suggested Partition Construction Between Mechanical Equipment Room and Critical Spaces

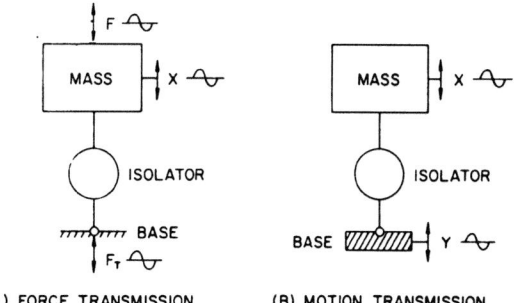

(A) FORCE TRANSMISSION (B) MOTION TRANSMISSION

Fig 16-5. Single degree freedom vibration isolation system

Vibration Isolation.—By analog, vibration of mechanical machinery in buildings can be illustrated as a one degree of freedom system (i.e., by motion in the vertical direction only) as shown in Fig. 16-5.

$$E = 100 \left[1 - \frac{1}{\left(f_d/f_n\right)^2 - 1} \right] \qquad (5)$$

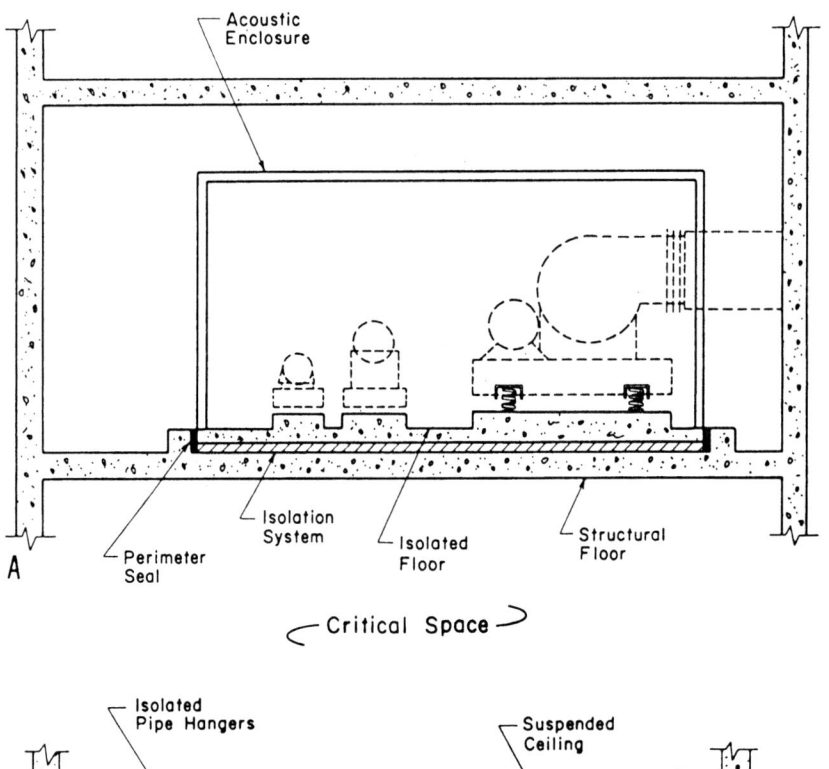

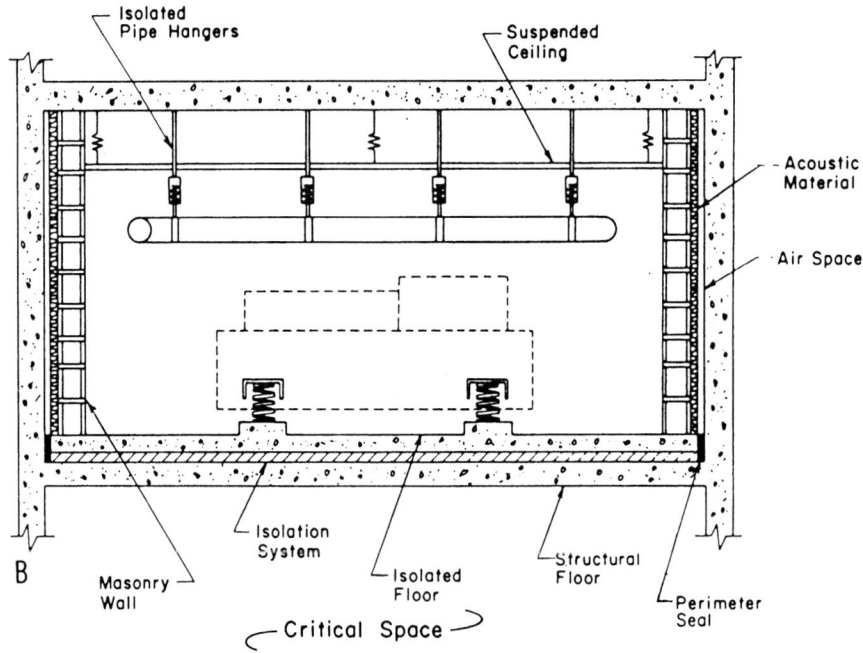

Fig 16-6. Two Structural Methods for Isolating Mechanical Equipment Noise

The elements of this analogous system are a rigid body or mass, which represents the equipment to be isolated, and an isolator through which it is connected to the structure. The effectiveness E of the isolator is determined by the reduction of the transmitted force or motion from the equipment to the structure The efficiency of isolation devices can be predicted from the formula:

The f_d should be taken as the rotational speed (Hz or rpm) of the equipment or the driver, whichever is lower. For instance, in the case of fan operation the use of rpm times the number of blades in determining the disturbing frequency often will lead to improper isolation, since most often imbalance occurs at rotor speed and not at the blade passage speed. In all cases, isolators must be selected for the lowest rotational speed of motor or equipment.

The natural frequency f_n can be computed from the static deflection of the equipment on the isolator system. The formula for natural frequency is

$$f_n = 188 \sqrt{\frac{1}{D}} \qquad \text{Hz} \qquad (6)$$

where D = static deflection of the machinery on the isolator system, given in inches.

Figs. 16-7 and 16-8 depict the isolation efficiency as a function of static deflection and disturbing frequency. In most normal situations the 90% isolation criterion is used and the appropriate isolator static deflection is obtained from these charts for the lowest disturbing frequency of the equipment to be isolated. Therefore, proper isolators can be selected when the weight of the equipment and the required static deflections are known. Fig. 16-7 shows the isolation efficiency for steel springs that have low internal damping. Since internal damping increases the transmitted force Fig. 16-8 applies for materials such as cork, rubber, neoprene, or felt, which have greater internal damping than steel springs. These isolation relationships apply for rigid floors, which are massive in comparison with the machinery and isolators considered. Table 16-5 shows appropriate corrections to be made to the isolation efficiency graphs tor various floor constructions to account for change in floor mass and flexibility.

Isolation Mount Selection.—In selecting isolation systems it is necessary to obtain all or some of the following information:

The extent of needed information depends upon the complexity and seriousness of the resulting vibration or noise problem. For noncritical installations, 80% isolation efficiency is usually adequate. In extremely critical situations, 90 to 95% isolation efficiency may be necessary. In critical situations, a more detailed analysis should be performed where actual floor vibration amplitudes are calculated and resulting noise levels predicted. These more detailed analysis procedures are necessary when considerations include:

1) location where equipment is to be mounted;

2) operating characteristics: power, rpm, strokes per minute, starting torque;

3) direction and magnitude of principal forcing frequencies;

4) equipment weight and weight per mount;

5) number, size and location of mounting ft;

6) equipment attachments, such as pipe, duct, and electrical conduit;

7) structure characteristics to which equipment is to be mounted; and

8) required isolation efficiency.

Table 16-5. Minimum Mounting Deflections for Various Types of Floors

Operating Speed, Rpm	Type of Floor			
	Basement	Rigid Concrete	Upper Story Light Concrete	Wood
	Deflection, in.			
300	1.50	3.00	3.50	4.00
600	0.60	1.00	1.50	2.00
900	0.25	0.50	1.00	1.25
1200	0.20	0.45	0.80	1.00
3600	0.03	0.20	0.50	1.00
7200	0.03	0.20	0.50	1.00

Further considerations are these:

1) The required isolation efficiency is very high (say, 98% or greater);

2) The driving forces are such that they cause rotational as well as translational motions of the machinery;

3) There are combined periodic and shock forces; and

4) Support structures (such as roofs) are flexible.

Recommended mounting systems for a variety of equipment are given in Table 16-6, with the mount types illustrated in Table 16-7. Note that there is no standard method for presenting isolator performance ratings. Most manufacturers will present curves representing load versus deflection, or load versus natural frequency. However, some will only give the natural frequency at the rated load. If the natural frequency at only one load is given (usually the maximum load), the natural frequency at an intermediate load can be obtained from:

$$f_n' = f_n \sqrt{\frac{W}{W'}} \qquad \text{Hz} \qquad (7)$$

where f_n = natural frequency at rated load W; and

$f_{n'}$ = natural frequency at rated load W'.

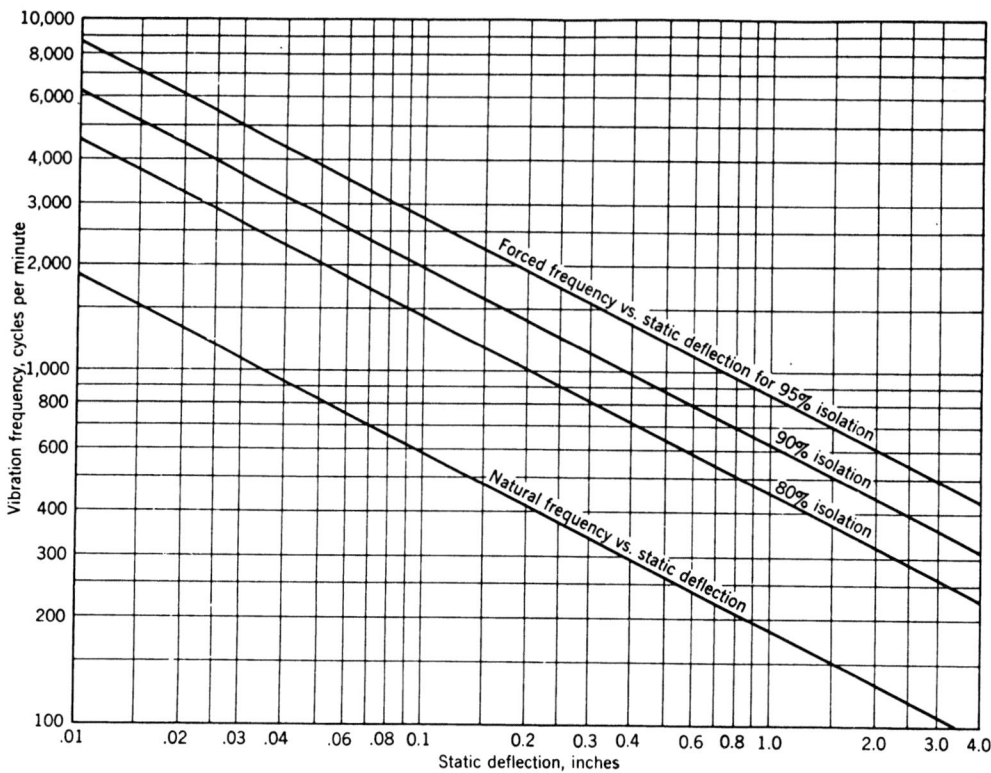

Fig 16-7. Isolation efficiency graph for cork, rubber, or felt mountings

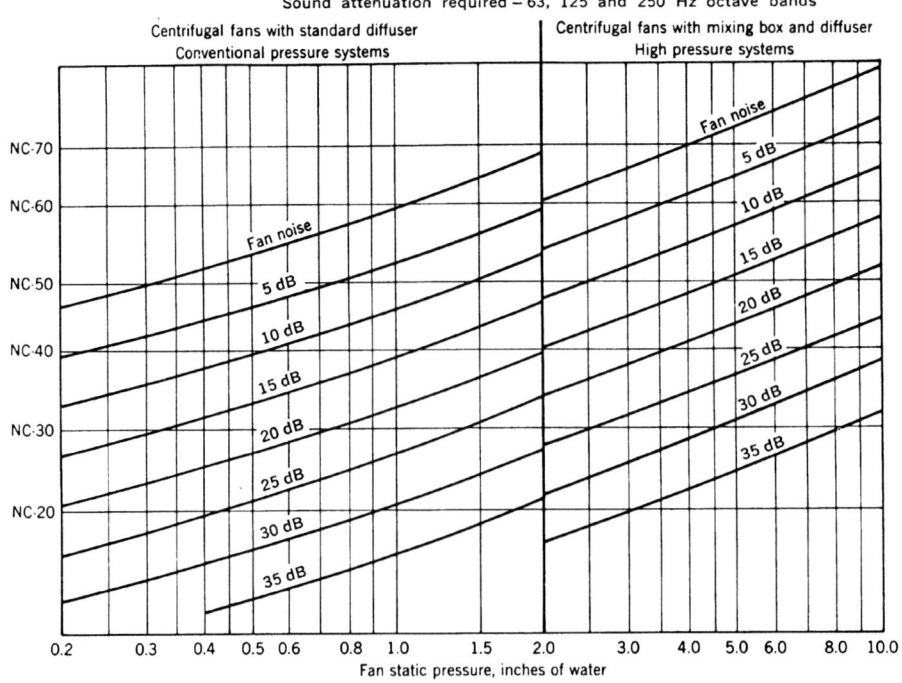

Fig 16-8. Sound Attenuation required 63, 125, and 250 Hz octave length

Table 16-6. Guide for Selecting Vibration Isolating System for Some Mechanical and Electrical Equipment

Equipment	Power Range	Speed Range (rpm)	Minimum Area — Mount Type (See Table 16-7)			Normal Area — Weight Ratio (See note 1)			Critical Area — Deflection, in (See note 2)		
			Minimum	Normal	Critical	Minimum	Normal	Critical	Minimum	Normal	Critical
Centrifugal and axial flow fans	< 3 hp	All	NN	2	3	...	...	2	...	10	1.5
	3 – 25 hp	< 600	2	3	3	...	2	3	10	1.5	20
		600 – 1200	2	2	3	...	...	2	5	10	15
		1200	2	2	3	...	...	2	5	10	10
	> 125 hp	< 600	2	3	3	...	2	3	15	20	30
		600 – 1200	2	3	3	...	2	2	10	15	20
		>1200	2	3	3	...	2	2	5	10	10
Motor pump assemblies	< 20 hp	450 – 900	2, 3	3	3	1.5	2 – 3	3 – 4	1.5	1.5	3.0
		900 – 1800	2, 3	3	3	2.5	1.5 – 2.5	2 – 3	1.5	1.0	2.0
		> 1800	2, 3	3	3	2.5	1.5 – 2.5	2 – 3	1.0	0.75	1.5
	20 – 100 hp	450 – 900	3	3	3	2 – 3	2 – 3	3 – 4	1.5	1.5	4.0
		900 – 1800	3	3	3	1.5 – 2.5	2 – 3	2 – 3	1.0	1.0	3.0
		> 1800	3	3	3	1.5 – 2.5	1.5 – 2.5	2 – 3	0.75	1.0	2.0
	> 100 hp	450 – 900	3	3	3	2 – 3	3 – 4	3 – 4	2.0	2.0	5.0
		900 – 800	3	3	3	2 – 3	2 – 3	2 – 3	1.5	1.5	4.0
		> 1800	3	3	3	1.5 – 2.5	2 – 3	2 – 3	1.0	1.0	3.0
Internal combustion engines and engine driven equipment	< 25 hp	All	2	2	3	...	2 – 3	3 – 4	0.35	0.35	2.5
	25 – 100 hp	All	2	2	3	...	2 – 3	3 – 4	0.35	1.75	3.5
	> 100 hp	All	2	2	3	...	2 – 3	3 – 4	0.35	2.50	5.0
Reciprocating type air compressors, 1 to 2 cylinders	< 20 hp	300 – 600	4	NR	NR	4 – 8	...	...	4.0	...	...
		600 – 1200	4	4	NR	2 – 4	3 – 6	...	2.0	4.0	...
		> 2400	4	4	4	1 – 2	2 – 3	3 – 6	1.0	2.0	4.0
	20 – 100 hp	300 – 600	4	NR	NR	6 – 10	...	...	5.0	...	...
		600 – 1200	4	NR	NR	3 – 6	...	...	3.0	...	...
		> 1200	4	4	NR	2 – 3	3 – 6	...	1.5	3.0	...
Refrigeration reciprocating compressors and package chiller assemblies	10 – 50 tons	600 – 900	2	3	3	...	2 – 3	3 – 4	2.0	2.0	3.0
		900 – 1200	2	3	3	...	2 – 3	3 – 4	1.5	1.5	2.0
		> 1200	2	3	3	...	2 – 3	2 – 3	1.0	1.5	2.0
	> 50 tons	600 – 900	3	3	4	2 – 3	3 – 4	4 – 6	2.0	3.0	3.0
		900 – 1200	3	3	3	...	3 – 4	3 – 5	2.0	2.0	2.0
		> 1200	3	3	3	...	2 – 3	3 – 4	1.5	2.0	.20
Refrigeration rotary compressor, and packaged chiller, assemblies	100 – 500 tons	> 3000	2	2	3	...	...	2 – 3	0.75	1.0	1.5
	500 – 1000 tons	> 3000	2	2	3	...	...	3 – 5	1.0	1.5	1.5
Absorption refrigeration assemblies	All sizes		1	2	2	...	...	...	0.25	0.50	1.00
Cooling towers, propeller type (see note 5, below)	< 25 hp	150 – 300	NN	2	2	...	...	...	...	5.0	5.0
		300 – 600	NN	2	2	...	...	...	...	3.0	3.0
		> 600	NN	2	2	...	...	...	...	3.0	3.0
	25 – 150 hp	150 – 300	NN	2	2	...	...	...	...	6.0	6.0
		300 – 600	NN	2	2	...	...	...	...	4.0	4.0
		> 600	NN	2	2	...	...	...	...	3.0	3.0
	> 150 hp	150 – 300	NN	2	2	...	...	...	...	6.0	6.0
		300 – 600	NN	2	2	...	...	...	...	5.0	5.0
		> 600	NN	2	2	...	...	...	...	4.0	4.0
Cooling towers centrifugal type	< 23 hp	450 – 900	NN	2	2	...	...	...	...	1.0	1.5
		900 – 1800	NN	2	2	...	...	...	...	0.75	1.0
		> 1800	NN	2	2	...	...	...	...	1.5	0.75
	25 – 150 hp	450 – 900	NN	2	2	...	...	...	...	1.0	2.0
		900 – 1800	NN	2	2	...	...	...	...	1.0	1.5
		> 1800	NN	2	2	...	...	...	...	0.75	1.0
	> 150 hp	450 – 900	NN	2	2	...	...	...	...	2.0	3.0
		900 – 1800	NN	2	2	...	...	...	...	1.5	1.5
		> 1800	NN	2	2	...	...	...	...	1.0	1.0
Transformers	< 10 kva		1	1	2	...	...	...	0.13	0.13	0.25
	10 – 100 Kva		1	2	2	...	...	...	0.13	0.25	0.50
	> 100 kva		1	2	2	...	...	...	0.25	0.50	0.50

1. Weight ratio $= \dfrac{\text{Weight of inertia block or base}}{\text{Weight of equipment mounted on inertia block or base}}$

2. Deflection of the combined equipment and inertia block on the mount. For normal and critical areas these deflections may have to be increased, depending on the floor flexibility. For normal areas, the deflection should be three to six times the floor deflection and critical areas six to ten times the floor deflection (see text).

3. NN denotes not needed; mount machine directly on the floor.

4. NR denotes not recommended, machine cannot be suitably isolated.

5. Minimum location is on a slab outside of building. To minimize waterfall noise from rooftop location over critical areas, place two or three layers of neoprene pad between tower and springs, or between tower and roof if the propeller and drive assembly are vibration isolated from the tower.

6. Minimum Area: Basement or on grade slab location.

7. Normal Area: Upper floor location, but not above or adjacent to a critical area, private offices, classrooms, conference rooms, operating rooms, etc.

8. Critical Area: Upper floor location above or adjacent to private offices, classrooms, conference rooms, operating room., etc.

Table 16-7. Mount Types

Mount Type	Schematic Illustration	
1		Pad mounts of sufficient layers to obtain desired static deflection at load rates of 25 – 60 psi (45 durometer neoprene), or 145 – 150 psi (65 durometer neoprene). Floor should be level or self leveling pads used to insure rated loading.
2		Assembly of equipment bolted to stiff steel frame to maintain alignment of components. Frame mounted on springs, general purpose elastomer mounts, or pads, depending on the amount of static deflection required.
3		Assembly of equipment bolted to inertia block, which is supported on steel springs with the top of the springs mounted as high as possible on the block. Bottom of springs may rest on pedestals or block can be recessed into the floor.
4		Same as Type 3 except that tops of springs are close to the height of the center of gravity of the combined block and equipment assembly.

Airborne Noise Through Ducts.—Noise output from a fan is maximum at the fan discharge and almost equally as loud at the fan intake. This, and the fact that acoustically untreated ducts act like speaking tubes or as highly efficient airborne sound transmitters, makes transmission of fan noise through duct work a major problem. The severity of the problem increases as the fan horsepower increases. In the past the material most frequently used to reduce or attenuate fan noise transmission through ductwork was duct lining. However, the introduction of unit sized air conditioning silencers on the market has given the mechanical engineer another tool for the reduction of noise in the ventilating system. In many localities it will be found that the use of a silencer in a duct as small as 12×12 inches is less expensive than providing acoustical duct lining to achieve an equal amount of sound attenuation. Recent designs now provide practically negligible pressure drop through air conditioning silencers and therefore do not require increased horsepower and fan sizes.

Detailed methods of calculating duct lining or duct silencer noise reduction required for a specific system are outlined in the following section entitled *Calculation of Sound Levels in Ducted Systems*.

Fig. 16-8 gives an approximate procedure for determining the amount of sound attenuation required in the most critical octave bands 63, 125, and 250 Hz. This chart is for estimation purposes only and should not replace computations described in the next section. The curves for Fig. 16-8 are based on a fan delivery of 10,000 cfm and a system consisting of 40 ft of duct having two 90 degree elbows and one branch take-off. For other flow rates at the fan, modify the required sound attenuation multiply by the expression:

$$10\log_{10}\left(\frac{Q}{10000}\right)$$

where Q = actual cfm.

Note that this expression is a negative if Q is less than 10,000 cfm. If less than 40 ft of duct, or fewer take-offs or elbows are used, add 5 dB to the attenuation required. If an axial fan is used instead of a centrifugal fan, add 5 dB to the sound attenuation required.

Regenerated Noise.—Air flow, especially at high velocities, is quite capable of creating noise as it passes through the air conditioning system. Middle and high frequency noise can be generated at grilles, diffusers and other orifices; low and middle frequency noise is frequently generated at take-offs, elbows, etc.

High velocity systems may be subjected to regenerated noise at various duct fittings. It is strongly recommended that high velocity systems, when used in critical areas, be thoroughly analyzed by an acoustical consultant or other experienced persons. Most grille and diffuser manufacturers submit noise output data with their literature giving noise output as related to the velocity of air through the open area of the grille and the pressure drop across the grille.

See *Acoustical Problems in High Velocity Air Distribution*.

Other Mechanical Noise Sources.—*Condenser Water and Chilled Water Piping:* In addition to the necessity of isolating vibrating piping from the structure to avoid structural transmission of noise from the piping, piping can also be an airborne source of noise. Condenser water or chilled water mains installed horizontally above suspended ceilings will frequently generate and transmit noise in excess of criteria standards to critical spaces below when the suspended ceiling is transparent to sound, as are most acoustical tile ceilings. The solution to this problem is usually to substitute a suspended plaster ceiling for the acoustical tile ceiling and, if necessary, cement the acoustical tile to the underside of the plaster, or to box the piping with wire lath and plaster or equivalent material.

Steam Pressure Reducing Valves: Noise levels as high as 115 dB at a distance of a few feet from a large pressure reducing valve in a high velocity steam system are possible. Since this noise can be transmitted either as structure-borne or airborne, the steam pressure reduction valve and piping for a distance of approximately 30 diameters in each direction should be isolated from the structure.

Adequate sound barriers must also be provided to attenuate the airborne noise transmission. It is strongly recommended that steam pressure reduction valves be located in noncritical areas. Any deviation from this recommendation should be discussed with an experienced acoustical authority.

Transformers: Iron core transformers also generate noise, usually at the fundamental frequency of 120 Hz. Other harmonics up to 1200 Hz may also be detected. The noise output from transformers is a function of the size of the unit in kva rating.

Location of a transformer in excess of 500 kva should be the subject of special analysis.

Cooling Towers: Control of noise of cooling towers is treated separately later in this section.

Specifications: Neglect of acoustical problems in mechanical systems can result in a completely unsatisfactory acoustical environment. Corrective measures taken after a building has been completed are rarely fully satisfactory and always greatly more expensive than if the design had incorporated necessary acoustical precautions.

Mechanical specifications and drawings should clearly define the work to be done. Clauses such as "the contractor shall make the job vibration less and noiseless" places engineering responsibility upon the contractor in excess of his limited knowledge of the field. Furthermore, such vague wording actually handicaps the more experienced contractor who might, because of his experience, over-engineer the solution at a cost higher than a less experienced competitor.

Calculation of Sound Levels from HVAC Systems

In this section the details necessary for the computation of the sound pressure levels from HVAC systems will be described and illustrated. The approximate method, using Fig. 16-8 of the previous section, is simpler for estimating required noise attenuation. However, for critical situations it is recommended that more accurate, detailed calculations be made, as outlined in this section.

Description of Decibels.—The mathematical decibel scale follows a logarithmic pattern. The decibel is used to describe the intensity level or energy level of a physical quantity, and is defined as ten times the logarithm to the base 10 of the ratio of a power or energy quantity to a reference value of the same physical quantity:

$$L_E = 10 \log_{10}\left(\frac{E}{E_{ref}}\right) \quad dB \qquad (8)$$

In acoustics the decibel is used for acoustic power and acoustic pressure expressed by the following:

$$L_W = 10 \log_{10}\left(\frac{W}{W_{ref}}\right) \qquad (9)$$

$$L_P = 10 \log_{10}\left(\frac{P}{P_{ref}}\right)^2 \qquad (10)$$

In Equation (3) it can be seen that the energy is proportional to the square of the pressure; therefore, the pressure term must be squared since the decibel is defined as a ratio of power.

Addition of Decibels.—Since decibels are logarithmic quantities, the summation of two decibel values requires the sum of the energy values:

$$L_{W1} = 10 \log_{10}\left(\frac{W_1}{W_{ref}}\right)$$

$$L_{W2} = 10 \log_{10}\left(\frac{W_2}{W_{ref}}\right)$$

$$L_{W1} + L_{W2} = 10 \log_{10}\left(\frac{W_1 + W_2}{W_{ref}}\right) dB \qquad (11)$$

And since power is related to the square of pressure,

$$L_{P1} = 10 \log_{10}\left(\frac{P_1}{P_{ref}}\right)^2$$

$$L_{P2} = 10 \log_{10}\left(\frac{P_2}{P_{ref}}\right)^2$$

$$L_{P1} + L_{P2} = 10 \log\left(\frac{P_1^2 + P_2^2}{P_{ref}^2}\right) dB \qquad (12)$$

To add a series of decibel values the antilog first must be calculated.

$$L_W = 10 \log_{10}\left(\frac{W}{W_{ref}}\right) \qquad (13)$$

$$\frac{W}{W_{ref}} = 10^{\frac{L_W}{10}} \qquad (14)$$

Then 10 times the log of the sum of the antilogs gives the sum of the decibel values:

$$L_{W1} + L_{W2} = 10 \log_{10}\left(10^{\frac{L_{W1}}{10}} + 10^{\frac{L_{W2}}{10}}\right) \qquad (15)$$

The basic equation for the summation of decibels, whether power or pressure level, is given as follows:

$$L_W = 10 \log_{10}\left(10^{\frac{L_{W1}}{10}} + 10^{\frac{L_{W2}}{10}} + \ldots 10^{\frac{L_{Wn}}{10}}\right) \qquad (16)$$

$$L_P = 10 \log_{10}\left(10^{\frac{L_{P1}}{10}} + 10^{\frac{L_{P2}}{10}} + \ldots 10^{\frac{L_{Pn}}{10}}\right) \qquad (17)$$

As an example consider the addition of 90 dB and 94 dB sound pressure level:

$$L_P = 10 \log_{10}\left(10^{\frac{L_{P1}}{10}} + 10^{\frac{L_{P2}}{10}} + \ldots 10^{\frac{L_{Pn}}{10}}\right)$$

$$= 10 \log_{10}\left(10^{\frac{90}{10}} + 10^{\frac{94}{10}}\right)$$

$$= 10 \log_{10}(10^9 + 10^{9.4})$$

$$= 10 \log_{10}(1 \times 10^9 + 2.51 \times 10^9)$$

$$= 10 \log_{10}(3.51 \times 10^9)$$

$$= 10(0.5453 + 9)$$

$$= 95.5 \ dB$$

It is obvious that when the added dB values Equation (15) differ by 10 or more, the higher of the values can be chosen as a sufficiently accurate answer. With a modern engineering calculator the addition of logarithmic values can be done quite easily without performing the intermediate steps shown.

Octave Bands and One-Thirds Octave Bands.—

Often linear frequency scale (100 Hz, 200 Hz, 300 Hz, etc.) is inconvenient for assessing acoustical frequencies, which range from 20 Hz to 20,000 Hz. The practical method is to separate this audible frequency range into ten unequal segments called *octave bands*. An octave higher means a doubling in frequency; e.g., 63 Hz, 125 Hz, 250 Hz, etc.

For scientific measurement of sound, certain frequency ranges from low to high have been established as guides over the range of audible sound. For each octave band the frequency of the upper limit is twice that of the lower band limit, as shown in Table 16-8. Also, the center frequencies have been standardized for scientific measurements so that each succeeding octave band center frequency is two times the frequency of the previous band, as shown in Table 16-8.

Fig 16-9a. Uniform radiation over $\frac{1}{4}$ of sphere, $Q = 4$ two reflecting surfaces

Fig 16-9b. Uniform hemispherical radiation, $Q = 2$ single reflecting surfaces

Fig 16-9c. Uniform spherical radiation, $Q = 1$ no reflecting surfaces

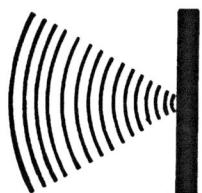

Fig 16-9d. Uniform radiation, Q depends on direction

Each octave band is sometimes separated into three ranges, referred to as one-third octave bands. These ranges have also been standardized for scientific measurements as given in Table 16-8. Portable sound measuring instruments measure the sound pressure level in decibels for each octave band or one-third octave band, the octave band measurements being most commonly used. Octave band measurements are necessary to determine the NC criterion of a building space described previously in this section.

Table 16-8. Frequency Limits for Octave Bands and one-third Octave Bands

Octave Bands			one-third Octave Bands		
Lower Band Limit, Hz	Center Frequency, Hz	Upper Band Limit, Hz	Lower Band Limit, Hz	Center Frequency, Hz	Upper Band Limit, Hz
11	16	22	14.1	16	17.8
			17.8	20	22.4
			22.4	25	28.2
22	31.5	44	28.2	31.5	35.5
			35.5	40	44.7
			44.7	50	56.2
44	63	88	56.2	63	70.8
			70.8	80	89.1
			89.1	100	112
88	125	177	112	125	141
			141	160	178
			178	200	224
177	250	355	224	250	282
			282	315	355
			355	400	447
355	500	710	447	500	562
			562	630	708
			708	800	891
710	1000	1420	891	1000	1122
			1122	1250	1413
			1413	1600	1778
1420	2000	2840	1778	2000	2239
			2239	2500	2818
			2818	3150	3548
2840	4000	5680	3548	4000	4467
			4467	5000	5623
			5623	6300	7079
5680	8000	11360	7079	8000	8913
			8913	10000	11220
			11200	12500	14130
11360	16000	22720	14130	16000	17780
			17780	20000	22390

The Sabin.—The *sabin* is an important unit of sound absorption expressing the total amount of sound absorption obtained from a given area of material from a component such as a window or door, or even from occupants in a room. Mathematically, the sabin is not a coefficient but is expressed in square feet for a panel of a single material as

$$A = \alpha S \qquad (18)$$

where A = absorption of the panel in sabins, (ft^2);

α = absorption coefficient, dimensionless; and

S = surface area of the panel (ft^2).

Table 16-9. Typical Values for Sound Absorption Coefficients of Building Materials

Materials	Frequency, Hz						
	125	250	500	1000	2000	4000	8000
	Absorption Coefficient α						
Cellulose fiber ceiling tile #1 mounting	0.05 to 0.10	0.20 to 0.25	0.50 to 0.80	0.50 to 0.99	0.45 to 0.90	0.30 to 0.70	0.30 to 0.75
Same, #7 mounting	0.30 to 0.40	0.30 to 0.45	0.35 to 0.65	0.45 to 0.99	0.50 to 0.90	0.50 to 0.75	0.50 to 0.80
Mineral fiber ceiling tile #1 mounting	0.02 to 0.10	0.15 to 0.25	0.55 to 0.75	0.60 to 0.99	0.60 to 0.99	0.50 to 0.90	0.50 to 0.95
Same #7 mounting	0.40 to 0.70	0.40 to 0.95	0.45 to 0.95	0.55 to 0.99	0.65 to 0.99	0.50 to 0.95	0.50 to 0.95
Brick, unglazed	0.03	0.03	0.03	0.04	0.05	0.07	0.06
Brick, glazed painted	0.01	0.01	0.02	0.02	0.02	0.03	0.03
Carpet, heavy on concrete	0.08	0.24	0.57	0.69	0.71	0.73	0.74
Same with latex backing on hair felt or foam pad	0.08	0.27	0.39	0.34	0.48	0.63	0.72
Light carpet	0.01	0.05	0.10	0.20	0.45	0.65	0.66
Concrete block, unpainted	0.36	0.44	0.31	0.29	0.39	0.25	0.25
Concrete block, painted	0.10	0.05	0.06	0.07	0.09	0.08	0.08
Draperies, hung straight							
10 oz per yd^2	0.03	0.04	0.11	0.17	0.24	0.35	0.40
14 oz per yd^2	0.07	0.31	0.49	0.75	0.70	0.60	0.60
18 oz per yd^2	0.14	0.35	0.55	0.72	0.70	0.65	0.65
Floors, concrete or terrazzo	0.01	0.01	0.01	0.02	0.02	0.02	0.02
Asphalt, rubber, or cork tile on concrete	0.02	0.03	0.03	0.03	0.03	0.02	0.02
Wood	0.15	0.11	0.10	0.07	0.06	0.07	0.06
Glass, large panes of heavy plate	0.18	0.06	0.04	0.03	0.02	0.02	0.02
Common window glass	0.35	0.25	0.18	0.12	0.07	0.04	0.03
Gypsum board	0.29	0.10	0.05	0.04	0.07	0.09	0.08
Marble or glazed tile	0.01	0.01	0.01	0.01	0.02	0.02	0.02
Plaster, smooth finish	0.01	0.01	0.02	0.03	0.04	0.05	0.04
Rough finish	0.14	0.10	0.06	0.05	0.04	0.03	0.03
Sheet metal panels	0.05	0.04	0.03	0.03	0.02	0.01	0.01
Water, as in a swimming pool	0.01	0.01	0.01	0.01	0.02	0.03	0.02
Wood paneling, $\frac{3}{8}$" thick	0.28	0.22	0.17	0.09	0.10	0.11	0.09
Air, sabins per 1000 cu ft at 50% relative humidity	0.00	0.10	0.30	0.90	2.30	7.20	28.00
Absorption of Seats and Audience Sabins per Square Foot of Seating Area per Unit							
Audience seated in upholstered chairs, per ft^2 of floor area	0.60	0.74	0.88	0.96	0.93	0.85	0.80
Unoccupied cloth covered seats, per ft^2 of floor area	0.49	0.66	0.80	0.88	0.82	0.70	0.65
Wooden pews, occupied, per ft^2 of floor area	0.57	0.61	0.75	0.86	0.91	0.86	0.80
Pew cushions (without pews), sabins each	0.75 to 1.10	1.00 to 1.70	1.45 to 1.90	1.50 to 2.00	1.40 to 1.70	1.40 to 1.60	1.40 to 1.55
Chairs, unoccupied, metal or wood, sabins each	0.15	0.19	0.22	0.39	0.38	0.30	0.30

The amount of absorption in sabins is defined by Equation (18), where the absorption coefficient α is determined by a specified method of measurement in an acoustic laboratory.

The absorption of a system composed of a number of materials with different sound absorption coefficients can be determined from the relation:

$$A = \alpha_1 S_1 + \alpha_2 S_2 + \ldots \alpha_n S_n = \sum_{(i=1)}^{(i=n)} \alpha_i S_i \quad (19)$$

where A = total absorption in sabins;

α_i = absorption coefficient of various materials (dimensionless); and

S_i = surface area of various materials, ft^2.

For example, the total absorption of an empty room would be computed from:

$$A = \alpha_{floor} S_{floor} + \alpha_{walls} S_{walls} + \alpha_{ceiliing} S_{ceiliing} + \alpha_{windows} S_{windows} + \alpha_{doors} S_{doors} \quad (20)$$

If there are other materials in the room, they must be included. Because the absorption coefficient varies with frequency, the total absorption A will also vary with frequency. The usual computational methods use octave bands with the center frequency of the octave band given.

Again, it is important to realize that the absorption coefficient α cannot be calculated but must be determined experimentally. Typical values of this coefficient are given in Table 16-9. Supplier catalogs are the usual sources of coefficients for specific materials. A comprehensive source of these data is a bulletin entitled Performance Data Architectural Acoustical Materials, published by the Acoustical Materials Association. Another source is the Compendium of Materials for Noise Control.

Determination of Sound Pressure Level.—The sound pressure level is usually prescribed in octave bands to, room usage criteria. This was described previously under "*NOISE AND VIBRATION CONTROL*" with specific values in Table 16-2 of that section. The sound pressure level can be computed from the sound power level of noise sources and the room characteristics from the relation:

$$L_P = L_w + 10 \log_{10}\left(\left[\frac{Q}{4\pi n}\left(\frac{1}{r_1^2} + \ldots + \frac{1}{r_n^2}\right) + \frac{4}{R}\right]\right) \quad (21)$$
$$+ 10 \text{ dB}$$

where L_P = sound pressure at a location in questions above;

L_w = sound power level at dB from sources in the room;

Q = directivity factor (dimensionless) (See Figs. 16-9a - 16-9d);

n = number of sound sources of equal sound power level;

r_1, r_2, r_n = distances from sources, ft and;

R = room constant in ft^2.

The sound power level L_w must be provided be the manufacturer of the equipment to be installed in the space. For air flow systems, L_w must be computed as described later in this section. The directivity factor Q is a dimensionless number which accounts for the directional character of the source or the placement of the source in the room. Figs. 16-9a through 16-9d give directivity factors for various sound radiation conditions. For a sound source near a wall $Q = 2$ for a source such as a diffuser suspended from and some distance from a ceiling. a nearly uniform radiation can result with $Q = 1$.

The room constant R accounts for the amount of acoustic energy absorbed by the materials of the space such as walls, floor, ceiling, and occupants. It is computed from:

$$R = \frac{\bar{\alpha}S}{1 - \bar{\alpha}} \quad (22)$$

The room absorption term αS is obtained from the following relation:

$$\alpha S = \alpha_1 S_1 + \ldots + \alpha_n S_n + A_1 + A_n + \alpha_{air} V \quad (23)$$

The value for α for use in Equation (22) can be determined from Equation (23) by dividing by the total surface area in the room:

$$S = S_1 + S_2 + \ldots + S_n$$

Table 16-10. Manufacturer Provided Sound Power Levels for Fan Coil Unit in Fig. 16-10

Octave Band Center Frequency, Hz	125	250	500	1000	2000	4000	8000
Sound Power Level, L_w, dB re 10^{-12} watts	57	52	49	40	37	31	21

Example 1: Determination of sound pressure level for a nonducted source.

As an example of the use of Equation (21) to predict the sound pressure level in a room, consider the executive office, as shown in Fig. 16-10, which has a fan coil unit. The office has wood paneling on three walls, glass windows on one wall, heavy carpeting, and acoustical ceiling panels. It is desired to compute the noise criteria (NC) value for the office.

First the octave band sound power levels are to be obtained from the manufacturer of the fan coil unit. For this particular unit the values shown in Table 16-10 were provided.

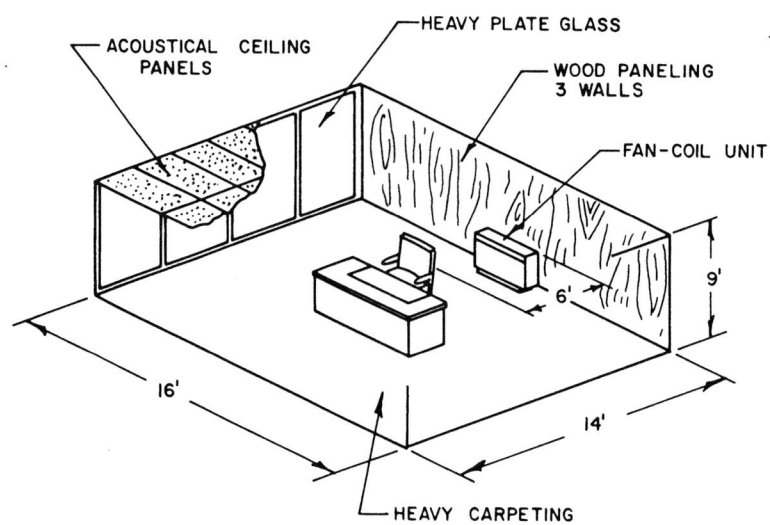

Fig 16-10. An office for which NC level is to be computed

Table 16-11. Calculation of the Room Constant *R*, for Example 1

	Computation	Octave Band Center Frequency, Hz						
		125	250	500	1000	2000	4000	8000
1	Window wall ($S_1 = 126$ ft²)							
	α_1	0.18	0.06	0.04	0.03	0.02	0.02	0.02
	$\alpha_1 S_1$ (sabins)	22.68	7.56	5.04	3.78	2.52	2.52	2.52
2	Paneled walls ($S_2 = 414$ ft²)							
	α_2	0.28	0.22	0.17	0.09	0.10	0.11	0.09
	$\alpha_2 S_2$ (sabins)	115.92	91.08	70.38	37.26	41.40	45.54	37.26
3	Floor ($S_2 = 224$ ft²)							
	α_3	0.08	0.27	0.39	0.34	0.48	0.63	0.74
	$\alpha_3 S_3$ (sabins)	17.92	60.48	87.36	76.16	107.52	141.12	165.76
4	Ceiling ($S_4 = 224$ ft²)							
	α_4	0.36	0.42	0.62	0.86	0.87	0.81	0.72
	$\alpha_4 S_4$ (sabins)	80.64	94.08	138.88	192.64	194.88	181.44	161.28
5	Air in room ($V = 2016$ ft³)							
	α_{air}	0.00	0.10	0.30	0.90	2.30	7.20	28.00
	$\alpha_{air}V/1000$ (sabins)	0.00	0.20	0.60	1.81	4.64	14.52	56.45
6	$\sum\alpha_i S_i$	237.16	253.2	301.66	309.84	346.32	385.14	423.27
7	Calculation of $\bar\alpha = \dfrac{\sum\alpha_i S_i}{S}$ ($S = 988$ ft²). Row 6 divided by S.	0.24	0.26	0.31	0.323	0.36	0.39	0.43
8	$R = \dfrac{\bar\alpha S}{1-\bar\alpha}$ rounded	312	342	438	458	548	631	743

Calculation of the room constant R is illustrated in Table 16-11. For each room surface the acoustic absorption coefficients are obtained from the manufacturer of the material or, in the case of glass, the values are obtained from Table 16-9. The acoustic absorption of air per 1000 ft^3 is determined from Table 16-11.

In Table 16-11, rows 1 through 4, the absorption (in sabins) for each room surface is computed by multiplying the surface area by the absorption coefficients. The absorption for the air in the room is computed in row 5 by dividing the room volume in cubic feet by 1000 and multiplying by the air absorption α_{air} per 1000 ft^3. The total absorption of the room is given in row 6, which is the sum of the absorption (in sabins) of the room surfaces and the air in the room from rows 1 through 5. The average absorption coefficient a is computed in row 7 by dividing the total absorption values, in sabins, by the total surface area of the room; i.e., the values in row 6 are divided by the room surface area to give the values in row 7. Finally, the room constant R is computed in row 8 from the values in rows 6 and 7.

Using the values of room constant computed in Table 16-11, the octave band sound pressure levels will now be calculated using Equation (21). From Fig. 16-9b, the directivity factor Q is 2 because the fan coil unit is against one wall and hemispherical radiation from the wall is assumed. For only one noise source, n is 1; and r_1 is the distance from the unit to the receiver location, which is 6 ft in this example. The sound pressure level is then computed in octave bands from

$$L_p = L_w + \text{Correction}$$

$$L_p = L_w + 10\log\left[\frac{Q}{4\pi n}\left(\frac{1}{r_1^2}\right) + \frac{4}{R}\right] + 10 \text{ Db}$$

For this 125 Hz, Octave band center frequency the computation is as follows:

$L_w = 57$, From Table 16-10

$R = 312$ from Table 16-11

$Q = 2$, From Fig. 16-9b

$$
\begin{aligned}
L_p &= L_w + 10\log\left[\frac{2}{4\pi r_1^2} + \frac{4}{312}\right] + 10 \\
&= L_w + 10\log\left(\frac{2}{4\pi 6^2} + \frac{4}{312}\right) + 10 \\
&= L_w + 10\log(0.0044 + 0.0128) + 10 \\
&= (L_w + 10\log[0.0172] + 10) \\
&= L_w - 17.6 + 10 \\
&= L_w - 7.6 \\
&= 57 - 7.6 \\
&= 49 \text{ dB}
\end{aligned}
$$

This procedure is repeated for every octave band center frequency. Results are shown in Table 16-12. Note that in row 4 of Table 16-12 the final values are rounded to the nearest whole decibel.

Determination of the NC level is accomplished by plotting the resulting sound pressure levels from Table 16-12 on an NC criterion chart as shown in Fig. 16-11 which indicates that the highest penetration is the NC-35 curve. Thus, the level at the listener location in Fig. 16-10 meets an NC-35 criterion. Referring to Table 16-9 of the previous section, it is shown that an NC-35 criterion is acceptable for an executive office. If the computed level had exceeded the NC 35 value, alternate systems would have been considered. For instance, a fan coil unit with lower sound power levels could have been specified. Alternatively, ceiling panels with larger acoustic absorption values could have been used. Possibly, a combination of both approaches would satisfy the criterion.

Table 16-12. Calculation of Sound Pressure Levels

	Computation	Octave Band Center Frequency, Hz						
		125	250	500	1000	2000	4000	8000
1	$10 \times \log\left[\frac{2}{4\pi 6^2} + \frac{4}{R}\right]$ dB (R from Table 16-11)	−17.6	−17.9	−18.7	−18.8	−19.3	−19.7	−20.1
2	Add 10 decibels	+10	+10	+10	+10	+10	+10	+10
3	Correction, dB	−7.6	−7.9	−8.7	−8.8	−9.3	−9.7	−10.1
4	$L_P = L_w + \text{Correction}$ dB (L_w from Table 16-10 values rounded)	49	44	40	31	28	21	11

Note in this example the necessity of obtaining the octave band sound power levels for the unit to be installed to allow us to compute the sound pressure levels and the NC criteria. A unit designated as meeting some NC level is meaningless if the room constant for which the unit is to be installed is not known. Therefore, equipment manufacturers are encouraged to provide octave band sound power levels L_W and not NC levels or sone values.

Noise in Ducted Systems.—In the remainder of this section, in-duct noise sources will be treated. An analysis of the sound generation and propagation in a ducted system requires some information in addition to that given in previous sections. The airborne sound inside a ducted system that radiates into an occupied space involves the following factors:

1) sound power generated by the fan;

2) distribution of sound in the ducted system;

3) attenuation provided by the duct (acoustically treated, or bare duct);

4) attenuation provided by elbows;

5) attenuation provided by commercial silencers or attenuators;

6) generation of sound due to air flow in fittings, elbows, grilles, etc; and

7) sound transmitted through duct walls.

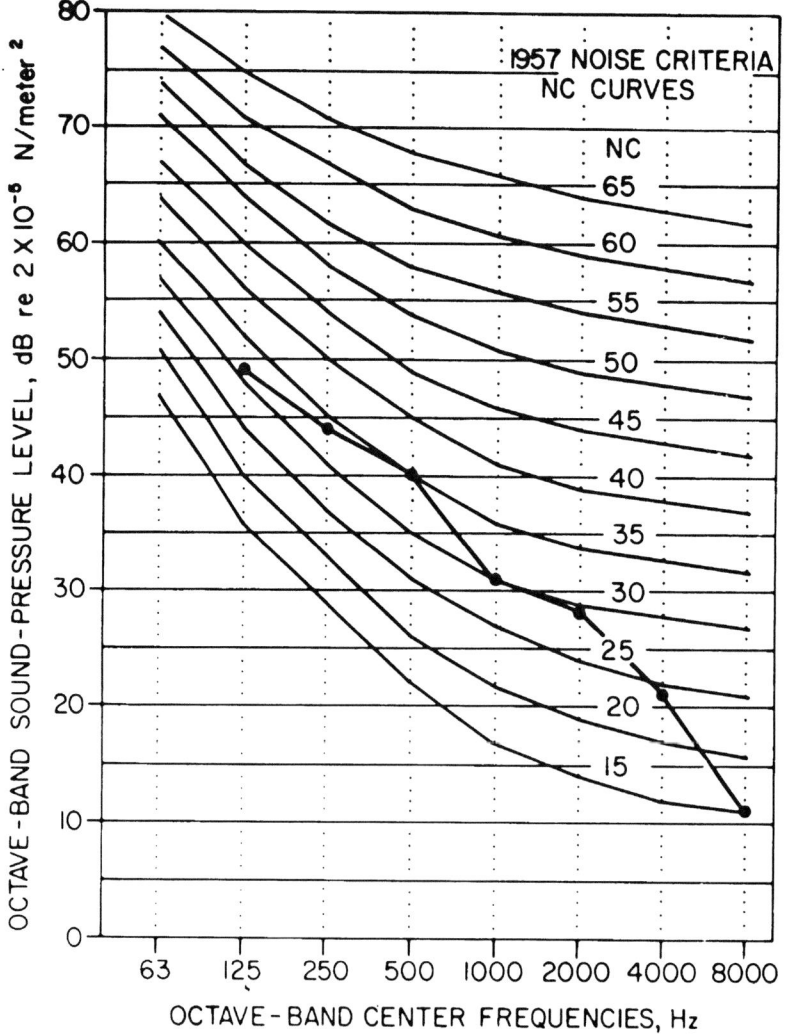

Fig 16-11. Determination of noise criteria for Example 1

Table 16-13. Acoustic Properties of Various Fan Types

Type	Design	Specific Sound Power Level, K_w Center Frequency Hz								BFI	Applications
		63	125	250	500	1000	2000	4000	8000		
		dB re 10^{-12} watt and 1 cfm at 1 inch ftp									
Centrifugal Fans											
Air-foil		35	35	34	32	31	26	18	10	3	Highest efficiency of all centrifugal fan design contains 10 to 16 blades of airfoil shape. Used for general heating, ventilating, and air conditioning systems, usually applied to central station units where the horsepower saving will be significant. Can be used on low, medium, and high pressure systems and will operate satisfactorily in parallel. Also used in large sizes, for clean air industrial applications where power savings will be significant. Can be used on industrial exhaust systems, where the air cleaning system is of high efficiency.
Back-ward Inclined Back-ward Curved		35	35	34	32	31	26	18	10	3	Efficiency is only slightly less than that of the airfoil fan. Contains 10 to 16 blades. Used for the same general applications as the airfoil fan. Can be used in industrial applications where the gas is essentially clean, but does not meet the standards required for air-foil fan selection.
Radial		48	45	43	43	38	33	30	29	5-8	Simplest of all centrifugal fans; relatively low efficiency, usually has 6 to 10 blades; includes both radial blades (R), and modified radial blades (M). Used primarily for industrial exhaust, including dirty gas fans and recirculating gas fans. This design also used for high pressure industrial applications.
Forward Curved		40	38	38	34	28	24	21	15	2	Efficiency less than the airfoil and backwardly curved fans, this fan is usually fabricated of lightweight and low cost construction. It may have from 24 to 64 blades. This design will be the smallest of the centrifugal fan types and operates at the lowest speed. Used primarily in low pressure heating, ventilating, and air conditioning applications, such as: domestic furnaces, small central station units, and packaged air conditioning equipment.

Table 16-13. *(Continued)* **Acoustic Properties of Various Fan Types**

Type	Design	Specific Sound Power Level, K_w								BFI	Applications
		Center Frequency Hz									
		63	125	250	500	1000	2000	4000	8000		
		dB re 10^{-12} watt and 1 cfm at 1 inch ftp									
Axial Fans											
Vane axial		42	39	41	42	40	37	35	25	6-8	High efficiency axial flow fan with airfoil blades and high pressure capability. Blades may be fixed or adjustable and the hub diameter is usually greater than 50% of the fan tip diameter. There may be from 3 to 16 blades. This fan design has guide vanes down stream from the wheel which permits good air flow pattern on the discharge side of the fan. Used for general heating, ventilating, and airconditioning applications in low, medium, and high pressure systems. May also be used in industrial applications such as: drying ovens, paint spray booths, and fume exhaust systems.
Tube axial		44	42	46	44	42	40	37	30	6-8	This fan is more efficient than the propeller fan design and can develop a more useful pressure capability. The number of blades may vary from 4 to 8 and the hub is usually about 50% of the fan tip diameter. The blades may be of airfoil or single thickness cross section. The fan is built without downstream guide vanes. Used in low and medium pressure ducted heating, ventilating, and air conditioning applications where the poor air flow pattern downstream from the fan is not detrimental. This fan is also used in some industrial applications such as: drying ovens, paint spray booths and fume exhaust systems.
Propeller		51	48	49	47	45	45	43	31	5-7	Low efficiency wheels are usually of inexpensive construction and are limited to very low pressure applications. Usually contains 2 to 8 blades of single thickness construction attached to a relatively small hub. The housing is a simple circular ring or orifice plate. This fan is used for low pressure, high volume air moving applications such as air circulation within a space or as exhaust fans in a wall or roof.
Tubular centrifugal		46	43	43	38	37	32	28	25	4-6	This fan usually has a wheel similar to the airfoil or backwardly inclined wheel, described above, which is built into an axial flow type housing. This results in lower efficiencies than the centrifugal fans of similar wheel design. The air is discharged radially from the wheel and must change direction by 90° to flow through the guide vane section. Used primarily for low pressure return air systems in heating, ventilating, and air conditioning applications.

Fan Noise Generation.—Table 16-13 gives information on the principal types of fans used in commercial installations. The fan noise is given in terms of the specific sound power levels in octave bands and the blade frequency increment (*BFI*). The specific sound power level (K_w) is defined as the sound power level generated by a fan operating at a flow rate of 1 cfm and a pressure of 1 inch of water. Fans generate a tone at the blade pass frequency over and above the sound level generated by air flow. In order to account for this blade pass tone, the sound power level must be increased in the octave band in which the blade frequency occurs. The amount of increase is listed in Table 16-13 for each fan under the column labeled *BFI*. The blade pass frequency is determined from

$$B_f = \frac{\text{rpm} \times \text{no. of blades}}{60} \quad \text{(Hz)} \quad (24)$$

The number of blades and the rpm are determined from the catalog used for fan selection to meet design flow requirements.

Estimating Fan Noise.—In general, it is desirable to obtain fan sound power information from the fan manufacturer. There may be times, however, when this is not possible or the fan is to be operated at a condition not covered by manufacturers data. For such cases the following procedure may be used to estimate the fan generated sound power.

The specific sound power levels (K_W) given in Table 16-13 provide a basis for estimating the sound power levels of fans L_W with corrections as functions of flow rate (Q), the pressure rise across the fan (P) and the blade frequency increment (*BFI*). Sound power is estimated from:

$$L_W = K_W + (10\log_{10}Q + 20\log_{10}P) + BFI \quad (25)$$

The term $(10 \log_{10} Q + 20 \log_{10} P)$ in Equation (25) may be calculated directly or obtained graphically from Fig. 16-12.

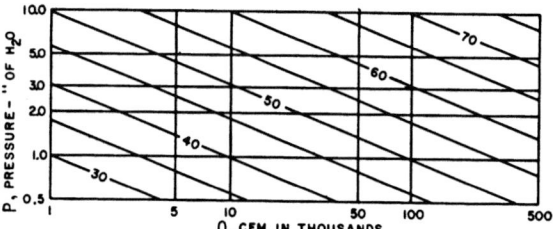

Fig 16-12. Correction factors

Equation (25) predicts the total sound power level generated by a fan that includes the inlet and outlet combined. If only the inlet sound power level or the outlet sound power level is desired, 3 dB must be subtracted from the values computed. This assumes that the inlet and outlet of the fan generate equal sound power levels. The reason for subtracting 3 dB is a result of how decibel values combine or subtract. As computed from Equation (15), whenever two equal sound power levels are combined the result is 3 dB greater than the values being added. Conversely, to find the sound power level that corresponds to one-half the total sound power, we must subtract 3 dB from the total sound power level. This will be illustrated in the following example.

Example 2: Estimate the sound power level from the outlet of a radial blade fan operating at 10,000 cfm, and 2 in. of wg. The fan has 16 blades and will operate at 500 rpm.

Table 16-14. Calculation of Sound Power Level for Fan Outlet for Example 2

Calculations	Octave Band Center Frequency, Hz							
	63	125	250	500	1000	2000	4000	8000
Specific sound level K_W dB (Table 16-13)	48	45	43	43	38	33	30	29
Correction term, $10 \log_{10}Q + 20 \log_{10}P$ (dB)	46	46	46	46	46	46	46	46
Blade frequency increment, *BFI* dB (Table 16-13)	0	8	0	0	0	0	0	0
Correction in dB to convert to sound power at fan outlet alone	−3	−3	−3	−3	−3	−3	−3	−3
Sound power level dB for fan outlet	91	96	86	86	81	76	73	72

Solution: A) The specific sound power levels. K_W for a radial type fan are obtained from Table 16-12 and listed in row 1 of Table 16-14.

B) Compute the bracketed term in Equation (18) for $Q = 10000$ cfm and $P = 2$ in. wg:

$$10 \log_{10}Q + 20\log_{10}P$$
$$= 10 \log_{10}10000 + 20\log_{10}2$$
$$= 40 + 6$$
$$= 46$$

C) Thus, 46 dB is listed for every octave band in row 2 of Table 16-14.

Determine the blade pass frequency from Equation (24)

$$B_f = \frac{500 \times 16}{60} = 133 \quad \text{(Hz)}$$

Note that 1.33 Hz falls within the 125 Hz octave band as shown in Table 16-8 of this section. Figure 4 lists a blade frequency increment *BFI* of 5 to 8 dB for a radial fan, therefore the maximum value of 8 dB will be listed for the 125 Hz octave band and zeros are listed for all other octave bands in row 3 of Table 16-14.

D) Correct for the sound power level of the outlet only. Equation (25) predicts the total sound power level from inlet plus outlet. Therefore subtract 3 dB, as shown in row 4, to correct for outlet sound power level of the fan.

E) Compute the octave band sound power level of the outlet by adding rows 1 through 4 of Table 16-14. The resulting sound power level, in decibels, is given in row 5. These values represent the sound power levels radiated into the duct system by the fan.

Distribution of Sound Power at Branch Takeoffs.—

At a tee section, or other branch take-off, the sound power upstream of the take-off propagates into each of the duct elements at the take-off location. The proportion of sound power that transmits from a main air supply duct into a branch take-off is approximately in the same ratio as the duct area ratios at the branch location. As illustrated by Equation (15), sound levels increase (or decrease) by logarithmic ratios; therefore, if a main duct has airborne sound with a level of 63 dB and this duct divides into two equal area ducts, the sound level will be 60 dB in each. In other words, cutting the sound power in half will result in a 3 dB reduction. The decibel reductions for other area ratios at branch take-offs are given in Table 16-15.

For multiple outlets the *cfm* at each outlet will be approximately in proportion to the area ratio; therefore, the values in Table 16-15 can be converted to percentage of *cfm* of each outlet to the total fan *cfm*, as given in Table 16-16.

Table 16-15. Sound Power Level Division at Branch Take Offs

Area of continuing duct, in percent, of the total area of all ducts after branch take-off	5	10	15	20	30	40	50	80
Decibels to be subtracted from power level before take-off in order to get power level in continuing duct	13	10	8	7	5	4	3	1

Table 16-16. Allotment of Fan Sound Power to Each Air Outlet

cfm in Percent of Total Fan *cfm*	⅕	½	1	2	5	10	20	50
Decibels to be subtracted from the up stream sound power level to get fan sound power level per outlet	27	23	20	17	13	10	7	3

Attenuation of Untreated Duct.—Untreated sheet metal duct walls will absorb sound energy.

For round ducts, the sound attenuation with or without thermal insulation is 0.03 decibel per linear foot for frequencies below 1000 Hz, and, it rises to 0.2 decibel per linear foot at 8000 Hz. Attenuation values for rectangular sheetmetal ducts, round elbows, and square elbows are given in Tables 16-17, 16-18, and 16-19.

Table 16-17. Natural Attenuation in Bare, Rectangular Sheet Metal Ducts

Duct	Size, in.	63	125	250	Above 250
		Attenuation, dB/ft			
Small	6 × 6	0.2	0.2	0.15	0.1
Medium	24 × 24	0.2	0.2	0.1	0.05
Large	72 × 72	0.1	0.1	0.05	0.01

Table 16-18. Attenuation of Round Elbows

Diameter or Dimensions, in.	63	125	250	500	1000	2000	4000	8000
5 to 10	0	0	0	0	1	2	3	3
11 to 20	0	0	0	1	2	3	3	3
21 to 40	0	0	1	2	3	3	3	3
41 to 80	0	1	2	3	3	3	3	3

Table 16-19. Attenuation of Square Elbows without Turning Vanes, in Decibels (dB)

Duct width D in.	63	125	250	500	1000	2000	4000	8000
(A) No lining								
5	...	...		1	5	7	5	3
10	...	...	1	5	7	5	3	3
20	...	1	5	7	5	3	3	3
40	1	5	7	5	3	3	3	3
(B) Lining ahead of elbow								
5	...	...	...	1	5	8	6	8
10	...	...	1	5	8	6	8	11
20	...	1	5	8	6	8	11	11
40	1	5	8	6	8	11	11	11
(C) Lining after elbow								
5	...	...	...	1	6	11	10	10
10	...	...	1	6	11	10	10	10
20	...	1	6	11	10	10	10	10
40	1	6	11	10	10	10	10	10
(D) Lining ahead of and after bend								
5	...	...	...	1	6	12	14	16
10	...	...	1	6	12	14	16	18
20	...	1	6	12	14	16	18	18
40	1	6	12	14	16	18	18	18

Duct Lining Attenuation.—Direct lining in ducts may be used for both thermal insulation and sound attenuation. The sound attenuation can be estimated from Equation (26).

$$\text{Lined duct attenuation} = 12.6 L \alpha^{1.4}\left(\frac{P}{S}\right) \text{ (dB)} \quad (26)$$

where L = length of linear duct, ft;

P = perimeter of duct inside the lining, in;

S = cross sectional area of the duct inside the lining, in^2; and

α = acoustic absorption coefficient of the lining material (a function of frequency).

The limitations of Equation (26) are:

1) Smallest duct dimension should not exceed 18 in. nor be less than 6 in.

2) Ratio of duct width to height should not exceed 2/1.

3) The absorption coefficient α should be representative for the entire octave band.

4) Air flow velocities should not exceed 4000 fpm.

5) Equation (26) does not allow for line of sight propagation of sound, which, limits high frequency attenuation. In a straight 12 in. duct, for instance, the attenuation in the 8000 Hz octave band will be only about 10 dB for any lining length over 3 ft. The attenuation in the next lower octave band (4000 Hz) will be about midway between 10 dB and the value calculated from Equation (26). The frequency above which the 10 dB limit applies is inversely proportional to the shortest dimension of the duct.

In selecting the duct lining material the following factors should be considered:

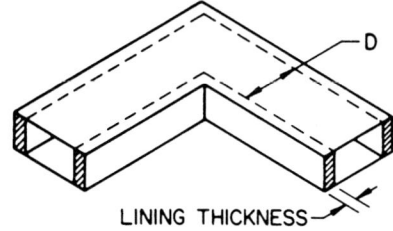

Fig 16-13. Illustration of duct width D for Table 16-19

1) For the absorption of frequencies below 500 Hz, the lining material should be 2 to 12 inches thick. Thin materials, particularly when mounted on hard solid surfaces, will absorb only the high frequencies.

2) It has been shown that increased absorption at frequencies below 700 Hz may be realized by using a perforated facing in which the area of the perforations is from 3 to 10% of the surface area. Such facings, however, decrease sound absorption at higher frequencies.

3) Any air space behind the lining material will have considerable effect. Absorption coefficients should be based on the particular mounting method intended to be used.

Sound absorbing materials suitable for use in air ducts are available in the form of blankets and semirigid boards. Specifications and absorption coefficients for most materials can be obtained from the Acoustical and Insulating Materials Association (AIMA).

Fig. 16-13 illustrates the correct application of an acoustic lining material in a square or rectangular elbow; the attenuation that can be obtained with this arrangement is given in Table 16-19.

Example 3: Determine the acoustic attenuation of a 24 by 36 in. duct, 20 ft long. The lining material is 1in. glass fiber with absorption coefficients as given in row 1 of Table 12. These values must be obtained from the supplier of the acoustic material.

Solution: The perimeter of the duct inside the lining is,

$$P = 2(22 + 34) = 112 \text{ in.}$$

The cross sectional area inside the lining is,

$$S = 22 \times 34 = 748 \text{ in}^2$$

For the 20 ft long duct, the attenuation is computed:

$$\text{Attenuation} = 12.6 L \alpha^{1.4}\left(\frac{P}{S}\right)$$

$$= 12.6 \times 20 \times \alpha^{1.4} \times \left(\frac{112}{748}\right)$$

$$= 37.7 \times \alpha^{1.4} \qquad (\text{dB/ft})$$

The values for $\alpha^{1.4}$ are given in row 2 of Table 16-20 and the attenuation values, in decibels, are given in row 3. In most calculations these values would be rounded to the nearest decibel.

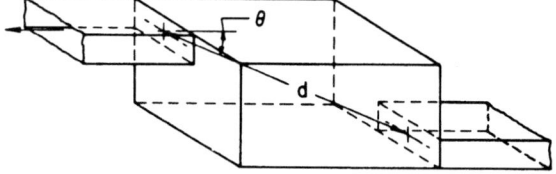

Fig 16-14. Diagram of a sound absorbing plenum

Table 16-20. Attenuation of a Lined Duct, Example 3

Row No.	Calculations	Octave Band Center Frequency, Hz							
		63	125	250	500	1000	2000	4000	8000
1	Absorption coefficient α of duct liner material	0.08	0.11	0.34	0.70	0.81	0.86	0.85	0.89
2	$\alpha^{1.40}$	0.029	0.045	0.220	0.607	0.745	0.810	0.797	0.849
3	Attenuation, dB = $37.7\alpha^{1.40}$	1.1	1.7	8.3	22.9	28.1	30.6	30.1	32.0

Sound Attenuation of Plenums.—When large values of sound attenuation are required, a sound absorption plenum will often be advantageous. The geometry of a sound absorbing plenum is shown in Fig. 16-14.

A relation given in Equation (27) has been developed for approximating the acoustic attenuation of a plenum

Plenum attenuation

$$= 10\log_{10}\left[\frac{1}{S_E\left(\dfrac{\cos\theta}{2\pi d^2} + \dfrac{1-\alpha}{\alpha S_W}\right)}\right] \quad \text{(dB)} \qquad (27)$$

where α = sound absorption coefficient of the lining material (frequency dependent);

 S_E = plenum exit area, ft^2;

 S_W = plenum wall surface area ft^2;

 d = distance between entrance and exit, ft (Fig. 16-14);

 θ = angle d makes with the normal to the entrance opening, degrees (Fig. 16-14).

For sound frequencies sufficiently high, where wavelength of sound given by:

$$\text{Wave length of sound} = \frac{1128}{\text{Frequency, Hz}} \quad \text{(ft)} \qquad (28)$$

is less than any of the plenum dimensions (height, width, or length), Equation (27) is accurate within a few decibels. At lower frequencies, when the wavelength of sound becomes greater than the plenum dimensions, Equation (27) is conservative and the actual attenuation exceeds the calculated value by 5 to 10 decibels.

Example 4: Determine the attenuation of a plenum as shown in Fig. 16-14. The exit duct is 10 inches in diameter, the surface area of the plenum is 42 ft^2, the distance d is 2.44 ft, and the angle θ is 15°. Compare the attenuation of a bare sheet metal plenum with the plenum covered with one inch of glass fiber.

Solution: The attenuation, in octave bands, is computed from Equation (27) with the following constants:

$$S_E = \pi\left(\frac{5}{12}\right)^2 = 0.55$$

$$d^2 = 5.95 \text{ ft}^2$$

$$\cos\theta = 0.966$$

$$S_W = 42 \text{ ft}^2$$

The values for the absorption coefficient α of sheet-metal panels are listed in row 1 of Table 16-21. These values are taken from Table 16-9. Note that α for 63 Hz can be considered the same as that for 125 Hz. The calculated values for $1-\alpha$ are given in row 2; the values of $\dfrac{1-\alpha}{\alpha S_W}$ are given in row 4. The value for the argument $\dfrac{\cos\theta}{2\pi d^2} + \dfrac{\alpha S_W}{1-\alpha}$ from the log quantity of Equation (27) is

given in row 5 The computed values for the attenuation of the plenum as computed from Equation (27) are given in row 6. These are the values for the attenuation, in decibels, for the various octave bands. For the 4000 and 8000 Hz center frequency octave bands the resulting attenuation (row 6) is calculated to be −1.17 dB, which would indicate that sound is generated. Since this violates the definition of attenuation of a plenum, as given by Equation (27), which does not include a term for noise generation, noise cannot be generated and the true attenuation is zero. Thus, a zero value for the attenuation is recorded in row 6 for the 4000 and 8000 Hz frequencies.

To determine the attenuation of the plenum with the inside surfaces treated with one inch of glass fiber, the calculations are repeated with the absorption coefficients for the glass fiber treatment as given in row 7 of Table 13. Those values must be obtained from the supplier of the acoustic absorption material. Values greater than $\alpha = 100$ should not be used for this calculation because the complete surface area is to be treated and values of greater than 1.00 are obtained from a sample in a test room. The usual procedure is to use a value of 1.00 for any material's absorption coefficient that is reported as greater than 1.00. This is the case for the value of α for the 8000 Hz octave band in this example.

The steps shown in rows 8, 9, 10, and 11 are identical to the computation for the sheet metal plenum without acoustic treatment. The final values for attenuation are shown in row 12, which are octave band values of the plenum attenuation, in decibels. As seen in comparison of rows 6 and 12, the addition of the sound treatment is most effective in octave bands above 250 Hz. The attenuation of the plenum was not changed in the 63 Hz and 125 Hz octave bands. To increase attenuation at the lower octave bands, a material that has higher values for the absorption coefficient at low frequency must be used or angle θ must be made larger.

Duct Lining and Elbows.—An elbow in a lined duct can improve the sound attenuation. If the wavelength, as calculated by Equation (28), is less than the width of the duct (Fig. 16-13, dimension D), the sound attenuation is improved as compared to a straight duct of equivalent length. On the other hand, if the wavelength is greater than the duct width, the sound attenuation is not improved. The sound attenuation of an elbow involves the following:

1) Only the lining on the sides of the duct is effective in attenuating the sound level, as shown in Fig. 16-13.

2) The attenuation of the elbow should be added to the attenuation calculated for lengths of lined duct without elbows as calculated by Equation (26).

3) For best results, the sides of the duct should be lined, both before and after the elbow, for a length of at least two duct widths. This length is based on a lining thickness of at least 10 percent of the duct width.

4) If the duct is lined only before or after the elbow. There is still some gain in attenuation, rows (B) and (C) of Table 16-19.

5) The attenuation that can be credited to the duct lining is the difference between the total attenuation in rows (B),

(C), or (D), of Table 16-19, and the attenuation of the unlined elbow row (A).

6) The listed increases in elbow attenuation are obtained only with duct linings, not with sound traps or lined plenums.

Table 16-21. Computation Sound Attenuation for Example 4

Row No.	Calculations	Octave Band Center Frequency, Hz							
		63	125	250	500	1000	2000	4000	8000
1	Absorption coefficient α for sheet metal panel	0.05	0.05	0.04	0.03	0.03	0.02	0.01	0.01
2	Calculation of $1-\alpha$	0.95	0.95	0.96	0.97	0.97	0.98	0.99	0.99
3	Calculation of $\frac{1-\alpha}{\alpha}$	19.00	19.00	24.00	32.33	32.33	49.0	99.0	99.0
4	Calculation of $\frac{1-\alpha}{\alpha S_w}$	0.452	0.452	0.571	0.769	0.769	1.167	2.357	2.357
5	$\frac{\cos\theta}{2\pi d^2} + \frac{\alpha S_w}{1-\alpha}$	0.478	0.478	0.597	0.795	0.795	1.193	2.383	2.383
6	Attenuation dB Equation (27)	5.8	5.8	4.8	3.6	3.6	1.8	0 (−1.17)	0 (−1.17)
7	Absorption coefficient α for 1 in glass fiber	0.05	0.06	0.20	0.65	0.90	0.95	0.98	1.00
8	Calculation of $1-\alpha$	0.95	0.94	0.80	0.35	10	0.05	0.02	0.00
9	Calculation of $\frac{1-\alpha}{\alpha}$	19.00	15.70	4.00	0.54	0.11	0.053	0.020	0.00
10	Calculation of $\frac{1-\alpha}{\alpha S_w}$	0.452	0.374	0.095	0.013	0.0026	0.0013	0.00048	0.00
11	$\frac{\cos\theta}{2\pi d^2} + \frac{\alpha S_w}{1-\alpha}$	0.478	0.400	0.121	0.039	0.028	0.0271	0.0263	0.0258
12	Attenuation dB Equation (27)	5.8	6.6	11.8	16.7	18.0	18.3	18.4	18.5

Open End Reflection Loss.—The sudden expansion of the fluid at the open end of a duct into a room or work space will cause some of the sound passing through the duct to reflect back into the system at the opening plane of the duct. Because of this phenomenon, only a portion of the sound energy is radiated from an open duct; the remaining energy is reflected. This effect is most pronounced at low frequencies, but is negligible at high frequencies. In duct system analysis, this result can be treated as an end reflection loss as given as a function of duct size and frequency in Table 16-22.

Air Flow Noise.—The fan is the major noise source in an air supply system, but as mentioned earlier in this chapter, air flow interaction with other elements in the system can be of significance. Turbulence in the flow is of major importance, and in extreme cases of flow separation, considerable sound power can be produced throughout the system. Estimates can be made for the sound

power generation of typical duct system elements from the following relation

$$L_w = F + G + H \qquad \text{(dB)} \qquad (29)$$

where L_w = octave band sound power level, in decibels, re 10^{-12} watts;

F = spectrum function determined from flow characteristics;

G = velocity function that account for the flow velocity through the duct element in decibels; and

H = correction function for the octave band f of interest.

The values of the spectrum function F are determined from a non-dimensional flow parameter called the Strouhal number, computed from,

$$S_t = \frac{5fD}{V} \tag{30}$$

where f = octave band center frequency Hz;

     D = duct diameter, inches or for rectangular ducts,

$$D = \sqrt{\frac{4}{\pi} \times \text{area}} \;\; ; \text{and}$$

V = average air flow velocity in the duct, fpm.

Table 16-22. Duct End Reflection Loss

Duct dia in.	Duct size in²	Octave Band Center Frequency, Hz							
		63	125	250	500	1000	2000	4000	8000
		Reflection Loss, dB							
5	25	17	12	8	4	1	0	0	0
10	100	12	8	4	1	0	0	0	0
20	400	8	4	1	0	0	0	0	0
40	1600	4	1	0	0	0	0	0	0
80	6400	1	0	0	0	0	0	0	0

The value of the spectrum function F in Equation (29) can be determined for elbows and branch take-offs from Figs. 8, 9 and 10. In all of these figures, the Strouhal Number S_t must be computed from Equation (30) for entry to the figures.

Values for the velocity function G can be determined from Fig. 16-18 and 16-19 for elbows and branch take offs as a function of the average flow velocity in the duct element.

The values for the octave bandwidth correction function H are obtained from Table 16-24. The values of H are not a function of the duct element, but rather depend only on the octave band of interest.

The effect of flow generated sound power for 90° elbows is easily seen in Fig. 16-18. For a doubling of the average flow velocity in the duct element, the sound power increases approximately 12 dB.

Two possibilities exist for the control of noise due to this effect:

1) Size the duct elements to minimize flow velocity and therefore obtain minimum flow noise source generation; or

2) Utilize high velocity systems with additional silencers to attenuate flow noise. There is a limitation with the second method: The air flow through silencers will also generate noise and thus reduce the attenuation that can be achieved. This will be treated in the next section.

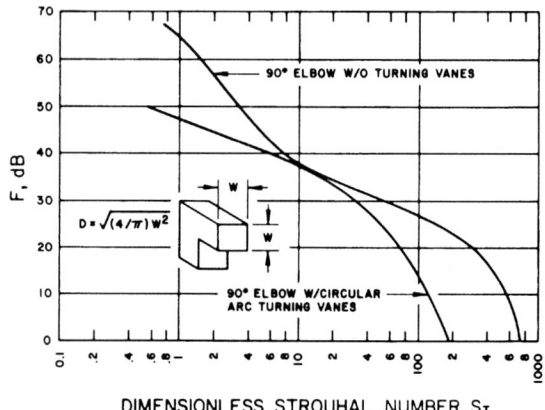

Fig 16-15. Spectrum function F for square cross section 90° elbow

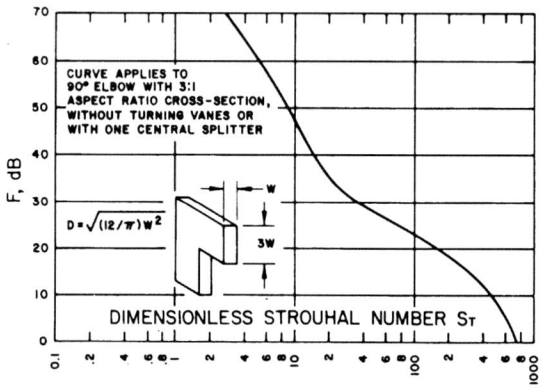

Fig 16-16. Spectrum function F for regular cross section 90° elbow

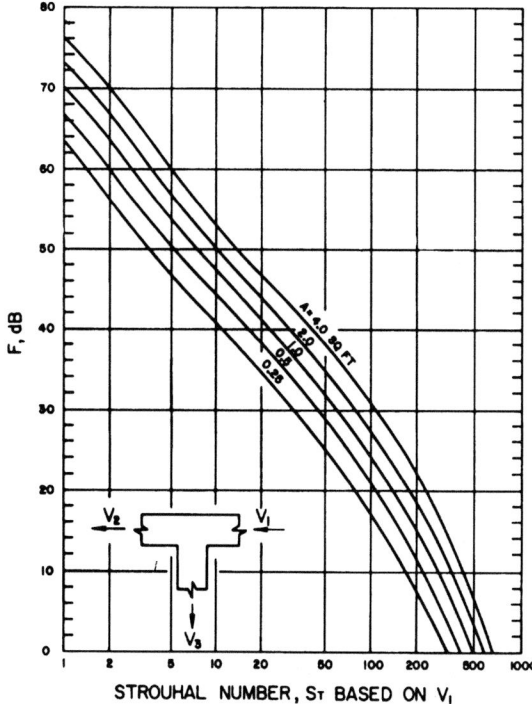

Fig 16-17. Spectrum function *F* for 90° branch take-offs

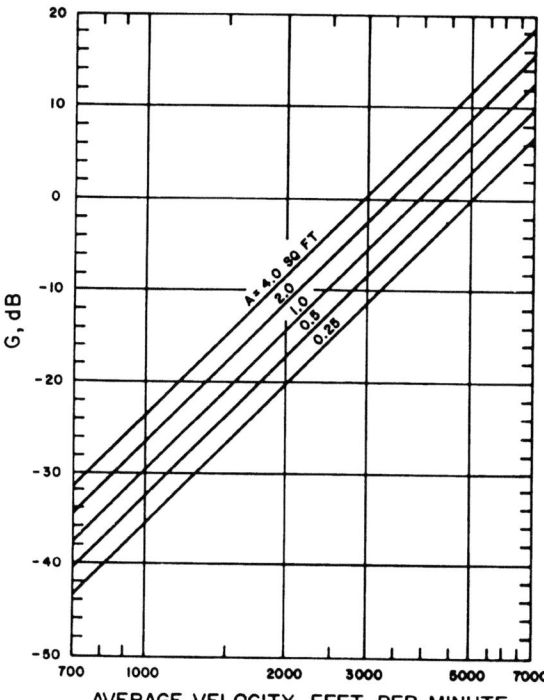

Fig 16-18. Velocity function *G* for 90° elbows

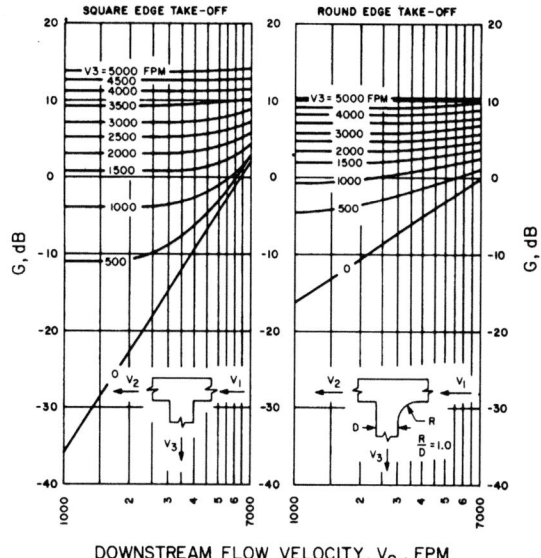

Fig 16-19. Velocity function *G* for 90° branch take-offs

Example 5: A 36 by 24 inch rectangular 90° elbow without turning vanes handles a flow rate of 8000 cfm air. Determine the sound power generated by the flow in this elbow.

Solution: Step 1. The equivalent duct diameter *D* is

$$D = \left(\frac{4}{\pi} \times 24 \times 36\right)^{\frac{1}{2}} = 33.2$$

Average velocity of the duct is

$$V_{avg} = \frac{Q}{A}$$

$$= \frac{8000}{2 \times 3} = 1333 \text{ fpm}$$

Using Equation (30), the Strouhal number is computed for each octave band. Equation (30) becomes

$$S_t = \frac{5D}{V}f = 0.125f$$

These values are computed and listed in separate rows in Table 16-23.

Step 2. The spectrum function F is obtained from Fig. 16-15 for square cross-section, 90° elbows without turning vanes. This condition is closer to the actual situation than Fig. 16-16. The values for the spectrum function are given in row 2 of Table 16-23.

Step 3. The values for the velocity function *G* are obtained from Fig. 16-18 for an average velocity of 1333 fpm and a cross-sectional area of 6 square feet. These values are given in row 3 of Table 16-23.

Step 4. The values for the octave bandwidth function *H* are obtained from Table 16-23 and listed in row 4 of Table 16-23.

Step 5. The sound power levels for the various octave bands are obtained by summing $F + G + H$, which is the sum of rows 2, 3, and 4 of Table 16-23. The result is given in row 5. The values are the sound power levels, in decibels, generated by the air flow in the elbow.

Table 16-23. Sound Power Level Generated by a 90° Elbow, from

Row No	Calculations	Octave Band Center Frequency, Hz							
		63	125	250	500	1000	2000	4000	8000
1	S_t [Equation (30)]	7.8	15.5	31	62	125	250	500	1000
2	Spectrum function F from Fig. 16-15	48	35	33	30	26	20	10	0
3	Velocity function G from Fig. 16-18	−17	−17	−17	−17	−17	−17	−17	−17
4	Octave band width function H Table 16-24	16	19	22	25	28	31	34	37
5	Sound power levels dB $F + G + H$ sum of rows 2, 3, and 4	47	37	38	38	37	34	27	20

Table 16-24. Octave Bandwidth Correction Function H

Octave Band Center Frequency, Hz	H, dB	Octave Band Center Frequency, Hz	H, dB
63	16	1000	28
125	19	2000	31
250	22	4000	34
500	25	8000	37

Example 6: A 36 by 24 inch air duct has a square edged 90° branch take-off. The branch take-off is 18 by 12 inches. If the upstream main duct flow rate is 8000 cfm and the branch flow rate is 1000 cfm, determine the octave band sound power level downstream of the take-off in the main duct and downstream of the branch take off.

Solution: Step 1. Compute the main air duct equivalent diameter

$$D = \left(\frac{4}{\pi} \times 24 \times 36\right)^{\frac{1}{2}} = 33.2 \text{ in.}$$

Step 2. Compute the Strouhal number for each octave band. First, the upstream average velocity is computed from

$$V_{\text{avg}} = \frac{Q}{A}$$

The Strouhal number is computed for each octave band center frequency from Equation (30):

$$S_t = \frac{5D}{V}f = 0.125f$$

These values are recorded in row 1 of Table 16-25.

Step 3. Determine the spectrum function F from Fig. 16-17 for the branch take-off using the area $A = 12 \times 18/144 = 15.5$ ft^2. The values are recorded in row 2 of Table 16-25.

Step 4. Determine the velocity function G from the left hand plot in Fig. 16-19. The downstream main duct velocity is $7000/6 = 1167$ fpm and the branch take-off velocity is $1000/1.5 = 667$ fpm. The value for G is found to be −8 dB and is recorded in row 3 of Table 16-25.

Step 5. Values for the octave band width correction function H are obtained from Table 16-24 and are recorded in row 4 of Table 16-25.

Step 6. The octave band sound power levels L_W (dB) are obtained by $F + G + H$; the sum of row 2, row 3, and row 4 of Table 16-25. These values are given in row 5 of the table.

Step 7. The values for the spectrum function F for the main duct are obtained from Fig. 10 using $A = 6$ ft^2. The curves in the figure are extrapolated to give values for 6 ft^2 by drawing a line parallel to the 4 ft^2 line at a distance one half of the spacing of the lines in the figure. The values for F are given in row 6 of Table 16-25.

Step 8. The values for the velocity function G and the correction function H are the same as given in rows 3 and 4, respectively, in Table 16-25.

Step 9. The sound power levels L_W (dB) are obtained by the sum of F (main duct) $+ G + H$, which is the sum of rows 3, 4, and 6. The resulting sound power level generated in the main duct is given in row 7.

Table 16-25. Sound Power Level Generated by a Branch Take-off

Row No.	Calculations	Octave Band Center Frequency, Hz							
		63	125	250	500	1000	2000	4000	8000
1	Strouhal number S_t Equation (30)	78	15.5	31	62	125	250	500	1000
2	Spectrum function F for branch, Fig. 16-15	51	45	38	31	23	13	2	...
3	Velocity function G Fig. 16-18	−8	−8	−8	−8	−8	−8	−8	−8
4	Octave band width correction function H Table 16-24	16	19	22	25	28	31	34	37
5	Sound power level L_W db for the branch. Sum values in rows 2, 3, and 4.	59	56	52	48	43	36	28	29
6	Spectrum function F for main duct, Fig. 16-15	57	51	44	37	30	20	9	...
7	Sound power level L_W dB for the main duct. Sum values in rows 3, 4, and 6.	65	62	58	54	50	43	35	29

The values in rows 5 and 7 of Table 16-25 are the octave band sound power levels, in decibels, generated by the air flow in the take-off and main branch, respectively.

Flow Noise Generation of Silencers.—Duct silencers are intended to attenuate sound that has been generated upstream of the silencer unit. In order to obtain maximum sound attenuation in a silencer, the flow is disturbed by baffles, liners, splitters, etc. Air flow over the sound attenuation surfaces can act as a flow noise generator; therefore, a silencer can itself be a generator of sound power. The self-generated sound power of a silencer with a center body can be predicted from Equation (31):

$$L_W = -145 + 55\log_{10}V + 10\log_{10}A$$
$$-45\log_{10}\frac{P}{100} - 20\log_{10}\frac{460+T}{530} \quad (31)$$

Equation (31) predicts the same sound power level for all octave bands, which agrees with experiments. This equation may be treated as a method of predicting the maximum sound power level of silencers without regard to flow streamlining the unit. Streamlining the baffles in the silencer may also reduce the self-generated sound power by as much as 10 dB.

When selecting silencers one should determine if the source attenuation provided by the supplier includes the self noise of the silencer. If the silencer is tested under no flow conditions, or if the tests are made at a flow velocity different from the application, Equation (31) may be used to estimate the effects of flow on the silencers acoustic performance.

Example 7: Determine the sound power level generated by a triangular duct silencer in a 36 by 36 in. duct with a flow of 8600 cfm of 75°F air. The silencer has an open area of 80 percent.

Solution: Compute L_W from Equation (31) as follows:

Step 1: Determine the flow velocity in the silencer:

$$V = \frac{8600}{3 \times 3} = 956 \text{ fpm}$$

Calculate the term $55\log_{10}V$ from Equation (31):

$$55\log_{10}(956) = 55(2.98) = 164 \text{ dB}$$

Step 2. Compute $10\log_{10}A$, where $A = 9$ ft^2:

$$10\log_{10}(9) = 10(0.95) = 9.5 \text{ dB}$$

Step 3. Compute the term $-45\log_{10}P/100$, where $P = 80\%$

$$-45\log_{10}\left(\frac{80}{100}\right) = -45\log_{10}(8) = -45(-0.097)$$
$$= 4.4 \text{ dB}$$

Step 4. Compute the term $-20\log_{10}460 + T/530$
Where $T = 75$ °F

$$-20\log_{10}\left(\frac{460+75}{530}\right) = -20\log_{10}(1.01)$$
$$= -0.08 \text{ dB}$$

Step 5. Compute the sound power level generated by the air flow in the silencer from the above calculated values.

$$L_W = -145 + 164 + 9.5 + 4.4 - 0.08$$
$$= 33 \text{ dB}$$

The value of $L_W = 33$ dB is the sound power level generated by the air flow through the silencer for each octave band.

Sound Transmission Through Duct Walls.—In some instances the sound produced inside a duct system is transmitted through the walls of the duct into a building space causing a noise problem. To correct this condition. the sound transmission loss of the duct walls must be considered. For a rectangular duct cross section the flat surfaces are treated as flat plates and the transmission loss is determined from Equation (32):

$$TL = 20\log_{10}W + 20\log_{10}f - 33 \text{ dB} \quad (32)$$

where TL = duct wall transmission loss, dB;
W = weight lb/ft^2 of the duct wall panel; and
f = frequency, Hz.

Transmission loss TL is computed for the octave band center frequencies and used to determine the reduction in sound power level from the inside to the outside of the duct.

Ducts with round cross-sections behave differently from rectangular cross-sections at low frequencies because of the added stiffness due to curvature. At high frequencies, a round duct has transmission loss much like a rectangular duct wall. The frequency separating the low from the high frequency region for a circular cross section duct is called the ring frequency f_r, given by:

$$f_r = \frac{c_l}{\pi D} \text{ Hz} \quad (33)$$

where f_r = ring frequency, Hz
c_l = speed of sound in duct wall material, m/s (5100 m/s for sheet metal)
D = nominal duct diameter, m.

In the frequency region, at the ring frequency or below it, the transmission loss is determined by first finding the nominal transmission loss from:

$$TL_{nominal} = 10\log_{10}\left(\frac{t}{D}\right) + 50 \quad (\text{dB}) \quad (34)$$

where $TL_{nominal}$ = nominal transmission loss at or below the ring frequency for a circular duct, dB
t = wall thickness of the duct, m; and
D = nominal duct diameter, m.

The nominal transmission loss is corrected for frequencies equal to and below the ring frequency by the values given in Table 16-27. For frequencies greater than the ring frequency for a circular duct, the transmission loss is computed from Equation (32).

Example 8: Compute the transmission loss for an 18 inch diameter sheet metal duct made from 15 gage material 0.0673 inch thick.

Solution: Step 1. Compute the ring frequency for the duct. The duct diameter is 18 inches or 0.4572 meter. The speed of sound c_l in the duct wall material is 5100 m/s, therefore:

$$f_r = \frac{c_l}{\pi D} = \frac{5100}{\pi \times 0.4572} = 3550 \text{ Hz}$$

From Table 16-8, this frequency is within the octave band with center frequency of 4000 Hz. This means the circular duct analysis applies for 4000 Hz and below, and the flat plate analysis applies above 4000 Hz.

Step 2. Compute the nominal transmission loss of the duct from Equation (34)

$$\frac{t}{D} = \frac{0.0673}{18} = 0.0037$$

This value is entered in row 1, Table 16-26, for every octave band of 4000 Hz or less.

Step 3. Enter the correction function from Table 16-27 for all octave bands starting with 1 f_r equal to 4000 Hz, ½ f_r equal to 2000 Hz, etc. These corrections are given in row 2.

Step 4. Determine the transmission loss for the duct. For 4000 Hz and below add the values in row 1, and row 2 of Table 16-26. For the 8000 Hz octave band, which is above the ring frequency, use Equation (32) to compute the transmission loss for standard 15 gage sheet metal:

$$TL = 20\log_{10} W + 20\log_{10} f - 33$$
$$= 20\log_{10} 2.8125 + 20\log_{10} 8000 - 33$$
$$= 54.1 \text{ dB}$$

This value is given in row 3 for the 8000 Hz octave band.

The transmission loss values given by row 3 of Table 16-26 can be used to determine the sound power levels outside a duct if the sound power levels in octave bands inside the duct are known, simply by subtracting the duct transmission loss. The sound pressure levels in a space can thus be computed using Equation (21) with the sound power levels L_W outside the duct as the source in the space.

Table 16-26. Calculation of Duct Wall Transmission Loss for Example 8

Calculations	Octave Band Center Frequency, Hz							
	63	125	250	500	1000	2000	4000	8000
1. Nominal transmission loss, dB Equation (34)	25.7	25.7	25.7	25.7	25.7	25.7	25.7	…
2. Correction factors from Table 16-27, dB	−7	−6	−5	−4	−3	−2	−4	…
3. Transmission loss for the duct wall, dB	18.7	19.7	20.7	21.7	22.7	23.7	21.7	54.1

Table 16-27. Corrections Factor for Transmission Loss

Frequency	$\frac{1}{64}f_r$	$\frac{1}{32}f_r$	$\frac{1}{16}f_r$	$\frac{1}{8}f_r$	$\frac{1}{4}f_r$	$\frac{1}{2}f_r$	$1 f_r$
Correction, dB	−7	−6	−5	−4	−3	−2	−4

Calculation of Sound Levels in Ducted Systems.—

Determination of sound levels from ducted systems requires the use of all previous material presented in this section. In the following example the procedure for predicting room space sound levels from a ducted air supply system will be illustrated.

Example 9: Compute the sound pressure levels, in octave bands for the listener location for the system shown in Fig. 16-20. The supply fan is of the radial blade type with 16 blades operating at 2 inches of water pressure drop and 500 rpm to supply 10,000 cfm of air.

Solution: Step1. The first step is to obtain octave band sound power levels for the fan outlet from the manufacturer. If these values are not available they may be estimated by using the procedure of Example 2. The sound power level for the fan is given in row 1 of Table 16-28.

Step 2. Determine the attenuation from the fan to the first branch take-off. The attenuation in dB/ft is obtained from Table 16-17, times the length (15 ft) gives the attenuation values in row 2 of Table 16-28.

Step 3. Determine the attenuation of the branch take off. The take-off has an area of 24 ×18 = 432 in² and the continuing duct has an area of 24 × 30 = 720 in². The percent area of the take off to the total area of duct after the take-off is 432/1152 = 40% (rounded). From Table 16-15 the reduction at the take-off is 4 dB as entered in row 3 of Table 16-28.

Step 4. Compute the sound power levels at location 3. This is done by adding rows 1, 2, and 3 with the result given in row 4.

Step 5. The sound power level of the sound generated by air flow through the first branch take-off must be computed. The procedure is identical to that of Example 6. For this example the resulting sound power levels were computed to be: 73, 69, 65, 64, 57, 53, 48, and 37 dB for the octave bands from 63 Hz to 8000 Hz. In general, these values must be combined logarithmically with the values given in row 4 to obtain the total sound power levels at location 3 which are due to the fan sound power transmitted through the duct systems, plus the air flow take off generated noise at the branch. In this example, the air flow generated sound power is 10 dB (or greater) less than the sound power levels given in row 4, therefore, by use of Equation (15), the sound power level of the combined sources is equal to the larger values which are given by row 4. Thus the sound power level of the branch takeoff can be neglected in this example." However, this may not always be the case in general.

Step 6: Compute the attenuation from Step 3 to Step 4 as shown in row 5.

Step 7: Obtain the attenuation of the square elbow at point 4 from Table 16-19. Use values for a 20 in duct width with no lining and record these values in row 6.

Step 8: Determine the sound power location at point 5 by adding values from rows 4, 5, and 6. This result is given in row 7.

Step 9: Calculate the sound power level of the air flow noise generated by the square elbow at point 4. This is done by a similar calculation to that shown in Example 5. For this example the resulting sound power levels are less by 10 dB (or more) than the sound power from the fan as given in row 7 and will not add to the levels in row 7.

Step 10: Compute the attenuation from point 5 to point 6 as shown in row 8. The attenuation values in dB/ft are obtained from Table 16-17.

Step 11: Obtain attenuation of the branch take off at point 7 from Table 16-15. The area of the 6 × 24 duct=144 in^2; the 24 ×18 duct = 432 in^2. Therefore, the percent area of the take-off to the total area after the branch take-off is 144/576 = 25%. From Table 16-15 for 25%, interpolate from the table to obtain 6 dB attenuation, as given in row 9.

Step 12: Calculate the sound power level at location 7 by adding the values in rows 7, 8, and 9.

Step 13. The sound power level for flow generated is due to flow at the branch take-off at location 7. For this example the sound power levels will be 10 dB (or more) below the levels given by row 10 and will not add to the levels in row 10.

Step 14. Determine the attenuation from point 7 to 8. Use the attenuation values in dB/ft for a small duct from Table 16-17. The attenuation is given in row 11.

Step 15. Obtain the open end reflection attenuation for the duct at location 8 from Table 16-22. Use the 100 in^2 duct size, values from Table 16-22, as listed in row 12.

Step 16. The sound power level at the diffuser at point 9 is calculated by adding values in rows 10, 11, and 12, with the result in row 13.

At location 9 the sound power level generated by air flow through the diffuser must be obtained from manufacturer data for the required air flow. The sound power levels in decibels must be combined logarithmically with the sound power levels in row 13 using Equation (8). For this example it will be assumed that the sound power levels due to air flow through the diffuser are less than 40 decibels for every octave band, therefore the air flow noise can be neglected compared to the levels given in row 13.

The sound power levels for the second diffuser located at point 11 will be computed by continuing the calculations as follows:

Step 17: The attenuation from point 6 to 10 is obtained from Table 16-15 using the same areas as were computed in Step 11. The area of the continuing duct at point 10 is 576 in^2 the area of duct at point 7 is 144 in^2. Therefore the percent area at point 10 of the total continuing duct after the take-off (576 + 144) in^2 is 576/720 = 80%. From Table 16-15 the attenuation is 1 dB, as shown in row 14.

Step 18. Compute the attenuation from point 10 to point 11 as shown in row 15.

Step 19. Obtain the attenuation of the branch take-off at point 12 from Table 16-15; with the percent area of the take off equal to 25% resulting in an attenuation of 6 dB by interpolation the value is given in row 16.

Step 20. Compute the attenuation from point 12 to 13 as shown in row 17.

Step 21. Obtain the end reflection loss from Table 16-22 for the 100 in^2 duct size. These values are listed in row 18.

Step 22. The octave band sound power levels at location point 14 are obtained by summation of values in rows 7, 8, 14, 15, 16, 17, and 18 with the result in row 19.

The sound power level for the air flow noise for the diffuser at location point 14 must be determined and added logarithmically to the levels in row 19. If this diffuser is identical to the one at location point 9, the contribution to the sound power levels of row 19 can be neglected.

Note in the example that the resulting sound power levels at the two diffusers are entirely due to the fan generated noise, which is attenuated through the duct system; air flow generated noise is negligible. This may not always be true in a ducted system. Therefore the flow generated noise should always be computed and compared to the fan noise at locations of interest.

To compute the sound pressure levels in octave bands at the listener location in Fig. 16-19 Equation (21) must be used for each of the two sources, which are the two diffusers (locations point 9 and 14), since the sound power level is not the same for each source. These calculations are described below and shown in Table 16-28.

C) Step 23. Determine the correction values to convert sound power level L_W at the source to sound pressure level L_W at the listener location, from Equation (21):

$$L_P = L_W + 10\log_{10}\left[\frac{Q}{4\pi r_1^2} + \frac{4}{R}\right] + 10$$

D) For this example room constant R must be determined for the space as illustrated by Example No. 1. For this case the same values for room constant R will be used as in Example 1. These values are listed in row 3 of Table 16-30. Note that the value for R for the 63Hz band was computed as in Example 1, The value of Q is determined from Fig. 16-1, to be 2 for a source near the ceiling and $r_1 = 14$ ft. Therefore

$$L_P = L_W + 10\log_{10}\left[\frac{2}{4\pi(14)^2} + \frac{4}{R}\right] + 10$$

E) The correction term for the 63-Hz band becomes

$$\text{correction} = 10\log\left[0.0008 + \frac{4}{243}\right] + 10$$

$$= -7.6 \text{ dB}$$

F) This value is given in row 4 of Table 16-30 and subsequent values are computed in row 4 in a similar manner.

G) Step 24. Determine the correction values for the source at location point 14:

$$L_P = L_W + 10\log_{10}\left[\frac{2}{4\pi(12)^2} + \frac{4}{R}\right] + 10$$

$$\text{correction} = 10 \times \log_{10}\left[0.0011 + \frac{4}{R}\right] + 10 \text{ dB}$$

These values are given in row 5 of Table 16-30.

Step 25. Calculate the sound pressure level at the listener location due to source at point 9. This is done by adding rows 1 and 4 with the results in row 6.

Step 26. Calculate the listener location sound pressure level due to source at point 14 by adding values in rows 2 and 5. The results are in row 7.

Step 27. Compute the total sound pressure level at the listener location by combining logarithmically the values in rows 6 and 7, using Equation (17). For the 63 Hz band:

$$L_P = 49.6 \text{ dB} + 46.8 \text{dB}$$

$$= 10\log_{10}(10^{4.96} + 10^{4.68})$$

$$= 10\log_{10}(91201 + 47863)$$

$$= 51 \text{ dB}$$

The same procedure is used to obtain the remaining values in row 8 of Table 16-28. The usual procedure is to perform calculations rounded to the nearest one-tenth decibel and then round the final sound pressure levels to the nearest decibel, as in row 8.

If the sound pressure levels from row 8, Table 16-30 are plotted on the Noise Criteria curves, for example as in Fig. 16-11, the resulting value will be NC-54 as determined by the noise criteria, which has the highest penetration by the plotted sound pressure levels. Under the heading of offices an NC-34 is unacceptable for general open offices. An NC-54 is acceptable for tabulation and computation rooms where office machines are located. In order to reduce the sound pressure levels resulting from the duct system in this example, additional noise attenuation must be provided in the system. To achieve an NC criteria below NC-50 a section of lined duct will be sufficient. To calculate lined duct attenuation, see Example 2. If either the duct from point 1 to point 2 or the duct from point 3 to point 4 in Fig. 16-20 were lined with a 1-in. thickness of glass fiber, the resulting level at the listener location would be below NC-50.

Table 16-28.

Table 16-29. Calculation of Ducted System Sound Power levels for Example 9

Calculation	Octave Band Center Frequency, Hz							
	63	125	250	500	1000	2000	4000	8000
1. Fan sound power level from manufacturer, dB	91	96	86	86	81	76	73	72
2. Attenuation from point 1 to point 2 dB/ft =	0.20	0.20	0.10	0.05	0.05	0.05	0.05	0.05
Attenuation, dB =	−3.0	−3.0	−1.5	−.7	−.7	−.7	−.7	−.7
3. Attenuation from point 2 to point 3, dB	−4.0	−4.0	−4.0	−4.0	−4.0	−4.0	−4.0	−4.0
4. Sound power level at point 3, dB	84.0	89.0	80.5	81.3	76.3	71.3	68.3	67.3
5. Attenuation from point 3 to point 4 dB/ft =	0.2	0.2	0.1	0.05	0.05	0.05	0.05	0.05
Attenuation, dB =	−5.2	−5.2	−2.6	−1.3	−1.3	−1.3	−1.3	−1.3
6. Attenation of elbowat point 4, dB	−0.0	−1.0	−5.0	−7.0	−5.0	−3.0	−3.0	−3.0
7. Sound power level at point 5, row 4 plus rows 5 and 6	78.8	82.8	72.9	73.0	70.0	67.0	64.0	63.0
8. Attenuation from point 5 to point 6 dB/ft =	0.2	0.2	0.1	0.05	0.05	0.05	0.05	0.05
Attenuation, dB =	−1.6	−1.6	−0.8	−0.4	−0.4	−0.4	−0.4	−0.4
9. Attenuation of take off at point 7, dB	−6.0	−6.0	−6.0	−6.0	−6.0	−6.0	−6.0	−6.0
10. Sound power level at point 7, dB row 7 plus rows 8 and 9	71.2	75.2	66.1	66.6	63.6	60.6	57.6	56.6
11. Attenuation from point 7 to point 8 dB/ft^2 =	0.2	0.2	0.15	0.1	0.1	0.1	0.1	0.1
Attenuation, dB =	−2.0	−2.0	−1.5	−1.0	−1.0	−1.0	−1.0	−1.0
12. End reflection loss at point 8, dB	−12.0	−8.0	−4.0	−1.0	0.0	0.0	0.0	0.0

Table 16-29. *(Continued)* **Calculation of Ducted System Sound Power levels for Example 9**

Calculation	Octave Band Center Frequency, Hz							
	63	125	250	500	1000	2000	4000	8000
13. Sound power level at point 9, dB row 10 plus rows 11 and 12	57.2	65.2	60.6	64.6	62.6	59.6	56.6	55.6
14. Attenuation from point 6 to point 10, dB	−1.0	−1.0	−1.0	−1.0	−1.0	−1.0	−1.0	−1.0
15. Attenuation from point 10 to point 11, dB/ft	0.20	0.2	0.1	0.05	0.05	0.05	0.05	0.05
Attenuation, dB	−2.0	−2.0	−1.0	−0.5	−0.50	−0.5	−0.5	−0.5
16. Attenation from point 11 to point 12, dB	−6.0	−6.0	−6.0	−6.0	−6.0	−6.0	−6.0	−6.0
17. Attenuation from point 12 to point 13, dB	−2.0	−2.0	−1.5	−1.0	−1.0	−1.0	−1.0	−1.0
18. End reflection loss at point 13, dB	−12.0	−8.0	−4.0	−1.0	0.0	0.0	0.0	0.0
19, Sound power level at point 14 row 7 plus rows 8, 14, 15, 16, 17, and 18	54.2	62.2	58.6	63.1	61.1	58.1	55.1	54.1

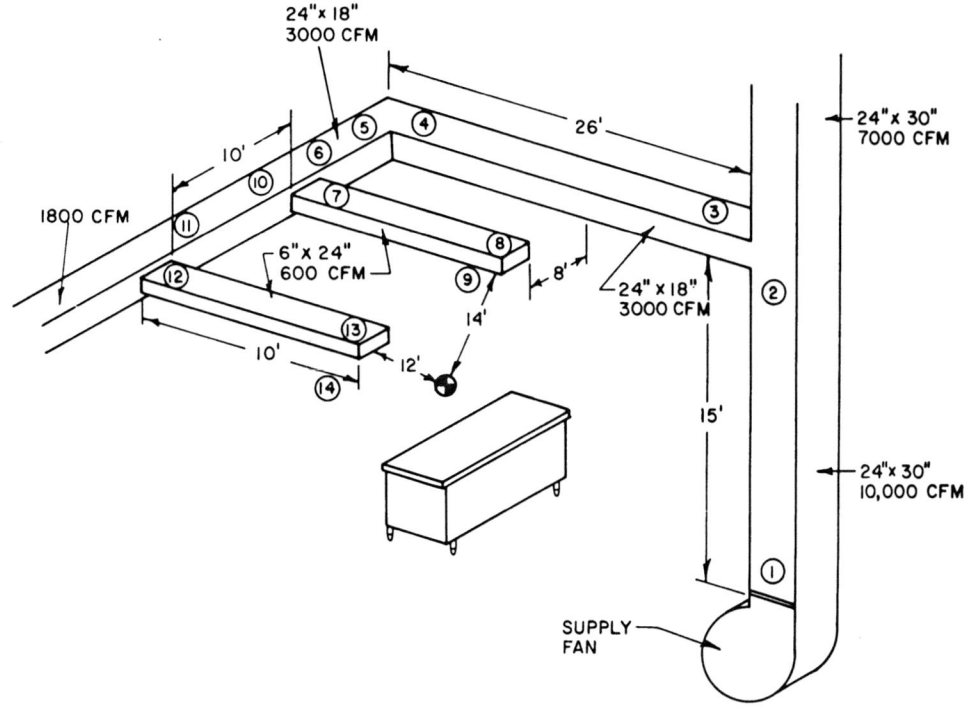

Fig 16-20. Ducted air supply system

Table 16-30. Computation of Sound Pressure for Example 9

Computation	Octave Band Center Frequency, Hz							
	63	125	250	500	1000	2000	4000	8000
1. Sound power level, dB, at point 9. From row 13 Table 16-26	57.2	65.2	60.6	64.6	62.6	59.6	56.6	55.6
2. Sound power level, dB, at point 14. From row 19 Table 16-26	54.3	62.2	58.6	63.1	61.1	58.1	55.1	54.1
3. Room constant R ft^2 for space	243	312	342	438	458	548	631	743
4. Correction for source at point 9, dB	−7.6	−8.6	−9.0	−10.0	−10.2	−10.9	−11.4	−12.1
5. Correction for source at point 14, dB	−7.8	−8.5	−8.9	−9.9	−10.1	−10.8	−11.3	−11.9
6. Sound pressure level due to source at point 9, dB, row 1 plus row 4	49.6	56.6	51.6	54.6	52.4	48.7	45.9	43.5
7. Sound pressure level due source at point 14, dB, row 2 plus row 5	46.8	53.7	49.7	53.2	51.0	47.3	43.8	42.2
8. Sound pressure level at listen er location, dB (rounded)	51	58	54	57	55	51	48	46

Control of Cooling Tower Noise

Major sources of cooling tower noise are fan, water, motor, speed reducing gears or belt, and external sources.

Fan Noise.—Sound level produced by a given type of cooling tower is primarily a function of total horsepower of the fans. For induced draft towers with axial flow fans, sound power (Fig. 16-21) can be determined from

$$PWL = 95 + 10\log \text{ (fan hp dB) re } 10^{-12} \text{ (watt) (35)}$$

For forced draft centrifugal towers, sound power (Fig. 16-22) is

$$PWL = 84 + 10\log \text{ (fan hp dB) re } 10^{-12} \text{ (watt) (36)}$$

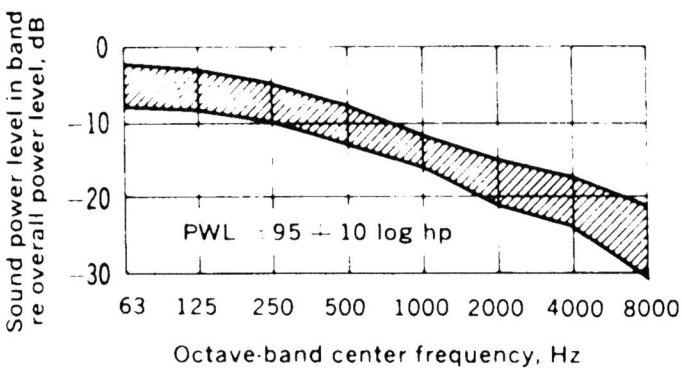

Fig 16-21. Sound spectrum for axial flow tower fans

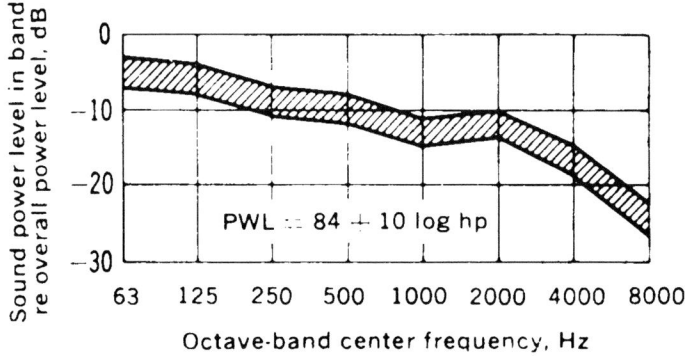

Fig 16-22. Sound spectrum for centrifugal flow tower fans

Sound power spectrums from Fig. 16-21 and 16-22 and Equations (35) and (36) can be converted by standard methods to average free field sound pressure levels at moderately large distance from the tower.

Sound pressure levels close to induced draft, axial flow towers at the fan discharge are

$$SPL = 105 + 10\log(\text{hp}) - 3 - 10\log A \qquad \text{(dB) (37)}$$

and at the air intake,

$$SPL = 105 + 10\log(\text{hp}) - 6 - 10\log A \qquad \text{(dB) (38)}$$

where A is area in ft^2 of the discharge and intake, respectively.

Even though the equations and curves are based on field tests performed on a limited number of cooling towers, they serve as valuable design aids in the formative stages of design or when no other data are available. These data can be supplemented before design is completed by actual rating data supplied by the cooling tower manufacturer.

Equations (35) and (36) indicate that, for a given tower type noise generation is a function of fan horsepower, and for a given horsepower, the forced draft centrifugal type is quieter than the axial flow induced draft type. Although, for a given duty, the centrifugal type requires more horsepower than the axial flow tower, it will be found that, for a given specific duty, the centrifugal type, despite its higher horsepower, is quieter than the axial flow induced draft rooting tower.

Air cooled condensers circulate a larger quantity of air per ton than cooling towers. Thus, it can be expected that, for a given cooling capacity, their fans will be noisier than those of cooling towers. Evaporative condensers handle lesser air quantities than cooling towers and, for a given cooling capacity, their fans can be expected to be quieter. This advantage is partially offset because the circulating pump, usually mounted directly adjacent to an evaporative condenser, generates additional noise.

Fan vibrations can be transmitted to the equipment casing or structure. They can be isolated by high deflection springs.

Water Noise.—The sound of water flowing through the tower and into the drain pan is of the intensity and general characteristics shown in Fig. 16-23. Airborne water noise will ordinarily be a factor only in the high frequency end of the spectrum since its level in the lower frequencies is usually below that of the cooling tower fan. Where the fan is operated at reduced speed in order to achieve lower fan sound levels, the water noise may become audible. The impact of the water will be transmitted as a moderate structure borne vibration from the tower into the building unless isolating pads are provided beneath the basin.

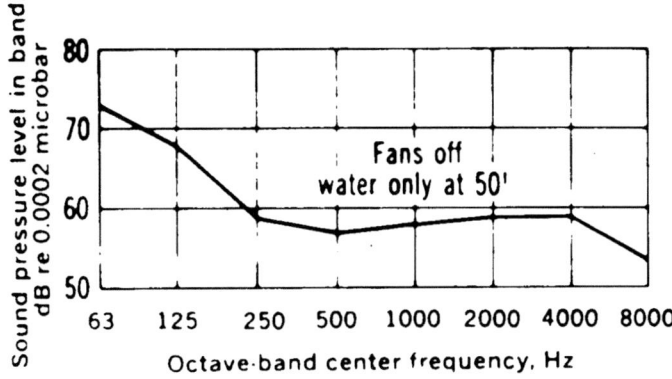

Fig 16-23. Tower water noise spectrum

Drive Components.—Fan cooled electric motors can be a source of disturbing sound when large quantities of air are circulated over the motor. Fig. 16-24 indicates the sound measured at a tower compared with the manufacturer's published data for the tower. The peak in the third

octave band was traced to the integral cooling fan for the 60 hp driving motor.

Noise from belt or gear drives is not ordinarily significant unless the drives are misaligned or damaged. The drives may be vibration generators and should be isolated with the fan and motor.

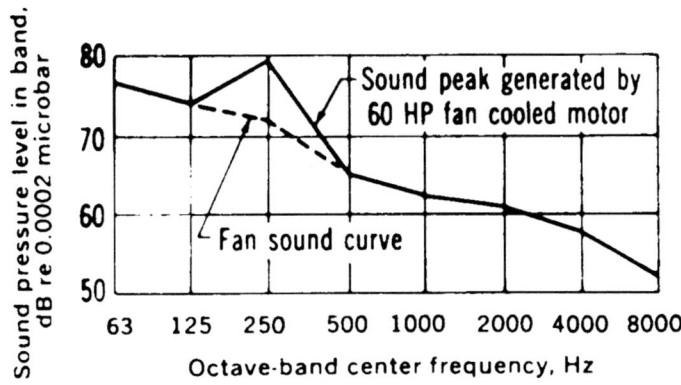

Fig 16-24. Tower water noise spectrum

External Noise Sources.—Both air cooled and evaporative condensers are directly connected to refrigeration compressors. Fig. 16-25 shows sound levels measured at

the side of an air cooled condenser located approximately 150 ft from the refrigeration compressor it serves.

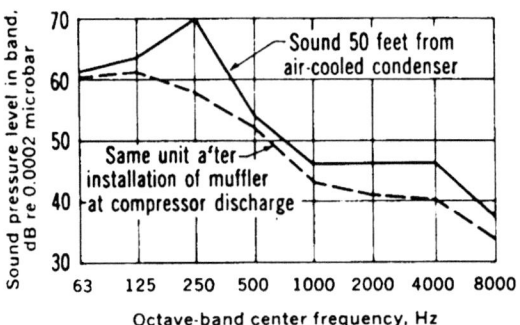

Fig 16-25. Tower water noise spectrum

The high intensity sound in the third octave band was identified as being produced by pulsations being carried along the refrigeration pipe with the hot gas, and radiating from the inlet manifold of the condenser. The lower curve shows measurements taken at the same position after the manufacturer's standard discharge muffler had been installed in the piping near the compressor, resulting in a significant reduction in the critical octave band.

Simila,r although usually more moderate, conditions can result from sound generated by condenser water pumps and transmitted through the water or pipe wall.

Configuration Factors.—Shape, size, and arrangements of major components all have a bearing on the sound characteristics of a tower. Fig. 16-26 shows adjustments to sound pressure levels that should be made for different cooling tower configurations of induced and forced draft fan towers.

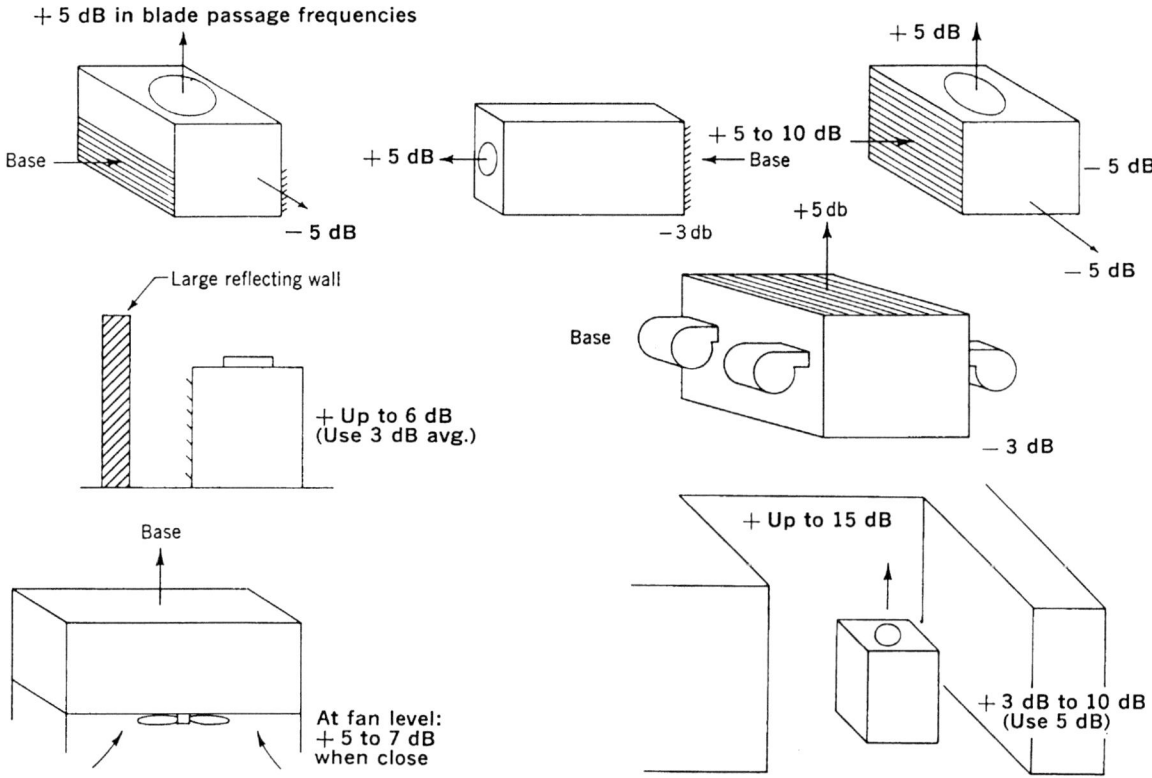

Fig 16-26. Effect of tower configuration and location on base sounds levels

It can be seen that for an axial flow induced draft type tower it is desirable to arrange the fan discharge so that it is not overlooked by windows or similar occupied areas and, if possible, to place the encased tower sides in a position where sound criteria are most critical.

Induced draft towers are constructed with the fan at the top, discharging vertically upward or, in the case of smaller units, at the sides, discharging horizontally. Air is drawn into louvers near the bottom or along the side of the tower casing. A higher intensity sound, especially at the blade passage frequencies, will be radiated from the fan discharge side of the tower than from either the louvered or encased sides. More sound will be radiated from sides containing louvered openings than from those that are completely encased.

Similar adjustments must be made for forced draft towers since these have fans located along the sides of the casing and have no inlet louvers. As such, they ordinarily produce the highest noise intensity over the top with lesser sound levels on the sides facing the fans and are quietest along the cased sides.

Location.—A cooling tower or condenser in an open field radiates sound in all directions. The far field sound levels previously noted are based on such a condition. Intensity of tower sound will be reduced as its distance from the observer increases.

If the equipment is located sufficiently close to a wall or if it is placed within a court so that large, massive surfaces receive the sound waves and reflect them, an observer located opposite the reflecting surfaces will hear higher sound intensities than he or she would if both listener and tower were located in a completely open area. For a single-wall surface the sound levels received by the observer will be increased as much as 6 dB with an average of approximately 3 dB, a good design value. Where the tower is located in a court, depending on how confined the enclosure, the sound levels can be expected to be anywhere from 3 dB to 10 dB, or more, higher than they would be in an open field; a 5 dB increase may be used for design. Baffle walls will reflect higher frequency sound if they are located close to the equipment if they are large relative to the equipment dimensions, and massive, and have no openings. Otherwise, they are useful primarily for their psychological effect in that they may conceal the sound source and confuse the observer.

Reducing Sound Generated.—A given tower operating with lowered fan speed and reduced horsepower will be quieter than when operating at rated speed. The noise reduction is often greater than would be expected due to reduction in horsepower. This indicates that some effects of air velocity on noise generation tend to build up (and reduce) faster than the horsepower. The most significant noise reductions take place in octave bands where sound peaks or pure tones are fan generated.

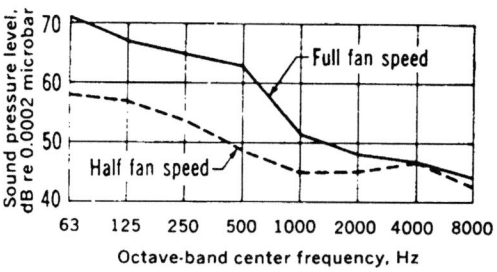

Fig 16-27. Effect of half speed operation

Half-Speed Operation.—When the cooling tower or condenser is located where chief complaints are likely to occur at night and where the nature of the cooling load is such that a reduction in capacity can be tolerated, operation of the cooling tower fans at part-speed during the night or other off-peak hours is an economical and very satisfactory method of achieving sizable reductions in tower sound levels and power consumption. Fig. 16-27 shows a representative axial flow induced cooling tower operated at both normal and half-speed. Power is reduced by a factor of 8 and average noise reduction is almost 12 dB. Significantly, the greatest noise reduction is in the octave band containing the blade passage frequency where sound level peaks often occur. Fan operation should be kept constant at the low level, since changes in sound intensity, due to cycling, are often more disturbing than constant higher sound levels.

Oversizing of the Tower.—If conditions are critical and if maximum capacity must be maintained at all hours the cooling tower may be oversized to permit a lower fan horsepower. The degree of oversizing determines sound reduction achieved. Most towers, when operated at half-speed, produce approximately 65% of capacity at full fan speed. Therefore, to obtain a noise reduction of as much as 12 dB, a 50% larger tower should be utilized.

Changing Leaving Conditions.—The most critical heat transfer condition a cooling tower must satisfy is the approach of the leaving water temperature to the design wet bulb. It is common for designers to require this difference to be as little as 7°F. If all other conditions remain the same, a standard 7°F approach tower selection is made and then the fans are slowed down to permit a wider approach to the wet bulb temperature, reduced sound levels will result. Fig. 16-28 shows the sound level for the base selection and for that of a different wet bulb approach.

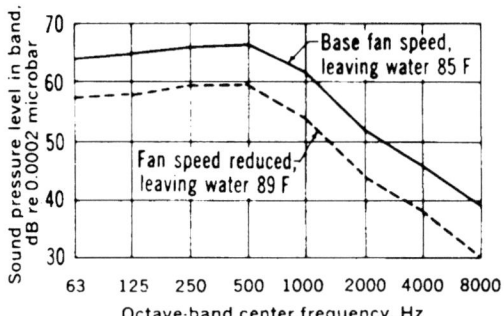

Fig 16-28. Effect of changing leaving water conditions on tower sound level

Operating the refrigeration plant with higher temperature condenser water will result in a reduced capacity of the refrigeration equipment. The effect of condenser water temperatures on capacity is dependent on the type of equipment used.Fig. 16-29 indicates that small capacity reductions result by raising inlet condenser water temperature for reciprocating and centrifugal electric compression units, but that sizable reductions in capacity result for absorption equipment.

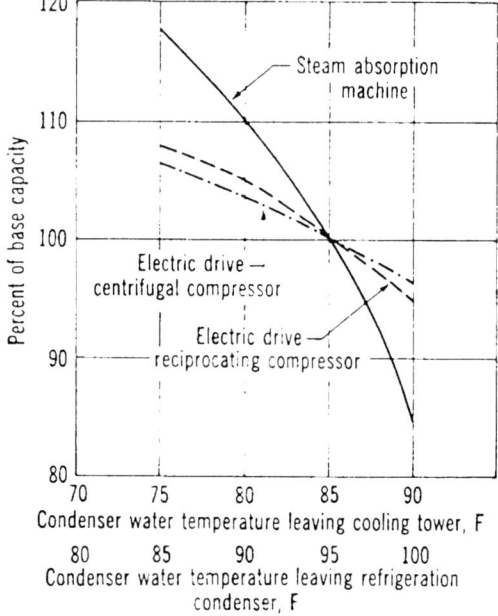

Fig 16-29. Effect of refrigeration system with changes in condensing temperatures

Sound Absorbers.—External sound absorbers applied to cooling tower inlets and discharge reduce the sound radiated from the towers. It is well to attempt an installation that will be satisfactory from a sound standpoint without need for this equipment, but if necessary, to make provision for additional attenuation that may be required. In existing installations where modifications to the tower are not practical or where a deficiency between the

desired and the actual sound level exists after modifications are made, sound absorbers can be successfully applied. Sound absorber sound ratings and their effect on equipment performance are generally available from the various manufacturers.

Obtaining Desired Sound Levels.—In order to insure a satisfactory installation, the sound generated by a cooling tower or remote condenser should be specified as an important performance factor.

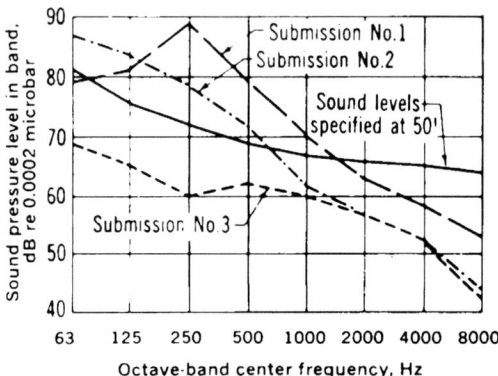

Fig 16-30. Manufacturers cooling tower submissions to meet sound level specifications

Required sound levels in each frequency band a given distance from the unit can be set forth after evaluating the characteristics of the area, the location of the tower and the sound characteristics of the available equipment. The sound performance can be confirmed either by manufacturers certified data or by performing tests at the manufacturers plant before shipping. See Fig. 16-30

Acoustical Problems in High Velocity Air Distribution

With a knowledge only of the noise spectrum generated by various air moving devices and the attenuating factors of duct systems, a low velocity air distribution system for air conditioning can be designed with reasonable assurance that the end environment for the spaces served will be as predicted.

Not so with high velocity systems, where excessive system noise is often generated within the distribution system itself and does not originate at the fan. System generated noise is the most costly to rectify.

System Noise Falls into Two Categories.—The first is *fan noise*, which is either totally or primarily generated by the air moving device (the acoustical designer of low-velocity, conventional fan duct systems is primarily concerned with the attenuation of fan noise).

The second is distribution system generated noise (*commonly called regenerated noise*), which is other than fan noise and is introduced into the duct system by the turbulent energy of the air stream in either the distributing duct system or terminal devices.

The commonly used term regenerated noise is a little misleading in that it implies that it is fan noise that was generated previously and then reintroduced into the system.The acoustical designer of high velocity systems must consider both fan noise and distribution system generated noise.

Distribution system generated noise is more commonly found in, though not restricted to, high velocity systems. It is caused by the turbulent pattern of the air stream, particularly at fittings generated by air piling up within the duct, which tends to excite the duct panel. Where air pile-up or turbulence at a duct fitting or fire damper occurs, the following conditions have been found:

1) The higher the velocity across a poorly designed duct fitting, the greater the turbulent energy of the air stream acting against the duct panel.

2) The higher the static pressure acting on the duct panel, the greater the resistance of the duct panel to excitation by the turbulent energy of the air stream.

3) The higher the spring rate or stiffness of the duct fitting panel in the area of the air stream turbulence the greater the resistance to panel excitation. Curved panel faces tend to provide more stable panel conditions and greatly increase the panels resistance to diaphragming due to turbulence of the air stream.

4) The greater the obstruction to the air stream within the duct, the greater is the air pile up and turbulent energy of the air stream.

5) The larger an insufficiently braced and supported duct panel, the lower is the frequency, when it occurs, of distribution system generated noise.

6) The larger the duct panel, the more critical is the (a) velocity at the duct fitting, (b) design of the fitting (c) construction of the duct panel, and the more complex is the aerodynamics situation at the fitting.

When distribution system generated noise occurs, the resulting transmitted noise is generally characterized by a predominantly low frequency quality. These low frequency noise levels of high intensity are normally radiated as airborne noise through the duct walls and panels of terminal devices in the area where the generation of noise occurs, and transmitted through the distribution system and terminal devices as air- and structure-borne noise.

The curves of Fig. 16-31 and 16-32 represent field measured octave band analyses of distribution system generated noise.

Quality of distribution system generated noise is dependent on size and type duct construction, type of fittings, and type of terminal devices used. Predominantly low frequency noise, often below 31.5 cycles per second (Hz), is transmitted from large, insufficiently braced, rectangular ducts, where noise generation occurs. As duct size decreases and panel stiffness increases, higher frequency noise (either first/second band) is transmitted from noise generating ducts and/or fittings.

Generally, present day damping compounds, applied either internally, externally, or to both surfaces of diaphragming duct that is generating noise due to a turbulent air stream, have been found to have little or no effect on the diaphragming action of the duct panel or the resulting noise transmitted. Unfortunately, acoustical lining and/or factory-built sound traps are also relatively ineffective in attenuating low frequency noise.

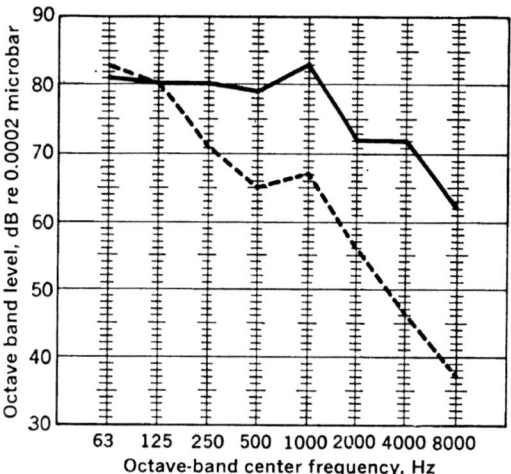

— Octave band sound pressure levels as measured within mechanical equipment space.

---- Octave band sound pressure levels as measured directly under shaft take-off, three floors removed from mechanical equipment space.

Fig 16-31. Noise band in first octave band is greater in tenant space

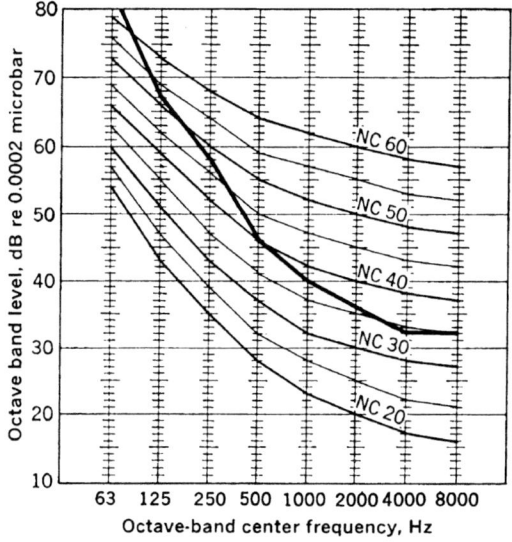

Fig 16-32. Typical curve of high velocity air distribution system generated noise

Corrective measures aimed at distribution system generated noise usually must involve modification of the duct fittings and/or special sound barrier construction to prevent or reduce transmitted noise through ceiling construction. In cases of noise generated by terminal devices, such as dual duct mixing units on perimeter walls, reduction of radiated noise from the terminal device and the adjacent high pressure ductwork may be achieved by special enclosures.

Following are recommendations for acoustical considerations in design and layout of high velocity systems. These recommendations are based primarily on empirical data and field experience. It is hoped that research in the respective areas will soon minimize reliance on empirical information and reduce all design steps to more rational terms.

Air Handling Apparatus Rooms.—Always select fan equipment for operation at the point of maximum static efficiency. This will prove also to be the optimal point acoustically. For quietest fan operation, it is important that not too large size fan equipment be selected. The design engineer, by selecting a smaller fan operating at higher speed, can attain the same air flow rate and static pressure and move the point of operation over to the right on the fan performance curve where there is assurance of staying in the normal operating range despite small changes in system resistance.

Location of fan equipment within casings should provide sufficient clearance between fan inlets and casing walls. Orientation of the fan with respect to fresh intake air should be such as to provide an approximately balanced air flow to each fan inlet with the best aerodynamic flow conditions to the fan inlets.

In push-through apparatus rooms for single duct systems, it is important to avoid sudden expansion (greater than 15° included angle) directly at the fan discharge. This condition can set up turbulence, noise, and vibration in the sheet metal casings. The method of discharge with respect to orientation of the connecting supply duct immediately downstream of the fan discharge should be in accordance with the fan manufacturer,s recommendations.

Unfortunately, on blow-through apparatus rooms the above conditions cannot be met because of the obvious space conditions. The turbulence created and the high pressures existing within the casing necessitate special casing construction. This aspect is discussed below.

A compromise of fan quality will always prove to be expensive and will result in a substandard installation.

Selection of Fan Isolation Bases.—Fan and driving motor base should be integral and rigid, without flexure caused by belt tension or torque applied.

Base should be sufficiently rigid to maintain belt centers at all times. Separate fan and motor bases or bases inadequately stiffened will result in maintenance problems and vibration/noise transmission.

Mountings and bases should be designed to accept the dynamic thrust introduced by high fan discharge static pressures.

All isolation elements should be stable, unrestrained (without external snubbers) and must provide adequate spring rate to properly isolate the lowest forcing frequency.

Where large items of fan equipment are supported on lightweight slabs, spring rates of the supporting mountings must be substantially reduced to compensate for the resiliency and the mass of the floor slab.

Apparatus Casings.—Inadequately stiffened apparatus casings generate low frequency noise due to the diaphragming of unstable panel walls. These low frequencies may be airborne through the fan inlets and distribution system or through architectural sound barriers. Where energies are sufficiently great and apparatus casing walls are fixed at floor and roof slabs, casing walls also may transmit structurally borne noise and/or vibration. Construction standards developed for low pressure apparatus casings are utterly inadequate for large high pressure and medium pressure systems and create serious acoustical problems on a great many installations.

It is recommended, therefore, that apparatus casings subjected to higher pressures be adequately braced and stiffened. On larger apparatus casings that handle over, say, 40,000 cfm, one of the following should be considered: (a) double wall factory insulated panels, (b) cellular casings, or (c) masonry casings.

Masonry casings internally insulated and made airtight will provide the optimal construction for achieving acoustical results.

Shape of High Pressure Apparatus Casings: On blow-through air handling plants, savings in energy realized by tapered casing designs are rather small. Apparatus casings should be arranged to form plenums of rectangular shape. Rectangular plenums permit better and tighter panel joint constructions, thereby reducing the possibility of air leaks, which may cause whistles and hissing noises. These noises are often transmitted structurally and are also airborne. For large dual duct air handling plants, improved acoustical conditions result when the cold and warm plenums are split vertically, or in the direction that produces the smallest span or panel in the direction of the air stream. Less danger of panel flutter vibrations, which generate noise, results. The vertical split of apparatus casings will also provide other functional and maintenance advantages.

Dampers and Air Valves.— Avoid band or automatic dampers in high velocity systems, since such devices when closed or partially opened produce noise and rumble usually of a low frequency characteristic. The exception to the above is the off-on damper usually installed in the discharge of multiple supply fans. Such dampers must be of streamlined construction.

Use of air balancing valves in water-air system zone duct mains produces noise. Such equipment noise should be adequately attenuated downstream of the valve.

Flexible Connectors.— Install flexible connectors of appropriate construction at all duct connections to high pressure apparatus casings and to supply and return fans. This will reduce fan casing noise transmitted through the duct wall.

Flexible connectors should be installed with a minimum of one inch greater length than the distance between fan and connecting duct.

Air Distributing Systems

Duct Velocities.—In designing high velocity duct systems, every effort should be made to reduce the total fan horsepower and to handle air at moderate velocities. This will assure a quieter system, reduce duct leakages and will allow, in the majority of cases, approach to the point of maximum cost economy. The chief justification for high duct velocity is space limitation created by past and present architectural and structural practices. In modern buildings, high duct velocities must be used where space limitations exist. In cases where these restriction do not exist, the duct velocities should be reduced.

Choice of Duct Design Method.—For high velocity duct systems it is immaterial what duct design method is selected for sizing of high pressure ducts. None of the commonly used duct design methods will, by themselves, produce an economical and quiet duct system. On large and medium installations, a combination of several design methods may be used advantageously. The important point is not to use high velocities or friction rates when space conditions will permit a larger duct. If, for example, the equal friction method is selected, it does not mean that the entire (longest) duct run should be sized at the initial high friction rate. Two, three, and more friction rates can be selected from consideration of space available for the ductwork.

Ductwork Adjacent to Apparatus Room.—Where no space restrictions exist between apparatus casings and duct riser shafts, duct sizes should be increased. An appreciable savings in horsepower requirements can be achieved and the system will be improved acoustically.

When high velocity mains handling large air quantities penetrate walls containing fire dampers, duct offsets or turns immediately before or after fire dampers should be avoided.

All efforts should be made to reduce turbulence at fire dampers.

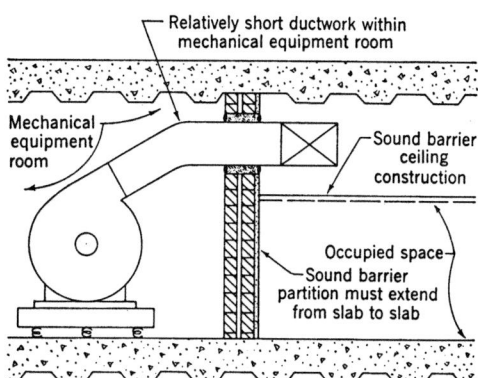

Fig 16-33. Ductwork is short, use special barrier

Where ductwork within mechanical spaces leading from the fan discharge to the occupied space is relatively short (less than 15 ft) before entering adjoining critical occupied spaces, consideration must be given to the noise radiated from the duct wall. Special sound barrier constructions separating the noise radiating duct and the occupied space may be required to contain the duct radiated noise. See Fig. 16-33.

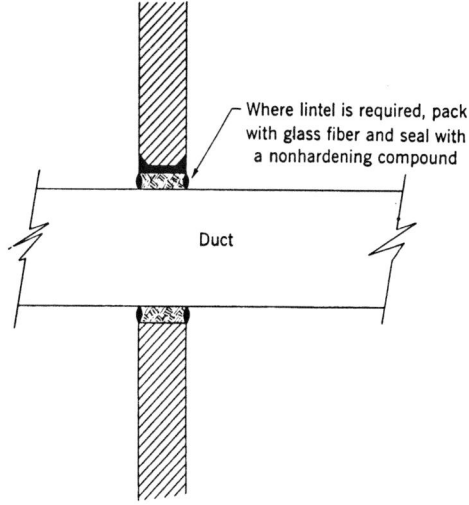

Fig 16-34. Ductwork through partition from mechanical to occupied space

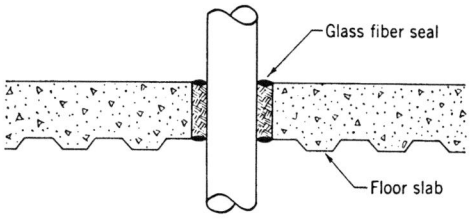

Fig 16-35. Penetration of floor slab by duct (outside of shaft)

All duct penetrations of partitions separating mechanical spaces from occupied spaces should be lined if required, sleeved with ½-inch fiber glass, and sealed with a nonhardening compound to reduce structurally borne transmitted duct wall noise into the building structure. All duct penetrations of floor slabs (outside of shafts) shall be similarly treated. See Figs. 16-34 and 16-35.

Duct Connections to Apparatus Casings.— In order to reduce turbulence, conserve energy, and reduce generation of noise, rectangular and circular high velocity ducts should be connected to supply plenums with fittings that will reduce abrupt velocity change in the air stream. Fittings shall be prism or shoe type (for rectangular duct), or bell mouth shaped (for circular duct) connections to apparatus casings.

Type Duct Construction.—From the viewpoint of distribution system generated noise, the rank order of design preference of duct construction (assuming the same velocity and static pressure) is (a) circular, (b) flat oval, and (c) rectangular.

Where vertical space is available, installation of circular duct will result in a slightly less expensive and generally quieter distribution system.

Where space is available to permit use of rectangular ducts with large aspect ratios, lower air velocities could be used, which would result in quieter and more economical distribution systems.

The above rank order also holds if one is rating duct construction from the viewpoint of duct wall stiffness to resist duct flutter, where conditions of turbulence occur.

The primary cause of distribution system generated noise, as previously discussed, is turbulence within the duct. There have been many high velocity systems with rectangular ductwork where design acoustical criteria have been maintained primarily because well designed fittings were installed and adequate high velocity duct construction was used.

Quieter distribution systems using rectangular duct and flat oval construction are provided when greater care is given to the design of duct fittings and duct panel bracing. The rectangular high pressure duct construction is now standardized and can be found in the *SMACNA High Velocity Duct Manual*. The newly developed construction will greatly reduce generation of noise in the distributing systems caused by excitation of duct panels due to turbulent air flow.

Fittings for High Velocity Ductwork.— It is imperative that, on high velocity systems, only smoothly designed fittings and take-offs be used. No fittings with a sharp or rough edges in the air stream can be tolerated. Fittings should be designed for gradual velocity changes of the airstream.

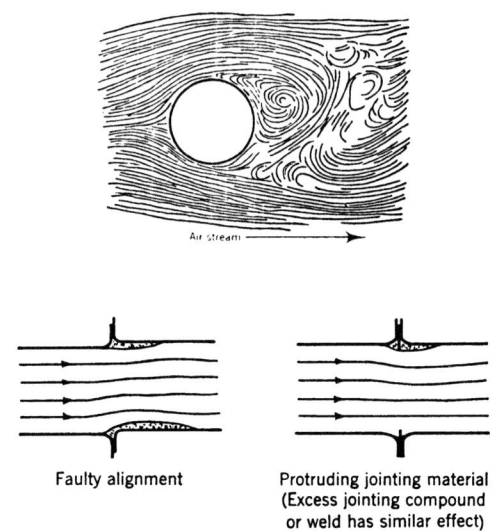

Fig 16-36. Turbulence due to round obstruction, duct misalignment and protruding edge in air stream

Probably the greatest part of acoustical problems on high velocity systems is created by improperly constructed and installed take off fittings, especially on rectangular ductwork. The generation of noise is exceptionally severe when holes in the ductwork for mounting fittings are cut smaller than the free area of the fittings, thus exposing raw edges to the air stream. The same problem is encountered with round ductwork when tap offs have to be mounted in the field in existing ductwork. One type of properly constructed and mounted fittings for rectangular ductwork is shown elsewhere in this handbook in connection with design of high velocity double duct systems.

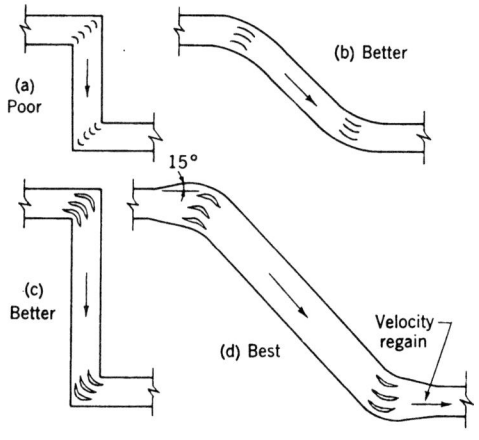

Fig 16-37. Air stream turns, good and bad

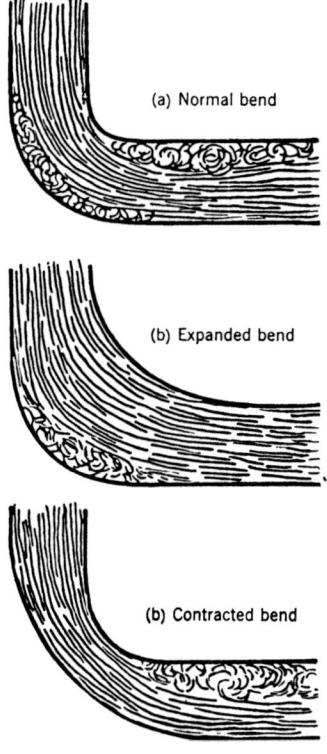

Fig 16-38. Air pattern in bends of various patterns

Fig. 16-36 indicates the turbulent pattern of air stream due to faulty duct alignment or obstructions in high velocity duct systems.

Always allow sufficient length of straight duct between fittings. Successive fittings in high velocity systems generate noise due to the turbulence created in the airstream. 5 equivalent diameters should be considered the absolute minimum between successive fittings. When this design is not possible, straightening vanes should be used to improve the condition as shown in Fig. 16-37.

Square elbows should be vaned and vanes should be of streamlined construction. Vanes should be extended on the downstream side for a minimum of 6 inches. All vanes should be rigidly designed and installed. See Fig. 16-38 indicating turbulent air pattern in normal, expanded and contracted radius bends.

Take-Off Fittings (Shafts and Mains).—For duct main branch take-offs or shaft take-offs, conical fittings (for circular duct), prism shaped shoe fittings (for rectangular duct), should be used; 90° duct main or shaft take-offs should not be tolerated for larger sizes (say, over 8 inches diameter) and high velocities (say, over 2000 fpm). All efforts where large duct panels are involved, at shaft take-off and main duct branch take-offs, should be made to reduce the velocity even further. See Fig. 16-39.

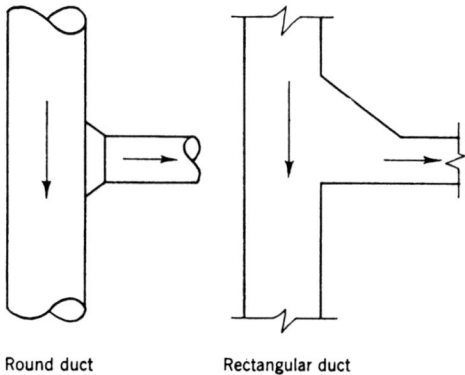

Fig 16-39. Tap-off from main or riser

Where shaft take-off conditions do not permit adequate space conditions to provide conical or prism-type taps, it is recommended that 10 gage duct be installed to permit the fire damper to be located further downstream of the tap within the 10 gage duct. The shaft wall thickness may then be utilized to permit the installation of conical or prism-type tap and thereby provide better aerodynamic take-off conditions and approach conditions to the fire damper. See Fig. 16-40.

When possible, the fire damper should be constructed with blades directed out of the airstream. Under no circumstances should the blades be permitted to extend into the shaft airstream.

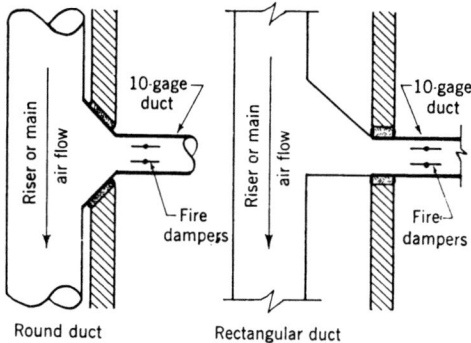

Fig 16-40. Where shaft take-off space is inadequate, use extra heavy duct

Dual Duct Area Ratio.— The practice of under sizing warm ducts on dual duct systems has resulted in many acoustically unsatisfactory installations. It should be kept in mind that maximum demand on warm duct will be created not during steady heat flow conditions under maximum winter load, but under a great many partial load operating conditions. The warm shaft ducts and horizontal mains should not be made less than 70–75% of the corresponding cold duct in area. The warm connections between mixing units and high velocity should always be the same size as cold connections.

Velocities Through Flexible Connections to the Terminal Devices.—At no time should excessively high velocities be maintained (maximum of 2200–2500 fpm) in flexible tubing to the terminal devices. Flexible tubing, especially when not straight, generates noise. Flexible tubing must be free of sharp offsets or bends. The inlet collars to the unit must not be distorted in any way or be allowed to project into the air stream.

Limit the Extent of High Velocity Ductwork.—In laying out a distributing system for all air overhead distribution, one must not simply follow the technique used in low pressure layouts by running high pressure ductwork over an entire conditioned area. The extent of high pressure mains on each floor must be limited to well defined areas and air distributed to individual rooms by low pressure, internally lined, ductwork. One should consider the high pressure ductwork to be a high velocity plenum, which remains intact for the life of the structure. In order to have maximum future flexibility and to avoid the danger of obsolescence of the system, all future changes due to shifting loads and partition changes should be confined to low pressure ductwork and mixing units.

Dampers as a Noise Generating Source.—Dampers are a source of noise generation in all types of fan systems. Volume dampers in conventional systems located at, or in close proximity to, air outlets will generate noise even though more than adequate fan noise, attenuation may have been provided in the distribution system. Adequate natural duct attenuation or acoustical lining should be provided before air outlets.

The use of balancing volume dampers in dual duct systems should be avoided. They are practically useless and are a source of noise and an unnecessary expense. Splitter dampers in high velocity systems should also be avoided as they generate noise and can cause distribution troubles.

Sound Barrier for High Velocity Ductwork.—Adequate sound barrier construction should be installed between all high velocity ductwork and occupied areas. Particular attention should be given to ceiling constructions in critical areas adjoining shaft take-offs, unavoidably poor duct fittings, and very large terminal devices, and where air valves are located in ceilings of critical spaces.

The relatively new concept of unified ceiling systems, which has been developed to integrate the functions of air distribution within the slab construction, greatly reduces the possibility of problems caused by radiated distribution system noise.

All high velocity ductwork and terminal devices should be installed free of any contact with ceilings and their supports.

Sound Traps.—Factory built sound traps should be selected for the minimum practical pressure drop, and not greater than 0.4 inch of water. The manufacturer's rating of attenuation with air flow and the sound power generated in the sound trap by the air flow should be balanced to provide useful net effective attenuation. There have been installations where the sound trap was replaced with straight duct and a quieter installation resulted.

When mixing unit, induction unit, and air valve manufacturers provide data regarding the attenuation properties of their equipment under air flow conditions, it may be possible to reduce acoustical treatment requirements in air distribution systems. Sound traps should be located with good entrance and discharge airflow conditions. Poor entrance and discharge conditions will considerably increase the pressure drop and the noise radiation from the duct panels. When space limitations are severe, however, it is less objectionable to reduce the duct length between the trap and the elbow before it than to reduce the space downstream of the trap.

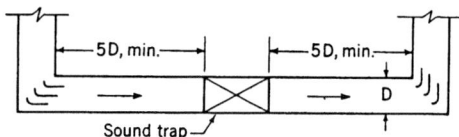

Fig 16-41. Locate sound traps with long straight inlet and discharge duct sections to provide best approach and leaving air pattern to trap

These data may show that, for high velocity systems, consideration of fan noise in certain duct schemes may be unnecessary and that acoustical lining or sound traps may be necessary only on the low pressure side of the system. There presently are indications that little or no attenuation is provided by acoustical treatment subjected to air stream velocities of greater than approximately 3,000 fpm due to the self-generating noise qualities of the acoustical treatment. Maximum attenuation is indicated under no-air-flow conditions with the attenuation falling off as the velocity increases across the face of the sound trap or surface area of the acoustical lining.

Crossover of Horizontal Dual Duct Mains Near Air Shafts.— Probably the most critical part of a high velocity, dual duct layout is the area near the riser shaft. Because of the space limitations, the crossover of horizontal mains cannot always be made with adequately designed and properly arranged fittings. When this is the case, noise and rumble may be generated in the crossover ductwork. It may be found desirable on such installations to eliminate the crossovers entirely by carrying three supply ducts in the shaft instead of two; say, two warm and one cold duct, as shown in Fig. 16-42.

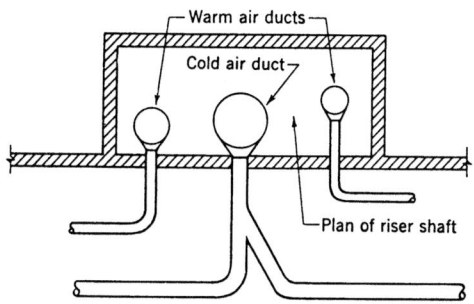

Fig 16-42. Typical duct connections to risers to avoid crossovers

Testing of High Pressure Ductwork.—Leaks in high pressure ductwork or apparatus casings create objectionable high frequency noise in occupied spaces. It is imperative that high velocity ductwork be pressure tested before insulation is applied and before the system in operation. The ductwork should be tested in convenient sections and the objectionable air leaks eliminated. Many acoustical problems on high velocity installations have been caused by failure to test the ductwork during installation. All high velocity duct or apparatus casing joints and seams must be made airtight with a long life sealant. Cloth, plastic, or foil adhesive tapes should not be used as the primary sealer but rather used in conjunction with mastic sealers.

For a suggested method of sealing and testing, see *SMACNA High Velocity Duct Manual.*

Terminal Devices.—*Acoustical Performance:* The acoustical performance of high velocity, all air or water air systems depends to a large degree on the acoustical performance of the installed terminal devices. Improper selection or compromise with the acoustical and functional characteristics of terminal devices for these systems, regardless of whether the distribution system and fan noise has been completely attenuated, can create excessive noise and exceed the design criterion.

Similarly, in conventional velocity systems, where considerable balancing adjustment is required at the diffuser or where volume dampers are located in close proximity to outlets, noise generation will occur regardless of the extent of acoustical treatment provided in the distribution duct.

Pressure reducing air valves and single and dual duct mixing units, while providing some attenuation of fan noise, also create a self-generating noise which is both radiated from the equipment surface and transmitted through the connecting duct in the form of air and structure borne noise. On smaller capacity units the radiated noise is normally attenuated by most ceiling constructions.

Generally, most air valve or mixing unit equipment manufacturers present acoustical data that reflect only the airborne noise through the equipment outlets. Little data

are presently available regarding the radiated noise values. Where the radiated noise factor of the equipment may be critical, two acoustical performance ratings will be required to fully analyze the condition. Acoustical performance ratings should be conducted:

1) With only the equipment located inside the test chamber and the outlets outside the chamber; and

2) With the equipment located outside the test chamber and only the outlet inside the chamber.

Under window unit induction or air mixing devices, when acoustically tested without enclosures within the chamber, will transmit the total radiated (through the equipment surfaces) and airborne (through the outlets) noise.

Some protection of radiated mixing unit casing noise may be provided by proper sound attenuation enclosure constructions. These enclosures will result in quieter equipment installations. With window induction units, however, to the induction air openings, special sound barrier enclosure constructions will provide relatively little radiation noise protection.

Flutter in Dual Duct Mixing Units: To prevent flutter of volume controllers in medium or high velocity dual duct systems, each mixing unit should be equipped with positive stabilizers. Where bad fittings adjacent to the unit or foreign matter within the duct system occur, flutter of volume controllers in mixing units not equipped with positive stabilizers may take place. The flutter may also be caused by a combination of excessively low pressure at the mixing unit and air pulsations in the air stream. This condition may cause a chain reaction to occur to other units not equipped with stabilizers. Flutter of volume controllers creates objectionable noise transmission to occupied areas.

Two Motor Dual Duct Units: Two-motor dual duct units may be noisy in operation when the demand on the mixing unit is for warm air only. When this occurs, the constant volume feature of the unit is suspended and considerably greater volumes of warm air may be handled by the mixing units than the design engineer intended. These higher volumes of warm air often create velocity conditions within the warm air duct, mixing box, and mixing box outlets which cause the equipment to operate with excessive noise.

Inlets to High Velocity Terminal Points: Carelessness on the part of the installer in connecting flexible tubing to high velocity terminal devices may change the acoustical characteristics of such devices. A sharp bend in the flexible tubing may expose a raw edge of the inlet collar, thus causing a loud hiss or a whistle, changing totally the acoustical characteristics of the units.

Warm Connections to Dual Duct Mixing Units: Warm runouts to the mixing units should be made the same size as cold connections, even if the unit is designed to handle less warm air than cold air under normal operating conditions. There will be many sets of operating conditions that force more warm air through warm connections than intended as designed. This may cause generation of noise in the warm flexible tubing.

Large Terminal Units: Large terminal devices say, handling over 1200–1500 cfm, and operating under high pressures, should be separated from high and low velocity ducts by a flexible connection.

Large capacity mixing units may create excessive noise in the immediate area of the equipment radiating noise. Care should be exercised in the location of the large capacity mixing units (1200 cfm and larger) in ceilings of critical spaces. It is preferable that these units be located in noncritical spaces, or sound barrier ceiling construction should be installed where they cannot be relocated.

Particular attention should be paid to where the radiated noise travels when terminal units are exposed in room with no suspended acoustical ceiling below, where a relatively sound transparent ceiling such as perforated metal pans or very light glass fiber ceiling tiles or boards is used, or where the acoustical design (NC) objective is critical.

Alternatively, a number of smaller units with the same total capacity may be installed to reduce the radiated noise transmission factor. The records of recent installations indicate that there is no real economic justification in using only air units of large capacities. Only small cost advantages can be gained by increasing units to over 1200 –1500 cfm.

Grilles, Registers and Diffusers: Select all terminal outlets to be at least 5 dB below the design criterion required for the space usage.

It must be remembered that, as the static pressure in the branch duct to the terminal air outlets increases, the outlet opening must be decreased to restrict the flow to design volume. At these higher duct pressures noise generation occurs in the damper restriction. The quality of this noise generation is characterized by high frequency transmission.

Radiation Protection at Wall Openings for Duct or Pipe.—The air conditioning engineer should be acquainted with the means for shielding ductwork and other openings that penetrate protective barriers around radiation facilities, particularly X-ray rooms.

Protection against radiation from X-ray tube, cyclotron, radium, or other radioactive material is primarily a question of shielding to reduce the level of radiation to a safe or specified amount, of maintaining safe distances from the rays, and/or of limiting the time of exposure.

The prime consideration in preventing penetration of rays is density of the shielding material. Lead is the densest of any commonly available. Where space is at a premium, particularly in modern buildings, and where

utmost radiation protection is demanded, lead is invariably used. Lead is useful, especially where neutrons and gamma rays are concerned, in that it does not itself become contaminated and emit harmful rays.

Lead, usually in sheet form, is used to line the walls, floor, and often the ceiling of rooms containing radiation facilities. Openings through the barrier for air ductwork, piping, service boxes, conduit, etc., require shielding, usually obtained by a lead barrier around or behind these building utilities of sufficient coverage and thickness to prevent penetration of these rays.

Shielding of duct and other openings in the protective barrier of radiation facilities depends on energy of radiation, orientation of the beam, dimensions and location of opening in the protective barrier, geometrical relationship between the radiation source and opening, and geometrical relationship between opening and persons, materials or instruments to be protected. The complexity of these factors requires the services of a radiological physicist, who determines extent of shielding, materials for shielding (usually lead or concrete), and thickness of the shielding material. After the radiological physicist has done the basic design for this shielding, the protective barrier contractor provides the required shielding for the openings.

Design of ductwork, piping, etc., should anticipate some of the problems encountered both in the design and installation of shielding. Also, coordination between air conditioning contractor and shielding fabricator can best be achieved by understanding and forethought on the part of the air conditioning designer.

Figs. 16-43 to 16-47 give some idea of the area of shielding required around ductwork. They show various duct installations that penetrate the protective barrier for walls or partitions of X-ray rooms. Lead shielding is used to cover these openings, the approximate extent of which is indicated in terms of simple equations involving the opening dimensions and wall thickness. These are conservative estimates, which will aid the air conditioning designer in understanding what to expect as to the area of shielded ductwork. The radiological physicist actually determines for each case the lead thickness and the exact amount of shielding required.

Note in Fig. 16-46 that protective shielding deals with primary radiation, while Figs. 16-43 to 16-47 show protection against scattered or secondary radiation. Primary radiation comes directly from the radiation source; scattered radiation has deviated in direction; and secondary radiation is emitted by an irradiated material. Primary radiation requires more protection because its energy level is higher.

Because sheet lead is not structurally self supporting, it must be mounted to prevent sagging by its own weight. For lead thicknesses up to 3.5 mm, sheet lead can be readily shaped around round and small rectangular ducts, say 24-inch maximum diameter or width, with all joints overlapped at least ½ inch. To hold these lead sheets in place, 1-inch wide iron bands should be placed around the periphery of the duct on approximately 12-inch centers, care being taken not to cut into the lead when the bands are bolted up.

When lead thickness is greater than 3.5 mm or duct width exceeds 24-inches, lead shielding should be laminated on a plywood or similar structural core, which is made in sections or panels to conform to the sides of the duct. The laminated sections are mechanically fastened at the seams and corners. These joints are lapped with sheet lead angles or lead strips, the width of which is twice the thickness of the lead, but not less than ½ inch in any case. Nails, bolts, screws or other fasteners used to secure the lead sheet or panel must be covered with lead of thickness equal to the lead sheet. Lead headed nails may be used as shown in Fig. 16-45.

For lead shielding of 1.0 mm or less, flexible leaded vinyl sheets can be used for easy forming to complex shapes and contours. The flexible leaded vinyl sheets can be applied in layers where heavier than 1.0 mm lead shielding is required. If the duct has a flexible connection or is made of a flexible material, the flexible vinyl sheets could be applied over it more readily than other forms of shielding.

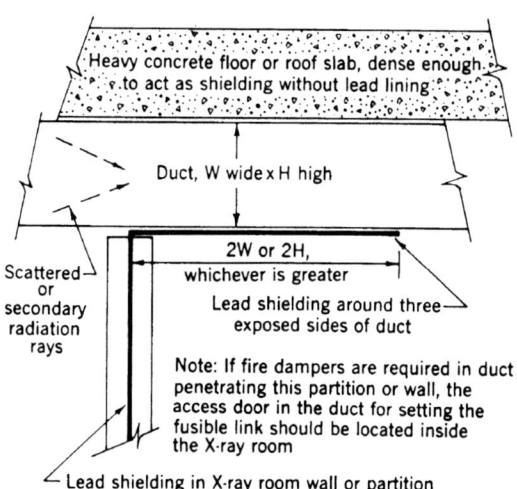

Fig 16-43. Elevation of section through X-ray room

Duct hangers are best installed on the outside of the lead shielding so that the hanger rods or straps do not have to pierce the shielding. The lead shielding adds considerably to the weight of the duct, so the hangers should be substantial, with such adequate anchoring in the slab above them as fish plates. For rectangular ducts, trapeze hangers would be the most practical. For design purposes, estimate each $\frac{1}{16}$ inch of lead at 4 lb/ft^2.

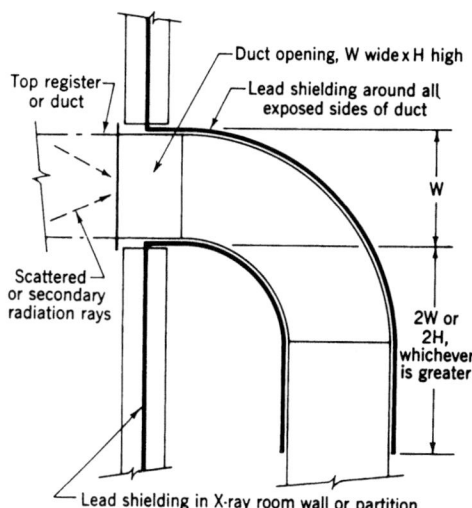

Fig 16-44. Elevation of Section Through X-ray Room

Tests for radiation leakage are usually made after a room is finished and equipment is installed. It is very important to install all shielding properly during the course of construction because it is expensive to make corrections to the finished protective barrier. Moreover, equipment such as dampers should never be put in the shielded section of the ductwork, as repairs to this equipment would be very costly if the shielding had to be dismantled.

A simple way to avoid penetration of the protective barriers lead lining by pipes or wires is to offset them as close behind the lead lining as possible so that they can be backed with a lead sheet of sufficient size to prevent passage of the rays at any angle. This lead patch method is also used for electric switch boxes located in a wall.

Medical Installations.—The extent of the protective barrier for medical installations is summarized below so that the air conditioning designer can tell whether ducts or pipes running through such spaces are likely to be a problem.

For medical radiographic and fluoroscopic rooms, the lead shielding generally does not extend above a line 7 ft 0 inch from the finished floor; if the service lines and ducts can be located above this line, shielding around them is obviously unnecessary. For X-ray therapy rooms, lead shielding may extend to the ceiling or structural slab. The ceiling or slab above and the floor may also be lead lined, depending upon output of the machine and other conditions. For industrial X-ray work, wall shielding may extend to the ceiling. Both ceiling and floor in some cases will require lead lining.

For shielding in super voltage rooms, special conditions may apply. In any event, the radiological physicist should be consulted in the design of the proper protective measures. Where concrete is considered for the shielding material, it is often more practical to use lead of equivalent density shielding value for the shielding of openings. Where recesses occur in concrete barriers for equipment, lead backing, equivalent to the thickness of the concrete removed, should be provided.

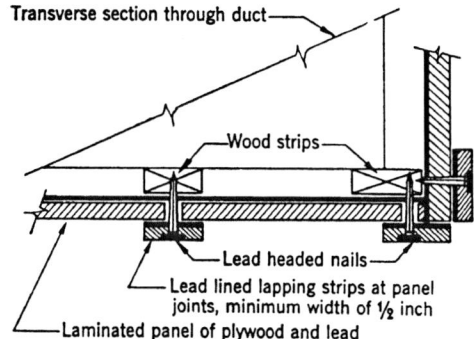

Note: Let duct rest on wood strips for support. Substantial trapeze hangers should be used for supporting shielding enclosure. Hanger rods must be rigid enough to prevent any sway of the enclosure

Fig 16-45. Elevation of section through X-ray room

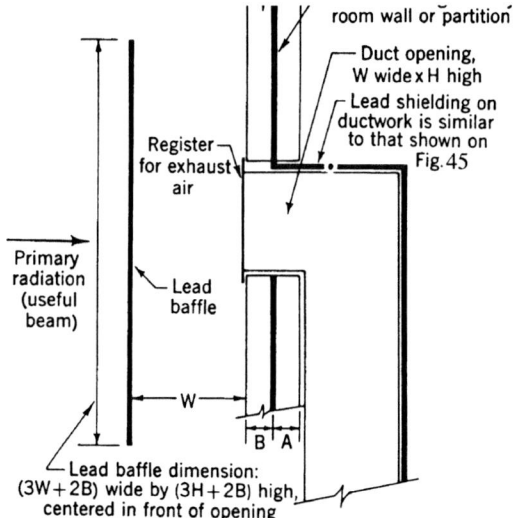

Note: Where duct runs straight without offset, lead shielding is similar to that shown on Fig.46

Fig 16-46. Elevation of section through X-ray room

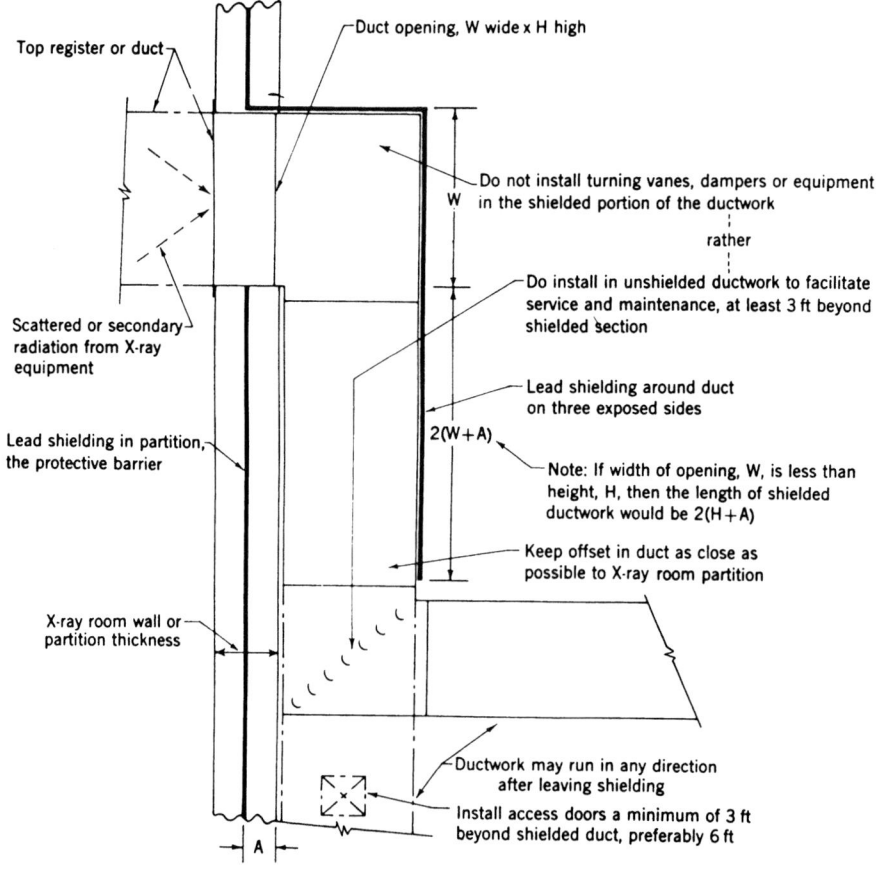

Fig 16-47. Plan view of duct running through partition of X-ray room, exposed to secondary or scattered radiation*

MOTORS AND STARTERS

NEMA Motor Classifications

NEMA is the National Electrical Manufacturers Association, a nonprofit trade organization supported by manufacturers of electrical apparatus and supplies. NEMA standards are designed to eliminate misunderstandings between manufacturer and purchaser. NEMA also assists purchasers in selecting and obtaining the proper product for their particular needs. Some standards included in the NEMA Standards for Motors and Generators have frequent application in the air conditioning, heating, ventilating, plumbing, and fire protection fields. Portions of these standards are described or repeated in the following pages. Reference will be made to these standards in other parts of this section.

The following are NEMA criteria for motor classification:

Classification by Size.—A motor may be classified as either a fractional horsepower motor or an integral horsepower motor.

Classification by Application.—Motors normally are classified under one of the following application designations:

General-Purpose Alternating-Current (ac) Motor: An induction motor of open construction, with standard operating characteristics and mechanical construction, for use under usual service conditions without restriction to a particular application or type of application.

Definite-Purpose Motor: A motor having standard ratings and standard operating characteristics or mechanical construction for use under service conditions other than usual, or for use on a specified type of application.

Special-Purpose Motor: A motor with special operating characteristics or special mechanical construction, or both.

Industrial Direct-Current (dc) Motor.

Classification by Electrical Type.— The following electrical motor types are recognized:
- ac induction motor
- ac wound rotor induction motor
- ac synchronous motor
- ac series motor
- Single-phase, split-phase, squirrel cage motor
- Single-phase, resistance-start, squirrel cage motor (a form of split-phase motor)
- Single-phase, capacitor, squirrel cage motor (This may be of a capacitor-start, a permanent-split capacitor, or a two-value capacitor type.)
- Single-phase, shaded-pole, squirrel cage motor
- Single-phase, repulsion, wound-rotor motor
- Single-phase, repulsion-start induction, wound rotor motor
- Single-phase, repulsion-induction, wound-rotor motor
- dc, shunt-wound motor (This may be either a straight shunt-wound motor or a stabilized shunt-wound motor.)
- dc, series-wound motor
- dc, compound-wound motor
- Universal, series-wound motor
- Universal, compensated series motor

Classification of Polyphase Motors by Design Letter.— Polyphase, squirrel cage, integral-horsepower induction motors may be classified under design letters A, B, C, or D. Such motors are designed to withstand full voltage when started and usually have a "slip at rated load" of less than 5%. However, design D motors have a slip at rated load of 5% or more, as do design A and design B motors with two or more poles. Characteristics pertaining to each of the above mentioned design letters are given in what follows:

Design A Motor: locked rotor torque in accordance with Table 17-1. Breakdown torque in accordance with Table 17-1.

Table 17-1. NEMA Standard Locked Rotor Torque of Single Speed Polyphase 60 and 50 Hz Squirrel Cage Integral Horsepower Motors with Continuous Ratings

	Designs A and B								Design C		
	Synchronous Speed (Hz)										
60	3600	1800	1200	900	720	600	514	1800	1200	900
50	3000	1500	1000	750	...	...	...	1500	1000	750
hp	Percent of Full Load Torque[a]										
½	...	...	...	140	140	115	110	...	...	...
¾	...	...	175	135	135	115	110	...	...	...
1	...	275	170	135	135	115	110	...	...	...
1½	175	250	165	130	130	115	110	...	...	...
2	170	235	160	130	125	115	110	...	...	...
3	160	215	155	130	125	115	110	...	250	225
5	150	185	150	130	125	115	110	250	250	225
7½	140	175	150	125	120	115	110	250	225	200
10	135	165	150	125	120	115	110	250	225	200
15	130	160	140	125	120	115	110	225	200	200
20	130	150	135	125	120	115	110			
25	130	150	135	125	120	115	110			
30	130	150	135	125	120	115	110	200 for all sizes above 15 hp		
40	125	140	135	125	120	115	110			
50	120	140	135	125	120	115	110			
60	120	140	135	125	120	115	110			
75	105	140	135	125	120	115	110			
100	105	125	125	125	120	115	110	For design D motors [a]		
125	100	110	125	120	115	115	110			
150	100	110	120	120	115	115	...			
200	100	100	120	120	115	...	...			

[a] These values represent the upper limit of application for these motors.

Note: The locked rotor torque of a motor is the minimum torque it will develop at rest for all angular positions of the rotor, with rated voltage applied at rated frequency.

The locked rotor torque of Design D, 60 and 50 hertz 4, 6, and 8 pole single speed, polyphase squirrel cage motors rated 150 hp and smaller, with rated voltage and frequency applied, is 275% of full load torque, which represents the upper limit of application for these motors.

For motors larger than 200 hp, see NEMA Standard MG 1-12.37.

Design B Motor: Locked rotor torque in accordance with Table 17-1. Breakdown torque in accordance with Table 17-1. Locked rotor current not to exceed Table 17-2.

Design C Motor: locked rotor torque in accordance with Table 17-1. Breakdown torque in accordance with Table 17-1. locked rotor current not to exceed Table 17-2.

Design D Motor: locked rotor torque to be 275% of full load torque. locked rotor current not to exceed Table 17-2.

Table 17-2. Characteristics of Three Phase Squirrel Cage Induction Motors

	60 Cycle (Hz), Rated at 230 V			50 Cycle (Hz), Rated at 380 V	
hp	Locked Rotor Current, Amperes	Design Letters	hp	Locked Rotor Current, Amperes	Design Letters
½	20	B, D	1 or less	20	B, D
¾	25	B, D	1½	27	B, D
1	30	B, D	2	34	B, D
1½	40	B, D	3	43	B, C, D
2	50	B, D	5	61	B, C, D
3	64	B, C, D	7½	84	B, C, D
5	92	B, C, D	10	107	B, C, D
7½	127	B, C, D	15	154	B, C, D
10	162	B, C, D	20	194	B, C, D
15	232	B, C, D	25	243	B, C, D
20	290	B, C, D	30	289	B, C, D
25	365	B, C, D	40	387	B, C, D
30	435	B, C, D	50	482	B, C, D
40	580	B, C, D	60	578	B, C, D
50	725	B, C, D	75	722	B, C, D
60	870	B, C, D	100	965	B, C, D
75	1085	B, C, D	125	1207	B, C, D
100	1450	B, C, D	150	1441	B, C, D
125	1815	B, C, D	200	1927	B, C
150	2170	B, C, D			
200	2900	B, C			
250	3650	B			
300	4400	B			
350	5100	B			
400	5800	B			
450	6500	B			
500	7250	B			

Classification of Single-Phase, Induction Motors by Design Letter.—The following single phase motor types are designed to withstand full voltage starting and have the characteristics noted:

Design N Motor: Fractional horsepower motor with a locked rotor current not to exceed the values in Table 17-3.

Design O Motor: Fractional horsepower motor with a locked rotor current not to exceed the values in Table 17-3.

Design L Motor: Integral horsepower motor with a locked-motor current not to exceed the values in Table 17-4.

Design M Motor: Integral-horsepower motor with a locked rotor current not to exceed the values in Table 17-4.

Table 17-3. Characteristics of Single-Phase Fractional HP 2, 4, 6, and 8-pole, 60-hertz Motors

	Locked Rotor Current, Amp			
	115 V		230 V	
hp	Design O	Design N	Design O	Design N
⅙ and smaller	50	20	25	12
¼	50	26	25	15
⅓	50	31	25	18
½	50	45	25	25
¾	...	61	...	35
1	...	80	...	45

Table 17-4. Characteristics of Single-Phase Integral HP Motors

	Locked Rotor Current, Amperes		
	Design L		Design M
hp	115 V	230 V	230 V
½	45	25	...
¾	61	35	...
1	80	45	...
1½	...	50	40
2	...	65	50
3	...	90	70
5	...	135	100
7½	...	200	150
10	...	260	200
15	...	390	300
20	...	520	400

Torque, Speed, and Horsepower Ratings for Single-Phase Induction Motors.—The horsepower rating of a single-phase induction motor is based upon a minimum value of breakdown torque. The range in breakdown torque to be expected for any horsepower and speed is given in Table 17-7. The breakdown torque of a general purpose motor is no less than the higher figure in the applicable torque range. The locked rotor torque of a general-purpose motor is no less than the value given in Table 17-7 for the applicable horsepower and speed.

Classification by Environmental Protection and Method of Cooling.—This classification refers to the amount of protection provided against the environment in which the motor operates, and to the arrangement of ventilating openings or other means of cooling.

Open Machine: One having ventilating openings that permit passage of external cooling air over and around the windings.

Drip-Proof Machine (Often Referred to as Open Drip-Proof Machine): An open motor in which ventilating openings are so constructed that successful operation is not interfered with when drops of liquid or solid particles strike or enter the enclosure at any angle from 0 to 15° downward from the vertical.

Machine with Encapsulated Windings: An ac squirrel cage motor having random windings filled with an insulating resin, which also forms a protective coating.

Totally Enclosed Machine: One so enclosed as to prevent free exchange of air between inside and outside of case. The enclosure, however, is not airtight.

Totally Enclosed Fan-Cooled Machine: A totally enclosed motor equipped for exterior cooling by means of a fan, or fans, integral with the motor but external to the enclosing parts.

Explosion Proof Machine: A totally enclosed motor or totally enclosed fan-cooled motor designed and built to withstand an explosion of gas or vapor within it and to prevent ignition of gas or vapor surrounding the motor by sparks, flashes, or explosions that occur within the motor casing.

With the exception of the open motor, which is seldom used, the motor enclosure and ventilating types classified above are most frequently utilized in the air conditioning, heating, ventilating, plumbing, and fire protection fields for other than hermetic or accessible hermetic service.

Other types classified by protection and cooling, but not frequently encountered, are listed below:

Splash-proof machine

Guarded machine

Semi-guarded machine

Drip-proof, fully guarded machine

Open, externally ventilated machine

Open pipe-ventilated machine

Weather-protected machine

Machine with sealed windings

Totally enclosed, fan-cooled, guarded machine

Dust ignition proof machine

Totally enclosed pipe ventilated machine

Totally enclosed water-cooled machine

Totally enclosed water-air-cooled machine

Totally enclosed air-to-air cooled machine.

Standard Voltages and Frequencies for Motors.—

Single-Phase ac Motors: 60 Cycles: 115 and 230 volts.

50 cycles: 110 and 220 volts.

ac Polyphase Motors: 60 Cycles: 115, 200, 230, 460, 575, 2300, 4000, 4600 and 6600 volts.

50 Cycles: 220 and 380 volts.

Universal Motors: 110 and 230 volts

dc Fractional-Horsepower Motors: 115 and 230 volts

Industrial dc Motors: $\frac{1}{2}$– 10 horsepower: 120 and 240 volts

15 – 200 Horsepower: 240 volts.

250 – 600 Horsepower: 250 and 500 volts.

600 –800 Horsepower: 500 and 700 volts.

Permissible Variation from Rated Voltage Induction motors: ± 10% (with rated frequency).

Universal Motors, except Fan Motors: ± 6%.

dc Motors: ±6%.

Permissible Variation from Rated Frequency: ± 5%.

Permissible Combined Variation of Voltage and Frequency: ± 10%, provided the frequency variation does not exceed 5%.

Locked Rotor kva: The nameplate of every ac motor, rated $\frac{1}{20}$ hp, and larger, is marked with the caption "Code" followed by a letter selected to show locked rotor kva per *hp.* Table 17-8 shows each code letter in relation to its designated range of locked rotor kva/hp. The majority of poly phase motors used in air conditioning, heating, ventilating, plumbing, and fire protection, have the code letter F. This code letter is not related to the design letter classification of an ac induction motor.

Service Factors: The maximum permissible loading of a motor is obtained by multiplying the rated horsepower by the service factor shown on the nameplate. Open, or open drip-proof, polyphase, general-purpose motors having a design A, B, or C classification, and usually have a service factor of 1.15 for rated horsepowers of 1, or greater. For horsepowers less than 1, the service factors for these motors are generally greater than 1.15 but no greater than 1.4. Totally enclosed, totally enclosed fan-cooled, explosion proof, and splash-proof motors generally have a service factor of 1.0 and should not be loaded over the nameplate rating.

Table 17-5. Basis of HP and Speed Ratings for Single Phase Induction Motors

60	50	60	50–25	60	50	60	50–25		Frequencies, hertz
3600	3000	1800	1500	1200	1000	900	750		Synchronous Speeds, rpm
3450[a]	2850[a]	1725[a]	1425[a]	1140[a]	950[a]	850[a]	...		Fractional-hp Nominal Speeds
								milli hp	
0.35–0.55	0.42–0.66	0.7–1.1	0.85–1.3	1.1–1.65	...	...	...	1	The figures at left are for motors rated less than $\frac{1}{20}$ hp. Breakdown torques in oz-in.
0.55–0.7	0.66–0.85	1.1–1.45	1.3–1.75	1.65–2.2	...	...	...	1.5	
0.7–1.1	0.85–1.3	1.45–2.2	1.75–2.6	2.2–3.3	...	...	...	2	
1.1–1.8	1.3–2.2	2.2–3.6	2.6–4.3	3.3–5.4	...	...	...	3	
1.8–2.7	2.2–3.2	3.6–5.4	4.3–6.6	5.4–8.1	...	...	...	5	
2.7–3.6	3.2–4.3	5.4–7.2	6.6–8.6	8.1–11	...	...	...	7.5	
3.6–5.5	4.3–6.6	7.2–11	8.6–13	11–17	...	...	...	10	
5.5–9.5	6.6–11.4	11–19	13–23	17–29	...	...	...	15	
9.5–15	11.4–18	19–30	23–36	29–46	...	...	...	25	
15–24	18–28.8	30–48	36–57.6	46–72	...	...	...	35	
								hp	
2.0–3.7	2.4–4.4	4.0–7.1	4.8–8.5	6.0–10.4	7.2–12.4	8.0–13.5	...	$\frac{1}{20}$	The figures at left are for fractional-hp motors. Breakdown torques in oz-ft.
3.7–6.0	4.4–7.2	7.1–11.5	8.5–13.8	10.4–16.5	12.4–19.8	13.5–21.5	...	$\frac{1}{12}$	
6.0–8.7	7.2–10.5	11.5–16.5	13.8–19.8	16.5–24.1	19.8–28.9	21.5–31.5	...	$\frac{1}{8}$	
8.7–11.5	10.5–13.8	16.5–21.5	19.8–25.8	24.1–31.5	28.9–37.8	31.5–40.5	...	$\frac{1}{6}$	
11.5–16.5	13.8–19.8	21.5–31.5	25.8–37.8	31.5–44.0	37.8–53.0	40.5–58.0	...	$\frac{1}{4}$	
16.5–21.5	19.8–25.8	31.5–40.5	37.8–48.5	44.0–58.0	53.0–69.5	58.0–77.0	...	$\frac{1}{3}$	
21.5–31.5	25.8–37.8	40.5–58.0	48.5–69.5	58.0–82.5	69.5–99.0	b	b	$\frac{1}{2}$	The figures at for integral-hp motors. Breakdown torques in lb-ft.
31.5–44.0	37.8–53.0	58.0–82.5	69.5–99.0	5.16–6.9	b	b	b	$\frac{3}{4}$	
44.0–58.0	53.0–69.5	5.16–6.8	6.19–8.2	6.9–9.2	b	b	b	1	
3.6–4.6	0.3–5.5	6.8–10.1	8.2–12.1	9.2–13.8	b	b	b	1½	
4.6–6.0	5.5–7.2	10.1–13.0	12.1–15.6	13.8–18.0	b	b	b	2	
6.0–8.6	7.2–10.2	13.0–19.0	15.6–22.8	18.0–25.8	b	b	b	3	
8.6–13.5	10.2–16.2	19.0–30.0	22.8–36.0	25.8–40.5	b	b	b	5	
13.5–20.0	16.2–24.0	30.0–45.0	36.0–54.0	40.5–60.0	b	b	b	7½	
20.0–27.0	24.0–32.4	45.0–60.0	54.0–72.0	b	b	b	b	10	

[a] These approximate full load speeds apply only for fractional hp motor ratings.
[b] These are ratings for which no torque values have been established.

Table 17-6. Basis of HP and Speed Ratings for Single Phase Induction Motors

Shaded Pole and Permanent-Split Capacitor Motors (except for permanent-split capacitor hermetic motors)						
60	50	60	50	60		Frequencies, Hz
1800	1500	1200	1000	900		Synchronous Speeds, rpm
					milli hp	
0.89–1.1	1.1–1.3	1.3–1.6	1.6–1.9	1.7–2.1	1	The figures at left are breakdown torques in oz-in.
1.1–1.4	1.3–1.7	1.6–2.1	1.9–2.5	2.1–2.7	1.25	
1.4–1.7	1.7–2.0	2.1–2.5	2.5–3.0	2.7–3.3	1.5	
1.7–2.1	2.0–2.5	2.5–3.1	3.0–3.7	3.3–4.1	2	
2.1–2.6	2.5–3.1	3.1–3.8	3.7–4.6	4.1–5.0	2.5	
2.6–3.2	3.1–3.8	3.8–4.7	4.6–5.7	5.0–6.2	3	
3.2–4.0	3.8–4.8	4.7–5.9	5.7–7.1	6.2–7.8	4	
4.0–4.9	4.8–5.8	5.9–7.2	7.1–8.7	7.8–9.5	5	
4.9–6.2	5.8–7.4	7.2–9.2	8.7–11.0	9.5–12.0	6	
6.2–7.7	7.4–9.2	9.2–11.4	11.0–13.6	12.0–14.9	8	
7.7–9.6	9.2–11.4	11.4–14.2	13.6–17.0	14.9–18.6	10	
9.6–12.3	11.4–14.7	14.2–18.2	17.0–21.8	18.6–23.8	12.5	
12.3–15.3	14.7–18.2	18.2–22.6	21.8–27.1	23.8–29.6	16	
15.3–19.1	18.2–22.8	22.6–28.2	27.1–33.8	29.6–37.0	20	
19.1–23.9	22.8–28.5	28.2–35.3	33.8–42.3	37.0–46.3	25	

Table 17-6. *(Continued)* **Basis of HP and Speed Ratings for Single Phase Induction Motors**

Shaded Pole and Permanent-Split Capacitor Motors (except for permanent-split capacitor hermetic motors)						
60	50	60	50	60		Frequencies, Hz
1800	1500	1200	1000	900		Synchronous Speeds, rpm
23.9–30.4	28.5–36.3	35.3–44.9	42.3–53.9	46.3–58.9	30	
30.4–38.3	36.3–45.6	44.9–56.4	53.9–68.4	58.9–74.4	40	
					hp	
3.20–4.13	3.80–4.92	4.70–6.09	5.70–7.31	6.20–8.00	$\frac{1}{20}$	
4.13–5.23	4.92–6.23	6.09–7.72	7.31–9.26	8.00–10.1	$\frac{1}{15}$	
5.23–6.39	6.23–7.61	7.72–9.42	9.26–11.3	10.1–12.4	$\frac{1}{12}$	
6.39–8.00	7.61–9.54	9.42–11.8	11.3–14.2	12.4–15.5	$\frac{1}{10}$	
8.00–10.4	9.54–12.4	11.8–15.3	14.2–18.4	15.5–20.1	$\frac{1}{8}$	The figures at left are break-down torques in oz-ft.
10.4–12.7	12.4–15.1	15.3–18.8	18.4–22.5	20.1–24.6	$\frac{1}{6}$	
12.7–16.0	15.1–19.1	18.8–23.6	22.5–28.3	24.6–31.0	$\frac{1}{5}$	
16.0–21.0	19.1–25.4	23.6–31.5	28.3–37.6	31.0–41.0	$\frac{1}{4}$	
21.0–31.5	25.4–37.7	31.5–47.0	37.6–56.5	41.0–61.0	$\frac{1}{3}$	
31.5–47.5	37.7–57.3	47.0–70.8	56.5–84.8	3.81–5.81	$\frac{1}{2}$	
47.5–63.5	57 –76.5	4.42–5.88	5.30–7.06	5.81–7.62	$\frac{3}{4}$	The figures at left are break-down torques in lb-ft.
3.97–5.94	4.78–7.06	5.88–8.88	7.06–10.6	7.62–11.6	1	
5.94–7.88	7.06–9.56	8.88–11.8	10.6–14.1	11.6–15.2	$1\frac{1}{2}$	

The breakdown torque range includes the higher figure down to horizontal line, but not including, the lower figure.

The horsepower rating of motors designed to operate on two or more frequencies shall be determined by the torque at the highest rated frequency.

Table 17-7. Minimum Locked Rotor Torques of Single Phase Induction Motors

		Minimum locked rotor Torque						
		60-cycle speed, Hz			50-cycle speed, Hz			
Synchronous Speed		3600	1800	1200	3000	1500	1000	Units of Torque
Approximate Full Load Speed		3450	1725	1140	2850	1425	950	
Horsepower	$\frac{1}{8}$		24	32	...	29	39	torque in oz-ft.
	$\frac{1}{6}$	15	33	43	18	39	51	
	$\frac{1}{4}$	21	46	59	25	55	70	
	$\frac{1}{3}$	26	57	73	31	69	88	
	$\frac{1}{2}$	37	85	100	44	102	120	
	$\frac{3}{4}$	50	119	8.0	60	143		torque in lb-ft.
	1	61	9.0	9.5	73			
	$1\frac{1}{2}$	4.5	12.5	13.0				
	2	5.5	16.0	16.0				
	3	7.5	22.0	23.0				
	5	11.0	33.0	...				
	$7\frac{1}{2}$	16.0	45.0	...				

Approximate full load speeds are for fractional horse power motor ratings only. Units for torque (see right hand column of table), in ounce-ft are above the lines and in lb-ft below the lines.

Table 17-8. Locked Rotor kva of ac Motors

Designation Letter	locked rotor kva/hp[a]	Designation Letter	Locked Rotor kva/hp[a]	Designation Letter	Locked Rotor kva/hp[a]
A	0–3.15	G	5.6 – 6.3	N	11.2 – 12.5
B	3.15–3.55	H	6.3 – 7.1	P	12.5 – 14.0
C	3.55 – 4.0	J	7.1 – 8.0	R	14.0 – 16.0
D	4.0 – 4.5	K	8.0 – 9.0	S	16.0 – 18.0
E	4.5 – 5.0	L	9.0 – 10.0	T	18.0 – 20.0
F	5.0 – 5.6	M	10.0 – 11.2	U	20.0 – 22.4
				V	22.4 – and up

[a] Locked rotor kva/hp range includes the lower figure, but not including the higher figure. For example, everything under 3.15 is in letter A, and 3.15 and above are in letter B.

The National Electrical Code

The National Electrical Code (NEC) is sponsored by the National Fire Protection Association (NFPA), under the auspices of the American National Standards Institute (ANSI). The National Electrical Code is purely advisory, as far as the NFPA and ANSI are concerned, but is offered for use in law and for regulatory purposes in the interest of life and property protection.

The NEC has been adopted in its entirety, in edited versions, or in part, by various state and local agencies throughout the United States having regulatory and enforcement jurisdiction over the installation of electrical work.

Included are the following subjects:

Marking on motors and multimotor equipment marking on controllers

Sizing of conductors

Motor and branch-circuit running over current protection (commonly referred to as "overload protection")

Motor branch-circuit, short-circuit, and ground fault protection

Motor-feeder, short-circuit, and ground-fault protection

Motor control circuits

Motor controllers

Disconnecting means requirements over 600 volts

Table 17-9. Motor HP and Full Load Currents for Single Phase Motors

hp	Full Load Current, Amp	
	115 V	230 V
⅙	4.4	2.2
¼	5.8	2.9
⅓	7.2	3.6
½	9.8	4.9
¾	13.8	6.9
1	16	8
1½	20	10
2	24	12
3	34	17
5	56	28
7½	80	40
10	100	50

To obtain full load currents of 208 and 200 volt motors, increase corresponding 230 volt, full load currents by 10 and 15%, respectively.

Grounding.—In addition, the NEC provides for the special considerations necessary for circuits supplying sealed (hermetic-type) motor compressors. The NEC also gives attention to air conditioning and/or refrigerating equipment incorporating a sealed (hermetic-type) motor-compressor supplied from an individual branch circuit. Included are the following subjects:

Marking on sealed (hermetic-type) motor compressors and equipment Marking on controllers

Means for disconnecting

Branch-circuit, short-circuit, and ground-fault protection

Sizing of conductors

Controllers for motor compressors, and motor compressor and branch-circuit overload protection.

Table 17-10. Motor HP and Full Load Currents for Three-Phase Motors

	Full-Load Current, Amp								
	Induction Type Squirrel Cage and Wound Rotor					Synchronous Type Unity Power Factor			
hp	115 V	230 V	460 V	575 V	2300 V	230 V	460 V	575 V	2300 V
½	4	2	1	0.8	...	...	...	...	...
¾	5.6	2.8	1.4	1.1	...	...	...	...	...
1	7.2	3.6	1.8	1.4	...	...	...	...	...
1½	10.4	5.2	2.6	2.1	...	...	...	...	...
2	13.6	6.8	3.4	2.7	...	...	...	...	...
3	...	9.6	4.8	3.9	...	...	...	...	...
5	...	15.2	7.6	6.1	...	...	...	...	...
7½	...	22	11	9	...	...	...	...	...
10	...	28	14	11	...	...	...	...	...
15	...	42	21	17	...	...	...	...	...
20	...	54	27	22	...	...	...	...	...
25	...	68	34	27	...	53	26	21	...
30	...	80	40	32	...	63	32	26	...
40	...	104	52	41	...	83	41	33	...
50	...	130	65	52	...	104	52	42	...
60	...	154	77	62	16	123	61	49	12
75	...	192	96	77	20	155	78	62	15
100	...	248	124	99	26	202	101	81	20
125	...	312	156	125	31	53	126	101	25
150	...	360	180	144	37	302	151	121	30
200	...	480	240	192	49	400	201	161	40

NEC tables list full load currents, versus horsepower for non hermetic ac motors and for dc motors. These tables are used to determine the ampacity of conductors and the rating of switches and branch circuit over current devices. However, separate motor running over current (overload) protection is based on the motor nameplate current rating. The full load currents listed in the tables are not necessarily identical with the full load currents marked on various manufacturer motor nameplates for corresponding horsepower ratings. Nevertheless, the table information can be taken as representative for ac motors that are running at usual speeds, with normal torque characteristics, and for dc motors running at a base speed. The NEC tables repeated are here:

Table 17-9: *Full Load Current*: Single-phase ac motors

Table 17-10: *Full Load Current*: Three-phase ac motors

Table 17-11: *Full Load Current*: Two-phase ac motors, (4-wire)

Table 17-12: *Full Load Current*: dc motors.

Table 17-11. Motor HP and Full Load Currents for Two Phase (4-Wire) Motors

	Full-Load Current, Amp								
	Induction Type Squirrel Cage and Wound Rotor					Synchronous Type Unity Power Factor			
hp	115 V	230 V	460 V	575 V	2300 V	220 V	440 V	550 V	2300 V
½	4	2	1	0.8	...	...	...	...	...
¾	4.8	2.4	1.2	1.0	...	...	...	...	...
1	6.4	3.2	1.6	1.3					
1½	9	4.5	2.3	1.8	...				
2	11.8	5.9	3	2.4	...	...	...	...	...
3	...	8.3	4.2	3.3	...	...	...	...	...
5	...	13.2	6.6	5.3	...	...	...	...	...
7½	...	19	9	8	...	...	...	...	...
10	...	24	12	10	...	...	...	...	...
15.	...	36	18	14	...	...	...	...	...
20	...	47	23	19	...	...	...	...	...
25	...	59	29	24	...	47	24	19	...
30	...	69	35	28	...	56	29	23	...
40	...	90	45	36	...	75	37	31	...
50	...	113	56	45	...	94	47	38	...
60	...	133	67	53	14	111	56	44	11
75	...	166	83	66	18	140	70	57	13
100	...	218	109	87	23	182	93	74	17
125	...	270	135	108	28	228	114	93	22
150	...	312	156	125	32	...	137	110	26
200	...	416	208	167	43	...	182	145	35

Table 17-12. Full Load Currents for DC Motors (Amperes)

	Armature Voltage Rating					
hp	90 V	120 V	180 V	240 V	500 V	550 V
¼	4.0	3.1	2.0	1.6	...	...
⅓	5.2	4.1	2.6	2.0	...	...
½	6.8	5.4	3.4	2.7	...	...
¾	9.6	7.6	4.8	3.8	...	...
1	12.2	9.5	6.1	4.7	...	...
1½	...	13.2	8.3	6.6	...	...
2	...	17	10.8	8.5	...	...
3	...	25	16	12.2	...	...
5	...	40	27	20	...	...
7½	...	58	...	29	13.6	12.2
10	...	76	...	38	18	16
15	...	...	...	55	27	24
20	...	...	...	72	34	31
25	...	...	...	89	43	38
30	...	...	...	106	51	46
40	...	...	...	140	67	61
50	...	...	...	173	83	75
60	...	...	...	206	99	90
75	...	...	...	255	123	111
100	...	...	...	341	164	148
125	...	...	...	425	205	185
150	...	...	...	506	246	222
200	...	...	...	675	330	294

Table 17-13. Locked Rotor Current Conversions

	Motor Locked Rotor Current Amperes						
Max hp Rating	Single-Phase		Two-or Three-Phase				
	115 V	230 V	115 V	200 V	230 V	460 V	575 V
½	58.8	29.4	24	14	12	6	4.8
¾	82.8	41.4	33.6	19	16.8	8.4	6.6
1	96	48	42	24	21	10.8	8.4
1½	120	60	60	34	30	15	12
2	144	72	78	45	39	19.8	15.6
3	204	102	...	62	54	27	24
5	336	168	...	103	90	45	36
7½	480	240	...	152	132	66	54
10	600	300	...	186	162	84	66
15	...	...	...	276	240	120	96
20	...	...	...	359	312	156	126
25	...	...	...	442	384	192	156
30	...	...	...	538	468	234	186
40	...	...	...	718	624	312	246
50	...	...	...	862	750	378	300
60	...	...	...	1035	900	450	360
75	...	...	...	1276	1110	558	444
100	...	...	...	1697	1476	738	588
125	...	...	...	2139	1860	930	744
150	...	...	...	2484	2160	1080	864
200	...	...	...	3312	2880	1440	1152

The NEC also incorporates a locked rotor current conversion table relating to the horsepower and voltage rating of typical motors. The locked rotor values in the table are used in determining ratings of some disconnect devices and controllers for sealed (hermetic type) motor compressors. The table values are representative and do not necessarily agree exactly with manufacturers actually locked rotor currents. Table 17-13 gives the NEC locked rotor conversion table. The listed values are applicable to full voltage (across the line) starting, and it is useful to relate them to various schemes for reduced voltage and part winding starting. Table 17-10 in previous section, derived from NEMA, also can be used for this purpose.

Motor and Load Dynamics, and Motor Heating

Torque-Speed Relationships for a Typical Three-Phase Induction Motor.—Fig. 17-1a shows the torque-speed curve and Fig. 17-1b the current speed curve of a 100 hp, 1760, 4-pole, 3-phase, NEMA Design B induction motor. It can be seen from Fig. 17-1a that the locked rotor torque (torque at start up when voltage is applied and the motor has not yet begun to rotate) is 125% of the full load torque. As the motor accelerates and picks up speed, the torque increases to a maximum value known as the "break down torque," which for this motor is 200% of the full load torque while occurring at about 80% of the full load speed.

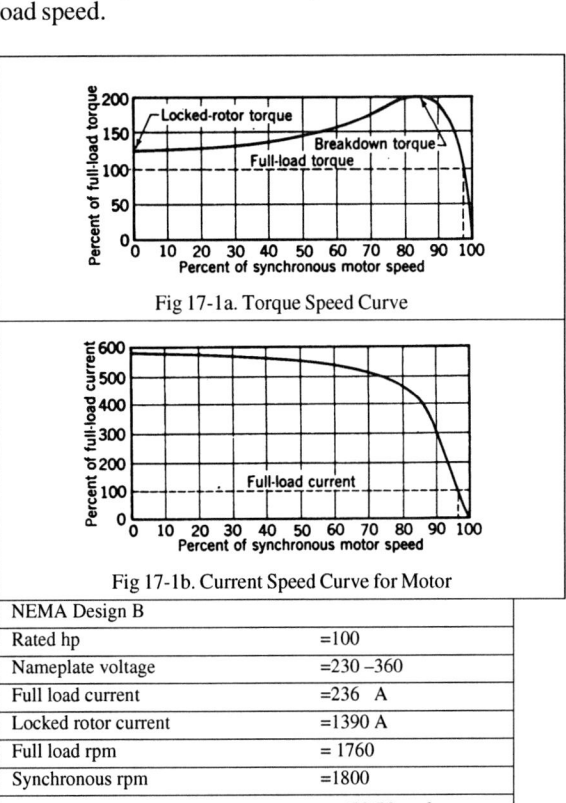

Fig 17-1a. Torque Speed Curve

Fig 17-1b. Current Speed Curve for Motor

NEMA Design B	
Rated hp	=100
Nameplate voltage	=230 –360
Full load current	=236 A
Locked rotor current	=1390 A
Full load rpm	= 1760
Synchronous rpm	=1800
Full load torque	$= \dfrac{5250 \times hp}{rpm}$ $= \dfrac{5250 \times 100}{1760}$ $= 300$ lb-ft
Locked rotor torque	$= 1.25 \times 300$ $= 375$ lb-ft
Breakdown torque	$= 2.00 \times 300$ $= 600$ lb-ft
kva	$= \dfrac{3 \times E \times I}{1000}$

Locked rotor kva	$= \dfrac{1.73 \times 230 \times 1390}{1000}$ $= 553$
Locked rotor kva/ hp	$= \dfrac{553}{100}$ $= 5.53$
Code Letter *F*	

As the motor continues its acceleration, the torque drops sharply until the motor torque is in balance with the load torque at approximately 98% of synchronous speed. Therefore, if the driven load is the same as the motor rating, in this case 100 hp, the motor speed will balance out at the rated speed of 1760, which is a revolutions slip of 40 from the 1800 synchronous motor speed. If the driven load is less than 100 hp, the revolutions slip will be less than 40; however, even under a no-load condition, the motor speed will not reach the synchronous speed due to friction and windage losses.

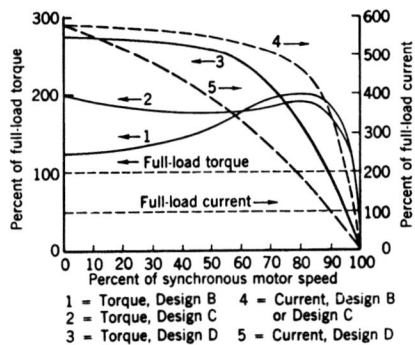

Fig 17-2. Torque current relationships for 100 hp, 1800 rpm motor; locked rotor kva/hp = 5.52; Code letter F

In Fig. 17-1b the current at start up (locked rotor current) is almost 600% of the full load current. As the motor accelerates towards full load speed, there is no significant decrease in the current drawn by the motor until the motor speed is roughly 85% of the full load speed. At this point the motor current drops off rapidly as the motor speed continues to increase to the point where the motor torque is shown in balance with the load current at approximately 96% synchronous speed.

Three-phase induction motors have five NEMA design classes that provide variations in motor characteristics. These variations are obtained by differences in rotor design. The three most commonly used classes are NEMA Design B, NEMA Design C, and NEMA Design D. Fig. 17-2 compares the torque-speed and current-speed curves of a 100-hp motor for the three designs.

Torque-speed relationships of driven loads normally fall within three general categories: constant horsepower, constant torque, and variable torque. These are represented by the curves in Fig. 17-3, the solid lines representing theoretical relationships. For example, curve A for theoretical constant horsepower is derived by making the torque multiplied by the speed equal to a constant. Curve B, by definition, shows a theoretical constant torque at all speeds. Curve C for theoretical variable torque is derived by letting torque be proportional to speed.

This variable-torque relationship is equivalent to the horsepower varying as the square of the speed.

Fig. 17-3 also shows some of the many actually driven loads that approach the theoretical curves. Actual curves, however, are seldom coincident with theoretical curves. For instance, the curve for a shearing machine (similar to that of a lathe) approaches the configuration of the theoretical constant horsepower curve. The curve as shown for a reciprocating or rotary compressor, under constant suction and discharge pressures and without unloaders, can be considered close to the configuration of the constant torque curve. In this curve there is a sudden sharp increase in load torque at zero speed to breakaway torque, and then a drop-off. The gradual increase in torque thereafter, which is proportional to speed, results from internal friction in the compressor. The curve for a centrifugal fan, pump, or compressor approaches the theoretical variable torque curve. In this actual curve, the torque varies almost as the square of the speed (horsepower varies as the cube of the speed); however, in the theoretical curve the torque is proportional to the speed.

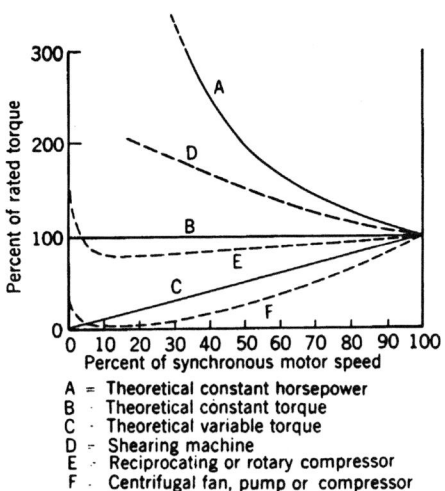

Fig 17-3. Load Torque Relationships for 100 hp, 1800 rpm motor; locked rotor kva/hp =5.52; Code letter F

Torque, Inertia, and Acceleration Time.—Starting from rest, a motor will accelerate in speed as long as its torque output is greater than the resisting torque of the driven load. Eventually, as the motor continues to pick up speed, its generated torque will decrease. At some point, the motor torque will exactly equal the resisting load torque, and acceleration will cease.

The time to accelerate through the entire starting period is a function of:

1) the difference between the motor output torque and the load torque; and

2) the inertia of the motor-load system. The difference between generated-motor and resisting-load torques through the entire starting period can be analyzed by plotting in graphical form the motor and load torques in relation to motor speed. Manufacturer data will usually supply the inertia of both a motor and a driven machine.

Torque normally is used in calculations in engineering units of lb-ft. For rotating bodies, the moment of inertia is frequently referred to as the "flywheel effect". Mathematically it is expressed as Wk^2, in units of lb-ft^2; where W is the weight of the rotating body, and k is its radius of gyration with respect to its rotational axis.

The next section illustrates the derivation of the formula for motor acceleration time and its application for a graphical solution. In Fig. 17-4, the torques of the motor and load are plotted against motor speed. The graph then is divided into numerous finite vertical increments in which the average T_r-T_l as well as the RPM_2-RPM_1 of each increment can be measured. The time to accelerate in seconds within each increment is given by the formula

$$\Delta t = Wk^2 \frac{(RPM_2 - RPM_1)}{308(T_r - T_l)}$$

where, in this instance, Wk^2 is the inertia of the motor plus the load referenced to the motor speed. The total time to accelerate is the sum of all the incremental time periods.

As can be seen from the formula for acceleration time, a large flywheel effect results in a relatively long acceleration period. Centrifugal compressors and large fans are characteristic of loads having large inertias. Acceleration periods approaching one minute for large centrifugal compressors are not uncommon. On the other hand, reciprocating compressors have low inertias. Thus, their acceleration periods are usually of short duration.

Frequently the load speed differs from the motor speed. For example, a V-belt driven fan or compressor usually rotates at a lower speed than the motor that drives it. Also, a centrifugal compressor driven through a gear assembly generally rotates at a higher speed than the motor. In making motor-load system torque and inertia calculations, it is necessary to relate the torque and inertia values to either the motor or the load speed. Industrial practice usually relates these values to the motor speed. By so doing, the load torque vs. speed curve can be shown on the same chart as the motor torque vs. speed curve.

Table 17-14 lists the mathematical relations for referencing the various torques and inertias to motor and load speeds in situations where the load and motor speeds differ. For example, if a centrifugal compressor is geared to be driven at twice the motor speed, the equivalent inertia

(Table 17-14, line 4) is given by $\left(\dfrac{w_l}{w_r}\right) \times J_l$. Thus, the equivalent inertia is $\left(\dfrac{w_l}{w_r}\right)^2 \times J_l$ times the compressor inertia. From this, it can be seen that a small, high-speed centrifugal compressor may have an equivalent inertia which is as great as a large, centrifugal compressor of equal capacity but slower speed. Both may have equally prolonged acceleration periods.

Dynamics of the Motor and the Load (Motor Speed is same with Load Speed).—

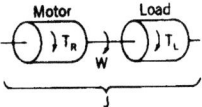

Equivalent motor load system:

$$J = \int \frac{Z^2 dW}{g} = \frac{Wk^2}{g}$$

$$T_r = T_l + J\frac{dw}{dt}$$

Steady state:

$$\frac{dw}{dt} = 0, \ T_r = T_l$$

Acceleration time:

$$dt = J\frac{dw}{T_r - T_l} = J\left(\frac{1}{T_r - T_l}\right)dw$$

$$t = J \int_{w_1}^{w_2} \frac{dw}{T_r - T_l}$$

Graphical solution of acceleration time:

$$dt = J\left(\frac{1}{T_r - T_l}\right)dw$$

$$= \frac{Wk^2}{32.2}\left(\frac{1}{T_r - T_l}\right)\frac{(RPM_2 - RPM_1)2\pi}{60}$$

$$= \frac{Wk^2(RPM_2 - RPM_1)}{308(T_r - T_l)}$$

$$t = \sum \frac{Wk^2(RPM_2 - RPM_1)}{308(T_r - T_l)}$$

g = acceleration due to gravity, 32.2 ft/sec^2

k = radius of gyration, ft

J_r = polar moment of inertia of motor, lb-ft sec^2

J_l = polar moment of inertia of load, lb-ft sec^2

J = polar moment of inertia of motor plus load, referenced to motor speed, lb-ft sec^2

RPM_r = revolutions per minute of motor

RPM_l = revolutions per minute of load

RPM_s = revolutions per minute of motor at synchronus speed

$RPM_2 - RPM_1$ = revolutions per minute increment of speed, referenced to motor speed

RPM = revolutions per minute of motor at final speed after acceleration

$SLIP = (RPM_s - RPM_r)/RPM_s$

Revolution SLIP $= RPM_s - RPM_r$

T_r = motor torque, lb-ft

T_l = load torque, lb-ft

$T_r - T_l$ = net accelerating torque, referenced to motor speed, lb-ft

t = accelerating time, sec

W_r = weight of rotating motor, lb

W_l = weight of rotating load, lb

W = weight of rotating motor and load, lb

$W_r k_r^2$ = flywheel effect of motor, lb-ft^2

$W_l k_l^2$ = flywheel effect of load, lb-ft^2

Wk^2 = flywheel effect of motor plus load, referenced to motor speed, lb-ft^2

Z = distance from the axis of rotation to center of gravity of an element, ft

w_r = rotating speed of motor, radians per second

w_l = rotating speed of load, radians per second

w = rotating speed of motor and load when both rotate at same speed, radians per second

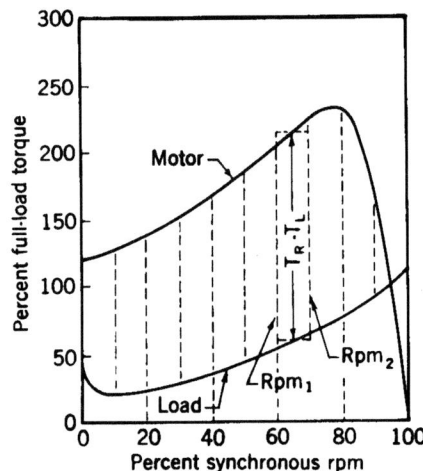

Fig 17-4. Dynamics of motor and load

Table 17-14. Dynamics of Motor and Load
(motor speed differs with load speed)

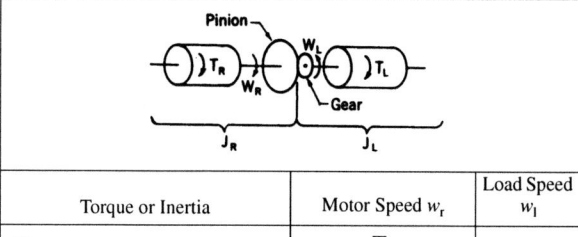

Torque or Inertia	Motor Speed w_r	Load Speed w_l
Motor torque	T_r	...
Load torque	$\dfrac{w_l}{w_r} \times T_l$	T_l
Motor and pinion inertia	J_r	...
Load and gear inertia	$\left(\dfrac{w_l}{w_r}\right)^2 \times J_l$	J_l
Motor and pinion flywheel inertia	$W_k k_k^2$	...
Load and gear flywheel inertia	$\left(\dfrac{w_l}{w_r}\right)^2 \times W_l k_l^2$	$W_l k_l^2$
	$\dfrac{w_l}{w_r} = \dfrac{\text{RPM}_l}{\text{RPM}_r}$	

Motor Heating and Motor Life.—The next section derives mathematically the calculation for energy absorbed by the rotor during an increment of acceleration time. It also denotes how the total energy absorbed by the rotor during the acceleration period can be derived graphically with the same motor vs. speed and load vs. speed curves as used previously for determining the acceleration time.

It is obvious that the energy absorbed by the rotor is greater when the acceleration time increases. Also, a motor will heat up more during starting when it is applied to a load having a greater inertia (Wk^2) and, to some extent, a greater load torque during the starting period.

Dissipation of heat to the surrounding air is limited during starting, thus most of the heat absorbed by the rotor produces a temperature rise in the iron and copper of the motor itself. The newer design motors on the market contain less iron than previous designs and consequently have less thermal storage capacity. When a motor-load system has a prolonged acceleration period, consultation with the motor manufacturer is suggested to determine that motor overheating will not occur.

Frequent starting of a motor-load system also can cause motor overheating, since there may not be sufficient running time between starts to dissipate the heat absorbed during each starting period. And again, this problem becomes more severe when the acceleration periods are prolonged. Good practice is to obtain maximum recommended starts per hour, or starts per day, from the motor manufacturer when frequent starting of a high inertia load is required.

A special, severe case of motor overheating can occur under locked rotor conditions. This takes place when the locked rotor torque of the motor is less than the breakaway torque of the load. In this situation the motor cannot begin to rotate, and the slip remains at 100%.

The newer designed, open, drip-proof motors have theoretical lives of roughly, say, 20,000 hours when run at rated loads in an ambient temperature of 40°C (104°F). When run at a 1.10 service factor, or a 10% overload, the theoretical life is cut to 10,000 hours. When run at 90% rated load, the theoretical life increases to 40,000 hours. The decrease in lifespan results from a high temperature rise within the motor, which decreases insulation life.

The most common cause for motor overheating is overloading. Referring to the torque-speed curve of Fig. 17-1a, a motor will continue to function without an appreciable increase in slip if the torque or load imposed on the motor is increased almost to the point of double the rated motor load. The current drawn by the motor is almost proportional to the increase in load to about 150% of rated load, where it then increases at a faster rate. The increased current in the stator winding and the increased rotor losses at higher loads raise the motor temperature and reduce motor life.

For a constant load a reduction in voltage applied to the motor terminal causes an inversely proportional increase in the current drawn by the stator. The increased current, if significant, can cause an excessive temperature rise in the motor. On the other hand, an increase in voltage does not necessarily decrease the total motor current. If the flux density in the motor core has approached saturation, an increase in voltage might require an increase in the magnetizing component of the motor current, which is greater than the reduction in the load or effective component of the motor current. The increased magnetizing current not only reduces the power factor but can cause heating due to additional resistance losses in the stator winding. The increase in flux density causes a greater loss in the motor core contributing to an increase in motor heating. Excessive voltage also can contribute to the breakdown of motor winding insulation. Motor manufacturers generally will not warrant their equipment if the voltage applied to the motor terminals differs by more than 10% from the nameplate value.

Other causes of decreased motor life are dust, dirt, chemicals, and oil or grease, which can be deposited on motor windings and in motor bearings when the motor is operated in a dirty environment. The erosion of insulation, the decrease in heat dissipation capability, and the contamination of bearings also contribute to motor destruction. Totally enclosed fan-cooled (TEFC) or explosion-proof motors generally are recommended for dirty environments.

Either a lack of effective air movement or high temperatures in spaces surrounding working motors can cause excessive temperatures within motors and can reduce motor life.

Rotor Heating During Starting.—*Slip* is equal to the ratio of the I^2R losses in the rotor to the total nonreactive power delivered to the rotor; therefore I^2R losses at any instant are equal to the nonreactive power multiplied by the slip. Energy absorbed by the rotor during an invrement of time is a function of I^2R losses multiplied by the increment of time. Total energy absorbed by the rotor during accleration is the summation of energy absorption for all increments of time:

Effective power delivered to motor

$$= \frac{T_r \times 2\pi \times \mathrm{RPM}_s}{33000} \times 0.746$$

$$= \mathrm{RPM}_s \times \frac{T_r \times 2\pi \times 0.746}{33000} \quad \text{(kw)}$$

I^2R rotor loss $=$ power slip loss

$= slip \times$ effective power delivered to motor

$$= \frac{\mathrm{RPM}_s - \dfrac{(\mathrm{RPM}_2 + \mathrm{RPM}_1)}{2}}{\mathrm{RPM}_s} \times \mathrm{RPM}_s \times \frac{T_r \times 2\pi \times 0.746}{33000}$$

$$= \left[\mathrm{RPM}_s - \left(\frac{\mathrm{RPM}_2 + \mathrm{RPM}_1}{2}\right)\right] \times \frac{T_r \times 2\pi \times 0.746}{33000} \quad \text{(kw)}$$

Energy absorbed by rotor

$= I^2R$ rotor loss $\times \Delta t$

$$= \left[\mathrm{RPM}_s - \left(\frac{\mathrm{RPM}_2 + \mathrm{RPM}_1}{2}\right)\right] \times \frac{T_r \times 2\pi \times 0.746}{33000}$$

$$\frac{Wk^2(\mathrm{RPM}_2 - \mathrm{RPM}_1)}{308(T_r - T_l)}$$

$$= \frac{1}{2.16 \times 10^6}\left[\mathrm{RPM}_s - \left(\frac{\mathrm{RPM}_2 + \mathrm{RPM}_1}{2}\right)\right]$$

$$\frac{Wk^2(\mathrm{RPM}_2 - \mathrm{RPM}_1) \times T_r}{(T_r - T_l)} \quad \text{(kw-sec)}$$

Total energy absorbed by rotor during accleration, KW-sec.

Graphical solution

$$= \sum \frac{1}{2.16 \times 10^6}\left[\mathrm{RPM}_s - \left(\frac{\mathrm{RPM}_2 + \mathrm{RPM}_1}{2}\right)\right]$$

$$\frac{Wk^2(\mathrm{RPM}_2 - \mathrm{RPM}_1) \times T_r}{(T_r - T_l)} \quad \text{(kw-sec)}$$

Portion of total energy absorbed by rotor for acclerating the rotating mass (load torque neglected)

$$\text{Kinetic energy} = \frac{1}{2}JW^2 \quad \text{(lb-ft)}$$

$$\text{Kinetic energy} = \frac{1}{2}JW^2 \times \frac{0.746}{550}$$

$$= \frac{1}{2} \times \frac{Wk^2}{32.2} \times \frac{(2\pi \times \mathrm{RPM})^2}{3600} \times \frac{0.746}{550}$$

$$= \frac{0.231 \times Wk^2 \times \mathrm{RPM}^2}{10^6} \quad \text{(kw-sec)}$$

Single Phase Motors

If one lead of a three-phase (polyphase) motor is disconnected from the line while the motor is running, it will continue to operate on the phase that remains connected providing the connected load is not too great. However, the speed will be reduced. In this case rotation is maintained by the pulsating field produced by the single phase that is connected to the line and by the field set up by the rotating rotor. A polyphase motor at rest will not start if only two of its leads are connected to the line since the single-phase pulsating field does not rotate and hence is unable to initiate rotation of the rotor.

A single-phase induction motor, then, must have some auxiliary means of providing a rotating field for starting. The most common method of providing this in single-phase induction motors is to add an auxiliary (starting) winding displaced from the main winding in both time and space. This second winding is generally separated in space by 90 electrical degrees from the main winding. Rotation is produced by creating an electrical phase displacement between the currents in the two windings. If the starting winding remained in the circuit under normal load conditions, losses would be excessive, the motor would overheat, and the starting winding would burn out. For this reason the starting winding is disconnected at approximately 75% of the motor's rated speed. This means that some disconnecting device also must be provided in each motor.

Types of Motors.—*Split-Phase:* The split-phase motor is a single phase induction motor having an auxiliary starting winding that has a high ratio of resistance to reactance as compared to the main winding connected in parallel with it. See Table 17-15. In this type of motor the auxiliary or starting winding is disconnected either by a centrifugally operated starting switch or by a relay when the motor reaches about three quarters of rated speed. These motors have from low to medium starting torque depending on their rating. For ratings above $\frac{1}{6}$ hp the locked rotor or starting torque is kept low because of locked rotor current limitations, which will be discussed later. Split-phase motors have a relatively low cost and are simple in construction compared with most other single-phase motors of the same ratings.

Some split-phase motors, for use on infrequently started devices, are provided with higher starting torques that can be obtained with the normal starting currents for this type of motor. In these cases the starting current is above the NEMA value for single-phase fractional horsepower motors.

There are various methods of obtaining two speed operation of split-phase motors. One common means is shown in Table 17-15.

When the split-phase motor drives through a belt, it is frequently provided with built-in thermal protection to prevent damage from overloading due to a tight belt or incorrect pulley ratio.

Capacitor: The capacitor motor, a modification of the split-phase type, is an induction motor whose auxiliary winding is connected in series with a capacitor. In small sizes, it is generally built in two types: the *capacitor-start type* and the *permanent split capacitor type*. In larger sizes it may combine the features of both types and so is called a capacitor-start-and-run-motor; a *capacitor-start-capacitor run motor*; or a *two-value capacitor motor*.

The principles of operation and the construction of the capacitor start motor are similar to the split phase motor except for the addition of the electrolytic capacitor. The capacitor start fractional horsepower motor is manufactured in ratings of from $\frac{1}{6}$ to $\frac{3}{4}$ hp. It is a general-purpose motor suitable for most applications.

The permanent-split capacitor motor uses a continuous-duty, oil-filled capacitor during both the starting and running periods. This type of motor has low starting current and torque, and the main and auxiliary windings are in the circuit at all times. No centrifugal starting switch or relay is used. The speed control is obtained by impressing different voltages on the main winding by means of a transformer or a reactor (choke coil or autotransformer), or by using a main winding, which is tapped in a manner that reduces the amount of the main winding for higher speed operation.

The capacitor-start-and-run-motor generally uses an intermittent duty electrolytic capacitor during the starting period and a continuous-duty, oil-filled capacitor during both the starting and running periods. Advantages of the running capacitor are that it can improve the power factor of the motor and can increase the value of the breakdown torque.

For ratings of $\frac{1}{3}$ hp and above, many capacitor-start and capacitor-start and run motors are manufactured for dual-voltage operation. In the case of a 115/230-volt capacitor-start motor, the main winding is made in two sections. The sections are connected in parallel for 115-volt operation and in series for 230-volt operation. The auxiliary winding and the capacitor connect across one section of the main winding. Wiring connections for operation at the desired voltage can be made at the motor terminal board following instructions supplied by the motor manufacturer.

Shaded-Pole: Another type of single-phase motor is the "shaded-pole motor". The starting torque of a shaded-pole motor is provided by an auxiliary permanently short-circuited winding or windings placed around a portion of the main pole. This winding is frequently a copper strap wrapped around a portion of the pole. The flux through the shaded section of the pole lags behind the flux in the rest of the pole, thus producing the effect of a rotating field and providing a starting force. The starting current and torque of this type motor are very low compared with other types of single phase motors. The shaded-pole motor is rugged and simple in construction. Its low efficiency, due to losses produced by the shading coils, has limited its application to the smaller ratings.

Repulsion-Start: Although repulsion-start induction motors are in use, they have been supplanted largely by the capacitor-start motors. The repulsion start induction motor starts on the repulsion principle. Single-phase power is applied to the stator winding. This induces current flow in the rotor winding, which is similar to that of a dc commutator motor. The brush axis is displaced several degrees from the line of flux flow. This permits an unbalanced current flow in the two halves of the rotor and the resultant torque starts the motor. As it approaches full speed, the armature coils are short circuited by a centrifugal mechanism, and the motor then operates on the induction principle with the same characteristics as a split-phase or capacitor-start motor. In some motors the brushes are lifted when the armature windings are short-circuited in order to reduce brush wear and noise. The advantage of the repulsion-start induction motor is extra high starting torque with low starting current. It has the disadvantages of a wound armature, brushes, armature short-circuiting mechanism, brush-lifting mechanism and their attendant maintenance and increased cost.

This type of motor is characterized by a very high starting torque with relatively low starting current. However, the torque of the motor decays rapidly as it comes up to speed, and even the best designs tend to be deficient in torque at the switching speed. To overcome this, it is common to build the motors with an excess of starting torque, sometimes as high as 500%, so that the torque at switching speed is high enough, say 200%, to insure successful operation.

Table 17-15. Application Data for Fractional Horsepower Single-Phase Motors

Type of Motor		Wiring Diagram	Horse-power Range	Speed Data			Approximate Torque (4-Pole Motors)		Built-in Starting Mechanism	Application Data
				Rated Speed	Speed Characteristics	Speed Control	Starting	Break down		
Split Phase	Normal purpose low locked rotor ampres		$\frac{1}{20}$ to $\frac{1}{3}$	1725 1140 860	Constant	None	Medium to low	Medium	Centrifugal switch[a]	For oil burners, fans, blowers, low locked rotor current minimizes light flicker, making motor suitable for frequent starting. For applications up to $\frac{1}{3}$ hp where medium starting and break-down torques are sufficient.
	High starting current		$\frac{1}{4}$ to $\frac{1}{3}$	1725	Constant	None	Medium	High	Centrifugal switch[a]	Ideal for sump pumps. For continuous and intermittent duty, where operation is infrequent and locked rotor current in excess of NEMA values is not objectionable. May cause light flicker on underwired or overloaded lighting circuits.
	Two speed (two windings)		$\frac{1}{8}$ to $\frac{1}{4}$	1725/1140 1725/860	Two speed	1-pole double throw switch	Medium	Medium	Centrifugal switch[a]	For belted furnace blowers, attic ventilating fans, similar belted medium-torque jobs. Simplicity permits operation with any 1-pole, double-throw switch or relay. Starts well on either-speed thus used with thermostatic or other automatic control. Tight belt or incorrect pulley ratio may overload motor.
Capacitor	General purpose capacitor start		$\frac{1}{6}$ to $\frac{3}{4}$	1725 1140 860	Constant	None	High	High	Centrifugal switch[a]	Ideal for all heavy duty drives, such as compressors, pumps, stokers, refrigerators, air conditioning. All purpose motor for high starting torque, low starting current. Quiet, economical. High efficiency and power factor. Single voltage in $\frac{1}{6}$, $\frac{1}{4}$ hp. 1725 rpm ratings dual voltage in others.
	Two speed capacitor start (two windings)		$\frac{1}{6}$ to $\frac{3}{4}$	1725/1140 1725/860	Two speed	1-pole double throw switch	Medium	Medium	Centrifugal switch[a]	Supplements line of 2-speed split-phase motors. Used on identical applications requiring horsepower ratings from $\frac{1}{3}$ to $\frac{3}{4}$ hp.
	Permanent split (single value)		$\frac{1}{20}$ to $\frac{3}{4}$	1625 1075 825	Constant or adjustable varying	Autotransformer or tapped winding	Very low	low	None	For direct connected fan drives, particularly unit heaters. Not for belt drives. Same motor adaptable for 115 or 230 volts for 1-speed, 2-speed, or multi-speed service by use of 1-pole, single-throw switch, 2-pole, double-throw switch, or speed controller, respectively. Fan load must be accurately matched to motor output for proper speed control. All rating dual voltage and dual rotation.
	Capacitor start and run		$\frac{1}{3}$ to $\frac{3}{4}$	1725 1140 860	Constant	None	Medium to high	High	Centrifugal switch[a]	Same as described above for general-purpose capacitor start.
Shaded pole			$\frac{1}{300}$ to $\frac{3}{4}$	1550 1050 800	Constant or adjustable varying	Autotransformer or tapped winding	Very low	low	None	Constant speed, switchless motor for low power application. Used for fans, small blowers, unit heaters. With fan load accurately matched to motor output, proper speed control can be obtained by means of series choke, auto transformer or tapped winding.

[a] May use current switching relay $\frac{1}{6}$ to $\frac{1}{4}$ horsepower and potential switching relay $\frac{1}{4}$ to $\frac{3}{4}$ horsepower in lieu of centrifugal switch.

Repulsion-Induction.—The term *repulsion-induction* is applied to a few types of motors in which the rotor carries a wire-wound repulsion winding, with its commutator and a squirrel cage winding. The motor gets its starting ability from the repulsion winding and its running torque from the combination of the two rotor windings. The change from the starting to the running condition is made electrically and magnetically so that there is no abrupt change in characteristics.

Commercial motors of this type have a relatively high starting torque in the 250–325% range, and low starting current. Efficiency is competitive with all the other types and the power factor is extremely high. Because of the smooth transfer from the starting to the running condition, this type of motor excels in severe starting and accelerating duty, especially at low voltage.

Large Single-Phase Motors.—Large single-phase motors vary in size from ¾ hp through 5 hp, and above. The three general types of large single-phase motors frequently used are the capacitor motor (either capacitor-start or capacitor-start-and-run), the repulsion-start induction-run motor, and the repulsion-induction motor. Each manufacturer has its own variation of the circuits and the mechanical devices used in the motor.

No practical single-phase motor has yet been invented that has the simplicity of the polyphase, squirrel-cage induction motor, and most large single-phase motors have some type of extra device to make them start. This is either integrally mounted or supplied as an external part. Great ingenuity has been shown by designers and manufacturers in making simple yet rugged devices.

However, the fact remains that single-phase motors are more expensive and more complicated than polyphase induction motors and, therefore, should be used only when polyphase power is not available. A possible exception is in the fractional horsepower field where the driven devices are small and are apt to be of less importance.

Here, the expense of three-phase wiring and switches outweighs the other consideration.

Starting torque in fractional horsepower single-phase induction motors is proportional to several factors, including the product of the current in the two windings and the size of the angle between these currents.

In a typical split-phase motor, the current (at starting) in the main winding usually leads the current in the auxiliary winding by 20 to 30 degrees. This creates the needed revolving magnetic field during starting. The starting torque of a normal purpose split-phase motor is low, about 140% of full load torque.

In the case of a capacitor-start or capacitor-start-and-run-motor of the same rating, the current (at starting) in the auxiliary winding leads the current in the main winding by 7.5 to 8.5 degrees. Because of this, the starting torque of these motors is comparatively high about 275 to 375% of full load torque. From this it is evident that a capacitor-start motor can be expected to produce from two to three times as much starting torque per ampere as can a split-phase motor.

Since the capacitor-start motor is more expensive the question might be raised as to why the starting current of the split-phase motor should not be increased to obtain the required starting torque. For example, if 25 oz-ft of starting torque is required, why not obtain it from a split-phase motor with about 40 amperes starting current instead of from a capacitor-start motor with about 15 amperes starting current? One reason is that excessive starting currents on frequent starting applications may result in objectionable light flicker. In order to avoid this, many utilities restrict the use of single-phase motors with high starting currents.

Frequently used rules are:

1) Automatically controlled single-phase motors for general use cannot draw starting currents greater than 20 amperes (plus 15% tolerance) at 115 volts or more than 25 amperes (plus 15% tolerance) at 230 volts.

2) Manually controlled single-phase motors for general use cannot draw starting currents greater than 40 amperes (plus 15% tolerance) at 115 volts, or more than 50 amperes (plus 15%) at 230 volts.

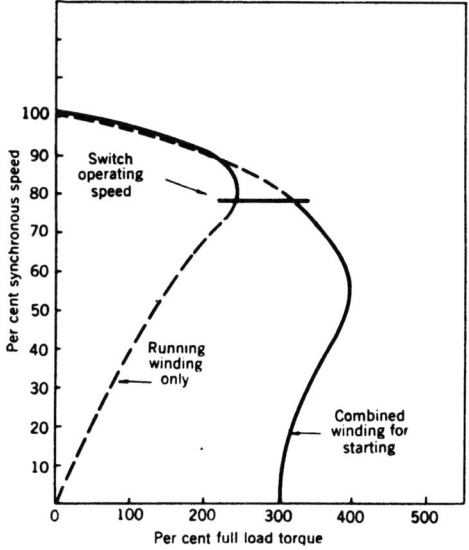

Fig 17-5a. Speed torque curve for a capacitor start motor

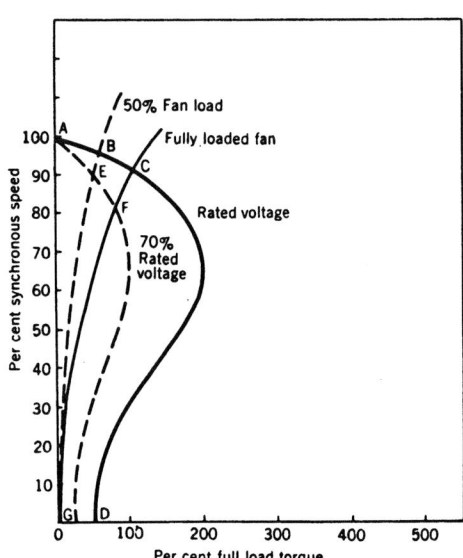

Fig 17-5b. Speed torque curve for a permanent split capacitor start motor

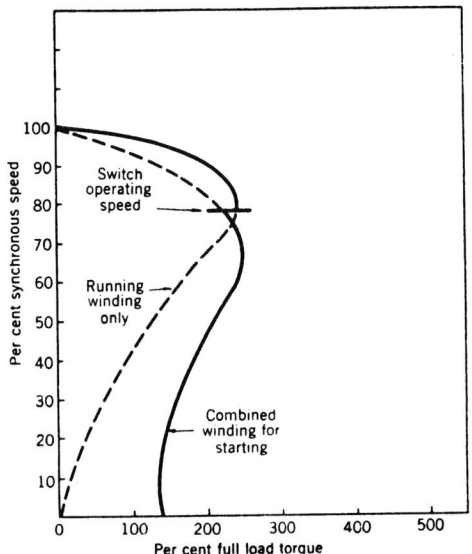

Fig 17-5c. Speed torque curve for a normal purpose split phase motor

3) Motors that draw starting currents greater than these values can be used if approved by the local utility.

Table 17-14 gives NEMA maximum locked rotor currents for four single-phase design letter motors; however, the locked-rotor currents of 60-cycle, single-phase general-purpose motors shall not exceed the values shown for the Design N motors. The locked-rotor torques of single-phase general purpose induction motors, with rated voltage and frequency applied, shall not be less than those given in Table 17-7.

Fig. 17-5a through 17-5e show speed-torque curves for various single-phase, fractional horsepower motors. Gen-

erally speaking, capacitor-start-type-motors have the locked-rotor torque and locked-rotor-current characteristics required for a single-phase, general-purpose motor classification.

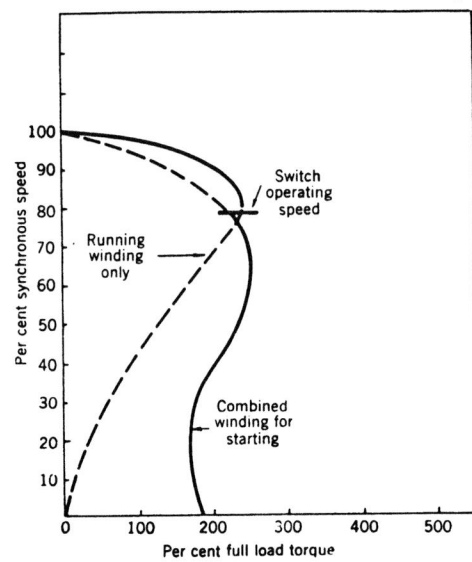

Fig 17-5d. Speed torque curve for a permanent split phase motor having a high starting current

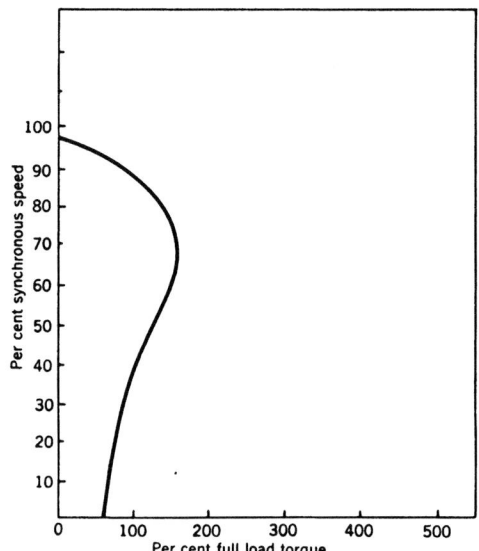

Fig 17-5e. Speed torque curve for a shaded pole motor

Suggested types of applications, for which each motor is best suited, are summarized in Table 17-16.

Application.—*Nameplate Data:* When selecting motors for an application, the motor must first be matched to the power supply. The motor nameplate ordinarily gives the name of the manufacturer, rating in horsepower and speed, temperature rise and duty cycle, power supply frequency and voltage, full-load, amperes, service factor, locked kva code number, and manufacturer identification number.

If the motor nameplate is not accessible, the information regarding power supply should be available at the point the apparatus is connected to the line. Power supply information includes voltage frequency and full-load amperes. A motor should be connected only to a power source that matches its rating.

Motors in agreement with NEMA standards can be operated successfully at rated load with a variation of plus or minus 10% in voltage or plus or minus 5% in rated frequency, or a combined variation of 10%. However, this operation is not necessarily in accordance with standards established for operation at rated voltage and frequency.

Table 17-16. Suitable Application

Fig. No. and Type Motor	Suitable Applications
Fig. 17-5a Capacitor start motor	Motor has starting current within the NEMA standard and has high starting torque. It is suitable for general purpose use since it can start heavy loads without causing excessive light flicker on normal circuits.
Fig. 17-5b Permanent split-capacitor motor	Motor has very low starting torque and low starting current. Value of capacitance of the oil-filled capacitor must be selected to provide satisfactory full load operation. With a fan-type load accurately matched to motor characteristics, this motor, with a controller, can provide very good multispeed and dual-voltage operation.
Fig. 17-5c Split-phase motor	Motor has a starting current above the NEMA standard and is suitable for frequent starting.
Fig. 17-5d Split-phase motor with high starting current	Motor has a starting current above the NEMA standard and is suitable for infrequent starting or where the higher starting current is not objectionable.
Fig. 17-5e Shaded-pole motor	Motor has very low starting torque. Speed when driving a fan-type load can be adjusted by means of a series choke coil or autotransformer or tapped winding. Low efficiency and power factor have limited its use to the smaller ratings.

Loading.—In general, the most obvious means of checking a load on a motor is by comparing the amperes taken by the motor to that shown on the nameplate. Although this is not the best method of checking load and cannot be relied on entirely, it is usually the one most available and for that reason it is quite often used. Particularly with regard to single-phase motors, the full-load amperes may be only 40 to 50% greater than the no-load amperes and in some motors may actually be no greater. Furthermore, variations in applied voltage and in motor construction will have considerable effect on the full-load amperes for single-phase motors.

If it is necessary to calibrate accurately the load on a motor, a much better criterion is to determine the watts taken by the motor. The watts supplied to the motor when driving the required load together with the voltage at which the test is run, with any duty cycle variations,

should be submitted to the manufacturer with the nameplate identification of the motor. With this information the manufacturer can usually give the actual load that the motor is driving. In connection with this, it is usually helpful to submit also the watts input with motor running without load; this permits the manufacturer to estimate the load more accurately. The variation in watt-meter reading between no load and full load normally is from 300 to 700%, depending on size of motor.

Multispeed Operation: When applying motors by matching the full-load amperes, it must be remembered that a 15% change in current may mean a 25 to 35% change in load; and when one loads a motor to 115% of its full-load amperes, the motor may be considerably overloaded.

An induction motor is used for speed control only in connection with a fan or blower. There are two methods of obtaining this speed control in a single-phase motor. The first method is by changing the number of poles using two different windings–one for the high speed, one for the low. The windings are arranged so that if one connection is used, it will operate at the speed of a four-pole motor, and if another connection is used, it will operate at the speed of six- or eight-pole motor. With this arrangement slight variations in voltage or fan load do not greatly change the operating speeds. Another method of speed control is varying the voltage to either a shaded pole or permanent-split capacitor motor or by utilizing a tapped winding. This method should be applied only to direct-connected fans or blowers.

In Fig. 17-5b the solid curve ABCD represents the torque produced by the motor at various speeds at rated voltage. The fan or blower curve represents the torque required to drive the fan at each speed. When the output torque of the motor at a given speed equals the torque required to drive the fan at this speed, the motor will operate at the speed indicated by point C. If the voltage to the motor is reduced, the output torque of the motor will be along dashed curve AEFG. Under these conditions the motor will operate at the speed of point F. Speed is controlled by varying the voltage to the motor. This works most successfully only with fan-type loads, in which torque required increases with speed, and on motors having no starting switch. Any voltage setting can be used to obtain a desired speed. However it must be realized that with low-voltage settings the starting torque is reduced so that the motor may not start. For this reason, this method of speed control is applied only to direct-connected fans and blowers as the friction in a belt may prevent the motor from starting on low speeds. Also, the fan and motor must be matched to obtain proper speed control. A fan that will not properly load a motor (such as that shown in Fig. 17-5b as 10% fan load) will not give proper speed control. On reduced voltage, the speed would only be reduced to point E.

There are many methods for reducing the effective voltage to the motor. Among these are autotransformers, connecting dual-voltage motors for high voltage and applying the lower voltage, or having an intermediate winding connected into the circuit to reduce effectively the voltage to the main winding.

As can be seen, variation of fan load or applied voltage will result in a variation in motor speed. Multispeed motors ordinarily operate at a lower full-load speed with the load point nearer the breakdown or maximum torque point since this method facilitates varying the speed.

Motor Protection.—Protection of motors is described in appropriate electrical codes and the National Electric Code. For example, most codes require all automatically started motors, regardless of size, to have overload protection. However, attention is directed to a particular type of motor protection called *inherent overheating protection*. This type of protection refers to a temperature or a temperature-and-current-sensing device that disconnects the motor from the line when the temperature of the winding becomes excessive under any abnormal condition. Since, in many instances, temperature is the reason for motor failure, an inherent device frequently offers improved protection so that short overloads or delayed starting will not cause nuisance outages unless such conditions will severely damage the motor.

In fractional horsepower single-phase motors there are two windings, the starting and the main. The main winding has considerable thermal capacity and operates whenever the motor is turned on. The starting winding has relatively little thermal capacity and is connected only during starting. The inherent protector guards the starting winding by tripping out in a short time when the current is high, such as under locked rotor conditions. It protects the main winding by being sensitive to temperature: it removes the motor from the line when the main winding temperature becomes excessive.

Two types of protection are in common use the automatic-reset and manual-reset types. With the automatic-reset type, the motor cools to a safe temperature and automatically resets and attempts to start. If conditions are changed so that temperatures do not then become excessive, the motor will continue its operation. If conditions are still unsafe, it will again remove the motor from the line. This cycling will continue until the motor is shut off. If for some reason it would be hazardous for a motor to start after once tripped, a manual-reset protector is used in which the operator must manually reset the protector before the motor will again start.

Motor Selection.—In selecting the type motor to use for a given application, the characteristics of the motors should be considered.

Fans and Blowers: For shaft-mounted fans and blowers little starting torque is required. However, some blowers have relatively high inertia and the motor must come up to speed quickly before the starting winding is damaged. Also, a long acceleration will draw a heavy current and cause lights to dim during acceleration.

A normal-purpose split-phase motor can be used if accelerating time is not excessive. The high-starting current, split-phase motor is the least expensive but should be used only where manual starting is used and starts are infrequent.

A two-speed, split-phase motor can be used if correct speeds can be obtained. Permanent-split capacitor or shaded-pole motor can be used if variable speed is desired. In this case, a shaded-pole motor is a low-performance motor, whereas the permanent-split capacitor motor operates at higher efficiencies and power factor and lower noise levels.

Capacitor-start or capacitor-start-and-run motors are used when starting time must be decreased on high inertia loads or on larger motors where the starting torque must be greater than that produced by a normal-purpose split phase motor.

The same remarks apply to belted fans and blowers, except that shaded-pole motors and permanent split capacitor motors should be omitted because their inherent low starting torque is not sufficient, to start a belted load under various conditions of belt tension.

Compressors: A compressor unit that does not have a sealed (hermetic) motor compressor may have a motor that drives a separate compressor by means of a belt. The belt-driven compressor requires a large starting torque as it may have to start under considerable back pressure with considerable friction and low line voltages. The line voltage usually drops when the motor is turned on. For these reasons the capacitor-start, capacitor start-and-run, and repulsion ac motors are used.

Sump Pumps: Sump pumps are usually operated very infrequently and are built as inexpensively as possible. Performance is of little importance and a high starting current split-phase motor will normally suffice. However, for a sump pump that starts regularly and often, a normal-purpose split-phase motor may be required because it has less tendency to produce flickering of lights.

Oil Burners: For oil burners the motor drives a blower and a pump, neither of which requires much starting torque. A normal-purpose split-phase motor is almost always used, except in the large commercial burners.

Hot Water Pumps: Hot water pumps operate at low pressures. The normal-purpose or high-starting current split-phase motors are satisfactory, depending on frequency of starting and running time.

Analysis of Application.—A general guide in selecting a motor to drive a newly designed machine is provided in Table 17-15. It is helpful to understand why a certain type of equipment is usually driven by one type of motor.

The belt-connected furnace blower application, for example, can be analyzed as follows:

Power supply	Usually single-phase, 60-cycle, alternating current is available.
Horsepower	$\frac{1}{6}$, $\frac{1}{4}$, $\frac{1}{3}$, $\frac{1}{2}$, or $\frac{3}{4}$ hp depending upon the design.
Torque	Belted blower load is fairly constant. Starting torque depends upon inertia of blower and tightness of the belt.
Locked-rotor or starting current	NEMA standards or utility regulations.
Overload protection	Desirable to protect motor against unusual conditions.
Mechanical features	Industry standard is open, resilient-mounted motor.
Locked-rotor or starting current	NEMA standards or utility regulations.

Assume that information on the blower used indicates that it can supply the required amount of air when operated at the desired speed with a motor output of 0.4 hp at 1725 rpm. This would indicate a load of 1.2 times the nameplate rating of a $\frac{1}{3}$-hp motor, or 0.8 times the nameplate rating of a $\frac{1}{2}$-hp motor. A $\frac{1}{3}$-hp, general-purpose, alternating-current motor has a service factor of 1.35 according to NEMA standards, and theoretically this motor could be used. However, the $\frac{1}{2}$-hp motor is recommended if the temperature in the area surrounding the motor is consistently hot.

In the belt-connected application, shaded-pole motor should not be used, due to the horsepower requirement. The starting torque of a permanent-split capacitor motor does not make it suitable for most belt-driven loads. Therefore, there is a choice between a split-phase motor and a capacitor-start motor for this application.

The choice between these two types of motors depends upon the effort required to start the blower and bring it up to operating speed. This will depend upon the tightness of the belt, the pulley ratio, and the inertia of the blower. If the belt is not too tight and the blower is lightweight, it is probable that a split-phase motor will be satisfactory. On this application the motor used should meet the NEMA standards for starting current and thus the high-starting-current type of the split-phase motor is not indicated. If the belt tension is high or the blower is heavy, the capacitor-start motor should be used.

On this application the motor should be provided with inherent overload protection to prevent overheating due to too much belt tension, incorrect pulley size, or incorrect installation.

Polyphase Motors

Alternating current, three-phase motors are common $\frac{1}{2}$-horsepower sizes, and larger, although they are available in smaller sizes. The 60 cycle nominal utility service voltage systems commonly used with three-phase motors are:

A) 120/208-V, 3-phase, 4-wire with grounded neutral
B) 265/460-V, 3-phase, 4-wire with grounded neutral
C) 115/230-V, 3-phase, 4-wire with grounded neutral
D) 230-V, 3-phase, 3-wire
E) 460-V, 3-phase, 3-wire.

The above voltages are nominal, and actual voltages vary, usually above their nominal values. High-voltage systems (2300-V, 4160-V, and 4800-V) are frequently used in industry for motors above 200 horsepower and for air conditioning system motors above 1000 horsepower.

Enclosure.—The "enclosure" of a motor refers to the arrangement of the ventilating openings or other means of cooling and the amount of protection provided against the atmosphere in which the motor operates. In the heating and ventilating field, motors that might be used include: open drip-proof totally enclosed; totally enclosed fan-cooled; explosion-proof enclosures; and motors with encapsulated windings.

The open motor is the basic standard and its ventilating openings do not protect the motor from dirt, water, or fumes. However, the present trend is to build such motors with considerable protection and in the case of many manufacturers, the open motor meets all the requirements of the drip-proof specification and is called an "*open drip-proof type*".

The *drip-proof type* is essentially an open motor with its ventilating openings arranged so that dripping water will not enter it. An elaboration of this type is the splash-proof motor, the openings of which offer further protection against splashing water. The latter usually carries a price premium of about 15% and is sometimes used in locations where splashing may occur followed by a period during which the motor can run in relatively dry air. The present trend is to use either the open drip-proof or totally enclosed motors, as dictated by the severity of the application, rather than the splash-proof type.

Totally enclosed, and *totally enclosed fan-cooled motors*, as their names imply, have no openings connecting the space around the windings with the outside air, and are generally used where dirt, dust, fumes, dampness, or outdoor conditions prevail. The smaller ratings are non ventilated, while the larger ones are fan-cooled by an external fan that blows air over the outside of the motor case. The price is about 150% of the open motor price, but this is often offset by a lower maintenance cost.

Explosion-proof motors are totally enclosed or totally enclosed fan-cooled motors so designed that they will not produce an explosion when operated in the flammable atmosphere for which they are approved. They are designed, manufactured, and tested under the strict supervision of Underwriters Laboratories, Inc. The price is about 180% of that of the open motor of the same rating.

Bearings.—Bearings in these types of motors are either of the rolling-contact or sleeve type. Almost all smaller fractional horsepower motors use wool-packed sleeve bearings while the larger motors usually have ball bearings; but roller or sleeve bearings are sometimes used. The larger sleeve-type bearings are lubricated with oil fed to the journal either by the capillary attraction of the wool waste or by a revolving oil ring, depending on the motor size and speed. If a motor is expected to carry some thrust load, at least one ball bearing or a tapered roller bearing is required unless some very special construction is used.

The pros and cons of ball versus sleeve bearings are legion, but some of the major points follow. Ball bearings will take thrust while the usual sleeve bearing will not. The ball bearing motor is not as apt to have objectionable end bump of the rotor under pulsating load as a sleeve-bearing motor. A sleeve-bearing motor often has a lower price. A sleeve-bearing motor may be quieter, but this is by no means universally true. A ball bearing generally requires less frequent lubrication, but on the other hand it probably requires a higher degree of skill in lubrication.

Quietness.—Certain types of motors are inherently noisier than others, but all commercial motors are reasonably quiet. Sometimes a special quiet motor is specified in the hope of reducing objectionable noise, but in the great majority of such cases the little gain that can be obtained from the special motor is of small consequence. It is better to provide some means of general noise suppression so that noise of the driven machine is reduced at the same time. On the other hand, poor running balance of the motor may be of considerable importance in producing noise.

In the special case of single-phase motors which have an inherent electrical imbalance, sound isolating mountings may prove very effective. These are sometimes incorporated in the motor itself by the motor manufacturer, or supplied as an external device. Here, again, it may prove better to isolate a sub-base carrying the motor and the driven machine, rather than the motor alone.

Polyphase, Squirrel Cage Induction Motors.—The induction motor is the most common type of ac polyphase motor. It is mechanically the simplest of all motors and consists of only a rotor, a stator, and two end-shields with the bearings. It is essentially a constant-speed machine, which means that the speed changes very little with load and cannot be adjusted. Induction motors are classified by starting torque, locked rotor current, and full load speed. The National Electrical Manufacturers Association Standards classify *squirrel cage induction motors* thus:

Design A. Normal starting torque, normal starting current.
Design B. Normal starting torque, low starting current.
Design C. High starting torque, low starting current.
Design D. High slip.

Design A motors are not commonly found at the present time, and Design B motors are used unless the extra starting torque of the Design C motor is required by the application.

Design B motors usually have 200% or greater breakdown torque, while Design C motors have slightly less. Breakdown torque is the greatest torque that the motor will carry at full voltage without a sudden change in speed. However, the maximum peak of the load torque should not exceed $\frac{2}{3}$ or $\frac{3}{4}$ of the value of the breakdown torque.

Fig. 17-2 shows speed-torque curves of 100 horsepower, 1800 rpm, Design B, Design C, and Design D motors. Table 17-1 of the first section on motor classifications gives the NEMA standards for horsepowers, speeds, frequencies, and locked rotor and breakdown torques for Designs A, B, and C polyphase squirrel cage induction motors.

General purpose open drip-proof induction motors are permitted by NEMA to have a service factor that defines the additional load that the motor will carry without reaching a temperature that will cause undue shortness of insulation life. The service factor multiplied by the nameplate rating of the motor gives the maximum horsepower to which the motor can be overloaded. Service factors are discussed at the beginning of this section. In the case of polyphase squirrel cage motors, these factors apply to Designs A, B, C, and F motors.

The additional horsepower obtained by applying the service factor can also be used as a safety factor to take care of the potential unknowns that can cause overloading of the motor. Generally, however, it is not advisable to operate a motor above its nameplate rating for air conditioning, heating, or ventilating services. Totally enclosed types of motors and motors with encapsulated windings normally have a service factor of 1.00. When one of these motors is used care must be taken that the motor not be overloaded.

NEMA also specifies the maximum locked rotor current for single-speed, three-phase, 60-cycle, and 50-cycle induction motors with rated voltage and frequency impressed. Table 17-2 gives these data.

The latter part of this section dealing with part winding and reduced voltage starters explains the significance of locked-rotor currents in motor applications and the relationship of locked-rotor currents to locked-rotor torques.

There are occasions when it is necessary to convert locked-rotor current to its equivalent locked rotor kva (kilovolt-amperes) or to convert full load running current to its equivalent full-load kva. The formula for a 3-phase motor is given by the following:

$$KVA = \frac{1.73 \times E \times I}{1000}$$

where E = voltage

I = locked rotor or full load line current.

NEMA requires that every alternating current motor rated $\frac{1}{20}$ hp and larger, except for polyphase wound-rotor motors, shall have a code letter marking on its nameplate indicating locked motor KVA/hp. Table 17-8 of "*Motor Classification*" shows the range in locked-rotor KVA/hp for each code letter. In this case, the lockedrotor KVA/hp range includes the lower figure, up to, but not including, the higher figure.

The National Electric Code segment, earlier in this section, discusses full-load currents and locked-rotor currents of motors and includes Table 17-10 which gives the NEC full-load current values for three-phase ac motors. Table 17-13, in the same section, repeats the NEC locked-rotor current conversion table. Maximum permissible locked-rotor currents, as given by NEMA, generally differ slightly from the NEC values.

Speed Control.—Two general types of speed control are used for polyphase motors in air conditioning, heating, ventilating, and plumbing work. One type is *two-speed* in which the motor operates at either of two defined constant speed conditions. The other is variable speed in which speed variation is smooth and stepless.

Two-speed motors frequently are used in conjunction with centrifugal and axial fans applied to variable torque loads (systems resistance varies as the square of the speed or air flow). The centrifugal fan, pump, or compressor curve of Fig. 17-3 illustrates such a load. Typical examples would be a central station centrifugal fan operating at half speed for night heating, or an induced-draft, cooling-tower, axial flow fan operating at half speed for capacity reduction and reduced noise. Two-speed motors also are used in conjunction with reciprocating or rotary compressors applied to constant torque loads when other methods for achieving capacity reduction are not practical. The reciprocating or rotary compressor curve of this Fig. 17-3, mentioned above, illustrates such a load.

Industrial centrifugal gas compressors operating against relatively constant heads frequently use variable-speed drives. Prior to the acceptance of prerotation vanes, most centrifugal compressors used for refrigeration and water chilling service used variable-speed drives for capacity control. Variable-speed motors and drives frequently are used in conjunction with centrifugal pumps operating against a relatively constant head (constant torque load). A frequent example is a tankless, variable-speed house-pump booster system. In this application, a 20 to 25% variation from maximum speed generally is sufficient to reduce the pumping system to minimum capacity. The relatively small required variation in speed is important, since virtually all variable-speed drives generate heat and become inefficient at the lower speeds.

Two-Speed Polyphase, Squirrel Cage Induction Motors.—Polyphase induction motors are available for multi speed applications in two, three, or four speeds; however, they seldom can be justified at greater than two speeds for air conditioning, heating, and ventilating work.

Most two-speed motors are furnished for full-speed and half-speed operation. The ability to achieve capacity reduction of equipment is the biggest reason for their use, although other benefits of decreased noise and lower operating costs can be very important. For example, a refrigeration compressor without unloaders can operate at 50% capacity when connected to a two-speed motor.

Another example is that of a two-speed motor applied to the axial flow fan of an induced draft cooling tower. The noise level of the cooling tower would markedly decrease at half-speed operation, which can be of tremendous importance in a residential neighborhood during the evening when cooling loads generally are low. The use of a two-speed motor can eliminate or decrease fan cycling with its attendant transient noise effects. Finally, the two-speed motor may decrease operating costs, since its power consumption at half-speed is roughly $\frac{1}{6}$ the two types that are at full speed.

Two Speed Motors Come in Two Types.—Separate winding and single-winding consequent pole.

Each type can be furnished with one of the following characteristics:

1) constant horsepower

2) constant torque

3) variable torque.

Constant horsepower motors are used where the torque requirement increases as the speed decreases, such as applications with certain winches and machine tools. At one-half speed, maximum allowable torque is twice the high-speed value. These motors are not used in heating, ventilating, or air conditioning work.

Constant torque motors are suitable for driving machines where the required horsepower varies directly as the speed. This makes the constant torque motor suitable for reciprocating compressor or rotary compressor applications.

Table 17-17. Schematic Wiring and Starter Switching Circuits for a Two-Winding, Two-Speed Motor and for Constant Horsepower and Torque, and Variable Torque, Single Winding, Two Speed Motors

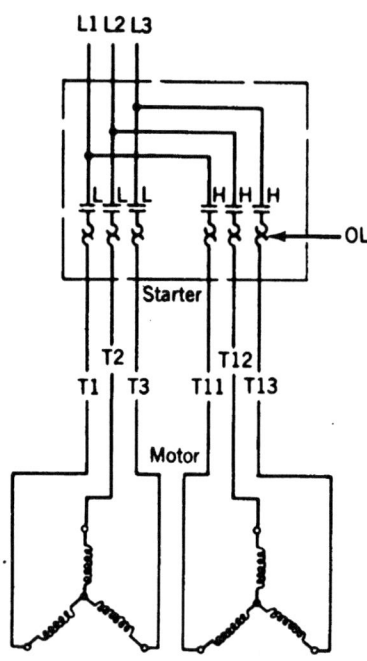

Two speed, two winding (separate winding) constant horsepower, constant torque, or variable torque

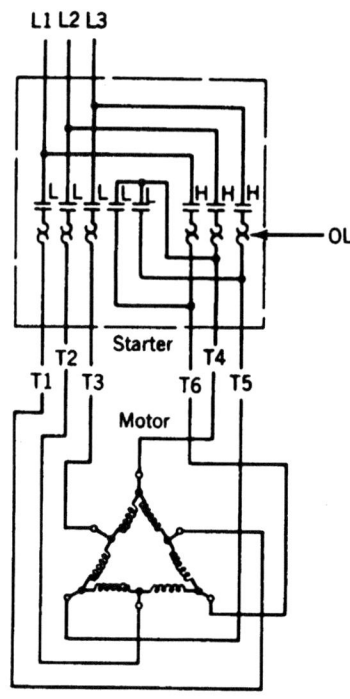

Two speed, single winding (consequent pole) constant horsepower

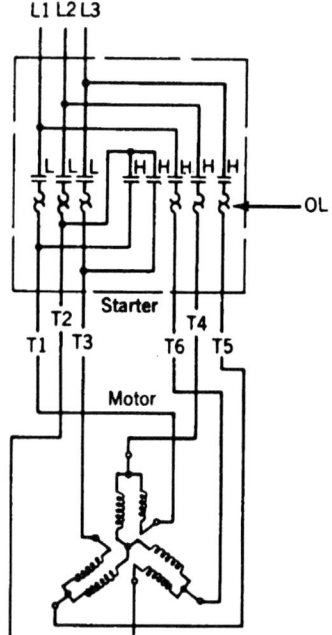

Two speed, single winding (consequent pole) variable torque

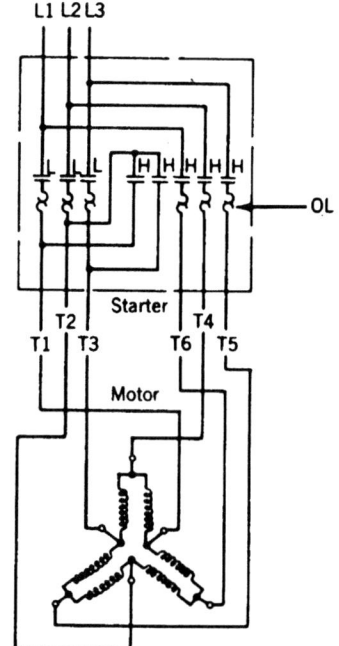

Two speed, single winding (consequent pole) consequent torque

Variable-torque motors are suitable for applications with loads that have torque requirements which are less than, or equal to, a torque requirement that varies directly with the speed. Fans and centrifugal pumps have torque requirements that vary roughly as the square of the speed and, therefore, fall under this category and can be driven by variable-torque motors. A variable-torque motor has a maximum horsepower output at low speed, which is ¼ that at high speed.

A separate, or two-winding, motor is more expensive than a single-winding, two-speed motor and usually operates at a lower power factor and efficiency. The two-winding motor does, however, have a simpler starter. A single-winding, consequent pole, two-speed motor can operate only at full speed and one-half full speed, while the two-winding motor can operate at full speed and, if so specified, a second speed which need not be one-half of full speed. Normally, a single-winding motor is used if the desired second speed is one-half full speed.

Table 17-17 in this section shows the schematic wiring and starter switching circuits for a two winding, two-speed motor and for constant horsepower, constant-torque and variable-torque, single-winding, two-speed motors.

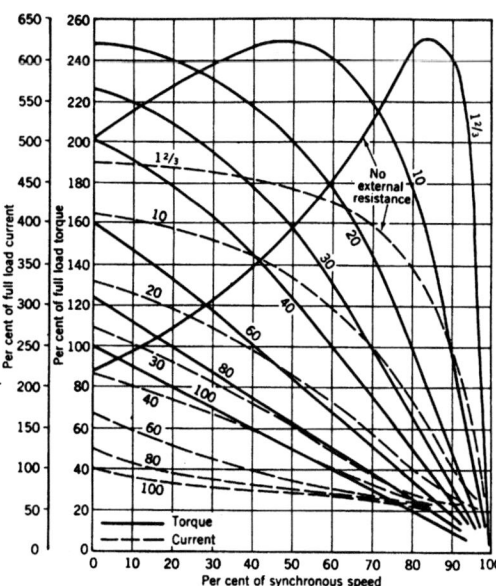

Fig 17-6. Family of speed torque curves and speed current curves for a single wound rotor induction motor

Wound-Rotor Polyphase Induction Motors.—The foregoing pointed out the advantage of variable-speed operation to obtain capacity reduction. The final section of this chapter, dealing with part winding and reduced-voltage starting, points out a frequent requirement for low starting currents for large motors without jeopardizing starting torques. The wound-rotor motor not only can provide adjustable speed operation but can provide a

decrease in starting current with an actual increase in starting torque. Adjustable-speed operation decrease in starting current increase in starting torque, acceleration, from the start, of a high-inertia load, or a combination of any of these factors can frequently justify the application of a wound-rotor motor to a load.

A wound-rotor induction motor has, as its name implies, a rotor that has polyphase windings or coils instead of the short-circuited rotor bars characteristic of a general purpose induction motor. The rotor windings are connected to collector assemblies or slip rings within the motor, which in turn permit the windings to be connected through brushes to external resistors. For an induction motor, at any given value of torque the slip will vary proportionally with the rotor resistance. Therefore, by adjusting the values of the external resistors, the speed torque characteristics of the motor can be changed.

Fig. 17-6 shows a family of speed-torque curves and speed-current curves applicable to a single wound-rotor induction motor. Each curve relates to a specific value of rotor resistance. The numbers on the curves indicate the secondary (rotor) resistance in percent of value required to give full-load torque at standstill.

External resistance or reactance may be varied manually or automatically. The most popular type of manual control is a drum switch, which cuts in or cuts out banks of external resistors. One method of automatic control uses pilot-controlled contactors, which switch the resistor banks in and out. Another method uses a saturable reactor in conjunction with pilot-controlled resistor banks.

The external resistors may be designed for intermittent or continuous duty. Intermittent duty resistors are generally utilized when the wound-rotor motor is used to provide a low starting current, extra-heavy starting ability, or slow acceleration of a high-inertia load. Continuous-duty resistors are used when speed control is desired and sustained operation at less than maximum speed is anticipated. Wound-rotor motors are seldom operated at less than 50% sustained speed since the power loss through the external resistors becomes severe and the operation is inefficient. Further, the problem of dissipating the heat developed in the resistors is aggravated.

Reference to Fig. 17-6 shows how ideal a wound rotor motor can be for satisfying severe power company inrush current requirements, while at the same time providing high starting torques. For example, the "80" secondary circuit resistance curves will provide a starting current which is only 120% of full load current and a starting torque that exceeds 120% of full load torque. Roughly, this is equivalent to 80% of the full-voltage locked-rotor torque and 21% of the full-voltage locked rotor current of a NEMA Design B, general purpose induction motor. In this case, the *torque efficiency* (see the section on part winding and reduced voltage starting) of the wound-rotor motor would be almost 400%, a performance which cannot be approached by any of the part winding or reduced-voltage starting methods.

Another advantage of the wound-rotor motor is its ability to accelerate from high-inertia starting loads. In this case, substantially all of the heat energy developed in the rotor circuit during acceleration is dissipated in the external resistors instead of heating the motor itself.

The wound-rotor motor is particularly well adapted for speed control of centrifugal compressors and centrifugal pumps operating between relatively fixed suction and discharge pressure conditions. In this case, a speed reduction of about 25% brings the equipment to its minimum required speed or to a hunting or surging condition. Prior to the widespread acceptance of pre-rotation vanes, use of wound-rotor motors provided the most acceptable method for varying capacities of centrifugal compressor refrigeration machines. At the present time some manufacturers are offering wound-rotor motors for use with variable-speed, tankless, pump booster systems.

Variable Speed.—For polyphase ac systems several types of variable-speed drives in addition to wound-rotor motors have been used.

At the present time, a variable-speed drive, up to about 100 hp (which frequently sees service) uses a modified form of a Design D induction motor in conjunction with a power supply having silicon-controlled rectifiers to vary the effective supply voltage. A typical speed-torque curve for a Design D motor is shown in Fig. 17-2. The torque varies as the square of the applied voltage, and a relatively small decrease in voltage will cause a significant slip in the presence of a load. Heat is generated when slippage occurs, and the SCR (start capacitor run) controlled, variable speed motor must be capable of dissipating this heat.

Other types of variable-speed drives suitable for polyphase alternating current systems are available. These include constant-speed polyphase induction motors, which drive their loads through some form of *torque transmitter*. One form of torque transmitter is the mechanical fluid drive; another is the electric magnetic drive, sometimes referred to as an eddy-current clutch.

Each of these drives achieves a variation in speed by providing a slip between the driving motor and driven load. The drives are inefficient in that torque conversion does not take place and the slip constitutes a loss that must be dissipated in the form of heat.

Among the most sophisticated in providing the greatest flexibility in speed and smooth control in conjunction with high efficiency are variations of the Ward Leonard system. In general, these utilize a constant-speed, ac induction motor which drives a dc adjustable-voltage generator and a small auxiliary dc constant voltage generator. The main adjustable voltage generator powers a shunt or compound dc motor which, in turn, drives the

load. The auxiliary dc generator provides excitation for the main generator and dc shunt fields.

Speed variation is accomplished by changing the output voltage of the generator through the use of rheostats or amplifiers, which vary the current in the shunt field of the generator. Variable-speed drives of this type are used with commercial elevators and with hoists, dredges, machine tools, steel mill drives and other industrial applications. This type of speed control system has not been used in air conditioning, heating, ventilating and plumbing services because applications in these fields do not justify the relative high cost of equipment.

Other types of sophisticated ac variable-speed drives are available but are too costly for air conditioning, heating, ventilating, and plumbing work. These include electronic rectification for use with dc motors, frequency conversion, and special forms of wound-rotor motors.

Synchronous Motors.—For many years synchronous motors have been direct-connected to large vertical reciprocating ammonia compressors and to the flywheels of large reciprocating horizontal ammonia compressors and air compressors. These machines operate at less than 500 rpm, and the synchronous motors that drive them are known as "engine types". In this case, the rotor of the synchronous motor is bolted on to the shaft extension of the compressor or flywheel and there are no rotor bearings or shaft supplied with the motor. Motors of this type are more efficient than induction motors of comparable speed and size, operate at a better power factor or provide power factor correction, and usually are less expensive than the induction motor.

Low inrush currents are characteristic of engine type synchronous motors. Where flywheel effect is lacking in the driven equipment, the rotor can be designed with a large inertia to provide this effect. The amount of flywheel effect required depends on the type of compressor and the method of its unloading during the starting period.

High-speed synchronous motors are designed for operation above 514 rpm, or in other words, have less than 14 poles in conjunction with a 60-cycle ac power supply. These motors are furnished complete with rotor shaft and bearings. Although these motors have been directly connected to, and have also driven reciprocating compressors via belt drive E, their most common application is to drive open type (non-hermetic) centrifugal refrigeration compressors through speed increasing gears.

Synchronous motor speeds generally are 1200 to 1800 rpm, although 3600 rpm synchronous motors are not uncommon in the extremely large sizes where the speed increaser cost goes up rapidly with a increase in gear ratio. Induction motors of compareable size and speed are less expensive than big speed synchronous motors. In the air conditioning field, synchronous motors can be justified generally only when improved power factor or power factor correction is desired.

Synchronous motors operate at fixed synchronous speed. During starting, they operate as an induction motor, utilizing a rotor amortisseur winding and separate rotor field winding, which is short circuited through a field discharge resistor. At the end of the starting period, a source of direct current excitation is applied to the field winding and the rotor pulled into synchronization. The source of dc excitation may be a small motor-generator set, a direct or belt drive generator connected to the motor shaft, or dry-type rectifier.

To provide a synchronous motor design that will pull into synchronization, one must have knowledge of the driven load. Both the required load torque at synchronization speed and the inertia of the load are chief considerations. Maximum slip at time of pull-in runs from 1 to 5%, depending on the load characteristics.

Acceleration time from startup to pull-in is directly related to the design of the rotor amortisseur winding. The graphical solution for acceleration time, described earlier in motor heating and motor life, is frequently used to determine acceleration time.

Usually, it is necessary for the motor manufacturer and the compressor manufacturer to combine their efforts to provide a satisfactory synchronous motor application.

Hermetic Type Motor Compressors

Hermetic motors that drive refrigeration compressors are types of definite-purpose motors. There are three main characteristics of hermetic motors that stand out from general-purpose open or totally enclosed motors.

1) Unlike a general purpose motor, which can be used to drive any number of types of machines, a hermetic motor is specially designed for a particular compressor model of a specific manufacturer.

2) The windings of the hermetic motor are submerged in the refrigerant atmosphere and generally are cooled by suction gas, although some hermetic motors of large size are cooled by discharge gas or refrigerant liquid injection or are water cooled. Thus, motor rating is dependent on the efficiency of refrigerant cooling. Efficiency of refrigerant cooling exceeds that of air cooling, and so the hermetic motor has less copper than an open motor driving a comparable load.

3) The hermetic motor is manufactured without a shaft. The compressor manufacturer attaches the squirrel cage rotor to an extension of the compressor shaft during assembly. The hermetic motor-compressor unit requires no shaft seal.

Refrigerant cooling efficiency is dependent on the design and application of the motor-compressor assembly, and the unit is rated in the amperes it can draw continuously without overheating. Hermetic motors are not horsepower rated, although reference to horsepower is often made to give an indication of approximate capacity.

Because of its decreased copper and its dependence on efficient refrigerant cooling, a hermetic motor is more susceptible to fast overheating and quick burnout in case of a stalled rotor, a malfunction in the refrigerant circuit, an excessive running load, a low voltage condition, or a disruption in the evaporator air flow. As a result, quick acting, sensitive, current and heat-sensing overload devices are desired for motor protection. This is particularly the case for single-phase hermetic motors where there is an increased probability of motor stalling on start-up.

Hermetic Compressors to 5 hp.—Hermetic motor-compressor units from fractional horsepower through 5 hp are most unique. For the most part, the few manufacturers who produce the compressor units supply them to a great number of other manufacturers who produce completely assembled air conditioning and refrigeration units, such as window air conditioners and heat pumps, domestic refrigerators and freezers, beverage coolers, vending machines, etc. Motor windings are furnished by a motor manufacturer to the compressor manufacturer who assembles the motor with the compressor. Most units of 5 hp and under are hermetically sealed in a steel shell. The shell cannot be opened in the field for inspection or service.

Present trend is for all units through 5 hp to have two pole, or 3450 rpm motors.

New units for use with window, residential and small commercial air conditioners through 5 hp (and some heat pumps) utilize *permanent split capacitor* motors, otherwise known as PSC types. Because of the limited starting torque available with permanent split-capacitor motors, their refrigeration systems must be designed with capillary tube liquid feed to permit equalization on shutdown. Most compressors have a single cylinder in the small sizes and two and three cylinders in the larger sizes.

For single-phase units requiring a higher starting torque, such as those used with refrigeration applications or where equalization on shutdown does not take place, a *resistance start-induction run* (RSIR), *capacitor start-induction run* (CSIR), or a *capacitor start-capacitor run* (CSR) motor must be used. Of the three types, the RSIR provides the lowest torque and its use is generally restricted to refrigerators and freezers in the $\frac{1}{20}$ to $\frac{1}{3}$-hp range when capillary tube liquid feed is used. The CSIR is generally used from $\frac{1}{6}$ to $\frac{1}{2}$ hp where high starting torque is required for refrigerators, freezers, and vending machines, which use thermostatic expansion valves. The CSR is used from $\frac{1}{3}$ hp through $1\frac{1}{2}$ hp and larger for such applications as vending machines, beer coolers, reach-in refrigerators, and small walk-in refrigerators.

Relays: A centrifugal speed switch is not practical in a hermetic unit; therefore, external hot-wire relays, current sensitive relays, or potential type relays are used to switch RSIR, CSIR, and CSR units off of their starting windings at the end of the starting period. In addition, kits from the compressor manufacturer often permit the addition of capacitors and potential type relays to PSC units after installation and operation to convert them to CSR units. This sometimes is necessary if the PSC unit is applied to a system which, for some reason, fails to fully equalize on shutdown.

The hot wire relay is used in conjunction with some smaller units and generally has been supplanted by the current type relay. Basically, the hot wire relay is a thermal time switch incorporating a straight, stiff wire, which quickly heats up when line current passes through it. After a short interval, the elongation of the wire causes a snap switch to open, which disconnects the motor start winding from the line. A second snap switch incorporated in the hot wire relay serves as overload protection and disconnects the entire motor from the line if excessive current should cause the hot wire to further elongate.

The current sensitive relay is more commonly used with RSIR and CSIR motors up through $\frac{1}{3}$ hp. A magnetic coil in series with the motor running winding closes a set of movable contacts immediately when the motor is initially energized at the beginning of the starting period. The movable contacts complete a circuit through the starting capacitor to the starting winding in the CSIR motor or to the starting winding in the RSIR motor. As the motor approaches full speed, the current drawn by the running winding decreases. At a predetermined speed, the magnetic coil drops out the movable contacts and disconnects the starting winding from the line.

The potential relay is commonly applied to CSIR and CSR units $\frac{1}{2}$ hp and larger. A potential coil, which operates a set of normally closed contacts is connected directly across the start winding. The normally closed contacts connect to the starting capacitor, which is in series with the coil. When the motor is first energized, the voltage drop across the capacitor is high, but the voltage drop across the coil is low; therefore, the contacts connect the capacitor to the line. As the motor gains speed, the start winding develops back EMF (a counter voltage) and, at a predetermined speed, the potential coil opens up the set of contacts. This disconnects the capacitor from the line. However, the potential coil keeps the contacts open due to the voltage induced in the open-circuited start winding when the motor is running at high speed.

Overload Protection: Overload protection is carefully selected and coordinated with the motor-compressor unit and furnished with the unit by the manufacturer. Overload protection by use of a hot wire relay already has been described. One prominent manufacturer provides overload protection for units through 5 hp in the following manner:

1) Single-phase units up through 1 hp have an overload device consisting of a snap-acting, thermostatic, bimetal disc and a heater located outside of the compressor shell, but inside of the terminal cover. Line current passes through the heater, which heats up the bimetal disc. The disc also is responsive to the heat of the compressor shell. In the event of excessive current, excessive shell temperature, or a combination of both, the bimetal disc opens up a pair of line-current switches, stopping the motor.

2) Single-phase units of 1 hp through $2\frac{1}{2}$ hp utilize a combination heater and bimetal disc housed within a tiny tin-plated steel can, which is inserted in the end-turns of the motor windings within the compressor shell. This internal line break overload protector functions in a manner similar to the overload protector described in the preceding paragraph, except that it is more responsive to motor-winding temperatures.

3) Single-phase units, $2\frac{1}{2}$ hp through 5 hp, utilize a two-pole contactor with an internal motor-winding thermostat and a supplementary exterior overload wired in series to the holding coil of the contactor. The internal thermostat causes the contactor to open and stop the motor in event of excessive motor-winding tempertaure. The supplementary overload opens the contactor under excessive locked rotor conditions for which the internal thermostat responds too slowly. The supplementary overload may be a bimetal disc with heater or a special circuit breaker.

4) Three-phase units have overload protection similar to that described in the preceding paragraph, except that two supplementary exterior overloads are used-one in each of two phases. In this case, a single internal thermostat is used.

Wiring Diagrams: The following wiring diagrams show examples of various starting devices and overload protectors used with hermetic motors.

Fig. 17-7 shows a hot wire relay used for starting and overload protection of an RSIR motor.

Fig. 17-8 shows a current sensitive relay used for starting and a line break bimetal disc and heater used for overload and heat protection of a CSIR motor.

Fig. 17-9 shows an internal line break bimetal disc and heater used for overload and heat protection of a PSC motor.

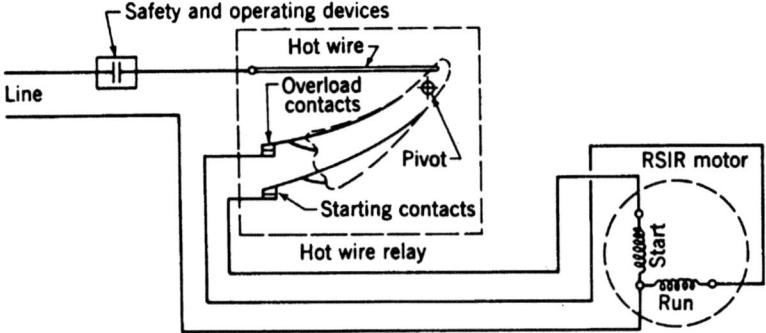

Fig 17-7. Hot wire relay with resistance start, induction run motor

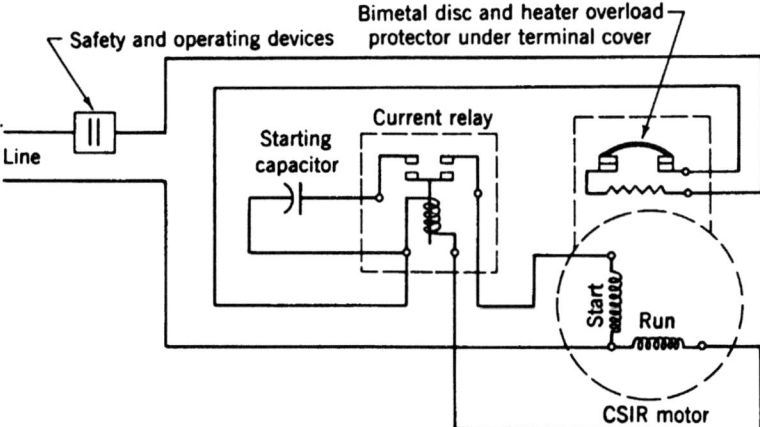

Fig 17-8. Current relay and overload with capacitor start, induction run motor

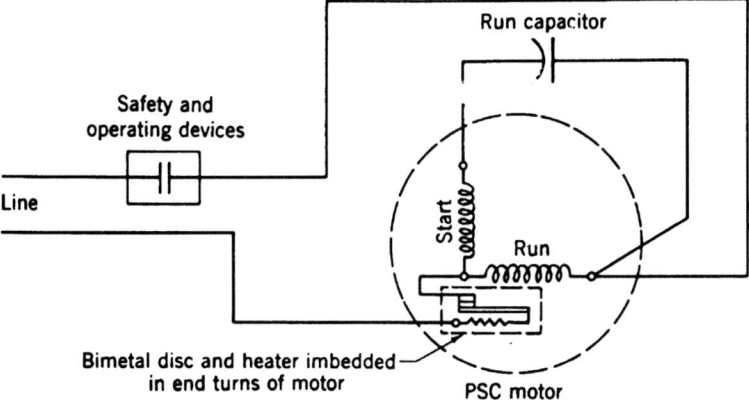

Fig 17-9. Permanent split capacitor motor with internal line break overload protection

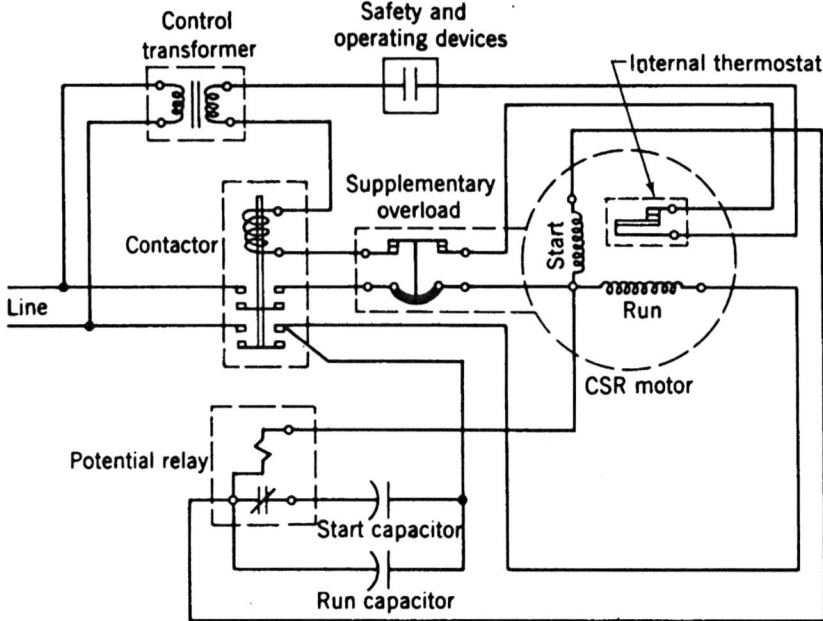

Fig 17-10. Capacitor start capacitor run motor with internal protection and potential relay

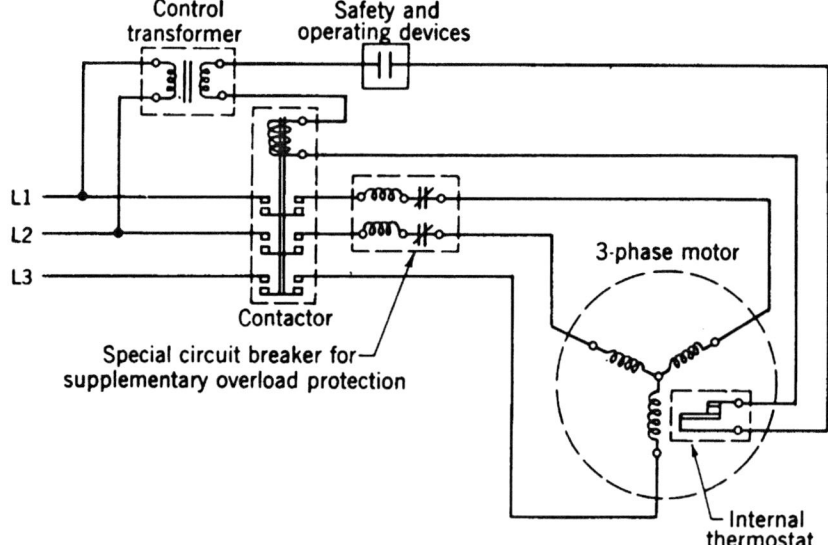

Fig 17-11. Three phase motor with internal protection

Fig. 17-10 shows a potential relay used for starting and a supplementary interior overload and internal motor winding thermostat and contactor used for overload and heat protection of a CSR motor.

Fig. 17-11 shows two supplementary exterior overloads and an internal motor winding thermostat used for overload and heat protection of a three-phase motor.

Although most motor compressor units of 5 hp and below are sealed hermetic types, accessible hermetic units can be inspected and serviced in the field, and motors can be replaced or repaired without necessarily removing the compressor.

Hermetic compressors above 5 hp are available although sealed hermetic units are available through 10 hp, most units above $7\frac{1}{2}$ hp are of the accessible hermetic type. Motors are three-phase and generally are furnished by motor manufacturers to compressor manufacturers who market compressors, condensing units, and water chilling units to the general air conditioning and refrigeration industry.

Motors generally have internal motor-winding thermostats, often one in each phase winding for large units. Starters are full-voltage part-winding or reduced-voltage types as required for the particular installation. Starters normally incorporate quick acting overloads for protection against locked rotor conditions, excessive loads, and low voltage conditions.

An overload relay utilized in some hermetic motors, makes use of a thermistor. The thermistor is a special semiconductor resistor that has a comparatively low, constant resistance up to a critical temperature point and has a great positive temperature coefficient of resistance within a narrow range above the critical temperature. The thermistor is tiny and can be placed in direct contact with the motor stator winding. It has very good thermal response and reacts much faster to increases in motor-winding temperatures than conventional internal motor-winding thermostats.

The thermistor is used in conjunction with a low-voltage bridge circuit or a low-voltage, rectified, direct current and a drop-out relay coil wired in series. On a rise in motor-winding temperature the increase in thermistor resistance above its critical temperature decreases the rectified current to the coil of the drop-out relay, causing the relay contacts to open. The drop-out relay contacts are wired in series with the starter holding coil, causing it to be de-energized and thereby stopping the compressor.

Most hermetic motors above 5 hp are suction gas cooled. Some of the hermetic motors driving the centrifugal compressors of large water cooling systems are cooled by discharge gas; others are cooled by chilled water circulated through a jacket, which forms the shell surrounding the motor. Increased attention is being given to liquid injection for hermetic motor cooling, as large centrifugal compressor water chilling systems tend towards the use of higher pressure refrigerants.

Starters

The National Electric Code includes, under the definition of "controller" any switch or device normally used to start and stop a motor. The recommendations of the code cover requirements for motor controllers in addition to requirements for motor running overcurrent protection, motor disconnecting means, motor branch circuit overcurrent protection, motor feeder overcurrent protection, and motor conductors. Although the manufacturer of mechanical equipment or the mechanical contractor who installs mechanical equipment frequently furnishes motor controllers and motor running overcurrent protection devices (overloads), requirements for the other devices must be incorporated and coordinated into each installation.

Motor Controllers.—National Electric Code requirements for nonhermetic motor controllers can be summarized as follows:

1) Motor controllers are not required for stationary motors $\frac{1}{8}$ hp or smaller that are so constructed that damage cannot occur from overload or failure to start. An example of this type motor is a clock motor.

2) For portable motors $\frac{1}{3}$ hp or smaller, the controller may be an attachment plug and receptacle.

3) For stationary motors 2 hp or less and 300 volts or less, the controller may be a general-use switch having an ampere rating at least twice the full-load rating of the motor. For A-C motors 2 hp or less, and 300 volts or less, an ac snap switch may be used to control a motor having a full-load current rating not exceeding 80% of the ampere rating of the switch.

4) For motors above 2 hp or greater than 300 volts, the controller must have a horsepower rating that shall not be lower than the horsepower rating of the motor. Devices that fall under this category include manual, horsepower-rated, push button switches up to about $7\frac{1}{2}$ hp, motor circuit switches which are rated in horsepower up to 50 hp, and contactors.

5) Also permitted for motors above 2 hp are branch-circuit type circuit breakers rated in amperes only. Each of these devices is capable of interrupting the locked rotor current of the motor it controls. These devices also are frequently used for motors 2 hp and smaller.

6) A controller for a hermetic type motor-compressor must have a continuous-duty, full-load, current rating not less than the nameplate rated load current or branch circuit selection current, whichever is greater, and locked rotor current, respectively, of the motor-compressor.

Overcurrent Protection.—Except for small, open ac motors with inherent overload protection and for single phase and small, polyphase hermetic-type motor-compressors, which have separate or inherent overload protection, most controllers incorporate overload protection (motor running overcurrent protection) in their enclosures.

The following summarizes National Electric Code requirements for motor running overcurrent protection:

1) Continuous duty motors, 1 hp or less, which are manually started and are within sight of the controller location and are not permanently installed, need no motor running overcurrent protection device, providing the branch circuit overcurrent protection device is properly rated for this purpose.

2) Any motor of 1 hp or less that is permanently installed is started automatically shall have a motor running overcurrent protection device (overload) separate from the motor and responsive to motor current or integral with the motor and approved for use with the motor it protects on the basis that it will prevent dangerous overheating due to overload or failure to start.

An integral device such as just described provides what is known as inherent overload protection. The code provides exceptions to the requirement for overload protection for high impedance motors, such as clock motors, and in some other cases where safety controls protect the motor against damage due to stalled rotor current.

Each continuous duty motor rated more than 1 hp shall be protected either by a separate motor-running, overcurrent protection device or by an approved inherent overload protector device.

Starters.—Starters used in heating, ventilating, air conditioning and plumbing work most often conform to the following general patterns:

1) Open motors on polyphase ac systems use magnetic contactors that interrupt all conductors. Separate overload protection is provided within the starter enclosure. Motors about 7½ hp and smaller sometimes use manual pushbutton starters with overloads, although magnetic starters are more popular even for fractional horsepower motors. Motor circuit switches using dual element fuses or time delay fuses for overload protection are seldom used.

2) Electrically operated circuit breakers sometimes are used for starters with very large squirrel cage induction motors, large synchronous motors, and for the primary controllers of large, wound-rotor induction motors. The circuit breakers usually function also as the motor branch circuit overcurrent protection device. Overcurrent running protection is provided by magnetic overload devices, which function to trip the electrically operated circuit breaker in event of overload.

3) Open, single-phase ac motors up to 1 hp generally use a manual toggle type snap switch motor starter. Overload protection is provided in the starter when the motor does not incorporate inherent overload protection. The speed selector switches of small, multispeed blower motors often function as the controllers.

4) Hermetic, three-phase motor compressors over 5 hp generally use conventional magnetic motor starters incorporating overloads. Internal motor-winding thermostats are wired in series with the overloads for added protection. Hermetic three-phase motor-compressors, 5 hp and smaller, frequently use contactors with the motors having inherent overload protectors or contactors with separate, special overload devices. (Refer to preceding part on hermetic type motor compressors for more details.)

Overload Protection.—A shortened insulation life due to excessive temperature rise is the most serious effect of motor overload. Generally, motor overload protection devices have inverse-time characteristics; that is, they respond more rapidly to increased currents. An attempt is made to match the overload protection device to the thermal characteristics of the motor.

Overload protection devices for motors without inherent protection fall into the following general categories: *thermal* and *magnetic*.

For small motors that are started manually without contactors, the overload device generally consists of a thermal bimetallic switch or thermal melting pot switch that directly interrupts the current to the motor. Most frequently, the switch is manually reset in the absence of a motor overload by a snap switch in the same enclosure which functions as the motor controller. Some ac snap switch controllers used with small, single-phase motors use time-delay fuses for overload protection. When motor circuit switches are used for starting larger motors, time-delay fuses are frequently used for overload protection.

Where contactors are used for motor controllers, the overload devices generally are overload relays. In this case, the thermal or magnetic element of the relay senses line current, but the switch or contact portion of the device interrupts the control circuit to the coil of the magnetic contactor.

Thermal bimetallic overload relays, thermal melting-pot relays and thermal induction relays are popular overload protection devices for ac motors up to around 200 hp in size. Magnetic overload relays are popular for this size motor and larger and are available for motors of smaller size.

The most popular type of magnetic overload relay includes a magnetic coil and plunger, which achieves an inverse-time relationship through the use of an oil dashpot, which offers resistance to the travel of the plunger. Adjustments to the overload setting can be made by varying the rate of oil flow in the dashpot. Another type of magnetic overload device uses electromagnetic induction from a coil to a movable core. No oil is required for this type.

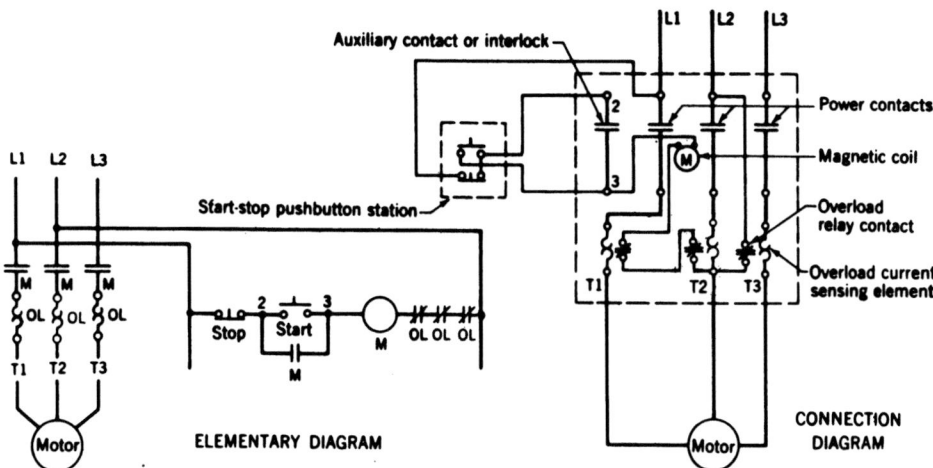

Fig 17-12. Full voltage size 1, 3-phase, magnetic starter; 3-wire control (low voltage protection)

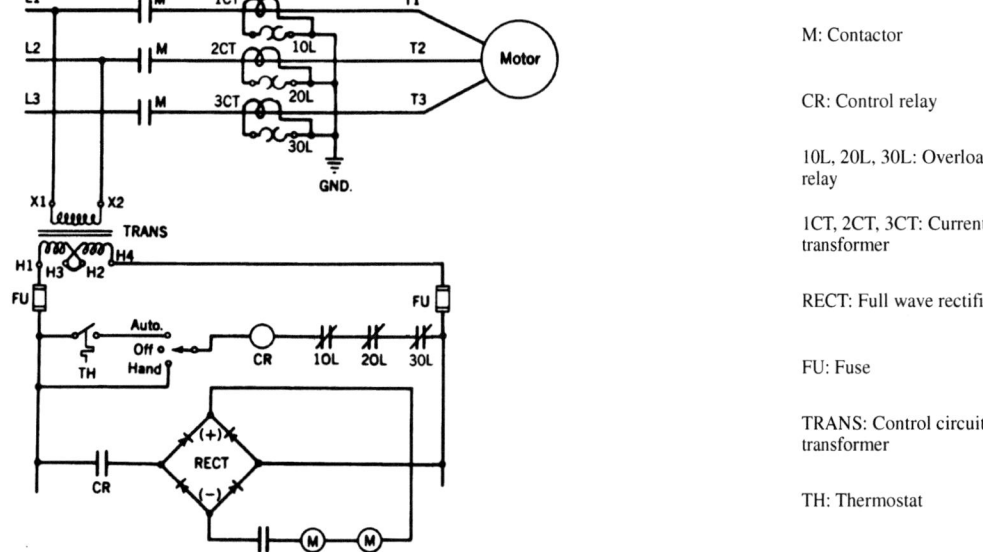

M: Contactor

CR: Control relay

10L, 20L, 30L: Overload relay

1CT, 2CT, 3CT: Current transformer

RECT: Full wave rectifier

FU: Fuse

TRANS: Control circuit transformer

TH: Thermostat

Fig 17-13. Full voltage, size 6, 3-phase, magnetic starter; 2-wire control (low voltage release)

Overload relays are available for manual reset from a pushbutton through the starter cover or enclosure cover, or are available for automatic reset. The manual reset type is most commonly used for most air conditioning, heating and ventilating motors; however, the automatic reset overload relay is popular with some types of packaged equipment that use external annunciators, reset relays or high impedance relays to reset safety devices.

Overload protection for non-hermetic motors sometimes use internal thermostats, or internal heaters and bimetal discs, plus supplementary overload protection as described for hermetic type motor-compressors. Thermistors, as described for hermetic type motor-compressors, are also sometimes used.

Starters for Large AC Motors.—Starters for large ac motors frequently use dc contactors. For the same static closing force, the frame and armature of a dc contactor can be smaller than that of an ac contactor. Furthermore, the impact force on closing of a dc contactor is smaller than the closing impact force of an ac contactor of the same size.

This means that for large motors, a dc magnetic contactor will be smaller and will require less massive support than an ac contactor. Another advantage is that the coil of a dc contactor does not have the large inrush current of an ac coil. Most frequently, the dc supply for a large starter comes from a full-wave selenium rectifier within the starter enclosure.

For large ac motors it becomes impractical to put the full-line motor current through the current-sensing portion of the overload relay. In this case a current transformer is utilized with each overload relay, which causes a small, accurate, percentage of the line motor current to pass through the overload relay. The current transformers normally are mounted within the starter enclosure. Adjustable magnetic overload relays and adjustable thermal induction relays are commonly used in conjunction with current transformers.

Starters are rated by NEMA in sizes for various horsepower motors at different voltages. Table 17-18 gives NEMA sizes of full-voltage starters for single phase and three-phase motors.

Fig. 17-12 shows the connection diagram and elementary diagram of a full-voltage, Size 1, three-phase magnetic starter. The connection diagram, sometimes referred to as the wiring diagram, shows all components and devices in their actual physical relationship to each other. The connection diagram gives the information for physically locating components and tracing wires or for wiring up a specific piece of equipment.

Table 17-18. Starter Size vs. Motor Horsepower for Full Voltage Starting

| Starter Size | Three Phase Motors | | |
	200 V/230 V		460 V/575 V
00	1½	1½	2
0	3	3	5
1	7½	7½	10
2	10	15	25
3	25	30	50
4	40	50	100
5	75	100	200
6	150	200	400
7	…	300	600
8	…	450	900

| Single-Phase Motors | | |
Starter Size	115 V	230 V
00	⅓	1
0	1	2
1	2	3
1P	3	5
2	3	7½
3	7½	15

On the other hand, the elementary diagram shows the system in a simplified manner, with no attempt made to indicate the various components and devices in their actual, relative positions. The elementary diagram gives the information for following easily the operation of the components and devices in the circuit.

Fig. 17-13 shows the elementary diagram of a typical full-voltage, Size 6, three-phase magnetic starter. The contactor has two dc coils wired in series, and the dc supply is provided from a full-wave rectifier in the starter. Current transformers are used to reduce the current through the current-sensing elements of the overload relays. A control-circuit transformer is used to decrease the voltage of the control circuit from line voltage to 230 V (shown) or 115 V.

Fig. 17-12 shows an arrangement where a 2-element momentary contact, start-stop pushbutton station controls the starter operation. The pushbutton stations can be remotely located or mounted in the starter cover and is wired into a normally open, auxiliary contact of the starter contactor. The control arrangement provides what is known as three-wire control, also known as low voltage protection or no voltage protection. In event of power interruption, the starter will drop out and will not pick up when power returns. In this case, the start button must be pressed to reclose the starter. This control arrangement provides protection to personnel who might be working on a machine after a power outage and has the additional advantage of preventing the simultaneous restarting of many motors in a large installation when voltage is re applied after a power interruption. Three-wire control from start stop push buttons is common for manually con-

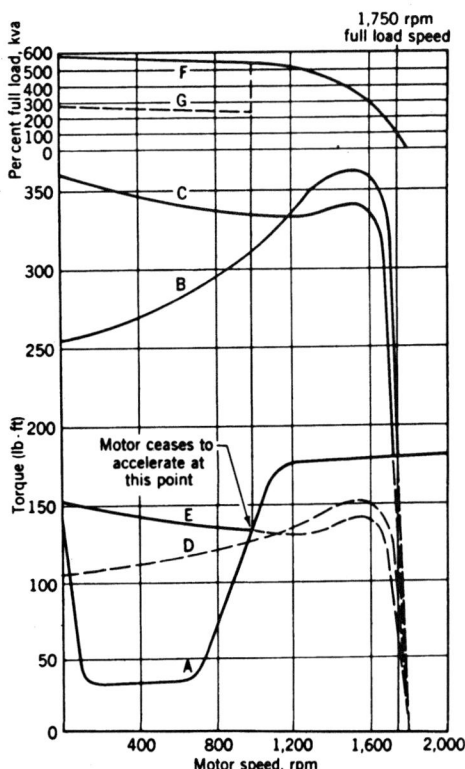

Fig 17-14. Torque speed and KVA speed curves
for 60 hp motor and compressor

trolled fans and pumps in air conditioning, heating, and ventilating applications.

Two-wire control, otherwise known as low voltage release or no voltage release, is used where motors are to be automatically started and stopped from devices such as thermostats, float switches, pressure switches, time clocks, etc. This arrangement permits the motor to restart automatically when voltage returns after a power interruption. Fig. 17-13 shows how a remote thermostat can be used to start and stop, automatically, a large motor using a two-wire control system. The auto offhand three-position selector switch, which can be remotely located or mounted in the starter cover, is used to bypass the thermostat if automatic operation is not desired.

Winding and Reduced-voltage Starting

Part-winding and reduced-voltage starting are used with large squirrel cage induction motors, large hermetic type motor-compressors, and large synchronous motors to reduce line disturbances to the serving electric utility's distribution system. On some occasions part-winding and reduced voltage starting can be very useful in preventing severe shocks to mechanical equipment caused by a motor's high starting torque.

Electric Utility Limitations.—Locked rotor current for a squirrel cage induction motor will be from $4\frac{1}{2}$ to 7 times full-load current, depending on the design of the particular motor. (See discussion earlier in this section on NEMA code letters). This large starting current, when associated with a big motor, could cause an excessive voltage drop through the electric utility's transformers and distribution system resulting in momentary dimming of lights, an undesired dip in voltage to computers and other electronic machines, and, conceivably, opening of magnetic starters serving other motors.

To protect their systems, electric utilities establish limitations on starting of large motors. These limitations generally take one of the following three forms:

1) *A maximum allowable current or power consumption per motor horsepower during any portion of the starting period:* This protects the power company in a general situation. Such limitations are defined in terms of amperes per horsepower and kilovolt-amperes (kva) per horsepower.

2) *A maximum permissible motor horsepower, or a maximum allowable current or power consumption during any portion of the starting period:* Generally, this recognizes the specific size of motor to be used, application of the motor, capacity of the power distribution system serving the motor, and location of the motor in the power distribution system. Such limitations are defined in terms of amperes and kva.

3) *A maximum allowable increase in current or power consumption per unit of time during the starting period:* This type of limitation generally occurs where a power company's automatic voltage regulator is capable of maintaining relatively constant voltage at the distribution point, providing a large change in load is not suddenly applied. Such limitations are defined in terms of amperes or kva per unit of time, or amperes or kva per horsepower per unit of time, in which case the unit of time is given in terms of seconds or fractions of a second. Generally, there is no definite limit to the ultimate value of the inrush current.

Minimizing Mechanical Shocks.—Most motors above 5 hp size have a starting (locked rotor) torque ranging from 100% to 200% of full-load torque. It is sometimes worthwhile to decrease this starting torque to minimize mechanical shocks when a motor is applied to a high-inertia load. A part-winding or reduced-voltage starter provides this reduction in torque.

A prime example is a large, centrifugal, V-belt driven fan. In many installations, start-up occurs with noticeable belt slippage. Use of an inexpensive part-winding motor and starter provides a *soft start,* which decreases or eliminates the slippage.

Application.—The power company limitation generally determines the required decrease to motor locked rotor line current. The part-winding or reduced-voltage starting method used to obtain this reduction in starting current will decrease the full-voltage torque speed characteristics of the motor during the starting period. In most cases, the decreased motor torque must still be enough to start and accelerate the driven load to full-load speed, or close to it, if the power company limitation is to be satisfied. Thus, power company limitation, type of part-winding and reduced-voltage starting used, nature of the driven load, and the speed-torque characteristics of the motor are interrelated and must be considered jointly.

An example of these interrelated factors follows:

Curve A, Fig. 17-14, shows the torque-speed load of an 8-cylinder, reciprocating, refrigeration compressor with automatic unloaders. The compressor is direct-connected to an open 60-hp motor. Starting and stopping is initiated by a medium-differential, suction pressure switch. The high side of the refrigeration system does not equalize to the low side on shutdown.

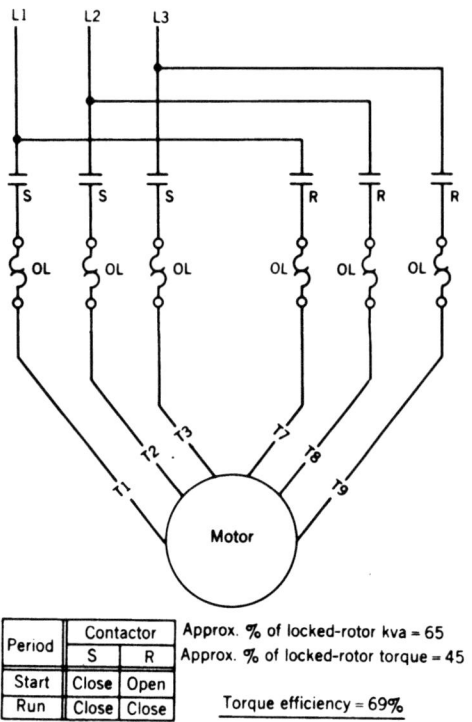

Period	Contactor	
	S	R
Start	Close	Open
Run	Close	Close

Approx. % of locked-rotor kva = 65
Approx. % of locked-rotor torque = 45

Torque efficiency = 69%

Fig 17-15. Part winding (one half winding start)

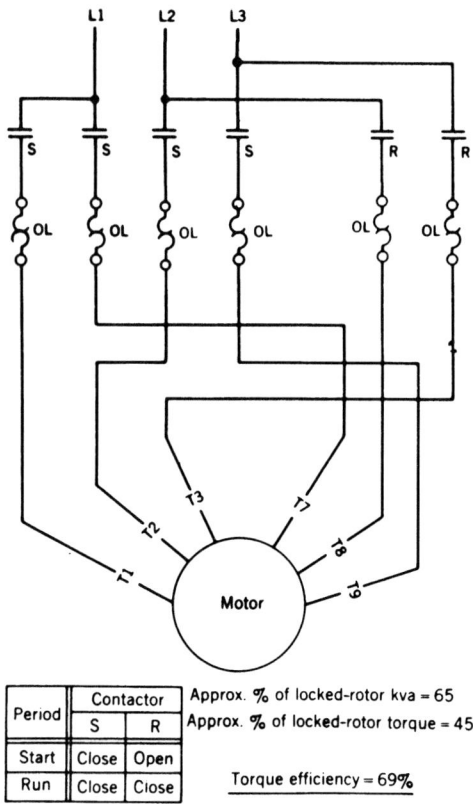

Period	Contactor	
	S	R
Start	Close	Open
Run	Close	Close

Approx. % of locked-rotor kva = 65
Approx. % of locked-rotor torque = 45

Torque efficiency = 69%

Fig 17-16. Part winding (two-thirds winding start)

Initial *breakaway torque* is required primarily to start two loaded cylinders against the high-side to low-side pressure difference. As the compressor begins to accelerate, the required torque drops to less than 25% of full-load torque since the remaining six cylinders are unloaded. After a short period, compressor oil pressure builds up sufficiently to load all 8 cylinders, and at this point, the required torque almost equals full-load torque.

Curve B shows the torque-speed curve of a NEMA Design B 60-hp motor, starting at full voltage. Since this curve lies entirely above the compressor torque-speed curve, the motor will start the compressor and accelerate it to full speed without difficulty.

Curve C shows the torque-speed curve of a NEMA Design C motor starting at full voltage. This motor also will start the compressor and bring it up to full load speed without difficulty.

Curve F shows the full voltage motor kva, in terms of percent full load kva, in this case applicable to both the NEMA Design B and the NEMA Design C motor. Locked-rotor kva is 5.8 times full load kva or about 5.5 kva/ hp.

Suppose the power company imposes a limitation of 3.0 kva/hp during any portion of the starting period. This would be equivalent to about 3.15 times full-load kva. An autotransformer reduced voltage starter on the 65% tap would cut the inrush kva down to about 2.7 kva /hp, more or less depending on the magnetizing current of the autotransformer within the starter. However, this reduction in starting kva would be accompanied by a decrease in motor torque.

Curve D shows the torque-speed curve of the NEMA Design B motor when energized through the autotransformer starter on the 65% tap. Notice that this motor now cannot overcome the required breakaway torque of the compressor. As a result, the motor stalls on the reduced-voltage starting step and, when full voltage is applied on the second step of starting, the inrush is the full 5.5 kva per hp.

Curve F shows the torque-speed curve of the NEMA Design C motor when energized through the autotransformer starter on the 65% tap. This motor can break the compressor away from the dead stop position, but it cannot maintain full compressor speed after all cylinders load up. When full voltage is applied, the inrush kva will exceed the power company limitation. Curve G shows the percent full-load kva at the point where the motor torque is in balance with the loaded compressor torque and full voltage is applied.

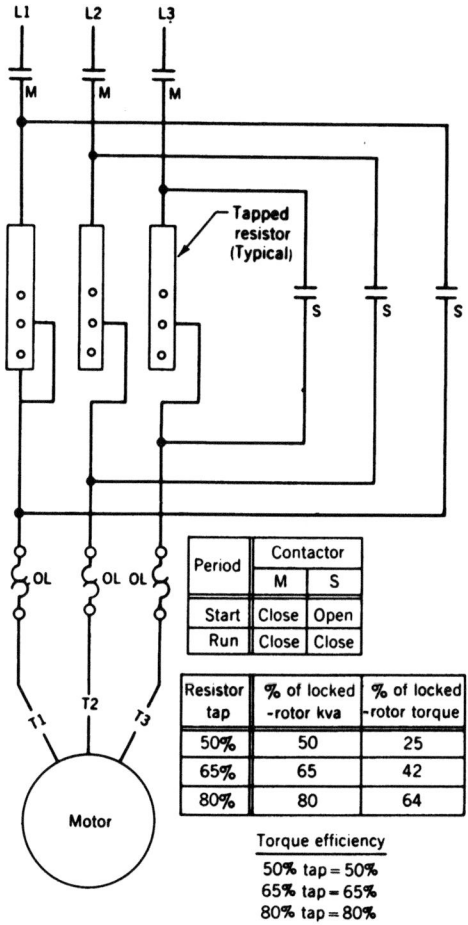

Period	Contactor	
	M	S
Start	Close	Open
Run	Close	Close

Resistor tap	% of locked-rotor kva	% of locked-rotor torque
50%	50	25
65%	65	42
80%	80	64

Torque efficiency
50% tap = 50%
65% tap = 65%
80% tap = 80%

Fig 17-17. Primary resistance (two step)

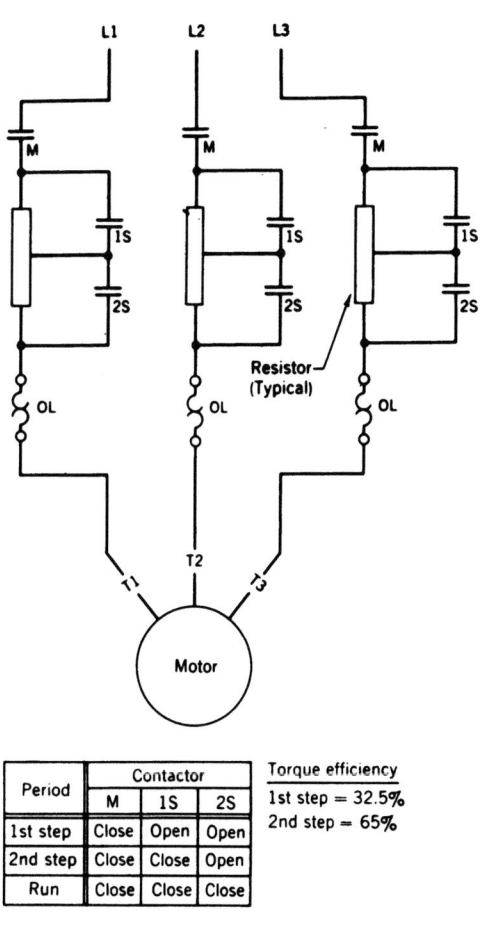

Period	Contactor			Torque efficiency
	M	1S	2S	1st step = 32.5%
1st step	Close	Open	Open	2nd step = 65%
2nd step	Close	Close	Open	
Run	Close	Close	Close	

	% voltage	% of locked-rotor kva	% of locked-rotor torque
1st step	32.5	32.5	10.6
2nd step	65	65	42

Fig 17-18. Primary Resistance (three step)

A satisfactory solution to this situation would be to use the autotransformer starter, the NEMA Design C motor and a compressor with externally operable cylinder unloaders. In this case the motor would be capable of starting the compressor, and the machine could be kept at 25% capacity during the entire starting period by operating the unloaders through a timing relay or through an interlock on the run contact or of the autotransformer starter.

The NEMA Design B motor could be used if the compressor discharge were equalized to its suction during shutdown or at the beginning of start-up. A check valve in the compressor discharge line in conjunction with a solenoid or bleed valve between compressor suction and discharge has been used frequently for this purpose.

Depending upon the type of power company limitation encountered, it is not always necessary to start or break away equipment on the first step of starting. For example, a limitation specifying a maximum allowable increase in current or kva per unit of time or current or kva per horsepower per unit of time does not establish a limit to the ultimate inrush current or kva. Thus, a motor that stalls on the first step of starting would be acceptable if its inrush at this time would not exceed the increment established by the power company.

Generally, centrifugal machines, with their rising torque-speed characteristics, present no problems regarding breakaway torques. However, it is desirable to keep these machines unloaded during the entire starting period to reduce acceleration time, and to approach full-load speed before full voltage is applied. Centrifugal refrigeration compressors almost always have the pre-rotation vanes kept automatically closed during the starting period when used with reduced-voltage starters. Large centrifugal pumps can be started against closed discharge valves to minimize loads during starting.

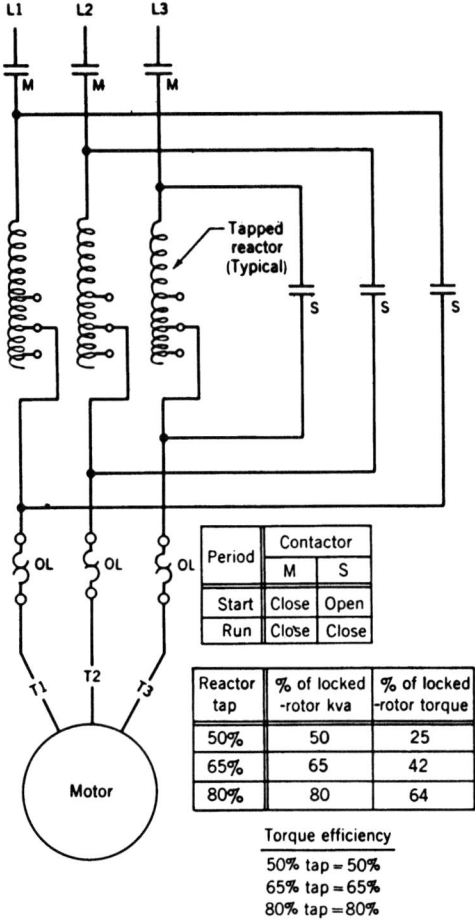

Period	Contactor	
	M	S
Start	Close	Open
Run	Close	Close

Reactor tap	% of locked-rotor kva	% of locked-rotor torque
50%	50	25
65%	65	42
80%	80	64

Torque efficiency
50% tap = 50%
65% tap = 65%
80% tap = 80%

Fig 17-19. Primary reactor (two step)

The effects of the inertia of the driven machine and motor should not be ignored when large equipment is involved. Acceleration time, from dead stop to full load speed, is a function of workload, friction load, and inertia of the driven machine as well as the inertia of the motor. Even though the workload is decreased due to unloading, a large inertia (Wk^2), in conjunction with a decreased torque due to reduced-voltage starting, may result in an abnormally long acceleration time. An over extended acceleration time could result in over heating of the driving motor, overheating of resistors or transformers used in reduced-voltage starters, or lack of lubrication in driven equipment that utilizes shaft-mounted oil pumps.

Types of Starters.—Fig. 17-15 through 17-23 identify and show wiring diagrams of the power switching circuits of the more commonly used part-winding and reduced voltage starters. Also included for each starting

method is the sequence in which the various contactors operate during the starting period.

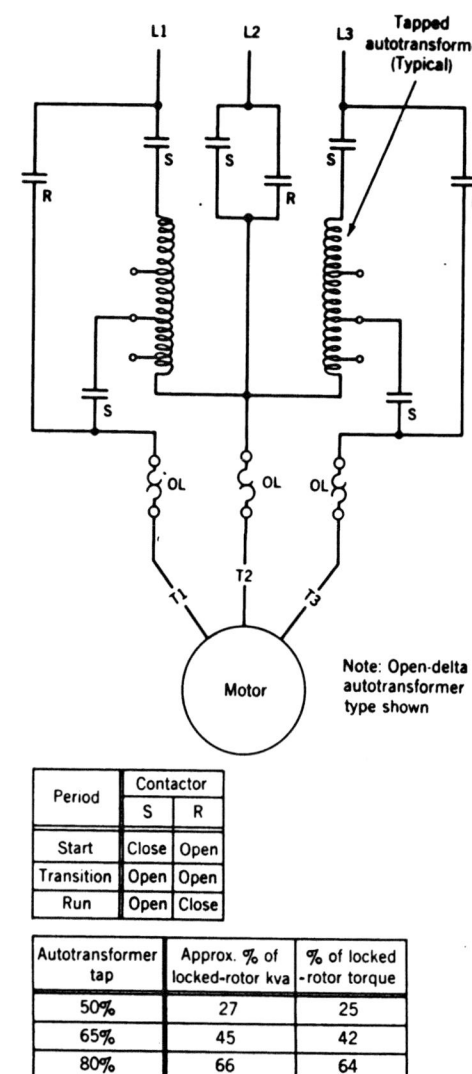

Note: Open-delta autotransformer type shown

Period	Contactor	
	S	R
Start	Close	Open
Transition	Open	Open
Run	Open	Close

Autotransformer tap	Approx. % of locked-rotor kva	% of locked-rotor torque
50%	27	25
65%	45	42
80%	66	64

Torque efficiency = Approx. 95% on all taps

Fig 17-20. Autotransformer (open circuit transition)

Open Circuit Transition.—It will be noticed from Fig. 17-20 and 17-22 that both autotransformer and star-delta starters include open-circuit transition types. The open-circuit transition starters function, in effect, to disconnect the motor from the line during the brief instant it takes to switch from the starting step to the running step. This is necessary to insure against an overlap of contacts, which would short-circuit part of the transformer winding in the autotransformer starter or cause a dead short in the star-delta starter.

At the instant full voltage is connected at the end of the open transition, there will be an inrush current of much shorter duration than the inrush that occurs when the motor is first started. This second inrush can be of a magnitude which equals or even exceeds the original inrush. If this second inrush is objectionable to the power company, then a closed circuit transition starter must be used.

Advantages and Disadvantages.—Each type of part-winding and reduced-voltage starter in common use has one or more distinct advantages and usually some disadvantages.

In many situations, the most significant characteristic of the starting method is the ratio of the percent of available motor locked rotor torque to the percent of motor locked rotor current or kva. This is defined as torque efficiency and is given by the formula

$$E_T = \frac{\% \text{ of full volt locked rotor torque}}{\% \text{ of full volt locked rotor kva or line current}}$$

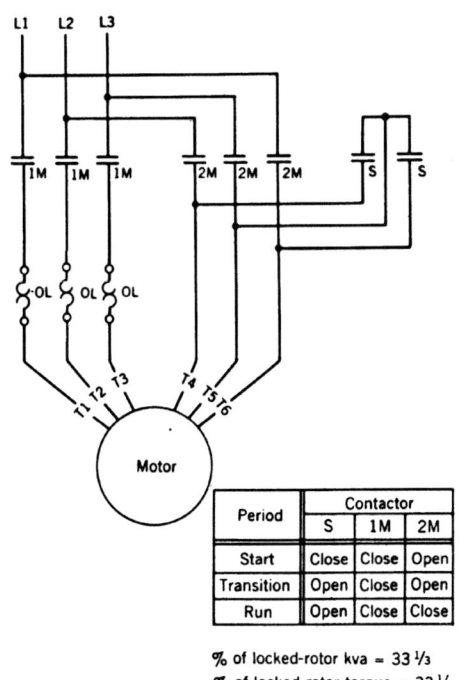

Fig 17-21. Star delta (open circuit transition)

Table 17-1 data include full-voltage, locked rotor torques of NEMA Design A, B, and C motors, fans, ranging while Table 17-2 gives locked rotor currents for these motors. The data refer to squirrel-cage induction motors.

The tabulated information in Fig. 17-15 through 17-23 show the percent of full voltage, locked rotor kva and the percent of full voltage, locked rotor torque available for each starting method. The particular starting method selected must not only decrease the inrush kva sufficiently to satisfy power company requirements, but must simultaneously permit enough torque to start and accelerate the load if the power company requirement is not an *increment* type of limitation. In other words, a high torque efficiency can often be a significant advantage in the selection of a reduced-voltage starting method.

The following summarizes advantages and disadvantages of the various methods of part-winding and reduced-voltage starters.

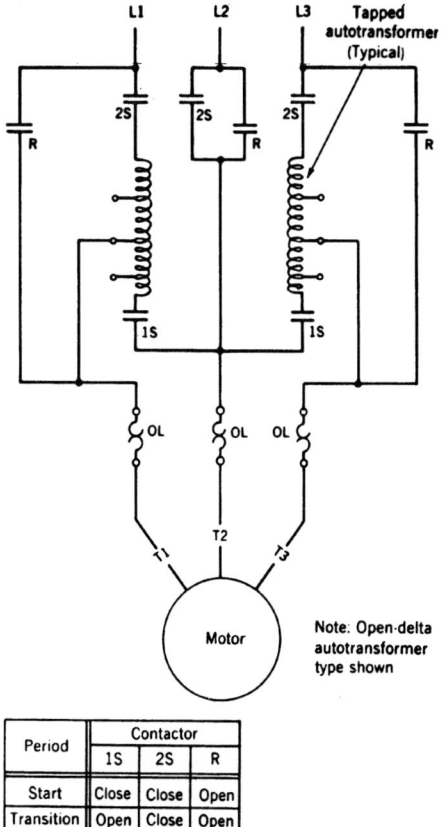

Fig 17-22. Autotransformer (closed circuit transition)

Period	Contactor		
	S	1M	2M
Start	Close	Close	Open
Transition	Open	Close	Open
Run	Open	Close	Close

% of locked-rotor kva = 33 ⅓
% of locked-rotor torque = 33 ⅓
Torque efficiency = 100%

Period	Contactor		
	1S	2S	R
Start	Close	Close	Open
Transition	Open	Close	Open
Run	Open	Open	Close

Autotransformer tap	Approx. % of locked-rotor kva	% of locked-rotor torque
50%	27	25
65%	45	42
80%	66	64

Torque efficiency = Approx. 95% on all taps

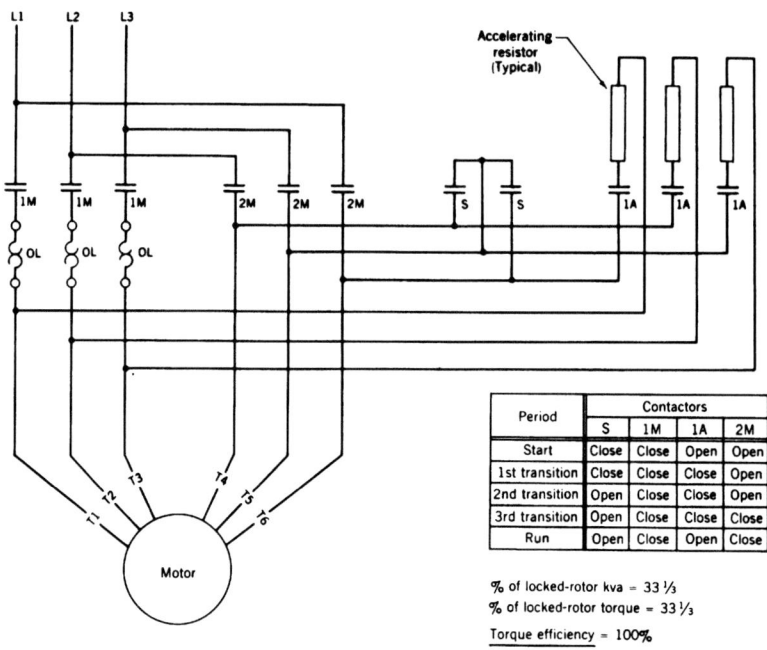

Period	Contactors			
	S	1M	1A	2M
Start	Close	Close	Open	Open
1st transition	Close	Close	Close	Open
2nd transition	Open	Close	Close	Open
3rd transition	Open	Close	Close	Close
Run	Open	Close	Open	Close

% of locked-rotor kva = 33 ⅓
% of locked-rotor torque = 33 ⅓
Torque efficiency = 100%

Fig 17-23. Star delta (closed circuit transition)

Advantages	Disadvantages
A. Part winding (½ winding start)	
1. Low cost.	1. Frequently will have torque dip at about half-speed during starting.
2. Closed transition.	2. Low torque efficiency.
	3. More severe heating and mechanical stresses on motor during starting.
B. Part winding (⅔ winding start)	
1. Low cost.	1. Low torque efficiency.
2. Closed transition.	2. Unbalanced line currents during starting.
	3. More severe heating and mechanical stresses on motor during starting.
C. Primary resistance (2-step)	
1. Closed transition.	1. Relatively expensive.
2. Tapped resistors permit field adjustment to inrush kva and starting torque.	2. Low torque efficiency.
D. Primary Resistance (3-step)	
1. Closed transition.	1. Expensive.
2. High power factor during starting step.	2. Low torque efficiency.
E. Primary reactor	
1. Closed transition.	1. Relatively low cost for high-voltage installations.

Advantages	Disadvantages
2. Tapped reactors permit field adjustment to inrush kva and staring torque.	2. Low torque efficiency.
Note: This starting method is particularly well adapted to high-voltage systems. Rarely used at low voltage.	
F. Autotransformer (open-circuit transition)	
1. High torque efficiency	1. Relatively expensive.
2. Tapped transformer permits field adjustment to inrush kva and starting torque.	2. Open-circuit transition.
G. Autotransformer (closed-circuit transition or korndorfer method)	
1. Closed Transition.	1. Expensive.
2. High torque efficiency.	
3. Tapped transformer permits field adjustment to inrush kva and starting torque.	
H. Star-Delta (open-circuit transition)	
1. High torque efficiency.	1. Open transition.
2. Particularly well adapted to long accelerating (starting) periods.	2. Low starting torque.
I. Star-Delta (closed-circuit transition)	
1. Closed transition.	1. Expensive.
2. High torque efficiency.	2. Low starting torque.
3. Particularly well adapted to long accelerating (starting)	

Useful Formulas.—Direct current circuits:

$$I = \frac{E}{R}$$

$$W = EI = I^2R = \frac{E^2}{R}$$

$$KW = \frac{W}{1000} = \frac{EI}{1000} = \frac{I^2R}{1000} = \frac{E^2}{1000R}$$

$$hp = \frac{W \times eff}{746} = \frac{KW \times eff}{0.746} = \frac{EI \times eff}{746}$$

Single-Phase AC Circuits:

$$va = EI$$

$$kva = \frac{va}{1000} = \frac{EI}{1000}$$

$$W = va \times PF = EI \times PF$$

$$KW = kva \times PF = \frac{EI \times PF}{1000}$$

$$hp = \frac{KW \times eff}{0.746} = \frac{kva \times PF \times eff}{0.746}$$

$$= \frac{EI \times PF \times eff}{431}$$

Three phase ac circuits:

$$va = 1.73 \times EI$$

$$kva = \frac{va}{1000} = \frac{1.73 \times EI}{1000}$$

$$W = va \times PF = 1.73 \times EI \times PF$$

$$KW = kva \times PF = \frac{1.73 \times EI \times PF}{1000}$$

$$hp = \frac{KW \times eff}{0.746} = \frac{kva \times PF \times eff}{0.746}$$

$$= \frac{1.73 \times EI \times PF \times eff}{431}$$

Power transmitted by shafting: $hp = \dfrac{T \times N}{5250}$

AC motor speed:

$$N_s = \frac{120 \times Hz}{P}$$

$$N = N_s(1 - s)$$

Letters and abbreviations used in the above formulas have these meanings:

I = current, amperes

E = potential difference, volts

R = resistance, ohms

W = power, watts

KW = power, kilowatts

va = apparent power, volt-amperes (present only in alternating current circuits with inductance and/or capacitance)

kva = apparent power, kilovolt-amperes

hp = output power, horsepower

eff = efficiency, expressed as a decimal fraction

PF = power factor, expressed as a decimal fraction (present only in alternating current circuits with inductance and/or capacitance)

T = torque, lb-ft

N = revolutions per minute at rated speed

N_s = revolutions per minute at synchronous speed

Hz = frequency, cycles per second, or Hertz

P = number of poles

s = slip expressed as a fraction of synchronous speed

Electric Motor Maintenance

Electric Motor Inspection Schedule.—Frequency and thoroughness of inspection depend upon such factors as 1) importance of the motor in the production scheme;

2) percentage of days the motor operates; 3) nature of service; and 4) winding conditions.

Weekly Inspection.—1) *Surroundings.* Check to see if the windings are exposed to any dripping water, acid, or alcoholic fumes; also, check for any unusual amount of dust, chips, or lint on or about the motor. See if any boards, covers, canvas, etc. have been misplaced that might interfere with the motor ventilation or jam moving parts.

2) *Lubrication of sleeve-bearing motors.* In sleeve-bearing motors check oil level if a gage is used and fill to the specified line. If the journal diameter is less than 2 inches, the motor should be stopped before checking the oil level. For special lubricating systems, such as wool-packed forced lubrication, flood and disk lubrication, follow instruction book. Oil should be added to bearing housing only when motor is at rest. A check should be made to see if oil is creeping along the shaft toward windings where it may harm the insulation.

3) *Mechanical condition.* Note any unusual noise that may be caused by metal-to-metal contact or any odor as from scorching insulation varnish.

4) *Ball or roller bearings.* Feel ball bearing or roller-bearing housings for evidence of vibration, and listen for any unusual noise. Inspect for creepage of grease on inside of motor.

5) *Commutators and brushes.* Check brushes and commutator for sparking. If the motor is on cyclic duty it should be observed through several cycles. Note color and surface condition of the commutator. A stable copper oxide-carbon film (as distinguished from a pure copper surface) on the commutator is an essential requirement

for good commutation. Such a film may vary in color all the way from copper to straw, chocolate to black. It should be clean and smooth and have a high polish. All brushes should be checked for wear and pigtail connections for looseness. The commutator surface may be cleaned by using a piece of dry canvas or other hard, non-linting material that is wound around and securely fastened to a wooden stick, and held against the rotating commutator.

6) *Rotors and armatures.* The air gap on sleeve-bearing motors should be checked, especially if they have been recently overhauled. After installing new bearings, make sure that the average reading is within 10%, provided reading should be less than 0.020 inch. Check air passages through punchings and make sure they are free of foreign matter.

7) *Windings.* If necessary clean windings by suction or mild blowing. After making sure that the motor is dead, wipe off windings with dry cloth, note evidence of moisture, and see if any water has accumulated in the bottom of frame. Check if any oil or grease has worked its way up to the rotor or armature windings. Clean with carbon tetrachloride in a well ventilated room.

8) *General.* This is a good time to check the belt, gears, flexible couplings, chain, and sprockets for excessive wear or improper location. The motor starting should be checked to make sure that it comes up to proper speed each time power is applied.

Monthly or Bimonthly Inspection.—1) *Windings.* Check shunt, series, and commutating field windings for tightness. Try to move field spools on the poles, as drying out may have caused some play. If this condition exists, a service shop should be consulted. Check motor cable connections for tightness.

2) *Brushes.* Check brushes in holders for fit and free play. Check the brush-spring pressure. Tighten brush studs in holders to take up slack from drying out of washers, making sure that studs are not displaced, particularly on dc motors. Replace brushes that are worn down almost to the brush rivet, examine brush faces for chipped toes or heels, and for heat cracks. Damaged brushes should be replaced immediately.

3) *Commutators.* Examine commutator surface for high bars and high mica, or evidence of scratches or roughness. See that the risers are clean and have not been damaged.

4) *Ball or roller bearings.* On hard-driven, 24-hour service ball or roller-bearing motors, purge out old grease through drain hole and apply new grease. Check to make sure grease or oil is not leaking out of the bearing housing. If any leakage is present, correct the condition before continuing to operate.

5) *Sleeve bearings.* Check sleeve bearings for wear, including end-play bearing surfaces. Clean out oil wells if

there is evidence of dirt or sludge. Flush with lighter oil before refilling.

6) *Enclosed gears.* For motors with enclosed gears, open drain plug and check oil flow for presence of metal scale, sand, or water. If condition of oil is bad, drain, flush, and refill as directed. Rock rotor to see if slack or backlash is increasing.

7) *Loads.* Check loads for changed conditions, bad adjustment, poor handling, or control.

8) *Couplings and other drive details.* Note if belt-tightening adjustment is all used up. Shorten belt if this condition exists. See if belt runs steadily and close to inside (motor edge) of pulley. Chain should be checked for evidence of wear and stretch. Clean inside of chain housing. Check chain lubricating system. Note inclination of slanting base to make sure it does not cause oil rings to rub on housing.

Annual or Biannual Inspection.—1) *Windings.* Check insulation resistance by using either a mega ohm meter or a voltmeter having a resistance of about 100 ohms per volt. Check insulation surfaces for dry cracks and other evidence of need for coatings of insulating material. Clean surfaces and ventilating passages thoroughly if inspection shows accumulation of dust. Check for mold or water standing in frame to determine if windings need to be dried out, varnished, and baked.

2) *Air gap and bearings.* Check air gap to make sure that average reading is within 10%, provided reading should be less than 0.020 inch. All bearings, ball, roller, and sleeve should be thoroughly checked and defective ones replaced. Waste-packed and wick-oiled bearings should have waste or wicks renewed if they have become glazed or filled with metal or dirt. Make sure that new waste bears well against shaft.

3) *Rotors (squirrel cage).* Check squirrel-cage rotors for broken or loose bars and evidence of local heating. If fan blades are not cast in place, check for loose blades. Look for marks on rotor surface indicating foreign matter in air gap or a worn bearing.

4) *Rotors (wound).* Clean wound rotors thoroughly around collector rings, washers, and connections. Tighten connections, if necessary. If rings are rough, spotted, or eccentric, refer to service shop for refinishing. See that all top sticks or wedges are tight. If any are loose, refer to service shop.

5) *Armatures.* Clean all armature air passages thoroughly if any are obstructed. Look for oil or grease creeping along shaft, checking back to bearing. Check commutator for surface condition, high bars, high mica, or eccentricity. If necessary, remachine the commutator to secure a smooth fresh surface.

6) *Loads.* Read load on motor with instruments at no load, full load, or through an entire cycle, as a check on the mechanical condition of the driven machine.

DESIGN PROCEDURE

ABBREVIATIONS AND SYMBOLS & DESIGN PROCEDURE

Design Procedure

Contract and Mechanical Drawings.—When construction of a new building or alteration in an existing building is contemplated, the owner usually contracts for the professional services of architects and engineers. To satisfy the owner's purpose, his requirements, and his budget limitations for the work to be done, these architects and engineers will prepare design drawings and work specifications for the project. The drawings and specifications are of four major categories —mechanical, structural, electrical, and architectural. The drawings are generally drawn to scales of $\frac{1}{8}$"=1'-0" or $\frac{1}{4}$"=1'-0", and this scale is noted on the drawing. Estimates are prepared from these drawings by various contractors, who will then submit bids for their phase of the installation. Bids are selected by the architect or engineer, and contracts signed on the basis of the design drawings, which are then identified as the *contract* drawings. Subsequent revisions to the contract drawings may involve additional costs or credits to the owner. The sheetmetal draftsman should check drawing number, scale, date, revision number (if any), orientation, and general notes of each design drawing used for reference while preparing *shop* drawings.

Basically, the *mechanical* drawings are schematic and intended to show general arrangements of equipment, sizes of ducts, piping, and wiring layouts. However, it is not uncommon for these drawings to locate ducts, pipes, or equipment by definite dimensions. If a draftsman is unable to achieve a location requirement, he should prominently note the reasons on his drawing.

HVAC Drawings.—Most significant to the draftsman are the heating, ventilating, and air conditioning drawings consisting of floor plans, mechanical equipment room (MER) layouts, plans and sections, details, schedules, flow control and riser diagrams. Drawing numbers are generally prefixed: **HVAC, AC, M,** or **H,** corresponding to heating, ventilating, and air conditioning, air conditioning, mechanical, or heating respectively. HVAC drawings show duct systems, piping for heating, cooling, refrigeration, and fuel oil. They may include pneumatic tube systems, snow melting devices, automatic temperature controls, and all mechanical equipment.

Double line layouts are used most often for ductwork, although single line drafting methods are not uncommon. The former distinguishes duct runs from piping layouts that are generally drawn single line, so that duct arrangements and space requirements can be clearly analyzed. Table 18-1 shows duct system symbols and nomenclature.

Floor Plans.—Design drawing sheets are usually of adequate size to indicate entire floor plan layouts. Build-ings of very large area often require more than one drawing per floor. Match lines are used to connect points of adjacent drawings, along with notes indicating the continuation drawing number, e.g., continued on Dwg. H-6.

HVAC floor plans indicate general arrangements of air inlets, outlets, and the related duct distribution systems. Using these drawings for reference, together with the corresponding structural and architectural design drawings, the sheetmetal draftsman responsibility is to locate air-system components on each shop drawing to conform to the intent of the design engineer.

Drafting procedures are affected by differences of duct construction standards for various types of systems and methods of fabrication. The draftsman should make a visual analysis of the floor plans, so that he may become aware of special material or construction requirements.

Duct materials for underground or below-grade installation are often specified as coated metal. Such materials must be ordered and the shop drawings prepared with sufficient lead time so that ducts can be installed according to job construction schedules and coordinated with work schedules of other mechanical and electrical trades.

Design drawings and specifications of duct systems used for boiler breechings, fume hoods, kitchen, dishwasher, and shower room exhausts, as well as inlet and discharge ducts for interior cooling towers and evaporative condensers, must be checked for requirements of types of materials, gages, watertight construction, expansion joints, and hanging details. (See Table 18-1 for smoke breeching, hanging details.) Concrete pour schedules at the job site will determine the sequence for making shop drawings. The drawings should indicate slab insert locations, slab, and concrete wall openings for ducts. Although, duct openings may be shown on architectural or structural drawings, they should be verified by the draftsman through field inspection, either personally or by a subordinate, during preparation of the drawing.

Plans must be checked against specifications of lined ducts to confirm net clear interior duct sizes, thickness, and extent of lining.

Single or double duct supply systems to terminal units or pressure-reducing control valves are known as high pressure ducts, and require special instructions from the draftsman. Ductwork downstream of mixing units or pressure-reducing boxes is low pressure, and generally requires acoustical lining for a specified distance. Accessibility to these units for maintenance must be considered by the draftsman.

Supply and return air grilles, registers, and diffusers are available in many types and styles. Manufacturer drawings indicate inside or outside dimensions for making sheetmetal collars or other special requirements for connection to the manufacturer's equipment. The draftsman should note on the shop drawing where special grilles or air turning devices are to be installed.

Table 18-1. Duct Drafting Symbols

2–Dimensional	Identification	1–Dimensional	2–Dimensional	Identification	1–Dimensional
W x D		48 X 16		Turning vanes	
	Outside air, return, spill or exhaust	UP　　　DN.		Full throat radius	
SUPPLY	Supply	UP　SECTIONS DN		Round	
DIA.		22"⌀　○		Splitter vanes	
	Acoustical lining			Rotated down	
	Duct below grade				
D	Inclined drop in direction of flow	DN. / D		Splitter damper with locking quadrant	
R	Inclined rise in direction of flow	R / R		Splitter damper with adjustable rod	
	Elbow down			Top register or top grille with air extractor	T.R. OR T.G.
	Elbow up			Ceiling register or ceiling grille	C.R. OR C.G.
	Rectangular to round			Transfer air grilles	T.G.
	Positive branch	N=		Tee branch tap	
	Lateral branch tap				
	Lateral			TRANSFER-AIR CEILING GRILLES (LINED SECTION) C.G. C.G.	
	Tee branch tap			TRANSFER-AIR DOOR LOUVER	
	Tee			TRANSFER-AIR UNDERCUT DOOR	

DRAFTING SYMBOLS

18–3

Table 18-1. *(Continued)* Duct Drafting Symbols

2–Dimensional	Identification	1–Dimensional	2–Dimensional	Identification	1–Dimensional
	Manual volume damper			Bottom register or bottom grille	
	Remote operated manual volume damper			Reheat coil (system)	ONE WAY LIGHT-AIR-TROFFER (CFM) / LAT / TWO WAY
	Round ceiling diffuser 15"φ CD 900 CFM 90° BAFFLE			Sleeve type fire damper	
	Rectangular ceiling diffuser 24 x 12 CD 2000 CFM ONE WAY BLO			Duct-type fire damper	BTM. OF SLAB / VIBRATION ELIM. FOR HANGING (TYPE) / ¾"φ T.R.
CONTINUOUS PLENUM 8 x 12	Lineal ceiling diffuser			Supply air (cfm, size) roof fan	
S.D. 12-6 FLEX	Single duct terminal unit (identification size, hand)			Exhaust air (cfm, size) roof fan	
FLEX D.D. 3-8	Dual duct terminal unit (identification, size, hand)			Weather cap	VIBRATION ELIM. FAN BASE (TYPE) / F. FL. / EQUIPMENT PAD
	Pressure control valve (size)			Ventilator	INERTIA BASE
SA	Sound absorber (dia., length, system)			Louver house	COIL STAND
SA	Sound absorber (L × W × H, system)			Roof gooseneck wire-mesh screen	
2000 CFM	Canopy hood (L × W × H, mounting height, cfm, duct size connection)		AD	Wall gooseneck automatic damper	
1200 CFM	Cabinet type fume hood (size, cfm, duct size)			Axial fan	
GBDD E-9 SCREEN	Propeller-type exhaust fan (protective screen, gravity back draft damper, louver and bird screen)		PA-3	Induction unit, enclosure, primary air riser, system number	

Table 18-1. *(Continued)* Duct Drafting Symbols

2–Dimensional	Identification	1–Dimensional	2–Dimensional	Identification	1–Dimensional
	Centrifugal and single inlet fan, motor, drive and belt guard		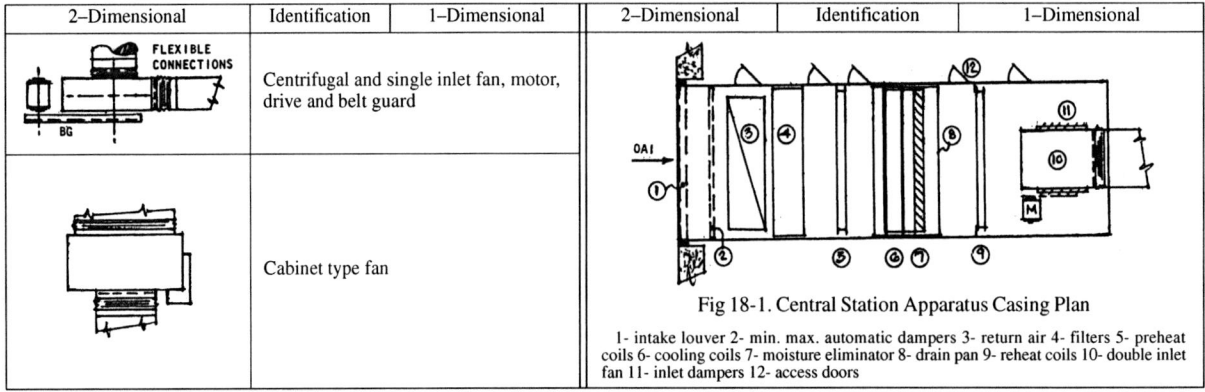		
	Cabinet type fan				

Fig 18-1. Central Station Apparatus Casing Plan

1- intake louver 2- min. max. automatic dampers 3- return air 4- filters 5- preheat coils 6- cooling coils 7- moisture eliminator 8- drain pan 9- reheat coils 10- double inlet fan 11- inlet dampers 12- access doors

Table 18-2. Standard Graphical Symbols for HVAC

Air Conditioning				Heating and Ventilation			
Identification	Symbol	Identification	Symbol	Identification	Symbol	Identification	Symbol
Capillary tube		Filter line		Air eliminator		Access door	
Compressor		Filter and strainer, line		Anchor		Adjustable blank off	
Compressor, rotary (enclosed crankcase, belted)		Float, high side		Expansion joint		Adjustable plaque	
Compressor, reciprocating (open crankcase, belted)		Float, low side		Hanger or support			
Compressor, reciprocating (open crankcase, direct-drive)		Gage		Heat exchanger		Automatic damper	
Motor compressor, reciprocating (direct connected, enclosed crankcase)		Pressure stat		Heat transfer surface (plan, indicate type, such as convector)			
Motor compressor, rotary (direct connected, enclosed crankcase)		Pressure switch		Pump (Indicate type, such as vacuum)		Canvas connection	
Motor compressor, reciprocating (sealed crankcase)		Pressure switch (with high pressure cut-out)		Strainer		Deflecting damper	
Motor compressor, rotary (sealed crankcase)		Receiver, horizontal		Tank (designate type)		Direction of flow	
Condensing unit (air-cooled)		Receiver, vertical		Thermometer		Duct (first figure is side shown)	
Condensing unit (water-cooled)		Scale trap		Thermostat		Duct section (exhaust or return)	
Condenser air cooled (finned, forced air)		Spray pond		Trap, boiler return		Duct section (supply)	
Condenser air cooled (finned, static)		Thermal bulb		Trap, blast thermostatic		Exhaust inlet, ceiling (indicate type)	
Condenser water cooled (concentric tube in a tube)		Thermostat (remote bulb)		Trap, float		Exhaust inlet, wall (indicate type)	

Table 18-2. *(Continued)* Standard Graphical Symbols for HVAC

Air Conditioning				Heating and Ventilation			
Identification	Symbol	Identification	Symbol	Identification	Symbol	Identification	Symbol
Condenser water cooled (shell and coil)		Valve, expansion, automatic	⊗	Trap, float and thermostatic		Fan and motor (with belt guard)	
Condenser water cooled (shell and tube)		Valve, expansion, hand	⊗	Trap, thermostatic			
Condenser evaporative		Valve, expansion, thermostatic		Unit heater (centrifugal fan type- plan)		Inclined drop (with respect to air flow)	
		Valve, compressor suction pressure limiting (throttling type, compressor side)		Unit heater (propeller fan type-plan)		Inclined rise (with respect to air flow)	
Cooling unit, finned (natural convection)		Valve, constant pressure, suction		Unit ventilator, plan		Intake louvers	
Cooling unit (forced convection)		Valve, evaporator pressure regulating (snap action)		Valve, check			
Cooling tower		Valve, evaporator pressure regulating (throttling type, evaporator side)		Valve, diaphragm		Louver opening	
Dryer		Valve, magnetic stop		Valve, gate		Supply outlet, ceiling (Indicate type)	
Evaporator, circular (Ceiling type, finned)		Valve, snap action		Valve, glove		Supply outlet, wall (Indicate type)	
Evaporator, manifolded (Bare tube, gravity air)		Valve, suction vapor regulating		Valve, lock and shield			
Evaporator, manifolded (finned, forced air)		Valve suction		Valve, motor operated		Vanes	
Evaporator, manifolded (finned, gravity air)		Valve water		Valve, pressure reducing			
Evaporator, plate coils (headered or manifolded)		Vibration absorber, line		Valve relief (either pressure or vacuum)		Volume damper	
				Vent point			

Table 18-3. Standard Graphical Symbols for Valves

Name of Valve	Flanged	Screwed	Bell & Spigot	Welded	Soldered
Angle valve, check					
Angle valve, gate (elevation)					
Angle valve, gate (plan)					
Angle valve, globe (elevation)					
Angle valve, globe (plan)					
Automatic bypass valve					
Automatic governor operated valve					

Table 18-3. *(Continued)* Standard Graphical Symbols for Valves

Name of Valve	Flanged	Screwed	Bell & Spigot	Welded	Soldered
Automatic reducing valve	▲				
Check valve, straight way	⊳	⊳	⊳	⊳	⊳
Cock	⊟	⊟	⊟	⊟	⊟
Diaphragm valve	⊠	⊠			
Float valve	⊠	⊠		⊠	⊠
Gate valve also used as stop valve	⊠	⊠	⊳⊲	⊠	⊠
Gate valve motor operated	⊠	⊠		⊠	
Globe valve	⊠				
Globe valve motor operated	⊠		⊠		
Hose valve, angle	⊿	⊿			
Hose valve, gate	⊠	⊠			
Hose valve, glove	⊠	⊠			
Lockshield valve	⊠	⊠			⊠
Quick opening valve	⊠	⊠		⊠	⊠
Safety valve	⊠	⊠	⊳⊲	⊠	⊠

Table 18-4. Standard Graphical Symbols for Piping

Air Conditioning			
Brine return	— — BR — —	Brine supply	—— B ——
Chilled or hot water flow (circulating)	—— CH ——	Chilled or hot water return (circulating)	— — CHR — —
Condenser water flow	—— C ——	Condenser water return	— — CR — —
Drain	—— D ——	Humidification line	—— H ——
Make-up water	—— · ——	Refrigerant discharge	—— RD ——
Refrigerant liquid	—— RL ——	Refrigerant liquid	— — RS — —

Heating			
Air relief line	—— · ——	Boiler blow-off	—— — ——
Compressed air	—— A ——	Condensate discharge	-o— -o— -o-
Feed water pump discharge	-oo- -oo- -oo-	Fuel-oil flow	—— FOF ——
Fuel-oil return	— — FOR — —	Fuel-oil tank vent	— — FOV — —
High pressure return	╫ — ╫ —	High pressure steam	╫ — ╫
Hot water heating return	— — — —	Hot water heating supply	————
Low pressure return	— — — —	Low pressure steam	————
Make-up water	—— · ——	Medium pressure return	╪ — ╪ —
Medium pressure steam	╪ — ╪ —		

Plumbing			
Acid waste	—— ACID ——	Cold water	—— · —— · —
Drinking water return	——·· ——·· ——	Fire line	—— F —— F ——
Gas	— G —— G —		
Hot water	—— ·· —— ·· —	Hot water return	—— ··· —— ··· —

Table 18-4. *(Continued)* Standard Graphical Symbols for Piping

Soil, waste, or leader (above grade)	——————	Soil, waste, or leader (below grade)	— — — —
Vacuum cleaning	—v———v—	Vent	— — — — —
Pneumatic Tubes			
Tube runs	— — — — — —		
Sprinklers			
Branch and head	—o———o—	Drain	— —s— — —s— —
Main supplies	———s———		
Compressed air	———A———	Drinking water flow	——·——·——

Table 18-5. Standard Graphical Symbols for Pipe Fittings

Name of Fitting	Flanged	Screwed	Bell & Spigot	Welded	Soldered
Bushing					
Cap					
Cross, reducing					
Cross, straight size					
Cross					
Elbow, 45°					
Elbow 90°					
Elbow, turned down					
Elbow, turned up					
Elbow, base					
Elbow, double branch					
Elbow, long branch					
Elbow, reducing					
Elbow, side outlet (outlet down)					
Elbow, side outlet (outlet up)					
Elbow, street					
Joint, connecting pipe					
Joint, expansion					

Table 18-6. American National Standard Abbreviations for Scientific and Engineering Terms

Description	Abb.	Description	Abb.	Description	Abb.	Description	Abb.
Absolute	abs	Cubic inch	in^3 or cu in	Greatest common divisor	gcd	Ounce-inch	oz-in
Alternating current	ac	Cubic meter	m^3 or cu m	High pressure	hp	Pennyweight	dwt
Ampere	amp	Cubic millimeter	mm^3 or cumm	Horsepower	hp	Pint	pt
Ampere-hour	amp hr	Cubic yard	yd^3 or cu yd	Horsepower-hour	hp-hr	Potential	pot
Angstrom unit	Å	Current density	cd	Internal	intl	Potential difference	pd
Antilogarithm	antilog	Cylinder	cyl	Hour	h or hr	Pound	lb
Arithmetical average	aa	Decibel	dB	Hyperbolic cosine	cosh	Pound-force foot	lb_f-ft or lb-ft
Atmosphere	atm	Degree	deg or°	Hyperbolic sine	sinh	Pound-force inch	lb_f-in or lb-in
Atomic weight	at wt	Degree Centigrade	°C	Hyperbolic tangent	tanh	Pound-force per square foot	lb_f/ft^2 or psf
Avoirdupois	avdp	Degree Fahrenheit	°F	Inch	in.	Pound-force per square inch	lb_f/in^2 or psi
Barometer	baro	Degree Kelvin	°K	Inch per second	in/s or ips	Pound per horsepower	lb/hp or php
Board feet (foot board measure)	fbm	Diameter	dia or Φ	Inch-pound	in-lb	Power factor	pf
Boiler pressure	bopress	Direct current	dc	Indicated horsepower-hour	iph	Quart	qt
Boiling point	bp	Dozen	doz	Intermediate pressure	ip	Reactive volt-ampere meter	RVA
Brinell hardness number	Bhn	Dram	dr	Internal	intl	Revolution per minute	r/min or rpm
British thermal unit	Btu	Efficiency	eff	Kilovolt-ampere/hour	KVA-h or kVah	Revolution per second	r/s or rps
Bushel	bu	Electric	elec	Kilowatt-hour meter	kw-hm	Root mean square	rms
Calorie	cal	Electromotive force	emf	Latitude	lat.	Round	rnd
Candle	cd	Elevation	el	Least common multiple	lcm	Secant	sec
Center to center	c to c	Engine	eng	Liquid	liq	Second	s or sec
Centimeter	cm	Engineer	engr	Logarithm (common)	log	Sine	sin
Centimeter-gram-second (system)	cgs	Engineering	engg	Logarithm (natural)	ln	Specific gravity	sp gr
Chemical	chem	Equation	Eq	Low pressure	lp	Specific heat	sp ht
Chemically pure	cp	External	ext	Lumen per watt	lm/W or lpw	Square	sq
Circular	circ	Fluid	fl	Magnetomotive force	mmf	Square centimeter	cm^2 or sq cm
Circular mil	cmil	Foot	ft	Mathematics (ical)	math	Square foot	ft^2 or sq ft
Coefficient	coef	Foot-candle	ftc	Maximum	max	Square inch	in^2 or sq in
Cologarithm	colog	Foot-Lambert	ftL or ftl	Mean effective pressure	mep	Square kilometer	km^2 or sq km
Concentrate	conc	Foot per minute	fpm	Melting point	mp	Square root of mean square	rms
Conductivity	cndct	Foot per second	fps	Meter	m	square	sq
Constant	const	Foot-pound	ft-lb	Meter-kilogram-second	mks	Standard	std
Cord	cd	Foot-pound-second (system)	fps	Microfarad	μF	Tangent	tan
Cosecant	csc	Free on board	fob	Mile	mi	Temperature	temp
Cosine	cos	Freezing point	fp	Mile per hour	mi/h or mph	Tensile strength	ts
Cost, insurance, and freight	cif	Frequency	freq	Milliampere	mA	Versed sine	vers
Cotangent	cot	Fusion point	fnpt	Minimum	min	Volt	V
Counter electromotive force	cemf	Gallon	gal	Molecular weight	mol wt	Watt	W
Cubic	cu	Gallon per minute	gpm	Molecule	mo	Watthour	Wh
Cubic centimeter	cm^3 or cc	Gallon per second	gps	National Electrical Code	NEC	Week	wk
Cubic foot	ft^3 or cu ft	Grain	gr	Ounce	oz	Weight	wt
Cubic feet per second	ft^3/sec or cfs	Gram	g			Yard	yd

Alternative abbreviations conforming to the practice of the International Electrotechnical Commission.

Ampere	A	Kilovolt-ampere	kVA	Microwatt	μW	Volt	V	Henry	H	Megawatt	MW	Millihenry	mH	Watt	W
Ampere-hour	Ah	Kilowatt	kW	Milliampere	mA	Volt-ampere	VA	Joule	J	Megohm	MΩ	Millivolt	mV	Watthour	Wh
Coulomb	C	Kilowatt hour	kWh	Millifarad	mF	Volt	VC	Kilovolt	kV	Microampere	μA	Ohm	ω	Volt	V
Farad	F	Microfarad	μF	Milliampere	mA	coulomb									

Only the most commonly used terms have been included. These forms are recommended for those whose familiarity with the terms used makes possible a maximum of abbreviations. For others, less contracted combinations made up from this list may be used. For example, the list gives the abbreviation of the term "feet per second" as "fps." To some, however, ft per sec will be more easily understood.

Lists of Abbreviations and Symbols

The following list of abbreviations is useful for shop drawings. Periods are used only when the abbreviation spells a word such as: arch., auto., flex., etc.

Abbreviation	Definition	Abbreviation	Definition
AA	All around	CCWDB	Counterclockwise down blast
ABV	Above	CCWTAD	Counterclockwise top angular down
AC	Air conditioning	CCWTAU	Counterclockwise top angular up
ACN	Asbestos-cloth neck	CCWTH	Counterclockwise top horizontal
AD	Access door	CCWUB	Counterclockwise up blast
ADJ	Adjustable	CD	Ceiling diffuser
AF	Angle frame	CEIL, CLG	Ceiling
	Air filter	CFM	Cubic feet per minute
AFF	Above finished floor	CG	Ceiling grille
AHU	Air-handling unit	CH	Ceiling height
AL	Aluminum	CIRC	Circumference
ALD	Automatic-louver damper	CL COLL	Clinch collar
AMBD	Automatic multiple-blade damper	COD	Clean-out door
AMT	Amount	COL	Column
APPROX.	Approximately	CONC	Concrete
ARCH.	Architect	CONN	Connection
ASB	Asbestos	CONT'D	Continued
ATC	Acoustical-tile ceiling	COP	Coefficient of performance
AUTO	Automatic	CR	Ceiling register
B	Bottom	CS	Concrete slab
BD	Bottom down	CT	Cooling tower
BEV	Bevel	CWBAD	Clockwise bottom angular down
BG	Bottom grille	CWBAU	Clockwise bottom angular up
BI	Black iron	CWBH	Clockwise bottom horizontal
BJ	Bar joist	CWDB	Clockwise down blast
BL	Building line	CWTAD	Clockwise top angular down
BLDG	Building	CWTAU	Clockwise top angular up
BLK	Black	CWTH	Clockwise top horizontal
BM	Beam	CWUB	Clockwise up blast
BO	By others	DEFL	Deflector
BOD	Bottom of duct	DEG	Degree
BOS	Back of slip	DET	Detail
BR	Bottom register	DIA	Diameter
BS	Below slab	DMPR	Damper
BTM	Bottom	DN	Down
BU	Bottom up	DT	Drop top, Duct turn
CANV	Canvas	DWDI	Double width, double inlet
CCWBAD	Counterclockwise bottom angular down	DWG	Drawing
EA	Exhaust air	HU	Humidifier
EB	Equal brake	HV	Heating and ventilating
EL	Elbow, Elevation	HVAC	Heating, ventilating and air conditioning
ELEV	Elevation	ID	Inside dimension
ENG, ENGR	Engineer	INCL	Inclusive
EQ	Equal	INT	Interior, Internal
EQUIP	Equipment	J	Joggle
EQUIV	Equivalent	JT	Joint
ESH	Electric strip heater	KD	Knocked down
ET	Equal taper	KE	Kitchen exhaust
EXH	Exhaust	KIT	Kitchen
FA	Free area, Fresh air	LCC	Lead-coated copper
FAI	Fresh air intake	LDR	Leader

Abbreviation	Definition	Abbreviation	Definition
FB	Flat bottom	LE	Large end
FC	Flexible connection, Full corners	LG	Long
FD	Fire damper	LH	Left hand
F Fl, FIN FL	Finished floor	LNG	Lining
FIN.	Finished	LP	Low pressure
FLBR	Fusible link bottom register	LVG	Leaving
FLEX.	Flexible	MA	Matched angles
FLG	Flange	MAX	Maximum
FLTR	Fusible link top register	MB	Mixing box
FP	Fire proofing	MD	Manual damper
FPM	Feet per minute	MFG	Manufacturing
FS	Flat slip	MIN	Minimum, Minute
FSAA	Flat slips all around	MISC	Miscellaneous
FSB	Flat slip on bottom	MO	Masonry opening
FST	Flat slip on top	NC	Normally closed
FT	Flat top	NEOP	Neoprene
FTG	Fitting, footing	NIC	Not in contract
FVD	Friction volume damper	NK	Neck
GA	Gage	NO	Number, Normally open
GAL	Gallon	NOM	Nominal
GALV	Galvanized	NR	Near
GC	General contractor	NTS	Not to scale
GI.	Galvanized iron	OA	Overall, Outside air
GPM	Gallons per minute	OAI	Outside air intake
HC	Hanging ceiling, Heating coil	OAL	Overall length
HD	Head	OBD	Opposed-blade damper
HGR	Hanger	OC	On center
HP	High Pressure	OD	Outside dimension
OH	Opposite hand	SS	Stainless steel
OPNG	Opening	ST	Sound trap
OPP	Opposite	STD	Standard
OS	Outside	STL	Steel
PBD	Parallel-blade damper	STR	Straight
R	Raw, Radius	SWSI	Single width single inlet
RA	Return air	T	Top
RE	Raw end	TC	Telescoping collar
REQ	Required	TD	Top down
RF	Roof fan or Return fan	TG	Top grille
RH	Reheat, Right hand	THK	Thick
RHC	Reheat coil	THR	Throat
ROVD	Remotely-operated volume damper	TOD	Top of duct
RPM	Revolutions per minute	TOIL	Toilet
RT	Raise top	TOS	Top of steel
SA	Supply air	TR	Top register
SD	Splitter damper	TU	Top up
SE	Small end, Slip end	TX	Toilet exhaust
SECT.	Section	TYP	Typical
SK	Sketch	UON	Unless otherwise noted
SL	Slab	US	Underside of slab
SLD	Slim-line diffuser	VD	Volume damper
SPL	Splitter	VE	Vibration eliminator
SQ	Square	VERT	Vertical

Table 18-7. Electrical Abbreviations and Symbols

Abbr.	Term	Abbr.	Term	Abbr.	Term	Symbol	Term
AFF	Above finished floor	PF	Primary feeds	F	Feeder	⬭	Fluorescent fixture
ATS	Automatic transfer switch	PB	Pull box	FBO	Furnished by others	◯	Recessed incandescent spot light
CL	Centerline	PC	Pull chain	HC	Hung ceiling	PB	Panel board
CSB	Cable support box	RP	Receptacle panel	LP	Lighting panel	MCC	Motor control center
DP	Distribution panel	RPC	Refrigeration power center	LC	Load center	———	Concealed conduit
EC	Empty conduit	S	Switchboard	MCC	Motor control center	– – – –	Conduit concealed in floor
EPC	Emergency power center	SS	Substation switchboard	NIC	Not in contract	— — —	Conduit run exposed
ERP	Emergency receptacle panel	T	Transformer	PC	Power center	—EC—	Empty conduit
ESB	Emergency switch board	VT	Vapor tight	PP	Power panel	——o	Conduit up
Exp. Jt.	Expansion joint	WP	Weather proof	PDC	Primary Distribution Center	——●	Conduit down
Exp.	Explosion proof	▭	Recessed fluorescent fixture surface or pendant-mounted	PF	Primary feeds	HCP	Heating control panel

The following list of symbols is useful for shop drawings:

Symbol	Represents	Symbol	Represents
&	and	φ	diameter
∠	angle	=	equals
×	times	±	plus or minus
c/c	center to center		

Table 18-8. Architectural Abbreviations

Abbr.	Term	Abbr.	Term	Abbr.	Term	Abbr.	Term
ABS	Absolute	DIA	Diameter	HW	Hot water	R	Riser
ACCUM	Accumulate	DIM	Dimension	H W PL	Hard white plaster	RAD	Radius
AC DL	Acoustical block	DN	Down	ID	Inside diameter	REC	Recess
ACOUS	Acoustic	DUPL	Duplicating	INSUL	Insulation	REG	Register
AC PLAS	Acoustical plaster	DUP REC	Duplex receptacle	INT	Interior	REINF	Reinforced
AC T	Acoustical tile	DWG	Drawing	INTERM	Intermediate	REQD	Required
ALUM	Aluminum	EDG	Edging	JAN	Janitor	REMOV	Removable
ASB	Asbestos	EL	Elevation	JT	Joint	RET	Retaining
AFF	Above finished floor	EC	Electric	LAB	Laboratory	R H	Relative humidity
AT	Asphalt tile	ELEV	Elevation	LC	Lead Coated	RM	Room
BAL	Balcony	EQ	Equipment	LECT	Lecture	S	Saddle
B B	Bulletin board	EXPJT	Expansion joint	LSJ	Long span joist	S.B.	Single bubbler
BD	Board	EXT	Exterior	LTG	Lighting	SECT	Section
BLKG	Blocking	EXTN	Extension	MA	Metal angle	SQ	Square
BM	Beam	F.A.	Fire alarm	MAX	Maximum	S.S.	Stainless steel
BR	Brick	F .B .	Flemish bond	MECH	Mechanical	ST	Steel
BSMT	Basement	F.E.	Fire extinguisher	MET	Metal	STOR	Storage
CAB	Cabinet	F DR	Floor drain	MEZZ	Mezzanine	STRUCT	Structural
C&HST	Coat & hat strip	F .G.	Fire gong	MIN	Minimum	SUSP	Suspended
CAV	Cavity	FH	Flat head	ML	Metal lathe	T	Thread
CB	Ceiling break	FHC	Fire hose cabinet	M.L.F.	Metal lath furring	T&G	Tongue & groove
CBL	Concrete block	F HR	Fire hose reel	MO	Masonry opening	TEMP	Tempered
CEM	Cement	FIN	Finished	N I C	Not in contract	THK	Thick
CHB	Chalk board	FL	Floor	NO	Normally open	TOW	Top of wall
CL	Centerline	FOLD	Folding	O C	On center	T.S.	Top of slab
CL	Closet	FP	Fireproofing	O D	Outside diameter	TV	Television
CLG	Ceiling	FP S C	Fire proof self closing	OH	Overhead	TYP	Typical
COL	Column	FTG	Footing	OPG	Opening	U.O.N.	Unless otherwise noted
COMP	Compressed	FX	Fixed	OPP HAND	Opposite hand	V	Volts
CONC	Concrete	GA	Gage	oz	Ounce	VAC	Vacuum
CONSTN	Construction	GALV	Galvanized	P & R	Projected & Recessed	VAT	Vinyl asbestos tile
CONT	Continuous	G.T.	Glazed Tile	P	Plaster	V.C.T.	Vitreous ceramic tile
CONTR	Contract	GEN	General	PART	Partition	VERM	Vermiculite
CONV	Convector	GRAV	Gravel	PL	Plate	VEST	Vestibule
CORR	Corridor	H	High	PLAS LAM	Plastic laminate	W	Wide
CTS	Centens	H&V	Heating & ventilating	PLAT	Platform	WB	Waste basket
C W	Cold water	HC	Hung ceiling	PREP	Preparation	W D	Window dimension
D.B.	Double bubbler	HCF	Hard cement finish	PROJ	Projection	WD	Wood
DET	Detail	HCONC	Hardened concrete	PT	Paint	WIN	Window
D F	Drinking fountain	HM	Hollow metal	PVC	Polyvinyl chloride	W.L.	Wire lath
DR	Drain	HR	Hand rail	HCP	Heating control panel	WP	Waterproofing
DR RM	Dressing room	HVAC	Heating, ventilating & air conditioning				

CLIMATIC DESIGN DATA

CLIMATIC DESIGN INFORMATION

This chapter provides tables of climatic conditions for locations in the United States, Canada, and around the world. The data for this chapter have been adapted from 2001 ASHRAE Fundamentals Handbook, "Weather Information", which in turn was developed from information available in previous ASHRAE Handbooks and publications.

As is evident from the chapters in this handbook, climatic data is needed for design, sizing, distribution, installation, and marketing of heating, ventilating, air-conditioning, dehumidification and smoke management equipment, as well as for other energy-related processes in residential, agricultural, commercial, and industrial applications. Warm-season temperature and humidity conditions correspond to annual percentile values of 0.4, 1.0, and 2.0. Cold season conditions are based on annual percentiles of 99.6 and 99.0. The use of annual percentiles to define the climatic design conditions ensures that they represent the same probability of occurrence anywhere, regardless of the seasonal distribution of extreme temperature and humidity.

Climatic Design Conditions

Annual design conditions for the United States appear in Table 19-1, for Canada, in Table 19-2, and for international locations, in Table 19-3.

The information provided in Tables 19-1 to 19-3 in the indicated column is from left to right is:
1) Name of station
2) Location (location, longitude, and elevation)
3) Heating dry-bulb temperature corresponding to 99.6%, and 99%
4) Cooling dry-bulb and mean wet-bulb temperature corresponding to 0.4%, 1.0%, and 2.0%
5) Evaporation dry-bulb and mean wet-bulb temperature corresponding to 1.0%, and 2.0%
6) Dehumidification dewpoint, humidity ratio and mean dry-bulb temperature corresponding to 1.0%, and 2.0%
7) Mean daily range, which is the mean of the difference between daily maximum and minimum dry-bulb temperatures for the warmest month (highest average dry-bulb temperature).

Applicability and Characteristics of the Design Conditions.

The sets of design values in this chapter represent different psychrometric conditions. Design data based on dry-bulb temperature represent peak occurrences of the sensible component of ambient outdoor conditions. Design values based on wet-bulb temperature are related to the enthalpy of the outdoor air. Conditions based on dewpoint relate to the peaks of the humidity ratio.

Heating Design Conditions: The 99.6% and 99.0% design conditions of Tables 19-1 to 19-3 are often used in

the sizing of heating equipment. In cold spells, dry-bulb temperatures below the design conditions can last for a week or more.

Cooling and Dehumidification Design Conditions: The 0.4%, 1.0%, and 2.0% dry-bulb temperatures and mean coincident wet-bulb temperatures of Tables 19-1 to 19-3 often represent conditions on hot, mostly sunny days. These are useful for cooling applications, especially air conditioning. The design conditions based on dewpoint temperatures are directly related to extremes of humidity ratio, which represent peak moisture loads from the weather.

Extreme dewpoint conditions may occur on days with moderate dry-bulb temperatures resulting in high relative humidity. These values are especially useful for applications involving humidity control, such as desiccant cooling and dehumidification, cooling-based dehumidification, and fresh air ventilation systems. The values are also used as a checkpoint when analyzing the behavior of cooling systems at part-load conditions, particularly when such systems are used for humidity control as a secondary function. The humidity ratio values correspond to the combination of dewpoint temperature and the mean coincident dry-bulb temperature calculated at the standard pressure at the elevation of the location.

Mean Daily Range: The mean daily range is the mean difference between the daily maximum and minimum temperatures during the hottest month. These values are calculated from the extremes of the hourly temperature observations. The true daily temperature range is generally about 2°F greater, for the same reason as explained in the previous section.

Additional Resources.—ASHRAE publications and CD-ROMS can be obtained from http://www.ashrae.org/.

NCDC (National Climate Data Center) publications and CD-ROMS can be obtained from http://www.ncdc.noaa.gov/.

Environment Canada publications and CD-ROMS can be obtained from Metrological Services of Canada http://www.msc-smc.ec.gc.ca/.

ASHRAE. 1994. Wind data for design of smoke control systems. Research Report RP-816.

ASHRAE. 1995a. Design data for the 1%, 2.5%, and 5% occurrences of extreme dew point temperature, with mean coincident dry-bulb temperature research Report RP-754.

ASHRAE. 1995b. *Weather data sets for ASHRAE research.* Research Report RP-889.

ASHRAE. 1997a. *Weather year for energy calculations 2 (WYEC2) Data and Toolkit* (CD-ROM).

ASHRAE. 1997b. Sequences of extreme temperature and humidity for design calculations. Research Report RP-828.

ASHRAE. 1997c. Updating the tables of design weather conditions in the *ASHRAE Handbook of Fundamentals*. Research Report RP-890.

ASHRAE. 1998. Design Weather Sequence Viewer (CD-ROM).

ASHRAE. 1999. *Weather Data Viewer* 2.1 (CD-ROM).

ASHRAE. 2001. *ASHRAE Handbook of Fundamentals*.

ASHRAE. 2001. *International Weather for Energy Calculations (IWEC)* (CD-ROM).

ASHRAE. 2005. *Weather Data Viewer*, Version 3.0 (CD-ROM).

Environment Canada. 1983-1987. Principal station data. PSD 1 to 134. Atmospheric Environment Service, Downsview, Ontario.

Environment Canada. 1993a. Canadian climate normals (1961–1990).

Environment Canada. 1993b. Canadian weather energy and engineering data sets (CWEEDS files) and Canadian weather for energy calculations (CWEC files) user's manual.

Marion, W. and Urban. K. 1995. User's manual for TMY2s, typical meteorological years, derived from the 1961–1990 National Solar Radiation Data Base.

NREL/SP-463-7668, E95004064. National Renewable Energy Laboratory, Golden, CO.

NCDC. 1991. Surface airways meteorological and solar observing network (SAMSON) data set. National Climatic Data Center, Asheville, NC.

NCDC. 1992a. Monthly normals of temperature, precipitation, and heating and cooling degree-days. In *Climatography of the U.S. #81*.

NCDC. 1992b. Annual degree-days to selected bases (1961-1990). In *Climatography of the U.S. #81*.

NCDC. 1994. U.S. division and station climatic data and normals.

NCDC. 1996. International station meteorological climate summary (ISMCS) Version 4 (CD-ROM).

NCDC. 1999. Engineering weather data (CD-ROM).

ASHRAE publications and CD-ROMS can be obtained from http://www.ashrae.org/.

NCDC (National Climate Data Center) publications and CD-ROMS can be obtained from http://www.ncdc.noaa.gov/.

Environment Canada publications and CD-ROMS can be obtained from Metrological Services of Canada http://www.msc-smc.ec.gc.ca/.

Table 19-1. Air Conditioning Design Data—United States

Station	Location Lat.	Location Long.	Location Elev.	Heating 99.6% DB	Heating 99% DB	Cooling 0.4% DB	Cooling 0.4% MWB	Cooling 1% DB	Cooling 1% MWB	Cooling 2% DB	Cooling 2% MWB	Evaporation 1% DB	Evaporation 1% MWB	Evaporation 2% DB	Evaporation 2% MWB	Dehumidification 1% DP	Dehumidification 1% W	Dehumidification 1% MDB	Dehumidification 2% DP	Dehumidification 2% W	Dehumidification 2% MDB	Range of DB
ALABAMA																						
Anniston	33.58	85.85	610	19	24	95	76	93	76	90	75	78	88	77	86	76	137	82	75	133	81	19.6
Birmingham	33.57	86.75	630	18	23	94	75	92	75	90	74	77	88	76	87	74	131	82	73	127	81	18.7
Dothan	31.32	85.45	400	28	32	95	76	93	76	92	76	79	88	78	87	76	139	82	76	136	82	17.5
Huntsville	34.65	86.77	643	15	20	94	75	92	74	90	74	77	88	76	86	74	130	82	73	126	81	18.5
Mobile	30.68	88.25	220	26	30	94	77	92	76	91	76	79	88	78	87	76	139	83	76	135	82	16.5
Montgomery	32.30	86.40	203	24	27	95	76	93	76	91	76	78	89	78	88	75	134	84	75	130	83	18.7
Muscle Shoals/Florence	34.75	87.62	551	16	21	96	76	94	75	92	74	78	89	77	87	75	133	82	74	130	81	20.0
Ozark, Ft. Rucker	31.28	85.72	299	28	31	95	77	94	77	92	76	79	89	78	88	77	142	84	76	138	83	18.0
Tuscaloosa	33.22	87.62	171	20	24	95	77	94	77	92	76	79	89	78	88	76	137	83	75	134	82	19.6
ALASKA																						
Adak, NAS	51.88	176.65	13	19	23	59	55	57	53	55	51	53	57	51	54	51	55	56	49	51	53	9.7
Anchorage, ElemendorfAFB	61.25	149.80	213	–13	–8	71	58	69	57	66	56	58	66	57	64	55	65	61	53	61	60	12.6
Anchorage, Ft. Richardson	61.27	149.65	377	–19	–13	74	60	71	58	68	57	59	69	58	66	54	63	62	53	61	61	15.5
Anchorage, Intl Airport	61.17	150.02	131	–14	–9	71	59	68	57	65	56	58	66	57	63	55	64	61	53	61	60	12.6
Annette	55.03	131.57	112	13	17	74	61	70	59	66	57	60	68	58	65	56	68	63	55	65	61	10.5
Barrow	71.30	156.78	13	–41	–36	57	51	52	49	48	46	49	52	46	48	46	46	51	44	42	48	10.6
Bethel	60.78	161.80	151	–28	–24	72	59	68	57	64	55	58	66	56	63	55	64	60	53	60	58	13.4
Bettles	66.92	151.52	643	–49	–44	79	61	75	59	72	58	61	73	59	70	56	67	64	54	63	63	19.4
Big Delta, Ft. Greely	64.00	145.73	1283	–45	–39	78	59	75	58	71	56	59	72	58	69	54	65	63	52	61	61	17.3
Cold Bay	55.20	162.73	102	6	10	60	54	57	53	55	52	54	56	53	55	53	59	55	51	56	54	7.4
Cordova	60.50	145.50	43	–4	1	70	59	67	57	63	56	58	65	56	62	54	62	60	53	60	59	13.5
Deadhorse	70.20	148.47	56	–36	–34	66	57	61	54	58	53	55	62	53	58	51	56	59	49	51	56	13.7
Dillingham	59.05	158.52	95	–20	–13	69	57	66	56	62	54	57	64	55	61	53	61	59	52	57	57	13.1
Fairbanks, Eielson AFB	64.67	147.10	548	–33	–31	81	61	78	60	75	59	62	75	60	72	56	69	66	54	63	66	19.4
Fairbanks, Intl Airport	64.82	147.87	453	–47	–41	81	61	77	59	74	58	61	74	59	71	56	68	64	54	64	63	18.6
Galena	64.73	156.93	151	–33	–31	78	61	74	59	71	58	61	71	59	69	56	69	65	54	63	64	15.3
Gulkana	62.15	145.45	1578	–44	–39	77	58	73	56	69	55	57	70	56	67	51	60	60	50	55	59	20.3
Homer	59.63	151.50	72	0	4	65	56	62	55	60	54	56	61	55	59	53	60	58	52	57	57	11.9
Juneau	58.37	134.58	23	4	7	74	60	69	58	66	57	59	68	58	64	56	67	61	55	64	60	13.3
Kenai	60.57	151.25	95	–22	–14	68	55	65	55	62	54	56	63	55	61	53	60	58	52	58	57	13.3
Ketchikan	55.35	131.70	95	13	20	71	60	68	59	66	58	60	67	59	64	57	71	62	56	68	61	10.5
King Salmon	58.68	156.65	49	–24	–19	71	58	67	56	64	55	57	65	56	62	54	62	60	52	58	58	15.2
Kodiak, State USCG Base	57.75	152.50	112	7	12	68	58	65	56	62	55	57	63	56	61	55	64	59	53	61	57	11.2
Kotzebue	66.87	162.63	16	–36	–31	68	59	64	58	61	56	58	64	56	61	55	65	61	54	62	59	8.8
McGrath	62.97	155.62	338	–47	–42	77	60	73	58	70	56	59	70	58	67	55	65	62	54	62	61	17.4
Middleton Island	59.43	146.33	46	18	21	62	54	60	51	59	51	54	59	53	57	51	56	56	50	54	55	5.8
Nenana	64.55	149.08	361	–51	–44	80	60	76	59	73	57	60	73	59	70	55	65	65	53	60	63	21.2
Nome	64.50	165.43	23	–31	–26	69	57	65	55	61	54	56	63	55	60	53	60	59	51	56	57	10.9
Northway	62.97	141.93	1722	–34	–32	78	58	74	57	71	56	58	71	57	69	53	62	61	51	60	59	20.0
Port Heiden	56.95	158.62	95	–6	–2	64	54	61	52	59	51	54	60	52	58	50	54	57	49	51	55	9.7
Saint Paul Island	57.15	170.22	30	–2	3	54	51	52	50	51	49	50	52	49	50	49	52	51	48	50	50	5.4
Sitka	57.07	135.35	66	16	21	66	59	64	58	61	57	59	62	58	60	57	71	60	56	68	59	9.2
Talkeetna	62.30	150.10	358	–28	–21	77	60	73	58	70	57	60	70	58	67	56	67	62	54	64	61	16.4
Valdez	61.13	146.35	33	4	7	69	56	66	55	62	54	56	64	55	61	53	59	57	52	57	56	12.2
Yakutat	59.52	139.67	30	–3	2	66	56	63	55	60	54	57	60	56	59	55	64	57	54	62	57	12.0
ARIZONA																						
Flagstaff	35.13	111.67	7011	1	8	85	56	83	55	80	55	60	73	59	72	56	88	64	55	83	63	27.6
Kingman	35.27	113.95	3389	22	27	99	64	97	63	95	62	67	85	66	86	62	92	75	59	85	76	24.8
Page	36.93	111.45	4278	20	24	99	62	97	62	95	61	65	86	64	86	58	85	74	56	80	74	23.8
Phoenix, Intl Airport	33.43	112.02	1106	34	37	110	70	108	70	106	70	75	96	74	95	69	111	84	67	104	85	23.0
Phoenix, Luke AFB	33.53	112.38	1089	35	38	110	71	107	71	105	71	76	97	75	96	71	118	85	69	111	86	25.2
Prescott	34.65	112.42	5043	15	20	94	60	91	60	89	60	66	80	64	79	61	98	71	60	93	70	25.4
Safford, Agri Center	32.82	109.68	3117	21	26	102	66	99	66	97	65	71	89	69	88	66	106	76	64	102	77	34.7
Tucson	32.12	110.93	2556	31	34	104	65	102	65	100	65	71	87	70	86	67	111	76	66	106	77	29.4
Winslow	35.02	110.73	4882	10	14	95	60	93	60	91	59	64	81	63	80	59	91	69	58	85	69	27.4
Yuma	32.65	114.60	207	40	44	111	72	109	72	106	72	78	95	77	95	74	127	88	71	117	89	23.8
ARKANSAS																						
Blytheville, Eaker AFB	35.97	89.95	256	12	18	97	78	95	77	93	77	80	91	78	89	77	142	86	76	135	85	18.7
Fayetteville	36.00	94.17	1250	6	13	95	76	93	75	90	74	77	89	76	87	74	132	84	72	124	81	21.4
Ft. Smith	35.33	94.37	463	13	19	99	76	96	76	93	75	78	91	77	90	74	130	84	73	126	83	21.5
Little Rock, AFB	34.92	92.15	312	16	21	97	77	95	77	92	76	79	91	78	89	76	137	85	75	133	84	19.5
Texarkana	33.45	93.98	390	20	25	97	77	95	77	93	76	79	90	78	89	76	139	85	75	135	84	20.5
CALIFORNIA																						
Alameda, NAS	37.78	122.32	13	40	42	83	65	79	64	76	63	65	76	64	73	61	80	69	60	78	67	14.8
Arcata/Eureka	40.98	124.10	217	30	32	70	60	67	59	65	58	61	65	60	64	59	75	63	58	71	62	15.5
Bakersfield	35.43	119.05	492	32	35	104	70	101	69	99	69	71	96	70	95	62	85	83	60	79	83	26.5
Barstow/Daggett	34.85	116.78	1926	28	32	107	69	105	67	102	67	71	95	69	95	63	91	85	59	81	85	27.8
Blue Canyon	39.28	120.72	5285	21	24	84	59	81	57	79	56	60	78	58	75	52	69	70	50	64	68	16.6
Burbank/Glendale	34.20	118.35	774	39	41	98	69	95	69	92	68	72	89	71	86	67	103	78	66	98	77	23.4
Fairfield, Travis AFB	38.27	121.93	62	31	34	98	67	94	67	91	66	69	90	67	88	61	79	74	59	75	73	29.0
Fresno	36.77	119.72	328	30	32	103	70	101	70	98	69	71	96	70	94	62	85	84	61	80	82	30.9

Table 19-1. *(Continued)* Air Conditioning Design Data—United States

Station	Lat.	Long.	Elev.	Heating 99.6% DB	99% DB	Cooling 0.4% DB	0.4% MWB	1% DB	1% MWB	2% DB	2% MWB	Evap 1% DB	1% MWB	Evap 2% DB	2% MWB	Dehum 1% DP	1% W	1% MDB	2% DP	2% W	2% MDB	Range of DB
Lancaster/Palmdale	34.73	118.22	2346	22	24	101	66	98	65	96	64	69	91	67	90	60	84	81	58	78	81	27.9
Lemoore, Reeves NAS	36.33	119.95	236	30	32	103	72	101	71	98	70	73	96	71	94	65	94	87	62	85	86	32.9
Long Beach	33.82	118.15	39	40	43	92	67	88	67	84	66	70	82	69	80	66	96	75	65	92	75	16.7
Los Angeles	33.93	118.40	105	43	45	85	64	81	64	78	64	69	76	68	75	66	95	73	65	92	72	10.9
Marysville, Beale AFB	39.13	121.43	112	31	34	101	70	98	69	95	68	71	95	69	92	61	80	82	60	76	81	29.0
Merced, Castle AFB	37.38	120.57	187	30	32	99	69	97	69	94	68	71	93	69	92	62	82	84	60	78	81	30.2
Mount Shasta	41.32	122.32	3543	16	21	91	62	88	61	85	60	63	84	61	82	53	69	73	51	64	71	32.0
Mountain View, Moffet NAS	37.42	122.05	39	36	39	88	65	84	65	80	64	67	80	65	78	61	80	73	60	76	72	18.0
Ontario	34.05	117.60	942	35	38	102	71	98	70	95	69	73	92	72	90	68	106	80	66	101	78	27.7
Oxnard, Pt. Mugu NAWS	34.12	119.12	7	39	41	83	62	79	64	77	64	69	75	67	74	66	97	73	65	93	72	14.6
Paso Robles	35.67	120.63	837	26	29	102	68	98	67	95	65	68	94	67	91	58	75	73	57	71	71	37.8
Red Bluff	40.15	122.25	354	29	32	105	70	102	69	98	67	71	95	69	93	62	85	80	61	80	78	29.5
Riverside, March AFB	33.88	117.27	1539	34	36	101	68	98	68	95	67	71	91	70	90	65	97	80	62	90	79	29.0
Sacramento, Mather Field	38.55	121.30	95	30	32	101	69	97	68	95	67	69	94	68	92	60	77	77	58	74	76	33.7
Sacramento, McClellan AFB	38.67	121.40	75	31	34	102	70	98	69	95	68	71	95	69	92	61	80	81	60	77	79	29.7
Sacramento, Metro	38.70	121.58	23	31	33	100	69	97	69	94	68	70	94	69	91	61	79	80	59	76	78	33.3
Salinas	36.67	121.60	85	33	35	83	63	78	62	75	61	65	75	63	72	60	78	68	59	76	67	18.7
San Bernardino, NortonAFB	34.10	117.23	1158	34	36	103	70	101	70	97	69	73	94	71	92	66	101	83	65	95	82	31.5
San Diego, Intl Airport	32.73	117.17	30	44	46	85	67	81	67	79	67	71	78	70	77	68	104	76	67	99	74	8.9
San Diego, Miramar NAS	32.85	117.12	420	39	42	92	69	88	67	85	67	71	83	69	81	67	99	77	65	96	75	17.5
San Francisco	37.62	122.38	16	37	39	83	63	78	62	74	61	63	75	62	72	58	73	66	57	71	65	16.7
San Jose Intl Airport	37.37	121.93	56	35	38	93	67	89	66	86	65	68	85	67	83	61	81	76	60	78	74	22.3
Santa Barbara	34.43	119.83	10	34	37	83	64	80	64	77	64	67	76	66	74	65	91	71	63	85	70	18.0
Santa Maria	34.90	120.45	240	32	35	86	63	82	62	78	61	65	78	64	75	60	77	69	59	74	68	19.4
Stockton	37.90	121.25	26	30	32	100	69	97	68	94	67	70	94	68	92	60	78	78	59	75	77	30.4
Victorville, George AFB	34.58	117.38	2874	27	30	101	65	98	65	96	64	68	88	67	88	61	90	79	59	83	78	28.3
COLORADO																						
Alamosa	37.45	105.87	7543	−17	−11	84	55	82	55	80	54	59	74	58	73	54	81	62	52	77	62	31.2
Colorado Springs	38.82	104.72	6171	−2	4	90	58	87	58	84	58	62	77	61	76	57	88	66	56	83	65	24.9
Craig	40.50	107.53	6283	−20	−12	88	57	85	56	83	55	59	78	57	77	52	72	65	50	68	64	36.4
Denver	39.75	104.87	5331	−3	3	93	60	90	59	87	59	63	80	62	79	58	90	68	57	85	68	26.9
Eagle	39.65	106.92	6539	−13	−7	88	58	86	57	83	57	60	78	59	76	55	82	65	53	76	65	36.1
Grand Junction	39.12	108.53	4839	2	7	96	61	94	60	92	60	64	83	63	82	58	87	71	56	79	71	26.6
Limon	39.27	103.67	5364	−6	1	90	60	88	60	85	59	63	78	62	77	59	92	66	58	88	66	26.8
Pueblo	38.28	104.52	4721	−1	5	97	62	94	62	92	62	66	83	65	83	62	98	71	60	92	71	29.4
Trinidad	37.27	104.33	5761	−2	6	93	61	90	60	87	60	64	83	63	81	58	91	69	57	86	69	28.3
CONNECTICUT																						
Bridgeport	41.17	73.13	16	8	12	86	73	84	72	82	71	74	81	73	79	72	120	78	71	115	77	14.1
Hartford, Brainard Field	41.73	72.65	20	2	6	91	73	88	72	85	70	74	84	73	82	71	116	79	70	110	78	20.9
Windsor Locks, Bradley Fld	41.93	72.68	180	3	8	92	73	88	71	85	70	74	84	72	82	71	114	79	69	109	77	20.9
DELAWARE																						
Dover, AFB	39.13	75.47	30	14	18	93	76	89	75	87	74	78	86	76	84	76	135	82	74	129	81	16.2
Wilmington	39.68	75.60	79	10	14	91	75	89	74	86	73	76	85	75	83	74	125	81	72	120	80	17.0
FLORIDA																						
Apalachicola	29.73	85.03	20	31	35	92	79	90	78	89	78	80	87	79	87	78	145	84	77	141	84	13.3
Cape Canaveral, NASA	28.62	80.72	10	38	42	92	78	90	78	89	77	79	87	79	87	77	141	84	76	138	83	16.0
Daytona Beach	29.18	81.05	36	34	37	92	77	90	77	88	77	79	87	78	86	76	137	84	76	134	83	15.4
Ft. Lauderdale/Hollywood	26.07	80.15	23	46	50	92	78	90	78	89	78	80	87	79	87	78	145	84	77	141	84	11.3
Ft. Myers	26.58	81.87	16	42	47	94	77	93	77	92	77	80	88	79	87	78	144	83	77	140	83	16.9
Gainesville	29.68	82.27	151	30	33	94	77	92	77	90	76	79	88	78	87	76	139	83	76	136	82	17.3
Homestead, AFB	25.48	80.38	7	48	52	92	79	90	79	89	78	80	88	80	87	78	145	86	77	141	85	11.7
Jacksonville, Cecil Fld NAS	30.22	81.88	82	31	34	96	76	95	76	93	76	78	90	77	89	75	134	83	75	130	82	20.0
Jacksonville, Intl Airport	30.50	81.70	30	29	32	94	77	93	77	91	77	79	89	78	88	76	138	84	76	134	83	17.8
Jacksonville, Mayport Naval	30.40	81.42	16	34	39	95	78	92	78	90	77	80	89	79	88	77	142	85	77	139	85	15.3
Key West	24.55	81.75	20	55	58	90	79	89	79	89	79	80	87	80	87	78	146	85	77	143	85	8.1
Melbourne	28.10	80.65	36	38	43	93	79	91	79	89	79	81	88	80	87	79	150	85	78	146	85	15.5
Miami, Intl Airport	25.82	80.28	13	46	50	91	77	90	77	89	77	79	87	78	86	77	141	83	76	138	82	11.4
Miami, New Tamiami A	25.65	80.43	10	45	49	92	78	91	78	90	77	79	88	79	87	77	141	83	76	138	83	15.5
Milton, Whiting Field NAS	30.72	87.02	200	28	31	95	78	93	77	92	76	80	89	79	88	77	143	85	76	138	84	18.5
Orlando	28.43	81.32	105	37	42	94	76	93	76	92	76	79	88	78	87	76	139	82	76	136	81	16.6
Panama City, Tyndall AFB	30.07	85.58	16	33	37	91	79	89	79	88	79	82	87	81	86	80	154	85	79	150	84	12.2
Pensacola, Sherman AFB	30.35	87.32	30	28	32	93	78	92	78	90	77	80	88	79	88	78	144	85	76	138	85	15.3
Saint Petersburg	27.92	82.68	10	43	47	94	80	93	79	92	79	82	89	81	88	80	153	85	79	150	85	13.5
Sarasota/Bradenton	27.40	82.55	30	39	43	93	80	92	79	90	79	81	89	80	87	79	148	86	78	146	86	15.8
Tallahassee	30.38	84.37	69	25	28	95	77	93	76	91	76	79	88	78	87	76	138	82	76	135	82	19.8
Tampa, Intl Airport	27.97	82.53	10	36	40	92	77	91	77	90	77	79	88	78	87	77	140	84	77	137	83	15.0
Valparaiso, Eglin AFB	30.48	86.53	85	30	33	92	78	90	78	89	77	80	89	79	86	78	144	84	77	141	83	13.9
Vero Beach	27.65	80.42	26	39	43	92	77	90	78	89	77	79	88	79	87	77	139	84	76	137	84	15.7
West Palm Beach	26.68	80.12	20	43	47	91	78	90	78	89	77	79	88	78	87	77	139	84	76	137	83	13.1
GEORGIA																						
Albany	31.53	84.18	194	27	30	96	76	95	76	93	75	78	89	78	88	76	136	82	75	133	81	19.8

Table 19-1. *(Continued)* **Air Conditioning Design Data—United States**

Station	Location			Heating		Cooling						Evaporation				Dehumidification						Range of
				99.6%	99%	0.4%		1%		2%		1%		2%		1%			2%			
	Lat.	Long.	Elev.	DB		DB	MWB	DB	MWB	DB	MWB	DB	MWB	DB	MWB	DP	W	MDB	DP	W	MDB	DB
Athens	33.95	83.32	810	20	25	94	75	92	75	90	74	77	87	76	86	74	129	81	73	125	80	18.4
Atlanta	33.65	84.42	1033	18	23	93	75	91	74	88	73	76	87	75	85	73	128	81	72	124	80	17.3
Augusta	33.37	81.97	148	21	25	96	76	94	76	92	75	78	89	77	88	75	130	83	74	127	82	20.2
Brunswick	31.15	81.38	20	30	34	93	78	91	79	88	78	80	88	79	87	78	144	85	77	141	84	14.4
Columbus, Ft. Benning	32.33	85.00	233	23	27	97	76	94	76	92	76	79	89	78	88	76	136	83	75	133	82	20.5
Columbus, Metro Airport	32.52	84.93	397	23	27	95	76	93	75	91	75	78	88	77	87	75	134	82	74	130	82	18.0
Macon	32.70	83.65	361	23	27	96	76	94	75	92	75	78	89	77	88	75	132	82	74	129	82	19.3
Marietta, Dobbins AFB	33.92	84.52	1070	21	26	94	74	91	74	89	74	76	87	75	86	73	130	81	72	123	79	17.1
Rome	34.35	85.17	643	15	21	96	74	94	74	91	74	77	89	76	88	74	130	83	73	127	83	20.7
Savannah	32.13	81.20	49	26	29	95	77	93	76	91	76	78	89	78	87	76	135	83	75	132	82	17.5
Valdosta, Moody AFB	30.97	83.20	233	30	34	95	77	94	77	92	76	79	89	78	88	76	139	84	76	135	83	17.8
Valdosta, Regional Airport	30.78	83.28	203	28	31	95	77	94	76	92	76	79	89	78	88	76	139	82	76	136	82	19.4
Waycross	31.25	82.40	151	29	32	96	76	94	76	93	75	78	90	77	89	75	130	83	74	127	83	20.3
HAWAII																						
Ewa, Barbers Point NAS	21.32	158.07	49	59	61	92	73	90	72	89	72	75	86	75	85	72	118	82	71	113	82	15.8
Hilo	19.72	155.07	36	61	63	85	74	84	74	83	73	76	81	75	81	74	127	79	73	123	78	13.3
Honolulu	21.35	157.93	16	61	63	89	73	88	73	87	73	75	84	74	84	72	120	80	71	116	79	12.2
Kahului	20.9	156.43	66	59	61	89	74	88	74	87	73	76	85	75	84	73	122	80	72	118	80	15.6
Kaneohe, MCAS	21.45	157.77	10	67	68	86	75	85	74	84	74	77	82	76	82	75	133	81	74	128	80	7.4
Lihue	21.98	159.35	148	60	62	85	75	85	74	84	74	76	82	75	82	74	128	80	73	125	79	9.6
Molokai	21.15	157.10	449	60	61	88	73	87	73	86	72	75	83	74	83	73	124	79	71	118	79	13.3
IDAHO																						
Boise	43.57	116.22	2867	2	9	96	63	94	63	91	62	64	89	63	87	55	72	71	53	67	71	30.3
Burley	42.55	113.77	4150	−5	2	94	63	90	62	87	61	65	84	63	83	58	84	72	56	78	72	29.0
Idaho Falls	43.52	112.07	4741	−12	−6	92	61	89	60	86	60	63	82	61	81	56	81	69	54	73	68	34.0
Lewiston	46.38	117.02	1437	6	15	97	65	93	64	90	63	65	89	64	87	56	71	71	54	65	71	26.5
Mountain Home, AFB	43.05	115.87	2995	0	5	99	63	96	62	93	61	64	91	63	89	54	70	69	52	64	71	32.8
Mullan	47.47	115.80	3317	−1	7	87	62	84	61	80	60	63	79	62	77	58	80	68	56	75	66	28.1
Pocatello	42.92	112.60	4478	−7	0	93	61	90	60	87	59	62	83	61	82	55	76	70	53	70	69	32.1
ILLINOIS																						
Belleville, Scott AFB	38.55	89.85	453	3	10	95	78	93	77	90	76	78	90	77	88	76	136	85	74	131	84	19.8
Chicago, Meigs Field	41.78	87.75	623	−4	3	92	74	89	73	86	71	76	85	74	83	72	121	80	71	115	80	16.0
Chicago, OHare Intl A	41.98	87.90	673	−6	−1	91	74	88	73	86	71	75	85	74	83	72	123	82	71	115	80	19.6
Decatur	39.83	88.87	682	−2	3	94	76	91	75	88	74	78	89	76	86	75	133	84	73	127	83	20.0
Glenview, NAS	42.08	87.82	653	−3	4	93	75	89	73	87	71	76	87	74	84	72	120	82	70	113	81	17.6
Marseilles	41.37	88.68	738	−5	1	93	74	89	73	86	71	76	86	74	84	73	126	82	71	117	81	19.4
Moline/Davenport IA	41.45	90.52	594	−8	−3	93	76	90	74	87	73	77	87	75	85	73	127	83	72	120	82	20.0
Peoria	40.67	89.68	663	−6	−1	92	76	89	74	86	73	77	86	75	84	74	130	83	72	123	81	19.5
Quincy	39.95	91.20	768	−4	2	94	76	91	75	88	74	77	88	76	85	74	132	82	73	126	82	18.9
Rockford	42.20	89.10	741	−10	−4	91	74	88	73	85	71	75	85	74	82	73	124	81	71	116	79	19.8
Springfield	39.85	89.67	614	−4	2	93	76	91	75	88	74	77	88	76	85	75	132	84	73	125	82	19.4
West Chicago	41.92	88.25	758	−7	0	91	75	89	74	86	72	76	85	74	83	74	130	83	71	119	80	19.8
INDIANA																						
Evansville	38.05	87.53	387	3	9	94	77	92	76	90	75	78	89	77	87	75	132	84	73	126	83	19.8
Ft. Wayne	41.00	85.20	827	−4	2	90	74	88	73	85	71	75	84	74	82	72	124	81	71	117	79	19.9
Indianapolis	39.73	86.27	807	−3	3	91	75	88	74	86	73	77	86	75	83	74	131	82	73	125	81	18.9
Lafayette, Purdue Univ	40.42	86.93	607	−5	3	93	75	90	75	88	73	77	86	75	84	74	132	83	73	125	82	20.9
Peru, Grissom AFB	40.65	86.15	810	−3	4	93	75	89	75	87	73	77	86	75	83	75	134	83	73	127	81	18.5
South Bend	41.70	86.32	774	−2	3	90	73	87	72	85	71	75	84	73	81	72	123	80	71	116	78	18.6
Terre Haute	39.45	87.32	584	−3	5	93	76	90	76	88	75	78	87	76	85	76	136	84	74	131	82	19.6
IOWA																						
Burlington	40.78	91.13	699	−4	1	94	76	91	76	88	73	77	88	76	85	74	131	83	72	124	82	18.7
Cedar Rapids	41.88	91.7	869	−11	−5	93	75	89	74	86	72	76	86	74	84	74	129	83	71	120	80	20.0
Des Moines	41.53	93.65	965	−9	−4	93	76	90	74	87	73	76	87	75	85	73	126	83	71	120	81	18.5
Ft. Dodge	42.55	94.18	1165	−13	−7	92	75	88	73	86	71	75	86	74	83	72	123	82	70	116	79	18.5
Lamoni	40.62	93.95	1122	−6	0	96	74	92	74	89	72	76	87	75	85	73	127	82	71	120	80	18.9
Mason City	43.15	93.33	1214	−15	−10	91	74	88	73	85	71	75	85	74	82	73	126	82	71	118	80	20.8
Ottumwa	41.10	92.45	846	−5	0	95	75	92	75	88	73	76	88	75	86	74	130	83	72	121	81	18.7
Sioux City	42.40	96.38	1102	−11	−6	94	75	90	74	88	72	76	87	75	85	73	127	84	71	120	82	20.4
Spencer	43.17	95.15	1339	−16	−11	91	75	88	73	85	71	75	86	73	82	72	123	82	70	117	79	20.2
Waterloo	42.55	92.4	879	−14	−9	91	75	88	73	85	71	75	85	74	83	72	124	82	71	117	80	20.0
KANSAS																						
Concordia	39.55	97.65	1483	−4	3	100	73	96	72	93	72	76	89	74	88	72	123	82	70	118	81	22.5
Dodge City	37.77	99.97	2592	0	6	100	70	97	70	94	69	73	89	71	88	68	114	78	67	109	77	24.3
Ft Riley, Marshall AAF	39.05	96.77	1066	−2	5	99	75	96	74	93	74	77	90	75	88	73	130	83	71	120	82	22.7
Garden City	37.93	100.72	2890	−3	4	100	69	97	69	94	69	72	89	71	88	67	113	78	66	108	77	27.5
Goodland	39.37	101.70	3688	−3	2	97	66	94	66	91	65	69	84	68	84	65	106	73	63	100	73	26.5
Russell	38.87	98.82	1864	−4	3	100	72	96	72	94	72	75	90	73	88	71	120	82	69	116	80	24.1
Salina	38.80	97.65	1273	−3	4	101	74	97	73	94	73	76	90	75	89	72	123	83	71	118	82	23.0
Topeka	39.07	95.62	886	−2	4	96	75	93	75	90	75	78	89	76	88	74	132	85	73	126	83	20.3
Wichita, Airport	37.65	97.43	1339	2	8	100	73	97	73	94	73	76	90	74	89	72	123	82	71	118	81	22.2
Wichita, McConnell AFB	37.62	97.27	1371	2	10	100	73	97	73	94	73	76	90	74	89	72	124	83	71	119	82	21.8

Table 19-1. *(Continued)* Air Conditioning Design Data—United States

Station	Lat.	Long.	Elev.	99.6% DB	99% DB	0.4% DB	0.4% MWB	1% DB	1% MWB	2% DB	2% MWB	1% DB	1% MWB	2% DB	2% MWB	1% DP	1% W	1% MDB	2% DP	2% W	2% MDB	Range of DB
KENTUCKY																						
Bowling Green	36.97	86.42	548	7	14	94	76	91	75	88	74	77	87	76	86	75	132	82	74	127	81	20.0
Covington/Cincinnati A	39.05	84.67	876	1	7	91	74	89	73	86	72	76	86	74	83	73	126	81	72	120	80	18.9
Ft. Campbell, AAF	36.67	87.50	571	9	15	95	77	93	76	90	76	78	89	77	87	76	136	84	74	132	83	19.4
Ft. Knox, Godman AAF	37.90	85.97	755	9	15	94	76	92	74	89	74	77	88	76	86	74	132	83	73	126	82	19.4
Jackson	37.60	83.32	1381	7	14	90	74	87	73	85	72	76	85	74	83	73	130	81	71	122	79	18.2
Lexington	38.03	84.60	988	4	10	91	74	89	73	86	72	75	86	74	83	72	124	81	71	120	80	18.4
Louisville	38.18	85.73	489	6	12	93	76	90	75	88	74	77	88	76	86	74	129	84	73	125	82	18.2
Paducah	37.07	88.77	413	7	13	96	77	93	76	92	75	79	90	78	88	76	138	85	75	132	83	20.2
LOUISIANA																						
Alexandria, England AFB	31.33	92.55	89	27	30	95	78	94	78	92	77	80	90	79	89	77	142	85	76	138	85	18.4
Baton Rouge	30.53	91.15	69	27	30	94	78	92	77	91	77	79	88	78	87	77	141	84	76	137	83	16.7
Bossier City, Barksdale AFB	32.50	93.67	167	22	27	96	77	94	77	93	77	79	90	78	89	76	139	83	76	134	83	20.0
Lafayette	30.20	91.98	43	28	32	94	78	93	78	91	77	80	89	79	88	77	143	83	77	140	83	17.1
Lake Charles	30.12	93.22	33	29	32	93	78	91	78	90	77	80	88	79	87	78	145	84	77	141	83	16.2
Leesville, Ft. Polk	31.05	93.20	328	27	30	95	77	94	76	92	76	79	88	78	87	76	140	82	76	136	82	18.2
Monroe	32.52	92.03	79	22	27	96	78	94	78	93	77	80	90	79	89	77	143	85	77	139	84	19.3
New Orleans, Intl Airport	29.98	90.25	30	30	34	93	79	92	78	90	78	80	88	80	87	78	146	85	77	142	84	15.5
New Orleans, Lakefront A	30.05	90.03	10	35	39	93	78	92	78	90	77	80	87	79	87	78	145	84	77	141	83	11.9
Shreveport	32.47	93.82	259	22	26	97	77	95	77	93	76	79	90	78	89	76	135	83	75	132	83	19.1
MAINE																						
Augusta	44.32	69.80	351	−3	1	87	71	84	69	80	67	71	80	69	77	68	106	75	67	100	74	18.4
Bangor	44.80	68.83	194	−7	−2	87	71	84	69	81	67	71	81	69	77	68	104	75	67	99	73	20.5
Brunswick, NAS	43.88	69.93	75	−2	2	87	71	84	69	80	67	71	80	70	77	69	105	76	67	100	74	19.1
Caribou	46.87	68.02	623	−14	−10	85	69	82	67	79	66	70	77	68	76	68	104	75	66	97	72	19.5
Limestone, Loring AFB	46.95	67.88	745	−13	−9	84	68	80	66	78	64	69	76	67	74	67	101	72	65	94	71	18.7
Portland	43.65	70.32	62	−3	2	86	71	83	70	80	68	72	80	70	77	69	107	76	67	101	74	18.7
MARYLAND																						
Camp Springs, Andrews AFB	38.82	76.87	282	13	18	94	75	91	74	88	73	77	87	75	85	74	129	82	73	124	80	18.7
Baltimore, BWI Airport	39.18	76.67	154	11	15	93	75	91	74	88	73	76	86	75	85	74	125	81	72	120	80	18.8
Lex Park, Patuxent RiverNAS	38.28	76.40	39	16	21	93	76	91	75	87	74	77	87	76	85	75	131	83	74	125	82	15.8
Salisbury	38.33	75.52	52	13	18	93	77	90	76	88	75	78	86	77	85	76	137	82	75	132	81	18.7
MASSACHUSETTS																						
Boston	42.37	71.03	30	7	12	91	73	87	71	84	70	74	83	72	81	71	113	79	69	108	78	15.3
East Falmouth, Otis ANGB	41.65	70.52	131	11	14	85	72	82	72	79	69	74	78	72	76	72	118	76	71	113	75	14.6
Weymouth, S Weymth NAS	42.15	70.93	161	6	11	92	73	87	72	85	71	75	84	73	81	72	118	79	70	111	78	19.6
Worcester	42.27	71.88	1010	0	5	85	71	83	69	80	68	72	80	70	77	69	112	76	68	105	75	16.6
MICHIGAN																						
Alpena	45.07	83.57	692	−7	−1	87	71	84	69	81	67	72	81	70	78	69	107	76	67	100	74	22.9
Detroit, Metro	42.23	83.33	663	0	5	90	73	87	72	84	70	74	84	73	81	71	118	80	70	111	78	20.4
Flint	42.97	83.75	764	−2	3	88	73	86	71	83	70	74	82	72	80	71	116	78	69	110	77	20.6
Grand Rapids	42.88	85.52	804	0	5	89	73	86	71	84	70	74	83	72	81	71	118	79	70	112	77	20.7
Hancock	47.17	88.50	1079	−9	−4	86	71	83	69	80	67	71	80	70	77	69	109	76	67	103	74	20.6
Harbor Beach	44.02	82.80	600	9	12	90	71	86	69	83	68	72	83	70	80	68	106	80	67	100	78	14.4
Jackson	42.27	84.47	1001	−3	4	88	74	86	73	84	71	75	83	73	81	72	123	81	71	117	78	20.3
Lansing	42.77	84.60	873	−3	2	89	73	86	72	84	70	74	83	73	81	72	120	79	70	114	78	21.7
Marquette, Sawyer AFB	46.35	87.40	1220	−11	−6	86	69	83	68	79	65	70	79	68	75	67	106	74	66	99	73	22.1
Marquette/Ishpeming A	46.53	87.55	1424	−13	−8	85	69	82	67	78	65	70	78	68	75	67	104	75	65	98	72	22.1
Mount Clemens, ANGB	42.62	82.83	581	3	7	90	74	87	72	84	71	75	83	73	80	72	120	81	70	113	78	19.6
Muskegon	43.17	86.25	633	3	7	85	71	83	70	81	69	73	80	71	78	70	115	77	69	109	76	18.1
Oscoda, Wurtsmith AFB	44.45	83.40	633	0	3	89	72	86	71	83	69	73	83	71	79	70	112	79	68	106	77	21.4
Pellston	45.57	84.80	719	−9	−3	87	71	85	69	81	68	72	81	70	77	69	108	76	67	103	75	23.9
Saginaw	43.53	84.08	669	0	4	90	74	87	72	84	70	75	84	73	81	72	120	80	70	112	78	21.2
Sault Ste. Marie	46.47	84.37	725	−12	−7	83	69	80	68	77	66	70	77	68	74	67	103	74	65	95	72	21.9
Seul Choix Point	45.92	85.92	591	0	4	78	66	76	65	74	64	68	72	66	71	67	101	72	65	94	70	13.9
Traverse City	44.73	85.58	623	−3	2	89	71	86	70	83	68	72	82	70	80	69	109	78	67	103	76	22.0
MINNESOTA																						
Alexandria	45.87	95.40	1424	−20	−15	89	72	86	70	83	69	73	82	71	80	70	116	79	68	109	77	19.3
Brainerd, Pequot Lakes	46.60	94.32	1280	−24	−17	88	70	85	68	81	66	70	82	68	78	66	102	77	65	96	75	21.6
Duluth	46.83	92.18	1417	−21	−16	84	69	81	67	78	65	69	78	67	75	66	102	75	64	94	72	20.2
Hibbing	47.38	92.83	1352	−25	−20	85	70	81	68	78	66	71	78	68	75	68	108	76	66	101	73	23.2
International Falls	48.57	93.38	1184	−29	−23	86	69	83	67	80	66	70	79	68	77	67	103	75	65	96	73	21.8
Minneapolis–St. Paul	44.88	93.22	837	−16	−11	91	73	88	71	85	70	74	84	72	82	71	116	81	69	109	79	19.1
Redwood Falls	44.55	95.08	1024	−17	−12	92	74	88	72	86	70	75	85	73	82	72	123	81	70	116	80	20.7
Rochester	43.92	92.50	1319	−17	−12	88	72	85	71	82	70	74	82	72	80	71	120	79	69	111	77	19.7
Saint Cloud	45.55	94.07	1024	−20	−14	91	72	88	71	85	70	74	84	72	82	70	116	80	68	109	78	21.5
Tofte	47.58	90.83	791	−10	−6	79	64	75	62	71	61	64	72	63	70	61	83	69	59	77	68	13.0
MISSISSIPPI																						
Biloxi, Keesler AFB	30.42	88.92	33	31	35	92	79	91	78	89	78	80	88	80	87	78	147	85	78	144	84	13.0
Columbus, AFB	33.65	88.45	220	20	25	96	77	94	76	92	76	78	89	78	88	76	136	83	75	132	82	19.3
Greenwood	33.50	90.08	154	20	24	96	78	94	78	93	77	80	90	79	89	77	143	85	76	139	84	19.1
Jackson	32.32	90.08	331	21	25	95	77	93	76	92	76	79	89	78	88	76	138	83	75	134	82	19.2

Table 19-1. *(Continued)* **Air Conditioning Design Data—United States**

Station	Lat.	Long.	Elev.	99.6% DB	99% DB	0.4% DB	0.4% MWB	1% DB	1% MWB	2% DB	2% MWB	1% DB	1% MWB	2% DB	2% MWB	1% DP	1% W	1% MDB	2% DP	2% W	2% MDB	Range of DB
McComb	31.18	90.47	413	23	28	94	76	92	76	91	76	78	88	78	87	76	138	82	75	135	81	19.8
Meridian	32.33	88.75	308	21	25	96	77	94	76	92	76	78	90	77	88	75	134	83	74	130	83	20.3
Tupelo	34.27	88.77	361	18	22	96	76	94	76	92	75	78	89	77	88	75	134	83	74	131	82	18.9
MISSOURI																						
Cape Girardeau	37.23	89.57	341	6	13	96	77	94	77	91	76	78	90	78	88	76	136	85	75	132	83	19.8
Columbia	38.82	92.22	899	−1	5	95	75	92	75	89	74	77	88	75	86	74	130	83	72	124	82	20.3
Joplin	37.15	94.50	981	3	11	96	75	94	75	91	74	77	89	76	88	74	132	85	72	125	83	20.0
Kansas City	39.32	94.72	1024	−1	4	96	75	93	75	90	74	77	89	76	87	74	130	84	73	125	83	18.8
Poplar Bluff	36.77	90.47	479	8	13	95	77	92	76	90	76	78	88	77	87	76	138	83	75	133	82	20.0
Spickard/Trenton	40.25	93.72	886	1	6	96	74	93	73	89	72	76	88	75	86	73	128	83	71	118	81	19.6
Springfield	37.23	93.38	1270	3	9	95	74	92	74	89	74	76	88	75	86	73	128	83	72	124	81	20.8
St. Louis, Intl Airport	38.75	90.37	564	2	8	95	76	93	75	90	74	78	88	76	87	75	132	83	73	127	82	18.3
Warrensburg, Whiteman AFB	38.73	93.55	869	1	7	96	76	93	76	90	75	78	90	76	88	75	134	85	73	128	83	19.3
MONTANA																						
Billings	45.80	108.53	3570	−13	−7	93	63	90	62	87	61	64	84	62	83	57	78	71	55	74	70	25.8
Bozeman	45.78	111.15	4475	−20	−12	91	61	87	60	85	59	62	82	61	81	56	78	67	53	71	66	31.7
Butte	45.95	112.50	5545	−22	−14	86	57	84	56	80	55	58	76	57	76	52	70	63	50	66	62	31.5
Cut Bank	48.60	112.37	3855	−21	−16	87	60	84	59	80	58	60	79	59	77	54	70	65	51	65	63	26.1
Glasgow	48.22	106.62	2297	−22	−17	94	64	90	63	86	62	66	83	64	82	60	83	71	58	77	69	25.3
Great Falls, Intl Airport	47.48	111.37	3658	−19	−13	92	61	88	60	85	59	62	82	61	81	55	74	67	53	69	66	27.2
Great Falls, Malmstrom AFB	47.50	111.18	3527	−17	−11	93	62	89	61	86	60	63	83	62	81	57	78	69	54	71	68	26.3
Havre	48.55	109.77	2598	−25	−19	94	63	90	62	86	61	64	84	62	82	58	78	69	56	74	68	27.9
Helena	46.60	112.00	3898	−18	−10	90	60	87	59	84	59	61	81	60	80	55	73	66	52	68	66	28.0
Kalispell	48.30	114.27	2972	−12	−3	89	62	86	61	82	60	63	81	61	79	57	76	67	55	71	67	29.9
Lewistown	47.05	109.47	4167	−18	−12	89	61	86	60	82	59	63	80	61	78	56	79	69	54	74	67	28.3
Miles City	46.43	105.87	2628	−19	−13	97	66	93	65	90	64	67	86	66	84	61	88	75	59	82	73	25.9
Missoula	46.92	114.08	3189	−9	−1	91	62	88	61	85	60	63	82	62	81	56	76	68	55	71	66	31.3
NEBRASKA																						
Bellevue, Offutt AFB	41.12	95.92	1047	−5	1	95	76	91	75	88	74	77	88	76	86	74	134	83	73	127	82	18.4
Grand Island	40.97	98.32	1857	−8	−2	97	72	93	72	90	70	74	88	73	86	70	120	81	69	113	79	22.4
Lincoln	40.85	96.75	1188	−7	−2	97	74	94	74	91	73	76	89	75	87	73	130	83	71	121	82	22.3
Norfolk	41.98	97.43	1552	−11	−5	95	74	92	72	89	72	75	88	73	86	71	121	82	70	115	81	20.8
North Platte	41.13	100.68	2785	−10	−4	95	69	92	69	89	68	72	86	70	85	67	111	78	66	105	77	25.5
Omaha, Eppley Airfield	41.30	95.90	981	−7	−2	95	75	92	75	89	73	77	88	75	86	73	128	84	72	121	82	19.9
Omaha, WSO	41.37	96.02	1332	−8	−2	94	75	90	75	87	73	76	87	74	85	72	126	83	71	120	82	17.6
Scottsbluff	41.87	103.60	3957	−11	−3	95	65	92	64	89	64	68	85	66	84	62	97	74	60	91	73	28.9
Sidney	41.10	102.98	4304	−8	−1	95	63	92	63	89	63	66	84	64	84	60	91	72	58	86	71	27.9
Valentine	42.87	100.55	2598	−16	−8	97	68	94	67	90	67	71	89	69	87	65	103	78	63	94	77	26.5
NEVADA																						
Elko	40.83	115.78	5135	−5	1	95	60	92	59	90	58	61	84	60	84	54	75	66	51	67	67	38.4
Ely	39.28	114.85	6263	−6	0	89	56	87	56	85	55	59	78	58	78	53	75	64	50	68	65	34.6
Las Vegas, Intl Airport	36.08	115.17	2178	27	30	108	66	106	66	103	65	70	93	69	93	63	92	81	60	84	85	24.8
Mercury	36.62	116.02	3310	24	28	102	65	100	64	98	63	67	89	66	89	60	89	77	58	80	80	25.9
N. Las Vegas, Nellis AFB	36.23	115.03	1870	28	31	108	68	106	67	104	66	71	94	70	94	64	97	82	61	86	84	26.3
Reno	39.50	119.78	4400	8	13	95	61	92	60	90	59	62	86	60	85	53	69	69	50	63	68	37.3
Tonopah	38.05	117.08	5427	7	13	94	58	92	57	89	57	61	82	60	81	53	74	68	50	67	69	31.1
Winnemucca	40.90	117.80	4314	1	7	97	61	94	60	92	59	62	87	60	86	53	69	67	50	62	68	37.4
NEW HAMPSHIRE																						
Concord	43.20	71.50	344	−8	−2	90	71	87	70	84	68	73	82	71	79	70	111	77	68	105	76	24.1
Lebanon	43.63	72.30	597	−7	−3	88	71	86	69	83	68	72	82	70	79	69	108	77	67	103	75	23.0
Mount Washington	44.27	71.30	6266	−23	−19	60	56	58	54	56	54	56	57	54	56	56	84	57	54	78	55	8.5
Portsmouth, Pease AFB	43.08	70.82	102	4	9	89	72	85	70	83	70	73	82	72	79	71	113	77	69	106	76	18.2
NEW JERSEY																						
Atlantic City	39.45	74.57	66	8	13	91	74	88	73	86	72	76	84	75	82	74	125	80	72	120	79	18.1
Millville	39.37	75.07	82	10	15	92	75	89	74	87	73	76	86	75	83	74	129	80	73	125	80	18.7
Newark	40.70	74.17	30	10	14	93	74	90	73	87	71	76	85	74	83	73	121	80	71	116	80	15.9
Teterboro	40.85	74.07	10	10	14	92	76	89	74	87	73	77	87	75	83	74	128	82	72	119	81	18.4
Trenton, McGuire AFB	40.02	74.60	135	11	15	93	75	90	74	87	73	76	87	75	84	74	127	82	72	118	80	18.9
NEW MEXICO																						
Alamogordo, Holloman AFB	32.85	106.10	4094	20	23	98	63	96	63	93	63	67	85	67	85	62	98	72	61	92	73	30.2
Albuquerque	35.05	106.62	5315	13	18	96	60	93	60	91	60	64	82	64	81	60	93	69	58	89	69	25.4
Carlsbad	32.33	104.27	3294	19	23	101	65	98	66	96	66	71	87	70	85	68	116	76	67	111	75	25.4
Clayton	36.45	103.15	4970	1	9	94	62	91	62	88	62	65	84	65	82	60	94	71	59	90	70	26.1
Clovis, Cannon AFB	34.38	103.32	4295	10	15	96	64	93	64	91	65	69	83	68	83	65	109	74	64	105	73	24.5
Farmington	36.75	108.23	5502	8	13	94	60	92	60	89	60	64	83	63	82	58	90	68	57	85	69	28.8
Gallup	35.52	108.78	6470	1	5	89	57	87	56	85	56	61	76	60	75	57	90	64	56	85	64	30.6
Roswell	33.30	104.53	3668	14	20	98	65	96	65	94	65	69	86	68	85	65	108	73	64	104	73	24.8
Truth Or Consequences	33.23	107.27	4859	22	26	97	61	95	61	93	61	65	85	64	84	59	90	71	58	87	72	25.0
Tucumcari	35.18	103.60	4065	9	15	98	64	95	64	93	64	68	85	67	84	64	104	73	63	100	72	24.9
NEW YORK																						
Albany	42.75	73.80	292	−7	−2	90	71	86	70	84	69	73	82	71	79	70	111	77	68	106	76	23.7
Binghamton	42.22	75.98	1631	−2	2	85	70	82	69	80	67	71	79	70	77	69	111	75	67	106	74	17.5

Table 19-1. *(Continued)* **Air Conditioning Design Data—United States**

Station	Lat.	Long.	Elev.	99.6% DB	99% DB	0.4% DB	0.4% MWB	1% DB	1% MWB	2% DB	2% MWB	1% DB	1% MWB	2% DB	2% MWB	1% DP	1% W	1% MDB	2% DP	2% W	2% MDB	Range of DB
Buffalo	42.93	78.73	705	2	5	86	70	84	69	81	68	72	80	71	78	70	113	77	68	106	75	17.7
Central Islip	40.80	73.10	98	11	15	88	73	85	72	83	70	75	81	74	79	73	124	78	71	116	77	15.1
Elmira/Corning	42.17	76.90	955	−2	3	90	72	87	71	84	69	73	82	72	80	70	116	78	69	110	76	24.1
Glens Falls	43.33	73.62	328	−10	−4	88	73	85	71	83	70	74	82	72	80	71	116	79	69	108	76	22.1
Massena	44.93	74.85	213	−15	−10	87	72	84	71	82	69	73	81	71	79	70	111	78	68	105	76	21.8
New York, JFK Airport	40.65	73.78	23	11	15	91	74	88	72	85	71	75	84	74	82	72	120	80	71	114	79	13.9
New York, La Guardia A	40.77	73.90	30	13	17	92	74	89	73	86	72	76	85	74	83	73	125	80	71	116	80	14.6
Newburgh	41.50	74.10	492	6	10	88	74	85	72	83	70	74	83	73	80	72	119	80	70	111	78	17.1
Niagara Falls	43.10	78.95	591	4	7	87	72	85	71	83	69	74	81	72	79	71	116	78	69	111	76	18.9
Plattsburgh, AFB	44.65	73.47	236	−9	−4	86	71	83	69	80	68	72	80	70	78	69	108	76	67	102	75	19.6
Poughkeepsie	41.63	73.88	167	2	6	92	75	88	72	85	71	75	85	73	82	71	116	80	70	111	78	23.0
Rochester	43.12	77.67	554	1	5	89	73	86	71	83	70	74	82	72	80	71	116	79	69	109	77	20.1
Rome, Griffiss AFB	43.23	75.40	505	−5	1	88	71	86	70	83	69	73	82	71	79	70	111	78	68	105	76	21.8
Syracuse	43.12	76.12	407	−3	2	88	72	85	71	83	70	73	82	72	80	70	113	78	69	107	77	20.3
Watertown	44.00	76.02	325	−12	−6	85	71	83	70	80	69	72	80	71	77	70	111	77	69	106	75	20.5
White Plains	41.07	73.70	440	7	12	89	74	87	72	84	71	75	83	73	80	72	120	80	71	114	78	18.0
NORTH CAROLINA																						
Asheville	35.43	82.55	2169	11	16	88	72	85	71	83	70	73	82	72	80	71	123	78	70	118	76	19.4
Cape Hatteras	35.27	75.55	10	26	29	88	78	86	77	85	77	79	84	78	83	77	142	83	76	138	82	11.4
Charlotte	35.22	80.93	768	18	23	94	74	91	74	89	73	76	87	75	86	73	125	80	72	122	80	17.8
Cherry Point, MCAS	34.90	76.88	30	24	28	95	79	92	78	90	77	80	90	79	88	77	141	86	76	136	85	16.6
Fayetteville, Ft. Bragg	35.13	78.93	243	22	27	96	77	94	76	92	75	78	89	77	88	76	135	83	75	131	83	18.2
Goldsboro, Johnson AFB	35.33	77.97	108	22	27	96	77	94	76	91	76	78	89	77	87	76	135	83	75	132	82	18.5
Greensboro	36.08	79.95	886	15	19	92	75	90	74	88	73	76	86	75	85	73	127	81	72	123	80	18.6
Hickory	35.73	81.38	1188	18	23	94	73	91	72	88	72	75	85	74	84	73	128	80	71	120	78	19.1
Jacksonville, New RiverMCAF	34.72	77.45	26	23	27	94	79	92	78	89	77	79	89	78	87	77	140	85	76	136	84	17.1
New Bern	35.07	77.05	20	22	27	94	78	92	78	90	76	79	89	78	87	77	139	84	76	134	83	17.8
Raleigh/Durham	35.87	78.78	440	16	20	93	76	90	75	88	74	77	87	76	85	74	130	81	73	125	80	18.8
Wilmington	34.27	77.90	33	23	27	93	79	91	78	89	77	79	88	78	86	77	141	83	76	137	83	15.7
WinstonSalem	36.13	80.22	971	18	23	92	74	89	74	87	73	76	86	75	85	73	129	80	72	121	79	17.6
NORTH DAKOTA																						
Bismarck	46.77	100.75	1660	−21	−16	93	68	90	67	86	66	70	84	68	82	65	100	77	63	92	75	26.5
Devils Lake	48.10	98.87	1453	−23	−19	91	69	87	67	84	66	70	83	68	80	66	100	77	63	90	75	21.1
Fargo	46.90	96.80	899	−22	−17	91	71	88	70	85	69	73	84	71	81	69	112	80	67	104	77	22.3
Grand Forks, AFB	47.97	97.40	912	−20	−16	91	71	88	69	85	68	72	83	70	80	69	109	78	67	101	76	22.9
Minot, AFB	48.42	101.35	1667	−21	−16	94	68	90	67	86	66	70	85	68	82	65	100	78	63	90	75	24.7
Minot, Intl Airport	48.27	101.28	1716	−20	−16	92	67	88	66	84	65	69	83	67	80	64	96	75	62	89	73	22.9
Williston	48.18	103.63	1906	−24	−18	96	67	92	66	87	65	69	86	67	83	63	92	76	61	85	73	25.7
OHIO																						
Akron/Canton	40.92	81.43	1237	0	5	88	72	85	71	83	70	73	82	72	80	71	118	78	69	113	77	18.8
Cincinnati, Lunken Field	39.10	84.42	482	5	12	93	74	90	75	88	73	76	87	75	84	74	128	81	72	120	80	20.0
Cleveland	41.42	81.87	804	1	6	89	73	86	72	84	71	74	83	72	81	71	118	80	70	112	78	18.6
Columbus, Intl Airport	40.00	82.88	817	1	6	90	74	88	73	86	71	75	85	74	82	72	123	81	71	117	79	19.3
Columbus, Rickenbckr AFB	39.82	82.93	745	3	10	92	74	89	73	87	72	75	86	74	84	72	120	82	70	115	79	19.8
Dayton, Intl Airport	39.90	84.20	1004	−1	5	90	74	88	73	86	71	75	85	74	82	72	123	80	71	117	79	19.2
Dayton, WrightPatterson	39.83	84.05	823	1	8	92	74	89	74	87	73	76	86	74	84	73	127	83	71	119	81	19.8
Findlay	41.02	83.67	810	−2	4	90	74	87	72	85	71	75	83	73	81	72	121	80	71	116	78	18.9
Mansfield	40.82	82.52	1296	−1	4	88	73	85	72	83	71	74	83	73	80	71	122	79	70	116	78	17.8
Toledo	41.60	83.80	692	−2	3	90	73	87	72	85	71	75	84	73	81	72	122	80	70	115	78	20.9
Youngstown	41.27	80.67	1184	−1	4	88	72	85	70	83	69	73	82	71	79	70	116	78	69	110	76	20.6
Zanesville	39.95	81.90	899	2	9	90	74	88	73	86	71	75	85	74	82	72	120	80	71	116	78	20.7
OKLAHOMA																						
Altus, AFB	34.67	99.27	1378	13	19	102	73	100	73	97	73	76	92	75	91	72	124	83	71	119	82	23.6
Enid, Vance AFB	36.33	97.92	1306	5	12	101	74	98	74	95	73	76	91	75	90	71	121	83	70	116	82	21.8
Lawton, Ft. Sill/Post Field	34.65	98.40	1188	12	19	99	73	97	73	95	73	76	90	75	89	73	129	82	71	121	81	20.7
McAlester	34.88	95.78	771	10	17	98	76	96	76	93	76	78	91	77	89	75	137	83	74	133	83	21.8
Oklahoma City, Tinker AFB	35.42	97.38	1293	10	17	98	74	96	75	94	74	77	91	76	89	74	132	85	72	123	83	19.4
Oklahoma City, W. Rogers A	35.40	97.60	1302	9	15	99	74	96	74	94	73	76	90	75	89	72	125	82	71	120	81	21.2
Tulsa	36.20	95.90	676	9	14	100	76	97	76	94	75	78	92	77	90	74	132	85	73	127	84	19.5
OREGON																						
Astoria	46.15	123.88	23	25	29	76	64	72	62	69	61	63	71	62	68	60	76	66	59	74	65	14.2
Eugene	44.12	123.22	374	21	26	91	67	87	65	83	64	67	84	65	81	60	78	73	59	74	71	27.6
Hillsboro	45.53	122.95	203	19	24	92	69	88	67	84	65	68	86	66	82	61	82	75	60	78	72	26.6
Klamath Falls	42.15	121.73	4091	4	10	91	64	87	62	85	61	64	84	63	81	57	80	73	55	75	71	34.2
Meacham	45.52	118.40	4055	−9	0	87	59	84	58	80	57	59	80	58	78	50	63	64	49	59	64	33.7
Medford	42.37	122.87	1329	21	24	98	67	95	66	91	65	67	91	66	88	58	76	74	56	71	73	33.7
North Bend	43.42	124.25	13	30	32	71	60	69	60	67	59	61	67	60	66	58	73	64	57	70	63	12.8
Pendleton	45.68	118.85	1496	3	11	97	64	94	63	90	62	64	90	63	87	55	68	69	53	62	70	27.2
Portland	45.60	122.60	39	22	27	90	67	86	66	83	64	67	84	65	80	60	78	72	59	75	71	21.6
Redmond	44.25	121.15	3077	1	9	93	62	89	61	86	59	62	86	60	83	52	65	67	50	60	66	35.0
Salem	44.92	123.00	200	20	25	92	67	87	66	83	64	67	85	65	81	59	76	73	58	72	71	27.9
Sexton Summit	42.62	123.37	3842	21	24	83	60	80	59	77	58	61	77	59	74	53	69	68	52	66	66	18.9

Table 19-1. *(Continued)* **Air Conditioning Design Data—United States**

Station	Lat.	Long.	Elev.	99.6% DB	99% DB	0.4% DB	0.4% MWB	1% DB	1% MWB	2% DB	2% MWB	1% DB	1% MWB	2% DB	2% MWB	1% DP	1% W	1% MDB	2% DP	2% W	2% MDB	Range of DB
	Location			Heating		Cooling						Evaporation				Dehumidification						Range of DB
PENNSYLVANIA																						
Allentown	40.65	75.43	384	5	10	90	73	88	72	85	71	74	84	73	82	71	117	79	70	111	78	19.4
Altoona	40.30	78.32	1503	5	10	89	72	86	70	83	69	72	83	71	80	69	113	77	68	109	76	19.4
Bradford	41.80	78.63	2142	−6	−1	83	69	80	68	78	66	70	77	68	75	68	111	73	66	105	72	21.2
Du Bois	41.18	78.90	1818	0	5	86	70	84	69	81	67	71	79	70	78	69	112	74	67	108	73	19.4
Erie	42.08	80.18	738	2	7	85	72	83	70	80	70	73	80	71	78	70	115	77	69	109	76	15.6
Harrisburg	40.20	76.77	308	9	13	92	74	89	73	86	72	76	85	74	83	73	123	80	72	118	79	18.8
Philadelphia, Intl Airport	39.88	75.25	30	11	15	92	75	89	74	87	73	77	86	75	84	74	126	81	73	121	80	17.7
Philadelphia, Northeast A	40.08	75.02	121	11	15	93	76	90	74	88	73	77	87	75	84	74	129	82	72	121	82	19.1
Philadelphia, Willow Gr NAS	40.20	75.15	361	10	14	93	75	90	74	88	72	76	87	75	85	73	125	82	71	116	81	19.4
Pittsburgh, Allegheny Co. A	40.35	79.93	1253	4	11	90	72	87	71	85	70	74	84	72	81	70	117	78	69	113	77	18.0
Pittsburgh, Intl Airport	40.50	80.22	1224	2	7	89	72	86	70	84	69	73	82	71	80	70	115	78	68	109	77	19.5
Wilkes–Barre/Scranton	41.33	75.73	948	2	7	88	71	85	70	83	69	73	81	71	79	70	115	77	69	109	76	18.8
Williamsport	41.25	76.92	525	2	7	90	73	87	71	84	70	74	83	73	80	72	118	78	70	113	77	20.3
RHODE ISLAND																						
Providence	41.73	71.43	62	5	10	89	73	86	74	83	70	74	82	73	80	72	118	78	70	112	77	17.4
SOUTH CAROLINA																						
Beaufort, MCAS	32.48	80.72	39	28	31	95	78	93	78	92	77	80	89	79	88	77	141	85	76	137	84	16.7
Charleston	32.90	80.03	49	25	28	94	78	92	77	90	77	79	88	78	87	77	139	83	76	134	83	16.2
Columbia	33.95	81.12	226	21	24	96	76	94	75	92	74	77	89	77	87	75	130	81	74	127	81	19.9
Florence	34.18	79.72	148	23	27	96	76	94	76	92	76	78	89	78	88	76	136	83	75	132	82	19.8
Greer/Greenville	34.90	82.22	971	19	23	93	74	91	74	88	73	76	87	75	85	73	126	80	72	122	80	18.2
Myrtle Beach, AFB	33.68	78.93	26	25	29	93	79	90	78	88	78	80	88	79	87	78	144	86	77	140	84	14.4
Sumter, Shaw AFB	33.97	80.47	243	24	29	95	76	93	75	90	75	77	88	76	86	75	132	82	74	129	81	18.5
SOUTH DAKOTA																						
Chamberlain	43.80	99.32	1739	−13	−7	98	72	94	71	90	70	74	89	72	87	70	116	82	68	109	80	23.8
Huron	44.38	98.22	1289	−17	−12	95	72	91	71	88	70	74	87	72	84	70	117	81	69	110	79	24.1
Pierre	44.38	100.28	1742	−14	−9	99	70	95	69	91	68	72	89	71	86	68	109	80	66	102	78	25.6
Rapid City	44.05	103.07	3169	−11	−5	95	65	91	65	88	64	68	84	67	82	63	98	75	61	92	73	25.3
Sioux Falls	43.58	96.73	1427	−16	−11	94	73	90	72	87	71	75	87	73	84	71	119	82	69	112	80	22.1
TENNESSEE																						
Bristol	36.48	82.40	1519	9	14	89	72	87	72	85	71	74	84	73	82	71	120	79	70	116	77	19.2
Chattanooga	35.03	85.20	689	15	20	94	75	92	75	89	74	77	88	76	86	74	130	82	73	125	81	19.5
Crossville	35.95	85.08	1880	7	15	89	73	87	72	85	72	74	83	73	82	72	125	79	71	121	78	19.8
Jackson	35.60	88.92	433	12	18	95	77	93	76	91	76	78	90	78	88	75	135	85	75	132	84	19.8
Knoxville	35.82	83.98	981	13	19	92	74	90	74	87	73	76	86	75	85	73	127	81	72	123	80	18.1
Memphis	35.05	90.00	285	16	21	96	78	94	77	92	77	79	91	78	89	76	137	86	75	133	84	16.8
Nashville	36.13	86.68	591	10	16	94	76	92	75	90	74	77	88	76	86	74	130	82	73	126	81	19.1
TEXAS																						
Abilene	32.42	99.68	1791	16	22	99	71	97	71	95	71	74	89	73	88	70	119	80	69	115	79	20.5
Amarillo	35.23	101.70	3606	6	12	96	67	94	66	92	66	70	86	69	85	65	107	75	64	104	74	23.3
Austin	30.30	97.70	620	25	30	98	74	96	74	94	74	77	88	76	87	75	134	80	74	130	80	20.1
Beaumont/Port Arthur	29.95	94.02	23	29	32	94	79	92	79	91	78	81	89	80	88	79	148	85	78	145	84	15.9
Beeville, Chase Field NAS	28.37	97.67	190	28	33	101	77	98	77	96	77	81	91	80	90	78	148	85	78	144	84	21.6
Brownsville	25.90	97.43	20	36	40	95	78	94	77	93	77	79	88	79	88	77	142	83	77	140	82	16.5
College Station/Bryan	30.58	96.37	322	22	29	98	75	96	75	94	75	78	89	78	88	76	138	81	75	134	81	21.4
Corpus Christi	27.77	97.50	43	32	36	95	78	94	78	92	78	80	89	79	88	78	146	83	77	143	83	16.5
Dallas/Ft. Worth, Intl A	32.90	97.03	597	17	24	100	74	98	74	96	74	77	91	76	90	74	130	82	73	126	81	20.3
Del Rio, Laughlin AFB	29.37	100.78	1083	28	32	101	72	98	73	96	72	77	90	76	89	74	131	82	72	124	81	20.9
El Paso	31.80	106.40	3917	21	25	101	64	98	64	96	64	69	84	68	84	65	109	73	64	103	74	28.0
Ft. Worth, Carswell AFB	32.77	97.45	650	18	24	100	75	97	75	96	75	78	91	77	90	75	135	84	74	130	84	19.3
Ft. Worth, Meacham Field	32.82	97.37	709	19	24	100	75	98	74	96	74	77	90	76	89	74	131	82	73	127	82	20.0
Guadalupe Pass	31.83	104.80	5453	13	19	92	61	89	60	87	60	65	80	64	79	60	96	71	59	91	71	20.9
Houston, Hobby Airport	29.65	95.28	46	29	34	94	77	93	77	92	77	80	88	79	87	78	144	83	77	141	82	16.6
Houston, Inter Airport	29.97	95.35	108	27	31	96	77	94	77	92	77	79	89	79	88	77	141	83	76	137	83	18.2
Junction	30.50	99.77	1713	19	23	100	72	98	71	96	71	75	88	74	87	71	121	79	70	118	79	24.8
Killeen, Ft. Hood	31.07	97.83	1014	20	27	98	74	96	73	95	74	77	89	76	88	74	132	81	73	128	80	21.4
Kingsville, NAS	27.50	97.82	49	31	36	97	77	96	78	95	78	80	91	80	90	78	144	84	77	141	84	19.8
Laredo	27.55	99.47	509	32	36	102	73	101	74	98	74	78	91	77	89	75	136	81	75	132	81	21.2
Lubbock, Intl Airport	33.65	101.82	3241	11	17	97	67	95	67	93	67	72	86	71	85	68	115	76	67	111	76	22.1
Lubbock, Reese AFB	33.60	102.05	3337	11	18	98	67	95	67	93	67	72	86	71	85	68	115	77	66	110	77	23.8
Lufkin	31.23	94.75	289	23	27	97	76	95	77	93	76	79	89	78	89	76	139	83	75	134	82	20.9
Marfa	30.37	104.02	4859	15	19	94	62	92	61	89	62	67	81	66	80	63	103	71	62	98	71	31.3
McAllen	26.18	98.23	108	34	40	100	76	98	76	97	76	80	90	79	89	77	143	82	77	140	82	20.7
Midland/Odessa	31.95	102.18	2861	17	22	99	67	97	67	95	67	72	86	71	86	68	115	75	67	111	75	23.7
San Angelo	31.37	100.50	1909	20	24	100	70	97	70	95	70	74	89	73	88	70	118	79	69	116	78	22.3
San Antonio, Intl Airport	29.53	98.47	794	26	30	98	73	96	73	94	74	77	87	76	86	75	135	81	74	132	80	19.1
San Antonio, Kelly AFB	29.38	98.58	689	27	32	99	74	97	74	96	74	78	88	77	88	76	140	82	75	136	81	20.5
San Antonio, Randolph AFB	29.53	98.28	761	27	31	98	74	96	74	94	74	77	89	76	88	75	134	81	74	132	81	22.3
Sanderson	30.17	102.42	2838	23	28	97	67	95	68	94	68	73	86	72	86	69	119	78	68	114	77	20.7
Victoria	28.85	96.92	118	29	33	95	76	94	76	92	77	79	88	78	87	77	141	82	76	139	82	17.4
Waco	31.62	97.22	509	22	26	101	75	99	75	97	75	78	92	77	91	74	131	82	74	127	82	21.6

Table 19-1. *(Continued)* **Air Conditioning Design Data—United States**

Station	Location			Heating		Cooling						Evaporation				Dehumidification						Range of
	Lat.	Long.	Elev.	99.6%	99%	0.4%		1%		2%		1%		2%		1%			2%			DB
				DB	DB	DB	MWB	DB	MWB	DB	MWB	DB	MWB	DB	MWB	DP	W	MDB	DP	W	MDB	
Wichita Falls, Sheppard AFB	33.98	98.50	1030	14	19	103	74	100	73	98	73	76	92	75	91	72	124	82	71	120	81	23.9
UTAH																						
Cedar City	37.70	113.10	5623	2	8	93	59	91	59	88	58	62	80	61	79	57	85	68	55	78	68	28.5
Ogden, Hill AFB	41.12	111.97	4787	6	11	93	61	90	60	87	60	64	81	62	81	57	83	73	55	77	73	22.0
Salt Lake City	40.78	111.97	4226	6	11	96	62	94	62	92	61	65	85	64	85	58	84	73	56	77	73	27.7
VERMONT																						
Burlington	44.47	73.15	341	−11	−6	87	71	84	69	82	68	72	81	70	78	69	109	77	67	102	75	20.4
Montpelier/Barre	44.20	72.57	1165	−10	−6	85	70	83	68	80	67	70	80	69	77	67	106	75	66	99	73	21.1
VIRGINIA																						
Ft. Belvoir	38.72	77.18	69	12	18	95	78	93	76	89	75	78	89	77	87	75	133	85	74	127	83	20.9
Hampton, Langley AFB	37.08	76.37	10	21	24	94	78	91	77	88	76	79	89	78	86	76	136	84	75	132	83	14.9
Lynchburg	37.33	79.20	938	12	17	93	74	90	74	88	73	76	87	75	85	73	125	80	72	120	79	18.2
Newport News	37.13	76.50	43	18	22	95	78	92	77	89	76	78	89	77	87	76	135	83	75	132	82	18.2
Norfolk	36.90	76.20	30	20	24	93	77	91	76	88	75	77	87	77	85	75	130	82	74	126	81	15.3
Oceana, NAS	36.82	76.03	23	22	25	94	77	91	76	88	75	78	87	77	86	76	134	83	74	129	82	15.7
Quantico, MCAS	38.50	77.30	13	16	21	94	77	92	76	89	74	78	89	76	87	75	130	85	73	125	83	18.5
Richmond	37.50	77.33	177	14	18	94	76	92	75	89	74	78	88	76	86	75	131	82	74	126	81	19.1
Roanoke	37.32	79.97	1175	12	17	92	73	89	72	87	71	74	86	73	84	71	118	79	70	115	78	19.6
Sterling	38.95	77.45	322	9	14	93	75	90	74	88	73	76	87	75	85	73	125	81	72	120	80	21.0
Washington, R. Reagan A	38.85	77.03	66	15	20	95	76	92	76	89	74	78	88	76	86	75	132	83	74	127	81	16.6
WASHINGTON																						
Bellingham	48.80	122.53	157	15	21	79	65	76	64	74	62	65	75	63	72	60	78	70	59	74	67	16.7
Hanford	46.57	119.60	732	5	12	100	67	96	65	93	64	66	94	65	90	56	68	75	53	62	74	26.5
Olympia	46.97	122.90	200	18	23	87	67	83	65	79	64	66	81	64	78	60	76	71	58	73	69	25.2
Quillayute	47.95	124.55	203	23	27	80	62	74	61	70	59	62	72	60	67	58	74	63	57	71	62	15.4
Seattle, Intl Airport	47.45	122.30	449	23	28	85	65	81	64	78	62	65	79	63	76	59	74	69	57	71	68	18.3
Spokane, Fairchild AFB	47.62	117.65	2461	1	7	92	62	89	61	85	60	63	84	61	82	55	71	68	53	67	67	26.1
Stampede Pass	47.28	121.33	3967	3	10	78	57	74	56	71	54	57	71	56	69	51	65	61	50	62	58	16.0
Tacoma, McChord AFB	47.13	122.48	322	18	24	86	65	82	63	78	62	65	80	63	76	59	76	70	58	72	68	22.5
Walla Walla	46.10	118.28	1204	4	12	98	66	95	65	92	64	67	91	65	88	58	76	72	57	71	72	27.0
Wenatchee	47.40	120.20	1243	3	9	95	67	92	65	88	63	66	89	64	85	57	73	75	55	68	74	25.2
Yakima	46.57	120.53	1066	4	11	95	65	92	64	88	63	66	89	64	86	57	71	74	55	67	72	31.1
WEST VIRGINIA																						
Bluefield	37.30	81.20	2858	5	12	85	69	83	69	80	67	71	79	70	77	68	116	75	67	111	73	16.4
Charleston	38.37	81.60	981	6	11	91	73	88	73	86	71	75	85	74	82	72	123	80	71	118	78	19.1
Elkins	38.88	79.85	1998	−2	5	85	71	83	70	81	69	72	80	71	78	69	116	77	68	111	75	21.1
Huntington	38.37	82.55	837	6	11	91	74	89	73	86	72	76	85	74	83	73	127	81	72	121	79	19.1
Martinsburg	39.40	77.98	558	8	14	94	74	91	73	88	72	75	86	74	85	72	120	80	71	116	79	21.8
Morgantown	39.65	79.92	1247	4	11	89	72	87	71	85	70	74	83	73	82	71	119	78	70	115	76	20.3
Parkersburg	39.35	81.43	860	4	11	91	74	88	72	86	72	75	85	74	82	72	122	80	71	118	78	19.6
WISCONSIN																						
Eau Claire	44.87	91.48	906	−18	−13	90	73	87	71	84	70	74	83	72	81	71	116	80	69	109	78	20.6
Green Bay	44.48	88.13	702	−13	−8	88	73	85	72	82	70	74	82	72	80	71	116	79	69	109	77	20.7
La Crosse	43.87	91.25	663	−14	−8	91	74	88	73	85	71	75	84	74	82	73	125	81	71	117	78	20.1
Madison	43.13	89.33	866	−11	−6	90	73	87	72	84	70	74	84	72	82	71	118	80	69	111	78	21.9
Milwaukee	42.95	87.90	692	−7	−2	89	74	86	72	83	70	74	83	72	81	71	119	80	70	111	78	16.6
Wausau	44.93	89.63	1201	−15	−9	88	71	85	70	82	69	72	82	71	78	69	113	77	68	108	75	19.6
WYOMING																						
Big Piney	42.57	110.10	6969	−22	−15	83	54	80	53	78	52	55	74	53	74	48	64	60	45	57	59	32.8
Casper	42.92	106.47	5289	−13	−5	92	59	89	58	86	58	61	80	60	79	55	78	66	53	73	65	30.4
Cheyenne, Warren AFB	41.15	104.82	6142	−7	0	87	58	85	57	82	57	61	76	60	75	56	85	65	55	80	64	25.7
Cody	44.52	109.02	5095	−14	−7	91	59	87	58	84	57	60	81	58	80	52	69	66	50	64	65	25.4
Gillette	44.35	105.53	4035	−16	−7	94	61	91	61	87	60	63	83	62	82	57	80	69	54	73	68	28.6
Lander	42.82	108.73	5558	−14	−7	90	59	87	58	85	57	61	80	59	80	53	74	68	51	69	67	26.7
Rock Springs	41.60	109.07	6759	−9	−2	86	54	84	54	82	53	57	74	56	74	51	71	61	49	66	61	27.7
Sheridan	44.77	106.97	3967	−14	−8	93	62	90	61	86	61	64	83	63	81	58	82	71	56	76	69	29.1
Worland	43.97	107.95	4245	−22	−13	96	63	93	63	90	62	66	86	64	84	59	86	75	57	80	73	31.0

Lat. = North latitude, Long. = West Longitude DB = Dry bulb temperature °F, Elev. = Elevation ft DP = dewpoint temperature °F MWB = mean coincident wet-bulb temperature°F, MDB = mean coincident dry-bulb temperature °F, W= humidity ratio, grains of moisture per lb of dry air.

Table 19-2. Air Conditioning Design Data—Canada

Station	Location			Heating		Cooling						Evaporation				Dehumidification						Range of
				99.6%	99%	0.4%		1%		2%		1%		2%		1%			2%			
	Lat.	Long.	Elev.	DB	DB	DB	MWB	DB	MWB	DB	MWB	DB	MWB	DB	MWB	DP	W	MDB	DP	W	MDB	DB
ALBERTA																						
Calgary Intl	51.12	114.02	3556	−22	−17	83	60	80	59	77	57	61	75	59	73	55	74	65	53	69	64	22.0
Cold Lake	54.42	110.28	1785	−31	−26	82	64	78	62	75	60	64	76	62	72	60	82	69	58	76	67	20.0
Coronation	52.07	111.45	2595	−27	−23	85	62	82	60	78	59	63	78	61	75	58	78	67	56	73	66	22.1
Edmonton Intl Airport	53.30	113.58	2372	−28	−23	82	63	78	62	75	60	64	75	62	73	59	83	69	57	77	66	21.8
Fort McMurray	56.65	111.22	1211	−32	−29	84	64	80	62	76	60	64	76	62	73	59	78	68	57	74	66	22.0
Grande Prairie	55.18	118.88	2195	−32	−27	81	62	78	60	75	58	62	74	60	71	57	76	65	55	71	63	20.9
Lethbridge	49.63	112.80	3048	−22	−16	88	61	84	61	81	60	63	79	61	77	57	78	69	55	73	67	24.8
Medicine Hat	50.02	110.72	2349	−24	−19	90	63	87	62	84	61	64	83	62	80	58	78	69	56	72	68	25.0
Peace River	56.23	117.43	1873	−32	−27	81	62	78	60	75	59	62	75	60	71	58	76	67	56	71	65	21.4
Red Deer	52.18	113.90	2969	−27	−21	82	62	79	61	76	59	63	75	61	73	58	80	69	56	74	66	22.9
Rocky Mtn. House	52.43	114.92	3245	−25	−20	80	62	78	61	75	59	63	75	61	72	58	81	68	56	76	66	22.5
Vermilion	53.35	110.83	2028	−30	−25	83	64	80	62	77	61	64	77	62	74	60	83	69	58	77	67	22.0
Whitecourt	54.15	115.78	2566	−30	−24	80	61	77	60	74	59	62	74	60	71	58	80	67	57	75	64	23.4
BRITISH COLUMBIA																						
Abbotsford	49.03	122.37	190	15	20	85	67	80	66	77	64	66	79	64	76	61	80	73	59	76	70	21.4
Cape St. James	51.93	131.02	302	25	29	64	59	62	58	60	57	59	61	58	60	58	71	59	57	69	59	7.6
Castlegar	49.30	117.63	1624	5	9	92	64	88	63	84	62	65	83	63	81	59	78	70	57	74	68	27.9
Comox	49.72	124.90	79	21	25	80	63	76	62	73	61	63	74	62	71	59	75	66	58	71	65	16.4
Cranbrook	49.60	115.78	3081	−15	−8	88	61	85	60	81	59	62	80	60	78	55	72	66	53	67	65	24.8
Fort Nelson	58.83	122.58	1253	−33	−30	82	62	78	60	75	59	62	74	60	72	58	75	66	56	70	64	21.1
Fort St. John	56.23	120.73	2280	−30	−25	79	61	76	59	73	58	61	72	59	70	57	74	65	55	69	63	18.7
Kamloops	50.70	120.45	1135	−8	−1	93	65	88	63	85	62	65	85	63	81	57	74	69	56	69	68	24.7
Penticton	49.47	119.60	1129	5	10	90	65	87	64	83	63	65	83	64	81	59	76	72	57	72	71	26.5
Port Hardy	50.68	127.37	72	22	26	68	59	65	58	63	57	59	64	58	62	57	69	61	56	67	60	12.4
Prince George	53.88	122.68	2267	−25	−18	81	60	78	59	74	58	61	74	59	71	56	73	64	54	67	62	23.2
Prince Rupert	54.30	130.43	112	7	13	66	58	63	57	61	56	58	62	57	60	57	69	60	56	66	59	10.4
Quesnel	53.03	122.52	1788	−22	−14	85	62	81	60	77	59	62	77	61	74	57	75	65	56	71	63	25.4
Sandspit	53.25	131.82	20	21	25	68	60	65	59	63	58	60	64	59	62	58	71	61	57	69	60	8.6
Smithers	54.82	127.18	1716	−19	−12	81	61	77	59	73	58	61	74	59	71	56	70	64	54	65	62	22.0
Spring Island	50.12	127.93	322	29	31	68	60	66	59	63	58	60	64	59	62	58	74	61	57	71	60	8.8
Terrace	54.47	128.58	712	−2	2	83	62	78	60	74	59	62	76	60	72	56	69	64	55	65	64	17.1
Tofino	49.08	125.77	79	25	29	72	62	68	60	66	58	60	67	59	64	58	73	62	57	71	60	12.2
Vancouver Intl	49.18	123.17	7	18	24	76	65	74	64	71	62	64	72	63	70	61	79	70	60	76	68	14.0
Victoria Intl Airport	48.65	123.43	62	23	26	79	63	75	62	72	61	63	74	61	71	58	71	67	57	69	65	18.4
Williams Lake	52.18	122.05	3084	−20	−14	83	59	79	57	75	56	59	75	57	72	53	67	61	51	62	60	22.0
MANITOBA																						
Brandon	49.92	99.95	1342	−29	−24	87	67	84	66	80	65	69	80	66	77	65	97	74	62	88	72	23.6
Churchill	58.75	94.07	95	−36	−33	77	62	72	60	67	58	61	70	58	66	56	68	65	53	60	62	16.7
Dauphin	51.10	100.05	1001	−28	−23	87	67	84	66	80	64	68	80	66	77	64	94	74	62	86	72	22.1
Portage La Prairie	49.90	98.27	883	−25	−21	88	68	85	67	81	65	69	80	68	78	66	99	75	64	92	73	20.5
The Pas	53.97	101.10	889	−32	−28	83	66	79	64	76	62	66	76	64	73	62	85	70	60	80	68	18.4
Thompson	55.80	97.87	715	−38	−34	83	64	79	62	76	60	64	75	62	73	60	78	69	58	73	66	23.0
Winnipeg Intl	49.90	97.23	784	−27	−23	87	68	84	67	81	66	70	80	68	78	66	99	75	64	92	73	20.5
NEW BRUNSWICK																						
Charlo	47.98	66.33	125	−14	−10	83	68	79	66	75	65	68	76	66	73	66	97	72	64	90	70	18.4
Chatham	47.00	65.45	102	−12	−7	86	69	83	67	79	65	69	78	68	75	67	98	73	65	92	71	20.3
Fredericton	45.87	66.53	66	−12	−7	86	69	83	68	79	66	70	79	68	76	67	99	75	65	93	72	20.7
Moncton	46.12	64.68	233	−10	−5	83	68	80	67	77	65	69	77	68	74	67	99	73	65	93	71	19.4
Saint John	45.32	65.88	358	−9	−4	78	65	75	64	72	62	66	72	64	69	64	90	69	62	84	66	16.9
NEWFOUNDLAND																						
Battle Harbour	52.30	55.83	26	−14	−10	65	58	60	55	58	53	56	60	54	57	54	62	58	52	57	55	10.4
Bonavista	48.67	53.12	89	3	7	74	65	71	63	68	62	65	69	63	67	63	85	68	61	80	66	11.7
Cartwright	53.70	57.03	46	−18	−15	75	62	70	59	67	58	61	68	59	66	57	70	65	55	64	63	17.5
Daniels Harbour	50.23	57.58	62	−7	−3	69	63	66	62	65	61	63	66	62	64	62	83	65	60	78	63	9.7
Deer Lake	49.22	57.40	72	−13	−7	81	66	77	64	74	62	66	74	65	71	64	88	71	61	81	69	21.4
Gander Intl Airport	48.95	54.57	495	−4	0	79	65	76	63	72	62	66	72	64	70	63	88	70	61	83	68	17.8
Goose	53.32	60.37	160	−24	−20	81	63	77	61	73	60	63	73	61	71	59	76	68	57	71	65	18.2
Hopedale	55.45	60.23	26	−21	−18	70	59	65	57	61	55	58	64	55	61	54	62	61	52	57	59	12.6
St. Johns	47.62	52.73	459	3	7	76	65	73	64	70	63	66	71	64	68	64	92	69	62	85	67	15.7
Stephenville	48.53	58.55	85	−2	3	74	64	70	63	67	63	65	69	64	68	64	88	68	62	83	66	12.4
Wabush Lake	52.93	66.87	1808	−33	−30	76	60	72	58	68	57	61	69	59	66	58	76	63	56	70	62	16.9
NORTHWEST TERRITORIES																						
Cape Parry	70.17	124.68	56	−34	−33	58	53	54	50	50	47	50	53	47	50	47	48	52	45	43	50	9.7
Fort Smith	60.02	111.95	666	−34	−32	82	63	78	61	75	60	63	75	61	72	59	76	67	57	71	66	21.4
Inuvik UA	68.30	133.48	223	−43	−40	78	60	75	59	71	57	60	72	58	69	53	61	65	52	57	64	18.4
Norman Wells	65.28	126.80	243	−40	−36	80	62	77	60	74	59	62	74	60	71	57	71	66	56	67	65	18.5
Yellowknife	62.47	114.45	676	−39	−36	77	60	74	59	70	57	60	71	59	68	56	68	65	53	62	63	14.4
NUNAVUT																						
Baker Lake	64.30	96.08	59	−41	−39	69	57	65	55	61	53	56	63	54	60	52	57	59	50	53	57	16.4
Cambridge Bay	69.10	105.12	89	−38	−35	60	53	57	51	53	48	51	56	49	53	48	50	53	46	46	51	12.4
Chesterfield	63.33	90.72	36	−35	−34	66	54	60	52	56	50	52	60	50	56	48	49	55	46	46	52	13.7
Coral Harbour	64.20	83.37	210	−40	−38	64	53	60	51	56	50	52	59	50	56	48	50	55	46	46	52	14.8
Hall Beach	68.78	81.25	26	−42	−38	56	50	52	47	49	45	48	52	45	49	44	42	50	42	39	47	9.9
Iqaluit (Frobisher)	63.75	68.55	108	−39	−36	60	50	57	48	53	46	49	55	47	53	44	43	52	42	40	50	12.4
Resolute	74.72	94.98	220	−42	−40	50	45	48	43	44	41	43	47	41	44	40	36	45	38	34	43	8.5

Table 19-2. *(Continued)* Air Conditioning Design Data—Canada

Station	Lat.	Long.	Elev.	Heating 99.6% DB	99% DB	Cooling 0.4% DB	MWB	1% DB	MWB	2% DB	MWB	Evaporation 1% DB	MWB	2% DB	MWB	Dehumidification 1% DP	W	MDB	2% DP	W	MDB	Range of DB
NOVA SCOTIA																						
Greenwood	44.98	64.92	92	−2	3	84	69	80	67	78	66	70	77	69	75	68	102	74	66	96	72	20.0
Halifax Intl Airport	44.88	63.50	476	−2	2	80	68	78	66	75	64	69	74	67	72	67	99	71	65	95	69	16.7
Sable Island	43.93	60.02	13	14	17	70	67	69	66	67	65	67	68	66	67	66	97	68	65	92	66	8.3
Shearwater	44.63	63.50	167	1	5	78	66	75	64	72	63	67	72	66	69	66	96	69	65	92	68	13.1
Sydney	46.17	60.05	203	−1	3	81	68	78	67	75	65	69	75	67	72	67	99	72	65	93	70	17.3
Truro	45.37	63.27	131	−9	−4	79	69	77	67	75	66	69	75	68	72	68	102	73	66	97	70	19.3
Yarmouth	43.83	66.08	141	7	10	73	66	71	64	69	63	66	69	64	67	65	93	68	63	86	66	13.1
ONTARIO																						
Armstrong	50.30	89.03	1152	−33	−30	81	66	78	65	75	63	67	75	65	73	64	94	71	61	85	69	24.7
Atikokan	48.75	91.62	1289	−31	−27	84	67	80	66	77	64	69	77	67	74	66	102	73	64	95	71	23.0
Big Trout Lake	53.83	89.87	735	−32	−30	79	64	75	62	72	61	65	72	63	70	62	84	68	60	78	67	16.4
Earlton	47.70	79.85	797	−27	−21	85	69	81	67	78	65	69	77	67	75	67	101	74	65	95	72	21.6
Geraldton	49.78	86.93	1152	−32	−28	81	66	78	65	75	63	67	75	65	73	65	97	72	62	87	69	22.1
Gore Bay	45.88	82.57	633	−12	−7	80	68	78	67	75	65	69	75	68	73	67	102	72	66	97	71	16.4
Kapuskasing	49.42	82.47	745	−30	−25	84	67	80	65	77	64	68	77	66	74	65	95	72	62	87	70	22.5
Kenora	49.78	94.37	1348	−27	−22	84	67	81	65	78	64	68	77	66	75	66	99	73	63	92	72	16.4
London	43.03	81.15	912	−3	2	85	71	83	70	80	69	72	80	71	77	70	113	77	68	108	75	19.8
Mount Forest	43.98	80.75	1362	−7	−3	83	70	80	68	77	67	70	77	69	75	68	109	74	67	103	73	20.3
Muskoka	44.97	79.30	925	−17	−11	84	69	80	68	78	66	70	77	68	75	68	106	74	66	100	72	20.7
North Bay	46.35	79.43	1217	−18	−13	81	67	78	66	76	64	68	75	67	73	66	102	72	65	96	70	17.1
Ottawa Intl	45.32	75.67	374	−13	−8	86	70	83	69	80	67	71	80	69	78	68	106	76	67	99	75	18.5
Sault Ste. Marie	46.48	84.52	630	−13	−8	83	69	79	67	76	65	69	76	67	74	67	102	73	65	95	71	20.9
Simcoe	42.85	80.27	791	−2	3	85	72	83	70	80	69	72	80	71	77	70	112	77	68	107	75	19.3
Sioux Lookout	50.12	91.90	1280	−30	−25	84	67	80	65	78	63	68	76	66	74	65	97	71	63	90	70	18.5
Sudbury	46.62	80.80	1142	−19	−14	84	67	81	66	78	64	68	77	66	74	66	99	72	64	92	71	19.9
Thunder Bay	48.37	89.32	653	−22	−18	84	68	80	66	77	64	68	77	66	73	65	93	72	62	86	70	21.3
Timmins	48.57	81.37	968	−28	−23	84	67	81	65	78	64	68	77	66	74	65	95	72	63	88	70	23.9
Toronto Intl	43.67	79.63	568	−4	1	87	71	84	70	81	68	72	80	70	78	69	110	77	68	104	75	20.1
Trenton	44.12	77.53	282	−8	−3	84	71	81	70	78	68	72	78	70	76	70	110	76	68	104	74	18.0
Wiarton	44.75	81.10	728	−5	0	82	70	80	69	77	67	70	77	69	75	68	106	75	67	101	73	18.0
Windsor	42.27	82.97	623	2	6	89	73	86	71	83	70	74	83	73	80	71	118	79	70	112	77	17.5
PRINCE EDWARD ISLAND																						
Charlottetown	46.28	63.13	177	−6	−2	79	69	77	67	74	65	69	74	67	72	67	99	72	65	94	71	15.1
Summerside	46.43	63.83	79	−5	−1	79	68	77	66	74	65	69	74	67	72	67	99	72	65	94	70	14.4
QUEBEC																						
Bagotville	48.33	71.00	522	−23	−19	84	67	80	65	77	63	68	76	66	74	65	93	72	62	85	70	19.8
Baie Comeau	49.13	68.20	72	−19	−14	75	63	71	61	69	60	63	69	61	67	61	79	66	59	75	64	17.1
Grindstone Island	47.38	61.87	194	−1	3	73	66	70	65	68	64	67	69	65	68	66	95	69	64	90	68	8.6
Kuujjuarapik	55.28	77.77	39	−33	−30	75	61	70	59	66	57	61	68	58	65	57	69	64	54	62	62	15.8
Kuujuaq	58.10	68.42	121	−34	−31	74	60	69	57	65	55	59	66	56	64	55	65	63	52	58	60	18.7
La Grande Riviere	53.63	77.70	640	−33	−30	78	62	75	60	71	58	62	70	60	68	59	77	65	57	70	63	21.2
Lake Eon	51.87	63.28	1841	−31	−27	74	60	70	58	67	57	61	67	59	64	58	78	63	57	74	62	16.4
Mont Joli	48.60	68.22	171	−12	−8	80	67	76	65	74	64	67	75	65	72	64	90	72	62	83	70	16.4
Montreal Intl	45.47	73.75	118	−12	−7	85	71	83	70	80	68	72	80	70	77	69	106	77	67	101	75	17.6
Montreal Mirabel	45.68	74.03	269	−16	−11	84	71	81	69	78	67	71	78	69	76	68	103	75	66	98	73	20.2
Nitchequon	53.20	70.90	1759	−33	−31	72	60	69	58	66	57	61	65	59	64	59	79	63	57	74	62	14.0
Quebec	46.80	71.38	240	−16	−11	84	70	80	68	78	66	70	77	68	75	68	103	75	66	95	73	19.1
Riviere Du Loup	47.80	69.55	486	−13	−10	79	68	76	67	74	65	69	74	67	72	67	99	72	65	93	70	15.5
Roberval	48.52	72.27	587	−23	−19	83	68	79	66	76	65	69	77	67	74	66	98	74	64	92	72	17.8
Schefferville	54.80	66.82	1709	−33	−31	74	58	69	57	66	55	59	66	57	64	56	71	62	53	64	60	16.0
Sept–Iles	50.22	66.27	180	−20	−15	72	60	69	59	67	58	62	67	60	65	60	77	64	58	73	62	13.9
Sherbrooke	45.43	71.68	791	−20	−14	84	70	80	68	78	66	70	78	68	75	67	103	75	66	97	73	22.3
St. Hubert	45.52	73.42	89	−12	−7	86	71	83	70	80	68	72	80	70	78	69	106	77	67	101	75	19.1
Ste. Agathe Des Monts	46.05	74.28	1296	−19	−15	81	68	78	66	76	65	69	75	67	73	67	103	72	65	97	70	19.4
Val dOr	48.07	77.78	1106	−27	−22	83	67	80	65	78	63	68	76	66	73	65	95	72	62	88	70	20.7
SASKATCHEWAN																						
Broadview	50.38	102.68	1975	−30	−25	87	65	83	64	79	63	66	79	64	76	62	89	71	60	83	70	23.8
Estevan	49.22	102.97	1906	−25	−21	90	66	86	65	83	64	68	81	66	79	63	92	73	61	86	71	23.8
Moose Jaw	50.33	105.55	1893	−26	−21	90	64	87	64	83	62	66	81	64	79	61	85	71	59	79	69	23.8
North Battleford	52.77	108.25	1798	−31	−26	86	64	82	63	78	61	65	78	63	76	60	83	69	58	77	68	21.1
Prince Albert	53.22	105.68	1404	−34	−29	84	65	81	64	78	62	65	77	64	75	61	84	71	59	78	69	21.8
Regina	50.43	104.67	1893	−29	−24	89	64	85	64	82	62	66	80	64	78	61	85	71	59	79	69	23.6
Saskatoon	52.17	106.68	1654	−31	−26	87	64	84	63	80	62	65	79	63	77	60	82	70	58	76	68	22.7
Swift Current	50.28	107.68	2684	−25	−21	88	63	84	62	80	61	64	79	62	77	59	82	68	57	76	67	23.0
Uranium City	59.57	108.48	1043	−38	−35	79	62	76	60	72	58	62	72	60	69	58	74	66	56	69	64	17.1
Wynyard	51.77	104.20	1841	−29	−25	85	64	81	64	78	62	65	77	63	75	61	85	70	59	81	68	20.7
Yorkton	51.27	102.47	1634	−30	−26	86	65	82	64	79	62	66	78	64	75	62	87	71	60	81	69	22.0
YUKON TERRITORY																						
Burwash	61.37	139.05	2644	−34	−32	73	57	69	55	66	53	56	68	54	64	50	58	58	48	55	57	21.4
Whitehorse	60.72	135.07	2306	−34	−31	77	57	73	55	69	53	56	70	55	67	50	58	59	48	55	58	20.9

Lat. = North latitude, Long. = West Longitude DB = Dry bulb temperature °F, Elev. = Elevation ft DP = dewpoint temperature °F MWB = mean coincident wet-bulb temperature°F, MDB = mean coincident dry-bulb temperature °F, W= humidity ratio, grains of moisture per lb of dry air.

Table 19-3. Air Conditioning Design Data—World Locations

Station	Lat.	Long.	Elev.	99.6% DB	99% DB	0.4% DB	0.4% MWB	1% DB	1% MWB	2% DB	2% MWB	1% DB	1% MWB	2% DB	2% MWB	1% DP	1% W	1% MDB	2% DP	2% W	2% MDB	Range of DB
ALGERIA																						
Algiers	36.72N	3.25E	82	36	38	95	71	92	71	89	72	76	85	75	83	73	125	81	72	118	80	20.9
Annaba	36.83N	7.82E	13	39	41	94	71	90	72	87	73	77	83	76	83	75	130	81	73	125	80	17.1
Biskra	34.80N	5.73E	285	41	43	108	69	106	69	103	69	71	97	71	96	63	86	82	61	82	83	20.0
Constantine	36.28N	6.62E	2276	31	33	100	66	96	67	93	66	70	87	69	86	65	100	76	63	94	75	27.0
El Golea	30.57N	2.87E	1302	33	35	109	69	107	68	104	68	71	101	69	99	60	80	84	58	76	85	25.7
Oran	35.63N	0.60W	295	35	38	92	69	89	69	86	69	74	83	73	81	72	119	79	71	115	79	18.4
Tebessa	35.48N	8.13E	2667	29	31	99	65	97	64	94	64	68	87	67	86	62	92	72	61	88	72	27.2
ARGENTINA																						
Buenos Aires	34.82S	58.53W	65	31	34	93	73	90	72	87	71	75	84	74	83	72	120	79	71	115	78	21.6
Comodoro Rivadavia	45.78S	67.50W	150	29	31	87	61	84	60	80	58	62	78	60	76	55	65	64	53	60	65	18.7
Cordoba	31.32S	64.22W	1555	31	34	94	73	91	72	89	71	76	86	74	84	72	127	82	71	120	80	21.1
Junin Airport	34.55S	60.95W	266	30	32	92	72	89	71	87	71	74	84	73	83	72	118	78	70	111	77	21.6
Formosa	26.20S	58.23W	196	40	44	98	76	96	76	94	76	80	90	79	89	77	141	84	76	136	83	18.5
Marcos Juarez	32.70S	62.15W	374	29	32	95	74	92	74	90	73	77	87	75	85	74	129	82	73	123	80	22.1
Mendoza	32.83S	68.78W	2309	30	33	96	68	93	67	91	67	71	87	70	85	66	106	80	65	100	79	22.1
Paso De Los Libres	29.68S	57.15W	229	36	39	96	74	94	75	92	73	78	88	76	86	75	132	83	74	126	82	20.2
Posadas	27.37S	55.97W	410	39	43	97	76	95	76	93	75	79	90	78	89	76	136	85	75	132	84	19.1
Reconquista	29.18S	59.67W	173	37	40	96	78	94	77	91	76	80	89	79	87	77	144	86	76	138	84	17.8
Resistencia	27.45S	59.05W	170	35	39	98	76	95	76	93	76	79	90	78	88	77	140	85	76	134	83	20.2
Rio Gallegos	51.62S	69.28W	62	17	22	76	57	72	55	70	54	57	70	55	67	51	56	61	49	52	60	19.4
Rosario	32.92S	60.78W	82	30	33	93	74	90	73	88	72	76	85	75	83	74	125	81	72	119	79	20.5
Salta Airport	24.85S	65.48W	3990	30	33	89	65	87	66	84	66	71	80	70	79	68	119	76	67	115	74	19.1
San Juan	31.57S	68.42W	1961	28	31	100	69	97	68	94	68	72	91	71	89	66	102	82	64	97	81	23.8
San Miguel De Tucuman	26.85S	65.10W	1476	37	40	96	74	93	74	91	74	78	88	76	87	75	138	84	74	132	83	17.5
ARMENIA																						
Yerevan	40.13N	44.47E	2919	7	11	96	69	94	69	91	67	70	90	69	88	63	95	82	61	90	81	24.5
ASCENSION ISLAND																						
Georgetown	7.97S	14.40W	259	69	70	86	75	85	75	85	75	76	83	76	82	74	130	80	74	126	80	7.7
AUSTRALIA																						
Adelaide	34.93S	138.52E	13	39	41	95	64	92	64	88	63	68	81	66	80	64	89	73	61	81	72	19.4
Alice Springs	23.80S	133.90E	1774	34	36	104	65	102	64	100	64	72	83	71	83	69	115	77	67	104	77	24.7
Brisbane	27.38S	153.10E	16	44	46	88	72	86	72	84	72	76	82	75	81	74	126	80	73	121	79	13.7
Cairns	16.88S	145.75E	22	56	59	91	78	90	77	88	77	80	87	79	86	78	146	84	77	141	83	13.1
Canberra	35.30S	149.18E	1893	26	29	90	63	87	63	83	62	66	78	65	77	62	90	70	60	84	68	23.9
Darwin	12.40S	130.87E	98	64	66	93	75	92	76	91	76	81	88	81	87	79	152	85	79	151	85	13.0
Kalgoorlie/Boulder	30.77S	121.45E	1181	36	38	102	65	99	64	95	63	68	85	67	86	63	90	71	61	84	71	24.5
Learmonth	22.23S	114.08E	19	49	51	105	70	102	70	99	70	78	87	77	87	76	134	83	74	127	83	23.6
Perth	31.93S	115.95E	95	41	43	99	67	95	66	91	65	70	85	69	83	66	95	74	64	91	74	22.5
Port Hedland	20.37S	118.62E	19	51	54	105	71	102	71	100	71	81	91	81	90	79	151	86	78	147	86	19.3
Sydney Intl Airport	33.95S	151.18E	10	42	44	90	68	85	67	82	68	72	79	71	78	70	111	76	69	107	75	12.1
Townsville	19.25S	146.75E	19	48	52	92	76	91	76	89	76	80	87	79	85	78	147	84	77	141	83	11.7
AUSTRIA																						
Aigen/Ennstal (Mil)	47.53N	14.13E	2129	2	7	82	66	79	64	76	63	66	76	64	74	61	88	72	60	83	69	20.0
Graz	47.00N	15.43E	1138	5	12	85	69	82	68	79	65	69	78	67	77	66	99	73	64	94	71	20.5
Innsbruck	47.27N	11.35E	1945	10	14	85	65	82	64	79	62	65	78	64	74	61	86	67	59	81	67	20.5
Klagenfurt	46.65N	14.33E	1482	4	9	85	66	82	65	79	63	66	79	65	76	62	88	71	61	84	68	23.0
Linz	48.23N	14.20E	1026	5	12	85	66	82	64	79	63	67	77	65	74	63	90	69	62	88	68	19.6
Salzburg	47.80N	13.00E	1476	7	12	86	67	82	65	79	64	66	80	65	77	61	85	71	60	83	70	18.9
Vienna, Hohe Warte	48.25N	16.37E	656	12	17	86	68	83	67	80	66	69	80	67	77	65	94	73	64	90	72	16.7
Vienna, Schwechat	48.12N	16.57E	623	9	14	86	67	83	66	80	65	67	79	66	78	63	88	72	62	83	71	19.1
Zeltweg	47.20N	14.75E	2237	0	5	82	66	79	65	76	63	66	76	64	74	62	89	72	60	85	69	21.1
AZORES																						
Lajes	38.77N	27.10W	180	46	48	80	71	78	71	77	69	72	77	71	75	70	111	75	69	106	74	11.3
BAHAMAS																						
Nassau	25.05N	77.47W	22	57	60	91	79	90	78	89	78	80	87	80	87	79	150	83	78	144	83	12.4
BAHRAIN																						
AlManamah	26.27N	50.65E	6	52	54	103	77	101	78	99	79	86	94	85	93	84	181	92	84	176	92	12.4
BELARUS																						
Babruysk (Bobruysk)	53.12N	29.25E	541	−9	2	82	65	79	65	76	63	67	76	65	74	63	88	71	61	83	69	20.7
Homyel (Gomel)	52.45N	31.00E	416	6	0	83	66	80	65	77	64	67	76	65	74	64	89	71	62	84	70	16.2
Hrodna (Grodno)	53.68N	23.83E	442	5	1	82	66	78	64	75	63	66	75	64	73	63	87	71	61	81	69	19.4
Mahilyow (Mogilev)	53.90N	30.32E	633	9	3	80	66	77	64	75	63	66	76	64	72	63	88	70	61	83	68	16.9
Minsk	53.87N	27.53E	767	5	0	81	65	78	64	75	62	66	75	64	73	62	85	69	60	80	69	17.3
Vitsyebsk (Vitebsk)	55.17N	30.13E	577	8	2	80	65	77	64	74	63	66	74	64	72	63	88	70	61	83	68	15.1
BELGIUM/LUXEMBOURG																						
Antwerp	51.20N	4.47E	45	16	21	82	68	79	66	76	65	68	77	66	74	65	91	73	63	85	71	16.2

Table 19-3. *(Continued)* Air Conditioning Design Data—World Locations

Station	Location Lat.	Location Long.	Location Elev.	Heating 99.6% DB	Heating 99% DB	Cooling 0.4% DB	Cooling 0.4% MWB	Cooling 1% DB	Cooling 1% MWB	Cooling 2% DB	Cooling 2% MWB	Evaporation 1% DB	Evaporation 1% MWB	Evaporation 2% DB	Evaporation 2% MWB	Dehumidification 1% DP	Dehumidification 1% W	Dehumidification 1% MDB	Dehumidification 2% DP	Dehumidification 2% W	Dehumidification 2% MDB	Range of DB
Brussels	50.90N	4.53E	190	15	21	82	67	79	66	76	65	68	77	66	74	64	90	72	62	85	71	16.9
Charleroi	50.47N	4.45E	629	15	21	82	67	79	65	76	64	67	76	65	73	63	89	71	62	85	69	16.7
Florennes	50.23N	4.65E	980	13	19	80	66	77	65	74	63	66	75	65	72	63	90	70	62	85	68	16.2
Koksijde	51.08N	2.65E	29	17	22	79	67	75	65	72	64	66	73	65	71	64	88	70	62	83	68	15.1
Luxembourg	49.62N	6.22E	1243	13	18	82	65	79	63	76	62	65	76	64	72	62	87	68	60	82	67	17.1
Oostende	51.20N	2.87E	16	18	22	77	66	73	65	70	63	66	72	64	70	64	88	69	62	83	67	14.0
Saint Hubert	50.03N	5.40E	1827	11	16	77	64	74	62	72	61	64	72	62	69	61	85	67	59	80	65	14.6
BENIN																					
Cotonou	6.35N	2.38E	29	71	72	90	79	89	80	89	80	81	88	81	87	80	153	85	79	151	85	8.6
Parakou	9.35N	2.62E	1289	65	67	98	71	97	71	95	71	78	90	77	89	74	135	84	74	132	83	20.7
BERMUDA																					
Hamilton, Bermuda	32.37N	64.68W	9	55	57	88	78	88	78	86	77	80	85	79	84	78	144	83	77	141	83	8.3
BOLIVIA																					
Cochabamba	17.45S	66.10W	8303	35	37	84	56	83	56	81	56	60	76	59	74	56	91	62	55	90	62	27.0
La Paz	16.52S	68.18W	13169	25	27	63	44	62	44	61	43	48	57	47	56	44	71	50	43	68	49	22.7
BOSNIA–HERZEGOVINA																					
Banja Luka	44.78N	17.22E	511	10	16	92	69	88	69	85	67	71	83	69	81	66	99	76	65	94	73	22.9
BRAZIL																					
Arch De Fernando	3.85S	32.42W	183	73	74	88	78	87	78	86	77	79	85	79	85	77	144	83	77	141	83	8.1
Belem	1.38S	48.48W	52	72	73	92	78	90	78	90	78	80	87	80	87	79	149	84	77	143	83	14.8
Brasilia	15.87S	47.93W	3480	48	51	89	65	88	65	86	65	70	79	70	79	68	118	72	68	116	72	23.4
Campinas	23.00S	47.13W	2168	47	50	92	73	90	71	88	72	75	84	74	83	73	134	78	72	128	77	17.8
Campo Grande	20.47S	54.67W	1824	46	50	95	71	93	71	92	71	76	86	76	86	74	134	80	73	132	79	18.4
Caravelas	17.63S	39.25W	13	61	63	89	77	88	77	87	77	78	85	78	85	77	140	81	76	137	80	13.7
Curitiba	25.52S	49.17W	2979	36	40	87	69	85	68	83	68	72	80	71	78	70	123	74	69	119	74	17.5
Fortaleza	3.78S	38.53W	82	72	73	90	78	90	78	89	78	80	87	79	86	79	149	81	77	143	81	11.2
Goiania	16.63S	49.22W	2450	53	55	93	67	92	68	91	68	74	84	73	84	71	125	77	70	123	76	23.0
Maceio	9.52S	35.78W	377	67	68	90	75	89	75	88	75	78	84	77	84	76	136	80	75	134	80	14.2
Manaus, E. Gomes A	3.03S	60.05W	6	70	71	97	78	95	78	94	78	82	89	81	88	80	158	85	79	151	83	20.3
Manaus, Ponta Pelada	3.15S	59.98W	275	71	73	94	77	93	78	92	78	80	88	80	88	79	151	84	78	146	83	14.2
Natal	5.92S	35.25W	170	70	71	90	78	90	77	89	77	79	86	79	86	77	142	82	77	141	82	12.2
Porto Alegre	30.00S	51.18W	9	40	43	95	76	92	75	90	74	77	87	76	86	75	132	82	74	126	80	17.1
Recife	8.07S	34.85W	62	70	71	92	78	91	78	90	78	79	88	79	88	77	142	83	77	140	83	11.3
Rio De Janeiro, Galeao	22.82S	43.25W	19	59	61	102	79	99	77	97	77	81	94	80	91	77	142	84	77	141	84	19.3
Salvador	12.90S	38.33W	19	68	70	90	78	88	78	88	78	80	86	79	85	77	142	84	77	141	84	10.8
Santarem	2.43S	54.72W	236	72	73	93	77	92	77	91	78	80	88	79	88	77	144	82	77	143	82	14.0
Sao Paulo	23.62S	46.65W	2634	48	50	89	69	88	69	86	69	72	81	71	80	70	122	75	69	120	75	14.9
Vitoria	20.27S	40.28W	13	61	63	93	77	92	77	90	77	79	87	78	86	77	141	81	76	137	82	14.6
BULGARIA																					
Botevgrad	42.67N	24.83E	7837	−7	−2	60	49	57	48	55	47	50	54	49	53	49	68	52	47	64	50	7.7
Burgas	42.48N	27.48E	91	17	21	87	72	84	71	82	69	73	81	71	79	70	111	77	68	104	76	20.0
Lom	43.82N	23.25E	108	14	18	90	74	87	72	85	71	73	85	72	83	69	108	81	68	102	79	19.1
Musala	42.18N	23.58E	9603	−10	−4	56	44	53	43	51	42	45	51	44	49	43	58	47	41	55	46	9.2
Plovdiv	42.13N	24.75E	606	14	19	93	70	90	70	87	69	72	87	70	84	66	99	80	65	94	78	21.4
Ruse	43.85N	25.95E	147	12	16	94	73	91	71	88	70	72	88	71	86	67	100	80	66	95	78	20.7
Sofia	42.65N	23.38E	1952	10	14	88	66	85	65	82	64	67	82	65	80	61	87	72	60	83	72	21.8
Varna	43.20N	27.92E	141	17	20	85	72	83	71	81	70	73	80	71	79	70	112	78	69	106	77	17.3
BRUNEI																					
Brunei Intl Airport	4.93N	114.93E	49	71	72	92	79	92	79	91	79	82	88	81	88	80	155	85	79	152	85	14.0
CANARY ISLANDS																					
Las Palmas	27.93N	15.38W	82	55	57	86	68	84	68	81	69	75	78	73	78	73	125	77	72	118	76	9.9
Santa Cruz De Tenerife	28.05N	16.57W	236	57	57	91	68	87	68	84	69	74	81	73	80	71	117	79	70	111	78	12.4
CAPE VERDE																					
Sal Island	16.73N	22.95W	180	63	64	86	75	85	75	84	75	77	82	77	81	76	136	80	75	133	80	8.8
CHILE																					
Antofagasta	23.43S	70.43W	393	50	52	77	68	75	67	74	65	68	74	67	73	66	97	73	65	92	71	10.4
Arica	18.33S	70.33W	193	52	55	83	71	81	69	79	68	72	78	70	78	69	107	78	67	100	76	11.9
Concepcion	36.77S	73.05W	52	35	37	76	63	74	62	72	61	64	71	63	70	61	80	66	60	78	65	20.2
Iquique	20.53S	70.18W	170	54	55	80	68	79	67	78	67	68	78	67	77	65	92	75	64	89	74	11.7
La Serena	29.92S	71.20W	479	42	44	72	63	71	63	70	62	64	70	63	69	61	81	67	60	78	66	11.9
Puerto Montt	41.42S	73.08W	282	28	30	73	62	70	61	68	60	62	68	61	67	60	77	65	58	72	64	17.6
Punta Arenas	53.00S	70.85W	121	23	25	64	54	61	53	59	51	54	60	53	58	51	55	56	49	52	55	13.0
Santiago	33.38S	70.78W	1561	29	32	89	65	88	65	86	64	67	84	66	82	60	81	75	59	78	74	31.5
Temuco	38.75S	72.63W	393	29	31	81	64	78	63	75	61	64	76	62	73	59	76	70	58	72	67	24.7
CHINA																					
Anda	46.38N	125.32E	492	−19	−16	87	69	85	68	82	67	73	80	71	78	71	115	77	69	108	75	14.4
Andirlangar	37.93N	83.65E	4146	−1	2	98	63	96	62	93	61	65	88	63	86	58	83	71	55	76	72	26.9
Anyang	36.12N	114..37E	249	18	21	94	73	92	74	90	74	79	86	78	84	78	144	84	76	138	83	14.4

Table 19-3. *(Continued)* Air Conditioning Design Data—World Locations

Station	Location Lat.	Long.	Elev.	Heating 99.6% DB	99% DB	Cooling 0.4% DB	MWB	1% DB	MWB	2% DB	MWB	Evaporation 1% DB	MWB	2% DB	MWB	Dehumidification 1% DP	W	MDB	2% DP	W	MDB	Range of DB
Baoding	38.85N	115.57E	62	13	16	94	72	91	72	89	73	78	85	77	84	76	139	83	75	132	82	14.8
Bayan Mod	40.75N	104.50E	4360	−5	−1	91	59	89	58	86	57	62	79	60	78	56	80	68	54	74	69	20.7
Beijing	39.93N	116.28E	180	13	15	94	71	91	71	89	71	78	84	76	83	76	134	82	74	130	81	15.7
Bengbu	32.95N	117.37E	72	22	24	95	80	93	79	90	77	82	90	80	88	79	152	87	78	147	86	11.9
Changchun	43.90N	125.22E	780	−12	−9	86	70	84	70	82	69	74	80	72	78	72	123	78	71	116	76	13.5
Changsha (576790)	28.23N	112.87E	223	29	31	96	80	94	80	92	79	81	90	81	90	79	153	86	78	148	85	12.6
Chengdu	30.67N	104.02E	1666	32	34	89	76	87	76	85	75	78	84	77	83	77	148	82	76	144	81	12.2
Dalian	38.90N	121.63E	318	10	13	86	74	84	72	82	72	76	80	75	78	75	132	78	73	126	78	9.9
Dandong	40.05N	124.33E	45	1	5	85	75	82	73	80	72	76	80	75	78	75	131	78	74	126	77	12.2
Datong	40.10N	113.33E	3507	−6	−3	87	63	85	62	82	62	68	77	66	76	65	104	72	63	98	72	19.3
Deqen	28.50N	98.90E	11443	18	20	67	52	65	52	63	52	54	61	54	60	52	90	57	51	87	56	12.1
Dinghai	30.03N	122.12E	121	31	33	90	81	88	80	86	79	81	87	80	85	79	151	85	78	148	84	9.7
Erenhot	43.65N	112.00E	3169	−20	−16	91	61	88	60	85	59	64	78	63	77	60	88	69	58	81	69	21.1
Fuzhou	26.08N	119.28E	278	40	42	96	81	94	80	92	80	81	92	80	90	79	150	88	78	148	86	13.9
Golmud	36.42N	94.90E	9215	0	4	80	52	78	51	75	50	53	72	51	71	45	62	60	43	57	58	18.9
Guangzhou	23.13N	113.32E	26	42	44	94	80	93	79	91	79	81	89	81	88	80	153	84	79	150	84	12.4
Guilin	25.33N	110.30E	544	34	36	94	78	92	78	91	78	80	87	80	87	78	150	83	78	147	83	13.3
Guiyang	26.58N	106.72E	3523	28	30	87	70	85	70	83	70	72	81	72	80	70	126	77	69	123	76	12.6
Hami	42.82N	93.52E	2424	0	3	97	66	94	65	92	64	68	89	66	87	61	87	77	58	80	75	23.9
Hangzhou	30.23N	120.17E	141	28	30	96	81	94	80	92	80	82	91	81	89	79	152	86	79	149	85	13.5
Harbin	45.75N	126.77E	469	−21	−16	87	69	84	68	82	68	74	79	72	78	72	119	78	70	111	76	15.3
Hefei	31.87N	117.23E	118	24	27	95	81	92	80	90	79	82	90	81	89	79	152	87	78	148	86	11.0
Hohhot	40.82N	111.68E	3494	−4	−1	88	64	85	63	82	62	68	77	66	76	65	106	73	63	99	72	18.9
Jinan	36.68N	116.98E	190	18	20	95	73	92	74	90	73	79	87	78	85	76	139	84	75	134	83	13.1
Jingdezhen	29.30N	117.20E	196	28	31	97	80	94	79	93	79	81	91	80	89	78	149	85	78	145	85	14.9
Jinzhou	41.13N	121.12E	229	2	5	88	72	85	71	83	70	76	81	75	79	74	130	79	73	124	79	13.5
Jixi	45.28N	130.95E	767	−14	−10	87	70	83	69	81	68	72	79	71	77	70	113	77	68	106	76	15.1
Kashi	39.47N	75.98E	4235	8	12	92	66	90	65	88	64	68	84	66	83	62	99	76	60	92	75	22.1
Korla	41.75N	86.13E	3061	6	10	95	67	93	65	90	65	68	87	66	86	61	89	78	59	83	76	19.1
Kowloon	22.33N	114.18E	78	48	51	92	79	91	79	90	79	81	87	81	87	79	152	85	79	150	85	8.1
Kunming	25.02N	102.68E	6207	32	34	80	63	78	63	77	63	67	75	67	74	65	118	71	65	116	71	15.3
Lanzhou	36.05N	103.88E	4980	10	13	89	64	86	63	84	62	66	80	65	78	62	99	73	60	92	72	20.0
Lhasa	29.67N	91.13E	11975	13	16	77	51	74	51	72	51	55	68	54	67	50	85	58	50	83	58	21.1
Liuzhou	24.35N	109.40E	318	38	40	95	78	94	78	92	78	80	89	80	89	78	148	85	78	145	84	12.6
Longzhou	22.37N	106.75E	423	43	45	96	80	95	80	93	79	82	91	81	90	79	155	86	79	152	85	13.7
Macau	22.20N	113.53E	193	44	47	92	81	90	81	89	80	82	88	81	88	80	157	86	80	156	86	7.6
Mudanjiang	44.57N	129.60E	242	−15	−12	87	71	84	69	81	68	72	80	71	78	70	113	78	68	106	76	16.0
Nanchang	28.60N	115.92E	164	30	32	96	80	94	80	92	80	82	90	81	89	80	155	87	79	151	86	12.4
Nanjing	32.00N	118.80E	39	23	26	94	81	92	80	89	79	82	89	81	88	80	154	87	79	150	86	11.2
Nanning	22.82N	108.35E	239	42	44	95	79	93	79	92	79	81	89	81	88	80	155	85	79	152	85	11.9
Nenjiang	49.17N	125.23E	797	−32	−27	86	67	82	66	80	66	70	77	69	75	68	106	74	66	100	73	17.1
Qingdao	36.07N	120.33E	252	19	21	85	74	83	74	81	74	78	80	77	80	77	140	80	76	136	79	8.1
Qiqihar	47.38N	123.92E	485	−18	−14	87	69	84	69	82	68	73	80	71	78	70	113	77	69	106	75	14.2
Shanghai	31.17N	121.43E	22	26	29	94	81	92	81	89	80	82	89	81	88	80	157	87	79	150	85	11.5
Shantou	23.40N	116.68E	9	44	47	91	80	90	80	89	80	81	87	81	87	79	153	85	79	150	84	9.4
Shaoguan	24.80N	113.58E	223	36	39	96	78	95	78	93	78	80	90	80	89	78	146	84	77	144	84	13.7
Shenyang	41.77N	123.43E	141	−6	−2	88	74	86	73	84	72	76	83	75	81	74	128	81	73	122	79	14.4
Shijiazhuang	38.03N	114.42E	265	14	17	95	72	92	72	90	73	79	85	77	84	77	141	83	75	134	82	15.5
Taiyuan	37.78N	112.55E	2555	4	8	89	69	87	68	85	68	73	81	72	80	71	125	78	69	117	77	19.6
Tangshan	39.67N	118.15E	95	7	10	90	74	88	73	86	72	78	83	76	82	76	136	82	74	130	80	13.9
Tianjin	39.10N	117.17E	16	14	17	92	74	90	73	88	73	78	85	77	84	77	139	83	75	133	82	13.0
Urumqi	43.78N	87.62E	3015	−10	−5	91	61	89	60	86	60	63	82	62	81	56	74	67	54	70	68	18.4
Weifang	36.70N	119.08E	167	12	15	93	73	90	73	88	73	79	85	78	83	77	142	83	76	136	82	14.9
Wenzhou	28.02N	120.67E	22	33	36	93	82	91	81	89	80	82	89	81	88	80	156	87	79	153	85	11.7
Wuhan	30.62N	114.13E	75	27	29	95	81	93	80	91	80	82	90	81	89	80	156	87	79	152	87	11.0
Xian	34.30N	108.93E	1305	20	23	95	73	92	73	90	72	77	87	76	85	74	134	83	73	128	81	16.0
Xiamen	24.48N	118.08E	456	43	45	91	79	90	79	88	79	80	87	80	86	78	150	84	78	148	83	10.6
Xining	36.62N	101.77E	7421	4	7	81	57	78	56	75	55	59	72	58	70	55	86	63	54	81	62	19.6
Xuzhou	34.28N	117.15E	137	19	22	94	77	91	76	89	75	80	88	79	86	78	148	85	77	143	84	12.2
Yaxian	18.23N	109.52E	22	59	62	91	80	90	80	89	80	82	88	82	87	80	157	86	80	155	86	9.5
Yichang	30.70N	111.30E	439	30	32	96	79	93	79	91	78	81	90	80	88	79	152	87	78	148	85	13.0
Yichun	47.72N	128.90E	761	−28	−24	86	69	83	67	80	67	71	79	69	76	68	106	75	67	101	73	18.2
Yinchuan	38.48N	106.22E	3648	−1	4	88	67	86	66	84	65	70	81	68	79	66	111	76	64	104	75	19.1
Yingkou	40.67N	122.20E	13	1	4	86	76	84	74	83	73	76	82	75	81	75	130	80	74	125	80	12.1
Yining	43.95N	81.33E	2175	−10	−3	91	67	89	66	86	65	68	85	66	83	62	89	74	60	85	73	23.0
Yueyang	29.38N	113.08E	170	30	32	94	81	92	80	91	80	82	90	81	89	80	155	88	79	150	86	9.0
Zhangjiakou	40.78N	114.88E	2381	1	4	89	65	87	65	84	64	71	80	69	79	67	111	76	66	104	75	17.1
Zhanjiang	21.22N	110.40E	91	46	48	93	80	92	80	90	80	82	88	81	87	80	158	85	80	155	85	8.5

Table 19-3. *(Continued)* Air Conditioning Design Data—World Locations

Station	Lat.	Long.	Elev.	Heating 99.6% DB	99% DB	Cooling 0.4% DB	MWB	1% DB	MWB	2% DB	MWB	Evaporation 1% DB	MWB	2% DB	MWB	Dehumidification 1% DP	W	MDB	2% DP	W	MDB	Range of DB
Zhengzhou	34.72N	113.65E	364	19	21	94	74	92	74	90	74	80	87	78	85	78	147	84	77	141	83	14.6
COLOMBIA																						
Bogota	4.70N	74.13W	8359	36	39	70	56	68	56	68	56	59	65	58	65	57	94	63	56	90	62	20.7
COOK ISLANDS																						
Rarotonga Island	21.20S	159.82W	22	62	64	85	78	85	78	84	77	79	83	79	83	78	146	82	77	142	82	8.3
CROATIA																						
Pula	44.90N	13.92E	206	25	27	89	71	86	69	84	68	72	82	71	81	69	109	77	68	103	75	19.1
Split	43.53N	16.30E	68	29	32	91	70	89	69	86	68	71	85	70	84	66	97	78	65	92	76	18.5
Zagreb	45.73N	16.07E	351	8	14	88	70	85	70	83	68	71	83	69	80	67	99	77	65	94	74	22.1
CUBA																						
Guantanamo	19.90N	75.15W	55	67	68	94	78	93	78	92	78	81	91	80	90	78	146	88	77	141	87	15.3
CYPRUS																						
Akrotiri	34.58N	32.98E	75	40	43	91	71	89	72	87	73	77	84	76	83	75	132	82	74	127	81	13.0
Larnaca	34.88N	33.63E	6	37	40	93	71	91	72	89	72	77	85	76	84	75	131	83	74	125	82	17.8
Paphos	34.72N	32.48E	26	39	42	88	76	86	76	85	76	78	85	77	83	76	137	84	75	132	83	15.5
CZECH REPUBLIC																						
Brno	49.15N	16.70E	807	6	12	85	66	82	65	79	64	67	79	65	76	63	88	71	61	83	70	19.4
Cheb	50.08N	12.40E	1545	4	10	83	65	80	64	77	62	65	76	63	74	61	84	68	59	80	67	19.4
Ostrava	49.68N	18.12E	839	1	9	85	67	82	65	78	64	67	79	65	76	63	88	71	61	84	70	20.7
Plzen	49.65N	13.27E	1194	2	9	84	67	81	65	78	64	67	78	65	75	63	89	73	61	84	69	20.3
Praded Mountain	50.07N	17.23E	4895	-2	2	65	55	63	54	60	53	56	60	54	58	54	74	57	52	70	56	9.7
Prague	50.10N	14.28E	1200	3	10	84	65	80	64	77	63	66	76	64	74	62	85	69	60	82	69	20.0
Pribyslav	49.58N	15.77E	1758	3	9	81	65	77	64	74	62	65	74	63	72	61	85	69	59	80	67	18.5
DENMARK																						
Alborg	57.10N	9.87E	9	8	15	77	63	74	61	71	60	63	71	61	69	59	75	67	58	71	65	15.1
Copenhagen	55.63N	12.67E	16	12	18	77	63	74	62	71	60	63	71	62	69	60	77	67	59	74	66	14.6
Hammerodde	55.30N	14.78E	36	20	22	73	64	70	63	68	62	64	69	63	67	63	85	67	61	80	66	7.0
Mon Island	54.95N	12.55E	49	18	22	74	65	71	63	69	62	65	70	63	67	62	84	68	61	80	66	10.1
Odense	55.47N	10.33E	55	14	18	78	64	75	63	72	61	64	73	62	70	61	79	68	59	75	66	17.3
Skagen	57.77N	10.65E	22	15	20	72	66	69	64	67	63	65	69	64	66	64	88	67	62	84	65	9.5
Tirstrup	56.30N	10.62E	82	9	16	77	64	75	62	72	61	64	71	62	69	61	80	66	59	75	65	17.8
ECUADOR																						
Guayaquil	2.15S	79.88W	29	67	68	92	76	91	76	90	76	79	87	79	85	77	143	83	77	141	82	13.3
Quito	0.15S	78.48W	9225	45	46	72	54	70	54	69	54	57	66	57	65	54	88	59	54	88	59	18.4
EGYPT																						
Alexandria	31.20N	29.95E	22	44	46	90	71	88	73	86	74	76	84	75	83	73	125	82	72	120	81	11.3
Cairo	30.13N	31.40E	242	45	46	100	69	97	69	95	69	74	87	74	86	71	117	78	70	112	78	23.9
Luxor	25.67N	32.70E	288	40	42	110	72	108	71	106	71	74	102	73	101	64	90	91	62	85	90	30.6
ESTONIA																						
Kopu/Cape Ristna	58.92N	22.07E	29	5	11	73	64	70	63	68	61	64	68	62	67	62	83	67	60	78	65	8.6
Tallinn	59.35N	24.80E	144	-4	3	77	64	74	62	71	61	64	71	62	69	61	82	68	59	76	66	14.8
FAEROE ISLANDS																						
Torshavn	62.02N	6.77W	127	26	28	58	54	56	53	55	53	54	56	53	54	54	62	55	53	60	54	5.4
FIJI																						
Nadi	17.75S	177.45E	59	61	63	90	77	89	77	88	77	79	86	79	85	77	143	83	77	140	82	14.2
Nausori	18.05S	178.57E	22	62	64	88	78	87	78	86	78	79	85	79	84	78	146	82	77	142	82	11.0
FINLAND																						
Helsinki	60.32N	24.97E	183	-11	-3	79	64	75	61	73	61	64	72	62	69	61	80	67	59	75	65	17.6
Jyvaskyla	62.40N	25.68E	475	-21	-13	78	62	75	61	71	60	63	72	61	69	60	78	65	58	72	64	17.6
Kauhava	63.10N	23.03E	144	-20	-14	77	62	74	61	70	59	63	70	61	68	60	76	65	58	71	64	18.0
Kuopio	63.02N	27.80E	334	-21	-14	78	62	75	61	71	60	63	71	62	69	60	79	66	58	74	65	12.8
Lahti	60.97N	25.63E	275	-15	-7	79	64	76	63	73	61	64	74	62	71	60	79	68	59	75	66	19.1
Pello	66.80N	24.00E	275	-25	-20	76	61	72	60	69	58	61	69	59	66	58	72	64	56	67	62	15.8
Pori	61.47N	21.80E	55	-12	-4	77	62	74	61	71	59	63	71	61	68	60	76	65	58	72	64	16.2
Suomussalmi	64.90N	29.02E	734	-21	-17	76	61	72	60	69	58	61	70	59	66	58	73	64	56	69	62	15.1
Tampere	61.42N	23.58E	367	-15	-8	79	62	76	61	73	60	63	72	61	70	59	76	66	58	71	64	18.7
Turku	60.52N	22.27E	193	-10	-3	79	63	75	61	72	60	63	72	61	69	60	77	66	58	73	65	16.4
FRANCE																						
Bordeaux	44.83N	0.70W	200	22	27	90	70	86	69	83	68	71	82	70	79	68	104	75	66	98	74	20.3
Clermont–Ferrand	45.78N	3.17E	1082	16	20	89	70	86	68	82	67	70	83	68	80	65	98	76	64	93	74	22.7
Dijon	47.27N	5.08E	744	14	20	88	68	84	68	81	67	70	80	68	78	66	99	74	64	93	72	20.9
Brest	48.45N	4.42W	337	27	30	78	65	74	65	71	64	65	72	64	68	64	89	67	62	85	66	13.7
Lyon	45.73N	5.08E	787	17	23	90	69	86	69	83	67	70	82	68	80	66	99	75	64	93	73	21.4
Marseille	43.45N	5.23E	118	25	28	90	71	87	70	85	69	73	82	71	81	70	111	78	68	104	77	18.7
Montpellier	43.58N	3.97E	19	25	29	90	71	87	70	84	69	75	81	73	80	73	123	78	71	116	76	18.5
Nancy	48.68N	6.22E	711	14	17	86	69	82	67	79	65	69	79	67	76	65	94	73	63	90	71	20.9
Nantes	47.17N	1.60W	88	23	27	86	68	83	68	79	66	70	79	68	76	66	97	73	65	92	70	18.2
Nice	43.65N	7.20E	32	35	37	84	74	83	73	81	72	76	80	75	79	75	131	80	73	123	79	12.2

Table 19-3. *(Continued)* Air Conditioning Design Data—World Locations

Station	Lat.	Long.	Elev.	Heating 99.6% DB	99% DB	Cooling 0.4% DB	MWB	1% DB	MWB	2% DB	MWB	Evaporation 1% DB	MWB	2% DB	MWB	Dehumidification 1% DP	W	MDB	2% DP	W	MDB	Range of DB
Nimes	43.87N	4.40E	203	26	30	92	69	89	69	87	68	72	83	71	81	69	107	76	67	100	75	19.6
Orleans	47.98N	1.75E	410	17	22	86	68	83	66	80	65	69	79	67	76	65	93	73	63	88	71	21.2
Paris, De Gaulle	49.02N	2.53E	357	18	23	86	69	82	68	79	66	69	79	67	76	66	97	74	64	91	72	18.7
Paris, Orly	48.73N	2.40E	314	19	23	86	69	82	67	79	65	69	79	67	76	65	93	73	63	88	71	18.4
St.–Quentin	49.82N	3.20E	331	17	22	82	68	79	67	76	65	68	77	66	74	65	94	72	63	88	70	18.9
Strasbourg	48.55N	7.63E	505	12	17	87	70	84	68	81	67	70	80	68	78	66	98	75	64	92	72	20.7
Toulouse	43.63N	1.37E	501	22	27	91	70	88	69	84	68	71	82	70	81	68	104	77	66	98	75	21.4
FRENCH POLYNESIA																						
Moruroa Island	21.82S	138.80W	9	67	68	87	79	86	78	85	78	80	84	79	83	78	147	82	78	144	82	6.8
Papeete, Tahiti	17.55S	149.62W	6	68	69	89	79	89	79	88	78	80	87	79	86	78	145	85	77	141	85	11.0
GERMANY																						
Aachen	50.78N	6.10E	672	14	19	83	66	80	65	77	64	67	78	65	75	63	88	71	61	83	70	15.5
Ahlhorn (Ger–AFB)	52.88N	8.23E	184	11	16	84	65	80	65	77	64	66	78	64	74	62	85	70	61	80	69	18.2
Berlin	52.47N	13.40E	160	11	15	86	66	82	65	79	64	67	79	65	75	62	85	70	61	80	69	16.7
Bitburg	49.95N	6.57E	1227	12	18	84	66	80	65	77	64	67	78	65	75	63	89	71	61	83	70	18.5
Bremen	53.05N	8.80E	16	12	16	82	66	79	65	76	63	66	76	65	73	63	85	71	61	80	68	18.0
Bremerhaven	53.53N	8.58E	36	15	19	81	66	77	64	73	63	66	74	65	72	64	88	70	62	83	69	11.7
Dresden	51.13N	13.78E	741	8	13	85	66	82	65	78	63	66	78	65	76	62	86	71	61	81	69	17.6
Dusseldorf	51.28N	6.78E	144	14	20	85	67	82	65	79	64	67	79	66	76	63	88	72	62	83	71	17.5
Eggebek (Ger–Navy)	54.63N	9.35E	72	11	17	80	65	77	63	73	62	65	74	63	71	61	80	68	59	75	67	17.3
Ehrenberg	50.50N	9.95E	3034	5	10	75	62	72	60	69	59	62	70	60	67	58	81	65	57	77	63	13.5
Frankfurt Am Main	50.05N	8.60E	370	12	17	87	67	83	66	80	64	67	80	66	77	63	88	71	62	83	70	19.8
Grafenwohr	49.70N	11.95E	1361	−2	5	85	66	82	66	79	64	66	79	65	76	62	88	71	61	83	69	25.0
Greifswald	54.10N	13.40E	19	9	15	81	66	77	65	74	63	66	75	64	72	63	85	70	61	80	68	16.4
Hamburg	53.63N	10.00E	52	11	16	82	66	79	64	75	63	66	76	64	73	62	85	70	61	80	68	16.7
Hannover	52.47N	9.70E	177	9	14	84	67	80	65	77	64	67	78	65	74	63	87	71	61	82	69	18.7
Heidelberg	49.40N	8.65E	357	14	19	90	69	86	67	83	66	69	84	67	80	64	92	75	63	87	71	20.0
Hof	50.32N	11.88E	1863	3	9	81	64	77	62	74	61	64	74	62	71	60	83	67	59	79	66	18.5
Husum (Ger–AFB)	54.52N	9.15E	121	12	17	79	64	76	64	72	62	65	73	63	70	62	84	68	61	79	66	15.5
Kap Arkona	54.68N	13.43E	134	17	21	74	65	71	64	69	62	65	70	63	68	62	85	68	61	80	67	9.2
Kiel/Holtenau (Ger Navy)	54.38N	10.15E	102	14	19	78	64	75	63	72	62	64	73	62	70	61	79	68	59	75	67	15.5
Koln	50.87N	7.17E	324	11	17	85	67	82	65	79	64	67	79	65	76	63	87	71	62	83	69	19.8
Lahr	48.37N	7.83E	511	11	17	86	69	84	68	80	66	69	81	68	78	65	94	74	64	91	73	20.7
Landsberg (Ger–AFB)	48.07N	10.90E	2060	5	10	83	66	79	64	77	63	65	77	64	74	61	85	70	59	80	69	20.2
Leck (Ger–AFB)	54.80N	8.95E	43	11	17	79	65	76	63	72	62	64	75	63	71	61	80	68	59	75	67	16.4
Leipzig	51.42N	12.23E	436	8	13	85	66	82	65	78	64	67	78	65	76	63	86	71	61	81	70	18.5
Memmingen (Ger–AFB)	47.98N	10.23E	2113	5	10	83	66	80	65	77	63	65	78	64	74	59	82	70	59	80	69	20.0
Munich	48.13N	11.70E	1735	4	10	84	66	81	64	78	63	66	78	65	76	62	87	71	60	83	69	20.2
Neuburg (Ger–AFB)	48.72N	11.22E	1270	3	10	85	66	81	65	79	64	66	80	65	76	61	85	71	59	79	69	22.7
Nordholz (Ger–Navy)	53.77N	8.67E	102	12	17	81	65	77	64	74	62	65	74	64	71	62	83	69	60	79	67	14.8
Ramstein (US–AFB)	49.43N	7.60E	780	11	16	86	68	83	66	80	65	67	79	66	78	63	88	72	61	83	71	22.3
Sollingen (Can–AFB)	48.77N	8.10E	419	13	17	87	69	84	68	81	66	69	81	68	78	66	97	74	64	92	72	19.8
Stuttgart	48.68N	9.22E	1374	9	14	84	66	81	65	78	63	66	78	65	76	62	87	71	60	83	70	19.4
GEORGIA																						
Batumi	41.65N	41.63E	19	29	32	82	73	80	72	79	71	74	79	72	77	72	118	78	71	113	76	10.4
Kutaisi (Kutaisi)	42.27N	42.63E	380	28	30	90	71	87	70	84	70	74	81	73	79	72	120	78	71	116	77	14.9
Sokhumi (Sukhumi)	42.87N	41.13E	42	29	31	84	73	82	73	80	72	75	80	74	79	73	122	78	72	118	77	13.1
Tbilisi	41.68N	44.95E	1532	21	24	92	70	89	70	87	69	72	86	70	84	67	105	79	65	99	78	18.4
GIBRALTAR																						
North Front	36.15N	5.35W	16	46	48	88	69	85	68	82	68	73	78	72	77	72	117	76	71	113	75	12.6
GREECE																						
Andravida	37.92N	21.28E	39	32	34	91	70	89	71	87	71	74	83	73	82	72	117	79	70	111	78	21.2
Athens	37.90N	23.73E	49	34	37	93	69	91	68	89	68	73	85	72	83	69	108	82	68	102	80	16.9
Elefsis (Hel–AFB)	38.07N	23.55E	102	33	36	97	70	95	68	92	68	73	88	71	86	68	103	82	66	96	80	18.2
Iraklion	35.33N	25.18E	127	41	44	88	66	86	67	84	68	73	81	72	80	70	110	79	68	104	79	10.6
Larisa	39.63N	22.42E	242	23	26	97	69	93	68	91	68	70	88	69	86	65	92	74	64	89	74	25.2
Preveza	38.95N	20.77E	13	36	38	88	71	86	71	84	72	75	82	74	81	73	122	79	72	118	79	14.4
Rodhos	36.40N	28.08E	36	41	44	90	71	87	71	86	70	75	82	74	81	73	122	79	72	117	79	10.1
Soudha	35.48N	24.12E	495	39	41	93	66	90	67	88	66	71	81	70	80	68	105	75	67	99	75	15.3
Thessaloniki	40.52N	22.97E	13	25	28	92	70	90	69	88	69	72	84	71	84	68	102	79	66	97	78	20.9
GREENLAND																						
Dundas, Thule Ab	76.53N	68.50W	193	−35	−33	54	44	51	43	48	41	43	50	42	48	37	33	45	36	31	44	8.3
Godthab	64.17N	51.75W	229	−12	−8	57	49	54	47	51	46	48	53	47	50	46	46	49	44	43	47	10.4
Kangerlussuaq	67.00N	50.80W	173	−42	−38	65	51	63	50	60	49	51	62	49	59	44	43	52	43	41	52	18.2
Narsarsuaq	61.18N	45.42W	85	−18	−12	65	50	62	49	60	47	51	58	50	57	48	49	50	46	46	49	12.2
GUAM																						
Andersen AFB (Guam)	13.58N	144.93E	606	74	75	88	79	87	79	87	78	80	85	80	85	79	154	83	78	150	83	7.6

Table 19-3. *(Continued)* Air Conditioning Design Data—World Locations

Station	Location Lat.	Location Long.	Location Elev.	Heating 99.6% DB	Heating 99% DB	Cooling 0.4% DB	Cooling 0.4% MWB	Cooling 1% DB	Cooling 1% MWB	Cooling 2% DB	Cooling 2% MWB	Evap 1% DB	Evap 1% MWB	Evap 2% DB	Evap 2% MWB	Dehum 1% DP	Dehum 1% W	Dehum 1% MDB	Dehum 2% DP	Dehum 2% W	Dehum 2% MDB	Range of DB
HUNGARY																				
Budapest	47.43N	19.27E	606	8	14	90	69	86	68	84	66	69	85	67	80	64	92	74	63	87	74	22.0
Debrecen	47.48N	21.63E	367	6	11	88	71	85	70	82	68	71	83	69	81	66	97	78	64	92	76	20.3
Nagykanizsa	46.45N	16.98E	462	8	14	87	70	84	69	81	68	70	82	69	80	66	97	75	65	92	73	22.7
Pecs	46.00N	18.23E	666	12	16	88	70	86	69	83	68	70	84	69	81	65	96	79	64	90	76	18.9
Siofok	46.92N	18.03E	354	12	17	86	71	83	70	80	69	71	81	70	79	68	103	79	66	97	76	14.6
Szombathely	47.27N	16.63E	725	10	15	86	69	83	68	80	67	69	80	68	78	65	97	75	64	92	72	19.8
ICELAND																				
Akureyri	65.68N	18.08W	88	8	11	66	56	63	54	61	53	55	62	53	60	51	57	58	49	52	56	9.5
Keflavik	63.97N	22.60W	177	17	20	59	52	57	51	55	51	52	55	51	54	51	57	53	50	54	52	7.6
Raufarhofn	66.45N	15.95W	32	10	13	60	53	56	51	54	50	52	56	50	53	49	52	54	48	50	52	7.4
Reykjavik	64.13N	21.90W	200	14	17	60	53	58	52	56	51	53	56	52	55	51	56	54	50	54	53	8.5
INDIA																				
Ahmadabad	23.07N	72.63E	180	52	55	108	74	106	74	103	75	83	92	82	91	81	161	87	80	157	86	22.9
Bangalore	12.97N	77.58E	3021	59	60	94	67	92	67	91	67	73	82	72	81	71	127	76	70	125	76	19.3
Bombay	19.12N	72.85E	45	62	64	95	73	93	74	92	75	81	88	81	88	80	153	86	79	150	85	9.4
Calcutta	22.65N	88.45E	19	54	56	99	78	97	79	95	79	84	92	83	91	82	167	89	82	164	88	18.0
Cuddalore	11.77N	79.77E	39	68	69	99	78	98	78	96	78	83	90	82	90	81	162	88	81	159	87	14.8
Goa/Panaji	15.48N	73.82E	196	67	69	93	77	92	77	91	77	82	88	81	87	80	158	86	79	153	85	10.4
Hyderabad	17.45N	78.47E	1788	58	60	105	71	103	71	101	71	76	88	76	87	74	135	80	73	133	80	18.9
Jaipur	26.82N	75.80E	1279	44	47	108	69	105	69	103	69	80	87	79	87	78	153	83	77	149	82	22.3
Madras	13.00N	80.18E	52	68	69	101	77	99	77	97	77	82	90	82	89	81	159	86	80	155	86	14.6
Nagpur	21.10N	79.05E	1017	53	55	110	71	108	71	106	70	79	88	79	87	77	148	83	77	145	82	22.9
New Delhi	28.58N	77.20E	708	44	46	107	72	105	72	103	73	82	91	81	90	80	158	86	79	155	86	21.6
Poona	18.53N	73.85E	1833	50	52	100	67	99	67	97	67	75	84	74	83	73	131	79	72	127	78	29.0
Sholapur	17.67N	75.90E	1571	61	63	105	71	104	71	102	70	78	92	77	90	75	141	83	74	136	82	21.1
Trivandrum	8.48N	76.95E	209	72	73	92	78	91	78	90	78	81	88	80	87	79	150	84	78	148	84	11.7
INDIAN OCEAN ISLANDS																				
Diego Garcia Isl.	7.30S	72.40E	9	73	75	90	80	89	79	88	79	81	86	80	86	80	157	84	79	151	84	9.4
IRELAND																				
Belmullet	54.23N	10.00W	32	30	32	70	62	66	61	64	60	62	65	61	63	61	79	64	59	76	62	8.8
Birr	53.08N	7.88W	236	24	28	76	64	72	63	69	61	64	70	62	67	61	81	66	60	78	65	14.9
Claremorris	53.72N	8.98W	226	26	28	73	64	70	62	67	61	63	68	62	65	61	82	65	60	78	64	13.9
Clones	54.18N	7.23W	291	25	28	74	64	71	62	68	61	63	69	62	67	61	80	66	59	76	65	13.7
Cork	51.85N	8.48W	531	29	32	71	62	68	61	66	60	63	67	61	65	61	82	64	60	78	63	12.1
Dublin	53.43N	6.25W	278	29	31	72	63	69	61	67	60	63	67	61	66	61	80	65	59	76	64	12.6
Kilkenny	52.67N	7.27W	209	25	28	76	64	72	62	70	61	64	70	62	68	61	82	66	60	78	65	15.8
Malin	55.37N	7.33W	82	31	33	67	61	65	60	63	59	61	64	59	62	59	76	62	58	72	61	7.6
Mullingar	53.53N	7.37W	341	25	28	74	64	70	62	67	61	63	69	62	66	61	81	66	60	78	64	14.4
Rosslare	52.25N	6.33W	82	32	34	68	62	66	61	64	60	62	65	61	64	61	79	64	59	76	62	8.8
Shannon	52.70N	8.92W	65	28	31	75	64	71	63	68	61	64	70	62	67	61	81	67	60	78	65	12.1
Valentia Observatory	51.93N	10.25W	45	31	33	71	63	68	62	66	61	64	67	62	65	62	83	65	61	80	64	9.4
ISRAEL																				
Jerusalem	31.78N	35.22E	2473	33	35	89	65	86	64	84	63	69	79	68	78	66	104	72	65	100	71	18.4
Lod	32.00N	34.90E	160	40	42	94	69	90	72	88	72	76	85	76	85	74	126	82	73	122	82	17.1
Ovda (Isr-AFB/Civ)	30.00N	34.83E	1417	36	39	100	65	97	65	95	65	71	87	69	85	66	102	78	64	95	76	25.0
Tel Aviv-Yafo	32.10N	34.78E	13	44	46	88	69	86	74	85	74	77	83	76	83	75	132	82	74	127	82	9.9
ITALY																				
Bologna/Borgo (AFB)	44.53N	11.30E	138	22	25	93	75	90	73	88	72	75	87	74	85	72	118	81	70	111	81	20.3
Brindisi	40.65N	17.95E	32	36	39	90	73	86	74	84	75	79	83	77	82	77	141	82	75	133	81	13.0
Catania	37.47N	15.05E	55	35	37	95	72	91	73	89	72	78	84	76	83	75	133	81	74	126	80	20.9
Genova	44.42N	8.85E	9	32	36	86	72	84	72	82	72	75	81	74	80	73	123	81	72	117	79	10.4
Messina	38.20N	15.55E	167	43	45	89	72	88	73	86	74	78	83	77	83	76	136	83	75	132	82	9.4
Milan, Linate	45.43N	9.28E	337	21	25	89	73	87	72	85	71	74	84	73	82	71	117	80	70	111	78	18.2
Milan, Malpensa	45.62N	8.73E	692	15	18	90	74	87	73	85	72	75	85	74	83	72	121	81	70	115	79	23.0
Naples	40.85N	14.30E	236	32	34	92	73	89	73	87	73	77	84	76	83	75	133	82	73	125	80	19.8
Palermo	38.18N	13.10E	111	44	46	92	71	88	73	86	75	79	84	78	83	77	142	83	76	137	82	9.5
Perugia	43.08N	12.50E	672	24	27	92	70	90	69	86	69	72	84	70	83	68	104	77	66	99	76	25.0
Pisa	43.68N	10.38E	3	26	29	89	72	87	71	85	71	75	83	73	82	72	118	79	71	113	78	21.2
Rome	41.80N	12.23E	9	30	32	87	74	86	74	84	74	78	82	76	81	76	136	81	75	131	80	17.8
Ronchi Legionari Ab	45.82N	13.48E	39	21	25	91	72	88	71	86	71	74	83	72	82	71	116	79	70	109	78	21.2
Torino	45.22N	7.65E	941	20	23	87	72	85	71	83	70	74	82	72	80	71	120	79	70	113	77	18.9
Venice	45.50N	12.33E	19	23	26	87	74	85	73	83	71	75	82	74	81	73	123	80	71	116	78	16.4
JAMAICA																				
Kingston	17.93N	76.78W	29	71	72	92	78	91	78	90	78	80	89	79	88	77	143	85	77	141	85	11.7
Montego Bay	18.50N	77.92W	9	70	71	90	79	90	79	89	78	80	88	79	87	77	142	85	77	141	86	11.3
JAPAN																				
Aomori	40.82N	140.77E	9	18	20	86	74	83	73	80	71	74	81	73	79	72	120	80	71	115	78	13.0

Table 19-3. *(Continued)* **Air Conditioning Design Data—World Locations**

Station	Lat.	Long.	Elev.	Heating 99.6% DB	Heating 99% DB	Cooling 0.4% DB	Cooling 0.4% MWB	Cooling 1% DB	Cooling 1% MWB	Cooling 2% DB	Cooling 2% MWB	Evap. 1% DB	Evap. 1% MWB	Evap. 2% DB	Evap. 2% MWB	Dehum. 1% DP	Dehum. 1% W	Dehum. 1% MDB	Dehum. 2% DP	Dehum. 2% W	Dehum. 2% MDB	Range of DB
Asahikawa	43.77N	142.37E	380	−2	2	86	73	82	70	80	68	73	81	71	77	70	112	78	68	106	76	15.7
Atsugi	35.45N	139.45E	213	29	30	90	77	88	76	86	76	78	84	77	84	76	135	82	75	132	81	11.7
Fukuoka	33.58N	130.45E	39	30	32	93	77	91	78	88	77	79	87	78	86	76	134	82	75	133	82	13.1
Hakodate	41.82N	140.75E	118	13	16	82	73	80	72	77	71	73	78	72	76	72	117	77	70	111	76	11.0
Hamamatsu	34.75N	137.70E	157	30	32	90	76	88	76	86	76	79	84	78	82	77	142	81	77	140	81	11.9
Hiroshima	34.40N	132.47E	173	30	31	91	78	89	77	87	77	78	87	78	85	76	138	83	76	134	82	11.7
Hyakuri (Jasdf)	36.18N	140.42E	114	19	23	89	78	86	77	84	76	78	84	77	83	77	139	82	75	134	81	13.3
Kadena	26.35N	127.77E	147	50	52	92	81	91	81	90	80	82	89	82	88	81	161	87	80	159	86	9.7
Kagoshima	31.57N	130.55E	16	33	35	91	78	90	78	88	77	79	86	79	85	77	142	83	77	140	83	11.2
Kumamoto	32.82N	130.72E	127	28	30	92	78	91	77	89	77	79	87	78	85	77	142	82	76	139	82	14.0
Maebashi	36.40N	139.07E	370	26	28	92	77	90	76	87	75	77	87	76	85	74	130	83	73	125	82	13.5
Maizuru	35.45N	135.32E	72	28	30	91	77	89	77	87	76	78	87	77	85	75	132	82	74	130	81	13.7
Matsumoto	36.25N	137.97E	2004	16	18	89	72	87	72	84	71	73	83	72	82	70	118	78	69	113	77	16.9
Matsuyama	33.83N	132.78E	111	31	33	91	77	89	76	87	76	77	86	77	85	75	133	82	74	129	82	12.1
Miho (Civ/Jasdf)	35.48N	133.25E	29	30	31	90	78	88	77	86	76	78	85	77	84	76	134	82	75	132	81	11.5
Miyako Jima Island	24.78N	125.28E	134	54	56	90	80	89	80	88	80	81	87	81	86	80	156	84	79	152	84	8.5
Morioka	39.70N	141.17E	515	14	18	87	75	84	73	82	71	75	82	74	79	73	125	79	72	120	78	13.9
Nagasaki	32.73N	129.87E	114	33	35	90	77	88	78	86	77	79	84	78	84	78	146	83	77	141	82	10.1
Nagoya	35.25N	136.93E	55	27	29	93	77	90	76	88	75	78	86	77	85	75	133	81	75	131	82	14.0
Naha	26.18N	127.65E	26	53	55	90	80	88	80	88	80	81	87	81	86	79	151	85	79	151	85	6.8
Naze	28.38N	129.50E	22	49	50	90	79	89	79	88	79	80	87	80	87	78	147	85	78	145	84	9.7
New Tokyo Intl A	35.77N	140.38E	144	23	25	89	78	87	78	85	76	78	85	77	83	77	141	82	75	134	81	13.5
Niigata	37.92N	139.05E	22	27	29	90	77	88	76	85	75	77	85	76	84	75	130	82	74	125	82	10.8
Nyutabaru (Jasdf)	32.08N	131.45E	269	28	31	90	78	88	78	86	77	79	85	78	83	77	143	82	77	141	82	11.0
Oita	33.23N	131.62E	42	30	32	91	78	89	77	87	77	78	86	78	85	76	136	82	75	133	82	12.2
Osaka	34.78N	135.45E	49	28	30	93	77	91	76	89	75	78	87	78	86	76	134	81	75	132	82	14.4
Owase	34.07N	136.20E	88	30	32	90	76	87	76	85	76	78	85	77	84	76	134	82	75	130	81	11.0
Sapporo	43.05N	141.33E	62	12	15	84	73	81	71	78	69	73	80	71	77	70	111	78	69	105	76	11.7
Sendai	38.27N	140.90E	141	24	26	86	75	84	74	81	73	76	82	75	80	74	129	80	73	124	78	9.5
Shimonoseki	33.95N	130.93E	62	33	35	88	77	87	77	85	76	78	85	77	84	76	136	82	75	133	82	7.9
Shizuhama (Jasdf)	34.82N	138.30E	32	30	32	91	79	89	78	86	77	79	86	79	84	77	143	83	77	140	82	11.9
Tokyo, Intl Airport	35.55N	139.78E	26	31	32	91	78	88	77	86	77	79	86	78	84	77	141	83	76	134	82	11.2
Tosashimizu	32.72N	133.02E	108	34	36	86	78	85	78	83	78	80	83	79	83	78	147	83	78	145	82	5.9
Wakkanai	45.42N	141.68E	36	11	13	77	71	74	69	72	68	70	74	69	72	69	106	73	67	100	72	7.6
JORDAN																						
Amman	31.98N	35.98E	2536	33	35	95	65	92	65	89	64	70	82	68	81	66	106	74	65	100	72	20.3
KAZAKHSTAN																						
Almaty (Alma Ata)	43.23N	76.93E	2778	−3	3	91	65	89	64	86	63	66	84	65	83	60	84	73	58	79	73	19.8
Aqmola (Tselinograd)	51.13N	71.37E	1141	−21	−17	89	64	85	62	82	62	65	79	64	78	61	83	69	59	77	69	19.4
Aqtobe (Aktyubinsk)	50.30N	57.23E	744	−19	−14	93	67	90	65	86	64	67	85	66	82	62	85	72	60	80	72	23.0
Atyrau (Guryev)	47.02N	51.85E	−49	−7	−3	97	68	94	67	91	66	70	85	69	84	66	96	76	64	89	76	20.2
Oral (Uralsk)	51.25N	51.40E	118	−18	−13	93	67	89	66	86	65	68	84	67	82	64	88	74	62	83	72	22.5
Pavlodar	52.28N	76.95E	403	−24	−19	90	67	87	65	84	63	67	80	66	79	63	86	71	61	80	71	20.2
Qaraghandy (Karaganda)	49.80N	73.13E	1820	−18	−13	89	61	85	61	82	60	63	78	62	77	59	78	67	57	74	66	20.3
Qostanay (Kustanay)	53.22N	63.62E	511	−21	−17	90	66	86	65	83	64	67	81	66	79	63	87	72	61	83	71	18.7
Semey (Semipalatinsk)	50.35N	80.25E	643	−25	−20	91	66	87	64	84	64	67	82	66	80	62	86	72	61	81	71	22.5
Zhambyl (Dzhambul)	42.85N	71.38E	2142	−5	1	96	64	93	64	90	63	65	88	64	86	58	78	72	56	73	72	25.0
KENYA																						
Arissa	0.47S	39.63E	482	70	71	99	74	98	74	97	74	78	89	77	88	75	135	81	75	132	80	19.1
Kisumu	0.10S	34.75E	3759	60	62	90	66	89	66	87	67	71	82	71	81	68	119	76	67	116	75	19.8
Lodwar	3.12N	35.62E	1689	69	71	100	69	99	69	98	69	74	86	74	87	72	125	79	71	120	79	19.8
Nairobi	1.32S	36.92E	5328	49	51	84	60	83	60	81	60	65	74	64	73	63	104	66	62	102	66	24.3
Nakuru	0.27S	36.10E	6236	47	48	84	57	83	57	82	57	63	73	62	72	60	97	65	59	95	65	27.5
KOREA, NORTH																						
Anju	39.62N	125.65E	88	−1	4	86	75	83	74	82	73	76	81	75	80	75	130	79	73	125	78	13.5
Chongjin	41.78N	129.82E	141	7	10	81	71	78	70	76	69	73	76	71	74	71	116	75	70	110	74	9.4
Changjin	40.37N	127.25E	3546	−19	−15	77	65	74	63	72	62	67	71	65	70	66	108	70	64	102	68	16.2
Haeju	38.03N	125.70E	265	10	13	86	75	84	73	82	72	76	81	75	79	75	132	79	74	128	78	10.8
Hamhung	39.93N	127.55E	124	7	10	87	73	84	72	81	71	75	82	74	78	73	124	79	72	119	77	12.1
Nampo	38.72N	125.37E	154	8	11	85	76	83	75	82	73	77	81	76	80	75	134	79	74	130	78	11.3
Pyongyang	39.03N	125.78E	124	3	7	87	75	85	74	83	72	76	82	75	80	75	130	80	74	125	79	13.7
Sinuiju	40.10N	124.38E	22	3	7	88	75	85	72	82	71	76	81	75	79	75	130	78	74	125	78	12.8
KOREA, SOUTH																						
Cheju	33.50N	126.55E	87	30	32	89	78	86	79	85	78	80	85	79	84	79	151	83	78	148	83	9.7
Inchon	37.48N	126.63E	229	12	15	87	76	84	74	82	73	76	82	75	80	75	131	80	74	127	79	10.4
Kangnung	37.75N	128.90E	88	16	20	90	75	87	74	85	72	76	85	75	82	74	126	82	73	122	80	10.4
Kwangju	35.13N	126.92E	236	19	22	90	78	88	76	85	75	78	85	77	83	76	139	82	76	135	81	12.6
Osan	37.08N	127.03E	39	7	11	90	78	88	76	86	75	78	85	77	83	77	139	83	75	132	82	14.4

Table 19-3. *(Continued)* Air Conditioning Design Data—World Locations

Station	Lat.	Long.	Elev.	Heating 99.6% DB	Heating 99% DB	Cooling 0.4% DB	Cooling 0.4% MWB	Cooling 1% DB	Cooling 1% MWB	Cooling 2% DB	Cooling 2% MWB	Evap 1% DB	Evap 1% MWB	Evap 2% DB	Evap 2% MWB	Dehum 1% DP	Dehum 1% W	Dehum 1% MDB	Dehum 2% DP	Dehum 2% W	Dehum 2% MDB	Range of DB
Seoul	37.55N	126.80E	62	7	10	89	77	86	75	84	74	78	83	77	80	77	142	81	76	134	79	14.4
Taegu	35.88N	128.62E	200	17	20	92	78	90	76	87	74	78	87	77	85	76	135	83	74	130	82	13.1
Taejon	36.30N	127.40E	255	12	15	90	76	88	75	86	74	77	84	76	83	76	136	81	75	131	80	14.4
Ulsan	35.55N	129.32E	108	20	22	91	78	89	77	86	76	78	86	78	84	76	138	83	76	134	82	11.5
KUWAIT																						
Kuwait	29.22N	47.98E	180	38	41	117	69	115	69	113	68	78	91	75	92	75	132	87	70	112	85	27.7
KYRGYZSTAN																						
Bishkek (Frunze)	42.85N	74.53E	2083	−8	−2	95	67	93	65	90	65	68	87	66	85	61	87	74	60	83	74	25.6
Tianshan (Mtn Stn)	41.92N	78.23E	11856	−27	−23	57	42	54	41	51	39	42	51	41	49	38	53	44	36	50	43	20.9
LATVIA																						
Liepaja	56.55N	21.02E	26	1	9	76	64	73	62	70	62	65	70	63	68	62	85	68	61	80	66	10.3
Riga	56.97N	24.07E	9	−3	4	79	65	76	64	73	62	66	73	64	71	63	85	69	61	80	68	14.2
LIBYA																						
Banghazi	32.08N	20.27E	433	44	46	99	72	95	71	92	70	76	86	75	85	74	127	81	72	123	80	16.7
Tripoli	32.67N	13.15E	265	39	41	107	76	103	74	100	73	78	94	76	90	74	130	84	73	123	83	24.8
LIECHTENSTEIN																						
Vaduz	47.13N	9.53E	1519	12	17	83	67	80	65	78	64	67	78	65	75	63	90	72	61	85	71	16.6
LITHUANIA																						
Kaunas	54.88N	23.88E	246	−4	3	80	67	77	65	74	63	67	75	65	72	63	88	71	62	83	68	16.6
Klaipeda	55.70N	21.15E	32	1	8	77	65	73	64	70	62	65	71	64	69	63	85	69	61	80	67	9.7
Vilnius	54.63N	25.28E	511	−5	2	81	65	78	64	75	62	66	74	64	72	62	85	70	61	80	68	16.2
MACEDONIA																						
Skopje	41.97N	21.65E	784	10	15	95	68	92	68	89	67	70	88	68	86	63	88	76	62	86	75	27.4
MADEIRA ISLANDS																						
Funchal	32.68N	16.77W	180	53	55	81	69	79	69	77	68	71	76	70	76	68	105	75	68	102	74	8.5
MALAYSIA																						
George Town	5.30N	100.27E	13	73	73	91	79	90	78	90	78	81	87	81	87	79	151	84	79	150	84	13.3
Kota Baharu	6.17N	102.28E	16	71	72	91	79	90	79	90	79	80	88	80	87	78	147	84	78	145	84	12.8
Kuala Lumpur	3.12N	101.55E	72	71	72	94	78	93	78	92	78	80	89	80	89	79	149	84	78	146	84	16.2
Kuantan	3.78N	103.22E	52	70	71	92	79	91	79	90	79	80	88	80	88	78	147	84	78	146	84	15.3
Malacca	2.27N	102.25E	29	72	72	92	78	91	78	90	78	81	88	80	87	79	150	84	78	147	83	15.3
Sitiawan	4.22N	100.70E	26	71	72	92	79	91	79	90	79	81	89	80	88	79	150	85	78	147	85	14.8
Kuching	1.48N	110.33E	88	71	72	93	79	92	78	91	78	80	89	80	88	78	148	85	77	143	83	15.8
Miri	4.33N	113.98E	59	72	73	90	79	89	79	89	79	81	87	81	87	79	152	85	79	150	84	11.9
MALI																						
Bamako	12.53N	7.95W	1250	59	62	104	69	103	69	101	69	78	89	78	88	76	140	82	75	139	82	22.1
MALTA																						
Luqa	35.85N	14.48E	298	44	46	92	71	88	72	86	72	76	82	75	82	74	127	80	73	125	79	14.4
MARSHALL ISLANDS																						
Kwajalein Atoll	8.73N	167.73E	26	76	77	89	79	88	79	88	79	80	87	80	86	78	147	85	78	146	85	7.6
MAURITANIA																						
Nouadhibou	20.93N	17.03W	9	55	57	92	69	88	69	86	69	74	81	73	81	72	118	78	70	112	77	15.8
Nouakchott	18.10N	15.95W	9	55	57	107	70	103	69	100	69	80	87	79	86	78	148	84	77	141	83	23.0
MEXICO																						
Acapulco	16.77N	99.75W	16	68	70	92	80	92	80	91	80	81	89	81	89	79	150	86	79	150	86	13.0
Merida	20.98N	89.65W	32	57	60	100	76	98	76	95	76	80	90	79	89	77	143	84	77	141	83	22.5
Mexico City	19.43N	99.08W	7329	39	42	84	57	82	57	80	56	61	73	60	72	57	92	64	57	92	63	24.8
Puerto Vallarta (766010)	20.68N	105.25W	19	59	60	92	81	91	81	90	80	82	90	81	89	79	153	87	79	150	86	14.2
Tampico (765491)	22.28N	97.87W	78	50	53	92	80	90	80	90	80	82	88	81	87	80	158	86	79	152	84	11.3
Veracruz	19.20N	96.13W	45	57	59	94	80	92	80	91	80	81	90	80	89	79	150	85	78	148	85	14.9
MICRONESIA																						
Chuuk Intl/Moen	7.47N	151.85E	7	75	76	88	80	88	80	87	79	81	87	80	86	79	148	85	78	147	85	7.4
MIDWAY ISLAND																						
Midway Island NAF	28.22N	177.37W	13	59	60	87	75	86	75	86	75	76	84	76	84	74	129	82	74	126	82	8.1
MOLDOVA																						
Chisinau (Kishinev)	47.02N	28.87E	590	6	10	86	67	84	66	81	65	68	80	67	78	64	92	74	63	87	72	16.4
MONGOLIA																						
Ulaanbataar	47.93N	106.98E	4317	−23	−19	82	60	78	59	75	58	61	73	59	71	56	80	66	55	75	64	17.6
Ulaangom	49.97N	92.08E	3070	−40	−37	82	61	79	60	77	59	62	76	60	73	56	75	68	54	70	66	19.3
MOROCCO																						
Al Hoceima	35.18N	3.85W	45	44	46	87	73	84	72	82	72	76	81	75	80	74	130	79	73	125	78	11.2
Casablanca	33.57N	7.67W	203	42	44	85	72	81	72	79	72	74	79	73	77	73	122	77	72	118	76	9.2
Casablanca/Nouasser	33.37N	7.58W	675	38	40	96	72	91	71	87	70	73	86	72	84	69	108	77	68	106	77	19.8
Midelt	32.68N	4.73W	4970	29	31	92	58	90	58	89	58	61	81	60	80	55	76	67	53	72	67	24.5
Ouarzazate	30.93N	6.90W	3740	33	35	100	62	98	61	97	61	64	89	63	89	56	77	71	54	71	71	24.7
Oujda	34.78N	1.93W	1541	34	36	98	70	94	69	91	69	72	87	71	85	68	111	78	67	106	77	24.7
Safi	32.28N	9.23W	147	42	44	94	71	89	70	85	70	73	83	72	81	70	111	77	69	107	75	14.8
Tanger	35.73N	5.90W	68	41	43	92	71	89	71	86	70	73	84	72	81	70	110	78	68	104	77	16.7

Table 19-3. *(Continued)* Air Conditioning Design Data—World Locations

Station	Lat.	Long.	Elev.	Heating 99.6% DB	99% DB	Cooling 0.4% DB	MWB	1% DB	MWB	2% DB	MWB	Evaporation 1% DB	MWB	2% DB	MWB	Dehumidification 1% DP	W	MDB	2% DP	W	MDB	Range of DB
NETHERLANDS																						
Amsterdam	52.30N	4.77E	−6	17	21	80	66	77	65	74	64	67	74	65	72	64	90	69	63	85	68	14.8
Beek	50.92N	5.78E	380	14	19	83	67	79	65	76	64	67	76	66	74	64	92	71	63	87	70	16.4
De Bilt	52.10N	5.18E	13	16	20	82	66	79	65	75	64	67	75	65	73	64	88	70	62	83	69	16.0
Eindhoven	51.45N	5.42E	72	16	21	83	67	80	65	77	64	67	77	65	74	63	87	70	62	83	69	17.8
Gilze/Rijen	51.57N	4.93E	42	15	20	82	66	79	65	76	63	67	76	65	73	63	87	69	62	83	68	17.3
Groningen	53.13N	6.58E	13	14	18	81	67	77	65	74	64	67	74	65	71	64	90	70	63	85	68	17.5
Leeuwarden	53.22N	5.75E	6	16	20	79	66	75	64	71	63	65	72	64	70	63	85	68	61	81	67	13.7
Rotterdam	51.95N	4.45E	−13	17	21	80	67	77	65	74	64	67	75	65	72	64	90	71	63	85	68	14.6
NETHERLANDS ANTILLES																						
Willemstad	12.20N	68.97W	219	74	75	91	80	90	80	90	79	81	88	81	87	79	153	86	79	150	86	9.5
NEW CALEDONIA																						
Noumea	22.27S	166.45E	236	61	62	88	76	86	76	85	75	78	84	77	82	76	139	81	75	134	80	9.4
NEW ZEALAND																						
Auckland	37.02S	174.80E	19	35	37	77	66	76	66	74	66	69	73	67	72	67	99	71	66	94	70	11.3
Christchurch	43.48S	172.55E	111	28	30	83	62	79	61	76	60	64	74	62	71	60	78	67	59	74	65	17.5
Taiaroa Head	45.77S	170.73E	249	38	39	69	57	66	57	64	56	60	63	59	62	58	74	61	57	71	60	8.6
Wellington (934340)	41.33S	174.80E	22	35	36	74	64	71	63	70	62	65	69	64	68	63	86	67	62	83	67	9.7
NIGER																						
Agadez	16.97N	7.98E	1646	51	53	108	67	107	67	105	66	74	92	73	91	70	116	82	68	111	82	22.5
Niamey	13.48N	2.17E	744	60	62	108	71	106	71	105	70	79	94	78	93	76	138	84	75	135	84	23.8
NORWAY																						
Bergen	60.30N	5.22E	164	16	20	73	59	68	57	65	55	59	64	58	63	57	70	60	56	66	59	11.5
Bodo	67.27N	14.37E	42	9	13	70	59	66	57	63	55	58	64	56	62	55	65	59	54	62	58	9.0
Oslo/Fornebu	59.90N	10.62E	55	0	5	80	63	77	62	73	60	63	71	62	69	60	78	66	59	74	65	15.8
Oslo/Gardermoen	60.20N	11.08E	669	−8	−2	78	60	75	58	71	57	60	70	59	67	57	71	62	55	66	61	18.0
Stavanger	58.88N	5.63E	29	13	18	73	59	70	58	66	57	60	66	59	64	58	74	62	57	69	61	11.3
Svinoy (Lgt–H)	62.33N	5.27E	134	28	29	64	57	61	56	60	56	58	60	56	59	56	68	59	55	65	58	4.1
Tromso	69.68N	18.92E	32	6	10	68	57	64	55	61	54	56	63	55	60	54	62	59	52	57	57	10.8
Trondheim	63.47N	10.93E	55	−1	6	75	60	71	59	68	58	61	68	60	65	59	75	64	57	70	61	12.4
Utsira	59.30N	4.88E	183	23	27	67	58	64	58	61	57	59	62	58	60	58	73	60	57	70	59	5.2
OMAN																						
Masqat	23.58N	58.28E	49	61	63	109	73	107	73	105	73	85	93	84	92	83	174	91	82	169	90	14.9
Salalah	17.03N	54.08E	65	63	65	92	71	91	76	90	76	82	87	81	87	80	158	86	79	152	85	9.7
Thamarit	17.67N	54.03E	1459	48	51	108	69	106	68	104	68	78	91	76	90	74	134	84	73	130	82	25.2
Turat Masirah	20.67N	58.90E	62	63	65	99	74	96	76	94	77	82	89	82	88	81	160	86	80	156	86	15.5
PANAMA																						
Panama	8.92N	79.60W	52	73	73	95	76	93	77	92	77	81	89	81	88	79	152	85	79	150	85	15.8
Tocumen	9.05N	79.37W	36	68	68	93	78	92	77	91	77	80	88	80	88	78	148	85	77	143	84	17.5
PARAGUAY																						
Asuncion	25.27S	57.63W	331	41	44	98	75	95	75	94	75	79	90	78	89	76	136	83	75	134	83	18.5
PERU																						
Arequipa	16.32S	71.55W	8267	42	43	75	55	74	54	73	53	58	69	57	69	54	85	62	53	83	61	23.4
Cuzco	13.55S	71.98E	10659	32	34	72	52	71	52	70	51	54	67	53	66	49	76	60	48	74	59	23.9
Iquitos	3.75S	73.25W	413	66	68	93	80	92	80	91	80	81	90	81	90	79	151	87	78	147	87	17.1
Lima	12.00S	77.12W	42	57	58	86	75	84	74	82	73	75	81	74	80	73	124	80	72	118	79	11.5
Pisco	13.75S	76.28W	22	53	55	86	75	83	73	82	72	74	82	73	80	72	117	81	70	111	79	12.4
Talara	4.57S	81.25W	295	60	61	90	76	88	75	87	74	78	84	77	83	76	139	82	75	134	81	14.2
PHILIPPINES																						
Angeles, Clark AFB	15.18N	120.55E	643	68	69	97	78	95	77	93	77	82	89	81	87	80	161	86	79	154	85	17.6
Baguio	16.42N	120.60E	4924	52	54	82	71	79	70	77	69	72	77	71	76	71	135	75	69	130	74	14.8
Cebu/Mandaue	10.30N	123.97E	78	73	74	93	81	92	81	91	80	82	90	81	89	79	152	87	79	150	87	12.4
Olongapo	14.80N	120.27E	56	70	71	98	77	96	77	95	78	82	90	81	89	79	152	86	79	150	86	17.1
Manila, Aquino Airport	14.52N	121.00E	68	69	71	95	81	93	80	92	79	82	90	82	89	80	158	88	79	152	87	15.8
POLAND																						
Bialystok	53.10N	23.17E	495	−4	3	81	66	78	65	75	64	67	75	65	73	64	90	71	62	84	69	19.1
Gdansk	54.38N	18.47E	452	1	9	80	65	77	63	73	62	65	73	63	71	61	82	68	59	77	67	17.5
Katowice	50.23N	19.03E	931	3	9	83	67	80	65	77	64	67	77	65	74	63	88	71	62	85	69	18.4
Kielce	50.82N	20.70E	856	−1	6	83	67	80	65	76	64	67	76	65	74	63	90	71	62	84	69	20.2
Kolobrzeg	54.18N	15.58E	16	10	16	80	65	75	63	71	63	65	72	64	70	63	85	68	61	80	67	12.1
Krakow	50.08N	19.80E	777	−1	6	85	69	81	67	77	65	68	79	67	76	64	93	73	63	88	71	19.6
Lodz	51.73N	19.40E	616	2	9	84	66	80	65	77	63	66	77	65	74	62	86	71	61	82	70	18.7
Lublin	51.22N	22.40E	787	−2	5	82	67	79	66	76	64	67	77	65	74	64	90	72	62	85	70	18.0
Poznan	52.42N	16.83E	301	3	11	85	66	81	64	78	63	67	78	65	75	63	86	71	61	80	69	19.6
Przemysl	49.80N	22.77E	918	1	7	82	67	79	66	76	64	67	76	66	74	64	92	72	63	88	70	14.9
Snezka	50.73N	15.73E	5291	−3	2	64	55	60	54	58	52	55	58	53	57	53	74	57	52	69	55	7.9
Suwalki	54.13N	22.95E	610	−5	2	80	66	77	65	74	63	66	74	64	72	63	88	70	61	83	68	18.5
Szczecin	53.40N	14.62E	9	7	13	83	67	80	66	77	64	67	77	66	74	64	90	72	62	84	70	16.9

Table 19-3. *(Continued)* Air Conditioning Design Data—World Locations

Station	Lat.	Long.	Elev.	Heating 99.6% DB	Heating 99% DB	Cooling 0.4% DB	Cooling 0.4% MWB	Cooling 1% DB	Cooling 1% MWB	Cooling 2% DB	Cooling 2% MWB	Evaporation 1% DB	Evaporation 1% MWB	Evaporation 2% DB	Evaporation 2% MWB	Dehumid. 1% DP	Dehumid. 1% W	Dehumid. 1% MDB	Dehumid. 2% DP	Dehumid. 2% W	Dehumid. 2% MDB	Range of DB
Torun	53.03N	18.58E	236	1	9	84	67	80	65	77	64	67	77	65	75	63	86	71	61	80	70	18.4
Warsaw	52.17N	20.97E	351	0	8	84	67	81	66	77	64	68	78	66	76	64	91	72	63	86	71	19.8
Wroclaw	51.10N	16.88E	396	2	10	84	67	81	66	78	64	67	78	66	76	63	88	71	62	83	71	19.1
PORTUGAL																					
Beja	38.02N	7.87W	810	36	38	99	70	95	68	92	67	70	92	69	89	63	89	74	62	85	73	29.5
Braganca	41.80N	6.73W	2270	26	28	92	65	88	64	85	63	66	85	64	83	59	81	70	58	78	69	24.3
Coimbra	40.20N	8.42W	459	35	38	93	70	89	69	85	68	71	85	69	83	65	96	76	64	92	74	21.4
Evora	38.57N	7.90W	1053	37	39	96	68	93	66	89	66	68	88	67	85	63	89	71	62	85	69	23.6
Faro	37.02N	7.97W	13	41	43	89	69	86	68	84	69	72	80	71	80	69	108	77	68	103	76	17.1
Lisbon	38.78N	9.13W	403	39	41	93	69	90	68	86	68	71	83	70	81	68	103	76	66	97	75	18.9
Portalegre	39.28N	7.42W	1935	34	37	94	66	91	65	88	64	67	87	66	85	61	85	69	59	81	69	19.4
Porto	41.23N	8.68W	239	35	37	86	67	82	66	79	65	68	78	67	75	65	93	70	64	92	69	17.3
Viana Do Castelo	41.70N	8.80W	59	33	35	90	70	86	69	82	67	70	83	69	80	66	96	74	65	92	72	18.7
PUERTO RICO																					
Ceiba, Roosevelt Rds	18.25N	65.63W	39	68	70	90	78	89	78	88	77	80	87	79	86	77	143	84	77	141	84	10.1
San Juan	18.43N	66.00W	62	69	69	92	77	90	78	89	78	80	87	79	87	78	146	84	77	143	84	12.2
QATAR																					
Ad Dawhah	25.25N	51.57E	32	51	53	109	71	107	72	105	72	86	93	85	93	84	180	91	83	171	92	19.4
ROMANIA																					
Bucharest	44.50N	26.13E	298	8	14	91	72	88	70	86	69	73	85	71	83	69	109	77	68	104	75	23.9
Cluj–Napoca	46.78N	23.57E	1354	4	8	85	68	82	67	79	65	69	78	67	76	65	99	73	64	93	71	20.5
Constanta	44.22N	28.63E	45	15	19	83	72	81	72	79	71	74	79	72	78	72	118	77	71	113	76	12.2
Craiova	44.23N	23.87E	639	10	15	92	74	89	73	86	71	74	86	73	83	71	118	80	69	110	79	22.0
Galati	45.50N	28.02E	236	7	12	89	72	86	70	84	69	72	83	71	80	69	108	77	67	102	75	20.2
Omul Mountain	45.45N	25.45E	8231	-13	-7	58	50	54	48	52	47	50	53	48	51	49	69	52	47	64	49	11.2
Satu Mare	47.78N	22.88E	406	0	6	88	71	85	69	82	68	71	83	69	80	67	100	76	65	94	74	23.2
Timisoara	45.77N	21.25E	288	9	14	92	70	88	69	85	67	70	85	69	82	66	96	74	64	91	73	23.0
RUSSIA																					
Abakan	53.75N	91.40E	803	-29	-24	85	64	82	63	78	62	66	77	64	75	62	85	70	60	80	69	18.9
Aldan	58.62N	125.37E	2237	-41	-37	81	61	77	60	74	59	62	74	60	71	58	77	66	56	72	65	18.4
Aleksandrovsk–Sahal	50.90N	142.17E	102	-17	-13	74	64	71	63	68	61	65	69	63	67	63	85	67	61	80	65	11.3
Anadyr	64.78N	177.57E	203	-37	-34	65	56	62	55	59	53	55	61	53	58	52	58	58	50	55	56	9.7
Apuka	60.45N	169.58E	26	-18	-14	61	55	58	53	56	52	54	57	53	55	53	60	56	51	56	54	8.5
Arkhangelsk	64.53N	40.47E	42	-29	-23	79	65	75	63	72	62	65	73	63	70	62	83	69	60	77	67	16.9
Armavir	44.98N	41.12E	524	4	10	90	69	87	69	84	68	71	82	70	81	68	104	77	66	98	75	21.8
Astrakhan	46.27N	48.03E	59	-1	4	94	71	91	69	88	68	72	85	71	83	69	105	78	67	99	76	19.4
Barnaul	53.40N	83.70E	826	-21	-16	85	66	81	64	78	63	67	78	65	75	63	88	72	61	83	70	16.9
Blagoveshchensk	50.25N	127.50E	449	-27	-23	86	69	83	69	80	67	72	78	70	77	69	109	76	68	104	74	16.6
Borzya	50.38N	116.52E	2244	-37	-32	83	63	80	62	77	62	66	75	64	73	62	92	70	61	87	69	19.1
Bratsk	56.07N	101.83E	1604	-32	-27	81	63	77	62	74	61	64	74	63	71	61	84	69	59	78	67	16.6
Bryansk	53.33N	34.23E	711	-8	-3	81	66	78	65	75	64	67	75	65	73	64	90	71	62	85	69	14.6
Chelyabinsk	55.30N	61.53E	744	-19	-15	85	66	82	65	79	64	67	78	66	76	63	90	72	62	85	70	16.6
Cherepovets	59.12N	37.93E	429	-25	-17	79	67	76	65	73	63	66	74	65	72	64	90	70	62	83	68	18.2
Chita	52.02N	113.33E	2247	-33	-29	84	65	80	63	77	61	66	76	64	73	62	91	70	60	85	68	20.5
Dudinka	69.40N	86.17E	62	-50	-44	76	62	72	60	67	58	61	70	59	67	57	69	66	55	64	63	14.4
Egvekinot	66.35N	179.12W	85	-34	-29	64	53	60	52	57	50	53	60	51	56	50	53	54	48	50	52	9.2
Groznyy	43.35N	45.68E	531	5	10	91	71	88	69	86	68	71	84	70	82	67	102	77	66	99	75	18.5
Habarovsk/Novy	48.52N	135.17E	236	-22	-18	86	70	83	69	80	68	72	79	70	78	69	108	76	67	102	73	16.2
Irkutsk	52.27N	104.35E	1683	-29	-24	81	63	78	62	74	61	65	74	63	72	61	86	68	59	80	67	20.0
Izhevsk	56.82N	53.27E	518	-21	-16	85	66	81	65	78	64	67	78	65	75	63	89	72	62	84	70	17.3
Juzno–Kurilsk	44.02N	145.87E	131	10	13	68	65	66	64	65	63	65	66	63	64	64	90	65	63	86	64	5.6
Juzno–Sahalinsk	46.92N	142.73E	102	-11	-6	78	68	75	67	72	65	68	72	66	70	67	99	71	64	91	69	14.0
Kaliningrad	54.70N	20.62E	88	-3	6	80	66	77	64	74	62	66	74	64	72	62	85	70	61	79	68	15.3
Kaluga	54.57N	36.37E	659	-12	-7	80	67	77	66	74	63	67	75	65	73	64	91	72	62	85	69	16.6
Kazan	55.78N	49.18E	380	-18	-12	85	67	81	66	78	64	68	77	66	75	64	91	73	62	85	71	16.6
Kirov	58.65N	49.62E	482	-27	-18	82	67	79	65	75	64	67	76	65	73	64	90	72	62	85	70	17.3
Kolpashevo	58.30N	82.88E	249	-37	-30	82	66	79	65	76	63	67	76	65	73	64	90	72	62	84	69	18.0
Krasnodar	45.03N	39.15E	108	3	9	90	71	87	70	84	69	72	83	71	81	69	106	78	67	100	77	21.1
Krasnoyarsk	56.00N	92.88E	908	-29	-24	83	65	80	63	77	62	66	76	64	73	62	88	70	61	82	69	19.1
Kurgan	55.47N	65.40E	259	-25	-19	87	67	83	66	80	65	68	80	67	77	64	90	73	63	85	72	18.7
Kursk	51.73N	36.27E	688	-9	-3	83	67	80	66	78	65	68	77	66	75	64	92	72	62	87	71	17.1
Kyakhta	50.37N	106.45E	2627	-21	-18	83	62	80	61	76	60	64	76	62	73	59	83	68	57	78	67	18.0
Magadan	59.58N	150.78E	387	-20	-15	65	55	61	53	59	52	55	59	54	57	53	61	56	52	58	55	9.7
Magnitogorsk	53.35N	59.08E	1253	-19	-15	85	65	82	64	79	62	66	78	64	76	62	86	72	60	80	70	18.9
Markovo	64.68N	170.42E	108	-54	-49	76	61	72	59	69	57	60	70	58	67	55	66	63	54	62	62	18.4
Moscow	55.75N	37.63E	511	-10	-4	82	67	79	65	76	64	67	76	65	73	64	90	72	62	85	70	14.8
Moscow, Vnukovo	55.65N	37.27E	666	-11	-6	81	66	77	65	75	63	67	76	65	73	63	88	69	61	83	68	16.4
Murmansk	68.97N	33.05E	167	-20	-12	74	59	70	57	66	56	59	68	57	65	55	64	63	53	60	60	12.2

Table 19-3. (Continued) Air Conditioning Design Data—World Locations

Station	Lat.	Long.	Elev.	Heating 99.6% DB	99% DB	Cooling 0.4% DB	MWB	1% DB	MWB	2% DB	MWB	Evaporation 1% DB	MWB	2% DB	MWB	Dehumidification 1% DP	W	MDB	2% DP	W	MDB	Range of DB
Nikolayevsk	53.15N	140.70E	223	−28	−23	78	67	75	65	73	64	67	73	65	71	64	90	71	62	85	68	15.5
Nikolskoe/Beringa	55.20N	165.98E	20	12	15	57	54	55	53	54	52	53	55	52	54	53	59	54	51	56	53	4.5
Nizhniy Novgorod	56.22N	43.82E	269	−17	−11	83	67	80	66	77	64	68	77	66	74	64	92	72	63	85	71	17.5
Nizhniy Tagil	57.88N	60.07E	846	−26	−20	83	65	80	64	76	63	66	76	64	74	63	88	71	61	83	68	18.4
Novokuznetsk	53.73N	87.18E	1010	−23	−17	83	64	80	64	77	63	66	77	65	74	62	88	71	61	83	70	17.8
Novosibirsk	55.03N	82.90E	580	−25	−19	83	66	80	64	77	63	67	77	65	74	62	91	71	62	85	70	16.9
Nyurba	63.28N	118.33E	423	−63	−58	84	66	80	64	76	61	66	77	63	73	62	84	71	59	76	68	22.9
Olekminsk	60.40N	120.42E	741	−54	−48	85	65	81	64	77	62	65	78	64	74	61	82	72	59	76	68	20.2
Omsk	54.93N	73.40E	403	−24	−18	87	66	84	64	81	64	67	80	65	78	62	85	72	61	80	70	19.3
Orel	53.00N	36.03E	666	−10	−4	82	66	80	66	77	64	67	76	65	74	64	90	72	62	85	70	16.6
Orenburg	51.78N	55.22E	357	−18	−13	92	66	88	65	85	64	67	83	66	80	62	85	72	61	80	71	20.9
Ozernaja	51.48N	156.48E	95	4	7	60	56	58	54	56	53	55	57	54	55	54	62	56	53	59	55	5.9
Penza	53.13N	45.02E	570	−14	−9	85	65	82	64	79	63	67	78	65	75	64	90	72	62	85	70	18.7
Perm	58.02N	56.30E	564	−24	−18	84	67	81	65	77	64	67	78	65	75	63	89	72	62	84	70	16.0
Petropavlovsk–Kamca	52.97N	158.75E	79	5	8	69	60	66	58	63	56	58	65	57	62	55	65	61	54	62	59	9.5
Petrozavodsk	61.82N	34.27E	367	−19	−11	77	64	73	62	70	60	64	71	62	69	61	82	67	59	76	65	13.7
Pskov	57.80N	28.42E	137	−13	−4	80	66	77	64	74	63	66	74	65	72	63	88	70	61	81	69	16.4
Rostov–Na–Donu	47.25N	39.82E	252	2	5	89	69	86	68	83	67	71	82	69	80	67	99	76	65	95	75	18.5
Rubtsovsk	51.50N	81.22E	705	−26	−20	87	67	84	66	81	64	68	79	66	77	64	92	71	62	87	71	20.2
Ryazan	54.62N	39.72E	557	−10	−6	83	67	80	66	77	64	68	77	66	74	64	92	72	63	87	71	14.9
Rybinsk	58.00N	38.83E	374	−19	−12	80	68	77	65	74	64	67	74	65	72	64	90	72	63	86	69	13.0
Samara (Kuybyshev)	53.25N	50.45E	144	−17	−12	88	68	85	67	82	66	70	81	68	78	65	94	76	63	88	73	20.5
Saratov	51.57N	46.03E	511	−8	−5	87	66	84	65	81	64	68	80	66	78	63	89	73	62	84	72	15.1
Smolensk	54.75N	32.07E	790	−9	−4	79	66	76	65	74	63	66	74	65	72	63	90	71	62	84	69	15.1
Sochi	43.45N	39.90E	52	28	30	83	73	81	73	80	72	74	80	73	78	72	120	78	71	116	77	13.5
St Petersburg	59.97N	30.30E	13	−9	−2	79	65	76	64	73	62	66	74	64	71	62	84	69	61	79	68	13.5
Svobodnyy	51.45N	128.12E	646	−35	−30	85	67	82	67	79	66	70	77	68	76	67	103	73	66	97	72	18.7
Syktyvkar	61.72N	50.83E	390	−32	−25	83	66	79	65	75	62	67	76	64	73	63	88	71	61	82	68	17.1
Tambov	52.73N	41.47E	456	−13	−8	86	67	83	66	80	64	68	78	66	76	64	92	73	63	86	71	18.5
Tayshet	55.95N	98.00E	990	−34	−29	83	64	79	63	76	62	66	76	64	73	62	86	70	60	81	68	19.3
Ufa	54.75N	56.00E	344	−24	−18	87	67	83	66	80	65	68	80	67	78	64	91	73	63	86	72	19.1
Ulan Ude	51.80N	107.43E	1673	−33	−29	85	63	82	62	78	61	65	76	63	74	61	84	70	59	79	68	20.7
Urup Island	46.20N	150.50E	230	12	14	63	59	60	57	57	56	58	59	56	57	57	71	58	55	65	56	9.2
Ustilimsk	58.03N	102.73E	1318	−40	−35	82	63	78	62	75	61	64	74	62	73	61	83	69	58	77	67	20.2
Ust–Kamcatsk	56.22N	162.47E	89	−23	−18	67	57	63	56	60	54	57	62	55	59	54	63	59	53	60	57	10.6
Vladimir	56.13N	40.38E	557	−16	−10	82	67	78	66	75	64	67	76	65	73	64	91	71	62	85	70	15.3
Vladivostok	43.12N	131.90E	604	−8	−4	78	69	75	67	72	66	70	73	69	71	69	110	72	68	104	70	8.6
Volgograd	48.68N	44.35E	475	−6	−2	90	65	88	65	85	64	68	82	66	80	63	89	72	62	84	72	18.9
Vologda	59.23N	39.87E	429	−27	−18	80	66	76	64	74	63	67	73	65	71	64	90	71	62	83	68	16.9
Voronezh	51.70N	39.17E	505	−9	−5	85	66	82	65	79	63	67	78	66	75	64	90	72	62	85	71	17.5
Yakutsk	62.08N	129.75E	337	−61	−58	85	66	81	64	78	62	66	78	64	75	61	82	71	59	76	72	21.2
Yekaterinburg	56.80N	60.63E	777	−22	−17	84	66	81	65	77	64	67	77	65	74	64	90	71	62	85	70	17.1
Yelets	52.63N	38.52E	551	−11	−6	84	67	81	66	78	64	68	77	66	74	64	92	72	63	88	70	17.1
Zyryanka	65.73N	150.90E	141	−56	−52	83	63	79	62	74	60	64	76	61	72	58	73	70	56	66	68	17.3
SAMOA																						
Pago Pago	14.33S	170.72W	9	72	73	88	80	88	80	87	80	81	86	81	86	79	153	85	79	150	85	9.4
SAUDI ARABIA																						
Abha	18.23N	42.65E	6837	41	44	87	56	86	56	84	56	66	75	65	74	63	111	71	62	108	71	21.4
Al Jawf	29.78N	40.10E	2244	32	35	105	63	103	62	101	61	64	95	63	96	55	70	66	52	63	67	26.3
Al Madinah	24.55N	39.70E	2070	48	50	113	65	110	65	109	64	68	97	67	98	60	82	75	57	76	76	23.8
Al Wajh	26.20N	36.47E	52	53	55	95	72	93	76	91	78	82	89	82	89	81	159	88	79	152	87	13.1
Arar	30.90N	41.13E	1811	32	34	107	68	105	68	103	67	71	100	69	98	60	81	90	57	75	86	25.6
At Taif	21.48N	40.55E	4753	42	45	97	65	95	65	94	65	70	87	69	87	65	109	80	63	102	79	20.9
Az Zahran	26.27N	50.15E	55	45	47	111	71	109	71	107	72	84	94	83	92	82	168	90	80	158	90	23.9
Hail	27.43N	41.68E	3323	31	34	105	65	104	64	102	64	67	97	65	97	57	80	72	55	74	71	28.3
Hafar Al Batin	28.33N	46.17E	1165	36	39	117	67	112	66	110	66	69	100	67	100	61	85	72	59	78	71	27.5
Jiddah	21.67N	39.15E	39	59	61	104	72	102	73	100	74	82	94	81	92	79	151	89	79	150	88	22.0
Jizan	16.90N	42.58E	9	68	70	102	83	100	83	99	83	86	98	85	97	83	171	96	82	168	95	12.6
Khamis Mushayt	18.30N	42.80E	6738	40	43	88	57	87	57	86	56	65	74	64	74	62	106	71	61	102	70	22.1
Makkah	21.48N	39.83E	1017	59	62	113	76	111	76	109	75	81	102	80	101	76	139	94	74	133	94	27.2
Qasim	26.30N	43.77E	2132	37	39	110	67	109	65	107	64	70	96	68	98	62	92	80	59	81	75	29.3
Rafha	29.63N	43.48E	1466	33	35	111	69	109	68	107	67	70	104	69	103	61	83	72	58	75	75	29.7
Riyadh	24.72N	46.72E	2007	41	44	111	64	110	64	108	64	67	97	66	96	60	83	72	57	76	72	25.2
Tabuk	28.37N	36.63E	2526	34	37	104	64	102	63	100	63	67	95	65	94	56	74	77	55	71	76	26.6
Turayf	31.68N	38.67E	2667	29	32	102	64	99	63	97	62	66	91	65	90	58	78	75	56	73	74	27.4
Yanbual Bahr	24.15N	38.07E	3	52	54	109	76	106	76	104	76	82	95	81	94	79	150	89	77	142	88	25.7
SENEGAL																						
Dakar	14.73N	17.50W	78	61	62	89	74	88	77	86	77	80	85	79	84	79	150	83	78	146	83	9.7

Table 19-3. *(Continued)* Air Conditioning Design Data—World Locations

Station	Lat.	Long.	Elev.	Heating 99.6% DB	99% DB	Cooling 0.4% DB	MWB	1% DB	MWB	2% DB	MWB	Evaporation 1% DB	MWB	2% DB	MWB	Dehumidification 1% DP	W	MDB	2% DP	W	MDB	Range of DB
Saint Louis	16.05N	16.45W	13	60	61	101	69	97	69	94	69	82	87	81	86	80	156	85	79	153	84	16.2
Tambacounda	13.77N	13.68W	164	63	65	106	70	104	70	103	70	80	89	79	88	78	146	84	77	142	83	22.7
Ziguinchor	12.55N	16.27W	75	61	63	101	72	98	71	96	72	82	90	82	89	80	156	87	80	153	86	27.7
SINGAPORE																						
Singapore	1.37N	103.98E	52	73	74	91	79	90	79	90	79	81	87	80	87	79	152	84	79	150	84	11.3
SLOVAKIA																						
Bratislava	48.20N	17.20E	427	9	14	89	69	86	68	83	67	69	83	68	80	65	92	75	63	88	74	22.1
Chopok Mountain	48.93N	19.58E	6601	−6	−3	59	52	56	51	54	50	52	55	51	53	51	71	53	49	67	52	7.9
Kosice	48.70N	21.27E	761	8	12	85	68	82	67	79	65	68	80	67	77	64	91	74	62	86	72	19.3
Lomnicky Stit (Peak)	49.20N	20.22E	8645	−12	−8	53	47	51	45	49	43	47	50	45	48	45	62	48	43	57	46	8.5
Zilina	49.23N	18.62E	1033	2	8	85	67	82	65	78	64	67	79	65	76	62	88	71	61	84	70	21.8
SLOVENIA																						
Ljubljana	46.22N	14.48E	1263	9	13	86	68	83	67	80	65	68	80	67	78	64	92	72	62	88	72	22.3
SOUTH AFRICA																						
Bloemfontein	29.10S	26.30E	4422	26	28	93	60	91	60	89	60	66	79	65	78	62	99	69	61	94	68	26.3
Cape Town	33.98S	18.60E	137	38	41	87	67	83	67	81	65	69	80	68	77	65	94	72	65	92	72	15.8
Durban	29.97S	30.95E	26	50	52	87	75	85	75	83	74	77	83	76	81	75	132	81	74	128	80	9.9
Johannesburg	26.13S	28.23E	5577	34	37	84	60	82	60	80	60	65	76	64	75	61	99	68	60	96	67	18.7
Marion Island	46.88S	37.87E	72	30	32	57	54	55	52	53	51	53	54	52	53	53	59	54	51	56	52	8.1
Port Elizabeth	33.98S	25.60E	196	43	46	85	66	81	68	79	68	72	77	71	76	70	112	74	69	108	74	12.1
Pretoria	25.73S	28.18E	4337	39	41	89	64	88	63	86	63	68	80	67	79	64	106	72	63	102	72	17.6
SPAIN																						
Barcelona	41.28N	2.07E	19	32	35	85	74	84	74	82	73	76	82	74	80	74	126	80	73	121	79	15.1
Granada	37.18N	3.78W	1833	25	28	99	67	96	67	93	66	69	89	68	88	63	92	75	61	85	74	33.7
La Coruna	43.37N	8.42W	219	39	41	77	65	74	65	72	64	66	72	65	71	64	90	69	63	87	68	9.4
Madrid	40.45N	3.55W	1909	24	26	97	69	94	68	92	67	70	91	68	89	62	90	80	60	84	79	29.2
Malaga	36.67N	4.48W	22	39	41	93	68	90	68	86	68	74	81	73	80	72	118	78	70	112	77	16.4
Palma	39.55N	2.73E	26	31	33	91	74	89	73	86	73	77	84	76	83	75	132	82	73	125	81	22.3
Salamanca	40.95N	5.50W	2608	23	25	93	65	90	64	86	63	65	86	64	83	59	82	69	57	78	68	28.6
Santander	43.47N	3.82W	213	36	39	80	67	76	67	75	66	69	74	68	73	67	102	72	66	97	71	9.4
Santiago De Compostela	42.90N	8.43W	1204	30	32	88	69	84	67	80	66	69	82	67	77	65	95	73	63	90	70	21.2
Sevilla	37.42N	5.90W	101	34	37	104	75	100	72	97	71	74	96	72	92	68	104	80	66	97	78	30.1
Valencia	39.50N	0.47W	203	34	36	90	71	88	72	86	72	75	83	74	82	73	125	80	72	118	80	16.6
Zaragoza	41.67N	1.05W	862	28	30	97	69	93	69	90	68	71	89	70	85	66	99	76	64	93	78	24.1
SWEDEN																						
Goteborg, Landvetter	57.67N	12.30E	554	3	10	78	62	75	60	72	59	62	71	60	68	59	76	64	57	71	62	14.9
Goteborg, Save	57.78N	11.88E	173	3	10	78	62	74	61	71	60	64	70	62	68	61	80	66	59	76	65	13.7
Jonkoping	57.77N	14.08E	761	−4	5	79	61	75	60	72	58	62	71	60	68	59	76	64	57	72	62	19.6
Kalmar	56.73N	16.30E	52	5	10	79	63	75	62	72	60	64	72	62	70	61	79	67	59	74	65	18.7
Karlsborg	58.52N	14.53E	334	2	9	76	63	73	61	70	60	63	70	61	68	60	77	66	58	73	65	14.2
Karlstad	59.37N	13.47E	180	−5	1	77	63	74	62	71	60	64	70	62	68	61	80	65	59	76	64	15.7
Kiruna	67.82N	20.33E	1482	−22	−17	70	56	66	54	63	52	56	63	54	61	52	62	59	50	57	57	13.7
Malmo	55.55N	13.37E	347	7	14	77	62	74	61	71	60	64	70	62	68	62	85	66	60	80	65	14.2
Ostersund/Froso	63.18N	14.50E	1213	−14	−7	74	58	70	57	67	55	58	67	57	65	54	66	61	53	62	60	13.5
Soderhamn	61.27N	17.10E	118	−7	0	77	62	73	60	70	59	62	71	60	68	58	74	65	57	69	64	16.2
Stockholm, Arlanda	59.65N	17.95E	200	−2	5	80	63	77	61	73	59	63	71	62	69	61	80	65	59	75	64	16.2
Stockholm, Bromma	59.35N	17.95E	36	−1	5	79	63	76	61	72	60	64	72	62	69	61	80	66	59	75	65	15.8
Sundsvall	62.53N	17.45E	32	−14	−8	75	62	72	59	69	58	62	68	60	66	59	76	64	58	71	62	15.8
Ungskar	56.03N	15.80E	9	11	16	71	65	68	63	67	62	64	68	63	66	63	85	67	61	80	65	6.8
Uppsala	59.88N	17.60E	134	−4	3	78	62	75	61	71	59	63	71	61	69	59	76	65	58	71	65	16.7
Visby	57.67N	18.35E	154	12	16	75	63	72	62	70	61	64	70	63	68	62	84	66	61	80	65	13.1
SWITZERLAND																						
Geneva	46.25N	6.13E	1364	18	23	86	66	83	65	80	64	67	80	65	77	62	89	71	61	84	70	22.1
Interlaken	46.67N	7.88E	1902	15	19	82	65	79	65	76	63	65	77	64	74	61	87	70	60	83	69	17.8
Jungfrau Mountain	46.55N	7.98E	11732	−15	−11	43	33	41	32	39	32	35	38	34	37	33	43	36	32	41	35	6.8
La Chaux-De-Fonds	47.08N	6.80E	3343	6	12	78	62	74	61	71	59	62	72	60	70	58	80	66	56	76	65	17.6
Locarno	46.17N	8.88E	649	21	24	84	70	82	69	80	67	71	80	69	78	67	102	76	66	97	74	17.8
Lugano	46.00N	8.97E	905	25	28	85	71	83	69	81	68	71	80	70	79	68	106	77	66	100	76	17.6
Payerne	46.82N	6.95E	1610	14	19	84	67	81	66	78	64	67	78	65	76	63	91	73	61	86	70	19.8
Saentis (Aut)	47.25N	9.35E	8202	−3	1	57	47	55	46	53	44	48	52	47	51	46	63	49	45	60	48	7.7
San Bernardino	46.47N	9.18E	5374	6	10	69	55	67	54	64	53	57	64	55	62	54	76	60	52	71	58	14.9
Zurich	47.38N	8.57E	1866	13	18	83	66	80	65	77	63	66	77	65	74	62	90	70	61	86	69	16.0
SYRIA																						
Damascus	33.42N	36.52E	1984	25	28	101	64	98	64	96	64	68	85	67	84	64	97	72	62	91	71	33.8
TAIWAN																						
Hsinchu	24.82N	120.93E	88	47	50	93	81	92	81	91	81	82	90	81	90	80	154	88	79	150	87	12.4
Hualien	23.98N	121.60E	62	53	55	90	80	89	80	88	80	81	87	81	87	79	153	86	79	149	86	9.7
Kaohsiung	22.58N	120.35E	29	52	55	92	79	90	79	90	79	81	87	80	87	79	151	84	79	150	84	11.5

Table 19-3. *(Continued)* Air Conditioning Design Data—World Locations

Station	Location Lat.	Location Long.	Location Elev.	Heating 99.6% DB	Heating 99% DB	Cooling 0.4% DB	Cooling 0.4% MWB	Cooling 1% DB	Cooling 1% MWB	Cooling 2% DB	Cooling 2% MWB	Evaporation 1% DB	Evaporation 1% MWB	Evaporation 2% DB	Evaporation 2% MWB	Dehumidification 1% DP	Dehumidification 1% W	Dehumidification 1% MDB	Dehumidification 2% DP	Dehumidification 2% W	Dehumidification 2% MDB	Range of DB
Taichung	24.18N	120.65E	367	46	48	94	82	93	82	91	81	83	91	82	90	81	162	89	80	159	89	15.1
Tainan (593580)	23.00N	120.22E	45	51	53	92	81	91	81	90	80	82	88	81	88	80	158	85	80	155	85	9.9
Taipei	25.07N	121.55E	19	48	50	94	80	93	80	92	80	81	90	81	90	79	150	86	79	148	86	13.3
Taipei Intl Airport	25.08N	121.22E	108	48	50	93	80	92	80	91	80	82	90	81	89	79	152	86	79	149	86	13.1
TAJIKISTAN																						
Dushanbe	38.55N	68.78E	2634	19	23	99	67	97	67	95	66	69	91	68	90	62	91	81	60	85	80	25.6
Khujand (Leninabad)	40.22N	69.73E	1404	17	21	99	67	96	66	94	66	69	91	67	90	61	84	79	59	79	78	23.0
THAILAND																						
Bangkok	13.92N	100.60E	39	65	68	99	80	97	79	95	78	83	91	82	89	81	160	87	80	156	87	16.7
Chiang Mai	18.78N	98.98E	1030	53	56	100	72	98	72	96	73	78	88	78	87	76	139	82	75	138	81	24.5
Chiang Rai	19.92N	99.83E	1295	49	52	98	72	96	72	94	73	79	88	78	87	76	144	83	76	141	82	25.0
Chumphon	10.48N	99.18E	16	66	68	95	79	94	79	92	79	81	91	80	90	78	147	87	78	145	86	16.7
Hat Yai	6.92N	100.43E	114	70	71	95	77	94	77	93	77	80	89	79	88	78	144	82	77	143	82	18.0
Phetchabun	16.43N	101.15E	380	56	59	101	78	99	78	97	78	81	91	81	90	79	150	87	78	148	86	20.9
Phrae	18.17N	100.17E	531	55	58	101	76	99	77	97	76	81	90	80	90	78	149	85	78	146	85	22.1
Tak	16.88N	99.15E	406	57	60	102	74	101	74	99	74	79	89	79	88	77	144	83	76	140	83	18.7
TRINIDAD & TOBAGO																						
Port of Spain	10.62N	61.35W	49	68	70	91	77	90	77	90	77	79	87	79	86	77	143	82	77	141	82	14.2
TUNISIA																						
Bizerte	37.25N	9.80E	9	38	40	97	72	92	72	89	72	76	84	75	83	73	123	81	72	118	80	18.2
Gabes	33.88N	10.10E	16	42	44	96	71	92	73	89	73	78	86	77	85	76	136	85	75	130	84	11.7
Gafsa	34.42N	8.82E	1030	36	38	105	68	101	69	98	68	72	90	71	89	67	104	78	66	99	78	23.8
Kelibia	36.85N	11.08E	98	42	44	89	73	86	73	85	73	77	82	76	81	75	133	81	74	127	80	13.1
Qairouan (Kairouan)	35.67N	10.10E	223	40	42	105	71	100	71	97	71	75	88	74	88	72	118	80	70	112	80	25.4
Tunis	36.83N	10.23E	13	41	43	98	73	94	73	91	73	77	86	76	85	74	128	82	73	123	81	21.8
TURKEY																						
Adana	37.00N	35.42E	216	32	34	97	71	94	71	92	72	78	87	77	86	75	133	82	74	128	82	19.8
Ankara	40.12N	32.98E	3113	2	8	90	63	86	63	84	62	64	83	63	81	57	78	72	55	74	70	28.4
Erzurum	39.92N	41.27E	5767	−23	−17	84	61	82	60	79	59	62	78	61	76	56	82	72	54	76	70	29.9
Eskisehir	39.78N	30.57E	2575	12	16	90	68	87	67	85	66	69	83	67	83	64	97	78	62	92	75	25.9
Istanbul	40.97N	28.82E	121	26	29	86	70	84	69	83	69	72	80	71	78	70	111	76	68	105	76	15.3
Izmir/Cigli(Cv/AFB)	38.50N	27.02E	16	28	31	96	72	93	71	91	70	73	90	72	89	67	98	82	66	95	81	23.0
Malatya	38.43N	38.08E	2785	10	16	97	68	95	67	93	66	68	93	67	91	59	82	85	57	77	83	27.4
Van	38.45N	43.32E	5449	6	9	84	59	82	66	80	66	68	80	66	78	64	108	78	62	101	77	19.4
TURKMENISTAN																						
Ashgabat (Ashkhabad)	37.97N	58.33E	688	20	23	104	67	102	67	99	67	72	92	70	91	64	92	85	63	87	84	24.1
Dashhowuz (Tashauz)	41.83N	59.98E	288	5	10	103	74	99	73	96	71	75	95	74	93	68	105	90	66	98	88	24.3
UNITED KINGDOM & NORTHERN IRELAND																						
Aberdeen/Dyce	57.20N	2.22W	213	22	27	71	62	68	60	65	58	61	67	60	64	59	75	64	57	70	62	13.0
Aberporth	52.13N	4.57W	439	26	29	72	62	68	61	65	60	62	66	61	64	61	80	64	59	77	62	9.4
Aughton	53.55N	2.92W	183	26	28	75	64	72	62	69	60	63	69	62	67	61	80	66	59	76	64	10.8
Aviemore	57.20N	3.83W	721	15	21	75	61	71	60	67	58	61	69	59	65	57	71	65	56	67	62	15.5
Belfast	54.65N	6.22W	265	27	29	72	62	69	61	67	60	62	67	61	65	60	78	65	58	74	64	12.8
Birmingham	52.45N	1.73W	324	21	24	78	64	75	62	72	61	64	72	62	70	61	80	67	59	76	65	16.9
Bournemouth	50.78N	1.83W	36	22	25	78	65	75	63	72	62	65	72	63	69	62	83	67	61	80	66	18.0
Bristol	51.47N	2.60W	36	26	29	79	65	76	63	73	62	65	73	63	70	62	82	68	60	78	66	12.8
Camborne	50.22N	5.32W	288	30	32	71	62	68	61	66	60	63	66	62	65	62	83	64	60	79	63	8.8
Cardiff	51.40N	3.35W	219	25	28	77	64	74	63	71	62	64	71	63	68	62	83	66	60	79	65	14.8
Edinburgh	55.95N	3.35W	134	21	25	72	61	69	60	66	59	61	67	60	65	59	74	64	57	71	63	14.6
Exeter	50.73N	3.42W	98	24	27	78	65	75	64	72	62	65	73	64	70	62	84	68	61	81	67	15.8
Finningley	53.48N	1.00W	55	23	26	78	64	75	63	72	61	64	72	62	70	60	78	67	59	75	65	17.3
Glasgow	55.87N	4.43W	26	21	24	75	63	71	61	67	59	62	69	60	66	59	75	65	58	71	63	14.6
Hemsby	52.68N	1.68E	45	27	29	74	65	71	63	69	62	64	70	63	67	62	83	67	61	79	65	13.9
Herstmonceux	50.87N	0.33E	55	24	27	76	65	74	63	71	62	65	72	63	69	62	83	67	61	80	66	15.3
Jersey/Channel Islands	49.22N	2.20W	275	28	31	76	65	73	63	70	62	64	71	63	68	62	83	65	61	81	65	11.0
Kirkwall	58.95N	2.90W	68	29	31	64	59	62	57	60	56	58	61	57	59	57	69	59	56	66	58	9.2
Lerwick	60.13N	1.18W	275	28	30	60	56	58	55	57	54	56	58	55	56	55	66	59	54	64	56	6.8
Leuchars	56.38N	2.87W	39	24	27	72	61	69	59	66	58	61	67	59	64	58	73	63	57	69	62	14.0
London, Gatwick	51.15N	0.18W	203	22	25	80	65	76	63	74	62	65	73	64	71	62	83	68	60	79	67	17.6
London, Heathrow	51.48N	0.45W	78	25	28	81	66	78	64	75	63	66	75	64	72	62	83	69	61	80	68	16.6
Lyneham	51.50N	1.98W	511	22	26	78	64	75	62	72	61	64	72	62	69	61	81	66	59	77	65	15.8
Lynemouth	55.02N	1.42W	98	28	31	69	61	67	60	65	58	61	65	60	64	59	76	63	58	73	62	8.8
Manchester	53.35N	2.27W	255	24	27	77	63	74	62	71	60	63	71	62	69	60	79	67	59	74	65	13.7
Nottingham	53.00N	1.25W	383	23	26	78	64	74	63	71	61	64	72	62	69	61	81	68	60	77	65	16.0
Oban	56.42N	5.47W	13	26	29	73	61	69	60	66	58	61	67	60	64	58	73	64	57	70	62	10.4
Plymouth	50.35N	4.12W	88	29	31	75	63	72	62	69	61	64	69	63	67	62	83	66	61	80	64	11.0
Stansted Airport	51.88N	0.23E	347	23	26	79	64	76	63	73	62	64	72	63	70	61	82	67	60	78	66	16.7
Stornoway	58.22N	6.32W	42	29	31	65	59	62	58	60	56	58	61	57	60	57	71	60	56	67	59	8.6

Table 19-3. *(Continued)* Air Conditioning Design Data—World Locations

Station	Lat.	Long.	Elev.	Heating 99.6% DB	99% DB	Cooling 0.4% DB	MWB	1% DB	MWB	2% DB	MWB	Evaporation 1% DB	MWB	2% DB	MWB	Dehumidification 1% DP	W	MDB	2% DP	W	MDB	Range of DB
Valley	53.25N	4.53W	36	27	30	74	63	70	61	67	60	62	68	61	65	60	78	64	59	75	63	10.6
Wyton Raf	52.35N	0.12W	134	22	26	79	64	76	63	73	62	65	73	63	71	62	82	68	60	78	66	16.7
UKRAINE																						
Chernihiv (Chernigov)	51.48N	31.28E	449	−7	−1	84	68	81	67	78	65	68	78	67	75	65	93	73	63	89	71	18.2
Chernivtsi (Chernovtsky)	48.27N	25.97E	787	2	7	83	68	80	66	78	65	68	78	66	76	64	92	73	63	88	72	16.2
Dnipropetrovsk	48.37N	35.08E	465	0	4	87	67	85	66	82	65	69	80	67	78	65	94	74	63	89	72	18.7
Donetsk	48.07N	37.77E	741	−1	3	86	66	83	66	80	65	68	80	67	76	64	92	73	63	88	72	19.6
Kerch	45.40N	36.42E	160	11	15	85	69	83	69	81	68	71	80	70	78	68	105	77	67	99	75	14.6
Kharkiv (Kharkov)	49.87N	36.13E	498	−3	2	85	67	83	65	80	65	68	78	67	76	65	93	73	63	88	71	16.4
Kherson	46.67N	32.62E	157	4	8	89	68	86	68	83	66	70	81	68	79	66	97	75	65	92	73	21.2
Kirovohrad (Kirovograd)	48.48N	32.25E	564	−2	2	86	65	83	65	80	64	67	78	66	76	64	90	72	62	85	70	20.5
Kryvyy Rih (Krivoy Rog)	47.93N	33.33E	410	0	4	87	67	85	66	82	65	68	80	67	78	64	92	73	63	87	72	21.1
Kyyiv (Kiev)	50.40N	30.45E	551	−2	3	83	67	80	66	77	65	68	77	66	75	65	93	73	63	88	71	16.6
Luhansk	48.60N	39.27E	203	−4	0	88	67	85	66	82	64	68	81	67	78	64	90	72	63	86	72	19.1
Mariupol (Zdanov)	47.07N	37.50E	229	4	8	84	71	82	70	80	69	72	79	71	78	69	109	77	68	103	75	15.1
Odesa	46.48N	30.63E	114	7	12	86	67	84	67	81	66	70	79	69	77	67	102	74	66	96	73	18.4
Poltava	49.60N	34.55E	521	−3	2	85	66	82	66	80	65	68	78	66	76	64	92	73	63	87	71	17.6
Rivne (Rovno)	50.58N	26.13E	767	−3	3	82	67	79	66	76	64	67	77	66	74	64	92	72	62	86	70	18.5
Simferopol	45.02N	33.98E	593	8	13	87	67	85	66	82	65	69	79	67	78	65	94	73	63	89	72	20.3
Sumy	50.88N	34.78E	570	−7	−1	84	67	81	66	78	64	68	77	66	75	64	92	72	63	88	71	17.1
Uzhhorod (Uzhgorod)	48.63N	22.27E	387	6	10	86	69	83	68	81	66	69	81	67	79	64	92	75	63	88	73	18.7
Vinnytsya (Vinnitsa)	49.23N	28.47E	977	−2	3	82	66	79	65	77	64	67	76	65	74	64	91	71	62	86	70	18.2
Zaporizhzhya	47.80N	35.25E	282	0	5	88	67	85	66	82	65	69	80	67	78	65	94	74	64	89	72	20.2
Zhytomyr (Zhitomir)	50.27N	28.63E	744	−4	2	82	67	79	65	77	64	67	77	65	74	64	91	71	62	86	70	18.9
UNITED ARAB EMIRATES																						
Abu Dhabi	24.43N	54.65E	88	52	54	111	74	108	74	106	75	85	94	85	93	84	178	91	82	169	90	23.0
Dubai	25.25N	55.33E	16	54	55	107	75	105	75	103	76	85	94	85	93	84	177	91	82	169	91	17.5
Ras Al Khaymah	25.62N	55.93E	101	49	52	111	76	109	77	107	77	85	99	84	98	82	169	93	81	160	92	22.7
Sharjah	25.33N	55.52E	108	49	51	110	77	107	77	106	77	85	97	84	96	82	169	91	81	160	91	23.9
URUGUAY																						
Colonia Del Sacramento	34.45S	57.83W	75	39	41	88	74	86	73	84	72	75	83	74	81	73	122	80	72	117	79	14.9
Montevideo	34.83S	56.00W	104	35	38	89	72	86	71	83	70	74	81	73	79	72	118	77	71	116	76	16.7
Paso De Los Toros	32.80S	56.52W	246	34	36	95	72	91	72	88	71	75	85	74	83	72	122	80	71	117	78	20.3
Rocha	34.48S	54.30W	59	34	36	89	73	86	72	83	71	75	82	74	80	72	123	78	72	118	77	19.1
Salto	31.38S	57.95W	111	34	37	98	74	95	74	92	74	77	89	76	87	74	129	83	73	123	81	22.0
Treinta Y Tres	33.22S	54.38W	151	33	35	92	73	89	72	86	71	75	84	74	81	73	123	79	72	118	78	20.9
UZBEKISTAN																						
Samarqand (Samarkand)	39.70N	67.00E	2375	12	17	96	67	94	66	92	66	68	89	67	89	60	85	77	58	80	76	24.8
Tashkent	41.27N	69.27E	1604	13	18	100	71	98	68	95	68	72	92	70	90	65	99	84	63	91	82	26.8
VANUATU																						
Luganville	15.52S	167.22E	144	66	68	87	78	86	78	85	77	79	84	79	84	78	146	82	77	143	82	10.4
VENEZUELA																						
Caracas	10.60N	66.98W	157	70	71	92	84	91	83	90	83	85	89	84	88	84	181	88	84	177	87	12.6
VIETNAM																						
Ho Chi Minh City	10.82N	106.67E	62	68	70	95	77	94	77	93	77	80	89	80	89	78	147	85	77	143	84	14.8
WAKE ISLAND																						
Wake Island	19.28N	166.65E	13	71	72	89	79	89	79	88	78	80	86	80	85	79	150	84	78	146	84	8.1
WALLIS & FUTUNA ISLAND																						
Wallis Islands	13.23S	176.17W	88	72	73	88	80	87	80	87	80	81	86	81	86	79	153	85	79	151	84	8.5
YUGOSLAVIA																						
Belgrade	44.82N	20.28E	324	11	16	92	71	89	70	86	69	71	85	70	83	67	99	78	65	94	76	22.1
Palic	46.10N	19.77E	344	10	15	90	70	87	69	84	67	70	84	69	82	65	94	76	64	90	75	20.3
Podgorica (Titograd)	42.37N	19.25E	108	25	27	95	71	93	71	90	70	72	89	71	87	67	99	80	66	96	78	21.1
ZIMBABWE																						
Harare	17.92S	31.13E	4931	45	46	86	62	84	61	83	61	67	76	67	74	65	112	69	65	110	69	21.1

Lat. = North latitude, Long. = West Longitude DB = Dry-bulb temperature °F, Elev. = Elevation ft DP = dewpoint temperature °F, MWB = mean coincident wet-bulb temperature°F, MDB = mean coincident dry-bulb temperature °F, W = humidity ratio, grains of moisture per lb of dry air.

Table 19-4. Monthly Percentiles of Wet-Bulb and Dry-Bulb Temperature for U.S. Locations

		Jan		Feb		Mar		Apr		May		Jun		Jul		Aug		Sep		Oct		Nov		Dec		Annual	
Location	%	WB	DB	WB	DB	WB	DB	WB	DB	WB	DB	WB	DB	WB	DB	WB	DB	WB	DB	WB	DB	WB	DB	WB	DB	WB	DB
ALABAMA																											
Birmingham	0.4	64.3	69.8	66.1	75.5	68.9	81.9	71.6	85.8	75.2	91.9	78.3	95.5	79.7	98.8	79.2	96.5	77.3	94.5	73.4	86.2	69.6	78.3	67.6	73.2	78.2	94.4
	1	62.8	67.3	64.4	73.1	67.6	79.8	70.5	84.3	74.3	89.6	77.5	93.9	79.0	96.6	78.4	94.6	76.6	92.6	72.1	84.6	68.1	76.5	66.1	71.4	77.2	92.1
	2	61.3	65.5	62.7	70.4	66.4	77.5	69.3	82.9	73.4	87.5	76.7	92.3	78.4	94.8	77.9	93.2	76	90.9	71.1	82.8	67.0	74.7	64.3	69.4	76.3	90.1
Huntsville	0.4	62.7	67.7	64.3	72.8	67.4	80.1	71.5	85.9	74.7	90.5	77.6	95.1	79.6	97.7	79.1	96.4	77.2	93.5	72.7	85.2	68.2	77.1	65.7	71.4	78.0	94.1
	1	60.9	65.6	62.5	70.3	66.0	77.8	70.0	84.0	73.6	88.5	77.0	93.4	79.0	96.1	78.3	94.8	76.4	91.4	71.4	83.5	66.6	75.0	63.8	69.0	77.0	91.7
	2	59.3	63.6	60.9	67.8	64.6	75.6	68.6	82.2	72.7	86.9	76.2	91.9	78.4	94.5	77.6	93.2	75.7	89.8	70.3	81.8	65.3	72.9	62.4	67	76.0	89.5
Mobile	0.4	69.8	75.0	70.6	77.2	71.9	82.0	74.5	86.4	76.8	91.7	80.0	95.4	80.4	96.3	80.3	95.3	79.3	93.4	76.5	88.1	73.9	81.6	72.4	76.8	79.4	93.8
	1	68.8	73.4	69.5	75.1	71.2	80.2	73.8	84.7	76.0	90.0	79.2	94.1	79.9	95.0	79.7	94.1	78.7	92.2	75.7	86.7	72.9	79.9	71.5	75.4	78.5	92.1
	2	67.6	71.6	68.4	73.4	70.5	78.7	72.9	83.3	75.3	88.5	78.4	92.9	79.4	93.9	79.3	92.9	78.2	91.0	74.8	85.4	71.8	78.4	70.6	74.1	77.9	90.5
Montgomery	0.4	66.9	74.0	68.2	77.0	70.2	83.0	73.3	86.1	76.3	92.1	79.4	97.3	80.6	97.9	80.4	97.9	78.7	95.6	75.2	88.9	71.7	81.8	70.2	78	79.3	95.2
	1	65.3	71.6	66.8	74.9	69.2	81.2	72.2	84.7	75.4	90.3	78.5	95.5	80.0	96.2	79.9	96.0	78.1	94.0	74	87.1	70.4	79.8	68.9	75.6	78.4	93.2
	2	63.8	69.2	65.4	72.7	68.2	79.5	71.1	83.4	74.6	88.8	78.0	94.0	79.4	94.9	79.3	94.4	77.4	92.4	73.0	85.5	69.1	77.9	67.3	73.4	77.5	91.3
ARIZONA																											
Flagstaff	0.4	41.3	57.5	43.4	61.2	45.2	64.0	49.3	72.4	53.2	79.0	58.8	89.3	63.2	88.4	63.2	85.6	60.3	82.0	53.4	77.4	46.9	66.7	42.3	58.3	61.4	85.1
	1	39.8	54.0	41.8	57.8	43.8	62.2	47.8	70.0	52.3	77.1	57.6	87.1	62.3	86.8	62.3	83.8	59.1	80.0	51.7	75.4	45.4	64.4	40.6	55.9	60.1	82.6
	2	38.5	51.2	40.3	55.2	42.7	60.4	46.7	68.0	51.3	75.4	56.4	85.2	61.6	85.3	61.5	82.3	58.1	78.6	50.6	73.3	44.1	61.8	39.1	53.2	58.9	80.1
Phoenix, Intl Airport	0.4	58.3	78.0	59.6	84.3	61.2	90.7	64.2	98.7	67.4	105.5	73.6	113.4	76.5	112.4	77.2	110.5	75.9	107.9	70.1	100.9	63.1	87.6	58.2	77.6	75.6	109.8
	1	56.9	75.6	58.4	81.8	60.0	88.3	63.1	96.5	66.4	103.4	72.0	111.6	76.0	110.9	76.5	109.0	75.1	106.1	69.2	98.8	61.5	85.6	56.8	75.5	74.7	107.6
	2	55.8	73.5	57.4	79.5	59.0	86.0	62.1	94.4	65.7	101.3	70.6	109.9	75.4	109.7	75.9	107.7	74.2	104.6	68.2	96.9	60.3	83.7	55.7	73.4	73.8	105.6
PIntl Airportrescott	0.4	47.5	64.7	49.5	70.2	50.6	74.5	53.5	81.6	58.5	87.4	63.3	96.9	68.5	97.3	69.0	94.7	65.8	90.9	59.2	85.5	52.3	73.4	48.0	64.2	66.7	93.5
	1	46.1	62.0	48.0	67.6	49.5	72.0	52.4	79.3	57.4	85.3	62.2	95.3	67.3	95.5	68.0	92.2	64.8	89.1	57.9	83.6	50.8	71.2	46.4	62.1	65.5	90.9
	2	44.6	59.6	46.5	65.1	48.5	69.8	51.5	77.1	56.4	83.5	61.2	93.5	66.5	93.9	67.1	90.6	63.9	87.4	56.7	81.4	49.6	69.2	45.0	60.1	64.4	88.6
Tucson	0.4	55.1	77.5	56.2	82.5	57.6	87.8	60.6	95.4	64.4	101.3	69.8	108.8	72.8	107.3	73.4	103.5	72.0	101.5	66.8	96.5	59.7	85	56.1	77	72.0	104.2
	1	54.0	74.6	55.1	79.5	56.4	85.1	59.4	92.8	63.5	99.3	68.9	106.6	72.2	105.4	72.8	102.1	71.2	100	65.9	94.3	58.5	82.9	54.4	75.1	71.1	101.9
	2	52.8	72.5	54.1	77.4	55.4	82.7	58.3	90.4	62.5	97.1	68.0	105.0	71.6	103.9	72.3	100.6	70.5	98.5	64.8	92.1	57.4	81.1	53.4	72.9	70.3	99.6
ARKANSAS																											
Fort Smith	0.4	61.1	70.0	61.7	75.5	67.4	82.5	71.5	87.8	76.1	90.5	79.4	96.9	80.1	102.7	80.2	102.4	78.1	96.9	73.4	89.8	67.8	79.7	64.0	72.2	78.8	98.6
	1	58.9	66.6	60.1	72.4	66.0	80.1	70.3	85.4	74.9	89.2	78.6	95.0	79.4	100.9	79.5	100.4	77.2	94.8	72.1	87.6	66.3	77.5	62.4	69.8	77.8	95.8
	2	56.3	63.7	58.7	69.2	64.5	77.7	69.1	83.5	73.8	87.7	77.9	93.5	78.7	99.2	78.8	98.6	76.4	93	70.7	85.2	64.9	75.2	60.4	67	76.9	93.2
Little Rock, AFB	0.4	64.2	71.3	64.3	76.3	69.3	81.9	73.0	85.9	76.6	91.2	80.5	97.1	81.3	102.2	81.3	100.9	79.3	95.9	74.9	88.7	69.8	79.5	66.7	72.4	80.0	97.4
	1	62.8	68.4	62.9	72.5	68.0	79.5	71.8	83.9	75.8	89.8	79.7	95.4	80.6	100	80.4	99	78.5	93.7	73.4	86.4	68.4	76.9	64.9	70.1	79.0	94.7
	2	60.7	65.9	61.1	69.7	66.8	77.2	70.7	82.2	75.0	88.3	78.9	94.0	80.1	98	79.8	97.1	77.7	92.1	72.2	84.6	67.2	74.7	63.1	67.6	78.0	92.4
CALIFORNIA																											
Arcata/Eureka	0.4	57.8	65.3	58.9	67.4	56.5	65.5	58.1	66.1	60.1	68.3	61.4	69.7	62.2	69.1	64.1	71.2	64.6	77.5	62.1	75.7	60.2	67.3	58.3	63.2	62.2	70.4
	1	56.5	62.6	57.4	64.3	55.4	62.3	56.4	63.3	58.9	65.1	60.1	67.0	61.2	67.3	62.9	69	63.3	72.9	60.8	71.4	59	65.1	56.9	61.5	60.7	67.4
	2	55.4	60.6	56.1	62.2	54.4	60.2	55.3	61.3	57.7	63.0	59.2	65.2	60.3	66.2	61.9	67.5	62.1	69.9	59.7	67.8	58	63.3	55.7	60.1	59.6	65.4
Bakersfield	0.4	61.1	72.0	62.0	77.5	63.8	82.5	66.3	93.1	69.4	100.4	72.5	106.4	74.4	107	75.0	106.1	72.8	102.9	68.7	96.8	62.8	81.9	59.4	70.8	72.7	103.9
	1	58.7	68.9	60.7	74.8	62.4	79.9	64.9	89.7	68.2	97.9	71.2	104.3	73.5	105.4	73.9	104.4	71.8	100.9	67.6	93.9	61.4	79.2	57.8	68.2	71.3	101.3
	2	57.0	66.3	59.4	72.6	61.2	77.5	63.5	87.2	67.2	95.6	70.2	102.2	72.6	104	72.9	102.8	70.9	99	66.6	91.8	60.2	76.7	56.2	66.2	70.1	98.8
Barstow/ Daggett	0.4	56.0	72.5	56.5	79.2	57.9	85.5	60.5	93.9	65.3	99.5	69.1	108.5	73.9	110.4	74.4	109.4	72.4	104.4	65	98.1	59.1	83.5	57.2	73.5	72.3	107.3
	1	54.0	70.3	55.2	76.5	56.9	82.8	59.4	91.2	64.1	97.5	68.1	107.1	73.1	108.9	73.4	107.9	71.2	102.7	63.8	95.7	57.5	80.7	54.1	71	70.8	104.9
	2	52.4	68.2	53.9	74.5	55.9	80.4	58.4	88.9	63.1	95.6	67.2	105.5	72.3	107.7	72.4	106.3	70	101.0	62.8	93.3	56.3	78.2	52.3	68.4	69.3	102.4
Fresno	0.4	59.4	66.9	61.4	74.2	64.2	80.1	66.2	91.0	70.0	99.1	72.4	104.9	74.7	106.5	75.3	105.4	72.4	101.9	68.3	95.6	61.8	78.8	59.2	66.5	72.9	103.2
	1	57.1	64.3	60.2	72.0	62.5	77.3	64.9	88.6	68.7	96.9	71.4	103.3	73.9	105.2	74.0	103.8	71.3	99.9	67.3	92.8	60.7	76.2	56.7	64.1	71.4	100.5
	2	55.4	62.2	59.0	69.8	61.2	75.2	63.5	85.8	67.4	94.8	70.4	101.4	73	103.4	73.0	102.0	70.3	97.9	66.2	90.0	59.7	74	55.0	61.9	70.1	97.9
Long Beach	0.4	60.4	82.0	61.6	81.7	62.6	83.1	65.0	88.8	67.3	88.7	69.4	92.3	71.7	92	73.5	94.0	73.4	97.6	69.4	95.8	65.1	87	61.1	80.6	71.4	91.7
	1	59.5	79.2	60.7	79.1	61.5	78.6	63.6	84.3	66.0	84.0	68.4	87.1	71.0	89	72.4	90.9	72.3	93.5	68.4	91.2	64.1	83.5	60.1	77.7	70.2	87.6
	2	58.8	75.8	59.8	76.3	60.5	75.6	62.5	80.6	64.8	79.8	67.4	83.8	70.2	86.7	71.4	88.3	71.4	90.4	67.5	87.4	63.1	80.5	59.1	74.8	69.0	84.3
Los Angeles	0.4	60.4	79.6	61.2	79.4	61.4	77.7	63.8	82.1	65.4	80.8	67.9	85.1	70.3	82.4	71.7	84.0	71.3	91.5	68.3	90.4	64.2	83.9	60.9	78.9	69.8	84.6
	1	59.5	76.6	60.2	75.8	60.5	73.7	62.6	77.2	64.3	75.9	66.8	78.9	69.4	80	70.9	81.9	70.3	87.1	67.3	85.9	63.3	80.5	59.8	75.8	68.6	80.6
	2	58.6	73.4	59.3	73.0	59.5	71.0	61.7	74.2	63.4	73.0	65.9	76.0	68.7	78.3	70.1	80.0	69.4	83.1	66.4	82.0	62.4	77.7	58.9	73	67.6	77.8
Sacramento, Metro	0.4	58.2	64.2	61.0	71.5	63.8	77.0	67.4	86.5	70.1	96.2	72.9	103.0	73.9	104.3	75.0	103.0	70.8	100.2	67.3	93.7	62.7	77.3	58.3	64	71.6	100
	1	56.4	61.7	59.3	69.3	62.0	74.5	65.4	84.1	68.6	93.5	71.5	100.4	72.5	101.9	72.4	100.9	69.8	97.7	66.2	91.0	61.3	74.8	56.5	62.1	70.0	96.8
	2	55.1	59.9	58.1	67.0	60.4	72.2	63.6	81.5	67.3	91.2	70.2	98.1	71.5	99.7	71.1	98.8	68.9	95.2	65.2	87.9	59.9	72	55	60.2	68.5	93.6
San Diego, Intl Airport	0.4	61.9	78.5	62.4	79.0	61.9	78.0	64.7	82.0	66.2	80.3	69.6	85.1	73.2	84.8	73.9	85.2	75.1	90.9	69.4	90	65.4	82.6	62.3	76.4	72.5	85
	1	61.0	75.8	61.4	76.3	61.1	74.8	63.7	78.5	65.1	76.2	68.4	80.1	72.1	82.6	73.1	83.5	73.9	87.4	68.6	85.4	64.4	79.2	61.0	74.2	71.0	81.4
	2	60.1	72.9	60.6	73.1	60.3	72.2	62.5	75.1	64.2	73.5	67.6	77.4	71.1	80.5	72.3	81.5	72.8	84.4	68	81.7	63.5	76.4	60.0	71.9	69.6	78.9
San Francisco	0.4	58.7	64.1	59.3	68.7	59.7	71.5	62.5	79.1	63.4	82.8	65.5	88.6	65.7	85.9	65.5	83	66.4	88.5	64.5	85.1	60.6	72.9	59.0	63.5	64.4	83.1
	1	57.3	62.1	58.1	66.0	58.4	68.2	60.3	74.6	61.9	78.7	63.8	83.2	64.4	81.1	64.3	79.5	65.0	84.9	63.4	81.4	59.6	70.1	57.9	61.7	63.0	78.1
	2	56.1	60.5	57.0	63.8	57.3	65.8	58.9	71.3	60.7	74.3	62.4	78.4	63.3	77.3	63.4	76.1	63.8	81.1	62.4	77.8	59.0	67.6	56.6	60.3	61.8	73.9
Santa Maria	0.4	60.2	77.9	61.9	78.9	61.7	78.4	63.7	87.1	63.2	80.0	64.3	86.2	68.8	88.2	67.5	84.7	69.5	91.6	65.4	91.4	62.1	83.1	59.8	78.8	66.3	85.9
	1	59.1	75.2	60.4	76.1	60.7	75.3	62.5	83.0	62.1	76.2	63.4	80.0	66.9	83.3	66.6	81.8	68.0	87.4	64.5	87.1	61	80.5	58.5	76.9	64.7	81.5
	2	58.1	73.0	59.4	73.4	59.4	72.6	61.2	79.1	61.1	73.2	62.5	76.8	65.5	79.9	65.6	79.6	66.3	83.5	63.7	83.5	60.2	78	57.3	74.4	63.5	78.1

Table 19-4. *(Continued)* **Monthly Percentiles of Wet-Bulb and Dry-Bulb Temperature for U.S. Locations**

		Jan		Feb		Mar		Apr		May		Jun		Jul		Aug		Sep		Oct		Nov		Dec		Annual	
Location	%	WB	DB	WB	DB	WB	DB	WB	DB	WB	DB	WB	DB	WB	DB	WB	DB	WB	DB	WB	DB	WB	DB	WB	DB	WB	DB
COLORADO																											
Alamosa	0.4	37.7	50.7	40.2	56.1	43.4	65.1	47.2	71.2	52.1	79.1	58.6	86.5	61.7	87.4	63.2	85.1	58.2	81.2	51.7	73.5	43.3	61.9	37.5	50.4	59.8	84.2
	1	35.6	47.7	38.1	53.7	41.9	63.1	46.1	69.2	51.0	77.1	57.4	85.1	60.5	86.1	61.0	83.7	56.7	79.7	50.3	72	42.1	59.7	35.7	47.8	58.6	82.1
	2	34.0	44.7	36.8	50.9	40.5	60.5	45.1	67.5	50.2	75.2	56.6	83.7	59.9	84.7	60.1	82.3	55.5	78.1	48.8	70.3	40.9	57.3	34.2	45.4	57.5	79.8
Boulder	0.4	44.0	63.2	46.3	67.6	48.0	73.5	53.2	80.2	58.8	85.8	64.4	94.4	66.9	96.4	66.1	94.7	62.5	90.5	54.4	82	48.7	72.5	45.0	66.3	64.5	92.8
	1	42.4	60.1	44.2	64.3	46.4	70.5	52.0	77.8	57.6	83.8	63.4	92.5	65.8	95.1	65.2	92.8	61.1	88.3	53.3	80.1	47.4	69.8	43.3	63	63.2	90.2
	2	40.9	57.3	42.4	61.2	45.2	67.9	50.9	75.4	56.6	81.7	62.4	91.0	65.0	93.7	64.3	91.2	60	86.2	52.4	78.1	46.1	67.2	41.7	59.7	62.0	87.4
Colorado Springs	0.4	42.2	61.8	44.3	66.0	46.0	70.7	50.8	77.5	56.5	83.5	61.9	92.3	64.8	93.8	64.4	91.1	60.9	86.5	53.1	80.2	46.0	70.4	42.3	62.7	62.8	89.8
	1	40.4	59.3	42.1	62.5	44.2	67.8	49.4	75.2	55.4	81.4	61.0	90.3	63.9	92.1	63.5	89.2	59.7	85	51.8	78.3	44.8	66.6	40.9	59.8	61.5	87
	2	38.9	56.2	40.1	59.1	42.9	64.7	48.4	73.0	54.4	79.2	60.2	88.2	63.1	90.5	62.9	87.5	58.7	83.2	50.7	76	43.7	64.3	39.4	57.1	60.5	84.2
Eagle	0.4	37.7	46.0	40.5	53.1	45.3	64.0	49.8	73.2	55.1	81.3	61.4	89.8	64.5	91.8	63.7	90.4	59.3	86.1	53.3	77	45.4	62.3	39.0	48.8	61.8	88.2
	1	36.4	43.5	38.9	50.5	43.6	61.1	48.5	70.7	54.0	79.5	59.8	88.0	63.2	90.2	62.5	88.6	58	84	51.6	74.9	43.6	59.2	37.4	46	60.3	85.8
	2	34.9	41.5	37.5	48.0	42.1	58.2	47.1	68.6	53.0	77.7	58.6	86.4	62.2	88.9	61.6	87.1	57	81.7	50.3	72.6	42.1	56.4	35.7	43.3	59.0	83.2
Grand Junction	0.4	40.7	50.8	45.6	60.6	49.8	71.4	53.4	81.1	58.8	88.3	63.6	98.5	67	99.4	66.8	97.6	63	91.8	56.5	81.3	48.8	66.1	42.9	52.5	65.1	96.2
	1	39.2	48.1	44.2	58.3	48.0	69.1	52.3	78.9	57.7	86.6	62.6	96.7	66.2	97.9	65.9	96.2	61.9	90	55.3	79.7	47.5	63.4	41.1	50.1	63.9	94
	2	37.6	45.8	42.6	55.6	46.6	66.5	51.2	76.6	56.7	84.9	61.6	95.0	65.4	96.7	65.1	94.8	61.0	88.2	54.1	77.7	46.2	60.9	39.2	47.6	62.8	91.6
Pueblo	0.4	46.5	66.4	48.5	72.0	49.7	77.0	55.3	83.1	61.2	91.1	66.9	100.6	68.9	101.1	69.4	98.4	65.1	94.0	57.0	86.4	49.5	74.8	46.6	67.6	67.4	97.2
	1	44.5	63.5	46.7	68.7	48.4	74.3	53.7	81.0	60.1	89.3	65.7	98.4	68.2	99.4	68.4	96.7	64.0	92.2	56.0	84.7	48.4	72.0	44.9	64.3	66.2	94.3
	2	42.9	60.9	44.8	65.4	47.4	71.7	52.6	78.9	59.0	87.4	64.8	96.2	67.4	97.8	67.7	95.0	63.1	90.2	55.1	82.5	47.4	69.4	43.2	61.5	65.1	91.6
CONNECTICUT																											
Bridgeport	0.4	50.0	52.7	48.3	52.9	52.2	59.9	60.9	74.8	69.2	80.4	73.7	87.9	77.4	91.6	77.9	89.0	75.9	86.1	68.8	75.8	63.1	67.1	54.4	57.6	75.8	86.4
	1	47.4	49.8	45.6	49.9	50.2	57.7	58.8	70.4	67.2	77.7	72.5	85.1	76.4	89.4	77.0	87.2	75.0	83.6	67.7	73.3	61.4	65.1	52.0	54.9	74.3	83.9
	2	44.4	47.5	43.4	47.1	48.6	55.0	56.3	66.4	65.3	75.4	71.5	82.8	75.3	87.0	76.2	85.7	74.0	81.4	66.3	71.7	59.9	63.2	50.2	52.8	73.1	81.6
Hartford, Brainard Field	0.4	51.3	55.5	52.8	59.4	58.9	71.4	64.6	83.3	71.6	90.2	75.5	93.1	78.0	95.2	77.7	93.0	75.8	90.4	68.5	80.0	64.4	71.2	56.8	60.3	75.8	91.2
	1	46.8	51.1	49.6	54.7	55.9	66.4	62.1	78.1	69.8	86.5	74.3	91.2	77.2	93.3	76.5	91.1	74.4	87.2	66.4	77.2	61.8	67.9	53.0	57.0	74.2	88.2
	2	42.7	47.0	45.6	51.3	53.0	62.1	60.0	73.7	68.3	83.4	73.3	88.9	76.2	91.5	75.4	89.2	73.1	84.2	65.0	74.4	59.3	64.6	49.4	53.1	72.7	85.4
DELAWARE																											
Wilmington	0.4	55.3	59.9	57.4	64.7	63.5	75.4	66.8	83.6	74.1	89.3	77.3	92.8	79.7	95.5	79.0	93.1	77.4	91.1	70.7	80.6	66.2	73.4	60.6	65.1	77.5	91.2
	1	52.4	56.2	54.8	61.1	60.6	71.8	65.1	80.1	72.1	86.6	76.2	90.8	78.6	93.5	78.1	91.2	76.3	88.8	69.4	78.0	63.5	70.1	58.1	61.9	76.2	88.7
	2	49.4	53.0	51.8	57.5	57.9	67.1	63.3	76.0	70.7	84.4	75.2	89.0	77.8	91.9	77.2	89.6	75.3	86.4	68.0	75.8	61.8	67.2	55.2	58.6	74.9	86.2
FLORIDA																											
Daytona Beach	0.4	71.0	81.0	71.1	83.2	72.3	85.7	74.5	88.9	77.1	91.5	79.4	93.9	80.4	94.5	80.3	93.4	79.5	90.5	77.6	87.5	74.8	83.6	72.7	81.5	79.4	91.8
	1	70.1	79.6	70.2	81.3	71.5	84.2	73.3	87.1	76.2	89.8	78.7	92.3	79.9	93.0	79.9	91.9	78.9	89.3	77.0	86.2	74.0	82.3	71.6	80.2	78.5	90.0
	2	69.3	78.0	69.2	79.0	70.8	82.4	72.5	85.4	75.4	88.1	78.2	90.9	79.3	91.7	79.3	90.6	78.4	88.4	76.3	85.1	73.2	81.1	70.5	78.8	78.0	88.4
Jacksonville, Intl Airport	0.4	69.9	80.0	70.4	82.2	72.1	86.1	74.6	89.6	77.5	93.9	80.1	96.5	81.4	97.2	81.0	95.4	79.8	93.1	77.4	89.3	74.2	82.8	71.6	80.8	79.9	94.4
	1	68.9	78.2	69.4	80.3	71.2	84.4	73.4	88.2	76.5	91.8	79.3	95.0	80.5	95.8	80.3	94.3	79.2	91.8	76.7	87.4	73.3	81.5	70.7	79.1	79.1	92.6
	2	67.9	76.2	68.3	78.3	70.3	82.6	72.4	86.7	75.5	90.1	78.6	93.5	80.0	94.5	79.7	93.2	78.6	90.6	76.0	85.8	72.4	80.2	69.6	77.6	78.3	90.8
Key West	0.4	75.7	82.0	76.0	82.3	77.0	84.0	78.3	86.4	79.9	88.2	81.3	90.4	81.3	91.4	81.5	91.5	80.9	90.5	80.2	88.3	78.7	85.1	76.6	82.4	80.6	90.3
	1	75.1	81.0	75.3	81.5	76.3	83.2	77.5	85.4	79.2	87.4	80.7	89.6	80.6	90.8	81.1	91.0	80.4	89.8	79.5	87.5	78.1	84.3	76.1	81.6	80.1	89.4
	2	74.4	80.2	74.7	80.7	75.7	82.3	77.0	84.4	78.4	86.8	80.2	89.1	80.3	90.2	80.5	90.3	80.1	89.2	79.0	87.0	77.4	83.5	75.5	80.7	79.5	88.6
Miami, Intl Airport	0.4	74.3	83.1	74.2	84.1	75.3	86.3	76.9	89.2	78.5	90.1	79.9	92.0	80.2	93.1	80.3	92.5	80.0	91.2	79.2	89.4	77.4	85.6	75.8	83.3	79.5	91.1
	1	73.7	82.0	73.4	82.7	74.5	85.0	76.0	87.5	77.5	88.8	79.2	90.7	79.5	91.8	80.0	91.5	79.4	90.3	78.4	88.3	76.9	84.7	74.9	82.2	79.0	89.9
	2	73.1	80.8	72.9	81.6	74.1	83.8	75.2	86.1	77.0	87.7	78.5	89.6	79.1	90.8	79.5	90.7	79.1	89.5	78.0	87.3	76.3	83.7	74.1	81.2	78.4	88.9
Tallahassee	0.4	70.7	76.7	70.5	79.2	72.4	84.4	74.4	89.1	77.2	93.2	79.9	96.8	80.9	97.0	80.4	96.3	79.4	94.3	76.8	89.3	73.3	82.5	72.6	78.8	79.5	94.6
	1	69.5	75.1	69.5	77.3	71.5	82.6	73.5	87.3	76.3	91.6	79.2	95.1	80.2	95.6	79.9	95.0	78.8	93.1	76.0	87.9	72.5	81.1	71.6	77.1	78.7	92.8
	2	68.2	73.3	68.3	75.3	70.6	80.9	72.6	85.6	75.5	90.2	78.5	93.8	79.5	94.4	79.4	93.7	78.2	91.9	75.2	86.5	71.9	79.7	70.3	75.5	78.1	91.2
Tampa, Intl Airport	0.4	72.3	81.2	72.4	82.4	74.2	84.7	76.1	87.9	78.2	92.2	80.1	93.8	81.3	93.3	81.1	93.7	79.9	92.8	78.3	89.9	75.7	86.0	74.2	82.9	80.0	92.4
	1	71.2	80.0	71.5	81.2	73.4	83.6	75.2	86.7	77.3	90.8	79.5	92.5	80.5	92.5	80.4	92.9	79.3	91.8	77.7	88.7	74.9	84.5	73.1	81.3	79.2	91.2
	2	70.3	78.7	70.7	79.8	72.5	82.6	74.3	85.6	76.5	89.7	79.0	91.5	80.0	91.9	79.9	92.1	78.8	91.1	77.1	87.6	74.1	83.3	72.1	80.0	78.4	90.1
West Palm Beach	0.4	73.6	82.9	74.1	84.1	75.0	86.5	76.3	89.2	78.3	90.1	80.0	91.9	80.4	93.6	80.4	92.7	80.2	91.2	78.7	89.0	77.0	85.5	75.0	83.3	79.6	91.2
	1	73.0	81.5	73.3	82.7	74.2	85.0	75.2	87.3	77.6	88.6	79.3	90.7	79.9	92.1	80.1	91.6	79.5	90.3	78.2	88.1	76.3	84.3	74.1	82.2	79.0	90.0
	2	72.3	80.3	72.5	81.4	73.4	83.5	74.3	85.5	76.9	87.5	78.7	89.7	79.4	91.0	79.6	90.9	79.1	89.5	77.5	87.1	75.5	83.1	73.3	81.1	78.4	88.9
GEORGIA																											
Athens	0.4	62.4	69.2	64.2	74.0	67.3	80.4	70.1	85.9	75.0	90.9	77.1	96.4	79.2	98.6	78.5	96.0	77.2	92.2	73.3	85.2	69.0	77.7	67.0	72.6	77.5	94.3
	1	60.9	66.4	62.5	71.4	65.9	78.4	68.8	84.2	73.8	89.0	76.4	94.4	78.4	97.0	78.0	94.1	76.3	90.6	71.7	83.2	67.6	75.9	65.3	69.9	76.5	91.9
	2	59.2	64.2	61.0	69.0	64.5	76.2	67.8	82.4	72.7	87.4	75.7	92.7	77.7	95.3	77.4	92.6	75.5	89.1	70.5	81.3	66.4	73.7	63.2	67.6	75.7	89.6
Atlanta	0.4	62.5	68.5	64.1	73.3	66.0	80.2	69.8	85.1	73.9	88.8	76.9	94.4	79.7	97.5	78.4	95.2	76.5	91.9	72.2	83.8	68.1	77.1	66.1	71.5	77.2	93.1
	1	61.1	66.3	62.8	71.0	64.9	78.1	68.2	83.3	72.7	87.3	76.0	92.7	78.4	95.5	77.5	93.4	75.5	89.9	70.8	82.0	67.0	75.0	64.3	69.4	76.0	90.7
	2	59.4	64.1	61.1	68.5	63.7	76.0	67.2	81.6	71.8	86.0	75.3	91.2	77.5	93.8	76.8	91.8	74.7	88.4	69.5	80.3	65.9	73.1	62.5	67.3	75.1	88.4
Augusta	0.4	65.1	73.6	66.7	77.8	68.5	83.3	71.9	88.5	75.9	93.1	78.6	98.7	80.4	100.3	80.1	98.0	78.1	94.9	74.5	88.0	71.1	81.9	68.4	76.8	78.7	96.2
	1	63.6	70.9	65.0	75.3	67.4	81.7	70.4	86.9	74.3	91.3	77.9	96.5	79.6	98.4	79.3	96.2	77.3	93.2	73.4	86.3	69.9	79.2	66.7	74.4	77.8	93.8
	2	62.0	68.2	63.4	72.9	66.2	79.7	69.2	85.2	73.3	89.6	77.2	94.7	79.1	96.7	78.4	94.9	76.6	91.6	72.3	84.5	68.7	77.2	65.1	71.8	76.9	91.7
Columbus, Metro Airport	0.4	66.3	72.9	66.9	76.2	69.8	83.1	72.4	87.5	75.9	91.3	79.3	97.1	80.3	99.0	79.7	97.2	78.1	94.5	74.8	88.3	70.7	80.3	69.8	76.4	78.6	95.3
	1	64.8	70.8	65.5	74.2	68.4	81.1	71.2	86.1	74.7	89.8	78.4	95.5	79.4	97.4	79.0	95.4	77.4	93.0	73.5	86.5	69.5	78.5	68.3	74.3	77.8	93.2
	2	63.5	68.3	64.3	72.0	67.4	79.4	70.2	84.5	73.9	88.6	77.6	94.2	78.8	95.8	78.4	94.2	76.8	91.5	72.5	84.5	68.6	76.8	66.8	72.4	77.0	91.4

Table 19-4. *(Continued)* **Monthly Percentiles of Wet-Bulb and Dry-Bulb Temperature for U.S. Locations**

		Jan		Feb		Mar		Apr		May		Jun		Jul		Aug		Sep		Oct		Nov		Dec		Annual	
Location	%	WB	DB	WB	DB	WB	DB	WB	DB	WB	DB	WB	DB	WB	DB	WB	DB	WB	DB	WB	DB	WB	DB	WB	DB	WB	DB
Macon	0.4	65.8	73.2	67.2	77.4	69.4	83.3	72.6	88.5	76.0	93.6	78.8	98.5	80.3	100.1	80.1	98.2	78.1	95.0	74.5	88.9	71.0	81.5	69.5	76.2	78.7	96.3
	1	64.4	70.8	65.8	75.0	68.3	81.4	71.2	86.7	75.0	91.9	78.1	96.8	79.4	98.3	79.3	96.3	77.4	93.4	73.6	86.9	69.7	79.2	67.9	74.2	77.8	94.0
	2	63.1	68.4	64.5	72.6	67.4	79.4	70.2	85.1	74.0	90.3	77.3	95.1	78.8	96.6	78.7	94.8	76.9	91.9	72.6	85.1	68.7	77.3	66.4	72.2	77.0	91.9
Savannah	0.4	67.3	76.6	68.2	79.5	70.1	84.3	73.2	89.3	76.5	93.2	79.2	97.4	81.0	99.0	80.4	96.2	78.5	93.2	76.4	87.5	72.6	81.9	69.8	78.4	79.3	95.0
	1	66.3	74.3	67.0	77.0	68.9	82.1	71.9	87.3	75.6	91.2	78.4	95.6	80.3	97.2	79.7	94.8	78.0	91.7	75.3	86.0	71.4	80.0	68.5	76.6	78.4	92.8
	2	65.2	72.0	65.8	74.7	67.9	80.1	70.7	85.3	74.7	89.5	77.9	93.8	79.5	95.3	79.2	93.5	77.4	90.3	74.2	84.4	70.6	78.3	67.2	74.2	77.6	90.7
HAWAII																											
Hilo	0.4	73.4	84.3	73.6	84.7	73.5	83.9	74.4	83.3	75.2	85.0	75.0	85.1	76.4	85.3	77.3	85.7	77.3	86.4	77.4	86.2	76.2	84.5	74.4	84.1	76.4	85.3
	1	72.8	82.9	72.9	83.2	72.7	82.7	73.4	82.2	74.4	83.8	74.4	84.1	75.7	84.3	76.5	84.8	76.6	85.4	76.5	85.3	75.5	83.6	73.9	82.8	75.6	84.3
	2	72.2	81.7	72.2	82.0	72.1	81.5	72.8	81.2	73.8	82.7	73.9	83.4	75.2	83.5	76.1	84.2	76.1	84.6	76.0	84.4	74.9	82.8	73.2	81.8	74.9	83.3
Honolulu	0.4	74.1	83.2	73.4	83.3	73.3	84.9	73.3	85.3	74.4	87.2	74.5	88.5	76.1	89.5	76.7	90.4	77.2	90.6	77.2	89.4	75.5	87.4	74.8	85.1	76.0	89.2
	1	73.4	82.3	72.6	82.5	72.4	84.0	72.6	84.5	73.8	86.3	73.9	87.8	75.3	88.9	75.8	89.6	76.3	89.7	76.4	88.6	74.9	86.4	74.1	83.7	75.1	88.3
	2	72.8	81.5	72.0	81.8	71.8	83.1	72.1	83.8	73.2	85.6	73.3	87.2	74.5	88.2	75.2	89.1	75.7	89.0	75.7	87.8	74.3	85.6	73.4	82.9	74.3	87.3
Kahului	0.4	73.9	83.7	73.4	84.2	73.4	86.2	73.5	86.2	75.8	88.0	75.5	89.2	76.5	90.0	77.3	90.3	77.3	90.3	77.3	89.3	75.8	87.5	75.1	85.1	76.4	89.0
	1	73.1	82.8	72.6	83.3	72.6	84.8	73.0	85.2	74.8	87.0	75.0	88.2	75.9	88.8	76.5	89.2	76.5	89.4	76.6	88.4	75.1	86.6	74.2	84.1	75.5	87.9
	2	72.4	81.9	72.1	82.4	72.0	83.6	72.4	84.2	74.0	86.1	74.3	87.3	75.3	87.8	75.9	88.3	76.0	88.5	76.0	87.7	74.4	85.6	73.4	83.3	74.8	86.8
Lihue	0.4	73.8	81.9	73.8	82.7	73.4	82.2	74.1	82.8	74.9	83.6	76.0	85.3	77.4	85.5	77.9	87.0	77.5	86.4	77.4	85.5	76.0	83.3	74.5	82.1	76.9	85.4
	1	73.1	80.8	72.8	81.3	72.8	81.2	73.3	81.7	74.3	82.8	75.2	84.3	76.5	85.0	77.2	86.0	77.1	85.8	76.6	84.9	75.3	82.5	74.0	81.0	76.1	84.5
	2	72.4	79.8	72.1	80.2	72.1	80.3	72.8	80.9	73.9	82.2	74.5	83.5	75.9	84.4	76.6	85.3	76.5	85.2	76.1	84.2	74.7	82.0	73.4	80.2	75.3	83.9
IDAHO																											
Boise	0.4	45.0	51.8	49.2	60.3	51.8	70.1	57.4	80.7	62.4	90.9	66.2	98.6	68.3	100.4	67.9	100.1	63.9	92.7	57.4	82.2	51.4	64.5	46.1	54.6	65.8	96.4
	1	43.9	49.8	47.2	57.4	50.3	67.0	55.8	77.7	60.6	88.0	65.0	96.0	67.1	98.4	66.5	97.8	62.6	90.2	56.3	79.3	50.2	61.7	44.4	51.9	64.3	93.5
	2	42.8	48.0	45.5	54.8	49.0	63.7	54.1	74.6	59.4	84.8	63.8	93.4	66.1	96.7	65.6	95.8	61.4	88.1	55.2	76.3	48.8	59.1	43.2	49.7	62.9	90.5
Pocatello	0.4	41.2	49.3	45.8	56.4	48.3	65.3	53.7	77.5	59.4	84.5	64.7	94.2	66.3	96.1	65.9	96.2	61.3	89.6	55.0	80.4	48.7	62.9	42.7	50.9	63.9	93.0
	1	39.7	46.0	43.6	53.3	46.9	62.5	52.1	75.0	58.0	82.5	63.2	92.0	65.3	94.7	64.4	94.3	60.1	87.5	53.9	77.6	47.1	60.3	40.8	48.1	62.4	90.1
	2	38.4	44.1	41.8	50.5	45.3	59.4	50.7	71.7	56.6	80.4	62.0	89.4	64.3	93.3	63.5	92.8	59.0	85.3	52.7	74.7	45.7	57.7	39.3	45.7	61.0	87.2
ILLINOIS																											
Chicago, OHare Intl Airport	0.4	51.3	53.8	51.1	57.4	62.2	73.7	66.8	83.1	72.9	88.7	76.5	93.0	79.8	95.6	79.3	94.0	76.1	90.3	68.8	82.7	61.9	69.9	57.7	61.3	77.2	91.1
	1	46.5	50.0	47.9	53.4	59.8	69.7	65.2	79.7	71.4	86.3	75.4	90.7	78.5	93.5	78.3	92.0	74.8	87.6	67.0	79.7	60.3	66.7	54.7	57.9	75.3	88.4
	2	42.5	45.8	44.8	49.6	57.5	65.8	63.6	75.9	70.1	84.1	74.4	89.1	77.5	91.5	77.2	89.9	73.5	85.1	65.3	76.5	58.7	63.9	50.1	53.7	73.6	85.5
Moline/Davenport Intl Airport	0.4	49.7	53.5	50.4	59.3	62.1	74.9	67.6	84.7	73.4	89.6	77.9	94.7	80.5	97.0	80.4	96.7	77.0	92.0	70.0	83.7	61.6	70.3	56.7	60.8	78.2	93.0
	1	45.1	49.9	47.9	54.7	59.9	70.9	65.9	81.5	72.1	87.6	76.6	92.8	79.5	95.2	79.3	93.6	75.5	89.0	68.2	80.9	60.0	67.0	53.6	56.5	76.5	90.0
	2	41.6	46.1	45.2	50.9	57.5	66.9	64.4	78.2	70.9	85.5	75.6	90.8	78.6	93.4	78.2	91.6	74.3	86.6	66.6	78.0	58.6	64.4	48.9	53.0	75.0	87.2
Peoria	0.4	52.0	54.5	52.6	59.6	63.3	75.0	68.8	83.2	74.2	87.9	78.3	93.2	81.1	97.0	80.2	96.2	77.3	90.4	69.5	82.2	62.3	70.6	58.5	61.2	78.4	91.9
	1	48.0	51.0	50.2	55.5	61.0	71.8	66.7	80.4	72.7	86.3	77.1	91.3	79.8	94.6	79.1	92.8	75.7	88.3	68.0	79.8	60.9	67.6	55.2	58.0	76.8	89.1
	2	44.2	47.4	47.9	52.3	58.9	67.8	65.0	77.5	71.3	84.4	76.0	89.6	78.8	92.7	78.1	90.7	74.4	86.1	66.5	77.0	59.4	64.6	51.3	54.5	75.1	86.4
Rockford	0.4	46.7	48.9	47.9	54.1	60.8	72.0	66.7	83.5	72.8	88.0	77.0	92.9	79.7	95.1	79.4	94.0	75.6	89.2	68.8	82.1	60.4	68.0	55.4	58.1	77.2	90.6
	1	42.6	45.2	45.2	49.7	58.2	68.1	64.9	79.9	71.1	86.3	75.5	90.7	78.7	93.0	78.2	91.3	74.4	87.0	67.2	78.9	59.0	64.3	51.9	54.0	75.3	87.8
	2	39.2	42.2	42.4	46.2	55.7	63.6	63.0	75.9	69.8	84.4	74.4	88.8	77.7	91.0	77.0	89.0	73.3	84.5	65.5	76.1	57.5	61.5	46.3	49.3	73.6	85.3
Springfield	0.4	55.1	58.6	55.8	62.4	64.5	76.2	69.9	84.2	75.3	90.2	78.5	95.3	81.8	97.8	80.8	96.2	77.8	92.4	70.4	85.2	64.2	73.1	60.1	63.2	79.0	93.4
	1	51.3	54.6	53.5	59.0	62.3	73.2	67.9	81.8	73.7	88.3	77.4	93.2	80.4	95.6	79.8	94.0	76.5	90.1	68.7	82.6	62.6	70.4	57.3	60.7	77.4	90.7
	2	47.8	51.3	50.7	55.9	60.6	69.9	66.3	79.4	72.4	86.4	76.4	91.6	79.5	93.8	78.8	91.9	75.3	88.0	67.5	79.9	61.2	67.4	54.2	57.0	75.9	88.1
INDIANA																											
Evansville	0.4	59.0	64.2	59.8	67.9	66.2	78.4	70.3	85.3	75.7	90.2	79.5	95.9	80.8	97.8	80.4	97.1	78.1	92.6	71.4	85.1	65.8	75.5	61.7	66.7	79.0	94.0
	1	56.7	60.9	57.9	64.3	64.4	75.4	68.9	83.4	74.5	88.5	78.4	94.0	80.0	95.5	79.5	94.9	77.1	90.9	70.0	83.0	64.4	73.2	59.6	64.3	77.7	91.6
	2	54.2	58.1	55.9	61.8	62.4	72.8	67.4	81.2	73.4	87.0	77.4	92.4	79.3	94.1	78.6	93.1	76.0	89.3	68.4	80.8	63.1	70.7	57.8	62.1	76.5	89.5
Fort Wayne	0.4	52.7	55.4	52.2	57.6	62.0	72.7	66.3	82.5	73.3	88.2	76.6	92.3	79.2	95.0	79.1	92.5	76.3	89.6	68.1	81.7	62.1	70.8	58.8	61.7	76.9	90.3
	1	49.0	51.6	49.7	53.6	60.0	69.7	64.9	79.6	71.6	86.2	75.5	90.5	78.1	92.5	78.0	90.3	74.9	87.1	66.5	79.2	60.5	67.5	56.3	58.7	75.2	87.7
	2	44.7	47.4	47.0	50.8	58.0	66.2	63.5	75.5	70.3	84.2	74.5	88.9	77.1	90.7	76.7	88.6	73.7	84.9	65.3	76.1	59.4	64.5	53.1	55.6	73.6	85.3
Indianapolis	0.4	57.4	60.5	56.1	62.6	63.3	75.2	67.5	82.0	74.0	87.9	78.3	92.1	80.2	95.5	80.1	93.1	77.0	90.3	69.9	82.2	64.4	72.5	59.8	63.6	78.1	90.8
	1	53.0	56.0	53.6	59.2	61.5	72.2	66.0	79.7	72.7	86.3	77.0	90.4	79.2	93.3	79.0	91.1	75.9	88.4	68.4	79.8	63.1	70.2	58.2	61.2	76.7	88.4
	2	49.4	52.3	51.1	56.2	59.9	69.2	64.8	76.9	71.4	84.6	75.8	88.8	78.4	91.4	78.0	89.4	74.8	86.4	67.1	77.3	61.6	67.6	55.9	58.8	75.2	86.2
South Bend	0.4	52.5	54.5	51.5	57.7	61.7	73.2	66.1	82.1	73.2	88.1	76.5	92.5	79.1	94.9	78.7	92.8	75.3	89.4	68.4	80.9	62.3	70.3	58.6	61.7	76.7	90.0
	1	49.0	51.3	48.6	53.6	59.5	69.5	64.6	78.6	71.3	86.1	75.3	90.3	78.0	92.4	77.7	90.3	74.3	86.2	66.9	78.4	60.8	66.9	56.6	58.9	74.9	87.4
	2	44.2	47.3	45.8	50.2	57.4	65.8	63.3	74.7	70.0	84.0	74.3	88.6	77.0	90.3	76.5	88.4	73.4	84.0	65.2	75.5	59.2	64.2	52.8	55.2	73.3	84.7
IOWA																											
Des Moines	0.4	47.1	52.8	50.6	60.9	60.9	76.1	67.3	84.7	73.2	87.5	78.1	94.9	80.2	98.5	78.9	97.8	76.6	91.6	69.4	83.1	61.0	68.8	56.3	59.9	77.6	93.4
	1	43.2	49.3	47.1	56.3	58.7	71.2	65.5	81.7	71.7	85.9	77.0	92.0	79.2	95.9	78.0	95.0	75.4	88.7	67.6	80.3	59.3	65.6	51.6	55.7	76.2	90.1
	2	40.4	45.9	44.6	52.4	56.2	67.1	63.9	78.1	70.1	84.1	75.9	90.0	78.2	93.9	77.1	92.4	74.3	86.3	65.8	77.5	57.5	63.1	45.9	51.6	74.7	87.2
Mason City	0.4	38.6	43.9	44.7	52.2	58.6	70.3	65.4	83.9	71.9	88.0	77.7	94.3	80.1	95.1	79.4	94.0	76.1	89.6	68.7	82.0	58.9	64.9	50.8	52.6	77.3	91.1
	1	36.8	40.4	41.6	46.9	55.4	63.9	63.6	79.9	70.2	85.7	76.2	91.7	78.9	93.0	78.1	91.4	74.2	86.5	66.4	78.5	56.9	61.8	42.7	46.1	75.4	88.0
	2	35.4	38.1	38.8	43.0	52.2	59.2	61.4	75.7	68.7	83.2	75.0	89.5	77.7	91.2	76.8	89.2	72.8	83.9	64.4	75.1	54.4	59.2	38.8	41.9	73.6	85.1
Sioux City	0.4	42.6	52.1	48.6	59.8	59.6	76.2	66.1	87.6	72.5	89.4	77.6	96.7	81.0	98.3	79.4	96.2	76.2	91.9	68.2	83.9	58.1	67.2	48.3	54.9	78.0	93.6
	1	40.4	48.1	45.8	55.2	56.5	71.5	64.3	83.7	71.0	87.3	76.6	94.0	79.6	95.8	78.4	94.1	74.9	89.1	66.5	80.8	56.0	64.3	43.6	50.9	76.3	90.4
	2	38.3	44.7	43.3	51.3	54.1	66.8	62.5	79.9	69.6	85.2	75.6	91.8	78.6	93.8	77.3	91.9	73.7	86.6	64.3	77.9	53.5	61.5	40.9	47.0	74.6	87.5

Table 19-4. *(Continued)* **Monthly Percentiles of Wet-Bulb and Dry-Bulb Temperature for U.S. Locations**

		Jan		Feb		Mar		Apr		May		Jun		Jul		Aug		Sep		Oct		Nov		Dec		Annual	
Location	%	WB	DB	WB	DB	WB	DB	WB	DB	WB	DB	WB	DB	WB	DB	WB	DB	WB	DB	WB	DB	WB	DB	WB	DB	WB	DB
Waterloo	0.4	41.4	46.2	46.1	53.1	59.8	72.6	65.8	83.0	72.8	87.9	77.4	93.2	79.9	95.7	79.2	95.1	76.3	89.8	68.8	81.9	59.4	66.0	53.8	56.7	77.2	91.2
	1	38.7	42.8	42.5	48.8	56.7	67.0	63.9	79.7	71.1	85.8	76.1	91.1	78.8	93.5	78.0	91.4	74.7	86.9	66.8	78.6	57.5	62.8	48.3	51.0	75.4	88.2
	2	36.9	40.5	40.1	45.1	53.7	62.3	62.1	75.6	69.6	83.6	75.0	89.3	77.6	91.7	76.9	89.5	73.3	84.4	64.8	75.5	55.1	60.2	42.6	46.4	73.7	85.4
KANSAS																											
Dodge City	0.4	49.2	66.1	53.3	74.9	58.9	82.3	65.1	87.9	70.8	93.4	74.8	101.3	75.4	104.2	75.2	102.7	72.3	97.7	66.2	89.7	59.1	76.2	50.8	66.3	73.7	100.1
	1	46.8	62.4	50.9	70.0	56.9	79.0	63.2	84.9	69.5	90.8	73.8	98.7	74.4	102.4	74.2	100.8	71.2	95.6	65.0	87.3	56.9	72.9	48.3	62.8	72.5	97.1
	2	44.7	58.6	48.7	66.0	55.2	75.4	61.7	82.3	68.1	87.9	72.9	96.7	73.7	100.9	73.4	99.1	70.4	93.4	63.7	84.4	55.0	69.5	46.2	59.1	71.4	94.0
Goodland	0.4	45.7	65.2	49.6	71.1	53.2	78.7	59.5	85.3	66.0	89.7	70.5	99.7	72.3	101.1	71.4	99.2	68.3	94.6	60.2	86.9	52.4	72.3	47.4	65.6	70.1	96.9
	1	43.8	60.8	47.2	66.4	51.3	74.2	58.3	82.0	64.7	86.9	69.6	97.0	71.3	99.2	70.4	97.3	67.2	92.2	58.8	84.2	50.6	69.8	45.3	61.9	69.0	93.8
	2	42.1	56.6	45.6	62.9	49.6	71.0	56.9	78.9	63.6	84.5	68.7	94.5	70.5	97.4	69.8	95.4	66.2	90.0	57.4	81.4	49.1	66.8	43.2	58.0	67.9	90.7
Topeka	0.4	54.5	62.3	56.7	69.4	63.8	80.1	70.1	86.4	74.6	88.8	79.4	95.5	80.9	101.3	80.1	100.2	77.8	95.5	71.6	87.3	63.9	74.1	58.1	64.4	78.8	95.9
	1	50.1	58.1	53.7	65.8	62.5	76.2	68.7	83.5	73.3	87.1	78.4	93.6	80.0	98.5	79.2	97.6	76.7	93.3	69.7	84.4	62.1	71.1	55.9	61.5	77.5	92.9
	2	47.3	54.8	50.8	62.0	60.4	73.0	67.1	81.1	72.0	85.2	77.4	91.8	79.1	96.4	78.4	95.4	75.7	91.0	68.1	81.7	60.4	68.4	52.1	58.8	76.2	90.3
Wichita, Airport	0.4	55.0	62.7	56.5	71.6	64.4	79.8	69.2	86.2	74.2	90.9	77.4	100.3	78.2	106.5	78.3	103.4	76.4	98.5	71.0	88.7	63.6	74.0	58.2	63.9	76.7	100.3
	1	50.3	59.2	54.6	67.9	62.6	76.4	67.9	83.1	72.8	88.5	76.4	98.1	77.3	103.7	77.3	101.3	75.3	95.7	69.2	85.6	62.0	71.0	55.4	61.2	75.5	97.3
	2	47.7	55.7	52.1	64.4	60.6	73.3	66.7	80.4	71.7	86.4	75.6	95.9	76.6	101.4	76.4	99.5	74.3	93.2	67.7	82.9	60.3	68.6	52.3	58.8	74.4	94.1
KENTUCKY																											
Covington/Cincinnati OH,Intl Airport	0.4	57.5	61.8	57.8	64.9	63.9	76.4	67.4	82.9	73.5	87.4	77.9	92.1	79.8	95.4	78.6	93.7	75.7	90.2	69.3	81.9	64.3	73.1	60.1	66.0	77.2	91.0
	1	55.5	59.1	55.9	62.1	61.9	73.6	66.1	80.7	72.3	85.8	76.7	90.5	78.8	93.2	77.5	91.5	74.9	88.4	68.0	80.0	62.8	70.2	58.6	63.3	75.7	88.6
	2	52.3	55.7	53.6	59.4	60.1	70.7	64.8	78.3	71.2	84.1	75.5	89.0	77.7	91.5	76.7	89.9	74.1	86.2	66.8	77.7	61.3	67.7	56.5	60.8	74.3	86.2
Lexington	0.4	57.7	63.8	58.3	66.4	64.1	76.7	67.8	82.4	73.7	87.3	76.5	91.3	78.9	94.8	77.9	93.9	75.9	90.1	69.9	81.8	65.0	74.6	60.5	67.0	76.6	90.7
	1	55.8	60.4	57.1	64.1	62.5	74.4	66.3	80.7	72.4	85.7	75.7	89.7	78.0	92.4	77.1	91.7	75.0	88.2	68.5	80.1	63.4	72.1	59.2	64.4	75.4	88.5
	2	53.6	57.7	55.4	61.7	60.8	71.7	65.0	78.7	71.4	84.1	74.9	88.5	77.1	91.1	76.2	90.1	74.1	86.6	67.3	78.1	61.9	69.5	57.9	62.2	74.2	86.3
Louisville	0.4	59.0	64.7	59.8	68.5	65.0	78.7	68.8	84.5	74.8	87.9	78.4	93.0	80.5	96.8	79.5	95.8	77.4	91.7	71.3	83.5	66.0	75.4	61.4	67.6	78.3	92.6
	1	57.0	61.9	58.1	65.5	63.5	75.9	67.4	82.8	73.8	86.5	77.5	91.4	79.5	94.5	78.9	93.7	76.4	89.9	70.0	81.4	64.6	72.8	59.8	65.2	77.1	90.4
	2	54.5	59.2	56.2	62.7	61.8	73.3	66.3	80.8	72.7	85.1	76.4	90.3	78.6	93.1	78.1	92.1	75.5	88.2	68.5	79.7	63.2	70.5	58.3	63.3	75.8	88.2
LOUISANA																											
Baton Rouge	0.4	70.0	77.1	71.1	78.7	73.0	83.7	74.7	86.8	78.3	91.7	80.3	95.2	81.2	95.3	81.3	95.4	80.0	93.3	77.4	89.3	74.1	82.7	73.0	78.8	80.1	93.6
	1	68.9	75.1	69.9	76.9	71.9	82.0	74.0	85.4	77.4	90.3	79.8	94.0	80.4	94.3	80.5	94.2	79.3	92.2	76.3	87.6	73.2	81.3	71.5	77.0	79.3	92.2
	2	67.8	73.1	68.5	74.9	71.0	80.4	73.3	84.1	76.5	89.1	79.2	93.0	80.0	93.3	80.1	93.1	78.5	91.1	75.2	86.1	72.2	79.8	70.5	75.5	78.4	90.8
Lake Charles	0.4	70.2	74.9	70.9	76.2	72.3	80.1	75.3	85.4	78.2	89.9	81.3	93.2	81.4	94.8	81.3	95.4	80.4	93.0	78.4	88.2	75.2	82.2	73.1	77.2	80.4	92.9
	1	69.3	73.4	69.8	74.6	71.6	78.6	74.4	83.6	77.5	88.4	80.4	92.2	80.8	93.7	80.7	94.1	79.9	91.8	77.5	87.0	74.2	80.8	72.1	75.8	79.8	91.4
	2	68.3	71.6	68.8	73.0	71.0	77.3	73.9	82.2	76.8	87.3	79.9	91.2	80.3	92.7	80.3	93.0	79.4	90.5	76.6	85.9	73.3	79.4	71.1	74.4	79.2	90.0
New Orleans, Intl Airport	0.4	71.0	77.4	72.3	78.5	74.4	82.4	76.4	85.7	78.4	90.0	81.3	94.1	82.5	95.8	82.3	95.1	81.3	92.4	78.3	88.4	75.3	82.4	73.5	79.0	81.2	93.1
	1	69.8	75.4	71.2	76.8	73.4	80.7	75.3	84.4	77.7	88.8	80.5	93.0	81.9	94.4	81.5	93.8	80.4	91.3	77.2	86.6	74.4	81.0	72.7	77.4	80.3	91.5
	2	68.7	73.4	70.1	75.1	72.5	79.3	74.5	83.3	77.2	87.7	80.0	92.0	81.2	93.3	81.0	92.6	79.9	90.3	76.2	85.3	73.4	79.6	71.6	76.1	79.5	90.1
Shreveport	0.4	66.9	76.0	67.7	79.2	70.4	84.0	74.3	86.5	77.5	90.6	80.4	96.2	80.2	99.7	80.3	99.6	79.3	96.6	76.4	90.2	72.1	81.6	69.7	76.4	79.3	96.7
	1	65.7	73.3	66.3	76.2	69.3	81.8	73.2	84.9	76.7	89.3	79.4	94.9	79.5	98.1	79.8	98.2	78.6	94.7	75.3	88.4	70.8	79.9	68.2	74.4	78.5	94.6
	2	64.7	70.6	64.8	73.9	68.4	79.7	72.3	83.6	75.8	88.1	78.6	93.5	79.2	96.6	79.3	96.9	78.0	93.2	74.2	86.5	69.7	78.2	66.8	72.5	77.9	92.6
MAINE																											
Caribou	0.4	43.2	43.8	43.2	47.1	46.6	55.5	57.3	69.8	67.2	84.0	72.8	87.4	75.3	89.3	74.9	87.0	70.6	81.3	64.3	72.9	57.3	59.4	46.0	47.1	72.3	84.9
	1	38.1	39.9	40.5	43.3	44.4	50.6	54.8	65.3	65.0	80.3	70.8	85.3	74.2	87.3	72.6	84.8	68.7	78.3	62.0	68.9	54.5	56.7	41.6	43.8	70.2	81.7
	2	35.6	37.6	37.4	40.1	42.3	47.6	51.9	61.2	63.4	77.2	69.2	83.2	73.1	85.2	71.3	82.8	67.1	75.9	59.6	65.4	51.6	54.3	38.7	40.3	68.2	78.8
Portland	0.4	47.0	49.1	46.2	50.6	51.9	60.8	58.9	72.6	68.5	84.3	73.3	89.6	76.4	91.2	76.2	89.9	73.7	85.7	64.3	75.4	58.1	63.9	51.8	54.3	73.7	86.4
	1	43.6	46.2	43.9	47.2	48.7	56.1	56.1	67.1	66.3	80.2	71.8	86.2	75.4	88.8	74.6	87.3	72.0	82.5	62.7	71.8	56.4	60.2	49.2	51.6	71.7	83.1
	2	40.3	43.3	41.8	44.7	46.2	52.2	53.7	63.1	63.9	75.9	70.4	83.4	74.1	86.5	73.4	85.1	70.1	79.2	61.3	68.6	54.6	58.0	46.6	48.9	69.8	80.0
MARYLAND																											
Glen Burnie/ Baltimore, BWI Airport	0.4	56.4	62.5	59.0	68.9	64.2	78.3	67.3	86.1	74.2	91.0	77.8	94.3	79.8	97.5	79.3	95.4	77.3	93.1	71.1	82.7	66.8	75.5	61.5	67.7	77.7	93.2
	1	53.8	58.4	56.3	64.2	61.6	74.5	65.8	82.6	72.8	88.3	76.6	92.6	78.8	95.5	78.2	93.3	76.3	90.6	69.9	80.0	64.4	72.2	59.0	64.3	76.3	90.6
	2	50.6	55.3	53.3	60.9	59.3	70.2	64.2	78.9	71.3	85.9	75.7	90.9	78.0	93.7	77.3	91.5	75.3	88.4	68.4	77.5	63.0	69.5	56.2	61.0	75.1	88.0
MASSACHUSETTS																											
Boston	0.4	54.1	57.6	53.4	58.9	58.1	69.3	63.4	80.8	70.6	88.1	75.3	93.2	77.3	95.6	77.5	92.4	75.3	89.8	68.2	78.9	64.0	70.7	58.1	61.9	75.4	90.5
	1	50.5	54.0	50.1	55.0	55.2	63.4	61.2	75.0	68.7	84.4	73.8	90.8	76.4	93.2	76.4	90.7	74.0	86.2	66.3	75.9	61.6	67.9	55.7	58.9	73.7	87.2
	2	46.5	50.8	46.8	51.6	52.5	59.2	58.9	70.7	67.0	81.1	72.5	88.1	75.5	90.9	75.2	88.5	72.8	83.2	64.8	73.3	59.5	64.7	52.6	56.3	72.2	84.1
Worcester	0.4	50.8	53.7	50.9	55.4	55.6	66.0	61.8	79.0	69.1	84.4	73.2	87.2	75.9	89.4	76.6	87.6	74.0	84.5	65.3	76.2	61.2	67.0	54.8	58.3	73.7	85.4
	1	46.6	50.4	47.5	51.7	52.9	62.1	59.2	74.0	67.1	81.5	71.6	85.3	74.8	87.7	74.9	85.3	72.3	81.8	63.6	73.5	59.0	63.9	52.5	55.7	71.8	82.7
	2	42.7	46.5	44.0	48.1	50.0	58.0	57.3	69.7	65.2	78.9	70.4	83.3	73.8	85.9	73.5	83.6	70.7	79.1	62.2	70.8	56.8	61.2	48.7	52.0	70.1	80.1
MICHIGAN																											
Alpena	0.4	42.3	45.3	43.0	47.7	55.1	63.1	63.7	81.6	69.9	85.0	73.5	90.9	76.9	93.1	76.0	89.5	73.0	84.8	65.7	76.1	58.1	63.7	51.0	54.7	73.6	87.4
	1	39.2	42.5	40.0	44.3	51.2	58.9	61.7	75.1	68.0	82.4	71.9	88.1	75.5	90.4	74.5	87.2	71.5	82.0	63.6	72.2	55.4	60.1	45.3	47.9	71.5	84.1
	2	36.9	39.7	37.6	41.5	47.4	54.5	58.8	70.2	66.4	79.4	70.5	85.3	74.1	88.0	73.4	84.9	69.8	79.2	61.4	69.0	52.5	57.0	41.0	43.4	69.6	80.8
Detroit, Metro	0.4	50.7	52.8	49.3	55.2	60.2	71.6	66.0	81.7	73.3	88.2	76.2	91.8	78.5	94.6	78.4	92.0	75.3	88.4	67.9	80.5	61.0	68.4	57.0	60.5	75.9	89.8
	1	45.9	48.9	46.5	51.0	57.4	67.3	64.2	78.2	71.7	85.6	75.0	89.9	77.4	92.2	77.0	89.8	74.0	86.0	65.8	77.1	59.2	65.2	53.8	57.1	74.2	87.0
	2	42.4	44.9	43.8	47.5	54.9	62.8	62.5	73.9	70.1	83.3	73.8	88.1	76.1	90.2	75.5	87.9	72.7	83.6	64.0	74.1	57.5	62.6	50.0	52.9	72.5	84.4

Table 19-4. *(Continued)* Monthly Percentiles of Wet-Bulb and Dry-Bulb Temperature for U.S. Locations

		Jan		Feb		Mar		Apr		May		Jun		Jul		Aug		Sep		Oct		Nov		Dec		Annual	
Location	%	WB	DB	WB	DB	WB	DB	WB	DB	WB	DB	WB	DB	WB	DB	WB	DB	WB	DB	WB	DB	WB	DB	WB	DB	WB	DB
Flint	0.4	48.3	51.1	47.1	51.7	59.3	69.5	65.5	80.8	73.0	86.2	74.9	91.1	78.6	93.0	78.1	90.3	74.7	87.6	67.2	78.9	60.8	67.9	56.6	60.1	75.3	88.3
	1	44.9	48.0	44.7	48.7	56.6	66.0	63.8	77.2	71.3	84.0	73.9	88.6	77.1	90.7	76.5	88.2	73.2	84.4	65.7	75.8	59.0	64.8	53.0	56.2	73.5	85.6
	2	40.9	44.1	42.1	45.6	53.6	61.7	62.1	73.2	69.5	81.9	72.9	86.7	75.7	88.8	75.1	86.4	72.0	81.9	63.9	73.0	57.3	62.1	48.8	51.6	71.8	83.1
Grand Rapids	0.4	48.6	50.5	48.3	52.4	60.0	69.9	66.3	80.7	72.2	87.6	75.8	91.3	78.2	92.5	78.0	91.9	74.8	87.2	68.3	79.2	60.5	67.6	56.1	59.0	75.8	89.2
	1	44.7	46.9	44.6	48.8	57.5	66.4	64.6	77.8	70.9	85.1	74.6	89.3	77.1	90.9	76.9	89.8	73.6	84.5	66.2	76.6	58.7	64.1	52.7	55.2	74.0	86.4
	2	40.2	43.1	41.9	45.3	54.4	62.4	62.7	73.7	69.5	82.7	73.5	87.7	76.0	89.4	75.7	87.5	72.4	82.1	64.4	73.9	57.3	61.4	47.6	50.6	72.3	83.8
Hancock	0.4	41.9	43.4	41.9	45.6	54.3	61.0	63.2	76.6	68.6	85.1	73.5	87.9	75.8	90.9	75.9	88.4	72.3	82.3	65.0	76.2	57.0	62.7	47.4	50.0	73.3	85.5
	1	38.1	40.6	39.4	43.0	50.9	56.1	60.6	71.9	67.2	82.4	72.2	85.5	74.7	88.1	74.5	86.1	70.8	79.5	63.2	73.0	55.1	59.6	43.1	45.5	71.3	82.6
	2	35.5	37.5	36.9	40.0	47.3	52.2	58.4	68.4	65.7	79.9	70.9	83.4	73.5	85.8	73.4	84.2	69.5	77.3	61.3	69.6	53.0	56.7	38.9	40.5	69.5	80.0
Lansing	0.4	49.2	52.2	48.7	52.3	60.1	70.1	66.7	80.5	73.2	87.2	76.0	91.7	78.5	93.3	77.6	92.5	75.3	87.9	67.7	79.6	60.9	68.6	56.5	59.0	75.9	89.4
	1	45.5	48.6	45.6	49.6	57.6	66.7	64.5	77.8	71.3	84.9	74.7	89.5	77.4	91.5	76.4	89.9	74.1	84.9	66.1	76.8	59.0	64.8	52.9	55.4	74.2	86.4
	2	41.4	44.4	42.8	45.9	54.9	62.6	62.8	73.6	69.8	82.4	73.6	87.5	76.3	89.8	75.5	87.6	73.0	82.4	64.4	73.6	57.5	61.8	48.3	50.8	72.6	83.7
Muskegon	0.4	45.9	47.7	44.5	48.9	58.1	66.7	64.2	77.0	70.3	83.9	73.3	87.3	76.4	89.1	77.2	88.5	73.8	83.6	66.5	75.8	59.2	64.1	53.1	55.2	74.5	85.4
	1	42.5	44.1	42.1	45.3	55.1	63.1	62.3	73.2	68.5	81.9	72.3	85.4	75.4	87.1	76.1	86.1	72.7	81.5	65.0	73.6	57.7	61.6	50.2	52.1	72.8	83.1
	2	39.2	41.4	39.8	42.6	52.4	59.6	60.3	70.1	67.2	79.8	71.2	83.8	74.5	85.6	75.0	84.2	71.5	79.8	63.5	71.2	56.2	59.7	45.9	48.3	71.2	80.9
Sault Ste. Marie	0.4	37.2	38.7	38.1	40.3	44.5	50.3	60.1	72.2	69.1	82.7	71.6	85.4	75.5	88.3	74.5	85.7	72.3	81.0	63.1	72.6	54.2	56.4	43.9	45.5	72.0	83.2
	1	35.2	36.4	36.1	38.6	42.5	47.1	57.2	67.3	66.8	79.8	69.8	82.8	74.0	85.9	73.0	83.6	70.1	77.7	61.0	68.2	51.6	54.4	39.6	41.1	69.8	79.9
	2	33.8	35.0	34.8	37.0	40.6	44.3	54.2	63.4	64.5	76.9	68.2	80.2	72.3	83.5	71.4	81.6	68.1	75.0	59.0	64.9	49.0	52.0	37.0	38.2	67.7	76.8
Traverse City	0.4	41.4	44.7	42.5	47.0	56.1	66.6	64.8	82.0	71.0	87.7	74.6	92.8	76.8	93.6	76.5	91.8	74.1	85.9	67.7	78.5	58.8	65.6	52.6	55.7	74.2	89.0
	1	38.6	42.3	39.7	44.4	53.2	62.3	63.0	77.3	69.2	84.7	73.1	89.7	75.6	91.5	75.0	88.7	72.6	83.4	65.7	75.3	56.9	61.9	47.1	50.0	72.3	85.6
	2	36.8	40.0	37.6	41.4	50.0	57.6	60.7	72.3	67.4	81.4	71.5	87.0	74.4	89.5	73.9	86.4	71.1	80.9	63.7	72.3	54.7	59.5	42.2	45.0	70.4	82.6
MINNESTOA																											
Duluth	0.4	34.7	39.2	37.8	44.5	46.2	55.1	57.5	73.6	66.4	82.7	71.8	85.7	74.6	89.3	73.6	88.0	70.6	81.6	61.8	72.5	52.0	57.6	38.6	41.0	71.5	84.3
	1	32.9	36.2	35.4	40.5	43.1	50.4	54.7	68.8	64.4	79.6	69.6	83.3	73.4	86.8	72.2	85.3	68.5	78.1	59.8	69.1	48.7	53.3	34.7	37.1	69.3	80.9
	2	31.5	33.9	33.6	37.8	40.3	46.7	51.8	64.8	62.7	77.0	67.8	80.9	72.1	84.6	70.9	82.9	66.8	75.8	57.7	65.9	45.2	50.2	33.2	35.1	67.1	78.0
International Falls	0.4	34.1	37.5	37.5	42.8	46.0	55.5	58.8	76.4	68.0	86.8	72.1	88.6	75.6	90.9	74.5	89.4	71.4	82.1	61.5	74.5	50.0	57.2	35.5	38.6	72.2	86.2
	1	32.1	34.7	35.2	40.3	43.5	51.5	56.4	72.0	66.4	83.6	70.3	86.2	74.0	88.4	73.1	86.5	68.9	79.1	59.1	70.6	46.8	52.6	33.1	35.4	69.9	82.8
	2	30.6	32.5	33.5	37.4	40.8	47.8	53.9	67.8	64.5	80.5	68.9	83.7	72.6	86.1	71.7	84.5	66.8	76.2	57.3	66.7	44.3	49.5	31.7	33.7	67.8	79.8
Minneapolis-St. Paul	0.4	37.4	42.0	43.3	50.1	56.7	67.0	64.4	82.1	71.0	88.4	76.4	93.6	78.8	96.1	78.1	94.0	75.2	89.0	67.2	80.0	57.2	63.9	46.3	49.3	76.0	91.0
	1	35.5	39.6	39.8	45.4	53.1	61.8	62.4	77.6	69.4	85.7	75.2	91.0	77.6	93.7	76.8	91.3	73.3	85.7	65.5	76.2	54.3	60.4	39.4	43.0	74.1	87.9
	2	34.2	37.6	37.5	42.1	50.0	57.8	60.3	73.8	67.9	83.0	74.0	88.7	76.4	91.5	75.4	89.2	71.6	83.0	63.2	73.1	51.7	57.4	37.0	40.2	72.2	85.0
Rochester	0.4	37.3	41.4	43.3	48.2	57.2	65.9	64.5	80.3	70.9	85.4	76.0	90.7	79.3	92.9	77.4	91.1	74.4	85.4	66.5	78.3	57.2	62.4	48.2	50.6	75.5	88.0
	1	35.7	38.4	39.1	43.3	53.9	60.4	62.3	76.1	69.3	83.2	74.8	88.3	77.4	90.7	76.2	88.2	72.5	82.9	64.6	74.9	55.1	59.8	41.8	43.8	73.6	85.1
	2	34.3	36.7	36.7	40.0	50.2	56.6	60.3	72.1	67.9	80.6	73.4	86.3	76.0	88.5	75.0	86.2	71.0	80.3	62.5	72.1	52.5	57.3	37.5	39.8	71.7	82.3
Saint Cloud	0.4	36.6	41.5	42.0	47.9	54.4	66.1	64.1	81.2	70.3	88.1	75.7	93.5	78.6	95.8	77.5	93.2	75.0	88.4	66.4	78.1	54.9	62.7	40.0	44.2	75.7	90.5
	1	35.1	39.3	39.1	44.4	51.1	60.2	61.8	77.2	68.9	85.1	74.5	90.5	77.3	93.3	76.4	91.0	73.0	85.5	64.7	75.4	52.0	58.6	37.0	40.6	73.8	87.5
	2	33.6	37.0	36.9	41.7	47.9	55.9	58.9	73.3	67.4	82.5	73.3	88.5	76.2	90.9	75.2	89.1	71.2	82.7	62.4	72.5	49.2	55.3	35.1	37.6	71.8	84.7
MISSISSIPPI																											
Jackson	0.4	67.9	75.4	69.1	78.6	71.2	83.6	74.1	86.4	77.0	91.4	80.1	96.9	80.8	98.5	80.5	97.6	79.2	95.9	76.1	88.8	72.5	81.8	70.6	77.2	79.6	95.3
	1	66.5	72.8	67.8	76.4	70.2	81.7	73.2	85.1	76.1	89.9	79.1	95.2	80.2	96.8	80.1	96.0	78.5	93.8	74.8	87.2	71.2	80.1	69.3	75.3	78.7	93.4
	2	65.2	70.3	66.4	73.9	69.2	79.9	72.2	83.6	75.1	88.7	78.4	93.9	79.7	95.2	79.5	94.8	78.0	92.3	73.6	85.6	70.0	78.4	68.1	73.4	78.0	91.8
Meridian	0.4	67.2	74.5	68.5	78.5	70.5	83.9	73.6	86.8	76.5	91.7	79.5	97.3	80.8	99.4	80.3	97.5	78.7	96.2	75.2	88.8	71.2	81.1	70.2	77.0	79.3	95.6
	1	65.8	72.1	67.2	75.8	69.5	81.9	72.5	85.1	75.5	90.2	78.5	95.5	80.1	97.3	79.5	96.0	78.1	94.0	74.0	86.7	70.1	79.4	69.2	75.0	78.3	93.5
	2	64.5	69.8	65.7	73.4	68.6	79.7	71.5	83.8	74.7	88.8	77.9	94.0	79.4	95.7	79.1	94.7	77.3	92.5	72.9	85.0	69.1	77.6	67.7	72.9	77.4	91.6
MISSOURI																											
Columbia	0.4	56.3	63.8	56.9	68.4	64.0	79.2	68.9	84.8	75.0	87.5	78.7	94.6	80.1	101.7	79.5	98.9	76.8	93.3	70.3	85.8	63.8	74.9	60.2	66.1	78.1	94.7
	1	53.2	59.0	54.8	64.9	62.3	76.1	67.4	82.7	73.3	86.0	77.7	92.0	79.3	97.4	78.4	96.5	75.7	91.1	68.8	82.8	62.2	72.1	57.7	63.5	76.8	91.6
	2	50.0	55.8	52.5	61.1	60.5	73.1	66.1	80.6	71.8	84.4	76.6	90.2	78.5	95.2	77.6	94.6	74.7	89.0	67.5	80.0	60.6	69.4	54.9	60.1	75.4	89.1
Kansas City	0.4	55.8	61.7	56.0	67.9	63.9	78.6	69.9	86.3	74.3	88.4	78.4	95.9	80.0	101.0	79.9	100.0	77.3	94.2	71.8	86.9	63.7	74.8	59.1	64.5	78.3	95.9
	1	51.7	58.6	53.3	64.1	62.1	75.5	68.5	83.1	72.7	86.9	77.6	93.4	79.3	98.7	79.0	97.7	76.3	92.0	69.4	84.2	62.4	71.6	56.5	62.2	77.1	92.8
	2	48.2	55.0	50.7	60.7	60.4	72.5	66.8	80.5	71.4	85.2	76.8	91.6	78.5	96.4	78.1	95.6	75.4	89.9	68.1	81.4	60.8	68.9	53.3	59.3	75.9	90.1
Springfield	0.4	56.4	65.1	58.8	70.7	64.6	78.4	69.4	84.2	74.1	86.4	78.2	94.0	79.5	99.5	78.5	98.6	76.5	93.1	70.9	86.4	64.5	74.9	60.7	67.5	77.5	94.7
	1	54.3	61.4	56.9	67.2	63.2	75.9	68.0	81.3	72.9	85.0	77.2	91.7	78.7	96.8	77.7	96.8	75.5	90.4	69.4	83.3	63.0	72.5	59.0	65.1	76.3	91.9
	2	52.3	58.5	54.8	64.2	61.7	73.2	66.9	79.4	71.7	83.6	76.2	89.9	77.9	94.8	77.0	95.0	74.7	88.5	67.9	80.8	61.6	70.2	56.7	62.5	75.2	89.3
St. Louis, Intl Airport	0.4	58.1	65.9	59.0	71.0	65.4	80.9	70.3	86.8	74.7	89.4	78.8	94.8	81.1	100.2	79.7	99.7	78.4	94.1	71.5	85.9	65.4	76.0	62.0	67.8	78.9	95.2
	1	54.8	61.0	56.7	66.8	64.0	77.5	68.4	84.2	73.5	87.9	77.8	93.2	80.2	97.7	79.0	96.8	77.1	92.1	70.3	83.2	64.2	73.3	59.7	64.5	77.5	92.5
	2	52.0	57.4	54.2	62.9	62.4	74.3	67.1	81.8	72.4	86.2	77.0	91.9	79.3	95.8	78.3	94.8	76.0	90.0	69.0	80.4	62.8	70.6	57.0	61.5	76.3	90.0
MONTANA																											
Billings	0.4	42.4	55.7	45.7	61.6	48.3	69.0	54.9	80.2	60.6	86.8	66.5	95.3	68.4	97.6	66.8	97.4	62.8	90.6	55.6	81.3	48.7	66.0	43.6	57.9	65.4	93.3
	1	40.4	52.6	43.2	58.0	46.7	65.6	53.3	76.5	59.4	83.7	65.2	92.5	67.2	95.6	65.5	94.9	61.3	88.1	54.5	77.6	46.9	62.8	41.6	54.5	63.9	90.2
	2	38.9	49.9	41.8	55.2	45.3	62.5	51.8	73.3	58.3	81.1	64.0	89.9	66.1	93.4	64.4	93.1	60.1	85.4	53.2	74.4	45.2	59.7	40.0	51.8	62.4	86.8
Cut Bank	0.4	43.4	54.5	43.8	56.2	45.3	61.7	51.6	74.4	57.5	80.3	61.6	86.7	66.3	89.8	63.7	93.2	59.8	87.1	53.7	77.9	47.2	61.8	43.3	53.8	62.2	87.3
	1	41.2	51.2	41.5	52.6	43.9	58.0	49.9	70.4	56.1	77.1	60.6	84.4	64.7	87.6	62.9	90.7	58.2	84.0	52.4	74.4	45.1	58.7	41.2	51.1	60.4	83.9
	2	39.3	47.9	39.7	50.0	42.1	54.4	48.2	66.7	54.6	74.5	59.6	82.2	63.2	85.8	61.9	88.6	56.9	80.9	51.3	71.4	43.3	55.1	39.5	48.0	58.9	80.3

Table 19-4. *(Continued)* **Monthly Percentiles of Wet-Bulb and Dry-Bulb Temperature for U.S. Locations**

		Jan		Feb		Mar		Apr		May		Jun		Jul		Aug		Sep		Oct		Nov		Dec		Annual	
Location	%	WB	DB	WB	DB	WB	DB	WB	DB	WB	DB	WB	DB	WB	DB	WB	DB	WB	DB	WB	DB	WB	DB	WB	DB	WB	DB
Glasgow	0.4	39.0	45.8	43.3	54.0	49.0	65.0	56.2	80.1	63.3	88.5	68.9	96.2	72.3	97.4	68.5	98.5	63.3	90.4	56.6	79.8	48.0	61.5	41.5	50.0	67.7	93.5
	1	37.4	43.3	41.0	49.5	46.7	61.6	54.2	76.4	61.6	85.0	67.3	92.8	70.6	95.2	67.2	96.0	62.0	87.3	55.1	75.9	46.1	57.9	39.1	46.8	65.5	90.0
	2	35.9	41.1	39.1	46.1	44.6	57.6	52.6	72.9	60.1	82.1	66.0	89.8	68.9	93.0	66.0	93.6	60.8	84.4	53.5	72.4	43.9	54.3	37.0	43.4	63.8	86.3
Great Falls, Intl Airport	0.4	43.6	56.0	45.4	60.5	48.0	66.6	54.3	78.7	60.3	78.7	65.1	92.2	67.3	95.4	65.1	96.6	61.0	89.8	55.1	80.2	47.9	64.6	44.5	57.1	63.9	91.8
	1	41.8	53.1	43.4	57.4	46.3	63.1	52.7	75.1	58.6	76.8	63.7	89.7	65.6	93.5	63.9	94.3	59.6	87.2	53.9	77.0	46.4	61.4	42.7	54.8	62.2	88.3
	2	40.2	50.7	41.8	54.8	44.8	60.1	51.1	71.7	57.1	75.8	62.5	86.9	64.4	91.6	62.9	92.3	58.5	84.7	52.5	74.2	45.1	58.7	41.0	52.1	60.7	84.9
Helena	0.4	41.4	52.6	44.3	56.7	47.3	66.8	53.7	76.6	59.0	77.7	64.7	91.8	65.5	95.1	64.3	94.6	61.4	88.2	54.2	76.9	47.0	60.9	42.5	54.2	63.0	90.4
	1	39.9	48.9	42.3	53.8	45.6	62.4	52.0	73.2	57.7	77.2	63.0	89.2	64.3	92.8	63.2	92.2	60.0	85.5	53.0	73.5	45.2	58.2	40.4	50.7	61.4	87.2
	2	38.5	46.5	40.7	51.2	44.0	59.1	50.4	70.2	56.5	75.0	61.7	86.4	63.3	90.8	62.2	90.0	58.7	82.4	51.7	70.5	43.5	55.3	39.0	47.8	60.1	83.8
Kalispell	0.4	40.9	44.6	42.1	49.3	47.4	61.0	55.2	75.1	61.3	79.4	65.4	88.1	67.6	92.5	66.6	93.5	61.8	85.4	55.2	72.5	48.0	54.4	42.0	47.0	64.6	89.1
	1	38.9	42.8	40.5	46.8	45.4	57.1	53.2	71.2	59.4	75.5	64.3	86.0	66.2	90.8	65.0	91.5	60.5	82.5	53.7	69.6	45.6	51.8	40.0	44.3	63.0	85.7
	2	37.4	41.2	39.1	44.5	43.5	54.0	51.4	67.5	57.9	73.3	63.1	83.7	65.1	89.1	64.0	89.5	59.4	79.8	52.3	66.3	43.8	49.5	38.5	42.2	61.4	82.2
Lewistown	0.4	42.7	53.7	44.6	57.2	46.9	64.6	52.9	75.4	59.6	77.5	65.4	87.1	68.1	93.1	66.1	94.7	62.3	88.4	56.3	79.5	48.1	64.9	43.4	56.2	64.4	89.4
	1	40.6	50.6	42.4	53.1	45.1	60.9	51.5	72.2	58.0	76.2	63.9	84.3	66.5	90.9	64.7	92.6	60.0	85.7	54.3	76.4	46.0	61.4	41.4	52.9	62.5	85.5
	2	38.9	48.1	40.4	50.5	43.6	57.3	50.0	69.1	56.5	72.9	62.7	81.8	65.1	88.5	63.4	90.3	58.5	83.0	52.7	73.4	44.2	58.1	39.8	50.1	60.9	82.1
Miles City	0.4	41.5	51.0	45.6	59.2	51.2	69.2	57.7	82.6	64.9	83.5	70.7	99.5	72.6	101.2	70.2	100.3	65.1	94.0	57.4	81.5	49.7	64.8	42.4	53.6	69.3	96.7
	1	39.7	47.5	43.4	55.1	49.3	65.3	55.7	78.4	63.2	82.1	69.3	95.4	71.3	98.9	68.9	98.2	63.8	90.9	56.2	77.7	47.5	61.0	40.4	49.5	67.3	93.4
	2	37.9	44.5	41.7	51.7	47.4	61.8	54.3	75.3	61.7	80.3	67.8	92.8	70.1	96.8	67.7	96.5	62.6	87.7	54.9	74.7	45.5	57.7	38.5	46.5	65.6	89.8
Missoula	0.4	40.8	45.2	42.8	52.3	48.4	63.6	55.8	77.0	62.1	80.2	66.1	91.6	67.1	95.4	66.5	95.8	61.9	87.6	55.3	75.0	47.6	56.4	41.7	47.9	64.6	91.4
	1	38.8	43.0	41.3	48.7	46.9	60.3	53.9	73.4	60.2	76.7	64.7	89.4	65.9	93.4	65.0	93.4	60.8	84.9	54.1	72.0	45.6	53.2	39.7	44.8	63.0	88.2
	2	37.5	41.4	40.0	46.2	45.2	57.4	52.4	70.0	58.6	75.0	63.6	86.7	64.8	91.7	63.9	91.5	59.6	82.1	52.6	68.5	44.0	50.6	38.2	41.9	61.5	84.6
NEBRASKA																											
Grand Island	0.4	44.9	58.8	49.9	66.1	58.4	79.0	65.4	87.8	71.2	83.6	76.3	99.2	78.0	101.6	77.4	99.2	73.8	94.3	66.1	85.8	57.1	70.2	47.4	61.1	75.6	96.6
	1	42.8	54.4	47.3	61.8	56.3	73.7	63.7	83.8	69.5	81.2	74.9	96.7	76.8	99.5	76.2	96.7	72.6	91.5	64.3	82.6	54.5	66.8	45.0	56.6	74.1	93.1
	2	40.4	50.1	45.4	57.4	53.9	69.5	61.8	80.0	68.2	80.1	73.7	94.3	76.0	97.4	75.2	94.6	71.4	89.1	62.5	79.8	52.6	63.9	42.6	52.7	72.6	89.7
Norfolk	0.4	44.7	58.1	48.7	63.6	58.3	76.7	66.3	90.1	71.1	84.4	76.8	97.7	78.3	99.5	78.1	97.5	74.3	93.9	64.2	83.5	57.6	68.0	46.2	57.2	76.4	95.0
	1	42.7	53.8	46.7	58.9	56.1	71.2	64.3	86.4	69.7	81.5	75.9	95.6	77.4	97.3	77.2	95.4	73.3	91.7	62.1	80.3	55.1	64.5	43.6	53.2	75.0	92.0
	2	40.1	49.2	44.4	54.9	54.1	66.7	62.3	82.4	68.3	79.5	74.8	93.1	76.5	95.2	76.3	93.6	72.2	89.5	60.6	77.2	52.6	61.5	41.4	49.5	73.4	89.0
North Platte	0.4	43.5	59.3	48.1	66.9	54.0	76.1	61.6	86.1	67.9	80.1	74.2	97.1	75.5	99.8	74.5	98.3	70.7	93.8	61.8	85.6	53.1	71.4	45.8	61.8	73.1	95.0
	1	41.6	54.8	46.3	62.9	52.0	72.6	60.0	82.5	66.5	79.3	72.5	94.1	74.4	97.7	73.4	95.9	69.3	91.4	60.0	82.7	51.1	68.0	43.4	57.9	71.5	91.7
	2	39.6	51.1	44.3	59.4	50.2	69.2	58.3	78.6	65.2	77.7	71.4	91.6	73.6	95.6	72.4	93.5	68.1	88.9	58.6	79.9	49.0	64.1	41.1	53.8	70.1	88.6
Omaha, Eppley Airfield	0.4	45.5	54.9	51.0	63.2	61.3	78.9	67.7	86.8	73.6	83.4	78.7	97.1	81.2	100.2	79.9	98.3	76.5	93.2	69.7	84.7	60.7	70.0	53.9	59.2	78.2	95.0
	1	43.2	51.2	47.9	58.6	59.1	74.2	66.0	83.4	72.1	83.6	77.5	94.7	79.8	97.7	78.8	95.8	75.4	90.6	68.0	81.9	58.8	67.1	48.9	55.7	76.6	91.8
	2	40.9	47.8	45.8	54.8	56.6	70.1	64.3	80.2	70.6	81.5	76.3	92.2	78.7	95.5	77.7	93.6	74.3	88.2	66.2	79.1	56.5	64.5	44.5	52.2	75.1	88.9
Scottsbluff	0.4	43.3	58.9	47.2	65.8	50.3	74.0	56.7	83.3	63.2	78.6	68.7	97.5	71.5	100.8	70.7	97.4	66.1	94.0	57.5	84.0	50.4	71.3	46.2	62.7	69.0	95.3
	1	41.7	55.5	45.1	61.4	48.6	70.3	55.4	80.5	62.0	78.1	67.6	94.9	70.4	98.6	69.4	95.2	64.9	91.3	56.0	81.2	48.6	68.1	43.7	59.7	67.5	92.2
	2	40.1	52.6	43.3	59.1	47.2	67.1	54.1	77.4	60.8	77.4	66.7	92.5	69.5	96.5	68.6	93.3	63.6	88.6	54.7	78.6	47.0	64.5	41.6	55.9	66.2	89.0
NEVADA																											
Elko	0.4	43.1	52.9	46.4	61.2	48.3	67.8	52.4	77.6	58.1	80.6	62.6	95.7	65.3	98.6	65.1	97.6	61.5	91.9	55.0	82.8	49.5	66.4	42.8	53.5	63.0	94.8
	1	41.3	49.8	44.7	57.5	46.9	65.0	51.0	75.2	56.6	77.9	61.3	93.5	64.2	96.8	64.1	95.5	60.0	89.9	53.4	80.0	47.5	63.7	41.4	50.8	61.4	92.3
	2	39.6	47.1	43.1	54.5	45.7	61.9	49.8	72.3	55.3	75.8	60.1	91.4	63.3	95.4	63.0	94.1	58.9	88.0	52.2	77.6	46.0	60.2	39.9	48.3	59.9	89.6
Ely	0.4	40.9	53.5	44.0	59.5	45.5	64.8	50.1	73.9	54.8	77.3	59.4	90.0	62.2	92.4	62.4	91.1	58.5	86.3	52.0	77.9	47.0	65.9	41.7	56.0	60.3	89.2
	1	39.4	50.2	42.0	56.3	44.1	62.1	48.5	71.7	53.5	75.0	58.1	88.5	61.2	91.0	61.3	89.7	57.4	84.5	50.8	76.1	45.0	62.8	39.7	53.2	59.0	87.0
	2	37.8	47.4	40.5	53.3	42.9	59.8	47.1	69.3	52.5	72.5	57.0	86.9	60.4	89.8	60.4	88.4	56.3	82.7	49.9	73.9	43.4	60.2	38.0	49.9	57.6	84.7
Las Vegas, Intl Airport	0.4	52.4	68.8	55.0	76.6	56.8	84.0	60.2	92.9	64.2	91.0	68.6	109.5	73.1	111.2	73.4	109.8	70.2	103.9	62.9	95.7	56.8	79.5	52.1	68.1	71.4	107.9
	1	50.6	66.3	53.5	73.8	55.4	81.7	58.9	90.8	63.2	89.3	67.3	108.0	72.2	109.8	72.5	108.0	69.1	102.5	61.7	93.7	55.5	77.4	50.4	65.6	70.1	105.6
	2	49.0	64.1	52.1	71.4	54.4	79.5	57.7	88.6	62.2	89.9	66.2	106.4	71.4	108.5	71.8	106.6	68.1	100.9	60.5	91.3	54.3	75.1	48.9	63.6	69.0	103.2
Reno	0.4	46.9	59.5	49.4	66.5	49.8	71.6	54.2	80.2	59.2	81.6	63.3	94.9	65.1	98.5	65.0	97.4	60.8	92.7	57.0	84.9	50.9	69.7	47.5	60.6	63.0	94.6
	1	44.7	56.8	47.5	63.6	48.3	68.8	52.5	77.9	58.0	80.3	62.1	93.0	64.1	96.8	63.9	95.7	59.9	90.4	55.7	82.6	49.6	67.2	45.7	57.9	61.6	92.1
	2	43.1	54.3	46.0	61.1	47.1	66.2	51.3	75.2	56.9	79.9	60.9	91.2	63.2	95.2	62.9	94.3	59.1	88.6	54.5	80.2	48.4	64.5	44.1	55.2	60.3	89.5
Tonopah	0.4	44.6	58.1	45.6	63.2	48.0	69.8	51.1	79.1	56.2	80.9	61.2	94.9	64.2	97.0	64.2	96.3	60.3	90.1	54.4	83.1	48.4	68.6	43.2	56.6	62.2	93.9
	1	42.5	55.0	44.3	61.2	46.6	67.7	49.7	76.3	55.0	79.3	59.8	93.2	63.2	95.7	63.3	94.7	59.3	88.3	53.1	81.0	46.9	66.1	41.4	54.8	60.8	91.6
	2	40.9	52.6	43.0	59.1	45.2	65.2	48.6	73.7	53.9	77.1	58.4	91.4	62.3	94.5	62.4	93.1	58.3	86.8	52.1	78.8	45.5	63.7	40.2	52.8	59.5	89.4
Winnemucca	0.4	47.0	57.7	49.0	64.5	50.6	71.7	53.8	81.0	59.2	85.5	63.5	97.7	66.2	100.5	65.3	100.1	60.8	93.4	55.9	85.2	50.2	69.3	46.7	58.7	63.4	96.8
	1	44.5	54.7	47.2	61.7	48.9	68.6	52.3	78.3	57.9	81.0	62.3	95.9	65.0	98.9	64.1	98.0	59.9	91.6	54.8	82.5	48.9	66.1	45.0	55.8	61.8	94.4
	2	43.0	52.3	45.5	59.2	47.4	65.8	51.2	75.6	56.8	80.6	61.0	93.9	63.9	97.3	63.1	96.3	59.0	89.6	53.7	80.0	47.6	63.5	43.3	53.1	60.3	91.8
NEW HAMPSHIRE																											
Concord	0.4	48.3	52.1	48.1	54.1	55.7	67.5	63.5	81.4	70.1	85.0	74.5	92.0	76.7	94.4	76.4	91.7	74.1	87.7	66.3	78.9	61.7	68.5	54.1	57.6	74.4	89.7
	1	42.7	47.4	45.0	50.0	51.8	62.1	60.7	76.0	68.3	81.6	73.0	89.7	75.7	92.2	75.1	89.5	72.7	85.1	64.4	75.4	58.8	64.8	49.6	53.3	72.7	86.5
	2	39.1	43.7	42.1	46.3	49.2	57.4	58.5	72.0	66.4	78.9	71.9	87.2	74.9	90.1	73.8	87.6	71.3	82.4	62.9	72.2	56.3	61.5	45.0	48.8	71.1	83.8
NEW JERSEY																											
Atlantic City	0.4	55.9	61.2	57.0	65.4	62.1	75.2	66.3	83.0	74.2	85.2	77.0	93.9	79.3	95.4	78.9	93.0	77.1	90.7	70.8	83.9	65.9	70.6	60.1	64.5	77.2	91.3
	1	53.9	57.2	54.5	60.7	59.4	69.8	64.5	79.3	72.0	79.4	75.9	91.4	78.3	93.6	77.9	90.8	76.1	88.0	69.4	81.5	64.1	68.4	58.3	61.8	75.9	88.3
	2	51.9	54.8	52.3	57.2	56.7	65.1	62.3	74.8	70.3	79.6	74.9	89.2	77.5	91.7	77.0	89.0	75.0	85.5	68.2	79.5	62.4	66.1	56.3	59.6	74.7	85.6

Table 19-4. *(Continued)* Monthly Percentiles of Wet-Bulb and Dry-Bulb Temperature for U.S. Locations

		Jan		Feb		Mar		Apr		May		Jun		Jul		Aug		Sep		Oct		Nov		Dec		Annual	
Location	%	WB	DB	WB	DB	WB	DB	WB	DB	WB	DB	WB	DB	WB	DB	WB	DB	WB	DB	WB	DB	WB	DB	WB	DB	WB	DB
Newark	0.4	55.8	60.2	55.7	63.3	62.6	75.2	65.6	84.4	72.9	86.8	76.4	94.9	79.0	97.9	78.2	94.9	77.1	92.7	70.1	88.4	65.4	78.4	59.8	64.4	76.7	93.0
	1	51.8	56.3	52.7	59.5	59.2	70.6	63.9	80.2	71.5	83.6	75.2	92.9	77.9	95.6	77.3	92.4	76.1	89.9	68.8	86.3	63.2	75.3	57.2	61.1	75.5	90.0
	2	48.4	52.6	50.1	55.5	56.1	66.1	62.2	76.1	70.0	81.0	74.1	90.9	76.9	93.5	76.5	90.5	75.1	86.9	67.5	84.1	61.6	72.6	54.0	57.8	74.2	87.3
NEW MEXICO																											
Albuquerque	0.4	45.1	60.5	47.2	68.1	50.1	75.5	54.0	83.1	59.2	90.3	64.2	99.6	66.4	99.5	66.8	95.1	64.5	91.9	58.6	83.9	51.4	70.6	45.1	60.9	65.3	95.6
	1	43.3	58.0	45.8	65.7	48.6	73.4	52.7	80.9	57.9	88.2	63.3	97.6	65.8	97.6	66.2	93.9	63.6	89.9	57.4	81.5	49.8	68.4	43.4	58.3	64.4	93.0
	2	41.9	55.5	44.5	63.1	47.4	71.2	51.6	79.1	56.9	86.4	62.4	95.7	65.3	96.0	65.5	92.5	62.9	87.9	56.2	79.5	48.3	66.1	42.2	55.8	63.5	90.5
Tucumcari	0.4	49.5	69.9	52.2	76.5	54.8	81.5	59.9	87.3	65.1	94.3	69.3	102.3	71.2	100.7	70.9	98.3	68.7	94.1	62.8	88.4	55.6	78.4	50.4	70.2	69.4	97.6
	1	47.8	67.3	50.3	73.1	52.7	78.4	58.4	85.6	63.9	92.3	68.3	99.8	70.3	99.0	70.1	96.7	67.8	92.3	61.4	86.3	54.2	75.3	49.0	67.7	68.4	95.1
	2	46.3	64.6	48.9	69.9	51.2	76.1	57.0	83.5	62.8	90.5	67.4	97.8	69.7	97.6	69.3	95.4	67.1	90.4	60.3	84.1	52.5	72.6	47.5	65.1	67.4	92.6
NEW YORK																											
Albany	0.4	48.6	52.3	48.0	53.7	55.6	67.2	63.5	81.4	70.6	89.2	74.5	92.0	76.8	94.0	76.4	91.8	74.2	87.7	66.4	78.9	61.7	68.4	54.1	57.4	74.4	89.6
	1	42.7	47.5	45.0	50.0	51.8	62.1	60.8	76.0	68.9	86.1	73.2	89.6	75.8	91.8	75.1	89.4	72.7	85.0	64.7	75.5	58.9	64.7	49.5	53.2	72.7	86.4
	2	39.0	43.6	42.3	46.3	49.3	57.3	58.5	72.1	66.9	83.0	72.0	87.0	74.9	89.9	73.9	87.5	71.3	82.3	63.1	72.2	56.4	61.4	45.1	48.9	71.2	83.6
Binghamton	0.4	49.1	51.8	49.5	54.3	57.5	69.3	62.3	79.5	69.6	83.5	72.8	86.1	75.1	88.9	74.3	86.9	73.0	83.7	64.3	74.8	59.8	65.3	54.2	57.4	72.6	84.9
	1	45.4	48.1	47.1	50.7	54.5	64.6	60.9	75.6	68.2	81.3	71.3	84.2	74.0	87.0	73.2	85.0	71.6	81.5	63.0	72.2	58.0	62.9	51.5	54.2	71.1	82.2
	2	41.3	44.5	44.0	47.7	52.0	60.4	59.1	71.7	66.8	79.2	70.2	82.3	72.9	85.4	72.1	83.1	70.5	79.2	61.7	70.0	55.7	60.5	47.7	50.9	69.5	79.7
Buffalo	0.4	50.3	53.9	50.5	55.5	57.7	70.2	63.7	78.8	70.4	84.1	73.9	87.9	75.6	89.9	75.5	88.2	74.2	85.2	65.8	76.9	60.2	67.4	56.4	60.3	73.8	86.0
	1	45.5	50.1	47.7	52.6	54.9	65.8	61.9	75.5	69.1	82.0	72.4	86.1	74.9	87.9	74.3	86.2	72.8	83.1	64.4	74.7	58.7	65.0	53.7	57.5	72.2	83.6
	2	42.7	46.5	44.7	49.4	52.8	61.2	59.9	72.1	67.5	80.0	71.2	84.4	74.1	86.2	73.3	84.6	71.6	80.8	63.1	72.4	56.6	62.8	50.4	54.2	70.8	81.3
Massena	0.4	45.0	49.8	46.8	51.0	54.7	64.5	63.6	78.1	71.2	86.8	75.4	88.7	77.5	91.2	76.8	89.2	74.7	84.6	65.9	76.1	59.5	66.3	51.9	55.5	74.7	87.2
	1	41.4	45.0	43.7	47.4	51.5	59.9	61.1	73.8	69.7	83.6	74.1	86.8	76.2	89.6	75.2	87.1	73.2	82.0	64.4	73.8	57.1	62.8	48.0	51.1	72.8	84.4
	2	38.9	42.0	41.1	44.7	48.6	55.9	58.7	69.9	67.9	80.6	72.7	84.8	75.0	87.9	73.9	85.3	71.5	79.7	62.6	71.1	54.6	59.1	43.8	46.7	71.0	81.7
New York, John F Kennedy Airport	0.4	53.2	57.7	54.3	60.9	59.1	70.6	64.6	80.3	72.4	88.4	75.7	92.7	78.0	95.4	78.2	92.1	76.3	90.2	69.6	79.1	64.1	71.6	57.5	61.1	76.3	90.5
	1	50.6	54.4	51.7	57.5	56.2	66.3	62.6	76.1	70.8	85.3	74.4	90.4	77.2	93.2	77.2	90.0	75.3	87.8	68.3	76.6	61.9	67.9	55.4	58.9	74.9	87.7
	2	47.9	51.8	49.1	54.4	53.5	62.5	60.5	72.7	69.1	82.6	73.3	88.4	76.3	91.2	76.3	88.4	74.3	85.1	66.9	74.2	60.2	65.2	53.0	56.4	73.6	85.1
Rochester	0.4	49.5	53.9	50.6	55.5	59.0	72.4	65.2	81.1	71.8	87.1	76.1	89.9	77.9	93.2	77.3	90.5	75.2	87.6	66.8	78.9	61.3	68.3	57.0	60.9	75.4	88.5
	1	45.0	50.1	47.7	52.1	56.2	66.4	63.4	77.7	70.5	84.4	74.6	88.1	76.8	91.1	75.7	88.5	73.9	85.3	65.3	76.5	59.1	65.5	53.0	57.4	73.5	85.8
	2	42.5	46.7	44.4	49.0	53.6	62.1	61.5	73.9	69.1	82.2	73.3	86.5	75.8	89.2	74.4	86.4	72.6	82.6	63.9	73.8	57.3	63.1	49.6	53.6	71.8	83.1
Syracuse	0.4	49.5	55.1	50.3	57.2	58.9	72.2	65.1	81.4	71.9	86.8	74.9	90.0	77.5	92.0	77.2	90.5	75.0	87.2	66.2	78.8	61.4	69.2	56.2	60.3	74.9	88.1
	1	44.8	49.6	46.9	52.5	55.5	67.0	63.1	77.4	70.3	84.5	73.7	87.9	76.3	90.3	75.8	88.3	73.7	84.7	64.9	75.6	59.5	66.0	53.1	57.2	73.2	85.4
	2	41.7	45.9	44.0	48.9	52.7	62.2	60.8	73.7	68.5	81.8	72.6	86.0	75.2	88.5	74.4	86.2	72.4	82.3	63.5	72.8	57.1	63.0	48.6	53.6	71.6	82.9
NORTH CAROLINA																											
Asheville	0.4	57.8	64.6	59.1	69.7	62.1	76.3	66.2	82.7	71.2	84.6	74.7	89.5	76.5	91.7	75.6	90.0	73.4	86.4	68.4	79.5	64.4	73.2	62.2	67.8	74.5	87.8
	1	55.7	61.6	57.0	66.1	60.9	73.9	64.4	80.5	69.7	82.5	73.6	87.4	75.7	90.2	74.9	88.1	72.6	84.4	67.2	77.5	63.1	71.1	60.3	64.9	73.3	85.3
	2	53.9	59.2	55.2	63.2	59.7	71.4	63.2	78.5	68.8	81.0	72.7	85.7	74.9	88.4	74.2	86.5	71.9	82.9	66.1	75.6	61.6	68.8	58.3	62.4	72.2	83.2
Cape Hatteras	0.4	66.2	69.4	65.6	70.6	67.5	73.7	69.4	78.4	75.7	83.7	79.2	87.4	81.3	90.3	81.1	89.4	79.0	87.3	76.1	82.9	71.5	77.1	68.7	72.3	79.9	87.5
	1	64.9	67.8	64.0	68.3	66.2	72.0	68.4	76.5	74.4	81.9	78.4	85.9	80.7	88.9	80.4	88.3	78.3	86.1	74.8	81.0	70.5	75.6	67.5	70.9	78.9	86.2
	2	63.3	66.3	62.7	66.4	65.1	70.3	67.5	74.9	73.5	80.3	77.7	84.8	80.2	87.8	79.8	87.3	77.6	85.1	73.7	79.4	69.5	74.0	66.2	69.5	78.0	84.8
Charlotte	0.4	61.5	68.2	63.0	73.2	65.4	80.5	69.0	86.4	74.4	90.2	77.1	94.2	78.1	97.9	77.8	95.7	76.2	91.8	72.2	84.2	68.2	77.8	66.2	70.9	76.8	93.5
	1	59.9	65.3	61.4	69.9	64.2	77.7	67.6	84.5	73.0	88.3	76.1	92.5	77.4	96.1	77.2	94.0	75.4	90.3	70.9	82.4	67.1	75.3	64.0	68.7	75.8	91.1
	2	57.9	63.1	59.5	67.3	62.8	75.1	66.4	82.5	71.9	86.4	75.3	90.9	76.9	94.4	76.6	92.5	74.7	88.8	69.6	80.5	65.7	73.1	61.9	66.2	74.9	88.9
Greensboro	0.4	61.0	66.7	62.0	71.8	65.4	80.3	68.4	85.8	74.3	88.9	77.5	93.5	78.9	96.1	78.2	94.7	75.7	91.1	71.1	83.1	67.9	76.3	65.0	70.0	77.1	92.2
	1	58.6	64.2	60.1	68.0	64.0	76.9	67.2	83.9	72.7	87.1	76.3	91.7	78.1	94.6	77.4	92.7	74.9	89.3	69.8	81.1	66.4	73.8	62.7	67.6	76.0	89.9
	2	56.3	61.6	58.4	65.4	62.5	74.0	66.0	81.6	71.7	85.4	75.4	90.1	77.3	92.8	76.8	91.1	74.2	87.5	68.5	79.2	64.8	71.7	60.8	64.8	74.9	87.6
Raleigh/Durham	0.4	63.1	69.5	64.0	74.0	66.3	81.4	69.2	87.3	74.8	89.7	78.2	94.1	79.8	96.6	79.2	94.8	76.9	91.6	72.7	84.4	68.5	78.2	66.6	72.4	77.9	92.8
	1	61.4	66.9	62.2	70.7	65.1	78.6	67.9	85.0	73.6	87.9	77.2	92.2	78.9	94.9	78.4	93.0	76.1	89.7	71.3	82.1	67.5	75.6	64.5	70.0	76.8	90.3
	2	59.5	64.4	60.4	67.7	63.7	76.0	66.7	82.8	72.5	86.2	76.2	90.5	78.1	93.4	77.8	91.4	75.3	88.0	70.3	80.1	66.1	73.6	62.4	67.6	75.7	88.2
Wilmington	0.4	67.5	73.4	68.0	76.1	69.5	81.7	72.8	87.5	76.9	90.9	80.1	94.8	82.1	96.6	81.4	95.0	79.4	92.0	76.5	85.7	73.2	80.1	70.0	75.8	80.2	93.1
	1	66.1	70.9	66.4	73.8	68.4	78.9	71.5	85.2	75.7	88.7	79.2	92.7	81.2	95.0	80.8	93.4	78.5	90.1	75.4	83.7	71.9	78.2	68.1	73.7	79.2	90.8
	2	64.7	68.7	64.9	71.5	67.2	76.4	70.1	82.8	74.6	86.8	78.4	91.0	80.4	93.4	80.2	92.1	78.1	88.5	74.2	82.1	70.5	76.6	66.6	71.7	78.3	88.7
NORTH DAKOTA																											
Bismarck	0.4	38.7	45.9	43.6	53.1	50.5	67.3	59.1	81.7	68.3	88.2	73.0	95.2	76.2	98.7	73.2	98.1	68.9	92.5	59.5	80.4	50.1	64.0	40.1	48.9	72.1	93.4
	1	37.2	43.0	40.9	49.0	47.7	61.5	57.1	77.8	66.2	85.1	71.3	92.3	74.7	95.7	72.0	95.7	67.1	88.8	57.8	76.6	47.3	59.1	37.9	44.4	70.0	89.8
	2	35.8	40.8	38.6	45.0	45.2	57.0	55.1	73.7	64.2	82.1	70.0	89.0	73.1	92.9	70.9	93.3	65.4	85.5	56.3	73.1	45.1	55.1	36.2	41.5	68.1	86.2
Fargo	0.4	35.9	39.4	40.6	46.0	51.5	61.5	62.4	82.1	70.2	88.7	76.4	92.5	78.4	95.5	77.1	96.0	73.5	90.0	63.7	79.0	52.3	60.3	39.2	44.4	75.1	91.2
	1	34.3	37.3	37.7	42.3	48.0	57.1	59.8	77.6	68.4	86.3	74.5	90.1	77.0	92.8	75.5	93.5	71.6	86.8	61.6	74.9	49.2	56.8	35.6	39.5	73.0	87.8
	2	33.0	35.3	35.7	39.1	45.3	52.8	57.3	73.0	66.8	83.6	72.8	87.6	75.6	90.4	74.2	91.1	69.5	83.8	59.7	71.4	47.0	53.4	33.7	36.5	70.9	84.8
Minot, Intl Airport	0.4	38.1	43.5	41.5	50.0	48.7	64.1	57.9	80.8	66.6	88.5	71.3	94.0	75.3	96.1	73.4	96.4	68.3	90.7	59.0	78.1	49.1	60.7	38.9	46.3	71.1	91.9
	1	36.8	41.9	39.3	46.1	46.3	58.8	56.1	76.8	64.5	85.0	69.9	90.4	73.6	93.5	72.0	94.2	65.5	87.0	57.3	74.5	46.3	56.7	37.1	43.1	68.9	87.9
	2	35.4	39.9	37.3	43.1	43.9	54.4	54.1	72.3	62.7	81.8	68.4	87.5	71.9	91.0	70.4	91.9	63.7	83.5	55.8	71.1	44.3	53.5	35.4	40.5	66.8	84.3
OHIO																											
Akron/Canton	0.4	53.1	56.6	53.5	58.8	60.0	73.1	65.0	80.3	72.4	85.9	75.2	89.8	77.2	92.0	76.8	90.6	74.0	86.7	66.8	77.9	61.7	69.5	57.6	61.9	74.9	88.0
	1	50.6	53.8	51.1	56.1	58.1	69.7	63.2	77.8	70.4	83.6	74.1	87.8	76.1	89.8	75.6	88.2	73.0	84.7	65.3	75.9	60.0	66.8	55.7	59.4	73.3	85.3
	2	47.3	50.7	49.1	53.6	56.3	66.2	61.8	75.1	68.6	81.7	72.9	86.1	75.2	88.3	74.4	86.2	72.0	82.7	63.9	73.8	58.6	64.5	53.2	57.1	71.8	82.9

Table 19-4. *(Continued)* **Monthly Percentiles of Wet-Bulb and Dry-Bulb Temperature for U.S. Locations**

		Jan		Feb		Mar		Apr		May		Jun		Jul		Aug		Sep		Oct		Nov		Dec		Annual	
Location	%	WB	DB	WB	DB	WB	DB	WB	DB	WB	DB	WB	DB	WB	DB	WB	DB	WB	DB	WB	DB	WB	DB	WB	DB	WB	DB
Cleveland	0.4	54.1	58.5	54.2	59.3	61.9	74.4	66.3	81.2	73.1	86.6	76.0	90.4	77.9	92.6	77.5	90.5	75.2	88.1	67.8	79.5	63.0	70.7	57.7	63.5	75.6	88.6
	1	50.9	54.6	51.6	56.7	59.3	70.6	64.5	78.7	71.3	84.5	74.8	88.4	77.0	90.8	76.3	88.6	74.1	85.8	66.1	76.8	60.9	68.0	55.8	60.2	74.0	86.0
	2	47.0	51.3	48.8	53.6	57.1	67.2	63.0	75.5	69.8	82.7	73.6	86.9	76.0	89.2	75.1	86.6	73.0	83.8	64.5	74.5	59.3	65.1	53.3	57.4	72.4	83.5
Columbus, Intl Airport	0.4	55.4	59.4	55.5	61.9	62.1	75.8	66.4	82.3	74.2	88.3	77.2	91.7	78.6	94.2	78.1	92.6	75.7	89.8	68.6	80.8	63.0	72.0	58.7	63.3	76.5	90.3
	1	52.8	56.2	53.7	59.1	60.1	72.9	64.9	80.3	72.4	86.4	76.1	90.1	77.4	92.1	77.2	90.8	74.4	87.7	67.1	78.9	61.4	69.4	56.9	61.1	75.0	87.9
	2	49.1	52.8	51.2	56.4	58.4	69.3	63.4	77.4	70.8	84.3	74.9	88.6	76.6	90.6	76.1	89.0	73.3	85.8	65.7	76.7	59.8	66.5	54.7	58.6	73.5	85.5
Dayton, Intl Airport	0.4	55.5	59.1	55.8	61.9	62.4	74.6	66.9	81.6	73.6	87.5	76.9	92.1	78.5	95.2	78.4	93.1	75.2	89.4	68.4	80.6	63.7	72.0	59.0	62.6	76.4	90.3
	1	53.2	55.9	53.4	58.7	60.3	71.7	65.3	79.3	72.1	85.9	75.5	90.2	77.6	92.7	77.2	90.8	74.3	87.3	67.0	78.4	62.1	69.3	57.2	60.5	74.9	87.9
	2	49.4	52.4	51.2	55.5	58.7	68.6	63.9	76.4	70.7	84.0	74.5	88.6	76.6	90.7	76.2	89.0	73.2	85.4	65.6	76.1	60.4	66.6	54.6	58.2	73.5	85.6
Mansfield	0.4	54.3	58.3	53.6	59.9	60.9	73.2	64.5	80.5	72.2	84.0	75.7	89.8	78.0	92.1	77.5	89.5	74.5	86.7	67.3	78.3	62.6	69.9	58.3	62.3	75.5	87.8
	1	51.9	55.6	51.4	56.4	58.8	70.2	63.3	78.0	70.2	82.2	74.6	87.7	76.7	90.2	76.4	87.7	73.4	84.8	66.0	75.8	61.0	68.0	56.3	59.7	74.1	85.3
	2	48.4	52.2	49.2	53.9	56.7	66.9	62.1	75.3	68.5	80.4	73.7	85.7	75.8	88.4	75.3	86.2	72.4	82.9	64.7	73.8	59.3	65.3	54.0	57.2	72.6	83.0
Toledo	0.4	52.2	55.1	51.6	56.9	61.0	73.2	66.0	82.8	73.3	89.3	76.0	92.8	78.9	94.5	79.4	92.7	75.9	89.6	67.7	81.1	61.8	69.9	57.7	61.0	76.5	90.3
	1	48.8	51.6	48.7	53.3	58.3	69.6	64.3	79.7	71.7	86.7	75.0	90.7	77.9	92.4	77.9	90.3	74.6	87.0	66.0	78.3	60.0	66.8	55.1	58.2	74.8	87.4
	2	44.3	47.7	45.8	50.1	56.3	65.5	62.9	75.5	70.2	84.3	74.0	88.8	76.7	90.3	76.5	88.2	73.4	84.6	64.6	75.4	58.3	63.8	52.2	54.9	73.2	84.8
Youngstown	0.4	52.6	55.7	53.2	59.3	60.1	73.4	64.4	81.5	72.0	85.4	74.6	89.1	77.1	91.7	76.1	90.3	74.1	87.0	66.6	78.1	61.9	70.2	57.4	62.3	74.4	87.5
	1	49.6	52.6	50.6	56.0	57.9	69.4	62.9	78.6	70.0	83.6	73.7	87.2	76.0	89.6	74.9	87.7	73.0	84.6	65.1	76.0	60.1	67.1	55.5	59.5	72.9	85.0
	2	46.1	49.5	48.2	52.7	55.9	65.9	61.5	75.4	68.4	81.8	72.4	85.6	74.9	88.0	73.8	85.8	71.9	82.6	63.7	73.5	58.2	64.3	53.0	56.7	71.3	82.6
OKLAHOMA																											
Oklahoma City, Will Rogers Airport	0.4	58.8	67.6	60.3	76.2	65.8	81.8	70.3	87.0	75.3	90.5	78.4	97.0	78.1	103.8	77.6	102.1	76.6	97.3	72.9	89.7	66.4	77.4	61.7	69.0	76.9	99.2
	1	55.6	64.3	58.4	72.8	64.3	79.1	69.4	84.6	74.2	88.6	77.4	95.0	77.4	101.9	77.0	100.4	75.7	95.4	71.4	86.8	64.5	75.1	60.0	66.4	75.9	96.2
	2	52.6	61.9	56.7	69.6	62.9	76.5	68.2	82.4	73.1	86.8	76.7	93.3	76.8	100.0	76.3	99.0	75.0	93.3	69.6	84.3	63.0	72.7	57.9	64.2	75.1	93.5
	0.4	59.0	68.3	61.2	75.5	67.4	82.4	72.0	87.8	76.6	89.7	80.5	96.8	81.0	104.1	79.9	102.9	78.7	97.7	73.6	90.5	67.6	79.0	63.5	70.2	79.2	99.6
Tulsa	1	57.3	65.0	59.7	72.2	65.6	79.5	70.6	85.4	75.4	88.3	79.5	95.0	80.2	101.9	79.2	101.3	77.8	95.2	72.3	87.4	66.1	76.4	61.3	67.7	78.1	96.7
	2	54.5	62.2	57.9	69.0	64.0	76.8	69.4	83.3	74.4	86.9	78.6	93.5	79.4	100.1	78.4	99.8	76.9	93.3	70.9	85.1	64.6	74.0	59.2	65.1	77.1	94.0
OREGON																											
Astoria	0.4	53.3	57.8	55.6	62.6	54.6	64.2	57.2	68.7	63.2	75.5	65.5	77.0	66.8	79.8	68.8	81.6	66.6	82.5	62.5	74.2	57.1	62.2	55.4	58.4	65.0	76.4
	1	52.3	55.8	54.1	59.6	53.2	61.1	55.5	65.1	61.3	71.5	63.4	72.9	65.2	75.7	66.6	77.5	65.2	79.5	60.7	70.7	55.9	60.1	53.8	56.5	63.0	72.0
	2	51.5	54.4	52.6	57.5	52.2	58.5	54.3	61.9	59.5	67.8	61.9	69.7	63.8	72.8	64.7	73.8	63.8	75.5	59.5	67.7	55.1	58.5	52.8	55.1	61.5	68.9
Eugene	0.4	55.6	59.1	56.5	62.7	57.9	67.8	62.3	75.1	68.7	83.9	69.9	91.1	70.8	96.0	70.5	96.7	67.8	91.9	62.9	81.6	58.9	64.1	56.2	59.0	68.5	91.2
	1	54.1	57.1	55.2	60.5	56.3	65.3	60.3	72.0	66.4	81.0	68.3	87.4	69.4	93.3	69.3	93.7	66.4	89.0	61.7	77.6	57.3	61.5	54.3	57.2	66.8	87.1
	2	52.8	55.4	53.7	58.3	54.8	63.1	58.7	69.2	64.6	78.0	67.0	84.8	68.2	91.0	68.1	91.1	65.4	86.0	60.4	73.9	56.0	59.7	52.8	55.3	65.2	83.4
Medford	0.4	51.4	60.5	54.7	68.0	57.4	73.4	62.0	82.8	67.2	92.1	69.4	98.5	70.9	102.2	70.2	103.5	67.5	98.3	62.5	88.7	55.8	66.3	52.6	59.2	68.6	98.3
	1	49.9	57.9	52.9	64.4	55.4	70.6	60.0	79.6	65.1	88.5	68.3	95.6	69.7	100.4	69.3	100.6	66.3	95.6	61.3	84.7	54.2	63.4	50.9	56.4	67.1	94.8
	2	48.8	55.3	51.4	61.6	54.0	67.4	58.2	76.6	63.3	85.3	67.1	93.1	68.8	98.3	68.2	98.2	65.1	92.9	60.1	81.2	53.0	60.9	48.9	54.2	65.5	91.2
North Bend	0.4	57.0	61.8	58.0	65.5	56.3	64.4	57.4	68.0	61.0	71.1	62.2	70.9	62.7	71.3	64.2	72.3	63.9	78.2	62.0	74.9	59.5	65.4	57.5	62.0	62.3	71.2
	1	55.8	59.9	56.4	62.8	55.0	61.7	56.0	64.0	59.3	66.6	61.0	68.4	61.9	69.9	63.1	70.6	62.6	73.3	60.7	70.4	58.4	63.4	56.3	60.1	61.1	69.0
	2	54.5	58.2	55.1	60.4	54.0	59.8	54.9	61.6	58.1	64.3	59.9	66.8	61.1	68.7	62.3	69.7	61.6	70.8	59.7	67.6	57.4	61.8	55.2	58.6	60.0	67.2
Pendleton	0.4	51.4	59.4	52.7	62.4	54.2	67.7	59.1	78.6	65.4	89.3	67.0	96.5	69.4	102.0	67.0	101.0	64.1	92.0	59.4	80.7	53.8	64.7	51.4	60.2	65.9	96.6
	1	49.0	57.4	50.8	59.5	52.6	65.1	57.3	75.1	63.5	86.1	65.7	94.2	67.6	99.7	66.0	98.3	62.9	89.7	57.9	77.5	51.9	62.0	49.4	57.3	64.3	93.0
	2	47.3	55.1	49.1	57.3	51.2	62.4	56.0	71.9	61.6	83.0	64.4	91.7	66.3	97.4	65.2	96.1	61.9	87.3	56.7	74.9	50.3	59.3	47.9	55.1	62.8	89.6
Portland	0.4	54.1	57.9	55.8	62.8	56.3	68.5	61.4	76.4	67.2	86.5	69.2	91.3	70.9	96.4	71.2	97.3	68.3	91.2	63.1	80.0	57.8	63.3	54.9	58.4	68.8	90.3
	1	52.4	56.2	54.2	60.3	55.0	66.2	59.4	73.3	64.9	83.5	67.7	87.7	69.6	92.5	69.9	93.3	67.1	88.6	61.6	76.3	56.1	61.2	53.3	56.3	67.1	86.2
	2	51.2	54.6	52.6	58.4	53.6	63.9	57.9	70.4	63.2	80.1	66.4	84.9	68.5	89.5	68.8	90.1	65.8	85.5	60.5	73.1	54.7	59.5	51.7	54.6	65.4	82.6
Redmond	0.4	47.8	57.9	49.7	61.9	51.0	69.3	55.8	78.9	61.6	86.3	64.6	92.5	65.5	97.0	65.3	97.3	61.8	91.0	57.5	82.7	51.7	65.8	48.5	57.7	63.4	92.6
	1	45.6	54.5	47.9	59.5	49.1	65.7	54.1	75.4	59.7	83.3	63.3	90.1	64.4	94.9	64.3	94.8	60.7	88.4	56.1	80.0	50.0	62.2	46.4	55.1	61.8	89.2
	2	44.1	51.8	46.5	56.9	47.6	62.7	52.5	71.6	57.9	80.1	61.8	87.7	63.4	93.0	63.3	92.5	59.7	85.9	54.9	76.5	48.3	58.8	44.6	52.9	60.3	85.8
Salem	0.4	54.5	58.7	56.3	63.7	56.9	67.9	61.4	75.5	67.1	85.6	69.9	93.0	71.0	96.8	70.5	97.8	67.4	92.7	63.2	81.7	58.0	63.1	55.3	58.8	68.4	91.7
	1	53.3	56.8	54.8	60.5	55.4	65.6	59.2	72.4	65.2	82.6	68.1	89.1	69.6	93.9	69.2	94.5	66.3	89.5	61.5	77.4	56.5	60.8	53.4	56.7	66.7	87.4
	2	52.0	55.1	53.5	58.6	54.1	63.2	57.7	69.5	63.5	79.5	66.7	86.0	68.4	91.2	68.1	91.3	65.3	86.4	60.1	74.0	55.1	59.2	52.3	55.1	65.0	83.4
PENNSYLVANIA																											
Allentown	0.4	53.9	57.0	54.3	61.3	61.9	74.2	65.4	84.0	72.0	88.6	75.4	92.2	77.8	94.8	77.4	92.3	75.5	90.2	68.4	79.2	64.5	71.5	58.5	61.8	75.5	90.4
	1	49.1	52.9	51.3	56.5	59.0	69.8	63.6	79.6	70.7	86.0	74.2	90.2	76.8	92.9	76.2	90.2	74.5	87.6	67.3	76.5	62.6	68.2	54.4	57.7	74.2	87.7
	2	44.6	48.8	47.4	52.9	56.0	65.7	62.0	75.3	69.2	83.6	73.2	88.2	75.8	91.0	75.2	88.5	73.4	85.2	65.9	74.2	60.5	65.3	50.1	53.6	72.8	85.2
Bradford	0.4	48.8	50.9	48.7	53.2	57.6	68.0	61.5	78.0	68.8	82.0	71.3	84.0	74.0	87.2	73.7	85.2	72.0	80.9	64.1	74.4	59.3	65.1	54.1	56.3	71.6	82.8
	1	44.6	47.5	46.0	50.0	55.2	63.9	59.9	74.8	66.9	80.2	70.3	82.3	72.9	85.1	72.2	83.0	70.3	79.1	62.5	72.0	57.7	62.5	51.4	53.8	70.0	80.4
	2	41.2	44.2	43.5	47.4	52.7	60.3	58.3	71.5	65.4	78.1	69.4	81.0	72.0	83.4	71.1	81.2	69.0	77.1	61.3	69.8	55.7	60.1	48.7	50.9	68.4	78.0
Erie	0.4	52.4	56.7	52.2	57.7	59.9	72.7	64.5	77.7	72.1	83.3	74.2	87.5	77.1	88.9	76.1	87.6	74.3	85.7	66.2	78.2	61.2	69.5	57.6	63.1	74.3	85.3
	1	49.0	53.3	49.7	54.6	57.2	68.2	62.7	75.2	70.0	81.4	73.0	85.6	75.8	86.5	74.8	85.8	73.0	83.0	64.6	75.1	59.5	66.4	55.3	59.4	72.8	82.8
	2	44.7	49.6	46.9	51.4	54.9	64.6	61.1	72.7	68.2	79.3	71.9	83.9	74.7	85.1	73.9	83.9	71.8	80.7	63.3	72.5	57.8	63.7	52.2	56.3	71.3	80.4
Harrisburg	0.4	53.6	59.6	53.7	62.3	62.5	75.6	66.7	84.7	74.4	89.1	76.9	93.5	79.6	97.1	79.2	94.0	77.2	91.2	69.4	80.2	65.4	72.2	58.8	63.2	77.2	91.9
	1	48.9	53.7	50.6	57.5	59.6	71.4	65.1	81.5	72.6	86.7	75.5	91.3	78.5	94.6	78.0	91.9	76.0	88.8	68.2	77.5	63.4	69.5	54.6	59.1	75.5	89.0
	2	44.7	49.6	48.1	53.8	57.0	67.3	63.3	77.4	70.9	84.3	74.6	89.3	77.4	92.6	76.9	89.9	74.7	85.9	66.8	75.0	60.9	66.7	50.5	54.4	74.2	86.4

Table 19-4. *(Continued)* **Monthly Percentiles of Wet-Bulb and Dry-Bulb Temperature for U.S. Locations**

		Jan		Feb		Mar		Apr		May		Jun		Jul		Aug		Sep		Oct		Nov		Dec		Annual	
Location	%	WB	DB	WB	DB	WB	DB	WB	DB	WB	DB	WB	DB	WB	DB	WB	DB	WB	DB	WB	DB	WB	DB	WB	DB	WB	DB
Philadelphia, Intl Airport	0.4	56.3	60.0	57.3	63.8	63.3	75.6	67.1	85.5	74.0	90.7	77.5	93.8	79.9	96.6	79.4	94.2	77.7	91.3	71.2	81.1	66.7	74.1	60.6	64.0	77.8	92.1
	1	53.9	56.8	55.0	60.4	60.9	71.6	65.3	80.8	72.4	87.4	76.5	91.9	78.9	94.3	78.4	92.2	76.7	88.9	69.9	78.5	64.5	70.4	58.5	61.3	76.5	89.4
	2	50.3	53.7	52.2	57.1	58.3	67.3	63.5	76.6	71.0	84.9	75.5	90.0	78.1	92.5	77.5	90.5	75.6	86.8	68.4	76.2	62.6	67.4	55.5	58.7	75.1	87.0
Pittsburgh, Intl Airport	0.4	54.1	59.0	54.7	61.8	60.6	75.3	64.8	81.9	71.4	86.4	74.4	90.5	76.8	93.0	76.3	91.7	74.3	87.8	66.7	78.6	61.4	71.2	57.5	63.6	74.4	88.6
	1	51.1	55.5	51.9	58.3	58.6	72.0	63.3	79.6	70.1	84.4	73.4	88.3	75.7	90.8	75.1	89.3	73.0	85.6	65.2	76.9	60.0	68.4	56.1	61.1	72.9	85.9
	2	47.9	52.3	49.5	55.4	56.7	68.5	61.8	76.8	68.4	82.4	72.3	86.6	74.7	89.0	74.0	87.1	71.8	83.5	63.7	74.8	58.4	65.8	53.8	58.2	71.4	83.6
Wilkes-Barre/ Scranton	0.4	52.2	56.2	53.1	57.9	59.8	72.1	63.9	82.5	71.0	86.5	74.3	89.3	76.4	92.6	75.7	89.5	74.2	86.3	66.9	77.2	62.4	68.9	56.6	60.3	74.2	87.8
	1	48.6	51.8	50.3	54.4	57.2	67.5	62.2	78.5	69.3	84.2	73.1	87.5	75.4	90.4	74.7	87.7	73.2	84.2	65.4	74.8	60.5	65.9	53.2	56.3	72.8	85.1
	2	43.8	47.7	47.2	51.5	54.5	64.1	60.4	74.9	67.8	82.0	72.1	85.6	74.5	88.3	73.9	85.9	72.0	82.2	64.0	72.4	58.4	63.5	49.6	52.7	71.4	82.6
Williamsport	0.4	49.9	53.6	52.2	57.1	60.4	73.4	65.1	83.8	72.1	89.2	75.3	91.3	77.8	95.0	77.2	91.3	75.1	87.9	67.7	77.8	62.7	68.6	54.7	57.2	75.5	89.5
	1	45.3	49.2	48.8	54.1	57.4	69.1	63.7	79.5	70.3	86.1	74.2	89.0	76.9	92.3	76.2	89.3	73.9	85.5	66.5	75.2	60.7	65.9	50.7	53.4	74.0	86.5
	2	42.0	45.4	45.3	50.8	54.3	64.5	62.0	76.1	68.9	83.7	73.2	86.9	75.9	90.1	75.2	87.3	72.8	83.1	65.0	72.5	58.4	63.3	46.9	50.4	72.7	83.8
RHODE ISLAND																											
Providence	0.4	54.8	57.2	53.4	58.5	57.4	67.5	63.2	79.6	70.8	87.3	75.4	91.2	78.1	94.4	78.1	91.2	75.7	89.4	68.9	78.0	64.0	70.1	58.1	61.5	75.7	89.2
	1	51.2	54.3	50.5	54.8	54.8	63.2	60.6	74.3	68.8	83.7	73.7	88.8	76.9	92.0	76.6	89.2	74.4	85.7	67.1	75.4	61.8	67.1	55.8	59.1	74.1	86.0
	2	47.5	50.9	47.8	52.2	52.5	59.6	58.7	70.6	66.9	80.3	72.4	86.5	75.8	89.5	75.6	87.2	73.3	82.5	65.7	73.1	59.9	64.3	53.2	56.3	72.7	83.2
SOUTH CAROLINA																											
Charleston	0.4	66.9	75.1	68.2	78.0	69.4	83.2	72.8	88.3	76.8	92.0	80.3	95.8	82.2	97.2	81.0	95.2	79.4	92.3	76.3	87.1	72.4	81.3	69.8	76.9	80.0	93.7
	1	65.7	72.9	66.6	75.5	68.4	80.8	71.3	86.3	75.8	90.2	79.4	93.9	81.2	95.5	80.3	93.8	78.6	90.9	75.4	85.1	71.4	79.4	68.4	75.0	79.0	91.6
	2	64.4	70.3	65.2	73.1	67.3	78.6	70.2	84.2	74.8	88.2	78.5	92.1	80.4	94.1	79.6	92.6	78.0	89.4	74.4	83.4	70.5	78.0	67.0	73.0	78.1	89.6
Columbia	0.4	66.5	74.6	67.0	78.2	68.4	84.4	71.9	89.5	75.8	93.0	78.3	97.8	79.8	100.8	79.4	98.1	78.1	94.3	74.4	87.6	70.8	81.4	68.6	76.6	78.3	96.1
	1	64.7	71.3	65.1	75.4	67.4	82.1	70.5	87.9	74.5	91.4	77.4	96.1	79.0	98.8	78.6	96.3	77.4	92.6	73.4	85.7	69.5	79.3	67.1	74.5	77.4	93.7
	2	62.9	68.5	63.5	72.6	66.3	79.7	69.3	86.1	73.4	90.0	76.7	94.4	78.4	96.8	78.2	94.9	76.7	91.3	72.4	84.0	68.4	77.3	65.3	72.0	76.5	91.5
Greer/Greenville	0.4	61.0	68.8	62.6	72.5	65.1	80.0	69.5	85.8	74.3	90.4	76.7	94.8	78.4	97.4	77.7	94.8	75.9	90.8	71.6	83.6	67.7	77.1	65.2	69.9	76.6	93.1
	1	59.2	65.2	60.4	69.9	64.0	77.5	67.7	84.1	73.1	88.1	76.0	92.9	77.6	95.7	77.0	93.0	75.2	89.1	70.2	82.1	66.3	74.4	62.9	67.9	75.6	90.7
	2	57.3	62.7	58.6	66.9	62.6	75.0	66.4	82.3	72.0	86.3	75.3	91.3	77.0	93.9	76.3	91.5	74.5	87.4	69.1	80.2	64.9	72.4	61.2	65.5	74.8	88.3
SOUTH DAKOTA																											
Huron	0.4	40.6	49.0	45.0	56.5	56.2	72.6	63.7	84.5	71.0	87.3	76.9	96.3	78.8	100.4	77.5	99.5	73.6	94.8	64.4	82.1	53.9	65.3	42.9	51.8	76.1	95.1
	1	38.5	44.9	42.7	51.9	52.8	66.9	62.1	80.2	69.7	84.7	75.4	93.2	77.5	98.4	76.4	96.6	72.2	91.1	62.5	78.4	51.7	61.3	40.2	47.5	74.2	91.4
	2	36.7	41.8	40.6	47.5	50.0	61.4	60.2	76.0	68.0	82.5	74.1	90.8	76.7	95.7	75.3	93.9	70.8	87.9	60.7	74.8	49.1	58.0	38.0	43.9	72.4	88.0
Pierre	0.4	42.3	53.0	46.2	60.6	53.7	72.5	61.5	85.4	69.2	90.3	75.1	99.4	77.1	105.3	74.6	103.1	71.7	97.6	61.5	85.3	52.4	67.6	43.3	54.5	74.0	98.8
	1	40.1	48.8	44.1	56.6	51.4	68.0	59.9	81.6	67.5	87.4	73.8	95.9	75.8	102.1	73.8	100.3	70.0	94.2	60.0	81.0	49.9	63.6	41.1	50.5	72.3	94.7
	2	38.2	45.4	42.1	52.2	49.0	63.2	58.1	77.6	66.1	84.6	72.5	92.8	74.7	99.6	72.9	97.9	68.4	90.7	58.5	77.4	47.7	59.7	39.2	47.2	70.8	90.9
Rapid City	0.4	44.2	59.4	46.3	63.7	51.1	72.6	57.4	82.3	65.0	86.9	71.2	97.7	72.1	100.9	71.2	98.8	66.1	94.3	57.3	84.1	49.9	69.6	45.3	60.9	69.8	95.1
	1	42.2	56.0	44.3	60.2	49.1	68.4	55.7	79.4	63.4	84.2	69.8	93.1	71.0	98.1	70.0	96.6	64.7	91.2	56.0	80.7	48.4	66.0	42.9	57.2	68.1	91.2
	2	40.4	52.6	42.7	56.8	47.4	64.7	54.3	75.8	62.1	81.5	68.5	89.6	70.2	95.4	68.9	94.3	63.3	88.5	54.8	77.7	46.5	62.4	41.1	53.6	66.5	87.6
Sioux Falls	0.4	40.0	48.5	45.3	56.1	57.6	73.3	64.1	85.3	70.6	87.9	76.5	95.6	78.5	99.4	77.9	96.7	74.6	91.6	66.3	81.5	55.9	64.7	44.8	52.3	76.2	93.9
	1	37.8	44.3	42.9	51.3	54.5	68.1	62.4	81.1	69.1	85.4	75.3	93.1	77.5	97.0	76.9	94.5	73.0	88.8	64.1	78.1	53.4	61.8	40.5	47.4	74.5	90.3
	2	36.0	41.0	40.4	47.6	51.7	63.1	60.5	76.5	67.9	82.8	74.1	90.7	76.6	94.8	75.8	92.4	71.5	86.2	62.0	74.9	50.9	58.9	38.4	43.6	72.7	87.2
TENNESSEE																											
Bristol	0.4	57.0	64.4	59.0	68.6	62.6	76.6	67.0	82.4	72.1	86.2	75.2	90.3	76.6	92.6	76.3	92.3	73.9	88.5	68.8	81.2	64.2	74.8	60.6	69.2	75.0	89.0
	1	55.2	61.4	57.1	65.6	61.1	74.0	65.4	80.5	70.8	84.3	74.2	88.6	75.9	90.9	75.5	90.0	73.0	87.1	67.2	79.4	62.8	72.1	58.9	65.4	73.9	86.8
	2	53.5	58.9	55.2	62.8	59.7	71.8	64.0	78.7	69.8	82.8	73.3	87.2	75.2	89.3	74.9	88.0	72.2	85.6	66.0	77.7	61.3	69.7	57.1	62.7	72.7	84.8
Chattanooga	0.4	60.7	66.4	62.3	72.4	66.2	80.2	69.3	86.2	74.8	90.4	77.7	94.7	80.0	98.8	79.3	96.6	76.9	93.0	72.4	84.5	67.4	76.4	64.5	70.3	77.8	94.1
	1	59.0	63.8	60.5	69.4	64.6	77.7	68.1	84.2	73.8	88.4	77.0	93.0	78.8	96.7	78.3	94.9	76.1	91.0	70.9	82.4	65.9	73.9	62.8	67.6	76.7	91.6
	2	57.1	61.7	59.0	66.6	63.2	75.2	67.0	82.5	72.8	86.5	76.2	91.5	78.1	94.9	77.5	93.2	75.3	89.2	69.7	80.8	64.6	71.7	61.0	65.3	75.7	89.4
Knoxville	0.4	59.7	66.4	61.2	71.0	65.7	78.1	69.2	84.0	74.3	88.1	77.3	92.3	79.0	95.7	77.9	94.5	75.9	91.1	71.2	82.4	66.6	75.9	64.3	70.7	76.9	91.9
	1	58.1	63.9	59.5	68.2	64.0	75.8	67.9	82.2	73.2	86.3	76.3	90.5	78.1	94.2	77.2	92.5	75.2	89.2	69.7	80.8	65.1	73.3	61.9	67.8	75.8	89.5
	2	56.0	60.9	58.0	65.6	62.5	73.6	66.6	80.5	72.1	84.9	75.5	89.3	77.3	92.6	76.5	91.1	74.4	87.6	68.3	79.2	63.7	71.1	59.8	64.6	74.8	87.3
Memphis	0.4	63.8	69.5	65.2	74.5	69.1	80.6	72.4	86.1	76.9	91.1	80.3	96.2	81.8	100.1	81.4	97.8	79.3	95.7	74.8	87.1	69.4	78.9	67.3	72.1	80.1	95.7
	1	62.2	67.3	63.2	71.6	67.9	78.6	71.3	84.2	76.0	89.5	79.3	94.7	81.1	98.0	80.5	96.1	78.4	92.9	73.2	85.3	68.2	76.7	65.3	70.0	79.1	93.5
	2	60.5	65.2	61.4	69.2	66.4	76.5	70.3	82.6	75.0	88.2	78.5	93.4	80.4	96.3	79.8	94.7	77.5	91.2	71.7	83.7	67.1	74.5	63.4	67.7	78.1	91.7
Nashville	0.4	62.2	67.3	63.0	71.9	66.9	80.2	70.5	85.5	75.4	89.5	78.2	95.3	79.5	97.9	79.0	97.3	77.2	93.5	72.5	84.7	67.9	77.5	64.7	70.2	78.0	94.2
	1	60.1	65.0	61.3	69.5	65.4	77.8	69.1	83.6	74.1	87.9	77.3	93.4	78.9	96.2	78.3	95.4	76.3	91.5	71.0	83.3	66.4	74.9	62.7	68.0	77.0	91.7
	2	58.1	62.8	59.7	67.3	64.0	75.2	67.9	82.0	73.2	86.4	76.6	91.9	78.2	94.5	77.7	93.5	75.5	90.0	69.8	81.7	65.1	72.7	61.1	66.0	76.0	89.6
TEXAS																											
Abilene	0.4	60.7	75.7	61.2	80.9	66.9	87.3	71.2	92.2	74.7	97.0	77.2	100.3	76.1	102.0	75.4	100.8	75.1	97.6	72.4	91.3	66.9	82.0	62.3	74.7	75.1	98.9
	1	58.5	72.6	59.7	77.8	65.3	84.4	69.9	89.9	73.5	94.7	76.1	98.1	75.2	100.4	74.8	99.4	74.2	95.6	71.3	89.1	65.7	79.4	60.9	72.3	74.1	96.8
	2	56.3	69.9	58.2	74.7	64.0	81.6	68.8	87.5	72.5	92.5	75.3	96.2	74.5	99.1	74.2	98.2	73.5	94.0	70.3	87.1	64.4	77.2	59.6	69.9	73.2	94.6
Amarillo	0.4	50.4	70.1	52.9	76.2	58.0	82.0	62.4	88.5	67.7	94.1	71.4	100.4	72.3	99.1	72.1	97.5	70.1	94.2	64.9	88.5	58.4	77.4	52.5	70.2	70.8	96.2
	1	48.3	66.5	50.8	72.3	55.9	79.6	61.2	85.7	66.7	92.1	70.6	97.7	71.5	97.5	71.3	96.0	69.2	92.3	63.6	86.2	56.2	74.9	50.2	67.3	69.7	93.8
	2	46.2	63.4	49.1	68.8	54.1	76.5	59.9	83.4	65.6	90.0	69.9	95.5	70.9	96.3	70.5	94.4	68.4	90.6	62.4	84.1	54.7	72.5	48.2	64.4	68.9	91.5
Austin	0.4	68.1	77.7	67.8	82.7	71.4	87.1	74.7	89.9	78.3	93.1	79.0	97.8	78.5	100.3	78.3	101.1	78.3	97.9	76.6	91.7	72.7	84.1	69.3	78.3	78.0	98.3
	1	66.8	75.3	66.6	79.3	70.4	84.0	73.6	87.7	77.3	91.4	78.3	96.0	78.0	99.1	77.6	99.8	77.5	96.2	76.0	90.1	71.6	81.8	68.2	76.0	77.2	96.4
	2	65.3	73.2	65.5	76.6	69.5	81.5	72.8	85.9	76.3	89.9	77.8	94.4	77.4	98.0	77.2	98.6	77.1	94.7	75.2	88.5	70.8	80.2	67.2	74.1	76.4	94.4

Table 19-4. *(Continued)* Monthly Percentiles of Wet-Bulb and Dry-Bulb Temperature for U.S. Locations

		Jan		Feb		Mar		Apr		May		Jun		Jul		Aug		Sep		Oct		Nov		Dec		Annual	
Location	%	WB	DB	WB	DB	WB	DB	WB	DB	WB	DB	WB	DB	WB	DB	WB	DB	WB	DB	WB	DB	WB	DB	WB	DB	WB	DB
Beaumont/ Port Arthur	0.4	70.4	75.0	70.5	77.3	72.6	80.8	76.4	86.0	79.1	90.0	82.0	94.2	82.4	96.1	82.3	96.9	81.4	94.3	79.0	89.3	75.6	83.0	73.5	77.8	81.4	94.0
	1	69.3	73.6	69.4	75.4	71.8	79.2	75.6	84.2	78.3	88.7	81.3	93.0	81.8	94.9	81.6	95.2	80.8	93.0	78.2	87.9	74.7	81.3	72.1	76.3	80.5	92.4
	2	68.3	72.2	68.5	73.7	71.1	77.8	74.8	82.6	77.6	87.5	80.5	92.0	81.3	93.9	81.2	94.0	80.3	91.7	77.4	86.4	73.8	80.0	71.0	74.9	79.9	90.9
Brownsville	0.4	72.4	82.1	73.0	84.3	74.8	88.8	77.8	91.3	80.0	92.4	81.0	95.5	80.2	96.6	80.2	96.5	80.5	95.2	79.3	91.7	76.6	87.3	74.5	83.8	80.0	95.1
	1	71.6	80.4	71.9	82.2	74.0	86.5	77.0	89.4	79.3	91.4	80.4	94.4	79.5	95.7	79.7	95.8	80.0	94.3	78.8	90.6	76.1	85.9	73.8	82.3	79.4	93.8
	2	71.0	79.0	71.1	80.4	73.3	84.3	76.2	87.9	78.7	90.5	80.0	93.4	79.3	94.8	79.4	95.0	79.4	93.2	78.3	89.4	75.4	84.8	73.1	81.0	78.9	92.5
Corpus Christi	0.4	72.4	80.8	72.2	84.1	75.3	88.0	77.9	89.9	80.5	91.4	81.6	94.4	81.0	96.3	81.2	96.8	81.4	95.2	80.1	91.5	77.1	86.2	73.7	82.7	80.7	94.9
	1	71.4	78.7	71.1	81.0	74.0	84.9	77.1	87.9	79.7	90.1	81.1	93.4	80.4	95.5	80.5	95.8	80.8	94.0	79.3	90.0	76.3	84.6	72.7	80.8	80.1	93.5
	2	70.4	68.3	70.1	67.1	73.1	68.2	76.3	73.5	79.1	77.1	80.5	78.5	80.1	94.7	80.3	95.0	80.3	92.8	78.6	88.8	75.4	83.4	71.9	79.2	79.4	92.2
El Paso	0.4	51.6	70.7	53.8	77.0	55.4	82.8	61.0	90.4	64.5	96.4	69.3	105.6	71.3	103.2	71.3	99.6	69.8	96.5	65.1	89.8	58.1	78.5	53.2	70.4	69.9	100.5
	1	50.1	68.0	52.3	74.5	54.3	80.7	59.2	88.2	63.3	94.9	68.4	103.5	70.5	101.4	70.6	98.3	69.1	95.1	63.8	87.9	56.4	76.5	51.5	68.7	69.0	97.9
	2	48.8	65.8	51.1	72.3	53.2	79.0	57.7	86.4	62.3	93.3	67.6	101.9	69.9	99.9	70.0	97.0	68.4	93.5	62.7	86.0	55.1	74.6	50.1	66.6	68.1	95.6
Fort Worth, Meacham Field	0.4	64.4	74.7	65.1	79.4	69.8	84.5	73.8	89.1	77.5	92.8	79.4	100.1	79.4	103.7	78.5	102.5	78.3	98.2	75.2	92.7	70.4	82.8	67.0	75.7	78.2	100.0
	1	63.1	71.8	63.8	76.7	68.5	81.9	72.7	86.2	76.3	91.0	78.6	97.3	78.5	101.6	78.0	101.2	77.5	96.7	74.3	90.0	69.4	80.4	65.6	73.2	77.3	97.8
	2	61.5	69.2	62.4	74.1	67.6	79.5	71.7	84.2	75.4	89.3	77.9	95.9	78.0	100.1	77.4	100.1	77.0	95.0	73.4	87.9	68.4	78.3	64.4	70.7	76.4	95.6
Houston, Inter-continental Airport	0.4	70.3	78.3	70.8	81.0	72.6	83.7	76.3	88.0	78.3	91.4	80.5	96.3	80.5	98.4	80.4	98.9	80.3	95.3	78.2	90.5	75.1	84.8	72.2	79.1	79.9	95.9
	1	69.4	76.3	69.7	78.4	71.7	81.8	75.2	86.0	77.7	90.2	80.0	94.9	80.1	96.9	80.0	97.5	79.7	93.9	77.3	89.1	74.2	83.2	71.2	77.7	79.2	94.0
	2	68.6	74.5	68.5	76.2	71.0	80.2	74.3	84.4	77.1	89.0	79.4	93.6	79.6	95.7	79.4	96.2	79.2	92.6	76.6	87.6	73.3	81.6	70.2	76.2	78.5	92.3
Lubbock, Intl Airport	0.4	53.8	72.9	55.8	79.0	60.5	84.4	64.7	90.3	69.9	97.0	73.8	101.7	74.1	100.1	73.4	97.9	72.5	94.5	67.6	89.0	61.3	79.6	56.2	72.4	72.5	97.3
	1	51.8	69.7	54.1	75.3	58.9	82.1	63.6	87.8	68.9	94.6	72.7	99.5	73.2	98.2	72.8	96.5	71.5	92.9	66.3	86.9	59.5	77.2	53.6	69.6	71.5	94.9
	2	49.4	66.7	52.4	72.5	57.3	79.4	62.7	85.9	67.9	92.4	71.9	97.6	72.5	96.8	72.2	95.0	70.7	91.5	65.2	85.0	58.1	74.8	51.7	67.0	70.5	92.6
Lufkin	0.4	69.1	77.1	69.0	78.7	72.0	84.9	75.7	87.0	78.1	90.9	80.2	95.5	80.4	99.0	80.3	100.5	80.3	96.3	77.6	91.1	72.8	82.9	71.4	77.3	79.4	96.5
	1	67.8	74.8	67.9	76.4	71.0	82.3	74.5	85.6	77.2	89.7	79.5	94.3	79.8	97.7	79.5	98.4	79.4	94.9	76.5	89.3	71.8	80.8	69.9	75.8	78.8	94.5
	2	66.7	72.7	66.6	74.7	70.0	80.1	73.7	84.3	76.4	88.7	79.1	93.2	79.3	96.2	79.2	97.0	78.7	93.5	75.4	87.7	71.0	79.2	68.5	74.3	78.1	92.7
Midland/Odessa	0.4	56.7	75.1	58.5	81.3	62.8	87.1	67.1	92.9	70.7	99.2	74.2	102.4	74.0	101.8	73.4	101.1	72.3	97.8	69.7	91.1	64.3	82.2	58.2	75.5	72.6	99.3
	1	54.7	72.2	56.6	78.0	61.4	84.4	66.1	90.8	69.9	96.9	73.3	100.4	73.2	100.0	72.6	99.6	71.5	95.4	68.5	88.9	62.5	79.8	56.7	73.0	71.6	96.9
	2	52.8	69.7	55.0	75.3	60.0	82.2	65.1	88.6	68.9	95.0	72.4	98.8	72.4	98.4	72.1	98.1	71.0	93.6	67.5	87.1	61.0	77.4	54.8	70.5	70.7	94.7
San Angelo	0.4	61.5	77.5	61.5	82.3	66.6	88.5	70.6	93.8	74.2	99.3	76.2	101.1	75.4	102.1	75.2	102.4	75.0	98.0	72.8	91.5	67.9	83.3	62.8	76.6	74.7	99.5
	1	60.0	74.6	60.3	79.4	65.4	85.5	69.5	91.7	73.3	96.6	75.4	99.0	74.8	100.6	74.5	100.4	74.2	96.2	71.8	89.2	66.5	80.6	61.6	73.9	73.8	97.3
	2	57.9	71.7	59.1	76.5	64.3	83.1	68.6	89.7	72.4	94.2	74.7	97.1	74.2	99.5	74.0	99.0	73.5	94.5	70.8	87.3	65.3	78.7	60.5	71.8	73.0	95.2
San Antonio, Intl Airport	0.4	67.4	78.4	67.9	83.0	71.1	87.9	74.7	91.3	78.0	95.4	79.5	98.3	78.9	99.5	78.1	100.2	78.2	96.8	76.4	91.9	72.5	84.3	69.4	78.2	78.0	97.5
	1	66.4	75.6	66.8	80.4	70.2	85.0	74.1	88.6	77.0	92.9	78.6	96.7	78.2	98.2	77.4	98.7	77.4	95.4	75.8	90.2	71.5	82.2	68.3	76.4	77.1	95.8
	2	65.4	73.5	65.7	77.8	69.4	82.5	73.3	86.8	76.2	90.9	78.0	95.2	77.5	97.2	77.0	97.6	77.0	94.2	75.1	88.6	70.8	80.4	67.4	74.6	76.4	94.0
Victoria	0.4	70.4	78.4	70.5	81.1	72.8	85.0	76.2	87.9	79.1	91.4	80.4	95.3	80.2	97.2	80.1	98.1	80.2	95.6	78.4	90.9	76.0	85.1	72.8	79.8	79.5	95.4
	1	69.5	76.6	69.4	78.4	72.0	82.6	75.3	86.3	78.2	89.7	80.0	94.2	79.6	96.1	79.5	96.7	79.5	94.2	77.8	89.3	74.9	83.4	71.6	78.3	79.1	93.9
	2	68.8	74.9	68.5	76.5	71.3	80.9	74.5	85.0	77.5	88.5	79.4	93.1	79.3	95.2	79.2	95.5	79.1	92.8	77.2	88.0	74.1	81.9	70.8	77.0	78.4	92.4
Waco	0.4	65.6	76.3	66.3	80.5	70.6	85.7	75.0	90.1	77.9	93.2	80.1	99.6	79.3	103.0	79.1	104.0	79.1	99.2	76.4	93.1	71.6	84.2	67.7	77.0	78.5	100.7
	1	64.4	73.6	65.1	77.6	69.6	83.0	73.9	87.4	77.1	91.8	79.2	98.1	78.5	101.8	78.4	102.2	78.3	97.4	75.5	91.2	70.7	81.8	66.4	74.4	77.7	98.7
	2	63.0	70.9	63.9	75.1	68.4	80.6	72.8	85.4	76.2	90.4	78.4	96.5	78.1	100.8	78.0	101.0	77.6	96.1	74.7	89.1	69.7	79.8	65.3	72.2	77.0	96.6
Wichita Falls, Sheppard AFB	0.4	60.6	73.5	62.7	80.4	67.8	88.0	72.5	91.6	76.4	96.7	79.0	103.3	78.4	106.7	77.9	105.2	77.2	100.1	74.4	92.7	67.7	81.6	63.0	73.7	77.2	102.6
	1	58.0	70.6	60.7	76.9	66.5	84.7	71.4	89.1	75.2	94.3	78.0	100.2	77.5	105.1	77.2	103.4	76.3	98.3	73.0	90.0	66.4	79.2	61.5	71.1	76.3	99.9
	2	55.4	67.5	58.8	73.6	65.0	81.2	70.2	86.6	74.2	92.0	77.2	98.4	76.9	103.4	76.5	102.0	75.7	96.5	71.7	87.9	65.2	76.9	59.7	68.5	75.4	97.5
UTAH																											
Cedar City	0.4	44.8	58.0	46.5	63.7	48.3	69.5	51.9	77.0	56.9	85.1	61.9	95.1	66.1	96.4	65.4	94.5	61.5	89.7	55.1	81.4	49.0	68.2	44.6	59.0	63.6	93.0
	1	42.3	54.4	45.2	60.7	47.1	67.0	50.6	74.9	55.9	82.5	60.4	93.4	64.9	95.0	64.4	93.1	60.6	88.1	53.8	79.6	47.6	66.0	42.7	56.3	62.3	90.6
	2	40.6	51.0	43.6	58.1	45.9	64.7	49.5	72.7	54.9	80.6	59.2	91.4	64.0	93.5	63.5	91.6	59.8	86.4	52.7	77.6	46.3	63.7	41.2	53.7	61.1	88.2
Salt Lake City	0.4	44.1	52.8	47.3	60.7	51.0	69.7	55.9	80.5	61.7	87.2	65.7	98.2	68.2	99.7	68.5	98.1	64.1	92.7	57.2	82.0	51.2	67.0	44.3	56.1	66.1	96.4
	1	42.0	50.3	46.0	58.1	49.5	67.2	54.4	77.7	60.2	85.3	64.2	96.5	67.1	98.4	67.3	96.5	63.0	90.5	56.1	79.5	49.5	64.1	43.0	53.3	64.7	94.2
	2	40.4	47.5	44.7	55.5	48.3	64.7	53.4	75.2	59.0	83.7	63.0	94.5	66.2	97.1	66.2	95.3	62.1	88.7	55.1	77.0	48.2	61.5	41.4	50.0	63.5	91.8
VERMONT																											
Burlington	0.4	45.4	49.0	48.4	52.3	56.0	66.0	63.1	78.8	70.4	86.8	74.2	89.6	76.2	92.2	75.9	89.3	74.6	84.1	64.8	74.7	59.7	65.8	53.6	56.2	73.9	87.4
	1	41.8	45.0	43.4	47.2	52.3	61.0	60.8	73.4	68.4	83.5	72.9	87.3	75.1	90.2	74.4	87.0	72.9	81.6	63.1	72.2	57.5	63.0	49.0	53.1	72.0	84.3
	2	38.2	41.8	40.7	44.4	49.3	56.5	58.2	69.8	66.5	80.4	71.5	85.3	74.1	88.0	73.1	85.2	71.1	79.2	61.7	69.6	54.9	60.4	44.4	48.5	70.3	81.5
VIRGINA																											
Lynchburg	0.4	58.4	67.6	60.7	72.2	64.8	80.2	66.9	87.7	74.7	88.1	76.6	92.7	78.3	96.6	77.5	95.2	75.8	92.6	70.8	82.7	66.5	76.7	63.1	70.3	76.5	92.7
	1	56.1	63.2	58.3	67.7	63.1	76.8	65.7	84.7	73.1	86.6	75.8	91.1	77.5	94.8	76.8	93.4	75.1	90.2	69.6	80.9	65.2	74.2	61.3	67.1	75.5	90.1
	2	53.6	59.9	56.0	64.8	61.3	73.4	64.6	82.3	71.7	84.8	75.0	89.5	76.9	93.3	76.1	91.7	74.3	88.3	68.2	79.1	63.9	71.5	59.0	63.5	74.5	87.9
Norfolk	0.4	63.5	70.5	65.3	74.4	67.1	81.0	69.1	86.5	75.3	90.1	78.4	94.7	80.3	96.7	79.7	95.7	77.9	93.2	73.1	84.6	69.3	78.8	66.6	72.7	78.5	93.2
	1	61.7	67.2	63.3	70.9	65.7	78.0	67.8	84.1	73.7	88.0	77.4	92.5	79.5	95.1	79.1	93.5	77.0	90.7	71.9	82.2	68.2	76.4	64.6	70.4	77.4	90.7
	2	59.5	64.6	61.0	67.8	64.1	74.8	66.6	81.7	72.4	86.2	76.7	91.0	78.8	93.5	78.3	91.7	76.2	88.3	70.9	79.7	66.8	74.1	62.9	68.1	76.5	88.2
Richmond	0.4	62.1	68.1	62.7	73.0	66.7	81.8	68.9	89.1	75.8	91.6	78.8	95.6	80.7	97.6	80.0	96.3	77.9	93.9	72.3	85.1	69.1	79.0	65.4	71.5	78.8	94.1
	1	59.6	64.8	60.8	69.7	65.1	78.7	67.8	86.1	74.4	89.5	77.8	93.6	80.0	96.0	79.2	94.3	76.9	91.7	71.3	82.5	67.5	76.1	63.1	69.2	77.6	91.6
	2	56.8	62.2	58.6	66.4	63.3	75.2	66.7	83.5	73.2	87.5	77.0	91.9	79.2	94.6	78.4	92.6	76.1	89.4	70.1	80.3	66.0	73.5	61.0	66.0	76.4	89.2

Table 19-4. *(Continued)* **Monthly Percentiles of Wet-Bulb and Dry-Bulb Temperature for U.S. Locations**

		Jan		Feb		Mar		Apr		May		Jun		Jul		Aug		Sep		Oct		Nov		Dec		Annual	
Location	%	WB	DB	WB	DB	WB	DB	WB	DB	WB	DB	WB	DB	WB	DB	WB	DB	WB	DB	WB	DB	WB	DB	WB	DB	WB	DB
Roanoke	0.4	56.3	65.9	58.9	70.8	63.4	79.6	65.9	86.0	72.7	88.5	75.2	92.5	77.1	96.6	76.5	94.8	74.9	91.3	69.3	82.4	65.5	75.5	60.8	68.2	75.2	91.7
	1	54.0	62.0	56.5	67.1	61.4	76.3	64.8	83.2	71.2	86.5	74.3	90.9	76.2	94.4	75.7	92.3	74.0	89.2	67.9	80.3	63.7	72.7	59.0	65.3	74.1	89.3
	2	51.9	59.0	54.2	63.8	59.7	73.1	63.7	80.6	70.0	84.4	73.4	89.3	75.4	92.5	75.1	90.4	73.1	87.0	66.7	78.4	61.9	70.1	56.6	62.5	73.1	86.8
Sterling	0.4	57.0	63.0	59.1	68.5	64.0	78.4	67.3	85.5	74.6	89.3	77.6	93.5	79.5	96.9	78.6	94.9	77.9	92.8	70.7	82.8	66.7	75.6	62.2	68.8	77.4	92.6
	1	53.3	59.3	57.0	64.2	61.9	74.9	66.0	82.6	73.2	87.2	76.6	91.8	78.5	94.9	77.8	92.9	76.4	90.4	69.5	80.4	64.9	72.7	59.8	64.8	76.1	90.0
	2	50.5	55.2	54.0	61.0	60.0	71.0	64.6	79.6	71.6	85.2	75.6	89.9	77.6	93.2	77.0	91.3	75.2	88.4	68.1	77.9	63.0	70.0	56.9	61.5	74.9	87.6
WASHINGTON																											
Olympia	0.4	53.4	55.2	54.3	61.4	55.0	66.2	59.4	74.8	64.6	84.1	68.1	88.7	70.0	92.2	70.4	92.8	66.8	86.7	61.6	74.4	55.8	59.9	53.3	55.7	67.7	87.1
	1	51.8	53.8	53.1	58.4	53.7	63.4	57.5	71.3	63.1	80.4	66.7	85.2	68.8	89.2	69.0	90.0	65.3	83.1	60.3	71.0	54.5	57.8	51.6	53.5	65.9	83.0
	2	50.5	52.4	51.9	56.0	52.3	60.9	55.9	68.0	61.5	77.1	65.5	82.5	67.6	86.4	67.8	87.1	64.3	80.7	59.0	67.8	53.3	56.1	50.5	52.2	64.1	79.4
Quillayute	0.4	52.4	56.0	53.8	61.8	52.7	62.5	55.5	69.9	61.5	79.6	63.6	82.2	65.7	84.5	67.0	85.3	65.1	82.9	60.5	72.7	55.7	59.4	53.1	54.6	63.8	79.5
	1	50.9	53.4	52.3	58.3	51.5	59.6	54.3	66.2	59.6	74.8	62.1	76.6	64.3	80.6	65.2	80.9	63.6	79.8	59.2	68.5	54.9	57.2	52.2	53.4	61.8	73.9
	2	50.1	51.8	50.8	55.4	50.5	57.1	53.1	62.7	58.0	69.8	60.2	72.0	62.7	76.4	63.9	76.9	62.3	76.0	58.2	65.3	54.0	55.7	51.3	52.4	60.2	69.5
Seattle, Intl Airport	0.4	52.0	56.2	53.6	62.9	53.7	64.7	58.5	74.0	63.7	82.6	66.3	86.8	68.1	89.9	69.1	90.6	66.0	84.8	60.8	73.5	55.5	61.4	52.8	55.8	66.3	85.0
	1	50.6	54.4	52.4	59.8	52.4	62.4	56.7	70.4	62.1	78.9	65.2	83.7	67.0	86.7	67.8	87.4	64.7	81.8	59.5	70.4	54.3	58.9	51.2	54.1	64.6	81.4
	2	49.7	52.8	51.2	57.2	51.3	60.1	55.0	67.2	60.5	75.5	63.9	80.9	66.0	84.3	66.6	84.6	63.5	79.1	58.5	67.4	53.1	57.2	50.1	52.6	63.0	77.7
Spokane, Fairchild AFB	0.4	44.6	48.4	47.5	53.5	50.7	62.5	57.5	75.8	62.2	85.7	65.4	91.5	66.9	96.3	66.3	96.5	62.5	88.8	57.8	76.3	50.1	55.7	46.0	49.3	64.5	92.1
	1	42.5	46.0	45.8	51.2	49.1	59.6	55.0	71.3	60.0	82.5	64.0	89.3	65.6	94.2	65.3	94.2	61.3	85.7	56.0	73.1	48.3	53.0	43.7	46.8	62.9	88.7
	2	41.0	43.8	44.3	49.2	47.6	57.0	53.1	68.0	58.6	79.4	62.9	86.7	64.6	92.4	64.3	92.2	60.1	83.4	54.5	70.2	47.0	51.1	42.1	44.9	61.4	85.2
Yakima	0.4	47.0	55.7	49.9	60.7	53.3	68.1	59.1	78.5	64.3	90.0	67.1	95.6	70.7	99.7	69.7	99.8	66.0	90.7	60.4	79.8	52.5	62.1	48.2	55.7	67.4	65.4
	1	45.3	52.4	48.4	58.5	51.8	65.4	57.0	75.9	62.5	86.8	65.8	93.0	69.0	97.7	68.4	97.2	64.5	88.3	58.7	76.8	51.1	59.7	45.9	52.1	65.6	64.3
	2	43.5	50.2	46.9	56.0	50.1	63.0	55.2	73.1	60.8	83.9	64.7	90.7	67.5	95.8	67.4	95.0	63.4	86.2	57.1	73.6	49.6	57.6	43.9	49.1	64.1	63.0
WEST VIRGINA																											
Charleston	0.4	57.3	66.6	58.3	70.1	62.9	79.7	66.2	86.3	73.8	88.3	76.3	91.4	78.4	94.1	77.6	93.7	75.7	90.2	69.5	81.9	64.3	76.6	60.4	70.1	76.2	73.0
	1	55.6	62.9	56.6	67.0	61.4	77.1	65.0	83.9	72.4	86.6	75.3	90.0	77.4	92.2	76.7	91.6	74.7	88.0	68.1	80.2	62.8	73.9	58.9	66.8	74.9	72.5
	2	53.8	60.3	54.9	64.1	59.8	74.6	63.9	82.0	70.9	85.3	74.4	88.6	76.5	90.6	75.8	89.6	73.8	86.1	66.8	78.2	61.3	71.6	57.4	64.4	73.7	71.3
Elkins	0.4	54.3	61.3	55.7	65.1	60.4	75.5	64.2	81.1	69.7	83.3	73.4	85.9	75.4	88.9	74.8	88.2	73.1	84.5	67.0	77.9	62.2	72.4	58.9	66.4	73.3	70.5
	1	52.7	58.6	54.2	62.1	58.5	72.4	62.6	79.1	68.7	81.7	72.4	84.4	74.6	87.1	73.8	86.4	72.1	83.1	65.4	76.1	60.3	69.8	56.9	63.4	71.9	69.6
	2	50.6	56.0	52.4	59.8	56.9	69.9	61.4	77.1	67.7	80.3	71.4	83.2	73.6	85.5	72.9	84.5	71.2	81.5	64.1	74.4	58.8	67.4	54.9	60.4	70.6	68.6
Huntington	0.4	57.9	65.9	58.5	69.7	63.3	80.3	67.4	86.1	74.5	87.9	77.4	91.6	79.1	94.8	78.8	93.9	75.4	90.5	69.4	82.1	64.8	76.4	60.8	69.7	77.0	74.3
	1	56.2	62.7	56.8	66.9	61.8	77.2	65.8	83.9	73.1	86.4	76.3	90.2	78.1	92.7	77.6	92.0	74.7	88.2	68.2	80.3	63.2	73.6	59.4	66.7	75.7	73.4
	2	54.2	59.9	55.0	63.8	60.1	74.5	64.6	81.8	71.7	85.0	75.3	88.8	77.3	91.2	76.7	90.3	73.9	86.4	67.0	78.4	61.7	71.1	57.6	64.0	74.4	72.2
WISCONSIN																											
Eau Claire	0.4	38.0	41.8	42.6	47.9	56.3	66.7	64.6	82.4	71.7	87.6	76.1	92.6	78.8	95.5	78.1	92.9	74.4	87.2	67.1	78.3	57.2	62.6	47.8	50.2	75.7	73.3
	1	35.8	39.5	39.4	44.2	52.7	61.7	62.7	77.6	70.1	85.5	74.8	89.9	77.4	93.1	76.6	90.4	72.8	84.4	65.4	75.2	54.8	59.4	40.2	42.8	73.8	71.1
	2	34.4	37.3	37.4	41.4	49.3	57.4	60.8	74.0	68.5	83.3	73.4	87.9	76.1	90.7	75.2	88.3	71.4	81.7	63.3	72.2	51.8	57.1	37.2	39.7	71.9	69.6
Green Bay	0.4	39.4	41.9	40.9	43.9	56.8	64.7	65.5	80.0	72.5	85.5	76.2	91.9	78.4	92.5	78.3	90.8	74.5	85.3	67.5	76.9	57.9	62.7	48.4	50.3	75.5	73.2
	1	37.2	39.5	38.2	41.8	52.8	59.1	63.2	75.5	70.9	83.4	74.9	89.4	77.1	90.3	76.5	88.4	73.1	82.6	65.2	73.6	55.7	59.5	43.9	45.8	73.6	71.5
	2	35.5	37.8	36.6	39.8	49.2	55.0	60.9	71.0	69.0	81.1	73.6	86.9	75.9	88.3	75.0	86.1	71.3	80.2	62.9	70.9	53.3	56.4	39.3	41.6	71.7	69.9
La Crosse	0.4	40.9	44.4	44.3	50.3	58.0	70.2	65.8	83.2	73.4	88.1	77.6	93.8	80.8	96.0	79.6	94.2	76.4	89.2	68.3	79.3	58.7	64.4	50.4	52.5	77.3	74.4
	1	38.0	41.5	41.1	46.6	55.1	64.4	63.8	79.3	71.1	86.0	76.2	91.3	79.3	93.5	78.0	91.5	74.9	86.2	66.6	76.5	57.0	61.2	44.2	47.0	75.3	72.7
	2	35.9	39.4	38.8	43.6	51.9	60.5	61.9	75.4	69.5	83.5	74.8	89.2	77.7	91.6	76.8	89.3	73.3	83.3	64.6	74.1	54.2	59.0	39.5	42.5	73.6	71.3
Madison	0.4	43.6	47.4	44.9	51.1	59.2	70.0	65.2	81.4	72.0	86.7	76.6	91.8	78.8	94.4	78.3	92.5	75.2	87.4	67.6	79.3	59.1	65.9	52.5	55.4	76.0	73.3
	1	40.0	43.3	41.9	46.9	56.4	65.7	63.4	78.0	70.5	84.7	75.0	89.9	77.4	92.2	76.8	90.2	73.5	85.0	66.0	76.4	57.4	62.6	48.0	50.0	74.0	71.8
	2	37.2	40.5	39.4	43.9	53.6	61.6	61.5	74.1	69.1	82.7	73.7	88.3	76.3	90.1	75.5	88.1	72.0	82.7	64.2	73.6	55.6	59.4	43.0	46.0	72.2	70.4
Milwaukee	0.4	45.7	48.7	45.5	51.0	59.8	70.3	65.3	80.9	72.1	85.5	76.0	92.1	79.0	93.8	78.5	93.0	75.9	87.8	68.3	79.7	60.2	66.6	54.3	57.0	76.3	74.0
	1	41.5	44.4	42.5	46.7	57.3	65.6	63.5	76.3	70.4	83.3	74.8	89.8	77.7	91.5	77.6	90.3	74.2	84.8	66.1	75.9	58.5	63.2	49.3	52.1	74.3	72.1
	2	38.6	41.4	39.9	44.3	53.6	60.9	61.4	72.2	68.8	80.9	73.6	87.2	76.6	89.5	76.2	87.7	72.6	82.2	64.1	72.7	56.5	60.3	45.4	47.9	72.4	70.4
WYOMING																											
Casper	0.4	39.3	50.0	42.6	57.1	46.7	66.1	51.4	76.7	57.2	83.2	62.8	93.5	64.4	95.8	64.3	93.7	59.5	89.2	52.4	78.7	45.9	63.3	40.8	53.6	62.4	58.6
	1	37.9	47.3	40.7	53.1	44.6	62.7	50.1	73.7	56.1	81.2	61.8	91.2	63.5	94.2	63.2	92.1	58.3	86.9	51.3	76.2	44.2	60.6	39.3	50.4	61.0	57.8
	2	36.6	45.3	39.2	50.5	43.3	60.1	48.9	71.0	55.0	79.1	60.8	88.8	62.6	92.5	62.2	90.6	57.3	84.7	50.3	73.4	42.6	58.0	37.9	48.2	59.8	57.5
Cheyenne, Warren AFB	0.4	39.9	56.0	42.4	60.2	44.8	66.9	50.3	74.3	56.4	80.9	62.3	88.7	64.4	91.7	64.3	89.6	60.1	85.2	51.8	77.1	45.3	65.3	41.2	58.2	62.3	57.5
	1	38.4	53.3	40.5	57.0	43.3	63.7	49.2	72.2	55.2	78.6	61.3	86.6	63.4	90.0	63.0	87.8	58.6	83.3	50.4	75.2	44.0	63.0	39.5	55.7	60.9	57.0
	2	37.1	50.9	38.9	54.1	41.9	60.3	48.1	69.5	54.1	76.3	60.3	84.6	62.6	88.4	62.0	86.1	57.3	81.3	49.3	72.8	42.5	60.4	38.1	52.8	59.6	56.9
Lander	0.4	38.6	50.4	41.8	55.2	45.3	65.0	51.6	75.4	56.4	81.7	62.2	92.0	64.4	94.3	64.3	92.2	59.4	86.7	52.9	77.4	45.5	61.4	40.2	52.6	62.1	58.7
	1	37.1	47.6	39.9	52.0	43.6	61.9	49.9	72.8	55.2	79.9	61.1	89.5	63.4	92.4	63.0	90.5	58.2	84.6	51.4	74.4	43.8	58.8	38.4	49.8	60.5	57.8
	2	35.8	45.3	38.2	49.4	42.4	58.9	48.5	69.9	54.2	77.7	60.0	87.3	62.5	90.9	61.8	89.0	57.0	82.6	50.3	71.9	42.2	56.0	36.9	47.3	59.2	57.2
Rock Springs	0.4	37.3	45.1	39.7	50.7	42.9	60.7	47.8	71.2	52.2	77.9	57.4	88.0	60.9	90.2	59.6	88.2	57.4	83.1	49.2	72.8	43.3	57.8	38.5	47.4	58.2	54.3
	1	35.9	42.5	37.8	47.7	41.4	57.5	46.5	69.2	51.1	76.0	56.3	86.0	59.6	88.4	58.7	86.8	55.4	81.4	48.1	70.8	41.7	55.3	36.8	44.5	56.8	53.8
	2	34.5	40.2	36.4	45.2	40.0	54.8	45.3	66.8	50.2	74.0	55.2	84.2	58.7	86.9	57.9	85.3	54.1	79.3	47.0	68.7	40.2	53.0	35.2	42.2	55.5	53.3
Sheridan	0.4	41.4	55.0	44.9	59.8	48.7	69.6	55.9	78.6	61.4	85.2	67.4	95.1	68.6	98.1	66.4	97.0	62.8	92.0	55.7	81.7	48.7	68.4	43.6	59.2	65.6	62.2
	1	39.9	51.4	42.9	56.1	47.2	66.3	53.6	75.5	60.3	82.6	66.1	91.4	67.1	95.9	65.4	95.1	61.0	89.1	54.3	78.4	46.8	64.7	41.7	55.6	64.1	61.1
	2	38.7	48.8	41.2	53.4	45.7	62.5	52.1	72.7	59.2	80.0	65.0	88.4	66.1	93.6	64.5	93.1	59.9	86.3	53.0	75.2	45.2	60.6	39.8	51.9	62.6	60.8

WB = wet-bulb temperature°F, DB = dry-bulb temperature, °F .

Table 19-5. City Water Temperature

State and City and Water Source (W = well; S = surface)	Month						Probable Monthly Maximum Temperature
	April	May	June	July	August	September	
	Temperature, °F						
ALABAMA							
Anniston (W)	...	...	65.0	66.0	67.0	65.0	70
Birmingham	63.0	73.0	78.0	82.0	81.0	79.0	85
Gadsden (S)	...	...	76.0	78.0	82.0	80.0	85
Tuscaloosca	...	...	64.0	69.0	70.0	71.0	74
ARAKANSAS							
Fort Smith (S)	...	...	77.0	75.0	80.0	77.0	83
Little Rock (WS)	...	...	85.0	88.0	86.0	82.0	89
N. Little Rock (S)	...	...	80.0	82.0	85.0	80.0	88
Pine Bluff (W)	...	...	75.0	78.0	80.0	75.0	83
ARIZONA							
Tucson (W)	...	...	80.0	80.0	80.0	80.0	80
CALIFORNIA							
Alameda	...	...	59.0	62.0	64.0	64.0	67
Alhambra (W)	...	...	68.0	68.0	68.0	68.0	68
Berkeley	...	...	59.0	62.0	64.0	64.0	67
Fresno (W)	...	...	72.0	72.0	72.0	72.0	...
Glendale (WS)	...	...	68.0	68.2	68.2	67.3	71
Los Angeles	63.0	68.0	73.0	74.0	76.0	75.0	79
Oakland	55.0	57.0	59.0	62.0	64.0	64.0	67
Pasadena (WS)	...	...	68.0	73.0	74.0	74.0	77
Pomona (W)	...	...	67.0	...	...	...	...
Richmond	...	...	59.0	62.0	64.0	64.0	67
Riverside (W)	...	...	72.0	74.0	74.0	73.0	77
Sacramento (S)	...	...	70.7	79.7	80.6	77.0	83
San Bernardino (WS)	67.0	67.0	67.0	67.0	67.0	67.0	67
San Francisco	60.0	60.0	60.0	60.0	60.0	60.0	...
San Jose (WS)	...	...	68.0	73.0	73.0	73.0	76
Santa Ana (W)	...	...	69.0	69.0	69.0	69.0	69
Santa Barbara (S)	...	...	...	...	70.0	80.0	...
Stockton (W)	...	...	70.0	70.0	70.0	70.0	70
COLORADO							
Colorado Springs (S)	...	...	57.0	60.0	62.0	60.0	65
Denver	54.3	61.7	63.0	70.9	70.7	68.0	74
Pueblo (S)	...	...	69.0	74.0	74.0	70.0	77
CONNECTICUT							
Bridgeport	43.0	45.0	53.0	62.0	65.0	66.0	69
Hartford	44.0	54.0	59.0	66.0	70.0	69.0	73
New Haven	50.0	...	...	...	70.0	60.0	74
Waterbury	47.0	64.0	68.0	74.0	74.0	73.0	...
Stamford (S)	...	...	69.0	76.0	67.5	68.5	71
Stratford	...	...	61.0	63.0	64.0	64.0	67
DISTRICT OF COLUMBIA							
Washington	49.0	49.0	43.0	67.0	73.0	75.0	...
DELAWARE							
Wilmington	52.0	68.0	73.0	78.0	79.0	73.0	82
FLORIDA							
Jacksonville	79.2	80.6	84.8	86.3	86.7	82.4	90
Miami	From 70 to 75 year round						
Orlando (S)	...	...	84.0	86.0	87.0	86.0	90
Pensacola (W)	...	...	70.0	70.0	70.0	70.0	...
Tampa	80.0	85.0	87.0	85.0	85.0	83.0	...
West Palm Beach	...	...	84.2	85.6	86.2	84.9	89
GEORGIA							
Atlanta	59.0	71.5	78.1	83.5	79.5	77.8	87
Augusta (S)	...	...	82.0	84.0	85.0	79.0	88
Columbus (S)	...	...	75.0	80.0	80.0	79.5	83
Rome (S)	...	...	77.0	78.0	77.0	72.0	81
Savannah (W)	72 year round						...
ILLINOIS							
Aurora (W)	...	...	60.0	60.0	60.0	60.0	
Belleville	...	...	80.0	90.0	86.0	83.0	93
Bloomington (S)	...	...	69.8	78.8	78.8	68.0	82
Champaign (W)	...	...	58.0	58.5	56.0	56.0	...

Table 19-5. *(Continued)* **City Water Temperature**

State and City and Water Source (W = well; S = surface)	April	May	June	July	August	September	Probable Monthly Maximum Temperature
				Month			
				Temperature, °F			
Chicago	39.2	47.1	55.4	68.0	69.4	62.5	...
Denville (S)	...	...	79.5	84.0	83.0	75.0	87
Decatur (S)	...	...	75.9	78.6	83.3	73.8	86
E. St. Louis (S)	...	...	80.0	90.0	86.0	83.0	93
Elgin (W)	...	...	57.0	56.0	56.0	54.0	...
Evanston (S)	...	...	57.0	67.0	72.0	66.0	75
Freeport (W)	...	...	56.0	56.0	56.0	56.0	...
Granite City	...	...	80.0	90.0	86.0	83.0	93
Maywood (W)	...	...	60.0	60.0	60.0	60.0	...
Moline (S)	...	...	74.2	85.9	80.8	72.6	89
Oak Park (S)	...	...	68.2	70.0	75.0	73.0	78
Peoria	54.0	54.0	56.0	56.0	56.0	54.0	...
Quincy (S)	...	...	73.4	82.2	79.9	71.6	85
Rockford (W)	...	...	55.0	55.0	55.0	55.0	58
Springfield (S)	...	...	76.6	79.9	80.6	76.3	84
Waukegan (S)	...	...	54.5	65.6	69.8	64.7	...
INDIANA							
Elkhart (W)	...	...	57.0	58.0	60.0	58.0	...
Evansville	56.0	66.0	85.0	84.0	83.0	74.0	87
Fort Wayne	49.0	67.0	73.0	79.0	78.0	73.0	82
Gary	41.0	50.0	60.0	70.0	70.0	65.0	...
Hammond (S)	...	...	70.0	78.0	82.0	82.0	85
Indianapolis	53.0	68.0	73.0	80.0	82.0	77.0	85
Lafayette (W)	...	...	53.0	53.0	53.0	53.0	...
Marion (W)	...	...	54.0	54.0	55.0	55.0	...
Muncie (WS)	...	...	70.5	75.5	74.4	68.4	79
South Bend			Averages 60 year round				
IOWA							
Burlington (S)	...	...	...	81.0	87.0	86.0	90
Cedar Rapids (S)	...	...	71.4	82.5	79.2	68.0	...
Council Bluffs (S)	...	...	76.0	80.5	81.5	72.7	85
Des Moines	44.1	49.1	58.2	65.7	72.9	71.1	77
Dubuque (W)	...	...	59.0	60.0	60.0	59.0	...
Fort Dodge (W)	...	...	52.0	52.0	52.0	52.0	...
Mason City	...	...	...	...	59.0	...	...
Ottumwa (S)	...	...	72.5	77.5	77.5	72.5	81
Sioux City (W)			Average 54.0				...
Waterloo (W)			Average 54.0				...
KANSAS							
Hutchinson (W)			Average 60.0				...
Kansas City	63.0	78.0	84.0	93.0	91.0	85.0	...
Salina (W)	...	...	58.0	60.0	62.0	62.0	...
Topeka (WS)	...	...	76.0	84.0	80.0	74.0	87
KENTUCKY							
Ashland (S)	...	...	77.0	80.6	82.4	73.4	85
Covington (WS)	...	...	75.0	82.0	81.0	77.0	85
Louisville	49.0	69.0	77.0	82.0	82.0	77.0	85
Paducah (S)	...	...	76.0	84.0	80.0	74.0	87
LOUISIANA							
Alexandria (W)	...	...	85.0	86.0	86.0	86.0	89
New Orleans	66.0	77.0	86.0	89.0	90.0	90.0	93
Shreveport (S)	...	...	88.0	91.0	89.0	84.0	...
MAINE							
Portland (S)	...	...	56.3	64.0	66.0	64.0	69
MARYLAND							
Baltimore	47.0	53.0	61.0	66.0	70.0	64.0	73
Cumberland	...	...	59.0	62.0	65.0	69.0	72
Hagerstown (S)	...	...	82.0	83.0	82.0	79.0	...
MASSACHUSETTS							
Brockton (S)	...	...	53.0	58.0	62.0	62.0	65
Brookline (W)	...	...	57.0	62.0	67.0	66.0	70
Cambridge	43.0	55.0	64.0	72.0	74.0	68.8	...
Chicopee (S)	...	...	61.5	66.4	66.7	74.0	68.8
Holyoke (S)	...	...	69.0	74.0	72.0	68.0	74
Leominster (S)	...	...	65.0	71.0	74.0	64.0	77
Lowell	50.0	50.0	50.0	50.0	50.0	50.0	...

Table 19-5. *(Continued)* **City Water Temperature**

State and City and Water Source (W = well; S = surface)	April	May	June	July	August	September	Probable Monthly Maximum Temperature
				Month			
				Temperature, °F			
New Bedford	42.0	48.0	60.0	68.0	71.0	69.0	74
Quincy (S)	...	...	65.0	70.0	70.0	70.0	73
Springfield	41.0	49.0	52.0	54.0	55.0	54.0	...
Taunton (S)	...	...	65.0	70.0	70.0	70.0	73
Westfield (S)	...	...	56.0	61.0	63.0	58.0	...
Weymouth (S)	...	...	68.0	73.4	75.0	68.0	78
Worcester	46.0	53.5	65.0	70.0	73.0	68.5	76
MICHIGAN							
Ann Arbor (W)	...	...	58.0	62.0	62.5	61.5	66
Battle Creek (WS)	...	...	52.0	51.0	52.0	52.0	...
Bay City (S)	...	...	70.0	78.0	75.0	67.0	81
Dearborn	...	...	64.0	75.0	74.0	68.0	78
Detroit	41.0	56.0	64.0	75.0	74.0	68.0	78
Grand Rapids	54.0	66.0	71.0	73.0	74.0	68.0	78
Highland Park	...	...	64.0	73.0	74.0	71.0	77
Jackson (W)	...	...	52.0	52.0	52.0	52.0	...
Kalamazoo (W)	...	...	52.0	52.0	52.0	52.0	55
Lansing (W)	...	...	57.5	58.0	59.0	59.0	62
Maskegon (S)	...	...	49.0	46.0	68.0	66.0	71
Pontiac (S)	...	...	Average 55°F				...
Saginaw (S)	...	...	70.0	78.0	75.0	70.0	81
MINNESOTA							
Duluth	33.4	52.7	57.6	70.6	66.6	58.7	...
Minneapolis	40.5	61.2	69.3	80.2	73.0	67.6	83
Rochester (W)	...	...	53.0	55.0	58.0	56.0	...
St. Cloud (S)	...	...	68.0	77.0	70.0	64.0	80
Winona (W)			Average 55°F				...
MISSISSIPPI							
Jackson (S)	...	...	80.0	82.0	74.0	74.0	85
Meridian (WS)	...	...	78.0	86.0	86.0	82.0	89
MISSOURI							
Hannibal (S)	...	...	78.0	80.0	80.0	75.0	83
Jefferson City (S)	...	...	65.0	70.0	80.0	76.0	83
Springfield (WS)	...	...	68.0	74.0	76.0	75.0	79
St. Louis	53.0	69.0	77.0	85.0	83.0	75.0	88
NEBRASKA							
Lincoln (W)	...	...	58.0	59.0	59.0	59.0	...
Omaha	50.8	55.8	68.0	80.9	79.4	69.1	84
NEW HAMPSHIRE							
Berlin (S)	...	...	58.0	66.0	63.0	56.0	69
Nashua (W)	...	...	52.0	58.0	67.0	65.0	70
NEW JERSEY							
Atlantic City (WS)	...	...	71.6	72.5	68.0	64.4	71
Elizabeth	43.3	48.8	51.7	54.7	61.3	66.7	70
Newark	45.0	56.0	64.0	68.5	71.5	70.5	75
Paterson	46.0	49.2	54.6	55.9	59.0	64.0	...
Woodbridge (S)			Average 51.8°F				...
NEW YORK							
Albany	40.0	52.0	60.0	56.0	66.0	65.0	69
Amsterdam (S)	...	...	44.0	50.0	57.0	57.0	60
Binghamton (S)			Ranges from 34.0 to 74.0				...
Buffalo	32.0	37.0	62.0	71.0	73.0	66.0	76
Ithaca	...	...	61.1	71.6	70.8	67.5	75
Jamestown (W)			Average 48°F				...
Lackawanna (S)	...	...	...	75.0	75.0	...	...
Mount Vernon (S)	...	...	60.0	64.0	67.0	68.0	71
Newburgh (S)			Average 54°F				...
New York	45.0	55.0	63.0	70.0	70.0	69.0	73
Niagra Falls (S)	...	...	59.9	69.8	68.0	66.2	73
N. Tonawanda (S)	...	...	66.0	67.0	78.0	73.0	81
Poughkeepsie (WS)	...	...	68.9	75.2	76.6	71.3	78
Rochester	41.9	52.8	62.3	68.0	68.9	64.6	72
Schenectady (W)	...	...	51.0	55.0	57.0	59.0	60
Syracuse	44.2	50.5	59.8	66.4	70.4	67.7	73
Troy (S)	...	...	67.5	70.0	72.5	69.5	76
Utica	43.2	53.6	63.0	70.0	70.2	67.6	73

Table 19-5. *(Continued)* **City Water Temperature**

State and City and Water Source (W = well; S = surface)	April	May	June	July	August	September	Probable Monthly Maximum Temperature
				Temperature, °F			
Watertown (S)	...	...	69.0	72.0	71.0	67.0	75
White Plains	...	...	...	...	...	52.0	...
Yonkers	60.0	69.0	75.0	75.0	79.0	78.0	...
NORTH CAROLINA							
Asheville (S)	...	...	68.0	69.0	74.0	76.0	79
Charlotte (S)	...	...	76.0	81.0	80.0	77.0	84
Durham (S)	...	...	72.0	74.7	76.2	74.4	79
High Point (S)	...	...	75.0	78.0	...	73.0	...
Raleigh (S)	...	...	77.0	83.4	81.8	79.0	...
Wilmington (S)	...	...	86.0	86.0	84.2	80.6	89
NEW MEXICO							
Alburquerque (W)				Average 72°F			...
OHIO							
Akron	43.7	61.0	69.3	74.3	74.7	69.4	78
Alliance (WS)	...	...	64.4	68.0	68.0	64.4	71
Cincinnati	49.0	66.0	76.0	82.0	81.0	77.0	85
Cleveland	39.0	50.0	58.0	68.0	73.5	71.0	77
Cleveland Heights (S)	...	...	58.0	68.0	73.5	71.0	77
Columbus	46.0	64.0	72.0	76.0	76.0	74.0	79
Elyria (W)	...	...	66.0	70.0	72.0	66.0	75
Findlay (WS)	...	...	63.0	61.7	60.8	59.0	64
Hamilton (W)	...	...	63.0	65.0	65.0	64.0	...
Lima (S)	...	...	71.6	74.7	77.4	73.4	80
Mansfield (W)				Average 50°F			...
Newark (S)	...	...	67.0	70.0	70.0	64.0	73
Norwood (W)				Average 60°F			...
Portsmouth (S)	...	...	77.0	80.6	78.8	75.2	82
Sandusky	...	...	64.4	75.2	75.2	66.2	78
Steubenville	...	...	60.0	63.0	68.0	67.0	71
Toledo	48.0	66.0	72.0	87.0	85.0	72.0	...
Warren	...	...	73.2	78.6	76.5	71.2	82
Youngstown	43.0	50.5	58.5	62.5	66.0	68.5	72
OKLAHOMA							
Muskogee (S)	...	...	80.4	87.7	90.7	83.8	94
Oklahoma City	55.4	68.0	73.4	77.2	77.0	72.4	80
Tulsa	62.2	70.0	77.2	81.8	81.8	79.1	85
OREGON							
Portland	43.7	50.0	56.0	62.0	55.0	51.6	65
PENNSYLVANIA							
Allentown (S)	...	...	62.0	70.0	69.0	61.0	72
Bethlehem (WS)	...	...	70.6	74.0	75.0	62.7	78
Bradford (WS)	...	...	57.0	60.0	60.0	56.0	63
Butler (S)	...	...	55.0	65.0	70.0	70.0	73
Catbondale (S)	...	...	60.0	65.0	70.0	65.0	73
Duquesne (W)	...	...		Ranges from 56.0 to 68.0			...
Easton (S)	...	...	54.0	65.0	65.0	60.0	68
Erie	36.9	53.7	63.8	72.3	72.9	69.8	76
Hazleton (S)				Average 65°F			...
Homestead				Ranges from 60.0 to 75.0			...
Johnstown (S)	...	...	53.5	57.7	59.5	58.7	63
Lancaster (S)	...	...	70.0	76.0	77.0	72.0	80
Norristown (S)	...	...	...	...	84.0	...	...
Philadelphia	40.0	68.0	71.0	79.0	77.0	72.0	82
Pittsburgh	46.4	66.2	75.2	80.6	80.6	75.2	84
Reading	46.4	59.9	70.7	78.8	76.1	71.6	82
Scraton	...	58.2	64.1	70.3	70.9	67.9	74
Sharon (S)	...	...	71.0	74.0	73.0	67.0	77
Uniontown (WS)	...	...	65.0	68.0	68.0	65.0	71
Wilkinsburg (S)	...	...	75.0	79.0	77.0	75.0	82
Williamport (WS)	...	...	62.0	66.0	65.0	63.0	68
RHODE ISLAND							
Central Falls	...	...	70.0	74.0	74.0	67.0	77
Cranston	...	...	62.0	64.0	65.0	63.0	68
E. Providence (S)	...	...	50.0	55.0	60.0	60.0	63
Newport (S)	...	...	66.0	70.2	70.2	59.1	73
Pawtucket (S)	...	...	70.0	74.0	74.0	67.0	77

Table 19-5. *(Continued)* **City Water Temperature**

State and City and Water Source (W = well; S = surface)	April	May	June	July	August	September	Probable Monthly Maximum Temperature
				Temperature, °F			
Providence	48.0	56.0	62.0	64.0	65.0	63.0	68
SOUTH CAROLINA							
Charleston (S)	...	...	81.0	83.0	85.0	80.0	...
Columbia				Average 75°F			...
Greensville (S)	...	...	70.0	76.0	76.0	71.0	79
Spartanburg (S)	...	...	72.5	78.8	78.8	75.3	82
SOUTH DAKODA							
Sioux Falls (W)				Average 55°F			...
TENNESSEE							
Chattanooga	64.0	67.0	73.0	79.0	79.5	76.5	83
Jackson (W)	...	...	68.0	68.0	70.0	70.0	73
Knoxville	59.2	75.6	81.5	84.0	84.3	79.9	87
Nashville	61.0	76.0	84.0	88.0	88.0	84.0	91
TEXAS							
Abilene (WS)	...	...	70.0	75.0	80.0	80.0	83
Amarillo (W)	...	...	63.0	65.0	65.0	65.0	68
Austin (S)	...	...	84.0	84.0	85.0	79.0	88
Beaumont (S)	...	...	88.0	88.0	87.0	87.0	91
Brownsville (S)	...	...	84.0	86.0	87.0	89.0	92
Dallas	65.0	66.0	77.0	82.0	82.5	74.0	86
El Paso	80.0	82.0	84.0	85.0	85.0	84.0	88
Port Worth	62.0	72.0	81.0	83.0	83.0	81.0	86
Houston	84.0	84.0	84.0	84.0	84.0	84.0	...
Laredo (S)	...	...	84.2	83.3	84.6	78.5	88
Lubbock (S)	...	...	67.0	67.0	67.0	66.0	80
San Angelo (S)	...	...	75.0	78.0	80.0	77.0	83
San Antonio	76.0	76.0	76.0	76.0	76.0	76.0	...
Texarkana (WS)	...	...	77.0	83.0	86.0	86.0	89
Waco (S)	...	...	79.5	83.1	84.6	79.8	88
UTAH							
Ogden (WS)				Average 60.0°F			...
Salt Lake CIty	50.0	50.0	58.0	58.0	57.0	50.0	61
VERMONT							
Burlington (S)	...	...	58.0	63.0	66.0	68.0	71
VIRGINIA							
Lynchburg (S)	...	...	62.0	67.0	73.0	73.0	76
Newport News (WS)	...	...	77.0	82.0	82.0	76.0	85
Norfolk	62.0	70.0	77.5	83.0	83.0	79.5	...
Petersburg (S)	...	...	75.4	75.4	78.0	71.6	81
Richmond	56.8	69.6	74.7	80.4	79.5	73.4	83
WASHINGTON							
Everett (S)	...	...	54.0	60.0	62.0	50.0	65
Spokane				Averages 4, year round			...
Tacoma	49.0	51.0	53.0	59.0	61.0	60.0	...
Yakima (S)	...	...	56.0	61.5	65.0	62.0	68
WEST VIRGINIA							
Charleston (S)	...	...	79.0	83.0	82.0	77.0	85
Clarksburg (S)	...	...	75.0	76.0	77.0	72.0	80
Wheeling (S)	...	...	75.8	80.9	75.5	76.4	...
WISCONSIN							
Appleton	...	...	67.0	76.0	72.0	67.0	79
Beloit (W)				Averages 57.0			
Eau Claire (W)	...	...	50.0	51.0	53.0	62.0	65
Fond du Lac (W)	...	...	54.0	56.0	56.0	54.0	59
Kenosha (S)	...	...	56.0	59.0	67.0	60.0	70
La Crosse				Average 52.0			...
Madison (W)	...	...	53.0	52.0	53.0	52.0	56
Milwaukee	38.4	42.8	49.7	57.0	60.0	56.6	...
Manitowoc (W)	...	...	48.0	53.0	57.0	58.0	61
Superior (W)	...	...	56.2	61.5	64.4	62.9	67

The foregoing tabulation was compiled from data collected in a single year of the cities listed. While long term averages might show slightly different figures, it should be borne in mind that well water temperatures usually reflect annual mean dry-bulb temperatures of the air, while surface water temperatutes vary more closely with saesonal wet-bulb averages.

UNITS AND CONVERSIONS

U.S. Customary Unit System

Linear Measures

1 mile = 1760 yards (yd) = 5280 feet (ft)
1 yard = 3 feet = 36 inches (in.)   *1foot* = 12 inches (in.)
1 mil = 0.001 inch (in.)
1 fathom = 2 yards (yd) = 6 feet (ft)   *1 rod* = 5.5 yards (yd) = 16.5 feet (ft)
1 hand = 4 inches (in.)   *1span* = 9 inches (in.)
1 micro-inch = one millionth inch or 0.000001 inch

(1 micrometer or micron one millionth meter = 0.00003937 inch).

Surveyor's Measure

1 mile = 8 furlongs = 80 chains
1 furlong = 10 chains = 220 yards
1 chain = 4 rods = 22 yards = 66 feet = 100 links
1 link = 7.92 inches

Nautical Measure

1 league = 3 nautical miles
1 nautical mile = 6076.11549 feet = 1.1508 statute miles
1 knot = nautical unit of speed = 1 nautical mile per hour
1 degree at the equator = 60 nautical miles = 69.047 statute miles
360 degrees = 21,600 nautical miles = 24,856.8 statute miles = circumference at equator.

Square Measure

1 square mile = 640 acres = 6400 square chains
1 acre = 10 square chains = 4840 square yards (yd^2) = 43,560 square feet (ft^2)
An acre is equal to a square, the side of which is 208.7 feet (ft^2)
1 square chain = 16 square rods = 484 square yards (yd^2) = 4356 square feet (ft^2)
1 square rod = 30.25 square yards (yd^2) = 272.25 square feet (ft^2)= 625 square links
1 square yard = 9 square feet (ft^2)
1 square foot = 144 square inches (in^2)

Measure Used for Diameters and Areas of Electric Wires

1 circular inch = area of circle 1 inch in diameter = 0.7854 square inch (in^2)
1 circular inch = 1,000,000 circular mils
1 square inch = 1.2732 circular inch = 1,273,239 circular mils
1 circular mil = the area of a circle 0.001 inch in diameter

Cubic Measure

1 cubic yard = 27 cubic feet (ft^3)
1 cubic foot = 1728 cubic inches (in^3)

The following measures are also used for wood and masonry:

1 cord of wood = $4 \times 4 \times 8$ feet = 128 cubic feet (ft^3)
1 perch of masonry = $16\frac{1}{2} \times 1\frac{1}{2} \times 1$ foot = $24\frac{3}{4}$ cubic feet (ft^3)

Shipping Measure

For measuring entire internal capacity of a vessel:

1 register ton = 100 cubic feet (ft^3)

For measurement of cargo:

Approximately 40 cubic feet (ft^3) of merchandise is considered a shipping ton, unless that bulk would weigh more than 2000 pounds (lb), in which case the freight charge may be based upon weight
40 cubic feet = 32.143 U.S. bushels = 31.16 imperial bushels

Dry Measure

1 bushel = 1.2445 cubic feet (ft^3) = 2150.42 cubic inches (in^3) (U.S. or Winchester struck bushel)

1 bushel = 4 pecks = 32 quarts = 64 pints

1 peck = 8 quarts = 16 pints

1 quart = 2 pints

1 heaped bushel = 1¼ struck bushel

1 cubic foot = 0.8036 struck bushel

1 British Imperial bushel = 8 Imperial gallons = 1.2837 cubic feet = 2218.19 cubic inches

Liquid Measure

1 U.S. gallon = 0.1337 cubic foot (ft^3) = 231 cubic inches (in^3) = 4 quarts = 8 pints

1 quart = 2 pints = 8 gills   *1 pint* = 4 gills

1 British Imperial gallon = 1.2009 U.S. gallon = 277.42 cubic inches

1 cubic foot = 7.48 U.S. gallons

Old Liquid Measure

1 barrel = 31½ gallons   *1 hogshead* = 2 barrels = 63 gallons

1 pipe or *butt* = 2 hogsheads = 4 barrels = 126 gallons

1 tierce = 42 gallons   *1 puncheon* = 2 tierces = 84 gallons

1 tun = 2 pipes = 3 puncheons

Apothecaries' Fluid Measure

1 U.S. fluid ounce = 8 drachms = 1.805 cubic inch (in^3) = $\frac{1}{128}$ U.S. gallon

1 fluid drachm = 60 minims

1 British fluid ounce = 1.732 cubic inch (in^3)

Avoirdupois or Commercial Weight

1 gross or long ton = 2240 pounds   *1 net or short ton* = 2000 pounds

1 pound = 16 ounces = 7000 grains

1 ounce = 16 drachms = 437.5 grains

The following measures for weight are now seldom used in the United States: *1 hundred-weight* = 4 quarters = 112 pounds (*1 gross or long ton* = 20 hundred-weights); *1 quarter* = 28 pounds; *1 stone* = 14 pounds; *1 quintal* = 100 pounds

Troy Weight, Used for Weighing Gold and Silver

1 pound = 12 ounces = 5760 grains

1 ounce = 20 pennyweights = 480 grains

1 pennyweight = 24 grains

1 carat = 3.086 grains (used in weighing diamonds)

1 grain Troy = 1 grain avoirdupois = 1 grain apothecaries' weight

Apothecaries' Weight

1 pound = 12 ounces = 5760 grains

1 ounce = 8 drachms = 480 grains

1 drachm = 3 scruples = 60 grains

1 scruple = 20 grains

Measures of Pressure

1 pound per square inch = 144 pounds per square foot (lb/ft^2) = 0.068 atmosphere = 2.042 inches of mercury at 62°F = 27.7 inches of water at 62° F = 2.31 feet of water at 62° F

1 atmosphere = 30 inches of mercury at 62° F = 14.7 pounds per square inch (lb/in^2) = 2116.3 pounds per square foot (lb/ft^2) = 33.95 feet of water at 62°F

1 foot of water at 62°F = 62.355 pounds per square foot (lb/ft^2) = 0.433 pound per square inch (lb/in^2)

1 inch of mercury at 62°F = 1.132 foot of water = 13.58 inches of water = 0.491 pound per square inch (lb/in^2)

Miscellaneous

1 great gross = 12 gross = 144 dozen

1 quire = 24 sheets

1 gross = 12 dozen = 144 units

1 ream = 20 quires = 480 sheets

1 dozen = 12 units

1 ream printing paper = 500 sheets

1 score = 20 units

Table 20-1. Fractional Inch Measure Equivalents

Fraction of Inch	Decimal Inch	Millimeter	Fraction of Inch	Decimal Inch	Millimeter
1/64	0.015625	0.397	1/2	0.5	12.700
1/32	0.03125	0.794		0.511811	13
	0.0393701	1	33/64	0.515625	13.097
3/64	0.046875	1.191	17/32	0.53125	13.494
1/16	0.0625	1.588	35/64	0.546875	13.891
5/64	0.078125	1.984		0.5511811	14
	0.0787402	2	9/16	0.5625	14.288
3/32	0.09375	2.381	37/64	0.578125	14.684
7/64	0.109375	2.778		0.5905512	15
	0.1181102	3	19/32	0.59375	15.081
1/8	0.125	3.175	39/64	0.609375	15.478
9/64	0.140625	3.572	5/8	0.625	15.875
5/32	0.15625	3.969		0.6299213	16
	0.1574803	4	41/64	0.640625	16.272
11/64	0.171875	4.366	21/32	0.65625	16.669
3/16	0.1875	4.763		0.6692913	17
	0.1968504	5	43/64	0.671875	17.066
13/64	0.203125	5.159	11/16	0.6875	17.463
7/32	0.21875	5.556	45/64	0.703125	17.859
15/64	0.234375	5.953		0.7086614	18
	0.2362205	6	23/32	0.71875	18.256
1/4	0.25	6.350	47/64	0.734375	18.653
17/64	0.265625	6.747		0.7480315	19
	0.2755906	7	3/4	0.75	19.050
9/32	0.28125	7.144	49/64	0.765625	19.447
19/64	0.296875	7.541	25/32	0.78125	19.844
5/16	0.3125	7.938		0.7874016	20
	0.3149606	8	51/64	0.796875	20.241
21/64	0.328125	8.334	13/16	0.8125	20.638
11/32	0.34375	8.731		0.8267717	21
	0.3543307	9	53/64	0.828125	21.034
23/64	0.359375	9.128	27/32	0.84375	21.431
3/8	0.375	9.525	55/64	0.859375	21.828
25/64	0.390625	9.922		0.8661417	22
	0.3937008	10	7/8	0.875	22.225
13/32	0.40625	10.319	57/64	0.890625	22.622
27/64	0.421875	10.716		0.9055118	23
	0.4330709	11	29/32	0.90625	23.019
7/16	0.4375	11.113	59/64	0.921875	23.416
29/64	0.453125	11.509	15/16	0.9375	23.813
15/32	0.46875	11.906		0.9448819	24
	0.4724409	12	61/64	0.953125	24.209
31/64	0.484375	12.303		1.000000	25.4

U.S. System And Metric System Conversion

Length and Area

Table 20-2. Conversion of Linear Measure

From	Multiply by Factor To Obtain								
	Millimeter	Centimeter	Meter	Kilometer	Inches	Feet	Yards	Miles	Nautical Miles
Millimeter	1	0.1	0.001	0.000001	0.0393	0.00328	0.0010	6.2137E-07	5.3958E-07
Centimeter	10	1	0.01	0.00001	0.3937	0.03280	0.0109	6.2137E-06	5.3958E-06
Meter	1000	100	1	0.001	39.3700	3.28084	1.0936	6.2137E-04	0.00053958
Kilometer	1000000	100000	1000	1	39370.0787	3280.83990	1093.6132	0.6213	0.5395878
Inch	25.4	2.54	0.0254	0.000025	1	0.08333	0.0277	1.5782E-05	1.3705E-05
Feet	304.8	30.48	0.3048	0.000304	12	1	0.3333	0.0001893	0.0001644
Yard	914.4	91.44	0.9144	0.000914	36	3	1	0.00056812	0.0004933
Mile	1609344	160934.4	1609.344	1.609344	63360	5280	1760	1	0.868382
Nautical Mile	1853266.3	185326.63	1853.266	1.853266	72963.24	6080.27	2026.7566	1.151566	1

Table 20-3. Conversion of Area

From	Multiply by Factor To Obtain							
	$Millimeter^2$	$Centimeter^2$	$Meter^2$	$Kilometer^2$	$Inch^2$	$Feet^2$	$Yards^2$	$Miles^2$
$Millimeter^2$	1	0.01	1.0E-06	1.0E-12	0.0015	1.E-05	1.19E-06	3.86E-13
$Centimeter^2$	100	1	0.0001	1.0E-10	0.155	0.001	0.000119	3.86E-11
$Meter^2$	1.0E+06	10000	1	1.0E-06	1550.0	10.76	1.1959	3.86E-07
$Kilometer^2$	1.0E+12	1.0E+10	1.E+06	1	1.5E+9	10.7E+6	1195990.	0.3861
$Inch^2$	645.16	6.4516	6.4E-04	6.45E-10	1	0.00694	0.000771	2.49E-10
$Feet^2$	92903.04	929.03	0.092	9.29E-08	144	1	0.1111	3.5E-08
$Yard^2$	836127.36	8361.27	0.836	8.36E-07	1296	9	1	3.22E-07
$Miles^2$	2.58E+12	2.58E+11	2.5E+6	2.5899	4.E+10	2.78E+7	3097600	1

Mass and Density

Table 20-4. Mass Conversion

From	Multiply by Factor To Obtain								
	Gram	Kilogram	Ton (Metric)	Ounce (avoir)	Ounce (Troy)	Grain	Pound	Ton (Short)	Ton (Long)
Gram	1.00	0.001	0.00000	0.035	0.0321	15.43236	0.0022	1.1E-06	9.84E-07
Kilogram	1000.00	1.00	0.001	35.273	32.15	15432.36	2.2046	0.00110	0.00098
Ton (Metric)	1000000.0	1000.00	1.000	35273.97	32150.74	1.5E+7	2204.62	1.10231	0.98421
Ounce (Avoir)	28.35	0.02835	0.00003	1.000	0.911	437.500	0.0625	0.00003	0.00003
Ounce (Troy)	31.10	0.03110	0.00003	1.0971	1.000	480.00	0.0685	0.00003	0.00003
Grain	0.065	0.00006	0.00000	0.0022	0.002	1.00	0.00014	0.00000	0.00000
Pound	453.59	0.45359	0.00045	16.000	14.58	7000.00	1.0000	0.00050	0.00045
Ton (Short)	907184.8	907.1848	0.90718	32000.00	29166.66	1.4E+7	2000.00	1.00000	0.89286
Ton (Long)	1016046.0	1016.046	1.01605	35840.01	32666.66	1.5E+7	2240.00	1.1200	1.00000

Table 20-5. Density Conversion

From	Multiply by Factor To Obtain						
	Gram/mL	$Grams/cm^3$	Kg/m^3	$Lb/inch^3$	$Lb/feet^3$	Lb/gallon	$Tons/yards^3$
Gram per mL	1	1	1000	0.03613	62.43	8.345	0.8428
$Grams/cm^3$	1	1	1000	0.03613	62.43	8.345	0.8428
$Kilogram/m^3$	0.001	0.001	1	0.000036	0.062	0.0083	0.00084
$Lb/inch^3$	27.67783	27.67783	27677.83	1.0	1727.926	230.9714	23.32687
$Lb/feet^3$	0.01601	0.01601	16.01	0.000578	1	0.1336	0.01349
Lb/US gallon	0.11983	0.11983	119.83	0.004329	7.481126	1	0.10099
$Tons /yards^3$	1.18652	1.18652	1186.52	0.042869	74.07451	9.9015	1

Volume and Flow

Table 20-6. Volume Conversion

From	Multiply by Factor To Obtain									
	Centi meter^3	Meters ^{3}	Inches^3	Feet^3	Yards^3	Liter	Gallon (US)	Gallon (UK)	Quart (US)	Quart (UK)
Centimeter ^{3}	1.00	0.000	0.061	0.000	0.000	0.001	0.000	0.000	0.001	0.001
Meters ^{3}	1000000	1.000	61023.7	35.315	1.308	1000.00	264.17	219.969	1057.08	880.282
Inches ^{3}	16.38	0.000	1.000	0.001	0.000	0.016	0.004	0.004	0.017	0.014
Feet^3	28316.8	0.028	1728.00	1.000	0.037	28.317	7.481	6.229	29.933	24.927
Yard^3	764554.0	0.765	46656.0	27.000	1.000	764.555	201.97	168.178	808.198	673.024
Liter	1000.00	0.001	61.024	0.035	0.001	1.000	0.264	0.220	1.057	0.880
Gallon (US)	3785.41	0.004	231.000	0.134	0.005	3.785	1.000	0.833	4.001	3.332
Gallon (UK)	4546.09	0.005	277.420	0.161	0.006	4.546	1.201	1.000	4.806	4.002
Quart (US)	946.00	0.001	57.728	0.033	0.001	0.946	0.250	0.208	1.000	0.833
Quart (UK)	1136.00	0.001	69.323	0.040	0.001	1.136	0.300	0.250	1.201	1.000

Table 20-7. Flow Conversion

From	Multiply by Factor To Obtain									
	meter^3/sec	meter^3/min	Liter/sec	Liter/min	Feet^3/sec	Feet^3/min	gallon (US)/sec	gpm (US)	gallon (UK)/sec	gpm (U.K.)
meter^3/sec	1	60	1000	60000	35.287	2117.2	264.172	15850	219.96	13198.
meter^3/min	0.0166	1	16.66	1000	0.588	35.28	4.4028	264.17	3.666	219.96
Liter/sec	0.001	0.06	1	60	0.0352	2.11	0.2641	15.85	0.219	13.198
Liter/ min	1.6E-05	0.001	0.0166	1	0.00058	0.035	0.0044	0.264	0.00366	0.219
Feet^3/sec	0.0283	1.700	28.338	1700.31	1	60	7.4862	449.17	6.233	374.01
Feet^3/min	0.00047	0.0283	0.4723	28.33	0.0166	1	0.1247	7.486	0.103	6.233
gallon (US)/sec	0.0037	0.2271	3.7854	227.12	0.1335	8.014	1	60	0.8326	49.96
gpm(U.S.)	6.3E-05	0.0037	0.0630	3.78	0.0022	0.133	0.01666	1	0.0138	0.832
gallon (UK)/sec	0.00454	0.2727	4.546	272.76	0.1604	9.625	1.2	72.056	1	60
gpm(U.K.)	7.5E-05	0.0045	0.0757	4.54	0.0026	0.160	0.02	1.2	0.0166	1

Table 20-8. Pressure Conversion

From	Multiply by Factor To Obtain											
	Atmo-sphere	Pascal (n/m^2)	Dyne/cm^2	Bar	Kilogram / centimeter^2	Kilo-gram /meter^2	psia (pound/ inch^2)	Pound /foot^2	Inch of Water	Inch of Mercury	Millime-ter of Mercury	Tons/ foot^2
Atmosphere	1	101325	1013000	1.01325	1.033	10330	14.6959	2116.216	407.1893	29.9212	760	1.058
Pascal (n/m^2)	9.869E-06	1	9.997	0.00001	1.019E-05	0.1019	0.000145	0.02088	0.004018	0.0002952	0.0075	1.044E-05
Dyne/cm^2	9.871E-07	0.1000	1	1.0E-06	1.019E-06	0.0101	1.450E-05	0.00208	0.0004019	2.95E-05	0.00075	1.044E-06
Bar	0.98692	100000	999753.27	1	1.019491	10194.917	14.5037	2088.5434	401.8645	29.5299	750.061	1.04416
Kilogram/centimeter^2	0.96805	98088.09	980638.92	0.98088	1	10000	14.22642	2048.6123	394.1813	28.9653	735.721	1.024201
Kilogram/meter^2	9.68E-05	9.808809	98.063	9.8E-05	0.0001	1	0.001422	0.2048	0.039418	0.00289	0.07357	0.000102
Psia (pound/inch^2)	0.06804	6894.78	68930.79	0.06894	0.07029	702.917	1	144.000	27.70768	2.03602	51.715	0.071992
Pound/foot^2	0.00047	47.88	478.684	0.000478	0.000488	4.8813	0.006944	1	0.19241	0.01413	0.3590	0.000499
Inch of Water	0.00245	248.84	2487.786	0.002488	0.002536	25.3690	0.036091	5.19713	1	0.07348	1.8664	0.002598
Inch of Mercury	0.03342	3386.39	33855.594	0.03386	0.034524	345.2401	0.491153	70.72632	13.6087	1	25.400	0.035359
Millimeter of Mercury	0.00131	133.32	1332.894	0.00133	0.001359	13.5921	0.019336	2.7844	0.53577	0.03937	1	0.0013921
Tons/Foot^2	0.94517	95770.32	957466.918	0.95770	0.97637	9763.7051	13.89026	2000.2047	384.8670	28.2809	718.336	1

Table 20-9. Thermal Conductance Conversion

From	Multiply by Factor To Obtain									
	Btu-ft/ h-ft^2-°F	Btu-in./ h-ft^2-°F	Btu-in. / sec-ft^2-°F	Cal/cm-s-°C	Kcal/m-s-°C	Kcal / m-h-°C	Erg / cm-s-°C	Joules / m-h-°C	Watt/ft-°C	Watt/m-°K
Btu-ft/ h-ft^2-°F	1	0.0833	300	241.9	2419	0.672	0.000005	0.5778	1.895	0.5778
Btu-in./ h-ft^2-°F	12.000	1	3600.14	2902.91	29029.16	8.0643	6.93E-05	6.93387	22.7409	6.93387
Btu-in./ sec-ft^2-°F	0.0033	0.00027	1	0.806	8.0633	0.0022	1.92E-08	0.00192	0.00631	0.00192
Cal/ cm-s-°C	0.0041	0.00034	1.24013	1	10	0.002778	2.38E-08	0.00238	0.00783	0.00238
Kcal/m-s-°C	0.0004	3.4E-05	0.12401	0.1	1	0.000277	2.38E-09	0.00023	0.00078	0.000239
Kcal/ m-h-°C	1.4880	0.124	446.428	359.97	3599.70	1	8.59E-06	0.85982	2.81994	0.859829
Erg/ cm-s-°C	173070.2	14421.94	51921079.9	41865697	418656974	116303.2	1	100000	327968	100000
Joules/m-h-°C	1.7307	0.1442	519.21	418.6569	4186.569	1.163032	0.00001	1	3.27968	1
Watt /ft-°C	0.5277	0.0439	158.31	127.651	1276.517	0.354617	3.04E-06	0.3049	1	0.30490
Watt/m-°K	1.7307	0.1442	519.21	418.656	4186.569	1.163032	0.00001	1	3.27968	1

Force, Energy, Work, Torque and Power Conversion

Table 20-10. Conversion of Force

From	Multiply by Factor To Obtain						
	Newton	Dyne	Kg_f	Kip	Lb_f	Poundal	Ounce-force
Newton	1	100000	0.1019	0.00022	0.2248	7.233	3.5969
Dyne	0.00001	1	1.01E-06	2.248E-09	0.0000022	0.000072	3.59E-05
Kg_f	9.806	980665	1	0.0022	2.20453	70.93149	35.27396
Kip	4448.398	444839857	453.610	1	1000	32175.269	16000.63
Lb_f	4.448	444839.85	0.453	0.001	1	32.175269	16.00063
Poundal	0.138	13825.52	0.014	3.107E-05	0.031079	1	0.4972
Ounce-force	0.278	27801.39	0.028	6.249E-05	0.062497	2.010874	1

Table 20-11. Energy and Work Conversion

From	Multiply by Factor To Obtain									
	Joules	$Ft-lb_f$	Ft-Poundal	Btu	Kg-m	Calories	Watt-hour	Erg	Therm	eV
Joules	1	0.737	23.730	0.00094	9.807	0.238	0.00027	1.0E+7	9.4E-9	6.2415
$Ft-Lb_f$	1.355	1	32.174	0.00128	13.296	0.323	0.00037	1.3E+7	1.2E-08	8.462
Ft-Poundal	0.042	0.031	1	3.9E-05	0.413	0.010	1.1E-05	421401.	3.9E-10	0.263
Btu	1055.07	778.181	25037.30	1	10347.1	251.95	0.29307	1.0E+9	0.00001	6585.25
Kg-m	0.101	0.075	2.4197	9.6E-05	1	0.024	2.8E-05	1.0E+6	9.6E-10	0.63
Calories	4.187	3.088	99.37	0.00396	41.067	1	0.00116	4.1E+6	3.9E-08	26.14
Watt-Hour	3600	2655.21	85429.29	3.41208	35305.2	859.68	1	36E+9	3.4E-05	22469.4
Erg	1.0E-6	7.3E-8	2.37E-06	9.4E-11	9.8E-07	2.3E-08	2.7E-11	1	9.4E-16	6.2E-07
Therm	1.0E+8	7.7E+6	2.5E+9	1E+5	1.0E+9	2.5E+7	29307.6	1E+15	1	6.5E+7
eV	0.160	0.118	3.80	0.00015	1.57	0.038	4.4E-05	1.6E+5	1.5E-09	1

Table 20-12. Bending Moment or Torque Conversion

From	Multiply by Factor To Obtain					
	Dyne-centimeter	Kilogram-meter	Newton-milimeter	Newton-meter	Ounce-inch	Pound-feet
Dyne-centimeter	1.00	1.019E-08	1.000E-04	1.000E-07	1.416E-05	7.375E-08
Kilogram-meter	98070000.	1.0000	9807.00	9.8070	1388.788	7.2333
Newton-milimeter	10000.00	0.0001	1.00	0.0010	0.141	0.0007
Newton-meter	10000000.0	0.1020	1000.00	1.0000	141.611	0.7376
Ounce-inch	70615.52	0.0007	7.061	0.0071	1.000	0.0052
Pound-feet	13558180.0	0.1383	1355.81	1.3558	192.000	1.0000

Table 20-13. Power Conversion

From	Multiply by Factor To Obtain								
	Horsepower	Watts	Kilowatts	Kg_f-m/s	Ft-Lb_f/s	Ft-lb_f/hr	Calories/sec	Btu/sec	Btu/hr
Horsepower	1	745.699	0.7456	76.04	550	33000	178.1	0.7068	2544.48
Watts	0.00134	1	0.001	0.1019	0.7375	44.25	0.2388	0.00094	3.4122
Kilowatts	1.34102	1000	1	101.971	737.56	44253.7	238.835	0.94783	3412.20
Kg_f-m/s	0.01315	9.8066	0.0098	1	7.23	433.9	2.3421	0.00929	33.4623
Ft-lb_f/s	0.00181	1.3558	0.0013	0.1382	1	60	0.3238	0.00128	4.6263
Ft-lb_f/hr	3.0E-05	0.0225	2.2E-05	0.0023	0.0166	1	0.0053	2.1E-05	0.0771
Calories/sec	0.0056	4.1869	0.00418	0.4269	3.088	185.28	1	0.00396	14.2868
Btu/sec	1.4148	1055.03	1.05503	107.583	778.155	46689.3	251.980	1	3600
Btu/hr	0.00039	0.29306	0.00029	0.0298	0.216	12.969	0.0699	0.00027	1

Velocity and Acceleration
Table 20-14. Velocity Conversion

From	Multiply By Factor To Obtain						
	cm/sec	m/sec	km/hr	ft/sec	ft/min	ft/hr	knot
cm/sec	1.00	0.01	0.036	0.032808	1.9685	118.11026	0.01944
m/sec	100.00	1.00	3.60	3.2808	196.8504	11811.0236	1.94384
km/hr	27.78	0.27778	1.00	0.91344	54.6806	3280.8399	0.53995
ft/sec	30.48	0.3048	1.09728	1.00	60.00	3600.00	0.59248
ft/min	0.5080	0.00508	0.018288	0.016667	1.00	60.00	0.0098
ft/hr	0.008467	8.47E-05	3.05E-05	2.78E-04	0.016666	1.00	1.6E-04
knot	51.444	0.51444	1.852	1.687808	101.2687	6076.11549	1.00

Table 20-15. Conversion of Acceleration

From	Multiply by Factor To Obtain						
	cm/sec^2	m/sec^2	km/hr^2	ft/sec^2	ft/min^2	$miles/hr^2$	knot/sec
cm/sec^2	1	0.01	129.6	0.0328	118.11	80.529	0.01942
m/sec^2	100	1	12960	3.280	11811.02	8052.970	1.94260
km/hr^2	0.007716	7.71E-05	1	0.00025	0.911	0.6213	0.00014
ft/sec^2	30.48	0.3048	3950.20	1	3600	2454.545	0.59210
ft/min^2	0.0084	8.46E-05	1.097	0.00027	1	0.681	0.00016
$mile/hr^2$	0.0124	0.000124	1.609	0.0004	1.466	1	0.00024
knot/sec	51.44444	0.514444	6671.46	1.6888	6080	4145.45	1

Measures of the Quantity of Thermal Energy.—The unit of quantity of thermal energy used in the United States is the British thermal unit, which is the quantity of heat or thermal energy required to raise the temperature of one pound of pure water one degree F. (American National Standard abbreviation, Btu; conventional British symbol, B.Th.U.) The French thermal unit, or *kilogram calorie,* is the quantity of heat or thermal energy required to raise the temperature of one kilogram of pure water one degree C. One kilogram calorie = 3.968 British thermal units = 1000 gram calories. The number of foot-pounds of mechanical energy equivalent to one British thermal unit is called the *mechanical equivalent of heat,* and equals 778 foot-pounds.

In the modern metric or SI system of units, the unit for thermal energy is the *joule* (J); a commonly used multiple being the kilojoule (kJ), or 1000 joules. See page 8 for an explanation of the SI system. One kilojoule = 0.9478 Btu. Also in the SI System, the *watt* (W), equal to joule per second (J/s), is used for power, where 1 watt = 3.412 Btu/hour

1 horsepower-hour = 0.746 kilowatt-hour = 1,980,000 foot-pounds = 2545 Btu (British thermal units) = 2.64 pounds of water evaporated at 212°F = 17 pounds of water raised from 62° to 212°F

1 kilowatt-hour = 100 watt-hours = 1.34 horsepower-hour = 2,655,200 foot-pounds = 3,600,000 joules = 3415 Btu = 3.54 pounds of water evaporated at 212°F = 22.8 pounds of water raised from 62° to 212°F

1 horsepower = 746 watts = 0.746 kilowatt = 33,000 foot-pounds per minute = 550 foot-pounds/second = 2545 Btu/hour = 42.4 Btu/minute = 0.71 Btu/second = 2.64 lbs of water evaporated per hour at 212°F

1 kilowatt = 1000 watts = 1.34 horsepower = 2,654,200 foot-pounds/hour = 44,200 foot-pounds/minute = 737 foot-pounds/second = 3415 Btu/hour = 57 Btu/minute = 0.95 Btu/second = 3.54 pounds of water evaporated per hour at 212°F

1 watt = 1 joule/second = 0.00134 horsepower = 0.001 kilowatt = 3.42 Btu/hour = 44.22 foot-pounds per minute = 0.74 foot-pounds/second = 0.0035 pound of water evaporated per hour at 212°F

1 Btu (British thermal unit) = 1052 watt-seconds = 778 foot-pounds = 0.252 kilogram-calorie = 0.000292 kilowatt-hour = 0.000393, horsepower-hour = 0.00104 pound of water evaporated at 212°F

1 foot-pound = 1.36 joules = 0.000000377 kilowatt-hour = 0.00129 Btu = 0.0000005 horsepower-hour

1 joule = 1 watt-second = 0.00000078 kilowatt-hour = 0.00095 Btu = 0.74 foot-pound

Metric Systems Of Measurement

Measures of Length

10 millimeters (mm) = 1 centimeter (cm)

10 centimeters = 1 decimeter (dm)

10 decimeters = 1 meter (m)

1000 meters = 1 kilometer (km)

Square Measure

100 square millimeters (mm²) = 1 square centimeter (cm²)

100 square centimeters = 1 square decimeter (dm²)

100 square decimeters = 1 square meter (m²)

Surveyors Square Measure

100 square meters (m²) = 1 are (a)

100 ares = 1 hectare (ha)

100 hectares = 1 square kilometer (km²)

Cubic Measure

1000 cubic millimeters (mm³) = 1 cubic centimeter (cm³)

1000 cubic centimeters = 1 cubic decimeter (dm³⁾)

1000 cubic decimeters = 1 cubic meter (m³)

Dry and Liquid Measure

10 milliliters (ml) = 1 centiliter (cl)

10 centiliters = 1 deciliter (dl)

10 deciliters = 1 liter (l)

100 liters = 1 hectoliter (hl)

1 liter = 1 cubic decimeter = the volume of 1 kilogram of pure water

at a temperature of 39.2°F

Measures of Weight

10 milligrams (mg) = 1 centigram (cg)

10 centigrams = 1 decigram (dg)

10 decigrams = 1 gram (g)

10 grams = 1 dekagram (dag)

10 dekagrams = 1 hectogram (hg)

10 hectograms = 1 kilogram (kg)

1000 kilograms = 1 (metric) ton (t)

Table 20-16. International System (SI) Units

Physical Quantity	Name of Unit	Unit Symbol	Definition
Basic SI Units			
Length	meter	m	Distance traveled by light in vacuum in $\frac{1}{299,792,458}$ second.
Mass	kilo-gram	kg	Mass of the international prototype, which is in the custody of the bureau international des poids et mesures (BIPM) at Sèvres, near Paris.
Time	second	s	The duration of 9,192,631,770 periods of the radiation corresponding to the transition between the two hyperfine levels of the ground state of the cesium-133 atom.
Electric Current	ampere	A	The constant current that, if maintained in two parallel rectilinear conductors of infinite length, of negligible circular cross section, and placed at a distance of 1 meter apart in a vacuum, would produce between these conductors a force equal to 2×10^{-7} N/m length.
Thermodynamic Temperature	degree kelvin	K	The fraction 1/273.16 of the thermodynamic temperature of the triple point of water.
Amount of Substance	mole	mol	The amount of substance of a system which contains as many elementary entities as there are atoms in 0.012 kg of carbon-12.
Luminous Intensity	candela	cd	Luminous intensity, in the perpendicular direction, of a surface of $1/600,000$ m^2 of a black body at the temperature of freezing platinum under a pressure of 101,325 N/m^2.
SI Units Having Special Names			
Force	newton	$N = kg\text{-}m/s^2$	That force that, when applied to a body having a mass of 1 kilogram, gives it an acceleration of one meter/sec^2.
Work, energy, quantity of heat	joule	$J = N\text{-}m$	The work done when the point of application of a force of one newton is displaced through a distance of 1 meter in the direction of the force.
Electric charge	cou-lomb	$C = A\text{-}s$	The quantity of electricity transported in 1 second by a current of 1 ampere.
Electric potential	volt	$V = W/A$	The difference of potential between two points of a conducting wire carrying a constant current of 1 ampere, when the power dissipated between these points is equal to 1 watt.
Electric capacitance	farad	$F = C/V$	The capacitance of a capacitor between the plates of which there appears a difference of potential of 1 volt when it is charged by a quantity of electricity equal to 1 coulomb.
Electric resistance	ohm	$\Omega = V/A$	The resistance between two points of a conductor when a constant difference of potential of 1 volt, applied between these 2 points, produces in this conductor a current of 1 ampere, this conductor not being the source of any electromotive force.
Magnetic flux	weber	$Wb = V\,s$	The flux which, linking a circuit of one turn produces in it an electromotive force of 1 volt as it is reduced to zero at a uniform rate in 1 second.
Inductance	henry	$H = V\,s/A$	The inductance of a closed circuit in which an electromotive force of 1volt is produced when the electric current in the circuit varies uniformly at the rate of 1 ampere/second.
Luminous flux	lumen	$1m = cd\,sr$	The flux emitted within a unit solid angle of 1 steradian by a point source having a uniform intensity of 1 candela.
Illumination	lux	$lx = lm/m^2$	An illumination of 1 lumen/m^2.

Heat and Power.—The british thermal unit is $\frac{1}{180}$ of the heat required to raise the temperature of 1 lb of water from 32°F to 212°F. It is substantially equal to the quantity of heat required to raise 1 lb of water from 63°F to 64°F.

One Btu equals $\frac{1}{3416}$ kw-hr

1 Btu equals .293 w-hr

1 w-hr equals 3.415 Btu

1 Kilowatt (1000 Watts) equals 1.3405 hp (56.93 Btu per minute)

1 Mechanical hp equals 0.746 kw (42.44 Btu/minute)

1 Boiler hp equals 33471.9 Btu/hour

1 Btu will warm 55 ft³ dry air 1°F at 70°F temperature, barometric pressure 29.921 in (Weight .07492 lb/ft³)

Specific heat for dry air at temperature range from 32°F to 212°F equals 0.24 Btu/Lb-°F

Heating Value of Various Fuels.—Natural gas equals 850 to 1150 Btu/ft³, manufactured gas equals 500 to 550 Btu/ft³.

Blast furnace gas equals 85 to 100 Btu/ft³.

Fuel oil (industrial) equals 140000 to 150000 Btu/gal.

Bituminous coal equals 12000 Btu/lb.

Pressure.—1 Atmosphere equals 14.7 lb/in².

1 inch at water gauge pressure has a corresponding velocity of 4005 fpm.

1 Mile /hour wind equals 5280 ft/hr (88 fpm).

Wind Velocity to Pressure

V	P	V	P	V	P
5	0.1	35	4.9	65	16.9
10	0.4	40	6.4	70	19.6
15	0.9	45	8.1	75	22.5
20	1.6	50	10.0	80	25.6
25	2.5	55	12.1	100	40.0
30	3.6	60	14.4		

Formula $P = 0.004 V^2$ Where: V= Wind Velocity, mph, P= Pressure, lbs/ft²

The quantity of heat, in Btu, required to raise the temperature of 1 lb of a substance 1°F

Specific Heat of Various Materials

Air (at 70°F)	0.24	Lead-Solid	0.031
Aluminum	0.22	Lead-Fluid	0.037
Bake-dough	0.60	Nickel	0.11
Brass	0.089	Paper	0.32
Carbon	0.204	Steel	0.1175
Copper	0.094	Tin-Solid	0.056
Glass	0.20	Tin-fluid	0.064
Iron-gray	0.11	Water (at 70°F)	1.0
Iron-cast	0.16	Zinc	0.093

Binary Multiples.—The International Electro-technical Commission has assigned the following prefixes to represent exponential binary multiples. This avoids confusion with standard SI decimal prefixes when representing powers of 2, as in bits and bytes.

Symbol	Name	Binary Power	Symbol	Name	Binary Power
Ki	kibi	2^{10}	Ti	tebi	2^{40}
Mi	mebi	2^{20}	Pi	pebi	2^{50}
Gi	gibi	2^{30}	Ei	exbi	2^{60}

Example 1: $2 \text{ Ki} = 2 \times 2^{10} = 2 \times 1,024 = 2,048$. This does *not* equal $2 \text{ K} = 2 \times 10^3 = 2,000$.

Example 2: 1 mebibyte $= 1 \times 2^{20} = 1,048,576$ bytes. Again this does *not* equal 1 megabyte $= 1 \times 10^6 = 1,000,000$ bytes, a value that is often confused with 1,048,576 bytes.

The greek letters are frequently used in mathematical expressions and formulas. The greek alphabet is given below.

Greek Letters and Standard Abbreviations

A	α	Alpha	I	ι	Iota	R	ρ	Rho
B	β	Beta	K	κ	Kappa	Σ	σ ς	Sigma
Γ	γ	Gamma	Λ	λ	Lambda	T	τ	Tau
Δ	δ	Delta	M	μ	Mu	Υ	υ	Upsilon
E	ε	Epsilon	N	ν	Nu	Φ	φ	Phi
Z	ζ	Zeta	Ξ	ξ	Xi	X	χ	Chi
H	η	Eta	O	o	Omicron	Ψ	ψ	Psi
Θ	ϑ θ	Theta	Π	π	Pi	Ω	ω	Omega

Terminology of Sheet Metal

Air Conditioning: The process of treating air in an enclosed space to control, simultaneously, its temperature, humidity, cleanliness, and distribution, and to satisfy the requirements of the space for human comfort conditions or for a particular manufacturing operation.

Ambient Air: The surrounding air, encompassing all sides.

Anemometer: A rotating-vane instrument for measuring air velocity.

Aspect Ratio, Rectangular Duct : For straight duct, the ratio of the $AR = \dfrac{W}{D}$ long side to the short side. For elbows, it is the ratio of the depth to the cheek width $AR = \dfrac{D}{W}$.

Attenuation Box: An airtight device that reduces the sound and pressure levels of conditioned air for distribution to a space.

Baffle: A sheet metal partition to deflect air flow.

Blow: The horizontal distance of an airstream from a supply outlet to a terminal velocity of 75 rpm at $6\frac{1}{2}$ feet above the floor.

Boot: a ratio size scoop installed in the airstream at the connection of a clinch-collar-branch to the main.

Branch: A duct connection to or from the main run.

Bypass: A path of air diverted around a system element.

Casing: An airtight sheet-metal enclosure which contains one or more pieces of apparatus of the air-handling-system.

Ceiling Diffuser: A ceiling outlet which distributes air in a desired pattern of planes.

Central Fan System: A system located in an equipment room for heating, ventilating, or air conditioning which distributes air through ducts to various parts of a building.

Cheek: The portion of a rectangular duct elbow in the plane of the turn.

Collar: A short section of duct which connects to another duct or piece of equipment.

Compound Offset: A duct fitting which changes its path in plan and ELEV (elevation), but remains parallel to the original line of the run.

Condensation: Liquid formed from a vapor by the extraction of heat.

Condenser: A chamber used to liquefy a gas.

Cooling Tower: An apparatus which cools water by evaporation to the outside air, to be used in the refrigeration cycle of an air conditioning system.

Coupling: A short collar which is used as a connection piece for round duct.

Curb: A concrete peripheral band, generally $4'' \times 4''$ or $6'' \times 6''$, used as a subbase of an apparatus casing.

Cuts: Detailed DWGS (drawings) of related equipment in air-handling systems.

Damper: A device of one or more blades used to control the volume of air in a duct system.

Datum: A fixed plane from which heights in a building are measured.

Developed Length: The true length of a duct along its centerline.

Direct Expansion: An air conditioning system that uses a cooling coil (evaporator), wherein the refrigerant is used as the medium of heat transfer.

Direct Fired Unit: A device in which air passes over a heat exchanger of metal plates, which were heated by the flame itself.

Drawband: Flat bar, or metal strips, with bolted ends, which are used to make airtight connections on round objects.

Electrolytic CONN (Connection) : A duct connection of dissimilar metals separated by a gasket of non-conducting material to prevent premature corrosion.

Equivalent Length : The linear feet of ST (straight) duct of a DIA (diameter) offering the same resistance to flow as a particular fitting or piece of apparatus in an air-handling system.

Evaporator : The part of a cooling system in which the refrigerant liquid is vaporized, such as a direct expansion coil, or the shell and tube chilled water section.

Exhaust Air: Air that is expelled from a building.

Filter: A device that removes impurities from the air.

Fire Damper: A damper in a duct system normally held open by a fusible link which melts at a preset temperature and thence allows the damper blades to close by gravity.

Fitting: A duct section that changes position or size from one end to the other.

Flexible Conduit: A factory made nonrigid round duct generally used for connections to terminal boxes in HP (high pressure) systems.

Flexible CONN (Connection): Canvas, asbestos, or neoprene connections to and from vibration isolated equipment.

Free Area: Actual, net clear space for air pressure.

Fusible Link: A connection joined by metal of a low melting point for use in fire dampers.

Gooseneck: An air inlet or air discharge fitting on the exterior of a BLDG (building). The OPNG (opening) is at an acute angle to the horizontal, so as to prevent the entry of snow or rain.

Grille: A decorative or functional open-type cover for an air outlet or inlet.

Head: A sheet metal closure for the end of a branch or main, usually a recessed pan type on rectangular ducts.

Heel: The outside, long portion of an elbow at RT (right angle) to the radius of the turn.

Humidifier: A device to place additional moisture into an airstream.

Inch of Water: A pressure equivalent in a duct system which would raise a column of 62°F water 1in high, or equal to 5.197 lbs/ft^2.

Induction: The movement of ambient air caused by the velocity of the primary air outlet.

Inertia Base: A concrete base of approximately three (3) times the weight of an object supported and mounted on floating spring type VE (vibration eliminators).

Infiltration : Air leakage into a building.

Insert: A hanging device placed onto a slab deck form prior to the concrete pour.

Insulation (Thermal): A material used to retard the flow of heat.

Joggle: Two opposite bends, each less than 90°, in a sheet of metal surfaces parallel.

Joint: A straight section of duct with the same opening on both ends.

Knocked Down: Sheet metal parts that will be assembled on the job.

Lateral: A round duct fitting with the branch at less than 90° to the line of the run.

Linear Diffuser: A long, narrow, supply-air ceiling outlet

Lining: An interior duct covering for thermal and acoustical valves.

Louver: A wall type air intake or discharge of horizontal, angular metal slats spaced in a parallel overlapping arrangement to exclude rain and snow.

Louver Damper: A volume control of parallel multiple blades.

Make-up Air: Outside air brought into a building to replenish the volume discharged by an exhaust system.

Mixing Box: An airtight device supplied by a hot-air duct and a cold air duct. A thermostat actuates proportioning dampers which mix the air in the box to the required temperature and thence distribute it to the space.

Moisture Eliminators: An arrangement of a series of vertical angular metal slats formed with edges to divert the saturated air leaving the cooling coils so that water droplets impinge on the slats and drain into a base pan.

Multiple Elbow: A rectangular duct elbow with connections at equally spaced degree angles, the sum of which is the degree of the elbow.

Offset: A fitting or fittings which change the location of the duct in plan or elevation with the line of the run parallel to the original.

Pitot Tube: An instrument consisting of two tubes, one within the other, for air pressure measurements in duct systems.

Plenum: An air space or enclosure containing a pressure other than ambient.

Quadrant DMPR (Damper): A manual damper with a device to position the damper from fully closed to fully open.

Radius of Diffusion: Distance in feet, from the centerline of a ceiling diffuser which is safely served with air motion.

Recirculated Air: Air that has been supplied to a space and thence returned to the equipment for redistribution.

Recovery EL (elbow): A round pipe elbow, that repositions a branch duct from a rotated lateral to a level plane.

Reducer: A duct fitting with a cross section area larger on one end than on the other.

Register: A decorative or functional open-type cover for an air outlet or inlet with an internal damper for volume adjustments.

Return Air: Air that has circulated in a treated space and shall flow back to the air-handling apparatus.

Riser: Vertical ducts for a distance of more than one floor.

Rotate: The turn of a round duct FTG (fitting) to change the centerline elevation of the run, or branch.

Run: A continuous line of duct joints and fittings in a fairly straight path.

Safing: Metal filler pieces fitted along the perimeter of filters, coils, and other equipment to prevent passage of bypass air.

Set: See *Offset.*

Sleeve: A metal form which provides a clear opening in a concrete pour for a duct or pipe.

Solid: A flush-type sheet metal closure for the end of a branch or main duct.

Sound Absorber: A device which reduces the sound level of airflow in a duct.

Spiral Pipe: Straight sections of round duct formed from continuous strip metal drawn through a machine and lock seamed into a helix.

Split System: A combination system of air ducts and hot water or steam perimeter radiation.

Splitter: A hinged sheet of metal to divert air into a branch duct as required.

Static Pressure: In a duct, air pressure that exerts itself in all directions.

Superstructure: That portion of an arrangement for suspended equipment which supports the hangers.

Supply Air: Air that has passed through the apparatus and shall be distributed to the space.

Teardrop: A streamlined, airtight cover for a foreign object in the airstream of a duct system.

Tee: A branch connection 90° to the main.

Telescoping Collars: Two short duct sections that fit snugly, one within the other, so as to allow adjustment for a finished alignment.

Throat: The inside, short portion of an elbow at RT (right angle) to the radius of the turn.

Throw: See *Blow.*

Total Pressure: The sum of static and velocity pressures in a duct system.

Transition: A duct FTG (fitting) that changes the size of cross section of one end to the other.

Trap Seal: A U-shape portion of pipe in which water remains to prevent the passage of air or gas.

Turning Vanes: A series of small radius blades evenly spaced along the diagonal, and parallel to the turn of a square throat, square heel elbow.

Velocity Pressure: In a duct system, the pressure exerted by air motion in the direction of flow.

Velometer: A direct reading air velocity instrument primarily used for testing and balancing.

Ventilation: The introduction, distribution, and movement of outside air in a building.

Volume: The 3-dimensional measurement of an object.

Warm Air Heating: An air system that satisfies comfort design requirements for a building or space during the heating season.

Wye: A Y-shaped FTG (fitting) at the end of a duct that splits into two branches at angles less than 90° to the run.

Zoning: A system that is controlled to maintain separate design conditions in different portions of a building.

A

Abbreviations scientific and engineering terms 18-8
Absorption split systems 13-4
AC motors 17-5
Acoustical problems
    air handling room 16-42
    apparatus casings 16-42
    dampers in duct 16-42
    fan isolation base 16-42
    flexible connectors 16-43
    high velocity system 16-40
Adiabatic mixing 3-3, 3-5
Air
    binding 15-41
    composition 2-1
    compressor 9-73
    discharge pipe capacities 9-78
    discharge through orifice 9-78
    flow control 12-27
    handling 14-1–14-96
    horsepower 14-1
    infiltration in fuel oil piping 12-18
    mixing streams 3-3
    pipe sizing 9-73
    piping pressure loss 9-72
    pressurization 15-64
    regulators 9-73
    removal from system 15-49
    supply outlets 14-56
    to air heat pumps 13-38
    to water heat pumps 13-40
    venting 15-52
Air conditioning process 3-1–3-8
    heating and cooling 3-1
Air conditioning system 13-1–13-116
    absorption split system 13-4
    air handler selection 13-49
    air handling apparatus 13-77
    air motion 13-14
    air systems 13-23, 13-30–13-34
    all-water systems 13-27
    apparatus casing 13-79
    apparatus floor area 13-77
    attic or crawl space 13-5
    automatic control 13-81
      cold air plenum 13-85
      cold deck control 13-82
      counter and parallel flow 13-98
      damper 13-88
      damper operation 13-88
      day cycle 13-88
      dual duct constant volume 13-94
      dual duct mixing box 13-93
      dual duct system 13-95
      dual duct variable volume 13-94
      economizer cycle 13-88
      face and bypass control 13-94–13-95
      freeze prevention 13-97
      hot deck control 13-84
      hot plenum 13-85
      hot water 13-90
      hot water converter 13-94
      hot water pressure 13-92
      hot water reheat 13-92–13-94
      hot water system 13-91
      mixed air 13-85
      mixed air control 13-88
      mixed air section 13-82
      mixing box control 13-94
      multizone unit 13-84
      night cycle 13-88
      night operation 13-89
      preheat control 13-91
      pressure control 13-94
      rooftop multizone units 13-81
      rotary air to air heat exchanger 13-95
      single duct variable volume 13-95
      summer cycle 13-88
      summer operation 13-95
      unit ventilator 13-88

Air conditioning system   (continued)
    automatic control
      variable speed control 13-95
    automatic control
      winter cycle 13-88
      winter operation 13-96
      winterizing chilled water system 13-97
      zone day-night operation 13-91
      zone mixing dampers 13-88
    backlash 13-79
    basic arrangement 13-69, 13-75
      ceiling plenum 13-70
      floor layouts 13-69
      office building 13-73
    carryover 13-79
    check lists 13-114
      air distribution 13-116
      drain facilities 13-115
      duct system 13-116
      electric power facilities 13-115
      heating load 13-115
      hot water heating supply 13-115
      refrigeration facilities 13-115
      sewer facilities 13-115
      steam supply facilities 13-115
      water facilities 13-115
    cold storage 13-58
    constant volume mixing unit 13-76
    construction details 13-80
    control 13-9, 13-26
    control panel location 13-9
    cooling considerations 13-20
    dehumidification 13-59
    direct solar heating 13-56
    double duct 13-9
    duct joints 13-80
    energy requirements 13-19
    equipment maintenance 13-108
    evaporative air conditioning 13-14–13-16
    fans 13-79
    furnace mounting 13-7
    heat pumps 13-36–13-44
    heat recovery 13-22–13-29
    heat recovery air system 13-30
    heat recovery water system 13-30
    heating and cooling calculations 13-19
    high velocity dual duct 13-60
      advantages 13-60
      air quantities 13-64
      cycles 13-60
      design factors 13-66
      design high pressure ducts 13-67
      design velocities 13-66
      double fan with dehumidifier 13-61
      large vs. small ducts 13-65
      low pressure ducts 13-68
      maximum velocity 13-66
      single fan with dehumidifier 13-60–13-61
      sizing 13-65
      system design 13-64, 13-68
    horizontal package units 13-1
    humidity control 13-10
    initial costs 13-18
    installation of equipment 13-107
    installations in roof 13-8
    installed costs 13-79
    insulation 13-79
    lighting heating cooling system 13-22
    location on roof 13-105–13-106
      advantages 13-105
      automatic control 13-105
      multiple units 13-105
      size of system 13-105
      ventilation 13-106
    machinery space 13-106
    maintenance 13-112
    multizone 13-8–13-9
    multizone units 13-4
    noise 13-79
    outdoor conditions 13-14
    overlapping 13-21
    refrigeration chassis 13-2
    remote condensers 13-2
    remote condensing units 13-3
    rooftop 13-6

Air conditioning system *(continued)*
  selection procedure 13-10
  services to equipment 13-107
  servicing of
    air handling system 13-107
    compresser oil 13-107
    condenser 13-107
    cooling plant 13-107
    refrigeration unit 13-108
    water system 13-107
  single package installations 13-5
  single package units 13-1
  single package year round units 13-2
  slab or ground level 13-6
  solar augmented heat pump 13-57
  solar energy 13-54
  solar heating description 13-54
  solar heating domestic water 13-56
  solar heating operation 13-54
  solar heating storage tank 13-56
  sound lining 13-79
  split systems 13-7
  thermostat location 13-10
  utility off-peak cooling 13-57
  variable affecting costs 13-80
  variable volume system 13-17–13-21
  ventilation air 13-9
  vertical package units 13-1
  vibration 13-106
  wall condensing units 13-8
  well water 13-54
  well water precooling 13-55
  well water refrigerant condensing 13-55
  winter to summer tank transition 13-58
  year round remote units 13-3
  zoning 13-69
  zoning installation 13-8
Air distribution system 16-43
  dampers as a noise generating source 16-46
  dual duct area ratio 16-45
  duct connectors 16-44
  duct design method 16-43
  duct in machine room 16-43
  duct off fittings 16-45
  duct velocity 16-43
  flutter in dual duct mixing units 16-47
  grilles, registers and diffusers 16-48
  high velocity ductwork 16-44, 16-46
  inlets to high velocity terminal points 16-47
  large terminal units 16-48
  noise in flexible connections 16-46
  sound barrier for high velocity ductwork 16-46
  sound traps 16-46
  terminal devices 16-47
  testing of high pressure ductwork 16-47
  two motor dual duct units 16-47
  warm connections 16-47
Air filters 9-73, 14-78
  characteristics 14-80
  dry filters 14-78
  electronic air cleaner 14-79
  selection 14-79
  viscous impingement 14-78
Air handling units
  trap 15-112–15-116
Air space thermal resistance 5-19
Air volume
  humidifying or dehumidifying 14-74
  required 14-75
  sensible heating or cooling 14-74
Airborne noise through ducts 16-13
Aircraft air heater 15-83
ANSI Standard abbreviations 18-8
Apothecaries
  fluid measure 20-2
  weight 20-2
Apparatus casing 13-79
Apparatus casing construction 14-77
Application range 14-2
Atmospheric pressure 20-2
Attenuation 16-1
Automatic control 13-81
  cold air plenum 13-85
  cold deck control 13-82

Automatic control *(continued)*
  counterflow and parallel flow 13-98
  damper 13-88
  damper operation 13-88
  day cycle 13-88
  dual duct constant volume 13-94
  dual duct mixing box 13-93
  dual duct system 13-95
  dual duct variable volume 13-94
  economizer cycle 13-88
  face and bypass control 13-94–13-95
  freeze prevention 13-97
  hot deck control 13-84
  hot plenum 13-85
  hot water 13-90
  hot water converter 13-94
  hot water pressure 13-92
  hot water reheat 13-92–13-94
  hot water system 13-91
  mixed air 13-85
  mixed air control 13-88
  mixing box 13-94
  multizone unit 13-84
  night cycle 13-88
  night operation 13-89
  preheat control 13-91
  pressure control 13-94
  rooftop multizone units 13-81
  rotary air to air heat exchanger 13-95
  single duct variable volume 13-95
  summer cycle 13-88
  summer operation 13-95
  unit ventilator 13-88
  variable speed control 13-95
  winter cycle 13-88
  winter operation 13-96
  winterizing chilled water system 13-97
  zone day night operation 13-91
  zone mixing dampers 13-88
Automatic control of dual duct system 13-95
Avoirdupois or commercial weight 20-2

B

Backlash 13-79
Balancing
  air flow 14-96
  and testing 14-99
  booster fan systems 14-98
  circuits 15-53
  duct distribution 14-98
Band pressure level 16-1
Bandwidth correction 16-6
Bare pipe radiation 15-34
Barrel liquid capacity 20-2
Below grade wall U-factors 6-3
Belts 13-114
Binary multiples 20-10
Blocked tight static pressure 14-2
Boiler
  cast iron 15-77
  cast iron radiators 15-78
  common return header 15-3
  connected load 15-73
  direct return connections 15-3–15-4
  draft loss 15-76
  drip end 15-7
  effect of load variation 15-70
  emergency protection 15-69
  furnace volume 15-73, 15-75
  gas fired 15-75
  grate area 15-73, 15-75
  hand fired 15-75
  Hartford connection 15-3
  heat emission 15-78
  heating surface 15-73
  heating value of coal 15-73
  hot water system 15-69
  mechanically fired steel boilers 15-74
  nameplate 15-75
  oil fired 15-74, 15-76
  overhead connections 15-4
  pipe sizing 15-71
  pipe, valves, and fittings 15-69

Boiler *(continued)*
    piping 15-15
    piping connections to boilers 15-1
    ratings 15-30, 15-73, 15-75–15-76
    return header drip 15-6
    return piping 15-6
    return trap 15-29
    stack dimensions 15-76
    steam header drip 15-6
    steam main drop 15-6
    steam main rise 15-6
    steam mains 15-6
    stoker fired 15-75
    supply and return piping 15-6
    supply header drip 15-6
    supply piping 15-6
    valve installation 15-69
    venting of piping 15-70
    welded joints 15-70
Boiler horsepower 12-31
Boiling point
    calcium chloride 15-81
    ethylene glycol 15-81
    glycerine 15-81
    glycol 15-81
    oil 15-82
    tetraanyl silicate 15-82
    tetracresyl silicate 15-81
Brake horsepower 14-2
Branch trunk duct losses 14-60
Breeching
    access 14-85
    aerodynamics 14-84
    construction 14-83, 14-85
    design 14-83
    design and construction 14-83
    expansion 14-83
British standard thermal units, (Btu) 20-7
Broadband noise 16-1
Building material resistances 5-17, 5-21–5-26
Built up roofing coefficient of transmission 5-14
Byte 20-10

C

Canning 15-30
Carat 20-2
Carnot cycle 1-4
Carryover 13-79
Cast iron radiators, capacity 15-79
Cavitation on pump 15-68
Ceiling
    by metal coefficient of transmissions 5-15
    by wood coefficient of transmissions 5-15
Centimeter-gram-second system of measurement 20-8
Cfm and scfm 14-1
Check valve 9-139–9-141
Cheese vats 15-31
Chimney
    draft 14-90
    sizing 14-94
    velocities 14-90
Circular mil gage for wires 20-1
Circulating pumps 15-66–15-67
    boilers 15-69
    cavitation effects 15-68
    construction 15-68
    for boiler 15-69
    net positive suction head 15-68
    seals 15-68
CLF
    hooded equipments 7-45–7-46
    people 7-44–7-45
    unhooded equipments 7-44
Climatic
    cooling design data 19-1
    data 19-1–19-38
    data applicability 19-1
    data characteristics 19-1
    design condition 19-1
    desumidification design data 19-1
    heating design data 19-1
    mean daily range 19-1
Closed system 1-2

Cloud point 12-15
CLTD
    conduction through glass 7-31
    multi family 7-49
    roofs 7-9
    single family 7-49
    walls 7-11
Code number
    thermal properties 7-27
    walls and roofs 7-27
Coefficient of performance 1-4, 1-6, 13-36
Coefficient of transmissions
    built up roofing 5-14
    ceiling by metal 5-15
    ceiling by wood 5-15
    flat masonry roof 5-14–5-15
    flat metal roof 5-15
    frame ceiling 5-14
    frame floor 5-14
    frame partitions 5-12
    frame walls 5-11–5-12
    masonry cavity walls 5-13
    masonry partitions 5-13
    masonry walls 5-11–5-12
    pitched roof 5-16
Cold air plenum 13-85
Cold deck control 13-82
Combustion 12-1–12-20
    air flow control 12-27
    air heater bypassing 12-17
    air infiltration in piping 12-18
    basics 12-1
    chemistry 12-1
    control errors 12-20
    control strategy 12-20
    draft control 12-24
    draft measurements 12-17
    efficiency 12-3
    efficiency losses 12-4
    energy losses 12-7
    excess air cost 12-3
    feedwater control 12-23
    firing rate 12-18
    flue gas 12-6
    flue gas recirculation 12-28
    fuel composition 12-1
    fuel oil 12-16
    fully metered control 12-22
    grate 12-16
    natural gas 12-15
    oxygen sensor 12-17
    oxygen trim 12-26
    parallel positioning 12-21
    radiation loss 12-5
    reaction 12-1
    safe burner set up 12-3
    short circuiting 12-16
    single pressure regulator 12-19
    stack losses 12-5
    theory 12-1
    tramp air 12-16
    troubleshooting 12-15, 12-17
    varying fuel flow 12-2
    varying oxygen content 12-2
    water in the fuel oil 12-18
    wet atomizing steam 12-18
Combustion control
    air considerations 12-12
    atomizing media 12-12
    cloud point 12-15
    considerations 12-11
    draft 12-13
    elevation 12-13
    firing considerations 12-14
    flashpoint 12-15
    flue gas considerations 12-13
    flue gas recirculation 12-14
    fuel oil firing considerations 12-14
    natural gas efficiency 12-8
    nitrogen content 12-15
    no. 2 oil efficiency 12-9
    no. 6 oil efficiency 12-10
    pour point 12-15
    pressure and flow basics 12-11
    saving fuel 12-7

Combustion control   *(continued)*
   sulfur content 12-15
   temperature 12-13
   viscosity considerations 12-14
Compressed air
   pipe sizing 9-73
   receiver 9-74
   system 9-72
   system testing 9-74
Compressed liquid 1-1
Compresssors 13-114
Concrete block 15-31
Concrete, ready mix 15-31
Condensate drains 14-77
Condensate return pump 15-29
Condenser 13-113
Condensing units in wall 13-8
Condensing water circuit 13-111, 13-113
Conduction 5-1
Connections
   heating units to risers 15-8
   mains to downfeed risers 15-8
   offset 15-9
   risers to heating unit 15-9
   runout 15-9
Conservation of energy 1-3, 3-1–3-3
   cooling and dehumidifing 3-2
Conservation of energy equations 3-1
Conservation of mass 1-3, 3-1–3-3
Conservation of mass equations 3-1
Continuity equation 1-6
Control valve sizing 9-142–9-143
Controls 13-9
   basic factors for designing 15-96
   bonnet air temperature 15-96
   continuous air circulation 15-94
   continuous blower circulation 15-95
   errors 12-20
   fan switch 15-94
   intermittent blower operation 15-95
   limit switch 15-94
   room thermostat 15-94
   strategies 12-20
   temperature drop of air in ducts 15-96
   thermostatics 15-94
   valve sizing 9-142
Convection 5-2
Convection coefficient 5-3
Convector piping details 15-4
Conversion
   fractional inch to millimeter 20-3
   millimeter to fractional inch 20-3
Cookers, coil 15-31
Cookers, jacketed 15-32
Cooling and dehumidification 3-2
Cooling and dehumidifing 3-2
Cooling load 5-33
Cooling load calculation 7-1
   CLF method 7-6–7-49
   CLTD method 7-6–7-49
   cooling coil load 7-1
   heat extraction rate 7-1
   heat gain 7-1
   heat source 7-1
   latent heat gain 7-1
   radiation heat gain 7-1
   residential 7-35
   SCL method 7-6–7-49
   sensible heat gain 7-1
   space cooling load 7-1
   thermal storage 7-1
   transfer function method 7-1
Cooling of fuel oil in atomizers 12-18
Cooling tower 13-99–13-105
   estimating data 13-101, 13-103
   natural draft 13-102
   tower height 13-103
   water requirements 13-104
   wet bulb temperature 13-103
   wind velocity 13-102
Cooling tower noise control 16-36
   configurations 16-38
   fan noise 16-36
   half speed operation 16-39

Cooling tower noise control   *(continued)*
   leaving condition changed 16-39
   location 16-39
   oversizing the tower 16-39
   reducing generated sound 16-39
   sound absorbers 16-40
   water noise 16-37
Cooling water 13-113
Cooling water system 13-112–13-113
Cooling, heat recovery 13-45
Counterflow and parallel flow 13-98
Cubic measure 20-1

D

Damper control 13-88
Damper operation 13-88
Dampers 13-113
Day cycle 13-88
Decibel 16-1
Degree days 11-1–11-8
Degree of saturation 2-2
Dehumidification 13-59
Demand load 9-28
Demand weights of fixtures 9-30
Density effects 14-4
Design lateral load 14-77
Dew point temperature 2-4
Direct fired unit heater 15-83
Distilleries 15-32
Domestic water, solar heating 13-56, 13-58
Double duct system 13-9
Draft
   burning coal 14-95
   control 12-24, 14-92
   foot of chimney 14-95
   measurements 12-17
Drip end 15-7
Dripping riser 15-12
Dry cleaning 15-32
Dry measure 20-2, 20-8
Dryers 15-32
Dual duct
   constant volume control 13-94
   mixing box control 13-93
   variable volume control 13-94
Duct
   box plenum system 15-88
   characteristics 15-88
   design 8-9
   design by computer 14-72
   design methods 8-12
   design procedures 8-13
   design velocities 8-11
   equal friction method 8-12
   equivalent lengths of fittings 15-105
   equivalent rectangular ducts 8-6
   extended plenum system 15-88
   fibrous glass construction 14-73
   fitting friction loss 8-14
   fitting loss coefficient
      bellmouth, plenum to round 8-24
      conical diffuser 8-26
      damper, butterfly 8-19
      elbow mitered 8-18
      elbow mitered with vane 8-18
      elbow with splitter vane 8-17
      elbow without vanes 8-17
      elbow Z shaped 8-19
      exhaust system 8-26
      fire damper 8-27
      return system 8-26
      round tap to rectangular main 8-25
      tee converging 8-26, 8-31, 8-33–8-34
      transition in rectangular 8-25
      transition rectangular to round 8-25
      transition round to rectangular 8-27
      transition round to round 8-26
      varaiable inlet outlet areas 8-24
      wye converging 8-36
      wye 30 degree converging 8-28
      wye, 45 degree 8-30, 8-32
   fitting loss coefficient tables 8-17–8-37
   flat and oval duct 8-5

Duct *(continued)*
    individual system 15-88
    rectangular 8-5
    resistance in low pressure ducts 8-15
    static regain method 8-13, 8-15
    trunk system 15-88
    turns 14-28
    vibration and noise 8-12
Duct design 8-1, 8-17
Duct design data
    diffuser, free discharge 8-21
    plenum to rectangular 8-21
    sudden contraction 8-21
    Tee type, diverging 8-23
    transition, rectangular to rectangular 8-22
    transition, round to rectangular 8-22
    wye type diverging 8-22
    45 degree entry branch 8-24
    90 degree elbow 8-21
Duct joints 13-80
Duct roughness 8-5
Ducts 13-113
    air balancing 14-52
    air distribution 14-56
    air flow 14-37, 14-53
    air quantities 13-64
    air supply outlets 14-56
    air turning hardware 14-52
    branches and discharges 14-51
    cycles 13-60
    degree of roughness 14-40
    density of air 14-39
    design air velocities 14-47
    design considerarion 8-9
    design velocities 8-12, 13-66
    double fan dual duct 13-61
    dynamic loss 8-7
    elbows 8-14
    energy equation 8-1
    equal friction method 8-14
    factors for design 13-66
    fan system interface 8-8
    fire and smoke management 8-9
    flexible ductwork 14-62
    four types 14-53
    friction chart 8-4–8-5
    friction losses 8-2, 14-40
    friction of air 14-41–14-44
    good turns 14-50
    high pressure ducts 13-67
    high velocity 13-60
    high velocity advantages 13-60
    high velocity design 14-71
    high velocity system 14-59
    insulation 8-9
    large vs. small in size 13-65
    local loss coefficients 8-7
    losses in rectangular elbows 14-46
    losses in round elbows 14-45
    losses in round fittings 14-45
    low pressure ducts 13-68
    maximum velocity 13-66
    noise control 8-12
    non circular 8-5
    pitot traverse 14-39–14-40
    pressure change in a system 8-8
    pressure head 8-1
    pressure losses 14-48–14-49, 14-61
    recommended velocities 8-11, 14-57
    rectangular and round equivalents 14-47
    rectangular shape 14-40
    return air ducts 13-68
    return air plenums 14-54
    roughness factors 8-2
    roughness values 8-5
    sectional losses 8-7
    single fan dual duct 13-60–13-61
    sizing 13-65
    static pressure 14-37, 14-66
    static pressure loss 14-60
    static regain 14-59, 14-63, 14-65
    system design 13-64, 14-56
    system leakage 8-11
    tap off fitting 14-62

Ducts *(continued)*
    testing and balancing 8-12
    turns 14-51
    velocity 14-37
    velocity pressure 14-37–14-38
Dust collectors 14-78–14-79
    dry centrifugal types 14-82
    electrostatic precipitators 14-83
    fabric collectors 14-82
    wet collectors 14-82

E

Economizer control cycle 13-88
Emissivities 5-4
Energy 1-2
    internal 1-2
    kinetic 1-2
    potential 1-2
    thermal 1-2
Energy equation 8-1
Energy esimation
    base temperature 11-1
    degree days 11-1–11-8
        abroad 11-8
        application 11-2
        different bases 11-9–11-20
        U.S. cities 11-9–11-20
    empirical constants 11-7
    fuel consumption 11-4
    future demands 11-5
    guide of operation 11-2
    limitations 11-7
    load factors 11-7
    operational hours 11-7
    65 deg, as base 11-1
Enthalpy 1-1, 2-4
Entropy 1-1
Equation of state 2-1
Equipment arrangement 13-44
Equipment losses 14-60
Equipment maintenance 13-108
    air distribution 13-108
    air handling 13-108
    central system schedule 13-111
    cooling 13-108
    schedule 13-110–13-111
    water using 13-108
Equivalent direct radiation 15-1
Equivalent length of elbow 9-2
Erosion 9-3
Ethylene glycol 15-81
Evaporative air conditioning 13-14–13-16
    air motion 13-14
    outdoor conditions 13-14
Evaporative condensers 13-113
Exbi 20-10
Excess air 12-3
Excess air measurement 12-6
Exhaust air heat recovery 13-31
Expansion conditions 15-65
Expansion joints 15-9
Expansion loops 15-9
    swing type 15-10
Expansion of piping 9-134–9-135
Expansion tank 15-65
    sizing 15-53, 15-65
Expansion valves 13-112
Extrinsic property 1-1

F

Face and bypass control 13-94–13-95
Fan 13-79
    acoustic properties 16-21
    air entry position 14-20
    axial fan 14-16
    backward inclined fan 14-14
    blade pitch variation 14-31
    class limits 14-16
    coil unit 13-48
    comparison 14-36
    discharge connections 14-27

Fan   (continued)
  discharge dampers 14-30
  double inlet 14-27
  flywheel effect 14-36
  formulas 14-31
  forward curve centrifugal fan 14-14
  horsepower and actual capacity 14-32
  inlet connections 14-26
  inlet dampers 14-29
  inlet effects 14-23
  inlet vanes 14-30
  laws 14-3
  noise generation 16-23
  operating limit 14-18–14-19
  operating point 14-11
  paralleling 14-11
  performance curve 14-11
  performance data 14-36
  performance modulation 14-29
  radial blade fans 14-15
  scroll volume control 14-29
  selection 14-21, 14-34
  single inlet 14-27
  size change 14-3
  speed modulation 14-31
  static pressure 14-1
  surge 14-11
  system resistance curve 14-11
  system surge 14-11
  terminology 14-1
  total pressure 14-1
  tubular centfifugal fan 14-15
  types 14-14
  velocity pressure 14-1
Feed mills 15-33
Feedwater control 12-23
Filling pressure 15-53
Filters 13-113
Filters and ducts 13-112–13-113
Fin efficiency 1-16
Fin tube piping 15-4
Fins and extended surfaces 1-15
Fire dampers 14-56
Fire protection 14-56
Fire protection equipments 9-143
Firing rate 12-18
First law of thermodynamics 1-3
Fixture units with demand 9-28
Fixtures demand weights 9-30
Flash point 12-15
Flash steam
  calculations 15-39
  condensate quantity 15-44–15-45
  quantities 15-43
Flash tank
  capacities 15-42
  dimension 15-39, 15-45
  sizing 15-40
Flash trap 15-29
Flat masonry roof coefficient of transmission 5-14
Flat roof by metal coefficient of transmission 5-15
Flat roof by wood coefficient of transmission 5-15
Float trap 15-27–15-28
Floor furnace 15-83
Flow meter piping 12-31–12-32
Flowwork 1-2
Flue gas composition 12-6
Flue gas recirculation 12-28
Flush valve capacity 9-30
Forced convection 1-12
Forced draft 14-92
Fractional inch to millimeter conversion 20-3
Frame ceiling coefficient of transmissions 5-14
Frame floor coefficient of transmissions 5-14
Frame partitions coefficient of transmissions 5-12
Frame walls coefficient of transmissions 5-11–5-12
Free delivery 14-2
Freeze prevention 10-19, 13-97
Freeze up protection 15-16
Freezing point
  calcium chloride 15-81
  glycerine 15-81
  glycol 15-81
  oil 15-82

Freezing point   (continued)
  tetra anyl silicate 15-82
  tetra cresyl silicate 15-81
French thermal unit 20-7
Friction
  chart 1-9, 15-47–15-48
  chart, duct 8-4
  hot water piping 15-46
  rate 15-23
Friction loss 1-9, 8-2
  copper piping 9-5
  equivalent length of elbow 9-2
  flanged pipe fitting loss 9-2
  K factors 9-2
  plastic piping 9-5
  screwed pipe fitting loss 9-2
  steel piping 9-5
  tee fitting 9-6
  valve and fitting equivalents 9-7–9-27
  valve and fitting loss 9-6
Fuel composition 12-1
Fuel consumption degree days 11-4
Fuel oil 12-16
Fuel oil handling 12-33
  alarm signals 12-39
  automatic pump alternation 12-38
  automatic start-stop system 12-38
  automatic valves 12-38
  back-up pump operation 12-38
  burner loop system 12-34
  continuous operation 12-38
  day tank 12-33
  entrained air 12-37
  flow rate 12-33
  gravity head 12-36
  intermittent operation 12-38
  maximum inlet pressure 12-36
  multiple day tank 12-33
  multiple pump 12-34
  piping system 12-37
  pump controls 12-37
  pump discharge pressure requirements 12-37
  required capacity 12-36
  safety shutdown 12-39
  standby generator application 12-33
  standby generator loop systems 12-34
  strainer pressure drop 12-36
  suction line losses 12-36
  tank overflow 12-37
  tank venting 12-37
Fully metered control 12-22
Furnace mounting 13-7
Future needs degree days 11-5

G

Gallons into cubic inches 20-2
Gas laws 2-1
Gas piping 9-59–9-72
  capacities 9-59
  pressure loss 9-63–9-70
  residential 9-59
  sizes for residential 9-59
  solution 9-62
  tables 9-62
Gas pressurization 15-64
Gas properties 2-1, 12-1
Gate valve 9-139–9-141
Gibi 20-10
Globe valve 9-139–9-141
Ground level installations 13-6
Ground source heat pumps 13-41

H

Hanger spacings 15-16
Heat 1-2
  coefficients of transmission 5-27
  exchanger 1-18
  mechanical equivalent 20-7
  quantity measurement 20-7
  scales 20-7
  storage 15-63

Heat (continued)
    thermal energy 20-7
    transfer 1-11
Heat anticipators 13-43
Heat emission
    bare radiators 15-79
    bathroom radiators 15-80
    enclosure effects 15-78
    front wall radiators 15-80
    pipe coils 15-80
    propeller unit capacities 15-80
    radiator finish 15-78
    ultra slender tubular 15-80
    unenclosed ratiators 15-79
    unit ventilators 15-80
    wall radiators 15-80
Heat gain
    computer equipment 7-6
    cooking appliances 7-3–7-5
    copier 7-6
    laboratory equipment 7-6
    laser printer 7-6
    medical equipment 7-6
    occupants 7-2
    office equipment 7-6
Heat load
    coefficients F2 6-4
    floor slab 6-5
    infiltration 6-6
    ventilation 6-6
Heat loss
    bare pipe 9-146–9-156
    coefficient 9-158
    cold surface temperature 9-158
    heat conductivity 9-158
    in piping 9-144
    insulated pipe 9-157, 9-159–9-176
Heat pumps
    air to air 13-38
    air to water 13-40
    coefficient of performance 13-36
    electrohydronic heat recovery 13-44
    equipment arrangement 13-44
    fan coil units 13-48
    ground source 13-41
    heat anticipators 13-43
    heating performance factor 13-37
    installation factors 13-42
    operating factors 13-42
    optimized data 13-47–13-48
    outdoor temperature effects 13-42
    performance factor 13-37
    reverse cycle principle 13-36
    sources 13-41
    thermostats 13-43
    types 13-37
    water to air 13-40
    water to water 13-39
Heat recovery 13-22–13-29, 13-44
    air systems 13-23, 13-30–13-34
    all water systems 13-27
    control 13-26
    cooling cycle 13-45
    supplementary heat 13-47
    system design 13-47
    temperature limit 13-45
Heat transfer coefficient 1-12
    combined network 5-9
    parallel network 5-8
    series network 5-6
Heating and cooling media 15-81
    brine 15-81
    calcium chloride 15-81
    ethylene glycol 15-81
    glycerine 15-81
    glycol 15-81
    oil 15-82
    tetraanyl silicate 15-82
    tetracresyl silicate 15-81
Heating and humidification 3-3
Heating load 5-33, 6-1
    floors 6-1
    infiltration 6-1
    roofs 6-1

Heating load (continued)
    ventilation 6-1
    walls 6-1
    walls below grade 6-2
    windows 6-1
Heating of fuel oil in atomizers 12-18
Heating performance factor 13-37
Heating system
    cast iron radiators 15-79
    enclosure effects 15-78
    forced air system 15-127
    gravity circulation 15-128
    hot water heater 15-124–15-125
    radiator emission 15-78
    steam or vapor 15-126–15-127
Henry's constant 10-4
Horsepower
    electric motor ratings 17-1–17-2, 17-4
Hot deck control 13-84
Hot plenum control 13-85
Hot water control 13-90
Hot water heating system 15-49
    affecting conditions 15-60
    affecting design conditions 15-60
    air pressurization 15-64
    air removal 15-49
    air venting 15-52
    balancing circuits 15-53
    boiler emergency protection 15-69
    boiler recirculating pump 15-69
    boilers 15-69
    branch pipe sizing 15-59
    cavitation effects 15-68
    checking pipe size 15-58
    circulating pumps 15-66–15-67
    combination piping system 15-60
    compare with steam 15-63
    compressed air 15-54
    district steam 15-50
    effect of load variation 15-70
    expansion conditions 15-65
    expansion tank sizing 15-53
    expansion tanks 15-60–15-61
    filling pressure 15-53
    gas pressurization 15-64
    generator 15-6
    heat storage 15-63
    high temperature drop 15-63
    HTW for process steam 15-66
    main pipe sizing 15-59
    net positive suction head 15-68
    nitrogen pressurization 15-64
    nitrogen pressurizing tank 15-66
    one pipe diversion 15-50
    one pipe diversion system 15-59
    one pipe series 15-50, 15-60
    operating water 15-49
    pipe size check 15-59
    pipe sizing 15-71
    pipe, valves and fittings 15-69
    piping design 15-55
    piping details 15-54
    pressure drop in fittings 15-56–15-57
    pressure limitation 15-49
    pressurization of HTW system 15-63
    preventing backflow 15-53
    prevention of freezing 15-49
    pump construction 15-68
    pump location 15-52–15-53
    pump specifications 15-67
    reduce tank size 15-54
    seals 15-68
    service water 15-49
    steam pressurization 15-63
    steam pressurizing tank 15-65
    summer cooling 15-50
    system adaptability 15-50
    temperature 15-61
    two pipe direct return 15-50
    two pipe direct reverse 15-58
    two pipe return reverse 15-58
    two pipe reversed return 15-52
    types 15-50
    valve installation 15-69
    venting of piping 15-70

Hot water heating system   *(continued)*
    waste steam heat 15-50
    water circulation below mains 15-49
    water velocity 15-52
    welded joints 15-70
Hot water pressure control 13-92
Hot water reheat control 13-92–13-94
Hot water reheat converter 13-94
Hot water system 13-91
HTW for process steam 15-66
Humidity control 13-10
Humidity ratio 2-2
Hydronic
    close expansion tank 10-7
    cooling 10-1
    design layout 10-18
    diaphragm tank 10-7
    equipment layout 10-18
    freeze prevention 10-19
    heating 10-1
    medium temperature 10-1
    open expansion tank 10-7
    pipe sizing 10-18
    piping layout 10-19
    pressure drop 10-19
    pump selection 10-19
    temperature classification 10-1

I

Ideal gas 2-1
Impulse trap 15-29
Indoor air quality 4-1
    air filter types 4-8
    carbon media filters 4-10
    fiber foam filters 4-10
    HEPA filters 4-10
    outdoor air requirements 4-7
    ozone 4-10
    pollutants and sources 4-5
    pollutants concentration 4-1, 4-5
    procedure 4-6
    standards 4-5
    ultraviolet light 4-10
    ventilation procedure 4-1
    ventilation rates 4-2
Industrial unit heater piping 15-5
Infiltration heat loss 6-6
Installation in attic 13-5
Installation in crawl space 13-5
Installation of equipment 13-107
Insulation 13-79
    prevent sweating 9-177
Internal heat
    air systems 13-30
    exhaust air heat recovery 13-31
    refrigeration heat 13-31
    refrigeration service 13-31
    water systems 13-30
Intrinsic property 1-1
Inverted bucket trap 15-29
Isolation efficiency 16-10

K

Kibi 20-10
Kilns 15-34

L

Laundries 15-34
Layout plan of piping 9-132
Lead lag control 12-28
Leaking glands 13-112
Length, measures 20-1, 20-8
Lifting trap 15-29
Lighting heating cooling system 13-22
Liquid, measure 20-2, 20-8
LMTD method 1-19
Load estimating 5-1
Lubricants, electric motors 17-39
Lubrication of motors 17-39

M

Machinery space 13-106
Masonery walls coefficient of transmissions 5-12
Masonry partitions coefficient of transmissions 5-13
Masonry walls coefficient of transmissions 5-11
Mebi 20-10
Mechanical efficiency 14-2
Mechanical equivalent of heat 20-7
Metric International System of Units 20-9
Microinch 20-1
Mil 20-1
Minimum deflections 16-9
Minimum elevation in drip traps 15-7
Mixed air control 13-85, 13-88
Mixed air section 13-82
Mixing air streams 3-3
Mixing box control 13-94
Moist air properties 2-6–2-7, 2-18
Moisture 13-112
Moody's friction chart 1-9
Mortar mixes 14-77
Motors
    acceleration time 17-9
    analysis of application 17-18
    application 17-17
    application data 17-14
    bearings 17-20
    capacitor 17-13
    capacitor run 17-28–17-29
    capacitor start 17-28
    classification by cooling 17-3
    classifications 17-1
        application 17-1
        electrical type 17-1
        size 17-1
    compressors 17-18, 17-25
    constant hp 17-21–17-22
    constant torque 17-21
    current relay 17-27
    DC types 17-7
    design letters 17-1–17-2
    dynamic loads 17-8
    dynamics 17-11
    dynamics of load 17-10
    enclosure 17-19
    fans and blowers 17-18
    full load currents 17-6–17-7
    heating 17-8, 17-11
    heating during starting 17-12
    hermetic compressor 17-25
    hermetic type 17-25
    hot wire relay 17-27
    hp and full load currents 17-6–17-7
    hp and speed ratings 17-4
    hp ratings 17-14
    induction run motor 17-27
    inertia 17-9
    internal line break 17-27
    life 17-11
    loading 17-17
    locked rotor current 17-2
    locked rotor current and torque ratings 17-1
    locked rotor kva 17-5
    locked rotor torque 17-5
    multispeed operation 17-17
    NEC code 17-6
    oil burners 17-18
    open machine 17-3
    overload with capacitor start 17-27
    permanent split capacitor 17-27
    polyphase 17-19
    polyphase induction motor 17-23
    protection 17-18
    quietness 17-20
    repulsion induction 17-15
    repulsion start 17-13
    selections 17-18
    shaded pole 17-13
    single phase 17-12, 17-15
    speed control 17-21
    speed data 17-14

Motors   *(continued)*
    squirrel cage induction 17-20–17-21
    sump pump 17-18
    synchronous speed 17-24
    three phase 17-6, 17-28
    torque and speed 17-2
    torques 17-9–17-10, 17-14
    two phase 17-7
    types 17-12, 17-14, 17-21
    variable speed 17-24
    variable torque 17-22–17-23
    voltage and frequencies 17-3
    wiring diagram 17-22
Motors and starters 17-1
Motors, electric
    armature rotors 17-40
    ball or roller bearings 17-39
    brushes 17-39
    commutators 17-39
    inspection schedule 17-39–17-40
    lubrication, proper 17-39
    maintaining and repairing 17-39–17-40
    maintenance 17-39
    mechanical condition 17-39
    monthly inspection 17-40
    rotors and armatures 17-40
    squirrel cage rotors 17-40
    weekly inspection 17-39
    windings 17-40
Mount types 16-12
Multizone system 13-9
Multizone unit control 13-84
Multizone units 13-4

N

National Electric Code (NEC) 17-6
Natural attenuation in ducts 16-24
Natural convection 1-12
Natural gas 12-15
Nautical measure 20-1
Net positive suction head 10-11, 15-68
Night cycle 13-88
Night operation 13-89
Nitrogen content 12-15
Nitrogen pressurization 15-64
Nitrogen pressurizing tank 15-66
Noise and vibration 16-1–16-50
    addition of decibels 16-14
    air flow noise 16-27
    airborne noise through ducts 16-13
    attenuation 16-1
    attenuation of a lined duct 16-25
    band pressure level 16-1
    bandwidth correction factor 16-6
    broadband noise 16-1
    calculation of sound levels 16-14
    condenser water and chilled water piping 16-13
    continuous noise 16-1
    cooling tower location 16-39
    cooling tower noise control 16-36
    cooling waters 16-13
    decibel 16-1, 16-14
    drive components 16-37
    duct lining and elbows 16-26
    duct lining attenuation 16-24
    ducted system 16-20
    equipment room and critical spaces 16-7
    external noise source 16-37
    fan acoustic properties 16-21
    fan noise 16-36
    fan noise estimation 16-23
    fan noise generation 16-23
    flow noise by silencers 16-31
    frequency 16-1
    frequency limits for octave bands 16-15
    insertion loss 16-1
    isolation efficiency 16-10
    microbar 16-1
    minimum mounting deflections 16-9
    mount types 16-12
    natural attenuation 16-24
    noise criteria 16-2–16-3

Noise and vibration   *(continued)*
    octave band 16-1, 16-7, 16-15
    octave bandwidth correction 16-30
    open end reflection loss 16-27
    pitch 16-1
    ratings and standards 16-7
    regenerated noise 16-13
    sabin 16-15
    sound
        absorption coefficients 16-16
        attenuation 16-10, 16-27
        attenuation of plenums 16-25
        level of sources 16-2
        power allotment at branch 16-24
        power distribution in branch 16-24
        power level 16-23–16-24
        pressure level 16-1, 16-17
        transmission 16-7
    speech interference criteria 16-2
    steam pressure reducing valves 16-13
    transformers 16-13
    vibration isolation 16-7
    water noise 16-37
Noise criteria 16-2–16-3
    chart 16-20
Noise from fluid flow 1-11
Noise generation 9-3
Noise in ducted system 16-20
Noise on ducts 13-79

O

Off-peak space cooling 13-57
Open system 1-2
Operating water temperature 15-49
Optimized data equations 13-48
Optimized data for heat pump 13-47
Outdoor air load 5-32
Outdoor air requirements 4-4
Outdoor temperature effects 13-42
Oxygen sensor 12-17
Oxygen trim 12-26

P

Paper corrugators 15-35
Parallel positioning 12-21
Partial vapor pressure 2-3
Pebi 20-10
Performance factor 13-37
Pipe
    allowable spaces 9-134
    expansion 9-134
    layout plan 9-132
    layout plan length 9-133
Pipe fittings 9-97–9-129
    dimensions 9-97, 9-129
    taper pipe thread 9-97–9-129
Pipe sizing 9-1
    pressure drop 9-1
    valve and fitting loss 9-1–9-58
Piping
    allowances for aging 9-3
    anchor 15-10
    application 15-26
    around door 15-10
    around obstacle 15-10
    boiler 15-15
    capacities, high pressure 15-21
    capacities, low pressure 15-23
    capacities, medium pressure 15-21
    carrying capacity 9-80–9-90
    closed system 9-4
    color identification 9-143
    contraction 15-11
    corrosion resistance 9-136
        metal 9-138
    design 15-17
    dimensional capacities 9-80–9-90
    dimensions 9-80–9-90
    dripping riser 15-12
    dripping steam main 15-13
    erosion 9-3

Piping   (continued)
    expansion 15-11
    flush valve 9-30
    hydronic system 9-4
    identification method 9-144
    lifting condensate 15-14
    material, protective 9-143–9-144
    materials 9-4
    multiple coils 15-14
    noise 9-4
    noise generation 9-3
    obstructions 15-12
    one pipe system 15-17
    plastic material 9-29
    recessed below floor 15-10
    reducing main 15-10
    single coils 15-13
    sizing 15-18, 15-20
    steam bypass control 15-14
    steam flow 9-31
    steam riser 15-10
    supports 15-16
    thickness 9-80–9-90
    two pipe high pressure system 15-18
    two pipe low pressure system 15-19
    two pipe medium pressure system 15-19
    two pipe system 15-17
    two pipe vacuum system 15-23
    underwater corrosion 9-136
    vacuum lift 15-12
    water 9-3
    water hammer 9-4
Piping design
    checking 15-59
    checking pipe size 15-58
    combination system 15-60
    for branches 15-59
    for main 15-59
    one pipe diversion system 15-59
    one pipe series 15-60
    two pipe direct return system 15-58
    two pipe reversed return system 15-58
Piping identification 9-143
Plant master control 12-28
Plastic piping 9-29, 9-91–9-93
    above ground 9-93
    above ground installation 9-96
    below ground 9-93
    below ground installation 9-96
    chemical resistance 9-94
    codes and regulations 9-97
    design parameters 9-93
    elastomeric seals 9-91
    flanges 9-93
    flaring 9-93
    flow characteristics 9-94
    heat fusion 9-91
    insert fitting 9-93
    installation 9-96
    joining technique 9-91
    mechanical couplings 9-91
    pressure loss 9-92
    pressure ratings 9-94–9-96
    solvent cementing 9-91
    standards and identifications 9-93
    storage handling 9-96
    thermal expansion coefficients 9-93
    threading 9-93
    types 9-91
Plumbing water piping 9-28
Pneumatic pipe sizing 9-73
Pneumatic piping 9-72
Pour point 12-15
Prandtl number 1-12
Preheat control 13-91
Pressure control 13-94
Pressure drop 9-1
    air in pipe 9-75–9-77
    air piping 9-72
    gas piping 9-63–9-70
    in fittings 15-56–15-57
    liquids 9-79
    return piping 15-23
    supply piping 15-23
    vertical piping 9-32

Pressure head 8-1
Pressure loss
    disk type water meter 9-28
    plastic piping 9-92
Pressure ratings, plastic piping 9-94–9-96
Pressure required in fixtures 9-6
Pressure unit conversion 20-2
Pressurization of hot water system 15-63
Preventing backflow 15-53
Prevention of freezing 15-49
Process 1-3
Propeller unit heat capacities 15-80
Properties of gas 12-1
Property 1-1, 1-3
Psychrometric analysis 2-1
Psychrometric chart 2-8
Psychrometry 2-1
    air composition 2-1
    degree of saturation 2-2
    dew point temperature 2-4
    enthalpy 2-4
    graphical presentation 2-7
    humidity ratio 2-2
    ideal gas 2-1
    moist air properties 2-6, 2-18
    relative humidity 2-2
    saturation 2-4
    vapor pressure 2-3
    water properties 2-12
    wet bulb temperature 2-2, 2-5
Pump
    centrifugal 10-8
    change of performance 10-9
    condensate return 15-29
    construction 15-68
    location 15-52
    net positive suction head 10-11
    operating chsracteristics 10-8
    specifications 15-67
    vacuum 15-30
Pumping down 13-112
Pure substance 1-1
Purging system 13-112

Q

Quality of steam 1-1

R

Radiator capacity 15-79
Radiator emission 15-78
Rankine degrees 20-7
Ratings and standards 16-7
Ratings of boilers 15-73
Ream, paper 20-3
Refrigerant circuit 13-112
Refrigerant controls 13-112
Refrigerant effect 1-4, 1-6
Refrigerant storage in drums 13-112
Refrigeration chassis 13-2
Regenerated noise 16-13
Register 15-89
    capacity 15-101, 15-103–15-104
    loudness 15-106
    pressure loss 15-101, 15-103–15-104
Reheat system 13-9
Relation of air with temperature 14-8, 14-10
Relative humidity 2-2
Remote condensers 13-2
Remote condensing units 13-3
Replacing refrigerant 13-112
Residential cooling load calculation 7-35
Resistance of building materials 5-17, 5-21–5-26
Return intake
    capacity 15-105
    pressure loss 15-105
Reverse cycle principle 13-36
Reversibility 1-4
Reynolds number 1-7
    laminar flow 1-8
    turbulent flow 1-7
Riser drip 15-8

Roof as a location for AC system 13-105–13-106
  advantages 13-105
  automatic control 13-105
  multiple units 13-105
  size 13-105
  ventilation 13-106
Roof numbers 7-8
Roof top installation 13-6
Roof'top multizone units 13-81
Rotary air to air heat exchanger control 13-95
Rotating apparatus 13-114
Rotors
  heating during starting 17-12
  wound 17-23
Roughness factors 8-2
RPM change 14-3

S

Sabin 16-15
Saturated liquid 1-1
Saturated vapor 1-1
Saturation 2-4
SC for glass 7-50
SCL for glasses 7-36
Second law of thermodynamics 1-4
Selecting air handler units 13-49
Service water heating system 15-49
Servicing of
  air handling system 13-107
  compresser oil 13-107
  cooling plant 13-107
  refrigeration unit 13-108
  water system 13-107
Shear stress 1-6
Shipping measure 20-1
Short circuiting 12-16
Signs and abbreviations
  scientific and engineering 18-8
Simple heating and cooling 3-1
Single degree freedom vibration isolation 16-7
Single duct variable volume control 13-95
Single package installations 13-5
Single package units 13-1
Single package year round units 13-2
Single phase induction motors 17-2, 17-4–17-5
Single phase motors 17-12
Sizing cold water pipe 9-29
Slab installations 13-6
SLF for glass 7-50
Solar augmented heat pump 13-57
Solar energy 13-54
  cooling system 13-54
Solar heating 13-56
  operation 13-54
  storage tank 13-56
  systems 13-54
Solubility versus temperature 10-5
Sound
  absorption coefficients 16-16
  attenuation 16-10
  duct wall transmission loss 16-32
  level of sources 16-2
  levels in a duct 16-32
  power at branch take off 16-24
  power level in a duct 16-34
  pressure 16-35
  pressure level 16-7, 16-17
  transmission 16-7, 16-31
  transmission loss factor 16-32
Sound lining 13-79
Space heater 15-83
Specific heat 1-2
  constant pressure 1-2
  constant volume 1-2
  various materials 15-36
Speech interference criteria 16-2
Split phase motors 17-12
Split system installations 13-7
Spray nozzles 13-113
Squirrel cage induction motors 17-1–17-2
Standard air 14-1
Starters

Starters (continued)
  AC motors 17-31
  mechanical shocks 17-33
  motor controllers 17-29
  open circuit transition 17-36
  overcurrent protection 17-29
  overload protection 17-30
  properties 17-30
  size with hp 17-32
  types 17-36
  winding 17-33
Static efficiency 14-2
Steam
  ashpalt plants 15-30
  coils 15-12
  pressurization 15-63
  pressurizing tank 15-65
  riser 15-10
Steam boiler
  autoclaves 15-37
  cheese vats 15-31
  concrete block 15-31
  dry cleaning 15-34–15-35
  flat iron work 15-35
  laundries 15-34
  ovens 15-35
  paper corrugators 15-35
  paper making 15-36
  pasteurization 15-36
  platen presses 15-36
  process heating 15-36
  restaurants 15-37
  snow removal 15-37
  sterilizers 15-37
  tire recapping 15-38
  vacuum pans 15-38
  washers 15-38
Steam heating system 15-1–15-129
  auditorium type unit ventilator 15-5
  boiler feed system 15-1
  boilers
    common return header 15-3
    controlled system header drip 15-6
    direct return connection 15-3–15-4
    drip end 15-7
    Hartford connection 15-3
    overhead connections 15-4
    piping connections to boilers 15-1
    steam main 15-6
    steam using equipments 15-4
    supply and return piping 15-6
    supply header drip 15-6
    vacuum header drip 15-6
  convector piping details 15-4
  equivalent direct radiation 15-1
  fin tube piping 15-4
  hot water generator 15-6
  industrial unit heater piping 15-5
  piping connections to boilers 15-1
  steam supply to heating units 15-1
  traps 15-1
  unit heater piping 15-5
  unit ventilator piping 15-5
  vacuum heating pump 15-1
  vacuum pumps 15-1
Steam main
  bypass 15-14
  drip in riser 15-7
  dripping 15-13
  rise and drip 15-6
  splitting 15-7
Steam piping 9-32
  capacities 9-33
  chart 9-34–9-58
  equivalent length of fitting 9-34
  equivalent length of run 9-33
  formula 9-31
  initial pressure 9-33
  maximum velocity 9-33
  pressure drop 9-33
  pressure loss 9-31–9-58
  size 9-32
Stefan Boltzmann constant 1-14
Strainers 13-113
Subcooled liquid 1-1

Sulfur content 12-15
Summer cycle 13-88
Summer operation 13-95
Superheated vapor 1-1
Supplementary heat 13-47
Supply and return header drip 15-6
Surface conductance 5-18
Surface resistance 5-18
Surface temperature calculations 5-9
Surroundings 1-2
Surveyors measure 20-1, 20-8
Symbols
    abbreviations 18-8
    air conditioning piping 18-6
    fittings 18-7
    heating piping 18-6
    piping 18-6
    plumbing piping 18-7
    pneumatic tubes 18-7
    sprinklers 18-7
    valves, pipe fitting 18-5
System boundary 1-2
System design 13-47

T

Tank transition from winter to summer 13-58
Tanks and pans 13-113
Tebi 20-10
Temperature control 12-28
Temperature limit, heat recovery 13-45
Thermal
    conduction 1-11
    conduction problems 1-15
    conductivity 1-11, 5-1–5-2
    convection 1-12
    diffusivity 1-12
    energy 20-7
    radiation 1-14, 5-4
    resistance of air space 5-19
Thermodynamic
    cycles 1-4, 1-6
    fundamental 1-1
    system 1-2
Thermostat location 13-10
Thermostatic controls 15-94
Thermostatic trap 15-28
Thermostats 13-43
Through wall installations 13-5
Tip speed 14-2
Ton long and short 20-2
Ton, metric 20-8
Tramp air 12-16
Transmission of coefficients
    doors 5-28
    fenestrations 5-27
    wood 5-28
Trap
    air handling unit 15-112–15-116
    boiler return 15-29
    cleaning 13-112
    condensate capacities 15-26
    connection 15-8
    flash 15-29
    float 15-27
    float sizing 15-41
    impulse 15-29
    inverted bucket 15-29
    lifting 15-29
    pressure differential 15-26
    radiation load 15-26
    safety factor 15-26
    selection 15-26
    splitting 15-7
    thermostatic 15-8
    types 15-27
    upright bucket 15-28
    warm up load 15-26
Troubleshooting 12-15, 12-17
Troy weight for gold and silver 20-2
Types of heat pumps 13-37

U

Unheated temperature calculations 5-9
Unit
    conversions 20-8
    systems 20-8
Unit air conditioners 13-114
    air filters 13-114
    condensers 13-114
    cooling coil 13-114
    fans 13-114
    motors 13-114
    piping 13-114
Unit heater
    air stream direction 15-120
    circulation of air 15-120
    duct furnace 15-118
    enclosed furnace 15-118
    exposed wall 15-120
    floor mounted heavy duty type 15-117
    floor mounted vertical blower units 15-117
    full area heating 15-111
    gas fired 15-109, 15-118–15-119
    gas fired air heater 15-117
    industrial type 15-5
    installations 15-119
    obstructions 15-120
    occupants 15-120
    partial area heating 15-111
    performance factors 15-109
    piping 15-5
    propeller fan type 15-117
    sizing 15-118
    spot heating 15-111
    steam supplied 15-110
    suspended 15-109
    suspended blower type 15-117
    suspended heavy duty units 15-117
    temperature limits 15-109
    thermostat locations 15-120
    too buoyant air 15-109
    types 15-117
Unit systems 20-8
Unit ventilator 13-88, 15-5
    auditorium type 15-5
    piping 15-5
Upright bucket trap 15-28

V

Vacuum lift 15-12
Vacuum pump 15-30
Valve and fitting equivalents 9-7–9-27
Valve and fitting loss 9-1–9-58
Valves 13-113
    check 9-139–9-141
    gate 9-139–9-141
    globe 9-139–9-141
Variable speed control 13-95
Variable volume system 13-17–13-21
    cooling considerations 13-20
    energy requirements 13-19
    heating and cooling calculations 13-19
    initial costs 13-18
    overlapping 13-21
Velocity design criteria 9-3
Velocity pressure relation 8-3, 14-38
Ventilation 14-1
Ventilation heat loss 6-6
Vibration 13-106
Vibration in pipes 1-11
Vibration isolation 16-7
Viscosity 1-6
Viscosity of liquid 9-78

W

Wall furnace 15-83
Wall type
    mass inside insulation 7-28–7-30

Warm air heating 15-82
    air volume 15-97–15-99
    blower characteristics 15-87
    bonnet capacity 15-85
    bonnet efficiency 15-85
    bonnet pressures 15-100
    combustion air supply 15-93
    combustion and ventilation air 15-93
    combustion efficiency 15-85
    direct fired unit heater 15-83
    duct arrangement 15-91
    duct heat loss 15-85
    duct system 15-88
    duct transmission efficiency 15-85
    floor furnace 15-83
    flue gas loss 15-85
    forced air furnace 15-83
    furnace arrangement 15-91
    gravity furnace 15-82
    gravity hot air furnace 15-82
    heat input 15-85
    industrial warm furnace 15-83
    pipeless furnace 15-82
    rating of furnace 15-85
    register delivery 15-85
    register free areas 15-100
    register pressures 15-101
    register temperature 15-97–15-99
    registers 15-89
    return air intake 15-90
    selection of furnace 15-87
    selection procedure 15-87
    space heater 15-83
    stove 15-82
    testing of furnace 15-85
    thermostatic controls 15-94
    throw from registers 15-100
    trends 15-88
    unit heater 15-83
    wall furnace 15-83
Waste steam heat utilization 15-50
Water conditioning 15-16
Water flow velocity 15-49
Water gauge 14-1

Water hammer 15-11
Water in fuel oil 12-18
Water piping 9-3, 9-28
Water properties 2-12
Water to air heat pumps 13-40
Water to water heat pumps 13-39
Water velocities maximum 9-3
Water velocity 15-52
Weight
    avoirdupois or commercial 20-2
    measures 20-1, 20-3
    metric 20-8
    sheetmetal 14-75–14-76
    troy, for gold and silver 20-2
Well water
    AC systems 13-54
    precooling 13-55
    refrigerant condensing 13-55
Wet atomizing steam 12-18
Wet bulb temperature 2-2, 2-5
Wide open BHP 14-2
Window GLF 7-47–7-48
Winter cycle 13-88
Winter operation 13-96
Winterizing chilled water system 13-97
Wire, circular mil measurement 20-1
Work 1-2
    mechanical 1-2
    shaft 1-2

Y

Year round remote units 13-3

Z

Zone day night operation 13-91
Zone mixing dampers 13-88
Zone types
    CLF tables 7-31–7-34
    SCL tables 7-31–7-34
Zoning installations 13-8

NOTES

LaVergne, TN USA
05 August 2010
192140LV00008B/1/P